PUMA®

An Introduction

In 2010 Puma stands as one of the leading figures in global football. The brand sponsors many International football federations such as 2006 World Champions Italy and other prominent footballing nations including Uruguay, Switzerland and The Czech Republic. PUMA is renowned for its sponsorship of many African National football teams including reigning African Cup of Nations Champions Egypt. Puma's other African nations include Algeria, Cameroon, Ghana and the Ivory Coast.

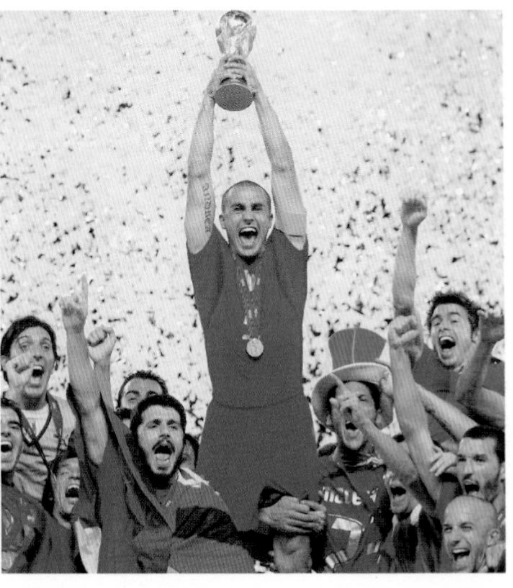

PUMA is well represented in terms of domestic football clubs across Europe, with Bordeaux, Lazio, Monaco, Sporting Lisbon and Villareal all provide International kudos. Back home PUMA sponsor English Premier League outfits Newcastle United Football Club and Tottenham Hotspur plus English Football League clubs Burnley, Cardiff City, Coventry City, Preston North End, Brentford, Colchester United, Leyton Orient, Sheffield Wednesday and Morecambe. SPL representation comes in the form of Hibernians, Motherwell and Stirling Albion.

PUMA has an association with many prestigious figures in the history of sport. Creating a heritage for the brand to be proud of. Olympic Champions Tommy Smith (200m in 1968), Heike Drechsler (Long Jump in 1992 & 2000) and Linford Christie (100m in 1992) have all represented the brand, as well as some of the biggest names in football including Eusebio, Pele, Diego Maradona, Johan Cruyff, Kenny Dalglish and more recently Paul 'Gazza' Gascoigne.

In the modern era on the World stage PUMA is represented by key icons such as Samuel Eto'o, Gianluigi Buffon and Raul Meireles . In the UK Puma represents many leading premiership and SPL figures, including Scott Brown, Aiden McGeady, Steven Davis, Shay Given, Nemanja Vidic, Peter Crouch, Michael Carrick, Nicolas Anelka and Diniyar Bilyaletdinov.

PUMA was founded in 1948 in Herzogenaurach, Germany by Rudolf Dassler. To this day the brand is synonymous with sport, particularly running shoes and football boots featuring the now globally recognised 'form stripe'. The company distributes its products in more than 120 countries, employs more than 9,000 people worldwide and has headquarters in Herzogenaurach, Boston, London and Hong Kong

PUMA is one of the world's leading Sportlifestyle companies that designs and develops footwear, apparel and accessories. It is committed to working in ways that contribute to the world by supporting Creativity, SAFE Sustainability and Peace, and by staying true to the principles of being Fair, Honest, Positive and Creative in decisions made and actions taken.

The PUMA Group owns the brands PUMA, Cobra Golf and Tretorn. It's Sport Performance and Lifestyle labels include categories such as Football, Running, Motorsports, Golf and Sailing. Sport Fashion features collaborations with renowned designer labels such as Alexander McQueen, Mihara Yasuhiro and Sergio Rossi.

GetConnected: Register for your chance to win with PUMA

The Non-League Club Directory & PUMA, through their licensee for PRO Teamsports – Genesis Sports, have teamed up to create the ultimate football playground for you to interact with thousands of other non-league players and clubs. You can share information, gloat or post that video of your 'prolific' centre forward heading the post!

You can also check out what PUMA have been up to and catch some exclusive video and action from their players and clubs.
Better yet, register on www.genesisports.co.uk/connected for your chance to win with PUMA throughout your season. Read on to find out what you or your team can win.

Team Competitions & Prizes

The Monthly Non-League Cup Competition
Success in any of the three Football Association national knock-out cup competitions (The F.A.Cup, F.A.Trophy or F.A.Vase) can bring publicity and excitement, but this season, if your league nominates one of your performances as outstanding for that month, you could be one of three lucky teams to win over £700 worth of PUMA gear, if we agree! However, don't throw away such a great prize by losing team discipline and picking up a caution or red card, as this will exclude you from our consideration.

The Monthly Fair Play Award
If your team can dominate without a booking for dissent or unsporting behaviour, you will automatically be entered into a draw at the end of each month to win £700 worth of PUMA gear! Make sure you register!

Player Competitions & Prizes

The Monthly Hat-trick Hotshot
This one is simple, or at least the concept is. Net a hat-trick and at the end of the month, you could win 1 of the 25 pairs of boots that PUMA are giving away each month, across the 24 leagues. If more than 25 players score a hat-trick that month, then it will go to a draw. Remember though, it's about hat-tricks, not dirty tricks. Pick up a booking or worse and your goals for that game are null and void, as far as this competition in concerned.

PUMA Players of the Year
At the end of every season PUMA will offer an annual boot sponsorship deal to the winners of the 'PUMA Player of the Season' and PUMA's 'England Player of the Year'. That's two chances to pick up an amazing boot deal. You will join PUMA's other top athletes, including the likes of Shay Given, Peter Crouch and Samuel Eto'o.

Video Star
The guys at genesissports will be rewarding the best video posts each month - as rated by you! Simply visit www.genesisports.co.uk/connected and post your video in the "your videos" section and if it gains enough votes, you could be in with a chance of winning one of many great prizes we are giving away each month. **Make sure you register!**

Non-League Club Directory Competition Terms and Conditions

1. Entrants to the Non-League Club Directory competitions are bound by these terms and conditions.

2. To qualify for any of the prizes, users must have previously registered their details on the 'GetConnected' website.

3. Discipline
    a. Should a player of a team receive a caution or is sent off during a match for dissent or unsporting behaviour, the team will become ineligible for the "Monthly Fair Play Award" for that month.
    b. Should a player of a team receive a caution or is sent off during a match for dissent or unsporting behaviour, the team will become ineligible for the "Monthly Non-League Cup Competition" for that match.
    c. Should a player of a team receive a caution or is sent off during a match for dissent or unsporting behaviour, the player will become ineligible for the "Hat-trick Hotshot Competition" for that match.

4. Withstanding point 2, nominees for the "Monthly Non-League Cup Competition" from each respective league will be reviewed by a panel of Non-League Club Directory editors, who will select three winners. Their decision will be final.

5. Nominees for the "PUMA Players of the Year" and PUMA's "England Player of the Year" from each respective league will be reviewed by a panel of Non-League Club Directory editors and PUMA, who will elect two winners. Their decision will be final.

6. Where prizes are decided by draw, the winner(s) will be drawn by an independent judge and the draw will take place within 7 days of the competition closing. The judge's decision is final. The winner will be notified by email and/or telephone/and/or post within 14 days of being selected followed by an official confirmation letter. The winner's name is available upon receipt of a written request to Marketing Department at Genesis Group International Limited, Unit 4 Alpha Point, Manchester, M22 4TE.

7. Prizes
    a. Team prizes given for the "Monthly Fair Play Award" & "Monthly Non-League Cup Competition" consist of; A Team Kit Bag, Sixteen Training Balls, A Football Bag and Two Match Balls (£700 RRP)
    b. Individual prizes given for "Hat-trick Hotshot Competition" consist of a new pair of PUMA Football boots of PUMA's choosing.
    c. Individual prizes given for "PUMA Players of the Year" and PUMA's "England Player of the Year" consist of a PUMA boot sponsorship agree ment to a maximum value of £500 RRP for the 2011/12 season only.

8. The following persons are not eligible to enter the Prize Draw: (i) employees of any business involved or associated with the Prize Draw (including Genesis Group International Limited and its associated companies) and (ii) any such person's family or household members. Genesis Group International Limited reserves the right to verify the eligibility of all entrants.

9. No cash alternatives will be offered. In the unlikely event that any of the prizes are not made available, Genesis Group International Limited reserves the right to offer an alternative prize of equal value.

10. Winners may be required to take part in promotional activity. In the event that the winners do take part in any promotional activity any and all rights in any photographs, images or any other similar material whatsoever vests in Genesis Group International Limited and the winner hereby assigns all rights in, title and interest to all and any such promotional material to Genesis Group International Limited.

11. The promoter of the Prize Draw is Genesis Group International Limited, Unit 4, Alpha Point, Manchester, M22 4TE.

12. The Company reserves the right to amend the terms and conditions from time to time.

13. The Company reserves the right to withdraw any of the promotions in the event of unforeseen circumstances.

14. These terms are governed by and construed in accordance with the laws of England. If any clause of the terms and conditions is declared to be invalid or unenforceable by a court of competent jurisdiction, the remaining provisions will nevertheless continue in full force without being impaired or invalidated in anyway.

PUMA®

NON-LEAGUE CLUB DIRECTORY 2011
ISBN 978-1-869833-68-8

Editors
Tony Williams
(Tel: 01823 490 684)
Email: t.williams320@btinternet.com
James Wright
6 Harp Chase, Taunton, Somerset TA1 3RY
(Tel: 07786 636659 Fax: 0800 048 8641)
Email: james@nlnewsdesk.co.uk

Published by Tony Williams Publications Ltd
(Tel: 01548 531 339)
Email: tw.publications@btinternet.com

Printed in the UK by CPI William Clowes Beccles NR34 7TL

Sales & Distribution
T.W. Publications (01548 531 339)

Front Cover:
Action from the F.A. Cup 1st Qualifying Round tie between Shortwood United and Witney United which ended in a 3-3 draw.
Photo: Peter Barnes.

NON-LEAGUE CLUB DIRECTORY 2011

(33rd Edition)

EDITORS
TONY WILLIAMS & JAMES WRIGHT

EDITORIAL ASSISTANTS
MIKE WILLIAMS, CRAIG POTTAGE, SARA WILLIAMS
AND SAM PERRY

BARRY W. BRIGHT
Vice Chairman
Football Association

FOREWORD

As each season dawns hordes of real football participants and followers wait for the next publication of the Non League Club Directory so professionally edited, with loving care, by Mike and Tony Williams and James Wright.

The finest encyclopedia of football information comprehensively covering Leagues and the clubs therein from Step 1 to Step 7; sprinkled with Football Association Competitions and then through the County Associations; Universities; The Armed Forces and onwards in a mosaic of statistics and photographs that do not exist in similar terms anywhere else in the world.

I've often wondered what the electricity accounts must be in the Williams' households as they obviously labour night and day to pull together such detail to ensure it reaches the printers in ample time and then onwards to eager purchasers.

As the season begins to evolve we begin to see whether the ambitions of those in the top echelons of Non League Football eager to taste or return to The Football League are well founded while down the Steps others - perhaps with not so well known household names – similarly seek success but find the fun, enjoyment and friendship of our great game of equal importance.

The game remains dependent on the great volunteer force. The men and women who week in and week out ensure that their League or club, often so important in communities, is well organised. Work quietly and diligently undertaken; not seeking praise or reward but obtaining personal satisfaction and pride from their efforts. To each and every one of them – 'Thank You'.

The FA Respect programme moves forward as The Football Association attempts to achieve an increase in the base number of registered referees in England; imposes zero tolerance for assaults on referees; requests an improvement in on-field player self discipline particularly in the area of dissent and urges a Step Change in Youth Football as to what is acceptable and unacceptable behaviour from parents and spectators.

We all have a collective responsibility to promote within football what is a fair and safe environment and to deal with that which diminishes such values.

Long may we continue to see the Non-League Club Directory produced; long may we continue to enjoy our involvement in the great game of Association Football; in difficult times long may we respect the values sport can bring to Society through the guardianship that each and every one of us have the responsibility for.

WIN NEXT YEAR'S NON-LEAGUE CLUB DIRECTORY

(AND HAVE A BIT OF FUN AT THE SAME TIME!)

NON-LEAGUE CLUB DIRECTORY PREDICTION COMPETITION

This year we have decided to re-introduce a popular competition that was run by the Cherry Red Non-League Newsdesk Annual for a number of years.

Entrants predict the 2010-11 champions of the top competitions, and the contestant with the most correct tips is the champion and receives next year's Directory FREE. Could not be simpler!

To enter, list your prediction for the champions of all three divisions of each of the Blue Square Conference, Ryman Isthmian, Zamaretto Southern and the Evo-stik Northern Premier Leagues PLUS the top divisions of each of 14 feeder leagues: Baker Joiner Midland Alliance, Cherry Red Combined Counties League, Essex Senior League, Hereward United Counties League, Koolsport Northern Counties League, Molten Spartan South Midlands League, Ridgeons Eastern Counties League, Safety Net Kent League, Skilltraining Northern League, Sussex County League, Sydenhams Wessex League, Toolstation Western League, Uhlsport Hellenic League League, Vodkat Northern West Counties League.

Entries should be emailed to james.m.wright.t21@btinternet.com or posted to Prediction Competition, 6 Harp Chase, Taunton TA1 3RY.

Rules:

By entering you agree that..

1) All entries must be received BEFORE November 1st 2010.
2) The number of second (or even third or fourth) places will be used as a tie-breaker if necessary.
3) The contact details of all entrants will be stored electronically and may be used to publicise future competitions or products of TW Publications (under no circumstances will they ever be divulged to any third party).
4) Participants' names and scores may be published in the Non-League Club Directory 2012, or on the Directory's website.
5) In the unlikely event that the Non-League Club Directory is not published in 2011, the winner will be entitled to a cash prize equivalent to the cover price of the current edition.
6) In the event of any dispute, the decision of the publisher is final.

ENTRY IS FREE, SO GIVE IT A GO. GOOD LUCK!

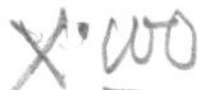

CONTENTS

THE DIRECTORY'S 'TEAM SHEET'

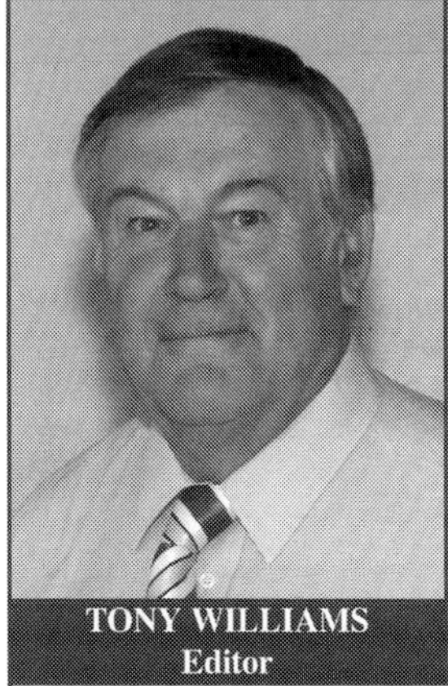

TONY WILLIAMS
Editor

Educated at Malvern College, one of the country's best football schools in the late sixties, he represented England Under 18 against Scotland at Celtic Park before serving as an administrative officer in the Royal Air Force for five years.

He was on Reading's books from the age of 16 to 22, but also represented F.A. Amateur XI's and the R.A.F. while playing mainly in the old Isthmian League for Corinthian Casuals, Dulwich Hamlet and Kingstonian and joining Hereford United and Grantham during R.A.F. postings.

After taking an F.A. Coaching badge he coached at Harrow Borough, Epsom & Ewell and Hungerford Town and was asked to edit Jimmy Hill's Football Weekly after initial experience with the Amateur Footballer. Monthly Soccer and Sportsweek followed before he had the idea for a football Wisden and was helped by The Bagnall Harvey Agency to find a suitable generous sponsor in Rothmans.

After launching the Rothmans Football Yearbook in 1970 as its founder and co-compiler with Roy Peskett, he was asked to join Rothmans (although a non-smoker!) in the company's public relations department and was soon able to persuade the Marketing Director that Rothmans should become the first ever sponsor of a football league.

After a season's trial sponsoring the Hellenic and Isthmian Leagues, it was decided to go national with the Northern and Western Leagues and for four years he looked after the football department at Rothmans, with Jimmy Hill and Doug Insole presenting a brilliant sponsorship package which amongst many other innovations included three points for a win and goal difference.

So Non-League football led the way with league sponsorship and two, now well accepted, innovations.

Sportsmanship and goals were also rewarded in a sponsorship that proved a great success for football and for Rothmans. Indeed the sportsmanship incentives could be of great value to-day in the Football Association's bid to improve the game's image by ridding the game of dissent and cheating.

After the cigarette company pulled out of their sports sponsorship Tony produced the first Non-League Annual and later The Football League Club Directory, launching 'Non-League Football' magazine with "The Mail on Sunday" and then "Team Talk."

After his ten years with Hungerford Town, he moved West and served Yeovil Town as a Director for seven years but was thrilled when David Emery's plans for the exciting Non-League Media emerged and came into reality, thus giving the grass roots of the game the publicity and promotion that he and his team had been attempting to set up since the Annual (now Directory) was launched in 1978.

T.W. Publications continues to help promote non-league football throughout the country and is providing information for the exciting 'Goalrun' website. The modern history of representative football outside the Football League titled 'Playing for England' is being finalised and this season Tony has also been invited to help with the new 'NonLeagueNews24.com' website and 'TheNonLeague24' magazine as Consultant Editor.

The aim of the company has always been to promote the non-league 'family,' its spirit and its general development. So a plaque from The Football Association inscribed 'To Tony Williams for his continued promotion of all that's good in football' was greatly appreciated as was the trophy to commemorate the thirtieth edition of the Directory and the recent GLS "Lifetime Award' for promoting non-league football.

CRAIG POTTAGE
Editorial Assistant

Craig has been a football aficionado since an early age and has always had an interest in players' careers. Craig has kept detailed records of non league players for the last few years and this is his fourth year involved in this publication.

Started work in Golf Course Design and Project Management moving onto his present career in Business Development for an IT Facilitation Company in Stevenage twelve years ago. Lives in the town with his wife and daughter. Has been an Arsenal season ticket holder for over twenty years and also goes to watch Stevenage Borough when time allows. Also been known to enjoy a beer or two.

JAMES WRIGHT
Editor

James Wright, brought up on the tiny island of St Agnes on the Isles of Scilly and, like his Midlands parents, a life-long Wolves fan, began his career in non-League journalism when joining Tony Williams's editorial staff at the Mail on Sunday Non-League Football magazine in August 1990. James soon assumed from Tony responsibility for the compilation of the Non-League Club Directory and edited the 1992, 1993, 1994 and 1995 editions of the best-selling annual. During this period, James was a founder member of the editorial team of Team Talk magazine, the top non-League periodical of the 1990s, and collated the acclaimed FA Cup Post War Club-by-Club Records. In 1995 James launched Non-League Newsdesk, a newsletter carrying up-to-date league tables and the week's results.

Over the six seasons James published the title, Newsdesk became an immensely popular, no frills, weekly. However, the 2000 launch of The Non-League Paper coupled with the proliferation of information on the internet saw Newsdesk sales dwindle. James decided to team up with the Paper, and for the past ten seasons has collected and collated the four or five pages of minor results and tables that appear each Sunday. The challenge has proved immensely enjoyable despite the fact that it prevents James from following his beloved Taunton Town on away days.

But James regards the highlight of his career to date as the 2000 launch of the Non-League Newsdesk Annual. During his years compiling the Directory he recognised the need for a much smaller publication to be available much earlier, i.e. in pre-season. The first edition of the Non-League Newsdesk Annual filled this void and was an immediate success outselling Alex Ferguson's official autobiography in the Sunday Times chart in its first week. The 2002 edition surpassed all others by reaching the number one slot - staying there for a further week.

Last year's merger of the Non-League Directory and the Newsdesk Annual saw James return to his journalistic roots. After publishing nine editions of the Annual independently, he is relishing the challenge of implementing some of the popular features of the Annual into the Directory.

James attends 100+ matches each season, and covers Taunton Town for the Somerset County Gazette. Outside football he is a qualified marine cartographer, and a keen long distance runner and local league tennis player. He also enjoys fishing, boating and gigging. He lives in the West Country with long-time partner Karen and eleven year old daughter Rosie.

MIKE WILLIAMS
Editorial Manager/Publisher

What started out as a holiday job in 1988 helping put together (literally in those days) the Non-League Club Directory and League Club Directory, in the end forged a career which saw him work for Coventry City Football Club, e-comsport in London and finally return to T.W. Publications in 2003.

During his eight year spell with TW Publications he learned the ropes of all aspects of publishing culminating in the roll of production manager for the Non-League Club Directory, Team Talk Magazine, the League Club Directory and many more publications published by the company.

1995 saw the opportunity to take up the post of Publications Manager at Coventry City Football Club, and the transfer was made in the April of that year. Sky Blue Publications was formed and the League Club Directory became their leading title. Re-branded as the Ultimate Football Guide he was to deal with all aspects of the book, from design to sales and was also put on a steep learning curve into the world of Premiership programme production. The three years spent at the Midland's club gave him a great insight into all departments of a Premiership club, having produced publications for them all.

Leaving Coventry F.C. in 1998, and after a spell working on a world wide football player database for e-comsport in London, he returned to the West Country in 2001 to set up his own design/publishing company, which incorporated working on the Directory again. 2009 saw the full time switch to TW Publications and the responsibilities of publishing the Directory.

Having gone to a rugby school his football playing career was delayed. However, becoming the youngest player to have played for the First XV and representing Torbay Athletics club at 100 and 200m proved his sporting background. At the age of 20 he begun his football career which, at it's height, saw him playing for Chard Town in the Western League Premier Division.

As club secretary for South Devon League side, Loddiswell Athletic, he has helped the club improve on and off the field as they strive for Premier Division football for the first time in the club's history. An achievement they missed by a single point last season. As well helping run the club, he also turns out for the Reserves, who also enjoyed a good season last term, the highlight of which was reaching the semi-finals of the Fred Hewings Cup.

SARA WILLIAMS
Editorial Assistant

Sara has been working behind the scenes at T.W. Publications for the past four years and has had her eyes firmly opened to the wonderful world of non-League football. From the administrative side to actually playing for Totnes & Dartington Ladies, she has experienced every part of the game at our level.

Born in Carshalton, Surrey, Sara showed an early interest in football and craved a Liverpool shirt, only to be bought a Chelsea top! (She has since made amends for this). Excelling in middle distance running, ultimately she represented her county at youth level, and often came up against her nemesis of the time, Donna Frasier.

Having worked in many different jobs Sara found her vocation in the animal care industry and qualified as a Vet Nurse in 2000 having worked for the P.D.S.A. Sara had 10 years working for Veterinary Surgeries in Surrey and Devon before leaving in 2007 to concentrate on T.W. Publications and her own line of children's books based on her experiences as a Vet Nurse.

Sara recently re-ignited her love of running by qualifying to run for the World Wildlife Fund in the London Marathon. No mean feat considering the last time she ran she was a teenager. However, she completed the event in a very respectable 4hrs 33mins.

ACKNOWLEDGMENTS

Once again another season has come and gone at break neck speed and even the World Cup seems an age ago now, however, as I write these words the new season is well and truly started and folders for next year's Directory (2012) already reside on my computer. You would think that with the whole season ahead of us, that putting the Directory together would be a relaxed affair, but as all club officials know, the close season is probably the busiest time of the football year. And so it is that when the season finishes the compilation of the Directory gathers pace, culminating in a very 'hectic' August.

As always it would not be possible to get the Directory to your homes if weren't for the support of the Football Association, club secretaries, programme editors, league officials, contributors and photographers and to them I extend by thanks. I can't name everyone who has helped along the way but in particular:

'OUR TEAM' OF PHOTOGRAPHERS

Peter Barnes, Graham Brown, Keith Clayton, Alan Coomes, 'Uncle Eric' Marsh,
Roger Turner, Bill Wheatcroft and Gordon Whittington.

FA COMPETITIONS DEPARTMENT

Steve Clark, Chris Darnell and Scott Bolton

CONTRIBUTORS

Dennis Strudwick (Football Conference)
Alan Allcock (Northern Premier League). Bruce Badcock (Isthmian League).
Jason Mills (Southern League)
Mike Brown (AFA). Arthur Evans (Photographer & reports).
Bill Mitchell & Stewart Davidson (Scottish Scene).
Craig Pottage & John Harman (Blue Square Players records).
Dr. Andrew Sarnecki (Pecking Order). Mike Simmonds (Schools).
And not forgetting James, Dad and Sara.

Thank you, Mike Williams.

James Wright is grateful to the following (and many) others for their help in compiling this current edition:

Richard Rundle, Nick House, Rowland Lyons, Rosie Wright, Karen Broom, John Shenton, Jane Phillips, John Shaw, Rob Errington, Margaret Errington, Jeremy Biggs, Jim Bean, Paul Rivers, Mrs S Moore, Graham Down, Ken Clarke, Brian King, Andrew Moffat, Phil Hiscox, Mike Sampson, Dave Lumley, Nigel Wood, Neil Juggins, Frank Harwood, Peter Francis, John Nisbet, Phil Mitcham, Arthur Green, Ann Bullock, Stephen Hosmer, Brian & Hilary Redmond, Steve Gilbert, Paul Redgate, Dave Braithwaite, Gary Berwick, Chris McCullough, Jim Wicks, Mary Ablett, Trevor Scorah, David Jarrett, Phil Annets, Roy Ainge, Bill Gardner, Jim Thorn, Peter Godfrey, John Thomas, Mark Rozzier, Dave Sponder, Ann Camm, Michael Stokes, Mike Hemmings, Ron Holpin, David Ward, Malcolm Pratt, Colin Goodwin, Rod Sutherland, Phil Potter, Dennis Johnson, Dave Marsay, Paul Birkitt, Kevin Bray, Mike Harvey, Dave Munday, Janet Hunt, Danny Braddock, Norman Pryce, Fiona Mitchell, Graham Thornton, Philip Rhodes, Jim Milner, Neville Butt, Dave Rattigan, David Wilcox, Rolant Ellis, Chas Rowland, R Griffiths, Ron Bridges, Tony Griffiths, Phil Woosnam, Alan Foulkes, William Davies, Glynn Jones, Trevor Syms, Martin Bryant, John Doe, Mike Markham, Sam Giles, David Holland, Les Bullock, Robin Goodwin-Davey, Elaine Waulmsley, Richard Mason, Peter Toft, Philip Coulthard, Geoff Jenkins, George McKitterick, Kevin Wilkinson, Richard Durrant, James Herbert, Alan Watkins.

A World Cup season usually manages to increase the general media coverage of the game and create interest among potential football followers who may not always be involved with football.

The 2009-2010 season itself didn't produce many outstanding achievements, although the form of Stevenage Borough as they took over from Oxford United as favourites for promotion to the Football League, was truly outstanding. From the turn of the year the Hertfordshire club lost only three league games, all by a 0-1 margin, drew just one match, kept fifteen clean sheets and confirmed their promotion as champions well before their end of season and before bidding farewell to Non--League football at The F.A.Trophy Final at Wembley.

After a record breaking F.A.Cup Year in 2008-2009 when eight non-league clubs reached the Third Round a comparatively disappointing three representatives didn't have much luck in the draw and there were few exciting headlines for our clubs.

The Changing Character of The Football Conference

The 'character' of non-league football's excellent pyramid of development is changing, although all non-league clubs fit into a system of leagues through which promotion can be gained if the required standards on and off the field are achieved. Clubs like Wycombe Wanderers (1993), Cheltenham Town (1999), Yeovil Town (2003), Burton Albion(2009) and now Stevenage Borough(2010) who were the giants of non-league football, strengthened their clubs appropriately and achieved their ambitions, thanks to winning the Conference Championship. Kidderminster Harriers and Rushden & Diamonds are back in the Conference now after spells in The Football League but although still at the top of the non-league pyramid, The Conference now possesses seven clubs whose fans probably consider their club's presence in this competition to be a low point in their history.

Many members of this season's Blue Square Premier Division, as the Conference is known at present, are re-building before hoping to return to League Two. Clubs such as Colchester United, Doncaster Rovers, Shrewsbury Town, Carlisle United, Exeter City, Torquay United and Oxford United have successfully achieved their aim, but looking at this season's line up, seven clubs who have been relegated are still desperately keen to reclaim their Football League membership - York City (relegated in 2004), Cambridge United (2005), Mansfield Town & Wrexham (2008), Luton Town (2009) with Darlington and Grimsby Town (2010).

Altrincham, Barrow, Bath City, Kettering Town, Southport and Tamworth are competing in the top non-league competition after spells in the regional divisions. Altrincham and Kettering Town could rightly consider themselves the 'senior' Conference clubs while Bath City and Barrow, also Alliance founder members, and Southport, have previously enjoyed many seasons in the top Non-league level. Clubs such as AFC Wimbledon and Newport County however, are really happy and proud to be contesting life just one step away from The Football League after recovering bravely from some very upsetting years.

So this leaves five clubs who will be hoping their surge up the non-league pyramid will enable them to follow the example of Burton Albion and Stevenage Borough who won their Football league places in the last two seasons.

Crawley Town and Fleetwood Town, with some exciting close season signings, will be the favourites, but Eastbourne Borough, Forest Green Rovers, Hayes & Yeading and Histon will at least be hoping for further consolidation at the top level of non-league football.

So it can be seen that the character of The Football Conference has changed and full marks to Chairman Brian Lee and his Board of Directors who have worked so hard to cope with the changing attitudes of senior non-league club officials. No doubt it will be a 'lively' season on and off the field and it will be interesting to see if another traditional non-league club can follow Burton Albion and Stevenage F.C. into the Football League.

England C - a very special England Team

One consistent source of good news has been the steady development of 'England C' who, despite a regular change of young personnel, continue to play well together. England caps at this level can be seen to be developing before moving back into the Football League. Paul Fairclough, Steve Burr and their excellent team of helpers that has given their youngsters a special pride in themselves on and off the field.

Non-League Football represents about 97% of our national sport. The purest of amateurs playing in village football and Sunday leagues look upwards through the county leagues, then the regional semi-professional competitions

through to the serious clubs, who are beginning to have thoughts about challenging for a Football League place. So they are aiming to reach the Blue Square North or South with the ultimate challenge of The Blue Square Premier.

The seriousness of competing within the top two steps of the game has encouraged practically all the Premier clubs to employ full time professional footballers, while many of those playing in the feeding leagues - Blue Square North and South are also being tempted to pay full time wages.This urge to keep up with the big spenders can bring disaster to many a club but it also enables very ordinary footballers to call themselves full time sportsmen.

The 'England C 'has taken the place of 'The England Semi-Professionals' and 'The National Game XI' who in their turn had replaced 'The England Amateurs,' but the best players in non-league football are those in the senior Blue Square leagues and they are nearly all full time. Realistically they are obviously playing at a lower level than players in The Premier League, The Championship and Leagues One and Two but they are representing England as the best players in non-league football.

The way this England team is coached and administered is beyond criticism and the results, quality of football and the way the young players return to The Football League, with improved understanding of the game and its responsibilities on and off the field, is greatly appreciated.

England Non-League XI?

However, there is a huge section of the English game, playing under the Non-League banner, but without an England team for which their best players can have ambitions to win international honours. Surely, there's enough money in senior football for our administrators to encourage some of it to filter down to provide us with a real England team to represent real non-league football I am sure the Football Association whose committees are packed with real football enthusiasts would be proud to set up a genuine England side for the very best of the thousands and thousands of footballers who are NOT MAKING A LIVING OUT OF THE GAME ON A FULL TIME BASIS. Surely they deserve it!

As a start, in the purest of amateur levels, perhaps the very best players from the teams competing in the successful 'F.A. National League Systems Cup' could be brought together for some representative matches. They would be greatly appreciated and might be surprisingly successful!

Surely The Football Association, who are responsible for the well being of all levels of the national game, would be thrilled to ensure that 97% of 'their footballers' had their own special international representative team or perhaps teams?

Guernsey our European Representatives

One of the most romantic and appealing football competitions is The F.A.National League Systems Cup, contested by league representative sides selected from clubs in thirty two leagues most of whom compete at Step 7 throughout England. Competitions from such different environments as The Dorset Premier League, the huge A.F.A. Southern Amateur League in London, Liverpool County Premier League, Birmingham & District AFA and The Humber Premier League are joined by squads representing the leagues in The Isle of Man, Jersey and Guernsey.

To be successful, these leagues need a good selection system and a dedicated coaching team and, since this competition was launched, the winners have come from Kent County League, Cambridgeshire, Mid Cheshire,The Isle of Man, The Southern Amateur League and now after a glorious run last season, Guernsey from the Channel Islands.

The winners represent England in The U.E.F.A. Regions' Cup which is held every two years, and this September, the cup winning squad from the little Guernsey League featuring only ten clubs will be competing against the rest of Europe in Croatia. This is a major honour for the Channel Islands and for Guernsey in particular, who have beaten such powerful leagues as Kent County, Northampton Town, Hertfordshire Senior, Southern Amateur, Dorset Premier and Liverpool County, averaging over three goals a match. Congratulations to all involved and I'm proud to have represented the green and whites while living on the Island in the seventies.

Respect

The Football Association received praise from all quarters of the game when they launched their 'Respect Programme,' but not necessary support. Some sections of the media took delight in highlighting the ugly scenes of dissent and the public were probably left with mixed feelings regarding the success of the scheme.

We are pleased to include a report from the F.A. Respect Manager Dermot Collins who is responsible for the development of Respect but let's look carefully at what we can do to help in the season ahead, rather than point a critical finger whenever dissent rears its ugly head.

Surely 'Respect' should be shown at all levels within our game and shown especially to the game itself which is the most popular in the world and can possibly influence more youngsters, sportsmen and sportswomen than any other aspect of modern life.

Spectators using foul mouthed abuse towards match officials or opponents cannot imagine how pathetic they sound or look and in no way do they help their club or the match situation. They will also irritate fellow supporters who may well decide to curtail their support. Some the very worst examples can be found amongst the parents watching their young and these incredibly sad characters can put their children off the game for life at a very early age.

Senior Club Officials who lose their self control are letting down their players, management and supporters and, as personnel in senior positions, they will automatically lose any respect they may have originally enjoyed.

Managers and Coaches can quickly lose the respect of their players by screaming abuse at the officials or opponents. Some players may also be encouraged to copy them and this will only bring more red and yellow cards and, understandably, referees are not likely to be giving foul mouthed players any benefit of the doubt on the field.

Players who constantly criticise, abuse and nag the officials can only harm their club's chances. Bookings will flow, followed by possible dismissals, decisions will go against them persistently and referees, who are only human, will be understandably biased against the club when visiting them in the future.

Everyone involved with non-league football, as a player, official or supporter, will recognise the difference between a happy and professional dedicated club, with a positive and sporting but competitive atmosphere, compared with a club where there is always a simmering anger and bitchiness that spring to life very easily.

A good chairman and his board will be able to appoint his management team that will help create the right atmosphere at their club. They will appeal to the right type of supporter and will all build a club that is respected as much as they are respecting the game itself!

Referees of course should also respect the game. Many of them are failed players and many have never enjoyed the benefits of being part of a team. They have always worked their way up the rankings as individuals and this can show on and off the field. Is it fair to think that many referees honestly want to blow the final whistle on an afternoon's work and not be remembered?

Most football people think of a good referee as one you do not notice, but just keeps the game flowing successfully and happily. But many referees, possibly because of the constant assessing, can develop as showmen once they realise that 'they are never wrong' and those types certainly want to be remembered.

There are times when the officious referee can really irritate but that is when the real character and discipline of a club official, manager, player or even supporter is truly tested. If you have played the game you soon realise that referees may know the laws of the game perfectly but many, especially the young, do not understand the game itself.

As a player, you know when a tackle is deliberate, whether you have received it or given it, but the referee doesn't necessarily and possibly never will. This can be desperate when yellow cards are given for tackles and praiseworthy self control is needed when you have been booked for an innocent tackle, or hurt deliberately by a tackle that hasn't been penalised.

Referees do need respect, but they too should also be aware that the game, and their position of power amongst players, also deserves their respect and understanding.

Television commentators and pundits can also respect the game and help by criticising and ridiculing, NOT glorifying, the clever professional who gets away with a crafty foul or simulation that gives a sickening example to the youngster learning the game

So another season is underway, and England have suffered the indignity of a terrible World Cup disappointment and the World Cup Final itself certainly wasn't a good advert for the 'beautiful game'. The distaste and jealousy concerning the huge salaries at the top of our game have encouraged mass criticism of football, so its a special time for all of us to stand up for the level of the game we love. It is a time in which we can show the rest of the sporting world that the national game in our country does produce the right type of sportsmen, who can play, administer and watch the game in the very best of spirits and we do understand the word RESPECT!

Tony Williams

Since this editorial was written, Tony Williams has been invited by The Football Association to help Dermot Collins, as The Respect Ambassador for The National Game (Non-League Football).

Respect

The Respect programme was launched in August 2008 and at the start of its third season it's appropriate to ask the question is it working?

Respect came into being as a response to widespread concern as to a loss of referees driven out of the game by verbal and physical abuse. There was unease as to some of the on field behaviour of players particularly in the professional game and in youth football the impact of pushy parents and aggressive coaches was ruining the experience for many young players.

Two years on – Respect has had an impact on tackling some of these troubling trends. Referee numbers are up by 8% and there are now record numbers of student referees undertaking the introductory course. Dissent cautions have declined dramatically in our senior professional leagues with both the Premier League and Football League Championship experiencing falls of 23 % and 31% respectively. Smaller decline have also been recorded in dissent and dismissals in the amateur game and in youth football the use of codes of conducts, pre match handshakes and designated spectator areas are beginning to have an impact on the raging touchline parents that make the game a misery for others.

The FA remains conscious that there is so much work to do - Assaults on Referees for instance have fallen by 13% but remain unacceptably high – There were 466 cases in the 2009/10 season. The FA remains committed to tackling these difficult problems with the assistance of our partner football organisations and the leagues, clubs and referees of this country. **Dermot Collins.**

The Non-League Club Directory

2009-2010
AWARDS

• ROLL OF HONOUR •

FOOTBALLER OF THE YEAR
Dale Roberts (Rushden & Diamonds)

MANAGER OF THE YEAR
Graham Westley (Stevenage Borough)

MERIT AWARDS
Aylesbury
Farnborough
Newport County
Whitley Bay

• MERIT AWARDS 2009-10 •

AYLESBURY

The little Buckinghamshire club entered the F.A.Challenge Cup on Saturday 15th August when they beat fellow Spartan South Midlands League club Langford 6-0 in the Extra Preliminary Round, with ace goalscorer Craig Henney recording what was to be his first of three F.A.Cup hat tricks. After a thrilling eight match run in which Leighton Town, Erith Town, Wingate & Finchey and Chesham United had been eliminated, Wealdstone eventually halted their progress after a thrilling 4-2 scoreline. Top scorer Henney finished with twelve F.A.Cup goals and the town of Aylesbury once again had enjoyed the F.A.Cup media headlines.

FARNBOROUGH

Outstanding football throughout the season brought promotion as Champions of The Zamaretto Premier Division to Farnborough who finished the campaign with an impressive goal tally of 100-44 and only failed to score in four of their 42 league games. With the emphasis on exciting passing football, Steve King's attacking players were not the biggest, but their all out attacking skills kept them at the top of their League, for all but a couple of weeks, throughout the entire campaign and they won the championship with three matches to play.

NEWPORT COUNTY

With just one victory in their first four league fixtures the doubters started muttering, but only one more defeat before the end of March proved manager Dean Holdsworth had built the right squad who played winning football. A total of 101 League and Cup goals was impressive enough, but a team that between 18th August and 30th January never conceded more than a single goal in a game and recorded sixteen clean sheets must be considered worthy champions. County are a fine all round side who should grace the Blue Square Premier and place themselves just one step away from retaining the treasured Football League membership.

WHITLEY BAY

Following the tradition that started in the days of The F.A.Amateur Cup, the North East of England have always expected to supply challengers for the 'junior' national knock out tournament. Whitley Bay have outlasted the famous Bishop Auckland and Crook Town, who have struggled to survive in the modern game, and 'The Bay' are still a regular challenger in the top three of the Northern League. However, importantly for the traditions of the area, they have proved themselves the very top club in recent F.A.Vase competitions. An Ian Chandler goal won the competition when the Final was played at Villa Park in 2002 and the match winner has now become the proud manager of Whitley Bay's winning Vase teams in the last two seasons. Can they become the first club to win three consecutive Wembley Finals?

NON LEAGUE FOOTBALLER OF THE YEAR

DALE ROBERTS

(Rushden & Diamonds)

Goalkeepers who are often considered a 'little mad' by their team mates, are always remembered, for their great saves or their tragic mistakes and it takes a strong character to cope with the pressures of the position. At the beginning of last season Dale Roberts' future at Rushden & Diamonds was in the balance when he lost his position as first choice goalkeeper and his future seemed in doubt. However, he battled back and not only helped his club to the Blue Square Premier Play-Offs by keeping twelve clean sheets in a fine second half of the season, but won the confidence of England Manager Paul Fairclough, who nominated him as England's Player of the Year after producing two brilliant displays against Hungary and Poland.

PAST WINNERS

2008-09	Aaron Webster (Burton Albion)
2007-08	Sean Canham (Team Bath)
2006-07	Jon Main (Tonbridge Angels)
2005-06	Stuart Thurgood (Grays Athletic)
2004-05	Terry Fearns (Southport)
2003-04	Andrew Forbes (Winchester City)
2002-03	Darren Way (Yeovil Town)
2001-02	Daryl Clare (Boston United)
2000-01	Ray Warburton (Rushden & Dia)
1999-00	Gary Abbott (Aldershot Town)
1998-99	Neil Grayson (Cheltenham Town)
1997-98	Phil Everett (Tiverton Town)
1996-97	Howard Forinton (Yeovil Town)
1995-96	Barry Hayles (Stevenage Boro)
1994-95	Kevan Brown (Woking)
1993-94	Chris Brindley (Kidderminster H.)
1992-93	Steve Guppy (Wycombe Wndrs)
1991-92	Tommy Killick (Wimborne Town)
1990-91	Mark West (Wycombe Wndrs)
1989-90	Phil Gridelet (Barnet)
1988-89	Steve Butler (Maidstone Utd)
1987-88	David Howell (Enfield)
1986-87	Mark Carter (Runcorn)
1985-86	Jeff Johnson (Altrincham)
1984-85	Alan Cordice (Wealdstone)
1983-84	Brian Thompson (Maidstone Utd)

NON LEAGUE MANAGER OF THE YEAR

GRAHAM WESTLEY
(Stevenage Borough)

You cannot really do much better as a Non-League Manager than win The Blue Square Premier and promotion to The Football League in style by eleven points and reach Wembley in The F.A.Trophy final. In his second spell at the club manager Graham Westley used the experience of his original successes at Broadhall Way and a very lively managerial spell at Farnborough. As a successful business man and a very confident character, his undoubted achievements had not always brought the respect that his managerial successes deserved, but having learnt from these experiences, his wonderful achievements with the club (now to be named Stevenage F.C.), were rightly acclaimed by the non-league football world.

PAST WINNERS

2008-09 Steve Fallon (Histon)
2007-08 Tony Greenwood (Fleetwood Town)
2006-07 John Still (Dagenham & Redbridge)
2005-06 Steve Burr (Northwich Victoria)
2004-05 Paul Fairclough (Barnet)
2003-04 Graham Turner (Hereford United)
2002-03 Gary Johnson (Yeovil Town)
2001-02 Nigel Clough (Burton Albion)
2000-01 Jeff King (Canvey Island)
1999-00 Jan Molby (Kidderminster Harr.)
1998-99 Brendan Phillips (Nuneaton Boro')
1997-98 Steve Cotterill (Cheltenham Town)
1996-97 Paul Futcher (Southport)
1995-96 Paul Fairclough (Stevenage Boro)
1994-95 Sammy McIlroy (Macclesfield T.)
1993-94 Bill Punton (Diss Town)
1992-93 Martin O'Neill (Wycombe Wndrs)

PECKING ORDER 2009-2010 by A J Sarnecki

Position in Season				Step	League	FA Cup			FA Trophy			FA Vase			C	T	V	Total
06-07	07-08	08-09	09-10			ent	xmt	won	ent	xmt	won	ent	xmt	won	pts	pts	pts	pts
						1		1	3	2/8	1	1	4/6	1				
1	1	1	1	1	FOOTBALL CONFERENCE Premier	24	240	27	24	192	38				291	302	0	593
3	3	2	2	2	FOOTBALL CONFERENCE North	22	132	32	22	132	23				186	221	0	407
2	2	3	3	2	FOOTBALL CONFERENCE South	22	132	32	22	132	22				186	220	0	406
5	4	6	4	3	ISTHMIAN Premier	22	88	29	22	44	28				139	138	0	277
6	6	5	5	3	NORTHERN PREMIER Premier	22	88	26	21	44	22				136	129	0	265
4	5	4	6	3	SOUTHERN Premier	21	84	31	21	42	23				136	128	0	264
new	11	9	7	4	NORTHERN PREMIER First North	22	44	27	22	0	22				93	88	0	181
9	7	7	8	4	SOUTHERN First Midland	22	44	27	22	0	21				93	87	0	180
11	9	10	9	4	SOUTHERN First South & East	22	44	35	22	0	12				101	78	0	179
8	10	8	10	4	ISTHMIAN First South	22	44	23	22	0	22				89	88	0	177
new	12=	12	11	4	NORTHERN PREMIER First South	22	44	19	22	0	18				85	84	0	169
10	8	11	12	4	ISTHMIAN First North	21	42	26	22	0	12				89	78	0	167
12	12=	13	13	5	NORTHERN First	22	0	24				22	26	39	46	0	87	133
13	14=	14	14	5	MIDLAND ALLIANCE	22	0	22				22	24	38	44	0	84	128
21	18	16	15	5	UNITED COUNTIES Premier	21	0	23				21	30	32	44	0	83	127
16	24	17	16	5	NORTH WEST COUNTIES Premier	21	0	19				22	24	27	40	0	73	113
14	16	15	17	5	EASTERN COUNTIES Premier	18	0	16				19	24	35	34	0	78	112
22	19	18	18	5	SPARTAN SOUTH MIDLANDS Premier	22	0	22				22	22	23	44	0	67	111
15	17	20	19	5	WESTERN Premier	20	0	14				20	26	28	34	0	74	108
20	22=	24	20	5	SUSSEX COUNTY First	20	0	16				20	16	34	36	0	70	106
19	14=	19	21	5	WESSEX Premier	22	0	19				22	22	20	41	0	64	105
18	20	22	22	5	COMBINED COUNTIES Premier	21	0	17				21	18	27	38	0	66	104
17	21	21	23=	5	NORTHERN COUNTIES EAST Premier	19	0	13				19	18	24	32	0	61	93
23	22=	23	23=	5	HELLENIC Premier	17	0	23				20	10	23	40	0	53	93
26	26	28	25	5	ESSEX SENIOR	14	0	7				17	12	14	21	0	43	64
24	25	25	26	5	KENT Premier	12	0	13				15	8	14	25	0	37	62
25	29	27	27=	6	NORTHERN Second	13	0	9				18	6	13	22	0	37	59
	new	34	27=	6	EAST MIDLAND COUNTIES	15	0	8				19	4	13	23	0	36	59
32	31	29=	29	6	WEST MIDLAND REGIONAL Premier	12	0	8				15	0	17	20	0	32	52
27	30	26	30	6	EASTERN COUNTIES First	11	0	7				18	6	7	18	0	31	49
33	32	29=	31	6	MIDLAND COMBINATION Premier	12	0	6				18	0	9	18	0	27	45
new	34	35	32	6	SOUTH WEST PENINSULA Premier	8	0	5				13	0	15	13	0	28	41
30	33	33	33	6	WESTERN First	10	0	6				15	0	9	16	0	24	40
28	28	32	34	6	NORTHERN COUNTIES EAST First	9	0	4				17	0	9	13	0	26	39
31	27	29=	35=	6	NORTH WEST COUNTIES First	8	0	2				15	6	7	10	0	28	38
37	35	37	35=	6	SPARTAN SOUTH MIDLANDS First	8	0	5				12	0	13	13	0	25	38
40	41	38	37	6	WESSEX First	7	0	2				10	0	7	9	0	17	26
34	36	36	38	6	SUSSEX COUNTY Second	8	0	4				9	0	1	12	0	10	22
41=	39	39	39	6	UNITED COUNTIES First	3	0	1				10	0	4	4	0	14	18
38	42=	40	40	6	COMBINED COUNTIES First	6	0	1				8	0	2	7	0	10	17
44=	40	43	41	6	HELLENIC First East	2	0	3				4	0	2	5	0	6	11
36	37	42	42	7	CENTRAL MIDLANDS Supreme	0	0	0				6	0	4	0	0	10	10
41=	44	41	43	6	HELLENIC First West	3	0	1				5	0	0	4	0	5	9
35	38	44=	44=	7	LEICESTERSHIRE SENIOR Premier	0	0	0				3	0	2	0	0	5	5
new	42=	44=	44=	7	SOUTH WEST PENINSULA First West	0	0	0				3	0	2	0	0	5	5
47=	47	46=	46	7	SUSSEX COUNTY Third	0	0	0				3	0	0	0	0	3	3
	52	46=	47=	7	WEST MIDLAND REGIONAL First	0	0	0				2	0	0	0	0	2	2
49=	49=	49=	47=	7	WEARSIDE	0	0	0				2	0	0	0	0	2	2
	48=	49=	47=	7	HERTS SENIOR COUNTY Premier	0	0	0				2	0	0	0	0	2	2
new	46	52=	50=	7	SOUTH WEST PENINSULA First East	0	0	0				1	0	0	0	0	1	1
		52=	50=	7	ESSEX OLYMPIAN Premier	0	0	0				1	0	0	0	0	1	1
		52=	50=	7	NORTH BERKSHIRE First	0	0	0				1	0	0	0	0	1	1
49=	48		50=	7	DORSET PREMIER	0	0	0				1	0	0	0	0	1	1
			50=	7	SPARTAN SOUTH MIDLANDS Second	0	0	0				1	0	0	0	0	1	1
			50=	7	WILTSHIRE Premier	0	0	0				1	0	0	0	0	1	1

Points are given for status (acceptance into each of the three competitions), for prestige (exemption from early rounds) and performance (number of wins, however achieved, even by walkover). Entry to the Vase is valued at one point, that to the Trophy at 3. Cup entry gives a further bonus of one point. The number of entries from each league is shown in the appropriate column. Points for exemptions are valued at two for each round missed. The entry in the table is of the total points so gained by the given league, not the number of teams given exemptions. Finally, all wins are valued at one point, regardless of opposition: giving extra points for defeating 'stronger' opponents would be too arbitrary. After all, if they lost then they were not stronger on the day!

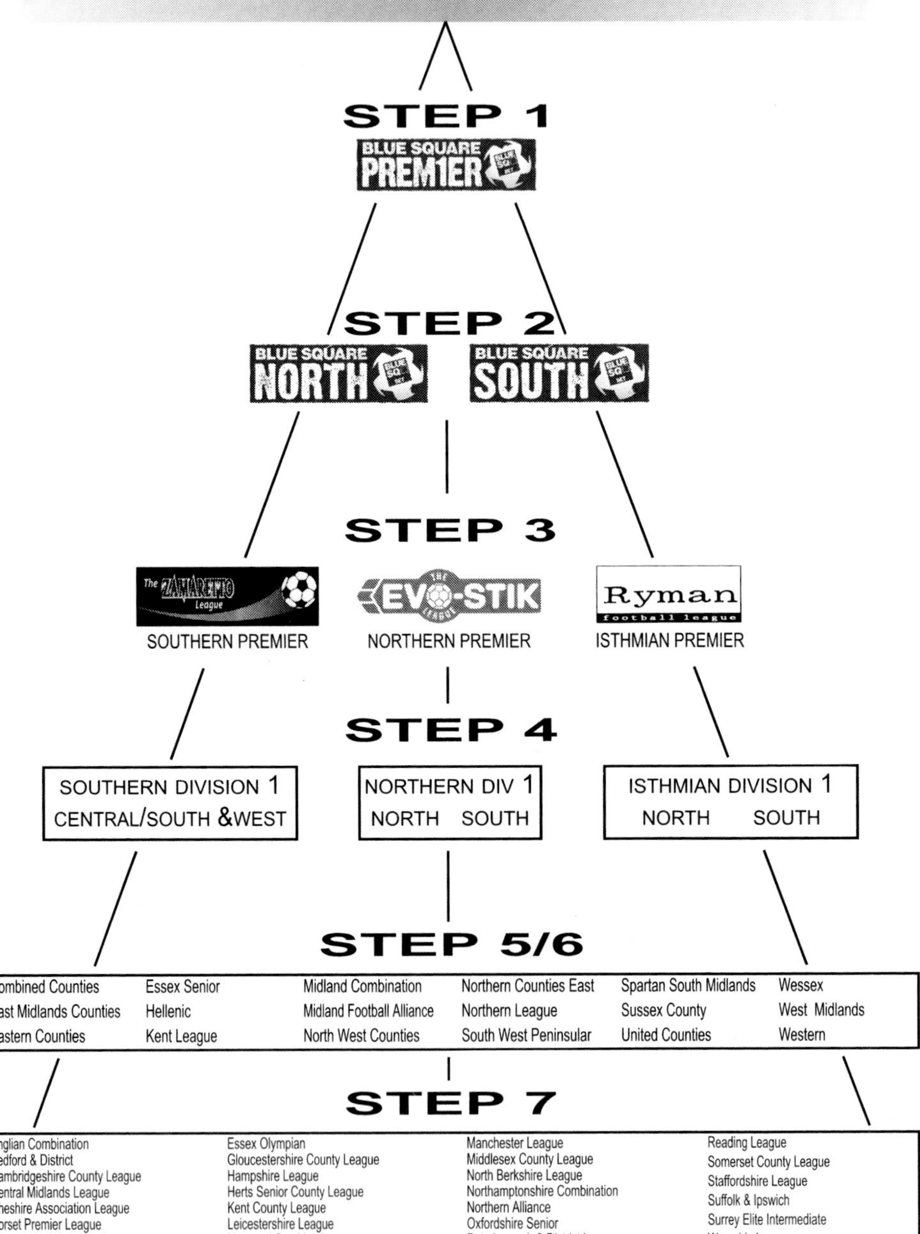
FOOTBALL LEAGUE
STEP 1
BLUE SQUARE PREMIER
STEP 2
BLUE SQUARE NORTH
BLUE SQUARE SOUTH
STEP 3
The ZAMARETTO League
SOUTHERN PREMIER
EVO-STIK
NORTHERN PREMIER
Ryman football league
ISTHMIAN PREMIER
STEP 4
SOUTHERN DIVISION 1
CENTRAL/SOUTH &WEST
NORTHERN DIV 1
NORTH SOUTH
ISTHMIAN DIVISION 1
NORTH SOUTH
STEP 5/6
Combined Counties
East Midlands Counties
Eastern Counties
Essex Senior
Hellenic
Kent League
Midland Combination
Midland Football Alliance
North West Counties
Northern Counties East
Northern League
South West Peninsular
Spartan South Midlands
Sussex County
United Counties
Wessex
West Midlands
Western
STEP 7
Anglian Combination
Bedford & District
Cambridgeshire County League
Central Midlands League
Cheshire Association League
Dorset Premier League
Essex & Suffolk Border League
Essex Olympian
Gloucestershire County League
Hampshire League
Herts Senior County League
Kent County League
Leicestershire League
Liverpool Combination
Manchester League
Middlesex County League
North Berkshire League
Northamptonshire Combination
Northern Alliance
Oxfordshire Senior
Peterborough & District League
Reading League
Somerset County League
Staffordshire League
Suffolk & Ipswich
Surrey Elite Intermediate
Wearside League

BLUE SQUARE PREM1ER

		P	W	D	L	F	A	GD	Pts
1	Stevenage Borough	44	30	9	5	79	24	55	99
2	Luton Town	44	26	10	8	84	40	44	88
3	Oxford United	44	25	11	8	64	31	33	86
4	Rushden & Diamonds	44	22	13	9	77	39	38	79
5	York City	44	22	12	10	62	35	27	78
6	Kettering Town	44	18	12	14	51	41	10	66
7	Crawley Town	44	19	9	16	50	57	-7	66
8	AFC Wimbledon	44	18	10	16	61	47	14	64
9	Mansfield Town	44	17	11	16	69	60	9	62
10	Cambridge United	44	15	14	15	65	53	12	59
11	Wrexham	44	15	13	16	45	39	6	58
12	Salisbury City (-10 pts)	44	21	5	18	58	63	-5	58
13	Kidderminster Harriers	44	15	12	17	57	52	5	57
14	Altrincham	44	13	15	16	53	51	2	54
15	Barrow	44	13	13	18	50	67	-17	52
16	Tamworth	44	11	16	17	42	52	-10	49
17	Hayes & Yeading United	44	12	12	20	59	85	-26	48
18	Histon	44	11	13	20	44	67	-23	46
19	Eastbourne Borough	44	11	13	20	42	72	-30	46
20	Gateshead	44	13	7	24	46	69	-23	46
21	Forest Green Rovers	44	12	9	23	50	76	-26	45
22	Ebbsfleet United	44	12	8	24	50	82	-32	44
23	Grays Athletic (-2)	44	5	13	26	35	91	-56	28
24	Chester City - Did not finish the season - results expunged.								

PROMOTION PLAY-OFFS

SF(1) Rushden & Diamonds 1 Oxford United 1 29/04/10 Att: 4535
SF(1) **York City** 1 Luton Town 0 29/04/10 Att: 6204
SF(2) **Oxford United** 2 Rushden & Diamonds 0 03/05/10 Att: 11963
SF(2) Luton Town 0 **York City** 1 03/05/10 Att: 9781
F **Oxford United** 3 York City 1 16/05/10 Att: 38957 (at Wembley Stadium)

	1	2	3	4	5	6	7	8	9	10	11	12	13	14	15	16	17	18	19	20	21	22	23
1 AFC Wimbledon	-	1-1	0-2	0-0	1-1	2-0	3-0	2-0	2-0	0-2	5-0	4-0	1-2	0-1	1-1	2-0	0-1	0-1	4-0	0-3	0-1	2-2	0-1
2 Altrincham	0-1	-	0-1	0-2	0-0	3-0	1-1	2-2	3-2	1-1	3-2	2-1	2-0	3-2	0-1	1-2	0-1	2-2	5-0	0-1	0-0	1-3	0-0
3 Barrow	2-2	0-3	-	0-1	4-1	3-2	2-0	1-1	3-3	2-2	1-1	0-0	0-2	1-0	0-1	3-1	1-1	1-6	0-1	0-0	1-0	2-1	0-0
4 Cambridge United	2-2	0-0	0-2	-	0-1	0-1	4-0	7-0	3-0	3-0	4-1	2-1	0-2	2-0	3-4	3-2	1-1	2-2	3-1	1-3	2-0	2-0	0-1
5 Crawley Town	2-1	1-0	0-1	1-0	-	2-2	2-1	3-1	1-4	1-1	1-0	2-0	2-1	2-2	2-1	0-2	1-2	2-1	2-0	0-3	2-0	1-0	3-1
6 Eastbourne Boro'	1-0	2-2	2-1	2-2	0-2	-	1-2	1-0	2-1	2-2	3-1	1-1	0-1	0-0	0-1	1-2	1-0	1-1	0-1	0-6	1-1	2-1	3-1
7 Ebbsfleet United	2-2	1-2	1-4	1-3	0-0	3-2	-	4-3	2-0	2-1	1-2	0-1	1-2	0-0	1-6	2-1	0-2	0-0	1-2	2-1	0-1	0-1	1-0
8 Forest Green R.	2-5	4-3	1-0	1-1	1-0	1-1	0-0	-	1-0	2-1	0-0	2-0	1-2	1-1	0-1	1-4	0-1	1-0	3-1	0-1	3-4	0-2	2-1
9 Gateshead	1-0	1-0	2-1	2-0	2-1	3-0	1-3	3-1	-	3-0	0-0	0-3	0-2	0-2	0-1	1-3	0-1	0-0	2-1	0-1	1-1	1-0	1-2
10 Grays Athletic	2-4	0-3	3-3	2-0	2-3	1-0	0-3	2-1	0-0	-	0-0	0-1	0-0	1-3	0-2	1-1	0-4	0-3	0-2	1-2	1-0	0-2	0-4
11 Hayes & Yeading	1-0	1-2	1-1	3-0	2-1	1-1	4-2	2-3	3-2	4-0	-	0-2	1-2	2-2	2-3	1-1	2-1	1-6	3-4	1-1	2-2	0-1	1-1
12 Histon	1-3	0-0	2-2	1-1	0-1	2-0	1-0	5-2	0-0	0-0	3-3	-	1-0	1-1	0-2	0-5	3-4	0-1	2-0	0-2	1-0	0-0	1-1
13 Kettering Town	1-2	2-0	2-1	0-1	1-1	4-0	3-0	0-2	4-0	2-0	0-1	1-1	-	0-2	0-0	2-2	1-1	0-3	1-2	1-1	0-0	2-2	0-1
14 Kidderminster H.	0-1	3-0	1-2	1-0	1-0	0-2	2-2	2-1	3-2	4-1	1-0	3-0	0-1	-	1-2	3-1	3-1	1-1	0-1	0-2	0-0	2-0	0-1
15 Luton Town	1-2	0-0	1-0	2-2	3-0	4-1	2-3	2-1	2-1	6-0	8-0	6-3	0-1	3-1	-	4-1	2-1	0-2	4-0	0-1	2-1	1-0	1-1
16 Mansfield Town	0-1	1-1	4-1	2-1	4-0	1-1	3-0	1-0	0-2	0-0	3-1	1-1	0-0	3-3	0-0	-	2-1	3-2	4-2	2-3	0-0	0-1	0-1
17 Oxford United	2-0	1-0	1-0	0-0	3-1	4-0	4-2	0-0	2-1	5-0	1-2	2-0	1-1	0-0	2-0	2-0	-	1-0	1-0	2-1	0-1	1-0	2-1
18 Rushden & Dia.	0-1	0-1	4-1	1-1	1-1	2-0	2-0	4-2	8-0	5-4	2-1	2-1	0-0	2-1	1-1	1-0	1-1	-	0-2	1-0	3-2	0-0	0-1
19 Salisbury City	0-2	4-1	3-0	2-1	2-2	1-1	3-1	1-3	0-1	2-0	3-1	3-0	2-0	1-0	1-1	0-1	1-1	1-3	-	0-1	1-0	1-1	1-0
20 Stevenage Boro'	0-0	1-1	4-0	4-1	2-0	2-0	3-0	2-0	5-3	1-1	4-0	1-0	2-0	2-0	0-1	3-1	1-0	2-1	3-1	-	1-1	0-0	1-0
21 Tamworth	2-2	0-2	3-0	0-0	0-1	1-1	3-4	0-0	1-0	2-1	0-2	1-3	1-3	2-1	1-1	2-4	0-0	0-1	2-0	1-0	-	2-1	2-3
22 Wrexham	1-0	1-1	0-0	2-2	2-0	3-0	1-1	1-0	0-0	2-1	0-2	3-0	1-2	2-2	3-0	2-1	0-1	0-1	1-2	0-1	0-0	-	1-0
23 York City	5-0	2-1	3-0	2-2	2-0	0-1	1-0	2-0	1-0	1-1	4-1	3-1	2-0	3-2	0-0	3-0	1-1	0-0	1-2	1-1	1-1	2-1	-

		P	W	D	L	F	A	GD	Pts
1	Southport	40	25	11	4	91	45	46	86
2	Fleetwood Town	40	26	7	7	86	44	42	85
3	Alfreton Town	40	21	11	8	77	45	32	74
4	Workington	40	20	10	10	46	37	9	70
5	Droylsden	40	18	10	12	82	62	20	64
6	Corby Town	40	18	9	13	73	62	11	63
7	Hinckley United	40	16	14	10	60	52	8	62
8	Ilkeston Town	40	16	13	11	53	45	8	61
9	Stalybridge Celtic	40	16	7	17	71	64	7	55
10	Eastwood Town	40	15	9	16	50	55	-5	54
11	AFC Telford United	40	14	9	17	52	55	-3	51
12	Northwich Victoria (-10)	40	15	13	12	62	55	7	48
13	Blyth Spartons	40	13	9	18	67	72	-5	48
14	Gainsborough Trinity	40	12	11	17	50	57	-7	47
15	Hyde United	40	11	12	17	45	72	-27	45
16	Stafford Rangers	40	10	14	16	59	70	-11	44
17	Solihull Moors	40	11	9	20	47	58	-11	42
18	Gloucester City	40	12	6	22	47	59	-12	42
19	Redditch United	40	10	8	22	49	83	-34	38
20	Vauxhall Motors	40	7	14	19	45	81	-36	35
21	Harrogate Town	40	8	6	26	41	80	-39	30
22	Farsley Celtic - Did not finish - results expunged.								

PROMOTION PLAY-OFFS - SEMI-FINALS

SF(1) **Droylsden** 2 Fleetwood Town 0 28/04/10 Att: 1104
SF(1) Workington 0 **Alfreton Town** 1 28/04/10 Att: 1483
SF(2) **Alfreton Town** 3 Workington 1 02/05/10 Att: 1475
SF(2) **Fleetwood Town** 3 Droylsden 1 aet (5-3p) 02/05/10 Att: 2862
F **Fleetwood Town** 2 Alfreton Town 1 09/05/10 Att: 3592

	1	2	3	4	5	6	7	8	9	10	11	12	13	14	15	16	17	18	19	20	21
1 AFC Telford Utd	-	2-0	1-1	2-4	1-2	1-1	0-0	2-2	0-1	2-1	2-2	4-0	0-0	1-2	3-0	0-0	0-2	2-1	0-1	5-1	1-0
2 Alfreton Town	4-0	-	1-0	1-0	5-0	1-1	1-4	1-0	3-1	3-1	3-2	4-0	2-0	3-2	3-0	3-0	1-1	3-1	3-5	2-2	2-0
3 Blyth Spartans	4-0	2-0	-	1-2	2-2	1-3	2-3	2-1	0-3	1-0	6-1	4-3	1-4	0-1	1-0	2-0	0-2	2-2	4-1	3-2	0-0
4 Corby Town	1-2	1-2	4-2	-	1-0	1-1	0-2	2-2	3-6	3-0	1-1	2-0	2-2	1-0	2-2	1-2	1-1	3-2	5-1	4-1	0-2
5 Droylsden	1-5	0-0	2-1	1-2	-	0-1	2-0	4-1	2-2	5-0	0-0	1-0	2-0	5-1	6-1	5-3	0-3	7-1	3-2	1-1	0-1
6 Eastwood Town	1-1	2-1	4-2	0-1	2-1	-	0-1	1-0	0-3	1-0	1-0	2-0	0-3	1-1	3-1	2-1	0-3	0-0	1-3	0-0	1-2
7 Fleetwood Town	3-1	2-2	4-2	4-2	3-0	3-1	-	2-2	3-1	2-2	3-1	1-1	1-0	0-3	8-0	3-0	4-0	2-1	2-0	4-2	4-0
8 Gainsborough Trinity	0-1	3-2	2-0	2-0	4-2	1-4	2-0	-	1-0	1-1	1-1	2-1	0-0	1-4	3-0	0-0	2-4	1-3	1-3	2-0	0-1
9 Gloucester City	0-1	1-2	3-1	1-2	1-4	1-3	1-2	1-0	-	0-1	3-5	2-0	0-1	0-1	2-0	1-0	2-2	2-0	1-2	1-0	0-2
10 Harrogate Town	0-3	0-4	2-5	0-4	2-2	0-1	0-1	2-0	1-1	-	3-1	2-0	0-1	2-1	3-2	0-1	2-3	1-4	0-4	3-0	1-2
11 Hinckley United	2-0	2-1	1-1	1-1	1-1	0-0	0-2	2-0	1-0	3-2	-	1-2	1-0	1-1	5-1	0-3	4-1	3-1	0-0	1-1	1-2
12 Hyde United	1-1	1-5	0-3	1-3	2-1	1-0	2-1	3-2	1-1	1-0	3-2	-	1-1	1-1	3-2	1-1	1-1	1-0	2-1	2-2	0-2
13 Ilkeston Town	2-1	0-0	2-1	3-2	1-0	1-0	0-1	0-0	0-0	3-3	0-1	1-1	-	1-1	3-2	1-0	3-2	2-3	3-2	4-0	1-3
14 Northwich Victoria	2-0	1-1	5-1	2-2	2-5	4-3	0-3	0-1	1-0	3-2	0-1	3-1	4-1	-	0-2	2-0	1-1	2-2	2-1	0-0	2-3
15 Redditch United	3-1	3-0	2-2	1-0	1-3	1-2	0-0	0-3	4-1	2-0	0-2	0-0	2-2	1-1	-	1-4	2-2	1-2	1-4	1-1	2-1
16 Solihull Moors	0-1	1-1	1-1	3-0	1-2	2-1	1-2	0-1	0-1	1-0	2-4	3-0	0-3	1-1	1-2	-	1-1	1-1	2-2	4-0	1-2
17 Southport	3-0	1-3	3-2	4-0	3-3	5-1	5-0	0-0	3-2	3-1	1-1	4-1	1-1	2-1	2-0	3-0	-	4-2	2-1	3-0	2-0
18 Stafford Rangers	2-0	1-1	1-1	0-2	2-2	3-3	2-2	2-1	1-0	1-0	2-3	1-1	0-1	2-2	0-1	2-3	1-2	-	0-2	3-1	2-0
19 Stalybridge Celtic	0-3	0-1	0-1	1-3	2-2	1-0	2-3	3-2	4-1	3-0	0-0	2-4	1-0	1-1	3-0	4-1	0-1	2-2	-	3-1	2-2
20 Vauxhall Motors	3-1	1-1	1-1	2-4	1-2	3-2	2-1	2-2	0-0	1-2	1-1	1-0	4-2	1-0	0-5	0-2	1-3	2-2	3-2	-	1-1
21 Workington	2-1	1-1	3-1	1-1	0-1	1-0	1-0	1-1	2-0	1-1	0-1	2-2	0-0	0-1	1-0	1-0	0-2	1-1	1-0	1-0	-

		P	W	D	L	F	A	GD	Pts
1	Newport County	42	32	7	3	93	26	67	103
2	Dover Athletic	42	22	9	11	66	47	19	75
3	Chelmsford City	42	22	9	11	62	48	14	75
4	Bath City	42	20	12	10	66	46	20	72
5	Woking	42	21	9	12	57	44	13	72
6	Havant & Waterlooville	42	19	14	9	65	44	21	71
7	Braintree Town	42	18	17	7	56	41	15	71
8	Staines Town	42	18	13	11	59	40	19	67
9	Welling United	42	18	9	15	66	51	15	63
10	Thurrock	42	16	13	13	66	60	6	61
11	Eastleigh	42	17	9	16	71	66	5	60
12	Bromley	42	15	10	17	68	64	4	55
13	St Albans City	42	15	10	17	46	55	-9	55
14	Hampton & Richmond Boro'	42	14	9	19	56	66	-10	51
15	Basingstoke Town	42	13	10	19	49	68	-19	49
16	Maidenhead United	42	12	12	18	52	59	-7	48
17	Dorchester Town	42	13	9	20	56	74	-18	48
18	Bishop's Stortford	42	12	11	19	48	59	-11	47
19	Lewes	42	9	15	18	49	63	-14	42
20	Worcester City	42	10	10	22	48	60	-12	40
21	Weston-super-Mare	42	5	8	29	48	93	-45	23
22	Weymouth	42	5	7	30	31	104	-73	22

PROMOTION PLAY-OFFS - SEMI-FINALS

SF(1) **Bath City** 2 Chelmsford City 0 27/04/10 Att: 1425
SF(1) **Woking** 2 Dover Athletic 1 27/04/10 Att: 3080
SF(2) Chelmsford City 0 **Bath City** 1 01/05/10 Att: 1650
SF(2) Dover Athletic 0 Woking 0 01/05/10 Att: 2970
F **Bath City** 1 Woking 0 09/05/10 Att: 4865

	1	2	3	4	5	6	7	8	9	10	11	12	13	14	15	16	17	18	19	20	21	22
1 Basingstoke Tn	-	1-0	0-2	0-1	2-3	2-1	2-1	1-3	0-1	1-2	1-1	1-1	0-0	1-5	1-1	0-1	0-4	1-1	2-1	2-1	1-2	0-1
2 Bath City	4-3	-	2-2	2-4	0-0	1-0	2-0	0-0	0-2	1-3	1-1	1-1	1-0	1-1	0-0	2-0	1-0	2-1	1-0	2-0	5-0	1-1
3 Bishop's Stortford	0-2	1-5	-	0-0	3-0	0-1	2-0	0-2	0-1	0-1	1-0	0-0	1-2	0-0	2-0	2-2	0-0	0-4	3-0	0-1	0-3	2-1
4 Braintree Town	1-2	2-0	2-0	-	1-1	2-1	2-0	1-2	1-1	1-1	0-2	3-0	2-0	1-2	2-2	2-0	3-1	1-0	1-0	3-2	1-0	0-0
5 Bromley	2-0	1-2	1-1	1-1	-	3-3	3-1	2-2	3-0	1-2	0-2	3-0	1-2	2-3	2-0	0-2	2-3	0-1	1-1	4-0	3-1	2-0
6 Chelmsford City	1-2	4-3	3-0	1-1	1-2	-	1-0	1-1	2-2	1-0	1-1	2-1	1-1	0-0	2-0	0-1	1-0	3-1	2-2	2-1	0-2	1-0
7 Dorchester Town	6-1	2-2	2-0	5-0	0-0	0-3	-	1-3	1-2	2-1	4-3	1-1	4-2	0-0	3-0	2-2	1-0	1-2	4-2	0-0	1-1	1-1
8 Dover Athletic	2-3	2-1	2-0	0-0	1-0	0-1	4-1	-	2-1	4-2	4-0	2-0	1-1	1-2	1-1	0-0	1-0	2-0	5-3	2-0	0-2	0-2
9 Eastleigh	6-0	1-1	1-1	1-2	6-1	3-1	2-0	1-2	-	0-0	0-1	1-0	0-3	1-4	0-1	0-0	2-8	1-3	3-1	4-0	0-2	4-1
10 Hampton & Rich.	0-1	3-1	1-3	2-2	0-2	2-1	1-2	1-4	4-1	-	1-1	1-2	4-0	0-4	3-0	1-4	1-1	2-2	2-1	3-0	0-2	2-2
11 Havant & W"ville	0-2	2-2	2-1	1-1	2-1	5-2	0-1	2-1	2-2	1-1	-	1-1	1-0	4-0	0-1	1-0	1-1	2-2	6-0	3-1	1-1	3-2
12 Lewes	0-0	1-2	2-1	2-2	1-0	0-2	5-0	6-2	1-2	1-0	0-3	-	1-2	0-3	0-0	1-1	1-1	3-1	2-0	1-1	0-2	3-3
13 Maidenhead U.	3-2	1-2	4-0	0-0	4-0	0-2	1-2	0-0	0-3	2-1	0-2	1-1	-	1-3	0-3	2-1	0-2	2-0	0-0	1-1	1-2	1-1
14 Newport County	1-0	1-0	1-0	1-0	2-0	4-0	3-0	3-0	5-1	3-1	2-0	2-2	4-1	-	5-0	1-0	5-0	2-2	2-0	1-1	1-0	1-0
15 St Albans City	2-0	0-2	2-4	1-1	2-0	0-1	2-1	1-2	2-1	1-2	1-1	1-1	1-0	0-1	-	1-3	1-0	1-2	2-1	2-1	0-1	2-0
16 Staines Town	0-1	1-1	2-2	2-1	2-2	0-1	3-0	0-0	1-2	4-0	1-2	2-1	1-1	1-0	4-3	-	3-0	1-1	3-0	3-1	3-0	0-1
17 Thurrock	0-0	3-1	2-2	1-2	3-6	1-1	5-2	0-2	3-2	0-2	0-0	3-1	2-2	2-1	0-0	1-2	-	3-2	2-1	2-1	2-2	2-1
18 Welling United	1-1	0-2	0-2	0-0	0-2	0-1	1-1	0-1	1-2	2-0	1-0	1-0	3-1	0-2	3-2	3-0	2-2	-	3-1	7-1	1-2	1-0
19 Weston-s-Mare	1-1	0-2	1-3	1-2	3-3	1-2	0-2	3-1	2-2	1-1	1-2	3-2	1-4	1-4	2-3	0-1	1-3	1-2	-	3-0	1-1	3-1
20 Weymouth	0-6	0-2	2-6	1-1	1-5	1-4	2-0	1-2	0-5	1-0	0-1	3-1	0-5	1-3	0-2	1-2	0-0	0-3	1-2	-	0-0	2-1
21 Woking	4-2	1-3	1-0	0-0	2-1	1-2	3-1	2-0	0-0	3-1	2-0	2-0	1-1	0-1	0-1	0-0	0-1	0-5	2-1	4-0	-	1-0
22 Worcester City	1-1	0-2	1-1	2-3	1-2	1-2	4-0	1-0	4-1	0-1	0-2	1-2	1-0	1-4	0-0	0-0	1-2	0-1	4-1	3-1	3-2	-

PLAY-OFF FINAL ACTION...

Constable fires home the second goal against York City.

York's 'keeper, Ingram, thwarts Oxford United's Matt Green.

However, Ingram can do nothing to stop Green's shot this time as he scores Oxford's first of the final.

Photos: Keith Clayton.

A.F.C. WIMBLEDON

Chairman: Erik Samuelson
Secretary: David Charles (T) 020 8547 3528
(E) david.charles@afcwimbledon.co.uk

Additional Committee Members:
Ivor Heller, Nigel Higgs, Keith McGuiness.

Manager: Terry Brown
Programme Editor: David Charles (E) david.charles@afcwimbledon.co.uk

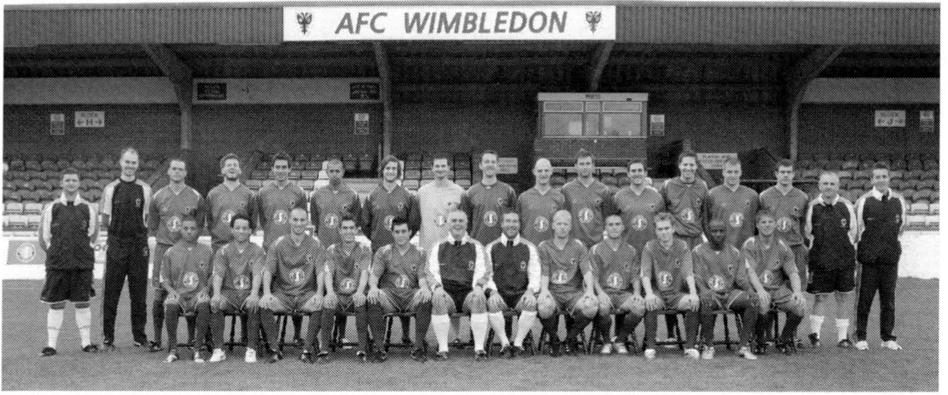

Back row (standing) Simon Bassey (coach) Mike Rayner (physio) Steve Watson, Luke Garrard, Steve Wales, Simon Sweeney, Paul Smith, Josh Lennie, Andy Little, Darren Grieves, Antony Howard, Mark Rooney, Michael Haswell, Jon Boswell, Stephen Goddard, John Morris (Reserve manager) Steve West(kit man)
Front row (seated) Byron Bubb, Wes Daly, Simon Sobihy, Paul Barnes, Lee Kersey, Dave Anderson (manager) Jon Turner (assistant manager) Steve Butler, Chris Gell, Joe Paris, Roscoe Dsane, Richard Butler.

Club Factfile

Founded: 2002 **Nickname:** Dons
Previous Names: None
Previous Leagues: Combined Counties 2002-04. Isthmian 2004-08.

Club Colours (change): All dark blue. (All yellow).

Ground: Kingsmeadow, Kingston, Surrey KT1 3PB (T) 020 8547 3528
Capacity: 4,500 **Seats:** 1,047 **Covered:** 2,700 **Clubhouse:** Yes **Shop:** Yes
Previous Grounds: Bottom Meadow (Shared with Sandhurst Town)
Simple Directions
From Kingston: From the one way system take Richmond Road (A308) towards Kingston Hospital. Turn right onto Cambridge Road (A2043), and Kingsmeadow is less than a mile on the right. From Central London: Take the A3 out of London, exiting at New Malden/Worcester Park. Cross over the A3, and take the Malden Road (A2043) towards Kingston. Follow this to the next roundabout. Take the first exit into Kingston Road (A2043 still) and Kingsmeadow is one mile on the left. From M25 Junction 10, take the A3 northbound into London. At the exit for New Malden/Worcester Park, turn off and take the left into Malden Road (A2043) towards Kingston Follow this to the next roundabout. Take the first exit into Kingston Rd (A2043 still) and Kingsmeadow is one mile on the left.

Record Attendance: 4,722 v St. Albans City - 25/04/09
Record Victory: 9-0 v Slough - 2006-07
Record Defeat: 0-4 v Hampton & Richmond B. (H) - 01/04/06. 0-4 v Walton & Hersham (A) - 02/04/05
Record Goalscorer: Kevin Cooper - 107 in 105 appearances (July 04 - May 07)
Record Appearances: Anthony Howard - 148
Additional Records:

Senior Honours: Combined Counties League & Cup 2003-04. Isthmian Division 1 2004-05. Surrey Senior Cup 2004-05. Conference South 2008-09.

10 YEAR RECORD

00-01	01-02	02-03	03-04	04-05	05-06	06-07	07-08	08-09	09-10
		CC 3	CCP 1	Isth1 1	Isth P 4	Isth P 5	Isth P 3	Conf S 1	Conf 8

AFC WIMBLEDON

No.	Date	Comp	H/A	Opponents	Att:	Result	Goalscorers	Pos
1	8/8/09	BSP	H	Luton Town	4488	D 1-1	Main pen 80	9
2	11/8/09	BSP	A	Eastbourne Borough	3108	L 0-1		17
3	15/8/09	BSP	A	Kettering Town	1746	W 2-1	Kedwell 2 (9, pen 66)	12
4	18/8/09	BSP	H	Salisbury City	3591	W 4-0	Moore 2 (11, 90), Kedwell 2 (pen 70, 88)	6
5	22/8/09	BSP	A	Altrincham	1438	W 1-0	Kedwell 82	4
6	29/8/09	BSP	H	Oxford United	4304	L 0-1		7
7	31/8/09	BSP	A	Grays Athletic	1762	W 4-2	Johnson 10, Main 2 (pen 21, pen 62), Kedwell 90	3
8	5/9/09	BSP	A	Tamworth	1669	D 2-2	Kedwell 2 (49, 59)	6
9	12/9/09	BSP	H	Cambridge United	4128	D 0-0		10
10	19/9/09	BSP	A	Ebbsfleet United	2005	D 2-2	Moore 28, Montague 90	12
11	22/9/09	BSP	H	Crawley Town	3408	D 1-1	Kedwell 76	12
12	26/9/09	BSP	H	Histon	3392	W 4-0	Moore 13, Taylor 56, Gregory 75, Kedwell pen 78	10
13	29/9/09	BSP	A	Rushden & Diamonds	1624	W 1-0	Montague 2	4
14	3/10/09	BSP	H	Kidderminster Harriers	3601	L 0-1		8
15	10/10/09	BSP	A	Forest Green Rovers	1921	W 5-2	Taylor 1, Main 2 (11, 80), Kedwell 2 (23, 58)	6
16	17/10/09	BSP	H	Kettering Town	3745	L 1-2	Main 22	8
17	14/11/09	BSP	A	Barrow	1614	D 2-2	Godfrey 63, Main 76	10
18	21/11/09	BSP	H	York City	4016	L 0-1		12
19	24/11/09	BSP	H	Ebbsfleet United	2942	W 3-0	Moore 2 (42, 73), Kedwell 63	10
20	28/11/09	BSP	A	Kidderminster Harriers	1788	W 1-0	Kedwell 20	9
21	1/12/09	BSP	A	Salisbury City	1157	W 2-0	Main 2 (63, 69)	6
22	5/12/09	BSP	H	Gateshead	3209	W 2-0	Gregory 22, Wellard 60	6
23	26/12/09	BSP	H	Hayes & Yeading United	3659	W 5-0	Kedwell 2 (6, 17), Cumbers 10, Main 2 (31, 79)	4
24	28/12/09	BSP	A	Stevenage Borough	3033	D 0-0		5
25	1/1/10	BSP	A	Hayes & Yeading United	1829	L 0-1		5
26	16/1/10	BSP	H	Mansfield Town	3584	W 2-0	Elder 3, Taylor 22	4
27	23/1/10	BSP	A	Wrexham	3276	L 0-1		5
28	6/2/10	BSP	H	Forest Green Rovers	3272	W 2-0	Elder 8, Hendry 9	5
29	13/2/10	BSP	A	Cambridge United	3087	D 2-2	Taylor 2 (42, 55)	8
30	20/2/10	BSP	A	Luton Town	7736	W 2-1	Elder 28, Kedwell 64	6
31	23/2/10	BSP	A	Oxford United	6250	L 0-2		7
32	6/3/10	BSP	H	Altrincham	3388	D 1-1	Judge 76	8
33	9/3/10	BSP	A	Crawley Town	1569	L 1-2	Kedwell 1	7
34	13/3/10	BSP	H	Eastbourne Borough	3358	W 2-0	Poole 42, Kedwell 85	7
35	22/3/10	BSP	H	Barrow	3019	L 0-2		7
36	27/3/10	BSP	H	Rushden & Diamonds	3640	L 0-1		8
37	30/3/10	BSP	H	Wrexham	3149	D 2-2	Og (Sinclair) 87, Poole pen 90	7
38	3/4/10	BSP	A	Histon	867	W 3-1	Poole 32, Hatton 36, Kedwell 53	6
39	5/4/10	BSP	H	Stevenage Borough	3840	L 0-3		7
40	7/4/10	BSP	A	York City	2667	L 0-5		7
41	10/4/10	BSP	A	Mansfield Town	2470	W 1-0	Kedwell 9	6
42	13/4/10	BSP	H	Grays Athletic	3015	L 0-2		6
43	20/4/10	BSP	H	Tamworth	3015	L 0-1		8
44	24/4/10	BSP	A	Gateshead	1304	L 0-1		8
	Chester	**record**	....	**. expunged 08/03**				
	31/10/09	BSP	A	Chester City	1666	L 1-3	Main 45	10
	Cups							
1	24/10/09	FAC 4Q	A	Crawley Town	2204	D 1-1	Hatton 43	
2	27/10/09	FAC 4QR	H	Crawley Town	2467	W 3-1	Main 15, Moore 66, Kedwell 90	
3	9/11/09	FAC 1	A	Millwall	9453	L 1-4	Taylor 81	
4	12/12/09	FAT 1	H	Boreham Wood	1306	W 2-1	Kedwell 83, Cumbers 90	
5	19/1/10	FAT 2	H	Altrincham	1450	W 3-1	Wellard 39, Main 49, Judge 72	
6	30/1/10	FAT 3	H	Workington	2301	L 2-3	Elder 15, Kedwell pen 62	

Home Attendances:	
Highest:	4488 v Luton Town
Lowest:	2942 v Ebbsfleet United
Average (08-09):	3496 (3219)
Top Goalscorer:	Kedwell - 24 (21 League, 3 Cup) in 45 appearances - 53% strike rate
Most Appearances:	Hatton - 46 (34+6 League, 6 Cup)

PULLEN	GARRARD	JOHNSON	LORRAINE	HUSSEY	TAYLOR	GODFREY	GREGORY	DUNCAN	HATTON	KEDWELL	MOORE	MAIN	WELLARD	BROWN	JUDGE	CONROY	ADJEI	INNS	MONTAGUE	TURNER	ASHTON	CUMBERS	LITTLE	HENDRY	RAPSON	BLANCHETT	POOLE	ELDER	HARMSWORTH	JACKSON	STENNING	PARKER	STAFFORD	
1	12	16	22	3	8	11	15	14	7	9	18	10	17	13	6	2	4	5	19	20	24	25	23	26	21	27	28	29	35	36	37	30	38	
X	X	X	X	X	X	X	X	X	X	X	S	S	S	U	U																			1
X	X	X	X	X	X	X	X	X	S	X	S	X		U	U	U																		2
X		X	X	X	X	U	X	S	X	X	X	X	U	U	S	X																		3
X	X	X	X	X	S	U	X	S	X	X	X	X	X	U	S																			4
X		X	X	X	X	S	X	X	X	X	X	S	U	U	S	X																		5
X	U	X	X	X	X	S	X	X	X	X	X	S	S	U		X																		6
X	X	X	X	X		X	S	S	S	X	X	X	X	U		U	X																	7
X		X		X	S	S	X	U	X	X	X	X	U	S		X	X	X																8
		X	X	X	S		X	X	X	X	X	S	X	X		X	U		S	U														9
X		X	X	X	X		X	S	X	X	X	X		U		X	S	U	S															10
X	X	X	X	X	X		X	S	X	X	X	U		U			X	U	S															11
X		X	X	X	X		X	S	X	X	X	X		U		U	X	S	S															12
X	U	X		X	X	U	X	S	X	X	X			U		S	X	X	X															13
X		X		X	X		X	S	X	X	X	S		U		S	X	X	X															14
X		X	X	X	X		X	X	X	X	X	X		U		S	U	S	S															15
X		X	X		X		X		X	X	X	X	S	U		X	U	X	S															16
		X	X		X	X	X	U	X		X	X	S	X	S	S		X	X	U														17
		X	X		X	X	X		X	X	S	X	S	X	X	X			S	U		U												18
		X	X		X	S	X		U	X	X	X	X	X	X	X			S			S	U											19
		X	X		X	S	X		S	X	X	S	X	X	X	X			U	U				X										20
		X	X		X	S			S	X		X	X	X	X	X	X		U	U		S		X										21
		X	X		X	S	X		U	X		X	X	X	X	X	S		S	U				X										22
		X	X		X	S	X		S	X		X	X	X	X	X	S			U		X												23
		X	X		X	X		X	X			X	X	X		S	X		X	U		U			S									24
	S	X	X		X				X			X	X	X	X	U	X		X	U		X		S	S									25
U		X			X				X	U		X	S	X	X	S	X		S					X		X	X	X						26
U		X	X		X			U	X	X			X	X	S	S	X		S					X		X		X						27
X		X	X		X		X		X	X		U	X	U		S								X		X	S	X				S		28
X			X		X		X		X	X		S	X	U	X	U								X		X	S	X				S		29
X			X		X		X	U	X	X		U	S	U	X	S								X		X	X	X						30
X			X		X	U	X		X	X		S	S	U	X	S								X		X	X	X						31
X			X		X	U	X	X	X	X	S		S	U	X									X		U	X	X						32
X			X		X	S	X	X	X	X	S		S	U	X									X		U	X	X						33
X			X					X	X	X			X	U	X	X	X										X	X	S		U		S	34
X		U	X					X	X	X	X	X	X	U	X	X	S									U	X	S						35
X		X	X				X	U	X	X	X		X	U	X	U	S							X			X	S						36
X		X	X				X	U	X	X	X		X	U	U	X								X		X	S	S						37
U		X	U				S	X	X	X				X	X	X	X							S		X	X	X		S				38
U		X	X				X		X	X	X		X	X	U	X	U							X		X	S	S						39
X		S	X				X	S	S		X		X	U	X	X	X									X	X	X						40
U		X	X				X	X	X	X	X		S	X	X	S	X							X			U	S						41
		X				S	X		X	X	X			X	X	X	X							S	U	X	X	S		U				42
		X	X			X	X			X	S		X	U	X		U			X				X			S	X	S	X				43
		X				U	X			X	X		X	X		X	X			U				X			X		S	X	S		S	44
X		S	X		X	S	X			X	X	X	X	U	X			X	S		X													
X		X	U		X	S	X	X	X	X	X	X	X	U	U		S	X	U															1
X		X	S		X	S	X	X	X	X	X	X	X	U	U			X	U															2
X		X	X		X	X	X	S	X	X	X	X	U	U	U	U		X	U			U												3
		U	X		S	X		X	X	S		S	X	X	X	X	X		X	U		X												4
U		X	X					U	X	X		X	X	X	X	X	X		X										U	U	U			5
U		X	S		X	X		S	X	X		U	X	X	X		X									X		X				S		6
Total League Appearances																																		
26	5	36	37	15	29	7	35	13	34	39	25	19	21	17	21	21	17	5	5	1	0	2	0	17	0	11	12	12	0	2	0	0	0	X
0	1	1	0	0	3	10	2	9	6	0	6	8	11	1	5	11	5	2	11	0	0	2	0	3	2	0	5	6	3	1	1	2	2	S
5	2	1	1	0	0	6	0	6	2	1	0	3	3	26	4	6	5	2	2	10	0	2	1	0	1	3	1	0	0	1	1	0	0	U
Total Cup Appearances																																		
3	0	5	3	0	4	3	3	3	6	5	3	4	5	3	3	2	3	3	2	0	0	1	0	0	0	1	0	1	0	0	0	0	0	X
0	0	0	2	0	1	2	0	2	0	1	0	1	0	0	0	0	1	0	0	0	0	0	0	0	0	0	0	0	0	0	0	1	0	S
2	0	1	1	0	0	0	0	1	0	0	0	1	1	3	3	1	0	0	3	1	0	1	0	0	0	0	0	0	1	1	1	0	0	U
Total Goals																																		
0	0	1	0	0	5	1	2	1	1	21	6	11	1	0	1	0	0	0	2	0	0	1	0	1	0	0	3	3	0	0	0	0	0	Lge
0	0	0	0	0	1	0	0	0	1	3	1	2	1	0	1	0	0	0	0	0	0	1	0	0	0	0	0	1	0	0	0	0	0	Cup

AFC WIMBLEDON

CURRENT SQUAD AS OF BEGINING OF 2010-11 SEASON

GOALKEEPERS		SQ NO.	HT	WT	D.O.B	AGE	P.O.B	CAREER	APPS	GOA
Seb	Brown	1	6'00"	12 12	24/11/89	20	Sutton	Brentford Rel c/s 09, St Albans (WE) 10/07, AFC Wimbledon 8/09	18	0
Jack	Turner	20			17/9/92	17		AFC Wimbledon, Bedfont Green (SL) 2/10	1	0
DEFENDERS										
Andre	Blackman	3			10/11/90	19		Arsenal (Yth), Tottenham (Yth), Portsmouth (Scholar) 7/07 Rel c/s 09, Bristol C 7/09 Rel 10/09, Leicester (Trial) 10/09, Southend (Trial) 2/10, AFC Wimbledon 6/10		
Ryan	Jackson	2			31/7/90	20		AFC Wimbledon	3	0
Brett	Johnson	6	6'01"	13 00	15/8/85	25	Hammersmith	Ashford T (Midd), Reading (Trial), Aldershot 2/04, Northampton £30,000 6/05 Rel c/s 08, Gravesend (L) 11/05, Grays (6ML) 1/06, Luton (Trial) 3/08, Brentford 8/08 Rel c/s 09, AFC Wimbledon 8/09	37	1
Jack	Stafford				3/11/91	18		AFC Wimbledon	2	0
Ismael	Yakabu	5	6'01"	12 09	5/4/85	25	Kano, Nig	Barnet Rel c/s 10, AFC Wimbledon 7/10		
MIDFIELDERS										
Kennedy	Adjei				10/2/88	22	Accra, Ghana	Croydon A, AFC Wimbledon 7/08, Sutton U (SL) 5/10	22	0
Steven	Gregory	4	6'01"	12 04	19/3/87	23	Aylesbury	Wycombe Rel 5/08, Hayes & Yeading (3ML) 8/07, Havant & W (L) 1/08, Hayes & Yeading 7/08, AFC Wimbledon Undisc 5/09	37	2
Sam	Hatton	7			7/2/88	22	St Albans	St Albans (Yth), Stevenage, Northwood (L) 3/06, Yeading (2ML) 8/06, Maidenhead (L) 11/06, Yeading (L) 2/07, AFC Wimbledon 5/07	40	1
Christian	Jolley	12			12/4/88	22		Woking (Yth), Local, Kingstonian 9/09, AFC Wimbledon 5/10		
Lee	Minshull	14			11/11/85	24		Ramsgate, Tonbridge 2/09, AFC Wimbledon 5/10		
Sammy	Moore	15	5'08"	9 00	7/9/87	23	Deal	Chelsea (Yth), Ipswich, Brentford (6ML) 7/07, Stevenage 1/08 Rel 5/08, Dover 6/08, AFC Wimbledon 7/10		
James	Stenning				26/11/90	19		AFC Wimbledon	1	0
Ricky	Wellard	8			9/5/88	22		Ashford T, AFC Wimbledon 6/09	32	1
Rashid	Yussuf	23	6'01"	10 07	23/9/89	20	Poplar	Charlton Rel c/s 09, Northwich (2ML) 11/08, Ebbsfleet (SL) 3/09, Gillingham 8/09 Rel c/s 10, AFC Wimbledon 6/10		
FORWARDS										
Matt	Harmsworth							AFC Wimbledon	3	0
Danny	Kedwell	9			22/10/85	24	Kent	Chatham, Tonbridge A 7/02, Fisher 10/02, Lordswood 3/03, Maidstone U 5/03 Rel 2/04, Gillingham (Trial) 1/04, Chatham 3/04, Herne Bay 7/04, Kidderminster (Trial) 12/04, Welling 7/05, Grays 5/07, AFC Wimbledon 9/08	39	21
Jon	Main	10	5'10"		7/3/81	29	Greenwich	VCD Ath, Cray W, Tonbridge A 1/06, Wolves (Trial) 3/07, Norwich (Trial) 3/07, AFC Wimbledon Undisc 11/07	27	11
Luke	Moore	11	5'11"	11 07	27/4/88	22	Gravesend	Gravesend/Ebbsfleet, AFC Wimbledon 6/09	31	6
Mark	Nwokeji	17	5'10"	11 04	30/1/82	28	London	Charlton (Jun), Colchester (Jun), Harlow, Leatherhead, Protec Academy, Chesham 8/02, Walton & H 9/03, St Albans 1/06, Staines (Dual) 2/06 Perm 2/06, Dag & Red 5/08 Rel c/s 10, Luton (6WL) 11/09, Luton (SL) 1/10, AFC Wimbledon 6/10		

Loanees		SN	HT	WT	DOB	AGE	POB	From - To	APPS	GOA
(M)Luis	Cumbers		6'00"	11 10	6/9/88	21	Chelmsford	Gillingham (2ML) 11/09 - Dover (L) 2/10 Rel c/s 10, Welling 6/10	4	1
(D)Danny	Blanchett		6'00"	11 07	12/3/88	22	Wembley	Peterborough (SL) 1/10 -	11	0
(F)Nathan	Elder		6'01"	13 12	5/4/85	25	Hornchurch	Shrewsbury (SL) 1/10 -	18	3
(F)Josh	Parker							QPR 1/10 -	2	0

Departures		SN	HT	WT	DOB	AGE	POB	From - To	APPS	GOA
(D)Nathan	Ashton		5'08"	09 07	30/1/87	23	Plaistow	Wycombe 10/09 - Rel 11/09	0	0
(D)Chris	Hussey				2/1/89	21	Hammersmith	Woking (Yth) - Coventry (3ML) 10/09 Undisc 1/10	15	0
(D)Luke	Garrard		5'10"	10 09	22/9/85	24	Barnet	Northwood 3/06 - Boreham Wood (3ML) 10/09 Perm 1/10	6	0
(G)Andy	Little		6'03"	13 10	3/10/74	35	Sheffield	Crawley 6/05 - Croydon Ath 2/10	0	0
(D)Jay	Conroy		6'02"	12 02	2/3/86	24	Ryegate	Northwich 3/09 - Rel 4/10	32	0
(M)Derek	Duncan		5'10"	10 11	23/4/87	23	Newham	Ebbsfleet 6/09 - Rel 4/10, Ebbsfleet 7/10	22	1
(M)Elliott	Godfrey		5'08"	11 03	22/2/83	27	Toronto, Can	Hampton & R 6/08 - Rel 4/10, Staines (L) 3/10	17	1
(M)Will	Hendry		5'11"	12 10	10/11/86	23	Slough	Maidenhead 11/09 - Rel 4/10, Gabala (Aze) 7/10	20	1
(M)Alan	Inns				5/6/82	28	Reading	Hampton & R 5/08 - Rel 4/10, Woking 5/10	7	0
(D)Ben	Judge				22/5/77	33	Redhill	Bromley 3/08 - Rel 4/10, Croydon Ath 7/10	26	1
(D)Paul	Lorraine				12/10/83	26		Woking 5/09- Rel 4/10, Ebbsfleet 6/10	37	0
(F)Ross	Montague		6'00"	12 11	1/11/88	21	Twickenham	Brentford 8/09 - Rel 4/10, Basingstoke 5/10	16	2
(M)Glenn	Poole		5'07"	11 04	3/2/81	29	Barking	Grays 1/10 - Rel 4/10, Barnet 6/10	17	3
(G)James	Pullen		6'02"	14 00	18/3/82	28	Chelmsford	Eastleigh (L) 1/08 Perm 2/08 - Rel 4/10, Chelmsford 7/10	26	0
(F)Peter	Rapson				5/2/92	18		Yth - Rel 4/10, Walton Casuals (L) 3/10, Sutton U 5/10	2	0
(M)Lewis	Taylor		6'00"	11 07	1/8/86	24	Sutton	Horsham 5/08 - Rel 4/10, Tonbridge A 7/10	32	5

Do you remember when...

Wimbledon F.C.

the original parent club of AFC Wimbledon turned professional and left The Isthmian League to join the Southern League in 1964-1965.

They won their first Southern Premier Championship in 1974-1975 and retained the title for three years. It's interesting to note the fortunes of the three runners-up who were Nuneaton Borough (3points behind), Yeovil Town (8pts) and Minehead (5pts)!

The 1975-1976 squad with their league and cup double are:

Back row, left to right: A.Batsford (Manager), S.Rice, R.Guy, K.Tilley, T.Vansittart, J.Bryant, D.Donaldson and P. Upfold.

Front row: R.Connell, G.Aitken, W.Holmes, D. Bassett, I.Cooke, H. Falconer and W.Edwards.

ALTRINCHAM

Chairman: Geoffrey Goodwin
Secretary: Derek Wilshaw (T) 01625 928 1045
(E) dwilshaw@altrinchamfootball.co.uk
Additional Committee Members: Grahame Rowley, George Heslop, Noel White, Andrew Shaw, Paul Daine, Brian Flynn.
Manager: Graham Heathcote.
Programme Editor: Grahame Rowley. (E) altrinchamprog@yahoo.co.uk

Back Row (L-R): Matty Crowell, Danny Holmes, Dale Johnson, Robbie Williams, James Coates, Stuart Coburn, Marc Joseph, Michael Twiss, Tom McCready. Middle: Charles Heathcote (kitman), Damian Reeves, Chris Denham, James Smith, Shaun Densmore, Nicky Clee, Anthony Danylyk, Ryan Brown, Matt Doughty, Ian Senior (goalkeeping coach). Front: Sean Riley (physio), George Heslop (company secretary), Derek Wilshaw (secretary), Robbie Lawton (captain), Graham Heathcote (manager), Grahame Rowley (vice-chairman), Paul Daine (director), Ken McKenna (assistant manager).Missing from the photo is Kevin Holsgrove.

Club Factfile

Founded: 1903 **Nickname:** The Robins
Previous Names: Broadheath FC 1893-1903.
Previous Leagues: Manchester 1903-11. Lancashire C. 1911-19. Cheshire C. 1919-68. Northern Premier 1968-79,97-99. Conference 1979-97, 99-
Club Colours (change): Red & white stripes/black/red. (All white)

Ground: Moss Lane, Altrincham, Cheshire WA15 8AP (T) 0161 928 1045
Capacity: 6,085 **Seats:** 1,154 **Covered:** Yes **Clubhouse:** Yes **Shop:** Yes
Previous Grounds: Pollitts Field 1903-10.
Simple Directions
From M6 junction19, turn right towards Altrincham into town centre (approx 15 minutes). Turn down Lloyd Street, past Sainsburys on the right. Tesco Extra on left. Then follow signs for Altrincham F.C.

Record Attendance: 10,275 - Altrincham Boys v Sunderland Boys English Schools Shield 1925.
Record Victory: 9-2 v Merthyr Tydfil - Conference 1990-91.
Record Defeat: 1-13 v Stretford (H) - 04.11.1893.
Record Goalscorer: Jack Swindells - 252 (1965-71).
Record Appearances: John Davison - 677 (1971-86).
Additional Records: Transfer fee paid - £15k to Blackpool for Keith Russell. Received - £50k from Leicester for Kevin Ellison.

Senior Honours: Cheshire Senior Cup Winners 1904-05, 33-34, 66-67, 81-82. F.A. Trophy Winners 1977-78, 85-86.
Football Alliance Champions 1979-80, 80-81. N.P.L. Premier Champions 1998-99.
Conference North & South Play-off Winners 2004-05.

10 YEAR RECORD

00-01	01-02	02-03	03-04	04-05	05-06	06-07	07-08	08-09	09-10
NP P 7	NP P 9	NP P 14	NP P 12	Conf N 5	Conf 22	Conf 21	Conf 21	Conf 15	Conf 14

ALTRINCHAM

No.	Date	Comp	H/A	Opponents	Att:	Result	Goalscorers	Pos
1	8/8/09	BSP	H	Ebbsfleet United	914	D 1-1	Senior 39	10
2	11/8/09	BSP	A	Barrow	1969	W 3-0	Kearney 37, Senior 78, Crowell 81	3
3	15/8/09	BSP	A	Hayes & Yeading United	401	W 2-1	Denham 22, Little 81	2
4	18/8/09	BSP	H	Histon	698	W 2-1	Denham 23, Johnson 40	2
5	22/8/09	BSP	H	AFC Wimbledon	1438	L 0-1		5
6	29/8/09	BSP	A	Kidderminster Harriers	1415	L 0-3		9
7	5/9/09	BSP	A	Kettering Town	1269	L 0-2		11
8	8/9/09	BSP	A	Cambridge United	2749	D 0-0		14
9	12/9/09	BSP	H	Crawley Town	817	D 0-0		14
10	19/9/09	BSP	A	Grays Athletic	674	W 3-0	Denham 10, Og (Uddin) 62, Senior 65	13
11	22/9/09	BSP	H	Tamworth	843	D 0-0		13
12	26/9/09	BSP	A	Stevenage Borough	2093	D 1-1	Williams 22	13
13	29/9/09	BSP	H	Gateshead	769	W 3-2	Danlyk 2, Denham 90, Doughty 90	10
14	3/10/09	BSP	A	Rushden & Diamonds	1168	W 1-0	Kearney 82	7
15	10/10/09	BSP	H	Mansfield Town	1642	L 1-2	Burns 64	10
16	17/10/09	BSP	H	Luton Town	1762	L 0-1		11
17	31/10/09	BSP	A	Oxford United	5609	L 0-1		13
18	14/11/09	BSP	H	Forest Green Rovers	1119	D 2-2	Williams 13, Senior 22	11
19	24/11/09	BSP	A	Tamworth	630	W 2-0	Doughty 71, McAliskey 88	9
20	1/12/09	BSP	H	Barrow	832	L 0-1		11
21	5/12/09	BSP	A	Histon	676	D 0-0		11
22	16/1/10	BSP	A	Ebbsfleet United	875	W 2-1	Senior 14, Young 53	11
23	23/1/10	BSP	H	Hayes & Yeading United	895	W 3-2	Senior 2 (31, 80), Little 40	11
24	30/1/10	BSP	H	Wrexham	1821	L 1-3	Doughty pen 87	11
25	6/2/10	BSP	H	Salisbury City	777	W 5-0	Young 16, Clee 38, Densmore 61, Senior 2 (80, 90)	11
26	13/2/10	BSP	A	Crawley Town	688	L 0-1		11
27	16/2/10	BSP	H	Eastbourne Borough	590	W 3-0	Doran 17, Denham 28, Senior pen 68	11
28	20/2/10	BSP	A	Eastbourne Borough	810	D 2-2	Denham 44, Senior 68	10
29	23/2/10	BSP	A	Gateshead	489	L 0-1		10
30	27/2/10	BSP	H	Grays Athletic	881	D 1-1	Senior 73	11
31	6/3/10	BSP	A	AFC Wimbledon	3388	D 1-1	Senior pen 51	11
32	9/3/10	BSP	A	Wrexham	2114	D 1-1	Young 82	11
33	13/3/10	BSP	H	York City	1236	D 0-0		11
34	16/3/10	BSP	H	Kettering Town	690	W 2-0	McAliskey 34, Densmore pen 42	10
35	20/3/10	BSP	H	Rushden & Diamonds	1035	D 2-2	Densmore 34, Denham 90	10
36	23/3/10	BSP	A	Mansfield Town	2364	D 1-1	Young 70	10
37	27/3/10	BSP	A	Forest Green Rovers	1043	L 3-4	Senior 12, Williams 39, Densmore pen 45	10
38	3/4/10	BSP	H	Kidderminster Harriers	889	W 3-2	Denham 2 (26, 43), Young 49	10
39	5/4/10	BSP	A	York City	3005	L 1-2	Denham 63	10
40	10/4/10	BSP	H	Oxford United	1356	L 0-1		12
41	14/4/10	BSP	H	Stevenage Borough	907	L 0-1		13
42	17/4/10	BSP	A	Luton Town	7374	D 0-0		13
43	20/4/10	BSP	A	Salisbury City	671	L 1-4	Senior 90	14
44	24/4/10	BSP	H	Cambridge United	1546	L 0-2		14
	Chester	**record**	**. . . . .**	**. expunged 08/03**				
	31/8/09	BSP	H	Chester City	1737	D 1-1	Little 22	10
	21/11/09	BSP	A	Chester City	1132	W 3-1	Little 22, Williams 33, Senior 90	10
	Cups							
1	24/10/09	FAC 4Q	A	Mansfield Town	2410	L 0-3		
2	12/12/09	FAT 1	A	Wrexham	1065	D 0-0		
3	15/12/09	FAT 1R	H	Wrexham	407	W 1-0	Young 70	
4	19/1/10	FAT 2	A	AFC Wimbledon	1450	L 1-3	Danlyk 59	

Home Attendances:	
Highest:	1821 v Wrexham
Lowest:	590 v Eastbourne Borough
Average (08-09):	901 (1084)
Top Goalscorer:	Senior - 15 (15 League, 0 Cup) in 44 appearances - 34% strike rate
Most Appearances:	Williams - 47 (39+4 League, 4 Cup)

COBURN 1	YOUNG 5	SMITH 2	DOUGHTY 3	KEARNEY 4	DANLYK 16	DENSMORE 6	CROWELL 8	SENIOR 19	DENHAM 10	JOHNSON 14	CLEE 11	LITTLE 9	WILLIAMS 12	SAUNDERS 13	HEFFERNAN 20	LAWTON 7	MOFFATT 22	EDWARDS 17	PEARSON 21	THAKER 24	THORNLEY 15	SHERIDAN 26	BURNS 25	WELCH 18	BENNETT 20	BRYAN 27	SMART 28	OWENS 27	MCALISKEY 17	CARDEN 24	DORAN 21	MOYO-MODISE 8	BROWN 27	
X	X	X	X	X	X	X	X	X	X	X	S	S	S	U	U																			1
X	X	X	X	X	X	X	X	X	S	X	U	S	S	U	X																			2
X	X	X	X	X	S	X	X	X	X	X	S	S	U	U	X																			3
X	X	X	X	X	U	X	X	X	X	X	S	S	X	U	U																			4
X	X	X	X	X	U	X	X	X	X	X	S	S	X	U	S																			5
X	X	X	X	X	X	X		X	X	X	S	S	S	U	X	U																		6
X	X	X	X	X	X			U	X	X	X		X	U	S		X		S	U														7
X	X	X	X	X	X			X	X	X	X		X	U	S	U			S	S														8
X	X	X	X	X	X	X		X	X	S	X		X	U	U	S			U															9
X		X	X	X	X	X		X	X	X	X		X	U	S				S	S	U													10
X		X	X	X	X	X		X	X				X	U	S				U	U	S	X	X											11
X		X	X	X	X	X		X	X		S		X	U	S				U			X	X	S										12
X		X	X	X	X	X		X	X		X		X	U		S			U			X	S	S										13
X	S	X	X	X	X	X		X	X		X	S	X	U		S						X		U										14
X	S	X	X	X	X	X		X	X		X	X	X			S						U	S	U										15
X	X	X		X	X	X			U		X	X	X	U		X			S			S	X	S										16
X	X		X		X	X					X	X	X	U		X			S				X	S	U	X	U							17
X	X		X		X	X		X	X		S	X	X	U		X			U				X	S				S						18
X	X	X	X	X	X	X		X	S		S	X	X	U		X								U					S					19
X	S	X	X	X	X	X		X	X		S	X	X	U		S								U					X					20
X	X	X	X	X	X	X		X	S		U		X	U		X			U					U					X					21
	X	X	X	X	X	X		X	S		S	S	X	X		X								U					X	U				22
X	X	X	S	S	X	X		X	S		X	X	X	U		X								U					X					23
X	X	X	X	X	X	X		X	S		X	U	S	U		X													X	S				24
X	X	X	X	X	X	X		X	X		S		X	U											U				X	S	S			25
X	X	X		X	X	X		X	X		X		X	U										U					U	S	X	S		26
	X	X		X	X	X		X	X		X	S	X	X															U	U	X	S	S	27
	X	X		X	X	X		X	X		X	U	X	X		X								U					S			U	S	28
X	X	X		X	X	X		X	X		X	S	X	U		S								U					X				S	29
X	X	X		X	S	X		X	X		X	X	X	U		X													S			U	S	30
X	X			X	X	X		X	X		X	U	X	U		S								U					S		X		X	31
X	X			X	X	X		X	X		X	S	X	U		S								U							X	S	X	32
X	X				X	X		X	X		X	X	X	U										S					U	S	X	S	X	33
X	X				X	X		X	U		X	U	X	U										U					X	X	X	U	X	34
X	X				X	X		X	S		U	S	X	U		X								X					X	S	X		X	35
X	X	U				X		X	X			S	X	U		X								S	U				X	X	X		X	36
X	X	S			U	X		X	X			S	X	U		X								X					X	S	X		X	37
X	X				X	X		X	X			S	X			X								S					X	X	S		X	38
X	X	X			X	X		X	S			X	X	U		X								U					S	S	X		X	39
X	X	X			X	X		S	S			X	X	U		X								U					X	S	X		X	40
U	X	X			X	X		X			X	S	X	X		X								U					U	S	X		X	41
X	X	X			X	X		X	S		X	S	X	U		X								U						S	X		X	42
X	X	X			X	X		X			X	S	X	U		X								U					X	S	S		X	43
X	X	X			X	X		X			X	X	X	U		X								S					S	S	X		U	44
X	X	X	X	X	S				X	X	S	X	X	U	S		X	X	U															
X	X		X		X	X		X			X	X	X	U		X			U				S	S				S	X					
X	S	X	X	X	X	X					X	X	X	U		X				U			X	S	S	U								
X	X	X	X	X	X	X		X	S		X	S	X	U		X			U					U										
X	X	X		X	X	X		X	X		S	X	X	U		X			U					S	U									
	X	X	X	X	X	X		X	X		S	S	X	X		X			U					U	U									
Total League Appearances																																		
40	37	34	23	29	38	42	5	40	28	9	24	12	39	4	3	20	1	0	0	0	0	4	5	2	0	1	0	0	14	3	14	0	13	X
0	3	1	1	1	2	0	0	1	10	1	11	18	4	0	6	8	0	0	5	2	1	1	2	9	0	0	0	1	6	12	3	4	4	S
1	0	1	0	0	3	0	0	1	2	0	3	4	1	38	3	2	0	0	6	2	1	1	0	18	3	0	1	0	4	2	0	3	1	U
Total Cup Appearances																																		
3	3	4	3	4	4	4	0	3	2	0	2	2	4	1	0	4	0	0	0	0	0	0	1	0	0	0	0	0	0	0	0	0	0	X
0	1	0	0	0	0	0	0	0	1	0	2	2	0	0	0	0	0	0	0	0	0	0	0	2	1	0	0	0	0	0	0	0	0	S
0	0	0	0	0	0	0	0	0	0	0	0	0	0	3	0	0	0	0	3	1	0	0	0	2	2	1	0	0	0	0	0	0	0	U
Total Goals																																		
0	5	0	3	2	1	4	1	15	10	1	1	2	3	0	0	0	0	0	0	0	0	0	1	0	0	0	0	0	2	0	1	0	0	Lge
0	1	0	0	0	1	0	0	0	0	0	0	0	0	0	0	0	0	0	0	0	0	0	0	0	0	0	0	0	0	0	0	0	0	Cup

ALTRINCHAM

CURRENT SQUAD AS OF BEGINING OF 2010-11 SEASON

GOALKEEPERS		SQ NO.	HT	WT	D.O.B	AGE	P.O.B	CAREER	APPS	GOA
Richard	Acton	23	6'02"	14 00	16/10/79	29	Manchester	Man City Rel 98, Woodley Sports, Runcorn c/s 99, Hyde 3/01, Altrincham 9/02, TNS 3/04, Altrincham c/s 04, Woodley Sports (Dual) 8/04, Bangor C 9/04, Altrincham 2/05, Woodley Sports (Cover) 2/05, TNS 7/05, Altrincham c/s 05 Rel c/s 08, Altrincham 11/08	2	0
Stuart	Coburn	1	6'01"	14 00	5/5/75	35	Manchester	Maine Road, Irlam, Trafford 94/95, Altrincham 3/97, Leigh RMI 5/02, Altrincham 10/03	40	0
Russell	Saunders	13	6'02"	12 06	3/1/89	21	Bury	Wigan Rel 5/08, Altrincham (L) 9/07, Gainsborough (L) 3/08, Stalybridge 7/08, Ashton U 1/09, Altrincham 7/09, Colne (Dual) 9/09, Rossendale (Dual) 11/09	4	0

DEFENDERS										
Ryan	Brown	27	5'10"	11 02	15/3/85	25	Stoke	Port Vale Rel c/s 05, Leek T 8/05, Northwich 6/06, Altrincham (SL) 2/10, Altrincham 5/10	17	0
Matt	Doughty	3	5'11"	11 00	2/11/81	28	Warrington	Chester, Rochdale 7/01 Rel 5/04, Halifax 5/04, Altrincham 6/08	24	3
James	Smart	28			1/10/92	17		Altrincham	0	0
James	Smith	2	5'10"	11 08	17/10/85	24	Liverpool	Everton (Sch), Liverpool, Ross County (3ML) 1/07, Stockport (3ML) 8/07 Stockport 1/08, Altrincham (Trial) 9/08, Vauxhall Motors 10/08, Altrincham 11/08	35	0
Robbie	Williams	12	6'05"		6/7/87	23	Blackpool	TNS/The New Saints Rel c/s 09, Newtown (3ML) 11/06, Caersws (4ML) 9/08, Altrincham 7/09	43	3

MIDFIELDERS										
John	Bennett	20			26/9/91	18		Altrincham	0	0
Adam	Carden	24			24/7/85	25	Southport	Southport, Man City (Trial), Runcorn 8/03, Witton 3/04, Accrington, Prescot Cables 8/05, Radcliffe B 12/05 Rel 1/06, Burscough c/s 06, Warrington (L) 2/07, FCUM 9/07, Altrincham 12/09	15	0
Nicky	Clee	11			30/8/83	27	Huddersfield	Local, Ossett A 12/02, Ashton U 8/04, Hyde U 6/05, Altrincham 7/09	35	1
Anthony	Danlyk	16	5'08"	11 08	1/2/83	27	Stoke	Stoke (Jun), Stone Dominoes, Leek T 3/02, Belper 8/04, Leek T 6/05, Witton 5/07, Leek T 9/07, Altrincham 6/08	40	1
Shaun	Densmore	6	6'03"	14 09	11/11/88	21	Liverpool	Everton Rel c/s 08, Bradford C (Trial) 7/08, Altrincham 9/08	42	4
Tom	Kearney	4	5'09"	10 12	7/10/81	28	Liverpool	Everton, Bradford C 3/02 Rel 5/06, Halifax c/s 06, Wrexham 6/08 Rel 7/09, Altrincham 7/09	30	2
Robbie	Lawton	7	6'00"	11 08	14/6/79	31	Liverpool	Marine, Vauxhall Motors, Caernarfon, Vauxhall Motors 7/99, Altrincham 6/06	28	0

FORWARDS										
Chris	Denham	10	6'00"	12 11	14/9/82	27	Manchester	Prestwich Heys, Stand Ath c/s 01, Bamber Bridge (2ML) 10/01, Stalybridge 8/02, Radcliffe 7/03, Stalybridge 12/03, Droylsden 6/05, Ashton U 8/05, Droylsden 10/05, Altrincham 6/08, Stalybridge (L) 3/09	38	10
Dale	Johnson	14	6'00"	11 08	3/5/85	25	Ashton	Woodley Sports, Hyde U 2/04, Droylsden (6WL) 3/08, Altrincham 6/08	10	1
Damien	Reeves	8	5'09"	11 10	18/12/85	24	Doncaster	Leeds Rel c/s 05, Scarborough (Trial) c/s 05, Barnsley (Trial) 9/05, Wakefield & Emley 10/05, Farsley Celtic 1/06, Histon 6/08, Northwich 1/09, Farsley Celtic 3/09, Alfreton 7/09, Guiseley (L) 9/09, AFC Telford 11/09, Bradford PA 3/10, Altrincham 6/10		
Michael	Twiss	9	5'11"	13 03	28/12/77	32	Salford	Man Utd Rel c/s 00, Sheff Utd (SL) 8/98, Norwich (Trial) 2/00, Preston (Trial) 3/00, Tranmere (Trial) 3/00, Port Vale 7/00 Rel c/s 01, Chesterfield (Trial) 7/01, Leigh RMI 8/01, Chester 5/02, Morecambe 5/04 Rel 3/10, Stalybridge 3/10 Rel 4/10, Altrincham 5/10		

Loanees		HT	WT	DOB	AGE	POB	From - To	APPS	GOA
(M)Danny	Edwards	5'09"	11 04	24/4/91	19	Burton	Port Vale 8/09 -	0	0
(D)Scott	Moffatt			7/2/90	20	Manchester	Man Utd 8/09 -	1	0
(F)Aaron	Burns	5'10"		8/11/87	22	Manchester	Northwich (2ML) 9/09 - GAP Connahs Quay (SL) 1/10, Chester FC 6/10	7	1
(F)Rod	Thornley			2/4/77	33		Ashton U (Dual) 9/09 -	1	0
(M)Sam	Sheridan			30/11/89	20		Bolton 9/09 -	5	0

Departures		HT	WT	DOB	AGE	POB	From - To	APPS	GOA
(M)Matthew	Crowell	5'09"	10 10	3/7/84	26	Bridgend	Southampton, Bristol C (Trial) 3/03, Wrexham 7/03 Rel 12/07, Northwich 1/08, Central Coast Mariners (Trial) 5/09, Altrincham 7/09, Central Coast Mariners (Aust) 8/09	5	1
(D)Danny	Heffernan	6'02"	11 08	25/5/87	23	Bolton	Ashton U (Dual) c/s 09 - New Mills (Dual) 9/09, Woodley Sports 7/10	9	0
(M)Tejal-Ross	Thaker	5'10"	11 00	25/11/89	20		Ashton U NC 9/09 - Ashton U (Dual) 9/09, Winsford 10/09	2	0
(F)Antonio	Bryan			4/10/89	20	Manchester	Man Utd 10/09 - Rel 11/09	1	0
(D)Andy	Owens	6'03"	13 05	15/10/89	20		Stafford R 11/09 - Rel 1/10, Rhyl	1	0
(D)Andrew	Pearson	6'00"	13 04	21/12/89	20	Manchester	Salford C 8/09 - Rel 1/10, Rhyl	5	0
(F)Clive	Moyo-Modise	5'10"	11 00	20/9/87	22	London	Bradford C 2/10 - Rel 3/10, Ashton U (Dual) 3/10	4	0
(F)Colin	Little	5'10"	11 00	4/11/72	37	Wythenshawe	Halifax 7/04 - Man Utd (Yth Coach) c/s 10	30	2
(F)John	McAliskey	6'04"	12 01	2/9/84	25	Huddersfield	Witton 11/09 - Rel 5/10	20	2
(D)Michael	Welch	6'03"	11 12	11/1/82	28	Crewe	Northwich c/s 09 - Rel 5/10, Bamber Bridge (Dual) 1/10	11	0
(M)Peter	Doran	5'08"	11 04	30/11/88	21	Liverpool	Welshpool 1/10 - Rel 5/10	17	1
(F)Chris	Senior	5'06"	9 01	18/11/81	28	Huddersfield	Halifax 7/07- Darlington 5/10	41	15
(D)Greg	Young	6'02"	12 03	24/4/83	27	Doncaster	Halifax 1/08 - York C 5/10	40	5

Do you remember when...

Altrincham

Seen here with the Alliance Championship Trophy and Bob Lord Challenge Trophy won in 1980-1981

Back row, left to right: Graham Tobin, Malcolm Bailey, Gary Hulmes, John Owens, John Connaughton, Graham Barrow, Graham Heathcote, Jeff Johnson, Barry Howard and John Evans (Physio). Front Row: Peter Warburton (Coach), John Rogers, Stan Allan, John King (Captain), Tony Sanders (Manager), Barry Whitbread, John Davison and Ivan Crossley.

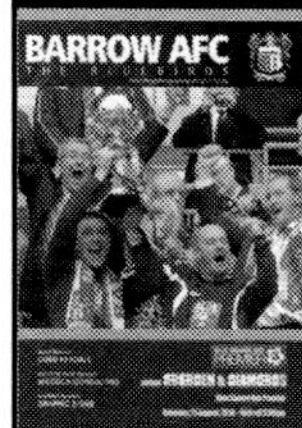

BARROW

Chairman: Brian Keen
Secretary: Russell Dodd (T) 07789 757 639
(E) secbafc@aol.com
Additional Committee Members: Keith Allen; Neil Chalker; Maurice Duffy; Tony Keen; Ian Laird; Dave Ryder; Martin Lewis; Bob Herbert
Manager: Dave Bayliss and Darren Sheridan
Programme Editor: Bob Herbert (E) robertbobherb@aol.com

BackRow (L-R): Barry Postlethwaite (Kit Man); Lee Woodyatt; Carlos Rogan; Lee Hunt; Paul Tait; Tim Deasy; Aaran Walker; Paul Jones; Andy Bond; Steve McNulty; Liam Enright (Physio); Les Potter (Asst Physio)
Front Row; Jason Walker; Ryan Elderton; Nick Rogan; Mark Boyd; Ashley Winn; Dave Bayliss (Joint Mgr); Brian Keen (Chairman); Darren Sheridan (Joint Mgr); Matt Henney; Mike Pearson; Paul Brown; Chris Thompson.

Club Factfile

Founded: 1901 **Nickname:** Bluebirds
Previous Names: None
Previous Leagues: Lancashire Combination 1901-21. Football League 1921-72. Northern Premier 1972-79, 83-84, 86-89, 92-98, 99-04. Conference 1979-83, 84-86, 89-92, 98-99.
Club Colours (change): White & blue/blue/white (Green & yellow/green & yellow/black)

Ground: Holker Street Stadium, Wilkie Road, Barrow-in-Furness LA14 5UW (T) 01299 823 061
Capacity: 4,500 **Seats:** 1,000 **Covered:** 2,200 **Clubhouse:** Yes **Shop:** Yes
Previous Grounds: Strawberry & Little Park, Roose.
Simple Directions
M6 Junction 36, onto A590 signposted Barrow. Follow A590 all the way to the outskirts of Barrow (approx. 27 miles) entering via Industrial route. In a further 2 miles you pass the Fire Station on the right hand side, take next left into Wilkie Road, the ground is on the right.

Record Attendance: 16,854 v Swansea Town - FA Cup 3rd Round 1954
Record Victory: 12-0 v Cleator - FA Cup 1920
Record Defeat: 1-10 v Hartlepool United - Football League Division 4 1959
Record Goalscorer: Colin Cowperthwaite - 282 (December 1977 - December 1992)
Record Appearances: Colin Cowperthwaite - 704
Additional Records: Paid £9,000 to Ashton United for Andy Whittaker (07/94)
Received £40,000 from Barnet for Kenny Lowe (01/91)
Senior Honours: Lancashire Senior Cup 1954-55. Lancashire Challenge Trophy 1980-81. Northern Premier League 1983-84, 88-89, 97-98. FA Trophy 1989-90, 2009-10.

10 YEAR RECORD

00-01	01-02	02-03	03-04	04-05	05-06	06-07	07-08	08-09	09-10
NP P 6	NP P 8	NP P 2	NP P 3	Conf N 16	Conf N 14	Conf N 16	Conf N 5	Conf 20	Conf 15

BARROW

No.	Date	Comp	H/A	Opponents	Att:	Result	Goalscorers	Pos
1	8/8/09	BSP	A	Cambridge United	2990	W 2-0	Logan 62, Walker pen 90	4
2	11/8/09	BSP	H	Altrincham	1969	L 0-3		11
3	15/8/09	BSP	H	Stevenage Borough	1254	D 0-0		14
4	18/8/09	BSP	A	Mansfield Town	3188	L 1-4	Walker 60	19
5	22/8/09	BSP	A	Eastbourne Borough	971	L 1-2	Jones 90	20
6	29/8/09	BSP	H	Tamworth	1051	W 1-0	Walker pen 77	17
7	31/8/09	BSP	A	Wrexham	3760	D 0-0		17
8	5/9/09	BSP	H	Rushden & Diamonds	1089	L 1-6	Bond 53	17
9	8/9/09	BSP	H	York City	1120	D 0-0		17
10	12/9/09	BSP	A	Luton Town	6264	L 0-1		17
11	19/9/09	BSP	H	Forest Green Rovers	1065	D 1-1	Shaw 67	17
12	22/9/09	BSP	A	Kettering Town	1150	L 1-2	Shaw 13	17
13	26/9/09	BSP	A	Salisbury City	876	L 0-3		17
14	29/9/09	BSP	H	Mansfield Town	1040	W 3-1	Walker 2 (7, 50), Kamara 68	17
15	3/10/09	BSP	H	Oxford United	1561	D 1-1	Shaw 29	18
16	10/10/09	BSP	A	Crawley Town	1051	W 1-0	Walker pen 76	16
17	17/10/09	BSP	H	Ebbsfleet United	1241	W 2-0	Shaw 76, Cook 86	15
18	31/10/09	BSP	A	Grays Athletic	736	D 3-3	Shaw 33, Kamara 38, Jones 86	16
19	14/11/09	BSP	H	AFC Wimbledon	1614	D 2-2	Og (Lorraine) 32, Walker 48	16
20	21/11/09	BSP	A	Oxford United	5629	L 0-1		16
21	24/11/09	BSP	H	Grays Athletic	863	D 2-2	Walker 19, Nelthorpe 77	17
22	1/12/09	BSP	A	Altrincham	832	W 1-0	Nelthorpe 85	16
23	5/12/09	BSP	H	Hayes & Yeading United	1164	D 1-1	Walker 52	16
24	26/12/09	BSP	H	Gateshead	1727	D 3-3	Goodfellow 4, Bond 51, Blundell 60	15
25	23/1/10	BSP	A	Rushden & Diamonds	1134	L 1-4	Blundell 82	18
26	6/2/10	BSP	H	Luton Town	1579	L 0-1		20
27	13/2/10	BSP	H	Kettering Town	1160	L 0-2		20
28	16/2/10	BSP	A	Gateshead	503	L 1-2	Walker 35	21
29	27/2/10	BSP	A	Ebbsfleet United	1146	W 4-1	Chadwick 3 (27, 28, 68), Walker pen 83	20
30	6/3/10	BSP	H	Cambridge United	1325	L 0-1		21
31	9/3/10	BSP	A	Stevenage Borough	1538	L 0-4		21
32	16/3/10	BSP	H	Wrexham	1066	W 2-1	Og (Westwood) 67, Chadwick 76	20
33	23/3/10	BSP	A	AFC Wimbledon	3019	W 2-0	Boyd 51, Chadwick 75	19
34	27/3/10	BSP	H	Eastbourne Borough	1302	W 3-2	Chadwick 25, Bond 2 (pen 64, pen 82)	17
35	29/3/10	BSP	H	Histon	994	D 0-0		16
36	31/3/10	BSP	A	Forest Green Rovers	786	L 0-1		16
37	3/4/10	BSP	A	Tamworth	817	L 0-3		18
38	8/4/10	BSP	H	Kidderminster Harriers	1253	W 1-0	Bolland 3	17
39	10/4/10	BSP	A	Hayes & Yeading United	312	D 1-1	Bolland 78	17
40	13/4/10	BSP	A	York City	2154	L 0-3		17
41	15/4/10	BSP	H	Crawley Town	970	W 4-1	Og (Smith) 34, Wiles 61, Chadwick 78, Walker 86	15
42	17/4/10	BSP	H	Salisbury City	1173	L 0-1		15
43	20/4/10	BSP	A	Kidderminster Harriers	1036	W 2-1	Walker 2 (18, 43)	15
44	24/4/10	BSP	A	Histon	753	D 2-2	Chadwick 47, Wiles 54	15
	Cups							
1	24/10/09	FAC 4Q	H	Chester City	1579	D 1-1	Rutherford 65	
2	27/10/09	FAC 4QR	A	Chester City	1287	W 4-0	Bond 2 (73, 77), Walker 75, Cook 90	
3	7/11/09	FAC 1	H	Eastleigh	1655	W 2-1	Cook 36, Walker 90	
4	28/11/09	FAC 2	A	Oxford United	6082	D 1-1	Bond pen 43	
5	8/12/09	FAC 2R	H	Oxford United	2754	W 3-1	Bolland 38, Logan 49, Goodfellow 66	
6	12/12/09	FAT 1	A	Kettering Town	763	W 1-0	Walker 49	
7	2/1/10	FAC 3	A	Sunderland	25190	L 0-3		
8	19/1/10	FAT 2	A	Maidenhead United	301	W 1-0	Bolland 8	
9	2/2/10	FAT 3	H	Gateshead	1200	D 1-1	Bond pen 63	
10	9/2/10	FAT 3R	A	Gateshead	312	W 3-2	Walker pen 36, Og (Jones) 44, Bond 73	
11	2/3/10	FAT 4	H	York City	1525	W 2-1	Bolland 5, Walker pen 35	
12	13/3/10	FAT SF 1	A	Salisbury City	1782	W 1-0	Blundell 75	
13	20/3/10	FAT SF 2	H	Salisbury City	3070	W 2-1	Walker 2 (pen 51, 89) (W 3-1 agg)	
14	8/5/10	FAT Final	W	Stevenage Borough	21223	W 2-1 aet	McEvilly 79, Walker 107	

Home Attendances:
Highest: 1969 v Altrincham
Lowest: 863 v Grays Athletic
Average (08-09): 1169 (1552)

Top Goalscorer: Walker - 22 (14 League, 8 Cup) in 49 appearances - 45% strike rate
Most Appearances: Spender - 55 (41 League, 14 Cup)

TOMLINSON 21	SPENDER 2	DUGDALE 17	JONES 4	NEWTON 3	RUTHERFORD 15	BOND 7	LOGAN 11	HULBERT 6	GREEN 10	WALKER 9	PEARSON 12	BOYD 8	TAYLOR 19	DEASY 1	MORRIS 18	BOLLAND 5	SHERIDAN 14	FOLEY 10	JELLEYMAN 20	SHAW 22	BAYLISS 16	ROGAN 23	KAMARA 24	WAINWRIGHT 25	COOK 19	NELTHORPE 23	BOWERY 10	GOODFELLOW 25	BLUNDELL 26	ROTHERY 27	WILES 24	CHADWICK 22	POWELL 23	MCEVILLY 10	EDWARDS 3	BROWN 16	OWEN 17	
X	X	X	X	X	X	X	X	X	X	X	S	S	S	U	U																							1
X	X	X	X		X	X	X	X	X	X	X	U	S	U	U	S																						2
X	X	U	X	X	X	X	X	X	U	X	S	X	U	U		X																						3
X	X	S	X	X	X	X	X	X		X	U	X	U	U		X	U																					4
X	X	X	X	X	S	X	X	X		X	U	S	X	U	U			X																				5
U	X	U	X		X	S	S	X		X	U	X		X		X		X	X	X																		6
U	X	U	X		S	U	X	X		X	U	X		X		X		X	X	X																		7
U	X	U	X		X	S	X	X		X	U	X		X	U	X			X	X																		8
U		X	U		X	X	X	S		X	X	X	X	X		X	U		X		U																	9
U	X	X	U		X	X	X	S		X	X	X	S	X		X				X		S																10
U	X	X	U		S	X	X	X		U	X	X		X	U	X				X		X																11
U	X	X	S		X	X	X				X			X	S	X	X		X	X	U	S																12
U	X	X	X		S		S	X			X			X	U		X		X	X		S	X	X														13
X	X	U	X		S	X	S	X		X	X			U					X	X		S	X	X														14
X		X	X		U	X	U	X		X	X			U			U		X	X		U	X	X														15
X	X	U	X		X	X	U			X	X	S		U			X		X	X				X	U													16
X	X	U	X		X	X	S	X		X	X	S		U					X	X				X	S													17
X		X	X		X	X	S	X		X	X	S		U			U		X	X			X		S													18
X	X		X		S	X		X		X	X	U		U		U			X	S			X		X	X												19
X	X		X		S	X	S	X		X	X	U		U		U			X				X			X	X											20
X	X				X	X	S	X		X	X	U		U		X	U		X	X						X	S											21
X	X				X	X	U	U			X	X		U		X	X		X							X	S		X	S								22
X	X				X	X		S		S	X	X		U		X	X		X							X		S	X	U								23
X	X		U			X		X		X	X	U		U		X			X							X	S	X	X	S								24
U	X		U		X	X	X	X		X	X	S		X		X			X										S		S	X						25
U	X		S		X	X	X			X	X	X		X		X			X										S		S	X	U					26
U	X		X		X	X	S	X		X	X	U		X		U			X										S		X	X						27
U	X		X		S	X	S			X	X	X		X		X	X		X											U	X	S					28
U	X		X		X	X	X	X		X	U	S		X		X			X										S		S	X						29
U	X		X		X	X	X	X		X	U	U		X		X			X										U			X		S				30
U	X		X		X	X		X		X	U	S		X		X			X											X	X	S	S				31
U	X		X		X	X		X		X	S	U		X		X														X		X	S			X	S		32
U	X				X		X	X		S	X	X		X		X														X		S	X			X	S	U	33
U	X				X	S	X	X		X	X	X		X		X														S		S	X		U	X			34
U	X		U		S	S	X	X			X	X		X		X														X		X	X		S	X			35
U	X		U		X	X	X	X			X	U		X		X														X		S	X		S	X			36
U	X		X		X	X	S	X			U	S		X		X														S		X	X		X	X			37
U	X		X			X	S	X		X	U	U		X		X			X										S		X	X			X			38
U	X		X			X	X	X		X	X	X		X		X			U										S		S	S			X			39
U	X		X		X	X	X	X		S	X	U		X		X														X		S	X		U				40
X	X		X		X	X	S	X		X	U	S		U		X														S		X	X			X			41
X	X		X		X	X	S			S	U	X		U		X														X		X	X			X		S	42
X	X		X		U	X		X		X	X	X		U		X																X	S		U	X		S	43
X	X		X				X			U	X	X		U			X		S										X		S	X		S	X		X	44
X	X	U	X		X	X	X	X		X	X	S		U			U		X	X	U		S		U													1
X	X	U	X		X	X	S			X	X	S		U	U		X		X	X	U		X		S													2
X	X		X		X	X	S	X		X	X	U		U		U	U		X	U	U		X		X													3
X	X		U		X	X	S	X		U	X	X		U		X	S		X				U					X	X	U								4
X	X		U		X	X	S	X		X	X	U		U		X	U		X		U							X	X	S								5
	X		U			X	X	X		X	X	U		X		X	U		X								S	X	X	S								6
U	X		U		X	X	S	X		X	X	U		X		X	U		X		U							X	X	S								7
U	X		U		X	X	X	X		X	X	S		X		X	U		X										X		S							8
U	X		U		X	X	X	X		S	X	U		X		X			X										X		S		X					9
U	X		X		S	X	X			X	X	X		X		U	X		X										S		X		U					10
U	X		X		X	X	X	X		X		U		X		X	U		X		U								X		S							11
U	X		X		X	X	S	X		X	U	U		X		X														X		X			S	X			12
U	X		X		X	X	S	X		X	U	U		X		X														X		X			S	X			13
X	X		X		X	X	S	X		X	U	S		U		X														X		X			S	X			14
Total League Appearances																																						
20	41	10	30	4	29	36	22	34	2	32	29	19	2	24	0	31	7	3	25	13	0	1	6	5	1	6	1	1	10	0	9	17	0	1	12	0	1	X
0	0	1	2	0	9	4	13	3	0	4	3	10	3	0	1	1	0	0	1	1	0	4	0	0	2	0	3	1	9	2	9	3	2	5	0	2	2	S
24	0	7	7	0	2	1	3	1	1	2	12	11	2	20	6	3	5	0	1	0	2	1	0	0	1	0	0	0	1	1	1	0	1	3	0	0	1	U
Total Cup Appearances																																						
6	14	0	8	0	12	14	6	12	0	12	10	2	0	8	0	10	2	0	11	2	0	0	2	0	1	0	0	4	10	0	4	0	1	0	3	0	0	X
0	0	0	0	0	1	0	8	0	0	1	0	4	0	0	0	0	1	0	0	0	0	0	1	0	1	0	1	0	1	3	3	0	0	3	0	0	0	S
7	0	2	6	0	0	0	0	0	0	1	3	8	0	6	1	2	7	0	0	1	6	0	1	0	1	0	0	0	0	1	0	0	1	0	0	0	0	U
Total Goals																																						
0	0	0	2	0	0	4	1	0	0	14	0	1	0	0	0	2	0	0	0	5	0	0	2	0	1	2	0	1	2	0	2	8	0	0	0	0	0	
0	0	0	1	0	1	5	1	0	0	8	0	0	0	0	0	3	0	0	0	0	0	0	0	0	2	0	0	1	1	0	0	0	0	1	0	0	0	

BARROW

CURRENT SQUAD AS OF BEGINING OF 2010-11 SEASON

GOALKEEPERS		SQ NO.	HT	WT	D.O.B	AGE	P.O.B	CAREER	APPS	GOA
Alan	Martin	21			1/1/89	21	Glasgow	Motherwell (Yth), Leeds United 07/07, Barrow (L) 09/08, Accrington Stanley (L) 08/09, Barrow (L) 08/10		
DEFENDERS										
Dave	Bayliss		6'00"	12 11	8/6/76	34	Liverpool	Rochdale, Luton 12/01 Rel c/s 05, Chester (2ML) 12/04, Bristol R (Trial) 4/05, Oxford U (Trial) 5/05, Wrexham 7/05 Rel c/s 06, Rochdale (L) 2/06, Lancaster 7/06, Barrow 11/06 Joint Man	0	0
Phil	Bolland		6'02"	13 08	26/8/76	34	Liverpool	Altrincham, Salford C 10/95, Trafford 3/96, Knowsley U 8/96, Southport c/s 97, Oxford U 7/01, Chester (2ML) 1/02 £15,000 3/02, Peterborough 1/06 Rel c/s 06, Chester 6/06, Wrexham 1/08, Cambridge U 7/08 Rel 6/09, Barrow 7/09	32	2
Paul	Jones		6'01"	11 09	3/6/78	32	Liverpool	Tranmere Rel c/s 97, Blackpool (L) 2/97, Barrow 8/97, Leigh RMI 8/99, Oldham 11/99 Rel c/s 02, Colwyn Bay 8/02 Rel 8/02, Hyde 3/03, Barrow 6/06	32	2
Phil	Morris				21/12/89	20		Barrow, Holker Old Boys (Dual)	1	0
Simon	Spender		5'11"	11 00	15/11/85	24	Mold	Wrexham Rel 4/09, Barrow (SL) 3/09, Barrow 5/09	41	0
MIDFIELDERS										
Marc	Boyd		5'10"	12 04	22/10/81	28	Carlisle	Newcastle Rel c/s 02, Carlisle (Trial) 3/02, Port Vale 7/02, Carlisle 3/04 Rel c/s 04, Gretna 7/04 Rel 1/06, Macclesfield (SL) 1/05, Accrington 2/06, Southport 6/06, Sligo R c/s 07, Barrow 1/08	29	1
Robin	Hulbert		5'10"	12 02	14/3/80	30	Plymouth	Swindon, Newcastle (SL) 2/98, Bristol C £25,000 3/00, Shrewsbury (SL) 3/03, Telford 11/03, Port Vale 7/04 Rel c/s 08, Darlington 8/08 Rel c/s 09, Barrow 6/09	37	0
James	Owen		5'09"	10 07	14/1/91	19	Caernarfon	Chester Rel 1/10, Barrow 3/10	3	0
Michael	Pearson		5'11"	11 01	19/1/88	22	Bangor	Liverpool (Sch), Oldham Rel c/s 08, Farsley Celtic (2ML) 10/07, Barrow 7/08	32	0
Paul	Rutherford		5'08"	10 11	10/7/87	23	Moreton	Liverpool (Yth), Greenleas, Chester 10/05 Rel c/s 09, Bournemouth (Trial) 7/08, Barrow 7/09	38	0
Darren	Sheridan		5'05"	11 05	8/12/67	42	Manchester	Leeds U (Trainee) Rel c/s 86,Local, Maine Road, Mossley, Curzon Ashton, Winsford, Barnsley £10,000 8/93, Wigan 7/99 Rel c/s 01, Oldham 7/01 Rel c/s 04, Clyde 6/04, St Johnstone 7/05, Barrow 1/07 Joint Man	7	0
Simon	Wiles		5'11"	11 04	22/4/85	25	Preston	Blackpool Rel c/s 08, Macclesfield (L) 10/06, Macclesfield (SL) 1/07, Macclesfield (6ML) 7/07, Dunfermline 8/08 Rel 8/09, USA, Barrow 1/10	18	2

FORWARDS										
Gregg	Blundell		5'11"	12 03	3/10/77	32	Liverpool	Tranmere 7/96, Knowsley U 11/96, Vauxhall Motors, Northwich £8,500 1/01, Doncaster £25,000 3/03, Chester £100,000 7/05, Darlington Undisc 1/07 Rel c/s 09, Accrington (2ML) 11/08, Chester 7/09, Barrow (5WL) 11/09 Perm 1/10	19	2
Nick	Chadwick		6'00"	12 08	26/10/82	27	Market Drayton	Everton, Derby (L) 2/03, Millwall (6WL) 11/03, Millwall (SL) 3/04, Plymouth £250,000 2/05 Rel 6/08, Cheltenham (Trial) 9/08, Hereford 9/08, Shrewsbury 1/09 Rel c/s 09, Darlington (Trial) 7/09, Chester 8/09, Barrow 1/10	20	8
Danny	Forrest		5'10"	11 07	23/10/84	25	Keighley	Bradford C Rel 5/06, Halifax (SL) 8/05, Halifax 6/06, Hucknall (L) 1/08, Crawley 5/08 Rel 5/10, Barrow 6/10		
Jason	Walker		6'02"	14 04	21/3/84	26	Barrow	Dundee, Morton 7/04, Morecambe 1/07, Barrow 3/07, Doncaster (Trial) 7/09	36	14

Loanees		**SN**	**HT**	**WT**	**DOB**	**AGE**	**POB**	**From - To**	**APPS**	**GOA**
(F)Aaron	Taylor		5'08"	11 11	9/3/90	20	Morecambe	Morecambe (5WL) 8/09 - Rel 5/10	5	0
(F)David	Foley		5'04"	08 09	12/5/87	23	South Shields	Hartlepool 8/09 - Rel 2/10	3	0
(F)Jon	Shaw		6'00"	13 01	10/11/83	26	Sheffield	Rochdale (3ML) 8/09 - Gateshead (5WL) 11/09, Rel 1/10, Mansfield 1/10 Rel 5/10, Gateshead 5/10	14	5
(F)Nick	Rogan		5'10"	12 12	15/10/83	26	Blackpool	Fleetwood 9/09 -	5	0
(M)Neil	Wainwright		6'00"	12 00	4/11/77	32	Warrington	Morecambe 9/09 -	5	0
(F)Andy	Cook		6'01"	11 04	18/10/90	19	Bishop Auckland	Carlisle (3ML) 10/09 -	3	1
(M)Craig	Nelthorpe		5'10"	11 00	10/6/87	23	Doncaster	York C (7WL) 11/09 - Luton (SL) 1/10, Rel 5/10, Gateshead 6/10	6	2
(F)Jordan	Bowery		6'01"	12 00	2/7/91	19	Nottingham	Chesterfield (6WL) 11/09 -	4	0
(M)Gavin	Rothery		5'09"	10 12	22/9/87	22	Morley	Carlisle (6WL) 11/09 - Rel c/s 10	2	0
(M)Marc	Goodfellow		5'08"	10 00	20/9/81	28	Burton	Burton (5WL) 11/09 - Kidderminster (SL) 1/10	2	1
(M)Kayledon	Brown				15/4/92	18	Derry	West Brom (SL) 3/10 -	2	0

Departures		SN	HT	WT	DOB	AGE	POB	From - To	APPS	GOA
(F)Darren	Green		6'00"	11 00	15/5/89	21	Preston	Stockport 8/09 - Rel 8/09, Kendal T 12/09	2	0
(D)Sean	Newton		6'02"	13 00	23/9/88	21	Liverpool	Droylsden 7/09 - AFC Telford (2ML) 8/09 Perm 10/09	4	0
(M)Malvin	Kamara		5'11"	13 00	17/11/83	26	Southwark	Huddersfield 9/09 - Rel 12/09, Colorado Rapids (Trial) 10/09, Guiseley 2/10, Ossett T 3/10	6	2
(D)Adam	Dugdale		6'03"	12 07	12/9/87	22	Liverpool	Royal Racing Football Club Montegnee (Bel) 7/09 - Rel 2/10, Hyde U (L) 11/09, AFC Telford (L) 1/10 Perm 2/10	11	0
(D)Gareth	Jelleyman		5'10"	10 06	14/11/80	29	Holywell	AFC Telford 8/09 - Rel 5/10	26	0
(F)Luke	Powell				2/11/90	19		ex Everton (Scholar) 1/10 - Rel 5/10	2	0
(M)Carlos	Logan		5'07"	11 00	7/11/85	24	Wythenshawe	Flixton 8/08 - Rel 5/10	35	1
(G)Tim	Deasy		6'01"	13 05	1/10/85	24	Salford	Stockport 8/07 - Rel 5/10	24	0
(G)Stuart	Tomlinson		6'01"	14 07	10/5/85	25	Ellesmere Port	Crewe 8/09 - Port Vale 5/10	20	0
(F)Lee	McEvilly		6'00"	13 00	15/4/82	28	Liverpool	Marine 3/10 - Sligo R 6/10	6	0
(D)Paul	Edwards		5'11"	10 12	1/1/80	30	Manchester	ex Port Vale 3/10 - Rel 6/10	12	0
(M)Andrew	Bond		5'10"	11 06	16/3/86	24	Wigan	Crewe 7/06 - Colchester 6/10	40	4
(M)Rob	Grainey				13/4/90	20		Holker OB 1/10 -		

Do you remember when...

Barrow

The club have a 100% record in F.A.Trophy finals at Wembley. They beat Stevenage Borough 2-1 last season and in 1989-1990 they won 3-0 against Leek Town. This was the first year back in their third spell in the top non-league competition finishing 14th, 10th and 22nd.

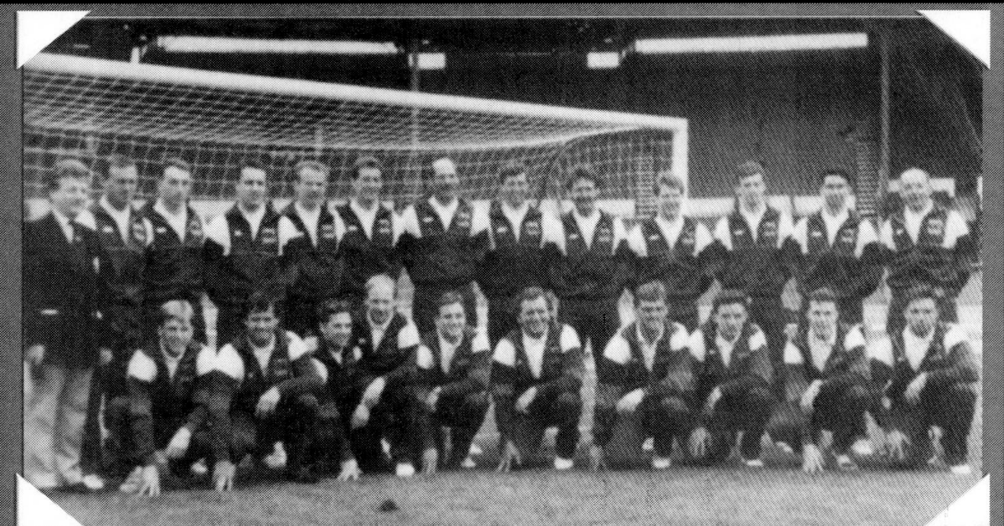

Back row, left to right: Keith Nelson (Football Secretary), Billy Gilmour, Lee Copeland, Garry Messanger, Kenny Lowe, Ken Gordon, Mick Cloudsdale (Physio), Peter McDonnell, Kevin Proctor, Jimmy Capstick, Malcolm Jackson, Glen Skivington and Terry Rhodes (Trainer).

Front Row: Steve Higgins, Neil McDonald (Assistant Manager), Stuart Todhunter, Peter Farrell, Neil Doherty, Ray Wilkie (Manager), Colin Cowperthwaite, Paul Ferris and Ian Burgess.

BATH CITY

Chairman: Geoff Todd
Secretary: Quentin Edwards **(T)** 07785 795 532
(E) qcath@blueyonder.co.uk
Additional Committee Members:
Phil Weaver, Andrew Pierce, Paul Williams
Manager: Adie Britton and Lee Howells
Programme Editor: Mark Stillman **(E)** mark@chrisstillman.co.uk

Back row (L-R): Dave Lukins (physio), John Freegard (coach), Luke Ruddick, Matt Coupe, Jake Reid, Gethin Jones, Danny Webb, Ryan Robinson, Gordon Rieck, Sekani Simpson, Sido Jombati, Adie Britton (manager), Vicky Gardiner (physio)
Front Row: Scott Murray, Joe Burnell, Hector Mackie, Mark Badman, Darren Edwards, Kaid Mohamed, Adam Connolly, Jim Rollo, Lewis Hogg, Adie Harris, Lee Phillips, Marc Canham.

Club Factfile

Founded: 1889 **Nickname:** The Romans
Previous Names: Bath AFC 1889-92. Bath Railway FC 1902-05. Bath Amateurs 1913-23 (Reserve side)
Previous Leagues: Western 1908-21. Southern 1921-79, 88-90, 97-2007. Alliance/Conference 1979-88, 90-97.

Club Colours (change): Black & white/black/black (All red)

Ground: Twerton Park, Twerton, Bath, Somerset BA2 1DB **(T)** 01225 423 087
Capacity: 8,840 **Seats:** 1,017 **Covered:** 4,800 **Clubhouse:** Yes **Shop:** Yes
Previous Grounds: The Belvoir Ground 1889-92 & 1902-15. Lambridge Show Ground 1919-32.
Simple Directions
Take Junction 18 off M4. 3rd exit off roundabout and follow A46 (10 miles) to Bath City Centre. Along Pulteney Road then right into Claverton Street and then follow A36 Lower Bristol Road (1.5 miles). Left under Railway bridge (signs Bath City FC) into Twerton High Street and ground is 2nd turning on left.

Record Attendance: 18,020 v Brighton & Hove Albion - FA Cup
Record Victory: 8-0 v Boston United - 1998-99
Record Defeat: 0-9 v Yeovil Town - 1946-47
Record Goalscorer: Paul Randall - 106
Record Appearances: David Mogg - 530
Additional Records: Paid £15,000 to Bristol City for Micky Tanner. Received £80,000 from Southampton for Jason Dodd.

Senior Honours: Southern Lge Western Div.2 1928-29. Southern Lge Western Division 1933-34. Southern League 1959-60, 77-78, 2006-07. Southern League Cup 1978-79. Somerset Premier Cup 1951-52, 52-53, 57-58, 59-60, 65-66, 67-68, 69-70, 77-78, 80-81, 81-82, 83-84, 84-85, 85-86, 88-89, 89-90, 93-94, 94-95, 2007-08.

10 YEAR RECORD

00-01	01-02	02-03	03-04	04-05	05-06	06-07	07-08	08-09	09-10
SthP 15	SthP 17	SthP 14	SthP 16	SthP 6	SthP 2	SthP 1	Conf S 8	Conf S 8	Conf S 4

BATH CITY

No.	Date	Comp	H/A	Opponents	Att:	Result	Goalscorers	Pos
1	8/8/09	BSS	A	Chelmsford City	1216	L 3-4	Evans 33, Edwards pen 44, Perrott 81	16
2	11/8/09	BSS	H	Maidenhead United	472	W 1-0	Edwards 65	9
3	15/8/09	BSS	H	Welling United	479	W 2-1	Jones 17, Holland 85	8
4	17/8/09	BSS	A	Havant & Waterlooville	1181	D 2-2	Badman 77, Edwards pen 79	6
5	22/8/09	BSS	H	Hampton & Richmond B.	507	L 1-3	Mohamed 61	10
6	29/8/09	BSS	A	Dorchester Town	507	D 2-2	Badman 25, Edwards 41	12
7	31/8/09	BSS	H	Worcester City	620	D 1-1	Perrott 64	12
8	5/9/09	BSS	A	Bishops Stortford	467	W 5-1	Mohamed 2 (9, 81, Edwards 2 (23, 56), Hogg 65	9
9	8/9/09	BSS	H	Eastleigh	507	L 0-2		11
10	12/9/09	BSS	H	Lewes	429	D 1-1	Mohamed 53	12
11	19/9/09	BSS	A	Dover Athletic	1069	L 1-2	Edwards 90	13
12	3/10/09	BSS	A	Newport County	1410	L 0-1		16
13	17/10/09	BSS	H	Basingstoke Town	685	W 4-3	Jones 2 (44, 71), Og (Hankin) 47, Perrott 90	13
14	27/10/09	BSS	A	Weymouth	675	W 2-0	Holland 55, Perrott 72	13
15	31/10/09	BSS	H	Bromley	585	D 0-0		13
16	10/11/09	BSS	A	Staines Town	425	D 1-1	Mohamed 65	14
17	14/11/09	BSS	H	Chelmsford City	543	W 1-0	Douglas 32	12
18	1/12/09	BSS	H	Woking	447	W 5-0	Mohamed 8, Edwards 2 (10, 76), Holland 37, Stolcers 74	10
19	5/12/09	BSS	H	Newport County	1404	D 1-1	Jombarti 14	9
20	8/12/09	BSS	A	Braintree Town	434	L 0-2		10
21	19/12/09	BSS	A	Woking	1190	W 3-1	Mohamed pen 28, Edwards 45, Hogg 74	9
22	26/12/09	BSS	A	Weston-Super-Mare	659	W 2-0	Edwards 2 (33, 40)	8
23	16/1/10	BSS	A	Thurrock	275	L 1-3	Mohamed pen 90	10
24	23/1/10	BSS	H	Bishops Stortford	558	D 2-2	Connolly 33, Hogg 46	10
25	30/1/10	BSS	A	St Albans City	383	W 2-0	Holland 5, Hogg 79	10
26	2/2/10	BSS	H	Weston-Super-Mare	548	W 1-0	Mohamed 34	8
27	6/2/10	BSS	H	Dover Athletic	667	D 0-0		9
28	13/2/10	BSS	A	Maidenhead United	250	W 2-1	Mohamed 43, Edwards 45	7
29	16/2/10	BSS	H	Havant & Waterlooville	428	D 1-1	Edwards 90	7
30	20/2/10	BSS	H	Weymouth	656	W 2-0	Connolly 74, Edwards 75	6
31	27/2/10	BSS	A	Welling United	572	W 2-0	Mohamed 41, Gilroy 90	3
32	6/3/10	BSS	H	Thurrock	603	W 1-0	Edwards 38	3
33	13/3/10	BSS	A	Eastleigh	655	D 1-1	Mohamed pen 29	5
34	16/3/10	BSS	A	Hampton & Richmond B.	411	L 1-3	Mohamed 37	5
35	20/3/10	BSS	H	Braintree Town	619	L 2-4	Gilroy 74, Holland 79	6
36	27/3/10	BSS	A	Basingstoke Town	524	L 0-1		8
37	2/4/10	BSS	H	Dorchester Town	738	W 2-0	Hogg 27, Mohamed 55	8
38	5/4/10	BSS	A	Worcester City	832	W 2-0	Hogg 2 (37, 85)	6
39	10/4/10	BSS	H	Staines Town	762	W 2-0	Holland 58, Edwards 90	5
40	17/4/10	BSS	A	Bromley	508	W 2-1	Mohamed 18, Holland 68	6
41	20/4/10	BSS	A	Lewes	603	W 2-1	Edwards 11, Jones 61	4
42	24/4/10	BSS	H	St Albans City	1030	D 0-0		4
	Cups							
1	26/9/09	FAC 2Q	A	Willand Rovers	442	W 5-0	Edwards 3 (14, 40, 45), Pelecaci 34, Mohamed 37	
2	10/10/09	FAC 3Q	A	Bishops Cleeve	398	W 4-1	Edwards 2 (pen 16, 71), Badman 2 (39, 41)	
3	24/10/09	FAC 4Q	H	AFC Totton	740	W 3-2	Evans 24, Connolly 30, Jones 47	
4	7/11/09	FAC 1	A	Grimsby Town	2107	W 2-0	Holland 32, Edwards 52	
5	21/11/09	FAT 3Q	A	Maidenhead United	272	L 0-1		
6	28/11/09	FAC 2	H	Forest Green Rovers	3325	L 1-2	Hogg 43	
7	27/4/10	PO SF1	H	Chelmsford City	1425	W 2-0	Mohamed pen 60, Mackie 87	
8	1/5/10	PO SF2	A	Chelmsford City	1650	W 1-0	Mohamed 53 (W 3-0 agg)	
9	9/5/10	PO Final	H	Woking	4865	W 1-0	Mohamed pen 56	

Home Attendances:	
Highest:	1404 v Newport County
Lowest:	428 v Havant & Waterlooville
Average (08-09):	585 (618)
Top Goalscorer:	Edwards - 24 (18 League, 6 Cup) in 49 appearances - 49% strike rate
Most Appearances:	Rollo - 50 (40+1 League, 9 Cup)

PUDDY	JOMBARTI	ROLLO	COUPE	HOLLAND	BROWNING	SIMPSON	CONNOLLY	EDWARDS	BADMAN	EVANS	JONES	PERROTT	CORNWALL	CALDWELL	GWINNETT	MOHAMED	DOUGLAS	HOGG	PERRIN	DUNN	TAYLOR	PELECACI	HART	HOWELLS	ROBINSON	STOLCERS	HARRIS	COLLIER	BARTLETT	MACKIE	GILROY	SLOCOMBE	
X	X	X	X	X	X	X	X	X	X	X	S	S	S	U	U																		1
X	X	X	X	X	S	X	X	X	X	X	X	S	U			S	U																2
X	X	X	X	X	S	X	X	X	X		X	X	U		U	S		S															3
X	X	X	X	X	X	X	X	X	X		U	S	S		U	S		X															4
	X	X	X	X	X	X	X	X		U	X	S			U	S		X	X	U													5
	X	X	X		S	X	X	X	X		X	S		U	S	X		X	X	U													6
	X	X	X		S	X	X	X			X	X		U	U	X		X	X	U	S												7
	X	X	X			X	X	X		U	X	X		S	S	X		X	X														8
	X	X	X			X	X	X		S	X	X		U	S	X		X	X		U												9
		X	X	U		X	X	X		X	X	X		S	U	X		X	X		U												10
		X	X		X		X	X	X	X		X		U	S			X	X			X	S	U									11
	X	X			X		X	X	X	X	X	S		U	U			X	X			X	U										12
	X	X	U	X	U	S	X	X	X	X	X	S			U	X			X			X											13
	X	U	X	X	U	X	X	X	X	X	X	S					S	X				S			X								14
	X	X	U	X	U	X	X	X	X	S	X	X					S	X				S			X								15
	X	X	S	X	U	X	X		X	U	X	S				X	X	X				S			X								16
	X	X	X	X	S	X	X	U	X	U		S				X	X	X				U			X								17
	X	X		X	U	X	X	X	X		X	U				X	S	X				S			X	S							18
	X	X		X	S	X	X	X	X	U	X			U		X	S	X							X	S							19
	X	X	U	X		X	X	S	X	S	X					S	X	X		U					X	X							20
	X	X	X	X	U	X	X	X		U	X			U		X	U	X							X	S							21
	X	X	X	X	S	X	X	X		U	X			U		X	S	X							X	S							22
	X	X	X	X		X	X	X	U		X			U		X	U	X							X	S	U						23
	X	X	U	X		X	X	X			X			U		X	S	X		U					X	S	X						24
	X	X	U	X		X	X	X	X		X			S		X	U	X							X	S	U						25
	X	X	U	X		X	X	X	X		X			U		X	S	X							X		S	U					26
	X	X	S	X		X	X	X	X		X			U		X	S								X		X		U				27
	X	X	X			X	X	X	X		X			U		X	S							U	X		S		X	S			28
	X	S	X	X		X	X	X	X		X			U		X									X		U		X	U	S		29
	X	X	X	X		X	X	X	X		X			U											X		S		S	S	X		30
	X	X	X	X	U	X	X	X	X							X								U	X		X		S	S	S		31
	X	X		X		X	X	X	X		X	U				X		X							X		S		U	S	S		32
	X	X		X	U	X	X	X	X		X	U				X		X							X		S		S		S		33
	X	X	X	X	U	X	X	X	X			S				X		X							X		U		S		S		34
	X	X	U	X	U		X	X	X		X					X		X							X		U		X	S	S		35
		X	U	X	U	X	X	X	X		X					X	S	X						U	X		X					U	36
	X	X	U	X	U	X	X	X	X	U	X					X	S	X							X		S						37
	X	X	U	X	S	X	X	X		S	X					X	S	X						U	X		X						38
	X	X	U	X	S	X	X	X		U	X					X	U	X							X		X			S			39
	X	X	U	X	S	X	X	X		U	X					X	U	X							X		X			S			40
	X	X	S	X		X	X	X	X	U	X					X	U								X		X		S	U			41
	X	X	X			X	X	X	X	S	X			U		X	U		U						X				X	S			42
		X	X		X		X	X		X	X	S		S	U	X		X	X	U		X	S										1
	X	X	S		X	S	X	X	X	S	X	U		U	U	X		X	X	U		X											2
	X	X	U	X	S	X	X	X	X	X	X	S		U	U			X		U		S			X								3
	X	X	U	X	U	X	X	X	X	U	X	S				X	S	X	U			U			X								4
	X	X	X	X	U	X	X	X	X	S		S				X		X				S		U	X								5
	X	X		X	U	X	X	X	X	U	X	S		U		X	S	X	U			S			X								6
	X	X	X			X	X	X	X	S	X					X	U	X	U						X				U	S			7
	X	X	S	X	S	X	X	X		U	X					X		X							X		X		U	S			8
	X	X	U	X	S	X	X	X		U	X					X		X							X		X		S	S			9
Total League Appearances																																	
4	39	40	22	33	5	38	42	39	30	7	36	7	0	0	0	31	3	31	9	0	0	3	0	0	29	1	8	0	4	0	1	0	X
0	0	1	3	0	10	1	0	1	0	5	1	11	2	3	4	5	12	1	0	0	1	4	1	0	0	7	6	0	5	8	6	0	S
0	0	1	12	1	12	0	0	1	1	11	1	3	2	17	8	0	8	0	1	5	2	1	1	5	0	0	5	1	2	2	0	1	U
Total Cup Appearances																																	
0	8	9	3	6	2	7	9	9	6	2	8	0	0	0	0	8	0	9	2	0	0	2	0	0	7	0	2	0	0	0	0	0	X
0	0	0	2	0	3	1	0	0	0	3	0	5	0	1	0	0	2	0	0	0	0	3	1	0	0	0	0	0	1	3	0	0	S
0	0	0	3	0	3	0	0	0	0	4	0	1	0	3	3	0	1	0	3	3	0	1	0	1	0	0	0	0	2	0	0	0	U
Total Goals																																	
0	1	0	0	7	0	0	2	18	2	1	4	4	0	0	0	15	1	7	0	0	0	0	0	0	0	1	0	0	0	0	2	0	Lge
0	0	0	0	1	0	0	1	6	2	1	1	0	0	0	0	4	0	1	0	0	0	1	0	0	0	0	0	0	0	1	0	0	Cup

BATH CITY

CURRENT SQUAD AS OF BEGINING OF 2010-11 SEASON

GOALKEEPERS	HT	WT	D.O.B	AGE	P.O.B	CAREER	Apps	Gls
Ryan Robinson	6'02"	13 02	13/10/82	27	Tebay	Blackburn, Wigan (Trial) 9/02, Southend 7/03 Rel c/s 04, Wivenhoe (L) 10/03, Morecambe 9/04 Kendal T (L) 9/04, Southport (L) 8/06, Southport (L) 9/06, Forest Green 1/07, Bath C 5/09	29	0
DEFENDERS								
Matt Coupe			7/10/78	31	St Asaph	Bristol C, Forest Green, Gloucester c/s 99, Clevedon T 9/99, Bath C c/s 01, Aberystwyth, Forest Green 1/02, Chippenham (L) 1/03, Bath C 2/03	25	0
Gethin Jones	5'11"	12 04	8/9/81	28	Carmarthen	Carmarthen, Cardiff 8/00 Rel c/s 03, Weymouth (L) 9/02, Merthyr 8/03, Bath C 6/05	37	4
Jim Rollo	6'00"	11 00	22/5/76	34	Wisbech	Walsall, Yate 9/95, Cardiff C 3/97 Rel c/s 98, Forest Green 7/98 Rel c/s 99, Cirencester (L) 10/98, Bath C (L) 1/99, Clevedon c/s 99, Merthyr, Bath C 5/02	41	0
Luke Ruddick			3/3/90	20		Brentford, Ashford T (Middx), Walton Casuals 9/08, Hampton & R 10/08 Harrow 11/08, Salisbury 11/08, Bath C 6/10		
Sekani Simpson	5'10"	11 10	11/3/84	26	Bristol	Bristol C (Sch) Rel c/s 05, Forest Green (L) 3/04, Tamworth (L) 9/04, Forest Green 7/05 Rel 5/06, Weston-Super-Mare 8/06 Rel 9/06 Bath C 10/06	39	0
Danny Webb	6'01"	11 08	2/7/83	27	Poole	Southampton (Scholar), Southend 12/00, Brighton (SL) 12/01, Brighton (L) 11/02, Hull C 12/02, Lincoln C (L) 3/03, Cambridge U (2ML) 12/03 Perm 2/04 Rel c/s 05, Weymouth 6/05, Yeovil 12/05, Rushden & D (L) 1/07, Woking (L) 3/07, Marsaxlokk (Mal) 7/07, AFC Wimbledon 7/07 Rel 5/08, Chelmsford 7/08 Rel 9/08, Havant & Waterlooville 10/08, Salisbury 11/08, Bath C 5/10		
MIDFIELDERS								
Mark Badman			21/12/79	30	Bath	Bristol C Rel c/s 99, Clevedon 7/99, Bath C 10/01, Chippenham 5/02, Bath C 8/08	30	2
Joe Burnell	5'10"	11 01	10/10/80	29	Bristol	Bristol C, Wycombe 7/04 Rel c/s 06, Northampton 8/06 Rel c/s 08, Oxford U 7/08 Rel 7/09, Exeter 7/09 Rel c/s 10, Bath C 7/10		
Marc Canham	5'11"	12 03	11/9/82	27	Wegburg, Ger	Colchester Rel 6/03, Bournemouth (Trial) c/s 03, Team Bath 8/03, Yeovil (Trial) 2/05, Hayes & Yeading 7/09 Rel 5/10, Bath C 6/10		
Adam Connolly	5'09"	12 04	10/4/86	24	Manchester	Cheltenham Rel c/s 08, Newport C (Trial) 7/08, Hednesford 8/08, Bath C 9/08	42	2
Adie Harris			21/2/81	29		Cardiff, Llanelli, Merthyr, Haverfordwest, Hornchurch 7/04, Haverfordwest c/s 05, Bath C 7/05, Haverfordwest 6/06 Rel 11/06, Bath C 12/06, Newport C 6/08, Weston-Super-Mare 4 fig 1/09 Rel 1/10, Bath C 1/10	14	0
Lewis Hogg	5'09"	11 11	13/9/82	26	Bristol	Bristol R Rel c/s 03, Barnet 8/03, Weston-s-Mare 12/03, Bath C 5/06	32	7
Sido Jombarti			20/8/87	23	Portugal	Weymouth 7/07 Rel 4/08, Cambridge U (Trial) 4/08, Basingstoke 7/08, Bath C 5/09	39	1
Hector Mackie			10/5/88	22	Inverness	Waltham Forest, Tottenham (Trial), Redbridge 4/05, Welling, Stevenage 7/06, Cambridge C (L) 8/06, Wealdstone (L) 12/06, Diss T (L) 2/07, Welling (L) 3/07, St Albans 7/07, Potters Bar 10/07, St Albans 10/08, Weymouth 6/09 Rel, Team Bath, Bath C (Trial) 1/1	8	0
Scott Murray	5'10"	11 06	26/5/74	36	Aberdeen	Fraserburgh, Aston Villa £35,000 3/94, Bristol C £150,000 12/97, Reading £650,000 7/03, Bristol C £500,000 3/04 Rel c/s 09, Cheltenham (3ML) 9/08, Yeovil 7/09 Rel c/s 10, Bath C 7/10		
FORWARDS								
Darren Edwards			4/8/80	30	Bristol	Bristol Manor Farm, Mangotsfield 98, Bristol R (Trial) 4/02,, Tiverton 1/04, Mangotsfield 9/04, Yate T 1/05, Bath C 12/06	40	18
Kaid Mohamed	5'11"		23/7/84	26	Cardiff	Ely Rangers, Cwmbran c/s 03, Llanelli 1/05, Cwmbran 7/05, Llanelli 12/05, Carmarthen 2/06, Wrexham (Trial) c/s 07, Swindon 8/07, Torquay (2ML) 1/08, Forest Green 7/08 Rel c/s 09, Newport C (L) 1/09, Bath C 8/09, Port Talbot (Trial) 5/10	36	15
Lee Phillips	5'10"	12 00	16/9/80	29	Penzance	Plymouth, Weymouth (3ML) 12/00 Perm 3/01, Exeter 2/05, Torquay £17,500 6/07, Rushden & D Undisc 5/08, Weymouth 1/09 Rel 2/09, Cambridge U 3/09 Rel 4/10, Bath C 7/10		
Jake Reid			22/6/87	23		Yeovil (Yth), Team Bath, Paulton (L) 1/07, Yate T (L) 3/07, Chippenham 6/07, Mangotsfield (L) 1/08, Yate (L) 3/08, Weymouth 8/09, Grays 12/09, Weymouth 1/10 Rel 3/10, Salisbury 3/10, Bath C 7/10		

Loanees	HT	WT	DOB	AGE	POB	From - To	APPS	GOA
(G)Willem Puddy	5'10"	11 07	4/10/87	22	Salisbury	Cheltenham (3ML) 7/09 - Oxford C (L) 11/09, Rel c/s 10	4	0
(F)Dave Gilroy	5'11"	11 05	23/12/82	29	Yeovil	Newport C (6WL) 2/10 - Rel 5/10, Woking 6/10	7	2

Departures	HT	WT	DOB	AGE	POB	From - To	APPS	GOA
(D)Callum Hart	6'00"	11 00	21/12/85	24	Cardiff	ex Weymouth 9/09 - Rel 10/09, Weston-Super-Mare 10/09		
(M)Florin Pelacaci			6/1/80	30	Baia Bare (Rom)	Gloria Bistrita 9/09 - Turo C 1/10, Barnet (Trial), Brimsdown 3/10, Hendon (Dual) 3/10	7	0
(F)Lee Roache	5'09"	11 00	30/4/84	26	Leytonstone	Eastleigh 3/10 - Hemel Hempstead 3/10		
(M)Andrejs Stolcers	5'10"	11 00	7/8/74	36	Riga, Lat	JFK Olimps Rīga (Lat) 12/09 - Hayes & Yeading 2/10 Rel 5/10	8	1
(M)Aaron Cornwall			28/2/87	23	Bristol	Halesowen T NC 8/09 - Chippenham (Dual), Almondsbury T (L) 2/10	2	0
(M)Mike Perrott			24/3/89	21		Team Bath 7/09 - Frome T (3ML) 12/09 Perm 3/10, Chippenham 6/10	18	4
(F)Stuart Douglas	5'09"	12 05	9/4/78	23	Enfield	Weymouth 6/08 - Rel 5/10, Newport C (6WL) 2/10	15	1
(G)Steve Perrin	5'11"		27/10/70	29	Melksham	Chippenham 2/07 - Retired 5/10	9	0
(M)Marcus Browning	6'00"	12 10	22/4/71	39	Bristol	Weymouth 7/09 - Rel 5/10	15	0
(M)Richard Evans	5'09"	11 08	19/6/83	27	Cardiff	Newport C 10/08 - Rel 5/10, Weston-Super-Mare (3ML) 1/10, Haverfordwest 6/10	12	1
(D)Chris Holland	6'00"	10 06	29/8/80	30	Taunton	Team Bath 8/05 - Rel 5/10, Eastleigh 5/10	33	7
(D)Scott Bartlett			30/5/79	31	Salisbury	Weston-Super-Mare 2/10 - Rel 6/10, Forest Green 6/10	9	0
(D)Sean Clohessy	5'11"	12 07	12/12/86	23	Croydon	Salisbury 7/10 - Southend 7/10		
(M)Lee Collier			5/12/79	30		Mangotsfield 1/10 - Fleet T 7/10	0	0
(G)Owen Dunn			9/5/89	20		Team Bath 8/09 -	0	0
(D)Raiff Gwinnett			9/11/90	19		Weymouth 8/09 -	4	0
(D)Lee Howells	5'11"	11 12	14/10/68	41	Fremantle, Aust	Mangotsfield (Pl/Coach) c/s 07 -	0	0
(D)Jordan Rose			22/11/89	20		Paulton (Dual) 3/10 -		
(M)Ashley Caldwell			21/4/90	20		Forest Green 8/08 - Paulton R (Dual) 7/09, Frome T (Dual) 2/10	3	0
(M)Martin Slocombe			8/11/88	21	Weston-Super-Mare	Chippenham (Dual) 3/10 -	0	0
(F)Jamie Taylor	5'11"	11 00	4/4/91	19		Swindon (Scholar) 7/09 - Paulton R (Dual) 7/09	1	0

Do you remember when...

Bath City

Bath City were promoted into The G.M. Vauxhall Conference from the Southern Premier Division having finished as runners-up in 1989-1990 with George Rooney as manager.

They finished 20th in their first senior campaign and Tony Ricketts took over for the 1991-1992 season in which they finished 9th.

Back row, (L-R): Dean Radford, Paul Hirons, Ian Hedges, David Singleton, Jim Preston, Graham Withey, Alan Churchward, Richard Crowley, Paul Randall and Adie Mings.
Middle Row: Bob Westlake (Assistant Physio), Dave Monks (Physio), Martin Boyle, David Payne, Rob Cousins, Keith Brown, Gary Smart, Chris Townsend, Peter Aitken (Ass. Manager), Phil Morris (Reserves Manager).
Front Row: Ian Weston, Phil Underhill, Chris Banks, Tony Ricketts (Manager), Dave Palmer, Sean Lundon and Jerry Gill.

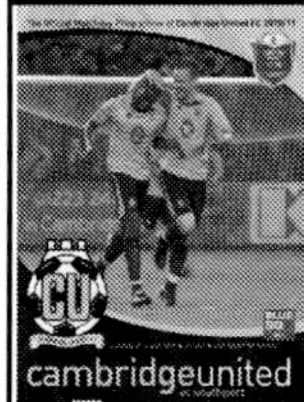

CAMBRIDGE UNITED

Chairman: Paul Barry
Secretary: Lisa Baldwin (T) 07769 217 871
(E) lisa-baldwin@cambridge-united.co.uk
Additional Committee Members: Jez George, Adrian Hanauer, Colin Proctor, Robert Smith, Claudine Bone, Will Jones
Manager: Martin Ling
Programme Editor: Will Jones (E) will.jones@cambridge-united.co.uk

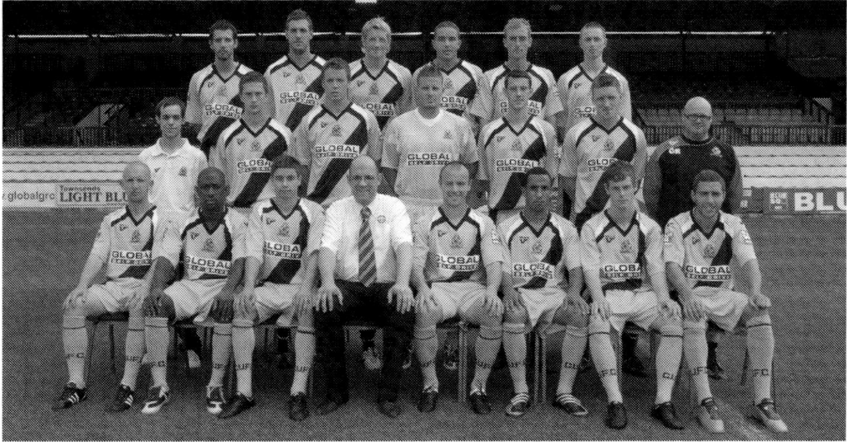

Back Row (L-R): Anthony Tonkin, Dan Gleeson, Wayne Hatswell, Jai Reason, Mark Beesley, Chris Holroyd.
Middle row: James Wynne (kit manager), Darryl Coakley, Josh Coulson, Danny Potter, Rory McAuley, Ben Farrell, Greg Reid (physio).
Front row: Andy Parkinson, Courtney Pitt, Sam Ives, Dan Crick (sponsor), Paul Carden (player assistant-manager), Jordan Patrick, Adam Marriott, Robbie Willmott. Not pictured: Martin Ling (manager), Danny Crow, Lee Phillips.

Club Factfile

Founded: 1912 **Nickname:** The U's
Previous Names: Abbey United 1919-51.
Previous Leagues: United Counties. Eastern Counties 1951-58. Southern 1958-70. Football League 1970-2005.

Club Colours (change): All amber and black (Sky blue & black/sky blue/sky blue)

Ground: Abbey Stadium, Newmarket Road, Cambridge CB5 8LN (T) 01223 566 500
Capacity: 9,217 **Seats:** 2,500 **Covered:** 5,000 **Clubhouse:** Yes **Shop:** Yes
Previous Grounds:
Simple Directions
A14 towards Cambridge and Newmarket, leave A14 at Junction with B1047. Turn right at top of slip road, follow road through Fen Ditton to TJunction and traffic lights. Turn right at lights, and go straight over at roundabout. Ground is on left hand side approximately 1/2 mile from roundabout.

Record Attendance: 14,000 v Chelsea - Friendly 01/05/1970
Record Victory: 5-1 v Bristol City - FA Cup 5th Round 1989-90
Record Defeat: 0-7 v Sunderland - League Cup 2nd Round 2002-03
Record Goalscorer: John Taylor - 86 (1988-92, 96-2001)
Record Appearances: Steve Spriggs - 416 (1975-87
Additional Records: Paid £192,000 to Luton Town for Steve Claridge 11/92. Received £1m from Manchester United for Dion Dublin 08/92 and from Leicester City for Trevor Benjamin 07/2000
Senior Honours: Football League Division Division Four 1976-77. Three 1990-91.

10 YEAR RECORD

00-01		01-02		02-03		03-04		04-05		05-06		06-07		07-08		08-09		09-10	
FL 2	19	FL 2	24	FL 3	12	FL 3	13	FL 2	24	Conf	12	Conf	17	Conf	2	Conf	2	Conf	10

CAMBRIDGE UNITED

No.	Date	Comp	H/A	Opponents	Att:	Result	Goalscorers	Pos
1	8/8/09	BSP	H	Barrow	2990	L 0-2		19
2	11/8/09	BSP	A	Ebbsfleet United	1523	W 3-1	Holroyd 2 (15, 71), Reason 49	9
3	18/8/09	BSP	H	Crawley Town	2733	L 0-1		10
4	22/8/09	BSP	A	Tamworth	1316	D 0-0		10
5	29/8/09	BSP	H	Gateshead	2417	W 3-0	Holroyd 2 (41, pen 90)	6
6	31/8/09	BSP	A	Rushden & Diamonds	2344	D 1-1	Hatswell 65	8
7	5/9/09	BSP	H	Forest Green Rovers	2646	W 7-0	Crow 2 (44, pen 51), Holroyd 2 (47, 65), Ives 2 (68, 74), Beesley 90	5
8	8/9/09	BSP	H	Altrincham	2749	D 0-0		6
9	12/9/09	BSP	A	AFC Wimbledon	4128	D 0-0		8
10	19/9/09	BSP	H	Wrexham	2823	W 2-0	Hatswell 9, Willmott 80	4
11	22/9/09	BSP	A	York City	2321	D 2-2	Reason 79, Beesley 83	5
12	26/9/09	BSP	H	Luton Town	4870	L 3-4	Pitt 20, Holroyd 2 (pen 33, 65)	9
13	29/9/09	BSP	A	Grays Athletic	976	L 0-2		12
14	4/10/09	BSP	A	Histon	2371	D 1-1	Holroyd 81	12
15	10/10/09	BSP	H	Ebbsfleet United	3668	W 4-0	Pitt 45, Holroyd pen 53, Willmott 81, Crow 90	8
16	17/10/09	BSP	A	Hayes & Yeading United	744	L 0-3		10
17	31/10/09	BSP	H	Kidderminster Harriers	3508	W 2-0	Holroyd 13, Hatswell 31	8
18	14/11/09	BSP	H	Kettering Town	3088	L 0-2		9
19	21/11/09	BSP	A	Luton Town	7458	D 2-2	Crow 2 (81, pen 90)	9
20	24/11/09	BSP	H	Rushden & Diamonds	2612	D 2-2	Carden 60, Saah 65	11
21	5/12/09	BSP	A	Eastbourne Borough	1217	D 2-2	Og (Austin) 23, Saah 47	10
22	26/12/09	BSP	H	Stevenage Borough	4439	L 1-3	Crow pen 5	10
23	28/12/09	BSP	A	Mansfield Town	3368	L 1-2	Holroyd 42	12
24	1/1/10	BSP	A	Stevenage Borough	3406	L 1-4	Crow 38	12
25	16/1/10	BSP	H	Eastbourne Borough	2969	L 0-1		14
26	23/1/10	BSP	H	York City	2646	L 0-1		14
27	6/2/10	BSP	A	Crawley Town	1108	L 0-1		15
28	13/2/10	BSP	H	AFC Wimbledon	3087	D 2-2	Crow 18, Phillips 68	16
29	20/2/10	BSP	A	Forest Green Rovers	930	D 1-1	Crow 22	18
30	2/3/10	BSP	H	Oxford United	3002	D 1-1	Saah 18	18
31	6/3/10	BSP	A	Barrow	1325	W 1-0	Neilson 73	16
32	9/3/10	BSP	A	Kettering Town	1248	W 1-0	Crow 76	16
33	13/3/10	BSP	H	Histon	4417	W 2-1	Neilson 67, Carden 85	15
34	16/3/10	BSP	H	Salisbury City	2028	W 3-1	Coulson 23, Murray 32, Neilson 74	15
35	20/3/10	BSP	A	Wrexham	2105	D 2-2	Crow pen 83, Marriott 90	13
36	24/3/10	BSP	H	Tamworth	2121	W 2-0	Crow 2 (51, 68)	12
37	27/3/10	BSP	H	Grays Athletic	3125	W 3-0	Crow 3 (30, 37, 63)	11
38	30/3/10	BSP	A	Kidderminster Harriers	1141	L 0-1		12
39	3/4/10	BSP	A	Gateshead	841	L 0-2		13
40	5/4/10	BSP	H	Mansfield Town	2823	W 3-2	Coulson 25, Phillips 50, Crow pen 90	11
41	10/4/10	BSP	A	Salisbury City	1245	L 1-2	Hudson 31	13
42	13/4/10	BSP	A	Oxford United	5219	D 0-0		13
43	17/4/10	BSP	H	Hayes & Yeading United	2940	W 4-1	McAuley 16, Crow 2 (27, 78), Marriott 87	10
44	24/4/10	BSP	A	Altrincham	1546	W 2-0	Marriott 2 (75, 90)	10
	Chester	**record**	....	**. expunged 08/03**				
	15/8/09	BSP	A	Chester City	1757	W 4-2	Holroyd 3 (pen 45, 74, 89), Willmott 45	4
	1/12/09	BSP	H	Chester City	2239	W 1-0	Crow 90	10
	Cups							
1	25/10/09	FAC 4Q	A	Lincoln United	837	W 3-1	Willmott 2 (35, 39), Hatswell 41	
2	7/11/09	FAC 1	H	Ilkeston Town	2395	W 4-0	Holroyd 5, Reason 64, Pitt 71, Marriott 86	
3	28/11/09	FAC 2	H	York City	3505	L 1-2	Tonkin 84	
4	12/12/09	FAT 1	H	Luton Town	1665	W 3-1	Crow 6, Holroyd 2 (30, 36)	
5	19/1/10	FAT 2	H	Eastbourne Borough	913	D 2-2	Crow 2 (pen 34, pen 85)	
6	26/1/10	FAT 2R	A	Eastbourne Borough	525	W 2-0	Ives 13, Reason 57	
7	2/2/10	FAT 3	H	Salisbury City	1237	D 0-0		
8	9/2/10	FAT 3R	A	Salisbury City	592	L 1-2	Crow 80	

Home League Attendances	
Highest:	4870 v Luton Town
Lowest:	2028 v Salisbury City
Average (08-09):	2955 (3570)
Top Goalscorer:	Crow - 23 (19 League, 3 Cup) in 49 appearances - 47% strike rate
Most Appearances:	Crow - 49 (37+4 League, 8 Cup)

POTTER 1	COAKLEY 21	HATSWELL 6	GLEESON 2	COULSON 4	CARDEN 15	WILLMOTT 11	PARKINSON 8	REASON 14	HOLROYD 9	BEESLEY 7	PITT 26	IVES 20	PATRICK 23	WALKER 31	MCAULEY 12	CROW 10	TONKIN 3	SAAH 5	PHILLIPS 27	CHALLINOR 25	MARRIOTT 22	FARRELL 16	HUDSON 28	PALMER 3	PARTRIDGE 6	RUSSELL 17	MURRAY 8	BERRY 24	BROWN 30	ROBERTS 25	WILLOCK 29	NEILSON 18	
X	X	X	X	X	X	X	X	X	X	X	S	S	S	U	U																		1
X	X	X	X	X	X	X	X	X	X	X	U	S	U	U	S																		2
X	X	X	X	X	X	X	X	X	X	X	S	U			U	S	S																3
X		X	X	U	X	X	X	X	X	S	U	S		U		X	X	X															4
X		X	X	U	X	X	X	X	X	S	U	S		U		X	X	X															5
X		X	X	U	X	X	X	X	X	S	U	S			U	X	X	X															6
X		X	X	U	X	X	X	X	X	S	U	S				X	X	X	S														7
X		X	X	U	X	X	X	X	X	U	U	S				X	X	X	S														8
X		X	X	U	X	X	X	X	X	S	U	S				X	X	X	S														9
X		X	X	U	X	X	X	X	X	S		U				X	X	X	U	S													10
X		X	X	U	X	X	X	X	X	S	S	U				X	X	X	S														11
X		X	X	U	X	X	U	X	X	X	X	S				S	X	X	S														12
X		X	X	U	X	X	U	X	X	S	X	S				S	X	X	X														13
X		X	X	U	X	X	U	X	X	U	X	U				X	X	X	S														14
X		X	X	U	X	X	S	X	X		X	S		U		X	X	X	S														15
X		X	X	U	X	X		X	X		X	S		U		X	X	X	S	U													16
X		X	X		X	X	X	X	X			S	U		S	X	X	X	S	U													17
X		X		U	X	X	U	X	X		X	S			X	X	X	X	S	S													18
X		X		U	X	X	X	X	X		S	U		U	X	S	X	X	X														19
X	X	X	X		X		X	X	X		X	U		U	U	X		X	S		U												20
X	X	X		U	X	X	U	S	S	S	X	X			X	X		X	X														21
X		X	X		X	X	U	S	X	S	X	X			S	X	X	X			U												22
X	S		X	X		X	U	X	X	S	X	X		U	X	X	X				U												23
X	S			X		X	S	X	X	U	X	X			X	X	X	X			U		U										24
X	U			X	X	X	X	S	X	S	S	X		U	X	X							X	X									25
X	U	X		U	X	X	S	X				X		U	X	X		X	X		S			X									26
	U		X	X		X		X		S		X		X	U	X			X		S			X	X	X	S						27
			X	X		S		X		U		S		U	X	X			X		U			X	X	X	X		X				28
			X	X		X		X		U		S		U	X	X			X					X	X	X			X	S	S		29
			X	S	X			S		U		X			X	X		X	X					X	X	X			X	U	S		30
				X	X			U		U		U		U	X	X		X	X					X		X			X	X	S	X	31
				X	X			U		U				U	X	X		X	S					X		X	U		X	X	X	X	32
			S	X	X			U		U					X	X		X	S					X		X	S		X	X	X	X	33
			X	X	X			S				U			X	X		X	S		S				X		X		X	U	X	X	34
			X	X	X			S							X	X		X	S		S			U	X		X		X	U	X	X	35
			X	X	X			X							S	X		X	X		U			U	X	S	X		X		S	X	36
			X	X	X			X							S	X		X	X		S			U	X	U	X		X		S	X	37
				X	X			X							S	X		X	X		U			U	X	S	X		X	X	S	X	38
				U	X	X		U							X	X		X	S		S			X	X	X	S		X	X	X	X	39
U				X	X			X							X	X		X	X		U			S	X	X	S		X		U	X	40
U	U			X				X				X			X				X		X		X	X		X	S	S	X		S	X	41
U			X	X	X			U							X	X		X	X		S			X		X	U		X		S	X	42
			X	X	X										X	X		X			X			X		X			X			X	43
U			X	X	X	S		S							X	X		X	X		S			X		X			X		U	X	44
X	X	X	X	X	X	X	X	X	X	X	U	S		U	S	S																	
X	X			X	X	X	U	X	X		X	S		U	X	X		X	S		S												
X		X		U	X	X	S	X	X		X	U		U	X	X	X	X	S	U	S												1
X		X		U	X	X		X	X		X	U	U	U	X	X	X	X	S	S	S												2
X	U	X	X	U		X	U		X		X	X	U	U	X	X	X	X			S	U											3
X		X	X		X	X	S	S	X	S	X	X		U	U	X	X	X															4
X	X	X		U	X	X	U	X	X	S		X		U	X	X		X			S												5
X	X			X	X	S		X	X			X	U	U	X	X		X	X		S		U										6
X	X		X	X	X	S		X		X		X		U		X			X		S		U		X	S							7
	X		X	X		X		X		X		X	U	X	U	X			U		S				X	X		U					8

Total League Appearances

26	5	23	31	22	38	28	15	31	24	4	11	9	0	1	21	37	19	35	16	0	2	0	2	14	11	13	6	0	17	5	5	14	X
0	2	0	1	1	0	2	3	7	1	13	5	16	1	0	6	4	1	0	16	2	8	0	0	1	0	2	5	1	0	1	8	0	S
4	4	0	0	18	0	0	7	5	0	9	7	8	2	15	5	0	0	0	1	2	8	0	1	4	0	1	2	0	0	3	2	0	U

Total Cup Appearances

7	4	5	4	3	6	6	0	6	6	2	4	6	0	1	5	8	4	6	2	0	0	0	0	0	2	1	0	0	0	0	0	0	X
0	0	0	0	0	0	2	2	1	0	2	0	0	0	0	0	0	0	0	2	1	7	0	0	0	0	1	0	0	0	0	0	0	S
0	1	0	0	4	0	0	2	0	0	0	0	2	4	7	2	0	0	0	1	1	0	1	2	0	0	0	0	1	0	0	0	0	U

Total Goals

0	0	3	0	2	2	2	0	2	12	2	2	2	0	0	1	19	0	3	2	0	4	0	1	0	0	0	1	0	0	0	0	3
0	0	1	0	0	0	2	0	2	3	0	1	1	0	0	0	4	1	0	0	0	1	0	0	0	0	0	0	0	0	0	0	0

CAMBRIDGE UNITED

CURRENT SQUAD AS OF BEGINING OF 2010-11 SEASON

GOALKEEPERS		SQ NO.	HT	WT	D.O.B	AGE	P.O.B	CAREER	APPS	GOA
LSimon	Brown	30	6'02"	15 00	3/12/76	33	Chelmsford	Tottenham Rel c/s 99, Lincoln C (L) 12/97, Fulham (L) 8/98, Kingstonian (3ML) 9/98, Aylesbury (SL) 2/99, Colchester 7/99 Rel c/s 04, Hibernian 7/04, Brentford 6/07 Rel c/s 09, Darlington (5ML) 8/08, Northampton 9/09 Rel 1/10, Cambridge U 2/10	17	0
Danny	Naisbitt	1	6'01"	11 12	25/11/78	31	Bishop Auckland	Middlesbrough (Trainee), Walsall, Bromsgrove (Trial) c/s 99, Barnet 8/99 Rel 9/03, Carlisle (L) 8/02, Southend (Trial), Harlow 9/03, Brentford 10/03, Cambridge C 11/03, Dag & Red 12/03 Rel 2/04, Peterborough 3/04, Hendon 3/04, Welling 3/04, AFC Wimbledon		
DEFENDERS										
Darryl	Coakley	18			9/2/91	19	Bury St Edmunds	Ipswich (Yth), Cambridge U (Yth) Pro c/s 09	7	0
Josh	Coulson	4	6'03"	11 11	28/1/89	21	Cambridge	Cambridge C (Yth), Cambridge U c/s 06	23	2
Blaine	Hudson	26			28/10/91	18	Gorleston	Norwich (Yth), Cambridge U 5/08	2	1
James	Jennings	3	5'10"	11 02	2/9/87	22	Manchester	Macclesfield, Altrincham (2ML) 1/08, Kettering 7/09, Cambridge U Undisc 5/10		
David	Partridge	6	6'00"	13 05	26/11/78	31	Westminster	West Ham, Dundee U £40,000 3/99 Rel c/s 02, L.Orient (3ML) 1/02, Motherwell 7/02, Bristol C £150,000 7/05 Rel 8/07, MK Dons (SL) 1/06, L.Orient (L) 7/06, Brentford (L) 1/07, Swindon (L) 3/07, Brentford 12/07 Rel 1/08, St Patricks 1/08, Cambridge U 1/10	11	0
Kevin	Roberts	2	6'02"	14 00	10/3/87	23	Liverpool	Chester Rel 2/10, Cambridge U 2/10	6	0
Brian	Saah	5	6'03"	12 03	16/12/86	23	Rush Green	L.Orient Rel c/s 09, Southend (Trial) 7/09, Tranmere (Trial) 7/09, Cambridge U 8/09	35	3
MIDFIELDERS										
Luke	Berry	27			12/7/92	18		Cambridge U	1	0
Paul	Carden	15	5'09"	11 10	29/3/79	31	Liverpool	Blackpool, Rochdale (Trial) 2/98 Perm 3/98, Hull C (Trial), Chester 3/00, Doncaster £10,000 7/01, Chester 11/01 Rel c/s 05, Peterborough 7/05 Rel 10/06, Burscough 10/06, Burton (3ML) 10/06 Perm 1/07, Accrington 5/07 Rel 5/08, Cambridge U (6WL) 11/07, Cambridge U (SL) 1/08, Cambridge U 5/08	38	2
Jack	Eades	28						Notts Forest (Scholar), Cambridge U (CRC) c/s 08		
Liam	Hughes	29						Scunthorpe (Yth), Cambridge U (CRC) c/s 08		
Sam	Ives	17			24/6/91	19	Cambridge	Cambridge C (Yth), Cambridge U	16	2
Rory	McAuley	12	5'10"	12 06	16/10/89	20	Blackpool	Cambridge U	27	1
Adam	Miller	8	5'11"	11 06	19/2/82	28	Hemel Hempstead	Ipswich (Scholar), Southend (Trial) 8/00, Canvey Island 10/00, Southend (Trial), Grays PE 8/02, Gravesend 9/03, Aldershot 10/03, QPR £50,000 11/04, Peterborough (L) 9/05, Stevenage 1/06, Gillingham (6WL) 11/07 Undisc 1/08 Rel c/s 10, Dag & Red (2ML) 11/09		
Jordan	Patrick	20			3/2/91	19	Honolulu	Cambridge C (Yth), Cambridge U (Yth) c/s 06 Pro c/s 09	1	0
Simon	Russell	7	5'07"	10 06	19/3/85	25	Hull	Hull C, Kidderminster 7/04, York C 8/08 Rel 5/10, Tamworth (3ML) 9/09, Cambridge U (SL) 1/10, Cambridge U 5/10	15	0
Robbie	Willmott	11	5'09"	12 01	16/5/90	20	Harlow	Cambridge U	30	2
FORWARDS										
Daryl	Clare	10	5'09"	11 00	1/8/78	32	Jersey	Grimsby Rel c/s 01, Northampton (3ML) 11/99, Northampton (L) 11/00, Cheltenham (L) 12/00, Boston U 7/01, Chester £25,000 10/02, Boston U Undisc 11/04, Crawley 8/05 £60,000, Burton 3/06, Rushden & D 5/08, Mansfield (SL) 3/09, Mansfield 5/09, Gateshead (3ML) 10/09 Perm 1/10, Cambridge U £10,000 6/10		

Adam	Marriott	19			14/4/91	19	Brandon	Norwich (Yth), Cambridge C (Yth), Cambridge U (Yth) c/s 06 Pro c/s 09	10	4
Conal	Platt	14	5'09"	10 10	14/10/86	23	Preston	Liverpool, Bournemouth 5/06 Rel c/s 07, Morecambe (L) 11/06, Weymouth (SL) 2/07, Weymouth 8/07, Rushden & D (SL) 2/08, Forest Green 5/08, Cambridge U 6/10		
Danny	Wright	9	6'02"	13 08	10/9/84	25	Southampton	Attleborough, Dereham c/s 05, Grimsby (Trial) 12/05, Histon 3/07 Rel 4/10, Peterborough (Trial) 11/09, Cambridge U 5/10		

Loanees		**HT**	**WT**	**DOB**	**AGE**	**POB**	**From - To**	**APPS**	**GOA**
(M)Scott	Neilson	6'00"		15/5/87	23	Enfield	Bradford C (SL) 3/10 -	14	3

Departures		**HT**	**WT**	**DOB**	**AGE**	**POB**	**From - To**	**APPS**	**GOA**
(F)Jon	Challinor	5'11"	11 11	2/12/80	29	Northampton	Rushden & D £15,000 8/08 - Forest Green (L) 8/09, Mansfield (6WL) 11/09 Perm 1/10 Rel 4/10	2	0
(D)Anthony	Tonkin	5'11"	12 01	17/1/80	30	Newlyn	Forest Green 7/08 - Oxford U Undisc 1/10	20	0
(D)Wayne	Hatswell	6'00"	13 10	8/2/75	35	Swindon	Rushden & D Undisc 1/08 - Dundalk (Pl/Coach) 1/10	23	3
(F)Chris	Holroyd	5'11"	12 03	24/10/86	23	Macclesfield	Chester 8/08 - Brighton £60,000 1/10	25	12
(F)Andy	Parkinson	5'10"	12 12	27/5/79	31	Liverpool	Notts County 7/08 - Rel 2/10, Gateshead 2/10 Rel 5/10	18	0
(G)Danny	Potter	5'11"	13 00	18/3/79	31	Ipswich	Stevenage 5/07 - Rel 4/10, Torquay 5/10	26	0
(M)Jai	Reason	5'11"	13 01	9/1/90	20	Southend	Ipswich (SL) 2/09 Perm 7/09 - Rel 4/10	38	2
(F)Lee	Phillips	5'10"	12 00	16/9/80	29	Penzance	Weymouth 3/09 - Rel 4/10, Bath C 7/10	32	2
(F)Callum	Willock	6'01"	12 08	29/10/81	28	Waterloo	Crawley 2/10 - Rel 4/10, Ebbsfleet 7/10	13	0
(D)Aiden	Palmer	5'08"	10 10	2/1/87	23	Enfield	Bishops Stortford 1/10 - Rel 4/10, Bishops Stortford 7/10	15	0
(M)Antonio	Murray	5'08"	11 00	15/9/84	25	Cambridge	Chelmsford 2/10 - Rel 4/10, Histon 6/10	11	1
(F)Mark	Beesley	5'10"	11 10	10/11/81	28	Burscough	Forest Green Undisc 1/08 - Rel 4/10, Chester (2ML) 10/09, AFC Telford (L) 3/10	17	2
(M)Courtney	Pitt	5'07"	10 08	17/12/81	28	Paddington	Boston U 9/05 - Rel 4/10, York C (SL) 1/10	16	2
(M)Ben	Farrell	6'00"	11 11	20/7/86	24	Cambridge	Bedford 1/08 Rel 4/10, Histon (L) 8/09, Weymouth (SL) 1/10	0	0
(D)Dan	Gleeson	6'03"	13 02	17/2/85	25	Cambridge	Notts County 5/07 - Luton 5/10	32	0
(F)Danny	Crow	5'10"	11 00	26/1/86	24	Great Yarmouth	Peterborough 9/08 - Luton 5/10	41	19
(G)Laurie	Walker	6'00"	11 09	8/2/90	20		Millwall -	1	0

Do you remember when...

Cambridge United

Cambridge United competed in The Football League from 1970 to 2005 and in 1968-69 campaign they won The Southern Premier League & Cup double.

Back row, left to right: Geoff Proctor, Jack Woolley, Mick Brown, John Gregson, Terry Eades, Keith Barker, Gerry Baker, Robin Hardy, Bill Leivers, Rodney Slack, Jackie Scurr, Peter Leggett, Phil Baker, Paddy Harris and Matt Wynn.
Front Row: Brian Grant, Mel Slack, Roly Horrey, Bill Cassidy, Dennis Walker, Jimmy Thompson, Tony Butcher and John Saunders.

CRAWLEY TOWN

Chairman: Victor Marley
Secretary: Dave Pottinger **(T)** 01293 410 000
(E) secretary@crawleytownfc.com
Additional Committee Members:
Alan Foot, Alan Williams, Bruce Winfield, Susan Carter, Gayle Vowels
Manager: Steve Evans
Programme Editor: Gayle Vowels **(E)** gaylevowels@crawleytownfc.com

Back Row (L-R): Mithun Nayee, Danny Forrest, Jamie Stevens, Brad Thomas, Nick Carter, Lewis Killeen, Jon Paul Pittman.
Middle: Denise McLean, Steven Trussell, Jake Wright, Adam Quinn, Simon Rayner, Steve Fletcher, Glenn Wilson, Richard Munn, Phil Jarman.
Front: Sam Pinault, Thomas We, Simon Stone, Chris Giles, Paul Raynor, Steve Evans (Manager), Dannie Bulman, Jamie Cook, Isaiah Rankin, Anton Rents Douglas.

Club Factfile

Founded: 1896 **Nickname:** Red Devils
Previous Names: None
Previous Leagues: Sussex County 1951-56. Metropolitan 56-63. Southern 64-2000.

Club Colours (change): All red (White/purple/purple)

Ground: Broadfield Stadium, Brighton Road, Crawley RH11 9RX **(T)** 01293 410 000
Capacity: 4,996 **Seats:** 1,080 **Covered:** 4,200 **Clubhouse:** Yes **Shop:** Yes
Previous Grounds: Malthouse Farm 1896-1914, 38-40, Victory Hall & Rectory Field 18-38, Yetmans Field 45-49, Town Mead 49-53, 54-97, Ifield Rec. 53-54
Simple Directions
Exit the M23 at junction 11 (Pease Pottage), take the 4th exit and continue to roundabout (landmarked by large football), take the first exit which enters stadium car park.

Record Attendance: 4,522 v Weymouth - Southern League 06/03/04
Record Victory: 10-0 v Chichester United - Sussex League 1955 and v Crowborough - Sussex Floodlit Cup 2001
Record Defeat: 0-10
Record Goalscorer: Phil Basey - 108 (1968-72)
Record Appearances: John Maggs - 652 (1963-73, 75-79)
Additional Records: Received £75,000 from Brentford for Jay Lovett in 2000

Senior Honours: Sussex Senior Cup 1988-89, 90-91, 2003-04. Southern League 2003-04.

10 YEAR RECORD

00-01	01-02	02-03	03-04	04-05	05-06	06-07	07-08	08-09	09-10
SthP 11	SthP 4	SthP 7	SthP 1	Conf 12	Conf 17	Conf 18	Conf 15	Conf 9	Conf 7

CRAWLEY TOWN

No.	Date	Comp	H/A	Opponents	Att:	Result	Goalscorers	Pos
1	8/8/09	BSP	A	Mansfield Town	3264	L 0-4		23
2	11/8/09	BSP	H	Forest Green Rovers	776	W 3-1	Cook 2, Hutchinson 20, Ademeno 55	12
3	15/8/09	BSP	H	Wrexham	1014	W 1-0	Cook 50	7
4	18/8/09	BSP	A	Cambridge United	2733	W 1-0	Cook 26	5
5	22/8/09	BSP	H	Gateshead	881	L 1-4	Rents 82	7
6	29/8/09	BSP	H	Grays Athletic	846	D 1-1	Louis 6	10
7	1/9/09	BSP	A	Luton Town	6389	L 0-3		14
8	5/9/09	BSP	A	York City	2139	L 0-2		16
9	8/9/09	BSP	H	Histon	798	W 2-0	Carruthers 87, Louis 90	13
10	12/9/09	BSP	A	Altrincham	817	D 0-0		13
11	19/9/09	BSP	H	Kettering Town	901	W 2-1	Ademeno 58, Willock 68	11
12	22/9/09	BSP	A	AFC Wimbledon	3408	D 1-1	Louis 38	11
13	26/9/09	BSP	H	Rushden & Diamonds	925	W 2-1	Louis 27, Willock 58	8
14	29/9/09	BSP	A	Oxford United	5675	L 1-3	Louis 27	11
15	3/10/09	BSP	A	Ebbsfleet United	987	D 0-0		11
16	10/10/09	BSP	H	Barrow	1051	L 0-1		13
17	17/10/09	BSP	A	Kidderminster Harriers	1276	L 0-1		14
18	31/10/09	BSP	H	York City	975	W 3-1	Forrest 2 (53, 89), Smith 78	12
19	14/11/09	BSP	H	Mansfield Town	883	L 0-2		14
20	21/11/09	BSP	A	Hayes & Yeading United	342	L 1-2	Smith 34	14
21	24/11/09	BSP	H	Salisbury City	603	W 2-0	Smith 50, Killeen 87	13
22	28/11/09	BSP	A	Gateshead	467	L 1-2	Malcolm 29	13
23	1/12/09	BSP	H	Oxford United	1319	L 1-2	Pinault 17	14
24	5/12/09	BSP	A	Tamworth	729	W 1-0	Kileen 14	13
25	26/12/09	BSP	H	Eastbourne Borough	979	D 2-2	Ademeno 7, Wilson 21	12
26	28/12/09	BSP	A	Grays Athletic	505	W 3-2	Ademeno 3 (2, 5, 6)	10
27	1/1/10	BSP	A	Eastbourne Borough	1726	W 2-0	Ademeno 3, Wilson 31	10
28	23/1/10	BSP	H	Kidderminster Harriers	800	D 2-2	Ademeno 13, Cogan 63	10
29	6/2/10	BSP	H	Cambridge United	1108	W 1-0	Cogan 8	10
30	13/2/10	BSP	H	Altrincham	688	W 1-0	Ademeno 58	10
31	20/2/10	BSP	A	Wrexham	2475	L 0-2		11
32	27/2/10	BSP	H	Luton Town	2118	W 2-1	Smith 2 (55, 87)	10
33	2/3/10	BSP	A	Salisbury City	581	D 2-2	Cogan 27, Wilson 55	10
34	6/3/10	BSP	A	Stevenage Borough	2230	L 0-2		10
35	9/3/10	BSP	H	AFC Wimbledon	1569	W 2-1	Forrest 18, Ademeno 52	9
36	13/3/10	BSP	H	Ebbsfleet United	983	W 2-1	Malcolm 75, Ademeno 86	8
37	27/3/10	BSP	H	Stevenage Borough	1229	L 0-3		9
38	2/4/10	BSP	A	Rushden & Diamonds	1703	D 1-1	Malcolm 48	9
39	5/4/10	BSP	H	Hayes & Yeading United	860	W 1-0	Forrest pen 57	8
40	10/4/10	BSP	A	Histon	499	W 1-0	Hutchinson 49	8
41	13/4/10	BSP	A	Forest Green Rovers	601	L 0-1		8
42	15/4/10	BSP	A	Barrow	970	L 1-2	Smith 57	8
43	17/4/10	BSP	H	Tamworth	755	W 2-0	Forrest pen 58, Smith 64	7
44	20/4/10	BSP	A	Kettering Town	800	D 1-1	Forrest pen 18	7
	Cups							
1	24/10/09	FAC 4Q	H	AFC Wimbledon	2204	D 1-1	Forrest 13	
2	27/10/09	FAC 4QR	A	AFC Wimbledon	2467	L 1-3	Louis 27	
3	12/12/09	FAT 1	A	Bashley	335	W 3-2	Rents 4, Wilson 16, Og (Middleton) 64	
4	18/1/10	FAT 2	A	Chelmsford City	715	L 1-2	Malcolm 46	

Home League Attendances	
Highest:	2118 v Luton Town
Lowest:	603 v Salisbury City
Average (08-09):	913 (1204)

Top Goalscorer:	Ademeno - 11 (11 League, 0 Cup) in 34 appearances - 32% strike rate
Most Appearances:	Pinault - 44 (38+2 League, 4 Cup)

RAYNER 1	BROADHURST 6	RENTS 3	GILES 5	WILSON 16	SMITH 23	HUTCHINSON 4	POWELL 24	LOUIS 9	COOK 11	ADEMENO 8	RUSK 2	COGAN 17	MALCOLM 15	JORDAN 22	FORREST 7	PINAULT 10	KILLEEN 14	CARRUTHERS 12	COLLINS 28	DJILALI 11	BARTON 27	QUINN 21	WILLOCK 24	RAYNOR 39	LAKE-EDWARDS 25	CARTER 19	HUGGINS 26	NAPPER 18	LOKANDO 12	KING 27	LANGSTON 5	
X	X	X	X	X	X	X	X	X	X	X	S	S	S	U	U																	1
X	X	X	X		X	X	U	S	X	X	X		S	U	S	X	X															2
X	X	X	X		X	X	U	S	X	X	X	S	S	U		X	X															3
X	X	X	X		X	X	U	S	X	X	X	X	S	U	S		X															4
X	X	X	X		X	X		S	X	X	X	X	S	U	S	U	X															5
U	X	X		X		X	S	X	X	X		S	X	X	X	X	U	S														6
U	X	X				X		X				U	S	X	X	X	X	X	X	X	S	U										7
X		X				X	S	X			X	S	U		X	S	U	X	X	X	X	X										8
X	X	X				X		S		X	X	S		U	S	X	U	X		X		X	X									9
X	X	X				X		S		X	X	U		U	S	X	U	X		X		X	X									10
X	X	X		X				S		X	X	U	S	U	S	X		X		X		X	X									11
X	X	X		X		S		X			X	S	X	U	S	X	U	X				X	X									12
X	X	X		X	U	S		X			X	X	S	U	S	X	X					X	X									13
X		X		X	S	X		X			X	X	S	U	S	X	X					X	X	U								14
X	X	X			S	X		X			X	X	U	U	S	X	X					X	X		U							15
X	X	X		S	S	X		X		S	X	X		U	U	X	X					X	X									16
X		X	U	X	S	X		S			X	X	S	U	X	X	X					X	X									17
X			X	X	X	X		X			X	X	S	U	X	X	U					X	S			S						18
X	X		X	X	X	U				S	X	X	S	S	X	X	U					X	X									19
X	X		X	X	X	X					S	X	X	U		X	S					X	X				U	U				20
X	X		X	X	X	X				S	X		X	U		X	X					X				S		U	S			21
X	X			X	X	X				X	X		X	U		X	X							U		S	U	U	X			22
X	X	X		X	X	S				X	X		X	U		X	X					X				U			U	U		23
X		X		X	X					X	X	X	X	U		X	X					X	S			U			U	S		24
X	S	X		X	X	S				X	X	X	X	U		X	X					X	S			U						25
X	X	X		X	X	X				X		X	X	U		S	S					X	X			U		U				26
X	X	X		X	X	X				X	U	X	X	U		X	S					X	S			S						27
X		X	U	X	X	X				X	X	X	X	U	S	X	U					X	U									28
X	X	X			X	X				X	X	X	X	U	S	X	S					X			U					S		29
X		X		X	X	X				X	X	X	X	U	S	X	S					X						S		U		30
X	X	X			X	X					X	X	X	U	S	X	X					X		U		U		S				31
X	X	X		S	X	X				X	X	X	S	U	S	X	X					X						U				32
X	X	X		X		X				X	X	X	X	U	S	X	X							U		U		U				33
X	X	X		X	S	X				X	X	X	X	U	X	X	S									U		U				34
X	X	X		X	X					X	X	X	S	U	X	X	S									U		U			X	35
X	X	X		X	X					X	X	X	S	U	X	X	S					U				U					X	36
X	X	X		X	X	S				X	X	X	S	U	X	X	S					U									X	37
U	S	X		X	S	X				S	U	X	X	X	X	X	X					X									X	38
U	U	X			X	X				S	X	X	X	X	X	X						X				U		U			X	39
U	X	X		S	X	X				S	U	X	X	X	X	X						X				X		S				40
U		X		X	S	X				U	X	X	X	X	X	U						X				X		S			X	41
U		X		X	X	X				U	X	X	X	X	X	X	U							U				S			X	42
U	X	X		S	X	X				X	X	X	S	X	X	X	U											S			X	43
U	X	X		X	U	X				X	X	X	X	X	X	X	S							U				S				44
X		X	U	X	X	X		X			X	X	S	U	X	X	U					X	S		U	U						1
X	X		S	X	X	X		X			X	X	S	U	X	X	U					X	S		U	U						2
X	U	X		X	X					X	X	X	X	U		X	X					X	S			U				U		3
X	X	X		X	X					X	X	X	X	U	S	X	U					X	S			U						4
Total League Appearances																																
35	32	39	9	28	27	34	1	10	6	26	36	31	22	9	17	38	19	6	2	5	1	28	12	0	0	2	0	0	1	0	8	X
0	2	0	0	4	7	5	2	8	0	6	2	6	17	1	16	2	10	1	0	0	1	0	4	0	0	4	0	7	1	2	0	S
9	1	0	2	0	2	1	3	0	0	2	3	3	2	33	2	2	10	0	0	0	0	3	1	6	2	10	2	9	2	2	0	U
Total Cup Appearances																																
4	2	3	0	4	4	2	0	2	0	2	4	4	2	0	2	4	1	0	0	0	0	4	0	0	0	0	0	0	0	0	0	X
0	0	0	1	0	0	0	0	0	0	0	0	0	2	0	1	0	0	0	0	0	0	0	4	0	0	0	0	0	0	0	0	S
0	1	0	1	0	0	0	0	0	0	0	0	0	0	4	0	0	3	0	0	0	0	0	0	0	2	4	0	0	0	1	0	U
Total Goals																																
0	0	1	0	3	7	2	0	5	3	11	0	3	3	0	6	1	1	1	0	0	0	0	2	0	0	0	0	0	0	0	0	Lg
0	0	1	0	1	0	0	0	1	0	0	0	0	1	0	1	0	0	0	0	0	0	0	0	0	0	0	0	0	0	0	0	Cp

CRAWLEY TOWN

CURRENT SQUAD AS OF BEGINING OF 2010-11 SEASON

GOALKEEPERS		SQ NO.	HT	WT	D.O.B	AGE	P.O.B	CAREER	APPS	GOA
Nick	Jordan	12	6'02"	13 01	13/11/89	20	Aldershot	Portsmouth (Scholar) Rel c/s 08, Exeter 8/08 Rel c/s 09, Crawley 8/09	10	0
Michel	Kuipers	1	6'02"	14 03	26/6/74	36	Amsterdam, Holl	SDW Amsterdam (Holl), Bristol R 1/99 Rel c/s 00, Brighton 7/00 Rel c/s 10, Hull C (L) 8/03, Boston U (L) 11/05, Boston U (2ML) 2/06, Crawley 5/10		

DEFENDERS		SQ NO.	HT	WT	D.O.B	AGE	P.O.B	CAREER	APPS	GOA
Danny	Hall	6	6'02"	12 07	14/11/83	26	Ashton-under-Lyne	Oldham Rel c/s 06, Scarborough (L) 2/03, Shrewsbury 5/06, Gretna 1/08 Rel 5/08, Chesterfield 7/08 Rel c/s 10, Darlington (L) 11/09, Crawley 5/10		
Pablo	Mills	22			27/5/84	26	Birmingham	Derby, MK Dons (4ML) 8/05, Walsall (SL) 2/06, Rotherham 8/06 Rel c/s 10, Crawley (2ML) 8/07, Crawley 7/10		
Adam	Quinn	5			2/6/83	27	Sheffield	Sheff Wed, Carlisle (Trial) 3/02, Halifax 8/02, Crawley 8/08	28	0
Sam	Rents	3	5'09"	11 03	22/6/87	23	Brighton	Brighton Rel 5/08, Worthing (L) 11/05, Crawley 5/08	39	1
Darragh	Ryan	15	5'10"	10 10	21/5/80	30	Cuckfield	Brighton Rel c/s 99, Crawley 6/99, UCD c/s 00, Galway Hibs, Australia, Crawley (Trial) c/s 04, Bognor Regis 11/04, Burgess Hill 1/05, Worthing c/s 05, Haywards Heath, UCD 12/05, Cork 1/07, St Patricks 1/09, Stevenage 1/10 Rel 2/10, Crawley (Trial) 3/10, C		
Glenn	Wilson	16	6'01"	12 09	16/3/86	24	Lewisham	C.Palace Rel 5/06, AFC Wimbledon (L) 9/04, Bournemouth (Trial) 2/06, Rushden & D 6/06, Kidderminster (L) 3/07, Crawley 7/07	32	3

MIDFIELDERS		SQ NO.	HT	WT	D.O.B	AGE	P.O.B	CAREER	APPS	GOA
Barry	Cogan	17	5'09"	09 00	4/11/84	25	Sligo	Millwall, Barnet Undisc 8/06 Rel 5/07, Gillingham 7/07, Grays (SL) 3/08, Grays 7/08, Crawley 6/09	37	3
Jamie	Cook	18	5'10"	10 09	2/9/79	30	Oxford	Oxford U Rel 1/01, Darlington (Trial) 1/01, Boston U 2/01, Stevenage 2/03, Bath C (L) 2/04, Maidenhead 7/04, Witney U 9/05, Rushden & D (NC) 1/07, Havant & W 3/07, Crawley 7/07, Oxford U Undisc 9/09, Crawley 6/10	6	3
Chris	Flood	20			28/11/89	20		Andover (Yth), Winchester (Yth), Farnborough 6/07, Brentford, Thatcham (WE) 12/07, QPR 8/08 Rel 1/09, Eastleigh 3/09, Salisbury 8/09, Crawley £10,000 7/10		
Dean	Howell		6'01"	12 05	29/11/80	29	Burton	Notts County Rel c/s 00, Spalding (2ML) 12/99, Crewe 7/00 Rel c/s 01, Rochdale (L) 3/01, Southport 7/01, Morecambe 6/03, Halifax 7/04 Rel 4/05, Colchester 8/05, Halifax 2/06 Rel 5/06, Weymouth 6/06, Grays 1/07 Rel 5/07, Rushden & D 8/07, Aldershot 5/08 Rel c/s 10, Bury (L) 11/08, Crawley 7/10		
Eddie	Hutchinson	4	6'01"	13 00	23/2/82	28	Kingston	Sutton U, Brentford £75,000 8/00, Oxford U 7/06 Rel 4/09, Crawley 5/09	39	2
Steve	Masterton	11	6'00"	13 05	2/1/85	25	Irvine	Rengers (Yth), Kilmarnock, Clyde 1/05, Morton 5/08 Rel c/s 10, Crawley 6/10		
Byron	Napper	21			26/2/92	18		Crawley	7	0
Paul	Raynor		6'00"	12 11	29/4/66	44	Nottingham	Crawley Ass Man	0	0
Simon	Rusk	2	5'11"	12 08	17/12/81	28	Peterborough	Peterborough (Scholar), Cambridge C, Boston Utd 3/01 Rel c/s 07, Northwich 7/07 Rel 1/08, Rushden & D (L) 9/07, York C 1/08 Rel 5/09, Crawley 5/09	38	0
Ben	Smith	7	5'08"	11 06	23/11/78	31	Chelmsford	Arsenal (Trainee), Reading 4/97, Yeovil 3/98, Southend 6/01 Rel c/s 02, Hereford 6/02, Shrewsbury 6/04, Weymouth 1/06, Hereford Undisc 1/07 Rel c/s 09, Crawley 8/09	34	7
Sergio	Torres	8	6'02"	12 04	8/11/86	23	Mar Del Plata, Arg	Boca Juniors (Arg) (Yth), Banfield (Arg), Brighton (Trial), Molesey 1/04, Basingstoke 2/04, Wycombe Undisc 8/05, Peterborough £150,000 7/08, Lincoln C (L) 9/09, Lincoln C (2ML) 10/09, Crawley Undisc 7/10		

FORWARDS										
Liam	Enver-Marum	10	6'03"	12 00	17/11/87	23	London	Reading (Scholar) Rel c/s 06, Brighton (Trial) 7/06, Cambridge U 8/06, Woking 1/07 Rel 5/09, Eastbourne B 5/09 Rel 5/10, Crawley 6/10		
Michael	Malcolm	19	5'10"	11 07	13/10/85	24	Harrow	Wycombe (Yth), Tottenham £10,000 Rel c/s 05, Stockport 7/05 Rel c/s 07, Kettering 8/07 Rel 9/07, Rushden & D 9/07, Thurrock 12/07, Weymouth 1/08, Crawley (2ML) 11/08 Perm 1/09	39	3
Craig	McAllister	14	6'01"	12 07	28/6/80	30	Glasgow	Eastleigh, Basingstoke 3/02, Stevenage 5/04, Gravesend (L) 12/04, Eastleigh (3ML) 2/05, Woking 7/05, Grays 5/07, Rushden & D (L) 10/07, Rushden & D (2ML) 11/07, Oxford U 1/08 Rel 4/08, Exeter 5/08 Rel c/s 10, Barnet (5WL) 11/09, Rotherham (SL) 3/10, Crawley 6/10		
Matt	Tubbs	9			15/7/84	26	Bournemouth	AFC Bournemouth (Yth), Bolton Wanderers (Trainee), Dorchester, Salisbury 10/03, Bournemouth (6WL) 11/08, Crawley £70,000+ 6/10		

Loanees		HT	WT	DOB	AGE	POB	From - To	APPS	GOA
(M)Daniel	Powell	6'01"	13 03	12/3/91	19	Luton	MK Dons 8/09 - Forest Green Rovers (L) 10/09	3	0
(D)Chris	Carruthers	5'10"	12 03	19/8/83	27	Kettering	Oxford U 8/09 - York C (3ML) 9/09, Rel 1/10, York C 1/10	7	1
(D)Dominic	Collins	6'02"		15/4/91	19	Preston	Preston 9/09 -	2	0
(M)Adam	Barton	6'03"	12 01	7/1/91	19	Blackburn	Preston 9/09 -	2	0
(M)Kieron	Djelali	6'02"	13 01	1/1/91	19	London	C.Palace 8/09 - Chesterfield (L) 11/09	5	0
(D)Matt	Langston	6'02"	12 04	2/4/81	29	Brighton	Histon (6WL) 3/10 - Eastbourne B 6/10	8	0
(M)Liam	Bellamy			16/10/91	18		Charlton 4/10 -		

Departures		HT	WT	DOB	AGE	POB	From - To	APPS	GOA
(D)Chris	Giles	6'02"	13 00	16/4/82	28	Milborne Port	Forest Green 5/08 - Rel 1/10, Salisbury 1/10	9	0
(F)Callum	Willock	6'01"	12 08	29/10/81	28	Waterloo	Stevenage 9/09 - Rel 2/10, Cambridge U NC 2/10 Rel 4/10, Ebbsfleet 7/10	16	2
(M)Mbive 'Peggy'	Lokando			18/8/89	21	London	Leyton 11/09 - St Albans 2/10	2	0
(M)Josh	Huggins			3/11/90	19	Frimley	Hampton & R 8/09 - Rel, Didcot T 3/10	0	0
(D)Max	Lake-Edwards			20/8/90	20		Yth - Rel 3/10	0	0
(F)Ben	King			9/5/93	17		Yth - Rel 3/10	2	0
(M)Thomas	Pinault	5'10"	11 01	4/12/81	28	Grasse, Fra	Brentford 7/07 - Rel 4/10, France	40	1
(G)Simon	Rayner	6'04"	15 00	8/7/83	27	Vancouver, Can	Torquay 6/08 - Rel 4/10	35	0
(D)Karl	Broadhurst	6'00"	11 07	18/3/80	30	Portsmouth	Hereford 8/09 - Rel 4/10	34	0
(F)Mithan	Nayee	5'09"	11 02	3/3/90	20	Crawley	Yth - Rel 4/10		
(F)Jefferson	Louis	6'02"	13 02	22/2/79	31	Harrow	Wrexham 5/09 - Rel 5/10, Rushden & D (SL) 11/09, Gainsborough 6/10	18	5
(F)Danny	Forrest	5'10"	11 07	23/10/84	25	Keighley	Halifax 5/08 - Rel 5/10, Barrow 6/10	33	6
(M)Lewis	Killeen	5'09"	10 07	23/9/82	26	Peterborough	Halifax 5/08 - Rel 5/10, Droylsden 7/10	29	1
(F)Charles	Ademeno	5'10"	11 13	12/12/88	21	Milton Keynes	Southend 7/09 - Grimsby Tribunal 7/10	32	11
(M)Nick	Carter	5'10"	12 08	17/12/89	20	Eastbourne	Yth -	6	0

Do you remember when...

Crawley Town

Crawley Town 1994-1995 finished 11th with John Maggs as Manager.

Back row, left to right: Rob O'Shaughnessy, Neil Pearson, Paul Ashenden, Ian Chatfield, Matt Preston, Joff Vansittart and Colin Pates.
Front row: Mark Jenkins, Jack Dineen, Paul Adam, Viv Jeffery, Mickey Turner and Steve Payne.

DARLINGTON

Chairman: Raj Singh
Secretary: Lis Charlton (T) 01325 387 010
(E) lisa@darlington-fc.net
Additional Committee Members:
Graham Fordy, Andy Wilson, Phil Preston, Martin Walker,
Manager: Mark Cooper
Programme Editor: Martin Walker (E) martin.walker50@hotmail.com

Back row (L-R): Josh Gray, Tommy Wright, Michael Smith, Danny Hone, Liam Hatch, Kevin Austin, Joe Clarke, Gary Smith.
Middle: Craig Liddle (Head of Youth), Neil Maddison (Centre of Excellence Manager), Aaron Brown, Paul Terry, Chris Moore, Sam Russell, Kelvin Jack, John McReady, Curtis Main, Gareth Waite, Kevin Stonehouse (Football in the Community Manager).
Front: Tony Elliott (Goalkeeper Coach), Corey Barnes, Paul Arnison, Paul Terry, Richard Dryden (Assistant Manager), Ian Miller (Captain), Mark Cooper (Manager), Chris Senior, Jamie Chandler, Andrew Thompson (Kit man), Will Short (Physio).

Club Factfile

Founded: 1883 **Nickname:** The Quakers
Previous Names: None
Previous Leagues: Northern League 1883-1908, North Eastern 1908-21, Football League 1921-89, 91-2010, Conference 1989-90

Club Colours (change): White & black/white/white (All red)

Ground: Darlington Arena, Neasham Road DL2 1DL (T) 01325 387 000
Capacity: 25,000 **Seats:** 25,000 **Covered:** 25,000 **Clubhouse:** Yes **Shop:** Yes
Previous Grounds: Feethams > 2003, Reynolds Arena, Hurworth Moor
Simple Directions
Leave the A1(m) at junction 57 for Darlington. Follow road to roundabout. From here take the first exit off and follow road to second roundabout (Reg Vardy on right). Head straight over and follow signs for Teesside until you reach next roundabout. Turn left here and stadium is on right hand side.

Record Attendance: 21,023 v Bolton Wanderers - League Cup 3rd Round 14/11/1960
Record Victory: 9-2 v Lincoln City - Division 3 North 07/01/1928
Record Defeat: 0-10 v Doncaster Rovers - Division 4 25/01/1964
Record Goalscorer: Alan Walsh - 100, Jerry Best - 80
Record Appearances: Ron Greener - 490, John Peverell - 465, Brian Henderson - 463
Additional Records: Paid £95,000 to Motherwell for Nick Cusack January 1992.
Received £400,000 from Dundee United for Jason Devos October 1998

Senior Honours: Northern League 1895-96, 99-1900. North Eastern League 1912-13, 20-21.
Football League Division 3 1924-25, Division 4 1990-91, Division 3 North Cup 1933-34.
Durham Senior Cup 1919-20.

10 YEAR RECORD

00-01	01-02	02-03	03-04	04-05	05-06	06-07	07-08	08-09	09-10
FL 3 20	FL 3 15	FL 3 14	FL 3 18	FL 2 8	FL 2 8	FL 2 11	FL 2 6	FL 2 12	FL 2 24

DARLINGTON

No.	Date	Comp	H/A	Opponents	Att:	Result	Goalscorers
1	8/8/09	FL2	A	Aldershot Town	2866	L 1-3	Dowson 85
2	15/8/09	FL2	H	Bury	2310	L 0-1	
3	18/8/09	FL2	H	Crewe	1821	L 0-1	
4	22/8/09	FL2	A	Port Vale	4561	L 0-1	
5	28/8/09	FL2	H	Cheltenham	1840	D1-1	Gall 71
6	5/9/09	FL2	A	Lincoln City	3005	L 0-3	
7	11/9/09	FL2	A	Accrington	3228	L 1-2	Gall 59
8	19/9/09	FL2	H	Bournemouth	1999	L 0-2	
9	26/9/09	FL2	A	Grimsby Town	4014	D1-1	Main 81
10	29/9/09	FL2	H	Rochdale	1748	L 0-2	
11	3/10/09	FL2	H	Macclesfield	1763	L 0-1	
12	10/10/09	FL2	A	Dagenham & R	1981	L 0-2	
13	17/10/09	FL2	H	Shrewsbury	1958	W 2-1	Devitt 26, Thomas 56
14	24/10/09	FL2	A	Barnet	2313	L 0-3	
15	31/10/09	FL2	A	Hereford	2238	L 1-2	Collins 72
16	14/11/09	FL2	H	Burton	2404	W 1-0	Main 7
17	21/11/09	FL2	A	Chesterfield	3460	L 2-5	Collins 59, Hogg
18	24/11/09	FL2	H	Morecambe	1698	L 0-4	
19	1/12/09	FL2	A	Notts County	4606	L 0-4	
20	5/12/09	FL2	H	Bradford City	2744	L 0-1	
21	12/12/09	FL2	A	Torquay United	2434	L 0-5	
22	19/1/10	FL2	A	Rotherham	3234	W 2-1	Purcell 47, Smith 63
23	23/1/10	FL2	A	Crewe	3717	L 0-3	
24	26/1/10	FL2	H	Northampton	1694	L 1-2	Purcell 29
25	6/2/10	FL2	H	Rotherham	2231	W 2-0	Purcell 19, White 52
26	9/2/10	FL2	H	Lincoln City	1697	D 1-1	Dempsey 38
27	13/2/10	FL2	A	Morecambe	1741	L 0-2	
28	20/2/10	FL2	H	Chesterfield	2209	L 2-3	Purcell 27, 53
29	27/2/10	FL2	A	Bradford City	11532	L 0-1	
30	2/3/10	FL2	H	Port Vale	1582	L 1-3	Purcell 6
31	6/3/10	FL2	H	Torquay United	1819	L 1-3	Main 54
32	9/3/10	FL2	A	Bury	2123	D1-1	Purcell 32 (pen)
33	13/3/10	FL2	A	Northampton	4755	L 0-2	
34	20/3/10	FL2	H	Barnet	1463	L 1-2	Breen 57 (og)
35	23/3/10	FL2	H	Aldershot Town	1296	L 1-2	Arnison 85
36	27/3/10	FL2	A	Shrewsbury	5081	W 2-0	Purcell 8, Diop 87
37	3/4/10	FL2	A	Burton	2779	W 2-1	Gray 22, White 32
38	5/4/10	FL2	H	Hereford	2131	L 0-1	
39	10/4/10	FL2	H	Accrington	1545	D0-0	
40	13/4/10	FL2	A	Rochdale	5371	W 1-0	Mulligan 35
41	17/4/10	FL2	A	Bournemouth	6464	L 0-2	
42	20/4/10	FL2	A	Cheltenham	2836	D3-3	Purcell 2, Eastham 5 (og), Diop 27
43	24/4/10	FL2	H	Grimsby Town	1911	L 0-2	
44	27/4/10	FL2	H	Notts County	2112	L 0-5	
45	1/5/10	FL2	A	Macclesfield	1716	W 2-0	Miller 9, Smith 79
46	8/5/10	FL2	H	Dagenham & R	2720	L 0-2	
	Cups						
1	10/8/09	LGCP	H	Leeds United	4487	L 0-1	
2	1/9/09	JPT (N)	H	Lincoln City	828	W 1-0	Thorpe 27
3	6/10/09	JPT (N)	A	Leeds United	8429	L 1-2	Convery 45+1
4	7/11/09	FACP	A	Barnet	1654	L 1-3	Diop 73

Home League Attendances	
Highest:	2744 v Bradford City
Lowest:	1296 v Aldershot Town
Average:	1840

Top Goalscorer:	Purcell - 9 (9 League, 0 Cup) in 22 appearances - 41% strike rate
Most Appearances:	Miller - 43 (40 League, 3 Cup)

GOALKEEPERS		SN	HT	WT	DOB	AGE	POB	From - To	APPS	GOA
Kelvin	Jack	1	6'03"	16 00	29/4/76	34	Arima, Trin & Tob	Trin City United (Trin), Joe Public (Trin), Yavapai Roughriders (USA), VCU Rams (USA), Doc's Khelwalaas (Trin), W Connection (Trin), San Juan Jablotech (Trin), Reading 3/04 Rel 6/04, Blackpool (Trial) 7/04, Oldham (Trial) 7/04, Dundee 8/04 Rel 5/06, Gillingham 7/06 Rel 6/08, Barnsley (Trial) 2/08, Southend 2/10 Rel 5/10, Darlington 5/10		
Sam	Russell	23	6'00"	10 13	4/10/82	26	Middlesbrough	Middlesbrough Rel c/s 04, Gateshead (SL) 2/02, Darlington (L) 12/02, Scunthorpe (3ML) 8/03, Darlington 8/04 Rel c/s 07, MK Dons (Trial) 7/07, Rochdale 8/07 Rel c/s 09, Wrexham 8/09, Darlington 5/10		
DEFENDERS										
Paul	Arnison	2	5'10"	11 12	18/9/77	33	Hartlepool	Newcastle, Hartlepool (L) 3/00 Perm 3/00, Carlisle (3ML) 10/03, Carlisle 2/04 Rel c/s 08, Bradford C 7/08, Darlington 7/09		
Danny	Hone		6'02"	12 00	15/9/89	20	Croydon	Lincoln C, Darlington (6ML) 7/10		
Ian	Miller	6	6'02"	12 01	23/11/83	27	Colchester	Bury T, Ipswich 9/06, Boston U (2ML) 11/06, Darlington (2ML) 2/07, Darlington (6ML) 7/07 Perm 1/08		
Midfielders										
Michael	Brough	5	5'09"	11 07	1/8/81	29	Nottingham	Notts County Rel 1/04, Spalding (L) 1/00, Macclesfield (Trial) 1/04, Lincoln C (Trial) 2/04, Stevenage 3/04, Forest Green 1/06, Torquay 5/08, Salisbury (SL) 2/09, Stevenage (L) 9/09, Mansfield (5WL) 11/09 Perm 1/10 Rel 5/10, Darlington 7/10		
Jamie	Chandler	3	5'07"	11 02	24/3/89	21	South Shields	Sunderland, Darlington (4ML) 8/09, Darlington 7/10		
Josh	Gray	14	6'00"	11 11	22/7/91	19	South Shields	Darlington		
Chris	Lumsdon		5'10"	11 07	15/12/79	30	Newcastle	Sunderland, Blackpool (L) 2/00, Crewe (3ML) 9/00, Barnsley (2ML) 10/01 £350,000 12/01, Hartlepool (Trial) 7/04, Carlisle 8/04 Rel c/s 09, Darlington 7/09		
John	McReady	16						Darlington		
Chris	Moore	11					Newcastle	Newcastle (Jun), Bishop Auckland c/s 03, Whitley Bay 12/04 Rel c/s 05, Working Abroad, Whitley Bay 1/08, Darlington 3/10		
Gary	Smith	20	5'08"	10 10	30/1/84	26	Middlesbrough	Middlesbrough Rel c/s 04, Colchester (Trial) 11/03 Wimbledon (SL) 3/04, MK Dons 8/04 Rel c/s 07, Brentford 8/07 Rel c/s 09, Darlington 7/09		
Gareth	Waite	8					Thornaby	Thornaby, Spennymoor 1/08, Darlington 1/10		
Dominik	Werling	55	5'08"		13/12/82	27	Ludwigshafen, Ger	Waldhof Mannheim (Ger), Armenia Bielefild (Ger) 1/03, FC Union Berlin (Ger) 7/04, TSV Crauksheim (Ger) 7/05, SpVgg Bayern Hoff (Ger) 7/06, Sakarayaspor (Tur) 1/07, Barnsley (6ML) 7/07, FC Erzegebirge Aue (Ger) 7/08 Rel 9/08, Huddersfield 1/09 Rel c/s 09, Darlington 4/10		
FORWARDS										
Corey	Barnes	15	5'08"	10 08	1/1/92	18	Sunderland	Darlington		
Liam	Hatch		6'02"	12 03	3/4/82	27	Hitchin	Herne Bay, Gravesend 6/01, Ashford T (L) 2/02, Barnet £23,000 7/03, Peterborough £150,000 1/08, Darlington (SL) 8/08, Luton (SL) 6/09, Darlington (6ML) 7/10		
Curtis	Main	12	5'10"	10 07	20/6/92	18	South Shields	Darlington, Fulham (Trial) c/s 09, Middlesbrough (Trial) c/s 09		
Chris	Senior	10	5'06"	9 01	18/11/81	27	Huddersfield	Huddersfield, Wakefield-Emley 7/02, Scarborough 8/03 OOC 5/05, Halifax 8/05 Rel 5/07, Altrincham (SL) 1/07, Altrincham 7/07, Darlington 5/10		
Michael	Smith	17	5'11"	11 03	17/10/91	18		Darlington		
Tommy	Wright	9	6'00"	11 12	28/9/84	25	Kirby Muxloe	Leicester, Brentford (10WL) 9/03, Brentford (4ML) 12/03, Blackpool (4ML) 8/05, Barnsley £50,000 1/06, Walsall (7WL) 11/06, Darlington (L) 1/07 Undisc 1/07, Aberdeen £75,000 8/08 Rel 1/10, Grimsby 1/10, Darlington 5/10		

EASTBOURNE BOROUGH

Chairman: Len Smith
Secretary: Myra Stephens (T) 0775 417 4406
(E) footballsecretary@ebfc.co.uk

Additional Committee Members:
Mick Grimer, Mike Spooner, Angus Scott, Lorna Gosling

Manager: Garry Wilson
Programme Editor: Mike Spooner (E) media@ebfc.co.uk

Back Row (L-R): David Funnell (Kit), Dan Brown, Gary Elphick, Matt Langston, Andy Atkin, Richard Pacquette, Ben Austin, Ollie Rowe, Damian Karchinski (Kit) Middle Row: Dean Lightwood (Coach), Steve Eke (Coach), Kane Wills, Steve Brinkhurst, Darren Baker, Dan Knowles, Rikki Banks, Simon Weatherstone, Matt Smart, Ross Treleaven, Ray Tuppen (Sports Therapist)
Front Row: Neil Jenkins, Jamie Taylor, Matt Crabb, Nick Greenwood (Head Coach), Garry Wilson (Manager), Simon Johnson, Ethan Strevett, Nathan Crabb

Club Factfile

Founded: 1966 **Nickname:** Borough
Previous Names: Langney Sports > 2001
Previous Leagues: Eastbourne & Hastings, Sussex County, Southern

Club Colours (change): Red/black/red (All yellow)

Ground: Langney Sports Club, Priory Lane, Eastbourne BN23 7QH (T) 01323 766 265
Capacity: 4,151 **Seats:** 542 **Covered:** 2,500 **Clubhouse:** Yes **Shop:** Yes
Previous Grounds: None

Simple Directions
From M25 take M23/A23 eastbound to A27 Polegate by pass pick up and follow signs for crematorium 50yds past crem.turn right at mini roundabout into Priory Road Stadium 100yds on left.

Record Attendance: 3,770 v Oxford United - FA Cup 1st Round 05/11/05
Record Victory: 10-1 v Haywards Heath Town - Sussex County Division One 1991-92
Record Defeat: 0-8 v Sheppey United (A) - FA Vase 09/10/93 and v Peachaven & Tels (A) - Sussex Co. Div.1 09/11/93
Record Goalscorer: Nigel Hole - 146
Record Appearances: Darren Baker - 689
Additional Records: Paid £1,800 to Yeovil Town for Yemi Odoubade.
Received £15,000 from Oxford United for Yemi Odoubade.

Senior Honours: Sussex County League 1999-2000, 02-03. Sussex Senior Cup 2001-02.

10 YEAR RECORD

00-01	01-02	02-03	03-04	04-05	05-06	06-07	07-08	08-09	09-10
SthE 9	SthE 7	SthE 2	SthP 11	Conf S 5	Conf S 17	Conf S 7	Conf S 2	Conf 13	Conf 19

EASTBOURNE BOROUGH

No.	Date	Comp	H/A	Opponents	Att:	Result	Goalscorers	Pos
1	8/8/09	BSP	A	Wrexham	3726	L 0-3		21
2	11/8/09	BSP	H	AFC Wimbledon	3108	W 1-0	Jenkins 49	13
3	15/8/09	BSP	H	Rushden & Diamonds	941	D 1-1	Weatherstone 29	15
4	18/8/09	BSP	A	Grays Athletic	487	L 0-1		18
5	22/8/09	BSP	H	Barrow	971	W 2-1	Taylor 42, Atkin 45	12
6	29/8/09	BSP	A	Salisbury City	746	D 1-1	Weatherstone 69	15
7	31/8/09	BSP	H	Ebbsfleet United	1165	L 1-2	Taylor 69	16
8	5/9/09	BSP	A	Kidderminster Harriers	1307	W 2-0	N Crabb 37, Taylor 90	12
9	8/9/09	BSP	A	Stevenage Borough	1660	L 0-2		15
10	19/9/09	BSP	A	Oxford United	5688	L 0-4		14
11	22/9/09	BSP	H	Hayes & Yeading United	802	W 3-1	Og (Ruby) 44, Enver-Marum 2 (50, 55)	14
12	26/9/09	BSP	H	Tamworth	1053	D 1-1	Enver-Marum 56	14
13	29/9/09	BSP	A	Histon	633	L 0-2		15
14	3/10/09	BSP	H	Kettering Town	884	L 0-1		15
15	10/10/09	BSP	A	Gateshead	537	L 0-3		17
16	17/10/09	BSP	H	Mansfield Town	1207	L 1-2	Enver-Marum 68	18
17	31/10/09	BSP	A	Forest Green Rovers	789	D 1-1	M Crabb 39	18
18	14/11/09	BSP	H	Salisbury City	756	L 0-1		19
19	21/11/09	BSP	A	Mansfield Town	2922	D 1-1	McLaggon 44	20
20	24/11/09	BSP	H	Histon	703	D 1-1	Enver-Marum 42	19
21	1/12/09	BSP	A	Hayes & Yeading United	349	D 1-1	Taylor 9	20
22	5/12/09	BSP	H	Cambridge United	1217	D 2-2	Armstrong 15, Enver-Marum 25	20
23	26/12/09	BSP	A	Crawley Town	979	D 2-2	Enver-Marum 18, Taylor 47	20
24	28/12/09	BSP	A	Luton Town	6646	L 1-4	M Crabb 6	20
25	1/1/10	BSP	H	Crawley Town	1726	L 0-2		20
26	16/1/10	BSP	A	Cambridge United	2969	W 1-0	Taylor 55	18
27	23/1/10	BSP	A	Tamworth	883	D 1-1	Austin 40	19
28	6/2/10	BSP	H	Wrexham	972	W 2-1	Taylor 18, Enver-Marum 59	19
29	9/2/10	BSP	A	Rushden & Diamonds	1038	L 0-2		19
30	13/2/10	BSP	H	Luton Town	2018	L 0-1		19
31	16/2/10	BSP	A	Altrincham	590	L 0-3		19
32	20/2/10	BSP	H	Altrincham	810	D 2-2	Enver-Marum 3, Weatherstone pen 83	19
33	27/2/10	BSP	A	York City	2611	W 1-0	Enver-Marum 70	19
34	2/3/10	BSP	H	Stevenage Borough	903	L 0-6		19
35	6/3/10	BSP	H	Kidderminster Harriers	913	D 0-0		19
36	13/3/10	BSP	A	AFC Wimbledon	3358	L 0-2		19
37	20/3/10	BSP	H	Grays Athletic	1029	D 2-2	Taylor 2, Rooney 28	21
38	27/3/10	BSP	A	Barrow	1302	L 2-3	Taylor 2 (50, 57)	22
39	30/3/10	BSP	H	Gateshead	714	W 2-1	Weatherstone pen 64, Smart 66	20
40	3/4/10	BSP	H	Forest Green Rovers	1104	W 1-0	Rooney 51	20
41	5/4/10	BSP	A	Ebbsfleet United	1214	L 2-3	M Crabb 48, Benjamin 80	20
42	10/4/10	BSP	H	York City	1144	W 3-1	M Crabb 14, Atkin 2 (17, 32)	19
43	17/4/10	BSP	A	Kettering Town	932	L 0-4		20
44	24/4/10	BSP	H	Oxford United	2634	W 1-0	Weatherstone pen 84	19
	Chester	**record.**	**.....**	**. expunged 08/03**				
10	12/9/09	BSP	H	Chester City	968	D 1-1	Atkin 5	15
	Cups							
1	24/10/09	FAC 4Q	A	Tooting & Mitcham United	687	D 3-3	Crabb 42, Taylor 90, Elphick 90	
2	27/10/09	FAC 4QR	H	Tooting & Mitcham United	906	L 3-4 aet	Armstrong pen 13, Elphick 38, Austin 111	
3	12/12/09	FAT 1	A	Welling United	437	W 1-0	Enver-Marum 20	
4	19/1/10	FAT 2	A	Cambridge United	913	D 2-2	Taylor 14, Og (Hatswell) 33	
5	26/1/10	FAT 2R	H	Cambridge United	525	L 0-2		

Home League Attendances	
Highest:	3108 v AFC Wimbledon
Lowest:	703 v Histon
Average (08-09):	1001 (1387)
Top Goalscorer:	Taylor - 12 (10 League, 2 Cup) in 48 appearances - 25% strike rate
Most Appearances:	Taylor - 48 (39+4 League, 5 Cup)

	KNOWLES	PULLAN	BAKER	AUSTIN	JENKINS	M CRABB	JOHNSON	ARMSTRONG	BROWN	TAYLOR	ENVER-MARUM	SMITH	SMART	TRELEAVEN	JORDAN	ELPHICK	ATKIN	WEATHERSTONE	N CRABB	LIGHTWOOD	HURLEY	FRASER	ROWE	BENJAMIN	MCLAGGON	OPINEL	WALKER	ROONEY	NESSLING
	1	6	2	5	3	11	12	8	26	18	10	7	4	19	21	24	9	14	15	30	20	22	16	23	27	19	21	27	19
1	X	X	X	X	X	X	X	X	X	X	X	S	S	S	U	U													
2	X	X	X	X	X	X	S	X	X	X	X	X	S		U	U	S												
3	X	X	X	X	X	X		X	X	X	X	S	S		U	U	S	X											
4	X	X	U	X		X	U	X	X	X	X	S	X		U	X	S	X											
5	X	X	S	X	X	X		X	X	X	U	S	S		U	X	X	X											
6	X	X	U	X		X	S		X	X	S	X	X		U	X	X	X	S										
7	X	X	S	X		X	U	X	X	X	U		S		S	X	X	X	X										
8		X	X	X		X	U		X	X	S	U			X	X	X	X	X	U	U								
9	U	X	X	X		X	S		X	X	S	S	U		X	X	X	X	X										
10	U	X	U	X	X	X	X		X	X	S		S		X	X	X	X	S										
11	U	X	U	X	X	X	S		X	X	X	S	S		X	X		X	X										
12	U	X	U	X	X	X	U		X	X	X	S	U		X	X		X	X										
13	U	X	S	X	X	X	S		X	X	X	S	U		X	X		X	X										
14	U		X	X	X	X	U	S		S	X	X	X		X	X	X	X	S										
15	U		X	X	X	X	U	S	X	X	S	X	X		X	X	X	S											
16	U	X	X	X	X	X	U	X	X	X	S	X	U		X	S	X												
17	X	X	S	X	X	X	U	X	X	S	X		S		U	X		X				X							
18	X	X		X	X		U	X	X	S	X				U		S	X				U	X	X	X				
19	X		X	X		X	S	X	X	U	X				U	X	S	X				S		X	X				
20	X	X	X	X		X	U	X	X	S	X				U		U	X				S		X	X				
21	X		X	X		X	S	X	X	X	X				U	X	U	X					U	X	U				
22	X		X	X	X	X	X	X		X	X	S			U	X	S						S	X	U				
23	X	S	X	X	X	X	X	X	X	X	X		U		U	X	S		S										
24	X	X		X		X	X	X	X	X	X		U			X	S	S	S			X	U						
25	X	X		X	X	X	X	X	X	X	X		U			X	S	U	S				U						
26	X	X		X	X	X	X	X	S	X	X		U			X	S	U	S					X					
27	X	X	U	X	X	X	X	X		X	X	S	S		U	X		U	X										
28	X	X	X		X	X	X	X		X	X		S			X		U	S	U			S	X					
29	X	X	X			X	X	X		X	X		S			X		U	S	U			U	X		X			
30	X	X	X	X		X	X	X		X	X		U			X		U	S	U			U	X					
31		X	S	X		X	X	X		X	X		S			X		U	S	U				X		X	X		
32	X	X	X	X			X	X		X	X		X			X	S	S	S				U	X			U		
33	X	X	X	X	S	X	X	X		X	X					X	S	S	U	U				X					
34	X	X	X	X	S	X	X	X		X	X		S			X	S	U	U					X					
35	X	X		X	X	X	U	X		X	X		X			X	S	U	S				S	X					
36	X	U	X	X	X	X	X	X		X			X			X	S	S	S				U	X					
37	X	X	U	X	X	X	X			X	X		X			X	S	S	U					S				X	
38	X	X	X	U	X	S	X		U	X	S		X			X	X	S						X				X	
39	X		X	X	X	X	U		S	X	S		X			X	X	X					U	S				X	
40	X	U	X	X	X	X	U		S	X	S		X			X	X	X						S				X	
41	X	U	X	X	X	X	U		S	X	S		X			X	X	X						S				X	
42	X	U	X	X	X	X	S		S	X	S		X			X	X	X						U				X	
43	X	S	X	X		X	S		X	X			X			X	X	X	U	S				U				X	
44		U	X	X		X	S		X	X	S		X			X	X	X	U					S				X	X
	U	X	S		X	X	U	X	X		X	S	U		X	X	X	X	X										
1	U	X	U	X	X	X	U	X	X	X	S	U	X		X	X	X					U							
2	X	X	U	X	X	X	U	X	X	X	X	X	U	S	U	X	S	S											
3	X	U	X	X	X	X	X	X		X	X	X	S		U	X	S		U										
4	X	X	U	X	X	X	X	X		X	X		S		U	X	X	S	S										
5	X	X	U	X	X	X	X	X		X	X	S	U		U	X		S	X										
Total League Appearances																													
X	33	31	27	41	27	41	18	27	25	39	28	5	15	0	9	38	16	23	7	0	0	2	1	16	3	2	1	8	1
S	0	2	5	0	2	1	10	2	5	4	12	10	13	1	1	1	16	7	14	1	0	2	3	5	0	0	0	0	0
U	8	5	7	1	0	0	14	0	1	1	2	1	9	0	14	3	2	9	5	6	1	1	8	2	2	0	1	0	0
Total Cup Appearances																													
X	4	4	1	5	5	5	3	5	2	5	4	2	1	0	1	5	2	0	1	0	0	0	0	0	0	0	0	0	0
S	0	0	0	0	0	0	0	0	0	0	1	1	2	1	0	0	2	3	1	0	0	0	0	0	0	0	0	0	0
U	1	1	4	0	0	0	2	0	0	0	0	1	2	0	4	0	0	0	1	0	0	1	0	0	0	0	0	0	0
Total Goals																													
Lg	0	0	0	1	1	4	0	1	0	10	10	0	1	0	0	0	3	5	1	0	0	0	0	1	1	0	0	2	0
Cp	0	0	0	1	0	0	0	1	0	2	1	0	0	0	0	2	0	0	0	0	0	0	0	0	0	0	0	0	0

CURRENT SQUAD AS OF BEGINING OF 2010-11 SEASON

GOALKEEPERS		SQ NO.	HT	WT	D.O.B	AGE	P.O.B	CAREER	APPS	GOA
Rikki	Banks	21	6'03"	13 08	13/5/86	24	Brighton	C.Palace, Crawley (L) 2/06, Hendon (SL) 3/06, Worthing c/s 06, Lewes 6/08, Wycombe (Trial) 12/09, Eastbourne B 5/10		
Danny	Knowles	1	6'00"	12 00	7/1/86	24	Sidcup	Gillingham Rel 4/06, Hastings U (L) 8/04, Welling (4ML) 1/05, East Thurrock (3ML) 11/05, Grays 8/06 Rel 5/08, AFC Wimbledon (6WL) 11/07, Crawley (7DL) 3/08, Fisher (SL) 3/08, Weymouth 7/08 Rel 2/09, Woking 2/09 Rel 5/09, Eastbourne B 5/09	33	0
Dean	Lightwood				12/6/69	41		Newhaven, Ringmer, Saltdean, Shoreham, Lewes, Saltdean, Eastbourne B, Ringmer 8/03, Saltdean, Eastbourne B (Pl/Coach)	1	0
DEFENDERS										
Ben	Austin	5	5'09"	10 01	3/4/77	33	Hastings	Brighton (Jun), Eastbourne T, Eastbourne B 6/00	41	1
Darren	Baker	2	5'10"	09 06	23/11/74	35	Eastbourne	Brighton (Ass Sch), Littlehampton (Yth), Eastbourne B 6/92	32	0
Gary	Elphick	24	6'01"	13 02	17/10/85	24	Brighton	Brighton, Eastbourne B (L) 9/04, St Albans (SL) 12/04, Aldershot (2ML) 1/06, St Albans 3/06 Rel 12/07, Havant & W 12/07, Eastbourne B 5/09	39	0
Neil	Jenkins	3	5'06"	10 08	6/1/82	28	Carshalton	Wimbledon Rel c/s 02, Southend 8/02 Rel c/s 04, Crawley 6/04, Eastbourne B 7/06	29	1
Matt	Langston	6	6'02"	12 04	2/4/81	29	Brighton	Watford Rel c/s 03, Aldershot (L) 12/02, Barnet (SL) 3/03, Stevenage 8/03, Cambridge C 11/03, Histon 6/06, Crawley (6WL) 3/10, Eastbourne B 6/10		
Ollie	Rowe	17	6'01"	11 02	22/5/91	19	Eastbourne	Brighton (Scholar) Rel c/s 09, Ringmer c/s 09, Eastbourne T, Eastbourne B 11/09, Eastbourne T (Dual) 11/09	4	0
MIDFIELDERS										
Steven	Brinkhurst	16	5'11"	11 11	28/3/91	19	Lewes	Brighton Rel c/s 10, Bognor Regis (WE) 1/09, Lewes (L) 12/09, Lewes (L) 3/10, Eastbourne B 6/10		
Danny	Brown	26	6'00"	12 06	12/9/80	29	Bethnal Green	L.Orient, Barnet £40,000 5/99 Rel c/s 03, Oxford U 7/03 Rel c/s 05, Crawley 8/05 Rel 11/06, Cambridge U 11/06, Eastbourne B (2ML) 11/08, Perm 1/09	30	0
Matt	Crabb	11	5'10"	12 01	15/12/81	28	Eastbourne	Eastbourne U, Eastbourne B 7/00, Langney Sports (L) 8/00	42	4
Nathan	Crabb	15			26/6/85	25	Eastbourne	Eastbourne Utd Assoc, Eastbourne B 8/07	21	1
Simon	Johnson	8			14/4/91	19	Hailsham	Eastbourne B	28	0
Matt	Smart	4	5'10"	12 04	14/4/76	34	Crawley	Gillingham (Trainee, Crawley, Shoreham, Horsham, Wick, Horsham, Eastbourne B 7/01	28	1
Simon	Weatherstone	14	5'11"	11 00	26/1/80	30	Reading	Oxford U, Boston U 2/01, Yeovil £15,000 1/04, Hornchurch Undisc 9/04, Stevenage 11/04 Rel 5/06, Weymouth 6/06 Rel 5/08, Crawley 5/08 Rel 5/09, Eastbourne B 5/09	30	5

FORWARDS										
Andy	Atkin	9	6'00"	11 11	19/1/81	29	Hastings	Sidley U, Little Common, Sidley U c/s 00, Hooe Sports, Little Common, Eastbourne Utd Assoc 3/01, Eastbourne B 3/05	32	3
Richard	Pacquette	10	6'00"	12 06	23/1/83	27	Paddington	QPR Rel 6/04, Stevenage (L) 10/02, Dag & Red (L) 12/03, Mansfield (L) 2/04, MK Dons 9/04 Rel 11/04, Fisher 11/04, Brentford 11/04, Farnborough 12/04 Rel 1/05, Stevenage 1/05 Rel 1/05, Grimsby (Trial) 1/05, St Albans 2/05, Hemel Hempstead 3/05, Hampton & R 3/05, Worthing 7/05, Thurrock (L) 2/06, Havant & W 3/06, Maidenhead 3/08, Histon (L) 2/09, York C 7/09 Rel 5/10, Eastbourne B 6/10		
Jamie	Taylor	7	5'07"	11 11	16/12/82	27	Crawley	Broadbridge H, Horsham c/s 01, Aldershot 8/02 Rel 2/04, Horsham (L) 2/03, Carshalton (L) 12/03, Oakwood 2/04, AFC Wimbledon 3/04, Horsham 10/04, Woking 12/06, Dag & Red 3/07, Grays (SL) 2/08, Grays 5/08, Eastbourne B 7/09	43	10
Ross	Treleaven	19	5'09"	09 13	14/12/88	21	Brighton	Crowborough, Eastbourne B (Dual) 3/08 Perm c/s 08, Worthing (Dual) 8/08, Hastings U (Dual) 2/10	1	0

Loanees		SN	HT	WT	DOB	AGE	POB	From - To	APPS	GOA
(F)Joe	Benjamin		5'10"	11 04	8/10/90	19	Woodford	Northampton 11/09, (SL) 1/10 -	21	1
(F)Kayne	McLaggon		6'02"	12 06	21/9/90	19	Barry	Southampton 11/09 -	3	1
(D)Sacha	Opinel		5'09"	11 13	9/4/77	33	Saint Maurice (Fra)	Farnborough 2/10 -	2	0
(G)Mitchell	Walker				24/9/91	18	St Albans	Brighton 2/10 -	1	0
(M)Luke	Rooney				28/12/90	19	Bermondsey	Gillingham (SL) 3/10 -	8	2
(G)Greg	Nessling				11/4/84	26		Hastings U (Cover) 3/10 -	1	0

Departures		SN	HT	WT	DOB	AGE	POB	From - To	APPS	GOA
(F)Kane	Louis		5'11"	10 11	21/5/90	20	Brighton	Brighton 8/09 - Lewes 10/09		
(M)Danny	Smith		5'10"	10 07	7/6/89	21	Plymouth	Plymouth 5/09 - Rel 2/10, Weymouth NC 2/10	15	0
(G)Michael	Jordan		6'02"	13 02	7/4/86	24	Enfield	Stevenage 1/09 - Rel 2/10, Farnborough 2/10	10	0
(F)James	Fraser		5'09"	12 07	26/4/89	21	Brighton	Bristol R 10/09 - Sutton U (L) 1/10, Whitehawk (Dual), Eastbourne T (Dual) 2/10, Lewes 3/10 Rel 6/10	4	0
(D)Marc	Pullan		6'03"	14 06	28/2/74	36	Brighton	Worthing 1/06 - Rel 5/10, Lewes 6/10	33	0
(F)Liam	Enver-Marum		6'03"	12 00	17/11/87	22	London	Woking 5/09 - Rel 5/10, Crawley 6/10	40	10
(M)Paul	Armstrong		5'08"	10 09	5/10/78	31	Dublin	Crawley 6/06 - Rel 5/10, Whitehawk 7/10	29	1
(D)Matt	Hurley				14/6/85	25		Shoreham 8/09 - Burgess Hill (Dual) 3/10, Whitehawk 6/10	0	0

Do you remember when...

Eastbourne Boro'

Eastbourne Borough were known as Langney Sports until 2001-2002 and here we see the Sports' squad that won the Sussex League Championship in 1999-2000.

Back row, left to right: Garry Wilson (Manager), Duncan Kneller, Chris Dicken, John Snelgrove, Liam Barham, Neil Phillips, Tony Burt, Sean McFadden, Andy Agutter, Wayne Farrier and Nick Greenwood (Coach).
Front Row: Paul Stevens, Darren Baker, Matt Allen, Craig Willard, Paul Balch, Steve Willard, Daren Pearce and Simon Colbran.

FLEETWOOD TOWN

Chairman: Andrew Pilley
Secretary: (Ch. Exe) Steve Curwood **(T)** 07773 027 706
(E) steve.curwood@fleetwoodtownfc.com
Additional Committee Members:
Phil Brown, Steve Curwood, Peter Capper, Derick Thomas
Manager: Mickey Mellon
Programme Editor: Derick Thomas **(E)** press@fleetwoodtownfc.com

Back Row (L-R): Mark Peers, Andy Bell, Steve Foster, Phil Robinson, Rory Winters, Ricky Mercer, Ashley Dunn. Colin Potts.
Middle row: Danny Moore Physio, Russell Hitchin Physio, Paul Haddow, Adam Warlow, Nathan Pond, Mike Hale, Danny Hurst, Phil Doughty, Phil Denney,Simon Garner, Barry McCloughlin Kit Manager,
Front row: Kevin Leadbetter, Shaun Beeley, Kieran Walmsley, Andy Whittaker Coach, Tony Greenwood Manager, Nigel Greenwood Asst Manager, Jamie Milligan Captain, Warren Beattie, Lennie Reid.

Club Factfile

Founded: 1908 **Nickname:** The Fishermen
Previous Names: Fleetwood 1908, Fleetwood Wanderers 1997 then in the same year reverted to Fleetwood Freeport > 2002
Previous Leagues: Lancashire Combination 1908-68. Northern Premier 1968-76, 87-96, 2005-08, Cheshire 1977-82, North West Counties 1982-87, 97-2005.
Club Colours (change): Red and white/white/red (Amber & black stripes/black/amber)

Ground: Highbury Stadium, Park Avenue, Fleetwood, Lancashire FY7 6TX **(T)** 01253 770 702
Capacity: 3,000 **Seats:** 250 **Covered:** 1,200 **Clubhouse:** Yes **Shop:** Yes
Previous Grounds: Two locations before moving to Highbury in 1939
Simple Directions
Leave M6 J32 signposted M55. Leave M55 at J3. Take 3rd exit signposted Fleetwood. Stay on A585 for approx. 11.5 miles. At Eros Statue roundabout take 1st exit. At next roundabout take 6th exit onto Hatfield Avenue. Take 4th road on the left (Highbury Avenue). The entrance is on the right hand side between houses no. 65 & 67.

Record Attendance: 7,900 v Liverpool - 12/08/2003
Record Victory:
Record Defeat:
Record Goalscorer:
Record Appearances:
Additional Records:

Senior Honours: North West Counties Division Two 1998-99, Division One 2004-05. Northern Premier League Cup 2006-07.

10 YEAR RECORD

00-01		01-02		02-03		03-04		04-05		05-06		06-07		07-08		08-09		09-10	
NWC1	5	NWC1	14	NWC1	10	NWC1	3	NWC1	1	NP 1	2	NP P	8	NP P	1	Conf N	8	Conf N	2

FLEETWOOD TOWN

No.	Date	Comp	H/A	Opponents	Att:	Result	Goalscorers	Pos
1	8/8/09	BSN	A	Solihull Moors	279	W 2-1	Wilde 29, Milligan 38	6
2	11/8/09	BSN	H	Hyde United	1012	D 1-1	Wilde 22	7
3	15/8/09	BSN	H	AFC Telford	1309	W 3-1	Cahill 2 (29, 37), Clancy 62	3
4	18/8/09	BSN	A	Vauxhall Motors	224	L 1-2	Warlow 88	7
5	22/8/09	BSN	H	Eastwood Town	976	W 3-1	Clancy 65, Warlow 2 (74, 87)	3
6	29/8/09	BSN	A	Droylsden	449	L 0-2		6
7	31/8/09	BSN	H	Workington	1079	W 4-0	Milligan 9, Warlow 49, Wilde 61, Pond 72	5
8	5/9/09	BSN	A	Redditch United	230	D 0-0		7
9	12/9/09	BSN	H	Corby Town	1126	W 4-2	Seddon 3 (38, 52, 69), Warlow 74	3
10	19/9/09	BSN	A	Hyde United	501	L 1-2	Wilde 68	4
11	3/10/09	BSN	H	Gainsborough Trinity	1187	D 2-2	Warlow 2 (70, 78)	4
12	17/10/09	BSN	A	Gloucester City	363	W 2-1	Dodgson 72, Seddon 90	3
13	31/10/09	BSN	H	Alfreton Town	1297	D 2-2	Wilde 68, McNulty 87	7
14	10/11/09	BSN	H	Harrogate Town	812	D 2-2	Milligan 2 (pen 60, 87)	7
15	14/11/09	BSN	H	Redditch United	1167	W 8-0	Wright 1, McGuire 2 (11, 30), Milligan 59, Warlow 2 (64, 71), Rogan 2 (80, 82)	6
16	28/11/09	BSN	A	Alfreton Town	485	W 4-1	McNulty pen 32, Clancy 40, Seddon 2 (48, 82)	4
17	5/12/09	BSN	A	AFC Telford	1704	D 0-0		6
18	15/12/09	BSN	A	Northwich Victoria	489	W 3-0	Clancy 3 (10, 33, 41)	3
19	19/12/09	BSN	H	Stafford Rangers	1120	W 2-1	Milligan 2 (60, 87)	2
20	26/12/09	BSN	A	Southport	1840	L 0-5		2
21	28/12/09	BSN	H	Vauxhall Motors	1170	W 4-2	Rogan 31, Warlow 3 (62, 64, 79)	2
22	1/1/10	BSN	H	Southport	2541	W 4-0	Connors 30, Rogan 47, Clancy 66, Warlow 73	2
23	16/1/10	BSN	H	Ilkeston Town	1009	W 1-0	Cahill 56	2
24	23/1/10	BSN	H	Blyth Spartans	1033	W 4-2	Warlow 19, Rogan 2 (42, 58), Pond 85	1
25	30/1/10	BSN	H	Hinckley United	1442	W 3-1	Warlow 15, Mullan 45, Rogan 56	1
26	6/2/10	BSN	A	Corby Town	455	W 2-0	Warlow 23, Barry 83	1
27	13/2/10	BSN	H	Gloucester City	1267	W 3-1	Clancy 17, Rogan 2 (31, 37)	1
28	16/2/10	BSN	A	Eastwood Town	367	W 1-0	Clancy 90	1
29	20/2/10	BSN	A	Gainsborough Trinity	316	L 0-2		1
30	27/2/10	BSN	H	Northwich Victoria	1271	L 0-3		1
31	6/3/10	BSN	A	Hinckley United	642	W 2-0	Warlow 10, Clancy 37	1
32	13/3/10	BSN	H	Solihull Moors	1451	W 3-0	Warlow 2 (47, 52), Barry 87	1
33	20/3/10	BSN	A	Harrogate Town	431	W 1-0	Seddon 70	1
34	25/3/10	BSN	A	Stalybridge Celtic	587	W 3-2	Clancy pen 41, Warlow 2 (88, 90)	1
35	27/3/10	BSN	A	Stafford Rangers	480	D 2-2	Warlow 2 (52, 57)	1
36	3/4/10	BSN	H	Droylsden	1816	W 3-0	Thorpe 2 (45, 79), Warlow 55	1
37	5/4/10	BSN	A	Workington	731	L 0-1		2
38	10/4/10	BSN	A	Ilkeston Town	411	W 1-0	Clancy 45	2
39	17/4/10	BSN	A	Blyth Spartans	523	W 3-2	Warlow 2 (16, 58), Seddon 68	2
40	24/4/10	BSN	H	Stalybridge Celtic	3011	W 2-0	Clancy 2 (57, 78)	2
	Farsley Celtic record expunged 12/03							
9	8/9/09	BSN	A	Farsley Celtic	291	W 2-0	Seddon 14, Wilde 20	4
25	19/1/10	BSN	H	Farsley Celtic	611	W 2-0	Warlow 63, Milligan 73	1
	Cups							
1	26/9/09	FAC 2Q	H	Farsley Celtic	730	W 3-1	Wilde 9, McNulty 44, Warlow 57	
2	10/10/09	FAC 3Q	H	Vauxhall Motors	951	W 3-2	Hills 43, Clancy 45, Seddon 82	
3	24/10/09	FAC 4Q	A	Kidderminster Harriers	1257	D 0-0		
4	27/10/09	FAC 4QR	H	Kidderminster Harriers	1697	W 3-1	Seddon 25, Pond 51, Clancy 77	
5	7/11/09	FAC 1	A	Northampton Town	3077	L 1-2	Clancy 41	
6	21/11/09	FAT 3Q	H	Northwich Victoria	847	W 2-0	Cahill 12, Wilde 68	
7	11/12/09	FAT 1	A	Chester City	518	W 1-0	Warlow 60	
8	12/1/10	FAT 2	H	Dover Athletic	871	L 0-1		
9	28/4/10	PO SF1	A	Droylsden	1104	L 0-2		
10	2/5/10	PO SF 2	H	Droylsden	2862	W 3-1	Seddon 35, Milligan 42, Grand 110 (D 3-3 agg W 4-3 pens)	
11	9/5/10	PO Final	H	Alfreton Town	3592	W 2-1	Pond 8, Thorpe 79	

Home Attendances:	
Highest:	3011 v Stalybridge Celtic
Lowest:	812 v Harrogate Town
Average (08-09):	1179 (931)
Top Goalscorer:	Warlow - 28 (26 League, 2 Cup) in 42 appearances - 67% strike rate
Most Appearances:	Clancy - 45 (32+3 League, 9+1 Cup)

HURST	WOOLISCROFT	WRIGHT	MERCER	TAYLOR	POND	CLANCY	MILLIGAN	WILDE	ROGAN	WILLIAMS	WARLOW	MCGUIRE	CONNORS	CAHILL	MULLAN	DODGSON	MCNULTY	HILLS	BEELEY	JORGENSEN	SEDDON	GRUNDY	DELL	TORPEY	HALL	DOOTSON	COWAN	BARRY	FRANKS	THORPE	GRAND	WILLIAMSON	CAVANAGH	
X	X	X	X	X	X	X	X	X	X	X	S	S	U	U	U																			1
X	X	X	X	X	X	X	X	X		X	S	U	S	X	S	U																		2
X	X	X	X	X	X	X	X	X	U	S	S	U	S	X	X																			3
X	X	X	X	X	X	X		X	S	U	S	S	X	X	X		U																	4
X	X	X	X	X	X	X	X	X	U	U	X	X	U		S		U																	5
X	X	X	X	X	X	X	X	X	S		X	X			S	U	U	U																6
X		X	U	X	X	X	X	X	S		X	S		S	X	U	X		X															7
X		X	U	X	X	X		X	U		X	X	X	S	S	U	X		X															8
X		X		X	U	S		X			S	S	X	U	X	X	X		X	X	X													9
X		X		X	S		X	X			S	U	X	S	X	U	X		X	X	X													10
X				X	S		X	X			X	X	X	U	X	U	X	X	X	U	S													11
X		X		X	X	X	U	X				X		S		S	X	U	X	X	X	U												12
X		X		X	X	X	X	S				S	U	X	X	U	X		X		X			S										13
		X		X	X	X	X	X			S	U		S	X		X	U	X		X			S		X								14
		X		X	U	S	X	U	S		X	X		X	X		X	U	X					X		X								15
X		X		X	S	X	U	X			X	X	X	U	X		X		X		S			S										16
		X		X	U	X	U	S	U			X	X	X	X		X		X		X			S		X								17
		X		X	U	X	S	U	U		X	X	X		X		X		X		X			S		X								18
U		X		X	X	S	X	U	X				X	U	X			U	X		X			X		X								19
		X		X	S	X	X	X	S			X	S	U	X		X		X		X			U		X								20
X		X		X	U		X		X		X	X	S	U	X		X	S	X		S			X										21
X		X		X	X	X	S	U	X		X	X	X	U	U		X		X		S													22
X		X		X	X	X	X		U		X	U	S	X	X		X		X		U			U										23
X				X	X	X	X	S	X		X	S		U			X	X	X		U			X			U							24
		X		X	X	X	S		X		X	U		U	X		X		X		U					X	U	X						25
				X	X	X		U	X		X	X			U		X	S	X		S					X	X	X	S					26
	X	X		X	X	X	S	U	X		X	S		U	X		X				S					X		X						27
	X	X		X	X	X	U	U	X		S	X			U		X				X					X	U	X						28
	X	X		X	X	X	S	U	U		X	X		U	S		X				X					X		X						29
	X	X		X	S	X	S	S	X			X	U	U	X		X				X					X		X						30
X		X		X	U	X	U		U		X	X	X		U		X		X		S							X		X				31
X		X		X	U	X	U				X	X	X		X		X		X		S							S		X	U			32
X		X		X	U	X	U				X	X	X		S		X		X		S							X		X	S			33
X		X		X	S	X	U		U		S	X	X		S		X		X		X							X		X				34
X				X	X	X	S		U		X	X			S		X	X	X		U					U		X		X				35
X				X	X		S		U		X	X	X		U		X		X		S							X		X	U	X		36
X				X	S		U		S		X	X	X		X		X		X		S							X		X	U	X		37
X				U	X	X	X				X				U		X		X		U					S		X		X	X	X	U	38
				U	X	X	X		S		X		U		X		X	U			S					X		X		X	X	X		39
X		X		U	X	X	X		S		X				X		X		S		X					U		X			X	U		40
X		X		X	U	X		X			U	S	X	U	X	S	X		X	X	X													
X		X		X	X	X	X	U	S		S	U		X	X		X		X		X			S										
X		X	U	X	S		X	X			X	X	X	U		X	X	U	X	S	S	U												1
X				X	X	X	X	U			X	U	U		X		X	X	X	U	X	U												2
X		X		X	X	X	X	U				X	S	X	S	U	X	U	X		X	U	U											3
X		X		X	X	X	X	U	U			X	S	X	S	U	X	U	X		X	U												4
X		X		X	X	X	X	X	U			U		S	X		X	U	X		X	U			U									5
U				X	U	S		S	U		X	X	X	X	X		X	X	X					X		X								6
		X			X	X	X		X		X	X	S	U	X		X	U	X		S			S		X								7
X		X		X	X	X	S	U	X		X	X	X	U	S		X		X		S													8
X		X		U	X	X			S		X	X	U		U		X		X		X							X			X	U		9
X		X		U	X	X	X		S		X	U	S		X		X		X		X							S			X			10
X		X			X	X	X		U		X	U	S		X		X		X		X							U		S	X			11
Total League Appearances																																		
27	10	32	6	37	25	32	19	15	10	2	25	23	16	7	23	1	33	3	28	3	14	0	0	4	0	13	1	15	0	9	3	4	0	X
0	0	0	0	0	7	3	8	4	8	1	9	7	5	5	8	1	0	2	1	0	12	0	0	5	0	1	0	1	1	0	1	0	0	S
1	0	0	2	3	8	0	9	8	11	2	0	6	5	13	7	7	3	6	0	1	5	1	0	2	0	2	3	0	0	0	3	1	1	U
Total Cup Appearances																																		
9	0	9	0	7	9	9	8	2	2	0	8	7	3	3	6	1	11	2	11	0	7	0	0	1	0	2	0	1	0	0	3	0	0	X
0	0	0	0	0	1	1	1	1	2	0	0	0	5	1	3	0	0	0	0	1	3	0	0	1	0	0	0	1	0	1	0	0	0	S
1	0	0	1	2	1	0	0	4	4	0	0	4	2	3	1	2	0	5	0	1	0	5	1	0	1	0	0	1	0	0	0	1	0	U
Total Goals																																		
0	0	1	0	0	2	14	7	5	9	0	26	2	1	3	1	1	2	0	0	0	8	0	0	0	0	0	0	2	0	2	0	0	0	Lge
0	0	0	0	0	2	3	1	2	0	0	2	0	0	1	0	0	1	1	0	0	3	0	0	0	0	0	0	0	0	1	1	0	0	Cup

FLEETWOOD TOWN

CURRENT SQUAD AS OF BEGINING OF 2010-11 SEASON

GOALKEEPERS		SN	HT	WT	D.O.B	AGE	P.O.B	CAREER	APPS	GOA
Scott	Davies	16	6'00"	11 00	27/2/87	23	Blackpool	Morecambe Rel 6/10, Leek T (L) 3/06, Leek T (L) 8/06, Gillingham (Trial) 7/07, Fleetwood 6/10		
Danny	Hurst	1			14/11/80	29		Cheadle, Radcliffe 7/00, Sheff Wed (Trial) 2/03, Fleetwood 5 fig 1/07	27	0
DEFENDERS										
Shaun	Beeley	2	5'10"	11 04	21/11/88	21	Stockport	Oldham (Scholar) Rel c/s 07, Southport 8/07, Fleetwood 11/07, Salford C (L) 1/09	29	0
Junior	Brown	12	5'09"	10 12	7/5/89	21	Crewe	Crewe Rel c/s 08, Kidsgrove (L) 12/07, Witton (L) 3/08, FC Halifax c/s 08, Northwich 8/09, Fleetwood 6/10		
Joe	Camozzi							Fleetwood		
Peter	Cavanagh	26	5'09"	11 09	14/10/81	28	Bootle	Liverpool (Scholar), Accrington 9/01 Rel 8/09, Banned, Fleetwood 3/10	0	0
Jack	Duggan	21						Fleetwood		
Paul	Linwood	20	6'02"	12 08	24/10/83	26	Birkenhead	Tranmere, Wrexham (2ML) 8/05, Chester £15,000 8/06 Rel 5/09, Grimsby 7/09, Fleetwood 6/10		
Steve	McNulty	5	6'01"	13 12	26/9/83	26	Liverpool	Liverpool Rel 6/03, Chester (Trial) 3/03, Blackpool (Trial) 7/03, Burscough c/s 03, Vauxhall Motors £3,500 2/05, Barrow 6/07, Fleetwood £17,000 6/09	33	2
Adam	Sumner	22			4/12/91	18		Fleetwood		
Sam	Williamson		5'08"	11 09	15/10/87	22	Macclesfield	Man City, Wrexham (2ML) 11/08 Perm 1/09 Rel 4/10, Fleetwood (SL) 3/10, Fleetwood 5/10	4	0
Alan	Wright	3	5'05"	10 02	28/9/71	38	Ashton-under-Lyne	Blackpool, Blackburn 10/91, Aston Villa 3/95, Middlesbrough 8/03, Sheff Utd (3ML) 10/03 Perm 1/04 Rel c/s 07, Derby (SL) 2/06, Leeds (L) 10/06, Cardiff (6WL) 11/06, Doncaster (L) 2/07, Notts Forest (SL) 3/07, Oldham (Trial) 7/07, Cheltenham 10/07 Rel c/s 09, Fleetwood 7/09	32	1
MIDFIELDERS										
Anthony	Barry	4	5'07"	10 00	29/5/86	24	Liverpool	Everton (Trainee), Coventry, Accrington 4/05, Yeovil Undisc 1/06 Rel c/s 08, Chester 7/08 Rel 1/10, Wrexham 1/10, Fleetwood 1/10	16	2
Sean	Clancy	7	5'08"	09 12	16/9/87	22	Liverpool	Blackpool, Southport 8/06, Burscough (L) 3/07, USA, Shrewsbury NC 8/07, Altrincham 8/07 Rel 9/07, Burscough 9/07, Fleetwood Undisc 3/09	35	14
Steve	Connors	14			5/1/86	24	Liverpool	Witton, Bradford PA 5/07, Fleetwood 2/09	21	1
Ian	Craney	8	5'10"	12 07	21/7/82	28	Liverpool	Everton (Jun), Runcorn, Altrincham 9/00, Accrington £17,500 6/04 (04/05 38,10, 05/06 39,12), Swansea (6WL) 11/06, Swansea £150,000 1/07, Accrington (2ML) 9/07, Accrington £85,000 1/08, Huddersfield Undisc 8/08 Rel 4/10, Morecambe (SL) 7/09, Fleetwood 5/10		
Simon	Grand	13	6'00"	10 03	23/2/84	26	Chorley	Rochdale Rel c/s 04, Carlisle 8/04, Grimsby (L) 1/07 Undisc 1/07 Rel c/s 07, Morecambe 8/07 Rel c/s 08, Northwich 9/08, Chester (Trial) 9/08, Fleetwood 3/10	4	0
Jamie	McGuire	18	5'07"	11 01	13/11/83	26	Birkenhead	Tranmere Rel c/s 04, Northwich (L) 3/03, Northwich (2ML) 11/03, Cammell Laird c/s 04, Stockport (Trial) c/s 06, Droylsden 7/07, Fleetwood 5/09	30	2
Jamie	Milligan	25	5'06"	09 12	3/1/80	30	Blackpool	Everton, Blackpool 3/01 cc c/s 03, Macclesfield 8/03 Rel 9/03, Leigh RMI 9/03, Droylsden 9/03, Hyde 12/03, Fleetwood 12/05	27	7
Jamie	Mullan	11	5'06"	11 13	10/2/88	22	Nottingham	Notts County (Yth), Man Utd Rel c/s 07, Leeds (Trial) 5/07, Huddersfield (Trial) 8/07, Carlisle (Trial) 9/07, Rochdale 11/07, Northwich 1/08, Fleetwood £5,000 5/09	31	1
Nathan	Pond	6			5/1/85	25		Lancaster, Fleetwood, Bamber Bridge (Trial) 7/05	32	2

FORWARDS

		SN	HT	WT	DOB	AGE	POB	From - To	APPS	GOA
John	Miles	17	5'10"	12 09	28/9/81	28	Bootle	Liverpool, Port Vale (Trial) 3/02, Stoke 3/02, Crewe 8/02, Macclesfield (SL) 3/03, Macclesfield Undisc 5/03, Accrington 7/07, MK Dons (SL) 1/08, Fleetwood 6/10		
Nick	Rogan	9	5'10"	12 12	15/10/83	26	Blackpool	Kendal T, Morecambe 7/02 Rel 5/05, Workington (L) 3/05, Leigh RMI (Trial) 5/05, Lancaster 7/05, Southport 10/05, Barrow 2/06 Rel 5/09, Vauxhall Motors (L) 10/08, Fleetwood 6/09, Barrow (L) 9/09	18	9
Gareth	Seddon	19	5'11"	12 00	23/5/80	30	Burnley	Accrington, Atherstone, RAF Codsall, Everton (Trial), Bury 8/01 Rel c/s 04, Northwich (L) 1/03, Rushden & D 5/04 Retired 1/05, Padiham 8/05, Worcester 3/06, Hyde 6/06, Kettering Undisc 7/08, Fleetwood Undisc 9/09	26	8
Lee	Thorpe	15	6'00"	11 06	14/12/75	34	Wolverhampton	Blackpool Rel c/s 97, Bangor (L) 9/95, Lincoln C 8/97, L.Orient 5/02, Grimsby (6WL) 2/04, Bristol R 3/04, Swansea (L) 2/05 Perm 2/05 Rel c/s 06, Peterborough (2ML) 9/05, Torquay (SL) 2/06, Torquay 7/06, Brentford 7/07, Rochdale 1/08, Darlington 7/09 Rel 3	9	2
Magno	Vieira		5'09"	11 07	13/2/85	25	Bahia, Bra	Wigan Rel c/s 05, Northampton (2ML) 1/04, Carlisle (SL) 8/04, Year out, Barnet 7/06 Rel c/s 07, Crawley 6/07 Rel 5/08, Cambridge U (SL) 3/08, Wycombe 6/08 Rel c/s 09, Ebbsfleet 8/09, Fleetwood 7/10		
Adam	Warlow	10	6'02"	12 08	3/2/87	23	Southport	Crewe Rel c/s 07, Witton (SL) 8/06, Witton 5/07, Fleetwood 6/08	34	26

Loanees		SN	HT	WT	DOB	AGE	POB	From - To	APPS	GOA
(M)Michael	Hall				30/11/90	19		Blackburn 10/09 - Witton (L) 11/09	0	0
(D)Leigh	Franks				7/3/91	19		Huddersfield 1/10 -	1	0

Departures		SN	HT	WT	DOB	AGE	POB	From - To	APPS	GOA
(F)Chris	Williams		5'08"	9 00	2/2/85	25	Manchester	Stalybridge 2/09 - Rel 9/09	3	0
(M)Kevin	Leadbetter				10/9/79	30	Liverpool	Skelmersdale 5/08 - Rel 9/09, Skelmersdale (L) 8/09, Droylsden 10/09 Rel 7/10		
(D)Ricky	Mercer				22/11/83	26	Preston	Kendal 12/06 - Rel 10/09, Hyde U 10/09, AFC Fylde 7/10	6	0
(M)Claus	Jorgensen		5'10"	10 06	27/4/76	34	Holstebro, FOI	Port Vale 9/09 - Rel 10/09	3	0
(G)Aaron	Grundy		6'01"	12 07	21/1/88	22	Bolton	Cambridge U 8/09 - Witton 1/10, Chorley 6/10	0	0
(F)Andy	Bell		5'10"	12 06	4/2/84	26	Blackburn	Hednesford 2/06 - Kendal T (L) 11/09 Perm 12/09, Guiseley 3/10, AFC Fylde 7/10		
(D)Ashley	Wooliscroft		5'10"	11 02	28/12/79	30	Stoke	Newcastle T 5/09 - Stafford R (2ML) 10/09, Stafford R 3/10, Leek T (Dual) 3/10, AFC Telford 6/10	10	0
(D)Gavin	Cowan		6'04"	14 04	24/5/81	29	Hanover(Ger)	AFC Telford 1/10 - Gainsborough 3/10	1	0
(M)Lee	Dodgson				24/3/84	26	Lancaster	Lancaster 5/09 - Lancaster (L) 11/09, Vauxhall Motors (L) 2/10, Stalybridge 2/10	2	1
(F)Michael	Wilde				27/8/83	27	Birkenhead	TNS/The New Saints 1/09 - Rel 5/10, Chester FC 7/10	19	5
(F)Steve	Torpey		5'09"	10 08	16/9/81	28	Kirkby	AFC Telford £4,000 10/09 - Rel 5/10	9	0
(F)Tom	Cahill		5'10"	12 08	21/11/86	23	Derby	Rotherham 8/09 - Rel 5/10, Harrogate T (L) 3/10, AFC Fylde 7/10	12	3
(D)John	Hills		5'09"	12 08	21/4/78	32	St Annes-on-Sea	Blackpool 8/08 - Rel 5/10	5	0
(G)Craig	Dootson		6'04"	14 02	23/5/79	31	Preston	Alfreton 11/09 - Rel 5/10, Harrogate T 6/10	14	0
(D)Michael	Taylor		6'02"	13 10	21/11/82	27	Liverpool	TNS 1/09 - Rel 5/10, Hyde U 7/10	37	0
(D)Grant	Dell				11/8/92	18		Yth -	0	0
(D)Phil	Doughty		6'02"	13 02	6/9/86	23	Kirkham	Blackpool 8/08 - AFC Fylde (SL) 6/09		

Do you remember when...

Fleetwood Town

Fleetwood Town reached the F.A. Vase Final at Wembley in 1975 while competing in the North West Counties League.

Back row, left to right: AlanTuson (Trainer), Jimmy Bedson (Coach), Alan Kennerley, Chris O'Donnell, Laurie Milligan, Roy Dobson (Player/Assistant Manager), G Hudson, Steve Trainor, Stuart Robinson, Howard Taylor, Mickey Rudd and Alan Tinsley (Manager).

Front Row: Chris Robinson, Roy Whitehouse, Jimmy Hall, Glen Hadgraft, Norman Moran, Ian Cain, Keith Bowey, Mike Strachan and G.Benfold.

Mascot: I. Meeson.

FOREST GREEN ROVERS

Chairman: David Drew
Secretary: Colin Peake (T) 01453 834 860
(E) cpfgrfc@fsmail.net
Additional Committee Members: Bob Savage, Mike Bullingham, Mark Coles, Trevor Horsley, Glenn Hurley, Jamie Ponting, Rob Walker, Tom Williams, Heather Cook
Manager: David Hockaday
Programme Editor: Terry Brumpton (E) terrybrumpton@yahoo.co.uk

Back Row (L-R): James Baldwin, Ollie Cleaver, Luke Jones, Reece Styche, Ian Herring, Ross Dyer, Yan Klukowski
Middle: Mick Byrne (Coach), Ian Wrixon (Kit Manager), Callum Henry, Zak Jones, James Bittner, Jon Else, Tim Griggs (Therapist), Kevin Phillips (Coach)
Front Row: Scott Bartlett, Lee Smith, Lee Fowler, Jared Hodgkiss, David Hockaday (Manager), Mike Fowler, Steve Davies, James Norwood

Club Factfile

Founded: 1890 **Nickname:** Rovers
Previous Names: None
Previous Leagues: Stroud & District 1890-1922, Gloucestershire Northern Senior 1922-67, Gloucestershire Senior 1967-73, Hellenic 1973-82, Southern 1982-89.
Club Colours (change): Black & white stripes/black/black (All green)

Ground: The New Lawn, Smiths Way, Nailsworth, Gloucestershire GL6 0FG (T) 01453 834 860
Capacity: 5,141 **Seats:** 2,000 **Covered:** 1,000 **Clubhouse:** Yes **Shop:** Yes
Previous Grounds:
Simple Directions
Nailsworth is on the A46 between Stroud and Bath. At mini roundabout in town turn up Spring Hill towards Forest Green (signposted) and the stadium is at the top of the hill after the second roundabout.

Record Attendance: 4,836 v Derby County - FA Cup 3rd Round 03/01/2009
Record Victory: 8-0 v Fareham Town - Southern League Southern Division 1996-97
Record Defeat: 0-7 v Moor Green - Southern League Midland Division 1985-86
Record Goalscorer: Karl Bayliss
Record Appearances: Alex Sykes
Additional Records: Paid £20,000 to Salisbury City for Adrian Randall. Received £35,000 from Nuneaton Borough for Marc McGregor and from Oxford United for Wayne Hatswell.
Senior Honours: FA Vase 1981-82. Hellenic League 1981-82. Gloucestershire Senior Cup 1984-85, 85-86, 86-87. Gloucestershire Senior Professional Cup 1984-85, 86-86, 87-87.

10 YEAR RECORD

00-01	01-02	02-03	03-04	04-05	05-06	06-07	07-08	08-09	09-10
Conf 16	Conf 18	Conf 9	Conf 18	Conf 20	Conf 19	Conf 14	Conf 8	Conf 18	Conf 21

FOREST GREEN ROVERS

No.	Date	Comp	H/A	Opponents	Att:	Result	Goalscorers	Pos
1	8/8/09	BSP	H	Kettering Town	1074	L 1-2	Davies 68	16
2	11/8/09	BSP	A	Crawley Town	776	L 1-3	Smith 36	22
3	15/8/09	BSP	A	York City	1954	L 0-2		23
4	18/8/09	BSP	H	Luton Town	1805	L 0-1		23
5	22/8/09	BSP	A	Rushden & Diamonds	1056	L 2-4	Rigg 6, Stearn 82	23
6	29/8/09	BSP	H	Wrexham	1021	L 0-2		23
7	31/8/09	BSP	A	Oxford United	6338	D 0-0		23
8	5/9/09	BSP	A	Cambridge United	2646	L 0-7		23
9	8/9/09	BSP	H	Hayes & Yeading United	630	D 0-0		23
10	12/9/09	BSP	H	Ebbsfleet United	762	D 0-0		23
11	19/9/09	BSP	A	Barrow	1065	D 1-1	Rigg 62	23
12	22/9/09	BSP	H	Kidderminster Harriers	707	D 1-1	Rigg 54	23
13	26/9/09	BSP	H	Grays Athletic	911	W 2-1	Rigg 7, Preece 73	21
14	3/10/09	BSP	A	Mansfield Town	3022	L 0-1		20
15	10/10/09	BSP	H	AFC Wimbledon	1921	L 2-5	Rigg 7, Brown 16	21
16	17/10/09	BSP	A	Histon	823	L 2-5	Smith 9, Brown pen 89	22
17	31/10/09	BSP	H	Eastbourne Borough	789	D 1-1	Stonehouse 79	22
18	14/11/09	BSP	A	Altrincham	1119	D 2-2	Smith 30, Rigg 86	21
19	21/11/09	BSP	H	Stevenage Borough	757	L 0-1		21
20	24/11/09	BSP	H	Oxford United	1610	L 0-1		22
21	1/12/09	BSP	A	Wrexham	1808	L 0-1		23
22	5/12/09	BSP	H	Rushden & Diamonds	755	W 1-0	Preece 64	22
23	26/12/09	BSP	H	Salisbury City	1079	W 3-1	Rankin 29, Og (Webb) 45, Powell 69	21
24	28/12/09	BSP	A	Tamworth	868	D 0-0		21
25	16/1/10	BSP	H	Gateshead	805	W 1-0	Rankin 69	20
26	23/1/10	BSP	A	Ebbsfleet United	790	L 3-4	Rankin pen 19, Powell 2 (23, 71)	21
27	26/1/10	BSP	A	Hayes & Yeading United	291	W 3-2	Ameobi 22, Styche 2 (50, 87)	20
28	30/1/10	BSP	H	Mansfield Town	817	L 1-4	Ameobi 17	21
29	6/2/10	BSP	A	AFC Wimbledon	3272	L 0-2		21
30	13/2/10	BSP	A	Kidderminster Harriers	1421	L 1-2	Smith 59	21
31	20/2/10	BSP	H	Cambridge United	930	D 1-1	Hodgkiss 72	22
32	6/3/10	BSP	H	York City	892	W 2-1	Powell 22, Thorne 55	22
33	9/3/10	BSP	A	Luton Town	5884	L 1-2	Platt pen 81	22
34	16/3/10	BSP	A	Gateshead	485	L 1-3	Powell 39	22
35	20/3/10	BSP	A	Kettering Town	1032	W 2-0	Ameobi 68, Morris 86	22
36	23/3/10	BSP	A	Salisbury City	665	W 3-1	Ameobi 16, Smith 33, Styche 43	22
37	27/3/10	BSP	H	Altrincham	1043	W 4-3	Smith 19, Styche 69, Brown pen 74, Preece 77	20
38	31/3/10	BSP	H	Barrow	786	W 1-0	Morris 84	19
39	3/4/10	BSP	A	Eastbourne Borough	1104	L 0-1		21
40	5/4/10	BSP	H	Tamworth	1370	L 3-4	Powell 2, Platt 2 (41, pen 85)	21
41	10/4/10	BSP	A	Stevenage Borough	2524	L 0-2		21
42	13/4/10	BSP	H	Crawley Town	601	W 1-0	Platt 75	21
43	17/4/10	BSP	H	Histon	1204	W 2-0	Smith 39, Styche 44	19
44	24/4/10	BSP	A	Grays Athletic	940	L 1-2	Brown pen 66	21
	Chester	**record**	**........................**	**...expunged 08/03**				
14	29/9/09	BSP	A	Chester City	1019	W 2-1	Platt 18, Rigg 37	19
	Cups							
1	24/10/09	FAC 4Q	A	Mangotsfield United	946	W 2-1	Brown pen 7, Davies 82	
2	7/11/09	FAC 1	H	Mansfield Town	1149	D 1-1	Hodgkiss 28	
3	17/11/09	FAC 1R	A	Mansfield Town	2496	W 2-1	Platt 2 (40, 90)	
4	28/11/09	FAC 2	A	Bath City	3325	W 2-1	Smith 24, Preece 48	
5	12/12/09	FAT 1	A	Woking	956	L 0-1		
6	19/1/10	FAC 3	A	Notts County	4389	L 1-2	Rankin 63	

Home League Attendances	
Highest:	1921 v AFC Wimbledon
Lowest:	601 v Crawley Town
Average (08-09):	902 (955)
Top Goalscorer:	Smith - 8 (7 League, 1 Cup) in 46 appearances - 17% strike rate
Most Appearances:	Stonehouse - 49 (40+3 League, 6 Cup)

BURTON 1	TAYLOR 2	AYRES 4	PREECE 5	DAVIES 18	STONEHOUSE 6	CHALLINOR 24	ELSE 12	SMITH 11	PLATT 10	BROWN 7	MCDONALD 3	STEARN 14	PASS 17	LLOYD 8	PUGH 15	PALMER 19	ELLIS 26	ADAMS 25	RIGG 27	HENRY 21	WILKINSON 30	IMUDIA 28	SPENCE 29	THORNE 31	CURRAN 16	AMEOBI 24	CARLIN 13	HODGKISS 32	KING 26	FORD 25	POWELL 14	ROCASTLE 16	O'CEARUILL 29	JOYCE 25	RANKIN 33	OSMAN 34	BERRY 26	STYCHE 9	IRELAND 17	ARMSTRONG 26	MORRIS 25	
X	X	X	X	X	X	X	X	X	X	X	S	S	U	U																												1
X	X		X	X	X	X	S	X	X	X	X	X	U	S	U	U																									2
X	X		X	X	X	X	X	X	X	X	X	S	U	S	S																										3
X	X		X	X	X	X	U	X	X	X		S	U	S	U		X	X																							4
X			X	X	X	X	X		X	X		S	U	S	U		X	X	X	U																						5
X		X	X	S	X	X			S	X	X	X	U	S	U		X	X	X																						6
X		X	X	S	X	X			S	X	X	S	U	X	U		X	X	X																						7
X	X	X		U	X			X	S	X	X	U	S	X	S		X	X	X																						8
	X		X	S	X			X	S	X	X	U	X	X	U	U	X	X	X																						9
				X	X			X	X		X	U	U	S	U	S	X	X	X		X	X	X																			10
		U	X	X	X		U	X	X	X			U	S					X		X	X	X	X	S																	11
X		S	X	X	X			X	S	X			U	U					X			X	X	X	X																	11
X		X	X	X	X			S	X	X			U	S					X				X	X	U	X																	13
X		U	X		X		U	X	X	X				S					X				X	X		X	U	X	S													14
X			X	S	X			X	X	X				U					X				X	X		X	U	X	S	U												15
X			X	S	X		U	X		X				S	X				X					X			U	X	X	S	X											16
X			X	S	X			X	X	X	X		U						X							S		X	S	U	X	X										17
X			X	U	X		U	X	X	X	X		U						X									X	U		S	X	X									18
X			X		S			X	X	X	X		U						X					S				X	U		X	X	X	S								19
X			X	S	X			X	X	X			U											X		S		X	U		X	X	U	X								20
X			X	X	S			X		S	X		U											X		X		X	U		X	X	X	U								21
X			X		X			X	X	X	X		U													X		X	U		S	X	X	U	S							22
X					X		S	X	X	S										U	U			X		X		X			X	X	X	U	X							23
X			U		X		U	X	X	X										U	U			X				X			X	X	X	U	X							24
X			X		X		U		X	S												U			X		X		X			X	X	X		X	U						25
X			X		X		U	X		S												U			X		X		X			X	X	X		X	U	S					26
U			X		X			X	X	U												X			X		X		X			X	X	X			U	U	S				27
U			U		X			X	X	S												X			X		X		X			X	X	X		X		S	S				28
U			X				U	X	X	S	S											X			X		X		X			U	X	X		X			X				29
			X		S			X	X	X	X			U								U			S		X		X				S	X		X			X	X			30
			X		X			X	S	X	X										U			X		X		X			U	X			X			S	X			31
			X	U	X			X	X	X											U			S		X		X			X				X			S	X	X		32
						X		U	X	X	X										U	U			X		X		X			X				X			S	X	X		33
				S	X		S	X	X	S										U	U			X		X		X			X				X			X	X	X		34
			X	U	X		U	X	X	X											U					X		X					U		X			X	X	X	S	35
U			X	U	X		U	X	X	X																X		X					U		X			X	X	X	S	36
S			X	U	X			X	X	X																X		X			S		S		X			X	X	X	U	37
U			X	U	X			X	X												X			S		X		X			S		X		X			X		X	S	38
U			X	S	X			X		X											X			U		X		X			X		U		X			X		X	S	39
X		S	X	U	X			X	X	X														U		X		X			X				U			X		X	S	40
U		X	X		X			X	X	S														S		U		X			S				X			X	X	X	X	41
U		U	X		X			X	X	X	U													U		X		X			X								X	X	X	S	42
U		U	X		X			X	X	X	U													U		X		X			X								X	X	X	S	43
X		U	X		X			X	X	X	U										U					X		X			X				S			X		X	S	44
X		X	X	X	X		U	X	X	X				U	U	U			X				X			X	U																
X			X	X	X		U	X		X	X			U	U	U			X	U							U	X	X	U	X											1
X			X	S	X		U	X	X	X	X		U		U	U			X							X		X	U		U		X									2
X			X	U	X		U	X	X	X	X		U		U	U			X	U						U		X			X		X									3
X			X	U	X		U	X	X	X	X		U		U					U						X		X	U		S		X	X								4
X			U		X			X	S	S	X		U											X		X		X	X		X	X		S	X							5
X			X	U	X		S	X	X	X			U							U						X		X			X		X		X	U	S					6

Total League Appearances

25	6	6	37	10	40	7	3	39	34	33	14	2	1	3	1	0	7	7	15	0	7	3	6	18	1	25	0	31	1	0	19	14	13	1	17	0	0	13	11	13	1	X
1	0	2	0	9	3	0	3	1	6	8	2	5	1	10	2	1	0	0	0	0	0	0	0	5	1	2	0	0	3	1	5	1	1	1	2	0	2	5	0	0	8	S
9	0	5	2	8	0	0	12	0	0	1	3	3	17	4	7	2	0	0	0	5	11	0	0	4	1	1	3	0	5	2	2	0	4	4	1	3	1	0	0	0	1	U

Total Cup Appearances

6	0	0	5	1	6	0	0	6	4	5	5	0	0	0	0	0	0	0	3	0	0	0	0	1	0	4	0	6	2	0	4	1	4	1	2	0	0	0	0	0	0	X
0	0	0	0	1	0	0	1	0	1	1	0	0	0	0	0	0	0	0	0	0	0	0	0	0	0	0	0	0	0	0	1	0	0	1	0	0	1	0	0	0	0	S
0	0	0	1	3	0	0	4	0	0	0	0	0	5	1	4	3	0	0	0	4	0	0	0	0	0	1	1	0	2	1	1	0	0	0	0	1	0	0	0	0	0	U

Total Cup Appearances

0	0	0	3	1	1	0	0	7	4	4	0	1	0	0	0	0	0	0	6	0	0	0	0	1	0	4	0	1	0	0	5	0	0	0	3	0	0	5	0	0	2	Lg
0	0	0	1	1	0	0	0	1	2	1	0	0	0	0	0	0	0	0	0	0	0	0	0	0	0	0	0	1	0	0	0	0	0	0	1	0	0	0	0	0	0	Cp

Also played: Baldwin(16) U(1,3). Maxwell(14) S(12) U(13). Winter(2) U(25) U(Cup-5). Fowler(20) U(31) S(32,33).

FOREST GREEN ROVERS

CURRENT SQUAD AS OF BEGINING OF 2010-11 SEASON

GOALKEEPERS		SQ NO.	HT	WT	D.O.B	AGE	P.O.B	CAREER	APPS	GOA
James	Bittner		6'02"	13 01	2/2/82	28	Devizes	Swindon (Trainee), Fulham 7/00, Salisbury 11/01, Bournemouth 3/02, Torquay (Trial) 7/02, Cheltenham (Trial) 7/02, Chippenham 8/02, Southend (Trial) 7/03, Exeter 8/03 Rel 4/05, Torquay 6/05 Rel 5/06, Woking 12/06 Rel 5/07, Salisbury 6/07, Chippenham (L) 11/07, Forest Green 6/10		
Terry	Burton		6'02"	12 09	10/2/81	29	Hull	Hull C, Army, AFC Newbury, Wantage 7/06, Forest Green 8/07	26	0
Gavin	Carlin		6'05"	14 00	26/5/91	19	Derry	West Brom, Forest Green 9/09	0	0
DEFENDERS										
Lee	Ayres		6'02"	12 06	28/8/82	28	Birmingham	Walsall (Yth), Evesham, Kidderminster 6/01, Stourport (L) 02, Tamworth (L) 9/03, Tamworth 11/03, Notts County (Trial) 7/04, Burton £10,000 8/04 Rel 4/06, Bristol R (Trial) c/s 06, Moor Green/Solihull Moors c/s 06, Bristol R (Trial) 10/06, Redditch 7/08, Forest Green 6/10	8	0
Scott	Bartlett				30/5/79	31	Salisbury	Bournemouth (Jun), Amesbury T, Cirencester, Salisbury 2/00 Rel 2/09, Weston-Super-Mare 2/09, Bath C 2/10 Rel 6/10, Forest Green 6/10		
John	Else				8/6/89	21	Blackpool	Swindon (Yth), Reading (Yth), Bristol R (Yth), New College Academy, L.Orient (Res), Cirencester 8/07 Rel 2/08, Chippenham 3/08, Clevedon T 10/08, Forest Green, Stourport (L) 3/09	6	0
Callum	Henry				10/6/91	19		Forest Green, Frome T (L) 9/09	0	0
Luke	Jones		5'09"	11 09	10/4/87	23	Blackburn	Blackburn Rel c/s 06, Shrewsbury 11/06 Rel 4/08, Kidderminster (2ML) 1/08, Kidderminster 5/08 Rel 5/09, Mansfield 5/09 Rel 4/10, Forest Green 6/10		
MIDFIELDERS										
Craig	Armstrong		5'11"	12 09	23/5/75	35	South Shields	Notts Forest, Burnley (3ML) 12/94, Bristol R (L) 1/96, Bristol R (SL) 3/96, Gillingham (2ML) 10/96, Watford (L) 1/97, Watford (6WL) 3/97, Huddersfield £750,000 2/99, Sheff Wed £100,000 2/02, Grimsby (2ML) 2/04, Bradford C 1/05 Rel c/s 05, Cheltenham 7/05	13	0
Steve	Davies				27/4/89	21		Afan Lido, Cirencester 7/08, Forest Green 7/09	19	1
Lee	Fowler		5'07"	10 00	10/6/83	27	Cardiff	Coventry, Cardiff (L) 3/03, Huddersfield (3ML) 8/03 (Perm) 11/03, Grimsby (Trial) 7/05, Scarboough (2ML) 11/05 (Perm) 1/06 Rel c/s 06, Burton 5/06, Newport C (SL) 3/07, Newport C 5/07, Forest Green 6/08 Rel 5/09, Kettering 6/09 Rel 12/09, Oxford U 12/09		
Michael	Fowler		5'11"	11 13	22/8/81	29	Cardiff	C.Palace Rel c/s 01, Woking 8/01, Newport C 3/02, Welling 7/03, Cwmbran 10/03, Merthyr T 7/05, Gloucester 6/06, Salisbury 1/07 Rel 7/09, Forest Green 7/09	2	0
Ian	Herring		6'01"	11 12	14/2/84	26	Swindon	Swindon, Salisbury (L) 12/02, Chippenham (L) 3/03, Chippenham (L) 12/03 Perm 1/04, Salisbury 9/07, Weston-Super-Mare (SL) 3/08, Northwich 7/09, Forest Green 6/10		
Jared	Hodgkiss		5'06"	11 02	15/11/86	23	Stafford	West Brom Rel c/s 09, Aberdeen (5ML) 8/08, Northampton (SL) 3/09, Market Drayton 8/09, Forest Green 10/09	31	1
Sam	Mensah				19/5/89	21		Forest Green		
Ben	Pugh				3/6/89	21		Forest Green	3	0
Isaac	Shaze				25/6/89	21		Forest Green		
FORWARDS										
Ross	Dyer				12/5/88	22	Stafford	Hednesford, Forest Green 5/10		
Lee	Smith				8/9/83	26	Coney Hill	Gloucester, Cirencester 6/05, Weston-Super-Mare 6/07, Gloucester 9/07, Forest Green 6/10		
Reece	Styche		6'01"		3/5/89	21	Birmingham	Hednesford, Bromsgrove (L) 9/08, Chasetown 10/09, Forest Green 1/10	18	5

Loanees		HT	WT	DOB	AGE	POB	From - To	APPS	GOA
(F)Jon	Challinor	5'11"	11 11	2/12/80	29	Northampton	Cambridge U 8/09 - Mansfield (6WL) 11/09 Perm 1/10 Rel 4/10	7	0
(M)Steve	Adams	6'00"	12 00	25/9/80	29	Plymouth	Torquay 8/09 - Truro C (3ML) 10/09	7	0
(D)Mark	Ellis	6'02"	12 04	30/9/88	21	Plymouth	Torquay 8/09 -	7	0
(F)Sean	Rigg	5'09"	12 01	1/10/88	21	Bristol	Bristol R (3ML) 8/09 - Port Vale (SL) 11/09	15	6
(M)Lewis	Spence	5'09"	11 02	29/10/87	22	Lambeth	Wycombe 9/09 - Rushden & D 7/10	6	0
(M)Dave	King	6'00"	11 07	3/9/90	19		MK Dons 10/09 - Wealdstone (L) 1/10	4	0
(M)Daniel	Powell	6'01"	13 03	12/3/91	19	Luton	MK Dons (SL) 10/09 -	24	5
(F)Ben	Joyce	5'08"	11 04	9/9/89	20	Plymouth	Torquay (6WL) 11/09 - Weston-Super-Mare (SL) 1/10, Rel 5/10	2	0
(G)Danny	Ireland	6'02"	13 00	20/1/89	21	Sydney, Aust	Coventry (SL) 2/10 -	11	0
(M)Lee	Morris	5'10"	11 07	30/4/80	30	Blackpool	Hereford (SL) 3/10 - Rel 4/10, Kidderminster 7/10	9	2

Departures		HT	WT	DOB	AGE	POB	From - To	APPS	GOA
(D)James	Baldwin			14/5/89	21		Yth - Gloucester 8/09, Banbury U (Cover) 1/10	0	0
(F)Ross	Stearn	5'06"	10 07	17/9/81	18	Bristol	Bristol C (Scholar) NC 8/09 - Rel 9/09, Weston-Super-Mare 9/09, Almondsbury T 10/09	7	1
(F)Loren	Maxwell	6'01"	13 12	20/9/89	20		Glen Hoddle Academy 9/09 - Rel 10/09	1	0
(F)Chris	Curran			5/1/91	19	Enniskillen	Man Utd 9/09 - Rel, Portadown	2	0
(D)Andy	Taylor	6'00"		28/12/85	24	Liverpool	Austin Aztex (USA) 6/09 - Rel 11/09, Burscough 12/09	6	0
(F)Marcus	Palmer	6'00"	11 07	22/12/88	21	Gloucester	Solihull Moors 11/08 - Evesham 11/09, Bishops Cleeve 6/10	1	0
(D)Josh	Ford			28/6/90	20	Bristol	ex Rushden & D 10/09 - Rel 11/09, Tiverton 11/09, Weston-Super-Mare 1/10	1	0
(F)Andrew	Mangan	5'09"	10 03	30/8/86	24	Liverpool	Bury 5/08 - Wrexham Undisc 1/10		
(M)Ben	Osman	5'10"	10 13	24/9/90	19	Southampton	Weston-Super-Mare 1/10 - Frome T 2/10	0	0
(G)Thomas	Pass			21/12/91	18	Gloucester	Yth - Frome T (Dual) Perm	2	0
(D)Jack	Winter	5'10"	12 00	29/4/91	19	Hammersmith	ex Swindon (Scholar) 1/10 - Frome T 2/10	0	0
(M)Paul	Lloyd	5'09"	10 11	26/3/87	23	Preston	Workington 2/09 - Rel 2/10, Workington (L) 11/09, Burscough 3/10, Bamber Bridge 6/10	13	0
(M)Craig	Rocastle	6'01"	13 09	17/8/81	29	Lewisham	Dover 10/09 - Kansas City Wizards (USA)	15	0
(F)Tyrone	Berry	5'08"	10 02	20/2/87	23	London	York C 1/10 - Rel 3/10	2	0
(D)Oliver	Thorne			23/1/90	21		MK Dons 9/09 - Newport C 5/10	23	1
(M)Paul	Stonehouse	5'07"	11 03	13/7/87	23	Wegburg	Yth - Mansfield Undisc 6/10	43	1
(F)David	Brown	5'10"	12 06	2/10/78	31	Bolton	Barrow 1/09 (Pl/Ass Man) 6/09 - Rel 6/10, Wrexham 7/10	41	4
(F)Conal	Platt	5'09"	10 10	14/10/86	23	Preston	Weymouth 5/08 - Cambridge U 6/10	40	4
(M)Jonathan	Smith			17/10/86	23	Preston	Morecambe 7/07 - Rel 6/10, York C 6/10	40	7
(D)Mark	Preece	6'02"	13 07	3/6/87	23	Bristol	Bristol R 7/06 - Mansfield 7/10	37	3
(G)David	Wilkinson	5'11"	12 00	17/4/88	22	Croydon	C.Palace 9/09 - Rel 9/09, Truro C, Dover 10/09 Rel 11/09, Forest Green Rovers 12/09	7	0
(D)Jeffrey	Imudia			19/4/90	20		Southampton (Scholar) 9/09 -	3	0
(D)Joe	O'Cearuill	5'11"	12 11	9/2/87	23	Edmonton	Boreham Wood NC 11/09 -	14	0
(M)Curtis	McDonald	5'10"	10 08	24/3/88	22	Cardiff	MKS Swit (Pol) 8/08 -	16	0
(F)Tomi	Ameobi	6'03"	12 10	16/8/88	22	Newcastle	Bradford C 9/09 -	27	4
(F)Isaiah	Rankin	5'10"	11 00	22/5/78	32	London	Crawley 12/09 -	19	3

Do you remember when...

Forest Green Rovers

Frank Gregan's 1977-1978 squad won the Dr Martens League Championship (Southern League) and gained promotion to The Conference

Back Row, left to right: Dave Tyrrell (Physio), Alan McDougall (Scout), Mark Hallam, Chris Honor, Rob Cook, Justin Shuttleworth, Martin Woodhouse, Don Forbes, Martin Boyle, Tim Banks, Tommy Callinan (Assistant Manager) and Mike Kilgour (Coach).

Front Row: Tom Jones, Paul Hunt, Grantley Dicks, Paul McLoughlin, Frank Gregan (Manager), Gary Smart (Captain), Alex Sykes, Matthew Coupe, Toby Jackson and Steve Winter.

GATESHEAD

Chairman: Graham Wood

Secretary: Mike Coulson (T) 0191 478 883 (E) mike.coulson@gateshead-fc.com

Additional Committee Members:
Brian Waites, Jeff Bowron

Manager: Ian Bogie

Programme Editor: Jeff Bowron (E) jeffbowron@blueyonder.co.uk

Back Row (L-R): Carl Jones, Phil Turnbull, James Curtis, Tim Deasy, Gary Mulligan, Jon Shaw, Josh Gillies
Middle Graham Wood (Chairman), Martin Brittain, Andy Ferrell, Paul Heckingbottom, Ben Clark (C), Paul Farman, Alex Francis, Brian Wake, Steven Baptist, James Marwood, Brian Waites (Vice-chairman)
Front: Craig Nelthorpe, Jonny Allan, Nathan Fisher, Gary Neasham (Physio), Paul Bryson (Res. team manager), Ian Bogie (Manager), Terry Mitchell (Asst Manager), Kris Gate, Craig Baxter, David Brown

Club Factfile

Founded: 1930 **Nickname:** Tynesiders

Previous Names:

Previous Leagues: Football League 1930-60, Northern Counties east 1960-62, North Regional 1962-68, Northern Premier 1968-70, 73-83, 85-86, 87-90, Wearside 1970-71, Midland 1971-72, Alliance/Conf 1983-85, 86-87, 90-98

Club Colours (change): White/black/black (Blue/white/white)

Ground: International Stadium, Neilson Road, Gateshead NE10 0EF (T) 0191 478 3883

Capacity: 11,795 **Seats:** 11,795 **Covered:** 3,300 **Clubhouse:** Yes **Shop:** Yes

Previous Grounds: Redneugh Park 1930-71

Simple Directions
A1(M) to Washington Services, then A194(M) to first roundabout. Turn left onto A184 and the ground is situated approximately 3 miles on the left.

Record Attendance: 11,750 v Newcastle United - Friendly 07/08/95
Record Victory: 8-0 v Netherfield - Northern Premier League
Record Defeat: 0-9 v Sutton United - Conference 22/09/90
Record Goalscorer: Bob Topping - 120
Record Appearances: Simon Smith - 501 (1985-94)
Additional Records: Paid £9,000 to Dagenham & Redbridge for Paul Cavell.

Senior Honours: Northern Premier League 1982-83, 85-86, Conference North Play-off 2008-09.

10 YEAR RECORD

00-01	01-02	02-03	03-04	04-05	05-06	06-07	07-08	08-09	09-10
NP P 11	NP P 14	NP P 21	NP P 6	NP P 17	NP P 17	NP P 9	NP P 3	Conf N 2	Conf 20

GATESHEAD

No.	Date	Comp	H/A	Opponents	Att:	Result	Goalscorers	Pos
1	8/8/09	BSP	H	Histon	681	L 0-3		22
2	15/8/09	BSP	A	Luton Town	6829	L 1-2	Mackay 5	22
3	18/8/09	BSP	H	Tamworth	429	D 1-1	Harwood 86	22
4	22/8/09	BSP	A	Crawley Town	881	W 4-1	Gate 19, Brittain 2 (pen 37, pen 39), Armstrong 90	18
5	25/8/09	BSP	H	York City	1174	L 1-2	Francis 46	18
6	29/8/09	BSP	A	Cambridge United	2417	L 0-3		21
7	5/9/09	BSP	H	Hayes & Yeading United	519	D 0-0	Game abandond after 76 mins	21
8	8/9/09	BSP	A	Kettering Town	1230	L 0-4		22
9	12/9/09	BSP	H	Salisbury City	478	W 2-1	Gate 8, Richardson 39	20
10	19/9/09	BSP	A	Kidderminster Harriers	1286	L 2-3	Francis 12, Gate 62	20
11	22/9/09	BSP	H	Rushden & Diamonds	409	D 0-0		18
12	26/9/09	BSP	H	Oxford United	1144	L 0-1		19
13	29/9/09	BSP	A	Altrincham	769	L 2-3	Armstrong 6, Turnbull 68	21
14	3/10/09	BSP	A	Grays Athletic	592	D 0-0		21
15	10/10/09	BSP	H	Eastbourne Borough	537	W 3-0	Armstrong 2 (14, 17), Turnbull 84	19
16	31/10/09	BSP	A	Salisbury City	1050	W 1-0	Winn 85	20
17	14/11/09	BSP	A	Stevenage Borough	2203	L 3-5	Og (Griffin) 38, Clare 2 (69, 81)	20
18	21/11/09	BSP	H	Grays Athletic	506	W 3-0	Clare 3 (8, 57, 78)	19
19	24/11/09	BSP	A	York City	2302	L 0-1		20
20	28/11/09	BSP	H	Crawley Town	467	W 2-1	Clare 74, Gate 77	18
21	1/12/09	BSP	H	Mansfield Town	643	L 1-3	Mackay 45	18
22	5/12/09	BSP	A	AFC Wimbledon	3209	L 0-2		19
23	26/12/09	BSP	A	Barrow	1727	D 3-3	McDermott 2, Clare 2 (42, 57)	19
24	16/1/10	BSP	A	Forest Green Rovers	805	L 0-1		21
25	23/1/10	BSP	H	Luton Town	1218	L 0-1		22
26	26/1/10	BSP	H	Kettering Town	401	L 0-2		22
27	6/2/10	BSP	A	Mansfield Town	7261	W 2-0	Wake 2 (5, 48)	22
28	13/2/10	BSP	A	Hayes & Yeading United	296	L 2-3	Clare 2 (pen 39, 44)	22
29	16/2/10	BSP	H	Barrow	503	W 2-1	Winn 7, Turnbull 43	20
30	20/2/10	BSP	H	Ebbsfleet United	533	L 1-3	Winn 41	20
31	23/2/10	BSP	H	Altrincham	489	W 1-0	Baxter 74	19
32	2/3/10	BSP	A	Tamworth	483	L 0-1		21
33	6/3/10	BSP	A	Histon	645	D 0-0		20
34	13/3/10	BSP	A	Rushden & Diamonds	1414	L 0-8		20
35	16/3/10	BSP	H	Forest Green Rovers	485	W 3-1	Armstrong 10, Winn 42, Wake 80	18
36	23/3/10	BSP	H	Wrexham	614	W 1-0	Armstrong 50	17
37	27/3/10	BSP	A	Oxford United	5986	L 1-2	Armstrong 56	19
38	30/3/10	BSP	A	Eastbourne Borough	714	L 1-2	Baxter 72	19
39	3/4/10	BSP	H	Cambridge United	841	W 2-0	Clare 2 (38, pen 83)	19
40	5/4/10	BSP	A	Wrexham	2380	D 0-0		18
41	10/4/10	BSP	H	Kidderminster Harriers	602	L 0-2		20
42	17/4/10	BSP	A	Ebbsfleet United	1169	L 0-2		21
43	20/4/10	BSP	H	Stevenage Borough	702	L 0-1		21
44	24/4/10	BSP	H	AFC Wimbledon	1304	W 1-0	Clare 4	20
	Chester	**record**	**..........**	**...expunged 08/03**				
10	15/9/09	BSP	A	Chester City	994	L 1-2	Mackay 50	20
17	17/10/09	BSP	H	Chester City	631	L 0-1		19
	Cups							
1	24/10/09	FAC 4Q	H	Southport	402	W 3-0	Turnbull 2 (33, 90), Baxter 64	
2	7/11/09	FAC 1	H	Brentford	1151	D 2-2	Og (Price) 57, Winn 90	
3	17/11/09	FAC 1R	A	Brentford	1960	L 2-5	Armstrong 2 (58, 81)	
4	12/12/09	FAT 1	H	Harrogate Town	302	D 1-1	Richardson 84	
5	15/12/09	FAT 1R	A	Harrogate Town	160	W 2-0	Clare 62, Swailes 65	
6	19/1/10	FAT 2	H	Chippenham Town	216	W 1-0	Armstrong 59	
7	2/2/10	FAT 3	A	Barrow	1200	D 1-1	Curtis 70	
8	9/2/10	FAT 3R	H	Barrow	312	L 2-3	Sinclair 7, Clare 48	

Home League Attendances	
Highest:	1304 v AFC Wimbledon
Lowest:	401 v Kettering Town
Average (08-09):	535 (459)
Top Goalscorer:	Clare - 15 (13 League, 2 Cup) in 34 appearances - 44% strike rate
Most Appearances:	Turnbull - 48 (36+5 League, 6+1 Cup)

PROVETT 1	CURTIS 5	ROBINSON 3	JONES 6	BAXTER 2	GATE 4	TURNBULL 8	BRITTAIN 7	PHILLIPS 11	FORSYTH 18	MACKAY 21	FRANCIS 14	RICHARDSON 10	ARMSTRONG 9	FARMAN 13	SWAILES 15	HARWOOD 12	MCDERMOTT 17	PELONDE 20	ASCHERL 22	ONE 23	CAVE 19	WILLIAMS 24	CLARE 25	WINN 26	HAWORTH 27	KELTIE 29	SHAW 28	BAINS 21	BAPTISTE 16	SINCLAIR 22	WAKE 23	FERRELL 28	BUCHANAN 20	HECKINGBOTTOM 27	PARKINSON 12	HURREN 30	
X	X	X	X	X	X	X	X	X	X	X	S	S	S	U	U																						1
X	X	X	X	X	X	X		X	X	X	S	S	S	U	U	X																					2
X	X	X	U	X	X	X	X	X	S	X	S	X		U	X	S																					3
X	X	X	X	X	X	X	X	X	U	X	S	X	S	U		S																					4
X	X	X	X	X	X	X	X	X		X	S	X	S	U		S	U																				5
X	X	X		X	X	S	X	X		X	X	X	S	U		U	S	X																			6
X	X	X		X	X	S	X	X	U	X	X	S		U					X	X	U																7
X	X	X		X	X	X		X	S	S	X	S		U		X	X			X	U																8
X	X	X		X	X	X		S		X	U	X	S	U			S	X	X	X																	9
X		X		X	X	X		S	U	X	X		X	U	X	S	S			X	X																10
U	X	U		X	X	X		S		X	X	S	X	X	X	S				X	X																11
U	X	U		X	X	X		X		S	S	X	S	X	X					X	X	X															12
U	X	S		X	X	X		S		U	X	X	X	X	X					S	X	X															13
U	X	S		X	X	X		X		X	S		X	X	X		U			S	X	X															14
U	X	U		X	X	X		X	S	X	S		X	X	X		S				X	X															15
U	X	U		X	X	X		S		X			X	X			S	X		S	X		X	X													16
U	X			X	X	X					S		X	X		X		U		S	X	X	X	X	S												17
U	X			X	X	X				S	S		X	X	U					S	X	X	X	X	X												18
U				X	X	X		S		S	S			X	X			U		X	X	X	X	X	X												19
U	X			X	X	X								X	U					U	X	X	X	X	X	X											20
U	X			X	X			S		X		S	X	X	S		U				X	X		X	X	X											21
	X	X		X	X	X		X		U		S	S	X	X						U	S	X		X	X											22
U	X	X		X	X	U		X				S	U	X	X		X				U	X	X				X										23
U	X	U		X	X	S		X			S	X	S	X			X				X	X	X					X									24
U	X	X	U	X	X	X		X			S	S	X	X			X					S	X					X									25
U	X	X	U	X		X		X			S		X	X			U					X	X					X		X	S						26
U	X	X	X	U	X						S		X	X			S					X		X				U		X	X	X					27
U	X					X					U		S	X			S					X	X	X				U		X	X	X	X	X			28
U	X			X		X					U		S	X									X	X				S		S	X	X	X	X	X		29
U	X			X		X					S		S	X									X	X				X		U	X	X	U	X	X		30
U	X		X	X	X	S							S	X	U								X	X						U	X	X		X	X		31
U	X		X	X		X		S			S		S	X	U								X	X							X	X		X	X		32
U			X	X		X		U			S		S	X	X								X	X							X	X	U	X	X		33
U			X	X		X		S			X	S	X	X	X									X						S	X		U	X	X		34
U	X			X		X		S			S		X	X	X								X	X							S		U	X	X	X	35
U	X			X		X		S					X	X	X						X		X	X							S	X	U		X	S	36
U	X			X		X		S					X	X	X						X		X	X							S	X	U		X	S	37
X	X			X		X		S					X	U	X						U		X	S							X	X		X	U	X	38
U	X			X		X		S					X	X	X						S		X	X							S	X		X	X	U	39
U			U	X		X		S					X	X	X						X		X	X							S	X		X	X	S	40
U			S	X		X		S					X	X	X						X		X	X							U	X		X	X	S	41
U	X			X	X	S		S				X	X	X	X						U		X	X							S	X		X			42
U	X			X	X	X		X					X	X	X						U		X	X							S	S		X	S		43
U	X			X	X	X		X					X	X	X						U		X	X							S	S		X	S		44
X	X	X		X	X	X		S		X		X	U	U	S		S	X	X	X																	
X	U		S	X			X		S	X		X	X	X		U			S	X	X	X	X														
U	X	U		X	X	X		U			S		X	X	X		S	U		S	X	X	X	X													1
U	X	U		X	X	X		S			U		X	X		X	U	U		S	X	X	X	X													2
U	X	U		X	X	X		U			S		X	X	U	X	U			S	X	X	X	X													3
U	X	X		X	X	X		X		S		S	X	X	X	X					U	U	X														4
U	X	X		X	X			X		X		X	S	X	X		S				U	X	X				S										5
U	X	S		X	X	X		X			U	S	X	X			X				X	X	X						U								6
U	X	X	X	X	X	S						S	X	X	U		X					X	X							X	S						7
U	X	X	X	X	X	X					S			X	S		U				U	X	X							X	X						8
Total League Appearances																																					
11	38	15	9	42	30	36	6	18	2	14	7	9	23	33	22	3	4	3	2	7	17	14	26	23	5	3	1	4	0	3	9	14	2	15	12	2	X
0	0	2	1	0	0	5	0	17	3	4	19	10	15	0	1	5	7	0	0	5	1	2	0	1	1	0	0	1	0	2	9	2	0	0	2	4	S
32	0	5	4	1	0	1	0	1	3	2	3	0	1	11	6	1	4	2	0	1	8	0	0	0	0	0	0	2	0	2	1	0	6	0	1	1	U
Total Cup Appearances																																					
0	8	4	2	8	8	6	0	3	0	1	0	1	6	8	3	3	2	0	0	0	4	7	8	3	0	0	0	0	0	2	1	0	0	0	0	0	X
0	0	1	0	0	0	1	0	1	0	1	3	3	1	0	1	0	2	0	0	3	0	0	0	0	0	0	1	0	0	0	1	0	0	0	0	0	S
8	0	3	0	0	0	0	0	2	0	0	2	0	0	0	2	0	3	2	0	0	3	1	0	0	0	0	0	0	1	0	0	0	0	0	0	0	U
Total Goals																																					
0	0	0	0	2	4	3	1	0	0	2	2	1	7	0	0	1	1	0	0	0	0	0	13	4	0	0	0	0	0	0	3	0	0	0	0	0	Lg
0	1	0	0	1	0	2	0	0	0	0	0	1	3	0	1	0	0	0	0	0	0	0	2	1	0	0	0	0	0	1	0	0	0	0	0	0	Cp

GATESHEAD

CURRENT SQUAD AS OF BEGINING OF 2010-11 SEASON

GOALKEEPERS		SQ NO.	HT	WT	D.O.B	AGE	P.O.B	CAREER	APPS	GOA
Paul	Farman	13			2/11/89	19	North Shields	Newcastle (Scholar). Blyth c/s 08, Mansfield (Trial) 1/09, Newcastle Blue Star (Dual) 1/09, Gateshead 6/09	33	0
DEFENDERS										
Craig	Baxter	2	5'10"	09 10	27/9/86	23	Newcastle	Newcastle Rel c/s 06, Gateshead c/s 06	42	2
Ben	Clark	6	6'02"	13 00	24/1/83	27	Consett	Man Utd (Trainee), Sunderland, Hartlepool Undisc 10/04 Rel c/s 10, Gateshead 7/10		
James	Curtis	5			13/4/82	28		Kenneck Ryhope CA, Washington, Gateshead 6/03	38	0
Paul	Heckingbottom	3	6'00"	12 05	17/7/77	33	Barnsley	Man Utd (Trainee), Sunderland 7/95, Scarborough (SL) 10/97, Hartlepool (L) 9/98, Sheff Utd (Trial), Bolton (Trial), Stockport (Trial), Darlington 3/99 Rel c/s 02, Norwich 7/02, Bradford C 7/03, Sheff Wed 7/04, Barnsley Undisc 1/06, Bradford C (6ML) 7/07,	15	0
Carl	Jones	15	6'01"	12 02	3/9/86	23	Sunderland	Chester-le-Street, Hartlepool 9/04 Rel c/s 07, York C 8/07 Rel 1/08, Gateshead (L) 11/07, Gateshead (L) 1/08 Perm 1/08	10	0
MIDFIELDERS										
Martin	Brittain	7	5'08"	10 07	29/12/84	25	Newcastle	Newcastle Rel c/s 06, Hull C (Trial) 7/06, Brighton (Trial) 7/06, Kilmarnock (Trial) 8/06, Ipswich 8/06 Rel c/s 07, Yeovil (2ML) 10/06, Yeovil (SL) 1/07, Carlisle 8/07 Rel 8/07, Scunthorpe 12/07 Rel 12/07, Walsall 1/08 Rel c/s 08, Toronto FC (Trial) 3/08, Kidderminster 8/08 Rel 5/09, Gateshead 6/09	6	1
Andy	Ferrell	12	5'08"	11 05	9/1/84	26	Newcastle	Newcastle Rel c/s 04, Watford 7/04 Rel c/s 05, Hereford 8/05 Rel 5/07, Kidderminster (L) 3/07, Kidderminster 6/07, York C 5/09, Gateshead 2/10	16	0
Alex	Francis	14	6'02"	12 08	7/1/90	20	Gateshead	Newcastle (Scholar) Rel 5/08, Gateshead 6/08, Blyth (5WL) 11/09	26	2
Kris	Gate	4	5'07"	10 03	1/1/85	25	Newcastle	Newcastle Rel c/s 07, Grimsby (Trial) 11/05, Gateshead 9/07	30	4
Josh	Gilles	22			12/6/90	20		Sunderland Nissan, Newcastle Blue Star 1/09, Blyth 7/09, Whitley Bay 3/10, Gateshead 6/10		
James	Marwood	21	5'09"	11 05	21/5/90	20		Newcastle (Scholar) Rel c/s 09, Carlisle (Trial) 7/09, Blyth 11/09, Team Northumbria 2/10, Gateshead 6/10		
Craig	Nelthorpe	11	5'10"	11 00	10/6/87	23	Doncaster	Doncaster Rel 1/09, Hucknall (L) 12/05, Kidderminster (L) 10/06, Gateshead (2ML/Dual) 11/06, Halifax (L) 1/08, Darlington (SL) 3/08, Gateshead (3ML) 8/08, Oxford U 1/09, York C 5/09 Rel 5/10, Barrow (7WL) 11/09, Luton (SL) 1/10, Gateshead 6/10		
Phil	Turnbull	8	5'11"	11 08	7/1/87	23	South Shields	Hartlepool Rel c/s 07, Gateshead (L) 12/05, Blyth (L) 3/07, York 7/07, Gateshead 2/08	41	3
FORWARDS										
Jonny	Allan	10	6'00"	11 03	24/5/83	27	Penrith	Carlisle Rel c/s 02, Workington 8/02, Oxford U (Trial) 8/02 Northwich 8/02, Tranmere (Trial) 7/03, Lancaster 11/03, Halifax 12/03, Northwich 8/04, Gateshead 5/10		
Steve	Baptiste	16			12/10/90	19		Birtley T. Gateshead 2/09, Ashington (L) 2/10	0	0
Nathan	Fisher	18						Middlesbrough (Scholar), Gretna Rel c/s 08, York C (Trial) 7/08, Durham C, Chester-le-Street 12/08, Consett c/s 09, Chester-le-Street, Gateshead 6/10		
Jon	Shaw	9	6'00"	13 01	10/11/83	26	Sheffield	Sheff Wed Rel 11/04, York (2ML) 11/03, Burton 11/04, Cheltenham (Trial) 11/04, Halifax 8/07, Rochdale £60,000 7/08 Rel 1/10, Crawley (SL) 1/09, Barrow (3ML) 8/09, Gateshead (5WL) 11/09, Mansfield 1/10 Rel 5/10, Gateshead 5/10	1	0
Brian	Wake	17	6'00"	11 02	13/8/82	28	Stockton	Wolviston, Norwich (Trial) 1/99, Tow Law, Grimsby (Trial), Carlisle 5/02, Gretna 11/03, Scarborough (7ML) 5/05, Hamilton (SL) 1/06 Perm, Greenock Morton 1/08, Gateshead 1/10	18	3

Loanees		SN	HT	WT	DOB	AGE	POB	From - To	APPS	GOA
(F)Michael	Mackay		6'00"	11 07	11/10/82	27	Durham	Hartlepool (5ML) 8/09 -	18	2
(M)Peter	Winn		6'00"	11 09	19/12/88	21	Cleethorpes	Scunthorpe 10/09, (SL) 2/10 - Rel 5/10, Stevenage 7/10	24	4
(M)Andy	Haworth		5'11"	11 10	28/11/88	21	Lancaster	Blackburn 11/09 - Rochdale (L) 1/10	6	0
(M)Clark	Keltie		5'10"	11 09	31/8/83	27	Gateshead	Rochdale (5WL) 11/09 - Rel 12/09, Lincoln C 1/10	3	0
(D)Rikki	Bains		6'01"	13 00	3/2/88	22	Coventry	Darlington (SL) 1/10 - Rel 4/10	5	0
(D)Gavin	Hurren		5'08"	13 07	22/10/85	24	Birmingham	Tamworth 3/10 -	6	0

Departures		SN	HT	WT	DOB	AGE	POB	From - To	APPS	GOA
(M)Christophe	Ascherl				17/6/86	24		Mechterscheim (Ger) 8/09 - Bedlington 10/09, Sunderland RCA 1/10	2	0
(F)Armand	One		6'05"	17 04	15/3/83	27	Paris, Fra	Livingston 9/09 - Rel 11/09, Stranraer 1/10	12	0
(D)Stephane	Pelonde				21/3/87	23		Mondeville (Fra) 2/09 - Rel 12/09	3	0
(F)Darren	Forsyth		6'02"		21/2/88	22	Dublin	Bray W 7/09 - Rel 1/10, Dunston UTS (2ML) 10/09, Shelbourne	5	0
(M)Jamie	Harwood				27/9/84	25		Worksop 12/06 - Rel 2/10, Harrogate T (L) 10/09, Shildon 2/10	8	1
(D)Darren	Williams		5'10"	11 00	28/4/77	33	Middlesbrough	Dundee 9/09 - Rel 2/10, Gainsborough 3/10	16	0
(D)Mark	Robinson		5'09"	11 00	24/7/81	29	Guisborough	York C 6/09 - Gainsborough 3/10	17	0
(D)Chris	Swailes		6'02"	12 11	19/10/70	39	Gateshead	Hamilton 6/09 - Rel 5/10, Blyth (Pl/Ass Man) 6/10	23	0
(F)Andy	Parkinson		5'10"	12 12	27/5/79	31	Liverpool	Cambridge U 2/10 - Rel 5/10	14	0
(M)Wayne	Phillips				29/8/85	25	South Shields	Whitley Bay 7/07 - Rel 5/10, Harrogate T 7/10	35	0
(D)Phil	Cave				12/5/87	23	Newcastle	Livingston (SL) 2/09 Perm 8/09 - Rel 5/10, Blyth 7/10	18	0
(D)Wayne	Buchanan		6'02"	13 03	12/1/82	28	Bambridge	Lisburn Distillery 2/10 - Rel 5/10, Blyth (Trial) c/s 10	2	0
(M)Neale	McDermott		5'11"	11 02	8/3/85	25	Newcastle	R.A.A. Louviéroise (Bel) 7/09 - Rel 5/10	11	1
(F)Steven	Richardson				3/7/86	24	Gateshead	Durham C 6/09 - Rel 5/10, Spennymoor 5/10	19	1
(M)James	Sinclair		5'06"	10 05	22/10/87	22	Newcastle	San Jose Earthquake (USA) 1/10 - Rel 5/10	5	0
(F)Graeme	Armstrong		6'00"	12 08	28/6/83	27	Hexham	Dunston Fed £5,000 6/07 - Rel 5/10, Harrogate T 5/10	38	7
(F)Daryl	Clare		5'09"	11 00	1/8/78	32	Jersey	Mansfield (3ML) 10/09 Perm 1/10 - Cambridge U £10,000 6/10	26	13
(G)Jim	Provett		6'00"	13 04	22/12/82	27	Stockton	Harrogate T 2/09 - Rel c/s 10	11	0

Do you remember when...

Gateshead

Gateshead F.C. 1983-1984

16th in The Alliance

Premier League

Back row, left to right: Mr E.G.Hill (Chairman), Lance Jobling, David Parnaby, Kenny Dodds, Jim Pearson, Steve Higgins, Gordon Hindson and George Ramshaw (Assistant Manager).

Front Row: Tony Robinson, Bob Topping, Terry Hibbitt, Ray Wilkie (Manager), Kevin Pugh, Martin Henderson and Paul Grigg.

GRIMSBY TOWN

Chairman: John Fenty
Secretary: Ian Fleming **(T)** 07711 188 542
(E) ian@gtfc.co.uk
Additional Committee Members: Mike Parker, Ian Fleming, John Elsom, Mike Chapman, Peter Furneaux, Dave Smith, Dale Ladson
Manager: Neil Woods
Programme Editor: Lucie Ramsden **(E)** lucie@gtfc.co.uk

Club Factfile

Founded: 1878 **Nickname:** The Mariners
Previous Names: Grimbsy Pelham 1878-79
Previous Leagues: Football League 1892-2010

Club Colours (change): Black & white stripes/black/red (All sky blue)

Ground: Blundell Park, Cleethorpes, North East Lincolnshire DN35 7PY **(T)** 01472 605 050
Capacity: 10,033 **Seats:** Yes **Covered:** Yes **Clubhouse:** Yes **Shop:** Yes
Previous Grounds: Clee Park, Abbey Park

Simple Directions
From the North/West All routes follow M180 onto the A180 to Grimsby. At first roundabout go straight on then follow signs for Cleethorpes (A180) onto Grimsby Road. Blundell Park is situated behind the Drive Thru' McDonalds. From the South A46 (Lincoln) Follow A46 into Grimsby, go straight on at roundabout after dual carriageway, following signs to Cleethorpes. At the 'Grimsby Institute' get in the right hand lane and keep following signs for Cleethorpes. At Isaac's Hill roundabout turn left onto Grimsby Road, the ground is on the right hand side behind the Drive Thru' at McDonalds.

Record Attendance: 31,657 v Wolverhampton Wanderers - FA Cup 5th Round 20/02/1937
Record Victory: 9-2 v Darwen - Division 2 15/04/1899
Record Defeat: 1-9 v Arsenal - Division 1 28/01/1931
Record Goalscorer: Pat Glover - 180 (1930-39)
Record Appearances: John McDermott - 754 (1987-2007)
Additional Records: Paid £500,000 to Preston North End for Lee Ashcroft 11/08/1998
Received £1.5m from Everton for John Oster July 1997

Senior Honours: Football League Division 2 1900-01, 33-34, Division 3 North 1925-26, 55-56, Division 3 1979-80, Division 4 1971-72.
Division 2 Play-offs 1997-98.
League Group Cup 1982. Auto Windscreen Shield 1998.

10 YEAR RECORD

00-01	01-02	02-03	03-04	04-05	05-06	06-07	07-08	08-09	09-10
FL 1 18	FL 1 19	FL 1 24	FL 2 21	FL 2 18	FL 2 4	FL 2 15	FL 2 16	FL 2 22	FL 2 23

GRIMSBY TOWN

No.	Date	Comp	H/A	Opponents	Att:	Result	Goalscorers
1	8/8/09	FL2	A	Cheltenham	3654	L 1-2	Conlon 35
2	15/8/09	FL2	H	Crewe	5007	L 0-4	
3	18/8/09	FL2	H	Rotherham	4156	L 1-2	Sweeney 64
4	22/8/09	FL2	A	Bury	2799	W1-0	Conlon 20
5	29/8/09	FL2	H	Aldershot Town	3757	L 1-2	Conlon 81
6	5/9/09	FL2	A	Port Vale	5056	L 0-4	
7	12/9/09	FL2	H	Hereford	3173	W1-0	North 88
8	19/9/09	FL2	A	Torquay United	2575	W2-0	Nicholson 47 (og), Sweeney 65
9	26/9/09	FL2	H	Darlington	4014	D 1-1	Atkinson 21
10	30/9/09	FL2	A	Chesterfield	3329	L 2-3	Proudlock 70, Sweeney 87
11	3/10/09	FL2	A	Barnet	2497	L 0-3	
12	10/10/09	FL2	H	Burton	4002	L 1-2	Jones 4
13	17/10/09	FL2	H	Rochdale	3754	L 0-2	
14	24/10/09	FL2	A	Bournemouth	5270	L 1-3	Linwood 50
15	30/10/09	FL2	H	Accrington	4325	D2-2	Forbes 14, Conlon 90+5
16	14/11/09	FL2	A	Northampton	4028	D0-0	
17	21/11/09	FL2	A	Lincoln City	4981	D0-0	
18	24/11/09	FL2	H	Bradford City	3646	L 0-3	
19	28/11/09	FL2	A	Macclesfield	1409	D0-0	
20	5/12/09	FL2	H	Dagenham & R	3090	D1-1	Coulson 36
21	12/12/09	FL2	A	Shrewsbury	4850	D0-0	
22	18/12/09	FL2	H	Morecambe	3119	D1-1	Sweeney 67
23	28/12/09	FL2	H	Port Vale	4401	L 1-2	Conlon 90 (pen)
24	2/1/09	FL2	H	Bury	3463	D1-1	Akpa Akpro 60
25	16/1/10	FL2	H	Cheltenham	3334	D0-0	
26	23/1/10	FL2	A	Rotherham	3751	L 1-2	Fletcher 90+3
27	30/1/10	FL2	A	Aldershot Town	3195	D1-1	Grant 6 (og)
28	6/2/10	FL2	H	Notts County	4452	L 0-1	
29	13/2/10	FL2	A	Bradford City	11321	D0-0	
30	17/2/10	FL2	A	Notts County	5163	D1-1	Devitt 45
31	20/2/10	FL2	H	Lincoln City	6395	D2-2	Peacock 38, 46
32	23/2/10	FL2	H	Macclesfield	4813	D1-1	Devitt 42
33	27/2/10	FL2	A	Dagenham & R	2190	L 0-2	
34	6/3/10	FL2	H	Shrewsbury	3651	W3-0	Sinclair 45+3 (pen), 57, Akpa Akpro 64
35	9/3/10	FL2	A	Crewe	3272	L 2-4	Akpa Akpro 32, Sinclair 41
36	9/3/10	FL2	A	Morecambe	1882	D1-1	Coulson 59
37	9/3/10	FL2	H	Bournemouth	4428	W3-2	Devitt 27, Coulson 61, Chambers 90+1
38	27/3/10	FL2	A	Rochdale	4724	L 1-4	Chambers 43
39	2/4/10	FL2	H	Northampton	6482	L 1-2	Coulson 42
40	5/4/10	FL2	A	Accrington	1839	W3-2	Hudson 56, Coulson 59, Devitt 61
41	10/4/10	FL2	A	Hereford	2143	W1-0	Devitt 18
42	13/4/10	FL2	H	Chesterfield	5648	D 2-2	Wright 28, Akpa Akpro 57
43	17/4/10	FL2	H	Torquay United	5702	L 0-3	
44	24/4/10	FL2	A	Darlington	1911	W2-0	Lancashire 20, Akpa Akpro 45+3
45	1/5/10	FL2	H	Barnet	7033	W2-0	Atkinson 59, Hudson 90+3
46	8/5/10	FL2	A	Burton	4987	L 0-3	
	Cups						
1	11/8/09	LGCP	A	Tranmere	3527	L 0-4	
2	6/10/09	JPT (N)	A	Hartlepool	1675	W 2-0	Sweeney 6, Proudlock 34
3	7/11/09	FACP	H	Bath City	2103	L 0-2	
4	10/11/09	JPT (N) QF	A	Leeds United	10430	L 1-3	Sweeney 57

Home League Attendances
Highest: 7033 v Barnet
Lowest: 3090 v Dagenham & Redbridge
Average: 4156

Top Goalscorer: Sweeney - 6 (4 League, 2 Cup) in 43 appearances - 14% strike rate
Most Appearances: Atkinson - 41 (37 League, 4 Cup)

CURRENT SQUAD AS OF BEGINING OF 2010-11 SEASON

GOALKEEPERS		SQ NO.	HT	WT	D.O.B	AGE	P.O.B	CAREER	APPS	GOA
Kenny	Arthur	1	6'04"	13 08	2/12/78	31	Bellshill	Possil YMCA, Partick 6/97 Rel 5/07, Accrington 6/07, Rochdale 7/09 Rel c/s 10, Grimsby 6/10		
Nick	Colgan	13	6'01"	12 00	19/9/73	36	Drogheda	Drogheda, Chelsea Rel c/s 98, Crewe (L), 9/93, Grimsby (L) 10/94, Millwall (5WL) 9/95, Brentford (L) 10/97, Reading (L) 2/98, Bournemouth 7/98, Hibernian 7/99 Rel c/s 04, Stockport (5ML) 8/03, Barnsley 7/04, Dundee U (SL) 1/05, Ipswich 1/08 Rel c/s 08, Bradford C (Trial) 7/08, Sunderland 7/08 Rel c/s 09, Grimsby 7/09		
DEFENDERS										
Robert	Atkinson	25	6'01"	12 00	29/4/87	23	North Ferriby	Barnsley, Scarborough (2ML) 11/05 (SL) 1/06, Halifax (L) 11/06, Rochdale (L) 10/07, Grimsby (SL) 11/07, Grimsby (2ML) 10/08, Grimsby 1/09		
Scott	Garner	6	6'02"		20/9/89	19	Coventry	Leicester, Ilkeston (L) 10/08, Mansfield 1/09, Grimsby 7/10		
Mark	Gray	27			19/12/91	18		Grimsby, Spalding U (WE) 12/09		
Darran	Kempson	5	6'02"	12 13	6/12/84	25	Blackpool	Preston (Sch), Accrington (L) 2/04, Morecambe (3ML) 12/04 Perm 3/05, Crewe 7/06 Rel 5/07, Bury (SL) 2/07, Shrewsbury 7/07, Accrington (L) 2/08, Wrexham 7/08, Forest Green (2ML) 11/08, Accrington 7/09, Grimsby 6/10		
Lee	Ridley	3	5'10"	12 10	5/12/81	28	Scunthorpe	Scunthorpe Rel c/s 07, Cheltenham 7/07 Rel c/s 10, Darlington (6WL) 11/07, Lincoln C (SL) 1/08, Grimsby 6/10		
Robbie	Stockdale		5'11"	11 03	30/11/79	30	Middlesbrough	Middlesbrough, Sheff Wed (L) 9/00, West Ham (3ML) 10/03, Rotherham (SL) 2/04, Rotherham 7/04, Hull C 1/05 Rel c/s 06, Darlington (L) 2/06, Tranmere 7/06 Rel c/s 08, Grimsby 7/08 (Pl/Yth Dev Officer) 6/10		
Bradley	Wood	19	5'08"	11 00	2/9/91	18	Leicester	Grimsby		
MIDFIELDERS										
Peter	Bore	2	6'00"	12 02	4/11/87	22	Grimsby	Grimsby, York C (L) 9/08		
Michael	Cummins	8	6'00"	12 06	1/6/78	32	Dublin	Middlesbrough, Port Vale 3/00 Rel c/s 06, Darlington 7/06 Rel c/s 08, Rotherham 5/08 Rel c/s 10, Grimsby 6/10		
Adrian	Forbes	22	5'08"	11 10	23/1/79	31	Greenford	Norwich, Luton 7/01 £60,000 Rel c/s 04, Swansea 7/04 Rel c/s 06, Blackpool 7/06, Millwall Undisc 1/08 Rel c/s 09, Grimsby (SL) 2/09, Grimsby 7/09		
Josh	Fuller	20	5'09"	10 12	9/2/92	18	Grimsby	Grimsby		
Lewis	Gobern	7	5'10"	11 07	28/1/85	25	Birmingham	Wolves Rel c/s 09, Hartlepool (L) 11/04, Blackpool (2ML) 11/05, Bury (SL) 3/06, Colchester (SL) 1/09, MK Dons 7/09 Rel c/s 10, Grimsby 7/10		
Nick	Hegarty	21	5'10"	11 00	25/6/86	24	Hemsworth	Notts Forest (Jun), Sheff Wed (Jun), Grimsby, Whitby (L) 9/05, Willenhall (SL) 3/06, York C (L) 9/07		
Mark	Hudson	4	5'10"	11 03	24/10/80	29	Bishop Auckland	Middlesbrough, Chesterfield (3ML) 8/02, Carlisle (3ML) 12/02, Chesterfield 3/03, Huddersfield 7/05 Rel c/s 07, Rotherham Rel c/s 09, Blackpool 8/09 Rel 8/09, Gainsborough 9/09, Grimsby (Trial) 10/09, Grimsby 11/09		
Michael	Leary	14	5'11"	12 03	17/4/83	27	Ealing	Luton Rel c/s 07, Bristol R (3ML) 8/05, Walsall (SL) 1/06, Torquay (L) 11/06, Brentford (SL) 1/07, Barnet 7/07 Rel c/s 09, Grimsby 7/09		
Drew	Rhodes	26						Grimsby		
FORWARDS										
Charles	Ademeno	9	5'10"	11 13	12/12/88	21	Milton Keynes	Southend Rel 6/09, Bishops Stortford (2ML) 9/06, Cambridge U (L) 1/07, Welling (2ML) 11/07, Rushden & D (2ML) 2/08, Salisbury (5WL) 11/08, Salisbury (SL) 2/09, Crawley 7/09, Grimsby Tribunal 7/10		
Alan	Connell		5'11"	10 08	15/2/83	27	Enfield	Ipswich (Jun), Tottenham (Trial), Bournemouth 7/02, Torquay Undisc 7/05 Rel c/s 06, Hereford 7/06, Brentford 7/07, Bournemouth Undisc 8/08 Rel c/s 10, Grimsby 7/10		
Tom	Corner	23						Grimsby, Frickley (WE) 11/09		
Michael	Coulson	11	5'10"	10 00	4/4/88	22	Scarborough	Scarborough, Barnsley 7/06 Rel c/s 10, Northwich (L) 8/07, Chester (L) 10/09, Grimsby (SL) 11/09, Grimsby 5/10		
Nathan	Dixon	24	5'09"	11 07	15/4/92	18		Grimsby, Spalding U (WE) 12/09		
Chris	Jones	18	5'07"	10 00	12/9/89	20	Swansea	Swansea, Cambridge U (4ML) 8/08, Grimsby 7/09, Neath (SL) 1/10		
Lee	Peacock	10	6'00"	12 08	9/10/76	33	Paisley	Carlisle, Mansfield £90,000 10/97, Man City £500,000 11/99, Bristol C £600,000 8/00, Sheff Wed 7/04 Rel 1/06, Swindon 1/06, Grimsby 1/10		

HAYES & YEADING

Chairman: Derek Goodall

Secretary: Bill Gritt **(T)** 07710 102 004 **(E)** juneguk@aol.com

Additional Committee Members: Trevor Griffiths, John Bond, Derrick Matthews, Nick Griffin, Dean Goodall, Trevor Gorman, Colin Hanlan, Avril Radford, Simon East, Eric Stevens

Manager: Garry Haylock

Programme Editor: Andy Corbett **(E)** ac@andycorbett.com

Club Factfile

Founded: 2007 **Nickname:**

Previous Names: Hayes - Botwell Mission 1909-29. Hayes and Yeading merged to form today's club in 2007

Previous Leagues: Isthmian

Club Colours (change): Red/black/black (Blue/white/white)

Ground: Townfield House, Church Road, Hayes, Middlesex UB3 2LE **(T)** 0208 573 2075

Capacity: 6,500 **Seats:** 450 **Covered:** 2,450 **Clubhouse:** Yes **Shop:** Yes

Previous Grounds:

Simple Directions

Leave M25 at junction 16, follow A40 towards London, turn right onto A437, then turn left into A4020 (Uxbridge Road). Turn right into Church Road opposite the Adam and Eve Public House and the ground is 500 yards up on the right.

Record Attendance: 1,881 v Luton Town - Conference Premier 06/03/2010

Record Victory: 8-2 v Hillingdon Borough (A) - Middlesex Senior Cup 11/11/08

Record Defeat: 0-8 v Luton Town (A) - Conference Premier 27/03/10

Record Goalscorer: Josh Scott - 40 (2007-09)

Record Appearances: James Mulley - 137 (2007-10)

Additional Records:

Senior Honours: Conference South Play-offs 2008-09

10 YEAR RECORD

00-01	01-02	02-03	03-04	04-05	05-06	06-07	07-08	08-09	09-10
Conf 18	Conf 20	Isth P 7	Isth P 8	Conf S 12	Conf S 20	Conf S 16	Conf S 13	Conf S 4	Conf 17

HAYES & YEADING UNITED

No.	Date	Comp	H/A	Opponents	Att:	Result	Goalscorers	Pos
1	8/8/09	BSP	A	Kidderminster Harriers	1471	L 0-1		18
2	11/8/09	BSP	H	Stevenage Borough	681	D 1-1	Allen-Page 61	18
3	15/8/09	BSP	H	Altrincham	401	L 1-2	Fitzgerald 90	21
4	18/8/09	BSP	A	Rushden & Diamonds	1059	L 1-2	Gradwell 88	21
5	22/8/09	BSP	H	York City	606	D 1-1	Daly pen 54	21
6	29/8/09	BSP	A	Ebbsfleet United	884	W 2-1	Daly 3, Little 90	19
7	31/8/09	BSP	H	Sailsbury City	429	L 3-4	James 40, Fitzgerald 64, Binns 81	19
8	5/9/09	BSP	A	Gateshead	519	D 0-0	Match abandoned after 76 minutes	19
9	8/9/09	BSP	A	Forest Green Rovers	630	D 0-0		18
10	12/9/09	BSP	H	Tamworth	355	D 2-2	Green 31, S Canham 77	18
11	19/9/09	BSP	H	Histon	343	L 0-2		19
12	22/9/09	BSP	A	Eastbourne Borough	802	L 1-3	S Canham 72	20
13	26/9/09	BSP	A	Mansfield Town	3180	L 1-3	S Canham pen 60	22
14	29/9/09	BSP	H	Kettering Town	307	L 1-2	S Canham pen 45	23
15	10/10/09	BSP	A	Stevenage Borough	2120	L 0-4		23
16	17/10/09	BSP	H	Cambridge United	744	W 3-0	Fitzgerald 2 (24, 48), Cadmore 63	20
17	31/10/09	BSP	A	Tamworth	919	W 2-0	Mulley 16, Fitzgerald 28	19
18	14/11/09	BSP	A	Wrexham	2427	W 2-0	Little 2 (9, 11)	18
19	21/11/09	BSP	H	Crawley Town	342	W 2-1	S Canham 2 (32, pen 83)	17
20	24/11/09	BSP	A	Kettering Town	997	W 1-0	Watkins 85	16
21	1/12/09	BSP	H	Eastbourne Borough	349	D 1-1	Basham pen 90	17
22	5/12/09	BSP	A	Barrow	1164	D 1-1	James 81	17
23	26/12/09	BSP	A	AFC Wimbledon	3659	L 0-5		17
24	28/12/09	BSP	H	Ebbsfleet United	369	W 4-2	Watkins 36, Basham 2 (65, 70), James 86	15
25	1/1/10	BSP	H	AFC Wimbledon	1829	W 1-0	Marwa 59	14
26	16/1/10	BSP	A	York City	2403	L 1-4	Fitzgerald 90	15
27	23/1/10	BSP	A	Altrincham	895	L 2-3	James 21, Green 28	15
28	26/1/10	BSP	H	Forest Green Rovers	291	L 2-3	Basham 2 (12, 86)	15
29	30/1/10	BSP	H	Rushden & Diamonds	377	L 1-6	Fitzgerald 80	16
30	6/2/10	BSP	A	Histon	617	D 3-3	Watkins 33, Stolcers 62, Fitzgerald 81	16
31	9/2/10	BSP	H	Grays Athletic	251	W 4-0	Fitzgerald 13, Ruby 26, Allen-Page 2 (55, 61)	15
32	13/2/10	BSP	H	Gateshead	296	W 3-2	Cochrane 31, Mulley 63, Basham pen 77	14
33	27/2/10	BSP	H	Mansfield Town	427	D 1-1	Binns 42	13
34	6/3/10	BSP	H	Luton Town	1881	L 2-3	Cochrane 57, Cadmore 88	15
35	9/3/10	BSP	A	Oxford United	5045	W 2-1	Basham 2 (25, 43)	14
36	13/3/10	BSP	A	Grays Athletic	308	D 0-0		14
37	27/3/10	BSP	A	Luton Town	6761	L 0-8		15
38	2/4/10	BSP	H	Oxford United	1655	W 2-1	Marwa 2 (46, 65)	14
39	5/4/10	BSP	A	Crawley Town	860	L 0-1		14
40	10/4/10	BSP	H	Barrow	312	D 1-1	Marwa 64	14
41	13/4/10	BSP	A	Sailsbury City	755	L 1-3	Marwa 90	15
42	15/4/10	BSP	H	Kidderminster Harriers	318	D 2-2	Fitzgerald 2 (39, 70)	16
43	17/4/10	BSP	A	Cambridge United	2940	L 1-4	Green 74	16
44	24/4/10	BSP	H	Wrexham	446	L 0-1		17
	Chester	**record**	**........................**	**...expunged 08/03**				
15	3/10/09	BSP	H	Chester City	351	D 0-0		23
	Cups							
1	24/10/09	FAC 4Q	H	Staines Town	602	L 0-1		
2	12/12/09	FAT 1	A	Oxford United	1663	L 0-1		

Home Attendances:
Highest: 1881 v Luton Town
Lowest: 251 v Grays Athletic
Average (08-09): 389 (347)

Top Goalscorer: Fitzgerald - 11 (11 League, 0 Cup) in 31 appearances - 35% strike rate
Most Appearances: Green - 45 (43 League, 2 Cup)

OVERLAND 1	CADMORE 4	ALLEN-PAGE 2	RUBY 5	GREEN 3	MULLEY 7	BINNS 11	MARWA 6	COCHRANE 15	M CANHAM 8	GRADWELL 9	FITZGERALD 10	JAMES 17	PREDDIE 21	EL-ABD 14	LITTLE 19	DALY 24	S CANHAM 18	BAKER 25	ROCHESTER 16	FRASER-ALLEN 28	MEHMET 26	WEBB 33	WATKINS 34	PALMER 12	BASHAM 36	WASSMER 22	MASTERS 31	HARRIS 29	STOLCERS 30	WISHART 27	IDE 18	
X	X	X	X	X	X	X	X	X	X	X	S	S	U	U	U																	1
X	X	X	X	X	S	X	X	X	U	X	X	U	U	X		S																2
X	X	X	X	X	U		X	X	S	X	X	U	S	X	X	S																3
X	X	X		X	X	X	X	X	X	S	X	S	U	X	U	S																4
X	X	X	X	X	X	X		X	S	X	S	X	U	U	S	X																5
X	X	X	X	X	X	X	S		X	S	X	X	U	U	S	X																6
X	X		X	X	X	X	X	S	X	S	X	X	U	U	S	X																7
X		X	X	X	X	X	X	X		U	X	U	U	X	U	S	X															8
X		X	X	X	X	X	S	X	X	U	S	S	U	X		X	X															9
X	X		X	X	X	X	X	X	S		U	X	U	X	U	S	X															10
X	X	X	X	X	X	X	X	S	X	U	S	X	U			S	X															11
X	X	X	X	X	X	X	X	X	U		S	X	U		S	S	X															12
X	X	X	X	X	X	S	X		X		S			S	X	X	X	U	U													13
X	X	X		X	X	X	X	X	S		X	S		X	U	S	X	U														14
X	X		U	X	X	X			X	S		X		X	X	X	X	U		S	S											15
X	X	X	X	X	X	X			X	U	X			U	X	S	X	U			U											16
X	X	X	X	X	X		S		X		X	X		U	X	S	X	U			U											17
X	X	X	X	X	X		U	X	X			X		S	X		X	U					S	S								18
X	X	X	X	X	X	S	S	X			X	X		U	X		X	U					U									19
X	X	X	X	X	X	S	S	X	X		U	X			X		X	U					S									20
X	X		X	X	X	X	X		X		S	X		U	U		X	U					X		S							21
X	X	X	X	X	X	S	X		X		S	X		U	X			U					S		X							22
X	X	X	X		X	X	S	X	S		S	X		U	X			U					X		X							23
X	X	X	X	X	X	S	X		X		U	S		S	X			U					X		X							24
X	X	X	X	X	X	S	X		X		X	S		U	X			U					X	S								25
X	X	X	X	X		X	X		X	U	S	X		S	X			U						S	X							26
X		X	X	X	X	S	S	X	X		S	X		X	X			U							X	U						27
X	X	X	X	X	X	X	X	X	X		S			U	U			U					S		X							28
X	X	X	X	X	X	X	S	X	X		S			S	U			U					X		X							29
U	X	X	S	X		X	X	X	U		X				U								X				X	X	X	S		30
U	X	X	X	X		X	X	X	S		X			U	S												X	X	X	S		31
U	X		X	X	S	X	X	X	U					U									X		X		X	X	X	U		32
S	X		X	X	X	X	X	X	U			X			U								U		X		X	X	S			33
U	X		X	X		X	X	X	U			X		S	S								X				X	X	X	S		34
	X		X	X		U	X	X	X			X						U				U	X		X		X	X	S	S		35
U	X	X	X	X		X	X	X	X						S							S	X		X		X		U	U		36
U	X	X	X	X	S	U	X	X	X		X	S															X	X		S	X	37
U		X	X	X	X	X	X		X						U							X			X		X	X	S	U	S	38
U		X	X	X	X	X	X		X			X			U							S					X	X	S	S	X	39
U	X	X	X	X	X		X	U	X						X										X		X	X	S	S	S	40
U	X	X	X	X	U	X	X	X	X		X											X				S	X		U	S		41
	X	X	X	X	S		X	X	X		X							U				U	S				X	X	U	X		42
	X	X	X	X	S	X	X	X	X						S			U					S				X	X	U	X		43
	X	X	S	X	X	S	X	X	X						U			U					X			X	X	X		S		44
X	X			X	X	X	X		X	U	X	X		X		S	X	U		S	S											
X	X	X	X	X	X			U	X	U	X	X		S	X	S	X	U			S	U										
X	X	X	X	X	X	X	S	X	X		S	X			U			U					S		X							
Total League Appearances																																
29	39	36	39	43	31	29	32	29	30	4	16	20	0	9	15	6	14	0	0	0	0	2	11	0	13	1	15	13	4	2	2	X
1	0	0	2	0	5	8	8	2	6	4	13	7	1	6	8	10	0	0	0	1	1	2	6	3	1	1	0	0	5	9	2	S
10	0	0	1	0	2	2	1	1	6	5	3	3	11	14	13	0	0	21	1	0	2	2	2	0	0	1	0	0	4	3	0	U
Total Cup Appearances																																
2	2	2	2	2	2	1	0	1	2	0	1	2	0	0	1	0	1	0	0	0	0	0	0	0	1	0	0	0	0	0	0	X
0	0	0	0	0	0	0	1	0	0	0	1	0	0	1	0	1	0	0	0	0	1	0	1	0	0	0	0	0	0	0	0	S
0	0	0	0	0	0	0	0	1	0	1	0	0	0	0	1	0	0	2	0	0	0	1	0	0	0	0	0	0	0	0	0	U
Total Goals																																
0	2	3	1	3	2	2	5	2	0	1	11	4	0	0	3	2	6	0	0	0	0	0	3	0	8	0	0	0	1	0	0	Lge
0	0	0	0	0	0	0	0	0	0	0	0	0	0	0	0	0	0	0	0	0	0	0	0	0	0	0	0	0	0	0	0	Cup

HAYES & YEADING UNITED

CURRENT SQUAD AS OF BEGINING OF 2010-11 SEASON

GOALKEEPERS		SQ NO.	HT	WT	D.O.B	AGE	P.O.B	CAREER	APPS	GOA
Chris	Baker				28/3/88	22		Ash U, Hayes & Yeading 7/09, Beaconsfield SYCOB (L) 2/10	0	0
Lee	Harrison		6'02"	12 07	12/9/71	38	Billericay	L.Orient (Sch), Charlton Rel c/s 93, Fulham (L) 11/91, Gillingham (SL) 3/92, Fulham (SL) 12/92, Fulham c/s 93 Rel c/s 96, Barnet 7/96, Peterborough (3ML) 12/02 L.Orient (L) 3/03 £10,000 4/03 Rel 6/05, Peterborough 7/05 Rel 5/06, Barnet 7/06 Rel c/s 10, Hayes & Yeading 7/10		
DEFENDERS										
Tom	Cadmore		6'00"	13 01	26/1/88	22	Rickmansworth	Watford (Yth), Wycombe Rel 5/08, Yeading (3ML) 8/07, Hayes & Yeading 7/08	39	2
Adam	Green		5'11"	10 11	12/1/84	26	Hillingdon	Fulham Rel 5/06, Sheff Wed (L) 1/05, Bournemouth (L) 3/05, Bristol C (SL) 1/06, Grays 7/06 Rel 1/07, Woking 1/07 Rel c/s 08, Grimsby (Trial) 12/08, Hayes & Yeading 7/09	43	3
Esmond	James				4/2/90	20		Hayes & Yeading	27	4
Matt	Ruby				18/3/86	24	Chertsey	Woking Rel 8/08, Northwood (L) 10/05, Fleet T (L) 1/06, Basingstoke (L) 3/06, Bognor Regis (L) 3/07, Hayes & Yeading 8/08	41	1
Charlie	Wassmer				21/3/91	19		Hayes & Yeading, Harrow (L) 8/09	2	0
MIDFIELDERS										
Toby	Little				19/2/89	21		Hayes/Hayes & Yeading	23	3
Daniel	Mehmet				14/3/90	20		Hayes & Yeading	1	0
James	Mulley				30/9/88	21		Yeading/Hayes & Yeading, Charlton (Trial) 7/10	36	2
Bradley	Pritchard				19/12/85	24	Zimbabwe	C.Palace, Carshalton 12/04, Nuneaton B, Tamworth 6/08, Hayes & Yeading 7/10		
Nathan	Webb				5/6/92	18		Hayes & Yeading	4	0
FORWARDS										
Daniel	Wishart				28/5/92	18		Hayes & Yeading	11	0

Loanees		SN	HT	WT	DOB	AGE	POB	From - To	APPS	GOA
(F)George	Daly		5'11"	10 11	25/10/90	19	Wycombe	Wycombe (3ML) 8/09 -	16	2
(F)Sean	Canham		6'01"	13 01	26/9/84	26	Exeter	Notts County (3ML) 9/09 - Rel c/s 10, Hereford 7/10	14	6
(F)Steve	Basham		6'00"	12 00	2/12/77	32	Southampton	Luton (SL) 11/09 - Rel 5/10, Brackley 7/10	14	8
(D)Ed	Harris		6'01"	13 05	3/11/90	19	Roehampton	QPR (SL) 2/10 -	13	0

Departures		SN	HT	WT	DOB	AGE	POB	From - To	APPS	GOA
(G)Delroy	Preddie				14/7/76	34	Berkshire	Staines 8/07 - Rel 9/09, Walton & H 10/09	1	0
(F)Franck	Padovani		5'10"	11 04	22/4/85	25	Nice	Hereford 9/09 - Rel 11/09		
(M)Kraig	Rochester		6'01"	13 01	3/11/88	21	London	Dag & Red 9/09 - Rel 11/09	0	0
(D)Abdelhalim	El Kholti		5'10"	11 00	17/10/80	29	Annemasse (Fr)	Woking 9/09 - Rel 1/10		
(G)Simon	Overland		6'05"	10 01	28/12/85	24	London	Boreham Wood c/s 09 - Rel 5/10, Boreham Wood (Trial) 7/10	30	0
(D)Danny	Allen-Page		5'08"	10 13	30/10/83	26	London	Farnborough 7/06 - Rel 5/10	36	3
(M)Rambir	Marwa				10/1/80	30	Barkingside	St Albans (L) 11/07 Perm 12/07 - Rel 5/10, Ebbsfleet 7/10	40	5
(M)Marc	Canham		5'11"	12 03	11/9/82	27	Wegburg, Ger	Team Bath 7/09 - Rel 5/10, Bath C 6/10	36	0
(F)Rob	Gradwell		6'02"	13 07	16/12/90	19	Hillingdon	Birmingham (Scholar) c/s 09 - Rel 5/10, Lewes (L) 3/10, Lewes 5/10	8	1
(D)Sami	El-Abd				1/1/88	22	Brighton	Team Bath 7/09 - Rel 5/10, Lewes (L) 3/10, Chelmsford 7/10	15	0
(M)Dale	Binns				8/7/81	29	London	Maidenhead 2/09 - Rel 5/10, Farnborough 6/10	37	2
(F)Craig	Watkins				4/5/86	24	Croydon	Woking 11/09 - Rel 5/10, Met Police 6/10	17	3
(M)Andrejs	Stolcers		5'10"	11 00	7/8/74	36	Riga, Lat	Bath C 2/10 - Rel 5/10	9	1
(M)Jake	Lovell				20/9/90	19		Yth - Rel 5/10, Harrow (L) 8/09, AFC Hayes (L) 1/10		
(M)Justin	Cochrane		5'11"	11 07	26/1/82	28	Hackney	Aldershot T c/s 09 - Rel 5/10	31	2
(F)Scott	Fitzgerald		5'11"	12 00	18/11/79	30	Hillingdon	Basingstoke 8/08 - Wealdstone 6/10	29	11
(M)Kyle	Fraser-Allen		5'10"	11 07	12/2/90	20	Wanstead	Tottenham 9/09 -	1	0
(F)Charlie	Ide		5'09"	11 00	10/5/88	22	Sunbury	Carshalton 3/10 -	4	0
(F)Stafforde	Palmer				23/4/88	22		Yth - Maidenhead (3ML) 6/09, Eastleigh (SL) 2/10, Eastleigh 7/10	3	0
(G)Clark	Masters		6'03"	13 12	31/5/87	23	Hastings	Aldershot 2/10 -	15	0

Do you remember when...

Hayes F.C.

Hayes F.C. were Champions of the Icis Premier League (Isthmian) and Middlesex Cup Winners in 1995-1996, winning promotion to The Conference.

Hayes F.C. amalgamated with Yeading F.C in 2007-2008

Back row, left to right: Gary Williams, Darron Wilkinson, Paul Watkins, Jason Roberts, Russell Meara, Carl Bartley, Ross Pickett, Nathan Bunce and Eddie Mee.
Middle Row: Dave Killick (Youth Development Officer), Jimmy Sugrue, Jason Goodliffe, Steve Baker, Nick Roddis, Junior Haynes, Martin Randall, Karl Ballard (Sports Therapist) and Ray Girvan (Youth team Manager).
Front Row: Terry Brown (Manager), Freddie Hyatt, Lee Flynn, Derek Goodall (Chairman), Warren Kelly, Jon Brady, Willy Wordsworth (Assistant Manager).

HISTON

Chairman: Russell Hands
Secretary: Howard Wilkins (T) 01223 237 373
(E) secretary@histonfc.co.uk

Additional Committee Members:
Angelo Dama, Colin Petit, Mac McDonald, Paul Pleszko, Philip Biggs, Graham Eales

Manager: David Livermore
Programme Editor: Steve Wells (E) sjwells1@btinternet.com

Back Row (L-R): Alex Kaufman (Football in the Community Officer), Martin Smith (Sports Therapist), Jim Stevenson, Mamadou Gomes, Callum Stewart, Joe Welch, George Lawton, Romone McCrae, Remy Clerima, Danny Mills, Sekou Diarra, Dean Greygoose (Asst. Manager), John Beck (Manager - left club)
Front Row: Oluwafemi Ilesanmi, Lee Wootton, Daniel Sparkes, Antonio Murray, Erkan Okay, Zak Mills, Lewis Taaffe, Zac Attwood

Club Factfile

Founded: 1904 **Nickname:** The Stutes
Previous Names: Histon Institute
Previous Leagues: Cambridgeshire 1904-48, Spartan 1948-60, Delphian 1960-63, Eastern Counties 1966-2000, Southern 2000-05.

Club Colours (change): Red and black stripes/black/black (Royal blue with white piping/royal blue/royal blue)

Ground: The Glassworld Stadium, Bridge Road, Impington, Cambridge CB4 9PH (T) 01223 237 373
Capacity: 3,250 **Seats:** 450 **Covered:** 1,800 **Clubhouse:** Yes **Shop:** Yes
Previous Grounds:
Simple Directions
From the M11 (Northbound) Junc 14, take the A14 eastbound signed towards Newmarket. Take the first exit off the A14 and at the roundabout, take the first exit onto the B1049. Go straight over the traffic lights, past the Holiday Inn Hotel (on your right) and the entrance to the club is half a mile on your right.

Record Attendance: 6,400 v King's Lynn - FA Cup 1956
Record Victory: 11-0 v March Town - Cambridgeshire Invitation Cup 15/02/01
Record Defeat: 1-8 v Ely City - Eastern Counties Division One 1994
Record Goalscorer: Neil Kennedy - 292
Record Appearances: Neil Andrews and Neil Kennedy
Additional Records: Paid £6,000 to Chelmsford City for Ian Cambridge 2000. Received £30,000 from Manchester United for Guiliano Maiorana.

Senior Honours: Eastern Counties League Cup 1990-91, Eastern Counties League 1999-2000, Southern League Premier 2004-05, Conference South 2006-07.

10 YEAR RECORD

00-01	01-02	02-03	03-04	04-05	05-06	06-07	07-08	08-09	09-10
SthE 4	SthE 4	SthE 10	SthE 2	SthP 1	Conf S 5	Conf S 1	Conf 7	Conf 3	Conf 18

HISTON

No.	Date	Comp	H/A	Opponents	Att:	Result	Goalscorers	Pos
1	8/8/09	BSP	A	Gateshead	681	W 3-0	Wright 2 (45, 84), Hudson-Odoi 81	2
2	11/8/09	BSP	H	Grays Athletic	816	D 0-0		4
3	15/8/09	BSP	H	Oxford United	1433	L 3-4	Barker 46, Simpson 81, Langston 88	8
4	18/8/09	BSP	A	Altrincham	698	L 1-2	Simpson 15	14
5	22/8/09	BSP	H	Salisbury City	684	W 2-0	Frew 33, Wright 81	9
6	29/8/09	BSP	A	York City	1944	L 1-3	Wright 90	16
7	31/8/09	BSP	H	Stevenage Borough	1159	L 0-2		18
8	8/9/09	BSP	A	Crawley Town	798	L 0-2		18
9	12/9/09	BSP	H	Kidderminster Harriers	774	D 1-1	Hammond 85	18
10	19/9/09	BSP	A	Hayes & Yeading United	343	W 2-0	Knight-Percival 8, Simpson 38	15
11	22/9/09	BSP	H	Ebbsfleet United	647	W 1-0	Simpson 83	15
12	26/9/09	BSP	A	AFC Wimbledon	3392	L 0-4		15
13	29/9/09	BSP	H	Eastbourne Borough	633	W 2-0	Knight-Percival 2 (27, 73)	14
14	4/10/09	BSP	H	Cambridge United	2371	D 1-1	Langston 90	14
15	10/10/09	BSP	A	Tamworth	1090	W 3-1	Knight-Percival 2 (27, 77), Simpson 86	14
16	17/10/09	BSP	H	Forest Green Rovers	823	W 5-2	Knight-Percival 44, Barker 49, Simpson 71, Wright 2 (75, 90)	12
17	31/10/09	BSP	A	Mansfield Town	3162	D 1-1	Simpson pen 84	11
18	14/11/09	BSP	A	Rushden & Diamonds	1126	L 1-2	Tidswell 85	12
19	21/11/09	BSP	H	Wrexham	946	D 0-0		13
20	24/11/09	BSP	A	Eastbourne Borough	703	D 1-1	Hudson-Odoi 62	14
21	1/12/09	BSP	A	Grays Athletic	367	W 1-0	Smith 33	12
22	5/12/09	BSP	H	Altrincham	676	D 0-0		12
23	28/12/09	BSP	H	Kettering Town	716	W 1-0	Tann 59	11
24	23/1/10	BSP	A	Salisbury City	758	L 0-3		13
25	27/1/10	BSP	H	Luton Town	1543	L 0-2		13
26	2/2/10	BSP	H	York City	487	D 1-1	Hudson-Odoi 43	14
27	6/2/10	BSP	H	Hayes & Yeading United	617	D 3-3	Wright pen 14, Langston 41, Smith 90	14
28	9/2/10	BSP	A	Ebbsfleet United	731	W 1-0	Wright 72	13
29	13/2/10	BSP	A	Oxford United	5365	L 0-2		13
30	27/2/10	BSP	A	Kidderminster Harriers	1293	L 0-3		15
31	3/3/10	BSP	H	Rushden & Diamonds	583	L 0-1		15
32	6/3/10	BSP	H	Gateshead	645	D 0-0		14
33	9/3/10	BSP	H	Tamworth	350	W 1-0	Smith 11	13
34	13/3/10	BSP	A	Cambridge United	4417	L 1-2	Pugh 61	13
35	16/3/10	BSP	A	Stevenage Borough	2407	L 0-1		13
36	20/3/10	BSP	H	Mansfield Town	662	L 0-5		15
37	27/3/10	BSP	A	Wrexham	2335	L 0-3		14
38	29/3/10	BSP	A	Barrow	994	D 0-0		14
39	3/4/10	BSP	H	AFC Wimbledon	867	L 1-3	Og (Johnson) 54	15
40	5/4/10	BSP	A	Kettering Town	800	D 1-1	Smith 59	16
41	10/4/10	BSP	H	Crawley Town	499	L 0-1		18
42	13/4/10	BSP	A	Luton Town	7083	L 3-6	Spakes 69, Knight-Percival 74, Southam 87	18
43	17/4/10	BSP	A	Forest Green Rovers	1204	L 0-2		18
44	24/4/10	BSP	H	Barrow	753	D 2-2	Southam pen 27, Og (Jones) 90	18
	Chester	**record**	**..........**	**...expunged 08/03**				
8	5/9/09	BSP	A	Chester City	1171	L 0-2		18
	Cups							
1	24/10/09	FAC 4Q	A	Hinckley United	778	L 1-2	Oyebanjo 47	
2	19/1/10	FAT 1	A	Maidstone United	238	W 3-0	Wright pen 39, Tidswell 87, Tann 90. *fielded an ineligible player*	

Home Attendances:	
Highest:	2371 v Cambridge United
Lowest:	350 v Tamworth
Average (08-09):	700 (1402)
Top Goalscorer:	Wright - 9 (8 League, 1 Cup) in 28 appearances - 32% strike rate
Most Appearances:	Knight-Percival - 45 (43 League, 2 Cup)

Match	NAISBITT 1	OYEBANJO 21	LANGSTON 5	GWILLIM 3	TANN 2	SIMPSON 24	KENNEDY 7	BARKER 11	KNIGHT-PERCIVAL 18	WRIGHT 23	FREW 9	ANDREWS 8	HUDSON-ODOI 10	POPE 16	WELCH 27	BYGRAVE 6	LEABON 22	HAMMOND 17	FARRELL 29	SPARKES 14
1	X	X	X	X	X	X	X	X	X	X	X	S	S	S	U	U				
2	X	X	X	X	X	X	X	X	X	X	X		S	S	U		S	U		
3	X	X	X	X	X	X	X	X	X	X	X	S	S		S	U		U		
4		X	X	X	X	X	U	X	X	X	X		S		X	S	U	S	X	
5		X	X	X	X	X		X	X	X	X	X	S	S	X	U		U	U	
6		U	X	X	X	X		X	X	X		X	X	X	X	S	S	U	U	
7	X		X		X	X	S	X	X	X		X	X	X	U	X		S	S	U
8	X		X	X	X	X	U	X	X		X	U	U	X		X		S	X	U
9	X		X	X	X	X	S	S	X		X	X		X	U	X		S	X	
10	X		X	X	X	X	S	X	X		X	X	S	X	U	S			X	
11	X		X	X	X	X	X	X	X		X	X		X	U					
12	X	U	X	X	X	X	X	X	X	X	X			X	U	S				
13	X		X	X	X	X	X	X	X	X	S			X	U	S				
14	X		X	X		X	X	X	X	X	U	S		X	U	X				
15	X	U	X	X		X	X	X	X	X		S		X	U	X				
16	X	X	X	X	S	X	X	X	X	X	S	X			U	X				
17	X	X		X	X	X	X	X	X	X	U	U			U	X				U
18	X		X	X	X		X	X	X		X	U			U	X		S		
19	X	X	X	X	X		X	X	X		S	U	S		U	X				
20	X	X	X	X	X		X	X	X		S	S	X		U	X				
21	X	X	X	X	X		X	X	X		S	S			U	X				
22	X	X	X				X	X	X		U	X			U	X	X			U
23	X	X	X		X				X	X	S		X		U	X	S			
24	X	X	X	X	X				X	X	X		S		U	X				
25	X	X	X	X	X				X	X			X		U					S
26	X	X	X	X	X				X		S		X		U	X				S
27	X	X	X	U	X				X	X			X			X				
28	X	X	X		X				X	X	S		X			X				U
29	X		X	X	X				X	X	S		X			X				
30	X	S	X	X	X				X	X	X		S							S
31			X	X	X				X	X			X		U					
32				X	X											X				X
33				X	X				X							X				X
34		S		X	X				X							X				X
35		S		X	X				X							X				X
36		X		X	X				X							X				X
37		S		X	X				X	X						X				X
38		X		X	X				X	X										X
39		X		X	X				X	X										X
40		X		X	X				X	X										
41		X			X				X							X				X
42		X			X				X							X				X
43					X				X						X	X				X
44			X		X				X	X					X	X				
	X		X	X	X	X	S	X	X			S	X	X		X		S	X	U
Cup 1	X	X	X	X	S	X	X	X	X	X	U	X			U	X		S		U
Cup 2	X	X	X	X	X				X	X	X				U	X				U

Match	MASON-SMITH 34	TIDSWELL 12	OKAY 37	STEWART 15	JOSEPH-DUBOIS 38	CROOK 19	LONG 4	COX 29	SMITH 25	WERNDLY 28	TAFFE 35	YORK 26	SOUTHAM 8	KEY 13	STEVENSON 32	SHERINGHAM 7	KNIGHT 19	PUGH 24	VERMA 11	MILLS 20
1																				
2																				
3																				
4																				
5																				
6																				
7																				
8																				
9		U																		
10		U																		
11		U	S	U	U															
12			S		S															
13			X		U	U														
14			X			S	S													
15			X			S	S													
16						S	U													
17						X	S													
18		S				X	U	X												
19		X				S		X												
20		X				U	U													
21		S				U	X		X											
22		S		X			U		X											
23				X			X		X	U	U									
24		U	X	S					X	S										
25		X	X	S					X	U		S								
26		X	S	U					X				X							
27		S	S	X					X			U	X	U						
28		S	X						X				X	U	U					
29			X	U					X			U	X			S	U			
30		U	X						X				X			X	U			
31		S	X	U					X			U	X			X	X	S		
32		U	X	X					X		U	S	X	U	U	X	X	X		
33		X	X	U					X		U	U	X	U	U	X	X			
34		S	X	U					X			U	X	U		X	X	X		
35		U	X	U					X			U	X	U		X	X	X		
36		S	U	S					X			S	X	U		X	X	X		
37			X						X			U	X	U		S	X	X	S	
38		U	X						X			U	X			U	X	U	X	U
39			X	U					X			U	X	U		S	X	U	X	
40	U		X	U					X			X	X	U		S	X		X	
41		S	X	U					X		S	S	X	U		X	X		X	
42		S	X	S					X		U	U	X	U		X	X		X	
43		X	X	X					X		S	U	X			S	U		X	U
44		S	X	S					X		U	U	X			X	U		X	
	U																			
Cup 1																				
Cup 2		S	S	S					X	X										

Total League Appearances

	NAISBITT	OYEBANJO	LANGSTON	GWILLIM	TANN	SIMPSON	KENNEDY	BARKER	KNIGHT-PERCIVAL	WRIGHT	FREW	ANDREWS	HUDSON-ODOI	POPE	WELCH	BYGRAVE	LEABON	HAMMOND	FARRELL	SPARKES
X	27	23	31	35	40	17	15	21	43	26	13	8	10	10	5	28	1	0	4	11
S	0	4	0	0	1	0	3	1	0	0	9	6	9	3	1	5	3	5	1	3
U	0	3	0	1	0	0	2	0	0	0	3	4	1	0	22	3	1	4	2	5

	MASON-SMITH	TIDSWELL	OKAY	STEWART	JOSEPH-DUBOIS	CROOK	LONG	COX	SMITH	WERNDLY	TAFFE	YORK	SOUTHAM	KEY	STEVENSON	SHERINGHAM	KNIGHT	PUGH	VERMA	MILLS
X	0	6	21	5	0	2	2	2	24	0	0	1	19	0	0	10	12	5	7	0
S	0	11	4	5	1	4	3	0	0	1	2	4	0	0	0	5	0	1	1	0
U	1	8	1	10	2	3	4	0	0	2	5	12	0	12	3	1	4	2	0	2

Total Cup Appearances

	NAISBITT	OYEBANJO	LANGSTON	GWILLIM	TANN	SIMPSON	KENNEDY	BARKER	KNIGHT-PERCIVAL	WRIGHT	FREW	ANDREWS	HUDSON-ODOI	POPE	WELCH	BYGRAVE	LEABON	HAMMOND	FARRELL	SPARKES
X	2	2	2	2	1	1	1	1	2	2	1	1	0	0	0	2	0	0	0	0
S	0	0	0	0	1	0	0	0	0	0	0	0	0	0	0	0	0	1	0	0
U	0	0	0	0	0	0	0	0	0	0	1	0	0	0	2	0	0	0	0	2

	MASON-SMITH	TIDSWELL	OKAY	STEWART	JOSEPH-DUBOIS	CROOK	LONG	COX	SMITH	WERNDLY	TAFFE	YORK	SOUTHAM	KEY	STEVENSON	SHERINGHAM	KNIGHT	PUGH	VERMA	MILLS
X	0	0	0	0	0	0	0	0	1	1	0	0	0	0	0	0	0	0	0	0
S	0	1	1	1	0	0	0	0	0	0	0	0	0	0	0	0	0	0	0	0
U	0	0	0	0	0	0	0	0	0	0	0	0	0	0	0	0	0	0	0	0

Total Goals

	NAISBITT	OYEBANJO	LANGSTON	GWILLIM	TANN	SIMPSON	KENNEDY	BARKER	KNIGHT-PERCIVAL	WRIGHT	FREW	ANDREWS	HUDSON-ODOI	POPE	WELCH	BYGRAVE	LEABON	HAMMOND	FARRELL	SPARKES
Lge	0	0	3	0	1	7	0	2	7	8	1	0	3	0	0	0	0	1	0	0
Cup	0	0	0	0	1	0	0	0	0	1	0	0	0	0	0	0	0	0	0	0

	MASON-SMITH	TIDSWELL	OKAY	STEWART	JOSEPH-DUBOIS	CROOK	LONG	COX	SMITH	WERNDLY	TAFFE	YORK	SOUTHAM	KEY	STEVENSON	SHERINGHAM	KNIGHT	PUGH	VERMA	MILLS
Lge	0	1	0	0	0	0	0	0	4	0	0	0	2	0	0	0	1	1	0	0
Cup	0	1	0	0	0	0	0	0	0	0	0	0	0	0	0	0	0	0	0	0

HISTON

CURRENT SQUAD AS OF BEGINING OF 2010-11 SEASON

GOALKEEPERS		SQ NO.	HT	WT	D.O.B	AGE	P.O.B	CAREER	APPS	GOA
David	Knight		6'00"	11 07	15/1/87	23	Houghton-le-Spring	Middlesbrough, Darlington (2WL) 12/05, Oldham (L) 8/06, Swansea 8/07 Rel c/s 08, Mansfield 10/08 Rel 11/08, Middlesbrough 11/08, Darlington 7/09 Rel 12/09, Histon 2/10 (09/10 12,0), York C (Trial) 7/10	12	0
Joe	Welch		6'02"	12 12	29/11/88	21	Welwyn Garden	Southend Rel c/s 07, Diss T (L) 3/07, Bishops Stortford c/s 07 Rel 8/08, Cheshunt 8/08, Histon 10/08, Weymouth (2ML) 2/10	6	0
DEFENDERS										
Seb	Baxter				11/11/91	18		Histon		
Adam	Bygrave		5'09"	12 02	24/2/89	21	Walthamstow	Reading Rel c/s 08, Gillingham (SL) 11/07, Weymouth 5/08, Histon £5,000 1/09	33	0
Zak	Mills				28/5/92	18		Histon	0	0
Erkan	Okay		5'08"		29/1/85	25	Cambridge	Ipswich (Scholar), Aylesbury 3/04, Histon 7/04 Rel 1/09, Mildenhall (L) 6/05, Kettering (Trial) 1/09, Nuneaton T NC 1/09, Chelmsford 1/09 Rel 9/09, Histon 9/09 (Pl/Coach) 6/10	25	0
Lanre	Oyebanjo		6'01"	11 04	24/4/90	20	London	Brentford Rel c/s 08, Histon 7/08, Peterborough (Trial) 10/09	27	0
Joe	Stroud				1/4/92	18		Histon		
MIDFIELDERS										
Jay	Dowie				28/12/91	18		Histon		
Antonio	Murray		5'08"	11 00	15/9/84	25	Cambridge	Chelsea (Yth), Ipswich, Hibernian 1/05, Wycombe (Trial) c/s 06, Histon 8/06 Rel 5/09, Chelmsford 8/09 Rel 1/10, Cambridge U 2/10 Rel 4/10, Histon 6/10		
Lee	Smith				6/10/87	23		Bury T, Histon 8/09	24	4
James	Stevenson				17/5/92	18		Histon	0	0
Callum	Stewart		5'09"	12 06	1/10/90	19	Cambridge	Ipswich (Yth), Histon, Fulham (Trial) 4/10	10	0
FORWARDS										
Tyler	Campbell		6'00"	12 12	17/5/91	19	London	Histon, Harlow (SL) 6/09		
Sam	Mason-Smith				25/10/91	18		Histon	0	0
Daniel	Sparkes		6'04"	14 09	20/7/91	19	Peterborough	Histon	14	0
Lewis	Taffe				18/10/91	18		Histon	2	0
Andrew	Tidswell				1/2/90	20		Histon, Bury T (L) 8/09	17	1

Loanees		SN	HT	WT	DOB	AGE	POB	From - To	APPS	GOA
(M)Ben	Farrell		6'00"	11 11	20/7/86	24	Cambridge	Cambridge U 8/09 - Weymouth (SL) 1/10, Rel 4/10	5	0
(M)Billy	Crook		5'10"	11 00	23/8/90	20		Peterborough (2ML) 9/09 -	6	0
(D)Sam	Long		6'00"	11 02	4/9/90	19	Bexley	Grays (3ML) 9/09 - Rel 1/10, Tonbridge 2/10	5	0
(M)Sam	Cox		5'04"	10 03	10/10/90	19	Edgware	Tottenham 11/09 - Torquay (SL) 1/10, Barnet c/s 10	2	0
(F)Jack	Werndly				25/2/93	17		West Ham 12/09 -	1	0
(F)Charlie	Sheringham		6'01"	11 06	17/4/88	22	Chingford	Bishops Stortford 2/10 - Dartford 6/10	15	0
(F)Andy	Pugh		5'09"	12 02	28/1/89	21	Gravesend	Gillingham 3/10 - Rel c/s 10, Welling 6/10	6	1
(M)Aman	Verma				3/1/87	23	Birmingham	Leicester 3/10 -	8	0

Departures		SN	HT	WT	DOB	AGE	POB	From - To	APPS	GOA
(D)Nathan	Bowden-Haase				26/4/84	26		Hemel Hempstead 6/09 - Rel 8/09, Slough 8/09		
(F)Lee	Roache		5'09"	11 00	30/4/84	26	Leytonstone	Cambridge C Undisc 1/09 - Braintree 9/09, Eastleigh 2/10		
(F)Pierre	Joseph-Dubois				12/2/88	22	Paris, Fra	Weymouth 9/09 - Rel 10/09, Weymouth 12/09	1	0
(M)Neil	Andrews		5'11"	11 11	20/4/79	31	Cambridge	Cambridge C 7/97 - Rel 12/09, Bury T 12/09	14	0
(M)Jamie	Barker		6'01"	12 01	26/10/79	30	Cambridge	Yth - Rel 12/09, Cambridge C 12/09 Retired 6/10	22	2
(M)John	Kennedy		5'08"	10 07	19/8/78	32	Cambridge	Canvey Island 5/06 - Rel 12/09, Cambridge C 12/09	18	0
(D)Craig	Pope		5'10"	11 07	17/9/82	27	Islington	Cambridge C 5/07 - Rel 12/09, Thurrock 12/09	13	0
(M)Lee	Brennan		5'10"	12 02	11/11/91	18	Peterborough	Cambridge U (Yth) - Broxbourne, Cambridge C 12/09, Broxbourne 3/10		
(M)Josh	Simpson		5'10"	12 02	6/3/87	23	Cambridge	Cambridge C Undisc 9/08 - Peterborough (2ML) 11/09 Undisc 1/10	17	7
(F)Kieran	Leabon		5'11"	12 01	24/9/88	21	Chelmsford	Boston U 7/09 - Rel 2/10, Bury T (L) 9/09, Harrogate T (L) 11/09, Bury T 2/10	4	0
(F)Craig	Hammond				18/3/87	23		Royston 8/09 - AFC Sudbury (2ML) 1/10 Rel 4/10	5	1
(M)Nathaniel	Knight-Percival		6'00"	11 07	31/3/87	23	Cambridge	Yth - Wrexham 6/10	43	7
(M)Glen	Southam		5'07"	11 10	27/8/80	30	Enfield	Bishops Stortford 2/10 - Rel 4/10, Barnet 6/10	19	2
(F)Danny	Wright		6'02"	13 08	10/9/84	25	Southampton	Dereham 3/07 - Rel 4/10, Peterborough (Trial) 11/09, Cambridge U 5/10	26	8
(G)Danny	Naisbitt		6'01"	11 12	25/11/78	31	Bishop Auckland	Cambridge C 5/07 - Brighton (L) 3/10, Cambridge U 5/10	27	0
(D)Gareth	Gwillim		6'00"	12 06	9/2/83	27	Farnborough	Bishops Stortford 6/07 - Dag & Red 6/10	35	0
(D)Matt	Langston		6'02"	12 04	2/4/81	29	Brighton	Cambridge C 6/06 - Crawley (6WL) 3/10, Eastbourne B 6/10	31	3
(F)Michael	Frew				8/8/84	26	Peterborough	Cambridge C 5/09 - Brackley T (SL) 3/10, Corby T 6/10	22	1
(G)Lance	Key		6'04"	14 11	13/5/68	42	Kettering	Wivenhoe - Rel c/s 10, Rushden & D (Gk Coach) 7/10	0	0
(M)Max	York				25/11/91	18		Cambridge U (Yth) - Rushden & D 7/10	5	0
(D)Adam	Tann		6'00"	12 08	12/5/82	28	Fakenham	Notts County 7/09 - Chelmsford 7/10	41	1
(F)Bradley	Hudson-Odoi		5'08"		29/11/88	21	Ghana	Hereford 8/09 - Grays (L) 11/09	19	3

Do you remember when...

Histon

The 'Naughties' provided a vintage spell in the development of Histon Football Club. The Jewson Premier League (Eastern Counties) was won in 1999-2000 and the club from a village on the outskirts of Cambridge was on its way to eventually challenge for a Football League place in the Conference play offs in 2009.

The 1999-2000 squad: Back Row: Alan Dockerill (Jewson League), Steve Fallon (Manager, partly hidden), Andrew Jeffrey, Laurence Cullum, Dave Toombs, Paul Baker, Wayne Goddard, Shaun Harrington, Jamie Barker, Danny Potter and Lee Petrucciu (Physio). Front row, left to right: Neil Kennedy, Neil Andrews, Adrian Cambridge, Neil O'Donohue, Richard Chattoe and Zachery Nedimovic.

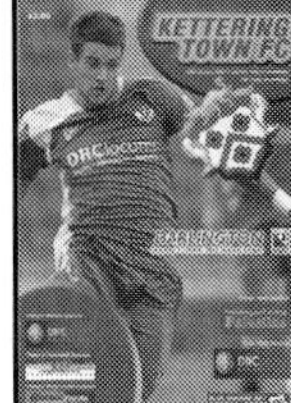

KETTERING TOWN

Chairman: Imraan Ladak

Secretary: Justin Boyd-Navazo **(T)** 07506 464 222 **(E)** info@ketteringtownfc.co.uk

Additional Committee Members:
Amanda deChoisy, Ken Samuel, Tony Reeves, Lee Thorn, Daniel Lee

Manager: Lee Harper

Programme Editor: Paul Cooke **(E)** companioncooke@btinternet.com

KETTERING TOWN FOOTBALL CLUB 2010-2011

Back Row:Patrick Noubissie,Luke Graham,Ian Roper,Nathan Abbey,Niall Cooper,John Dempster,Greg Taylor,Andre Boucaud
Middle Row:James Davidson(Physio),Marcus Kelly,Darren Wrack,SergeMakofo,Enzo Carrillo,Iyseden Christie,Mark Pryor,Brett Solkhon,James Dance,Sol Davis,Martin Harris,
Front Row:Jean Paul Marna,Ashley Westwood,Tommy Jaszczun(Coach),Lee Harper(Manager),Paul Furlong,Moses Ashikodi

Club Factfile

Founded: 1872 **Nickname:** The Poppies

Previous Names: Kettering > 1924

Previous Leagues: Midland 1892-1900, also had a team in United Counties 1896-99, Southern 1900-30, 1950-79, 2001-02, Birmingham 1930-50, Alliance/Conference 1979-2001, 02-03, Isthmian 2003-04

Club Colours (change): Red/black/black (White/white/green)

Ground: Rockingham Road, Kettering NN16 9AW **(T)** 01536 483 028

Capacity: 6,170 **Seats:** 1,800 **Covered:** 4,000 **Clubhouse:** Yes **Shop:** Yes

Previous Grounds: North Park and Green Lane

Simple Directions
Follow the A14 to junction 7. Take the A43 for one mile. At the first roundabout turn right onto the A6003 (Rockingham Road). The ground is 800 yards on the left.

Record Attendance: 11,536 v Peterborough - FA Cup 1st Round replay 1958-59

Record Victory: 16-0 v Higham YMCI - FA Cup 1909

Record Defeat: 0-13 v Mardy - Southern League Division Two 1911-12

Record Goalscorer: Roy Clayton - 171 (1972-81)

Record Appearances: Roger Ashby

Additional Records: Paid £25,000 to Macclesfield for Carl Alford 1994. Recieved £150,000 from Newcastle United for Andy Hunt.

Senior Honours: Southern League 1927-28, 56-57, 72-73, 2001-02. Conference North 2007-08.

10 YEAR RECORD

00-01	01-02	02-03	03-04	04-05	05-06	06-07	07-08	08-09	09-10
Conf 20	SthP 1	Conf 22	Isth P 9	Conf N 4	Conf N 6	Conf N 2	Conf N 1	Conf 8	Conf 6

KETTERING TOWN

No.	Date	Comp	H/A	Opponents	Att:	Result	Goalscorers	Pos
1	8/8/09	BSP	A	Forest Green Rovers	1074	W 2-1	Marna 2 (71, 81)	6
2	11/8/09	BSP	H	Oxford United	2240	D 1-1	Marna pen 11	5
3	15/8/09	BSP	H	AFC Wimbledon	1746	L 1-2	Thomas 74	11
4	18/8/09	BSP	A	Kidderminster Harriers	1368	W 1-0	Marna pen 85	7
5	22/8/09	BSP	A	Wrexham	3473	W 2-1	Spencer 25, Noubissie 48	6
6	29/8/09	BSP	H	Luton Town	3266	D 0-0		5
7	31/8/09	BSP	A	Mansfield Town	4034	D 0-0		7
8	5/9/09	BSP	H	Altrincham	1269	W 2-0	Ashikodi 84, Green 86	4
9	8/9/09	BSP	H	Gateshead	1230	W 4-0	Thomas 10, Ashikodi 32, Green 73, Spencer 82	2
10	12/9/09	BSP	A	York City	2275	L 0-2		5
11	19/9/09	BSP	A	Crawley Town	901	L 1-2	Marna pen 85	8
12	22/9/09	BSP	H	Barrow	1150	W 2-1	Ashikodi pen 28, Dempster 41	3
13	26/9/09	BSP	H	Ebbsfleet United	1345	W 3-0	Ashikodi 34, Green 77, Og (Crooks) 87	2
14	29/9/09	BSP	A	Hayes & Yeading United	307	W 2-1	Fowler 86, Green 90	2
15	3/10/09	BSP	A	Eastbourne Borough	884	W 1-0	Ashikodi 45	2
16	17/10/09	BSP	A	AFC Wimbledon	3745	W 2-1	Taylor 18, Thomas 20	3
17	31/10/09	BSP	H	Stevenage Borough	1844	D 1-1	Ashikodi 29	3
18	3/11/09	BSP	H	Wrexham	1186	D 2-2	Elding 5, Marna pen 90	3
19	14/11/09	BSP	A	Cambridge United	3088	W 2-0	Og (Hatswell) 3, Elding 90	3
20	21/11/09	BSP	H	Kidderminster Harriers	1348	L 0-2		3
21	24/11/09	BSP	H	Hayes & Yeading United	997	L 0-1		4
22	2/12/09	BSP	A	Luton Town	6608	W 1-0	Partridge 64	4
23	5/12/09	BSP	H	Salisbury City	1098	L 1-2	Elding pen 19	5
24	26/12/09	BSP	H	Tamworth	1250	D 0-0		5
25	28/12/09	BSP	A	Histon	716	L 0-1		6
26	19/1/10	BSP	A	Ebbsfleet United	587	W 2-1	Dance 30, Marna 63	5
27	23/1/10	BSP	A	Stevenage Borough	2136	L 0-2		6
28	26/1/10	BSP	A	Gateshead	401	W 2-0	Appiah 15, Wrack 40	4
29	6/2/10	BSP	H	York City	1375	L 0-1		8
30	13/2/10	BSP	A	Barrow	1160	W 2-0	Kelly 53, Marna 77	7
31	23/2/10	BSP	A	Tamworth	489	W 3-1	Appiah 16, Og (J Smith) 20, Dance 50	6
32	27/2/10	BSP	A	Rushden & Diamonds	2998	D 0-0		6
33	6/3/10	BSP	H	Grays Athletic	1131	W 2-0	Roper 10, Jennings 41	6
34	9/3/10	BSP	H	Cambridge United	1248	L 0-1		5
35	13/3/10	BSP	A	Oxford United	5836	D 1-1	Dance 42	5
36	16/3/10	BSP	A	Altrincham	690	L 0-2		6
37	20/3/10	BSP	H	Forest Green Rovers	1032	L 0-2		6
38	27/3/10	BSP	H	Mansfield Town	1188	D 2-2	Marna 4, Ebigbo 87	6
39	30/3/10	BSP	H	Rushden & Diamonds	2031	L 0-3		6
40	3/4/10	BSP	A	Grays Athletic	287	D 0-0		7
41	5/4/10	BSP	H	Histon	800	D 1-1	Jennings 37	6
42	17/4/10	BSP	H	Eastbourne Borough	932	W 4-0	Marna 2 (pen 43, pen 45), Kelly 59, Jennimgs 74	6
43	20/4/10	BSP	H	Crawley Town	800	D 1-1	Dempster 51	6
44	24/4/10	BSP	A	Salisbury City	1123	L 0-2		6
	Chester	**record.........................**		**... expunged 08/03**				
	Cups							
1	24/10/09	FAC 4Q	H	Redditch United	1403	D 1-1	Ashikodi 90	
2	27/10/09	FAC 4QR	A	Redditch United	1101	W 1-0 aet	Marna 120	
3	7/11/09	FAC 1	A	Hartlepool United	3428	W 1-0	Ashikodi 15	
4	29/11/09	FAC 2	H	Leeds United	4837	D 1-1	Roper 63	
5	8/12/09	FAC 2R	A	Leeds United	10670	L 1-5 aet	Elding 62	
6	12/12/09	FAT 1	H	Barrow	763	L 0-1		

Home Attendances:	
Highest:	3266 v Luton Town
Lowest:	800 v Histon
Average (08-09):	1239 (1615)
Top Goalscorer:	Marna - 12 (11 League, 1 Cup) in 40 appearances - 28% strike rate
Most Appearances:	Dempster - 47 (39+3 League, 4+1 Cup)

HARPER 1	JENNINGS 3	EADEN 2	GEOHAGHAN 23	DEMPSTER 6	ROPER 5	FOWLER 8	GREEN 7	SPENCER 9	SEDDON 19	BOUCAUD 17	MARNA 10	WRACK 4	TAYLOR 12	THOMAS 20	MCPIKE 18	NOUBISSIE 15	ASHIKODI 28	BUSSEY 19	CARAYOL 11	COOPER 13	HESLOP 16	ELDING 19	DANCE 14	DAVIS 23	PARTRIDGE 21	BAIN 7	KELLY 22	THELWELL 2	DOBSON 18	CHERRY 24	ABBEY 31	HADFIELD 8	CARILLO 27	APPIAH 11	ROBINSON 7	CHARLES 16	EBIGBO 25	PRYOR 26	
X	X	X	X	X	X	X	X	X	X	X	S	S	U	U	U																								1
X	X	X	X	S	X	X	X	X	S	X	X	U		S	U	X																							2
X	X	X	X	S	X	X	X		X	X	X	U	U	S	S	X																							3
X	X	X	X	X		X	X	X	X	X	S	S	U	S	U	X																							4
X	X	X	X	S	X	X	X	X	U	X	S	S		X	U	X																							5
X	X		X	X	X	X	X	X	S	X	S	U	U	X	U	X																							6
X	X		X	X	X	X	S	S	X	X		S	U	X	X	X																							7
X	X		X	X	X	X	X	X	S	X	X	U	U	S		X	S																						8
X	X		X	X	X	X	X	X		X	S	S	U	X		S	X																						9
X	X	U	X	X	X	X	X	X			S	X	S	S		X	X	U																					10
X	X	U	X	X	X		X	X		X	S	U	U	S		X	X		X																				11
X	U	X	U	X	X	X	X	S		X	S		X	X		S	X		X																				12
X	S	X	S	X	X	X	X	U		U	S		X	X		X	X		X																				13
X	S	X	S	X	X	X	X	S			U	U	X	X		X	X		X																				14
X	X	U	X	X	X	X	X	S			U	S	X	X		X	X			U																			15
X	X	U	X	X	X	X	X	S		S	S	U	X	X		X	X																						16
X	X		X	X	X		X	X		S	U	U	X	U		X	X		U		X																		17
X	X	U	X	X			X	U			S	X	X	S		X	X		S		X	X																	18
X			X	X	X	U	X	S		U		U	X	S		X	X				X	X	X																19
X			X	X	X	S	X	S		U	S		X	X		X	X			U	X	X																	20
X				X	X	X		S		X	X	U	X	X		X	S	U				X	X																21
X				X	X					X	X	S	X	U						U	X	X	S	X	X		X	U											22
					X					S	X	X	X	S		X		X		U	X	S	U			X	X	X	X										23
X	U			X						X		U	X	X		X				U	X	X	X	X	X		S			U									24
X										X		S	X	X		X		U		U	X	X	X	X		X	S	X		U									25
	X			X	X					X	X	X		S		X				U			X				X	X			X	S	U						26
	X			X	X					X	X	X	S	U		X				U			X				X	X			X	S		S					27
	X			X	X						X	X	S	S		X				U			X				X	X			X	U		X	S				28
	X			X	X					S		X	S	U		X				U			X				X	X			X	X		X	S				29
	X			X	X					S	S	X	X	U		X				U			X				X				X	X		X	S				30
	X			X	X					S	S	X	X	U		X							X				X	U			X	X		X	S				31
	X			X	X					S	S	X	X	S		X				U			X				X	U			X	X		X					32
	X			X	X					X	S	X	X	S									X				X	U			X	X		X		S	U		33
	X			X	X					X	S	S	X	U									X				X	U			X	X		X		X	S		34
	X			X	X					X	S	X	X	U		U							X				X	S			X	X		X		S			35
	X			X						X	S	X	X	S		U							X				X	X			X	X		X		U	S		36
	X			X	X					X	X		X	X		S				U			X					S			X	X		S		X	U		37
	X			X	X					X	X	S	X	X		X							X					U			X	X		S		U	S		38
	X			X	X					X	S	X	U	X		X							X					U			X	X		S		S	X		39
X	X			X	X					X	X		X	X		X				U			X									S		S		S	X	U	40
X	X			X	X					X	S	X	X	U		X				U			X									X		S		U	X		41
	X			X	X					X	X	X	X	S		X				U			X				X				X		S			U	S		42
	X			X	X					X	X	X	X	S		X				U			X				X				X		U			S	S		43
	X			X						X	X		X	X		X				U			X								X		S				X	X	44
X	X	U	X	S	X	X	X	X		S	X	U	X	X		X	S			U																			
X	X	U	X	X	X		X	S		X	S	S	X	X		X	X			U																			
X		X	X	X	X		X	S		U	S	U	X	S		X	X			U	X	X																	
X				X	X	U				X	S	U	X	S		X	X	U			X	X		X	X	U													
X				X	X	S				X		S	X	S		X		U		U	X	X		X	X	X				U									
X					X					X		S	X	S		X		U			X	X	X	X	X				X	U									
Total League Appearances										29	15	17	28	18	1	35	12	1	4	0	8	7	23	3	2	2	15	7	1	0	17	12	0	9	0	2	4	1	**X**
0	2	0	2	3	0	1	1	8	3	7	21	10	4	16	1	3	2	0	1	0	0	1	1	0	0	0	2	2	0	0	0	3	2	6	4	5	5	0	**S**
0	2	5	1	0	0	1	0	2	1	3	3	11	9	10	5	2	0	3	1	18	0	0	1	0	0	0	0	7	0	2	0	1	2	0	0	4	2	1	**U**
Total Cup Appearances										4	1	0	6	2	0	6	3	0	0	0	4	4	1	3	3	1	0	0	1	0	0	0	0	0	0	0	0	0	**X**
0	0	0	0	1	0	1	0	2	0	1	3	3	0	4	0	0	1	0	0	0	0	0	0	0	0	0	0	0	0	0	0	0	0	0	0	0	0	0	**S**
0	0	2	0	0	0	1	0	0	0	1	0	3	0	0	0	0	0	3	0	4	0	0	0	0	0	1	0	0	0	2	0	0	0	0	0	0	0	0	**U**
Total Goals										0	11	1	1	3	0	1	6	0	0	0	0	3	3	0	1	0	2	0	0	0	0	0	0	2	0	0	1	0	**Lge**
0	0	0	0	0	1	0	0	0	0	0	1	0	0	0	0	0	2	0	0	0	0	1	0	0	0	0	0	0	0	0	0	0	0	0	0	0	0	0	**Cup**

KETTERING TOWN

CURRENT SQUAD AS OF BEGINING OF 2010-11 SEASON

GOALKEEPERS		SQ NO.	HT	WT	D.O.B	AGE	P.O.B	CAREER	APPS	GOA
Nathan	Abbey		6'01"	11 13	11/7/78	32	Islington	Luton Rel c/s 01, Woking (L) 2/98 (97/98 4,0), Chesterfield 6/01 Rel c/s 02, Northampton 8/02 Rel c/s 03, Stevenage 8/03, Luton 10/03 Rel 10/03, St Albans 11/03, Macclesfield NC 11/03 Rel 11/03, Hayes 12/03, Ipswich Mon 12/03 Rel 1/04, Burnley 1/04 Rel 2/04, Burnley 3/04 Rel c/s 04, Boston U 7/04 Rel 1/06, L.Orient (6WL) 11/05, Bristol C 2/06 Rel 5/06, Torquay 7/06 Rel 12/06, Brentford (L) 12/06 Perm 1/07 Rel c/s 07, MK Dons 8/07 Rel c/s 09, Rushden & D 9/09 Rel 12/09, Kettering 1/10	17	0
Niall	Cooper				22/5/91	19		Sileby R, Kettering 7/09	0	0
Lee	Harper	1	6'01"	14 06	30/9/71	38	Chelsea	Sittingbourne, Arsenal £150,000 6/94, QPR £125,000 7/97 Rel c/s 01, Walsall 7/01, Northampton 7/02, MK Dons (3ML) 10/06 Perm 1/07 Rel c/s 07, Kettering 8/07 (Pl/Man) 11/09	26	0
DEFENDERS										
Sol	Davis		5'07"	12 04	4/9/79	30	Cheltenham	Swindon, Luton £600,000 8/02 Rel c/s 09, Peterborough (2ML) 9/07, Grimsby (Trial) 7/09, MK Dons 8/09 Rel c/s 10, Kettering (5WL) 11/09, Kettering 5/10	3	0
John	Dempster	6	6'00"	11 07	1/4/83	27	Kettering	Rushden & D, Oxford U 1/06 Rel 2/07, Kettering (L) 1/07 Kettering 3/07	42	2
Luke	Graham	2	6'03"	12 07	27/4/86	24	Kettering	Northampton, Aylesbury (L) 12/04, Kettering (2ML) 2/05, Forest Green (SL) 8/05, Kettering 5/06, Kings Lynn (SL) 10/08, Mansfield 5/09, York C (2ML) 11/09 Perm 1/10, Kettering 6/10		
Tommy	Jaszczun	15	5'11"	11 02	16/9/77	32	Kettering	Aston Villa, Blackpool £30,000 1/00 Rel c/s 04, Northampton 7/04, Rochdale 7/05, Cambridge U (SL) 1/06, Cambridge U 7/06 Ret 3/07, Kettering 5/07 Rel 3/09, Corby T 3/09 Rel 5/10, Kettering (Pl/Ass Man) 5/10		
Ian	Roper	5	6'03"	13 04	20/6/77	33	Nuneaton	Walsall Rel c/s 08, Luton 8/08, Kettering 7/09	38	1
Greg	Taylor	12	6'01"	12 01	15/1/90	20	Bedford	Rushden & D (Yth), Northampton Rel c/s 09, Kettering 6/09	32	1
Ashley	Westwood		5'11"	11 02	31/8/76	34	Bridgnorth	Man Utd, Crewe £40,000 7/95, Bradford C £150,000 7/98, Sheff Wed (L) 8/00 £150,000 9/00 Rel c/s 03, Northampton 7/03 Rel c/s 06, Chester 8/06 Rel 12/07, Swindon (SL) 3/07, Port Vale (4ML) 8/07, Stevenage 1/08 Rel 7/08, Lincoln C (Trial) 10/08, Wrexham 10/08, Kettering 7/10		
MIDFIELDERS										
Andre	Boucaud	8	5'10"	10 02	9/10/84	25	Enfield	Reading Rel c/s 04, Peterborough (SL) 3/03, Peterborough (2ML) 8/03, Walsall (Trial) 2/04, Peterborough 7/04, Aldershot (3ML) 9/05, Kettering 5/06, Wycombe 8/07 Rel c/s 08, Kettering 8/08	36	0
Ryan	Cherry				15/1/92	18		Kettering	0	0
James	Dance				15/3/87	23		Birmingham (Yth), Cheltenham (Scholar), Coleshill, Rushall O 6/09, Redditch 8/09, Kettering 11/09	24	3
Marcus	Kelly		5'07"	10 00	16/3/86	24	Kettering	Rushden & D, Oxford U 5/09, Kettering (6WL) 11/09, Perm 1/10	17	2
Patrick	Noubissie	23	5'10"	11 04	25/6/83	27	Bois-Colombes (Fra)	CS Brétigny-sur-Orge (Fra), Le Mée-sur-Seine SF (Fra), CS Sedan Ardennes (Fra), US Roye Foot Picardie 80 (Fra), Sporting Toulon (Fra) 7/05, Crewe 11/06 Rel 1/07, Swindon 1/07 Rel c/s 07, Hibernian 8/07 Rel c/s 08, Livingston (3ML) 8/07, Dundee (L) 3/08, Ayia Napa (Cyp) 7/08, Kettering 8/09	38	1
Mark	Pryor				21/8/92	18		Kettering	1	0
Brett	Solkhon		5'11"	12 06	12/9/82	27	Canvey Island	Ipswich (Yth), Arsenal (Yth), Rushden & D 7/00 Rel 1/03, Kettering 2/03 Rel 4/09, Corby 5/09, Brackley 3/10, Kettering 7/10		
Darren	Wrack	16	5'09"	12 10	5/5/76	34	Cleethorpes	Derby, Grimsby £100,000 7/96 Rel c/s 98, Shrewsbury (L) 2/97, Walsall 8/98 Rel c/s 08, Kettering 7/08	27	1

FORWARDS

		SN	HT	WT	DOB	AGE	POB	Career	APPS	GOA
Moses	Ashikodi	7	6'00"	11 09	27/6/87	23	Lagos, Nigeria	Millwall Rel 5/04, West Ham 8/04 Rel 1/06, Rushden & D (Trial) 7/05, Gillingham (3ML) 8/05, Rangers 1/06, Watford Undisc 1/07 Rel 2/09, Bradford C (SL) 3/07, Swindon (SL) 1/08, Hereford (5ML) 5/08, Luton (Trial) 2/09, Shrewsbury 2/09 Rel c/s 09, Kettering 9/09 Rel 12/09, Ebbsfleet 1/10, Kettering 6/10	14	6
Iyseden	Christie	9	5'10"	12 02	14/11/76	33	Coventry	Coventry Rel c/s 97, Bournemouth (L) 11/96, Mansfield (2ML) 2/97, Mansfield 6/97, L.Orient £40,000 7/99 Rel c/s 02, Rushden & D (Trial) 7/02, Mansfield 8/02 Rel c/s 04, Kidderminster 8/04, Rochdale £17,500 1/06, Kidderminster (4ML) 8/06 Perm 1/07, Stevenage 7/08 Rel 1/09, Kettering (4ML) 9/08, Torquay 2/09 Rel 5/09, Hibernians (Mal) (Trial) c/s 09, Kings Lynn 8/09, AFC Telford 9/09 Rel 10/09, Farnborough 10/09, Tamworth 11/09, Kettering 5/10		
Paul	Furlong		6'00"	13 08	1/10/68	41	Wood Green	Enfield, Coventry £130,000 7/91, Watford £250,000 7/92, Chelsea £2.3 mill 5/94, Birmingham C £1.5 mill 7/96, QPR (2ML) 8/00, Sheff Utd (L) 2/02, QPR (L) 8/02, QPR 9/02 Rel c/s 07, Luton 7/07 Rel c/s 08, Southend 7/08 Rel c/s 09, Barnet (SL) 1/09, Barnet 8/09 Rel c/s 10, Kettering (Pl/Coach) 7/10		
Jean-Paul	Marna	10			21/2/81	28		Paris St Germain (Fra), Berkhamsted, Kettering 7/06	36	11

Loanees		SN	HT	WT	DOB	AGE	POB	From - To	APPS	GOA
(M)Mustapha	Carayol		5'10"	11 11	10/6/89	20	Gambia	Torquay (3ML) 9/09 - Lincoln C c/s 10	5	0
(G)Nick	Bussey				21/9/84	25		Halesowen T (Dual) 9/09 - Rel 5/10	1	0
(M)Simon	Heslop		5'11"	11 00	1/5/87	23	York	Barnsley (2ML) 10/09 - Luton (SL) 3/10, Oxford U 6/10	8	0
(F)Anthony	Elding		6'01"	12 02	16/4/82	28	Boston	Crewe (2ML) 11/09 - Rel 1/10, Ferncvaros (Hun) 1/10	8	3
(M)Craig	Dobson		5'07"	10 06	23/1/84	26	Chingford	Mansfield (5WL) 11/09 - Rel 1/10, Farnborough 1/10 Rel 3/10, Sutton U 3/10	1	0
(M)Richie	Partridge		5'08"	11 00	12/9/80	29	Dublin	MK Dons (5WL) 11/09 - Stockport (L) 1/10	2	1
(F)Kitson	Bain		5'10"	12 08	26/5/82	28		Tranmere (5WL) 11/09 - Rel 5/10	2	0
(F)Kwesi	Appiah		5'11"	12 08	12/8/90	20	London	Peterborough (3ML) 1/10 -	15	2

Departures		SN	HT	WT	DOB	AGE	POB	From - To	APPS	GOA
(F)Jamie	Yates		5'07"	10 11	24/12/88	21	Sheffield	Rotherham 7/09 - Rel 8/09, Alfreton 9/09, Boston U (2ML) 9/09 Perm 11/09		
(F)James	McPike		5'10"	11 02	4/10/88	21	Birmingham	Birmingham 5/09 - Solihull Moors 9/09	2	0
(F)Gareth	Seddon		5'11"	12 00	23/5/80	30	Burnley	Hyde Undisc 7/08 - Fleetwood Undisc 9/09	7	0
(M)Ryan	Beswick				12/1/88	22	Walton-on-Thames	Leicester 5/09- Kings Lynn (2ML) 8/09, Solihull Moors 10/09		
(M)Mark	Cooper		5'08"	11 04	18/12/68	41	Wakefield	Hinckley U (Man) 5/07 - Peterborough (Man) 11/09 Rel 1/10, Darlington (Man) 6/10		
(D)Nicky	Eaden		5'10"	12 08	12/12/72	27	Sheffield	Solihull Moors 10/07, Peterborough (Ass Man) 11/09	8	0
(M)Lee	Fowler		5'07"	10 00	10/6/83	27	Cardiff	Forest Green 6/09 - Rel 12/09, Oxford U 12/09 Rel 3/10, Cirencester 3/10, Halesowen T 3/10 Rel 5/10, Forest Green 6/10	17	1
(F)Francis	Green		5'09"	11 04	25/4/80	30	Derby	Macclesfield 7/09 - Oxford U (5WL) 11/09 Perm 1/10 Rel 6/10, Brackley 6/10	20	4
(D)Exodus	Geohaghan		6'07"	11 11	27/2/85	25	London	Redditch U (L) 7/08 Undisc 8/08 - Peterborough (5WL) 11/09 Perm 1/10	19	0
(F)Anthony	Robinson				31/12/79	30	Birmingham	Rushall O NC 1/10 - Brackley 3/10	4	0
(D)James	Jennings		5'10"	11 02	2/9/87	22	Manchester	Macclesfield 7/09 - Cambridge U 5/10	36	2
(M)Danny	Thomas		5'07"	11 05	1/5/81	29	Leamington Spa	Macclesfield 8/09 - Tamworth 6/10	34	3
(F)Damian	Spencer		6'01"	14 05	19/9/81	28	Ascot	Cheltenham 7/09 - Kidderminster (3ML) 11/09, Aldershot (SL) 2/10, Aldershot 7/10	18	2
(M)Jordan	Hadfield		5'10"	11 04	12/8/87	23	Swinton	Ashton U NC 1/10 -	15	0
(F)Elliott	Charles		6'02"	13 00	23/12/90	19	Enfield	Barnet 3/10 -	7	0
(F)Pascal	Ebigbo		5'06"	10 10	22/6/87	23		Peckham 3/10 -	9	1
(D)Alton	Thelwell		6'00"	12 05	5/9/80	29	Islington	Newport C 12/09 -	9	0
(M)Enzo	Carillo				27/12/90	20		Buckingham T 1/10 -	2	0

Do you remember when...

Kettering Town

Kettering Town have been Runners-Up in the top competition four times. The first was in season 1980-1981 and this photo was taken in the following pre-season after achieving second place three points behind Altrincham in the second season of The Alliance Premier League.

Back row, left to right: Jim Conde (Assistant Manager), Rodney Marshall (Physio), Paul Haverson, Denis Martin, Peter Walters, Nicky Evans (top scorer with 29 goals), Peter Phipps, Steve McIlroy, and Malcolm Watts (Assistant Physio).
Front Row: John Flannagan, Derek Duggan, Sean Suddards (Captain), Colin Clarke (Manager), Fred Easthall and David Hofbauer.

KIDDERMINSTER HARRIERS

Chairman: Barry Norgrove
Secretary: David Colwell **(T)** 07713 149 644
(E) info@harriers.com
Additional Committee Members: Neil Savery, Oliver Hunt, Wayne Allen, John Baldwin, Robert Dignam, Gordon Howard, Keith Chandler, Helen MacDonald, Mat Wall
Manager: Steve Burr
Programme Editor: Matt Wall **(E)** matt.wall@harriers.co.uk

Back row (L-R): Matty Blair, Callum Gittings, Nick Wright, Dave Hankin, Tom Shaw, Mark Albrighton, Mike Willams
Middle row: Graham Devenport (Kit Manager), Gavin Crowe (Physio), Michael Briscoe, Andrew Stevens, Chris McPhee, Daniel Lewis, Tom Sharpe, Ade Ganderton (Backroom staff), Scott Mason (Backroom staff).
Front row: Lee Vaughan, Jack Byrne, Aaron Griffiths, Steve Burr (Manager), Keith Briggs (Captain), Gary Whild (Assistant Manager), John Finnigan (Player/coach), Kyle Hadley, Lee Morris.

Club Factfile

Founded: 1886 **Nickname:** Harriers
Previous Names: Kidderminster > 1891
Previous Leagues: Birmingham 1889-90, 91-1939, 47-48, 60-62. Midland 1890-91. Southern 1939-45, 48-60, 72-83. Birmingham Comb. 1945-47. West Midlands 1962-72. Conference 1983-2000. Football League 2000-05.
Club Colours (change): All red (All yellow)

Ground: Aggborough Stadium, Hoo Road, Kidderminster DY10 1NB **(T)** 01562 823 931
Capacity: 6,419 **Seats:** 3.175 **Covered:** 3,062 **Clubhouse:** Yes **Shop:** Yes
Previous Grounds:
Simple Directions
From North M5 Junc 3 onto A456 to Kidderminster, From South M5 Junc 6 onto A449 to Kidderminster. Alternatively M40/42 Junc 1 onto A38 to Bromsgrove/A448 to Kidderminster. (All routes follow Brown signs to (SVR) Steam Railway then follow signs to Aggborough). Aggborough is signposted at either end of Hoo Road.

Record Attendance: 9,155 v Hereford United - 27/11/48
Record Victory: 25-0 v Hereford (H) - Birmingham Senior Cup 12/10/1889
Record Defeat: 0-13 v Darwen (A) - FA Cup 1st Round 24/01/1891
Record Goalscorer: Peter Wassell - 432 (1963-74)
Record Appearances: Brendan Wassell - 686 (1962-74)
Additional Records: Paid £80,000 to Nuneaton Borough for Andy Ducros July 2000
Recieved £380,000 from W.B.A. for Lee Hughes July 1997
Senior Honours: FA Trophy 1986-87. Conference 1993-94, 1999-2000.

10 YEAR RECORD

00-01	01-02	02-03	03-04	04-05	05-06	06-07	07-08	08-09	09-10
FL 3 16	FL 3 10	FL 3 11	FL 3 16	FL 3 23	Conf 15	Conf 10	Conf 13	Conf 6	Conf 13

KIDDERMINSTER HARRIERS

No.	Date	Comp	H/A	Opponents	Att:	Result	Goalscorers	Pos
1	8/8/09	BSP	H	Hayes & Yeading United	1471	W 1-0	Barnes-Homer 35	8
2	11/8/09	BSP	A	Salisbury City	1034	L 0-1		10
3	15/8/09	BSP	A	Ebbsfleet United	865	D 0-0		13
4	18/8/09	BSP	H	Kettering Town	1368	L 0-1		17
5	22/8/09	BSP	A	Grays Athletic	754	W 3-1	Bennett 12, Smikle 28, McDermott 90	11
6	29/8/09	BSP	H	Altrincham	1415	W 3-0	Smikle 2 (11, 46), Barnes-Homer 23	8
7	31/8/09	BSP	A	Tamworth	1237	L 1-2	McPhee pen 73	11
8	5/9/09	BSP	H	Eastbourne Borough	1307	L 0-2		15
9	8/9/09	BSP	H	Mansfield Town	1378	W 3-1	Barnes-Homer 14, Caines 47, McPhee 69	12
10	12/9/09	BSP	A	Histon	774	D 1-1	McPhee 35	11
11	19/9/09	BSP	H	Gateshead	1286	W 3-2	Og (Swailes) 25, Smikle 40, Barnes-Homer 80	10
12	22/9/09	BSP	A	Forest Green Rovers	707	D 1-1	McPhee 16	10
13	26/9/09	BSP	A	York City	2509	L 2-3	Smikle 2, Barnes-Homer 62	12
14	29/9/09	BSP	H	Wrexham	1585	W 2-0	Smikle 50, Matthews 55	9
15	3/10/09	BSP	A	AFC Wimbledon	3601	W 1-0	Barnes-Homer 47	6
16	10/10/09	BSP	H	Luton Town	2927	L 1-2	Barnes-Homer 13	9
17	17/10/09	BSP	H	Crawley Town	1276	W 1-0	Caines 89	7
18	31/10/09	BSP	A	Cambridge United	3508	L 0-2		8
19	14/11/09	BSP	H	Oxford United	3569	W 3-1	Matthews 2 (2, 52), Barnes-Homer 18	8
20	21/11/09	BSP	A	Kettering Town	1348	W 2-0	Courtney 70, Barnes-Homer 82	8
21	24/11/09	BSP	A	Wrexham	2086	D 2-2	Smikle 33, McPhee 44	8
22	28/11/09	BSP	H	AFC Wimbledon	1788	L 0-1		8
23	1/12/09	BSP	H	Tamworth	1166	D 0-0		9
24	5/12/09	BSP	A	Stevenage Borough	1809	L 0-2		9
25	28/12/09	BSP	A	Rushden & Diamonds	1425	L 1-2	Matthews 68	9
26	23/1/10	BSP	A	Crawley Town	800	D 2-2	Finnigan 49, McPhee 85	9
27	26/1/10	BSP	H	Grays Athletic	1109	W 4-1	Smikle 26, Spencer 30, Finnigan 49, McPhee pen 60	9
28	6/2/10	BSP	A	Oxford United	5802	D 0-0		9
29	13/2/10	BSP	H	Forest Green Rovers	1421	W 2-1	Smikle 12, Spencer 90	9
30	27/2/10	BSP	H	Histon	1293	W 3-0	Smikle 4, Finnigan 56, Knights 59	9
31	2/3/10	BSP	H	Ebbsfleet United	1163	D 2-2	Knights 5, Smikle 77	9
32	6/3/10	BSP	A	Eastbourne Borough	913	D 0-0		9
33	16/3/10	BSP	A	Luton Town	5908	L 1-3	Lawrie 32	11
34	23/3/10	BSP	H	York City	1127	L 0-1		11
35	27/3/10	BSP	H	Salisbury City	1201	L 0-1		12
36	30/3/10	BSP	H	Cambridge United	1141	W 1-0	Smikle 18	10
37	3/4/10	BSP	A	Altrincham	889	L 2-3	Matthews 2 (15, 44)	11
38	5/4/10	BSP	H	Rushden & Diamonds	1463	D 1-1	Knights 54	12
39	8/4/10	BSP	A	Barrow	1253	L 0-1		12
40	10/4/10	BSP	A	Gateshead	602	W 2-0	McPhee 2 (74, 80)	10
41	15/4/10	BSP	A	Hayes & Yeading United	318	D 2-2	McPhee 56, Riley 80	10
42	17/4/10	BSP	H	Stevenage Borough	2564	L 0-2		11
43	20/4/10	BSP	H	Barrow	1036	L 1-2	Og (Edwards) 7	11
44	24/4/10	BSP	A	Mansfield Town	2734	D 3-3	Byrne 51, Knights 54, McPhee 74	13
	Chester	**record**	**.........**	**...expunged 08/03**				
25	26/12/09	BSP	H	Chester City	1755	W 2-0	Caines 16, Courtney 89	7
	Cups							
1	24/10/09	FAC 4Q	H	Fleetwood Town	1257	D 0-0		
2	27/10/09	FAC 4QR	A	Fleetwood Town	1697	L 1-3	Caines 89	
3	12/12/09	FAT 1	A	Matlock Town	460	W 2-0	Matthews 74, McPhee pen 90	
4	19/1/10	FAT 2	H	Lewes	654	W 3-2	Matthews 11, Knights 51, Caines 90	
5	1/2/10	FAT 3	A	Worcester City	1653	W 1-0	McPhee 53	
6	20/2/10	FAT 4	A	Oxford United	3358	W 2-1	Smikle 17, Matthews 84	
7	13/3/10	FAT SF 1	H	Stevenage Borough	2433	L 1-5	Caines 29	
8	20/3/10	FAT SF 2	A	Stevenage Borough	1622	D 0-0	(L 1-5 agg)	

Home Attendances:	
Highest:	3569 v Oxford United
Lowest:	1036 v Barrow
Average (08-09):	1338 (1688)
Top Goalscorer:	McPhee - 13 (11 League, 2 Cup) in 48 appearances - 27% strike rate
	Smikle - 13 (12 League, 1 Cup) in 51 appearances - 25% strike rate
Most Appearances:	Smikle - 51 (42+1 League, 8 Cup)

COLEMAN 1	DOLMAN 15	BAKER 3	RILEY 6	CAINES 5	SMIKLE 14	BENNETT 8	MCPHEE 7	BARNES-HOMER 9	KNIGHTS 20	MCDERMOTT 11	COURTNEY 2	HADLEY 16	FINNIGAN 4	SINGH 12	SHARPE 17	MATTHEWS 21	FARRELL 18	HAYWARD 19	ANDREW 23	SPENCER 24	CHARLES 25	GOODFELLOW 9	ATKINS 30	BIGNOT 22	LAWRIE 25	BOYES 26	BYRNE 27	PROSSER 33	KERRY 31	
X	X	X	X	X	X	X	X	X	X	X	S	S	S	U	U															1
X	U	X	X	X	X	X	X	X	X	X	X	S	S	U	S															2
X	U	X	X	X	X	X	X	X	X	S	X	S	U	U		X														3
X	U	X	X	X	X	X	X	X	X	S	X	U	U	U		X														4
X	S	X	X	X	X	X	X	X	S	S	X	X	X	U	U															5
X	U	X	X	X	X	X	X	X	S	S	X	X	X	U	S															6
X	U	X		X	X	X	X	X	S	X	X	S	X	U	X		S													7
X		X	X	X	X	X	X	X	S	U	X	X	S		U	X	S													8
X	S	X	X	X	X	X	X	X	X	X	X	U			U		U	U												9
X	U	X	X	X	X	X	X	X	X	X	X	U			U		U	U												10
X	U	X	X	X	X	X	X	X	X	X	X	S			U		S	S												11
X	U	X	X	X	X	X	X	X	X	X	X	S				S	U	U												12
X	U	X	X	X	X		X	X	X	X	X	U			U	X	S	S												13
X	S	X	X		X		X	X	X	X	X	S	X		U	X	U	S												14
X	S	X	X	S	X	X	X	X	X		X	U	X	U		X	U													15
X	U	X	X	S	X	X	X	X	X		X	S	X			X	U	S												16
X	U	X	X	X	X	X		X	X	S	X	U	X		S		X	U												17
X	U		X	X	X	X		X	X	S	X		X		U	X	U	U	X											18
X	S		X	X	X	X		X	X	X	X			U	U	X	S	S	X											19
X	U		X	X	X	X	X	X	X	S	X			U		X	S	S	X											20
X		S	X	X	X	X	X	X	S	X	X			U		X	S	U	X											21
X	X	U	X	X	X	X	X		X	S						X	S	U	X	X	S									22
X		U	X	X	X		X		S	X	X		X	U			S	S	X	X	X									23
X		U	X	X	X	X	X		S	X	X					X	S	U	X	X	S									24
X	U	U	X	X	X	X	X		X		X			U		X	X	U	X	S										25
X	U	X	X	X	X		X		X		X	S	X	U	U	X		S		X										26
U		X	X	X	X	S	X		U		X	S	X	X	S		X	X		X										27
X		X	X	X	X	X	X		S		X	U	X	U	U	X				S		X								28
X		X	X	X	X	X	X		S		X	U	X	U	U	X				S		X								29
		X	X	X	X	X	X		X		X		X	U	S	X						U	X	S	S					30
		X	X	X	X	X	X		X		X		X	U	U	X						S	X	U		S				31
		X	X	X	X	X	X		X		X			U	U	S						S	X	X	S	X				32
		X	X		X		X		S		X	S		U	X	X		U				X	X	U	X		X			33
		X	X	U	X	X	X		X		X			U	X	X						S	X		X	S	S			34
			X		X	X	X			S	X			U	X	S						X	X	U	S		X	X	X	35
			X		X	X	X		X	U	X			U	X	X						U	X		U		X	X	S	36
			X		X	X	X		X	U	X			U	X	X						S	X		S		X	X	S	37
		X	X		X	X	X		X	U	X			X	U	X							U		U		X	X	U	38
		X	X			X			X	S	U			X	S	X						X	U	X	S		X	X	X	39
		X	X		S	S	X		S				X	U	X	X						U	X		X		X	X	X	40
		X	X		X	X	X		X		S		X	U	X	S							X		U		S	X	X	41
		X	X		X	U	X		X		X		X	X	U	X							U		S		X	X	S	42
U		X	X		X	X	X		X		X		X	X		S						U			S		X	X	S	43
X		X	S		X	X	X		X		X		X	U	X	X						S			U		X		S	44
X	U	U	X	X	X	X	X		X		X			U		X	X	S	X	S										
X	U	X	X	X	X	U	X	X	X	X	X	S	X	U	U		S	U												
X	S	X	X	X	X	U	X	X	X	X	X	S	X	U	U		U	S												
U	S	U		X	X	X	X		X		X	U		X	U	X	X	X	X											
X	U	X	X	X	X	X	X		X		X		U	U		X	S	S		X										
U		X	X	X	X	X	X		U		X	S	X	X	U		X	U		X										
		X	X	X	X	X	X		X		X	U	X	U	U	S				X			X	S						
		X	X	X	X	X	X		X		X			U	U	S		U					X	X	S	X				
		X	X	U	X	X	X		X		X	U		U	X	X							X	U	X	U				
Total League Appearances																														
29	2	33	42	29	42	36	40	21	31	13	39	3	20	5	9	28	3	1	8	5	1	5	10	2	3	1	10	9	4	X
0	5	1	1	2	1	2	0	0	11	10	2	11	3	0	6	5	10	8	0	3	2	5	0	1	7	2	2	0	5	S
2	15	4	0	1	0	1	0	0	1	4	1	8	2	27	17	0	7	10	0	0	0	4	3	3	4	0	0	0	1	U
Total Cup Appearances																														
3	0	7	7	7	8	6	8	2	7	2	8	0	4	2	1	3	2	1	1	3	0	0	3	1	1	1	0	0	0	X
0	2	0	0	0	0	0	0	0	0	0	0	3	0	0	0	2	2	2	0	0	0	0	0	1	1	0	0	0	0	S
2	2	1	0	1	0	2	0	0	1	0	0	3	1	6	6	0	1	3	0	0	0	0	0	1	0	1	0	0	0	U
Total Goals																														
0	0	0	1	2	12	1	11	9	4	1	1	0	3	0	0	6	0	0	0	2	0	0	0	0	1	0	1	0	0	Lge
0	0	0	0	3	1	0	2	0	1	0	0	0	0	0	0	3	0	0	0	0	0	0	0	0	0	0	0	0	0	Cup

CURRENT SQUAD AS OF BEGINING OF 2010-11 SEASON

GOALKEEPERS		SQ NO.	HT	WT	D.O.B	AGE	P.O.B	CAREER	APPS	GOA
Danny	Lewis		6'01"	14 00	18/6/82	28	Redditch	Alvechurch (Yth), Garringtons, Studley c/s 02, Kidderminster 5/04 Rel 5/06, Moor Green 6/06, Redditch 6/07, Kidderminster 5/10		
Andrew	Stevens				19/4/87	23		Bedford T (Yth), Yeading, Bristol R (Trial) 5/05, Kingsbury T (L), Bedford T 2/07, Rugby T 8/08, Kidderminster 6/10		
DEFENDERS										
Mark	Albrighton		6'01"	12 07	6/3/76	34	Nuneaton	Nuneaton, Atherstone 8/95, Telford £15,000 10/99, Doncaster 5/02, Chester (2ML) 2/06, Boston U 5/06, Darlington (L) 11/06, Rushden & D (L) 1/07, Cambridge U 6/07, Stevenage 5/08 Rel 6/10, Kidderminster 6/10		
Michael	Briscoe		5'11"	12 00	4/7/83	27	Northampton	Harpole, Coventry 4/03 Rel c/s 04, Macclesfield 7/04 Rel 5/06, Burton (SL) 3/05, Kettering (Trial) c/s 06, Hucknall 9/06, Tamworth (L) 2/07, Tamworth 5/07, Halesowen T 8/08, Redditch 2/09, Tamworth 6/09, Kidderminster 7/10		
Gavin	Caines		6'01"	12 00	20/9/83	26	Birmingham	Walsall Rel c/s 04, Stafford R (2ML) 12/03, Cheltenham 7/04 Rel c/s 09, Kidderminster 8/09, Luton (SL) 3/10	31	2
Tom	Sharpe		6'02"	13 04	12/10/88	21	Nottingham	Notts Forest Rel 5/09, Bury (6WL) 11/07, Halifax (L) 1/08, Stalybridge (3ML) 9/08, Kidderminster 7/09	15	0
Lee	Vaughan		5'07"	11 00	15/7/86	24	Birmingham	Birmingham C (Yth), Portsmouth (Yth), Walsall 2/05, Willenhall (2ML) 8/05, AFC Telford 2/06, Kidderminster 5/10		
Mike	Williams		5'11"	12 00	27/10/86	23	Rhos-on-Sea	Wrexham Rel 4/10, Kidderminster 7/10		
Midfielders										
Keith	Briggs		5'10"	11 06	11/12/81	28	Glossop	Stockport, Norwich £65,000 1/03, Crewe (L) 8/04, Stockport 1/05 Rel 1/08, Shrewsbury 1/08 Rel 1/08, Mansfield 2/08 Rel c/s 08, Stalybridge 7/08, Kidderminster 5/10		
Jack	Byrne				20/7/89	21		Moor Green (Yth), Solihull B (Yth), Stratford T, Redditch 1/09, Kidderminster 3/10	12	1
John	Finnigan		5'08"	10 11	29/3/76	34	Wakefield	Notts Forest, Lincoln C (SL) 3/98, Lincoln C £50,000 6/98, Cheltenham 3/02, Kidderminster 7/09 (Temp Pl/Man) 12/09 (Pl/Ass Man) 1/10 12/09	23	3
Dave	Hankin		6'03"		25/3/85	25		Preston (Yth), Bamber Bridge, Squires Gate, Clitheroe 2/08, Stalybridge 6/09 Rel 4/10, Kidderminster 6/10		
Nathan	Hayward		5'08"	12 01	8/11/91	18	Kidderminster	Birmingham (Yth), Kidderminster, Wolves (Trial) 11/08, Redditch (SL) 3/10	9	0
Kevin	Holsgrove				9/1/88	22		Everton (Yth), NEWI Cefn Druids 8/07, Colwyn Bay 8/09, Hyde U 9/09, Kidderminster (Trial) 7/10		
Lee	Morris		5'10"	11 07	30/4/80	30	Blackpool	Sheff Utd, Derby £1.8 mill 10/99, Huddersfield (L) 3/01, Leicester £120,000 2/04 Rel 4/06, Bristol C (Trial) 5/06, Yeovil 8/06 Rel 3/08, Burton 8/08 Rel c/s 09, Hereford 7/09 Rel 4/10, Mansfield (5WL) 11/09, Forest Green (SL) 3/10, Bradford C (Trial) 7/10, Kidderminster 7/10		
Tom	Shaw		6'00"	12 00	1/12/86	23	Nottingham	Notts Forest (Jun), Rushden & D (7/04) Rel 7/08, Mansfield 8/08 Rel 10/08, Tamworth 10/08, Kidderminster 6/10		
FORWARDS										
Kyle	Hadley		5'08"	11 07	27/11/86	23		Old Hill T, Lye T, Stourbridge 6/07, Kidderminster 7/09, Redditch (SL) 3/10	14	0
Chris	McPhee		5'11"	11 09	20/3/83	27	Eastbourne	Brighton Rel 5/06, Aldershot (3ML) 8/05, Swindon (SL) 3/06, Torquay 7/06, Ebbsfleet 8/07 Rel 6/08, Weymouth 7/08 Rel 2/09, Kidderminster 2/09	40	11

Loanees		HT	WT	DOB	AGE	POB	From - To	APPS	GOA
(D)Danny	Andrew			23/12/90	19	Boston	Peterborough (2ML) 10/09 - Cheltenham (L) 1/10	8	0
(F)Damian	Spencer	6'01"	14 05	19/9/81	28	Ascot	Kettering (3ML) 11/09 - Aldershot (SL) 2/10, Aldershot 7/10	8	2
(F)Ryan	Charles	6'00"	11 13	30/9/89	20	Enfield	Luton (5WL) 11/09 - Rel 5/10, Rushden & D 6/10	3	0
(M)Marc	Goodfellow	5'08"	10 00	20/9/81	28	Burton	Burton (SL) 1/10 -	10	0
(F)James	Lawrie	6'00"	12 05	18/12/90	19	Belfast	Port Vale (SL) 2/10 - Rel c/s 10	10	1
(G)Ross	Atkins	6'00"	13 00	3/11/89	20	Derby	Derby (SL) 2/10 -	10	0
(F)Adam	Boyes	6'02"		1/11/90	19	Lingdale	Scunthorpe (SL) 2/10 -	3	0
(M)Luke	Prosser	6'02"	12 04	25/5/88	22	Enfield	Port Vale (SL) 3/10 - Rel c/s 10	9	0
(M)Lloyd	Kerry	6'02"	12 04	22/1/88	22	Chesterfield	Chesterfield 3/10 -	9	0

Departures		HT	WT	DOB	AGE	POB	From - To	APPS	GOA
(F)Matthew	Barnes-Homer	5'11"	12 05	25/1/86	24	Dudley	Wycombe 7/07 - Luton (5WL) 11/09 £75,000 1/10	21	9
(F)Aaron	Farrell	6'00"	12 06	24/4/86	24		Sutton Coldfield 7/09 - Rel 2/10, Worcester 2/10 Rel 2/10, Solihull B 3/10	13	0
(D)Zac	Costello			16/9/90	19		Cambridge U (Yth) 8/09 - Rel 3/10, Evesham (L) 11/09, Evesham (L) 1/10, Evesham 3/10		
(G)Dean	Coleman	6'01"	12 10	18/9/85	24	Dudley	Willenhall 7/07 - Rel 5/10, Halesowen T 6/10	29	0
(G)Jasbir	Singh	6'02"	13 05	12/3/90	20		Shrewsbury 8/09 - Rel 5/10, Solihull Moors 7/10	5	0
(M)Brian	Smikle	5'11"	11 09	3/11/85	24	Tipton	WBA 7/06 - Cheltenham 5/10	43	12
(D)Duane	Courtney	5'11"	11 03	7/1/85	25	Oldbury	The New Saints 7/09 - York C 5/10	41	1
(D)Liam	Dolman	6'01"	12 07	26/9/87	22	Brixworth	Northampton 8/09 - Rel 5/10, Corby (SL) 2/10, Corby T 5/10	7	0
(D)Lee	Baker	5'10"	12 01	20/1/89	20	Redditch	West Brom (5ML) 8/08 Perm 1/09 - Newport C 6/10	34	0
(F)Darryl	Knights	5'07"	10 01	1/5/88	22	Ipswich	Yeovil (SL) 1/08 Perm 5/08 - Rel 7/10, Newport C 7/10	42	4
(F)Robbie	Matthews			2/3/82	28	Wiltshire	Salisbury 8/09 - Rel 7/10	33	6
(M)David	McDermott	5'05"	10 00	6/2/88	22	Stourbridge	Walsall 8/08 - Rel 7/10, Halesowen T (L) 2/10	23	1
(D)Martin	Riley	6'00"	12 01	5/12/86	23	Wolverhampton	Shrewsbury 8/08 Rel 7/10	43	1
(D)Marcus	Bignot	5'07"	11 04	22/8/74	36	Birmingham	Millwall NC 2/10 -	3	0
(M)Dean	Bennett	5'10"	11 00	13/12/77	32	Wolverhampton	Chester c/s 08 -	38	1

Do you remember when...

Kidderminster Harriers

This squad were The Champions of the Conference in 1993-1994 but The Football League didn't pass Aggborough Stadium as up to their required standard for promotion.

Back row, left to right: Les Palmer, Richard Forsyth, Mark Yates, Jay Powell, Lee Hughes, Paul Webb, John Deakin and Delwyn Humphries.
Middle Row: Jim Conway (Physio), Mark Dearlove, Neil Cartwright, Darren Steadman, Kevin Rose, Jo Purdie, Martin Weir and Graham Allner (Manager).
Front Row: Paul Grainger, Chris Brindley, Simeon Hodson (Captain), Paul Davies, Paul Bancroft.

LUTON TOWN

Chairman: Nick Owen

Secretary: Adam Cockfield (T) 01582 411 622
(E) adam.cockfield@lutontown.co.uk

Additional Committee Members: Gary Sweet, Stephen Browne, Andrew Cook, Bob Curson, David Wilkinson, Mick Pattinson, Paul Ballantyne, Dave Hoskins, Andrew Barringer

Manager: Mick Harford

Programme Editor: Andrew Barringer (E) andrew.barringer@lutontown.co.uk

Club Factfile

Founded: 1885 **Nickname:** The Hatters

Previous Names:

Previous Leagues: Football League 1897-1900, 1920-2009. Southern 1900-20.

Club Colours (change): Orange/white/white (Blue, navy & white/white/orange)

Ground: Kenilworth Stadium, 1 Maple Road, Luton LU4 8AW (T) 01582 411 622

Capacity: 10,226 **Seats:** 10,226 **Covered:** All **Clubhouse:** Yes **Shop:** Yes

Previous Grounds: Excelsior, Dallow Lane 1885-97, Dunstable Road 1897-1905

Simple Directions

From the North: Exit the M1 at Junction 11, and join the A505 towards Luton. Follow the A505 for approximately 1.5 miles and Kenilworth Road is on your right as you leave the one-way system along Dunstable Road. To park, follow the one-way around, turning left, right and right again all in about 100 yards so that you do a complete U-turn and then take the second left into Ash Road. Continue down to the bottom, turn left at the end and the club is in front of you. Continue straight past the club and the road bends immediately over a dual carriageway bridge. Beyond this is plenty of street parking (and a great fish shop) if you are early. From the South: You can join the M1 from the M25 at Junction 21A, which is Junction 6 of the M1. Exit at Junction 11 and follow directions above in From the North. From the East: If you are on the A1, leave at Junction 8 of the A1(M) and take the A602 towards Hitchin, then follow the signs to Luton along the A505. When you come into Luton, head for the City Centre and once you reach the one-way system, follow signs to Dunstable and you will see Kenilworth Road on your left. From the West: Come in on the A505 and follow the directions above in From the North.

Record Attendance: 30,069 v Blackpool - FA Cup 6th Round Replay 04/03/59

Record Victory: 12-0 v Bristol Rovers - Division 3 South 13/04/36

Record Defeat: 0-9 v Small Heath - Division Two 12/11/1898

Record Goalscorer: Gordon Turner - 243 (1949-64)

Record Appearances: Bob Morton - 495 (1948-64)

Additional Records: Paid £850,000 to Odense for Lars Elstrup
Recieved £2,500,000 from Arsenal for John Hartson

Senior Honours: Football League Division 3 South 1936-37, Division 4 1967-68, Division 2 1981-82, Division 1 2004-05. League Cup 1988. League Trophy 2008-09

10 YEAR RECORD

00-01	01-02	02-03	03-04	04-05	05-06	06-07	07-08	08-09	09-10
FL 2 22	FL 3 2	FL 2 9	FL 2 10	FL 1 1	FLCh 10	FLCh 23	FL 1 24	FL 2 24	Conf 2

LUTON TOWN

No.	Date	Comp	H/A	Opponents	Att:	Result	Goalscorers	
1	8/8/09	BSP	A	AFC Wimbledon	4488	D 1-1	Craddock pen 14	12
2	11/8/09	BSP	H	Mansfield Town	7295	W 4-1	G Pilkington 2 (38, 65), Og (Perry) 80, Craddock pen 90	2
3	15/8/09	BSP	H	Gateshead	6829	W 2-1	Hall 21, Gallen 22	1
4	18/8/09	BSP	A	Forest Green Rovers	1805	W 1-0	Craddock 56	3
5	29/8/09	BSP	A	Kettering Town	3266	D 0-0		3
6	1/9/09	BSP	H	Crawley Town	6389	W 3-0	G Pilkington 2 (36, 62), Craddock 65	3
7	5/9/09	BSP	A	Salisbury City	2044	D 1-1	Gallen 27	3
8	8/9/09	BSP	A	Oxford United	10613	L 0-2		4
9	12/9/09	BSP	H	Barrow	6264	W 1-0	Newton 21	2
10	22/9/09	BSP	A	Wrexham	3448	L 0-3		9
11	26/9/09	BSP	A	Cambridge United	4870	W 4-3	Gallen 2 (48, pen 75), Jarvis 60, Howells 61	6
12	29/9/09	BSP	H	Stevenage Borough	8223	L 0-1		8
13	3/10/09	BSP	H	Tamworth	6297	W 2-1	Hall 19, Wright 24	5
14	10/10/09	BSP	A	Kidderminster Harriers	2927	W 2-1	Newton 76, Charles 90	5
15	17/10/09	BSP	A	Altrincham	1762	W 1-0	Newton pen 66	5
16	20/10/09	BSP	H	York City	6387	D 1-1	Hall 65	5
17	31/10/09	BSP	H	Rushden & Diamonds	7101	L 0-2		5
18	14/11/09	BSP	A	Grays Athletic	1668	W 2-0	Craddock 39, Gallen 50	5
19	21/11/09	BSP	H	Cambridge United	7458	D 2-2	Gnapka 61, Craddock 79	6
20	2/12/09	BSP	H	Kettering Town	6608	L 0-1		8
21	28/12/09	BSP	H	Eastbourne Borough	6646	W 4-1	Barnes-Homer 9, Gallen 2 (19, 36), Jarvis 75	7
22	23/1/10	BSP	A	Gateshead	1218	W 1-0	Og (Farman) 29	7
23	27/1/10	BSP	A	Histon	1543	W 2-0	Kovacs 52, Hall 72	7
24	30/1/10	BSP	H	Ebbsfleet United	6658	L 2-3	Hatch 27, Craddock 65	8
25	6/2/10	BSP	A	Barrow	1579	W 1-0	Hatch 83	7
26	9/2/10	BSP	H	Oxford United	8860	W 2-1	G Pilkington 90, Keane 90	5
27	13/2/10	BSP	A	Eastbourne Borough	2018	W 1-0	Hall 9	5
28	16/2/10	BSP	A	York City	3316	D 0-0		4
29	20/2/10	BSP	H	AFC Wimbledon	7736	L 1-2	Craddock 29	4
30	27/2/10	BSP	A	Crawley Town	2118	L 1-2	Barnes-Homer 78	5
31	2/3/10	BSP	A	Mansfield Town	3407	D 0-0		4
32	6/3/10	BSP	A	Hayes & Yeading United	1881	W 3-2	Hatch 23, Gnapka pen 30, Craddock 74	5
33	9/3/10	BSP	H	Forest Green Rovers	5884	W 2-1	Craddock 2 (pen 38, 90)	3
34	13/3/10	BSP	H	Wrexham	6538	W 1-0	Craddock 36	3
35	16/3/10	BSP	H	Kidderminster Harriers	5908	W 3-1	Howells 23, Gallen 2 (30, 57)	3
36	20/3/10	BSP	A	Ebbsfleet United	1923	W 6-1	Gnapka 3 (49, 76, 77), Gallen 50, Craddock 66, Barnes-Homer 90	2
37	27/3/10	BSP	H	Hayes & Yeading United	6761	W 8-0	Gallen 2 (7, 23), Gnapka 2 (11, 13), Keane 26, Craddock 2 (31, 56), Howells 35	3
38	30/3/10	BSP	H	Salisbury City	6892	W 4-0	Gnapka 35, Craddock 43, Howells 54, Heslop 74	2
39	3/4/10	BSP	A	Stevenage Borough	7024	W 1-0	Barnes-Homer 55	2
40	5/4/10	BSP	H	Grays Athletic	7860	W 6-0	Craddock 2 (32, 45), Gallen 3 (36, 41, 57), Hatch 80	2
41	10/4/10	BSP	A	Tamworth	2246	D 1-1	G Pilkington 15	2
42	13/4/10	BSP	H	Histon	7083	W 6-3	Howells 2 (29, 56), Craddock 3 (32, 50, pen 77)	2
43	17/4/10	BSP	H	Altrincham	7374	D 0-0		2
44	24/4/10	BSP	A	Rushden & Diamonds	4820	D 1-1	Craddock 9	2
	Chester	**record**	**..........**	**...expunged 08/03**				
5	22/8/09	BSP	H	Chester City	6563	D 0-0		3
22	5/12/09	BSP	A	Chester City	1352	D 0-0		7
	Cups							
1	24/10/09	FAC 4Q	H	Grays Athletic	2721	W 3-0	Blackett 10, Og (Rnkovic) 38, Hall 81	
2	7/11/09	FAC 1	H	Rochdale	3167	D 3-3	Basham 2 (4, 29), Newton 21	
3	11/11/09	FAC 1R	A	Rochdale	1982	W 2-0	Gallen 2 (60, 74)	
4	28/11/09	FAC 2	A	Rotherham United	3210	D 2-2	Craddock pen 21, Nwokeji 74	
5	8/12/09	FAC 2R	H	Rotherham United	2518	W 3-0	Newton 7, White 19, Gnapka 68	
6	12/12/09	FAT 1	A	Cambridge United	1665	L 1-3	Og (Hatswell) 68	
7	2/1/10	FAC 3	A	Southampton	18786	L 0-1		
8	29/4/10	PO SF1	A	York City	6204	L 0-1		
9	3/5/10	PO SF2	H	York City	9781	L 0-1	(L 0-2 agg)	

Home Attendances:
Highest: 8860 v Oxford United
Lowest: 5884 v Forest Green Rovers
Average (08-09): 6727 (6019)

Top Goalscorer: Craddock - 23 (22 League, 1 Cup) in 52 appearances - 44% strike rate
Most Appearances: G Pilkington - 53 (44 League, 9 Cup)

TYLER 1	BLACKETT 12	G PILKINGTON 6	EMANUEL 3	KEANE 4	BURGESS 11	NEWTON 7	HALL 14	CRADDOCK 10	REYNOLDS 21	GALLEN 20	HOWELLS 15	BASHAM 19	JARVIS 16	GORE 13	GNAPKA 18	MURRAY 23	BEAVAN 25	WATKINS 30	WHITE 5	NICHOLLS 8	PATRICK 31	DONNELLY 22	HATCH 9	CHARLES 17	ASAFU-ADJAYE 2	WRIGHT 24	NATHANIEL 33	WOOD 32	BARKER 34	K PILINGTON 26	NWOKEJI 27	BARNES-HOMER 29	CAIN 28	LACEY 36	NELTHORPE 22	POKU 37	KOVACS 5	HESLOP 35	
X	X	X	X	X	X	X	X	X	X	X	S	S	S	U	U																								1
X		X		X	X	X	X	X	X	X	S	S	X	U	S	X	U																						2
X	X	X		X	X		X	X		X	X	S	X	U	S	X	U	U																					3
X	X	X		X	X		X	X	X	X	U	U	S	U	U	X			X																				4
X	S	X		X	X	X		X		X	S	U	X	U		X			X	X		S																	5
X	S	X		X		X	S	X		X		U	X	U	X	X			X	X		S																	6
X	S	X		X		X	S	X		X		S	X	U	X	X			X	X		U																	7
X	X	X		X		X	X	X		X	U	U	X	U		S			X	X		S																	8
X	U	X		X		X	X	X		X	U	U	X	U	X	X			X				S																9
X	S	X				X	X	X	U	X			X	U	X	X			X			S	X	S															10
X	S	X				X	X	S	S	X	X		X	U	X	X			X				X	U															11
X	U	X				X	X	X			X		X	U	S	X			X	X				S	X	S													12
X	U	X				X	X	S			U		X		S	X			X	X			X	S	X	X													13
X	U	X				X	X	X			S		X	U	S	X			X	X				S	X	X													14
X		X			U	X	X	X	S		X	U		U	X				X	X				S	X	X													15
X		X			U	X	X	X	U		X	U		U	X				X	X				S	X	X													16
X		X			S	X	X	X		X	X		X	U	S	S			X	X				U	X														17
	X	X		X		X	U	X		X	S			U	X	X			X	X					U					X	S								18
	X	X		X	U	X		X		X	S		U	U	X	X				X				U	X					X									19
	X	X	S	X		X		X		X			U	U	X	X			X	X										X		S	U						20
	S	X		X		X	S	X		X	X		X	U	X					X					S					X	U	X							21
	X	X		X		S	X	X			X		X	U	X	X														X	S	X			S	U			22
		X		X		X	X	X		X	S			U	X	X				X			S		U					X		S					X		23
		X		X		X	X	X			U		U	S		X				X			X		S					X		X			S		X		24
X		X		X		X	X	X					S		X	X				X			X								S				S		X		25
X		X		X		X	X	X			U		X	U	S	X				X			X									S			S		X		26
X		X				X	X	X		U	S		X	U	X	X				X					U						S	X					X		27
X	S	X		X		X	X	X		U			X	U	S	X				X			X									S					X		28
X	U	X		X		X	X	X		X	S		X	U		X				X			S									S					X		29
X		X		X		X	X	X		X	U		X	U	S	X				X			S									S					X		30
X	U	X		X		X	X	S			X			U	X	X							X								S	X			S		X		31
X		X		X		X	X	S			X			U	X	X							X		U						U	X			S		X		32
X	U	X		X			X	X		X	S		S	U	X	X									X						U	X					X		33
X	U	X		X				X		X	X		S	U	X	X									X						S				U		X	X	34
X	U	X		X			S	X		X	X		U	U	X	X									X							S					X	X	35
X	S	X		X		U	U	X		X	X			U	X	X									X							S					X	X	36
X	S	X		X		U		X		X	X			U	X	X							S		X							S					X	X	37
X	X	X		X		S	U	X		X	X				X	X							S		X							U			S			X	38
X	X	X		X		S		X		X	X			U	X	X							S		X							S					U	X	39
X		X		X		U	U	X		X	X				X	X							S		X							S			S		X	X	40
X	X	X		X		U		X		S	X		S		X	X							X		X							S					U	X	41
X	X	X		X		X		X		X	X		U			X							S		X							S			U		U	X	42
X	X	X				X	X	X		X	X		U			X							S		X							S			U		U	X	43
X	S	X				X	S	X		X	X		X	U		X									U						S	X					X	X	44
X	X	X			X			X	X	X	S	X	X	U	U	S			X	X	U																		
	X	X	X	X		X	X	X			U		U	U		X			X											X	S	X	S						
X	X	X			X	X	X		X	X	X			U	S				X					X	S		S	U	U										
	X	X		X	X	X	U	S	U	X	S	X	U	X	X	X			X					U	U														
	U	X			X	S	X	X	U	X	X		X	X	S				X	X				S	X														
	X	X	U	X		X	S	X		X	S		U	U	X	X			X	X					U					X	S								
	X	X		X		X	S	S		X	S		X	U	X	X		U	X	X					U					X	U								
	X	X	S	X		X	U	S		X			X	U	X	X			X	X										X		S							
	X	X				X	X	X		X	X		X	U	S			S	U	X	U				X					X	S			U					
X	X	X		X		X	U	X		X	X			U	X	X							U									S					U	X	
X	X	X		X		X	S	X		X	X			U	X	X							S									S					U	X	
Total League Appearances																																							
37	13	44	1	33	5	32	27	40	3	30	21	0	21	0	26	38	0	0	16	22	0	0	10	0	18	4	0	0	0	7	0	8	0	0	0	0	17	11	X
0	10	0	1	0	1	3	5	4	2	1	10	4	6	1	9	2	0	0	0	0	0	4	10	6	2	1	0	0	0	0	7	14	0	0	8	0	0	0	S
0	9	0	0	0	3	4	4	0	2	2	7	7	6	36	2	0	2	1	0	0	0	1	0	3	5	0	0	0	0	0	3	1	1	0	3	1	4	0	U
Total Cup Appearances																																							
3	8	9	0	6	3	8	3	5	1	9	5	1	4	2	6	6	0	0	6	5	0	0	0	1	2	0	0	0	0	4	0	0	0	0	0	0	0	2	X
0	0	0	1	0	0	1	3	3	0	0	3	0	0	0	3	0	0	1	0	0	0	0	1	1	1	0	1	0	0	0	2	3	0	0	0	0	0	0	S
0	1	0	1	0	0	0	3	0	2	0	0	0	2	7	0	0	0	1	1	0	1	0	1	1	3	0	0	1	1	0	1	0	0	1	0	0	2	0	U
Total Goals																																							
0	0	6	0	2	0	3	5	22	0	15	6	0	2	0	8	0	0	0	0	0	0	0	4	1	0	1	0	0	0	0	0	4	0	0	0	0	1	1	Lge
0	1	0	0	0	0	2	1	1	0	2	0	2	0	0	1	0	0	0	1	0	0	0	0	0	0	0	0	0	0	0	1	0	0	0	0	0	0	0	Cup

LUTON TOWN

CURRENT SQUAD AS OF BEGINING OF 2010-11 SEASON

GOALKEEPERS		SQ NO.	HT	WT	D.O.B	AGE	P.O.B	CAREER	APPS	GOA
Kevin	Pilkington		6'01"	13 00	8/3/74	36	Hitchin	Man Utd Rel c/s 98, Rochdale (L) 2/96, Rotherham (3ML) 1/97, Celtic (SL) 3/98, Port Vale 7/98 Rel c/s 00, Macclesfield (Trial) 7/00, Wigan 8/00, Aberystwyth 9/00, Mansfield 9/00 Rel c/s 05, Notts County 7/05 Rel 5/10, Luton (2ML) 11/09, Luton 5/10	7	0
Mark	Tyler		6'00"	12 09	2/4/77	33	Norwich	Peterborough, Billericay (3ML) 1/96, Yeovil (L) 11/96, Hull C (L) 1/08, Watford (2ML) 9/08, Bury (2ML) 1/09, Luton 6/09	37	0
DEFENDERS										
Ed	Asafu-Adjaye		5'11"	12 04	22/12/88	31	Southwark	Luton, Walton & H (L) 3/07, Salisbury (3ML) 1/08	20	0
Shane	Blackett		6'00"	12 11	3/10/82	27	Luton	Dunstable, Arlesey 8/03, Dag & Red 5/04, Peterborough Undisc 1/07, Luton 7/09	23	0
Dan	Gleeson		6'03"	13 02	17/2/85	25	Cambridge	Cambridge U Rel 5/06, Welling (L) 9/03, Notts County 7/06, Cambridge U (SL) 3/07, Cambridge U 5/07, Luton 5/10		
Claude	Gnapka		6'02"	13 05	9/6/83	27	Marseille, Fra	Montpellier (Fra) (Yth), Marignane (Fra) 7/01, Beaucaire (Fra) 7/02, Racing Santander B (Spa) 7/03, Alaves B (Spa) 7/05, FC Vaduz (Lie) 7/06 Rel 12/06, Swindon 3/07, Peterborough 7/07 Rel c/s 08, Luton 8/08	35	8
Alex	Lacey				31/5/93	17		Luton	0	0
Fred	Murray		5'10"	11 12	22/5/82	28	Clonmel	Blackburn, Cambridge (3ML) 12/01 Perm 3/02, Northampton 7/04 Rel c/s 07, L.Orient (Trial) 7/07, Stafford R 8/07, Stevenage 1/08 Rel c/s 08, Exeter 9/08 Rel c/s 09, Grays 8/09, Luton (6ML) 8/09 Perm 1/10	40	0
George	Pilkington		5'11"	11 06	7/11/81	28	Rugeley	Everton Rel c/s 03, Exeter (2ML) 11/02, Port Vale 7/03 Rel c/s 08, Luton 8/08	44	6
Alan	White		6'01"	13 02	22/3/76	34	Darlington	Derby (Sch), Middlesbrough, Luton £40,000 9/97 Rel c/s 00, Colchester (6WL) 11/99, Colchester 7/00 Rel c/s 04, L.Orient 7/04, Boston U 3/05, Notts County 7/06, Peterborough (SL) 3/07, Darlington 7/07, Luton 7/09, Darlington (SL) 1/10	16	0
MIDFIELDERS										
Sam	Barker				29/5/92	18	St Albans	Luton, Leighton T (WE) 2/10	0	0
Andy	Drury		5'11"	12 08	28/11/83	26	Kent	Sittingbourne, Gravesend £1,700 7/03 Rel 5/06, Lewes 6/06 Rel 5/08, Stevenage 5/08, Luton 5/10		
Jake	Howells		5'09"	11 08	18/4/91	19	St Albans	Luton	31	6
Keith	Keane		5'09"	11 01	20/11/86	23	Luton	Luton	33	2
Adam	Murray		5'09"	10 00	30/9/81	28	Birmingham	Derby, Mansfield (SL) 2/02, Kidderminster (L) 8/03, Solihull 11/03, Burton 11/03, Notts County 11/03, Kidderminster 1/04, Mansfield 6/04, Carlisle Nominal 3/05, Torquay £10,000 8/06, Macclesfield £17,500 1/07, Oxford U Undisc 1/08, Luton 7/10		
Taylor	Nathaniel				16/1/92	18	London	Luton, Barton R (L) 2/10, Bedford T (L) 3/10	0	0
Adam	Newton		5'10"	11 06	4/12/80	29	Grays	West Ham Rel c/s 02, Portsmouth (2ML) 7/99, Notts County (SL) 11/00, L.Orient (6WL) 3/02, Peterborough 7/02, Brentford 6/08 Rel c/s 09, Luton 7/09	35	3
Kevin	Nicholls		6'00"	11 00	2/1/79	31	Newham	Charlton, Brighton (L) 2/99, Wigan £250,000 6/99, Luton £25,000 8/01, Leeds £700,000 7/06, Preston £700,000 7/07, Luton 8/08	22	0
Jonathan	O'Donnell				29/10/91	18		Watford (Yth), MK Dons (Yth), Hemel Hempstead, St Albans 7/09, Luton (Trial) 12/09, Luton 1/10, St Albans (L) 1/10		
Godfrey	Poku				22/7/90	20		Redbridge College, St Albans 8/09, Luton (Trial) 12/09, Luton 1/10, St Albans (L) 1/10	0	0
Adam	Watkins				8/9/91	18	Luton	Luton	0	0
Jack	Wood				16/4/92	18	London	Luton, Arlesey (L) 2/10, Aylesbury U (L) 3/10	0	0

FORWARDS

		SN	HT	WT	DOB	AGE	POB	From - To	APPS	GOA
Matthew	Barnes-Homer		5'11"	12 05	25/1/86	24	Dudley	Wolves (Sch) Rel c/s 04, Aldershot 9/04 Rel 11/04, Hednesford 2/05, Bromsgrove 3/05, Sracuse (USA), Virginia Beach Mariners (USA), Tividale 7/06, Willenhall 8/06, Wycombe 3/07 Rel 5/07, Kidderminster 7/07, Luton (5WL) 11/09 £75,000 1/10	22	4
Tom	Craddock		5'11"	11 10	14/10/86	23	Darlington	Middlesbrough, Wrexham (L) 10/06, Hartlepool (L) 2/08, Luton (3ML) 10/08, Luton £80,000 1/09	44	22
Danny	Crow		5'10"	11 00	26/1/86	24	Great Yarmouth	Norwich, Northampton (2ML) 2/05, Peterborough 8/05 Rel 9/08, Notts County (L) 10/08, Notts County (SL) 2/09, Cambridge U 9/08, Luton 5/10		
Kevin	Gallen		5'11"	12 10	21/9/75	34	Chiswick	QPR Rel c/s 07, Huddersfield 8/00 Rel c/s 01, Barnsley 7/01, QPR 11/01 Rel c/s 07, Plymouth (SL) 1/07, MK Dons 8/07, Luton (2ML) 11/08 Perm 1/09	31	15
Jordan	Patrick		5'08"	11 00	14/1/92	18	Luton	Luton, Spalding U (WE) 11/09	0	0

Loanees		SN	HT	WT	DOB	AGE	POB	From - To	APPS	GOA
(F)Liam	Hatch		6'02"	12 03	3/4/82	28	Hitchin	Peterborough (SL) 6/09 - Darlington (6ML) 7/10	20	4
(F)Callum	Reynolds				10/11/89	20	Luton	Portsmouth (6ML) 7/09 -	5	0
(F)George	Donnelly		6'02"	13 03	28/5/88	22	Plymouth	Plymouth 8/09 - Stockport (L) 1/10	4	0
(F)Ben	Wright		6'02"	13 05	10/8/88	22	Basingstoke	Peterborough 9/09 - Grimsby (2ML) 11/09, Barnet (L) 3/10	5	1
(F)Mark	Nwokeji		5'10"	11 04	30/1/82	28	London	Dag & Red (6WL) 11/09, (SL) 1/10 - Rel c/s 10, AFC Wimbledon 6/10	7	0
(M)Ashley	Cain		6'02"	12 06	27/9/90	19	Nuneaton	Coventry 11/09 - Oxford U (L) 2/10	0	0
(M)Craig	Nelthorpe		5'10"	11 00	10/6/87	23	Doncaster	York C (SL) 1/10 - Rel 5/10, Gateshead 6/10	8	0
(M)Simon	Heslop		5'11"	11 00	1/5/87	23	York	Barnsley (SL) 3/10 - Oxford U 6/10	11	1
(D)Gavin	Caines		6'01"	12 00	20/9/83	26	Birmingham	Kidderminster (SL) 3/10 -		

Departures		SN	HT	WT	DOB	AGE	POB	From - To	APPS	GOA
(M)Andy	Burgess		6'02"	11 11	10/8/81	29	Bedford	Rushden & D 5/09 - Mansfield (5WL) 11/09 Perm 1/10 Rel 4/10, FC Chester 7/10	6	0
(G)Shane	Gore		6'01"	12 00	28/10/81	28	Ashford	Maidenhead 8/09 - Rel 5/10	1	0
(M)Asa	Hall		6'02"	11 09	29/11/86	23	Sandwell	Birmingham 8/08 - Rel 5/10, Oxford U 5/10	32	5
(D)Rossi	Jarvis		5'11"	11 03	11/3/88	22	Fakenham	Norwich 8/08 - Rel 5/10, Barnet 7/10	27	2
(F)Steve	Basham		6'00"	12 00	2/12/77	32	Southampton	Exeter 8/09 - Rel 5/10, Hayes & Yeading (SL) 11/09, Brackley 7/10	4	0
(F)Ryan	Charles		6'00"	11 13	30/9/89	20	Enfield	Yth - Kidderminster (5WL) 11/09, Rushden & D 6/10	6	1
(D)George	Beavan		5'09"	12 02	12/1/90	20	Luton	Yth - Rel 5/10, Grays (4ML) 8/09	0	0
(D)Janos	Kovacs		6'04"	14 10	11/9/85	24	Budapest, Hun	Lincoln C 1/10 - Hereford 6/10	17	1
(D)Lewis	Emanuel		5'08"	11 12	14/10/83	26	Bradford	Bradford C 7/06 - Rel c/s 10, Southend (Trial) 8/08	2	0
(F)Taiwo	Atieno		6'02"	12 13	6/8/85	25	Brixton	Charleston Battery (USA) 3/10 -		

MANSFIELD TOWN

Chairman: Andrew Perry
Secretary: Laura Atherton (T) 01623 482 482
(E) laura.atherton@mansfieldtown.net
Additional Committee Members:
Steve Hymas,Steve Middleton and Andrew Saunders, Mark Stevenson
Manager: David Holdsworth
Programme Editor: Mark Stevenson (E) mark.Stevenson@mansfieldtown.net

Archive Photo.

Club Factfile

Founded: 1897 **Nickname:** The Stagds
Previous Names: Mansfield Wesleyans 1897-1906, Mansfield Wesley 1906-10
Previous Leagues: Mansfield & District Am. 1902-06, Notts & Dist. 1906-11, Central Alliance 1911-14, 15-21, Notts & Derbys' 1914-15, Midland 1921-26, Midland Combination 1926-31, Football League 1931-2008
Club Colours (change): Amber/blue/blue (Blue & white stripes/black/black)

Ground: Field Mill Stadium, Quarry Lane, Mansfield NG18 5DA (T) 01623 482 482
Capacity: 10000 **Seats:** **Covered:** All **Clubhouse:** Yes **Shop:** Yes
Previous Grounds: West Field Lane 1897-99, Ratcliffe Gate 1899-1901, 12-16, Newgate Lane 1901-12
Simple Directions
From the North: Take the M1 exiting at junction 29, then join the A617 to Mansfield, after around 6 miles turn right into Rosemary Street, then proceed to Quarry Lane where you should turn right to the ground. From the South: Take the M1 exiting at junction 28, then take the A38 to Mansfield, after around 6 miles turn right into Belvedere Street (at crossroads), then after a quarter of a mile turn right into Quarry Lane. From the East: Take the A617 to Rainworth, at the crossroads turn left, after 3 miles turn right into Nottingham Road, a left turn will take you into Quarry Lane where you find the ground. From the West: Take the M1 exiting at junction 28, then take the A38 to Mansfield, after around 6 miles turn right into Belvedere Street (at crossroads), then after a quarter of a mile turn right into Quarry Lane.

Record Attendance: 24,467 v Nottingham Forest - FA Cup 3rd Round 10/01/53
Record Victory: 9-2 v Rotherham United - Division 3 South 29/08/31
Record Defeat: 1-8 v Walsall - Division 3 North 19/01/33
Record Goalscorer: Harry Johnson - 104 (1931-36)
Record Appearances: Ron Arnold - 440 (1970-83)
Additional Records: Paid £150,000 to Carlisle United for Lee Peacock
Received £655,000 from Tottenham Hotspur for Colin Calderwood
Senior Honours: Football Division 4 1974-75, Division 3 1976-77. League Trophy 1987

10 YEAR RECORD

00-01	01-02	02-03	03-04	04-05	05-06	06-07	07-08	08-09	09-10
FL 3 13	FL 3 3	FL 3 23	FL 3 5	FL 2 13	FL 2 16	FL 2 17	FL 2 23	Conf 12	Conf 9

MANSFIELD TOWN

No.	Date	Comp	H/A	Opponents	Att:	Result	Goalscorers	Pos
1	8/8/09	BSP	H	Crawley Town	3264	W 4-0	Perry 2 (15, 43), Duffy 40, Speight 82	1
2	11/8/09	BSP	A	Luton Town	7295	L 1-4	Garner 17	8
3	15/8/09	BSP	A	Salisbury City	1147	W 1-0	Perry 68	5
4	18/8/09	BSP	H	Barrow	3188	W 4-1	Duffy 26, Speight 65, Clare 2 (pen 77, pen 90)	4
5	22/8/09	BSP	H	Ebbsfleet United	3269	W 3-0	Duffy 30, Briscoe 53, Speight 66	2
6	31/8/09	BSP	H	Kettering Town	4034	D 0-0		2
7	5/9/09	BSP	A	Grays Athletic	732	D 1-1	Speight 12	2
8	8/9/09	BSP	A	Kidderminster Harriers	1378	L 1-3	Duffy pen 88	3
9	12/9/09	BSP	H	Stevenage Borough	3251	L 2-3	Perry 2 (2, 16)	6
10	19/9/09	BSP	A	Rushden & Diamonds	1822	L 0-1		9
11	22/9/09	BSP	H	Oxford United	3933	W 2-1	Williams 21, Speight 25	7
12	26/9/09	BSP	H	Hayes & Yeading United	3180	W 3-1	Duffy 3 (37, pen 49, pen 62)	4
13	29/9/09	BSP	A	Barrow	1040	L 1-3	Nix 12	5
14	3/10/09	BSP	H	Forest Green Rovers	3022	W 1-0	Duffy pen 5	4
15	10/10/09	BSP	A	Altrincham	1642	W 2-1	Perry 7, Briscoe 46	4
16	17/10/09	BSP	A	Eastbourne Borough	1207	W 2-1	Perry 6, Duffy 12	4
17	31/10/09	BSP	H	Histon	3162	D 1-1	Williams 90	4
18	14/11/09	BSP	A	Crawley Town	883	W 2-0	Speight 11, Heckingbottom 77	4
19	21/11/09	BSP	H	Eastbourne Borough	2922	D 1-1	Challinor 68	4
20	28/11/09	BSP	A	Ebbsfleet United	850	L 1-2	Duffy pen 16	5
21	1/12/09	BSP	A	Gateshead	643	W 3-1	Hotchkiss 59, Burgess 69, Morris 90	4
22	5/12/09	BSP	H	Grays Athletic	2726	D 0-0		4
23	26/12/09	BSP	A	York City	4587	L 0-3		6
24	28/12/09	BSP	H	Cambridge United	3368	W 2-1	Perry 27, Speight 73	4
25	16/1/10	BSP	A	AFC Wimbledon	3584	L 0-2		5
26	30/1/10	BSP	A	Forest Green Rovers	817	W 4-1	Jones 2 (63, 86), Duffy 66, Speight 76	4
27	2/2/10	BSP	A	Wrexham	2689	L 1-2	Speight 48	4
28	6/2/10	BSP	H	Gateshead	7261	L 0-2		4
29	9/2/10	BSP	A	Stevenage Borough	1753	L 1-3	Shaw 39	6
30	13/2/10	BSP	A	Tamworth	1389	W 4-2	Duffy 17, Shaw 21, Nicholas 42, Sturrock 87	6
31	23/2/10	BSP	A	Hayes & Yeading United	427	D 1-1	Silk 90	7
32	2/3/10	BSP	H	Luton Town	3407	D 0-0		7
33	6/3/10	BSP	H	Salisbury City	2842	W 4-2	Challinor 30, Shaw 37, Perry 75, Duffy 90	7
34	13/3/10	BSP	H	Tamworth	2954	D 0-0		9
35	16/3/10	BSP	H	York City	2638	L 0-1		9
36	20/3/10	BSP	A	Histon	662	W 5-0	Garner 38, Briscoe 57, Sturrock 64, Burgess 69, Speight 75	8
37	23/3/10	BSP	H	Altrincham	2364	D 1-1	Speight 90	8
38	27/3/10	BSP	A	Kettering Town	1188	D 2-2	Challinor 10, Sturrock 33	7
39	3/4/10	BSP	H	Wrexham	2520	L 0-1		8
40	5/4/10	BSP	A	Cambridge United	2823	L 2-3	Speight 26, Nix 56	9
41	10/4/10	BSP	H	AFC Wimbledon	2470	L 0-1		9
42	13/4/10	BSP	H	Rushden & Diamonds	2031	W 3-2	Speight 2 (48, 77), Duffy pen 90	9
43	17/4/10	BSP	A	Oxford United	5712	L 0-2		9
44	24/4/10	BSP	H	Kidderminster Harriers	2734	D 3-3	Speight 3 (18, 25, 45)	9
	Chester	**record**	**........................**	**...expunged 08/03**				
6	29/8/09	BSP	A	Chester City	1734	W 1-0	Perry 2	2
27	23/1/10	BSP	H	Chester City	2882	W 4-0	Jones 2 (23, 34), Og (B Jones) 37, Speight 80	4
	Cups							
1	24/10/09	FAC 4Q	H	Altrincham	2410	W 3-0	Duffy 2 (19, 26), Perry 61	
2	7/11/09	FAC 1	A	Forest Green Rovers	1149	D 1-1	Garner 87	
3	17/11/09	FAC 1R	H	Forest Green Rovers	2496	L 1-2	Perry 71	
4	12/12/09	FAT 1	H	Tamworth	1467	L 0-2		

Home Attendances:

Highest:	7261 v Gateshead
Lowest:	2031 v Rushden & Diamonds
Average (08-09):	3092 (2424)
Top Goalscorer:	Speight - 17 (17 League, 0 Cup) in 37 appearances - 46% strike rate
Most Appearances:	Marriott - 48 (44 League, 4 Cup)

MARRIOTT 1	GARNER 6	GARDNER 2	JONES 5	MILLS 4	ARMSTRONG 12	WILLIAMS 11	NIX 26	BRISCOE 7	PERRY 19	DUFFY 9	SOMNER 8	SPEIGHT 17	CLARE 10	SANDERCOMBE 20	GRAHAM 15	ISTEAD 14	SILK 16	STURROCK 32	PORTER 25	ELEY 33	HECKINGBOTTOM 3	DOBSON 35	HOTCHKISS 34	BROUGH 36	CHALLINOR 25	BURGESS 37	MORRIS 18	SHAW 10	FOSTER 15	COLLETT 33	NICHOLAS 18	
X	X	X	X	X	X	X	X	X	X	X	S	S	S	U	U																	1
X	X	X	X		X	X	X	X	X	X	X	S	S	U	U	S																2
X	X		X		X	X	X	X	X	X	X	S	S	U	U	S	X															3
X	X		X		X	X	X	X	X	X	X	S	S	U	U	U	X															4
X	X		X		X	X	X	X	X	X	X	S	S	U	U	S	X															5
X	X		X	U	X	X	X	X	X	X	X	S	S	U	S		X															6
X	X		X	X		S	S		X	X	X	X	X	U	X	U	X	S														7
X	X	X	X	X		X	X	S	S	X	U	X	X		U		X	S														8
X	X		X	X	X	X		X	X	X	X	S		U	U	S	X		S													9
X	X		X	X	X	X	S	X		X	X	S	U		U	S	X	X														10
X	X	U			X	X	X	X		X	X	X	S		X	S	X	S	U													11
X	X	U			X	X	X	X		X	X	X	S		X	S	X	U	S													12
X	X	U			X	X	X	X	S	X	X	X			X	S	X	S		U												13
X	X			X		X	X		S	X	S	S	X		X	U	X	X		U	X											14
X	X			X	U	S		X	X	X	X	S			X	X	X	S		U	X											15
X	X		X	X	U	S			X	X	X	X				X	X	U		U	X	S										16
X	X		X	X	S	X			X	X		S				U	X	S		U	X	X	X									17
X	X		X	S	U	X			X	S	X	X				S	X	X		U	X			X								18
X	X		X		U	X		X	X	X	X							S		U	X	S	U	X	X							19
X		X	X		S	X		S		X	X						U	X		U	X			X	X	X	S					20
X		X	X		X	U		X	X		X			U			X	U					S	X	X	X	S					21
X			X		U	S		X	X	X	S			U			X				X		X	X	X	X	S					22
X	X		X			S			X	U	X	S		U			X				X		S	X	X	X	X					23
X	X			U		X		S	X	X	X	S		U			X				X		X	X		S	X					24
X	X		S			U		X	X	X	X	S		U			X				X		X	X		X		S				25
X			X		X	X		S	S	X	X	X				S	X						U	X	X				X	U		26
X			X		X	X		S	S	X	X	X				U	X						S	X	X				X	U		27
X			X		X	X		X	S	X	X	X					X						X	U	S			S	X	U		28
X			X	X		S	X	S	X	X							X	S						U	X			X	X	U	X	29
X	X			X		U	X	S	X	X							X	S						S	X			X	X	U	X	30
X	X			X		S	X		X	X							X	S						U	X	S		X	X	U	X	31
X			X	X		X	U	X	S	X							X	U						S	X			X	X	U	X	32
X				X		X	S	X	S	X	U						X	S						X	X			X	X	U	X	33
X				X		X	X	X	S	X	U						X	S						X		S		X	X	U	X	34
X				X			U	X	S	X	U	S					X	X						X	X	X			X	U	X	35
X	X			X			U	X	X		S	S					X	X						X	X	X		S		U	X	36
X	X			X			S	X	X		U	S					X	X						X	X	X		S		U	X	37
X	U			X			S	X	X	S		S					X	X						X	X	X			X	U	X	38
X				X		S		X	X	S	U	S					X	X						X	X	X			X	U	X	39
X				X			S	S	X		U	X					X	X						X	X	X		S	X	U	X	40
X	X			X		X	S	X	X		U	X					X	S							X			S	X	U	X	41
X	X			X			X	X	X	S	U	X				S	X									X		U	X	U	X	42
X	X		X	X		X		X	S	X	X	X				X		S							U	X		S		U		43
X	X			X		X	U	X	S	X	X	X				S	X									X		S	X	U		44
X	X		X		X	U	X	X	X	X	X	X	S	U	U	S	X															
X			X		X	X		X	S	X	X	X		U			X	S					X	U	S				X			
X	X		X	X	U	X			X	X	X	S			U	S	X	S		U	X	X	U									
X	X		X	X	U	S			X	X	U	X				X	X	S		U	X	S	U	X								
X	X	U	X	X	U	X		S	X	S		X				U	X	X		U	X		U	X								
X	X		U			S		X	S	X	X			S				U			X		X	X	X	X	X					
Total League Appearances																																
44	30	5	24	25	15	27	16	29	28	34	25	15	3	0	6	3	39	10	0	0	11	1	5	18	19	14	2	6	16	0	14	X
0	0	0	1	1	2	8	7	8	12	4	4	19	8	0	1	12	0	14	2	0	0	2	3	2	1	3	3	8	0	0	0	S
0	1	3	0	2	5	3	4	0	0	1	9	0	1	13	8	5	1	4	1	8	0	0	2	3	1	0	0	1	0	19	0	U
Total Cup Appearances																																
4	4	0	3	3	0	2	0	1	3	3	2	2	0	0	0	1	3	1	0	0	4	1	1	3	1	1	1	0	0	0	0	X
0	0	0	0	0	0	2	0	1	1	1	0	1	0	1	0	1	0	2	0	0	0	1	0	0	0	0	0	0	0	0	0	S
0	0	1	1	0	3	0	0	0	0	0	1	0	0	0	1	1	0	1	0	3	0	0	3	0	0	0	0	0	0	0	0	U
Total Goals																																
0	2	0	2	0	0	2	2	3	9	14	0	17	2	0	0	0	1	3	0	0	1	0	1	0	3	2	1	3	0	0	1	Lge
0	1	0	0	0	0	0	0	0	2	2	0	0	0	0	0	0	0	0	0	0	0	0	0	0	0	0	0	0	0	0	0	Cup

MANSFIELD TOWN

CURRENT SQUAD AS OF BEGINING OF 2010-11 SEASON

GOALKEEPERS		SQ NO.	HT	WT	D.O.B	AGE	P.O.B	CAREER	APPS	GOA
Neil	Collett				2/10/89	20	Coventry	Coventry Rel c/s 09, Nuneaton T 5/09, Mansfield 1/10	0	0
Alan	Marriott		6'01"	12 05	3/9/78	31	Bedford	Tottenham Rel c/s 99, Lincoln C 8/99 Rel c/s 08, Rushden & D 7/08, Mansfield 1/09	44	0
DEFENDERS										
Steve	Foster		6'01"	13 00	3/12/74	35	Mansfield	Mansfield, Telford 1/94, Woking 10/96, Bristol R £150,000 5/97 Rel c/s 02, Notts County (Trial) 7/02, Doncaster 8/02 (02/03 21,1) Rel 1/06, Scunthorpe 1/06 Rel c/s 07, Darlington 7/07 Rel 2/10, Blyth 3/10, Mansfield 5/10		
Mark	Preece		6'02"	13 07	3/6/87	23	Bristol	Bristol R Rel c/s 06, Gloucester (SL) 1/06, Kidderminster (Trial) 7/06, Forest Green 7/06, Weston-super-Mare (L) 1/07, Mansfield 7/10		
Kevin	Sandwith		5'11"	13 06	30/4/78	32	Workington	Carlisle, Barrow 9/98, Telford 2/99, Doncaster 5/01 Rel 9/02, Halifax 11/02, Lincoln C 3/04, Macclesfield 7/05, Swansea (Trial) 11/05, Chester 6/06 Rel c/s 08, Weymouth 7/08 Rel 2/09, Oxford U 2/09, Mansfield 5/10		
Gary	Silk		5'09"	13 07	13/9/84	25	Newport, IOW	Portsmouth Rel c/s 06, Barnet (L) 12/03, Wycombe (8ML) 7/04, Boston U (SL) 1/06, Notts County 7/06 Rel c/s 08, Mansfield 7/08	39	1
Chris	Smith		5'11"	11 06	30/6/81	29	Derby	Leeds (Yth), Reading Rel c/s 01, Hayes (L) 12/99, York (Trial) 3/01, Kidderminster (Trial) 4/01, York C 5/01 Rel c/s 04, Stafford R 8/04 Rel c/s 05, Worcester 7/05, Tamworth 5/08, Mansfield 7/10		
Ben	Turner				22/9/91	18		Mansfield, North Ferriby (L) 10/09, North Ferriby (L) 1/10		
Jason	Ventrella				22/4/92	18		Mansfield, Hucknall (L) 3/10		
MIDFIELDERS										
Conor	Higginson				27/1/92	18	Ollerton	Mansfield		
Steven	Istead		5'08"	11 04	23/4/86	24	South Shields	Newcastle (Yth), Hartlepool Rel c/s 06. Gateshead 7/06, Consett 1/07, Peterhead c/s 07, Ilkeston 6/08, Mansfield 6/09, Alfreton (6WL) 11/09	15	0
Gary	Mills		5'09"	11 06	20/5/81	29	Sheppey	Rushden & D, Yeovil (Trial) 6/06, Crawley 8/06, Rushden & D 1/07 Rel 5/07, Tamworth 6/07, Kettering 10/07, Stevenage 5/08, Mansfield 6/09	26	0
Tom	Naylor				28/6/91	19	Sutton-in-Ashfield	Mansfield, Belper (SL) 8/09		
Matt	Somner		6'00"	13 02	8/12/82	27	Isleworth	Brentford, Cambridge (2ML) 12/04 Perm 2/05, Bristol R NC 8/05, Aldershot 8/05, Notts County 6/06 Rel 6/08, Mansfield 7/08	29	0
Paul	Stonehouse		5'07"	11 03	13/7/87	23	Wegburg	Forest Green, Gloucester (L) 1/07, Mansfield Undisc 6/10		
Tyrone	Thompson		5'09"	11 02	8/5/81	29	Sheffield	Sheff Utd Rel c/s 03, Halifax (Trial) 9/01, Lincoln C (L) 10/02, Doncaster (L) 3/03, Huddersfield 8/03 Rel 4/04, Scarborough 6/04, Halifax 8/05, Crawley 6/07, Torquay 5/08 Rel c/s 10, Mansfield 7/10		
Ryan	Williams		5'04"	11 02	31/8/78	32	Chesterfield	Mansfield, Tranmere £70,000 + 8/97, Chesterfield (3ML) 11/99 £80,000 2/00, Hull C £150,000 7/01, Bristol R (2ML) 10/03 Perm 12/03, Forest Green (2ML) 12/04, Aldershot (L) 8/05, Aldershot 1/06 Rel 4/08, Weymouth 5/08 Rel 2/09, Mansfield 2/09	35	2
FORWARDS										
Louis	Briscoe		6'00"	11 13	2/4/88	22	Burton	Port Vale Rel 1/07, Stafford R (Trial), Moor Green 3/07, Leek T 7/07, Huston Dynamo (USA) (Trial) 3/08, Hednesford 6/08, Gresley R 9/08, Stafford R 11/08, Ilkeston 12/08, Mansfield 1/09	37	3
Robert	Duffy		6'01"	12 04	2/12/82	27	Swansea	Rushden & D Rel c/s 05, Stamford (L) 1/05, Peterborough (Trial) 7/05, Cambridge U 8/05, Kettering 9/05, Gainsborough 1/06, Stevenage 3/06 Rel 5/06, Oxford U 8/06 Rel 4/08, Wrexham (SL) 1/08, Mansfield (Trial) c/s 07, Newport C 7/08, Mansfield 1/09	38	14
Lee	Gregory				26/8/88	22		Sheff Utd (Scholar), Staveley MW, Mansfield 9/09, Glapwell (3ML) 9/09, Harrogate T (3ML) 12/09, FC Halifax (L) 3/10		
Kyle	Nix		5'06"	09 10	21/1/86	24	Sydney, Aust	Man Utd (Trainee), Aston Villa 7/02 Rel c/s 05, Sheff Utd 7/05 Rel c/s 06, Barnsley (SL) 2/06, Scunthorpe (Trial) 7/06, Buxton 11/06, Parkgate Rel c/s 07, Bradford C 7/07 Rel c/s 09, Mansfield 7/09, Sparta Rotterdam (Holl) (Trial) 7/10	23	2
Keigan	Parker		5'07"	10 05	8/6/82	28	Livingston	St Johnstone Rel c/s 04, Blackpool 7/04, Huddersfield 7/08, Hartlepool (2ML) 3/09, Oldham 7/09 Rel c/s 10, Bury (L) 3/10, Mansfield 7/10		

		SN	HT	WT	DOB	AGE	POB	From - To	APPS	GOA
Adam	Smith		5'11"	12 00	20/2/85	25	Huddersfield	Chesterfield Rel 6/08, Lincoln C (L) 1/08, Gainsborough 8/08, York C (2ML) 11/08, York C Undisc 1/09, Mansfield 5/10		

Loanees		SN	HT	WT	DOB	AGE	POB	From - To	APPS	GOA
(F)Levi	Porter		5'04"	10 05	6/4/87	23	Leicester	Leicester 9/09 -	2	0
(G)Ed	Eley		6'02"		1/3/91	19		Grimsby 9/09, 2ML 11/09 - Eastwood T 1/10 Rel 5/10	0	0
(M)Lee	Morris		5'10"	11 07	30/4/80	30	Blackpool	Hereford (5WL) 11/09 - Forest Green (L) 3/10, Rel 4/10, Kidderminster 7/10	5	1
(D)Andy	Nicholas		6'02"	12 08	10/10/83	26	Liverpool	Rotherham (SL) 2/10 -	14	1

Departures		SN	HT	WT	DOB	AGE	POB	From - To	APPS	GOA
(D)Joe	Lamplough				18/2/90	20	Hull	Hull C NC 8/09 - Glen Hoddle Soccer Academy 9/09		
(M)Jonathan	D'Laryea		5'10"	12 02	3/9/85	24	Manchester	Man City (3ML) 10/05 Perm 1/06 - Northwich (3ML) 8/09 Perm 11/09, Eastwood T Undisc 2/10		
(D)Luke	Graham		6'03"	12 07	27/4/86	24	Kettering	Kettering 5/09 - York C (2ML) 11/09 Perm 1/10, Kettering 6/10	7	0
(F)Daryl	Clare		5'09"	11 00	1/8/78	32	Jersey	Rushden & D (SL) 3/09 Perm 5/09 - Gateshead (3ML) 10/09 Perm 1/10, Cambridge U £10,000 6/10	11	2
(M)Craig	Dobson		5'07"	10 06	23/1/84	26	Chingford	ex Brentford 10/09 - Rel 1/10, Kettering (5WL) 11/09, Farnborough 1/10 Rel 3/10, Sutton U 3/10	3	0
(G)Timothy	Sandercombe		6'04"	13 12	15/6/89	21	Plymouth	Stafford R 5/09 - Weymouth 2/10, Worcester 7/10	0	0
(F)Jason	Bradley		6'03"	13 00	16/3/89	21	Sheffield	Darlington 7/09 - Rel 4/10, Newport (L) 8/09, Kings Lynn (L) 9/09, Harrogate T (SL) 12/09, Brackley T 6/10		
(F)Grant	Ryan		5'10"	12 06	5/2/91	19	Nottingham	Yth - Rel 4/10, Chasetown (L) 9/09, Chasetown (SL) 1/10		
(D)Nick	Langford				23/4/92	18		Yth - Rel 4/10, Grantham (L) 12/09		
(M)Craig	Armstrong		5'11"	12 09	23/5/75	35	South Shields	Kidderminster 6/09 - Rel 4/10, Forest Green (SL) 2/10, Forest Green (Pl/Coach) 6/10	17	0
(D)Paul	Heckingbottom		6'00"	12 05	17/7/77	33	Barnsley	Bradford C 6/09 - Gateshead (SL) 2/10, Rel 4/10, Gateshead 5/10	11	1
(M)Andy	Burgess		6'02"	11 11	10/8/81	29	Bedford	Luton (5WL) 11/09 Perm 1/10 - Rel 4/10, FC Chester 7/10	17	2
(M)Scott	Gardner		5'09"	11 04	1/4/88	22	Luxembourg	Leeds 2/09 - Rel 4/10, Eastwood T (L) 2/10	5	0
(D)Luke	Jones		5'09"	11 09	10/4/87	23	Blackburn	Kidderminster 5/09 - Rel 4/10, Forest Green 6/10	25	2
(F)Jon	Challinor		5'11"	11 11	2/12/80	29	Northampton	Cambridge U (6WL) 11/09 Perm 1/10 - Rel 4/10	20	3
(F)Blair	Sturrock		6'00"	11 00	25/8/81	29	Dundee	Swindon 8/09 - Rel 4/10, Southend 7/10	24	3
(M)Oliver	Hotchkiss				27/9/89	20	Houghton-le-Spring	Leeds (3ML) 10/09, Perm 1/10 - Rel 4/10	8	1
(D)Luke	Foster		6'02"	12 08	8/9/85	24	Mexborough	Oxford U Undisc 1/10 - Rel 5/10, Stevenage 5/10	16	0
(F)Jon	Shaw		6'00"	13 01	10/11/83	26	Sheffield	Rochdale 1/10 - Rel 5/10, Gateshead 5/10	14	3
(M)Michael	Brough		5'09"	11 07	1/8/81	29	Nottingham	Torquay (5WL) 11/09 Perm 1/10 - Rel 5/10, Darlington 7/10	20	0
(F)Jake	Speight		5'07"	11 02	28/9/85	24	Sheffield	Droylsden 5/09 - Bradford C £25,000 6/10	34	17
(F)Kyle	Perry		6'04"	14 05	5/3/86	24	Birmingham	Port Vale 7/09 - Tamworth 7/10	40	9
(D)Scott	Garner		6'02"		20/9/89	20	Coventry	Leicester 1/09 - Grimsby 7/10	30	2

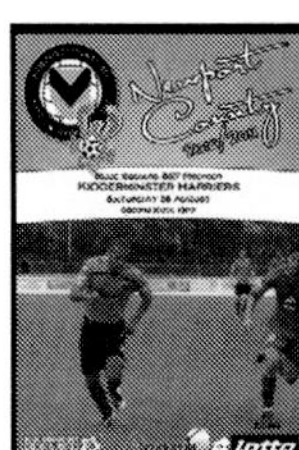

NEWPORT COUNTY

Chairman: Chris Blight
Secretary: Mike Everett (T) 07889 359 100
(E) mike.everett3@googlemail.com
Additional Committee Members: John Allison, ohn Bowkett, John Collingbourne, Howard Greenhaf, Nick McDonald, Matt Southall, Tim Harris, Phil Morgan
Manager: Dean Holdsworth
Programme Editor: Ray Taylor (E) rayncafc@aol.com

Back Row : Jonny Evans (Ass Physio), Wayne Turk, Lee Baker, Craig Reid, Giuseppe Sole, Andrew Hughes, Jake Harris, Scott Rogers, Tony Taggart, John Fitzgerald (Physio)
Centre Row : Bobby Morris (Staff), Chris Todd, Jamie Collins, Oliver Thorne, Glyn Thompson, Gary Warren (C), Glyn Garner, Robbie Matthews, Sam Foley, Paul Bignot, Tony Gilbert (Kit Manager)
Front Row : Darryl Knights, Eddie Odhiambo, Matthew Bishop (Coach), Fraser Skimming (Assistant Manager), Chris Blight (Chairman), Dean Holdsworth (Manager), John Bowkett (Director), Tim Harris (Director of Football), Ian Harris (Goalkeeping Coach), Danny Rose, Charlie Henry

Club Factfile

Founded: 1998 **Nickname:** The Exiles
Previous Names: Newport AFC after demise of Newport County in 1988-89, changed back again in 1999
Previous Leagues: Hellenic 1989-90, Southern 1990-2004

Club Colours (change): Amber/black/black (All white)

Ground: Newport Stadium, Langland Way, Newport, South Wales NP19 4PT **(T)** 01633 662 262
Capacity: 4,300 **Seats:** 1,236 **Covered:** 3,236 **Clubhouse:** Yes **Shop:** Yes
Previous Grounds:
Simple Directions
From M4 Junction 24: Follow A48 (Signposted City Centre, Newport International Sports Village) For 2.5 Miles. Turn left into Langland Way (adjacent to Carcraft), Take first left after BOC depot.

Record Attendance: 4,616 v Swansea City - FA Cup 1st Round 11/11/2006
Record Victory: 9-0 v Pontlottyn Blast Furnace (A) - Welsh Cup 01/09/90
Record Defeat: 1-6 v Stafford Rangers (A) - 06/01/96
Record Goalscorer: Chris Lillygreen - 93
Record Appearances: Mark Price - 275
Additional Records: Paid £5,000 to Forest Green Rovers for Shaun Chapple
Received £5,000 from Merthyr Tydfil for Craig Lima

Senior Honours: Hellenic League 1989-90. League Cup 1989-90. Gloucestershire Senior Cup 1993-94.
Southern League Midland Division 1994-95. Gwent FA Senior Cup 1996-97, 97-98, 99-2000, 00-01, 01-02, 03-04, 04-05.
Conference South 2009-10.

10 YEAR RECORD

00-01		01-02		02-03		03-04		04-05		05-06		06-07		07-08		08-09		09-10	
SthP	10	SthP	5	SthP	10	SthP	7	Conf S	18	Conf S	18	Conf S	6	Conf S	9	Conf S	10	Conf S	1

NEWPORT COUNTY

No.	Date	Comp	H/A	Opponents	Att:	Result	Goalscorers	Pos
1	8/8/09	BSS	A	Bishops Stortford	704	D 0-0		15
2	12/8/09	BSS	H	Hampton & Richmond B.	1185	W 3-1	Cochlin 21, Gilroy 71, Foley 90	6
3	15/8/09	BSS	H	Lewes	1201	D 2-2	Foley 48, Rose 86	11
4	18/8/09	BSS	A	Dorchester Town	609	D 0-0		11
5	22/8/09	BSS	H	Chelmsford City	1042	W 4-0	Foley 34, Cooper 45, Cochlin 73, Reid 90	7
6	29/8/09	BSS	A	Maidenhead United	497	W 3-1	Bradley 15, Reid 72, Warren 84	4
7	31/8/09	BSS	H	Weston-Super-Mare	1404	W 2-0	Reid pen 67, Gilroy 75	3
8	5/9/09	BSS	A	Welling United	552	W 2-0	Reid 2 (20, pen 67)	1
9	12/9/09	BSS	H	Eastleigh	1316	W 5-1	Reid 2 (24, 76), Henry 31, Rose 37, Foley 74	2
10	16/9/09	BSS	H	Weymouth	1509	D 1-1	Reid 2	2
11	19/9/09	BSS	A	Woking	1862	W 1-0	Foley 29	2
12	3/10/09	BSS	H	Bath City	1410	W 1-0	Henry 7	1
13	17/10/09	BSS	A	St Albans City	581	W 1-0	Henry 69	1
14	27/10/09	BSS	A	Staines Town	621	L 0-1		1
15	31/10/09	BSS	H	Basingstoke Town	1241	W 1-0	Collins 37	1
16	7/11/09	BSS	A	Dover Athletic	1680	W 2-1	Reid 2 (33, 72)	1
17	15/11/09	BSS	H	Bromley	2026	W 2-0	Rose 61, Morgan 89	1
18	28/11/09	BSS	A	Lewes	521	W 3-0	Rogers 24, Morgan 55, Henry 84	1
19	5/12/09	BSS	A	Bath City	1404	D 1-1	Reid pen 20	1
20	9/12/09	BSS	H	Thurrock	1603	W 5-0	Warren 17, Reid 3 (pen 35, 57, 87), Henry 45	1
21	19/12/09	BSS	H	Staines Town	1460	W 1-0	Henry 89	1
22	28/12/09	BSS	H	Dorchester Town	2151	W 3-0	Reid 2 (54, 67), Warren 84	1
23	1/1/10	BSS	H	Worcester City	2525	W 1-0	Foley 79	1
24	23/1/10	BSS	H	St Albans City	1412	W 5-0	Warren 22, Reid 2 (68, 82), Foley 90, Collins 90	1
25	30/1/10	BSS	A	Bromley	817	W 3-2	Cochlin 21, Henry 52, Foley 69	1
26	6/2/10	BSS	H	Welling United	1449	D 2-2	Collins 5, Morgan 58	1
27	10/2/10	BSS	A	Eastleigh	745	W 4-1	Reid pen 20, Foley 2 (23, 83), Henry pen 81	1
28	13/2/10	BSS	A	Chelmsford City	931	D 0-0		1
29	20/2/10	BSS	A	Hampton & Richmond B.	742	W 4-0	Reid 2 (7, 37), Turk 35, Foley 90	1
30	22/2/10	BSS	A	Worcester City	1017	W 4-1	Reid 9, Todd 2 (22, 39), Foley 40	1
31	27/2/10	BSS	H	Braintree Town	2117	W 1-0	Foley 62	1
32	2/3/10	BSS	A	Basingstoke Town	646	W 5-1	Rose 2 (9, 14), Douglas 39, Foley 49, Giles 84	1
33	6/3/10	BSS	A	Weymouth	1123	W 3-1	Morgan 3, Rose 76, Foley 84	1
34	12/3/10	BSS	H	Bishops Stortford	3084	W 1-0	Morgan 1	1
35	15/3/10	BSS	H	Havant & Waterlooville	4221	W 2-0	Foley 2 (24, 52)	CH
36	20/3/10	BSS	A	Thurrock	406	L 1-2	Warren 19	1
37	27/3/10	BSS	H	Woking	1742	W 1-0	Gilroy 90	1
38	3/4/10	BSS	H	Maidenhead United	1339	W 4-1	Gilroy 11, Reid 17, Rose 68, Rogers 72	1
39	6/4/10	BSS	A	Weston-Super-Mare	810	W 4-1	Henry 23, Gilroy 35, Cochlin 50, Rogers 70	1
40	10/4/10	BSS	A	Havant & Waterlooville	1020	L 0-4		1
41	17/4/10	BSS	H	Dover Athletic	3201	W 3-0	Morgan 3, Todd 15, Rose 67	1
42	24/4/10	BSS	A	Braintree Town	1187	W 2-1	Collins 7, Cochlin 11	1
	Cups							
1	26/9/09	FAC 2Q	A	Clevedon Town	623	W 3-1	Reid 2 (5, pen 14), Davies 90	
2	10/10/09	FAC 3Q	A	Paulton Rovers	703	L 0-1		
3	21/11/09	FAT 3Q	H	Braintree Town	684	W 2-1	Morgan 22, Gilroy 27	
4	12/12/09	FAT 1	A	Farnborough	805	W 3-1	Henry 22, Holgate 47, Reid 90	
5	20/1/10	FAT 2	H	York City	1040	D 0-0		
6	26/1/10	FAT 2R	A	York City	1469	L 0-1		

Home Attendances:	
Highest:	4221 v Havant & Waterlooville
Lowest:	1042 v Chelmsford City
Average (08-09):	1460 (853)
Top Goalscorer:	Reid - 26 (23 League, 3 Cup) in 46 appearances - 57% strike rate
Most Appearances:	Thompson - 48 (42 League, 6 Cup)

THOMPSON	BIGNOT	GILES	ROGERS	COOK	WARREN	ROSE	HENRY	REID	FOLEY	AKE	LEEK	GILROY	COCHLIN	TURK	BLACKBURN	DAVIES	COLBORNE	HARTRICK	BRADLEY	COOPER	DEERING	HUGHES	NEWMAN	SMITH	THELWELL	HOLGATE	MORGAN	THOMAS	COLLINS	PETERS	COUTTS	MORRIS	NICHOLLS	TODD	DOUGLAS	HUNT	
X	X	X	X	X	X	X	X	X	X	X	S	S	U	U	U																						1
X		X	X	X	X	X	X	X	X		U	S	X	X	U	S	U																				2
X	U	X	X	X	X	X	X	X	X			X	X	S	U	U		S																			3
X	X	X	X	U	X	X		X	X		S	S	X	X	U	U			X																		4
X	X	X	X	S	X	X		S	X			S	X	X	U	U			X	X																	5
X	X		X	X	X	X		S	S		X	X	X	X	U		U		X	S																	6
X	X		S	X	X	X	U	X	X			S	X	X	U		U		X	X																	7
X	X	U	X	X	X	X		X	X		S	S	X	X	U				S	X																	8
X	X	U	X	X	X	X	X	X	X			S	X	X	U				S		S																9
X		X	X	X	X	S	S	X	X			S	X	X			U		U	X	X																10
X	X	X	X		X	X	X	X	X			U	X	X	U	S	S				S																11
X	X	X	X	X		X	X	X	X			S	X	X	U		U			U	S																12
X	X		X	X	U	X	S	X	X				X	X	U										X	X	S	U									13
X	X	X	X		U	X	S	X	X				X	X	U										X	X	S	S									14
X	X	X	S		X	X	X	X	X				U	X	U										X	S	S		X								15
X	X	U	X		X	X	X	X	S				S	X	U										X	S	X		X								16
X	X	U	X		X	X	X	X	X				S	X	U										X	S	S		X								17
X	X		X		X		S	X	S			X	X	X	U			U							S	X	X		X								18
X	X	U	X		X		X	X	X				X	X	U											X	S		X	S	S						19
X	X	U	X		X		X	X	X				X	X	U			S								X			X	S	S						20
X	X	U	X		X		X	X	X				X	X	U			U									S		X	U	X						21
X		U			X	S	X	X	X				X	X	U											S	X		X		S	X	X				22
X	X	U	X		X	S		X	X				X	X	U											S	X		X			U	X				23
X	X		X		X	X	X	X	S			X	U		U												X		X			S	S	X			24
X	X		X		X	X	X	X	X			S	X		U												X		X			S	S	U			25
X	X		X		X	X	S	X	X			S	U	X	U												X		X			U		X			26
X	X		X		X	X	X	X	X				X	X	U												S		X			S	S	U			27
X	X		X		X	X	X		X			S	X	X	U												X		X			U	S	S			28
X	X		S		X	X	X	X	X				X	X	U												X		X			U		S	S		29
X		S	S			X	X	X	X				X	X	U												X		X			X	U	X	S		30
X	X	U	S		X	X	X	X	X				X	X	U												X		X					S	S		31
X	X	X	X		X	X	X	U	X				U	S	U												S		X					X	X		32
X	X	X	X		X	X		S	X	S			X	S	U												X		X					U	X		33
X	X		S		X	X	S	X	X	X			U	X	U												X		X					X	S		34
X	X	U	X		X	X	X	X	X				U	X	U												S		X					X	U		35
X	X	U	X		X	X	S	X	X				X	X	U												X		X					S	S		36
X	X	X	S		X	X	S	X				S	U	X	U												X		X					X		X	37
X	X		S		X	X	X	X		X		X	U	X	U	S											S		X					X			38
X	X	U	X			X	X	X		S		X	X	X	U												S		X					X		S	39
X	X		X		X	X	X	X		S		X	S	X	U												S		X					X		U	40
X	X		X		X	X	X	X	S	U		S	U	X	S												X		X					X			41
X	X		X		U	X	X	X	S	U		S	X	X	U												X		X					X			42
X	X	X	U	X		X	X	X	S			X	S	S	U	X	X			X		U	U														1
X	X		X	X		X	U	S	X			X	X	X	U		U			X		U	U	X	S												2
X	X		X		X	U		X	S			X	U	X	U			U							X	X	X		X								3
X	X	S			X		X	X	X				X	X	U			S								X			X	S	X						4
X	U	U	S		X	X	X	X	X			S	X	X	U												X		X			X					5
X	U		X		X	X	S	X	X			U	X	X	U												X		X			X					6
Total League Appearances																																					
42	37	13	33	10	36	35	27	37	32	3	1	7	29	36	0	0	0	0	4	4	1	0	0	0	5	5	17	0	28	0	1	2	2	12	2	1	X
0	0	1	8	1	0	3	8	3	6	3	3	15	3	3	1	3	1	2	2	1	3	0	0	0	1	5	12	1	0	2	3	3	4	4	5	1	S
0	1	13	0	1	3	0	1	1	0	2	1	1	10	1	40	3	5	2	1	1	0	0	0	0	0	0	0	1	0	1	0	4	1	3	1	1	U
Total Cup Appearances																																					
6	4	1	3	2	4	4	3	5	4	0	0	3	4	5	0	1	1	0	0	2	0	0	0	1	1	2	3	0	4	0	1	2	0	0	0	0	X
0	0	1	1	0	0	0	1	1	2	0	0	1	1	1	0	0	0	1	0	0	0	0	0	0	1	0	0	0	0	1	0	0	0	0	0	0	S
0	2	1	1	0	0	1	1	0	0	0	0	1	1	0	6	0	1	1	0	0	0	2	2	0	0	0	0	0	0	0	0	0	0	0	0	0	U
Total Goals																																					
0	0	1	3	0	5	8	9	23	17	0	0	5	5	1	0	0	0	0	1	1	0	0	0	0	0	0	6	0	4	0	0	0	0	3	1	0	Lge
0	0	0	0	0	0	0	1	3	0	0	0	1	0	0	0	1	0	0	0	0	0	0	0	0	1	1	0	0	0	0	0	0	0	0	0	0	Cup

NEWPORT COUNTY

CURRENT SQUAD AS OF BEGINING OF 2010-11 SEASON

GOALKEEPERS		SQ NO.	HT	WT	D.O.B	AGE	P.O.B	CAREER	APPS	GOA
Kieron	Blackburn	13			24/6/88	22	Newport	Newport C, Dinas Powys, Ton Pentre, Newport C 1/09	1	0
Glyn	Garner	21	6'02"	13 11	9/12/76	33	Pontypool	Cwmbran, Llanelli, Bury 7/00, L.Orient 5/05 Rel c/s 07, Shrewsbury 8/07, Rel 1/10, Grays 2/10 Rel 5/10, Newport C 7/10		
Glyn	Thompson	1	6'02"	13 01	24/2/81	29	Telford	Shrewsbury, Fulham £50,000 10/99, Mansfield (3ML) 1/00, Shrewsbury (L) 1/01, Northampton (2ML) 11/02, Northampton 3/03 Rel c/s 04, Walsall 8/04, Koge (Den), Rushden & D (Trial) 2/05, Waterford U (Trial) 2/05, Stafford R 1/05, Chesterfield 3/05 Rel c/s 05, Shrewsbury 7/05 Rel 5/06, Koje Boldklub (den), Hereford 6/06 Rel c/s 07, Newport C 7/07	42	0
DEFENDERS										
Lee	Baker	3	5'10"	12 01	20/1/89	21	Redditch	West Brom, Kidderminster (5ML) 8/08, Kidderminster 1/09, Newport C 6/10		
Paul	Bignot	2	6'01"	12 03	14/2/86	24	Birmingham	Crewe, Kidderminster (2ML) 10/06, Kidderminster 6/07 Rel 2/09, Newport C (3ML) 9/08, Newport C 2/09	37	0
Andrew	Hughes	18			5/6/92	18	Cardiff	Cardiff (Yth), Newport C	0	0
Oliver	Thorne	15			23/1/90	20		MK Dons (Scholar) Rel c/s 08, Wivenhoe 8/08, Cheshunt 9/08, Heybridge 12/08, Glen Hoddle Academy, Forest Green 9/09, Newport C 5/10		
Chris	Todd	6	6'01"	11 09	22/8/81	29	Exeter	Swansea Rel c/s 02, Drogheda 8/02, Exeter 1/03, Torquay £7,000 6/07 Rel 5/10, Salisbury (L) 2/09, Salisbury (5WL) 11/09, Newport C (SL) 1/10, Newport C 5/10	16	3
Gary	Warren	5			16/4/84	26		Mangotsfield, Team Bath c/s 07, Newport C 5/09	36	5
MIDFIELDERS										
Jamie	Collins	4	6'03"	12 00	28/9/84	25	Barking	Watford, Havant & W 2/05, Hampton & R 7/09, Newport C 10/09	28	4
Sam	Foley	10	6'00"	10 08	17/10/86	23	Upton	Cheltenham Rel c/s 08, Bath C (L) 3/08, Kidderminster 8/08, Redditch (2ML) 10/08, Newport C (SL) 2/09, Newport C 7/09	38	17
Ricky	Manship				17/11/90	19	Church Village	Newport C, Cinderford (L) 10/09		
Eddie	Odhiambo (Was Anaclet)	16	5'09"	10 00	31/8/85	25	Arusha, Tanzania	Southampton Rel 5/06, Chester (L) 12/04, Tamworth (3ML) 11/05, Oxford U 7/06, Stevenage 7/08, Newport C 7/10		
Scott	Rogers	8	5'11"	11 00	23/5/79	31	Bristol	Exeter (Jun), Bristol C (Trainee), Tiverton 7/97, Forest Green 8/03, Weston-super-Mare (L) 11/05, Bath C 3/06, Newport C (L) 1/09, Newport C 4/09	41	3
Daniel	Rose	7	5'07"	10 01	21/2/88	22	Bristol	Man Utd, Oxford U (SL) 1/07, Oxford U 8/07 Rel 4/08, Newport C 7/08	38	8
Tony	Taggart	17			7/10/81	28	London	Brentford Rel c/s 00, Farnborough c/s 00, Barnet 6/03, Farnborough 8/04, Weymouth 6/05, Havant & W 12/05, Eastleigh 7/08, Newport C 5/10		
Wayne	Turk	14			21/1/81	29	Gloucestershire	Oxford U (Trainee), Cirencester, Salisbury 7/00, Newport C (SL) 11/08 Perm 4/09	39	1
FORWARDS										
Charlie	Henry	11			1/7/87	23	Stevenage	Arlesey, Wycombe 11/05, Grays 3/06 Rel c/s 06, Haverhill R 7/06, Cambridge C 10/06, Dorchester 6/07, Havant & W 11/07, Newport C 6/09	35	9
Darryl	Knights	20	5'07"	10 01	1/5/88	22	Ipswich	Ipswich Rel c/s 07, L.Orient (Trial) 1/07, Yeovil (SL) 2/07, Yeovil 7/07 Rel 5/08, Cambridge U (2ML) 10/07, Kidderminster (SL) 1/08, Kidderminster 5/08 Rel 7/10, Newport C 7/10		

Robbie	Matthews	19			2/3/82	28	Wiltshire	Bournemouth (Yth), Swindon (Yth), Salisbury, Bemerton Heath Harlequins 11/01, Eastleigh c/s 02, Southampton (Trial), Bristol R (Trial) 2/03, Salisbury 9/04, Havant & W (6WL) 11/08, Crawley (SL) 1/09, Kidderminster 8/09 Rel 7/10		
Craig	Reid	9	5'10"	11 10	17/12/88	21	Coventry	Ipswich (Scholar), Coventry Rel c/s 06, Tamworth (L) 3/06, Falkirk (Trial) 7/06, Dunfermline (Trial) 7/06, Cheltenham 1/07 Rel c/s 08, Grays NC 8/08, Newport C (3ML) 9/08 Perm 12/08	40	23
Giuseppe	Sole	12			8/1/88	22		Woking, Basingstoke (L) 3/06, Ebbsfleet (SL) 1/09, Newport C 5/10		

Loanees		**SN**	**HT**	**WT**	**DOB**	**AGE**	**POB**	**From - To**	**APPS**	**GOA**
(F)Jason	Bradley		6'03"	13 00	16/3/89	21	Sheffield	Mansfield 8/09 - Kings Lynn (L) 9/09, Harrogate T (SL) 12/09, Rel 4/10, Brackley T 6/10	6	1
(M)Sam	Deering		5'05"	11 00	26/2/91	19	London	Oxford U 9/09 -	4	0
(F)Kerry	Morgan		5'10"	11 03	31/10/88	21	Merthyr	Swansea (SL) 10/09 -	29	6
(F)Casey	Thomas				14/11/90	19		Swansea 10/09 -	1	0
(D)Aaron	Morris		6'01"	12 05	30/12/89	20	Cardiff	Cardiff 12/09 -	5	0
(M)Ashley	Nicholls		5'11"	11 11	30/10/81	28	Ipswich	Bishops Stortford (2ML) 12/09 - Eastleigh 3/10, Maidenhead 6/10	6	0
(F)Stuart	Douglas		5'09"	12 05	9/4/78	32	Enfield	Bath C (6WL) 2/10 - Rel 5/10	7	1
(F)Ben	Hunt				23/1/90	20		Bristol R 3/10 - Dover 7/10	2	0

Departures		**SN**	**HT**	**WT**	**DOB**	**AGE**	**POB**	**From - To**	**APPS**	**GOA**
(F)Tom	Lyons		6'01"	11 04	22/2/88	22		Lewes 3/09 - Horsham 8/09, Dulwich H, Horsham 11/09		
(M)Dean	Grubb		5'09"	11 11	4/10/87	22	Weston-Super-Mare	Weymouth 9/09 - Rel 9/09, Wellington FC, Weston-Super-Mare 12/09		
(M)Kevin	Cooper		5'10"	10 04	8/2/75	35	Derby	Chesterfield 7/08 - Rel 10/09, Neath 1/10	5	1
(D)Aaron	Cook		6'01"	11 05	6/12/79	30	Caerphilly	Salisbury (SL) 11/08 Perm 4/09 - Rel 10/09, Eastleigh 10/09, Gosport B 7/10	11	0
(D)Alton	Thelwell		6'00"	12 05	5/9/80	29	Islington	ex L.Orient 10/09 - Kettering 12/09	6	0
(M)James	Coutts		5'06"	09 07	15/4/87	23	Weymouth	USA (Coaching) 12/09 - Rel 12/09, Dorchester NC 1/10	4	0
(F)Josh	Hartrick				20/12/91	18		Aberystwyth 8/09 - Haverfordwest 1/10	2	0
(F)Ashan	Holgate		6'02"	12 00	9/11/86	23	Swindon	Weston-Super-Mare 10/09 - Rel 1/10, Swindon Supermarine 3/10	10	0
(D)Anthony	Peters		6'05"		24/10/83	26		Cleveland 12/09 - Gainsborough 1/10 Rel 3/10	2	0
(M)Nathan	Davies				26/5/82	28	Pontypool	Yth - Rel 4/10, Leamington (L) 10/09, Weymouth (L) 2/10	3	0
(D)Martyn	Giles		6'00"	12 00	10/4/86	24	Cardiff	ex Hereford 6/08 - Rel 4/10, Llanelli 4/10	14	1
(D)Paul	Cochlin				23/8/83	27	Cardiff	Bath C 10/08 - Neath 5/10	32	5
(F)Dave	Gilroy		5'11"	11 05	23/12/82	27	Yeovil	Bath C 4/09 - Rel 5/10, Weston-Super-Mare (L) 10/09, Bath C (6WL) 2/10, Woking 6/10	22	5
(M)Takumi	Ake				26/4/84	26		Team Bath 6/09 -	6	0
(M)Scott	Armitage				19/11/90	19		Yth - Merthyr (3ML) 8/09		
(M)Kris	Leek				11/3/88	22	Newport	Yth - Merthyr (L) 9/09	4	0
(D)Gary	Colborne				12/9/90	19	Newport	Yth - Clevedon T (L) 11/09	1	0
(D)Matt	Smith		5'10"	12 00	5/10/88	21	Newport	Cardiff 1/09 - Cinderford (L) 9/09	0	0
Ryan	Newman							Yth -	0	0

Do you remember when...

Newport County

Newport County failed to complete the 1988-1989 season. The club was disbanded and returned as Newport AFC in the Hellenic League. (Reclaiming their original name in 1999). They have battled their way back to the Conference Premier this season and in 1994-1995 they won the Midland Section of the Southern League as they climbed up the pyramid.

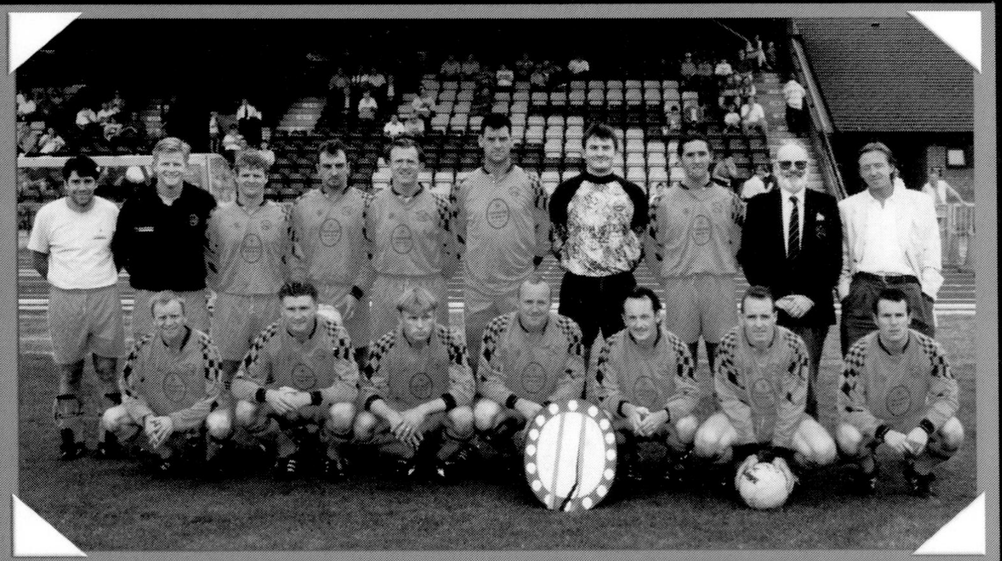

1994-1995 Back row, left to right: Linden Jones (Assistant Manager), Tom Johansen, David Webley, Mark Price, Will Foley, Brendan Dowd, Jon Roberts, Alex Smith, David Hando (Chairman) and Charlie Hopkins (Club's Lawyer).
Front Row: Kenny Latham, Craig Evans, Ray John, Steve Williams, Nigel Vaughan, Mark Tucker and Mark Spencer.

RUSHDEN & DIAMONDS

Chairman: Keith Cousins
Secretary: Matt Wild (T) 07813 019 090
(E) matt.wild@rd-fc.co.uk
Additional Committee Members:
Helen Thompson, Rachel Roberts, Matthew Banyard
Manager: Justin Edinburgh
Programme Editor: Gill Wignall (E) gill.wignall@rd-fc.co.uk

Club Factfile

Founded: 1992 **Nickname:** Diamonds
Previous Names: Irthlingborough Diamonds and Rushden Town merged in 1992
Previous Leagues: Southern 1992-96, Conference 1996-2001, Football League 2001-06

Club Colours (change): White & blue/blue/white (White & sky blue stripes/black/sky blue)

Ground: Nene Park, Irthlingborough, Northants NN9 5QF (T) 01933 652 000
Capacity: 6,635 **Seats:** **Covered:** All **Clubhouse:** Yes **Shop:** Yes
Previous Grounds: None
Simple Directions
Nene Park is situated three quarters of a mile north of the A45/A6 junction.

Record Attendance: 6,431 v Leeds United - FA Cup 3rd Round 1998-99
Record Victory: 9-0 v Weymouth (A) - Conference Premier 21/02/2009
Record Defeat: 1-7 v Cardiff City - Football League Trophy 16/10/2001
Record Goalscorer: Darren Collins - 153
Record Appearances: Gary Butterworth - 371 (1994-2000)
Additional Records: Received £25,000 from Kettering Town for Darren Collins November 2000

Senior Honours: Southern League Midland Division 1993-94. Northants Hillier Senior Cup 1993-94, 98-99.
Southern League Premier 1995-96. Conference 2000-01, Conference Shield 2000-01. Football League Division 3 2002-03.

10 YEAR RECORD

00-01	01-02	02-03	03-04	04-05	05-06	06-07	07-08	08-09	09-10
Conf 1	FL 3 6	FL 3 1	FL 2 22	FL 2 22	FL 2 24	Conf 12	Conf 16	Conf 11	Conf 4

RUSHDEN & DIAMONDS

No.	Date	Comp	H/A	Opponents	Att:	Result	Goalscorers	Pos
1	8/8/09	BSP	H	Salisbury City	1272	L 0-2		20
2	11/8/09	BSP	A	York City	2267	D 0-0		21
3	15/8/09	BSP	A	Eastbourne Borough	941	D 1-1	Akurang 58	19
4	18/8/09	BSP	H	Hayes & Yeading United	1059	W 2-1	Tomlin 62, Farrell 84	13
5	22/8/09	BSP	H	Forest Green Rovers	1056	W 4-2	Farrell 13, Byrne 27, Akurang 65, O'Connor 84	8
6	29/8/09	BSP	A	Stevenage Borough	1704	L 1-2	Akurang 58	14
7	31/8/09	BSP	H	Cambridge United	2344	D 1-1	Stuart 58	15
8	5/9/09	BSP	A	Barrow	1089	W 6-1	Farrell 2 (4, 58), Akurang 14, Pattison 38, Cousins 90, Reid 90	9
9	8/9/09	BSP	A	Ebbsfleet United	863	D 0-0		11
10	12/9/09	BSP	H	Grays Athletic	1192	W 5-4	Pattison 10, Tomlin 2 (56, pen 80), Reid 63, Akurang 90	9
11	19/9/09	BSP	H	Mansfield Town	1822	W 1-0	Akurang 90	5
12	22/9/09	BSP	A	Gateshead	409	D 0-0		6
13	26/9/09	BSP	A	Crawley Town	925	L 1-2	Farrell 10	11
14	29/9/09	BSP	H	AFC Wimbledon	1624	L 0-1		13
15	3/10/09	BSP	H	Altrincham	1168	L 0-1		13
16	17/10/09	BSP	H	Tamworth	1313	W 3-2	Tomlin 2 (4, 18), O'Connor 76	9
17	31/10/09	BSP	A	Luton Town	7101	W 2-0	Tomlin 84, Byrne 90	6
18	14/11/09	BSP	H	Histon	1126	W 2-1	Akurang 2 (37, 66)	7
19	21/11/09	BSP	A	Salisbury City	840	W 3-1	Terry 79, O'Connor 2 (83, 90)	7
20	24/11/09	BSP	A	Cambridge United	2612	D 2-2	Tomlin 13, Louis 26	6
21	1/12/09	BSP	H	York City	1117	L 0-1		7
22	5/12/09	BSP	A	Forest Green Rovers	755	L 0-1		8
23	28/12/09	BSP	H	Kidderminster Harriers	1425	W 2-1	Tomlin 2 (15, 57)	8
24	23/1/10	BSP	H	Barrow	1134	W 4-1	Louis 2 (14, 46), Farrell 57, Stuart 63	8
25	26/1/10	BSP	H	Wrexham	960	D 0-0		7
26	30/1/10	BSP	A	Hayes & Yeading United	377	W 6-1	Og 2 (Cadmore 4 Basham 51), Tomlin 18, O'Connor 45, Farrell 2 (71, 76)	7
27	6/2/10	BSP	A	Grays Athletic	476	W 3-0	O'Connor 39, Corcoran 72, Louis 81	6
28	9/2/10	BSP	H	Eastbourne Borough	1038	W 2-0	Louis 45, Corcoran 52	4
29	13/2/10	BSP	H	Stevenage Borough	1923	W 1-0	Wolleaston 88	4
30	16/2/10	BSP	A	Oxford United	7625	L 0-1		5
31	27/2/10	BSP	H	Kettering Town	2998	D 0-0		4
32	3/3/10	BSP	A	Histon	583	W 1-0	Tomlin pen 11	4
33	6/3/10	BSP	A	Tamworth	1016	W 1-0	Porter 83	3
34	13/3/10	BSP	H	Gateshead	1414	W 8-0	Stuart 6, Porter 45, Louis 2 (50, 78), Byrne 54, Tomlin 65, Farrell 81, Downer 85	4
35	20/3/10	BSP	A	Altrincham	1035	D 2-2	Og (McAliskey) 40, Terry 73	4
36	24/3/10	BSP	H	Oxford United	2970	D 1-1	Og (R Day) 59	4
37	27/3/10	BSP	A	AFC Wimbledon	3640	W 1-0	Farrell 55	4
38	30/3/10	BSP	A	Kettering Town	2031	W 3-0	Farrell 3, Byrne 12, Tomlin 64	4
39	2/4/10	BSP	H	Crawley Town	1703	D 1-1	Tomlin 45	4
40	5/4/10	BSP	A	Kidderminster Harriers	1463	D 1-1	Porter 26	4
41	10/4/10	BSP	H	Ebbsfleet United	1440	W 2-0	O'Connor 2 (27, 70)	4
42	13/4/10	BSP	A	Mansfield Town	2031	L 2-3	O'Connor 16, Smith 71	5
43	17/4/10	BSP	A	Wrexham	5672	W 1-0	O'Connor 17	4
44	24/4/10	BSP	H	Luton Town	4820	D 1-1	Byrne 20	4
	Chester	**record**	....	**...expunged 08/03**				
16	10/10/09	BSP	A	Chester City	1089	W 1-0	Tomlin 4	11
	Cups							
1	24/10/09	FAC 4Q	A	Workington	724	W 3-0	O'Connor 19, Corcoran 2 (81, pen 90)	
2	7/11/09	FAC 1	H	Hinckley United	1540	W 3-1	O'Connor 2 (31, 66), Byrne 82	
3	28/11/09	FAC 2	A	Brighton & Hove Albion	3638	L 2-3	Tomlin 14, O'Connor 40	
4	12/12/09	FAT 1	H	Billericay Town	696	W 1-0	O'Connor 73	
5	19/1/10	FAT 2	A	Workington	252	L 1-2	Farrell 50	
6	29/4/10	PO SF1	H	Oxford United	4535	D 1-1	Byrne 50	
7	3/5/10	PO SF2	A	Oxford United	11963	L 0-2	(L 1-3 agg)	

Home Attendances:	
Highest:	4820 v Luton Town
Lowest:	960 v Wrexham
Average (08-09):	1364 (1494)
Top Goalscorer:	Tomlin - 15 (14 League, 1 Cup) in 42 appearances - 36% strike rate
	O'Connor - 15 (10 League, 5 Cup) in 44 appearances - 34% strike rate
Most Appearances:	Porter - 50 (34+9 League, 7 Cup)

ROBERTS 1	ROBINSON 3	STUART 5	OSANO 2	DOWNER 6	REID 11	MCNAMARA 14	WOLLEASTON 8	O'CONNOR 7	AKURANG 25	TOMLIN 10	FARRELL 9	SMITH 19	PORTER 4	CORCORAN 16	COUSINS 12	PATTISON 18	BYRNE 20	BEECROFT 15	AISIEN 23	TERRY 24	ABBEY 31	MILLS 26	MCGUINESS 17	AINSLEY 23	LOUIS 27	DAY 13	MCDONALD 29	HUKE 22	THOMAS 11	
X	X	X	X	X	X	X	X	X	X	X	S	S	S	U	U															1
X	X	X	X		S	U	X	X	S	X	X		X	X	X	U	U													2
X		X	X	X	X	U	X	X	S	S	X		X	X	X	U	U													3
X		X	X	X	U	S	X	X	X	X	S		X	X	U	X	S													4
X		X	X	X	S	S		S	X	X	X		X	X	U	X	X	U												5
X	S	X	X	X	U			X	X	X	S	S	X	X		X	X	U												6
X	X	X	X	X	U			X	X	X	S	S	X		U	X	X		U											7
X	X	X	X		S			S	X	X	X	U	X		S	X	X		U	X										8
X	X	X	X		S			S	X	X	X	S	X		U	X	X		U	X										9
X	X	X	X		S			X	S	X	X	U	X	S	U	X	X			X										10
U	X	X	X	X	S			X	S	X	X		S		U	X	X			X	X									11
U	X	X	X	X	U				X	X	X	S	X	U	U	X	X				X									12
U	X	X	X	X	X				X		X	S	S	U	S	X	X			X	X									13
U	X	X	X	X	X				X		X	S	U	U	S	X	X			X	X									14
U	X	X	X	X	S			X	X		X	S	S		U	X	X			X	X									15
U	X	X	X					S	X	X	X	U	X	X	X	S	S			X	X									16
U	X	X	X					X	S	X	X		X	X	X	S	S			X	X	U								17
U	X	X	X	U					S	X	X		X	X		S	X			X	X	S			X					18
U	X	X	X	S		U		S	X		X		X	X	S	X	X			X	X									19
U	X	X	X	S				X	S	X	S		X	X	U		X			X	X				X					20
X	X	X	X	X				X	S	X	S		X			U	X			X				S	X	U				21
X	X	X	X					X	S	X	S		X	X		S	X			X				U	X	U				22
X	X	X	X	X		U	S	X	U	X	X		X				X			X					S	U				23
X	X	X	X	X			X			X	X	S	S	U		S	X			X					X	U				24
X	X	X	X	X			X	S		X	X	S	S	U			X			X					X	U				25
X	X	X	X	X			S	X		X	S	U	X	S			X			X					X	U				26
X	X	X		X			S	X		X	S	U	X	X		S	X			X					X	U				27
X	X	X		X		S	S	X			X	S	X	X		U	X			X					X	U				28
X	X	X	U	X			S	X	S		X	S	X	X			X			X					X	U				29
X	X	X	S	X			X	X	U	X	S		S	X			X			X					X	U				30
X	X	X	X	X				X	S	X	S		X	U		U	X			X					X	U				31
X	X		X	X		X		X	S	X	S	U	X	X		S	X								X	U				32
X	X		X	X				X	S	X	S	S	X	X		X	X								X	U	U			33
X	X	X	S	X				X		X	S	S	X	X		U	X			X					X	U				34
X	X	X	X					S	U	X	X	U	X	X		S	X			X					X	U				35
X	X	X	X	U				S	S	X	X		X	X		U	X			X					X	U				36
X	X	X	X			X	U	X	S	X	X		X	X			X								S	U		S		37
X	X	X	X			X	S	X		X	X		X	X			X								S	U		S	U	38
X	X	X	X			X	S	S	U	X	X		X				X			S					X	U		X		39
X	X	X	X	S		X	X	X	X			X	X			U	U			S					S			X		40
X	X	X	X	X			S	X	S	X	X	S	X				X			X						U		U		41
X	X	X	X			U		X	X			S	S			X	X	U		X					X	U		X		42
U	X	U	X	X		X		X	X			X	S			X	S	X								X	S	X		43
X		X	X				S		S	X	S	X	X			X	X			X					X	U	U	X		44
U	X	X	X		S			X	S	X	X		X	X	X	S	U			X	X									
U	X		X	X	U			X		X	X	U	X	X	X	S	S		U	X	X	S								1
U	X	X	X		S	U		X		X	X		X	X		S	X			X	X	S	U	U						2
U	X	X	X	X		S		X	S	X	X	U	X	U	X	S	X				X			U						3
X	X	X	X					X	S	X	X		X	X		S	X			X				U	S	U				4
X	X	X	X	X		U	S			X	X		X	U		U	X			X					X	U				5
X	X	X	X	X				X	S	X	X		X			U	X			X					S	U		S		6
X	U	X	X	X				X	S	X	S		X			S	X			X					X	U		X		7

Total League Appearances

33	39	41	39	26	4	7	8	29	16	34	26	3	34	22	4	17	36	1	0	29	10	0	0	0	20	1	0	5	0	X
0	1	0	2	3	7	3	9	9	17	1	15	16	9	2	4	8	4	0	0	2	0	1	0	1	4	0	1	2	0	S
11	0	1	1	2	4	5	1	0	4	0	0	7	1	7	10	8	3	3	3	0	0	1	0	1	0	22	2	1	1	U

Total Cup Appearances

4	6	6	7	5	0	0	0	6	0	7	6	0	7	3	2	0	6	0	0	6	3	0	0	0	2	0	0	1	0	X
0	0	0	0	0	1	1	1	0	4	0	1	0	0	0	0	5	1	0	0	0	0	2	0	0	2	0	0	1	0	S
3	1	0	0	0	1	2	0	0	0	0	0	2	0	2	0	2	0	0	1	0	0	0	1	3	0	4	0	0	0	U

Total Goals

0	0	3	0	1	2	0	1	10	8	14	11	1	3	0	1	2	5	0	0	2	0	0	0	0	7	1	0	0	0	Lge
0	0	0	0	0	0	0	0	5	0	1	1	0	0	2	0	0	2	0	0	0	0	0	0	0	0	0	0	0	0	Cup

RUSHDEN & DIAMONDS

CURRENT SQUAD AS OF BEGINING OF 2010-11 SEASON

GOALKEEPERS		SQ NO.	HT	WT	D.O.B	AGE	P.O.B	CAREER	APPS	GOA
Joe	Day	13			13/8/90	20	Brighton	C.Palace (Sch), Rushden & D 1/07, Brackley T (L) 3/09, Harrow (L) 10/09	1	0
Dale	Roberts	1	6'03"	11 06	22/10/86	23	Horden	Middlesbrough (Scholar), Sunderland (Scholar), Notts Forest, Eastwood T (SL) 3/06, Alfreton (SL) 7/06, Rushden & D (3ML) 1/08, Rushden & D (3ML) 10/08 Perm 1/09	33	0
DEFENDERS										
Jamie	Day	11	6'00"	11 09	7/5/86	24	High Wycombe	Peterborough Rel c/s 10, Man Utd (Trial), West Ham (Trial), Crawley (L) 9/04, Dag & Red (3ML) 11/09, Rushden & D 6/10		
Aynsley	McDonald	21			25/1/92	18	Earls Barton	Rushden & D, Wingate & F (L) 8/09, Banbury U (L) 1/10, Billericay (WE) 3/10	1	0
Justin	Miller	2	6'00"	11 10	16/12/80	29	Johannesburg, SA	Ipswich, L.Orient (3ML) 9/02, L.Orient 1/03 Rel c/s 07, Port Vale 7/07 Rel 4/08, Chelmsford 7/08 Rel 1/09, Bidvest Wits (SA) 1/09, Rushden & D 6/10		
Curtis	Osano	6	5'11"	11 04	8/3/87	23	Nakuru, Kenya	Reading Rel c/s 08, Aldershot T (3ML) 10/06, Woking (SL) 1/07, Rushden & D (SL) 7/07, Rushden & D 7/08	41	0
Kurt	Robinson	3	5'08"	11 00	21/10/89	20	Basildon	West Ham (Yth), Southend (Yth), Ipswich Rel 5/09, Northampton (6WL) 11/08, Rushden & D (SL) 1/09, Rushden & D 7/09	40	0
Jamie	Stuart	5	5'10"	11 00	15/10/76	33	Southwark	Charlton cc 12/97, Millwall 9/98 Rel c/s 01, Cambridge U (Trial) 7/01, Bury 10/01, Southend 6/03 Rel c/s 04, Hornchurch 7/04, Grays 11/04, Rushden & D 6/09	41	3
MIDFIELDERS										
Michael	Corcoran	16	5'10"	11 04	28/12/87	22	Coalisland	Cardiff, Oxford U (3ML) 1/07, Oxford U 7/07 Rel 1/08, Rushden & D 1/08	24	0
George	Cox				6/12/91	18	Bedford	Rushden & D, Northampton Spencer (L) 11/09, Spalding U (L) 1/10		
Shaun	Huke	20	5'11"	12 07	2/10/85	24	Reading	Rochedale Rangers (Aust), Peterborough Rel c/s 07, Kings Lynn (L) 8/03, Bedford T (L) 12/03, Heybridge (L) 3/04, Cambridge C (L) 9/04, Hornchurch (L) 11/04, Dag & Red 1/07 Rel 1/09, Central Coast Mariners (Aust) 1/09, Rushden & D 3/10	7	0
Matt	Johnson	18						Aveley, Rushden & D 6/10		
Joe	Keehan	15			7/1/87	23		Brighton (Yth), Whitehawk, Worthing 1/04, Crawley, Eastbourne B (L) 12/05 Perm 1/06, Worthing (3ML) 11/06 Perm 2/07, Horsham YMCA c/s 07, Worthing 1/08, Lewes 7/08, Rushden & D 6/10		
Max	Porter	4	5'11"	13 00	29/6/87	23	Hornchurch	Brighton (Yth), Gillingham (Yth), Southend (Sch), Cambridge U (6WL) 11/05 Perm 1/06, Bishops Stortford 6/06, Barnet Undisc 5/07 Rel c/s 09, Rushden & D 7/09	43	3
Alan	Power	14	5'07"	11 06	23/1/88	22	Dublin	Notts Forest Rel 5/08, Grays (3ML) 11/07, Hartlepool 7/08 Rel c/s 10, Rushden & D 6/10		
Lewwis	Spence	24	5'11"	13 03	29/10/87	22	Lambeth	C.Palace Rel c/s 08, C.Palace Baltimore (L) 4/07, Wycombe 6/08 Rel c/s 10, Forest Green (L) 9/09, Rushden & D 7/10		
Max	York	23			25/11/91	18		Cambridge U (Yth), Histon, Rushden & D 7/10		
FORWARDS										
Ryan	Charles	19	6'00"	11 13	30/9/89	20	Enfield	Luton Rel 5/10, Hitchin (SL) 3/07, Hinckley U (WE) 12/07, Kettering (L) 3/09, Kidderminster (5WL) 11/09, Rushden & D 6/10		
Neil	Cousins	12			23/4/82	28	Essex	Burnham R, Maldon T c/s 01, Braintree 7/02, Heybridge 12/02, Billericay c/s 04, Heybridge 11/05, Rushden & D 12/08	8	1
Craig	Farrell	9	6'00"	12 11	5/12/82	27	Middlesbrough	Leeds, Carlisle (2ML) 10/02 (Undisc) 12/02 Rel 5/05, Exeter c/s 05 Rel 5/06, York C 6/06, Oxford U (SL) 1/09, Rushden & D P/E 6/09	41	11
Aaron	O'Connor	8	5'10"	12 00	9/8/83	27	Nottingham	Ilkeston, Scunthorpe 12/02 Rel 2/03, Ilkeston 3/03, Nuneaton c/s 03, Ilkeston, Gresley R 7/04, Rushden & D (Trial) 6/06 Grays 1/07, Mansfield 8/08, Rushden & D 6/09	38	10
Nabil	Shariff	22			19/4/92	18	Milton Keynes	Rushden & D, Newport Pagnell (L) 9/09, Banbury (WE) 11/09		
Sam	Smith	17			20/5/90	20	Corby	Corby (Yth), Rushden & D 2/07, Corby T (L) 10/09, Hinckley U (L) 12/09	19	1
Lee	Tomlin	10	5'11"	10 09	12/1/89	21	Leicester	Leicester (Jun), Rushden & D 1/05, Liverpool (Trial) 4/06, Brackley (L) 10/07	35	14

Loanees		HT	WT	DOB	AGE	POB	From - To	APPS	GOA
(M)James	Reid	5'10"	11 04	28/2/90	20	Nottingham	Notts Forest (6ML) 7/09 - Rel 1/10, Lincoln C 3/10	11	2
(F)Cliff	Akurang	6'02"	12 03	27/2/81	29	Ghana	Barnet (SL) 7/09 - Rel 6/10, Thurrock 7/10	33	8
(M)Mark	Byrne	5'08"	11 00	9/11/88	20	Dublin	Notts Forest (SL) 7/09 - Barnet (6ML) 7/10	40	5
(F)Danny	Mills			2/8/91	19		Peterborough 10/09 -	1	0
(D)Jack	Ainsley	5'10"	11 00	17/9/91	18	Ipswich	Ipswich (2ML) 11/09	1	0
(F)Jefferson	Louis	6'02"	13 02	22/2/79	31	Harrow	Crawley (SL) 11/09 - Rel 5/10, Gainsborough 6/10	24	7
(F)Wesley	Thomas	5'10"	11 00	23/1/87	23	Barking	Dag & Red 3/10 - Cheltenham c/s 10	0	0

Departures		HT	WT	DOB	AGE	POB	From - To	APPS	GOA
(D)Bobby	Aisien			19/12/88	21		Wingate & F 8/09 - Kings Lynn (L) 9/09 Perm 10/09, Alfreton 12/09,		
							Billericay 3/10	0	0
(G)Nathan	Abbey	6'01"	11 13	11/7/78	32	Islington	ex MK Dons 9/09 - Rel 12/09, Kettering 1/10	10	0
(D)Jack	Higgins			30/7/91	19	Burnley	Boston U (Yth) 7/07 - Hemel Hempstead (3ML) 8/09, Rossendale 1/10		
(M)Robert	Wolleaston	5'11"	11 07	21/12/79	30	Perivale	Cambridge U 6/08 - Rel 5/10	17	1
(M)Jamie	McGuinness			4/5/90	20		Luton (Scholar) 7/08 - Rel 5/10, Bedford T (L) 8/09,		
							Weymouth (SL) 11/09	0	0
(M)Nicky	McNamara			11/12/89	20		Spalding U 3/09 - Rel 5/10	10	0
(M)Matt	Pattison			24/3/84	26	Surrey	Woking 6/09 - Rel 5/10, Basingstoke 5/10	25	2
(M)Lewis	Hilliard			2/10/90	19	March	Yth - Rel 5/10, Hemel Hempstead (3ML) 8/09		
(M)Jake	Beecroft			4/9/89	20		Yth - Rel 5/10 - Ilkeston (3ML) 9/09, St Albans (2ML) 1/10,		
							Tonbridge A 5/10	1	0
(M)Paul	Terry	5'10"	12 06	3/4/79	31	Barking	Grays 8/09 - Rel 6/10	31	2
(D)Simon	Downer	5'11"	12 08	19/10/81	28	Romford	Sutton U 1/09 - Rel 6/10, Sutton U 7/10	29	1

Do you remember when...

Rushden & Diamonds

Rushden & Diamonds won the Southern League championship in 1995-1996 and were promoted into the G.M.Vauxhall Conference where they finished 12th in their first season.

Back row, left to right: Steve Spooner, Andy Kirkup, Darren Collins, Steve Stott and Tim Wooding.
Middle Row: Billy Jeffrey, Steve Holden, Kevin Wilkin, Graham Benstead, Andy Lomas, Nick Ashby, Brendan Hackett and Paul Richardson.
Front Row: Ian King, David Holmes, Neil Smith Andy Peaks, Roger Ashby, (Manager), Carl Alford, Al James Hannigan and Garry Butterworth.

SOUTHPORT

Chairman: Charles Clapham
Secretary: Ken Hilton (T) 01704 533 422
(E) secretary@southportfc.net
Additional Committee Members: Sam Shrouder, Andrew Pope, Tim Medcroft, Stephen Porter, Gordon Medcroft, Roy Holden, Wes Hall, Russ Broadbent, Hayden Preece
Manager: Liam Watson
Programme Editor: Rob Urwin (E) rob@southportfcstats.co.uk

Back Row L to R: Kevin Lee, Rob Marsh-Evans, Steve Dickinson, Matty McNeil, Tony McMillan, Earl Davis, Chris Lever
Middle Row L to R: Alan Moogan, Liam Blakeman, Chris Simm, Robbie Williams, Shaun Gray, Michael Powell, Steve Daly, Tony Gray
Front Row L to R: Alan Collins, Mal Liptrot (Chief Scout), Ashley Winn, Chris Price (Asst Manager), Adam Flynn (Captain), Liam Watson (Manager), Matty McGinn, Dominic Morley (Coach), Danny Lloyd

Club Factfile

Founded: 1881 **Nickname:** The Sandgrounders
Previous Names: Southport Central, Southport Vulcan
Previous Leagues: Preston & District, Lancashire 1889-1903, Lancashire comb. 1903-11, Central 1911-21, Football League 1921-78, Northern Premier 1978-93, 2003-04, Conference 1993-2003
Club Colours (change): Yellow & black/yellow/yellow (White/black/white)

Ground: Haig Avenue, Southport, Merseyside PR8 6JZ (T) 01704 533 422
Capacity: 6,008 **Seats:** 1,660 **Covered:** 2,760 **Clubhouse:** Yes **Shop:** Yes
Previous Grounds: Sussex Road Sports Ground, Scarisbrick New Road, Ash Lane (later named Haig Avenue)
Simple Directions
Leave M6 at junction 26. Join M58 to junction 3. Join A570 signposted Southport, follow A570 through Ormskirk Town Centre following signs for Southport. At the big roundabout (McDonalds is on the left) take the fourth exit. Proceed along this road until you reach the 2nd set of pedstrian lights and take the next left into Haig Avenue.

Record Attendance: 20,010 v Newcastle United - FA Cup 1932
Record Victory: 8-1 v Nelson - 01/01/31
Record Defeat: 0-11 v Oldham Athletic - 26/12/62
Record Goalscorer: Alan Spence - 98
Record Appearances: Arthur Peat - 401 (1962-72)
Additional Records: Paid £20,000 to Macclesfield Town for Martin McDonald

Senior Honours: Lancashire Senior Cup 1904-05. Liverpool Senior Cup 1930-31, 31-32, 43-44, 62-63, 74-75, 90-91, 92-93, 98-99, Shared 57-58, 63-64. Football League Division 4 1972-73. Northern Premier League Challenge Cup 1990-91. Northern Premier League Premier Division 1992-93. Conference North 2004-05, 2009-10.

10 YEAR RECORD

00-01		01-02		02-03		03-04		04-05		05-06		06-07		07-08		08-09		09-10	
Conf	4	Conf	15	Conf	21	NP P	6	Conf N	10	Conf	18	Conf	23	Conf N	4	Conf N	5	Conf N	1

SOUTHPORT

No.	Date	Comp	H/A	Opponents	Att:	Result	Goalscorers	Pos
1	8/8/09	BSN	H	Gloucester City	780	W 3-2	McGinn 13, Davis 32, Kilheeney 52	5
2	11/8/09	BSN	A	Blyth Spartans	737	W 2-0	Simm 3, Kilheeney 59	3
3	15/8/09	BSN	A	Ilkeston Town	452	L 2-3	Kilheeney 67, Daly 83	6
4	18/8/09	BSN	H	Stalybridge Celtic	764	W 2-1	Kilheeney 2 (30, 42)	4
5	22/8/09	BSN	A	Alfreton Town	448	D 1-1	Simm 90	4
6	29/8/09	BSN	H	Harrogate Town	708	W 3-1	Marsh-Evans 51, Daly pen 70,McGinn 81	3
7	31/8/09	BSN	A	Northwich Victoria	724	D 1-1	Daly pen 84	3
8	5/9/09	BSN	H	Hinckley United	710	D 1-1	Kilheeney 88	4
9	8/9/09	BSN	H	Stafford Rangers	606	W 4-2	Kilheeney 3 (14, 71, 90), Davis 65	3
10	12/9/09	BSN	A	Gainsborough Trinity	530	W 4-2	Kilheeney 12, McGinn 39, Daly 2 (61, 70)	2
11	3/10/09	BSN	A	Solihull Moors	338	D 1-1	Lee 76	2
12	17/10/09	BSN	A	AFC Telford	1731	W 2-0	Simm 18, Kilheeney pen 23	2
13	27/10/09	BSN	A	Vauxhall Motors	323	W 3-1	Daly 71, Lee 87, Booth 90	1
14	31/10/09	BSN	H	Eastwood Town	831	W 5-1	Powell 5, Og 2 (McAughtrie 50, J Turner 52), Moogan 78, Daly 90	1
15	7/11/09	BSN	A	Workington	427	W 2-0	Lever 25, Daly 54	1
16	10/11/09	BSN	H	Redditch United	611	W 2-0	Winn 28, Powell 81	1
17	14/11/09	BSN	H	Ilkeston Town	904	D 1-1	Booth 66	1
18	28/11/09	BSN	H	Corby Town	815	W 4-0	Kilheeney 19, Powell 2 (35, 74), Simm 79	1
19	30/11/09	BSN	A	Hyde United	456	D 1-1	Daly 51	1
20	5/12/09	BSN	H	Solihull Moors	733	W 3-0	McGinn 2 (55, 66), Lever 83	1
21	26/12/09	BSN	H	Fleetwood Town	1840	W 5-0	Davis 2 (9, 78), Kilheeney 43, Powell 2 (50, 74)	1
22	1/1/10	BSN	A	Fleetwood Town	2541	L 0-4		1
23	23/1/10	BSN	H	AFC Telford	806	W 3-0	McGinn 2 (49, 76), Simm 90	2
24	30/1/10	BSN	A	Stafford Rangers	635	W 2-1	Daly 2 (pen 49, 90)	2
25	6/2/10	BSN	H	Blyth Spartans	738	W 3-2	Davis 31, Simm 2 (39, 81)	2
26	8/2/10	BSN	A	Hinckley United	394	L 1-4	Daly 60	2
27	27/2/10	BSN	A	Corby Town	418	D 1-1	Kilheeney 21	2
28	6/3/10	BSN	H	Gainsborough Trinity	851	D 0-0		2
29	9/3/10	BSN	A	Stalybridge Celtic	471	W 1-0	Daly 44	2
30	13/3/10	BSN	A	Redditch United	344	D 2-2	Davis 80, McGinn 85	2
31	16/3/10	BSN	H	Workington	709	W 2-0	Simm 27, Daly 45	2
32	20/3/10	BSN	H	Droylsden	815	D 3-3	Simm 18, McGinn 2 (pen 28, pen 89)	2
33	23/3/10	BSN	A	Gloucester City	301	D 2-2	Simm 39, Daly 53	2
34	27/3/10	BSN	H	Vauxhall Motors	826	W 3-0	Og (Winters) 31, Daly 61, Simm 75	2
35	3/4/10	BSN	A	Harrogate Town	458	W 3-2	Daly 36, Lever 46, Kilheeney 85	2
36	5/4/10	BSN	H	Northwich Victoria	1107	W 2-1	Powell 45, McGinn pen 89	1
37	10/4/10	BSN	A	Droylsden	584	W 3-0	Daly 25, McGinn pen 38, Kilheeney 41	1
38	17/4/10	BSN	H	Hyde United	1306	W 4-1	Kilheeney 2, Davis 13, McGinn pen 45, Barratt 50	1
39	20/4/10	BSN	H	Alfreton Town	2021	L 1-3	McGinn pen 19	1
40	24/4/10	BSN	A	Eastwood Town	1147	W 3-0	McGinn pen 8, Simm 50, lever 70	CH
	Farsley Celtic record expunged 12/03							
11	19/9/09	BSN	H	Farsley Celtic	743	L 2-3	Daly 20, Simm 90	2
28	13/2/10	BSN	A	Farsley Celtic	380	W 2-0	Daly 45, Kilheeney 73	2
	Cups							
1	26/9/09	FAC 2Q	H	Spennymoor Town	554	W 3-1	Daly pen 20, Powell 44, Aley 77	
2	10/10/09	FAC 3Q	A	Alfreton Town	613	D 2-2	Powell 2 (20, 90)	
3	13/10/09	FAC 3QR	H	Alfreton Town	533	W 2-1	McGinn 30, Kilheeney pen 79	
4	24/10/09	FAC 4Q	A	Gateshead	402	L 0-3		
5	21/11/09	FAT 3Q	A	Stourbridge	319	D 0-0		
6	24/11/09	FAT 3QR	H	Stourbridge	268	W 4-2	Lever 41, Daly 2 (52, pen 87), Og (Bennett) 84	
7	12/12/09	FAT 1	H	Gainsborough Trinity	478	D 2-2	Aley 7, Simm 57	
8	15/12/09	FAT 1R	A	Gainsborough Trinity	218	L 0-1		

Home Attendances:	
Highest:	2021 v Alfreton Town
Lowest:	606 v Stafford Rangers
Average (08-09):	811 (929)
Top Goalscorer:	Daly - 21 (18 League, 3 Cup) in 43 appearances - 49% strike rate
Most Appearances:	Flynn - 46 (40 League, 6 Cup)
	McMillan - 46 (40 League, 6 Cup)

MCMILLAN	LEVER	MARSH-EVANS	FLYNN	DAVIS	BARNES	WINN	MOOGAN	DALY	KILHEENEY	MCGINN	SIMM	POWELL	BOOTH	GRAY	BARRATT	ALEY	LEE	FINLEY	EASTHAM	LLOYD	HOLDEN	BATHURST	LAKE	PRICE	ONIBUJE	WILLIAMS	
X	X	X	X	X	X	X	X	X	X	X	S	S	S	U	U												1
X	X	X	X	X	S	X	X	S	X	X	X	X	U	U	S												2
X	X	X	X	X	X	X	X	S	X	X	X	S		U	S	U											3
X	X	X	X	X	X			X	X	X	S	X		U	X	S	S	U									4
X	X	X	X	X	S		U	X	X	X	X	X		U	S	S	X										5
X		X	X	X	X		U	X	U	X	X	X		S	X	S	X	S									6
X		X	X	X	X			S	X	X	X	X		U	X	S	X	U	U								7
X	U	X	X	X	X		S	X	X	X		X		U	X	S	X		U								8
X	U		X	X	S	S	X	X	X			X		X	X	X	X		U	S							9
X	U	X	X	X	S	X	X	S	X	X		X		U	X	S	X										10
X	U	X	X	X		U	X	X	X	X	X	X			S	S	X					U					11
X	X	X	X	X	S	X	X	U	X	X	X	X	S	U		S											12
X	X	X	X	X	U	X	X	S	X	X	X	X	S			U	S										13
X	X	X	X	X	U	X	X	S	X	X	X	X	S			U	S										14
X	X		X		S	X	X	X	X	X	S	X	U	X		S	X		U								15
X	X		X	X	U	X	U	S	X	X	X	X	S	X		S	X										16
X	X		X	X	U		X	X	X	X	S	X	X	X		S			U			U					17
X	X	X	X	X	S	X	X	U	X	X	X	X	S			S	U										18
X	U		X	X	S	X	X	X	X	X	S	X		X	S	U	X										19
X	X	X	X	X	S	X	X	S	X	X	X	X	S	U									U				20
X	X		X	X		X	X	S	X	X	X	X		X	U	S	S						U				21
X	X		X	X		X	X	S	X	X	X	X		X	U	S	S						U				22
X	X	S	X	X		X		X	X	X	S	X	S	X	U		X						U				23
X		S	X	X	X	X		X	X	X	S	X	U	X	S		X						U				24
X	X	X	X	X	S	X		S	X	X	X	X	X	U	S								U				25
X	X	X	X	U	X	X	X	X	U	X	X	U	S	X									U				26
X		S	X	X	U	X	X	X	X	X	S	X	S	X	X								U				27
X	X	X	X	X		X	X	S	X	X	X	X	S	S	U								U				28
X	X	X	X	X	S	X		X	S	X	U	X	X	U	X								U				29
X	X	X	X	X	U	X		X	X	X	S	X	S	U			X						U				30
X	X		X	X		X	X	X		X	X	X	S	S	U		X						U		S		31
X		U	X	X		X	X		X	X	X	X	S	X	S		X						U		S		32
X	X	X	X			X	X	X	S	X	X	X	U	X	S								U		S		33
X			X	X		X	X	X		X	X	X	S	X	S		X						U		S	U	34
X	X		X	X		X		X	S	X	S	X	X	X	X		S						U			U	35
X	X		X	X		X	X	S	X	X	X	X	S	U	U		X						U				36
X	X	U	X	X		X	X	X	X	X	S		S	S	X		X						U				37
X	X	U	X	X		X		X	X	X	S	X	S	S	X		X						U				38
X	X	S	X	X		X	X		X	X	X	X	S	U	S		X						U				39
X	X		X	X		X	X		X	X	X	X	S	S	S		X						U		U		40
X	X	S	X	X	S	X	X	X	X	X	S	U			X	U	X										
X	X	X	X	X	S	X	X	X	S	X	X	X		U	S								U				

MCMILLAN	LEVER	MARSH-EVANS	FLYNN	DAVIS	BARNES	WINN	MOOGAN	DALY	KILHEENEY	MCGINN	SIMM	POWELL	BOOTH	GRAY	BARRATT	ALEY	LEE	FINLEY	EASTHAM	LLOYD	HOLDEN	BATHURST	LAKE	PRICE	ONIBUJE	WILLIAMS	
X	X	X	U	X		S	X	X	X	X	S	X			X	S	X	U	U		U						1
X	X	X	X	X	U	X	X	S	X	S	X	X			U	X			U		U	U					2
X	X	X	X	X	U	X	X	X	S	X	X	X			U	S			U		U	U					3
X	X	X	X	X	S	X	U	X	U	X	X	X				S	X		U		U	S					4
X		X	X		X	X	X	X	U		X	S	X	X	U	S	X					S					5
X	X		X	X	X	X	U	X	U		S		X	X	X	X			U			S					6
U	S	X	X	X	X		U	X	U		X		X	X	X	X							X	S			7
U	X	X		X	X	X	U	S	X	U	X			X	X	X							X	U			8

Total League Appearances

MCMILLAN	LEVER	MARSH-EVANS	FLYNN	DAVIS	BARNES	WINN	MOOGAN	DALY	KILHEENEY	MCGINN	SIMM	POWELL	BOOTH	GRAY	BARRATT	ALEY	LEE	FINLEY	EASTHAM	LLOYD	HOLDEN	BATHURST	LAKE	PRICE	ONIBUJE	WILLIAMS	
40	29	21	40	37	8	32	27	22	33	39	24	36	4	15	11	1	21	0	0	0	0	0	0	0	0	0	X
0	0	4	0	0	11	1	1	13	3	0	12	2	20	6	12	14	6	1	0	1	0	0	0	0	4	0	S
0	5	3	0	1	6	1	3	2	2	0	1	1	4	15	7	4	1	2	5	0	0	2	21	0	1	2	U

Total Cup Appearances

MCMILLAN	LEVER	MARSH-EVANS	FLYNN	DAVIS	BARNES	WINN	MOOGAN	DALY	KILHEENEY	MCGINN	SIMM	POWELL	BOOTH	GRAY	BARRATT	ALEY	LEE	FINLEY	EASTHAM	LLOYD	HOLDEN	BATHURST	LAKE	PRICE	ONIBUJE	WILLIAMS	
6	6	7	6	7	4	6	4	6	3	3	6	4	3	4	4	4	3	0	0	0	0	0	2	0	0	0	X
0	1	0	0	0	1	1	0	2	1	1	2	1	0	0	0	4	0	0	0	0	0	3	0	1	0	0	S
2	0	0	1	0	2	0	4	0	4	1	0	0	0	0	3	0	0	1	5	0	4	2	0	1	0	0	U

Total Goals

MCMILLAN	LEVER	MARSH-EVANS	FLYNN	DAVIS	BARNES	WINN	MOOGAN	DALY	KILHEENEY	MCGINN	SIMM	POWELL	BOOTH	GRAY	BARRATT	ALEY	LEE	FINLEY	EASTHAM	LLOYD	HOLDEN	BATHURST	LAKE	PRICE	ONIBUJE	WILLIAMS	
0	4	1	0	7	0	1	1	18	17	15	12	7	2	0	1	0	2	0	0	0	0	0	0	0	0	0	Lge
0	1	0	0	0	0	0	0	3	1	1	1	3	0	0	0	2	0	0	0	0	0	0	0	0	0	0	Cup

SOUTHPORT

CURRENT SQUAD AS OF BEGINING OF 2010-11 SEASON

GOALKEEPERS		SQ NO.	HT	WT	D.O.B	AGE	P.O.B	CAREER	APPS	GOA
Steve	Dickinson				1/12/73	36		Bradford C Rel c/s 92, Guiseley 7/93, Southport 7/99, Guiseley c/s 06, Hucknall (L) 3/08, Leigh Genesis 5/08, Burscough 11/08, Alfreton 3/09, Bradford PA 6/09, Southport 5/10		
Damian	Eastham				14/4/92	18	Liverpool	Southport, Marine (Dual) 9/09	0	0
Anthony	McMillan				19/2/82	28	Wigan	Preston (Scholar), Wigan, Runcorn, Lancaster 3/05, Burscough 6/06, Lancaster (2ML) 11/06, Ashton U (L) 2/07, Colwyn Bay (L) 3/07, Southport 7/08	40	0
DEFENDERS										
Paul	Barratt				15/9/87	22	Manchester	Liverpool (Yth) Rel c/s 07, Worcester 8/07, Southport 11/07, Northwich 5/08 Rel 3/09, Fleetwood (L) 1/09, Southport 5/09, Hyde U (L) 10/09	23	1
Earl	Davis		6'01"	13 02	17/5/83	27	Manchester	Burnley, Southport (SL) 3/03, Southport 12/03, Swansea NC 1/04 Rel 2/04, Southport 2/04, Hyde U c/s 06, Burscough (3ML) 11/07 Perm 2/08, Southport 7/08	37	7
Adam	Flynn				12/10/84	25		Liverpool (Scholar), Prescot Cables 8/04, Burscough 6/07, Southport 7/08	40	0
Shaun	Gray				28/1/87	23	Ormskirk	Morecambe, Fleetwood (L) 1/06, Clitheroe (L) 8/06, Fleetwood 12/06, Prescot Cables (L) 1/08, Burscough 5/08, Southport 7/08, Burscough (L) 9/09	21	0
Alex	Grisedale				8/10/90	19	Liverpool	Southport, Burscough (L) 12/09		
Shaun	Holden				12/12/91	18	Fazackerley	Southport, Burscough (L) 12/09	0	0
Kevin	Lee		6'00"	11 10	4/11/85	24	Liverpool	Wigan, Accrington (L) 10/05, Blackpool (L) 3/06, Southport 7/06	27	2
Chris	Lever				13/2/87	23	Oldham	Oldham Rel c/s 07, Stalybridge (SL) 3/07, Southport c/s 07	29	4
Robert	Marsh-Evans		6'03"	12 08	13/10/86	23	Abergele	Chester Rel 1/08, Droylsden (L) 8/07, Vauxhall Motors (3ML) 9/07, Leigh RMI/Leigh Genesis 1/08 Rel 11/08, Vauxhall Motors 11/08, Southport 5/09	25	1
Robbie	Williams		5'10"	12 00	12/4/79	31	Liverpool	Liverpool (Ass Sch), Southport (Yth), St Dominics, Accrington 7/99, Southport (Trial) 7/09, Banned for 8 months, Southport 3/10	0	0
MIDFIELDERS										
Liam	Blakeman				6/9/82	27	Southport	Blackburn Rel c/s 02, Southport 7/02, Leigh RMI 11/02, St Helens 1/03, Burscough 7/03, Southport 1/06, AFC Telford 5/08, Southport 6/10		
Sam	Finley				4/8/92	18	Liverpool	Southport, Chorley (L) 11/09	1	0
Dan	Lloyd-McGoldrick				3/12/91	18	Liverpool	Southport, Marine (Dual) 9/09, Chorley (L) 11/09	1	0
Matty	McGinn				27/6/83	27	Fazackerley	Southport, Runcorn 8/02, Southport 7/05 Rel 9/06, Burscough 9/06, Southport 7/08	39	15
Connor	Millington				21/3/92	18	Liverpool	Southport, Skelmersdale (Dual) 9/09, Chorley (L) 11/09		
Alan	Moogan				22/2/84	26	Liverpool	Everton Rel c/s 04, Injured, Burscough c/s 06, Southport 7/08	28	1
Dominic	Morley				7/6/77	33	Liverpool	Liverpool (Trainee), Witton 7/95, Knowsley 8/96, Droylsden 4 fig 7/97, Southport c/s 99, Droylsden 8/00, Runcorn 10/01, Southport 5/04, Burscough 6/06 (Pl/Ass Man) 10/08, Southport (Pl/Coach) 5/10		
Mike	Powell				11/9/85	24	Ormskirk	Southport	38	7
Ashley	Winn		5'11"	11 02	1/12/85	24	Stockton	Middlesbrough (Yth), Oldham Rel 5/05, York C 8/05 Rel 5/06, Stalybridge (L) 3/06, Stalybridge 7/06, Barrow 7/08, Southport (L) 12/08, Southport 1/09	33	1

FORWARDS

Steve	Daly			10/12/81	28	Fazackerley	Wigan (Yth), Local, Runcorn 6/03, Southport 10/03, Droylsden 8/06, Burscough 5/08, Southport 7/08	35	18
Tony	Gray			6/4/84	26		Newton, Bangor C 9/04, Burscough 7/05, Southport 6/06, Droylsden 12/08, Southport 5/10		
Matty	McNeil	6'05"	14 03	14/7/76	34	Manchester	Burnley, Curzon Ashton, Altrincham, Woodley Sports 11/98, Stalybridge 9/99, Woking, Stalybridge, Runcorn 1/02, Hyde 8/03, Macclesfield (SL) 3/06, Macclesfield 7/06 Rel c/s 07, Stockport 7/07 Rel 1/10, Southport 5/10		
Chris	Simm	6'00"	12 08	10/4/84	26	Wigan	Congleton, Leigh RMI c/s 04, Wrexham (Trial) 7/07, Hyde 7/07, Southport 5/09	36	12

Departures		HT	WT	DOB	AGE	POB	From - To	APPS	GOA
(F)Jonathan	Bathurst			29/7/89	21		Skelmersdale 9/09 - Vauxhall Motors 12/09, Burscough 1/10	0	0
(F)Zac	Aley			17/8/91	19	Fazackerley	Yth - Blackburn 2/10	15	0
(G)Sean	Lake			19/9/87	22		Marine 12/09 - Rel 6/10	0	0
(M)Bradley	Barnes			12/12/88	21		Trafford 8/09 - FC Halifax (L) 3/10, Droylsden 7/10	19	0
(M)Robbie	Booth	5'07"	11 08	30/12/85	24	Liverpool	Burscough 7/08 - Vauxhall Motors (2ML) 8/09, Droylsden 7/10	24	2
(F)Ciaren	Kilheeney	5'11"	11 09	9/1/84	26	Stockport	Burscough 6/08 - Droylsden 7/10	36	17
(M)Chris	Price	5'09"	11 09	24/10/75	34	Liverpool	Burscough 7/08 -	0	0
(F)Fola	Onibuje	6'05"	14 09	25/9/84	25	Lagos, Ghana	Grays 3/10 -	4	0

Do you remember when...

Southport

Southport are now starting their fourth spell in The Conference Premier but this squad enjoyed a glorious season in 1992-1993 when they won promotion and The Northern Premier League, The Liverpool Senior Cup and The Lancashire ATS Challenge Trophy.

Back row, left to right: M.Morgan (Director), Chris Walmsley, Steve Joel (Assistant Manager), David Gamble, Alan McDonald, Paul Lodge, Paul Comstive, Paul Moore, Derek Goulding, L.Williams (Assistant Secretary), D.Knight (Physio), A.Pope (Director), T.Medcroft (Director) and Brian Kettle (Manager).
Front Row: Dave Fuller, Peter Withers, Roy Morris (Secretary), Charlie Clapham (Chairman), Steve Haw, Leroy Dove, Peter Quinlan and Richard Mitchell.

TAMWORTH

Chairman: Bob Andrews
Secretary: Rod Hadley (T) 01827 657 98 (Option 3)
(E) clubsec@thelambs.co.uk
Additional Committee Members: Stephen Lathbury, Brian Whitehouse, John Holcroft, Martin Newbold, Rod Hadley, Nick, Lunn, Dave Clayton
Manager: Gary Mills
Programme Editor: Dave Clayton (E) davec.tfc@hotmail.co.uk

Club Factfile

Founded: 1933 **Nickname:** The Lambs
Previous Names:
Previous Leagues: Birmingham Combination 1933-54, West Midlands (originally Birmingham League) 1954-72, 84-88, Southern 1972-79, 83-84, 89-2003, Northern Premier 1979-83
Club Colours (change): All red (All royal blue)

Ground: The Lamb Ground, Kettlebrook, Tamworth, Staffordshire B77 1AA (T) 01827 657 98
Capacity: 4,100 **Seats:** 518 **Covered:** 1,191 **Clubhouse:** Yes **Shop:** Yes
Previous Grounds: Jolly Sailor Ground 1933-34
Simple Directions
M42 Junction 10. Take A5/A51 to Town centre, then follow the signs for Kettlebrook and Tamworth FC.

Record Attendance: 5,500 v Torquay United - FA Cup 1st Round 15/11/69
Record Victory: 14-4 v Holbrook Institue (H) - Bass Vase 1934
Record Defeat: 0-11 v Solihull (A) - Birmingham Combination 1940
Record Goalscorer: Graham Jessop - 195
Record Appearances: Dave Seedhouse - 869
Additional Records: Paid £7,500 to Ilkeston Town for David Hemmings December 2000
Received £7,500 from Telford United for Martin Myers 1990
Senior Honours: Birmingham Senior Cup 1960-61, 65-66, 68-69. West Midlands League 1964-65, 65-66, 71-72, 87-88. FA Vase 1988-89. Southern League Premier Division 2002-03. Conference North 2008-09.

10 YEAR RECORD

00-01	01-02	02-03	03-04	04-05	05-06	06-07	07-08	08-09	09-10
SthP 12	SthP 2	SthP 1	Conf 17	Conf 15	Conf 20	Conf 22	Conf N 15	Conf N 1	Conf 16

TAMWORTH

No.	Date	Comp	H/A	Opponents	Att:	Result	Goalscorers	Pos
1	8/8/09	BSP	A	Stevenage Borough	2130	D 1-1	Pritchard 29	14
2	15/8/09	BSP	H	Grays Athletic	729	W 2-1	Pritchard 20, Sheridan 25	9
3	18/8/09	BSP	A	Gateshead	429	D 1-1	Wright 41	12
4	22/8/09	BSP	H	Cambridge United	1316	D 0-0		15
5	25/8/09	BSP	H	Wrexham	1290	W 2-1	C Smith 36, Sheridan 70	7
6	29/8/09	BSP	A	Barrow	1051	L 0-1		13
7	31/8/09	BSP	H	Kidderminster Harriers	1237	W 2-1	Wright 47, Rodman 63	6
8	5/9/09	BSP	H	AFC Wimbledon	1669	D 2-2	Sheridan 7, Wright 37	8
9	12/9/09	BSP	A	Hayes & Yeading United	355	D 2-2	Benjamin 57, Blackwood 68	7
10	19/9/09	BSP	H	Salisbury City	1003	W 2-0	Blackwood 13, Briscoe 17	3
11	22/9/09	BSP	A	Altrincham	843	D 0-0		4
12	26/9/09	BSP	A	Eastbourne Borough	1053	D 1-1	Sheridan 60	7
13	3/10/09	BSP	A	Luton Town	6297	L 1-2	Rodman 59	10
14	6/10/09	BSP	H	York City	1118	L 2-3	Tait 2 (18, 87)	10
15	10/10/09	BSP	H	Histon	1090	L 1-3	Wylde 48	12
16	17/10/09	BSP	A	Rushden & Diamonds	1313	L 2-3	Wright 8, Tait 90	13
17	31/10/09	BSP	H	Hayes & Yeading United	919	L 0-2		14
18	21/11/09	BSP	A	Ebbsfleet United	867	W 1-0	Pritchard 27	11
19	24/11/09	BSP	H	Altrincham	630	L 0-2		12
20	28/11/09	BSP	A	Grays Athletic	496	L 0-1		12
21	1/12/09	BSP	A	Kidderminster Harriers	1166	D 0-0		13
22	5/12/09	BSP	H	Crawley Town	729	L 0-1		14
23	26/12/09	BSP	A	Kettering Town	1250	D 0-0		14
24	28/12/09	BSP	H	Forest Green Rovers	868	D 0-0		14
25	16/1/10	BSP	A	Oxford United	5690	W 1-0	Christie 28	13
26	23/1/10	BSP	H	Eastbourne Borough	883	D 1-1	Christie 7	12
27	6/2/10	BSP	H	Stevenage Borough	841	W 1-0	C Smith 23	12
28	9/2/10	BSP	A	Wrexham	2435	D 0-0		12
29	13/2/10	BSP	H	Mansfield Town	1389	L 2-4	Wylde 19, Murdock 50	12
30	16/2/10	BSP	A	Salisbury City	586	L 0-1		12
31	23/2/10	BSP	H	Kettering Town	489	L 1-3	C Smith	14
32	2/3/10	BSP	H	Gateshead	473	W 1-0	Christie 56	13
33	6/3/10	BSP	H	Rushden & Diamonds	1016	L 0-1		13
34	9/3/10	BSP	A	Histon	350	L 0-1		17
35	13/3/10	BSP	A	Mansfield Town	2954	D 0-0		17
36	21/3/10	BSP	H	Oxford United	1572	D 0-0		16
37	24/3/10	BSP	A	Cambridge United	2121	L 0-2		16
38	27/3/10	BSP	A	York City	2863	D 1-1	C Smith 82	18
39	3/4/10	BSP	H	Barrow	817	W 3-0	Mitchell 45, Sheridan 46, Christie 78	17
40	5/4/10	BSP	A	Forest Green Rovers	1370	W 4-3	Shaw pen 6, Pritchard 37, Sheridan 64, Christie 74	15
41	10/4/10	BSP	H	Luton Town	2246	D 1-1	Lyttle 58	15
42	17/4/10	BSP	A	Crawley Town	755	L 0-2		17
43	20/4/10	BSP	A	AFC Wimbledon	3015	W 1-0	Wylde 26	16
44	24/4/10	BSP	H	Ebbsfleet United	1694	L 3-4	Christie 11, Wylde 40, Pritchard 58	16
	Chester record	**........................**		**...expunged 08/03**				
9	8/9/09	BSP	A	Chester City	1199	W 2-1	Tait 37, C Smith 59	5
19	14/11/09	BSP	H	Chester City	955	W 3-1	Mackenzie 10, Brown 69, Wright 76	13
	Cups							
1	24/10/09	FAC 4Q	A	Ilkeston Town	669	L 0-2		
2	12/12/09	FAT 1	A	Mansfield Town	1467	W 2-0	Christie 28, Pritchard 90	
3	19/1/10	FAT 2	A	Gainsborough Trinity	291	D 0-0		
4	26/1/10	FAT 2R	H	Gainsborough Trinity	392	W 2-1	Christie 12, Pritchard 43	
5	2/2/10	FAT 3	A	Guiseley	281	W 1-0	Murdock 77	
6	20/2/10	FAT 4	A	Salisbury City	1012	L 1-2	Shaw pen 88	

Home Attendances:	
Highest:	2246 v Luton Town
Lowest:	473 v Gateshead
Average (08-09):	1010 (814)
Top Goalscorer:	Pritchard - 7 (5 League, 2 Cup) in 47 appearances - 15% strike rate
Most Appearances:	Alcock - 47 (43 League, 4 Cup)
	Tait - 47 (41+1 League, 5 Cup)
	Sheridan - 47 (38+3 League, 6 Cup)
	Pritchard - 47 (40+1 League, 6 Cup)

ALCOCK 1	RODMAN 10	C SMITH 4	BRISCOE 16	TAIT 2	SHERIDAN 12	MACKENZIE 6	WRIGHT 7	WYLDE 5	SHAW 14	PRITCHARD 11	BLACKWOOD 3	BENJAMIN 22	LYTTLE 15	LAKE-GASKIN 21	NICHOLSON 9	HURREN 8	MILLS 18	BRUCE 20	APPS 23	RUSSELL 24	KORANTENG 26	ANDREW 25	BELFORD 19	GAUGHRAN 28	LOOKER 27	ÜLKER 29	LANGDON 17	BROWN 32	CHRISTIE 34	NEWBOLD 35	FANKEM 13	MURDOCK 9	J SMITH 17	MITCHELL 20	
X	X	X	X	X	X	X	X	X	X	X	S	S	S	U	U																				1
X	X	X	X	X	X	X	X	X	X	X	S	U	U	S	S																				2
X	X	X	X	X	X	X	X		X	X		U	X	U	S	U	U																		3
X	X	X	X	X	X	X	X		X	X	X	U	U	U	U	U																			4
X	X	X	X	X	X	X	X		X	X	X	U	S	U	U	U																			5
X	X	X	X	X	X	X	X		X	X	X	S	U	U	U	S																			6
X	X	X	X	X	X	X	X		X		X	U	X	U	S	U	U																		7
X	X	X	X	X	X		X		X		X	S	X	U	S	X	U	U																	8
X		X	X	X	X	U	X		X	X	X	S	X	X			S	U	U																9
X		X	X	X	X				X	X	X	U	X	X			U	U		X	S	U													10
X		X	X	X	X	S			X	X	X	U	X	X				U		X	U	S													11
X		X	X	X	X		S		X	X	X	U	X	X			U			X	U	S													12
X	X	X	X	X	X		X	U	X	X	X		S	U						X	U	U													13
X	X		X	X	X		X	X	X	X	X		X	S			U				U	S	U												14
X	X		X	X	X		X	X	X	X	X		X	S			U			S	U	S													15
X			X	X	X		X	S	X	X	X		X				U	U		X		S		X	U										16
X		U	X	X	X	X		X	X	X	X		U	X						X				S		S	U								17
X		X	X	X	X	X	X	S	X	X	X		U	U												S		X	S						18
X		X		X	X	X	X	X	U	X	X			S						X						U	U	X	S						19
X		X		X	X	X	X	X	U	X			U	U						X						U	X	X	S						20
X		X	S	X	X	X	X	X	U	X				U						X						U	X	X	S						21
X		X	S	X	X	X	X	X	U	X				S						X						S	X	X	U						22
X	X	X	X	X	X	X		X	X		S		U	U												U	U	X	X						23
X	X	X	X	X	X			X	X	X	U		U	U												U	U	X	X						24
X			X	X	X	X	X	X	X	X	X		U			S	U									S	S		X						25
		X	X	X	X	X	X	X	X	X	S		U	U													U		X		X	S			26
X		X	X		X		X	X	X	X	X		U	S		U													X		U	S	X		27
X		X	X		X	S		X	X	X	X		U	X		U													X		U	S	X		28
X		X	X	S	X	S		X	X	X	X			X		U													X		U	S	X		29
X		U	X	X	X	X		X	S	S	U		X	X		X													S			X	X		30
X	X	X	X	X	X	U		X	X	X	X		S	S																	U	S	X		31
X	X	X	U	X		X		X	X	X	X		U	X		U													X		U	S			32
X	X	X	U	X	S	X		X	X	X	X		U	X															X			S	U		33
X	X	X	S	X	X	U		X	X	X	X		U	X															X			S	S		34
X	X		X	X	X	U		X	U	X			X	S															X		U	X	X	S	35
X	X			X	X	U		X	U	X	S		X	S															X		U	X	X	X	36
X	X	X		X		S		X	U	X	X		X	S															X		U	S	X	X	37
X	X	X		X		U		X	S	X	X		X	S															X		U	S	X	X	38
X			U	X	X	S		X	X	X	X		X	S															X		U	S	X	X	39
X			S	X	X	S		X	X	X			X	X			U												X		U	U	X	X	40
X		X	S	X	X	S	U	X	X	X	X		X	S															X				X	U	41
X		X		X	X	S	S	X	X	X	X		X	S															X			U	X	U	42
X	X		X	X	S	X	X	X	S	X			U				U												X		U		X	X	43
X	X	X	U	X	S	X	X	X	U	X			S				X												X				X	S	44
X	X	X	X	X	X		X		X		X	S	X	X	U	U	U	U																	
X		X	X	X	X	X	X	S	X	X	X			U						U						S		X	S						
X			X	X	X	S	X	X	X	X	X		S				S			X			U	X											1
X		X	X	X	X	X		X	X	X			U	U									U			U		X	X	S					2
		X	X	X	X	X	S	X	X	X	X		U	S												U	U		X		X				3
		X	X	X	X	X	S	X	X	X				X			U						U				S		X		X				4
X		X	X		X	X		X	X	X	X			X															X			S	S		5
X	S	X	X	X	X	S		X	X	X	X		U	X															X			S	U		6
Total League Appearances																																			
43	23	33	29	41	38	21	23	31	33	40	29	0	19	12	0	2	1	0	0	10	0	0	0	1	0	0	3	7	20	0	1	3	15	6	X
0	0	0	5	1	3	8	2	2	3	1	5	4	5	14	4	2	1	0	0	1	1	5	0	1	0	4	1	0	5	0	0	11	1	2	S
0	0	2	4	0	0	6	1	1	8	0	2	8	16	14	4	8	11	5	1	0	5	2	1	0	1	5	5	0	1	0	12	2	1	2	U
Total Cup Appearances																																			
4	0	5	6	5	6	4	1	6	6	6	4	0	0	3	0	0	0	0	0	1	0	0	0	1	0	0	0	1	5	0	2	0	0	0	X
0	1	0	0	0	0	2	2	0	0	0	0	0	1	1	0	0	1	0	0	0	0	0	0	0	0	0	1	0	0	1	0	2	1	0	S
0	0	0	0	0	0	0	0	0	0	0	0	0	3	1	0	0	1	0	0	0	0	0	3	0	0	2	1	0	0	0	0	0	1	0	U
Total Goals																																			
0	2	4	1	3	6	0	4	4	1	5	2	1	1	0	0	0	0	0	0	0	0	0	0	0	0	0	0	0	6	0	0	1	0	1	Lge
0	0	0	0	0	0	0	0	0	1	2	0	0	0	0	0	0	0	0	0	0	0	0	0	0	0	0	0	0	2	0	0	1	0	0	Cup

TAMWORTH

CURRENT SQUAD AS OF BEGINING OF 2010-11 SEASON

GOALKEEPERS		SQ NO.	HT	WT	D.O.B	AGE	P.O.B	CAREER	APPS	GOA
Danny	Alcock		5'11"	11 03	15/2/84	26	Salford	Stoke, Barnsley 10/03 Rel c/s 04, Accrington 8/04 Rel 5/06, Stafford R 8/06, Tamworth 12/08	43	0
DEFENDERS										
Gavin	Hurren		5'08"	13 07	22/10/85	24	Birmingham	N.Forest Rel c/s 05, Kidderminster 7/05 Rel 4/08, Bromsgrove (L) 1/06, Mansfield 7/08 Rel 1/09, Kings Lynn 1/09, Crawley 2/09 Rel 5/09, Tamworth 6/09, AFC Telford (3ML) 9/09, Gateshead (L) 3/10	4	0
Des	Lyttle		5'09"	12 13	24/9/71	38	Wolverhampton	Leicester, Worcester 8/91, Swansea £12,500 7/92, Notts Forest £375,000 7/93 Rel c/s 99, Port Vale (6WL) 11/98, Watford 7/99, WBA (SL) 3/00, WBA 6/00 Rel c/s 03, Stourport 10/03, Northampton 11/03 Rel c/s 04, Boston U (Trial) 7/04, Forest Green 9/04 Rel 4/05, Worcester 7/05 Rel 5/07, Tamworth 8/07	24	1
Tom	Marshall		6'04"		16/11/87	22		Hednesford, Eastwood T 5/09, Chasetown (L) 10/09, Tamworth 6/10		
Aaron	Mitchell		6'05"		5/2/90	20	Nottingham	Notts Forest Rel 1/10, Ilkeston (2ML) 10/09, Burton (Trial) 2/10, Hucknall 3/10, Tamworth 3/10	8	1
Richard	Tait		5'11"		2/12/89	20	Galashiels	Curzon Ashton, Notts Forest 12/07 Rel 5/09, Tamworth (L) 3/09 Tamworth 5/09	42	3
Michael	Wylde		6'02"	13 02	6/1/87	23	Birmingham	Cheltenham Rel c/s 08, Cirencester (WE) 12/05, Kidderminster (SL) 3/08, Tamworth 7/08	33	4
MIDFIELDERS										
Seb	Lake-Gaskin		5'09"	12 01	24/2/91	19	Birmingham	West Brom (Scholar) Rel c/s 09, Tamworth 8/09	26	0
Neil	Mackenzie		6'02"	12 05	15/4/76	34	Birmingham	West Brom (Trainee), Stoke 11/95, Cambridge U (L) 3/99, Cambridge U £45,000 10/99 Rel 11/00, Kidderminster 11/00, Blackpool 7/01, Mansfield 8/02, Macclesfield (3ML) 11/04 Undisc 2/05, Scunthorpe (5WL) 11/05 Perm 1/06 Rel c/s 07, Hereford (L) 10/06, Notts County 7/07 Rel 1/09, Kidderminster (L) 9/08, Port Vale (L) 11/08, Burton (Trial) 1/09, Mansfield 1/09 Rel 4/09, Tamworth 6/09	29	0
Gary	Mills		5'11"	11 09	11/11/61	48	Northampton	Notts Forest cc 3/82, Seattle S (USA) 3/82, Derby Undisc 10/82, Seattle S (USA) 3/83, Notts Forest Undisc 7/83, Notts County Undisc 8/87, Leicester Undisc 3/89, Notts County £50,000 9/94 Rel c/s 96, Grantham (Pl/Man) c/s 96, Gresley R 7/98, Kings Lynn (Pl/Man) 11/98, Boston U 12/00, Tamworth (Pl/Man) 1/01, Coventry (Coach) 5/02, Notts County (Man) 1/04 left 11/04, Glapwell 4/05, Alfreton (Pl/Man) 5/05, Tamworth (Pl/Man) 1/07	2	0
Jake	Sheridan		5'09"	11 06	8/7/86	24	Nottingham	Notts County (Yth), Dunkirk, Notts County 8/05 Rel c/s 07, Tamworth 7/07	41	6
Jay	Smith		5'07"	12 00	24/9/81	28	Lambeth	Aston Villa, Southend (3ML) 8/02, Southend 11/02 Rel 1/07, Oxford U (SL) 3/06, Notts County (3ML) 11/06 Perm 1/07 Rel 1/09, Wigan (Trial), Eastwood T 12/09, Tamworth 1/10	16	0
Danny	Thomas		5'07"	11 05	1/5/81	29	Leamington Spa	Notts Forest (Trainee), Leicester 5/98, Bournemouth (L) 2/02 Undisc 2/02, Notts County (Trial) 3/04, Boston U 3/04 Rel c/s 06, Grimsby (Trial) 8/06, Cheltenham (Trial) 9/06, Shrewsbury 11/06, Hereford 1/07 Rel c/s 07, Macclesfield 7/07 Rel c/s 09, Kettering 8/09, Tamworth 6/10		
FORWARDS										
Kyle	Perry		6'04"	14 05	5/3/86	24	Birmingham	Walsall Rel c/s 05, Moor Green (L) 8/04, AFC Telford (SL) 9/04, AFC Telford c/s 05 Rel 7/06, Hednesford 7/06, Willenhall 9/06, Chasetown 6/07, Port Vale (Nominal) 1/08 Rel c/s 09, Northwich (L) 3/09, Mansfield 7/09, Tamworth 7/10		
Alex	Rodman		6'00"		15/12/87	22	Sutton Coldfield	Aston Villa (Trainee), Leamington 8/05, Alfreton (Trial) c/s 06, Grantham 8/06, Lincoln U 6/07 Rel 11/07, Gainsborough 11/07, Nuneaton 1/08, Tamworth 5/08	23	2
Nick	Wright		6'02"	12 00	25/11/87	22	Birmingham	Birmingham, Tamworth (L) 1/06, Bristol C (L) 10/06, Northampton (6WL) 11/06, Ashford T (L) 3/07, Halesowen T 8/07, Tamworth 10/07	25	4

Loanees		HT	WT	DOB	AGE	POB	From - To	APPS	GOA
(M)Simon	Russell	5'07"	10 06	19/3/85	25	Hull	York C (3ML) 9/09 - Cambridge U (SL) 1/10, Cambridge U 5/10	11	0
(D)Danny	Andrew			23/12/90	19	Boston	Peterborough 9/09 - Kidderminster (2ML) 10/09, Cheltenham (3ML) 1/10 Perm c/s 10	5	0
(D)Nathan	Koranteng			26/5/92	18	London	Peterborough 9/09 - Spalding U (L) 12/09, Boston U (L) 1/10	1	0
(D)Sam	Gaughran			29/1/90	20	Hunstanton	Peterborough 10/09 - Halesowen T (L) 3/10, Lowestoft 7/10	2	0
(F)Simon	Brown	5'10"	11 00	18/9/83	26	West Bromwich	Wrexham (2ML) 11/09 - Rel 3/10, Eastwood T 3/10, Corby T 6/10	7	0

Departures		HT	WT	DOB	AGE	POB	From - To	APPS	GOA
(F)Trevor	Benjamin	6'02"	13 07	8/2/79	31	Kettering	Kidsgrove 8/09 - Harrogate T 10/09 Rel 11/09, Woking 11/09	4	1
(M)Wayne	Looker			22/10/84	25		ex Histon 10/09 - Rel 10/09	0	0
(F)Stuart	Nicholson	5'10"	11 07	3/2/87	23	Newcastle	Newcastle Blue Star 1/09 - AFC Telford (L) 9/09, West Allotment Celtic 10/09	4	0
(F)Gölkan	Ülker	5'08"	11 00	15/9/86	23	Istanbul (Tur)	Long Buckby 10/09 - Rel 1/10, Shepshed D 1/10	4	0
(F)Adam	Newbold	6'00"	12 00	16/11/89	20	Nottingham	Stirling University 12/09 - Hucknall 1/10, Shepshed D 6/10	0	0
(G)Dale	Belford	5'10"	13 01	11/7/67	43	Tamworth	Atherstone T 6/09 - Atherstone T (Cover) 11/09, Willenhall (Dual) 12/09, Atherstone (Man) 2/10	0	0
(D)Dominic	Langdon	6'02"	11 00	14/9/88	21	Kettering	Rushden & D 7/07 - Brackley (L) 1/10 Perm	4	0
(M)Anthony	Bruce	5'10"	11 00	12/2/90	20	Birmingham	Bridgnorth 8/09 - Atherstone (2ML) 10/09 Perm 12/09	0	0
(M)Josh	Apps			7/6/90	20		Lewes 9/09 - Rel 12/09, Atherstone (L) 10/09	0	0
(D)Chris	Smith	5'11"	11 06	30/6/81	29	Derby	Worcester 5/08 - Mansfield 7/10	33	4
(F)lyseden	Christie	5'10"	12 02	14/11/76	33	Coventry	Farnborough 11/09 - Kettering 5/10	25	6
(M)Tom	Shaw	6'00"	12 00	1/12/86	23	Nottingham	Mansfield 10/08 - Kidderminster 6/10	36	1
(M)Michael	Blackwood	5'10"	11 04	30/9/79	30	Birmingham	Mansfield (SL) 3/09 Perm 5/09 - Brackley T 6/10	34	2
(D)Michael	Briscoe	5'11"	12 00	4/7/83	27	Northampton	Redditch 6/09 - Kidderminster 7/10	34	1
(M)Bradley	Pritchard			19/12/85	24	Zimbabwe	Nuneaton B 6/08 - Hayes & Yeading 7/10	41	5
(F)Jerome	Murdock			7/5/85	25		Shepshed D 1/10 - Barwell 7/10	14	1
(G)Chamberlin	Fankem			17/5/82	28		Walton Casuals - Willenhall (L) 12/09	1	0

Do you remember when...

Tamworth

In 1987-1988 Tamworth won the League and Cup double in the Banks' Brewery League (The West Midlands (Regional) League).

Back row, left to right: Benny Brown, Mark Bromley, Bobby Atkins, Shaun Hemming, Dave Shelton, Micky George, Mark Stanton and Russell Gordon
Front Row: Lionel Martin (Assistant Manager), Gary Smith, Corrigan Lockett, Carl Rathbone, Graham Smith (Manager), Martin Devaney, Danny McCormack and Ron Sims (Trainer).

WREXHAM

Chairman: Ian Roberts
Secretary: Geraint Parry (T) 07801 749 021
(E) gariant.parry@wrexhamfc.tv
Additional Committee Members:
Paul Atkinson, Geoff Moss, Paul Retout, Mike Turner, Dave Roberts
Manager: Dean Saunders
Programme Editor: TBA (E)

Back Row (L-R): Simon Brown, Silvio Spann, Hedi Taboubi, Wes Baynes, Andy Fleming, Luke Carding, Neil Taylor, Lamine Sakho, Jamie McCluskey. **Middle Row:** Alan Jones (Kit Manager), Matty Wolfenden, Marc Williams, Gareth Taylor, Sam Russell, Mansour Assoumani, Chris Maxwell, Christian Smith, Mike Williams, Kai Edwards, Mal Purchase (Fitness & Conditioning Coach), Mel Pejic (Physio). **Front Row:** Adrian Ceislewicz, Nathan Fairhhurst, Mark Jones, Curtis Obeng, Dean Saunders (Manager), Brian Carey (Assistant Manager), Matty Hurdman, Sam Williamson, Johnny Hunt, Obi Anoruo. (Archive Photo)

Club Factfile

Founded: 1872 **Nickname:** The Robins
Previous Names: Wrexham Athletic for the 1882-83 season only
Previous Leagues: The Combination 1890-94, 1896-1906, Welsh League 1894-96, Birmingham & District 1906-21, Football League 1921-2008
Club Colours (change): Red/white/white (All blue)

Ground: Racecourse Ground, Mold road, Wrexham LL11 2AH (T) 01978 262 129
Capacity: 15,500 **Seats:** 10,100 **Covered:** 15,500 **Clubhouse:** Yes **Shop:** Yes
Previous Grounds: Rhosddu Recreation Ground during the 1881-82 and 1882-83 seasons
Simple Directions
From Wrexham by-pass (A483) exit at Mold junction (A451). Follow signs for Town Centre and football ground is half a mile on the left hand side.

Record Attendance: 34,445 v Manchester United - FA Cup 4th Round 26/01/57
Record Victory: 10-1 v Hartlepool United - Division Four 03/03/62
Record Defeat: 0-9 v v Brentford - Division Three
Record Goalscorer: Tommy Bamford - 201 (1928-34)
Record Appearances: Arfon Griffiths - 592 (1959-79)
Additional Records: Paid £800,000 to Birmingham City for Bryan Hughes March 1997
Received £210,000 from Liverpool for Joey Jones October 1978
Senior Honours: Welsh FA Cup 1877-78, 81-82, 92-93, 96-97, 1902-03, 04-05, 08-09, 09-10, 10-11, 13-14, 14-15, 20-21, 23-24, 24-25, 30-31, 56-57, 57-58, 59-60, 71-72, 74-75, 77-78, 85-86, 94-95. Welsh Lge 1894-95, 95-96. Combination 1900-01, 01-02, 02-03, 04-05. Football Lge Div. 3 1977-78. FAW Prem. Cup 1997-98, 99-2000, 00-01, 02-03, 03-04. F. Lge Trophy 2004-05

10 YEAR RECORD

00-01	01-02	02-03	03-04	04-05	05-06	06-07	07-08	08-09	09-10
FL 2 10	FL 2 23	FL 3 3	FL 2 13	FL 1 22	FL 2 13	FL 2 19	FL 2 24	Conf 10	Conf 11

WREXHAM

No.	Date	Comp	H/A	Opponents	Att:	Result	Goalscorers	Pos
1	8/8/09	BSP	H	Eastbourne Borough	3726	W 3-0	Taboubi 34, G Taylor 2 (pen 61, 71)	3
2	15/8/09	BSP	A	Crawley Town	1014	L 0-1		16
3	18/8/09	BSP	H	York City	3371	W 1-0	G Taylor 58	9
4	22/8/09	BSP	H	Kettering Town	3473	L 1-2	Assoumani 56	14
5	25/8/09	BSP	A	Tamworth	1290	L 1-2	G Taylor 25	16
6	29/8/09	BSP	A	Forest Green Rovers	1021	W 2-0	Baynes 2 (29, 32)	12
7	31/8/09	BSP	H	Barrow	3760	D 0-0		12
8	12/9/09	BSP	H	Oxford United	3628	L 0-1		16
9	19/9/09	BSP	A	Cambridge United	2823	L 0-2		16
10	22/9/09	BSP	H	Luton Town	3448	W 3-0	G Taylor 2 (pen 6, 21), Jones 86	16
11	29/9/09	BSP	A	Kidderminster Harriers	1585	L 0-2		16
12	3/10/09	BSP	H	Salisbury City	2556	L 1-2	G Taylor 70	17
13	17/10/09	BSP	H	Grays Athletic	2495	W 2-1	Smith 5, G Taylor 39	16
14	20/10/09	BSP	A	Stevenage Borough	1763	D 0-0		16
15	31/10/09	BSP	A	Ebbsfleet United	969	W 1-0	Sakho 43	15
16	3/11/09	BSP	A	Kettering Town	1186	D 2-2	Og (Harper) 14, Westwood 22	14
17	14/11/09	BSP	H	Hayes & Yeading United	2427	L 0-2		15
18	21/11/09	BSP	A	Histon	946	D 0-0		15
19	24/11/09	BSP	H	Kidderminster Harriers	2086	D 2-2	Mike Williams 2 (26, 35)	15
20	1/12/09	BSP	H	Forest Green Rovers	1808	W 1-0	Baynes 89	15
21	5/12/09	BSP	A	York City	3006	L 1-2	Fleming 82	15
22	23/1/10	BSP	H	AFC Wimbledon	3276	W 1-0	G Taylor 29	16
23	26/1/10	BSP	A	Rushden & Diamonds	960	D 0-0		16
24	30/1/10	BSP	A	Altrincham	1821	W 3-1	Mangan 4, Baynes 37, Jones 74	13
25	2/2/10	BSP	H	Mansfield Town	2689	W 2-1	Baynes 28, Mangan 58	12
26	6/2/10	BSP	A	Eastbourne Borough	972	L 1-2	Mike Williams 76	13
27	9/2/10	BSP	H	Tamworth	2435	D 0-0		14
28	20/2/10	BSP	H	Crawley Town	2475	W 2-0	Mike Williams 59, Wolfenden 81	12
29	24/2/10	BSP	H	Stevenage Borough	2319	L 0-1		12
30	27/2/10	BSP	A	Salisbury City	948	D 1-1	Smith 69	12
31	6/3/10	BSP	H	Ebbsfleet United	2345	D 1-1	Mangan 15	12
32	9/3/10	BSP	H	Altrincham	2114	D 1-1	Baynes 33	12
33	13/3/10	BSP	A	Luton Town	6538	L 0-1		12
34	16/3/10	BSP	A	Barrow	1066	L 1-2	Jones 62	12
35	20/3/10	BSP	H	Cambridge United	2105	D 2-2	Mangan 9, Smith 14	12
36	23/3/10	BSP	A	Gateshead	614	L 0-1		12
37	27/3/10	BSP	H	Histon	2335	W 3-0	Holden 54, Mangan 2 (pen 63, 87)	13
38	30/3/10	BSP	A	AFC Wimbledon	3149	D 2-2	Og (Pullen) 50, Mangan 90	13
39	3/4/10	BSP	A	Mansfield Town	2520	W 1-0	Jones 42	12
40	5/4/10	BSP	H	Gateshead	2380	D 0-0		13
41	10/4/10	BSP	A	Grays Athletic	298	W 2-0	Westwood 30, N Taylor 76	11
42	17/4/10	BSP	H	Rushden & Diamonds	5672	L 0-1		12
43	20/4/10	BSP	A	Oxford United	4745	L 0-1		12
44	24/4/10	BSP	A	Hayes & Yeading United	446	W 1-0	Baynes 23	11
	Chester	**record**	**..........................**	**...expunged 08/03**				
11	27/9/09	BSP	H	Chester City	5913	D 0-0		15
	Cups							
1	24/10/09	FAC 4Q	A	FC Halifax	2843	W 1-0	Baynes 90	
2	7/11/09	FAC 1	H	Lowestoft Town	2402	W 1-0	G Taylor 89	
3	28/11/09	FAC 2	H	Swindon Town	3011	L 0-1		
4	12/12/09	FAT 1	H	Altrincham	1065	D 0-0		
5	15/12/09	FAT 1R	A	Altrincham	407	L 0-1		

Home Attendances:	
Highest:	5672 v Rushden & Diamonds
Lowest:	1808 v Forest Green Rovers
Average (08-09):	2485 (3367)
Top Goalscorer:	G Taylor - 10 (9 League, 1 Cup) in 30 appearances - 33% strike rate
Most Appearances:	Assoumani - 43 (38+1 League, 4 Cup)
	Baynes - 43 (24+14 League, 4+1 Cup)

	RUSSELL	N TAYLOR	MIKE WILLIAMS	ASSOUMANI	SPANN	FLEMING	TABOUBI	CIESELEWICZ	JONES	G TAYLOR	WOLFENDEN	MARC WILLIAMS	SMITH	BAYNES	MAXWELL	FAIRHURST	OBENG	WILLIAMSON	WESTWOOD	SINCLAIR	TSIAKLIS	SAKHO	MCCLUSKEY	MANGAN	ANORUO	HOLDEN	EDWARDS	BROWN	O'LEARY	MITCHLEY	HUNT	WALKER
	1	11	15	4	16	19	8	17	7	9	24	10	25	18	27	14	2	3	5	15	12	22	20	30	23	29	21	28	22	12	26	32
1	X	X	X	X	X	X	X	X	X	X	X	S	S	S	U	U																
2	X	X	X	X	S	X	X	X	X	X	X	S	U	S			X	U														
3	X	X	X	X	X	X	X	S	X	X	X	U	S	U			S	X														
4	X		X	X	X		X	S	X	X	X	S	X	S	U		X	X	U													
5		S	X	X	X	X		X	X	X		S	X	S	X	U	X		X	U												
6		X	U	X	U		X	S	X	U		X	S	X	X	X	X		X	X												
7		X	U	X		U	X	S	X	X		S	S	X	X	X	X		X	X												
8		X	U	X	U	S	X	S	X	X		X	U	X	X		X		X	X												
9		X	X	X			U	X	X	X		S	U	S	X	X	X		X		X	S										
10		X	U	X	X	X	U	S	X	X		X	X		X	U	X			X		S										
11		X	U	X	X	X	S	S	X	U		X	X	S	X		X			X		X										
12		X	U	X		S	X	S	X	X		X	X	U	X		X			X		X	S									
13		X	S	X		X	U	U	X	X		X	X	S	X		X			X		U	X									
14		X		X		X			X	X		X	X	U	X		X		U	X		U	X									
15			X	X	X	X		U	X	X		U	X	X	X	S		U	X			X	S									
16			X	X	X	X		U	S	X		U	X	X	X		X	U	X			X	U									
17	U	S	X	X	X	X	S	U		X		S	X	X	X		X		X			X										
18	U	U	X	X		X		S	U	X	U	X	X	X	X		X		X	X												
19		X	X			X		X	S	U	U	X	X	X	X	U	X		X	X			U									
20	U		X	U		X		S	X	X	S	X		X	X	S	X		X	X		X										
21	U	X	X	X		X		S	U	X	S	U		X	X	X	X			X		X										
22	X		S	X	X	X		U		X			X	X		U			X	X		X	S	X	S							
23	X		U	X	X	X							X	X	U	U	X		X	X		X	S	X	S							
24	X		S	X	X	X		U	S				X	X			U		X	X		X	X	X	S							
25	X		X	X	X	X			S		U		X	X	U		S		X				X	X	S	X						
26	X		X	X	X	X			X					X	U	U	U		X			S	X	X	U	X						
27	X	U	X	X	X	X					U			X	U	X	S		X	X			X	X	S	X						
28	X		X	X	X	X			S	S	S		X	X	U		U		X			X		X		X						
29	X		X	X	X	X			S	X	S		X	X	U		U		X				S	X		X						
30	X		X	X	X	X			X		U		X	X	U		S		X				U	X	S	X						
31	X	U	X	X	X	X			X		S		X	X					X	U		U	S	X		X						
32	X	S	S	X	X	X			X		S		X	X	U				X	X			U	X		X						
33	X	U	X	X	X	X			X		S		X	X	U		S		X			S		X		X						
34	X	U	X	X	X	X	U		X		S		X	X			S		X			X		X		S						
35	X	X	X		X	X			X		S		X	S					X			X		X		X	S					
36		X	X		X	X	X	S						S	X	S	X		X			X	U	X		X	U					
37	U	X				X	U				S			S	X		X		X	X				X		X	U	X	X	X		
38	U			S		X				X			X	S	X		X		X	X			U	X		X		X	X	S		
39		X		X		X		S	X	S				U	X		X		X				U	X			U	X	X	X		
40		X		X		X			X	S			U	S	X		X		X					X		S	U	X	X	X		
41	U	X		X		X			X	X			U	U	X		X		X					X			U	X	X	U		
42	U			X	S			X	X	X	S		X	S	X		X		X					X			U	X	X			
43			U	X	S		X	X		X			U	S	X		X		X					X				X	X	S	X	
44			X	X				X	X	U				X	X	X							S	X			U	X	X	S	S	X
		X	U	X	X	X	U	U	X	X		X	X	U	X		X			X		S										
1		U	X	X	S	X	U	S	X	X		X	X	S	X		X		U	X		U	X									
2	U	S	X	X		X	X	S	S	X	U	U		X	X	U	X		X			X	X									
3	U	X	X	U		X	U	S	U	X	U	X	X	X	X	U	X		X	X												
4	X		X	X	X	X	U	S	U		X	S		X	U	X	X		X			X										
5	X	X	U	X	X		X	S	X		S	X	S	X	U	X			X			X										
Total League Appearances																																
X	18	20	25	38	24	35	10	8	28	24	4	10	26	24	26	6	27	2	33	19	1	14	6	23	0	13	0	8	8	3	1	1
S	0	3	4	1	3	2	2	13	6	3	11	7	4	14	0	3	6	0	0	0	0	4	7	0	6	2	1	0	0	3	1	0
U	8	5	8	1	2	1	5	6	2	4	5	4	6	5	11	7	4	3	2	2	0	3	7	0	1	0	7	0	0	1	0	0
Total Cup Appearances																																
X	2	2	4	4	2	4	2	0	2	3	1	3	2	4	3	2	4	0	4	2	0	3	2	0	0	0	0	0	0	0	0	0
S	0	1	0	0	1	0	0	5	1	0	1	1	1	1	0	0	0	0	0	0	0	0	0	0	0	0	0	0	0	0	0	0
U	2	1	1	1	0	0	3	0	2	0	2	1	0	0	2	2	0	0	1	0	0	1	0	0	0	0	0	0	0	0	0	0
Total Goals																																
Lge	0	1	4	1	0	1	1	0	4	9	1	0	3	7	0	0	0	0	2	0	0	1	0	7	0	1	0	0	0	0	0	0
Cup	0	0	0	0	0	0	0	0	0	1	0	0	0	1	0	0	0	0	0	0	0	0	0	0	0	0	0	0	0	0	0	0

WREXHAM

CURRENT SQUAD AS OF BEGINING OF 2010-11 SEASON

GOALKEEPERS		SQ NO.	HT	WT	D.O.B	AGE	P.O.B	CAREER	APPS	GOA
Chris	Maxwell				30/7/90	20	Wrexham	Wrexham, Connahs Quay (6ML) 8/08	26	0
DEFENDERS										
Neil	Ashton		5'08"	12 06	15/1/85	25	Liverpool	Tranmere, Shrewsbury (SL) 12/04, Shrewsbury 6/05 Rel c/s 09, Macclesfield (SL) 1/08, Chester 7/09 Rel 2/10, Wrexham 6/10		
Chris	Blackburn		5'07"	10 06	2/8/82	28	Crewe	Chester Rel c/s 03, Northwich 8/03, Morecambe 2/04, Swindon 7/07 Rel 5/08, Weymouth (SL) 3/08 (07/08 13,2), Aldershot 5/08, Wrexham 5/10		
Kai	Edwards		6'00"	12 02	29/1/91	19		Wrexham	1	0
Johnny	Hunt				23/8/90	20		Wrexham	2	0
Cameron	Mawer		5'10"	11 06	21/2/86	24	Stevenage	Watford (Scholar), Wealdstone 1/05, Stoke, Stockport (Trial) c/s 05, Grays 7/05 Rel 5/08, Weymouth 7/08, Grays 8/09, Weymouth 2/10, Wrexham 7/10		
Curtis	Obeng		5'09"	11 00	14/2/89	21	Manchester	Man City Rel c/s 09, Wigan (Trial) 7/09, Wrexham 8/09	33	0
Frank	Sinclair		5'08"	12 09	3/12/71	38	Lambeth	Chelsea, West Brom (L) 12/91, Leicester £2 million 8/98 Rel c/s 04, Burnley 7/04 Rel c/s 07, Huddersfield (SL) 2/07, Huddersfield 7/07 Rel c/s 08, Lincoln C 7/08 Rel c/s 09, Wycombe (SL) 3/09, Wrexham 8/09	19	0
Declan	Walker				1/3/92	18		Wrexham	1	0
MIDFIELDERS										
Adrian	Cielslewicz		5'10"		16/11/90	19		Man City, Wrexham 6/09	21	0
Jay	Harris		5'07"	11 06	15/4/87	23	Liverpool	Everton Rel c/s 06, Accrington 8/06 Rel c/s 08, Chester 7/08 Rel 8/09, Banned, Enkopings SK (Swe), Wrexham 7/10		
Dean	Keates		5'06"	10 10	30/6/78	32	Walsall	Walsall Rel c/s 02, Hull C 8/02, Kidderminster Undisc 2/04 Rel c/s 05, Lincoln C 8/05, Walsall 1/06 Rel c/s 07, Peterborough 7/07 Rel 12/09, Wycombe 1/10 Rel c/s 10. Wrexham 7/10		
Nathaniel	Knight-Percival		6'00"	11 07	31/3/87	23	Cambridge	Histon, Wrexham 6/10		
Christian	Smith		6'02"	13 02	10/12/87	22	Crewe	Port Vale Rel c/s 07, Cambridge U (L) 1/07, Northwich (L) 3/07, Bury (Trial) 7/07, Clyde c/s 07 Rel 6/08, Wrexham 8/08 Rel 1/09, Macclesfield (Trial) 1/09, York C 1/09 Rel 5/09, Wrexham 8/09	30	3
Forwards										
Obi	Anoruo		5'10"	11 06	28/8/91	19	Nigeria	Wrexham, Newtown (4ML) 8/09	6	0
Wes	Baynes		5'11"	10 10	12/10/88	21	Chester	Wrexham	38	7
David	Brown		5'10"	12 06	2/10/78	31	Bolton	Man Utd, Hull (L) 3/98, Hull 7/98, Halifax (Trial) 8/01,Torquay 11/01, Chester 12/01, Telford 8/02, Hereford 6/03, Accrington 3/05 Rel 5/08, Burton (2ML) 11/06, Rushden & D (L) 1/08, Northwich (SL) 3/08, Barrow 10/08 Rel 1/09, Forest Green 1/09 (Pl/Ass Man) 6/09 Rel 6/10, Wrexham 7/10		
Kevin	Gall		5'08"	11 00	4/2/82	28	Merthyr	Cradiff (Yth), Newcastle, Bristol R 3/01, Yeovil 2/03 Rel 5/06, Carlisle 5/06 Rel c/s 09, Darlington (2ML) 1/08, Toronto FC (Trial) 3/08, Lincoln C (6ML) 7/08, Port Vale (L) 2/09, Yeovil (Trial) 7/09, Darlington 8/09 Rel 10/09, York C 11/09 Rel 5/10, Wrexham 7/10		
Andrew	Mangan		5'09"	10 03	30/8/86	24	Liverpool	Blackpool Rel c/s 05, Hyde U (SL) 3/05, Accrington 8/05 Rel c/s 07, Bury 7/07 Rel c/s 08, Accrington (L) 2/08, Forest Green 5/08, Wrexham Undisc 1/10	23	7
Andy	Morrell		5'11"	12 00	28/9/74	35	Doncaster	Newcastle Blue Star, Wrexham 12/98, Coventry 7/03, Blackpool 8/06 Rel c/s 08, Bury 8/08, Wrexham 6/10		
Gareth	Taylor		6'02"	13 08	25/2/73	37	Weston-Super-Mare	Southampton (Trainee), Bristol R 7/91, C.Palace £750,000 9/95, Sheff Utd P/E 3/96, Man City £400,000 11/98 Rel c/s 01, Port Vale (L) 1/00, QPR (2ML) 3/00, Burnley (SL) 2/01, Burnley 6/01, Notts Forest £500,000 8/03 Rel c/s 06, Crewe (SL) 1/06, Tranmere 7/06, Doncaster (L) 1/08 Undisc 2/08 Rel c/s 09, Carlisle (L) 3/09, Wrexham 6/09	27	9
Marc	Williams		5'09"	11 02	27/7/88	22	Colwyn Bay	Wrexham	17	0

Loanees		SN	HT	WT	DOB	AGE	POB	From - To	APPS	GOA
(M)Angelos	Tsiaklis		5'10"	10 12	2/10/89	20		Man City 9/09 - FCUM 3/10	1	0
(M)Luke	Holden		5'08"	11 00	24/11/88	21	Liverpool	Rhyl (SL) 1/10 -	15	1
(F)Danny	Mitchley		5'10"	10 08	7/10/89	20	Liverpool	Blackpool 3/10 -	6	0

Departures		SN	HT	WT	DOB	AGE	POB	From - To	APPS	GOA
(M)Anthony	Barry		5'07"	10 00	29/5/86	24	Liverpool	Chester 1/10 - Fleetwood 1/10		
(F)Simon	Brown		5'10"	11 00	18/9/83	26	West Bromwich	Mansfield 6/08 - Tamworth (2ML) 11/09, Rel 3/10, Eastwood T 3/10, Corby T 6/10		
(F)Lamine	Sakho		5'10"	11 02	28/9/77	32	Louga, Sen	Alki Larnaca (Cyp) 8/09 - Rel 3/10	18	1
(D)Mike	Williams		5'11"	12 00	27/10/86	23	Rhos-on-Sea	Yth - Rel 4/10, Kidderminster 7/10	29	4
(D)Sam	Williamson		5'08"	11 09	15/10/87	22	Macclesfield	Man City (2ML) 11/08 Perm 1/09 - Rel 4/10, Fleetwood (SL) 3/10, Fleetwood 5/10	2	0
(M)Mark	Jones		5'11"	10 12	15/8/83	27	Wrexham	Rochdale 7/09 - Rel 4/10, Bala T 6/10	34	4
(M)Heidi	Taboubi		5'10"	11 04	24/2/83	27	Cavaillon, Fra	AC Arles (Fra) 7/09 - Rel 4/10	12	1
(M)Nathan	Fairhurst		5'10"	10 05	16/10/89	20	Preston	Preston (SL) 11/08 Perm 7/09 - Rel 4/10	9	0
(M)Silvio	Spann		5'11"	10 12	21/8/81	29	Couva, Trin	West Connection (Trin) 8/07 - Rel 4/10	27	0
(M)Jamie	McCluskey		5'06"	08 09	6/11/87	22	Bellshill	ex St Johnstone 2/09 - Rel 4/10	13	0
(M)Steve	Abbott				31/7/82	28	Whiston	Team Bath 12/08 - Rel 4/10, The New Saints (SL) 7/09, AFC Telford 6/10		
(F)Matthew	Wolfenden		5'09"	11 08	23/1/87	23	Oldham	Oldham 7/09 - Rel 4/10	15	1
(G)Sam	Russell		6'00"	10 13	4/10/82	27	Middlesbrough	Rochdale 8/09 - Darlington 5/10	18	0
(D)Neil	Taylor		5'09"	10 01	7/2/89	21	St Asaph	Yth - Swansea 6/10	23	1
(D)Ashley	Westwood		5'11"	11 02	31/8/76	34	Bridgnorth	ex Stevenage 10/08 - Kettering 7/10	33	2
(M)Kristian	O'Leary		5'11"	12 09	30/8/77	33	Port Talbot	Swansea 3/10 - Neath 7/10	8	0
(D)Aaron	Brown		5'10"	11 11	14/3/80	30	Bristol	Gillingham 3/10 -	8	0
(D)Mansour	Assoumani		6'02"	12 00	30/1/83	27	Nice, Fra	ex Leeds 3/09 -	39	1
(M)Andrew	Fleming		6'01"	12 00	5/10/87	22	Liverpool	Yth -	37	1

WIN NEXT YEAR'S NON-LEAGUE CLUB DIRECTORY

(AND HAVE A BIT OF FUN AT THE SAME TIME!)

NON-LEAGUE CLUB DIRECTORY PREDICTION COMPETITION

This year we have decided to re-introduce a popular competition that was run by the Cherry Red Non-League Newsdesk Annual for a number of years.

Entrants predict the 2010-11 champions of the top competitions, and the contestant with the most correct tips is the champion and receives next year's Directory FREE. Could not be simpler!

To enter, list your prediction for the champions of all three divisions of each of the Blue Square Conference, Ryman Isthmian, Zamaretto Southern and the Evo-stik Northern Premier Leagues PLUS the top divisions of each of 14 feeder leagues: Baker Joiner Midland Alliance, Cherry Red Combined Counties League, Essex Senior League, Hereward United Counties League, Koolsport Northern Counties League, Molten Spartan South Midlands League, Ridgeons Eastern Counties League, Safety Net Kent League, Skilltraining Northern League, Sussex County League, Sydenhams Wessex League, Toolstation Western League, Uhlsport Hellenic League League, Vodkat Northern West Counties League.

Entries should be emailed to james.m.wright.t21@btinternet.com or posted to Prediction Competition, 6 Harp Chase, Taunton TA1 3RY.

Rules:

By entering you agree that..

1) All entries must be received BEFORE November 1st 2010.
2) The number of second (or even third or fourth) places will be used as a tie-breaker if necessary.
3) The contact details of all entrants will be stored electronically and may be used to publicise future competitions or products of TW Publications (under no circumstances will they ever be divulged to any third party).
4) Participants' names and scores may be published in the Non-League Club Directory 2012, or on the Directory's website.
5) In the unlikely event that the Non-League Club Directory is not published in 2011, the winner will be entitled to a cash prize equivalent to the cover price of the current edition.
6) In the event of any dispute, the decision of the publisher is final.

ENTRY IS FREE, SO GIVE IT A GO. GOOD LUCK!

YORK CITY

Chairman: Jason McGill
Secretary: Nick Bassett (T) 07885 539 956 (E) nick.bassett@ycfc.net
Additional Committee Members:
Sophie Hicks, Ian McAndrew, Rob McGill, Ross Porter
Manager: Martin Foyle
Programme Editor: Mark Comer (E) mark.comer@themaxdp.co.uk

Front row (L-R): Neil Barrett, Djoumin Sangare, Dean Lisles, Michael Gash, Greg Young, Richard Brodie, Michael Rankine, Levi Mackin, Chris Carruthers, Duane Courtney. Middle row: David McDermott, Jamie Hopcutt, Peter Till, David Knight, Andy Leaning (goalkeeping coach), Michael Ingham, Jonathan Smith, Andy McWilliams, George Purcell. Front row: Alex Lawless, Jeff Miller (physio), Andy Porter (assistant manager), Daniel Parslow, David McGurk, Martin Foyle (manager), Steve Torpey (youth team coach), James Meredith. Photo: Lewis Outing.

Club Factfile

Founded: 1922 **Nickname:** Minstermen
Previous Names:
Previous Leagues: Football League

Club Colours (change): Red/blue/red (All sky blue)

Ground: Bootham Crescent, York YO30 7AQ (T) 01904 624 447
Capacity: 9,496 **Seats:** 1,844 **Covered:** 7,000 **Clubhouse:** Yes **Shop:** Yes
Previous Grounds: Fulfordgate 1922-32
Simple Directions
From Tadcaster (A64) take left turning onto A1237 (Outer Ringroad) continue for approx 5 miles to A19 and then turn right into York. Continue for just over 1 mile and turn left into Bootham Crescent opposite Grange Hotel.

Record Attendance: 28,123 v Huddersfield Town - FA Cup 6th Round 1938
Record Victory: 9-1 v Southport - Division 3 North 1957
Record Defeat: 0-12 v Chester City - Division 3 North 1936
Record Goalscorer: Norman Wilkinson - 125 League (1954-66)
Record Appearances: Barry Jackson - 481 League (1958-70)
Additional Records: Paid £140,000 to Burnley for Adrian Randall December 1995
Received £1,000,000 from Manchester United for Jonathan Greening March 1998
Senior Honours: Football League Division 3 1983-84

10 YEAR RECORD

00-01	01-02	02-03	03-04	04-05	05-06	06-07	07-08	08-09	09-10
FL 3 17	FL 3 14	FL 3 10	FL 3 24	Conf 17	Conf 8	Conf 4	Conf 14	Conf 17	Conf 5

YORK CITY

No.	Date	Comp	H/A	Opponents	Att:	Result	Goalscorers	Pos
1	8/8/09	BSP	A	Oxford United	6403	L 1-2	Brodie 33	17
2	11/8/09	BSP	H	Rushden & Diamonds	2267	D 0-0		19
3	15/8/09	BSP	H	Forest Green Rovers	1954	W 2-0	Rankine pen 74, Smith 90	10
4	18/8/09	BSP	A	Wrexham	3371	L 0-1		15
5	22/8/09	BSP	A	Hayes & Yeading United	606	D 1-1	Pacquette 84	17
6	25/8/09	BSP	A	Gateshead	1174	W 2-1	Brodie 54, Gash 79	10
7	29/8/09	BSP	H	Histon	1944	W 3-1	Brodie 2 (12, pen 65), Smith 58	4
8	5/9/09	BSP	H	Crawley Town	2139	W 2-0	Brodie pen 6, Gash 10	7
9	8/9/09	BSP	A	Barrow	1120	D 0-0		8
10	12/9/09	BSP	H	Kettering Town	2275	W 2-0	Brodie 2 (57, 69)	4
11	22/9/09	BSP	H	Cambridge United	2321	D 2-2	Gash 2 (33, 89)	8
12	26/9/09	BSP	H	Kidderminster Harriers	2509	W 3-2	Brodie 2 (pen 10, 32), Gash 58	5
13	3/10/09	BSP	H	Stevenage Borough	2644	D 1-1	Sangare 90	9
14	6/10/09	BSP	A	Tamworth	1118	W 3-2	Ferrell 40, Brodie 61, Sangare 78	4
15	10/10/09	BSP	A	Salisbury City	1266	L 0-1		7
16	17/10/09	BSP	H	Oxford United	4302	D 1-1	Rankine 71	6
17	20/10/09	BSP	A	Luton Town	6387	D 1-1	Barrett 36	6
18	31/10/09	BSP	A	Crawley Town	975	L 1-3	Brodie 28	7
19	14/11/09	BSP	H	Ebbsfleet United	2629	W 1-0	Rankine 38	6
20	21/11/09	BSP	A	AFC Wimbledon	4016	W 1-0	Rankine 64	5
21	24/11/09	BSP	H	Gateshead	2302	W 1-0	Lawless 25	3
22	1/12/09	BSP	A	Rushden & Diamonds	1117	W 1-0	Brodie 73	3
23	5/12/09	BSP	H	Wrexham	3006	W 2-1	Carruther 6, Brodie 81	3
24	26/12/09	BSP	H	Mansfield Town	4587	W 3-0	Brodie 2 (21, pen 48), Gash 81	3
25	16/1/10	BSP	H	Hayes & Yeading United	2403	W 4-1	Carruthers 25, Brodie 2 (47, 58), Gall 83	3
26	23/1/10	BSP	A	Cambridge United	2646	W 1-0	Barrett 48	3
27	2/2/10	BSP	A	Histon	487	D 1-1	Purkiss 20	3
28	6/2/10	BSP	A	Kettering Town	1375	W 1-0	Rankine 16	3
29	13/2/10	BSP	A	Ebbsfleet United	1226	L 0-1		3
30	16/2/10	BSP	H	Luton Town	3316	D 0-0		3
31	27/2/10	BSP	H	Eastbourne Borough	2611	L 0-1		3
32	6/3/10	BSP	A	Forest Green Rovers	892	L 1-2	Mackin 34	4
33	9/3/10	BSP	H	Salisbury City	1867	L 1-2	Sangare 42	6
34	13/3/10	BSP	A	Altrincham	1236	D 0-0		6
35	16/3/10	BSP	A	Mansfield Town	2638	W 1-0	Pitt 61	5
36	23/3/10	BSP	A	Kidderminster Harriers	1127	W 1-0	Barrett 67	4
37	27/3/10	BSP	H	Tamworth	2863	D 1-1	Graham 57	5
38	30/3/10	BSP	A	Grays Athletic	323	W 4-0	Harsley 31, Brodie 2 (37, 42), Barrett 57	5
39	5/4/10	BSP	H	Altrincham	3005	W 2-1	McGurk 69, Brodie pen 90	5
40	7/4/10	BSP	H	AFC Wimbledon	2667	W 5-0	Rankine 2 (1, 70), Brodie 3 (pen 17, 22, pen 36)	4
41	10/4/10	BSP	A	Eastbourne Borough	1144	L 1-3	Rankine pen 45	5
42	13/4/10	BSP	H	Barrow	2154	W 3-0	Brodie 2 (40, 83), Gash 90	4
43	17/4/10	BSP	H	Grays Athletic	2854	D 1-1	Brodie 51	5
44	24/4/10	BSP	A	Stevenage Borough	5068	L 0-1		5
	Chester	**record**	**..........**	**...expunged 08/03**				
19	10/11/09	BSP	H	Chester City	2164	W 3-2	Brodie 3 (1, pen 32, 47)	6
	Cups							
1	24/10/09	FAC 4Q	H	Bedworth United	1869	W 2-0	Rankine 8, Brodie 42	
2	7/11/09	FAC 1	H	Crewe Alexandra	3070	W 3-2	Brodie 2 (39, 88), Pacquette 86	
3	28/11/09	FAC 2	A	Cambridge United	3505	W 2-1	Rankine 37, Brodie pen 40	
4	12/12/09	FAT 1	A	Hinckley United	506	D 0-0		
5	15/12/09	FAT 1R	H	Hinckley United	853	W 3-1	Brodie 3 (pen 35, 60, 90)	
6	2/1/10	FAC 3	A	Stoke City	15586	L 1-3	Barrett 22	
7	20/1/10	FAT 2	A	Newport County	1040	D 0-0		
8	26/1/10	FAT 2R	H	Newport County	1469	W 1-0	Pacquette 90	
9	30/1/10	FAT 3	H	Corby Town	2205	W 1-0	Ferrell pen 40	
10	2/3/10	FAT 4	A	Barrow	1525	L 1-2	Pacquette 70	
11	29/4/10	PO SF1	H	Luton Town	6204	W 1-0	Brodie 89	
12	3/5/10	PO SF2	A	Luton Town	9781	W 1-0	Carruthers 47 (W 2-0 agg)	
13	16/5/10	PO Final	W	Oxford United	38957	L 1-3	Og (Clarke) 42	

Home Attendances:

Highest: 4587 v Mansfield Town
Lowest: 1867 v Salisbury City
Average (08-09): 2560 (2360)

Top Goalscorer: Brodie - 34 (26 League, 8 Cup) in 51 appearances - 67% strike rate
Most Appearances: Meredith - 56 (42+1 League, 13 Cup)

INGHAM 24	MCGURK 5	MEREDITH 3	PARSLOW 6	PURKISS 2	FERRELL 8	MACKIN 17	LAWLESS 12	BARRETT 14	BRODIE 16	RANKINE 15	GASH 9	NELTHORPE 11	SANGARE 21	O'HARE 4	SMITH 7	PACQUETTE 10	MCWILLIAMS 20	MIMMS 13	CARRUTHERS 23	BOYES 25	GRAHAM 26	GALL 27	BERRY 28	PITT 28	CLARKE 25	HARSLEY 29	
X	X	X	X	X	X	X	X	X	X	X	S	S	U	U	U												1
X	X	X	X	X	X	X	X	X	X	X	S	S	U	U	S												2
X	X	X	X	X	X	X	X	X	S	X	X	S	U	U	S												3
X	X	X	X	X	X	X	X	X	S	X	X	S	U	U	S												4
X	X	X	X	X	S	X	X	X	S	X	X	U	U		X	S											5
X	X	X	X	X	X		X	X	X	S	X	U	S		U	X	S										6
X		X	X	X	X		X	X	X	S	X	S	X	U	X		S	U									7
X		X	X	X	X	S	X	X	X	U	X	U	X	U	X			U									8
X	U	X	X	X	X	U	X	X	X	S	X	U	X	U	X												9
X	S	X	X	X	X	S	X	X	X	S	X	U	X	U	X												10
X	S	X	X	X	X	X		X	X	S	X	U	X		X	U	S										11
X	S	X	X	X	X	X		X	X	S	X	U	X		X	U		U									12
X	U	X	X	X	X	X	S	X	X	S	X		X		X	U			S								13
X	U	X	X	X	X	X	S	X	X	X		U	X		X	S			S								14
X	X	X	X	X		X	X	X	X	X		S	X		S	S	U	U									15
X	S	X	X	X	X	U	X	X	X	X		U	X		X			U		S							16
X	U		X	X	X	S	X	X	X	X		U	X		X			U	X	S							17
X	X	S	X		X	S	X	X	X	X		S	X		U		U		X	X							18
X	X	X	X	X	U	S	X	X	X	X					X	S			X		U	U					19
X	X	X	X		S	X	X	X	X	X	S				U			U	X		X	U					20
X	X	X	X		S	X	X	X		X	X				S			U	X		X	S	U				21
X	X	X	X		S	X	X	X	X	X	S				S			U	X		X	U					22
X	X	X	X		U	X	X	X	X	X	S				U			U	X		X	U					23
X	X	X	X	U	S	X	X	X	X	X	S				U				X		X	S					24
X	X	X	X	S	U	X	X	X	X	X	S				U				X		X	S					25
X	X	X	X	X	S	X		X	X	X			S		U	S			X		X	U					26
X	X	X	X	X		X	X	U		X	X		S			S			X		X	U		U			27
X	X	X	X	X		X	X	S	X	X	S		S						X		X			U	U		28
X	X	X	X	X		X	X	S	X	X	S		U						X		X			S	U		29
X	X	X	X	S		X	X	X		X	X		U			S			X		X	U		U			30
X	X	X	X	U		X	X	X		X	X		U		S	S			X		X	S					31
X	X	X	X	X		X		X	X	S	U					X			X		X	S		S	U		32
X		X	U	X		U		X	X	X	S		X		S	X			X		X			S	X		33
X		X	U	X		X			X	S	X		X		X	U					X	U		X	X	S	34
X	S	X	U	X				X	X	S	X		X		S	U					X			X	X	X	35
X	U	X	U	X				X	X	S	X		X		S	U					X			X	X	X	36
X	U	X		X			U	X	X	S	X		X		S				S		X			X	X	X	37
X	S	X		X			S	X	X	S	X		X		U				U		X			X	X	X	38
X	X	X	U	X			S	X	X	S	X				U				S		X			X	X	X	39
X	X	X	U	X		X	X	X	X	X	S				S				X		X			U		S	40
X	X	X	U	X		X	X	U	X	X	S				S				X		X			S		X	41
X	X	X	U	X		X	X	X	X	X	S					S			X		X			U		U	42
X	X	X	U	X		X	X	X	X	X	S					S			X		X			S		U	43
X	X	X			X	X	X	S	X	S				S	U		X	X		X				U	X		44
X	X	X	X	X	S	S	X	X	X	X					X	U			X		U	S					
X	X	X	U	X	S	S	X	X	X	X		U	X		S		U	U	X	X							1
X	X	X	X	X		U	X	X	X	X		S			X	S		U	X	U	S						2
X	X	X	X		S	X	X	X	X	X	S				U		U	U	X		X	U	U				3
X	X	X	X	U	X	X	X		S	X	X				X			U	S		X	S					4
X	X	X	X	S	U	X	X	X	X	X	S							U	X		X	U					5
X	X	X	X	S	S	X	X	X	X	X	U		U			U		U	X		X	S					6
X		X	X	X	X			X	S	X	X		S		U	S		U	X		X	X					7
X	X	U	X	X	X		U	X		S		S		X	X		X	X		X	U						8
X	X	X	X	S	X	X	X			S	X		U		X	X			S		X	U					9
X	X	X	U	X		X		S		X	S		X		X	S		U	X			X			X		10
X	X	X	U	X		X	X	X	X	X	S				S	U		U	X		X						11
X	X	X	S	X		X	X	X	X	X	S		S					U	X		X			U			12
X	X	X	U	X		X	X	X	X	X	S		S					U	X		X			S			13
Total League Appearances																											
43	28	42	33	34	16	29	31	39	36	29	21	0	18	0	13	3	0	1	22	1	25	0	0	6	7	7	X
0	6	1	0	2	6	5	4	2	4	14	15	7	4	0	14	10	3	0	4	2	0	5	0	5	0	2	S
0	6	0	9	2	3	3	1	2	0	1	1	10	8	8	10	7	2	10	1	0	1	8	1	5	4	2	U
Total Cup Appearances																											
12	12	13	7	8	4	10	10	9	9	11	3	0	2	0	5	2	0	1	11	1	10	2	0	0	1	0	X
0	0	0	1	3	3	1	0	1	2	1	7	1	4	0	2	3	0	0	2	0	1	2	0	1	0	0	S
0	0	0	5	1	1	1	0	1	0	0	1	1	2	0	2	2	2	11	0	1	0	4	1	1	0	0	U
Total Goals																											
0	1	0	0	1	1	1	1	4	26	8	7	0	3	0	2	1	0	0	1	0	1	1	0	1	0	1	Lge
0	0	0	0	0	1	0	0	1	8	2	0	0	0	0	0	3	0	0	1	0	0	0	0	0	1	0	Cup

YORK CITY

current squad as of begining of 2010-11 season

GOALKEEPERS		SQ NO.	HT	WT	D.O.B	AGE	P.O.B	CAREER	APPS	GOA
Michael	Ingham	24	6'04"	13 12	7/9/80	28	Preston	Malachians, Cliftonville 7/98, Sunderland £30,000 7/99, Carlisle (2ML) 10/99, Coleraine (SL) 8/00, Stoke (L) 12/01, Stockport (2ML) 8/02, Darlington (L) 11/02, York C (SL) 1/03, Wrexham (SL) 3/04, Doncaster (L) 11/04, Coleraine (L),Wrexham 7/05 Rel c/s 07, Hereford 8/07 Rel c/s 08, York C 5/08	43	0
DEFENDERS										
Chris	Carruthers	11	5'10"	12 03	19/8/83	27	Kettering	Northampton, Hornchurch (L) 11/04, Kettering (L) 1/05, Bristol R (SL) 3/05, Bristol R Undisc 7/05 Rel c/s 08, Oxford U 7/08 Rel 1/10, Crawley (L) 8/09, York C (3ML) 9/09, York C 1/10	26	1
Duane	Courtney	2	5'11"	11 03	7/1/85	25	Oldbury	Derby (Yth), Birmingham (Scholar) Rel c/s 04, AFC Telford 9/04, Burnley £25,000 8/05 Rel 8/06, The New Saints 9/06 Rel c/s 09, Kidderminster 7/09, York C 5/10		
Alex	Lawless	7	5'11"	10 08	5/2/83	27	Llwynupion	Fulham, Torquay 7/05 Rel 5/06, Forest Green 8/06, York C 6/09	35	1
Dean	Lisles	19			5/5/92	18	York	York C		
David	McGurk	5	6'00"	11 10	30/9/82	27	Middlesbrough	Darlington, Bishop Auckland (L) 8/04, York (L) 9/04, York 6ML 8/05, York (SL) 1/06, York 6/06	34	1
Andy	McWilliams	20	5'08"		5/11/89	20	Stockton	York C	3	0
James	Meredith	3	6'00"	11 09	4/4/88	22	Albury, Aust	Derby Rel c/s 07, Cambridge U (L) 10/06, Chesterfield (L) 2/07, Sligo R 8/07 Rel 12/07, Shrewsbury 1/08 Rel 6/09, AFC Telford (SL) 10/08, York C 7/09	43	0
Daniel	Parslow	6	5'11"	12 05	11/9/85	24	Rhymney Valley	Cardiff Rel c/s 06, York C 8/06	33	0
Djoumin	Sangare	12	6'00"	12 08	16/12/83	26	Dunkerque	Wasquehal (Fra), Redbridge 9/04, Chelmsford 1/05, Redbridge 1/05, Lewes, St Albans (L) 8/05, Grays 8/06 Rel 5/07, St Albans (SL) 1/07, Stafford R 7/07, Salisbury 7/08, York C 7/09	22	3
Greg	Young	18	6'02"	12 03	24/4/83	27	Doncaster	Sheff Wed (Scholar), Shrewsbury (Trial) 3/02, Grimsby 7/02, Northwich (L) 10/04, Northwich (L) 12/04, Halifax 2/05, Northwich (L) 11/06, Alfreton (L) 8/07, Altrincham 1/08, York C 5/10		
MIDFIELDERS										
Neil	Barrett	14	5'10"	11 00	24/12/81	28	Tooting	Chelsea (Jun), Portsmouth (Trial) 3/01, Portsmouth 7/01, Dundee (3ML) 1/04, Dundee 7/04 Rel 9/05, Livingston 9/05 Rel 1/06, Exeter 9/06 Rel 12/06, Woking 1/07, Ebbsfleet 6/07, York C Undisc 6/09	41	4
Jamie	Hopcutt	21			23/6/92	18	York	York C		
Levi	Mackin	17	6'01"	12 00	4/4/86	24	Chester	Wrexham Rel 5/09, Droylsden (3ML) 1/08, York C (SL) 1/09, York C 5/09	34	1
George	Purcell	10	5'11"	11 09	8/4/88	22	Gravesend	Gillingham, Gravesend/Ebbsfleet 8/06, Heybridge (L) 9/07, Ramsgate (L) 2/09, Braintree 5/09, York C Undisc 7/10		
Jonathan	Smith	4	6'03"	11 02	17/10/86	23	Preston	Morecambe Rel 5/07, Fleetwood (3ML) 1/06, Bamber Bridge (L) 1/07, Forest Green 7/07 Rel 6/10, York C 6/10		
Peter	Till	8	5'11"	11 04	7/9/85	24	Walsall	Birmingham, Scunthorpe (3ML) 10/05, Boston U (SL) 1/06, L.Orient (L) 10/06, Grimsby (3ML) 11/06 Perm 1/07 Rel c/s 09, Chesterfield (SL) 1/09, Walsall 7/09 Rel c/s 10, York C 6/10		

FORWARDS

Richard	Brodie	16	6'02"	12 13	8/7/87	23	Gateshead	Whickham, Bolton (Trial), Newcastle Benfield c/s 06, York C 2/07, Barrow (L) 10/08	40	26
Michael	Gash	9	5'09"	12 01	3/9/86	23	Cambridge	Cambridge C, Cambridge U 6/06, Cambridge C (L) 1/07, Cambridge C 5/07, Ebbsfleet £20,000 7/08, York C £55,000 7/09	36	7
Michael	Rankine	15	6'01"	14 12	15/1/85	25	Doncaster	Armthorpe Welfare, Barrow 8/03, Scunthorpe 9/04, Barrow (L) 8/05, Lincoln C (Trial) 12/05, Altrincham (Trial) 12/05, Armthorpe Welfare 12/05, Alfreton 1/06, Rushden & D 7/06, Bournemouth (L) 10/08, York C £10,000 + P/E 6/09	43	8

Loanees		HT	WT	DOB	AGE	POB	From - To	APPS	GOA
(F)Adam	Boyes	6'02"		1/11/90	19	Lingdale	Scunthorpe 10/09 - Kidderminster (SL) 2/10	3	0
(M)Courtney	Pitt	5'07"	10 08	17/12/81	28	Paddington	Cambridge U (SL) 1/10 - Rel 4/10	11	1
(M)Paul	Harsley	5'08"	11 05	29/5/78	32	Scunthorpe	Chesterfield 3/10 -	9	1

Departures		HT	WT	DOB	AGE	POB	From - To	APPS	GOA
(F)Tyrone	Berry	5'08"	10 02	20/2/87	23	London	ex Grays 11/09 - Rel 12/09, Forest Green 1/10 Rel 3/10	0	0
(M)Andy	Ferrell	5'08"	11 05	9/1/84	26	Newcastle	Kidderminster 5/09 - Gateshead 2/10	22	1
(F)Michael	Emmerson			29/11/90	19	Middlesbrough	Yth - Ossett T (L) 12/09, Norton & Stockton Anciemts		
(M)Simon	Russell	5'07"	10 06	19/3/85	25	Hull	Kidderminster 8/08 - Tamworth (3ML) 9/09, Cambridge U (SL) 1/10, Cambridge U 5/10		
(F)Richard	Pacquette	6'00"	12 06	23/1/83	27	Paddington	Maidenhead 7/09 - Rel 5/10, Eastbourne B 6/10	13	1
(F)Kevin	Gall	5'08"	11 00	4/2/82	28	Merthyr	Darlington 11/09 - Rel 5/10, Wrexham 6/10	5	1
(M)Jamie	Clarke	6'02"	12 03	18/9/82	27	Sunderland	Grimsby 2/10 - Rel 5/10	7	0
(D)Alan	O'Hare	6'02"	12 02	31/7/82	28	Drogheda. Ire	Mansfield 6/09 - Rel 5/10, Gainsborough (2ML) 9/09, Gainsborough (SL) 1/10	0	0
(M)Craig	Nelthorpe	5'10"	11 00	10/6/87	23	Doncaster	Oxford U 5/09 - Rel 5/10, Barrow (7WL) 11/09, Luton (SL) 1/10, Gateshead 6/10	7	0
(G)Josh	Mimms	6'02"	12 12	5/8/89	21	Rotherham	Liverpool (Scholar) 10/07 - Rel 5/10, Gateshead (Trial) 7/10	1	0
(F)Adam	Smith	5'11"	12 00	20/2/85	25	Huddersfield	Gainsborough Undisc 1/09 - Mansfield 5/10	27	2
(D)Ben	Purkiss	6'02"	12 12	1/4/84	26	Sheffield	Gainsborough (SL) 3/07 Perm 8/07 - Oxford U 5/10	36	1
(D)Luke	Graham	6'03"	12 07	27/4/86	24	Kettering	Mansfield (2ML) 11/09 Perm 1/10 - Kettering 6/10	25	1
(G)Simon	Miotto	6'00"	13 07	5/9/69	40	Launceston	Herfolge BK (Den) 2/10 - Rel 7/10		

Anthony Howell side-foots past Stalybridge Celtic's Paul Philips to open the scoring for Alfreton.
Photo: Bill Wheatcroft.

Stevenage Borough's Beardsley shapes to cross under pressure from Luton Town's Murra.
Photo: Keith Clayton.

Farsley Celtic's Mark Jackson prepares to clear the danger under pressure from Alfreton's Paul Clayton.
Photo: Bill Wheatcroft.

Paul Clayton gets up highest, but sees his header go over the Stalybridge bar.
Photo: Bill Wheatcroft.

Farsley Celtic's 'keeper, Piotr Skiba, collects the ball safely during his side's match against Alfreton Town on the opening day of the 2009-10 season.
Photo: Bill Wheatcroft.

Drury keeps himself between Luton Town's Keane and the ball, to retain possession for Stevenage.
Photo: Keith Clayton.

STEVENAGE BOROUGH

No.	Date	Comp	H/A	Opponents	Att:	Result	Goalscorers	Pos
1	8/8/09	BSP	H	Tamworth	2130	D 1-1	Boylan pen 13	13
2	11/8/09	BSP	A	Hayes & Yeading United	681	D 1-1	Drury 48	14
3	15/8/09	BSP	A	Barrow	1254	D 0-0		17
4	18/8/09	BSP	H	Ebbsfleet United	1704	W 3-0	Beardsley 7, Byrom 74, Wilson 85	8
5	22/8/09	BSP	A	Oxford United	5775	L 1-2	Odubade 90	13
6	29/8/09	BSP	H	Rushden & Diamonds	1704	W 2-1	Boylan pen 7, Bostwick 74	11
7	31/8/09	BSP	A	Histon	1159	W 2-0	Laird 12, Odubade 62	4
8	8/9/09	BSP	H	Eastbourne Borough	1660	W 2-0	Ashton 28, Henry 68	7
9	12/9/09	BSP	A	Mansfield Town	3251	W 3-2	Beardsley 45, Odubade 59, Griffin 69	3
10	22/9/09	BSP	H	Grays Athletic	1803	D 1-1	Boylan 33	2
11	26/9/09	BSP	H	Altrincham	2093	D 1-1	Bostwick 90	3
12	29/9/09	BSP	A	Luton Town	8223	W 1-0	Laird 85	3
13	3/10/09	BSP	A	York City	2644	D 1-1	Og (Parslow) 34	3
14	10/10/09	BSP	H	Hayes & Yeading United	2120	W 4-0	Griffin 3 (17, 33, pen 74), Bostwick 90	2
15	17/10/09	BSP	H	Salisbury City	2009	W 3-1	Roberts 43, Griffin 60, Beardsley 82	2
16	20/10/09	BSP	H	Wrexham	1763	D 0-0		2
17	31/10/09	BSP	A	Kettering Town	1844	D 1-1	Byrom 2	2
18	14/11/09	BSP	H	Gateshead	2203	W 5-3	Griffin 3 (40, 45, 73), Odubade 45, Bostwick 90	2
19	21/11/09	BSP	A	Forest Green Rovers	757	W 1-0	Boylan 7	2
20	28/11/09	BSP	A	Salisbury City	851	W 1-0	Griffin 45	2
21	1/12/09	BSP	A	Ebbsfleet United	836	L 1-2	Odubade 21	2
22	5/12/09	BSP	H	Kidderminster Harriers	1809	W 2-0	Ashton 37, Cole 46	2
23	26/12/09	BSP	A	Cambridge United	4439	W 3-1	Odubade pen 27, Griffin 54, Beardsley 85	2
24	28/12/09	BSP	H	AFC Wimbledon	3033	D 0-0		2
25	1/1/10	BSP	H	Cambridge United	3406	W 4-1	Odubade 25, Boylan 2 (45, 62), Beardsley 50	1
26	23/1/10	BSP	H	Kettering Town	2136	W 2-0	Long 2 (63, 90)	1
27	6/2/10	BSP	A	Tamworth	841	L 0-1		2
28	9/2/10	BSP	H	Mansfield Town	1753	W 3-1	Odubade 2 (53, 69), Drury 73	1
29	13/2/10	BSP	A	Rushden & Diamonds	1923	L 0-1		2
30	24/2/10	BSP	A	Wrexham	2319	W 1-0	Bridges 45	2
31	2/3/10	BSP	A	Eastbourne Borough	903	W 6-0	Roberts 40, Bridges 47, Beardsley 71, Cole 3 (pen 83, 86, 90)	2
32	6/3/10	BSP	H	Crawley Town	2230	W 2-0	Bostwick 47, Boylan 90	1
33	9/3/10	BSP	H	Barrow	1538	W 4-0	Odubade 3 (28, 59, 84), Laird 45	1
34	16/3/10	BSP	H	Histon	2407	W 1-0	Ashton 18	1
35	23/3/10	BSP	A	Grays Athletic	515	W 2-1	Bostwick 65, Griffin 86	1
36	27/3/10	BSP	A	Crawley Town	1229	W 3-0	Odubade 2 (5, 33), Byrom 69	1
37	30/3/10	BSP	H	Oxford United	5744	W 1-0	Laird pen 52	1
38	3/4/10	BSP	H	Luton Town	7024	L 0-1		1
39	5/4/10	BSP	A	AFC Wimbledon	3840	W 3-0	Roberts 9, Wilson 11, Odhiambo 90	1
40	10/4/10	BSP	H	Forest Green Rovers	2524	W 2-0	Byrom 10, Laird pen 63	1
41	13/4/10	BSP	A	Altrincham	907	W 1-0	Griffin 82	1
42	17/4/10	BSP	A	Kidderminster Harriers	2564	W 2-0	Griffin 2, Byrom 62	CH
43	20/4/10	BSP	A	Gateshead	702	W 1-0	Laird pen 21	1
44	24/4/10	BSP	H	York City	5068	W 1-0	Bridges 35	1
	Chester	**record**	**..........**	**...expunged 08/03**				
10	19/9/09	BSP	A	Chester City	1089	W 1-0	Bostwick 7	2
21	24/11/09	BSP	H	Chester City	1487	W 2-0	Odubade 42, Roberts 66	2
	Cups							
1	24/10/09	FAC 4Q	A	Chelmsford City	1762	W 2-1	Griffin 63, Vincenti 90	
2	7/11/09	FAC 1	A	Port Vale	3999	D 1-1	Griffin 90	
3	17/11/09	FAC 1R	H	Port Vale	2914	L 0-1		
4	12/12/09	FAT 1	H	Ebbsfleet United	890	W 2-0	Beardsley 13, Bridges 89	
5	19/1/10	FAT 2	H	Vauxhall Motors	578	W 6-0	Roberts 21, Boylan 44, Bridges 2 (80, 83), Drury 84, Long 88	
6	30/1/10	FAT 3	H	Dover Athletic	1203	W 4-1	Sills 37, Beardsley 45, Bostwick 52, Odubade 88	
7	20/2/10	FAT 4	H	Workington	1510	W 2-1	Long 2 (55, 90)	
8	13/3/10	FAT SF 1	A	Kidderminster Harriers	2433	W 5-1	Bridges 2 (26, 43), Odubade 38, Beardsley 2 (70, 83)	
9	20/3/10	FAT SF 2	H	Kidderminster Harriers	1622	D 0-0	(W 5-1 agg)	
10	8/5/10	FAT Final	W	Barrow	21223	L 1-2 aet	Drury 10	

Home Attendances:	
Highest:	7024 v Luton Town
Lowest:	1538 v Barrow
Average (08-09):	2125 (1989)
Top Goalscorer:	Odubade - 16 (14 League, 2 Cup) in 46 appearances - 35% strike rate
Most Appearances:	Laird - 51 (42 League, 9 Cup)

DAY 16	HENRY 25	ROBERTS 14	LAIRD 3	BOSTWICK 24	DRURY 23	BYROM 13	MURPHY 7	LONG 8	BOYLAN 10	GRIFFIN 9	COLE 21	ODUBADE 11	ASHTON 5	BAYES 1	BEARDSLEY 20	WILSON 2	VINCENTI 30	BRIDGES 18	RAYNER 31	ODHIAMBO 4	ALBRIGHTON 6	BROUGH 17	SILLS 17	MAAMRIA 19	
X	X	X	X	X	X	X	X	X	X	X	S	S	S	U	U										1
X	X	X	X	X	X		X	S	X	X	X	S	U	U		X	S								2
	X	X	X	X	S	S	X		U	X	X		X	X		X	S	X	U						3
	X	X	X	X	S	S	X	U	X		X		X	X	X	X	S		U						4
	X	X	X	X		X	X	U	U		X	S	X	X	X	X	S			U					5
X	X	X	X	X		X		X	X		S	S	X		X	X	S		U		U				6
X	X	X	X	X		X		U	X		X	S	X		S		X		U	S	X				7
X	X	X	X	X		X		X	X	S	X	S	X		X				U	S	U				8
X	X	X	X	X		X		U	X	S	X	S	X	U	X					X	S				9
X	X	X	X	X	S	X			X	U	X	S		U	X		S			X	X				10
X		X	X	X	X		X	S	X	S	X	U		U	X		S			X		X			11
X		X	X	X	X	X	X			X	X	S		U	X		S			S	U	X			12
X		X	X	X	X	X	X			X	X	S		U	X		U			S	S	X			13
X	X	X		X	X	X	X	S	S	X		X		U	S		U			X		X			14
X	X	X	X	X	X	X	X	U		X		X	S	U	S		S					X			15
X	X	X	X	X		X	X	U		X	S	X	S	U	X		S					X			16
X	X	X	X	X		X				X	S	X	X	U	X		S	X		U	U				17
X	X	X	X	X	X			U		X	X	X	X	U	S		S	X		S					18
X	X	X	X	X	X	X	X		X		S	X		U	X		S			S	U				19
X	X	X	X	X	S	X				X	S	X	X	U	U			X		S	X				20
X	X	X	X	X	X	X	X	S		X	S	X		U	S			X			U				21
X	X		X		X	S	X		U	X	X		X	U	X		S	X		S	X				22
X	X		X	X		S	X	U	S	S		X	X	U	X			X		X	X				23
X	X		X	X		X	X	X	S			X	X	U	X		U	X		S	S				24
X	X		X	X		S	X	X	X			X	X	U	X		S	X		U	S				25
X	X	X		X		S		X	X		X	X	X	U	X		S	X			U		S		26
X	X		X	X		S	X	X		X	S	X	X	U	X			X			U		S		27
X		X	X	X	S	X		X	S		X	X	X	U	X			S			U		X		28
X		X	X	X	S	X		X	S		X	S	X	U	X			X			U		X		29
X	X	X	X	X		X		U	X		S		X	U	X		S	X			X		S		30
X		X	X	X		X		S			S	X	X	U	X		X	X		S	X			U	31
X	X	X	X	X	U	X		X	S		S	X	X	U	X			X			S				32
X	X	X	X	X	S	S		X	X		U	X	X	U	X			X					S		33
X	X	X	X		S	S	X	X			X	X	X	U	X			X			U		S		34
X	X	X	X	X	X	X	U			S	S	X	X	U	X			X					S		35
X	X	X	X	X	X	S		S		U	X	X	X	U	S			X					X		36
X	X	X	X	X	X	S		S		U	X	X	X	U	S			X					X		37
X	X	X	X	X	X	U			S	S		X	X	U	X	S		X					X		38
X	X	X	X	X	X	X				S			X	U	X	X	U			S	S		X		39
X	X	X	X	X	X	X		X		S			X	U	X	S	U	S					X		40
X	X	X	X	X	X	X		U		S		X	X	U		S	S	X					X		41
X	X	X	X	X	X	X				X	U	X	X	U	X	S		S					S		42
U			X	X	X		X	X	U	X	S			X		X	S	X		S	X		X		43
X	X	X	X	X	X	X		U		X		S	X	U	X	S		X					S		44
X	X	X	X	X	S	X			S	X	X	U	X	U	X					X	S				
X	X	X	X	X	X	X	X		X	U	S	X	S	U	X			S							
X	X	X	X	X	X	X		U		X	S	X	X	U	U		S	S		X	U				1
X	X	X	X	X	X	S		U		X	X	X	X	U	U		S	X		S	U				2
X	X	X	X	X	X	S	S		U	X	X	X	X	U	U		S	X		U					3
X	X		X	X			X	X		X	X	S	X	U	X		U	X		U	S				4
X	X	X			S		X	X	X	U	S	X	X	U	X			X		X	S				5
X	X	X	X	X				X	S	S	X	S	X	U	X			X			U		X		6
X		X	X	X		X		X	S		X	X	X	U	X		S	X			U		S		7
X	X	X	X	X	S	X					X	X	X	U	X		S	X			S		U		8
X	X	X	X		X	S	X	X			S	X	X	U	X			X			S		U		9
X	X	X	X	X	X	X		U		S		X	X	S	X	S	U	X							10
Total League Appearances																									
40	37	38	42	42	21	28	20	14	14	17	19	24	32	4	31	7	2	24	0	5	8	6	9	0	X
0	0	0	0	0	8	11	0	7	7	9	13	12	3	0	7	5	19	3	0	12	6	0	8	0	S
1	0	0	0	0	1	1	1	11	4	3	2	1	1	37	2	0	5	0	5	3	11	0	0	1	U
Total Cup Appearances																									
10	9	9	9	8	5	4	3	5	1	4	6	8	10	0	7	0	0	9	0	2	0	0	1	0	X
0	0	0	0	0	2	3	1	0	2	2	3	2	0	1	0	1	5	1	0	1	4	0	1	0	S
0	0	0	0	0	0	0	0	3	1	1	0	0	0	9	3	0	2	0	0	2	4	0	2	0	U
Total Cup Appearances																									
0	1	3	6	6	2	5	0	2	7	13	4	14	3	0	6	2	0	3	0	1	0	0	0	0	Lge
0	0	1	0	1	2	0	0	3	1	2	0	2	0	0	4	0	1	5	0	0	0	0	1	0	Cup

OXFORD UNITED

No.	Date	Comp	H/A	Opponents	Att:	Result	Goalscorers	Pos
1	8/8/09	BSP	H	York City	6403	W 2-1	M Green 88, Creighton 90	7
2	11/8/09	BSP	A	Kettering Town	2240	D 1-1	Sandwith 20	6
3	15/8/09	BSP	A	Histon	1433	W 4-3	M Green 16, Clist 47, Constable 2 (73, 77)	3
4	22/8/09	BSP	H	Stevenage Borough	5775	W 2-1	Potter 21, Murray 73	1
5	29/8/09	BSP	A	AFC Wimbledon	4304	W 1-0	Og (Conroy) 50	1
6	31/8/09	BSP	H	Forest Green Rovers	6338	D 0-0		1
7	5/9/09	BSP	A	Ebbsfleet United	1468	W 2-0	M Green 24, Clist 26	1
8	8/9/09	BSP	H	Luton Town	10613	W 2-0	Constable 5, Cook 16	1
9	12/9/09	BSP	A	Wrexham	3628	W 1-0	Constable 30	1
10	19/9/09	BSP	H	Eastbourne Borough	5688	W 4-0	M Green 25, Constable 28, Cook 45, Midson 87	1
11	22/9/09	BSP	A	Mansfield Town	3933	L 1-2	Constable 74	1
12	26/9/09	BSP	A	Gateshead	1144	W 1-0	M Green 62	1
13	29/9/09	BSP	H	Crawley Town	5675	W 3-1	Chapman 21, Kinniburgh 67, Midson 83	1
14	3/10/09	BSP	A	Barrow	1561	D 1-1	Foster 38	1
15	10/10/09	BSP	H	Grays Athletic	6150	W 5-0	Constable 2 (9, 24), Cook 43, Midson 2 (73, pen 90)	1
16	17/10/09	BSP	A	York City	4302	D 1-1	Clist 81	1
17	31/10/09	BSP	H	Altrincham	5609	W 1-0	Batt 65	1
18	14/11/09	BSP	A	Kidderminster Harriers	3569	L 1-3	Constable pen 30	1
19	21/11/09	BSP	H	Barrow	5629	W 1-0	Constable pen 27	1
20	24/11/09	BSP	A	Forest Green Rovers	1610	W 1-0	Constable 23	1
21	1/12/09	BSP	A	Crawley Town	1319	W 2-1	Chapman 83, Constable 90	1
22	5/12/09	BSP	H	Ebbsfleet United	5188	W 4-2	Potter 2 (4, 61), Constable 2 (9, 68)	1
23	28/12/09	BSP	A	Salisbury City	2677	D 1-1	Sodje 80	1
24	16/1/10	BSP	H	Tamworth	5690	L 0-1		2
25	23/1/10	BSP	A	Grays Athletic	1136	W 4-0	Clist 19, Potter 46, Constable 87, M Green 90	2
26	6/2/10	BSP	H	Kidderminster Harriers	5802	D 0-0		1
27	9/2/10	BSP	A	Luton Town	8860	L 1-2	M Green 74	2
28	13/2/10	BSP	H	Histon	5365	W 2-0	Deering 47, M Green 89	1
29	16/2/10	BSP	H	Rushden & Diamonds	7625	W 1-0	Chapman pen 86	1
30	23/2/10	BSP	H	AFC Wimbledon	6250	W 2-0	Constable 2 (14, 80)	1
31	2/3/10	BSP	A	Cambridge United	3002	D 1-1	M Green 42	1
32	9/3/10	BSP	H	Hayes & Yeading United	5045	L 1-2	Clist 53	2
33	13/3/10	BSP	H	Kettering Town	5836	D 1-1	F Green 36	2
34	21/3/10	BSP	A	Tamworth	1572	D 0-0		3
35	24/3/10	BSP	A	Rushden & Diamonds	2970	D 1-1	Deering 67	2
36	27/3/10	BSP	H	Gateshead	5986	W 2-1	Constable 52, M Green 90	2
37	30/3/10	BSP	A	Stevenage Borough	5744	L 0-1		3
38	2/4/10	BSP	A	Hayes & Yeading United	1655	L 1-2	Constable 45	3
39	5/4/10	BSP	H	Salisbury City	5741	W 1-0	Potter 86	3
40	10/4/10	BSP	A	Altrincham	1356	W 1-0	Constable 53	3
41	13/4/10	BSP	H	Cambridge United	5219	D 0-0		3
42	17/4/10	BSP	H	Mansfield Town	5712	W 2-0	Constable 2 (74, 86)	3
43	20/4/10	BSP	H	Wrexham	4745	W 1-0	Sandwith 82	3
44	24/4/10	BSP	A	Eastbourne Borough	2634	L 0-1		3
	Chester	**record**	**.......**	**expunged 08/03**				
4	18/8/09	BSP	H	Chester City	5135	W 4-0	Constable 3 (56, 83, 89), M Green 67	1
	Cups							
1	24/10/09	FAC 4Q	H	Thurrock	3296	W 2-0	Creighton 53, Clist 78	
2	7/11/09	FAC 1	H	Yeovil Town	6144	W 1-0	Midson 55	
3	28/11/09	FAC 2	H	Barrow	6082	D 1-1	Cook 9	
4	8/12/09	FAC 2R	A	Barrow	2754	L 1-3	Constable 90	
5	12/12/09	FAT 1	H	Hayes & Yeading United	1663	W 1-0	Midson 26	
6	19/1/10	FAT 2	H	Woking	1581	W 1-0	M Green 15	
7	30/1/10	FAT 3	A	Chelmsford City	1347	W 3-1	F Green 39, Midson 2 (64, 67)	
8	20/2/10	FAT 4	H	Kidderminster Harriers	3358	L 1-2	M Green 64	
9	29/4/10	PO SF1	A	Rushden & Diamonds	4535	D 1-1	Constable 28	
10	3/5/10	PO SF2	H	Rushden & Diamonds	11963	W 2-0	M Green 53, Constable 57 (W 3-1 agg)	
11	16/5/10	PO Final	W	York City	38957	W 3-1	M Green 15, Constable 20, Potter 90	

Home Attendances:
Highest: 10613 v Luton Town
Lowest: 4745 v Wrexham
Average (08-09): 5727 (4985)

Top Goalscorer: Constable - 26 (22 League, 4 Cup) in 44 appearances - 59% strike rate
Most Appearances: Clarke - 52 (43 League, 9 Cup)
Clist - 52 (40+1 League, 11 Cup)
Bulman - 52 (41+1 League, 10 Cup)

	CLARKE 21	CREIGHTON 6	SANDWITH 3	FOSTER 5	CHAPMAN 7	CLIST 11	MURRAY 8	BULMAN 4	KELLY 14	MIDSON 10	CONSTABLE 9	POTTER 15	M GREEN 24	RHODES 18	DAY 16	BATT 2	TURLEY 1	CARRUTHERS 23	PERRY 17	KINNIBURGH 22	COOK 25	WOODLEY 26	DEERING 20	F GREEN 19	SODJE 18	WEST 29	WRIGHT 14	TONKIN 18	FOWLER 17	HARGREAVES 5	GRANT 23	CAIN 22	CHALMERS 17
1	X	X	X	X	X	X	X	X	X	X	X	S	S	S	U	U																	
2	X	X	X	X	X	X	X	X		X	S	X	X	S	U	U	U																
3	X	X	X	X	X	X	U	X		X	X	U	X		S	S	U	X															
4	X	X	X	S	S	X	X	X		U	X	X	X	S	X	X	U																
5	X	X	X	X	X	X	X	X	X		X	S	S			X	U		S	U													
6	X	X	U	X	S	X	X	X	U		X	X	X			X	U		U	X													
7	X	X	S	X	S	X	X	X		S	X	U	X			X	U			X	X												
8	X	X	U	X	S	X	X	X		S	X	S	X			X	U			X	X												
9	X	X	S	X	S	X	X	X		S	X		X			X	U		U	X	X												
10	X	X	X	X	S	X	X	X		S	X	S	X			X	U		U		X												
11	X	X		X	S	X	X	X		S	X	U	X			X	U		U	X	X												
12	X	X		X	S	X	X	X		S	X		X			X	U		S	X	X	U											
13	X	X	S	X	X	X	X	X		X	X		X	U			U		S	X		S											
14	X	X	U	X	X	X	X	X		S	X		X			S	U		U	X	X												
15	X	X	U	X	X	X	X	X		S	X		X		U	S				X	X	S											
16	X	X	U	X	S	X	X	X		S	X		X		U	X			U	X	X												
17	X	X	U	X		X	X	X		X	X		X			X	U		S	X	S		S										
18	X	X		X	S	X	X	X	S	S	X		X		U	X	U			X			X										
19	X		X	X	S	X	X	X		X	X	S			U	X	U		X		X		S										
20	X	X	X	X	S	X		X		X	X				U	X	U		X		U			X	S								
21	X	X	X		X	X	X	X		X	S	S			U		U		X		X			X	S								
22	X	X	X		X	X	X	X		S	X	X				S	U		X		U			S	X								
23	X	X	X	X	X	X		X		X	X	X	S				U		U		S			X	S								
24	X	X			X	X	X	X		S	X	X	S		U	S	U							X			X	X					
25	X	S	S			X		X		X	X	X	S		X	X	U				U		X				X	X					
26	X	U				X		X		S	X	X	S		X	X	U				X		X				X	X		S			
27	X	U			S	X		X		X		X	S		X	X	U						X	S			X	X		X			
28	X	U			S	X		X		X		X	S		X	X	U						X	U			X	X		X			
29	X	U			S	X		X		X	X		S		X	X	U						X	S			X	X		X			
30	X	U			X	X		X			X		X		X	S	S						X				X	X		X	S	U	
31	X	S			X	X		X		S			X		X	X	U						S				X	X		X	X	U	
32	X	X			U	X		X		S			X		X	X	U						X				X			X	X	S	S
33	X	U			U	X		X		X			S		X	X	U						X	X			X	X			S		X
34	X	S				X		X			X		S		X	X	U						X	X			X	X		U	S		X
35	X	U				X		X			X		U		X	X	U						S	X			X	X		X	X		U
36	X	U			X	X		X			X	S	S		X		U				X		X				X	X			S		X
37	X	X			X	X		X			X	S	X		S		U						X				X	X		X	U		U
38	X	X			X	X				S	X	X	X		U	X	U						S	S			X	X					X
39	X	X	X		X			X		X	X	S			U	X	U				U		S	X			X	X					
40	X	X	S		X			X		X	X		S		U	X	U						X	X			X	X					S
41	X	X	X		X	X		X		S	X		X		U	X	U						S	X			X						U
42	X	X	X		X	X		X		X	X	S	X		S	X	U						S	U			X						
43	U		X		X			S		X		X	X		X	X	X				U	S	X				X			U			X
44	X	X	X		S	S							S		X	X	U				X	U	X					X		X	X		X
	X	X	X	U	S	X	X	X	S		X	X	X	S	X	X	U																
1	X	X	S	X	X	X	X	X	U	X				U	U	X	U		U	X	X		S										
2	X	X	U	X	U	X	X	X		X	X		X		U	X	U		S	X	S		S										
3	X	X	U	X	X	X	X	X		X	U	X			U	S	U		S	X	X		S										
4	X	X	X	X	X	X		X		S	X	X	S		U		U		X		X	U	U			U							
5	U		X	X	X	X	X			X		X	S		X		X		U		U		S	X	X								
6	X	S	X			X		X		S	X	X	X		X		U				U		S	X			X		X				
7	X	S	X			X		X		X	U	X	S		X	X	U						X	X			X			S			
8	U	X	X		X	X		X			X		X		U	X	X				X		S				X			U		S	
9	X	X	S		X	X		X		X	X	S	X		U	X	U						U				X	X					
10	X	X	U		X	X		X		X	X	S	X		U	X	U						S				X	X					
11	X	X	U		X	X		X		X	X	S	X		S	X	U						S				X	X					
Total League Appearances																																	
X	43	31	16	20	21	40	21	41	2	18	35	12	24	0	15	31	1	1	4	12	14	0	15	10	1	0	20	17	0	9	4	0	6
S	03	5	1	16	1	0	1	1	17	2	10	14	3	3	6	1	0	4	0	2	3	8	4	3	0	0	0	0	1	4	1	2	
U	18	6	0	2	0	1	0	1	1	0	3	1	1	13	2	39	0	7	1	5	2	0	2	0	0	0	0	0	2	1	2	3	
Total Cup Appearances																																	
X	98	5	5	8	11	4	10	0	8	7	5	6	0	3	7	2	0	1	3	4	0	1	3	1	0	6	3	1	0	0	0	0	
S	02	2	0	0	0	0	0	0	2	0	3	3	0	1	1	0	0	2	0	1	0	8	0	0	0	0	0	0	1	0	1	0	
U	20	4	0	1	0	0	0	1	0	2	0	0	1	7	0	9	0	2	0	2	1	2	0	0	1	0	0	0	1	0	0	0	
Total Goals																																	
Lge	0	1	2	1	3	5	1	0	0	4	22	5	10	0	0	1	0	0	0	1	3	0	2	1	1	0	0	0	0	0	0	0	0
Cup	0	1	0	0	0	1	0	0	0	4	4	1	4	0	0	0	0	0	0	0	1	0	0	1	0	0	0	0	0	0	0	0	0

A.F.C. TELFORD UNITED

Chairman: Lee Carter
Secretary: Mrs Sharon Bowyer (T) 07970 040 106
(E) sharon.bowyer@telfordutd.co.uk
Additional Committee Members:
Win Pryce, Ian Tyrer, David Topping, Ian Dosser, Anton Gunter, Steve Humbles
Manager: Andy Sinton
Programme Editor: James Baylis (E) james.baylis@ppmedia.co.uk

Back row from left to right: Derek Wellings (Kit manager), Shane Killock, Liam Murray, Sean Newton, Phil Trainer, Karl Broadhurst and Ruddy Farquharson (physio). Middle row, left to right: Darryl Smith (Goalkeeper coach), Danny Carey-Bertram, Ashley Woolliscroft, Will Richards, Daniel Platt, Steve Abbott, Ryan Young, Carl Rodgers, Stuart Whitehead, Andy Brown and John Psaras (First Team Coach). Front row left to right: Tyree Clarke, Martyn Naylor, Richard Davies, Darren Reid (Assistant Manager), Andy Sinton (Manager), Jon Adams, Sean Evans and Paul Harrison.

Club Factfile

Founded: 2004 **Nickname:** The Bucks
Previous Names: AFC Telford United was formed when Telford United folded in May 2004
Previous Leagues: As AFC Telford United: Northern Premier 2004-06
As Telford United: Southern 1969-79. Alliance/Conference 1979-2004
Club Colours (change): White/black/black (Yellow/black/black)

Ground: The Bucks Head Stadium, Watling Street, Wellington, Telford TF1 2TU **(T)** 01952 640 064
Capacity: 6,380 **Seats:** 2,004 **Covered:** 5,000 **Clubhouse:** Yes **Shop:** Yes
Previous Grounds:
Simple Directions
(Sat Nav follow TF1 2NW into Haybridge Road) From M54 Junction 6, A5223 towards Wellington, straight over first roundabout (retail park). Straight over second roundabout (B5067). Left at third roundabout (Furrows garage). Continue over railway bridge and follow road round to the right, then turn left into AFC Telford United Car Park.

Record Attendance: 4,215 v Kendal Town - Northern Premier League play-off final
Record Victory: 7-0 v Runcorn (A) - Northern Premier League Division One 2005-06
Record Defeat: 3-6 v Bradford P.A. (H) - Northern Premier League Division One 2005-06
Record Goalscorer: Kyle Perry - 32 (2004-06)
Record Appearances: Stuart Brock - 132 (2004-09)
Additional Records: Paid £5,000 to Tamworth for Lee Moore 08/12/06
Received £33,000 from Burnley for Duane Courtney 31/08/05
Senior Honours: Northern Premier League Division 1 Play-off 2004-05, Premier Division Play-off 2006-07. Conference League Cup 2008-09.

10 YEAR RECORD

00-01	01-02	02-03	03-04	04-05	05-06	06-07	07-08	08-09	09-10
Conf 6	Conf 9	Conf 15	Conf 12	NP 1 3	NP P 10	NP P 3	Conf N 2	Conf N 4	Conf N 11

AFC TELFORD UNITED

No.	Date	Comp	H/A	Opponents	Att:	Result	Goalscorers	Pos
1	8/8/09	BSN	H	Blyth Spartans	1847	D 1-1	Torpey 39	11
2	11/8/09	BSN	A	Stalybridge Celtic	587	W 3-0	Blakeman 38, Nolan 86, Adams 90	4
3	15/8/09	BSN	A	Fleetwood Town	1309	L 1-3	Andy Brown 90	9
4	18/8/09	BSN	H	Hinckley United	1665	D 2-2	Vaughan 52, Andy Brown pen 67	10
5	22/8/09	BSN	A	Gainsborough Trinity	434	W 1-0	Rodgers 85	7
6	29/8/09	BSN	H	Ilkeston Town	1682	D 0-0		7
7	31/8/09	BSN	A	Gloucester City	617	W 1-0	Nolan 65	7
8	5/9/09	BSN	H	Harrogate Town	1577	W 2-1	Torpey 60, Trainer 65	5
9	8/9/09	BSN	H	Northwich Victoria	1557	L 1-2	Cowan 40	8
10	12/9/09	BSN	A	Alfreton Town	610	L 0-4		9
11	19/9/09	BSN	A	Eastwood Town	616	D 1-1	Andy Brown 78	10
12	3/10/09	BSN	H	Droylsden	1542	L 1-2	Torpey 28	10
13	17/10/09	BSN	H	Southport	1731	L 0-2		11
14	31/10/09	BSN	H	Workington	1535	W 1-0	Trainer 88	10
15	3/11/09	BSN	A	Solihull Moors	404	W 1-0	Blakeman 77	10
16	1/12/09	BSN	H	Alfreton Town	1292	W 2-0	Andy Brown pen 9, Trainer 39	10
17	5/12/09	BSN	H	Fleetwood Town	1704	D 0-0		10
18	9/12/09	BSN	A	Corby Town	329	W 2-1	Cowan 25, Reeves 75	9
19	15/12/09	BSN	A	Redditch United	343	L 0-3		9
20	26/12/09	BSN	H	Stafford Rangers	2200	W 2-1	Blakeman 33, Gray 87	9
21	28/12/09	BSN	A	Hinckley United	815	L 0-2		9
22	19/1/10	BSN	A	Stafford Rangers	670	L 0-2		9
23	23/1/10	BSN	A	Southport	806	L 0-3		9
24	2/2/10	BSN	H	Vauxhall Motors	1169	W 5-1	Carey-Bertram 4 (18, 28, 58, 80), Brown 65	9
25	6/2/10	BSN	A	Droylsden	406	W 5-1	Trainer 2 (15, 90), Andy Brown 2 (pen 23, 90), Adams 87	7
26	9/2/10	BSN	H	Gainsborough Trinity	1304	D 2-2	Andy Brown 45, Trainer 83	7
27	13/2/10	BSN	H	Redditch United	1522	W 3-0	Reeves 2 (6, 23), Og (Bridgwater) 19	7
28	20/2/10	BSN	A	Harrogate Town	438	W 3-0	Newton 37, Reeves 69, Andy Brown pen 79	6
29	23/2/10	BSN	A	Northwich Victoria	539	L 0-2		7
30	27/2/10	BSN	A	Blyth Spartans	489	L 0-4		7
31	6/3/10	BSN	H	Solihull Moors	1525	D 0-0		7
32	13/3/10	BSN	A	Hyde United	472	D 1-1	Trainer 66	5
33	16/3/10	BSN	H	Eastwood Town	1323	D 1-1	Carey-Bertram 90	5
34	20/3/10	BSN	H	Stalybridge Celtic	1508	L 0-1		7
35	27/3/10	BSN	H	Hyde United	1708	W 4-0	Beesley 23, Blair 39, Andy Brown 85, Carey-Bertram 87	6
36	3/4/10	BSN	A	Ilkeston Town	548	L 1-2	Dugdale 70	9
37	5/4/10	BSN	H	Gloucester City	1572	L 0-1		9
38	10/4/10	BSN	A	Workington	619	L 1-2	Trainer 55	11
39	17/4/10	BSN	H	Corby Town	1503	L 2-4	Andy Brown 2 (7, 41)	11
40	24/4/10	BSN	A	Vauxhall Motors	387	L 1-3	Adams 26	11
	Farsley Celtic record expunged 12/03							
16	28/11/09	BSN	A	Farsley Celtic	399	L 1-3	Og (Skiba) 25	11
	Cups							
1	26/9/09	FAC 2Q	H	Pegasus Juniors	1136	W 4-1	Og (Robbins) 43, Carey-Bertram 48, Andy Brown 71, Torpey 90	
2	10/10/09	FAC 3Q	H	Worcester City	1459	D 0-0		
3	12/10/09	FAC 3QR	A	Worcester City	1062	W 1-0	Trainer 22	
4	24/10/09	FAC 4Q	A	Blyth Spartans	642	D 0-0		
5	27/10/09	FAC 4QR	H	Blyth Spartans	1398	W 4-0	Blakeman 24, Trainer 62, Andy Brown 2 (85, 88)	
6	7/11/09	FAC 1	H	Lincoln City	2809	L 1-3	Blakeman 49	
7	21/11/09	FAT 3Q	A	Stalybridge Celtic	422	D 1-1	Cowan 79	
8	24/11/09	FAT 3QR	H	Stalybridge Celtic	938	L 1-2	Killock 3	

Home Attendances:	
Highest:	2200 v Stafford Rangers
Lowest:	1169 v Vauxhall Motors
Average (08-09):	1550 (1973)
Top Goalscorer:	Andy Brown - 14 (11 League, 3 Cup) in 42 appearances - 33% strike rate
Most Appearances:	Young - 48 (40 League, 8 Cup)

YOUNG	VAUGHAN	JELLEYMAN	COWAN	TURNER	BLAKEMAN	ADAMS	RODGERS	TRAINER	ANDY BROWN	TORPEY	FIELD	CAREY-BERTRAM	EDWARDS	VERMIGLIO	NOLAN	JAGIELKA	WHITEHEAD	NEWTON	KILLOCK	HOWARTH	HURREN	CHRISTIE	NICHOLSON	THOMPSON	NURSE	EMBREY	REEVES	GRAY	EVANS	AARON BROWN	O'CONNOR	DUGDALE	BEESLEY	BLAIR	
X	X	X	X	X	X	X	X	X	X	X	S	S	S	U	U																				1
X	X	X	X	X	X	S	X	X	X	X	U	X		S	S	U																			2
X	X	X	X	X	X	S	X	X	X	X	U	X	U		S	U																			3
X	X	X	X	X	X	X	X	S	X	X		S	S	U	X	U																			4
X	X	X	X		S	X	X	X	X	S	X	X	U		S	U	X																		5
X	X				X		X	S	X	X	X	X	S		S	U	X	X	X	U															6
X	X		U		S		X	X	X	X	U	S	X		S	X	X	X	X																7
X	X		X		S	S		X	X	S	X	X	X			X	U	X	X	U															8
X	X		X		S	X		X	U	S	X	X	X			X	U	X	X	S															9
X	X		X		S	X		X		S	U	S				U	X	X	X		X	X	X												10
X	X		X		S	X	X	X	X	S						U	X	X	U		X	X	S												11
X	X		U		X	X	X	X	X	X		S	U			S	X	X	X		S														12
X	X		X		U	X	X	X	X	X	S	S					X	X	S		U			X											13
X	X		X		X	S		X	X		X	X	S				U	X	X		X			S		U									14
X	X		X		X	S		X	X		X	S	U				S	X	X		X			X		U									15
X	X		S			X	U	X	X			U					X	X	X					S	X		X	S	X						16
X	X		X			X	X	X	X								X	U	X					S	X	U	X	U	S						17
X	X		X		S			X	X								X	S	X		S			U	X	U	X	X	X						18
X	X		X		S	X	U	X	X								X	S	X					S	X	U	X		X						19
X	X				X	X	X	S	S								X	X	X					X	U		X	S	X						20
X	X		U		X	X	U	X	U								X	X	X					X	X		S	X	S						21
X						X	S	X				S					X	X	X					U	X		X	X	X	X	S	U			22
X					X	X	X	X	X			X					U	X	X					X	U		S	S			S	X			23
X	X				X	S	X	X	X			X					S	X	X					X	U		S				U	X			24
X	X				X	S	U	X	X			X					S	X	X					X	X		U				S	X			25
X	X				X	S	U	X	X								U	X	X	S				X	X		X				S	X			26
X	X				X	S	X	X	X								S	X	X	U				X	U		X				S	X			27
X	X				X	U	X	X	X			S					S	X	X					X	S		X				U	X			28
X	X				X	U	X	X	X			S					U	X	X					X	U		X				S	X			29
X	X				X		S	S	X			X					X	X	X						X		U		S		X	X			30
X	X				X	X	X	S	X			X					U	X	X						U		S		S		X	X			31
X	X				X	S	X	X	X			X					U	X	X	U				U			S				X	X			32
X	X				X	U	X	X	X			S					U	X	X					U			U				X	X	X		33
X	X				X		X	X									S	X	X					S			S				X	X	X	X	34
X					X	X	X	S	X			S	U				X	U	X					S							X	X	X	X	35
X					X	X	X	S	X			U					X	S	X					S					U		X	X	X	X	36
X					S	X	X	U	X			S					X	X		U				X					S		X	X	X	X	37
X	S				X	X	X	X	X			U					X	X						S					U		X	X	S	X	38
X	X				X	U	X	X	X			S	S				X	X						U					S		X		X	X	39
X	X				X	X	U	S	X			X	S				X	X						U							X	X	X	S	40
X	X		X		S	X	X	U				S					U		X		X				S		X	X	X						

YOUNG	VAUGHAN	JELLEYMAN	COWAN	TURNER	BLAKEMAN	ADAMS	RODGERS	TRAINER	ANDY BROWN	TORPEY	FIELD	CAREY-BERTRAM	EDWARDS	VERMIGLIO	NOLAN	JAGIELKA	WHITEHEAD	NEWTON	KILLOCK	HOWARTH	HURREN	CHRISTIE	NICHOLSON	THOMPSON	NURSE	EMBREY	REEVES	GRAY	EVANS	AARON BROWN	O'CONNOR	DUGDALE	BEESLEY	BLAIR	
X	S		X		X	X	X	U	X	S	S	X	X			X	U	X	X																1
X			X		X	X	X	X	X	X	U	U	S			U	X	X	U					S											2
X	X		X		U	X	X	X	X	X	S	X	U			U	X	X	S					S											3
X	X		X		U	S	X	X	S	U	U	X	U				U	X	X		X			X	X										4
X			X		S	X		X	X	U	X	X	S				U	X	X		X			S	X										5
X	X		X		X	X	X	X	X		U	U	U				U	X	X					X		U									6
X	X		X		X	X	X	X	X			S	S				X	X	X					S	U	U									7
X	X		X		X	X	S	X				S	X				X	S	X		X			X	U	U									8

Total League Appearances

YOUNG	VAUGHAN	JELLEYMAN	COWAN	TURNER	BLAKEMAN	ADAMS	RODGERS	TRAINER	ANDY BROWN	TORPEY	FIELD	CAREY-BERTRAM	EDWARDS	VERMIGLIO	NOLAN	JAGIELKA	WHITEHEAD	NEWTON	KILLOCK	HOWARTH	HURREN	CHRISTIE	NICHOLSON	THOMPSON	NURSE	EMBREY	REEVES	GRAY	EVANS	AARON BROWN	O'CONNOR	DUGDALE	BEESLEY	BLAIR	
40	34	5	15	4	27	21	26	31	34	8	6	14	3	0	1	3	21	30	29	0	4	2	1	12	9	0	10	3	5	1	11	17	7	6	X
0	1	0	1	0	9	10	2	8	1	5	2	14	6	1	5	1	6	3	1	2	2	0	1	8	1	0	6	3	6	0	6	0	1	1	S
0	0	0	3	0	1	4	6	1	2	0	4	3	5	2	1	7	9	2	1	5	1	0	0	6	6	5	3	1	2	0	2	1	0	0	U

Total Cup Appearances

YOUNG	VAUGHAN	JELLEYMAN	COWAN	TURNER	BLAKEMAN	ADAMS	RODGERS	TRAINER	ANDY BROWN	TORPEY	FIELD	CAREY-BERTRAM	EDWARDS	VERMIGLIO	NOLAN	JAGIELKA	WHITEHEAD	NEWTON	KILLOCK	HOWARTH	HURREN	CHRISTIE	NICHOLSON	THOMPSON	NURSE	EMBREY	REEVES	GRAY	EVANS	AARON BROWN	O'CONNOR	DUGDALE	BEESLEY	BLAIR	
8	5	0	8	0	5	7	6	7	6	2	1	4	2	0	0	1	4	7	6	0	3	0	0	3	2	0	0	0	0	0	0	0	0	0	X
0	1	0	0	0	1	1	1	0	1	1	2	2	3	0	0	0	0	1	1	0	0	0	0	4	0	0	0	0	0	0	0	0	0	0	S
0	0	0	0	0	2	0	0	1	0	2	3	2	3	0	0	2	4	0	1	0	0	0	0	0	2	3	0	0	0	0	0	0	0	0	U

Total Goals

YOUNG	VAUGHAN	JELLEYMAN	COWAN	TURNER	BLAKEMAN	ADAMS	RODGERS	TRAINER	ANDY BROWN	TORPEY	FIELD	CAREY-BERTRAM	EDWARDS	VERMIGLIO	NOLAN	JAGIELKA	WHITEHEAD	NEWTON	KILLOCK	HOWARTH	HURREN	CHRISTIE	NICHOLSON	THOMPSON	NURSE	EMBREY	REEVES	GRAY	EVANS	AARON BROWN	O'CONNOR	DUGDALE	BEESLEY	BLAIR	
0	1	0	2	0	3	3	1	8	11	3	0	6	0	0	2	0	0	1	0	0	0	0	0	0	0	0	4	1	0	0	0	1	1	1	Lge
0	0	0	1	0	2	0	0	2	3	1	0	1	0	0	0	0	0	1	0	0	0	0	0	0	0	0	0	0	0	0	0	0	0	0	Cup

AFC TELFORD

CURRENT SQUAD AS OF BEGINING OF 2010-11 SEASON

GOALKEEPERS	HT	WT	D.O.B	AGE	P.O.B	CAREER	APPS	GOA
Ryan Young			25/12/79	29	Birmingham	Plymouth (Trainee), Chasetown, Nuneaton, Halesowen T (L) 10/01, Hucknall T 2/02, Hednesford 5/03, Redditch 6/05, AFC Telford 9/05, Kettering 2/06, Willenhall 3/06, Hednesford 6/06, AFC Telford 5/07	40	0
DEFENDERS								
Shane Killock	6'00"	12 04	12/3/89	21	Huddersfield	Ossett A (Yth), Huddersfield, Hyde U (SL) 2/08, Harrogate T (L) 9/08, Oxford U (L) 1/09 Perm 2/09, AFC Telford (2ML) 8/09 Perm 10/09	30	0
Liam Murray	6'03"	11 00	1/8/85	25	Stafford	Shrewsbury Rel c/s 05, Leigh RMI (L) 3/05, Stafford R 8/05, Droylsden c/s 07, Redditch 2/08, Stafford R 2/09 Rel 5/09, Solihull Moors 6/09, Kings Lynn 7/09, Redditch 12/09, Solihull Moors 12/09, AFC Telford 6/10		
Sean Newton	6'02"	13 00	23/9/88	21	Liverpool	Chester, Southport (3ML) 8/07, Droylsden (SL) 2/08, Droylsden 8/08, Barrow 7/09, AFC Telford (2ML) 8/09 Perm 10/09	33	1
Stuart Whitehead	6'00"	12 02	17/7/76	34	Bromsgrove	Bromsgrove, Bolton 9/95 Rel c/s 98, Carlisle 7/98, Darlington 10/02, Telford 6/03, Shrewsbury 6/04, Kidderminster 5/06, AFC Telford 1/08	27	0
Ashley Wooliscroft	5'10"	11 02	28/12/79	30	Stoke	Stoke Rel c/s 01, Telford 9/01, Newtown 8/03, Leek T 9/03, Kidsgrove A 10/06, Hednesford 10/07, Stalybridge 10/07, Newcastle T 3/09, Fleetwood 5/09, Stafford R (2ML) 10/09, Stafford R 3/10, Leek T (Dual) 3/10, AFC Telford 6/10		
MIDFIELDERS								
Steve Abbott			31/7/82	28	Whiston	Congleton, St Helens, Leigh RMI, Team Bath 7/06, Wrexham 12/08 Rel 4/10, The New Saints (L) 7/09, AFC Telford 6/10		
Jon Adams			8/1/85	25		Leamington, AFC Telford	31	3
Matt Blair						RC Warwick, Stratford T 7/08, Bedworth 6/09, Redditch 11/09, AFC Telford 3/10	7	1
Sean Evans	5'09"	11 00	25/9/87	22	Ludlow	Shrewsbury (Yth), Man U (Yth 4/04) Rel c/s 08, Aberystwyth 8/08, Cinderford 1/09, Stourbridge 8/09, AFC Telford 11/09, Stourbridge (L) 1/10	11	0
Paul Harrison			1/1/85	25		Leeds Carnegie, AFC Halifax Rel 11/05, Glen Hoddle Academy (Spa), Galicia (Spa), AFC Telford 7/10		
Carl Rodgers			26/3/83	27	Chester	Chester (Yth), Caernarfon c/s 02, TNS 3/04, Colwyn Bay 5/04, AFC Telford 5/06	28	1
Phil Trainer	6'00"	12 00	3/7/81	29	Wolverhampton	Crewe Rel c/s 02, Hyde (3ML) 12/00, Hednesford (3ML) 11/01, Stalybridge (L) 3/02, Northwich 8/02, Kidsgrove 9/02, Halesowen 12/02, Tamworth 8/03, Stourport S (L) 9/03, Moor Green/Solihull Moors (L) 10/03 Perm 11/03, Oxford U 7/07 Rel 4/09, AFC Telford (SL) 1/09, AFC Telford 5/09	39	8
FORWARDS								
Andy Brown			3/3/86	24	Lincoln	Scunthorpe (Scholar), Harrogate T (L) 3/05, Hinckley 5/05, Nuneaton 7/07, AFC Telford 6/08	35	11
Danny Carey-Bertram	5'11"	13 00	14/6/84	26	Birmingham	WBA, Hereford 9/03 Rel 6/06, Cambridge U 6/06 Rel 1/07, Forest Green Rovers 1/07 Rel 4/08, Bath C 8/08, AFC Telford 10/08, Worcester (L) 12/09	28	6
Dave Howarth			19/12/91	18		AFC Telford, Blackburn (Trial) 9/09, Market Drayton (L) 11/09	2	0
Alex Meechan	5'08"	10 10	29/1/80	30	Plymouth	Swindon, Bristol C 7/98, Forest Green (2ML) 8/00, Yeovil (L) 11/00, Forest Green NC 12/00, Dag & Red 6/03, Forest Green (3ML) 11/03 Perm 2/04 Rel 6/04, Luton (Trial) 7/04, Leigh RMI 8/04 Rel 11/04, Halifax 11/04 Rel 4/05, Forest Green 7/05 Rel 1/07, Chester 1/07 Rel c/s 07, York C 7/07, Stalybridge 11/07, Altrincham 6/08 Rel 3/09, Stalybridge (L) 1/09, Stalybridge 3/09, Droylsden 7/09, AFC Telford 7/10		
Steve Thompson	5'07"	11 01	15/4/89	21	Peterlee	Middlesbrough Rel c/s 08, Port Vale 8/08 Rel 10/09, Stafford R (L) 9/09, AFC Telford 10/09	20	0

Loanees	HT	WT	DOB	AGE	POB	From - To	APPS	GOA
(D)Gavin Hurren	5'08"	13 07	22/10/85	24	Birmingham	Tamworth (3ML) 9/09 - Gateshead (L) 3/10	6	0
(F)Stuart Nicholson	5'10"	11 07	3/2/87	23	Newcastle	Tamworth 9/09 - West Allotment Celtic 10/09	2	0
(F)Andre Gray			26/6/91	19		Shrewsbury (2ML) 11/09 - Hinckley U (L) 3/10, Hinckley U 6/10	6	1
(F)Mark Beesley	5'10"	11 10	10/11/81	28	Burscough	Cambridge U 3/10 - Rel 4/10	8	1

Departures	HT	WT	DOB	AGE	POB	From - To	APPS	GOA
(D)Gareth Jelleyman	5'10"	10 06	14/11/80	29	Holywell	Rushden & D NC 7/09 - Barrow 8/09 Rel 5/10	5	0
(F)Matt Nolan	6'00"	12 00	25/2/82	28	Hitchin	Corby 6/09 - Lowestoft T 9/09	6	2
(D)Jimmy Turner	5'11"	11 04	4/10/83	26	Derby	Tamworth (L) 2/06 Perm 3/06 - Rel 9/09, Eastwood T 9/09, Halesowen T 2/10	4	0
(F)Iyseden Christie	5'10"	12 02	14/11/76	33	Coventry	Kings Lynn 9/09 - Rel 10/09, Farnborough 10/09, Tamworth 11/09, Kettering 5/10	2	0
(M)Steve Jagielka	5'08"	11 03	10/3/78	32	Manchester	Droylsden 6/07 - Hednesford 10/09	4	0
(F)Steve Torpey	5'09"	10 08	16/9/81	28	Kirkby	Stalybridge 6/09 - Fleetwood £4,000 10/09 Rel 5/10	13	3
(M)Tom Field			2/8/85	25	Liverpool	Vauxhall Motors 6/09 - Droylsden 11/09	8	0
(M)Jamie Vermiglio			10/6/82	28		Scarborough 5/07 - Chorley (L) 10/09, Northwich 12/09, Chorley 6/10	1	0
(M)Scott Embrey			3/8/91	19		Yth - Market Drayton (Dual) 11/09, Chasetown (L) 12/09 Perm 1/10	0	0
(D)Gavin Cowan	6'04"	14 04	24/5/81	29	Hanover(Ger)	Nuneaton 5/08 - Rel 1/10, Fleetwood 1/10, Gainsborough 2/10	16	2
(D)Aaron Brown	6'04"	14 07	23/6/83	27	Birmingham	Burton 1/10 - Truro C 2/10, Aldershot 3/10	1	0
(F)Damien Reeves	5'09"	11 10	18/12/85	24	Doncaster	Alfreton 11/09 - Bradford PA 3/10, Altrincham 6/10	16	4
(D)Lee Vaughan	5'07"	11 00	15/7/86	24	Birmingham	Walsall 2/06 - Kidderminster 5/10	35	1
(M)Kevin O'Connor	5'11"	12 02	19/10/85	24	Dublin	ex Wolves 1/10 - Worcester 6/10	17	0
(M)Liam Blakeman			6/9/82	27	Southport	Southport 5/08 - Southport 6/10	36	3
(D)Adam Dugdale	6'03"	12 07	12/9/87	22	Liverpool	Barrow (L) 1/10 Perm 2/10 - Rel c/s 10, Crewe 7/10	17	1
(M)Chris Nurse			7/5/84	26	Croydon	Rochester Rhinos (USA) 10/09 -	10	0
(M)Danny Edwards			27/10/83	26	Shrewsbury	Redditch 11/08 - Halesowen T (L) 11/09, Leamington 7/10	9	0

ALFRETON TOWN

Chairman: Wayne Bradley
Secretary: Bryan Rudkin (T) 07710 444 195
(E) waynebradley@healthcaremedia.co.uk

Additional Committee Members:
Steve Taylor, Sean Egan, Dave Gregory, Roger Thompson, Kev Miles

Manager: Nicky Law

Programme Editor: Chris Tacey (E) ctacey5087@aol.com

Back Row (L-R): Nicky Law (manager), Darren Stride, Aden Flint, Anton Brown, Matt Wilson, Ross Turner, Paddy Gamble, Anthony Wilson, Jake Moult, Anthony Howell, Paul Clayton,Paul Madin (physiotherapist), Russ O'Neill (assistant manager).
Front row: Kyle McFadzean (now Crawley Town), Jordan Hall, Ian Ross, Liam Hearn, Chris Hall, Nathan Arnold, Chris Shaw, Josh Law.

Club Factfile

Founded: 1959 **Nickname:** The Reds

Previous Names:

Previous Leagues: Central Alliance (pre reformation 1921-25) 59-61. Midland Combination 1925-27, 61-82. Northern Counties East 1982-87. Northern Premier 1987-99.

Club Colours (change): All red (All yellow)

Ground: Impact Arena, North Street, Alfreton, Derbyshire DE55 7FZ **(T)** 01773 830 277

Capacity: 3,600 **Seats:** 1,500 **Covered:** 2,600 **Clubhouse:** Yes **Shop:** Yes

Previous Grounds:

Simple Directions
From M1 Junction 28 Take A38 towards Derby for 2 miles. Then take slip road onto B600 Turn right at Tjunction towards town centre. At pedestrian crossing turn left into North Street and the ground is on the right hand side.

Record Attendance: 5,023 v Matlock Town - Central Alliance 1960
Record Victory: 15-0 v Loughbrough Midland League 1969-70
Record Defeat: 1-9 v Solihull - FAT 1997. 0-8 v Bridlington - 1992
Record Goalscorer: J Harrison - 303
Record Appearances: J Harrison - 560+
Additional Records: Paid £2,000 to Worksop Town for Mick Goddard
Received £7,000 from Ilkeston Town for Paul Eshelby

Senior Honours: Northern Counties East 1984-85, 2001-02. Northern Premier League Division 1 2002-03.
Derbyshire Senior Cup x7

10 YEAR RECORD

00-01	01-02	02-03	03-04	04-05	05-06	06-07	07-08	08-09	09-10
NCEP 3	NCEP 1	NP 1 1	NP P 4	Conf N 14	Conf N 17	Conf N 14	Conf N 16	Conf N 3	Conf N 3

ALFRETON TOWN

No.	Date	Comp	H/A	Opponents	Att:	Result	Goalscorers	Pos
1	11/8/09	BSN	H	Solihull Moors	453	W 3-0	Hearn 2 (47, 81), Brown 87	1
2	15/8/09	BSN	H	Vauxhall Motors	410	D 2-2	Todd 26, Brown 77	2
3	18/8/09	BSN	A	Eastwood Town	882	L 1-2	Pell 20	5
4	22/8/09	BSN	H	Southport	448	D 1-1	Clayton 45	6
5	29/8/09	BSN	A	Redditch United	291	L 0-3		9
6	31/8/09	BSN	H	Corby Town	575	W 1-0	Burke 50	8
7	5/9/09	BSN	A	Hyde United	368	W 5-1	Howell pen 14, Burke 28, Brown 43, Clayton 2 (71, 85)	6
8	8/9/09	BSN	A	Workington	337	D 1-1	Hearn 76	7
9	12/9/09	BSN	H	AFC Telford	610	W 4-0	Hearn 49, Clayton 69, Todd 2 (85, 90)	6
10	19/9/09	BSN	H	Stalybridge Celtic	537	L 3-5	Howell 13, Hearn 72, Todd 90	7
11	3/10/09	BSN	A	Blyth Spartans	462	L 0-2		9
12	17/10/09	BSN	A	Harrogate Town	401	W 4-0	Howell 2 (1, 23), Ross 2 (41, 54)	7
13	27/10/09	BSN	H	Gainsborough Trinity	517	W 1-0	Howell 66	6
14	31/10/09	BSN	A	Fleetwood Town	1297	D 2-2	Todd 53, Reeves 55	6
15	7/11/09	BSN	H	Stafford Rangers	462	W 3-1	Howell pen 33, Clayton 62, Hearn 79	5
16	10/11/09	BSN	H	Ilkeston Town	792	W 2-0	Todd 56, J Hall 89	3
17	14/11/09	BSN	A	Hinckley United	504	L 1-2	Howell 79	4
18	28/11/09	BSN	H	Fleetwood Town	485	L 1-4	Todd 30	5
19	1/12/09	BSN	A	AFC Telford	1292	L 0-2		6
20	12/12/09	BSN	H	Hyde United	302	W 4-0	Mills 11, Hearn pen 13, Ross 25, Law 73	5
21	19/1/10	BSN	A	Solihull Moors	161	D 1-1	Hearn 24	6
22	23/1/10	BSN	A	Vauxhall Motors	158	D 1-1	Hearn 4	6
23	26/1/10	BSN	H	Eastwood Town	560	D 1-1	Hearn 65	6
24	30/1/10	BSN	A	Gloucester City	310	W 2-1	Howell pen 70, Clayton 73	5
25	6/2/10	BSN	H	Harrogate Town	399	W 3-1	Brown 8, Clayton 35, Moult 53	5
26	13/2/10	BSN	A	Northwich Victoria	481	D 1-1	Howell 80	6
27	16/2/10	BSN	H	Workington	296	W 2-0	Law 55, Clayton 85	4
28	27/2/10	BSN	A	Stafford Rangers	466	D 1-1	Clayton 16	4
29	6/3/10	BSN	H	Gloucester City	410	W 3-1	Clayton 31, Hall 47, Hearn 54	3
30	9/3/10	BSN	H	Droylsden	410	W 5-0	Clayton 13, Moult 29, Hearn 3 (36, 56, 58)	3
31	13/3/10	BSN	A	Gainsborough Trinity	473	L 2-3	Clayton 2 (32, 89)	3
32	20/3/10	BSN	H	Blyth Spartans	441	W 1-0	Hearn 29	3
33	27/3/10	BSN	A	Stalybridge Celtic	530	W 1-0	Howell 20	3
34	3/4/10	BSN	H	Redditch United	477	W 3-0	Hearn 16, Howell 77, Nightingale pen 90	3
35	5/4/10	BSN	A	Corby Town	378	W 2-1	Clayton 10, Moult 52	3
36	10/4/10	BSN	H	Northwich Victoria	500	W 3-2	Flint 77, Moult 85, Og (Meadowcroft) 89	3
37	12/4/10	BSN	A	Droylsden	329	D 0-0		3
38	17/4/10	BSN	A	Ilkeston Town	584	D 0-0		3
39	20/4/10	BSN	A	Southport	2021	W 3-1	Clayton 2 (25, 82), Moult 53	3
40	24/4/10	BSN	H	Hinckley United	647	W 3-2	Hearn 2 (23, 45), Ross 40	3
	Farsley Celtic record expunged 12/03							
1	8/8/09	BSN	A	Farsley Celtic	285	W 3-0	Pell 40, Hearn 73, Roma 80	2
29	20/2/10	BSN	H	Farsley Celtic	428	W 6-2	Moult 10, Todd pen 25, Hearn 2 (39, 58), Bowler 2 (73, 88)	3
	Cups							
1	26/9/09	FAC 2Q	H	AFC Wulfrunians	353	W 6-0	Flint 1, Howell 2 (7, 45), Hearn 32, J Hall 41, Clayton 78	
2	10/10/09	FAC 3Q	H	Southport	613	D 2-2	Clayton 40, Hearn 74	
3	13/10/09	FAC 3QR	A	Southport	533	L 1-2	Howell 52	
4	21/11/09	FAT 3Q	A	Corby Town	306	D 1-1	Mills 9	
5	24/11/09	FAT 3QR	H	Corby Town	268	L 1-2 aet	Clayton 106	
6	28/4/10	PO SF1	A	Workington	1483	W 1-0	Hearn 55	
7	2/5/10	PO SF2	H	Workington	1575	W 3-1	Ross 37, Clayton 2 (48, 87) (W 4-1 agg)	
8	9/5/10	PO Final	A	Fleetwood Town	3592	L 1-2	Todd pen 75	

Home Attendances:	
Highest:	792 v Ilkeston Town
Lowest:	302 v Hyde United
Average (08-09):	481 (439)
Top Goalscorer:	Hearn - 21 (18 League, 3 Cup) in 41 appearances - 51% strike rate
	Clayton - 21 (16 League, 5 Cup) in 47 appearances - 45% strike rate
Most Appearances:	Clayton - 47 (33+6 League, 8 Cup)

DOOTSON	ROMA	MCFADZEAN	WILSON	PELL	ROSS	LAW	BROWN	CLAYTON	HEARN	HOWELL	TODD	REEVES	GAMBLE	BURKE	FLINT	J HALL	YATES	DUDLEY	KERRY	BOWLER	MILLS	ISTEAD	CURTIS SHAW	AISIEN	STAROSTA	MATTHEWSON	CHRIS SHAW	MOULT	MULDOON	C HALL	NIGHTINGALE	NORTH	TURNER	
X	X	X	X	X	X	X	X	X	X	X	S	S	U	U	U																			1
X	X	X	X	X	X	X	X	S	X	X	X	U	U	S	S																			2
X	X	X	X	X	X	X	X	S	X	X	X	S	U	U	S																			3
X	X	X	X		X	S	X	X	X	X	U	S	U	S	X	X																		4
X	X	X			X	S	X	U	X	X	S	X	U	X	X	X																		5
U	X	X		X	X	X	X	X	U	X	U	U	X	X	X	S																		6
X	X	X		X	X	X	X	X	S	X	U		U	X	X	S	S																	7
X	X	X	U	X	X	X	X	X	S	X			U	X	X	S	S																	8
X	X	X	X	X	U		X	X	X	X	S		U		X	X	U																	9
X	X	X	X	X	S	S	X	X	X	X	S		U	U	X	X																		10
X	X	X	U		S	S	X	X	X	X	X		U	S	X	X		X																11
U		X	X	X	X	S	X	X	X	X	X		X	S	X	S		U																12
U	U		X	X	X	S	X	X		X	X	X	X	X	X	S		U																13
U	U	X	X	X	X	S	X	X		X	X	X	X	U	X	S																		14
X	U	X	X	X	X	S	X	X	S	X	X	X		U	X	S																		15
	U	X	X	X	X	S		X	S	X	X	X	X	U	X	S			X															16
	X		U	X	X	S		X	S	X	X	X	X	S	X	X			X															17
	X			X	X	X		S		X	X		X		X	X			S	X	X													18
	X				X	X		X	S	X	X		X		X	X					X	X	U											19
	X	X	U		X	X		X	X		X		X						S		X	X	S	X	S	U								20
	U	X	X		U	X	X	S	X	X	X		X							U	X						X	X	U					21
	U	X	X		U	X	X	S	X	X	X		X							U	X						X	X	S					22
		X	X		X	X	X	X	X	X	S		X		U					U	S						X	X	S					23
	U		X		X	X	X	X	X	X	S		X		X					S	U						X	X	U					24
		U	X		X	X	X	X	X	X	S		X		X					U	S						X	X	U					25
		U	X		X	X	X	X	X	X	S		X		X					U	U						X	X	S					26
	U	S	X		X	X	X	X	X	X	U		X		X						S						X	X	S					27
	U	X			X	X	X	X	X		S		X		X					X	S						X	X	U	S				28
	U	X			X	X	X	X	X	S	U		X		X						U						X	X	U	X				29
	U	X			X	X	X	X	X	S	S		X		X					U	S						X	X		X				30
		X	S		X	X	X	X	X	X	S		X		X					U	U							X		X	S			31
		X	U		U	X	X	X	X	X	S		X		X						U						X	X		X	U			32
		X	S		U	X	X	X	X	X	U		X		X						U						X	X		X	U			33
		X	U		X	X	X	X	X	X	U		X		X						S						X	X		U	S			34
		X	U		X	X	X	X		X	U		X		X						S						X	X		U	X	S		35
	U		X		X	X	X	X	X	X	S				X						U						X	X			S	S	X	36
		X	U			X	X	X	S	X	X				X						U						X	X		S	X	U	X	37
	U	X	U		X	X	X	S	S		X				X						S						X	X			X	X	X	38
		X	S		X	X	X	X	X		S				X	X				U							X	X			U	U	X	39
		X	U		X	X	X	X	X		S				X	X				U							X	X			S	S	X	40
X	X	X	X	X	X	X	X	X	X	X	S	S	U	U	U																			
	U	X			X	X	X	X	X		X		X		X					S	S		X					X	S					

DOOTSON	ROMA	MCFADZEAN	WILSON	PELL	ROSS	LAW	BROWN	CLAYTON	HEARN	HOWELL	TODD	REEVES	GAMBLE	BURKE	FLINT	J HALL	YATES	DUDLEY	KERRY	BOWLER	MILLS	ISTEAD	CURTIS SHAW	AISIEN	STAROSTA	MATTHEWSON	CHRIS SHAW	MOULT	MULDOON	C HALL	NIGHTINGALE	NORTH	TURNER	
X	X	X	U	X	S	S	X	X	X	X	X		U	S	X	X																		1
U	U	X	X	U	X	X	X	X	X	X	U	U	X	U	X	S		X																2
U	U	X	X	U	X	X	X	X	X	X	S	S	X	U	X	S		X																3
	U		X	X	X	S		X		X	X	S	X		X	X			U	X	X													4
	U	U	X	X		X		X		X	X	S	X		X	X			S	X	X													5
		X	U		X	X	X	X	X	X	S				X	U					U						X	X			U		X	6
		X	U		X	X	X	X	X	X	S				X	U					S						X	X			U		X	7
		X	U		X	X	X	X	X	X	S				X	S					S						X	X			U		X	8

Total League Appearances

DOOTSON	ROMA	MCFADZEAN	WILSON	PELL	ROSS	LAW	BROWN	CLAYTON	HEARN	HOWELL	TODD	REEVES	GAMBLE	BURKE	FLINT	J HALL	YATES	DUDLEY	KERRY	BOWLER	MILLS	ISTEAD	CURTIS SHAW	AISIEN	STAROSTA	MATTHEWSON	CHRIS SHAW	MOULT	MULDOON	C HALL	NIGHTINGALE	NORTH	TURNER	
11	15	31	19	15	32	29	35	33	27	33	16	6	24	5	33	10	0	1	2	2	5	2	0	1	0	0	19	20	0	5	3	1	5	X
0	0	1	3	0	2	10	0	6	8	2	15	3	0	5	2	8	2	0	2	1	8	0	1	0	1	0	0	0	4	2	4	3	0	S
4	13	2	10	0	5	0	0	1	1	0	8	2	10	6	2	0	1	2	0	9	8	0	1	0	0	1	0	0	5	2	3	2	0	U

Total Cup Appearances

DOOTSON	ROMA	MCFADZEAN	WILSON	PELL	ROSS	LAW	BROWN	CLAYTON	HEARN	HOWELL	TODD	REEVES	GAMBLE	BURKE	FLINT	J HALL	YATES	DUDLEY	KERRY	BOWLER	MILLS	ISTEAD	CURTIS SHAW	AISIEN	STAROSTA	MATTHEWSON	CHRIS SHAW	MOULT	MULDOON	C HALL	NIGHTINGALE	NORTH	TURNER	
1	1	6	4	3	6	6	6	8	6	8	3	0	4	0	8	3	0	2	0	2	2	0	0	0	0	0	3	3	0	0	0	0	3	X
0	0	0	0	0	1	2	0	0	0	0	4	3	0	1	0	3	0	0	1	0	2	0	0	0	0	0	0	0	0	0	0	0	0	S
2	4	1	4	2	0	0	0	0	0	0	1	1	1	2	0	2	0	0	1	0	1	0	0	0	0	0	0	0	0	0	3	0	0	U

Total Goals

DOOTSON	ROMA	MCFADZEAN	WILSON	PELL	ROSS	LAW	BROWN	CLAYTON	HEARN	HOWELL	TODD	REEVES	GAMBLE	BURKE	FLINT	J HALL	YATES	DUDLEY	KERRY	BOWLER	MILLS	ISTEAD	CURTIS SHAW	AISIEN	STAROSTA	MATTHEWSON	CHRIS SHAW	MOULT	MULDOON	C HALL	NIGHTINGALE	NORTH	TURNER	
0	0	0	0	1	4	2	4	16	18	11	7	1	0	2	1	1	0	0	0	0	1	0	0	0	0	0	0	5	0	0	0	0	0	Lge
0	0	0	0	0	1	0	0	5	3	3	1	0	0	0	1	1	0	0	0	0	1	0	0	0	0	0	0	0	0	0	0	0	0	Cup

ALFRETON TOWN

CURRENT SQUAD AS OF BEGINING OF 2010-11 SEASON

GOALKEEPERS	HT	WT	D.O.B	AGE	P.O.B	CAREER	APPS	GOA
Paddy Gamble	5'10"	10 12	1/9/88	21	Bulwell	Notts Forest Rel 5/09, York C (2ML) 3/07, Stalybridge (SL) 7/07, Mansfield (5ML) 8/08, Alfreton 8/09	24	0
Ross Turner	5'11"	12 00	17/6/79	31	Sheffield	Stocksbridge PS, Worsborough Bridge, Scunthorpe 3/00 Rel c/s 00, Stocksbridge PS, Alfreton 11/01, Worksop 6/02, Bradford PA (L) 8/02, Bradford PA (L) 3/03, Ilkeston 11/03, Buxton 2/06, Sheffield 3/07, Retford U, Eastwood T 8/09, Retford U 11/09, Alfreton	5	0
DEFENDERS								
Aden Flint	6'06"		11/7/89	21		Pinxton FC, Alfreton (L) 10/08 Undisc 11/08, Matlock (L) 12/08	35	1
Kyle McFadzean	6'01"	13 04	20/2/87	23	Sheffield	Sheff Utd Rel c/s 07, Alfreton 6/07	32	0
Chris Shaw			18/12/83	26		Grantham, Gainsborough, Hucknall, Ilkeston 10/03, Eastwood T, Arnold 6/05, Eastwood T 10/05, Hucknall (2ML) 10/08, Grantham 1/09, Nantwich c/s 09, Corby T 10/09, Grantham (L) 12/09, Alfreton 12/09	19	0
MIDFIELDERS								
Nathan Arnold	5'08"	10 07	26/7/87	23	Mansfield	Mansfield Rel c/s 09, Grimsby (Trial) c/s 09, Hyde U 8/09, Alfreton 6/10		
Anton Brown			3/7/87	23		Mansfield (Scholar), Greenwood Meadows, Alfreton c/s 06	35	4
Chris Hall			3/3/83	27	Lincoln	Lincoln U, Burton 5/04, Gainsborough 6/07 Rel 2/10, York C (SL) 3/08, Alfreton 2/10	7	0
Jordan Hall			7/5/84	26		Chesterfield (Scholar), Hucknall, Buxton c/s 05, Hucknall (2ML) 1/08, Alfreton 3/08, Belper (L) 1/10, Matlock (L) 2/10	18	1
Josh Law			20/7/89	21		Chesterfield Rel c/s 08, Alfreton (SL) 10/07, Alfreton 5/08	39	2
Jake Moult	5'10"	10 05	10/2/89	21	Stoke	Port Vale (Scholar), Plymouth 7/07 Rel c/s 08, Kidderminster (SL) 3/08, Leek T 8/08, Stafford R 10/08, Alfreton 1/10	20	5
Ian Ross	5'10"	11 00	23/1/86	22	Sheffield	Sheff Utd, Boston U (3ML) 8/05, Bury (SL) 3/06, Notts County (SL) 7/06, Rotherham (2ML) 11/07 Perm 1/08 Rel c/s 08, Gainsborough 8/08, Alfreton 3/09 Rel 5/09	34	4
Matt Wilson			10/3/87	23		Darlington, Mackinlay Park, Sheffield Hallam Univ, Diddington T, Grantham, Alfreton 8/07, Worksop (3ML) 8/08	22	0
FORWARDS								
Paul Clayton			31/8/84	26		Barnsley (Scholar), Parkgate, Gainsborough 7/07, Alfreton 12/07	39	16
Liam Hearn			27/8/85	25		Santos, Hucknall c/s 06, Eastwood T 10/07, Chasetown 1/08, Quorn 1/08, Alfreton 9/08	35	18
Anthony Howell			27/5/86	24		Carlton T, Shepshed D 9/05, Carlton T 11/06, Grantham 3/07, Notts County (Trial) c/s 07, Eastwood T 6/07, Worksop 9/07, Eastwood (L) 1/08 Perm, Ilkeston 8/08, Mansfield 1/09 Rel 5/09, Alfreton (SL) 3/09, Alfreton 5/09	35	11
Anthony Wilson						Hallam, Belper c/s 07, Alfreton 5/10		

Loanees	HT	WT	DOB	AGE	POB	From - To	APPS	GOA
(D)Mark Dudley	5'10"	12 02	29/1/90	20	Doncaster	Derby 10/09 - Hinckley U (L) 11/09, Hinckley U (L) 2/10, Rel c/s 10	1	0
(M)Lloyd Kerry	6'02"	12 04	22/1/88	22	Chesterfield	Chesterfield 11/09 - Kidderminster (L) 3/10	4	0
(M)Steven Istead	5'08"	11 04	23/4/86	24	South Shields	Mansfield (6WL) 11/09 -	2	0

Departures	HT	WT	DOB	AGE	POB	From - To	APPS	GOA
(F)Jamie Yates	5'07"	10 11	24/12/88	21	Sheffield	Kettering 9/09 - Boston U (2ML) 9/09 Perm 11/09	2	0
(G)Craig Dootson	6'04"	14 02	23/5/79	31	Preston	Hyde 5/09 - Fleetwood 11/09 Rel 5/10, Harrogate T 6/10	11	0
(F)Damien Reeves	5'09"	11 10	18/12/85	24	Doncaster	Farsley Celtic 7/09 - Guiseley (L) 9/09, AFC Telford 11/09, Bradford PA 3/10, Altrincham 6/10	9	1
(D)Richard Pell			17/11/82	27	Boston	Blyth 5/09 - Byth Undisc 12/09, Harrogate T 6/10	15	1
(M)Carl Palmer			2/11/78	31		Kings Lynn 12/09 - Halesowen T (Dual) 12/09 Perm, Brackley T 3/10		
(M)Matty Burke			14/12/85	24		Vauxhall Motors 6/09 - Hyde U (3ML) 11/09 Perm 2/10	10	2
(M)Curtis Shaw			24/6/87	23	Nottingham	Kings Lynn 12/09 - Hucknall 3/10	1	0
(D)Bobby Aisien			19/12/88	21		Kings Lynn 12/09 - Billericay 3/10	1	0
(M)Andy Todd	6'00"	11 03	22/2/79	31	Nottingham	Rotherham 8/09 - Eastwood T 5/10	31	7
(F)Tyeisse Nightingale			12/10/85	24		Hucknall 3/10 - Eastwood T 6/10	7	1
(D)Dominic Roma	5'10"	11 11	29/11/85	24	Sheffield	Hinckley U 5/09 - Harrogate T 6/10	15	0
(F)Ben Mills			29/3/89	21	Stoke	Stafford R 11/09 - Stafford R 6/10	13	1
(M)Jack Muldoon			19/5/89	21		Glapwell 1/10 - Stocksbridge PS 6/10	4	0
(F)Danny North	5'09"	12 08	7/9/87	22	Grimsby	Grimsby 3/10 - St Patricks 6/10	4	0
(G)Lawrence Matthewson			22/4/88	22		ex Glapwell 12/09 - Belper (Dual) 1/10	0	0
(D)Ben Starosta	6'00"	12 00	7/1/87	23	Sheffield	ex Sheff Utd 12/09 -	1	0
(M)Kris Bowler			26/10/83	24		Matlock Undisc 7/07 - Worksop (3ML) 8/09	3	0
(M)Tom Curtis	5'08"	11 12	1/3/73	35	Exeter	Nuneaton 6/08 -		

BLYTH SPARTANS

Chairman: Tony Platten

Secretary: Ian Evans (T) 0790 598 4308 (E) generalmanager@blythspartans.com

Additional Committee Members:
K Scott, C Baxter, A Bowron S Ord, S Frake, Ms J Freeman, Brian Grey

Manager: Mick Tait

Programme Editor: Scott Dewhurst (E) samd_blyth@yahoo.co.uk

Back row (left to right): Tony Kennedy (Kit Manager), Michael Simm, Robert Dale, Nicky Deverdics, Daniel Groves, John Alexander, Neal Hooks, Jake Cunningham, Sam Grieveson, Callum Morris, Calvin Smith, Wayne Buchanan, Chris Swailes (Player Assistant Manager) and Susan Coates (Physio).
Front row (left to right): Eoin Ridley, Stephen Harrison, Liam O'Mahoney, Ian Graham, Mick Tait (Manager), Phil Cave, Paul Brayson, Stephen Turnbull, Michael Tait.

Club Factfile

Founded: 1899 **Nickname:** Spartans

Previous Names:

Previous Leagues: Northumberland 1901-07, Northern All. 1907-13, 46-47, North Eastern 1913-39, Northern Com. 1945-46, Midland 1958-60, Northern Counties 1960-62, Northern 1962-94, Northern Premier 1994-2006

Club Colours (change): Green & white stripes/black/green (White with red/white with red/white)

Ground: Croft Park, Blyth, Northumberland NE24 3JE (T) 01670 352 373

Capacity: 4,435 **Seats:** 563 **Covered:** 1,000 **Clubhouse:** Yes **Shop:** Yes

Previous Grounds:

Simple Directions
From the Tyne Tunnel, take the A19 signposted MORPETH. At second roundabout take the A189 signposted ASHINGTON. From A189 take A1061 signposted BLYTH. At 1st roundabout follow signs A1061 to BLYTH. Go straight across next two roundabouts following TOWN CENTRE/SOUTH BEECH. At next roundabout turn left onto A193 go straight across next roundabout, and at the next turn right into Plessey Rd and the ground is situated on your left. Team coach should the turn left into William St (3rd left) and reverse up Bishopton St to the designated parking spot.

Record Attendance: 10,186 v Hartlepool United - FA Cup 08/12/1956
Record Victory: 18-0 v Gateshead Town - Northern Alliance 28/12/1907
Record Defeat: 0-10 v Darlington - North Eastern League 12/12/1914
Record Goalscorer:
Record Appearances: Eddie Alder - 605 (1965-68)
Additional Records: Received £30,000 from Hull City for Les Mutrie

Senior Honours: North Eastern League 1935-36. Northern League 1972-73, 74-75, 75-76, 79-80, 80-81, 81-82, 82-83, 83-84, 86-87, 87-88. Northern League Division 1 1994-95. Northern Premier League Premier Division 2005-06.

10 YEAR RECORD

00-01	01-02	02-03	03-04	04-05	05-06	06-07	07-08	08-09	09-10
NP P 14	NP P 12	NP P 19	NP P 21	NP P 12	NP P 1	Conf N 7	Conf N 18	Conf N 15	Conf N 13

BLYTH SPARTANS

No.	Date	Comp	H/A	Opponents	Att:	Result	Goalscorers	Pos
1	8/8/09	BSN	A	AFC Telford	1847	D 1-1	Dale 3	12
2	11/8/09	BSN	H	Southport	737	L 0-2		16
3	15/8/09	BSN	H	Redditch United	458	W 1-0	Graham 60	12
4	22/8/09	BSN	H	Corby Town	458	L 1-2	Gillies 20	17
5	29/8/09	BSN	A	Hyde United	349	W 3-0	Brayson 52, Doninger 78, Graham 90	11
6	31/8/09	BSN	H	Droylsden	637	D 2-2	Dale 3, Harrison 72	11
7	5/9/09	BSN	A	Eastwood Town	575	L 2-4	Brayson 3, Boyle 77	12
8	8/9/09	BSN	A	Vauxhall Motors	176	D 1-1	Brayson pen 23	13
9	12/9/09	BSN	H	Solihull Moors	556	W 2-0	Dale 28, McCabe 51	11
10	19/9/09	BSN	A	Gloucester City	303	L 1-3	Dale 6	12
11	3/10/09	BSN	H	Alfreton Town	462	W 2-0	Dale 2 (19, 62)	11
12	17/10/09	BSN	H	Hinckley United	462	W 6-1	Tait 22, Harrison 34, Doninger 43, Graham 2 (45, 81), Brayson 49	10
13	31/10/09	BSN	H	Ilkeston Town	562	L 1-4	Webster 84	11
14	7/11/09	BSN	A	Solihull Moors	212	D 1-1	Brayson 69	11
15	14/11/09	BSN	H	Eastwood Town	527	L 1-3	Brayson 89	12
16	28/11/09	BSN	A	Redditch United	270	D 2-2	Brayson 2 (50, 62)	12
17	5/12/09	BSN	A	Stafford Rangers	483	D 1-1	Williams 65	13
18	16/1/10	BSN	H	Vauxhall Motors	384	W 3-2	Brayson 2 (18, 90), Dale 86	11
19	19/1/10	BSN	A	Northwich Victoria	357	L 1-5	Brayson 8	13
20	23/1/10	BSN	A	Fleetwood Town	1033	L 2-4	Brayson 2 (68, 87)	14
21	26/1/10	BSN	H	Stalybridge Celtic	393	W 4-1	Brayson 39, McCabe 65, Graham 68, Harrison 87	14
22	2/2/10	BSN	A	Stalybridge Celtic	269	W 1-0	Brayson 47	11
23	6/2/10	BSN	A	Southport	738	L 2-3	Graham 16, Brayson 47	13
24	9/2/10	BSN	H	Harrogate Town	407	W 1-0	McCabe 71	12
25	13/2/10	BSN	H	Stafford Rangers	466	D 2-2	Pell 43, Graham 46	11
26	27/2/10	BSN	H	AFC Telford	489	W 4-0	Graham 2 (16, 72), Brayson 2 (45, 76)	11
27	2/3/10	BSN	A	Workington	314	L 1-3	Brayson 66	14
28	6/3/10	BSN	H	Northwich Victoria	483	L 0-1		14
29	9/3/10	BSN	H	Workington	414	D 0-0		14
30	13/3/10	BSN	A	Ilkeston Town	360	L 1-2	Dale 53	14
31	20/3/10	BSN	A	Alfreton Town	441	L 0-1		14
32	22/3/10	BSN	A	Hinckley United	372	D 1-1	Brayson 45	14
33	27/3/10	BSN	H	Gloucester City	519	L 0-3		15
34	3/4/10	BSN	H	Hyde United	401	W 4-3	Tait 2 (17, 22), Brayson 44, Pell 58	13
35	5/4/10	BSN	A	Droylsden	294	L 1-2	Graham 35	13
36	10/4/10	BSN	A	Harrogate Town	287	W 5-2	Tait 4, Brayson 3 (18, 19, 74), Dale 33	12
37	13/4/10	BSN	H	Gainsborough Trinity	391	W 2-1	Tait 44, Brayson pen 76	12
38	17/4/10	BSN	H	Fleetwood Town	523	L 2-3	Brayson 2 (9, 60)	12
39	21/4/10	BSN	A	Corby Town	771	L 2-4	Brayson 62, Tait 72	13
40	24/4/10	BSN	A	Gainsborough Trinity	394	L 0-2		13
	Farsley Celtic record expunged 12/03							
4	18/8/09	BSN	A	Farsley Celtic	239	L 1-2	Dale 65	15
	Cups							
1	26/9/09	FAC 2Q	H	Ossett Albion	507	W 7-1	Tait 4 (29, 31, 63, 80), Brayson 85, Graham 88, Dale pen 90	
2	13/10/09	FAC 3Q	A	Salford City	271	D 2-2	Harrison 10, Doninger 24	
3	20/10/09	FAC 3QR	H	Salford City	534	W 2-1 aet	Brayson 30, Alexander 112	
4	24/10/09	FAC 4Q	H	AFC Telford	642	D 0-0		
5	27/10/09	FAC 4QR	A	AFC Telford	1398	L 0-4		
6	21/11/09	FAT 3Q	H	Stafford Rangers	442	W 2-0	Brayson 2 (70, 85)	
7	12/12/09	FAT 1	H	Ilkeston Town	419	W 2-0	Turnbull 22, Tait 27	
8	12/1/10	FAT 2	H	Guiseley	350	L 1-2	Og (Cotterill) 84	

Home Attendances:	
Highest:	737 v Southport
Lowest:	384 v Vauxhall Motors
Average (08-09):	464 (566)
Top Goalscorer:	Brayson - 32 (28 League, 4 Cup) in 43 appearances - 74% strike rate
Most Appearances:	Brayson - 43 (36 League, 7 Cup)
	Harrison - 43 (36 League, 7 Cup)

	BELL	HARRISON	BRACKSTONE	TAIT	WILLIAMS	LEESON	MCCABE	TURNBULL	ALEXANDER	WEBSTER	DALE	TODD	GRAHAM	BOYLE	REAY	NORTON	GILLIES	CRADDOCK	BRAYSON	DONINGER	TURNS	BAINS	MARWOOD	FRANCIS	PELL	FORSTER	BATES	HOOKS	FOSTER	SMITH	SLAUGHTER
1	X	X	X	X	X	X	X	X	X	X	X	S	U	U	U	U															
2	X	X	X	X	X	X	X	X	X	X	X	U	S	U	U	U															
3	X	X	X	X	X	X	X	X	X	U	U	X	X	U		U	S														
4	X	X	X	X	X			X	S	X	X	U	X	U	U	U	X	X													
5	X	X	X	X	X			X	U	X	S		S	S	U		X	X	X	X											
6	X	X	X	U	X		X	X	U		X		X	U	U		X	X	X	S											
7	X	X	X	X	X		X	X	U		X		U	S		U	S	X	X	X											
8	U	X	X	U	X	U	X	X	X	U	X			S		X	X	X	X												
9				X	X		X	X	X	S	X	U	S	X		U	X	X	X		X										
10		X	U	X	X			X	S		X	S	X	X			X	X	X		X										
11	X	X	X	X	X		X		S	X	X	U	X	U			U	X	X		U										
12	X	X		X	X		X		S	U	X	S	X	X		U	S	X	X	X											
13	X	X		X	X		X	X	S	S		U	X	X		U	U	X	X	X											
14	X	X	U	X	X		X	X	U	X		U	X	X		U	S		X			X									
15	X	X	U	X	X		X	X	S	X		S	U			U	X	X	X			X									
16		X	X	U	X			X	U			U	X	S		X	U		X	X		X	X	X							
17	U	X	X	X	X			X	U				X			X	U	S	X	X		X	U	X							
18	U	X	X	X			X	X	S		X	S	U			X	X	X	X				U		X						
19	U	X	X	X	X		X	X	S		X	U	U			X	X	X	X				S								
20	X	X		X	X		X	X	U		X	U	X			U	U	X	X	S						X					
21	X	X	S	X	X		X	X	S			U	X			U	U	X	X	X					X						
22	X	X	S	X	X		X	X	S		X	U				U	U	X	X						X		X				
23	X	X		X	X		X	X	U		X	U	X			U	U		X	X					X		S				
24	X	X	X	X	X		X	X	U		X	U	X			S	U		X						X		U				
25	U	X	X	X	X		X	X	U		X	U	X			X	S		X						X		U				
26	U		X	X	X			X	U		X	U	X			X	S	X	X						X		U	X			
27	X		X		X			X	S		X	U	X			U	U		X						X		X	X	X		
28	U		X		X			X	S		X	S				X	X		X						X		X	X	X	U	
29	U	X	X					X	U		X	X	U			X	X		X						X			X	X	U	
30	U	X	X	S	U			X	U		X	X	X			X	U		X						X			X	X		
31	U	X	X	X	X			U	U		X	U	X			X		U	X						X			X	X		
32	U	X		X	X			X	X		X					X		X	X									X	X		
33	S	X	X	X	X			X	X		X	S	S			X			X						X			X			
34	X	X	U	X	X			X	S		X	U	X			U			X						X			X	X		U
35	X	X	U	X	X			X	U		X	U	X			U			X						X			X	X		
36	X	X	X	X	X			X	S		X	U	X			U			X						X			X	U		
37	X	X		X	X			X	U		X		X			U		U	X						X			X	X		U
38	X	X	X	X	X			X	S			S	X			U		U	X						X			X	X		
39	X	X	X	X			X	X				X			X		U	X									X	X			
40	X	X	X	X	X				X			S	X			U		U	X						X			X	X		
	X	X		X	X	X	X	X	X	U	X	U	X	X	S	U	S														

	BELL	HARRISON	BRACKSTONE	TAIT	WILLIAMS	LEESON	MCCABE	TURNBULL	ALEXANDER	WEBSTER	DALE	TODD	GRAHAM	BOYLE	REAY	NORTON	GILLIES	CRADDOCK	BRAYSON	DONINGER	TURNS	BAINS	MARWOOD	FRANCIS	PELL	FORSTER	BATES	HOOKS	FOSTER	SMITH	SLAUGHTER
1	U	X	X	X	X			X	S	S	S	X	X	U			X	X	X	U	X										
2	X	X	X		X		X		U	U	X	X	X	U			U	X	X	X	U										
3	X	X	X	X	X		X	U	S	X	X	S		S		U	X	X	X												
4	X	X	X	X	X		X	U	U	U	X	U	X	S		U	S	X	X	X											
5	X	X	X	X	X		X	X	X	U		S	X	U		U	X	X		S											
6	U	X	U	X	X			X	X			U	X			X	U	X	X	X		X	U								
7	U		X	X	X		S	X	U		S		X			X	X	X	X	X		X	S								
8	U	X	X		X		X	X	U		X	U	X			X	S	X	X	X			U								
Total League Apperances																															
X	24	36	26	33	37	3	20	36	9	7	29	3	26	5	0	14	11	18	36	8	2	4	1	2	19	1	3	15	12	0	0
S	10	2	1	0	0	0	0	15	2	1	9	4	4	0	1	6	1	0	2	0	0	1	0	0	0	1	0	0	0	0	
U	11	0	5	3	1	1	0	1	16	3	1	20	6	6	5	21	11	5	0	0	1	0	2	0	0	0	3	0	1	2	2
Total Cup Apperances																															
X	4	7	7	6	8	0	5	5	2	1	4	2	7	0	0	3	4	8	7	5	1	2	0	0	0	0	0	0	0	0	0
S	0	0	0	0	0	0	1	0	2	1	2	2	0	2	0	0	2	0	0	1	0	0	1	0	0	0	0	0	0	0	0
U	4	0	1	0	0	0	0	2	4	3	0	3	0	3	0	3	2	0	0	1	1	0	2	0	0	0	0	0	0	0	0
Total Goals																															
Lge	0	3	0	6	1	0	3	0	0	1	9	0	10	1	0	0	1	0	28	2	0	0	0	0	2	0	0	0	0	0	0
Cup	0	1	0	5	0	0	0	1	1	0	1	0	1	0	0	0	0	0	4	1	0	0	0	0	0	0	0	0	0	0	0

BLYTH SPARTANS

CURRENT SQUAD AS OF BEGINING OF 2010-11 SEASON

GOALKEEPERS	HT	WT	D.O.B	AGE	P.O.B	CAREER	APPS	GOA
Jack Norton	6'00"		27/3/87	23		Darlington, Whitby 7/06, Darlington (L) 12/06, Guisborough, South Shields, Northallerton, Tow Law 1/08, Gateshead (Dual) c/s 08, Consett 2/09, Newcastle Blue Star 3/09, Blyth 8/09	15	0
DEFENDERS								
Phil Cave			12/5/87	23	Newcastle	Newcastle (Scholar), Gateshead 8/07, Livingston 7/08, Gateshead (SL) 2/09, Gateshead 8/09 Rel 5/10, Blyth 7/10		
Stephen Harrison			3/2/82	28	Hexham	Sunderland Rel c/s 02, Carlisle (Trial) 3/02, Bristol R (Trial) 4/02, Gateshead 7/02, Blyth 8/04, Gateshead 1/05, Durham C 6/06, Blyth 7/09	36	3
Chris McCabe			13/11/80	29		Jarrow Roofing, Sunderland Nissan, Blyth 12/04	20	3
Dan Smith	5'10"	10 07	5/10/86	23	Sunderland	Sunderland, Huddersfield (2ML) 1/06, Aberdeen 8/06 Rel c/s 08, Darlington (Trial), St Johnstone 8/08, Gateshead 11/08 Rel c/s 09, Ryhope CW 8/09, Blyth 3/10	0	0
Chris Swailes	6'02"	12 11	19/10/70	39	Gateshead	Ipswich, Peterborough £10,000 3/91 Rel c/s 91, Boston U 7/91, Birmingham (L) 3/92, Kettering £5,000 c/s 92, Bridlington T, Guisborough (L), Doncaster 10/93, Ipswich £150,000 3/95, Bury £200,000 11/97, Rotherham 7/01, Oldham 7/05 Rel 12/06, Hamilton 3/07 Rel c/s 09, Gateshead 6/09 Rel 5/10, Blyth (Pl/Ass Man) 6/10		
MIDFIELDERS								
Neal Hooks			3/7/87	23	Hexham	Ross C, Elgin (SL) 1/07, Newcastle Blue Star 7/07, Ilkeston 9/08, Sunshine George Cross (Aust) 2/09, Ilkeston 9/09, Blyth 2/10	15	0
Michael Tait			24/6/88	22		Darlington (Yth), Gretna Rel c/s 08, Newcastle Blue Star (SL) 1/08, Blyth 8/08, Newcastle Blue Star 9/08, Workington 11/08, Newcastle Blue Star 1/09, Blyth 6/09	34	6
Simon Todd			3/12/89	20		Darlington, Blyth (3ML) 8/08 (SL) 1/09 Perm 2/09, Ostavalls (Swe) 5/09, Blyth 8/09	12	0
Stephen Turnbull	5'10"	11 00	7/1/87	23	South Shields	Hartlepool Rel 5/08, Gateshead (L) 12/05, Bury (2ML) 11/06, Rochdale (L) 3/07, Gateshead 7/08 Rel 5/09, Blyth 6/09	36	0
Gareth Williams			1/4/80	30	Co Durham	Whickham, Whitley Bay, Blyth 8/00	37	1
FORWARDS								
John Alexander	5'11"	12 00	24/9/85	24	Middlesbrough	Darlington Rel c/s 04, Bishop Auckland (L) 12/02, Marske U, Billingham T, Blyth 7/09	24	0
Paul Brayson	5'07"	10 10	16/9/77	32	Newcastle	Newcastle, Swansea (3ML) 1/97, Reading £100,000 3/98, Cardiff (SL) 3/00, Cardiff 7/00 Rel c/s 02, Cheltenham 8/02 Rel 5/04, York C (Trial) 7/04, Northwich 8/04, Gateshead (L) 3/05, York C 6/07, Gateshead 1/08, Newcastle Blue Star 6/08, Durham C 6/09, Blyth Spartans 8/09	36	28
Robert Dale			11/6/84	26		Ryton, West Allotmment, Blyth, Oxford U (Trial) c/s 06	30	9
Ian Graham			4/2/87	23		Sunderland (Scholar), Newcastle Benfield, Blyth 6/09	30	10

Loanees	HT	WT	DOB	AGE	POB	From - To	APPS	GOA
(D)Rikki Bains	6'01"	13 00	3/2/88	22	Coventry	Darlington (2ML) 11/09 - Gateshead (SL) 1/10, Rel 4/10	4	0
(M)Alex Francis	6'02"	12 08	7/1/90	20	Gateshead	Gateshead (5WL) 11/09 -	2	0
(D)Richard Forster			16/8/81	29		Tow Law 1/10 -	1	0

Departures	HT	WT	DOB	AGE	POB	From - To	APPS	GOA
(D)Andrew Leeson	5'10"	11 00	27/9/83	26	Cape Town, SA	Newcastle Blue Star 12/05 - Rel 9/09, Whitby 9/09	3	0
(F)Sean Reay	6'01"	12 00	20/5/89	21	Jarrow	Darlington 10/08 - Shildon 9/09, Whitby 10/09, Jarrow Roofing 12/09	0	0
(G)Craig Turns			4/11/82	27		Durham C 9/09 - Spennymoor 10/09	2	0
(M)Adrian Webster	5'08"	10 09	11/10/80	29	Hawkes Bay, NZ	Kuopion Palloseura (Fin) 1/09 - Rel 11/09, Cockburn FC (Aust) 2/10	9	1
(D)Kenny Boyle			27/6/85	25		Whickham 8/07 - Dunston UTS, Spennymoor 2/10	9	1
(M)Mark Doninger	5'11"	12 00	19/10/89	20	Newcastle	Newcastle 8/09 - Derby (Trial) 1/10, Burton (Trial) 2/10, Sligo 2/10	10	2
(M)James Marwood	5'09"	11 05	21/5/90	20		Newcastle (Scholar) 11/09 - Team Northumbria, Gateshead 6/10	2	0
(F)Guy Bates			31/10/85	24		Walker Central 2/10 - Rel 3/10	4	0
(M)Josh Gilles			12/6/90	20		Newcastle Blue Star 7/09 - Whitley Bay 3/10, Gateshead 6/10	17	1
(D)Steve Foster	6'01"	13 00	3/12/74	35	Mansfield	Darlington 3/10 - Mansfield 5/10	12	0
(D)Richard Pell			17/11/82	27	Boston	Alfreton Undisc 12/09 - Harrogate T 6/10	19	2
(G)Marc Bell			9/10/82	27		Whitby 6/08 - Rel 6/10	25	0
(D)John Brackstone	5'11"	10 08	9/2/85	25	Hartlepool	Gateshead 2/09 - Bedlington 6/10	28	0
(F)Michael Hepplewhite			27/7/90	20		Jarrow Roofing 11/09 - Sunderland RCA 7/10		
(D)Darren Craddock	5'11"	12 02	23/2/85	25	Bishop Auckland	Newcastle Blue Star 6/09 - Whitby 7/10	19	0
(G)Sam Grieveson			6/7/92	18		Norwich 11/09 -		
(D)Richard Slaughter			4/8/90	20		Tow Law 3/10 -	0	0

BOSTON UNITED

Chairman: David Newton
Secretary: John Blackwell (T) 07860 663 299
(E) admin@bufc.co.uk

Additional Committee Members:
Neil Kempster, Chris Cook, Craig Singleton
Manager: Ron Scott and Paul Hurst
Programme Editor: Craig Singleton (E) craig.singleton@bufc.co.uk

Back row (L-R): James Cullingworth, Simon Ashton, Anthony Church, Kieran Murphy, Danny Davidson, Liam Parker, Miles Hunter, Jason Field. Middle row: Jason Hatfield (kit manager), Ryan Semple, Shaun Pearson, Aaron Butcher, Lee Canoville, Gareth Jelleyman, Katie Cooper (sports therapist).
Front row: Shane Clancy, Spencer Weir-Daley, Jamie Yates, Paul Hurst (manager), Rob Scott (manager), Danny Sleath, Marc Newsham, Harry Deane.

Club Factfile

Founded: 1933 **Nickname:** The Pilgrims
Previous Names: Reformed as Boston United when Boston Town folded in 1933
Previous Leagues: Midland 1933-58, 62-64, Southern 1958-62, 98-2000, United Counties 1965-66, West Midlands 1966-68, Northern Premier 1968-79, 93-98, 2008-10, Alliance/Conference 1979-93, 2000-02, 07-08, Football League 2002-07
Club Colours (change): Amber and black stripes/black/black (all white)

Ground: Jakemans Stadium, York Street, Boston PE21 6JN (T) 01205 364 406
Capacity: 6,645 **Seats:** 1,323 **Covered:** 6,645 **Clubhouse:** Yes **Shop:** Yes
Previous Grounds:
Simple Directions
A1 to A17 Sleaford to Boston-Over Boston Railway Station crossing, bear right at the Eagle Public House-To light over Haven Bridge-straight along John Adams Way(Dual Carriageway) -Turn right at traffic lights into main ridge, then right again into York Street (This is opposite Eagle Fisheries)-Ground is signposted after Railway crossing.

Record Attendance: 10,086 v Corby Town - Floodlights inauguration 1955
Record Victory: 12-0 v Spilsby Town - Grace Swan Cup 1992-93
Record Defeat:
Record Goalscorer: Chris Cook - 181
Record Appearances: Billy Howells - 500+
Additional Records: Paid £14,000 to Wycombe Wanderers for Micky Nuttell
Received £50,000 from Bolton Wanderers for David Norris 2000
Senior Honours: Central Alliance League 1961-62. United Counties League 1965-66. West Midlands League 1966-67, 67-68. Northern Premier League 1972-73, 73-74, 76-77, 77-78, League Cup 1973-74, 75-76. Southern League 1999-2000. Conference 2001-02.

10 YEAR RECORD

00-01	01-02	02-03	03-04	04-05	05-06	06-07	07-08	08-09	09-10
Conf 12	Conf 1	FL 3 15	FL 3 11	FL 2 16	FL 2 11	FL 2 23	Conf N 10	NP P 16	NP P 3

BOSTON UNITED

No.	Date	Comp	H/A	Opponents	Att:	Result	Goalscorers	Pos
1	Aug 15	Unibond P.	A	F.C.United	2482	W 2 - 1	Davidson 36 53	6
2	22		H	Kendal Town	1512	D 0 - 0		7
3	25		A	Frickley Athletic	338	W 1 - 0	Davidson 28	6
4	29		A	Guiseley	429	W 3 - 1	Sleath 67 Newsham 77 (pen) Canoville 78	2
5	31		H	Buxton	1471	D 2 - 2	Newsham 27 Clarke 90	
6	Sept 5		A	Burscough	280	L 1 - 3	Newsham 14	5
7	8		H	Matlock Town	1216	D 1 - 1	Camm 49	5
8	**12**	**F.A.C. 1Q**	**H**	**Loughborough Dynamo**	**941**	**W 4 - 2**	**Newsham 23 Suarez 27 Pearson 67 80**	
9	14		A	Bradford P.A.	455	D 2 - 2	Newsham 30 54	7
10	19		H	Whitby Town	1048	D 0 - 0		
11	22		H	Retford United	1008	L 0 - 1		11
12	**26**	**F.A.C. 2Q**	**A**	**Lowestoft Town**	**1134**	**L 0 - 1**		
13	Oct 5		A	Buxton	352	W 1 - 0	Suarez 85	
14	10		H	Ashton United	1259	W 3 - 0	Newsham 36 Pearson 45 Church 54	6
15	13		H	Worksop Town	1137	W 2 - 0	Davidson 50 Newsham 90	
16	**17**	**F.A.T 1Q**	**H**	**Chorley**	**889**	**W 3 - 2**	**Davidson 4 9 Sleath 66**	
17	24		A	Nantwich Town	693	W 4 - 0	Newsham 63 Davidson 78 84 Cotton 90	1
18	28		A	Stcksbridge Park Steels	362	L 1 - 2	Newsham 3	
19	**31**	**F.A.T 2Q**	**H**	**Quorn**	**917**	**D 0 - 0**		
20	**Nov 3**	**F.A.T. 2Qr**	**A**	**Quorn**	**271**	**L 2 - 3**	**Newsham 19 (pen) Church 87**	
21	7		H	North Ferriby United	1235	W 3 - 1	Newsham 45 Weir-Daley 63 76	3
22	14		H	Marine	1150	W 2 - 1	Weir-Daley 26 Suarez 69	
23	21		A	Ossett Town	246	W 5 - 0	Weir-Daley 14 Newsham 23 60 Pearson 65 Clarke 70	1
24	28		H	Burscough	1256	D 3 - 3	Church 32 Weir-Daley 41 Newsham 50	
25	Dec 5		A	Matlock Town	409	L 0 - 1		2
26	12		H	Bradford PA	1212	L 0 - 1		3
27	26		H	Stocksbridge P.S.	1365	W 3 - 2	Yates 1 Suarez 17 Weir-Daley 33	3
28	Jan 23		H	Durham City	1313	W10 - 0	Suarez 7 Sleath 10 Newsham 32 49 Korangfeng 33 75 DAVIDSON 3 (60 68 84) Yates 78	2
29	30		A	Kendal Town	293	L 0 - 1		3
30	Feb 6		H	Buxton	1151	W 2 - 1	Pearson 59 Parker 90	2
31	13		A	Ashton United	227	W 2 - 0	Davidson 67 Weir-Daley 90	2
32	27		H	Ossett Town	1250	W 7 - 0	Davidson 24 Weir-Daley 29 Pearson31 Church 35 69 Newsham 72 (p) Sleath 76	3
33	Mar 6		A	Durham City	230	W 4 - 1	WEIR-DALEY 3 (18 45 55) Semple 50	2
34	9		A	Retford Town	664	W 2 - 1	Sleath 30 Pearson 51	2
35	20		H	Nanntwich Town	1378	W 5 - 0	Newsham 17 Davidson 58 Weir-Daley 64 Sleath 72 Suarez 90	2
36	24		A	Whitby Town	275	L 0 - 2		
37	27		A	North Ferriby United	423	D 0 - 0		3
38	April 2		H	Frickley Athletic	417	W 4 - 2	Church 4 Pearson 54 Weir-Daley 71 Canoville73	
39	5		A	Hucknall Town	501	W 4 - 1	Newsham 13 48 Davidson 66 Weir-Daley 86	
40	10		H	Guiseley	1604	W 2 - 1	Sleath 80 (pen) Weir-Daley 90	2
41	14		A	Worksop Town	398	W 5 - 1	Weir-Daley 16 45 Suarez 50 Semple 59 Newsham 88	
42	17		H	F.C.United	2533	W 4 - 1	Canoville 70 Church 77 Weir-Daley 79 Davidson 88	1
43	24		A	Marine	1367	D 0 - 0		3
44	**27**	**Play Off S-F**	**H**	**North Ferriby United**	**2165**	**W 2 - 1**	**Yates 36 Newsham 41**	
45	**May 1**	**Play Off Final**	**A**	**Bradford P.A.**	**2327**	**W 2 - 1**	**Newsham 60 Church 93**	
					Goals	103 44		

Home Attendances:

Highest: 2533 v F.C. United

Lowest: 1008 v Retford United

Average (08-09): 1343 (1101)

Top Goalscorer: Newsham - 24 (League 20, FAC 1, FAT 1, Play-offs 2)

BOSTON UNITED

CURRENT SQUAD AS OF BEGINING OF 2010-11 SEASON

GOALKEEPERS	HT	WT	D.O.B	AGE	P.O.B	CAREER	APPS	GOA
Aaron Butcher			17/3/91	19		Peterborough (Yth), Boston U 7/07		
DEFENDERS								
Simon Ashton			20/2/92	18		Boston U		
Paul Canoville	6'01"	11 03	14/3/81	29	Ealing	Millwall (Ass Sch), Arsenal Rel c/s 01, Northampton (L) 1/01, Torquay 9/01 Rel c/s 05, Boston U 8/05 Rel c/s 07, Shrewsbury (SL) 1/07, Bournemouth (Trial) c/s 07, Notts County 7/07 Rel c/s 08, Grays 9/08 Rel 10/08, Halesowen T 10/08, Gainsborough (SL) 2/0		
James Cullingworth			18/9/87	22	Nottingham	Notts Forest, Shepshed D 1/07, Hucknall 7/07 Rel 9/08, Stafford R 10/08, Gainsborough 12/08 Rel 5/09, Boston U 6/09		
Kieran Murphy	5'11"	11 00	21/12/87	21	Kingston	MK Dons Rel 5/08, Aylesbury (L) 8/06, Maidenhead (L) 11/06, Hendon (L) 12/06, Walton & H (L) 3/07, Crawley (SL) 11/07, Ilkeston c/s 08, Boston U 5/10		
Liam Parker	6'01"	12 05	22/2/86	24	Boston	Grimsby Rel c/s 05, Boston T, Boston U 7/08		
Shaun Pearson			28/4/89	20		Spalding U, Stamford 6/08, Boston U 7/09		
MIDFIELDERS								
Anthony Church			29/3/87	22	Newham	Dag & Red (Yth), Ilford c/s 06, Redbridge, Newport C 7/08, Ilkeston 10/08, Boston U 7/09		
Shane Clancy			13/1/92	19		Boston U		
Gareth Davies	6'01"	12 10	4/2/83	27	Chesterfield	Sheff Utd (Yth), Buxton, Chesterfield 8/01 Rel 1/08, Stalybridge (L) 9/07, York C (Trial) 1/08, Halifax 2/08, Gainsborough 7/08 Rel c/s 09, Matlock c/s 09, Boston U 1/10		
Ryan Semple	5'11"	10 11	4/7/85	24	Belfast	Peterborough, Man Utd (Trial) 2/03, Farnborough (3ML) 11/03, Lincoln C 7/06 Rel 1/08, Chester (6WL) 11/06, Rushden & D (L) 8/07, Oxford U NC 2/08, Brackley T 3/08, Boston U (Trial) c/s 08, Deeping R 8/08, Haverhill R (Dual) 3/09, Gainsborough 6/09, Boston U 3/10		
Danny Sleath	5'08"	11 05	14/12/86	23	Matlock	Mansfield Rel 5/08, Gresley (L) 10/06, Alfreton (L) 2/07, Boston U (L) 11/07, Gainsborough (SL) 3/08, Eastwood T 9/08, Ilkeston 3/09, Boston U 7/09		
FORWARDS								
Danny Davidson	6'05"		23/10/79	30	Derby	Burton Rel c/s 00, Belper (L) 12/99, Rocester, Leek, Hereford 8/01, Stafford R 7/02, Crawley 8/04, Nuneaton 11/05 Rel 11/05, Tamworth 1/06 Rel 5/06, Moor Green/Solihull Moors 6/06, Alfreton 5/08 Rel 5/09, Matlock (L) 3/09, Boston U 8/09		
Miles Hunter			16/7/88	22		Lincoln C (Yth), Boston U (Yth), Deeping R, Bourne T, Sleaford T 7/09, Boston U 5/10		
Marc Newsham	5'10"	09 11	24/3/87	23	Hatfield, Yor	Rotherham Rel c/s 09, Gainsborough (L) 10/08, Sheffield FC (L) 12/08, Ilkeston (SL) 1/09, Boston U 6/09		
Mikel Suarez			28/9/86	23	Bilbao, Spa	Loughborough University, Nuneaton T (Trial) 7/09, Boston U 7/09		
Spencer Weir-Daley	5'09"	10 11	5/9/85	24	Leicester	Notts Forest Rel c/s 07, Macclesfield (2ML) 8/06, Lincoln C (3ML) 1/07, Bradford C (SL) 3/07, Notts County 7/07 Rel 1/09, Mansfield (Trial) 3/09, Ilkeston 9/09, Boston U 10/09		
Jamie Yates	5'07"	10 11	24/12/88	20	Sheffield	Rotherham Rel 5/09, Burton (3ML) 1/09, Kettering 7/09 Rel 9/09, Retford U 9/09, Alfreton 9/09, Boston U (2ML) 9/09 Perm 11/09		

Do you remember when...

Boston United

Boston United achieved a creditable 3rd place in The G.M. Vauxhall Conference in 1988-1989.

Back row, left to right: Ted Goddard (Physio), Alex Coupland, Lee Hurford, Gary Baines, Glenn Beech and Don Robinson (Trainer).
Middle row: Martin King, David Vaughan, Martin Hardy, John McKenna, David Cusack, Billy Millar, Allen Crombie, Warren Ward and Gerald Creane.
Front Row: Paul Shirtliff, Chris Cook, Gary Simpson, Georg Kerr (Manager), Ronnie Reid (Manager) Paul Wilson, David Beavon and Stewart Hamill.

CORBY TOWN

Chairman: Peter Mallinger

Secretary: Gerry Lucas **(T)** 07932 6333 43 **(E)** gerry21@googlemail.com

Additional Committee Members:
Michael Leech, David Dunham, Les Manning, Ian Hopewell

Manager: Graham Drury

Programme Editor: David Tilley **(E)** david.tilley59@tiscali.co.uk

Back row, left to right:- Glenn Walker, Chris Mackenzie, Tom Cross, Jack Drury, Michael Frew, Phil Gulliver.
Middle row, left to right:- Adam Webster, Andy Gooding, Danny Pitham, Simon Brown, Steve Towers, Asa Charlton, Liam Dolman, Chris Hope, Ben Mackey, Phil Watt, Steve Diggin, Ian Jackson (coach).
Front row, left to right:- Richard Lavery, Nathan Jarman, Danny Nicholls (assistant manager), Graham Drury (manager), Kevin Grundy (physio), Dean West, Andy Hall. Photo by David Tilley.

Club Factfile

Founded: 1947 **Nickname:** The Steelmen

Previous Names: Stewart & Lloyds (Corby) > 1947

Previous Leagues: United Counties 1935-52. Midland 1952-58. Southern 1958-2009

Club Colours (change): Black & white/black/black (Yellow/royal blue/blue)

Ground: Rockingham Triangle Stadium, Rockingham Road, Corby NN17 2AE **(T)** 01536 406 640

Capacity: 6,000 **Seats:** 300 **Covered:** 1,000 **Clubhouse:** Yes **Shop:** Yes

Previous Grounds:

Simple Directions
From A14, Exit at Jnc 7, Keep left, at first roundabout take A6003 Oakham/Uppingham stay on this road for approx. 7 miles (ignore signs for Corby to your right en route) straight over two roundabouts at second B.P. petrol station on right. at next roundabout approx 1 mile Ahead turn right onto A6116 for 300 yards entrance to Ground between Rugby Club and Rockingham Forest Hotel (Great Western).

Record Attendance: 2,240 v Watford - Friendly 1986-87

Record Victory: Not known

Record Defeat: Not known

Record Goalscorer: David Holbauer - 159 (1984-95)

Record Appearances: Derek Walker - 601

Additional Records: Paid £2,700 to Barnet for Elwun Edwards 1981
Received £20,000 from Oxford United for Matt Murphy 1993

Senior Honours: United Counties League 1950-51, 51-52. Southern League Premier Division 2008-09.
Northants Senior Cup x6.

10 YEAR RECORD

00-01	01-02	02-03	03-04	04-05	05-06	06-07	07-08	08-09	09-10
SthE 11	SthE 21	SthE 19	SthE 15	SthW 12	SthE 2	SthP 20	SthP 16	SthP 1	Conf N 6

CORBY TOWN

No.	Date	Comp	H/A	Opponents	Att:	Result	Goalscorers	Pos
1	8/8/09	BSN	H	Harrogate Town	505	W 3-0	Turner 23, Towers 53, Mettam 57	3
2	11/8/09	BSN	A	Stafford Rangers	531	W 2-0	Strachan 21, Mettam 35	2
3	15/8/09	BSN	A	Stalybridge Celtic	449	W 3-1	Gulliver 4, Solkhon 52, Defty 84	1
4	19/8/09	BSN	H	Ilkeston Town	787	D 2-2	Mettam 32, Mayo 72	1
5	22/8/09	BSN	A	Blyth Spartans	458	W 2-1	Mettam pen 39, Stallard 80	1
6	29/8/09	BSN	H	Gloucester City	633	L 3-6	Strachan 57, Mettam 68, Solkhon 89	2
7	31/8/09	BSN	A	Alfreton Town	575	L 0-1		6
8	5/9/09	BSN	H	Northwich Victoria	404	W 1-0	Stallard 80	3
9	9/9/09	BSN	H	Hinckley United	266	D 1-1	Diggin 42	5
10	12/9/09	BSN	A	Fleetwood Town	1126	L 2-4	Diggin 2 (67, 84)	7
11	19/9/09	BSN	A	Droylsden	422	W 2-1	Diggin 67, Mettam pen 82	5
12	3/10/09	BSN	H	Eastwood Town	603	D 1-1	Gulliver 24	6
13	17/10/09	BSN	A	Hyde United	318	W 3-1	Towers 2 (24, 75), Mettam 87	5
14	24/10/09	BSN	H	Stafford Rangers	475	W 3-2	Mettam 2 (6, 10), Mayo 88	2
15	7/11/09	BSN	H	Redditch United	505	D 2-2	Mettam 30, Defty 43	3
16	14/11/09	BSN	H	Workington	342	L 0-2		5
17	28/11/09	BSN	A	Southport	815	L 0-4		6
18	5/12/09	BSN	A	Vauxhall Motors	178	W 4-2	Mettam 20, Defty 2 (60, 86), Towers 82	5
19	9/12/09	BSN	H	AFC Telford	329	L 1-2	Towers 89	6
20	26/12/09	BSN	H	Gainsborough Trinity	360	D 2-2	Solkhon 3, Mettam 63	6
21	23/1/10	BSN	H	Solihull Moors	369	L 1-2	Diggin pen 80	8
22	6/2/10	BSN	H	Fleetwood Town	455	L 0-2		9
23	10/2/10	BSN	H	Droylsden	202	W 1-0	Mayo 6	8
24	13/2/10	BSN	A	Solihull Moors	249	L 0-3		8
25	27/2/10	BSN	H	Southport	418	D 1-1	Gulliver 2	10
26	2/3/10	BSN	A	Ilkeston Town	212	L 2-3	Mayo 17, Millar	12
27	6/3/10	BSN	H	Vauxhall Motors	261	W 4-1	Mettam 2 (48, 55), Defty 2 (53, 80)	10
28	9/3/10	BSN	A	Northwich Victoria	359	D 2-2	Mettam 58, Strachan 75	10
29	13/3/10	BSN	A	Workington	470	D 1-1	Mettam 7	10
30	20/3/10	BSN	H	Hyde United	287	W 2-0	Mettam 2 (pen 5, 84)	10
31	23/3/10	BSN	A	Gainsborough Trinity	276	L 0-2		11
32	27/3/10	BSN	A	Redditch United	301	L 0-1		11
33	29/3/10	BSN	A	Hinckley United	344	D 1-1	Hibbert 32	11
34	5/4/10	BSN	H	Alfreton Town	378	L 1-2	Diggin 69	11
35	8/4/10	BSN	A	Eastwood Town	342	W 1-0	Defty 75	11
36	10/4/10	BSN	H	Stalybridge Celtic	260	W 5-1	Mettam 44, Defty 3 (66, 78, 82), Walker 75	10
37	13/4/10	BSN	A	Harrogate Town	206	W 4-0	Towers 46, Defty 48, Hibbert 59, Walker 75	7
38	17/4/10	BSN	A	AFC Telford	1503	W 4-2	Mettam 2 (pen 25, pen 68), Diggin 2 (52, 90)	7
39	19/4/10	BSN	A	Gloucester City	175	W 2-1	Diggin 51, Mettam 65	7
40	21/4/10	BSN	H	Blyth Spartans	771	W 4-2	Defty 17, Towers 20, Diggin 2 (70, 78)	5
	Farsley Celtic record expunged 12/03							
15	31/10/09	BSN	A	Farsley Celtic	363	W 2-1	Lee 65, Diggin 67	2
	Cups							
1	26/9/09	FAC 2Q	A	Eastwood Town	474	L 1-2	Diggin 53	
2	21/11/09	FAT 3Q	H	Alfreton Town	306	D 1-1	Mettam 58	
3	24/11/09	FAT 3QR	A	Alfreton Town	268	W 2-1 aet	Og (Wilson) 97, Mettam 116	
4	12/12/09	FAT 1	H	Farsley Celtic	242	W 2-0	Diggin 25, Herbert 45	
5	20/1/10	FAT 2	A	Stalybridge Celtic	253	W 2-1	Diggin 47, Deeney 59	
6	30/1/10	FAT 3	A	York City	2205	L 0-1		

Home Attendances:	
Highest:	787 v Ilkeston Town
Lowest:	202 v Droylsden
Average (08-09):	391 (384)
Top Goalscorer:	Mettam - 24 (22 League, 2 Cup) in 43 appearances - 56% strike rate
Most Appearances:	Gulliver - 46 (40 League, 6 Cup)
	Mayo - 46 (40 League, 6 Cup)

OSBORN	WEST	JASZCZUN	GULLIVER	HOPE	STRACHAN	TURNER	TOWERS	STALLARD	METTAM	MAYO	WATT	DEENEY	DEFTY	MCGHEE	DIGGIN	SOLKHON	LEE	FRANCIS	SHAW	SMITH	HIBBERT	CROSS	PRICE	BOWLES	SANDY	WALKER	DOLMAN	MILLAR	GRAY	
X	X	X	X	X	X	X	X	X	X	X	S	S	S	U	U															1
X	X	X	X	X	X	X	X	X	X	X	U	S	S	U	S															2
X	X	X	X	X	X	X	X	X	X	X	U	U	S		S	S														3
X		X	X	X	X		X	X	X	X	X	U	S	U	S	X	S													4
X		X	X	X	X	X	X	S	X	X	X	U	X		S	U	S													5
X		X	X	X	X	S	X	X	X	X	X	U	U		X	S	S													6
X		X	X	X	X	X	X	U	X	X	X	U	S		S	S	X													7
X		U	X	X	X	S	X	S	X	X	U	X			X	X	X	S												8
X		U	X	X	X	S	X	S	X	X	U	X			X	X	X	S												9
X		X	X	X	U	U	X	X	S	X	X	X			S	X	X	S												10
X			X	X	U	U	X	U	S	X	X	X		S	X	X	X	X												11
X	X		X	X	X	U	X	U	S	X		U		U	X	X	X	X												12
X	X		X	X	X		X	S	X	X	U	S			X	X	X	S	U											13
X	X		X	X	X		X	X	X	X	S	X		S	X		U	S	U											14
X	X		X	X	X		X		X	X	U	X	X		S		S	S	U	X										15
X	X		X	X			X		X	X	U	S	X		S	X	X	S		U	X									16
X			X	X			X		X	X	X	U	S	S	S	X	X	U	X		X									17
X			X				X		X	X	X	X	X	U	X	X	S	X	S		S	U								18
X			X				X		X	X	X	X	X	U	X	X	S	S	S		X	U								19
X	S		X	U	X		X		X	X	X	X	S	U	X	X	S				X									20
X		U	X	X	X		X			X	X	X	U	S	X	X	S								X	S				21
X		X	X	U			X		X	X		X	S			X	X				X	U			S	S	X			22
X		X	X	U			X		X	X		X	U	S		X	X				X				U	S	X			23
X		X	X	U			X		X	X		X	U	S		X	X				X				U	S	X			24
X			X	S	U		X			X	U	X	X	S		X	U				X					X	X	X		25
X			X	X	S		X			X	U	X	X	S	U	X	S				X					X		X		26
X			X	X	U		X		X	X	S	X	X	S		X	U									X	X	S		27
X			X	X	S		X		X	X	U		X	X	S	X	U									X	X	S		28
X			X	X	S				X	X	U		X	X	U	X	S				X					X	X	S		29
X			X	X	X		X		X	X	U		X	S	U	S	S				X					X	X			30
X			X	U			X		X	X	X		X	S	S	X	S				X					X	X		U	31
X			X	S	U		X		X	X	X		X	X	S	S	U				X					X	X			32
X			X	X	S		X		X	X	X	U			S	S	X				X					X			U	33
	S		X	X	S		X		X	X	X	U	X	X	S						X	X				X			U	34
	X		X	S	X		X		X	X	X	U	X	S	U						X	X				X			S	35
	X		X	S	X		X		X	X	X	U	X	S	U						X	X				X			S	36
	X		X	S	X		X		X	X	X	U	X		U						X	X				X	S		S	37
	X		X	S	X		X		X	X	X		X	S	S						X	X				X	U		U	38
	X		X	S	X		X		X	X	X		X	S	X						X	X					U		S	39
	X		X	S	X		X		X	X	X	U	X	S	X						X	X					U		S	40
X	X		X	X	X		X		X	X	U	X	X		S		S	U	U	X										
X	S		X	X	U	X	X	U	S	X	U	X		S	X	X	X	X												1
X	U		X	X			X		X	X	X	X		S	S	X	X	X			S	U								2
X			X	X			X		X	X	X	U		S	S	X	X	S	X		X	U								3
X			X				X		X	X	X	X		X	X	S	S	X	S		X	U	U							4
X		U	X	X	X		X		X	X	X	X		S	X	X	S					U		U						5
X		S	X	X	U		X		X	X		X		S	S	X	X				X	U				X				6

Total League Apperances

OSBORN	WEST	JASZCZUN	GULLIVER	HOPE	STRACHAN	TURNER	TOWERS	STALLARD	METTAM	MAYO	WATT	DEENEY	DEFTY	MCGHEE	DIGGIN	SOLKHON	LEE	FRANCIS	SHAW	SMITH	HIBBERT	CROSS	PRICE	BOWLES	SANDY	WALKER	DOLMAN	MILLAR	GRAY	
33	14	11	40	25	22	5	39	7	34	40	21	16	20	4	13	22	13	3	1	1	21	7	0	0	1	14	10	2	0	X
0	2	0	0	8	5	3	0	4	3	0	3	4	8	16	15	6	12	8	2	0	1	0	0	0	1	4	1	3	5	S
0	0	3	0	5	5	3	0	3	0	0	12	13	4	7	7	1	5	1	3	1	0	3	0	0	2	0	3	0	4	U

Total Cup Apperances

OSBORN	WEST	JASZCZUN	GULLIVER	HOPE	STRACHAN	TURNER	TOWERS	STALLARD	METTAM	MAYO	WATT	DEENEY	DEFTY	MCGHEE	DIGGIN	SOLKHON	LEE	FRANCIS	SHAW	SMITH	HIBBERT	CROSS	PRICE	BOWLES	SANDY	WALKER	DOLMAN	MILLAR	GRAY	
6	0	0	6	5	1	1	6	0	5	6	4	5	0	1	3	5	4	3	1	0	3	0	0	0	0	1	0	0	0	X
0	1	1	0	0	0	0	0	0	1	0	0	0	0	5	3	1	2	1	1	0	1	0	0	0	0	0	0	0	0	S
0	1	1	0	0	2	0	0	1	0	0	1	1	0	0	0	0	0	0	0	0	0	5	1	1	0	0	0	0	0	U

Total Goals

OSBORN	WEST	JASZCZUN	GULLIVER	HOPE	STRACHAN	TURNER	TOWERS	STALLARD	METTAM	MAYO	WATT	DEENEY	DEFTY	MCGHEE	DIGGIN	SOLKHON	LEE	FRANCIS	SHAW	SMITH	HIBBERT	CROSS	PRICE	BOWLES	SANDY	WALKER	DOLMAN	MILLAR	GRAY	
0	0	0	3	0	3	1	7	2	22	4	0	0	12	0	11	3	0	0	0	0	2	0	0	0	0	2	0	1	0	Lge
0	0	0	0	0	0	0	0	0	2	0	0	1	0	0	3	0	0	0	0	0	0	0	0	0	0	0	0	0	0	Cup

CORBY TOWN

CURRENT SQUAD AS OF BEGINING OF 2010-11 SEASON

GOALKEEPERS	HT	WT	D.O.B	AGE	P.O.B	CAREER	APPS	GOA
Jack Drury						Corby T		
Chris Mackenzie	6'00"	12 09	14/5/72	38	Northampton	Corby T, Hereford £15,000 7/94 (97/98 7,0), L.Orient 10/97 Rel c/s 99, Nuneaton (L) 3/99, Nuneaton 8/99, Telford 6/03, Hereford (L) 4/04, Chester 5/04, Shrewsbury 5/06, Kidderminster (2ML) 9/07, Kidderminster Undisc 1/08 Rel 5/08, Hinckley U 6/08, Corby T	5/10	
DEFENDERS								
Asa Charlton	5'11"	12 00	7/12/77	32	Cosford	Stoke, Kidderminster, Willenhall 8/96, Telford c/s 97, Willenhall, Sandwell B, Rushall O c/s 99, Stourport S 7/01, Worcester 8/02, Halesowen T 1/03 Rel 10/04, Redditch 10/04, Mansfield 11/06 Rel 5/07, AFC Telford 5/07, Hednesford (L) 9/08, Redditch 10/08, Corby T 5/10		
Liam Dolman	6'01"	12 07	26/9/87	22	Brixworth	Northampton Rel c/s 09, Aylesbury (L) 8/05, Bishops Stortford (L) 1/06, Kettering (L) 2/06, Bishops Stortford (L) 3/06, Kidderminster 8/09 Rel 5/10, Corby (SL) 2/10, Corby T 5/10	11	0
Mark Duckett			2/5/83	27		Stevenage, Aylesbury (L) 12/00, Arlesey (L) 2/01, Hemel Hempstead (3ML) 8/01, Hitchin (L) 11/01, Aberystwyth 7/02, Cambridge C (Trial) 7/03, Braintree c/s 03, Bedford T 10/03, Barry T 1/04, Arlesey c/s 04, Erith & B 12/04, Hitchin c/s 05, Stamford 1/08, Corby 6/08 Rel 5/09, Brackley 6/09, Hitchin (L) 2/10, Harlow 6/10, Corby T NC 7/10		
Philip Gulliver	6'02"	13 05	12/9/82	27	Bishop Auckland	Middlesbrough Rel c/s 04, Blackpool (L) 11/02, Carlisle (L) 12/02, Bournemouth (SL) 3/03, Bury (2ML) 10/03, Scunthorpe (L) 1/04, Rushden & D 8/04, Hereford 7/06, Rushden & D 5/07 Rel 10/08, Oxford C 11/08, Corby 11/08	40	3
Chris Hope	6'01"	13 01	14/11/72	37	Sheffield	Darlington (Jun), Notts Forest 8/90, Kettering (SL) 1/93, Scunthorpe £50,000 7/93, Gillingham 7/00 £250,000 Rel 5/06, Rushden & D 7/06, Corby T 6/09	33	0
Danny Pitham			25/1/86	24		Burnley (Scholar) Rel c/s 04, Hinckley U c/s 04 Rel 5/05, Solihull B (L) 9/04, Rugby U (L) 1/05, Coalville 6/05, Bedworth 8/05, Atherstone T 1/07, Bedworth 3/07, Nuneaton T 11/08, Redditch (L) 2/10, Bedworth 2/10, Hinckley U 3/10, Corby T 6/10		
Philip Watt	5'11"	11 05	10/1/88	22	Rotherham	Rotherham (Yth), Lincoln C Rel 2/08, Grantham (WE) 2/06, Grantham (L) 9/06, Corby (L) 1/08, Corby 2/08	24	0
Dean West	5'10"	12 02	5/12/72	37	Morley	Leeds (Yth), Lincoln C, Bury P/E 9/95, Burnley 7/99, Lincoln C 7/04, Boston U P/E 9/04 Rel c/s 05, Kings Lynn 7/05, Corby T 7/08, Spalding U (L) 3/10, Bardon Hill (Dual 3/10	16	0
MIDFIELDERS								
Neil Cartwright			25/6/82	28	Wrexham	Hinckley U, Corby T 6/10		
Andy Gooding	5'07"	10 05	30/4/88	22	Coventry	Coventry Rel 1/08, Burton (2ML) 8/07, Rushden & D 1/08 Rel 5/08, Hinckley U 7/08, Corby T 5/10		
Chris Gray						Corby T	5	0
Andy Hall			25/1/86	24	Northampton	Coventry (Scholar), Kettering 7/05 Rel c/s 08, Halesowen T (SL) 3/08, Hinckley U 7/08, Corby T 5/10		
Neil King			8/4/83	27	Aylesbury	Aylesbury U, Brackley 7/01, Banbury U 8/05, Woodford U 9/05, Rugby T 2/08, Woodford U 7/09, Corby T 5/10		
Richard Lavery			28/5/77	33	Coventry	Bedworth, Hinckley A, Nuneaton, Stratford T, Massey Ferguson, Sutton Coldfield, Atherstone 11/99, Tamworth 2/00, Hinckley U 7/00, Nuneaton 7/01, Telford 7/03, Hinckley U 6/04, Leamington (L) 10/08, Corby T 6/10		
Jamie McGhee	5'08"	10 07	28/9/89	20	Grantham	Mansfield Rel 7/09, Corby T 7/09, Rugby T (L) 11/09, Spalding U (L) 3/10	20	0
Steve Towers			17/8/85	25		Oadby, Rothwell c/s 04, Corby 6/06 Rel 10/07, Stamford 10/07, Corby 5/08	39	7
Glen Walker			3/8/86	24		Sileby, Long Buckby c/s 09, Banbury U 11/09, Corby T 1/10	18	2
FORWARDS								
Simon Brown	5'10"	11 00	18/9/83	26	West Bromwich	West Brom, Kidderminster (SL) 3/04, Kidderminster (3ML) 7/04, Mansfield £50,000 12/04 Rel c/s 08, Wrexham 6/08 Rel 3/10, Rushden & D (5WL) 11/08, York C (SL) 1/09, Tamworth (2ML) 11/09, Eastwood T 3/10, Corby T 6/10		
Steve Diggin			2/11/87	22		Aston Villa (Yth), Wycombe (Yth), Cogenhoe, Kings Lynn 2/07, Cogenhoe 3/07, Corby 6/07	28	11
Michael Frew			8/8/84	26	Peterborough	Peterborough (Scholar), Yaxley 1/03, Lincoln C (Trial) 3/04 Nuneaton 8/04, Hucknall 3/06 (SL), Kings Lynn 6/06, Cambridge C 3/09, Histon 5/09, Brackley T (SL) 3/10, Corby T 6/10		
Ben Mackey	5'08"	11 09	27/10/86	23	Sutton Coldfield	Coventry Rel 2/05, Rugby U 3/05, Lincoln C (Trial) 7/05, Linfield (Trial) 7/05, RC Warwick, Leamington 5/06, Brackley 6/08, Corby T 6/10		

Loanees	HT	WT	DOB	AGE	POB	From - To	APPS	GOA
(F)Sam Smith			20/5/90	20	Corby	Rushden & D 10/09 - Hinckley U (L) 12/09	1	0
(M)Elliott Sandy			7/8/85	25		Brackley (2ML) 12/09 -	2	0
(G)Ian Brown			5/2/81	29		St Neots (Cover) 12/09 - Bedford T 5/10		

Departures	HT	WT	DOB	AGE	POB	From - To	APPS	GOA
(F)Lawrie Dudfield	6'01"	13 09	7/5/80	30	Southwark	Chelmsford 5/09 - Rel 7/09		
(D)Tom Bonner	6'00"	11 06	6/2/88	22	Camden	Solihull Moors 6/09 - Ilkeston 8/09		
(G)Ayden Duffy	6'05"	15 00	16/11/86	23	Kettering	Lincoln C 7/09 - Hyde U 9/09, Grantham 10/09, Lincoln Moorlands 2/10		
(G)Steven Norris	6'01"		3/10/90	19		Kings Lynn (Scholar) 6/09 - Spalding U (L) 9/09, Quorn 1/10		
(F)Mark Stallard	6'00"	13 06	21/10/74	35	Derby	Mansfield 7/09 - Rel 11/09	11	2
(F)Joe Francis			24/10/86	23		Kings Lynn 3/09 - Lowestoft T 12/09	11	0
(D)Chris Shaw			18/12/83	26		Nantwich 10/09 - Grantham (L) 12/09, Alfreton 12/09	3	0
(D)Geraint Price			7/2/91	19		Brooke House Academy 12/09 - St Neots 3/10	0	0
(G)Mark Osborn	6'02"	14 01	18/6/81	29	Bletchley	Halesowen T 7/08 - Hemel Hempstead 3/10	33	0
(M)Brett Solkhon	5'11"	12 06	12/9/82	27	Canvey Island	Kettering 5/09 - Brackley 3/10, Kettering 7/10	28	3
(F)Jason Lee	6'03"	13 08	9/5/71	39	Forest Gate	Kettering 3/09 - Ilkeston 3/10	25	0
(F)Ricky Millar			13/3/89	21		Cambridge C 2/10 - Stamford 3/10	5	1
(D)Tommy Jaszczun	5'11"	11 02	16/9/77	32	Kettering	Kettering 3/09 - Rel 5/10, Kettering (Pl/Ass Man) 5/10	11	0
(D)David Deeney	5'09"	10 06	12/1/87	22	Bulawayo, Zim	Hemel Hempstead 5/09 - Rel 5/10	20	0
(F)Jack Defty			7/9/81	28		Kings Lynn 6/09 - AFC Sudbury (L) 9/09, Kings Lynn Town 5/10	28	12
(D)Paul Mayo	5'11"	11 09	13/10/81	28	Lincoln	Mansfield 6/09 - Gainsborough 5/10	40	4
(F)Leon Mettam	5'09"	11 01	9/12/86	23	Lincoln	Stamford Undisc 2/08 - Gainsborough 5/10	37	22
(M)Leon Hibbert	6'04"		6/11/81	28	Watford	Barton R 7/08 - Slough (L) 10/09, Lincoln C (Trial) 5/10, Gainsborough 6/10	22	2
(M)Gavin Strachan	5'11"	11 07	23/12/78	31	Aberdeen	Notts County 7/09 - Hinckley U 6/10	27	3
(F)Nick Wellecomme			31/5/84	26	Stafford	Stafford R 6/10 - Stafford R 6/10		
(D)Gavin Hoyte	6'04"	12 06	24/6/86	24	Bedford	Grays 6/10 - Rel 7/10, Bedford T 7/10		
(G)Tom Cross			23/3/88	22		Sheffield FC 10/09 - Sheffield FC (L) 1/10	7	0
(D)Bradley Jones	5'11"	11 08	1/11/90	19		Stourbridge 2/10 -		
(M)Brian Bowles			24/1/91	19		Rugby T 1/10 -	0	0
(M)Scott Mitchell	5'11"	12 00	2/9/85	24	Ely	Kings Lynn 6/09 -		
(F)John Turner	5'10"	11 00	12/2/86	24	Harrow	Kings Lynn 1/09 -	8	1

DROYLSDEN

Chairman: David Pace
Secretary: Alan Slater (T) 07989 024 777
(E) alans83@btinternet.com

Additional Committee Members:
Bryan Pace, Stella Quinn

Manager: David Pace

Programme Editor: Steven Jarvis (E) stevenjjarvis@googlemail.com

Club Factfile

Founded: 1892 **Nickname:** The Bloods
Previous Names:
Previous Leagues: Manchester, Lancashire Combination 1936-39, 50-68, Cheshire County 1939-50, 68-82, North West Counties 1982-87, Northern Premier 1986-2004
Club Colours (change): All red (Silver/navy/navy)

Ground: The Butchers Arms Ground, Market Street, Droylsden, M43 7AY (T) 0161 370 1426
Capacity: 3,500 **Seats:** 500 **Covered:** 2,000 **Clubhouse:** Yes **Shop:** Yes
Previous Grounds:
Simple Directions
From junction 23 M60 follow signs A635 Manchester, then A662 signed Droylsden, at town centre traffic lights turn right into Market Street, through next set of lights and the main entrance to the ground is 75 yards on your left.

Record Attendance: 4,250 v Grimsby
Record Victory: 13-2 v Lucas Sports Club
Record Defeat: Not known
Record Goalscorer: E. Gillibrand - 275 (1931-35)
Record Appearances: Paul Phillips - 326
Additional Records: Received £11,000 from Crewe Alexandra for Tony Naylor 1990

Senior Honours: Northern Premier League Division 1 1998-99. Conference North 2006-07.
Manchester Premier Cup x3. Manchester Senior Cup x3.

10 YEAR RECORD

00-01	01-02	02-03	03-04	04-05	05-06	06-07	07-08	08-09	09-10
NP P 21	NP P 11	NP P 9	NP P 2	Conf N 3	Conf N 4	Conf N 1	Conf 24	Conf N 7	Conf N 5

DROYLSDEN

No.	Date	Comp	H/A	Opponents	Att:	Result	Goalscorers	Pos
1	8/8/09	BSN	H	Ilkeston Town	420	W 2-0	A Brown 62, Lloyd 85	4
2	10/8/09	BSN	A	Hinckley United	451	D 1-1	Brownhill 73	1
3	15/8/09	BSN	A	Gainsborough Trinity	300	L 2-4	Lloyd 87, Gray 90	10
4	17/8/09	BSN	H	Northwich Victoria	568	W 5-1	Gray 26, Whalley 2 (31, 64), Beck 71, P Brown 78	3
5	23/8/09	BSN	A	Gloucester City	340	W 4-1	Gray 2 (47, 53), Beck 54, Whalley 59	3
6	29/8/09	BSN	H	Fleetwood Town	449	W 2-0	Whalley 2, A Brown 10	1
7	31/8/09	BSN	A	Blyth Spartans	637	D 2-2	Whalley 8, Williams 88	2
8	5/9/09	BSN	H	Stafford Rangers	419	W 7-1	Gray 14, Sorvel 2 (28, 85), Yeo 38, P Brown 2 (64, 87), Meechan pen 82	2
9	7/9/09	BSN	H	Harrogate Town	376	W 5-0	Brownhill 38, Whalley 2 (44, 70), Gray 64, Meechan 87	1
10	12/9/09	BSN	A	Stalybridge Celtic	803	D 2-2	Whalley 37, P Brown 89	1
11	19/9/09	BSN	H	Corby Town	422	L 1-2	Gray 22	1
12	3/10/09	BSN	A	AFC Telford	1542	W 2-1	Whalley 18, Gray 90	1
13	10/10/09	BSN	A	Harrogate Town	348	D 2-2	Gray 57, P Brown 86	1
14	17/10/09	BSN	H	Workington	381	L 0-1		1
15	24/10/09	BSN	A	Eastwood Town	445	L 1-2	P Brown 75	3
16	31/10/09	BSN	H	Solihull Moors	293	W 5-3	Whalley 2 (23, 35), P Brown 53, Gray 2 (77, 84)	3
17	7/11/09	BSN	A	Vauxhall Motors	193	W 2-1	Gray 2 (2, 25)	2
18	28/11/09	BSN	H	Hyde United	436	W 1-0	Gray 59	2
19	5/12/09	BSN	H	Hinckley United	284	D 0-0		3
20	12/12/09	BSN	A	Stafford Rangers	363	D 2-2	Whalley 73, P Brown 76	3
21	23/1/10	BSN	H	Gainsborough Trinity	276	W 4-1	Prince 2 (11, 19), P Brown 2 (65, 72)	5
22	30/1/10	BSN	A	Ilkeston Town	366	L 0-1		6
23	3/2/10	BSN	A	Northwich Victoria	372	W 5-2	Prince 13, Whalley 15, Gray 2 (70, 82), Leadbetter 87	5
24	6/2/10	BSN	H	AFC Telford	406	L 1-5	Gray 33	6
25	10/2/10	BSN	A	Corby Town	202	L 0-1		6
26	13/2/10	BSN	A	Workington	383	W 1-0	Whalley 69	4
27	20/2/10	BSN	H	Vauxhall Motors	340	D 1-1	Whalley 55	5
28	6/3/10	BSN	A	Hyde United	518	L 1-2	Gray 59	5
29	9/3/10	BSN	A	Alfreton Town	410	L 0-5		5
30	13/3/10	BSN	H	Eastwood Town	1296	L 0-1		6
31	15/3/10	BSN	H	Gloucester City	244	D 2-2	Ellington 40, Halford 50	5
32	20/3/10	BSN	A	Southport	815	D 3-3	Og (Davis) 4, Lloyd 63, A Brown 76	5
33	23/3/10	BSN	A	Redditch United	148	W 3-1	Whalley 41, Gray 68, Leadbetter 87	5
34	27/3/10	BSN	A	Solihull Moors	208	W 2-1	A Brown 11, Gray 63	4
35	29/3/10	BSN	H	Stalybridge Celtic	508	W 3-2	Meechan 2 (11, 25), A Brown 34	4
36	3/4/10	BSN	A	Fleetwood Town	1816	L 0-3		4
37	5/4/10	BSN	H	Blyth Spartans	294	W 2-1	A Brown 14, Gray pen 72	4
38	10/4/10	BSN	H	Stalybridge Celtic	584	L 0-3		5
39	12/4/10	BSN	H	Alfreton Town	329	D 0-0		5
40	24/4/10	BSN	H	Redditch United	367	W 6-1	Gray 4 (pen 34, 39, pen 45, 60), Meechan 58, P Smith 83	5
	Farsley Celtic record expunged 12/03							
28	27/2/10	BSN	H	Farsley Celtic	248	L 1-2	Gray pen 27	5
	Cups							
1	26/9/09	FAC 2Q	H	FC Halifax Town	902	L 0-2		
2	21/11/09	FAT 3Q	A	Farsley Celtic	220	L 2-5	Prince 45, Gray pen 65	
3	28/4/10	PO SF1	H	Fleetwood Town	1104	W 2-0	Meechan 71, Gray pen 81	
4	2/5/10	PO SF2	A	Fleetwood Town	2862	L 1-3	Roche 113 (D 3-3 agg L 3-4 pens)	

Home Attendances:	
Highest:	1296 v Eastwood Town
Lowest:	244 v Gloucester City
Average (08-09):	394 (400)
Top Goalscorer:	Gray - 27 (25 League, 2 Cup) in 44 appearances - 61% strike rate
Most Appearances:	Gary - 44 (40 League, 4 Cup)

MAWSON	WOODYATT	BROWNHILL	RUFFER	CRYAN	WILLIAMS	A BROWN	GRAY	BECK	YEO	MEECHAN	LLOYD	P BROWN	ROCHE	BYRON	HOWARTH	HALFORD	WHALLEY	SORVEL	PICKFORD	GRAVES	CRAIG	BANIM	LEADBETTER	VAUGHAN	PHILLIPS	LAWTON	PRINCE	FIELD	G SMITH	BUTLER	OLUWA	CLANCY	MANSARAM	P SMITH	BARWICK	C BROWN	ELLINGTON	GRANT	
X	X	X	X	X	X	X	X	X	X	X	S	S	U	U	U																								1
X	X	X	X	X	X	X	X	X	X	X	S	S	U		U	U																							2
X	X	X	X	X	X	X	X	X	X	X	S	U		S	U		S																						3
		X		S		U	X	X	X		X	S	X	X	X	X	X	X	S	U																			4
	U	X	X			S	X	X	X			S	X	U	X	X	X	X	X	S																			5
X		X	U			X	X	X	X	S	S	S	X	X		X	X	X	U																				6
X	X	X	X		S		X	X	S	S	X	X		U		X	X	X			U																		7
X	U	X		U	S		X	X	X	S	X	S	X	X		X	X	X																					8
X	U	X		U	S		X	X	X	S	X	S	X	X		X	X	X																					9
X	U	X		S		S	X	X	X	U	X	S	X	X		X	X	X																					10
X		X		U		X	X	X	U	S	S	X	X	X		X	X	X				S																	11
		X		X	U	S	X	X	S	U	X	X	X	S	X	X	X		X																				12
	X			X	X	X	X	S	S	U		X	U	X	X	X	X	S	X																				13
		X		U	S	X	X	X	S	X		X	X	X	X	X		X					S																14
X		X		X		U	X	X	X	X		S	X	S		X		X	X				S	U															15
		X		S	U	X	X	X		S		X	U	X	X	X	X	X					S	X															16
U		X		X	S		X	X		S		X	U			X	X	X					X	X	X	U													17
		X		U		X	X	X		S		X	U	X		X	X							X	X		S	S	X										18
		X		U		X	X	X		X		X	U	X		X		X					S	X	X		S	U											19
		X		U		X	X			X		S	U	X		X	X	X					S	X	X		S	X											20
X		X		X			X	X		S		X	U	X	U		X	X					S	X			X	S											21
X		X		X			X	X				X	X	X	U	U	X	X					S				X	S		S									22
X		X		U			X	X		U		X	S	X		X	X	X					S	X			X	S											23
X		X		X			X			S		X	X	X	U	S		X					X	X			X	S		U									24
X		X		S			X	X		U		X	X	X		X	X	X					S	X			S	U											25
X		X		S		U	X			S		X	X	X		X	X	X					U	X			X	U											26
X		X		X			X			X		S	X	X		U	X	X						X			S	X		U	S								27
		S		U		X	X						U	X		X	X	X					X	X	X		X			X			S	S					28
		X		X		X	X			U			X	X		S	X	X						U	X		S						X	S	X				29
U		X		U		X	X				X		S			X	S							X	X		X							S		X	X	X	30
U		X		X		X	X				X		U			X	S	X						X	X		S							U			X	X	31
U		X		S		X	X			S	X		U	X		X	X	X						X	X		X							S					32
U		X		X		X	X			X	X		X				X	X					S	X	X		U			S				S					33
U		X		X		X	X			X			X			S	X	X					S	X	X		U							S		X			34
U		X		U		X	X			X			X			X		X					S	X	X		X			S				S		X			35
U		X		S		X	X			X			X	S		X		X					X	X	X					U				S		X			36
X				U		X	X			S	X		S	X			X	X					S	X	U					X				X		X			37
X		X		S		X	X			X	X		U	X			X	X					S	X	U									S		X			38
X		X		X		X	X			S	X		X			X	X	X					S	U	U									X		U			39
X		X		X		X	X			X	X		X			X	X	X					U	S	U		S							S					40
X		X		U		X	X				X	S	S	X		X	X	X						X			X				S	U							
X	U	X		U	U	X	X	X	X	S		S	X	X	U	X	X	X	S																				1
U		X		S			X	X		U		X	U	X		X	X	X						X	X		X	S											2
X		X		X		X	X			X	X		X			X	X	X					U	U	U		U							U					3
X		X		X		X	X			X	X		X	S		X	X	X					S	U	U									S					4
Total League Appearances																																							
21	5	37	5	17	4	24	40	22	10	14	14	15	22	24	6	28	29	33	4	0	0	0	4	21	13	0	9	2	1	2	0	0	1	2	1	6	2	2	X
0	0	1	0	8	5	3	0	1	4	14	5	11	3	4	0	3	3	1	1	1	0	1	15	1	0	0	8	5	0	3	1	0	1	10	0	0	0	0	S
8	4	0	1	12	2	3	0	0	1	6	0	1	13	3	6	3	0	0	1	1	1	0	2	3	4	1	2	3	0	3	0	0	0	1	0	1	0	0	U
Total Cup Appearances																																							
3	0	4	0	2	0	3	4	2	1	2	2	1	3	2	0	4	4	4	0	0	0	0	0	1	1	0	1	0	0	0	0	0	0	0	0	0	0	0	X
0	0	0	0	1	0	0	0	0	0	1	0	1	0	1	0	0	0	0	1	0	0	0	1	0	0	0	0	1	0	0	0	0	0	1	0	0	0	0	S
1	1	0	0	1	1	0	0	0	0	1	0	0	1	0	1	0	0	0	0	0	0	0	1	2	2	0	1	0	0	0	0	0	0	1	0	0	0	0	U
Total Goals																																							
0	0	2	0	0	1	6	25	2	1	5	3	10	0	0	0	1	16	2	0	0	0	0	2	0	0	0	3	0	0	0	0	0	0	1	0	0	1	0	Lge
0	0	0	0	0	0	0	2	0	0	1	0	0	1	0	0	0	0	0	0	0	0	0	0	0	0	0	1	0	0	0	0	0	0	0	0	0	0	0	Cup

DROYLSDEN

CURRENT SQUAD AS OF BEGINING OF 2010-11 SEASON

GOALKEEPERS	HT	WT	D.O.B	AGE	P.O.B	CAREER	APPS	GOA
Ian Fitzpatrick						Ashton U 1/09 - Rel	12	2
(F)Carl Lamb			10/11/84	24		The New Saints 7/08 - Rel 8/09	36	2
Paul Phillips			15/11/78	31	Manchester	Man Utd, Bury, Buxton, Curzon Ashton, Droylsden 12/99, Stalybridge 5/08, Droylsden 11/09	13	0
DEFENDERS								
Liam Brownhill			28/11/86	23	Altrincham	Stockport Rel c/s 05, Altrincham (Trial) c/s 05, Bangor C 8/05, Connahs Quay 10/05, Witton 12/05, Droylsden 6/08	38	2
Michael Byron	6'02"	11 03	16/8/87	23	Liverpool	Hull C Rel c/s 07, Scarborough (L) 8/06, Hinckley U (2ML) 10/06, Notts County (SL) 3/07, Notts County 9/07 Rel 1/08, Hinckley U (3ML) 11/07 Perm 2/08, Droylsden c/s 08	28	0
Colin Cryan	5'10"	13 00	23/3/81	29	Dublin	Sheff Utd Rel c/s 04, Scarborough (L) 10/02, Scarborough (L) 10/03, Scarborough 7/04 Rel 6/05, Lincoln C 8/05, Boston U 1/07 Rel c/s 07, Droylsden 7/07	25	0
Steve Halford	5'10"	12 10	21/9/80	29	Bury	Bury Rel 9/01, Chester 10/01, Accrington 1/02, Radcliffe B (L) 11/04, Droylsden (L) 2/05, Droylsden 7/05, Flixton (Dual) 10/08	31	1
Lee Roche	5'10"	10 11	28/10/80	29	Bolton	Man Utd Rel c/s 03, Wrexham (SL) 7/00, Burnley 7/03 Rel c/s 05, Wrexham 7/05 Rel c/s 07, Droylsden 10/07	25	0
James Vaughan	5'10"	12 09	6/12/86	23	Liverpool	Tranmere, Chester 1/06, Droylsden (L) 12/06, Wollongong Community (Aust) 4/09, Sydney FC (Aust), Gold Coast (Aust), Chester 8/09, Droylsden 10/09	22	0
MIDFIELDERS								
Bradley Barnes			12/12/88	21		Bolton (Yth), Flixton, Morecambe (Trial) 7/08, Barrow (Trial) 7/08, Trafford 9/08, Southport 8/09, FC Halifax (L) 3/10, Droylsden 7/10		
Steven Beck			4/6/84	26	Liverpool	Everton Rel 6/03, Wigan (Trial) c/s 03, TNS/The New Saints 7/03, Droylsden 10/08	23	2
Robbie Booth	5'07"	11 08	30/12/85	24	Liverpool	Everton (Scholar), Chester (Sch) (Pro) 3/05 Rel c/s 05, Southport 7/05, Burscough (L) 1/06, Burscough 9/06, Southport 7/08, Vauxhall Motors (2ML) 8/09, Droylsden 7/10		
Alex Brown			28/11/84	25		Crewe (Scholar), Witton 7/06, Droylsden 6/08	27	6
Tom Field			2/8/85	25	Liverpool	Everton (Trainee), Leigh RMI, TNS c/s 05, Stalybridge 8/05, Southport 10/05, Witton 11/05, Vauxhall Motors 12/05, Leigh RMI/Leigh Genesis 5/08, Vauxhall Motors 11/08, AFC Telford 6/09, Droylsden 11/09	7	0
Luke Holden	5'08"	11 00	24/11/88	21	Liverpool	Liverpool (Yth), Tranmere (Trainee), The New Saints 8/07 Rel 4/08, Cammell Laird 6/08, Bradford PA 10/08, Rhyl 1/09, Charlton (3ML) 9/09, Wrexham (SL) 1/10		
Lewis Killeen	5'09"	10 07	23/9/82	27	Peterborough	Sheff Utd Rel c/s 03, Halifax (3ML), Halifax 6/03, Crawley 5/08 Rel 5/10, Droylsden 7/10		
Rob Lloyd	6'00"	11 10	13/8/86	24	Chester	Crewe, Witton (2ML) 11/05, Witton (4ML) 10/06 Perm 2/07, FC Halifax 9/08, Droylsden 7/09 Rel 10/09, New Mills 11/09, Droylsden 2/10	19	3
Neil Prince	5'11"	10 07	17/3/83	27	Liverpool	Liverpool (Trainee), Torquay 8/02, Southport, Leigh RMI 3/03, Lancaster 8/03, Stalybridge 5/05, Hyde 7/06, Stalybridge 10/06, Southport c/s 07, Droylsden 7/08, Southport 3/09, Marine 7/09, Droylsden 11/09	17	3
Paul Smith	5'09"	11 09	13/3/91	19	Liverpool	Chester, Rhyl 8/09 Rel 1/10, Droylsden 3/10	12	1
Neil Sorvel	6'00"	12 09	2/3/73	37	Whiston	Crewe, Macclesfield 8/92, Crewe 6/99, Shrewsbury 7/05 Rel 1/07, Morecambe 1/07 Rel c/s 08, Southport (L) 1/08, Droylsden 7/08	34	2
Shaun Whalley	5'09"	10 07	7/8/87	23	Prescot	Southport, Chester 9/04 Rel c/s 05, Runcorn Halton 8/05, Witton 3/06, Accrington (2ML) 11/06 Perm 1/07 Rel c/s 08, Wrexham 6/08 Rel 5/09, Southport (SL) 2/09, Droylsden 8/09	32	16
FORWARDS								
Ciaren Kilheeney	5'11"	11 09	9/1/84	26	Stockport	Man City (Trainee), Mossley 1/03, Exeter 3/03, Droylsden 5/03, Radcliffe B 11/04, Ashton U 9/05, Burscough 9/06, Southport 6/08, Droylsden 7/10		

Loanees	HT	WT	DOB	AGE	POB	From - To	APPS	GOA
Chris Brown						Rochdale 3/10 -	6	0

Departures	HT	WT	DOB	AGE	POB	From - To	APPS	GOA
(M)Stuart Graves	5'11"	11 07	4/6/80	30	Bebbington	Bradford PA 7/09 - Colwyn Bay 9/09, Chester FC 5/10	1	0
(M)Carl Ruffer	5'08"	10 04	20/12/74	35	Chester	Bradford PA 11/08 - Salford C 9/09, Witton 10/09, Chester FC 6/10	5	0
(F)Jody Banim	5'08"	13 01	1/4/78	32	Manchester	Salford C 9/09 - Radcliffe B 9/09, Salford C 1/10, Stalybridge 1/10	1	0
(M)Steve Pickford			24/12/77	32	Ashton	Hyde U 7/08 - New Mills 11/09	5	0
(D)Lewis Craig			20/11/89	20		Barnoldswick T 7/09 - Witton 11/09	0	0
(D)Lee Woodyatt			16/7/83	27	Chester	Barrow 7/09 - Leigh Genesis 12/09, Chorley 5/10	5	0
(F)Simon Yeo	5'10"	11 08	20/10/73	36	Stockport	Macclesfield 7/09 - Harrogate T 12/09, New Mills 4/10	14	1
(M)Danny Williams	6'01"	13 00	12/7/79	31	Wrexham	Rhyl 7/09 - Bala T 1/10	9	1
(M)Paul Brown	5'11"	12 00	10/9/84	25	Liverpool	Barrow 6/09 - Rel 3/10, Witton 3/10, Vauxhall Motors 3/10	26	10
(F)Lee Ellington	5'10"	11 07	3/7/80	30	Bradford	Farsley Celtic 3/10 - Rel 3/10, Harrogate T 3/10	2	1
(F)Gareth Grant	5'10"	10 04	6/9/80	29	Leeds	Farsley Celtic 3/10 - Rel 3/10, Gainsborough 3/10	2	0
(G)Kyle Clancy			16/11/89	20		Burscough 2/10 - Marine 3/10	0	0
(G)Chris Howarth	6'02"	12 10	23/5/86	24	Bolton	Carlisle 8/09 - Witton 3/10	6	0
(F)Tony Gray			6/4/84	26		Southport 12/08 - Southport 5/10	40	25
(D)Chris Butler			18/10/84	25		Sligo R 1/10 - Marine 6/10	5	0
(F)Alex Meechan	5'08"	10 10	29/1/80	30	Plymouth	Stalybridge 7/09 - AFC Telford 7/10	28	5
(G)Craig Mawson	6'02"	13 04	16/5/79	31	Keighley	FC Halifax 8/08 - Hyde U 7/10	21	0
(D)George Horan			18/2/82	28		Rhyl 2/10 - Chester FC 7/10		
(M)Kevin Leadbetter			10/9/79	30	Liverpool	Fleetwood 10/09 - Rel 7/10	19	2
(D)Tim Lawton			27/2/91	19		Stockport (Yth) 11/09 -	0	0
(D)Patrece Liburd			1/3/88	22	Leeds	Farsley Celtic 3/10 -		
(D)Terry Barwick	5'11"	10 12	11/1/83	27	Sheffield	Goole AFC 3/10 -	1	0
(M)Grant Smith	6'01"	12 07	5/5/80	30	Irvine	Carlisle 11/09 -	1	0
(F)Darren Mansaram			25/6/84	26		Gainsborough 2/10 -	2	0
(F)Eniola Oluwa			7/11/84	25		Gregorians 1/10 -	1	0

EASTWOOD TOWN

Chairman: Tony Minnis
Secretary: Mrs Rachel Thornton — **(T)** 07971 655 983 **(E)** rachel@eastwoodtownfc.co.uk

Additional Committee Members:
Andy Cope

Manager: Paul Cox

Programme Editor: Andy Cope — **(E)** lydias.dad@googlemail.com

Back Row (L-R): Jermaine Holis, Adam Muller, Jonathan D'Laryea, Lee Stevenson, Anton Foster, Ryan Handbury, Kieran Kenlock.
Middle Row: Unknown, Matt Rhead, David Haggerty, Ian Deakin, Mat Bailey, John Danby, Adrian Hawes, Russell Cooke, Andy Todd
Front Row: Sam Ralph(Coach), Lindon Meikle, Michael Simpson, Rachel Thornton(Secretary), Paul Cox (Manager), Richard Cooper(Assistant Manager), Sam Duncum, Paul Riley, Nick Taylor (Physio).

Club Factfile

Founded: 1953 **Nickname:** The Badgers

Previous Names:

Previous Leagues: Notts Alliance 1953-61, Central Alliance 1961-67, East Midlands 1967-71, Midland Counties 1971-82, Northern Counties East 1982-87, 2003-04, Northern Premier 1987-2003, 04-09

Club Colours (change): Black & white/white/black & white (All sky blue)

Ground: Coronation Park, Eastwood, Notts NG16 3GL **(T)** 01773 711 819

Capacity: 5,500 **Seats:** 650 **Covered:** 1,150 **Clubhouse:** Yes **Shop:** Yes

Previous Grounds:

Simple Directions
M1 TRAVELLING SOUTH At junction 27, leave the motorway (A608) Heanor. At roundabout take 3rd exit A608. Past the Sandhills Tavern to a T- junction signposted Brinsley Heanor. Going through Brinsley will take you to Eastwood. At the lights turn left onto Nottingham Road. Look for the Fire Station on your right, then turn 1st right into Chewton Street. Ground is 150 metres on your right.
M1 TRAVELLING NORTH Exit junction 26. At roundabout take exit onto A610 Ripley. Leave the A610 at the first junction signed Ilkeston. Turn right at junction onto B6010, following the signs for Eastwood. Turn 1st left after the Man In Space pub into Chewton Street. Ground is 150 metres on your right.

Record Attendance: 2,723 v Enfield - FA Amateur Cup February 1965
Record Victory: 21-0 v Rufford Colliery - 1954-55
Record Defeat: 0-8 v Hucknall Town (A) - 2000-01
Record Goalscorer: Martin Wright - 147
Record Appearances: Arthur Rowley - 800+ with no bookings (1955-76)
Additional Records: Paid £500 to Gainsborough Trinity for Jamie Kay
Recieved £72,500 from Middlesbrough for Richard Liburd

Senior Honours: Midland League 1975-76. Northern Premier League Premier Division 2008-09
Notts Senior Cup x10

10 YEAR RECORD

00-01	01-02	02-03	03-04	04-05	05-06	06-07	07-08	08-09	09-10
NP 1 20	NP 1 8	NP 1 21	NCEP 2	NP 1 6	NP 1 7	NP 1 3	NP P 4	NP P 1	Conf N 10

EASTWOOD TOWN

No.	Date	Comp	H/A	Opponents	Att:	Result	Goalscorers	Pos
1	8/8/09	BSN	H	Northwich Victoria	768	D 1-1	Holland 7	13
2	11/8/09	BSN	A	Gloucester City	326	W 3-1	Knox 22, Nwadike 47, Holland 49	5
3	15/8/09	BSN	A	Harrogate Town	432	W 1-0	Hume 79	4
4	18/8/09	BSN	H	Alfreton Town	882	W 2-1	Meikle 40, Holmes 87	1
5	22/8/09	BSN	A	Fleetwood Town	976	L 1-3	Nwadike 70	3
6	29/8/09	BSN	H	Hinckley United	483	W 1-0	Holmes 79	4
7	31/8/09	BSN	A	Gainsborough Trinity	551	W 4-1	Meikle 37, Holland 65, Holmes 83, D Brown pen 87	1
8	5/9/09	BSN	H	Blyth Spartans	575	W 4-2	Holmes 11, Holland pen 13, Meikle 28, Knox 90	1
9	8/9/09	BSN	H	Stalybridge Celtic	575	L 1-3	Holmes 42	2
10	12/9/09	BSN	A	Stafford Rangers	507	D 3-3	Nwadike 14, M Smith 54, Og (Wilson) 74	4
11	19/9/09	BSN	H	AFC Telford	616	D 1-1	Meikle 67	3
12	3/10/09	BSN	A	Corby Town	603	D 1-1	Knox 82	3
13	17/10/09	BSN	A	Vauxhall Motors	197	L 2-3	Hume 2 (7, 82)	6
14	24/10/09	BSN	H	Droylsden	445	W 2-1	Knox 2 (25, 32)	5
15	27/10/09	BSN	H	Hyde United	480	W 2-0	Meikle 2 (21, 26)	2
16	31/10/09	BSN	A	Southport	831	L 1-5	Nwadike 89	5
17	14/11/09	BSN	A	Blyth Spartans	527	W 3-1	McAughtrie 62, M Foster 79, Holmes 87	2
18	28/11/09	BSN	A	Workington	296	L 0-1		3
19	1/12/09	BSN	H	Gloucester City	321	L 0-3		3
20	5/12/09	BSN	H	Harrogate Town	326	W 1-0	Holmes pen 45	2
21	16/1/10	BSN	A	Northwich Victoria	530	L 3-4	D Brown 20, Meikle 62, Holland 84	4
22	19/1/10	BSN	A	Redditch United	174	W 2-1	Holland 2 (30, 78)	4
23	23/1/10	BSN	H	Redditch United	457	W 3-1	R Gardner 20, Nwadike 63, Robinson 71	3
24	26/1/10	BSN	A	Alfreton Town	560	D 1-1	Meikle 22	4
25	6/2/10	BSN	H	Vauxhall Motors	372	D 0-0		4
26	13/2/10	BSN	A	Hyde United	352	L 0-1		5
27	16/2/10	BSN	H	Fleetwood Town	367	L 0-1		6
28	27/2/10	BSN	A	Solihull Moors	256	L 1-2	Holland 90	6
29	6/3/10	BSN	H	Stafford Rangers	442	D 0-0		6
30	13/3/10	BSN	A	Droylsden	1296	W 1-0	Meikle 47	7
31	16/3/10	BSN	A	AFC Telford	1323	D 1-1	Meikle 90	7
32	20/3/10	BSN	H	Workington	342	L 1-2	Whitehurst 23	8
33	23/3/10	BSN	A	Ilkeston Town	597	L 0-1		9
34	5/4/10	BSN	H	Gainsborough Trinity	398	W 1-0	D Brown 90	10
35	8/4/10	BSN	H	Corby Town	342	L 0-1		10
36	10/4/10	BSN	H	Solihull Moors	304	W 2-1	Holland 55, Meikle 79	7
37	15/4/10	BSN	A	Hinckley United	413	D 0-0		9
38	17/4/10	BSN	A	Stalybridge Celtic	384	L 0-1		10
39	20/4/10	BSN	H	Ilkeston Town	754	L 0-3		10
40	24/4/10	BSN	H	Southport	1147	L 0-3		10
	Farsley Celtic record expunged 12/03							
17	7/11/09	BSN	H	Farsley Celtic	411	W 2-1	Knox 30, Markel Bailey 44	4
	Cups							
1	26/9/09	FAC 2Q	H	Corby Town	484	W 2-1	Holland 2 (1, 45)	
2	10/10/09	FAC 3Q	A	Ilkeston Town	1128	D 1-1	Nwadike 21	
3	13/10/09	FAC 3QR	H	Ilkeston Town	1205	L 1-3	Knox 70	
4	21/11/09	FAT 3Q	H	Nantwich Town	312	L 0-3		

Home Attendances:	
Highest:	1147 v Southport
Lowest:	304 v Solihull Moors
Average (08-09):	451 (587)
Top Goalscorer:	Meikle - 11 (11 League, 0 Cup) in 44 appearances - 25% strike rate
Most Appearances:	Meikle - 44 (37+3 League, 4 Cup)

DEAKIN	COOKE	MARSHALL	NWADIKE	HUME	ROBINSON	R GARDNER	A FOSTER	KNOX	HOLLAND	MEIKLE	M FOSTER	M SMITH	HOLMES	PRENDERGAST	D BROWN	CHAMBERS	WHITEHURST	R TURNER	CHAPMAN	COOPER	CLARKE	RILEY	J TURNER	MCAUGHTRIE	BUDTZ	MARKEL BAILEY	J SMITH	GAUGHAN	STAIR	ELEY	ROSS	MATT BAILEY	D'LARYEA	S GARDNER	DUNCUM	DANBY	S BROWN	
X	X	X	X	X	X	X	X	X	X	X	S	S	S																									1
X	X	X	X	X			X	X	X	X	X	U	S	X	S	S	U																					2
	X	X	X	X	X	X	X	X	X	S	X	S	U		S	U		X																				3
	X		X	X	X		X	X	X	X	X	S	S		S	U	U	X	X																			4
	X		X	X	X		X	S	X	X	X	S	X		S	U		X	X	U																		5
			X	X	X		X	S	X	S	X	X	S	X	U	U		X	X		X																	6
			X	X	X		X	S	X	X	X	U	X		S	U	U	X	X		X																	7
X			X	X	X		X	S	X	X	X	U	X		X	U	U				X	S																8
X			X	X	X		X	S	X	X	X	U	X		X	U	U				X	S																9
			X	X	X		X	U	X	X	X	S	X		X	U	S	X			X	S																10
			X		X		X	X		X	X	S	X		U	S	S	X			X		X	X	U													11
	X		X		X		X	S	X	X	X	S	X		S	U		X			X		X		U													12
U	X		X	X	X	X	U	X		X	X		S		X		S	X			X			U														13
	X		X	X		X	X	X		X	X		U		U	S	U				S	X		X	X													14
	X		X		U	X	X	X		X	X		U		S	S	U					X	X	X	X													15
	X		X	X	U	X		X		X	X		S		U	S	U	X				X	X	X														16
	X		X		X	U		X	S	X	X		X		U	U	U					X		X	X	X												17
		X	X		X	X		S	X	X	X		S		U		U			U		X	X	X	X													18
	X	S	X			X		X	X	X	X		U		U					U		X	X	X	X	S												19
	U	X	X		X	X		S	U	X	X		X		X							X		U	X	U	X											20
	X	X				X	X		X	X		S	S		X							X	U		X	U	X	X	U									21
	X	X	X		X	X	X		X	X		S	X		U							X	U				U	U		X								22
	X	X	X		X	X	X		X	X		U	X		U							X	S				S	U		X								23
	X	X	X		X	X	X		X	X		X	S		U							X	U		X		S	S										24
	X	X	X		X	X	X		X	X		X	U		S							X			X	S		U	U									25
	X	X	X		X	X	X		X	X		S	S									X			X	U		U	U		X							26
	X	X	X			X	X		X	X		S	U							U		X			X	U		X	U		X							27
	X	X	X			X			X	S		S	X									X			X			U			U	X	X	X	S			28
X	X	U	U			U	X		X	X		S	X		S							X										X	X	X	X			29
X	X	S	X			S	X		X	X		U	S				X					X						U				X	X	X				30
	X	X	X			S	X		X	X			S		U		X					X						U			U	X	X			X		31
	X	X	X			U	X		X	X			U		U		X					X						S				X	S			X	X	32
	X	X	X		U	S	X		X	X		X	U				S					X										X	U			X	X	33
	X	U	S		X	X	X		X	X			U		S		U					X											X	X		X	X	34
	X	U			X	X	X		X	X			U		S		S					X						S					X	X		X	X	35
	X	X			X	X	X		S	X			U		S		U					X						S					X		X	X	X	36
	X	X	S		X	X	X		X	X			U		S		U					U											X	X		X	X	37
	X	X	X		X	X			X	X			U				S					U						S					X	X	S	X	X	38
	X	X			X		X		X	X			S		U		U					X				U		S					X		X	X	X	39
	X	X				X	X			X			X		S		U			S		X				U		X					X		S	X	X	40
	X		X		U	S		X		X	X		X		U	U	U					X	X	X	X	X												
	X		X		X		X	S	X	X	X	S	X		U	U	U	X			X	U	X		U													1
	X		X		X	X	X	S		X	X		X		X	U	S	X		U	S	U	X		U													2
	X		X	X	S	X	X	X		X	X		X		S	U	U	X			U	U	X		U													3
	X		X		X	S		X	S	X	X		X		S	U	U					X		X	X	X												4

Total League Appearances

DEAKIN	COOKE	MARSHALL	NWADIKE	HUME	ROBINSON	R GARDNER	A FOSTER	KNOX	HOLLAND	MEIKLE	M FOSTER	M SMITH	HOLMES	PRENDERGAST	D BROWN	CHAMBERS	WHITEHURST	R TURNER	CHAPMAN	COOPER	CLARKE	RILEY	J TURNER	MCAUGHTRIE	BUDTZ	MARKEL BAILEY	J SMITH	GAUGHAN	STAIR	ELEY	ROSS	MATT BAILEY	D'LARYEA	S GARDNER	DUNCUM	DANBY	S BROWN	
6	32	21	32	13	26	23	32	11	31	37	19	4	14	2	6	0	3	10	4	0	8	25	6	7	12	1	2	3	0	2	2	6	11	7	3	10	9	X
0	0	2	2	0	0	3	0	8	2	3	1	13	13	0	14	5	6	0	0	1	1	3	1	0	0	2	2	6	0	0	0	0	1	0	3	0	0	S
1	1	3	1	0	3	3	1	1	1	0	0	6	13	0	13	10	15	0	0	4	0	2	3	2	2	6	1	7	4	0	2	0	1	0	0	0	0	U

Total Cup Appearances

DEAKIN	COOKE	MARSHALL	NWADIKE	HUME	ROBINSON	R GARDNER	A FOSTER	KNOX	HOLLAND	MEIKLE	M FOSTER	M SMITH	HOLMES	PRENDERGAST	D BROWN	CHAMBERS	WHITEHURST	R TURNER	CHAPMAN	COOPER	CLARKE	RILEY	J TURNER	MCAUGHTRIE	BUDTZ	MARKEL BAILEY	J SMITH	GAUGHAN	STAIR	ELEY	ROSS	MATT BAILEY	D'LARYEA	S GARDNER	DUNCUM	DANBY	S BROWN	
0	4	0	4	1	3	2	3	2	1	4	4	0	4	0	1	0	0	3	0	0	1	1	3	1	1	1	0	0	0	0	0	0	0	0	0	0	0	X
0	0	0	0	0	1	1	0	2	1	0	0	1	0	0	2	0	1	0	0	0	1	0	0	0	0	0	0	0	0	0	0	0	0	0	0	0	0	S
0	0	0	0	0	0	0	0	0	0	0	0	0	0	0	1	4	3	0	0	1	1	3	0	0	3	0	0	0	0	0	0	0	0	0	0	0	0	U

Total Goals

DEAKIN	COOKE	MARSHALL	NWADIKE	HUME	ROBINSON	R GARDNER	A FOSTER	KNOX	HOLLAND	MEIKLE	M FOSTER	M SMITH	HOLMES	PRENDERGAST	D BROWN	CHAMBERS	WHITEHURST	R TURNER	CHAPMAN	COOPER	CLARKE	RILEY	J TURNER	MCAUGHTRIE	BUDTZ	MARKEL BAILEY	J SMITH	GAUGHAN	STAIR	ELEY	ROSS	MATT BAILEY	D'LARYEA	S GARDNER	DUNCUM	DANBY	S BROWN	
0	0	0	5	3	1	1	0	5	8	11	1	1	7	0	3	0	1	0	0	0	0	0	0	1	0	0	0	0	0	0	0	0	0	0	0	0	0	Lge
0	0	0	1	0	0	0	0	1	2	0	0	0	0	0	0	0	0	0	0	0	0	0	0	0	0	0	0	0	0	0	0	0	0	0	0	0	0	Cup

EASTWOOD TOWN

CURRENT SQUAD AS OF BEGINING OF 2010-11 SEASON

GOALKEEPERS	HT	WT	D.O.B	AGE	P.O.B	CAREER	APPS	GOA
Alex Goddard						Notts County, Eastwood T 9/07		
John Danby	6'02"	14 07	20/9/83	26	Stoke	Kidderminster Rel 5/06, Stourport (2ML) 2/03, Chester 5/06 Rel 3/10, Eastwood T 3/10	10	0
DEFENDERS								
Matt Bailey	6'05"	11 06	12/3/86	24	Nantwich	Nantwich (Yth), Stockport 11/02, Altrincham (L) 3/04, Scunthorpe (L) 8/04, Northwich 3/05, Crewe Undisc 5/05 Rel 5/08, Hereford (L) 9/05, Southport (L) 1/06, Lancaster (L) 3/06, Barrow (2ML) 1/07, Weymouth (SL) 3/08, Northwich 5/08, Hinckley U (L) 12/08, Eastwood T Undisc 2/10	6	0
Richard Cooper	5'08"	11 06	27/9/79	30	Nottingham	Notts Forest, York C (6WL) 3/01 Undisc 4/01 Rel c/s 04, Alfreton 7/04, Eastwood 8/05	1	0
Adrian Hawes			23/11/87	22		Heanor T, Hucknall 2/09, Motherwell (Trial), 8/09, Dag & Red (Trial) 10/09, Eastwood T 5/10		
MIDFIELDERS								
Russell Cooke			18/5/81	29		Notts County (Trainee), Hucknall c/s 99, Leigh RMI 8/03, Ilkeston 9/03, Hucknall c/s 04, Eastwood 6/08	32	0
Jonathan D'Laryea	5'10"	12 02	3/9/85	24	Manchester	Man City, Mansfield (3ML) 10/05, Mansfield 1/06, Northwich (3ML) 8/09 Perm 11/09, Eastwood T Undisc 2/10	12	0
Sam Duncum	5'09"	11 02	18/2/87	23	Sheffield	Rotherham Rel 5/08, York C (2ML) 2/08, Ilkeston 5/08, Eastwood T Undisc 2/10	6	0
Anton Foster			25/6/82	28		Ilkeston, Alfreton (L) (00/01), Eastwood (L) 1/03, Gedling T c/s 03, Belper c/s 04, Sheffield FC 8/05, Buxton 10/05, Eastwood T £10,000 7/08	32	0
Paul Riley	5'09"	10 07	29/9/82	27	Nottingham	Notts County Rel c/s 04, Hucknall (Trial) c/s 04, Alfreton 9/04, Ilkeston 10/04 Rel 11/04, Matlock 11/04, Eastwood T 9/09	28	0
Michael Simpson	5'07"	11 02	18/2/74	36	Nottingham	Notts County, Plymouth (2ML) 10/96, Wycombe (L) 12/96 £50,000 1/97 Rel c/s 04, L.Orient 7/04 Rel c/s 07, Burton 11/07 Rel c/s 10, Eastwood T 7/10		
Lee Stevenson			1/6/84	26	Sheffield	Sheff Wed (Scholar), Kings Lynn 3/03, Belper 11/06, Eastwood T 5/10		
Andy Todd	6'00"	11 03	22/2/79	31	Nottingham	Eastwood T, N.Forest 2/96, Scarborough 2/99, Eastwood T 5/99, Ilkeston 3/00, Eastwood T 7/01, Worksop 10/01, Hucknall 12/03, Burton 7/05, Accrington (SL) 1/06, Accrington Undisc 6/06, Rotherham 8/07 Rel c/s 09, Accrington (SL) 1/08, Eastwood T (3ML) 10/08		
FORWARDS								
Markel Bailey			14/1/90	20		Eastwood T	3	0
Lindon Meikle			21/3/88	22	Nottingham	Vernon Colts, Eastwood T 7/04	40	11
Adam Muller	5'11"	12 02	17/4/82	28	Thackley	Ossett T, Sheff Wed 5/00 Rel c/s 02, Worksop (SL) 3/01, Bournemouth (Trial) 2/02, Worksop 8/02, Wakefield & Emley (3ML) 9/03, Wakefield & Emley 7/04, Ilkeston (L) 1/06 Perm 2/06, Guiseley Undisc 6/08, Eastwood T 6/10		
Tyeisse Nightingale			12/10/85	24		Unity FC, Hucknall 7/09, Alfreton 3/10, Eastwood T 6/10		
Matt Rhead	6'04"		31/5/84	26	Stoke	Stallington, Kidsgrove Ath c/s 04, Eastwood T Undisc 10/07, Kidsgrove Ath (L) 9/08, Nantwich 6/09, Congleton (L) 12/09 Perm, Eastwood T 6/10		

Loanees	HT	WT	DOB	AGE	POB	From - To	APPS	GOA
(M)Scott Gardner	5'09"	11 04	1/4/88	22	Luxembourg	Mansfield 2/10 - Rel 4/10	7	0
Departures	HT	WT	DOB	AGE	POB	From - To	APPS	GOA
(M)Rory Prendergast	5'08"	12 00	6/4/78	32	Pontefract	Farsley Celtic 8/09 - Bradford PA 10/09, Goole AFC 11/09, Ilkeston 11/09 Rel 1/10, Goole AFC 3/10	2	0
(G)Alex Goddard			2/4/90	20		Notts County 9/07 - Grantham 9/09		
(D)Ben Chapman	5'06"	11 05	2/3/79	31	Scunthorpe	Kings Lynn 3/09 - Harrogate T 10/09, Frickley (L) 2/10	4	0
(D)Ryan Clarke			22/1/84	26		Grantham 8/09 - Rel 11/09, Northwich 12/09, Ilkeston 5/10	9	0
(G)Ross Turner			17/6/79	31		Retford U 8/09 - Retford U 11/09, Alfreton 3/10	10	0
(D)Mark Hume	6'02"	13 04	21/5/78	32	Barnsley	Buxton 9/08 - Bradford PA 11/09	13	3
(F)Paris Simmons			2/1/90	20		Derby 9/09 - Carlton T 11/09, Hucknall 6/10		
(M)Martin Foster	5'05"	9 10	29/10/77	32	Sheffield	Tamworth 6/09 - Harrogate T 12/09	20	1
(F)Peter Knox			30/9/79	30	Yorkshire	Hucknall 9/08 - Harrogate T 12/09, Worksop 5/10	19	5
(M)Dion Chambers			16/12/89	20	Nottingham	Swansea 7/09 - Worksop 12/09, Carlton, Hucknall 6/10	5	0
(M)Jay Smith	5'07"	12 00	24/9/81	28	Lambeth	ex Notts County 12/09 - Tamworth 1/10	4	0
(D)Jimmy Turner	5'11"	11 04	4/10/83	26	Derby	AFC Telford 9/09 - Halesowen T 2/10	7	0
(G)Jan Budtz	6'03"	13 05	20/4/79	31	Denmark	Hartlepool 9/09 - Rel 3/10	12	0
(D)Craig McAughtrie	6'04"	13 10	3/3/81	29	Burton	Kings Lynn 9/09 - Rel 4/10, Stafford R (SL) 1/10, Stafford R 5/10	7	1
(G)Ed Eley	6'02"		1/3/91	19		Grimsby 1/10 - Rel 5/10	2	0
(D)Lawrence Gaughan			14/2/90	20	Sheffield	Sheffield FC 12/09 - Rel 5/10	9	0
(M)Ross Gardner	5'08"	10 06	15/12/85	24	South Shields	Ilkeston 7/08 - Rel 5/10	26	1
(F)David Brown	5'11"	11 09	29/5/89	20	York	AFC Halifax 6/09 - Rel 5/10	20	3
(F)Ian Holmes	6'00"	12 05	29/6/85	25	Ellesmere Port	Mansfield 7/08 - Rel 5/10, Ilkeston 6/10	27	7
(F)Marc Smith			7/4/74	36	Doncaster	Guiseley (Undisc) 1/08 - Rel 5/10	17	1
(F)Ryan Whitehurst			6/9/89	20		Notts Forest 7/09 - Rel 5/10, Hucknall T 6/10	9	1
(M)Emeka Nwadike	6'00"	12 07	9/8/78	32	Camberwell	AFC Telford 6/09 - Gainsborough 5/10	34	5
(F)Simon Brown	5'10"	11 00	18/9/83	26	West Bromwich	Wrexham 3/10 - Corby T 6/10	9	0
(D)Paul Robinson			26/9/82	27		Hednesford 6/08 - Hucknall 6/10	26	1
(D)Tom Marshall	6'04"		16/11/87	22		Hednesford 5/09 - Chasetown (L) 10/09, Tamworth 6/10	23	0
(F)Danny Holland			18/2/83	27	Mansfield	Harrogate T Undisc 2/09 - FC Halifax 7/10	33	8
(G)Ian Deakin	6'00"	14 03	5/2/87	23	Birmingham	Notts Forest c/s 06 - Retford U (L) 10/09	6	0
(D)Josh Ross			13/9/91	18		Burton 2/10 -	2	0
(M)Theo Stair			1/8/91	19		Crewe 1/10 -	0	0

GAINSBOROUGH TRINITY

Chairman: Peter Swann
Secretary: Peter Wallace **(T)** 07841 163 110
(E) petewallace@aol.com
Additional Committee Members:
Karin Swann, P.F.C.Lobley, A.Lobley, Geoff Holmes, T.Bland, R.Coleman, G.H.Lyner
Manager: Brian Little
Programme Editor: Nicky Hodgson **(E)** nicky@the-sands.co.uk

Club Factfile

Founded: 1873 **Nickname:** The Blues
Previous Names:
Previous Leagues: Midland Counties 1889-96, 1912-60, 61-68, Football League 1896-1912, Central Alliance 1960-61, Northern Premier 1968-2004

Club Colours (change): All royal blue (All yellow)

Ground: The Northolme, Gainsborough, Lincolnshire DN21 2QW **(T)** 01427 613 295 (office) 613 688 (Social C)
Capacity: 4,340 **Seats:** 504 **Covered:** 2,500 **Clubhouse:** Yes **Shop:** Yes
Previous Grounds:
Simple Directions
The Northolme is situated on the A159, Gainsborough to Scunthorpe road, approximately a third of a mile north of the Town Centre. Public Car Park on the right 150 yards before the Ground. Any person parked illegally in the Streets around the Ground will be issued with a ticket from the Police.

Record Attendance: 9,760 v Scunthorpe United - Midland League 1948
Record Victory: 7-0 v Fleetwood Town and v Great Harwood Town
Record Defeat: 1-7 v Stalybridge Celtic - Northern Premier 2000-01 and v Brentford - FA Cup 03-04.
Record Goalscorer: Not known
Record Appearances: Not known
Additional Records: Paid £3,000 to Buxton for Stuart Lowe
Received £30,000 from Lincoln City for Tony James
Senior Honours: Midland Counties League 1890-91, 1927-28, 48-49, 66-67
Lincolnshire Senior Cup x12

10 YEAR RECORD

00-01	01-02	02-03	03-04	04-05	05-06	06-07	07-08	08-09	09-10
NP P 8	NP P 19	NP P 15	NP P 10	Conf N 11	Conf N 16	Conf N 12	Conf N 11	Conf N 13	Conf N 14

GAINSBOROUGH TRINITY

No.	Date	Comp	H/A	Opponents	Att:	Result	Goalscorers	Pos
1	8/8/09	BSN	A	Vauxhall Motors	260	D 2-2	Beckett 63, Parker 90	9
2	11/8/09	BSN	H	Workington	419	L 0-1		14
3	15/8/09	BSN	H	Droylsden	300	W 4-2	McMahon 2 (pen 25, pen 33), Hurst 66, Beckett 90	8
4	17/8/09	BSN	A	Hyde United	372	L 2-3	Beckett 13, Hurst 47	9
5	22/8/09	BSN	H	AFC Telford	434	L 0-1		14
6	31/8/09	BSN	H	Eastwood Town	551	L 1-4	Stamp 12	20
7	5/9/09	BSN	A	Solihull Moors	239	W 1-0	Hurst 32	18
8	8/9/09	BSN	A	Redditch United	246	W 3-0	Semple 43, McMahon 2 (48, 75)	12
9	12/9/09	BSN	H	Southport	530	L 2-4	Hurst 2 (32, 48)	13
10	19/9/09	BSN	H	Northwich Victoria	416	L 1-4	Stamp 46	17
11	3/10/09	BSN	A	Fleetwood Town	1187	D 2-2	Hudson 47, Hunt 80	17
12	17/10/09	BSN	H	Solihull Moors	320	D 0-0		16
13	24/10/09	BSN	H	Stalybridge Celtic	381	L 1-3	Peat pen 16	19
14	27/10/09	BSN	A	Alfreton Town	517	L 0-1		19
15	31/10/09	BSN	H	Gloucester City	378	W 1-0	Hudson 53	16
16	2/11/09	BSN	A	Hinckley United	441	L 0-2		17
17	14/11/09	BSN	H	Harrogate Town	421	D 1-1	Hudson 46	15
18	28/11/09	BSN	A	Gloucester City	246	L 0-1		20
19	5/12/09	BSN	A	Workington	293	D 1-1	Beckett 58	20
20	26/12/09	BSN	A	Corby Town	360	D 2-2	Burbeary 78, Og (Mayo) 88	19
21	16/1/10	BSN	H	Stafford Rangers	334	L 1-3	Beckett pen 90	19
22	23/1/10	BSN	A	Droylsden	276	L 1-4	Davies 35	19
23	6/2/10	BSN	H	Ilkeston Town	337	D 0-0		20
24	9/2/10	BSN	A	AFC Telford	1304	D 2-2	O'Hare 48, Beckett 90	20
25	13/2/10	BSN	A	Harrogate Town	310	L 0-2		20
26	20/2/10	BSN	H	Fleetwood Town	316	W 2-0	Burbeary 24, Beckett 87	20
27	23/2/10	BSN	H	Vauxhall Motors	229	W 2-0	Peat 62, Greaves 65	20
28	27/2/10	BSN	A	Stalybridge Celtic	423	L 2-3	Beckett 45, Aiston 49	20
29	6/3/10	BSN	A	Southport	851	D 0-0		20
30	9/3/10	BSN	H	Hyde United	298	W 2-1	Beckett 16, McMahon 77	20
31	13/3/10	BSN	H	Alfreton Town	473	W 3-2	Beckett 13, McMahon 35, Stamp 82	17
32	16/3/10	BSN	A	Ilkeston Town	252	D 0-0		16
33	20/3/10	BSN	H	Redditch United	312	W 3-0	Beckett 2 (20, 33), McMahon pen 24	15
34	23/3/10	BSN	H	Corby Town	276	W 2-0	McMahon 13, Stamp 85	14
35	27/3/10	BSN	A	Northwich Victoria	495	W 1-0	McMahon 82	12
36	5/4/10	BSN	A	Eastwood Town	398	L 0-1		12
37	10/4/10	BSN	H	Hinckley United	342	D 1-1	Beckett 30	13
38	13/4/10	BSN	A	Blyth Spartans	391	L 1-2	McMahon pen 43	13
39	17/4/10	BSN	A	Stafford Rangers	506	L 1-2	Beckett 11	14
40	24/4/10	BSN	H	Blyth Spartans	394	W 2-0	Hunt 32, Beckett 58	14
	Farsley Celtic record expunged 12/03							
6	29/8/09	BSN	A	Farsley Celtic	256	L 1-4	Mallon 54	18
	Cups							
1	26/9/09	FAC 2Q	A	Market Drayton Town	205	W 2-1	Semple 2 (40, 82)	
2	10/10/09	FAC 3Q	A	Nuneaton Town	930	L 0-1		
3	21/11/09	FAT 3Q	A	North Ferriby United	176	D 2-2	Beckett 2 (23, 29)	
4	24/11/09	FAT 3QR	H	North Ferriby United	226	D 3-3 aet	Stamp 8, Peat pen 90, Parker 98 (W 3-2 pens)	
5	12/12/09	FAT 1	A	Southport	478	D 2-2	Davies 51, Parker 86	
6	15/10/09	FAT 1R	H	Southport	218	W 1-0	McMahon 33	
7	19/1/10	FAT 2	H	Tamworth	291	D 0-0		
8	26/1/10	FAT 2R	A	Tamworth	392	L 1-2	Mallon 63	

Home Attendances:	
Highest:	551 v Eastwood Town
Lowest:	229 v Vauxhall Motors
Average (08-09):	360 (327)
Top Goalscorer:	Beckett - 17 (15 League, 2 Cup) in 41 appearances - 42% strike rate
Most Appearances:	Barnes - 47 (39 League, 8 Cup)

HERRIOTT	PICTON	GREAVES	PEAT	MOSES	HUNT	BURBEARY	DUNNING	BECKETT	MCMAHON	HALL	PARKER	MALLON	BARNES	DAVIES	SEMPLE	TOULSON	HURST	STAMP	AUSTIN	SPAFFORD	O'HARE	HUDSON	ALASSANE	BOYCE	AISTON	MANSARAM	PETERS	COWAN	WILLIAMS	ROBINSON	GRANT	
X	X	X	X	X	X	X	X	X	X	X	S	U	U	U	U																	1
U	X	X	X		X	X	X	X	X	X	X	S	X	S	U	U																2
U	X	X	X	S	S	X	X	X	X		X	S	X	X		U	X															3
U	X	X	X	S	S	X	X	X	X		X	S	X	X		U	X															4
S		U	X	X	X	X	X	X	X	S	X	S	X	U		X	X															5
	X	X	X		X	X	S		X	S	X	U	X	U	X	U	X	X														6
		X	X		X	X	X	X	U	S	X	U	X	U	X	X	X	S														7
U	X	X	X		X	X	X		S	U	X	U	X	U	X		X	X														8
	X	S	X		X	X	X		X	S	X	U	X	U	X		X	X	U													9
	X	X	X		X	X	X			U	X	S	X	U	X		X	X	U	U												10
		X	X	X	X	X	S	U	U		X	S	X		X		U	X			X	X										11
		X	X			X	U	X	S			S	X	X	X	X	X	S		U	X	X										12
		X	X		X	X	U	S				U	X	U	X	X	X	X		S	X	X										13
		X	X		X	X	X	X				S	X	U	U	X	S	X		S	X	X										14
			X		X	X	X	X		U		U	X	U	U	X	S	X			X	X	X									15
		U	X		X	X	X	X		S		S	X	S		X		X	U		X	X	X									16
			X		X	X	X	X	S	U	X	U	X	U	U	X		X				X	X									17
		U	X		X	X	X	X	X	S	X	S	X	U	S	X		X			X											18
U		X			X	X	X	X	X	S	X		X	X	S	X		U			X											19
U		X	X		X	X	X	X	X	S	X		X	X	S	X		S						U								20
		X	X		X	X	X	X	X	X	X	U	X	X	S			S						S	U							21
		U	X		U	X	X			S	X	U	X	X	S	X		X						X	X	X						22
		X	X			U	U	S	X	X			X	U		X		S			X			X	X	X	X					23
		X	X			S	U	X	X	X		U	X	U	U	X					X			X	X		X					24
U			X			S	X	X	X	X	S		X	U	S	X					X			X	X		X					25
U		X	X			X	X	X	X	U			X	U	U	X		S						X	X		X					26
U		X	X		U	X	X	X	X				X	U	U	X		U						X	X		X					27
U		X	X			X	X	X	X				X	S	S	X		S						X	X		X					28
U		S	X			X	X	X	X				X	X		X		S						X	X			X				29
U		X			U	X	X	X	X		U		X	X		X		S						X	X			X				30
		X			S	X	X	X	X		U		X	U		S		S						X	X			X	X	X		31
		U	U		X	X		X	X		S		X	S		X		S						X	X			X	X	X		32
		X	X		S	U		X	X		S		X	U		X		S						X	X			X	X	X		33
U		X			X	S		X	X		S		X	U		X		S						X	X			X	X	X		34
		X	U		X	S		X	X		U		X	S		X		S						X	X			X		X	X	35
		X	X		S	U		X	X		U		X			X		S						X	X			X	X	X	S	36
U		X	X		X	S		X	X		X		X	U		X		S							X				X	X	S	37
U		U	X		X	X		X	X		X		X	U		X		X						U					X	X	S	38
		X	X		X	S		X	X		S		X	U		X		S						X				X	X	X	U	39
		X	X		X	S		X	X		U		X	S		U		S						X	X			X	X	X		40
U	U	X	X	X			X		S	X	X	X	X	X	S	X	X	S														

HERRIOTT	PICTON	GREAVES	PEAT	MOSES	HUNT	BURBEARY	DUNNING	BECKETT	MCMAHON	HALL	PARKER	MALLON	BARNES	DAVIES	SEMPLE	TOULSON	HURST	STAMP	AUSTIN	SPAFFORD	O'HARE	HUDSON	ALASSANE	BOYCE	AISTON	MANSARAM	PETERS	COWAN	WILLIAMS	ROBINSON	GRANT	
		X	X	X	X	X	U	S		S	X	S	X		X	X		X	U			X										1
		X	X	X	X	X	U	S		S	X	S	X		X	X		X	U			X										2
U			X		X	X	X	X	S		X	S	X	U	U	X		X				X	X									3
		U	X		X	X	X	X	U	U	X	S	X	U	X	X		X				X										4
U		X	X		X	X	X	X	X	S	X		X	X	S	X		S														5
U		X	X		X	X	X	X	X	S	X		X	X	U	X		S														6
U		X	X		X	X	X	X	X	U	X	U	X	X		X		S								S						7
U		X	X		X	X	X	U	X	X	X	S	X	X	S			U								X						8

HERRIOTT	PICTON	GREAVES	PEAT	MOSES	HUNT	BURBEARY	DUNNING	BECKETT	MCMAHON	HALL	PARKER	MALLON	BARNES	DAVIES	SEMPLE	TOULSON	HURST	STAMP	AUSTIN	SPAFFORD	O'HARE	HUDSON	ALASSANE	BOYCE	AISTON	MANSARAM	PETERS	COWAN	WILLIAMS	ROBINSON	GRANT	
Total League Appearances																																
1	8	29	34	3	25	30	25	32	29	6	18	0	39	9	8	28	10	13	0	0	11	7	3	17	17	2	6	10	9	10	1	**X**
1	0	2	0	2	5	7	2	2	3	9	6	10	0	6	7	1	2	18	0	2	0	0	0	1	0	0	0	0	0	0	3	**S**
15	0	6	2	0	3	3	4	1	2	5	5	11	1	23	8	5	1	2	3	2	0	0	0	2	1	0	0	0	0	0	1	**U**
Total Cup Appearances																																
0	0	6	8	2	8	8	6	5	4	1	8	0	8	4	3	7	0	4	0	0	0	4	1	0	0	1	0	0	0	0	0	**X**
0	0	0	0	0	0	0	0	2	1	4	0	5	0	0	2	0	0	3	0	0	0	0	0	0	0	1	0	0	0	0	0	**S**
5	0	1	0	0	0	0	2	1	1	2	0	1	0	2	2	0	0	1	2	0	0	0	0	0	0	0	0	0	0	0	0	**U**
Total Goals																																
0	0	1	2	0	2	2	0	15	10	0	1	0	0	1	1	0	5	4	0	0	1	3	0	0	1	0	0	0	0	0	0	**Lge**
0	0	0	1	0	0	0	0	2	1	0	2	1	0	1	2	0	0	1	0	0	0	0	0	0	0	0	0	0	0	0	0	**Cup**

GAINSBOROUGH TRINITY

CURRENT SQUAD AS OF BEGINING OF 2010-11 SEASON

GOALKEEPERS	HT	WT	D.O.B	AGE	P.O.B	CAREER	APPS	GOA
Phil Barnes	6'01"	11 01	2/3/79	31	Sheffield	Rotherham, Blackpool £100,000 7/97 Rel c/s 04, Sheff Utd 7/04, Torquay (L) 2/05, QPR (L) 2/06, Grimsby Undisc 6/06 Rel 3/09, Gainsborough 4/09	39	0
Gavin Ward	6'03"	14 12	30/6/70	39	Sutton Coldfield	Aston Villa (Trainee), Shrewsbury 9/88 Rel c/s 89, West Brom 9/89, Cardiff C 10/89, Leicester £175,000 7/93, Bradford C £175,000 7/95, Bolton £300,000 3/96, Burnley (3ML) 6/98, Stoke 2/99 Rel c/s 02, Wigan (Trial) 7/02, Walsall 8/02 Rel c/s 03, Coventry C 8/03 Rel c/s 04, Barnsley (L) 4/04, Preston 8/04 Rel c/s 06, Tranmere 7/06, Chester 7/07, Wrexham 1/08 Rel 4/09, Hednesford 7/09, Gainsborough (Pl/Ass Man) 12/09		
DEFENDERS								
Andrew Boyce			5/11/89	20		Doncaster Rel c/s 09, Worksop (WE) 3/08, Worksop (SL) 8/08, Mansfield (Trial) 4/09, Kings Lynn 7/09, Gainsborough 12/09	18	0
Gavin Cowan	6'04"	14 04	24/5/81	29	Hanover(Ger)	Exeter (Trainee), Braintree 7/99, Canvey Island 12/02, Nuneaton (L) 12/04, Nuneaton (L) 2/05, Shrewsbury £5,000 + 3/05, Kidderminster (L) 8/06, Grays 1/07 Rel 6/07, Nuneaton (L) 3/07, Nuneaton 6/07, AFC Telford 5/08 Rel 1/10, Fleetwood 1/10, Gainsborough	10	0
Mark Greaves	6'01"	13 00	22/1/75	35	Hull	Gainsborough, Brigg T, Hull C 6/96, Boston U 8/02, Burton 7/07 Rel 5/08, York C 5/08 Rel 6/09, Gainsborough 7/09	31	1
Paul Mayo	5'11"	11 09	13/10/81	28	Lincoln	Notts Forest (Scholar), Lincoln C (Sch) 10/99 Pro 4/00, Dag & Red (L) 10/02, Watford £65,000 3/04, Lincoln C 8/05, Notts County 7/07, Darlington (L) 1/08, Mansfield 1/09 Rel 5/09, Corby T 6/09, Gainsborough 5/10		
Nathan Peat	5'09"	10 09	19/9/82	27	Hull	Hull C, Cambridge U (2ML) 12/03, Lincoln C (SL) 7/04, York 8/05 Rel 5/07, Harrogate T 6/07, Gainsborough 3/09	34	2
Neil Spafford			7/10/86	23		Boston T, Gainsborough 7/07, Brigg T (L) 12/09	2	0
Luke Waterfall	6'02"	12 11	30/7/90	20	Sheffield	Barnsley (Scholar), Tranmere 7/08 Rel c/s 09, Altrincham (L) 10/08, Oxford U (Trial) 7/09, York C (Trial) 7/09, Ilkeston 8/09, Gainsborough 5/10		
MIDFIELDERS								
Sam Aiston	6'01"	14 00	21/11/76	33	Newcastle	Newcastle (Trainee), Sunderland 7/95, Chester (SL) 2/97, Chester (2ML) 11/98, Stoke (2ML) 8/99, Shrewsbury (2ML) 12/99, Shrewsbury 7/00 Rel c/s 05, Tranmere 7/05 Rel c/s 06, Northampton 8/06, Burton (3ML) 8/07, Wrexham (2ML) 11/07 Perm 1/08 Rel 4/09, Hednesford 7/09, Gainsborough 1/10	17	1
Josh Davies			13/4/90	20		Gainsborough	15	1
Leon Hibbert	6'04"		6/11/81	28	Watford	Tring T, Welwyn Garden c/s 03, Berkhamstead 8/04, Hemel Hempstead c/s 06, Barton R 11/07, Corby T 7/08, Slough (L) 10/09, Lincoln C (Trial) 5/10, Gainsborough 6/10		
Lewis McMahon	5'09"	10 10	2/5/85	25	Doncaster	Sheff Wed, Notts County 7/05 Rel c/s 06, York C 8/06 Rel 5/07, Gainsborough 7/07	32	10
Emeka Nwadike	6'00"	12 07	9/8/78	32	Camberwell	Wolves, Shrewsbury 12/96 Rel c/s 98, Grantham 6/98, Kings Lynn 11/99, Ilkeston 1/01, Alfreton 6/03, Worcester 6/07, AFC Telford NC 3/08, Hinckley U (2ML) 11/08, Eastwood T 6/09, Gainsborough 5/10		
FORWARDS								
Luke Beckett	5'11"	11 02	25/11/76	33	Sheffield	Barnsley, Chester 6/98, Chesterfield £75,000 7/00, Stockport £100,000 12/01, Sheff Utd £50,000 11/04, Huddersfield (6WL) 1/05, Oldham (SL) 3/05, Oldham (SL) 7/05, Huddersfield £85,000 7/06 Rel 11/08, Gainsborough 11/08	34	15
Leon Mettam	5'09"	11 01	9/12/86	23	Lincoln	Lincoln C Rel c/s 07, Stamford 6/07, Corby T Undisc 2/08, Gainsborough 5/10		

Loanees	HT	WT	DOB	AGE	POB	From - To	APPS	GOA
(D)Jake Picton	6'00"	11 00	6/1/91	29	Pontefract	Scunthorpe (2ML) 8/09 -	8	0
(D)Alan O'Hare	6'02"	12 02	31/7/82	28	Drogheda. Ire	York C (2ML) 9/09, (SL) 1/10 - Rel 5/10	11	1
Departures	**HT**	**WT**	**DOB**	**AGE**	**POB**	**From - To**	**APPS**	**GOA**
(F)David Reeves	6'01"	13 08	19/11/67	42	Birkenhead	Sutton T (Pl/Coach) 12/07 - Rel 8/09		
(D)Adie Moses	5'10"	12 08	4/5/75	35	Doncaster	Mansfield 6/09 - Retired 11/09	5	0
(M)Matt Austin			15/2/89	21		Notts County c/s 08 - Rel 11/09	0	0
(M)Mark Hudson	5'10"	11 03	24/10/80	29	Bishop Auckland	Blackpool 9/09 - Grimsby (Trial) 10/09, Grimsby 11/09	7	3
(F)Glyn Hurst	5'10"	11 06	17/1/76	34	Barnsley	Chester 8/09 - Rel 11/09, Hyde U 12/09	12	5
(D)Idrissa Alassane			24/7/84	26		ex Aberdeen NC 10/09 - Rel 12/09	3	0
(F)Darren Mansaram			25/6/84	26		Dundalk 12/09 - Rel 2/10, Mansfield (Trial) 2/10, Droylsden 2/10	2	0
(F)Ryan Mallon	5'09"	11 08	22/3/83	27	Sheffield	York C (L) 12/05 Perm 1/06 - Worksop 2/10	10	0
(M)Chris Hall			3/3/83	27	Lincoln	Burton 6/07 - Rel 2/10, Alfreton 2/10	15	0
(M)Ryan Semple	5'11"	10 11	4/7/85	25	Belfast	Deeping R 6/09 - Boston U 3/10	15	1
(D)Anthony Peters	6'05"		24/10/83	26		Newport C 1/10 - Rel 3/10	6	0
(M)James Hunt	5'08"	10 03	17/12/76	33	Derby	Grimsby 7/09 - Rel 5/10	30	2
(M)Ryan Toulson			18/11/85	24		Harrogate T 5/09 - Guiseley 5/10	29	0
(F)Darryn Stamp	6'01"	11 10	21/9/78	31	Beverley	Northwich 6/09 - Rel c/s 10, Guiseley 7/10	31	4
(G)Luke Herriott			30/1/91	19		Mansfield c/s 09 -	2	0
(D)Ashley Burbeary			29/11/86	23		Droylsden 1/09 - Rel 7/10	37	2
(D)Wes Parker	5'08"	10 05	7/12/83	26	Boston	Boston U 5/09 -	24	1
(D)Mark Robinson	5'09"	11 00	24/7/81	29	Guisborough	Gateshead 3/10 -	10	0
(D)Darren Williams	5'10"	11 00	28/4/77	33	Middlesbrough	Gateshead 3/10 -	9	0
(M)Darren Dunning	5'06"	11 12	8/1/81	29	Scarborough	Harrogate T 5/09 -	27	0
(F)Gareth Grant	5'10"	10 04	6/9/80	29	Leeds	Droylsden 3/10 -	4	0

GLOUCESTER CITY

Chairman: Nigel Hughes
Secretary: Shaun Wetson (T) 07813 931 781
(E) swgcfc@gmail.com

Additional Committee Members:
Mike Dunstan

Manager: David Mehew
Programme Editor: Mike Dunstan (E) mikedunstan@blueyonder.co.uk

Back row, Ken Blackburn (Youth Coach), Matt Sysum, Jack Pitcher, Jack Harris, Sam Ellis, Tom Hamblin, Kev Sawyer, Ollie Hall, Ash Thomas, Mike Symons, Alex Allard, Matt Rose, Lee Marshall, Lee Randall (Kit Manager).
Middle Row : Doug Foxwell (Chief Scout), Kevin Allard (Exec), Mike Dunstan (Exec), Phil Warren (Supporters Trust), Adie Tandy (Physio), Dave Mehew (Manager), David Phillips (Chairman), Tim Harris (General Manager), Adrian Harris (Assistant Manager), Nigel Hughes (Exec), Dave Hatton (Youth Secretary), John Davis (Exec), Stewart Martyn (Goalkeeping Coach).
Front Row : Dr Bob Byrne (Club Doctor), Jack Twyman, Lee Smith, Tom Webb, Luke Ballinger, Neil Mustoe (Captain), Alex Sykes, James Upcott, Karl Nash, Jamie Reid, Shaun Wetson (Secretary). (Archive Photo)

Club Factfile

Founded: 1889 **Nickname:** The Tigers
Previous Names: Gloucester Y.M.C.A.
Previous Leagues: Bristol & District (now Western) 1893-96, Gloucester & Dist. 1897-1907, North Gloucestershire 1907-10, Gloucestershire North Senior 1920-34, Birmingham Combination 1935-39, Southern 1939-2000
Club Colours (change): Yellow & black/black/black (Sky blue/navy blue/sky blue)

Ground: Cheltenham Tn FC, The Abbey Business Stad., Whaddon Rd GL52 5NA (T) 01242 573558 (Cheltenham Town No.)
Capacity: 7,289 **Seats:** Yes **Covered:** Yes **Clubhouse:** Yes **Shop:** Yes
Previous Grounds: Longlevens 1935-65, Horton Road 1965-86, Meadow Park 1986-2007, Corinium Stadium Cirencester 2007-10
Simple Directions
From the North (M5) leave at Jnctn 10, follow road A4019) towards Cheltenham, keep going straight through traffic lights until you reach a roundabout, PC World will be on your left and McDonalds on your right. Turn left here, after 500 yards you will then come to a double roundabout, go straight over, keep going for another 300 yards then turn right into Swindon Lane, follow the road over the level crossing and 2 mini roundabouts until you come to a large roundabout, go straight over, signposted Prestbury, continue past Racecourse and turn right into Albert Road, follow this to the end then turn left at roundabout into Prestbury Road, 200yards turn into Whaddon Rd.

Record Attendance: Longlevens: 10,500 v Tottenham - Friendly 1952. Meadow Park: 4,000 v Dagenham & Red. - FAT 3rd Q Rnd 12/04/97
Record Victory: 10-1 v Sudbury Town (H) - FA Cup 3rd Qualifying Round 17/10/98
Record Defeat: 1-12 v Gillingham - 09/11/46
Record Goalscorer: Reg Weaver - 250 (1930s)
Record Appearances: Stan Myers & Frank Tredgett - (1950s)
Additional Records: Paid £25,000 to Worcester City for Steve Ferguson 1990-91
Received £25,000 from AFC Bournemouth for Ian Hedges 1990
Senior Honours: Southern League Cup 1955-56, Midland Division 1988-89, Premier Division Play-off 2008-09.
Gloucestershire Senior Cup x19

10 YEAR RECORD

00-01	01-02	02-03	03-04	04-05	05-06	06-07	07-08	08-09	09-10
SthW 13	SthW 14	SthW 5	SthW 2	SthP 15	SthP 13	SthP 10	SthP 6	SthP 3	Conf N 18

GLOUCESTER CITY

No.	Date	Comp	H/A	Opponents	Att:	Result	Goalscorers	Pos
1	8/8/09	BSN	A	Southport	780	L 2-3	Symons 5, J Harris 70	14
2	11/8/09	BSN	H	Eastwood Town	326	L 1-3	Symons 43	17
3	18/8/09	BSN	A	Solihull Moors	239	W 1-0	Hamblin 60	17
4	23/8/09	BSN	H	Droylsden	340	L 1-4	Marshall 73	19
5	29/8/09	BSN	A	Corby Town	633	W 6-3	Smith 3 (7, 58, 88), Ballinger 16, Hamblin 39, Sykes 54	15
6	31/8/09	BSN	H	AFC Telford	617	L 0-1		18
7	5/9/09	BSN	A	Vauxhall Motors	206	D 0-0		16
8	7/9/09	BSN	A	Hyde United	326	D 1-1	Symons 90	13
9	12/9/09	BSN	H	Workington	331	L 0-2		18
10	19/9/09	BSN	H	Blyth Spartans	303	W 3-1	Morford 2 (16, 72), Smith pen 59	14
11	3/10/09	BSN	A	Ilkeston Town	437	D 0-0		15
12	17/10/09	BSN	H	Fleetwood Town	363	L 1-2	Richards 52	15
13	31/10/09	BSN	A	Gainsborough Trinity	378	L 0-1		21
14	7/11/09	BSN	H	Hyde United	280	W 2-0	Smith 2 (20, 68)	17
15	14/11/09	BSN	A	Stafford Rangers	547	L 0-1		19
16	28/11/09	BSN	H	Gainsborough Trinity	246	W 1-0	Symons 9	16
17	1/12/09	BSN	A	Eastwood Town	321	W 3-0	Pitcher 38, Smith 39, J Harris 78	12
18	5/12/09	BSN	H	Northwich Victoria	316	L 0-1		14
19	8/12/09	BSN	A	Stalybridge Celtic	352	L 1-4	Smith pen 24	14
20	26/12/09	BSN	A	Redditch United	428	L 1-4	Hunt 89	15
21	1/1/10	BSN	H	Redditch United	378	W 2-0	Smith 10, Symons 57	12
22	23/1/10	BSN	A	Workington	304	L 0-2		15
23	26/1/10	BSN	H	Hinckley United	180	L 3-5	Hunt 2 (18, 90), Pitcher 46	16
24	30/1/10	BSN	H	Alfreton Town	310	L 1-2	Richards 64	17
25	2/2/10	BSN	H	Solihull Moors	215	W 1-0	Richards 4	16
26	13/2/10	BSN	A	Fleetwood Town	1267	L 1-3	Smith pen 64	15
27	20/2/10	BSN	H	Stalybridge Celtic	323	L 1-2	Smith pen 49	17
28	6/3/10	BSN	A	Alfreton Town	410	L 1-3	Rose 57	19
29	13/3/10	BSN	H	Vauxhall Motors	301	W 1-0	Symons 22	19
30	15/3/10	BSN	A	Droylsden	244	D 2-2	Smith 4, J Harris 80	18
31	20/3/10	BSN	A	Hinckley United	481	L 0-1		19
32	23/3/10	BSN	H	Southport	301	D 2-2	Symons 14, Smith 45	19
33	27/3/10	BSN	A	Blyth Spartans	519	W 3-0	Smith 3 (pen 13, 68, pen 90)	19
34	5/4/10	BSN	A	AFC Telford	1572	W 1-0	J Harris 13	18
35	10/4/10	BSN	H	Stafford Rangers	340	W 2-0	Richards 4, Morford 49	16
36	15/4/10	BSN	H	Harrogate Town	270	L 0-1		16
37	17/4/10	BSN	A	Northwich Victoria	421	L 0-1		17
38	19/4/10	BSN	H	Corby Town	175	L 1-2	Molyneaux 90	17
39	21/4/10	BSN	A	Harrogate Town	142	D 1-1	Richards 89	17
40	24/4/10	BSN	H	Ilkeston Town	350	L 0-1		18
	Farsley Celtic record expunged 12/03							
3	15/8/09	BSN	H	Farsley Celtic	241	L 3-4	Smith 2 (pen 47, 65), Ellis 75	18
27	6/2/10	BSN	A	Farsley Celtic	275	W 1-0	Hunt 11	14
	Cups							
1	26/9/09	FAC 2Q	A	Bashley	287	W 2-1	Pitcher 22, Marshall 73	
2	10/10/09	FAC 3Q	A	Dorchester Town	498	W 2-1	Pitcher 67, Hamblin 71	
3	24/10/09	FAC 4Q	H	Lowestoft Town	539	D 1-1	Og (Crane) 70	
4	27/10/09	FAC 4QR	A	Lowestoft Town	2247	L 2-4	Smith pen 39, Webb 84	
5	24/11/09	FAT 3Q	A	Truro City	217	L 0-1		

Home Attendances:	
Highest:	617 v AFC Telford
Lowest:	175 v Corby Town
Average (08-09):	313 (283)

Top Goalscorer:	Smith - 17 (16 League, 1 Cup) in 45 appearances - 38% strike rate
Most Appearances:	Smith - 45 (40 League, 5 Cup)

GREEN	SYSUM	MARSHALL	MUSTOE	KITE	ROSE	SMITH	PALMER	MORFORD	SYMONS	J HARRIS	PITCHER	ROBINSON	ELLIS	JAMES	A HARRIS	WIXEY	TWYMAN	HAMBLIN	BALLINGER	SYKES	BALDWIN	WEBB	RICHARDS	SEAVILL	B PREECE	DIALLO	MONHON	MEHEW	HUNT	C PREECE	MCCLENNAN	REID	ALDRICH	MOLYNEUX	LAKE	O'HARA	PLUMMER	LEWIS	HAYNES	
X	X	X	X	X	X	X	X	X	X	X	S	S	S	U	U																									1
X	X		X	X	X	X	X	X	X	X	X	S	S	S	U																									2
X	S		X	X	X	X	U	X	X	X	X	S	X	U		S		X																					3
X		S	X	X	X	X	S	X	X	X	X	U	S					X	X	U																			4
X	X	X	U		X	X	S	S	X		U	S						X	X	X	X	X																	5
X	U	X	X		U	X	X	X	X		S	S						X	S	X	X	X																	6
X	S	X			X	X	U	X	X	S	S	X	U						X		X	X	X																7
X	U				X	X	X	S	X	X	X		S		U				X	S	X	X	X																8
X		X			U	X	X	S	X	X	X		S					S	U	X	X	X	X																9
X		X			X	X	U	X	X	X	S				U			X	U	U	X	X	X																10
X		U	X		X	X	U	X		U	X			U	U			X		X	X	X	X																11
X		X	X		X	X	U	X	X		X				U			X		S	S	X	X	S															12
X	U	X	X		X	X	X		X		S		S					X		S	X	X		X	U														13
X		S	X		X	X	X	X	X	X	S							X		S	U		X	X	U														14
X		S	X		X	X	X	X	X	X	S				U			X		S	U		X	X															15
X		X	X		X	X		S	X	X	X				U			X		U	U	X	X				U												16
X		X	X		X	X	S	U	X	X	X							X		S	S	X	X				U												17
X		X	X		X	X	U	S	X	X	X			U				X			S	X	X				U												18
X		X	X			X	X	S	X	X	X			U				X			X	X	S			U	S												19
X		X				X	X		X	X	X		S					X			X		X		U			U	X	S	S								20
X		X	X		X	X		U	X	X	S							X			U	X	X		U				X	U									21
X		X	X		X	X		S	X	X	X				U			X				X	X					U				S								22
X		X	X		X	X		S	X		X				U			X			U	X	X						X			S	S							23
X		U	X		U	X		S	X	X	X			U							X	X	X						X			S	X							24
X		U	X		X	X		S	X	X	S										U	X	X						X			U	X	X						25
X			X		X	X	S	U	X	X	X							U				X	X						X				S	X	S					26
X			S		U	X	X	X	S	X	S							X				X	X						X				X	U	X					27
X			X		X	X	U	S	X	X	S							S				X	X						X				U	X	X					28
X			X		X	X	S	S	X	X					U			X				X	X					U	X						X	S				29
X			X		X	X	S	X	S	X	U							X				X	X						X					U	X	S				30
X			X		X	X	X	U	X	X	S							X					X					U	X					S	X	S				31
X			X		X	X		X	X	X	S			U				X				X	X					U					U		U	X				32
X			X		X	X		X	X	X	S							X				X	X					U					U		S	X	S			33
X			X		X	X		X	X	X								X				X	X					U					U	U	U	X	U			34
X			X		X	X		X	X	X	S							X				X	X											U	U	S	X	S			35
			X		S	X		X	S	X								X				X	U											S	X	X	U	X	X	X	36
X			U		X	X		S	X	X	X							X				X	X											X	S	S	X	U			37
X			X		X	X		S	X	U	S							X					X					U					S	X	X	X	X			38
X			X		X	X		X		X	X							X					X					U					X	U	S	S	S		X	39
X			X		X	X		X	U	S				S				X					X					S					X	X	U	X	X			40
X	X		X	X	X	X	X	S	X	X	X		X	U	U	S	U																								
X			X		X	X	U	S	X	X	X							U				X	X						X			S	U	X							
X		X	S		X	X	S	X			X			U	U			X	X	S	X	X	X																	1
X		X	U		X	X	U	X	X	S	X				U			X		U	X	X	X																	2
X	S	X	X		X	X	X	X	X		S			U	U			X		X	S	U	X																	3
X	U	X	S		X	X	U	S	X		X				U			X	X	S	X	X	X																	4
X		S	X			X	X	X		X	X				U			X		X	X	X				S	S	U													5
																																								6
Total League Appearances																																								
39	3	16	32	4	33	40	12	20	34	31	18	1	1	0	0	0	0	31	4	4	11	29	31	3	0	0	0	0	11	0	0	0	6	6	7	7	3	1	2	X
0	2	3	1	0	1	0	6	14	3	2	16	5	7	2	0	1	0	2	1	6	3	0	1	1	0	0	1	1	0	1	1	3	4	2	5	4	3	0	0	S
0	3	3	2	0	4	0	7	4	1	2	2	1	1	7	11	0	0	1	2	3	6	0	1	0	4	1	3	9	0	1	0	1	5	5	3	1	2	0	0	U
Total Cup Appearances																																								
5	0	4	2	0	4	5	2	4	3	1	4	0	0	0	0	0	0	5	2	2	4	4	4	0	0	0	0	0	0	0	0	0	0	0	0	0	0	0	0	X
0	1	1	2	0	0	0	1	1	0	1	1	0	0	0	0	0	0	0	0	2	1	0	0	0	0	1	1	0	0	0	0	0	0	0	0	0	0	0	0	S
0	1	0	1	0	0	0	2	0	0	0	0	0	0	2	5	0	0	0	0	1	0	1	0	0	0	0	0	1	0	0	0	0	0	0	0	0	0	0	0	U
Total Goals																																								
0	0	1	0	0	1	16	0	3	7	4	2	0	0	0	0	0	0	2	1	1	0	0	5	0	0	0	0	0	3	0	0	0	0	0	0	0	0	0	0	Lge
0	0	1	0	0	0	1	0	0	0	0	2	0	0	0	0	0	0	1	0	0	0	1	0	0	0	0	0	0	0	0	0	0	0	0	0	0	0	0	0	Cup

GLOUCESTER CITY

CURRENT SQUAD AS OF BEGINING OF 2010-11 SEASON

GOALKEEPERS	HT	WT	D.O.B	AGE	P.O.B	CAREER	APPS	GOA
Ollie Hall			11/1/92	18		Gloucester		
Ben Lewis			2/5/90	20		Oldland Abbotonians, Gloucester (Dual) 4/10, Gloucester Perm c/s 10	1	0
Kevin Sawyer			14/4/80	30	Swindon	Cirencester, Salisbury 8/02, Cirencester Undisc 8/06, Gloucester 5/07, Weston-Super-Mare (L) 3/08, Weston-Super-Mare 5/09, Gloucester 6/10		
DEFENDERS								
Rob Aldrich			16/4/86	24		Leominster, Pegasus Juniors 3/04, Gloucester 12/09	10	0
Ollie Barnes			10/3/87	23		Bristol C Rel c/s 06, Bristol R 7/06 Rel c/s 07, Gloucester (L) 1/07, Salisbury 7/07 Rel 5/08, Team Bath (SL) 3/08, Worcester 7/08 Rel 4/09, Weymouth 8/09 Rel 8/09, Dorchester 9/09, Clevedon (2ML) 12/09, Gloucester 7/10		
Mike Green	5'09"	11 04	18/12/84	25	Gloucester	Southampton, Chippenham (L) 12/03 (L) 3/04, Forest Green 3/04 Rel 4/05, Cinderford c/s 05, Bath C 6/06, Clevedon (3ML) 8/07 Dual 11/07, Weston-Super-Mare 12/07, Gloucester 6/10		
Tom Hamblin	6'01"		15/9/86	23		Mangotsfield (Yth), Bristol Manor Farm, Gloucester 5/06	33	2
Neil Mustoe	5'09"	12 10	5/11/76	33	Gloucester	Man Utd, Wigan Undisc 1/98 Cambridge U 7/98 Rel c/s 02, Hartlepool (Trial) 7/01, Cambridge C (L) 9/01, Gloucester 8/02, Stevenage 1/03, Yeovil 2/03 Rel c/s 03, Gloucester 8/03 Temp Man 1/06	33	0
Ryan O'Hara	5'08"	08 13	24/7/89	21		Swindon (Yth), Dundee (Yth), Gretna Rel 3/08, Forest Green (Trial) 3/09, Swindon Supermarine 9/08, Salisbury 7/09, Gloucester 3/10	11	0
Tomaso Parrinello			10/7/89	21		Bristol R Rel 2/09, Weston-Super-Mare (2ML) 12/08, Weston-Super-Mare 2/09, Gloucester 6/10		
Brandon Preece			16/3/93	17		Gloucester, Cirencester 11/08, Gloucester 9/09	0	0
MIDFIELDERS								
Adie Harris			5/3/64	46		Gloucester (Ass Man)	0	0
Jack Harris			7/6/89	21	Bristol	Avonmouth, Hallen, Gloucester c/s 08	33	4
Brett James			10/9/91	18		Gloucester	2	0
Adam Mann						Shortwood, Gloucester		
Darren Mullings	6'01"	12 00	3/3/87	23	Bristol	Bristol R, Clevedon (L) 12/06, Torquay 6/07 Rel 5/08, Tiverton (L) 11/07, Weston-Super-Mare 8/08, Gloucester 7/10		
James Palmer	5'07"	11 04	30/3/88	22	Bristol	Bristol R, Weston-Super-Mare 1/08, Gloucester (L) 1/09, Gloucester 6/09	18	0
Callum Preece			16/3/93	17		Gloucester, Cirencester 11/08, Gloucester 9/09	1	0
Marc Richards			8/11/81	28		Cheltenham (Yth), Cinderford, Weston-Super-Mare, Swindon Supermarine 2/02, Cinderford 10/02, Cirencester 7/03, Gloucester 3/07, Chippenham 8/08, Gloucester 10/08	32	5
Matt Rose			3/5/76	34	Cheltenham	Cheltenham, St Marks, Moreton T, Cirencester, Gloucester 8/99, Newport C 3/00, Weston-Super-Mare 4 fig 10/03, Gloucester 6/07	34	1
Cody Truchan			14/9/91	18		Gloucester		
Jack Twyman			19/9/91	18		Gloucester	0	0
Tom Webb			2/5/84	26		Luton (Yth), Gloucester 7/00, Viney St Swithins (L), Highworth T (L), Yate T (L) 8/09	29	0
FORWARDS								
James Hix							Gloucester	
David Mehew			29/10/67	42		Gloucester (Man)	1	0
Will Morford			28/4/86	24		Staunton & Corse, Tuffley Rovers, Slimbridge, Gloucester 10/07	34	3
Michael Symons			22/7/86	24	Gloucester	Ilfracombe, Barnstaple 7/04, Slimbridge (Dual) 12/04, Bideford 9/05, Cirencester 1/06, Clevedon T 3/07, Forest Green 8/08, Gloucester (L) 8/08, Gloucester (SL) 2/09, Gloucester 5/09	37	7

Loanees	HT	WT	DOB	AGE	POB	From - To	APPS	GOA
(G)Mike Green	6'01"	13 01	23/7/89	21	Bristol	Bristol R (SL) 7/09 -	39	0
(D)Alex Kite	6'00"	12 05	7/3/89	21	Kent	Bristol R 7/09 - Paulton R (L) 11/09, Chippenham (L) 1/10	4	0
(F)Ben Hunt			23/1/90	20		Bristol R (3ML) 12/09 - Newport C (L) 3/10, Dover 7/10	11	3
(M)Joe McClennan			11/6/91	19		Bristol C 12/09 - Warrington, Yate T 3/10	1	0
(F)Neikell Plummer			6/6/91	19		Bristol R 3/10 -	6	0
(D)Kyle Haines	5'11"	11 02	29/12/91	18	Wolverhampton	Cheltenham 3/10 -	2	0

Departures	HT	WT	DOB	AGE	POB	From - To	APPS	GOA
(F)Luke Ballinger			26/2/88	22	Bath	Mangotsfield 6/08 - Frome (Dual) 10/09	5	1
(D)Nelson Monhon			6/9/90	19		Minehead 11/09 - Salisbury 12/09	1	0
(M)Alex Sykes			2/4/74	36	Newcastle u Lyme	Bath C 6/06 - Bishops Cleeve (Pl/Ass Man) 12/09	10	1
(D)Lee Marshall			20/5/88	22		Paulton 6/08 - Paulton 2/10	19	1
(F)Jack Pitcher			13/6/83	27	Bristol	Clevedon T 5/07 - Rel 5/10, Mangotsfield 6/10	34	2
(F)Lee Smith			8/9/83	26	Coney Hill	Weston-Super-Mare 9/07 - Forest Green 6/10	40	16
(D)Lee Molyneux	6'00"	11 05	16/1/83	27	Portsmouth	Evesham 2/10 - Rel 6/10	8	0
(G)Danny Holdcroft			22/5/78	32	Chester	Larkhall 7/09 -		
(D)James Baldwin			14/5/89	21		Forest Green 8/09 - Banbury U (Cover) 1/10	14	0
(D)Greg Lake			5/10/88	21		Frome T 2/10 -	12	0
(D)Matt Sysum			29/8/89	21		Yth - Cirencester (L) 10/09	5	0
(M)Sam Ellis			10/1/90	20		Yth -	8	0
(M)Eddie Jones			6/6/91	19		Yth -		
(M)Jamie Reid			20/4/88	22	Gloucester	Yth - Cirencester 10/08, Gloucester 1/10	3	0
(M)Sam Robinson			2/9/89	20		Woking 8/09 - Cinderford (L) 9/09	6	0
(M)Dan Wixey			21/6/90	20		Yth -	1	0
(F)Nabi Diallo			27/12/90	19		Minehead 11/09 -	0	0
(F)Curtis Russell			7/4/92	18		Viney Hill 8/09 -		
(F)Shaun Seavill			24/9/86	23		Chippenham 10/09 -	4	0

GUISELEY

Chairman: Philip Rogerson
Secretary: Adrian Towers — **(T)** 07946 388 739 — **(E)** admin@guiseleyafc.co.uk

Additional Committee Members:
P.Rogerson, S Allen, S Parkin, J Gill, G Douglas, Bruce Speller, Keith Hanvey

Manager: Steve Kittrick
Programme Editor: Rachel O'Connor — **(E)** rachel.o@wharfedalenewspapers.co.uk

Back Row (L-R): Steve Kittrick (Manager), Wayne Benn (Asst Manager), Danny Ellis, Steve Burton, Ryan Crossley, Piotr Skiba, Lee Crooks, Tom Morgan, James Hanson, Danny Husband, Lee Pugh, Mark Whitehouse, Damian Dunne, Jordan Yorath, Martin Stringfellow (Physio).
Front Row: David Brown, Adam Muller, Alex Callery, Bailey Camfield, Dave Merris, Anthony Lloyd, Dean Walters, Brice Tianai, James Cotterill. (Archive Photo)

Club Factfile

Founded: 1909 **Nickname:** The Lions
Previous Names:
Previous Leagues: Wharfedale, Leeds, West Riding Counties, West Yorkshire, Yorkshire 1968-82, Northern Counties East 1982-91, Northern Premier 1991-2010

Club Colours (change): White/navy/navy (Yellow/blue/blue)

Ground: Nethermoor Park, Otley Road, Guiseley, Leeds LS20 8BT **(T)** 01943 873 223 (Office) 872 872 (Club)
Capacity: 3,000 **Seats:** 427 **Covered:** 1,040 **Clubhouse:** Yes **Shop:** Yes
Previous Grounds:
Simple Directions
From the West M62, M606 then follow signs to A65 through Guiseley to Ground on Right. From South and East M1 and M621 towards Leeds City Centre. Continue on M621 to Junction 2, follow Headingly Stadium signs to A65 towards Ilkley then as above. From North West From Skipton, A65 Ilkley, via Burley By-pass A65 towards Leeds, Ground quarter of a mile on left after Harry Ramsden's roundabout From North/NE A1M, leave at A59, towards Harrogate, then A658 signed Leeds Bradford Airport, at Pool turn right onto A659 Otley, continue towards Bradford/Leeds, to Harry Ramsden roundabout then A65 Leeds ground quarter of a mile on left.

Record Attendance: 2,486 v Bridlington Town - FA Vase Semi-final 1st Leg 1989-90
Record Victory: Not known
Record Defeat: Not known
Record Goalscorer: Not known
Record Appearances: Not known
Additional Records:

Senior Honours: Northern Counties East 1990-91. FA Vase 1990-91.
Northern Premier League Division 1 1993-94, Premier Division 2009-10, Challenge Cup 2008-09.

10 YEAR RECORD

00-01	01-02	02-03	03-04	04-05	05-06	06-07	07-08	08-09	09-10
NP 1 17	NP 1 11	NP 1 14	NP 1 9	NP P 10	NP P 14	NP P 6	NP P 6	NP P 3	NP P 1

GUISELEY

No.	Date	Comp	H/A	Opponents	Att:	Result	Goalscorers	Pos
1	Aug 15	Northern P.	H	Matlock Town	305	W 2 - 0	Muller 52 Cotterill 89	4
2	19		A	Whitby Town	361	W 2 - 1	Lloyd 20 Walshaw 90	
3	22		A	Ashton United	123	L 2 - 3	Walshaw 16 McIntosh 33	5
4	25		H	Ossett Town	240	D 1 - 1	Cotterill 83	5
5	29		H	Boston United	429	L 1 - 3	Lloyd 44 (pen)	
6	31		A	Marine	307	W 1 - 0	McMahon 45 (og)	
7	**Sept 12**	**F.A.C. 1Q**	**H**	**Whitley Bay**	**301**	**W 2 - 0**	**Burton 12 Fitzgerald 52**	
8	15		H	Nantwich Town	233	W 1 - 0	Reeves 53	
9	19		A	F.C.United	2106	W 2 - 1	Needham 22 27	4
10	22		A	Burscough	209	W 4 - 0	Ellis 9 Tuck 18 20 Lee 35	3
11	**26**	**F.A.C 2Q**	**H**	**Bamber Bridge**	**298**	**W 2 - 0**	**Needham 43 72**	
12	Oct 3		H	Worksop Town	276	L 1 - 2	Burton 64	5
13	**10**	**F.A.C 3Q**	**H**	**Kendal Town**	**405**	**D 1 - 1**	**Tuck 24**	
14	**13**	**F.A.C. 3Qr**	**A**	**Kendal Town**	**333**	**L 0 - 1**		
15	**17**	**F.A.T 1Q**	**A**	**Cammell Laird**	**101**	**W 3 - 0**	**Needham 37 Singh 39 Burton 82**	
16	24		A	Durham City	130	W 3 - 2	Needham 19 Tuck 41 Walshaw 60	5
17	27		A	Retford United	281	W 2 - 0	Tuck 5 Burton 74	5
18	**31**	**F.A.T 2Q**	**A**	**Frickley Athletic**	**254**	**W 3 - 0**	**Walshaw 43 76 Lloyd 85 (pen)**	
19	Nov 14		A	Kendal Town	277	L 1 - 2	Bentham 90	9
20	**21**	**F.A.T 3Q**	**H**	**F.C.Halifax**	**919**	**W 3 - 1**	**Walshaw 57 Bett 70 78**	
21	Dec 8		H	North Ferriby United	172	L 2 - 3	Ainge 16 Walshaw 49	9
22	**12**	**F.A.T 1**	**H**	**Redditch United**	**245**	**W 1 - 0**	**Ellis 62**	
23	15		H	Hucknall Town	135	W 3 - 0	Walshaw 5 Shiels 16 (og) Burton 27	
24	**Jan 12**	**F.A.T 2**	**A**	**Blyth Spartans**	**380**	**W 2 - 1**	**Burton 35 Fitzgerald 75**	
25	23		A	Worksop Town	184	W 3 - 1	Muller 21 Needham 50 Burton 55	7
26	25		H	Buxton	236	W 3 - 1	Walshaw 18 (pen) 45 Muller 79	
27	Feb 6		A	North Ferriby United	195	D 1 - 1	Walshaw 89	5
28	13		H	Stocksbridge P.S.	305	W 3 - 1	Walshaw 8 (pen) Muller 32 Holland 61	6
29	16		H	Whitby Town	190	W 3 - 1	Cotterill 4 Muller 49 Kamara 90	
30	20		A	Buxton	312	L 1 - 3	Walshaw 53 (pen)	5
31	27		H	Durham City	296	W 2 - 0	Needham 49 Holland 60	5
32	Mar 2		H	Kendal Town	275	W 1 - 0	Steel 54 (og)	
33	6		A	Nantwich Town	331	W 2 - 0	Walshaw 9 82(pen)	4
34	9		H	Burscough	239	W 2 - 1	Walshaw 18 39	
35	13		A	Hucknall Town	228	W 1 - 0	Askham 22	
36	20		H	Retford Town	421	D 1 - 1	Walshaw 53 (pen)	3
37	23		A	Stocksbridge Park Steels	178	W 4 - 2	Needham 17 80 Johnson 63 Walshaw 68	
23	27		H	F.C.United	841	W 2 - 0	Walshaw 11 (pen) Johnson 60	2
39	April 2		A	Ossett Town	265	W 4 - 1	Walshaw 18 Muller 40 Johnson 43 Rudd 61	
40	5		H	Bradford P.A.	1299	W 2 - 1	Walshaw 35 (pen) 66	
41	7		A	Bradford P.A.	909	W 4 - 2	Muller 12 Walshaw 38 (pen) 45 Merris 90	1
42	10		A	Boston United	1604	L 1 - 2	Walshaw 29 (pen)	1
43	13		A	Matlock Town	304	L 1 - 2	Johnson 65	
44	17		H	Marine	557	L 0 - 2		2
45	20		A	Frickley Athletic	292	W 2 - 1	Walshaw 18 (pen) 55 (pen)	
46	24		H	Ashton United	485	W 2 - 0	Walshaw 43 88	1
					Goals	90 45		

Home Attendances:	
Highest:	1299 v Bradford Park Avenue
Lowest:	135 v Hucknall Town
Average (08-09):	384 (408)
Top Goalscorer:	Walshaw - 30 (League 27 (11 Penalties), FAT 3)

GUISELEY

CURRENT SQUAD AS OF BEGINING OF 2010-11 SEASON

GOALKEEPERS	HT	WT	D.O.B	AGE	P.O.B	CAREER	APPS	GOA
Jon Worsnop			13/1/83	27	Bradford	Bradford (Sch), Chester 7/02 Rel c/s 03, Aberystwyth 7/03, Droylsden 5/04, Leigh RMI 2/05, Droylsden c/s 05, Mossley (L) 9/05, Bradford PA (L) 11/05, Witton (L) 3/06, Witton c/s 06, Ossett T Undisc 11/06, Bradford PA 3/07 Rel 5/09, Guiseley 6/09		
DEFENDERS								
Simon Ainge	6'01"	12 02	18/2/88	22	Shipley	Bradford C Rel c/s 09, Halifax (SL) 1/08, Cambridge U (SL) 3/09, Bradford PA c/s 09, Guiseley (L) 11/09 Perm 12/09		
James Cotterill	5'11"	12 04	3/8/82	28	Barnsley	Scunthorpe Rel c/s 03, Barrow 8/03 Rel 12/06, Ossett T 2/07, Guiseley 1/08		
Danny Ellis	6'00"	12 00	23/11/85	24	Bradford	Bradford C Rel c/s 06, Guiseley c/s 06		
Jez Fitzgerald			15/11/78	31		Morecambe (Yth), Darwen, Rossendale, Stalybridge 7/02, Accrington 3/04, Southport 5/04, Fleetwood 6/06, Leigh Genesis 6/08, Guiseley 11/08		
Jake McEneaney	5'11"	09 06	6/1/92	18	Skipton	Burnley Rel c/s 10, Guiseley 7/10		
Dave Merris	5'07"	10 06	13/10/80	29	Rotherham	Rotherham (Scholar), Guiseley 7/98, Harrogate T 9/99, York 8/03 Rel 5/06, Harrogate T 6/06, Guiseley 3/08		
Dave Syers			30/11/87	22		Ossett A, Harrogate T 3/09, Farsley Celtic 6/09, Harrogate T 3/10, Guiseley 7/10		
MIDFIELDERS								
Craig Bentham	5'09"	11 06	7/3/85	25	Bradford	Bradford C Rel 4/08, Farsley Celtic (3ML) 1/08, Farsley Celtic 6/08 Rel 7/09, Guiseley c/s 09		
David Briggs			27/4/84	26	Wakefield	Ossett T, Guiseley 2/09		
Chris Holland	5'09"	11 05	11/9/75	34	Whalley	Preston, Newcastle £100,000 1/94, Birmingham (2ML) 9/96 £600,000 10/96, Huddersfield £150,000 2/00, Boston U 3/04, Southport 1/07, Leigh Genesis 7/08, Fleetwood 11/08, Burscough 3/09, Guiseley 7/09		
Paddy Lauber	6'00"					Great Harwood, Rossendale, Clitheroe, Darwen, Padiham, Guiseley 1/10		
Liam Needham	5'11"	12 02	19/10/85	24	Sheffield	Sheff Wed Rel c/s 05, Notts County (Trial) 8/05, Gainsborough 8/05, Notts County 11/05 Rel 12/06, Gainsborough (L) 11/06, Gainsborough 12/06 Rel 5/09, Guiseley c/s 09		
Tom Penford	5'10"	11 03	5/1/85	25	Leeds	Bradford C Rel 5/08, Farsley Celtic 6/08 Rel c/s 09, FC Halifax 10/09, Guiseley 7/10		
Warren Peyton	5'09"	11 03	13/12/79	29	Manchester	Bolton, Rochdale 10/99 Rel c/s 00, Bury 9/00, Nuneaton 7/01, Doncaster 12/02, Leigh RMI 7/03 Rel c/s 05, Altrincham 11/05 Rel 5/09, Stalybridge 6/09, Guiseley 6/10		
Gavin Rothery	5'09"	10 10	22/9/87	22	Leeds	Leeds Rel 4/08, York C 10/08 (08/09 1,0), Harrogate T 12/08, Carlisle 3/09 Rel c/s 10, Barrow (6WL) 11/09 (09/10 2,0)		
Ryan Toulson			18/11/85	24		Halifax, Stocksbridge (L) 9/05, Altrincham (SL) 1/08, Harrogate T 6/08, Gainsborough 5/09, Guiseley 5/10		
Matt Young	5'08"	11 03	25/10/85	24	Leeds	Huddersfield Rel c/s 08, Harrogate T 7/08 Rel c/s 09, Farsley Celtic c/s 09, Guiseley 3/10		
FORWARDS								
Steve Burton	6'01"	12 11	9/10/83	26	Doncaster	Ipswich Rel 1/03, Boston U (2ML) 8/02, Doncaster 3/03 Rel c/s 04, Scarborough 6/04, Leigh RMI (L) 10/04, Canvey Island (L) 2/05, Crawley 3/05, Tamworth 8/06, Kettering 6/07, Harrogate T 12/07, Guiseley 6/08		
Simon Johnson	5'09"	11 09	9/3/83	27	West Bromwich	Leeds Rel 6/05, Hull C (2ML) 12/02, Blackpool (L) 12/03, Sunderland (6WL) 9/04, Doncaster (2ML) 12/04, Barnsley (SL) 2/05, Darlington 7/05 Rel c/s 07, Bradford C (Trial) 7/07, Hereford 8/07 Rel 4/09, Bury 8/09, Halesowen T 10/09 Rel 2/10, Burton (Trial) 2		
Joe O'Neill	6'00"	10 05	28/10/82	27	Blackburn	Preston, Bury (SL) 7/03, Mansfield (3ML) 8/04, Chester (3ML) 1/05, York 7/05 Rel 5/06, Altrincham 6/06 Rel 5/09, Stalybridge 6/09, Guiseley 6/10		
Darryn Stamp	6'01"	11 10	21/9/78	30	Beverley	Hessle, Scunthorpe 7/97 Rel c/s 01, Halifax (L) 2/00, Scarborough (L) 3/01, Scarborough 5/01, Northampton £30,000 5/02, Chester 8/03, Kidderminster (L) 11/04, Stevenage 1/05, York C (3ML) 10/06, Halifax 1/07, Northwich (SL) 3/08, Northwich 8/08, Gateshead (SL) 3/09, Gainsborough 6/09 Rel c/s 10, Guiseley 7/10		
James Walshaw			12/2/84	26		Ossett T, Lincoln C (Trial) 11/05, Bradford PA 3/07, Ossett T, Leek T 3/08 Farsley Celtic 7/08, Wakefield 11/08, Guiseley 3/09		

Do you remember when...

Guiseley

In the 1991-92 season Guiseley finished in Fourth place in the H.F.S. Loans League (N.P.L.) Division One with Mark Tennison scoring 24.

Back row, left to right: David Heely (Coach), Billy Roberts, Phil Wilson, D.Morgan, Paul Maxted, Mark Tennison, Allan Roberts, Bob Colville and Gordon Raynor (Manager)
Front Row: Ian Noteman, Michael Nagey, Vince Brockie, C. Hogarth, Richard Annan and Peter Atkinson.

HARROGATE TOWN

Chairman: Bill Fotherby
Secretary: Alan Williams (T) 0787 928 1207
(E) harrogatetown@unicombox.co.uk
Additional Committee Members: Andrew Thurkill, Brian Russell, Bernard Fotherby, Howard Matthews, George Dunnington
Manager: Simon Weaver
Programme Editor: Peter Arnett (E) peterarnett@btinternet.com

Club Factfile

Founded: 1919 **Nickname:** Town
Previous Names:
Previous Leagues: West Riding 1919-20, Yorkshire 1920-21, 22-31, 57-82, Midland 1921-22, Northern 1931-32, Harrogate & Dist. 1935-37, 40-46, W. Riding Co.Am. 1937-40, W. Yorks. 1946-57, N.C.E. 1982-87, N.P.L. 1987-2004
Club Colours (change): Yellow and black/black/black (Pink & black/white/pink)

Ground: The CNG Stadium, Wetherby Road, Harrogate HG2 7SA (T) 01423 883 671
Capacity: 3,291 **Seats:** 502 **Covered:** 1,300 **Clubhouse:** Yes **Shop:** Yes
Previous Grounds:
Simple Directions
A61 to Harrogate, turn right on to A658, and at roundabout take A661, proceed through second set of lights (Woodlands pub) ground approx. 500 mtrs on the right. From A1 Wetherby. Leave A1 at Wetherby on to A661 to Harrogate. Stay on this road and when reaching Harrogate at Woodland pub lights, ground 500mtrs on the right.

Record Attendance: 4,280 v Railway Athletic - Whitworth Cup Final 1950
Record Victory: 13-0 v Micklefield
Record Defeat: 1-10 v Methley United - 1956
Record Goalscorer: Jimmy Hague - 135 (1956-58 and 1961-76)
Record Appearances: Paul Williamson - 428 (1980-81, 1982-85, and 1986-93)
Additional Records:

Senior Honours: West Riding County Cup 1962-63, 72-73, 85-86. Northern Premier League Division 1 2001-02.
West Riding Challenge Cup x2.

10 YEAR RECORD

00-01	01-02	02-03	03-04	04-05	05-06	06-07	07-08	08-09	09-10
NP 1 11	NP 1 1	NP P 6	NP P 5	Conf N 6	Conf N 5	Conf N 6	Conf N 6	Conf N 9	Conf N 21

HARROGATE TOWN

No.	Date	Comp	H/A	Opponents	Att:	Result	Goalscorers	Pos
1	8/8/09	BSN	A	Corby Town	505	L 0-3		20
2	11/8/09	BSN	H	Vauxhall Motors	327	W 3-0	Maloney 3, McTiernan 31, Woodhouse 68	11
3	15/8/09	BSN	H	Eastwood Town	432	L 0-1		13
4	18/8/09	BSN	A	Workington	410	D 1-1	Dutton 70	14
5	22/8/09	BSN	H	Solihull Moors	272	L 0-1		15
6	29/8/09	BSN	A	Southport	708	L 1-3	Coleman 44	19
7	31/8/09	BSN	H	Hyde United	303	W 2-0	Coleman 11, Broadbent 76	14
8	5/9/09	BSN	A	AFC Telford	1577	L 1-2	Dutton 76	15
9	7/9/09	BSN	A	Droylsden	376	L 0-5		19
10	12/9/09	BSN	H	Redditch United	233	W 3-2	Sturdy 18, Harrison 21, Coleman 39	15
11	19/9/09	BSN	H	Stafford Rangers	339	L 1-4	Dutton 75	20
12	3/10/09	BSN	A	Northwich Victoria	536	L 2-3	Benjamin 2 (48, 49)	19
13	10/10/09	BSN	H	Droylsden	348	D 2-2	McTiernan 2, Benjamin 90	19
14	17/10/09	BSN	H	Alfreton Town	401	L 0-4		20
15	24/10/09	BSN	A	Solihull Moors	204	L 0-1		21
16	31/10/09	BSN	A	Redditch United	365	L 0-2		22
17	10/11/09	BSN	A	Fleetwood Town	812	D 2-2	Coleman 2 (62, 89)	22
18	14/11/09	BSN	A	Gainsborough Trinity	421	D 1-1	Leabon 73	22
19	28/11/09	BSN	H	Ilkeston Town	328	L 0-1		22
20	5/12/09	BSN	A	Eastwood Town	326	L 0-1		22
21	19/1/10	BSN	H	Hinckley United	142	W 3-1	Knox 2 (62, 88), Bradley 83	21
22	23/1/10	BSN	A	Stafford Rangers	525	L 0-1		21
23	6/2/10	BSN	A	Alfreton Town	399	L 1-3	Nowakowski 62	21
24	9/2/10	BSN	A	Blyth Spartans	407	L 0-1		22
25	13/2/10	BSN	H	Gainsborough Trinity	310	W 2-0	James 20, Muirhead 48	22
26	16/2/10	BSN	A	Vauxhall Motors	178	W 2-1	Knox 31, Yeo 34	20
27	20/2/10	BSN	H	AFC Telford	438	L 0-3		21
28	6/3/10	BSN	H	Stalybridge Celtic	365	L 0-4		22
29	13/3/10	BSN	A	Stalybridge Celtic	454	L 0-3		21
30	20/3/10	BSN	H	Fleetwood Town	431	L 0-1		21
31	23/3/10	BSN	H	Workington	201	L 1-2	Cahill pen 10	21
32	27/3/10	BSN	A	Ilkeston Town	304	D 3-3	Stamer 23, Ellington 2 (26, 79)	21
33	3/4/10	BSN	H	Southport	458	L 2-3	Syers 7, Radcliffe 90	21
34	5/4/10	BSN	A	Hyde United	356	L 0-1		21
35	10/4/10	BSN	H	Blyth Spartans	287	L 2-5	Ellington 6, Syers 48	21
36	13/4/10	BSN	H	Corby Town	206	L 0-4		21
37	15/4/10	BSN	A	Gloucester City	270	W 1-0	Knox 18	21
38	17/4/10	BSN	A	Hinckley United	424	L 2-3	Ellington 37, Syers 80	21
39	21/4/10	BSN	H	Gloucester City	142	D 1-1	Syers 77	21
40	24/4/10	BSN	H	Northwich Victoria	247	W 2-1	Syers 2 (9, 56)	21
	Farsley Celtic record expunged 12/03							
23	26/1/10	BSN	A	Farsley Celtic	315	L 1-2	Sturdy 68	21
	Cups							
1	26/9/09	FAC 2Q	A	Bradford Park Avenue	375	L 0-4		
2	21/11/09	FAT 3Q	A	FC United of Manchester	1166	W 3-2	James 15, Coleman 24, Nowakowski 52	
3	12/12/09	FAT 1	A	Gateshead	302	D 1-1	Dutton 80	
4	15/12/09	FAT 1R	H	Gateshead	160	L 0-2		

Home Attendances:	
Highest:	458 v Southport
Lowest:	142 v Gloucester City
Average (08-09):	319 (375)
Top Goalscorer:	Coleman - 6 (5 League, 1 Cup) in 11 appearances - 55% strike rate
Most Appearances:	Bloomer - 43 (40 League, 3 Cup)

	LAMB	HARRISON	SCOTT	WOODHOUSE	WEAVER	BLOOMER	BURRELL	MCTIERNAN	MALONEY	RYAN	DURHAM	EMMS	BROADBENT	HERNANDEZ	WOOD	DUTTON	STURDY	THOMAS	COLEMAN	CHAPMAN	DUNNING	HARWOOD	BENJAMIN	JAMESON	JAMES	NOWAKOWSKI	RATCHFORD	LEABON	IVANOV	GHAICHEM	YEO	FOSTER	KNOX	GREGORY	MUIRHEAD	BRADLEY	CAHILL	RADCLIFFE	SHEPHERD	STAMER	SYERS	ELLINGTON	
	X	X	X	X	X	X	X	X	X	X	X	S	S	U	U																												1
	X	X	X	X	X	X	S	X	X	S	X	X	S	U		X	U																										2
	X	X	X		X	X	X	X	X	S	X	X	S	U		X	U																										3
	X	X	X	X	X	X	U	X	X	S	X	X	U	U	U	X																											4
	X	X	X	X	X	X	S	X	X	X		X	S	U		X	U	S																									5
	X	X	X		X	X			X	X	X	X	U	U	S	X	U		X																								6
	U	X	X		X	X	S	X	U		S		X	X	X	X	X	U	X																								7
	U	X	U	X	X	X	S	X	S		S		X	X	X	X	X		X																								8
	U	X	X		X	X	S	X	X	S	X	S	U	X	X		X	X																									9
	U	X			X	X	X	X	X	U	S		U	X	X	X	X	U	X																								10
	U	X			X	X	X	X	X	U	S	S		X	X	X	X	S	X																								11
		X		X	S	X		X		S	S	U		X	X	X				X	X	X	X																				12
		X		X	X	X	S	X	S	X		S		U	U					X	X	X	X	X																			13
		X		X	X	X	S	X		X					S	S			X		X	X	X	X																			14
		X				X	S	S	S	X			U	U	X	X			X	X	X	X	X	X																			15
		X		S		X		X	X	S				U		X			X	X	U		X	X	X	X																	16
		X		X		X			X	S			X	U	X	X			S	X	S				X	U	X	X															17
		X		X		X		S	X	U			S	U	X	X			X	X	S				X		X	X															18
		X				X		X	X				X	U	X	S				X	U				X	X	X	X	S	S													19
		X		X		X		S		X			X	U	X	X				X	U				X	X	X		U	S													20
						X			X					U	U		X				X				X	X	X			U	S	X	X	X	X	S							21
						X			X					U			X			U	U				X	X	X			S	S	X	X	X	X	X							22
		X				X								U	X		X			X	U				X	S	X			U	S	X	X	X	X								23
		S				X		S	X					U	U		X				X				X	X	X				S	X	X	X	X								24
		S				X		U	X				S	U			X				X				X	X	X			U	X	X	X		X								25
		X				X		S	X				U	U			X				X				X		X			U	X	X	X	S	X								26
		X				X		S	X					U	U		X				X				X	X	X			S	X		X	S	X								27
		X				X			X				S	U	S		X				X				X		X				X			X	X	S	X						28
		U				X			X				X	U			X				X				X	X	X				S			S		S	X	X	X				29
		S				X			X				U	U			X				S				X	X	X				U	X		X				X	X	X			30
		X				X							U	U			X				U				X	S	X				U	X	X				X		X	X	X		31
		U				X								U			X				S				X	X	X					X	S				X	X	S	X	X	X	32
		U				X								X			X				U				X	X	U					X	S				S	X	X	X	X	X	33
		U				X								X			X				X				X	X	U					X	S			U	S		X	X	X	X	34
		U				X								X			X				X				X	X	U					X	U				X	U	X	S	X	X	35
		S				X			U								X				X				X	X	X					X	S				X	X	U	S	X	X	36
					U	X		U	X	U				X							X				X	X						X	X				S		X	U	X	X	37
					U	X		X	X	S				X							X					X	U					X	X				S		X		X	X	38
		U				X		U	X	S				U			X				S					X	X					X	X				X		X		X	X	39
		X				X		U	X	U				X			X									X	U					X	S				X	U	X		X	X	40
						X			X					U			X			U	S				X	X	X			U	S	X	X	X	X	X							
		X	X	X	X	U		X		S	S	X	U	X	X	X		S																									1
		X				X		X	X	X			X	U	X				X	X	S				X	S	X		S														2
		X		X		X		X					U	U	X	X				X	S				X	S	X		S	X	X												3
		X		X		X		X	X	S				U	X	X				X	S					S	X		U	X	X												4
Total League Appearances																																											
	6	26	8	11	13	40	4	16	26	7	6	5	6	12	12	15	23	1	9	9	16	4	5	4	22	19	18	3	0	0	4	17	11	6	8	1	8	5	10	5	10	9	X
	0	4	0	1	1	0	8	6	3	9	5	4	7	0	3	2	0	2	1	0	5	0	0	0	0	2	0	0	1	4	5	0	5	3	0	3	4	0	1	2	0	0	S
	5	6	1	0	2	0	1	4	2	5	0	1	8	26	6	0	4	2	0	1	7	0	0	0	0	1	5	0	1	4	2	0	1	0	0	1	0	2	1	1	0	0	U
Total Cup Appearances																																											
	0	4	1	3	1	3	0	4	2	1	0	1	1	1	4	3	0	0	1	3	0	0	0	0	2	0	3	0	0	2	2	0	0	0	0	0	0	0	0	0	0	0	X
	0	0	0	0	0	0	0	0	0	2	1	0	0	0	0	0	0	1	0	0	3	0	0	0	0	3	0	0	2	0	0	0	0	0	0	0	0	0	0	0	0	0	S
	0	0	0	0	0	1	0	0	0	0	0	0	2	3	0	0	0	0	0	0	0	0	0	0	0	0	0	0	1	0	0	0	0	0	0	0	0	0	0	0	0	0	U
Total Goals																																											
	0	1	0	1	0	0	0	2	1	0	0	0	1	0	1	3	1	0	5	0	0	0	3	0	1	1	0	1	0	0	0	0	4	0	1	1	1	1	0	1	6	4	Lge
	0	0	0	0	0	0	0	0	0	0	0	0	0	0	0	1	0	0	1	0	0	0	0	0	1	1	0	0	0	0	0	0	0	0	0	0	0	0	0	0	0	0	Cup

Also Played: GENT U(1), S(3,6). HOLMES X(Cup1). KNOWLES X(Cup1). WILLIAMS U(12) U(Cup1). REID S(16) U(Cup1,2). NAYLOR U(28,38).

HARROGATE TOWN

CURRENT SQUAD AS OF BEGINING OF 2010-11 SEASON

GOALKEEPERS	HT	WT	D.O.B	AGE	P.O.B	CAREER	APPS	GOA
Craig Dootson	6'04"	14 02	23/5/79	31	Preston	Preston (Yth), Morecambe, Bamber Bridge, Leigh RMI £4,000 7/00, Bradford PA (2ML) 10/01, Stalybridge 5/02, Bury 7/05 Rel 5/06, Hinckley (L) 1/06, Hyde 6/06, Alfreton 5/09, Fleetwood 11/09 Rel 5/10, Harrogate T 6/10		
Stephen Hernandez			17/8/89	21	Doncaster	Sheff Wed (Scholar), Sheff Utd Rel 7/09, Worksop (L) 9/07, Worksop (SL) 1/08, Harrogate T 8/09	12	0
DEFENDERS								
Matt Bloomer	6'00"	13 00	3/11/78	31	Grimsby	Grimsby Rel c/s 01, Hull C (Trial) 4/01, Hull C 7/01, Lincoln C (L) 3/02, Telford (3ML) 8/02, Lincoln C 12/02 Rel 5/06, Grimsby (L) 1/06, Cambridge U (2ML) 3/06, Cambridge U 7/06 Rel 1/07, Grimsby 1/07 Rel c/s 07, Boston U 7/07, Harrogate T 6/09	40	0
Simon Harrison	5'09"	10 08	24/12/88	21	Nether Edge	Rotherham, Matlock 8/08, Ilkeston 1/09, Harrogate T 6/09	30	1
Craig James	6'00"	13 00	15/11/82	27	Middlesbrough	Sunderland, Hibernian (SL) 8/02, Darlington (2ML) 11/03, Port Vale (L) 3/04 Undisc 4/04 Rel 5/06, Darlington 7/06, York C (SL) 3/07, Livingston 8/07 Rel c/s 08, Barrow 9/08 Rel 10/08, Darlington (Trial) 7/09, Harrogate T NC 10/09	22	1
Richard Pell			17/11/82	27	Boston	Notts Forest (Jun), York C (Ass Sch), Lincoln, USA, Boston T 7/99, Chesterfield (Trial), Gainsborough 8/04, Blyth 5/08 Rel 5/09, Alfreton 5/09, Byth Undisc 12/09, Harrogate T 6/10		
Josh Radcliffe			9/6/90	20		York C Rel 5/09, Harrogate RA (L) 10/08, Farsley Celtic 7/09, Harrogate T 3/10	5	1
Dominic Roma	5'10"	11 11	29/11/85	24	Sheffield	Sheff Utd Rel c/s 07, Boston U (L) 2/05, Notts County (Trial) 7/05, Tamworth (SL) 2/06, Hinckley U 7/07, Alfreton 5/09, Harrogate T 6/10		
Simon Weaver	6'01"	10 08	20/12/77	32	Doncaster	Sheff Wed Rel c/s 98, Doncaster (L) 2/97, Ilkeston, Grimsby (Trial) c/s 99, Nuneaton 2/00, Lincoln C 8/02, Macclesfield (2ML) 10/04, Kidderminster 12/04 Rel c/s 05, Scarborough 6/05 Rel 5/06, York C 8/06 Rel 8/06, Tamworth 8/06 Rel c/s 07, Salisbury (Trial) c/s 07, Boston U 12/07 Rel 5/08, Kings Lynn 5/08 Rel 1/09, Redditch 1/09, Ilkeston 2/09, Harrogate T (Pl/Man) 5/09	14	0
Michael Wood			13/1/90	20		Boston U, Harrogate T 8/09, Frickley (L) 2/10	15	1
MIDFIELDERS								
Steve Bowey	5'08"		10/7/74	36	Durham	Forest Green, Bristol R Rel (96/97), Gateshead, Q.o.South 2/02, York 6/06, Rel 5/07, Gateshead 5/07, Newcastle Blue Star 6/08 (Pl/Man 8/08), Bedlington 6/09, Ayr Utd 2/10, Harrogate T 5/10		
Luke Durham	5'10"	11 00	6/9/90	19		Huddersfield (Scholar) Rel c/s 09, Harrogate T 7/09	11	0
Martin Foster	5'05"	9 10	29/10/77	32	Sheffield	Leeds Rel c/s 98, Blackpool (L) 12/97, Morton 7/98, Doncaster 4/99, Ilkeston (L) 9/00, Forest Green AL 1/01, Halifax 7/04, Oxford U (SL) 1/07, Rushden & D 5/07, Tamworth 1/08, Eastwood T 6/09, Harrogate T 12/09	17	0
Adam Nowakowski			22/10/86	23		Ripon C, Harrogate T	21	1
Wayne Phillips			29/8/85	25	South Shields	Newcastle (Yth), Sunderland (Yth), Peterlee Newtown, Blyth 3/03 Rel 1/05, Whitley Bay 1/05, Gateshead 7/07 Rel 5/10, Harrogate T 7/10		
Liam Shepherd			14/1/90	20		York C Rel 5/09, Farsley Celtic 6/09, Harrogate T 3/10	11	0
Roy Stamer			14/5/78	31	Germany	Werder Bremen (Ger), Bochum (Ger), SC Wattenscheid (Ger) 7/01, Farsley Celtic, Guiseley c/s 05, Farsley Celtic 10/05, Bradford PA 9/08, Farsley Celtic 9/09, Harrogate T 3/10	7	1
FORWARDS								
Graeme Armstrong	6'00"	12 08	28/6/83	27	Hexham	Haltwhistle U, Queen of the South 7/00, Annan Ath, Dunston Fed c/s 04, Gateshead £5,000 6/07 Rel 5/10, Harrogate T 5/10		
Lee Ellington	5'10"	11 07	3/7/80	30	Bradford	Eccleshill Utd, Hull C, Altrincham (Trial), Exeter 3/00, Walton & H 4/00, Gainsborough 10/00, Stalybridge 7/05, Farsley Celtic 6/09, Droylsden 3/10 Rel 3/10, Harrogate T 3/10	9	4
Liam Hardy						Armthorpe Welfare, Harrogate T 6/10		
Jon Maloney	6'00"	11 12	3/3/85	25	Leeds	Doncaster Rel c/s 05, York (3ML) 12/04, University of Montevallo (USA) c/s 05, Harrogate T 7/09	29	1
Aiden Savory	6'00"	13 00	4/8/87	23	Leeds	Ossett T, Bradford PA c/s 09, Harrogate T 6/10		

Loanees	HT	WT	DOB	AGE	POB	From - To	APPS	GOA
(D)Rory Coleman	6'00"	11 09	22/12/90	19	Rotherham	Scunthorpe (3ML) 8/09 - Ilkeston (SL) 1/10	10	5
(F)James Knowles			7/6/90	20		Burton 9/09 -	0	0
(M)Jamie Harwood			27/9/84	25		Gateshead 10/09 - Rel 2/10, Shildon 2/10	4	0
(G)Arron Jameson	6'03"	13 01	7/11/89	20		Sheff Wed 10/09 - Matlock (L) 11/09	4	0
(F)Kieran Leabon	5'11"	12 01	24/9/88	21	Chelmsford	Histon 11/09 - Rel 2/10, Bury T 2/10	3	1
(F)Jason Bradley	6'03"	13 00	16/3/89	21	Sheffield	Mansfield (6ML) 12/09 - Rel 4/10, Brackley T 6/10	4	1
(F)Lee Gregory			26/8/88	22		Mansfield (3ML) 12/09 - FC Halifax (L) 3/10	9	0
(F)Tom Cahill	5'10"	12 08	21/11/86	23	Derby	Fleetwood (SL) 3/10 - Rel 5/10, AFC Fylde 7/10	12	1

Departures	HT	WT	DOB	AGE	POB	From - To	APPS	GOA
(D)Kevin Sharp	5'09"	11 11	19/9/74	35	Ontario, Can	Wigan (Pl/Ass Man) 6/09 - Rel 10/09		
(M)Dean Gent			29/5/85	25		Carlton 6/09 - Rel 9/09, Carlton, Hucknall 6/10	2	0
(M)Peter Holmes	5'11"	11 13	18/11/80	29	Bishop Auckland	Rotherham 9/09 - Ebbsfleet 10/09	0	0
(F)Trevor Benjamin	6'02"	13 07	8/2/79	31	Kettering	Tamworth 10/09 - Rel 11/09, Woking 11/09	5	3
(M)Mario Campagna			28/8/89	21		Knaresborough 8/09 - Ossett A 12/09		
(M)Brian Dutton	5'11"	12 00	12/4/85	25	Malton	Salisbury 7/09 - Northwich 12/09	17	3
(M)Leon Scott			5/6/86	24		Whitby 6/09 - Whitby (L) 10/09, Whitby 1/10	8	0
(M)Curtis Woodhouse	5'08"	11 00	17/4/80	30	Driffield	Mansfield 6/09 - Rel 2/10, Sheffield FC 2/10	12	1
(M)Jimmy Ghaichem			11/4/84	26		Goole AFC 11/09 - Ilkeston 3/10 Rel c/s 10	4	0
(F)Ben Muirhead	5'09"	11 02	5/1/83	27	Doncaster	Kings Lynn 12/09 - Buxton 3/10	8	1
(M)James Naylor			13/5/83	27		Harrogate T 2/10, Belper 3/10	0	0
(G)John Lamb			12/11/82	27		Ossett T 6/09 - Bradford PA 3/10	6	0
(F)Simon Yeo	5'10"	11 08	20/10/73	36	Stockport	Droylsden 12/09 - New Mills 4/10	9	0
(F)Peter Knox			30/9/79	30	Yorkshire	Eastwood 12/09 - Worksop 5/10	16	4
(D)Dave Syers			30/11/87	22		Farsley Celtic 3/10 - Guiseley 7/10	10	6
(D)Simon Sturdy			15/2/77	33	Yorkshire	Eastwood 6/09 - Matlock (2ML) 10/09, Frickley 7/10	23	1
(F)Daniel Broadbent	5'10"	12 00	2/3/90	20	Leeds	Huddersfield 8/09 - Frickley (L) 3/10, Frickley 7/10	13	1
(M)Richard Dunning			8/1/81	29		Guiseley 10/09 - Frickley 7/10	21	0
(D)Dave McTiernan			13/7/84	26		Newcastle Blue Star 6/09 - Whitby 7/10	22	2
(G)Kieron Williams			19/9/85	24			0	0
(D)Elijah Reid			6/10/89	20		Frickley 9/09 -	1	0
(D)Dominic Riordan						Stocksbridge PS 3/10 -		
(D)Warren Burrell	5'10"	10 06	3/6/90	20	Sheffield	Mansfield 8/09 -	12	0
(F)Ollie Ryan	5'09"	11 00	26/9/85	24	Boston	Boston U 6/09 - Belper (L) 1/10	16	0
(F)Zeph Thomas			14/11/89	20		AFC Emley 8/09 -	3	0
(M)Chris Emms			23/7/84	26		ECU Joondaloop (Aust) 7/09 -	9	0
(G)Aaron Ratchford			13/2/88	22		Guiseley 11/09 -	18	0
(D)Ben Chapman	5'06"	11 05	2/3/79	31	Scunthorpe	Eastwood T 10/09 - Frickley (L) 2/10	9	0
(F)Steven Ivanov			31/10/91	18	Bulgaria	Yth -	1	0

HINCKLEY UNITED

Chairman: Kevin Downes

Secretary: Ray Baggott (T) 07802 355 249 (E) raybaggott@yahoo.co.uk

Additional Committee Members: Robert Mayne, K Akeredolu, A Dyer, D Newman, P Savage, M Sutton, D Radburn, K Thompson, Dave Riche, Andy Gibbs

Manager: Dean Thomas

Programme Editor: TBA (E) andy.gibbs57@ntlworld.com

Front Row (L-R): Lloyd Kerry, Connor Franklin, Dan Dillon, Stuart Storer (coach), Dean Thomas (manager), Ben Fairclough, Danny Newton, James Reid. Middle: Andy Keeley (Physio), Nobby Radburn (Kit Manager), Steph Morley, Jacob Blackwell, Denham Hinds, Dan Haystead, Gavin Strachan, Andre Gray, Nicky Platnauer (Assistant Manager), Steve Cook (Youth Team Manager) Back: Alex Taylor,Jack Roberts, Gary King, Paul Lister, Richard Munday, James Mace, Chima Dozie, Andy Gundelach.

Club Factfile

Founded: 1997 **Nickname:** United

Previous Names: Today's club was formed when Hinckley Athletic and Hinckley Town merged in 1997

Previous Leagues: As United: Southern 1997-2004

Club Colours (change): Red with navy trim/navy/red (White with black trim/black/black)

Ground: The Greene King Stadium, Leicester Road, Hinckley LE10 3DR (T) 01455 840 088

Capacity: 4,329 **Seats:** 630 **Covered:** 2,695 **Clubhouse:** Yes **Shop:** Yes

Previous Grounds:

Simple Directions

M1 J21 take M69 (Coventry) or M6 J2 take M69 (Leicester). M69 J2 take A5 North. At 3rd roundabout (Dodwells). Take 2nd exit A47 Earl Shilton & Industrial Estates, follow A47 over three roundabouts & a set of traffic lights at next roundabout take 3rd exit B4668. Stadium is 100 yards on right.

Record Attendance: 2,278 v Nuneaton Borough - 10/12/2005

Record Victory: 9-1 v Rocester (A) - 28/08/2000

Record Defeat: 1-7 v Stalybridge Celtic (A) - Conference North 03/03/2009

Record Goalscorer: Jamie Lenton - 74

Record Appearances: Jamie Lenton - 280

Additional Records:

Senior Honours: Southern League Division 1 Western 2000-01

10 YEAR RECORD

00-01		01-02		02-03		03-04		04-05		05-06		06-07		07-08		08-09		09-10	
SthW	1	SthP	12	SthP	13	SthP	6	Conf N	12	Conf N	10	Conf N	4	Conf N	19	Conf N	10	Conf N	7

HINCKLEY UNITED

No.	Date	Comp	H/A	Opponents	Att:	Result	Goalscorers	Pos
1	8/8/09	BSN	A	Workington	462	W 1-0	Webster pen 66	7
2	10/8/09	BSN	H	Droylsden	451	D 1-1	Webster pen 35	2
3	15/8/09	BSN	H	Hyde United	381	L 1-2	West 10	11
4	18/8/09	BSN	A	AFC Telford	1665	D 2-2	Webster 8, Cartwright 36	11
5	22/8/09	BSN	H	Vauxhall Motors	243	D 1-1	Webster 47	11
6	29/8/09	BSN	A	Eastwood Town	483	L 0-1		14
7	31/8/09	BSN	H	Redditch United	413	W 5-1	Webster 5, West 2 (30, 64), Lavery 2 (38, 52)	10
8	5/9/09	BSN	A	Southport	710	D 1-1	Webster 68	11
9	9/9/09	BSN	A	Corby Town	266	D 1-1	Hall 34	11
10	19/9/09	BSN	H	Ilkeston Town	513	W 1-0	Dillon 70	9
11	3/10/09	BSN	A	Stafford Rangers	501	W 3-2	Cartwright 49, West 59, Lavery 72	7
12	17/10/09	BSN	A	Blyth Spartans	462	L 1-6	Taylor 75	9
13	31/10/09	BSN	H	Stalybridge Celtic	573	D 0-0		9
14	2/11/09	BSN	H	Gainsborough Trinity	441	W 2-0	Lavery 70, Taylor 81	9
15	14/11/09	BSN	H	Alfreton Town	504	W 2-1	Lavery 20, Webster 82	8
16	28/11/09	BSN	H	Stafford Rangers	515	W 3-1	Taylor 23, Franklin 67, Webster 79	7
17	1/12/09	BSN	A	Northwich Victoria	451	W 1-0	Webster 12	4
18	5/12/09	BSN	A	Droylsden	284	D 0-0		4
19	26/12/09	BSN	A	Solihull Moors	400	W 4-2	Smith 4 (41, 56, 64, 66)	3
20	28/12/09	BSN	H	AFC Telford	815	W 2-0	West 58, Collins 88	3
21	19/1/10	BSN	A	Harrogate Town	142	L 1-3	Dillon 35	3
22	23/1/10	BSN	A	Stalybridge Celtic	470	D 0-0		4
23	26/1/10	BSN	A	Gloucester City	180	W 5-3	Franklin 34, Mace 39, West 3 (44, 51, 59)	3
24	30/1/10	BSN	A	Fleetwood Town	1442	L 1-3	Mace 32	3
25	6/2/10	BSN	H	Northwich Victoria	486	D 1-1	Hall 56	3
26	8/2/10	BSN	H	Southport	394	W 4-1	Collins 20, Dillon 21, Gooding 66, Eribenne pen 72	3
27	13/2/10	BSN	A	Vauxhall Motors	200	D 1-1	Hall 90	3
28	15/2/10	BSN	H	Solihull Moors	471	L 0-3		3
29	22/2/10	BSN	A	Hyde United	307	L 2-3	Eribenne pen 27, Gooding 42	4
30	27/2/10	BSN	A	Ilkeston Town	362	W 1-0	Dillon 43	3
31	6/3/10	BSN	H	Fleetwood Town	642	L 0-2		4
32	20/3/10	BSN	H	Gloucester City	481	W 1-0	Taylor 4	4
33	22/3/10	BSN	H	Blyth Spartans	372	D 1-1	Franklin 55	4
34	27/3/10	BSN	H	Workington	395	L 1-2	Lavery 57	5
35	29/3/10	BSN	H	Corby Town	343	D 1-1	Gooding 11	5
36	5/4/10	BSN	A	Redditch United	428	W 2-0	Hall 11, Webster 29	5
37	10/4/10	BSN	A	Gainsborough Trinity	342	D 1-1	Mace 56	6
38	15/4/10	BSN	H	Eastwood Town	413	D 0-0		6
39	17/4/10	BSN	H	Harrogate Town	424	W 3-2	West 5, Lavery 16, Newton 79	5
40	24/4/10	BSN	A	Alfreton Town	647	L 2-3	Webster 9, Dillon 65	7
	Farsley Celtic record expunged 12/03							
10	12/9/09	BSN	H	Farsley Celtic	403	W 4-1	West 25, Hall 31, Cartwright 37, Gooding 44	10
	Cups							
1	26/9/09	FAC 2Q	H	Kirkley & Pakefield	322	W 2-1	West 39, Gooding 73	
2	10/10/09	FAC 3Q	A	Cambridge City	466	W 5-0	Webster 4 (7, 33, 45, pen 73), Gooding 67	
3	24/10/09	FAC 4Q	H	Histon	778	W 2-1	Giddings 2 (45, 63)	
4	7/11/09	FAC 1	A	Rushden & Diamonds	1540	L 1-3	Webster 64	
5	21/11/09	FAT 3Q	A	AFC Fylde	224	D 1-1	Webster 5	
6	24/11/09	FAT 3QR	H	AFC Fylde	194	W 7-3	Webster 5 (8, 24, 37, 80, 90), Taylor 22, Lavery 57	
7	12/12/09	FAT 1	H	York City	506	D 0-0		
8	15/12/09	FAT 1R	A	York City	853	L 1-3	West 48	

Home Attendances:
Highest: 815 v AFC Telford
Lowest: 343 v Corby Town
Average (08-09): 446 (530)

Top Goalscorer: Webster - 22 (11 League, 11 Cup) in 28 appearances - 79% strike rate
Most Appearances: Hall - 47 (39 League, 8 Cup)
MacKenzie - 47 (39 League, 8 Cup)
Taylor - 47 (29+10 League, 6+2 Cup)

MACKENZIE	MACE	GIDDINGS	LAVERY	COLLINS	FRANKLIN	HALL	GOODING	WEBSTER	WEST	DILLON	ERIBENNE	TAYLOR	CARTWRIGHT	LISTER	STORER	HAMILTON	BANCROFT	HINDS	BARKER	LANCASTER	JUPP	CONNOLLY	ROBERTS	DUDLEY	SMITH	YOUNG	NEWTON	HUTCHINSON	PICKERING	LAXTON	HEGGS	SIMMONDS	PLATNAUER	GRAY	JOACHIM	PITHAM	OGLEBY	
X	X	X	X	X	X	X	X	X	X	X	S	S	U	U	U																							1
X	X	X	X	X	X	X	X	X	X	X	S	S	S	U	U																							2
X	X	X	X	X	X	X	X	X	X	X	S	U	S	U		S																						3
X	X	X	X	X	X	X	X	X	U	U	X	S	X	U		U																						4
X	X		X	X	X	X	X	X	S	U	X	S	X	X	U	U																						5
X	X	X	X	X	X	X	X	X	S	U	X	S	X	U	U																							6
X	X	X	X		X	X	X	X	X	S		S	X	X	U	S	U																					7
X	X	X	X	X	X	X	X	X	X	U	S	S	X	U				U																				8
X	X	X	X	X	X	X	X		X	S	X	S	X	U	U	U																						9
X	X	X		X	X	X	X	X	S	X	X	S	X			U			U	U																		10
X	X	X	X	X		X	X		X	U		X	X	X	U	S			U																			11
	X	X	X	X		X	X	X	X	S	S	S	X	X		U						X	U															12
X		X	X		X	X	X	X	X	U	S	X	X	X	U	U							U															13
X		X	X		X	X	X	X	X	S	S	X	X	X	U	S							U															14
X	U		X		X	X	X	X		U	X	X	X	X	U	U							U	X														15
X	U		X	U	X	X	X	X	X	U	S	X	X	X		U								X														16
X	U		X	U	X	X	X	X	U		X	X	X	X		U								X														17
X	S		X	U	X	X	X	X	S	X	S	X	X	X		U								X														18
X	S		X	X	X	X	X		X	S		X	X	X	U										X		U	S										19
X	U			X	X	X	X		X	X		X	X	X		U									X	U	U	S										20
X	X			X	X		X		X	X		X	X	X	U	U											S	X										21
X	X			S	X	X	X		X	X	S	X	X	X	U	U							X				U											22
X	X			U	X	X	X		X	X	X	X	X	X	U	S							S				S											23
X	X			S	X	X	X		X	X	X	X	X	X		U							U				U											24
X				X	X	X	X		X	X	X	X	X			U							U	X			U		S	U								25
X				X	X	X	X		S	X	X	X	X	U									U	X			S		S		X							26
X				X	X	X	X		X	X	X	X	X	S									U	X			S		U		S							27
X					X	X	X		X	X		X	X	X		U							U	X			X		S			S	U					28
X					X	X	X		S	X	X	X	X	X									X	X			U		U			S						29
X			U		X	X	X		X	X		X	X	X		U							U	X			X		S			U						30
X			S		X	X	X		X	X		X	X	X									U	X			U							X	S	S		31
X	X		U		X	X	X			X	X	X		X		U							U				S							X		X		32
X	X		U		X	X	X			X	X	X		X									U		U		S							X		X	S	33
X	X		X		X	X	X	S	X	X		X		X	U								U				S							X				34
X	X		X		X	X	X	X	S	X		X		X									S		U		S							X				35
X	X		X		X	X	U	X	X	X		X	X	U									U				S									X		36
X	X		X		X	X	X	X	X			X	X	S		U							U				S									X		37
X	X		X		X	X	X	X	X			X	X	U									U		U		S									X		38
X	X		X		X	X	X	X	X	U		X	X	S		U							S				S									X		39
X	X		X		X	X	X	X	S	S		X		X		U							S				X									X		40
X	X	X			X	X	X	S	X	X	X	S	X	X	U	S																						

MACKENZIE	MACE	GIDDINGS	LAVERY	COLLINS	FRANKLIN	HALL	GOODING	WEBSTER	WEST	DILLON	ERIBENNE	TAYLOR	CARTWRIGHT	LISTER	STORER	HAMILTON	BANCROFT	HINDS	BARKER	LANCASTER	JUPP	CONNOLLY	ROBERTS	DUDLEY	SMITH	YOUNG	NEWTON	HUTCHINSON	PICKERING	LAXTON	HEGGS	SIMMONDS	PLATNAUER	GRAY	JOACHIM	PITHAM	OGLEBY	
X	X	X	U	X	X	X	X		X	X	X	S	X	U		U		U	U																			1
X	X	X	X			X	X	X	X	S	S	X	X	X	U	S					U																	2
X		X	X	X	X	X	X	X	S	X	X	S	X	S		U		U					U															3
X	U	X	X	S	X	X	X	X	S	U	X	X	X	X		U		U					U															4
X	X		X	U	X	X	X	X	S	S	X	X		X		U							U	X														5
X	U		X	U	X	X	X	X	S	S	X	X	X	X		S								X														6
X	U		X	X	X	X	X		X	S		X	X	X		U									X	U	U											7
X	S			X	X	X			X	X		X	X	X		U				U			X		X	U	S											8

Total League Appearances

39	25	13	25	17	38	39	39	22	27	22	15	29	32	25	0	0	0	0	0	0	0	1	2	11	2	0	3	1	0	0	1	0	0	5	0	7	0	X
0	2	0	1	2	0	0	0	1	8	6	10	10	2	3	0	5	0	0	0	0	0	0	4	0	0	0	12	2	4	0	1	2	0	0	1	1	1	S
0	4	0	3	4	0	0	1	0	2	9	0	1	1	10	15	21	1	1	2	1	0	0	17	0	3	1	7	0	2	1	0	1	1	0	0	0	0	U

Total Cup Appearances

8	3	4	6	4	7	8	7	5	4	3	5	6	7	6	0	0	0	0	0	0	0	0	1	2	2	0	0	0	0	0	0	0	0	0	0	0	0	X
0	1	0	0	1	0	0	0	0	4	4	1	2	0	1	0	2	0	0	0	0	0	0	0	0	0	0	1	0	0	0	0	0	0	0	0	0	0	S
0	3	0	1	2	0	0	0	0	0	1	0	0	0	1	1	6	0	3	1	1	1	0	3	0	0	2	1	0	0	0	0	0	0	0	0	0	0	U

Total Goals

0	3	0	7	2	3	4	3	11	9	5	2	4	2	0	0	0	0	0	0	0	0	0	0	0	4	0	1	0	0	0	0	0	0	0	0	0	0	Lge
0	0	2	1	0	0	0	2	11	2	0	0	1	0	0	0	0	0	0	0	0	0	0	0	0	0	0	0	0	0	0	0	0	0	0	0	0	0	Cup

HINCKLEY UNITED

CURRENT SQUAD AS OF BEGINING OF 2010-11 SEASON

GOALKEEPERS	HT	WT	D.O.B	AGE	P.O.B	CAREER	APPS	GOA
Danny Haystead	6'01"	11 09	13/2/86	24	Chesterfield	Sheff Utd Rel c/s 05, Scarborough (L) 11/04, Hinckley U 8/05 Rel c/s 07, Moor Green (L) 8/05, Quorn (SL) (06/07), Quorn c/s 07, Sheffield FC 2/08, Ilkeston 6/08, Hucknall 6/09, Hinckley U 6/10		
Denham Hinds			26/5/92	18		Leicester (Yth), Hinckley U, Oadby T, Hinckley U 9/09	0	0
DEFENDERS								
Connor Franklin			1/9/87	22	Leicester	Nuneaton, Hinckley U 6/08, Coventry (Trial) 3/10	38	3
Paul Lister			3/12/89	20	Sheffield	Burton, Grantham (SL) 11/08, Hinckley U 7/09	28	0
James Mace			5/3/85	25		Coleshill, Bedworth 1/07, Atherstone, Hinckley U 7/09	27	3
Richard Munday			24/8/87	23		Tamworth, Rushall O (L) 8/05, Solihull B, Loughborough D (Dual), Ilkeston 2/07, Stratford T, Romulus 8/09, Redditch 2/10, Hinckley U 6/10		
Leigh Platnauer			10/1/86	24		Hinckley U, Gresley R (Dual) 12/07, Oxford C (L) 2/10	0	0
Stuart Storer	5'11"	12 12	16/1/67	43	Harborough	Mansfield Rel 3/84, VS Rugby, Birmingham 7/84, Everton 3/87, Wigan (2ML) 7/87, Bolton (L) 12/87 £25,000 1/88, Exeter £25,000 3/93, Brighton £15,000 3/95 Rel c/s 99, Atherstone 9/99, Kettering 10/99 Rel 2/00, Chesham 2/00, Hinckley U 3/01	0	0
MIDFIELDERS								
Dan Dillon	5'09"	10 07	6/9/86	23	Huntingdon	Carlisle Rel 3/06, Workington (4ML) 8/05, Workington 3/06, Team Bath 7/06, Worcester (Trial) 5/09, Hinckley U 6/09	28	5
Louis Hamilton			28/2/91	19		Hinckley U, Hinckley Downes (Dual)	5	0
Jack Roberts	6'02"	10 00	10/11/90	19		Lincoln C (Scholar) Rel c/s 09, Hinckley U c/s 09, Coalville (Dual) 8/09, Loughborough D (L) 12/09	6	0
Gavin Strachan	5'11"	11 07	23/12/78	31	Aberdeen	Coventry, Dundee (3ML) 1/99, Motherwell (L) 2/02, Blackpool (Trial) 2/03, Peterborough 3/03, Southend 3/03 Rel c/s 03, Sheff Wed (Trial) 7/03, Hartlepool 8/03, Stockport (L) 10/05, Peterborough (L) 1/07, Peterborough 1/07 Rel 1/08, Notts County 1/08 Rel c/s 09, Corby 7/09, Hinckley U 6/10		
FORWARDS								
Andre Gray	5'11"	12 06	26/6/91	19	Wolverhampton	Shrewsbury Rel c/s 10, AFC Telford (2ML) 11/09, Hinckley U (L) 3/10, Hinckley U 6/10	5	0
Gary King	5'10"	11 04	27/1/90	20	Grimsby	Lincoln C Rel c/s 09, Boston U (2ML) 1/09, Accrington 8/09 Rel c/s 10, Hinckley U 6/10		
Ben Laxton			30/10/84	25		Hinckley Downes, Hinckley U	0	0
Daniel Newton			18/3/91	19		Hinckley Downes, Hinckley U (Dual) 12/09, Hinckley U 6/10	15	1
Alex Taylor			11/11/85	24	Wolverhampton	Kidderminster, Stafford R, Hinckley U 8/08	39	4
Adam Webster	6'01"	12 05	3/7/80	30	Thurmarston	Thurmarston, Notts County 2/99 Rel c/s 00, Grantham (L) 9/99, Bedworth (L) 12/99, Bedworth 7/00, Worcester £8,000 12/01, Hinckley U 2/08	23	11

Loanees	HT	WT	DOB	AGE	POB	From - To	APPS	GOA
(G)Wayne Connolly			30/12/78	31		Hinckley Downes 10/09 -	1	0
(D)Mark Dudley	5'10"	12 02	29/1/90	20	Doncaster	Derby 11/09, 2/10 - Rel c/s 10	11	0
(G)Dave Clarke			20/8/85	25		Sutton Coldfield (Dual) 11/09 -		
(F)Sam Smith			20/5/90	20	Corby	Rushden & D 12/09 -	2	4
(M)Sam Young			23/1/91	19		Hinckley Downes 12/09 -	0	0
(F)Andy Hutchinson			10/3/92	18		Lincoln C 12/09 -	3	0
(F)Liam Hebberd			8/1/85	25		Bardon Hill Sports (Dual) 3/10 -		
(F)Robert Ogleby			5/1/92	18		Coventry 3/10 - Hearts 4/10	1	0

Departures	HT	WT	DOB	AGE	POB	From - To	APPS	GOA
(G)Nick Jupp			6/5/89	21	Ashford	Yth - Rel 10/09, Coalville (Dual) 8/09, Shepshed D (L)	0	0
(M)Stuart Giddings	6'00"	11 08	27/3/86	24	Coventry	Coventry 9/08 - Darlington 11/09 Rel 4/10	13	0
(M)Andy Hall			25/1/86	24	Northampton	Kettering 7/08 - Corby T 5/10	39	4
(G)Chris Mackenzie	6'00"	12 09	14/5/72	38	Northampton	Kidderminster 6/08 - Corby T 5/10	39	0
(M)Andy Gooding	5'07"	10 05	30/4/88	22	Coventry	Rushden & D 7/08 - Corby T 5/10	39	3
(D)Danny Pitham			25/1/86	24		Bedworth 3/10 - Corby T 6/10	8	0
(F)Chukki Eribenne	5'10"	11 12	2/11/80	29	Westminster	Sutton U 8/09 - Ilkeston T 6/10	25	2
(M)Richard Lavery			28/5/77	33	Coventry	Telford 6/04 - Corby T 6/10	26	7
(M)Neil Cartwright			25/6/82	28	Wrexham	Yth - Corby T 6/10	34	2
(F)Matt West			11/3/90	20		Coventry (Scholar) 7/09 - Solihull Moors 6/10	35	9
(D)Nathan Bancroft			15/12/89	20		Yth - Rel c/s 10	0	0
(D)Lee Collins	6'01"	12 06	10/9/77	32	Birmingham	Solihull Moors 7/09 - Rel c/s 10	19	2
(M)Daniel Barker			22/4/88	22		South America c/s 09 - Rel c/s 10	0	0
(M)Sam Lancaster			17/2/86	24		Hinckley Downes - Rel c/s 10	0	0
(F)Carl Heggs			11/10/70	39		Redditch 2/10 - Rel c/s 10	2	0
(F)Julian Joachim	5'06"	12 02	20/9/74	35	Boston	Quorn 3/10 - Rel c/s 10	1	0
(F)Jarrod Pickering			11/8/86	24		Yth -	4	0
(F)Nicholas Pollard			4/11/82	27		Hinckley Downes 12/08 - Oadby T (Dual) 8/09		
(F)Leighton Simmonds			16/11/90	19		Kings Lynn 2/10 -	2	0

HYDE UNITED

Chairman: Stephen Hartley
Secretary: Tony Beard (T) 07778 792502
(E) aliandtony@ukonline.co.uk
Additional Committee Members:
A M Beard, D Farrington, A A Fruhwirth, J Whitehead, J Jackson
Manager: Neil Tolson
Programme Editor: Mark Dring (E) mark@dring16.fsnet.co.uk

Back Row (L-R): Andy Wilkinson(physio), Kylie WIlson, Danny Pollitt, Mark Lees, Michael Taylor, Dean Stott, Chris Rimmer, Greg Traynor, Will Burns, Craig Mawson, Chris Lynch, Matty Burke, Andy Smart, Lee Pugh, Scott McNiven
Front Row: Tom Manship, Ben Morris, Carlos Logan, Marcus Calvert, Scott Mooney, Mark Stewart, Lee Rick, Ashley Stott, Shaun Whalley

Club Factfile

Founded: 1919 **Nickname:** The Tigers
Previous Names: Hyde F.C.
Previous Leagues: Lancashire & Cheshire 1919-21, Manchester 1921-30, Cheshire County 1930-68, 1970-82, Northern Premier 1968-70, 1983-2004
Club Colours (change): White/navy/navy (Sky blue/white/sky blue)

Ground: Tameside Stadium, Ewen Fields, Walker Lane, Hyde SK14 2SB (T) 0871 200 2116
Capacity: 4,250 **Seats:** 660 **Covered:** 2,000 **Clubhouse:** Yes **Shop:** Yes
Previous Grounds:
Simple Directions
M60 (Manchester Orbital Motorway) to Junction 24. M67 to Hyde (Junction 3). Right at top of slip road and then left at lights. (Morrisons on left). Right at next lights (Lumn Road). Left at Give way sign. Ground entrance is on left, just after Leisure Pool. Please note for Satnav, use SK14 5PL

Record Attendance: 9,500 v Nelson - FA Cup 1952
Record Victory: 9-1 v South Liverpool
Record Defeat: 0-26 v Preston North End - FA Cup
Record Goalscorer: David Nolan - 117 in 404 appearances (1992-2003). Ged Kimmins - 117 in 274 appearances (1993-98)
Record Appearances: David Nolan - 404 (1992-2003)
Additional Records: Paid £8,000 to Mossley for Jim McCluskie 1989
Received £50,000 from Crewe Alexandra for Colin Little 1995
Senior Honours: Northern Premier League Division 1 2003-04, Premier Division 2004-05, League Cup x3
Cheshire Senior Cup x7. Manchester Premier cup x5.

10 YEAR RECORD

00-01	01-02	02-03	03-04	04-05	05-06	06-07	07-08	08-09	09-10
NP P 16	NP P 22	NP P 23	NP 1 1	NP P 1	Conf N 11	Conf N 8	Conf N 9	Conf N 20	Conf N 15

HYDE UNITED

No.	Date	Comp	H/A	Opponents	Att:	Result	Goalscorers	Pos
1	8/8/09	BSN	H	Stafford Rangers	401	W 1-0	Arnold 75	8
2	11/8/09	BSN	A	Fleetwood Town	1012	D 1-1	Arnold 58	9
3	15/8/09	BSN	A	Hinckley United	381	W 2-1	Douglas-Pringle 2 (55, 84)	5
4	17/8/09	BSN	H	Gainsborough Trinity	372	W 3-2	D McNiven 2 (56, 71), Eastham 76	1
5	22/8/09	BSN	A	Ilkeston Town	408	D 1-1	Smith 2	2
6	29/8/09	BSN	H	Blyth Spartans	349	L 0-3		5
7	31/8/09	BSN	A	Harrogate Town	303	L 0-2		9
8	5/9/09	BSN	H	Alfreton Town	368	L 1-5	D McNiven pen 60	10
9	7/9/09	BSN	H	Gloucester City	326	D 1-1	Mooney 36	9
10	12/9/09	BSN	A	Northwich Victoria	481	L 1-3	Rick 88	12
11	19/9/09	BSN	H	Fleetwood Town	501	W 2-1	D McNiven 2 (78, pen 82)	11
12	17/10/09	BSN	H	Corby Town	318	L 1-3	S McNiven 90	13
13	27/10/09	BSN	A	Eastwood Town	480	L 0-2		15
14	31/10/09	BSN	H	Vauxhall Motors	308	D 2-2	Stott 59, Mooney 76	14
15	7/11/09	BSN	A	Gloucester City	280	L 0-2		15
16	15/11/09	BSN	H	Northwich Victoria	718	D 1-1	Lynch 56	14
17	28/11/09	BSN	A	Droylsden	436	L 0-1		18
18	30/11/09	BSN	H	Southport	456	D 1-1	Manship 52	17
19	12/12/09	BSN	A	Alfreton Town	302	L 0-4		19
20	25/1/10	BSN	H	Ilkeston Town	269	D 1-1	Mooney 76	19
21	6/2/10	BSN	A	Redditch United	266	D 0-0		19
22	13/2/10	BSN	H	Eastwood Town	352	W 1-0	D McNiven pen 85	19
23	20/2/10	BSN	A	Stafford Rangers	507	D 1-1	D McNiven 39	19
24	22/2/10	BSN	H	Hinckley United	307	W 3-2	Mooney 69, Tolson 2 (90, 90)	18
25	27/2/10	BSN	A	Vauxhall Motors	249	L 0-1		18
26	2/3/10	BSN	A	Solihull Moors	167	L 0-3		19
27	6/3/10	BSN	H	Droylsden	518	W 2-1	Mooney 32, Lynch 83	17
28	9/3/10	BSN	A	Gainsborough Trinity	298	L 1-2	Mooney 35	17
29	13/3/10	BSN	H	AFC Telford	472	D 1-1	Arnold 67	18
30	16/3/10	BSN	A	Stalybridge Celtic	632	W 4-2	Burke 2 (11, 56), Arnold 2 (65, 90)	17
31	20/3/10	BSN	A	Corby Town	287	L 0-1		17
32	22/3/10	BSN	H	Stalybridge Celtic	706	W 2-1	D'Laryea 45, Arnold 88	16
33	27/3/10	BSN	A	AFC Telford	1708	L 0-4		17
34	3/4/10	BSN	A	Blyth Spartans	401	L 3-4	D McNiven 51, S McNiven 59, Og (Harrison) 75	17
35	5/4/10	BSN	H	Harrogate Town	356	W 1-0	D McNiven 30	17
36	10/4/10	BSN	H	Redditch United	301	W 3-2	D McNiven pen 34, Arnold 2 (80, 90)	14
37	13/4/10	BSN	A	Workington	493	D 2-2	D McNiven pen 2, Douglas-Pringle 75	14
38	17/4/10	BSN	A	Southport	1306	L 1-4	D McNiven pen 52	15
39	19/4/10	BSN	H	Workington	325	L 0-2		15
40	24/4/10	BSN	H	Solihull Moors	340	D 1-1	Arnold 39	15
	Farsley Celtic record expunged 12/03							
12	3/10/09	BSN	A	Farsley Celtic	326	L 0-3		12
23	8/2/10	BSN	H	Farsley Celtic	258	W 4-1	Rick 2 (20, 45), Holsgrove 39, Mooney 46	19
	Cups							
1	6/10/09	FAC 2Q	H	Salford City	276	D 2-2	Arnold 19, D'Laryea 35	
2	10/10/09	FAC 2QR	A	Salford City	391	L 0-1		
3	21/11/09	FAT 3Q	H	Nuneaton Town	328	D 3-3	Og (Pierpoint) 37, Mooney 78, Tolson 80	
4	24/11/09	FAT 3QR	A	Nuneaton Town	464	L 0-1		

Home Attendances:	
Highest:	718 v Northwich Victoria
Lowest:	269 v Ilkeston Town
Average (08-09):	354 (360)
Top Goalscorer:	D McNiven - 12 (12 League, 0 Cup) in 43 appearances - 28% strike rate
Most Appearances:	D McNiven - 43 (28+11 League, 4 Cup)

JONES	STOTT	LYNCH	S MCNIVEN	EASTHAM	D'LARYEA	SMITH	MANSHIP	D MCNIVEN	MOONEY	ARNOLD	RICK	LEES	BARRIE	ROWBOTHAM	ARMSTRONG	GEDMAN	KIRKBRIDE	ADAMS	DOUGLAS-PRINGLE	BERNSTEIN	DUFFY	CONVEY	HOLSGROVE	TOLSON	HARRISON	BURNS	BARRATT	THOMPSON	MERCER	DUGDALE	BURKE	HURST	RIMMER	HALSTEAD	LEA	ROUSE	
X	X	X	X	X	X	X	X	X	X	X	S	S	U	U	U																						1
X	X	X	X	X	X	X	X	X	X	X	U	U				S	U	U																			2
X	X	X	X	X	X	X	X	X	X	X		S				S	U	U	S																		3
X	X	X	X	X	X	X	X	X	S	X		U				X	S	U	S																		4
X	X	X	X	X	X	X	X	X	S	X		U				U	S	S	X																		5
X	X	X	X	X	X	X	X	X	X	X		U				S	U	S	S																		6
-U		X	X	X	X	X	X	U	X	S	X				S	X	S	X	X																		7
-U	X	X	X	X	U	X	X	S	X	S	S					X	X	X		X																	8
-X	X	X	X	X	U	U	X	X	X	U	X					U	S	X		X																	9
-X	X	X	X	X		S	X	X	X	S	X					U	U	X			X	S															10
-U		X	X	X		X	X	S	X	X	X		U			U	X				X	X	U														11
X	U	X	X		X		X	X	S	X	U	S					U						X				X	X	X								12
X	S	X	X		X		X	X	U	X	U	S					U						X				X	X	X								13
X	X	X	X				X	X	S	X	S	X		U									X	U		U	X		X								14
X	X	X	X				X	X	X	X	S	X		U									X			U	S	S	X								15
X	X	X	X		U			X	S		X	X		U									X	X	U	U	X			X							16
X		X	X		S		X	S	S		X	X		U									X	X		U			X	X	X						17
X		X	X		U		X	X	S		X	X		U									X	U		U			X	X	X						18
X		X	X		X		X	X	S		X	X		U									X	U	U	U			X			X					19
X	X		X		X		X	S	S		X	X		U					S				X						X		X	X	U				20
X	X		X		X		X	S	S	S	X	X		U									X						X		X	X	U				21
X	X	X	X		X		X	S	X	S	X	X		U					S				X								X	U					22
X	X	X			X		X	X	S	X	X	X		U					S				X								X	U	U				23
X	X	X			X		X	X	S	X	X	X		U					S				X	S							X	U					24
X	X	X			X		X	X	S	X	X	X		U					S				X								X	S	U				25
X	X	X			X		X	S	X	S	X	X		U					X				X			U					X		S				26
X	X	X	X		X		X	S	X	S	S	X		U					X				X						U		X						27
-X	X			X		X	S	X	S	U	X		U					X				X						X		X	S		X				28
X	X	X	X		X		X	S	S	X	U	X		U					X				X						U		X						29
-X	X	X		X		X	S	X	X	S	X		U									X	U					U		X			X				30
-X	X	X		X			S	X	X	S	X		U									X						X		X	S		X	U			31
-X	X	X		X			U	X	X	S	X		U					S				X	U					X		X			X				32
-X		X		X			X	X	X	S	X		U					S				X						X		X		U	X		S		33
-U	X	X		X			X	U	S	X	X		X					S				X						X		X			X		S		34
-X	X	X		X			X	S	X	U	X		U					S				X						X		X			X		U		35
-X	X	X		X			X	U	S	S	X		U					S				X			X			X		X					X		36
-	X	X		X			X	X	X	S	X		U					S				X			X			X		X		S			U		37
-S	X	X					X	X	X	U	X		U					S				X			X			X		X		X			S		38
-X	X	X					X	S	X	S	X		U					X				X			X			X		X		S			U		39
-X	X	X					S	X	X	X	X		U									X	S		X			S		X		X			U		40
U	X		X		X		X	X	S	X	X	X		U			S	X				X	X	S													
X	X	X	X		X		X	U	X	S	X	X		S									X								X	U	S				
U	X		X		X	U	X	X	X	X	X	X		U			S	X				X		S	U												1
X	U	X	X		X	X	X	X	X	X	U	X		U			U	X						S	U	U											2
X	X	X	X					X	S		X	X		U									X	X	U	U			U	X	X						3
X	X	X	X				U	X	X		U	X		U									X	S		U			X	X	X						4

Total League Appearances

23	29	35	35	11	32	7	27	28	18	28	14	31	0	1	0	1	2	2	10	1	2	2	30	2	0	5	4	2	19	3	23	3	2	7	0	1	X
0	2	0	0	0	1	0	1	11	18	7	14	5	0	0	0	4	2	4	15	0	0	0	1	2	0	0	1	1	1	0	0	3	3	0	0	3	S
0	5	0	0	0	2	2	1	1	4	0	8	4	1	28	1	1	8	4	0	0	0	0	0	6	2	7	0	0	3	0	0	3	5	0	1	4	U

Total Cup Appearances

3	3	3	4	0	2	1	2	4	3	2	2	4	0	0	0	0	0	2	0	0	0	1	2	1	0	0	0	0	1	2	2	0	0	0	0	0	X
0	0	0	0	0	0	0	0	0	1	0	0	0	0	0	0	0	1	0	0	0	0	0	0	3	0	0	0	0	0	0	0	0	0	0	0	0	S
1	1	0	0	0	0	1	1	0	0	0	2	0	0	4	0	0	1	0	0	0	0	0	0	0	3	3	0	0	1	0	0	0	0	0	0	0	U

Total Goals

0	1	2	2	1	1	1	1	12	6	9	1	0	0	0	0	0	0	0	3	0	0	0	0	2	1	0	0	0	0	0	2	0	0	0	0	0	Lge
0	0	0	0	0	1	0	0	0	1	1	0	0	0	0	0	0	0	0	0	0	0	0	0	1	0	0	0	0	0	0	0	0	0	0	0	0	Cup

HYDE UNITED

CURRENT SQUAD AS OF BEGINING OF 2010-11 SEASON

GOALKEEPERS	HT	WT	D.O.B	AGE	P.O.B	CAREER	APPS	GOA
Will Burns			31/5/88	22		Hyde U	5	0
Michael Jones	6'04"	12 05	3/12/87	22	Liverpool	Wrexham Rel 5/08, Hinckley U (L) 3/08, Northwich 5/08, Rhyl (SL) 1/09, Hyde U 7/09	23	0
Craig Mawson	6'02"	13 04	16/5/79	31	Keighley	Burnley, Lincoln (2ML) 9/00, Halifax 2/01 Rel c/s 01, Morecambe 8/01 Rel c/s 04, Oldham 8/04 Rel 10/04, Hereford 10/04, Halifax 6/06, FC Halifax 7/08, Droylsden 8/08, Hyde U 7/10		
DEFENDERS								
Thomas Cooper						Holwell Sports, Hyde U 3/10		
Nathan D'Laryea	5'10"	12 02	3/9/85	24	Manchester	Man City Rel c/s 07, Macclesfield (L) 1/07, Rochdale 7/07 Rel c/s 09, Farsley Celtic (2ML) 2/09, Hyde U c/s 09	33	1
Michael Lea	6'00"	12 00	4/11/87	22	Salford	Man Utd, Royal Antwerp (4ML) 8/07, Scunthorpe Undisc 7/08, Chester 7/09 Rel 3/10, Hyde U 3/10, Rochdale 3/10 Rel c/s 10, Hyde U 7/10	0	0
Mark Lees			23/7/88	22		Mossley, Curzon Ashton, Stalybridge, New Mills, Buxton 1/08, Ashton U 2/09, Hyde U 7/09	36	0
Chris Lynch	5'10"		29/12/84	25	Manchester	Wigan (Scholar) Rel c/s 04, Hyde U c/s 04	35	2
Scott McNiven	5'10"	10 08	27/5/78	32	Leeds	Oldham Rel c/s 02, Oxford U 7/02, Mansfield 7/04 Rel c/s 05, Chester Rel 5/06, Morecambe 8/06 Rel 8/06, Fleetwood 9/06, Guiseley 2/07, Farsley Celtic 6/07, AFC Fylde 7/08, Hyde U 8/09	35	2
Chris Rimmer			2/6/92	18		Hyde U 1/10	5	0
Ben Rowbotham			25/2/90	20		Hyde U	1	0
Andrew Smart	6'01"	14 00	17/3/86	24	Wythenshawe	Altrincham (Yth), Macclesfield, Northwich (SL) 1/07, Stalybridge 6/07, Hyde U 7/10		
Dean Stott			5/10/89	20		Burnley (Trainee) Rel c/s 08, Preston 5/08 Rel c/s 09, Hyde U 8/09	31	1
Michael Taylor	6'02"	13 10	21/11/82	27	Liverpool	Blackburn Rel c/s 04, Carlisle (3ML) 9/02, Rochdale (L) 3/03, Reading (Trial) 12/03, Wycombe (Trial) 3/04, Cheltenham 7/04, Forest Green (2ML) 3/06, Halifax 7/06 Rel 7/06, Lancaster 7/06 Rel 10/06, Barrow 10/06, Hyde U 10/06, TNS Undisc 8/07, Fleetwood 1/09 Rel 5/10, Hyde U 7/10		
MIDFIELDERS								
Matty Burke			14/12/85	24		Blackpool (Scholar), Salford C, Barrow, Vauxhall Motors c/s 08, Alfreton 6/09, Hyde U (3ML) 11/09 Perm 2/10	23	2
Tom Manship	5'08"	11 02	27/3/87	23	Melton Mowbray	West Brom (Yth), Mansfield (Scholar), Hinckley c/s 05, Rugby (L) 9/06, Grantham 10/06, Cheltenham NC 8/07, Hucknall (L) 11/07, Hucknall (L) 3/08, Hyde U 11/08	28	1
Lee Rick			18/6/89	21		Macclesfield (Yth), Hyde U	28	1
FORWARDS								
Daniel Douglas-Pringle	5'10"	11 07	8/12/84	25	Manchester	Man City (Scholar), Bury (Scholar), Chorley (L) 10/04 Perm 11/04, Leigh RMI 1/05 Rel 2/05, Woodley Sports 2/05, Alfreton 7/07, Curzon Ashton Undisc 9/07, Chorley 2/08, Woodley Sports 8/08, Hyde U 11/08	25	3
Glyn Hurst	5'10"	11 06	17/1/76	34	Barnsley	Tottenham Rel c/s 94, Barnsley 7/04 Rel c/s 97, Swansea (L) 12/95, Mansfield (2ML) 11/96, Emley 8/97, Ayr 3/98, Stockport 2/01, Chesterfield 12/01 Rel c/s 04, Notts County 7/04, Shrewsbury 1/06 Bury (4ML) 9/06 Perm 1/07 Rel c/s 09, Chester 7/09, Gainsborough 8/09 Rel 11/09, Hyde U 12/09	6	0
David McNiven	5'10"	12 00	27/5/78	32	Leeds	Oldham Rel c/s 00, Linfield (L) 3/97, Scarborough (L) 2/00, Southport (L) 3/00, York 8/00 Rel c/s 01, Chester 7/01, Hamilton 10/01, Northwich 7/02, Kidsgrove (L) 11/02, Leigh RMI 8/03, Q.O.South 7/04, Scarborough 1/06, Morecambe 6/06, Stafford R (L) 1/07, Stafford R 8/07, Farsley Celtic (L) 2/08, Hyde U 7/09	39	12
Scott Mooney			15/1/89	21		Asfordby Amateurs, Holwell Sports, Hyde U 7/09	36	6
Daniel Politt						Man City (Yth), Hyde U 7/10		
Neil Tolson	6'02"	12 04	25/10/73	36	Wordsley	Walsall, Oldham £150,000 3/92, Bradford C £50,000 12/93, Chester (L) 1/95, York £60,000 7/96 Rel c/s 99, Southend 7/99 Rel c/s 01, Retired, Leigh RMI 10/02, Kettering 1/03 Rel 1/03, Halifax 3/03, Hyde 7/03 Pl/Ass Man c/s 07, Radcliffe B (L) 2/06	4	2
Kyle Wilson	5'10"	12 11	14/11/85	24	Wallasey	Crewe Rel 5/06, Altrincham (2ML) 10/05 (05/06 7,0), Barrow (3ML) 12/05, Wrexham (Trial) c/s 06, Barrow 8/06, Tranmere (Rehab from injury), Barrow 6/07, Witton 11/07, Droylsden 1/08 (07/08 1,0), Fleetwood 1/08, Skelmersdale 3/08, FCUM 6/08, Macclesfield 5/09 Rel c/s 10, FCUM (L) 1/10, Hyde U 7/10		

Loanees	HT	WT	DOB	AGE	POB	From - To	APPS	GOA
(D)Ashley Eastham			22/3/91	19		Blackpool (2ML) 8/09 - Chesterfield (L) 11/09	11	1
(G)Matthew Convey	6'01"	11 12	5/11/89	20	Oman	Bradford C 9/09 -	2	0
(D)David Thompson			27/2/91	19		Bury 10/09 - Chorley 1/10	3	0
(D)Paul Barratt			15/9/87	22	Manchester	Southport 10/09 -	5	0
(D)Adam Dugdale	6'03"	12 07	12/9/87	22	Liverpool	Barrow 11/09 - AFC Telford (L) 1/10 Perm 2/10	3	0
(G)Mark Halstead			1/1/90	20		Blackpool 3/10 -	7	0
Departures	**HT**	**WT**	**DOB**	**AGE**	**POB**	**From - To**	**APPS**	**GOA**
(F)Paul Gedman			14/6/81	29		FC Halifax 7/09 - Salford C 9/09	5	0
(G)Ayden Duffy	6'05"	15 00	16/11/86	23	Kettering	Corby T 9/09 - Grantham 10/09, Lincoln Moorlands 2/10	2	0
(D)Lincoln Adams			17/9/79	30	Huddersfield	FC Halifax 7/09 - Rel 10/09, Salford C 12/09	6	0
(M)Robbie Smith			20/2/85	25		Padiham 7/09 - Rel 10/09	7	1
(M)Aiden Kirkbride	6'00"	10 07	26/11/90	19	Ormskirk	Wigan 7/09 - Prescot Cables 11/09, Chorley 1/10	4	0
(M)Nathan Arnold	5'08"	10 07	26/7/87	23	Mansfield	Mansfield 8/09 - Alfreton 6/10	35	9
(M)Paul Armstrong			3/4/86	24	Manchester	Connahs Quay 7/09 - Rel c/s 10	0	0
(M)Daniel Barrie	5'10"	11 07	1/10/90	19	Ormskirk	Wigan (Scholar) 7/09 - Rel c/s 10	0	0
(G)Elliot Bernstein			3/2/77	33		Hanwell T 8/08 - Rel c/s 10	1	0
(M)Greg Traynor	5'10"	11 00	17/10/84	25	Salford	Flixton 7/09 - Rel c/s 10		
(F)Domaine Rouse	5'06"	10 10	4/7/89	21	Stretford	ex Bury 3/10 - Rel c/s 10	4	0
(D)Ricky Mercer			22/11/83	26	Preston	Fleetwood 10/09 - AFC Fylde 7/10	20	0
(M)Gerry Harrison	5'10"	12 12	15/4/72	38	Lambeth	Northwich 2/05 -	0	0
(M)Kevin Holsgrove			9/1/88	22		Colwyn Bay 9/09 - Kidderminster 7/10	31	0

ILKESTON TOWN

Chairman: Gary Hodder
Secretary: Keith Burnand **(T)** 07887 832 125 **(E)** kfootball@tiscali.co.uk

Additional Committee Members:
Jim Cheetham, Steve Cooper, Andrew Raisin, Paul Martin

Manager: Kevin Wilson
Programme Editor: Terry Brumpton **(E)** terrybrumton@yahoo.co.uk

Back Row (L to R): Kevin Wilson (Manager), Jon Douglas, Luke Waterfall, Dan Holmes, Dan Lowson, Gary Ricketts,David Bevan, Tom Bonner, Keiran Murphy,(Capt.), David Graham, Steve Huntington (Coach)
Front row; Paul Winter (Physio), Alex White, Josh Burge, Liam Green, Sam Duncum, Paul Dempsey, Dan Holmes, Amari Morgan-Smith, Darren Caskey (Coach) (Archive photo)

Club Factfile

Founded: 1945 **Nickname:** The Robins
Previous Names:
Previous Leagues: Notts & Derbyshire 1945-47, Central Alliance 1947-61, Midlands counties 1961-71, 73-82, Southern 1971-73, 95-2004, N.C.E. 1982-86, Central Midlands 1986-90, West Midlands Reg. 1990-94, N.P.L. 2004-09

Club Colours (change): Red & white halves/red/red (Blue & black stripes/black/black)

Ground: New Manor Ground, Awsworth Road, Ilkeston, Derbyshire DE7 8JF **(T)** 0115 944 429 496
Capacity: 3,029 **Seats:** 550 **Covered:** 2,000 **Clubhouse:** Yes **Shop:** Yes
Previous Grounds: Manor Ground 1945-1992
Simple Directions
M1 Junction 26, take the A610 signed Ripley, leave at the first exit on to the A6096 signed Awsworth / Ilkeston, at the next island take the A6096 signed Ilkeston, keep on this road for about half a mile, then turn right into Awsworth Road, Signed Cotmanhay (Coaches can get down this road) the ground is about half a mile on the left hand side down this road. Car Parking available at the ground £1 per car.

Record Attendance: Manor Ground: 9,592 v Peterborough - FAC 4thQ 1955-56. New Manor: 2,538 v Rushden & D. - FAC 1st Rnd 1999/00
Record Victory: 14-2 v Codnor M.W. - 1946-47
Record Defeat: 1-11 v Grantham Town - 1947-48. 0-10 v VS Rugby - 1985-86
Record Goalscorer: Jackie Ward - 141
Record Appearances: Terry Swincoe - 377
Additional Records: Paid £7,500 to Southport for Justin O'Reilly 1998
Received £25,000 from Peterborough United for Francis Green

Senior Honours: Derbyshire Senior Cup 1948-49, 52-53, 55-56, 57-58, 62-63, 82-83, 92-93, 98-99, 99-00, 05-06, 06-07.
Central Alliance 1951-52, 52-53, 53-54, 54-55, League Cup 1957-58. Midland Counties League 1967-68. Central Midlands League Cup 1986-87. West Midlands Div.1 1991-92, Premier 93-94, Div.1 League Cup 91-92, Premier League Cup 93-94.

10 YEAR RECORD

00-01	01-02	02-03	03-04	04-05	05-06	06-07	07-08	08-09	09-10
SthP 14	SthP 10	SthP 21	SthW 10	NP 1 2	NP P 16	NP P 12	NP P 17	NP P 2	Conf N 8

ILKESTON TOWN

No.	Date	Comp	H/A	Opponents	Att:	Result	Goalscorers	Pos
1	8/8/09	BSN	A	Droylsden	420	L 0-2		18
2	11/8/09	BSN	H	Redditch United	310	W 3-2	Morgan-Smith pen 54, Bonner 58, D Holmes pen 75	13
3	15/8/09	BSN	H	Southport	452	W 3-2	Ricketts 2 (44, 50), D Holmes 60	7
4	18/8/09	BSN	A	Corby Town	787	D 2-2	Graham 50, Morgan-Smith 85	8
5	22/8/09	BSN	H	Hyde United	408	D 1-1	Morgan-Smith pen 90	8
6	29/8/09	BSN	A	AFC Telford	1682	D 0-0		8
7	5/9/09	BSN	A	Workington	355	D 0-0		8
8	8/9/09	BSN	A	Solihull Moors	246	W 3-0	Ricketts 2 (12, 17), Duncum 70	6
9	12/9/09	BSN	H	Vauxhall Motors	429	W 4-0	Duncum 2 (20, 77), White 36, Morgan-Smith pen 73	5
10	19/9/09	BSN	A	Hinckley United	513	L 0-1		6
11	3/10/09	BSN	H	Gloucester City	437	D 0-0		8
12	17/10/09	BSN	H	Northwich Victoria	547	D 1-1	Morgan-Smith pen 59	8
13	27/10/09	BSN	H	Stafford Rangers	395	L 2-3	Graham 35, Morgan-Smith pen 47	8
14	31/10/09	BSN	A	Blyth Spartans	562	W 4-1	Morgan-Smith 3 (7, 15, 58), Graham 30	8
15	10/11/09	BSN	A	Alfreton Town	792	L 0-2		8
16	14/11/09	BSN	A	Southport	904	D 1-1	D Holmes 41	9
17	28/11/09	BSN	A	Harrogate Town	328	W 1-0	O'Loughlin 34	9
18	5/12/09	BSN	A	Stalybridge Celtic	474	L 0-1		9
19	16/1/10	BSN	A	Fleetwood Town	1009	L 0-1		10
20	25/1/10	BSN	A	Hyde United	269	D 1-1	Waterfall 36	11
21	30/1/10	BSN	H	Droylsden	366	W 1-0	Morgan-Smith 71	9
22	6/2/10	BSN	A	Gainsborough Trinity	337	D 0-0		10
23	9/2/10	BSN	A	Vauxhall Motors	184	L 2-4	Godden 20, Dempsey 23	11
24	13/2/10	BSN	H	Stalybridge Celtic	435	W 3-2	Ricketts 21, Dempsey 74, Watts 90	10
25	20/2/10	BSN	A	Northwich Victoria	476	L 1-4	Dempsey 50	10
26	27/2/10	BSN	H	Hinckley United	362	L 0-1		13
27	2/3/10	BSN	H	Corby Town	212	W 3-2	Morgan-Smith 2 (pen 45, pen 80), Burge 85	11
28	6/3/10	BSN	A	Redditch United	316	D 2-2	O'Loughlin 2, Ricketts 39	13
29	13/3/10	BSN	H	Blyth Spartans	360	W 2-1	Morgan-Smith 2 (33, 37)	11
30	16/3/10	BSN	H	Gainsborough Trinity	252	D 0-0		9
31	20/3/10	BSN	A	Stafford Rangers	434	W 1-0	Ghaichem 40	9
32	23/3/10	BSN	H	Eastwood Town	597	W 1-0	Waterfall 12	8
33	27/3/10	BSN	H	Harrogate Town	304	D 3-3	Morgan-Smith 2 (67, 90), Watts 83	9
34	3/4/10	BSN	H	AFC Telford	548	W 2-1	Watts 78, Lee 85	8
35	7/4/10	BSN	H	Workington	316	L 1-3	Og (Andrews) 42	8
36	10/4/10	BSN	H	Fleetwood Town	411	L 0-1		9
37	13/4/10	BSN	H	Solihull Moors	251	W 1-0	Rodney 14	8
38	17/4/10	BSN	H	Alfreton Town	584	D 0-0		9
39	20/4/10	BSN	A	Eastwood Town	754	W 3-0	Rodney 12, Morgan-Smith pen 45, Ricketts 60	8
40	24/4/10	BSN	A	Gloucester City	350	W 1-0	Morgan-Smith 69	8
	Farsley Celtic record expunged 12/03							
7	31/8/09	BSN	H	Farsley Celtic	352	W 1-0	Duncum 15	4
	Cups							
1	26/9/09	FAC 2Q	H	Mildenhall Town	321	W 4-1	Dempsey 2 (17, 53), O'Loughlin 75, Graham 78	
2	10/10/09	FAC 3Q	H	Eastwood Town	1128	D 1-1	Morgan-Smith pen 70	
3	13/10/09	FAC 3QR	A	Eastwood Town	1205	W 3-1	Morgan-Smith 2 (41, 89), Ricketts 46	
4	24/10/09	FAC 4Q	H	Tamworth	669	W 2-0	Burge 30, Graham 69	
5	7/11/09	FAC 1	A	Cambridge United	2395	L 0-4		
6	21/11/09	FAT 3Q	H	Mossley AFC	271	D 1-1	Duncum 55	
7	24/11/09	FAT 3QR	A	Mossley AFC	183	W 2-0	Ricketts 2 (55, 60)	
8	12/12/09	FAT 1	A	Blyth Spartans	419	L 0-2		

Home Attendances:	
Highest:	597 v Eastwood Town
Lowest:	212 v Corby Town
Average (08-09):	402 (565)
Top Goalscorer:	Morgan-Smith - 19 (16 League, 3 Cup) in 46 appearances - 41% strike rate
Most Appearances:	Morgan-Smith - 46 (35+4 League, 7 Cup)

BEVAN	R HOLMES	BONNER	D HOLMES	O'LOUGHLIN	MURPHY	GREEN	DEMPSEY	RICKETTS	MORGAN-SMITH	DUNCUM	GRAHAM	DOUGLAS	WATERFALL	BURGE	WHITE	CASKEY	LOWSON	FAIRCLOUGH	ELEY	BEECROFT	HARRIS	WEIR-DALEY	DOYLE	HOOKS	COOMBES	MITCHELL	PALMER	MENDES	WATTS	PRENDERGAST	SHORT	GODDEN	COLEMAN	ZOOMERS	GHAICHEM	RODNEY	LEE	
X	X	X	X	X	X	X	X	X	X	X	S	S	U	U	U																							1
X		X	X	X	X	X	X	X	X	X	S	S	U	U	X	U																						2
X		X	X	X	X	X	X	X	X	X	S	U	U	U	X		U																					3
X		X	X	X	X	X	X	X	S	X	X	S	U	S	X		U																					4
U		X	X	X	X	U	X	X	S	X	X	S	U	X	X		X																					5
		X	X	X	X	S	X	X	X	X	S		X	S	U		X	X	U																			6
				X	X	X	X	X	X	X	S	S	X	U	X		X	U	U	X																		7
				X	X	X	X	X	X	X	S	S	X	U	X		X	S	U	X																		8
				X	X	X	X		X	X	X	S	X	U	X		X	S	U	X	S																	9
			U	X	X	X	X	X	X	X	S		X	S	X		X	S	U	X																		10
	U		X	X	X		X	X	X	X	S		X	S	X		X			X				S	U													11
	S	U		X	X	U			X	X	X		X	X	X		X			X	U			X	U													12
	U	X		X		U	X		X	X	X		X	X	X		X			X	U			S	U													13
	X	X				S	X		X	X	X		X	U			X			X	S			X	U	X	S											14
		X	S			U	X	X	X	X			X	X			X			X				X	U	X	S		U									15
		X	X	X		S	X	X	X	X			X	U			X			X				U	U	X	U											16
		X	X	X		U	X	X	X	X			X				X			S				U	U	X	U			X								17
		X	X	X			X	X	S	X			X				X							S	U	X	U		X	X	U							18
		X	X			S	X	X		X			X	S	X		X							X	U				S		U	X	X					19
		X	X	X		U	X	X	S	S			X	X	X	U	X							S								X	X					20
		X	X	X		U	X	X	X				X	S	X		X							U	U				U			X	X					21
		X	X	X		U	X	X	X				X	U	X		X							U	U				U			X	X					22
		X	X	X	U	U	X	X	X				X	S	X		X								U				S			X	X					23
		X	X	X		X	X	X	X				X	U	S		X							U	U				S			X	X					24
		U	S	X	X	X	X	X	X				X	S	X		X								U				X			S	X					25
		X	X	X	X	X	X	X	X				X	S	U	S	X								U				S			X						26
		X	X	X		X	X	X	X				X	S	U	S	X								U				S			X	X					27
		X	X	X	U	X		X	X				X	X	S	U	X								U				S			X	X					28
		X	X	X	X	X		X	X				X	X		U	X												S			U	U	X	S			29
		X	X	X	X	X		X	X				X	X	U	U	X								U				U					U	X			30
		X	X	X	X	X	S	X	X				X	X	U		X								U				S					U	X			31
		X	X	X	X	X	U	X	X				X	X		U	X								U				U						X	S		32
			X	X	X	X	U	X	X				X	X		S	X				U				U				S						X	X		33
		X	X	X	X	X	U		X				X	X		S	X								U				S						S	X	X	34
		X	X	X	X	X	U		X				X	X		S	X								U				S						S	X	X	35
		X	X	X	X	X	X		X				X	U		S					U				X				S						S	X	X	36
		X	X	U		X	X		X				X	X	X	U					U				X				X						S	X	S	37
		X	X	X		X	X		X				X	S	U	X	X				X				U				S							X	S	38
		X	X	X	X	U	X	X	X				X		U		X				S				U				S							X	X	39
		X	X	X	X		X	X	X				X	U	U		X				S				U				S							X	X	40
		X		X	X	X	X	X	X	X	S	U	X	S	S		X	X	U																			
	S		X	X	X		X	X	X		X		X	S	X	U	X			X	U	S	U															1
	U		X	X	X		X	X	X	X	S		X	S	X		X			X	U	U		S														2
	U	U	X	X	X		X	X	X	X	U		X	U	X	U	X			X	U			U														3
	U	X	X	X		U	X		X		X		X	X	X	U	X			X	U			S														4
	X	X	U			U	X		X	X			X	S		U	X			X	S			X		X		X	U									5
			X	X		U	X	X	X	X			X	S			X			X				U	U	X	S			X								6
		X	X	X		U	X	X	U	X			X	U			X							X	U	X	U			X								7
		S	X	X		U		X	X	X			X	S			X							X	U	X	S		X	X								8

Total League Appearances

BEVAN	R HOLMES	BONNER	D HOLMES	O'LOUGHLIN	MURPHY	GREEN	DEMPSEY	RICKETTS	MORGAN-SMITH	DUNCUM	GRAHAM	DOUGLAS	WATERFALL	BURGE	WHITE	CASKEY	LOWSON	FAIRCLOUGH	ELEY	BEECROFT	HARRIS	WEIR-DALEY	DOYLE	HOOKS	COOMBES	MITCHELL	PALMER	MENDES	WATTS	PRENDERGAST	SHORT	GODDEN	COLEMAN	ZOOMERS	GHAICHEM	RODNEY	LEE	
4	2	32	31	36	24	23	31	31	35	19	6	0	35	14	18	1	34	1	0	10	1	0	0	4	2	5	0	0	3	2	0	9	9	1	4	8	5	X
0	1	0	2	0	0	4	1	0	4	1	8	7	0	11	2	6	0	3	0	1	4	0	0	4	0	0	2	0	15	0	0	1	0	0	5	1	2	S
1	2	2	1	1	2	10	4	0	0	0	0	1	5	12	9	7	2	1	5	0	5	0	0	5	26	0	3	0	5	0	2	1	1	2	0	0	0	U

Total Cup Appearances

BEVAN	R HOLMES	BONNER	D HOLMES	O'LOUGHLIN	MURPHY	GREEN	DEMPSEY	RICKETTS	MORGAN-SMITH	DUNCUM	GRAHAM	DOUGLAS	WATERFALL	BURGE	WHITE	CASKEY	LOWSON	FAIRCLOUGH	ELEY	BEECROFT	HARRIS	WEIR-DALEY	DOYLE	HOOKS	COOMBES	MITCHELL	PALMER	MENDES	WATTS	PRENDERGAST	SHORT	GODDEN	COLEMAN	ZOOMERS	GHAICHEM	RODNEY	LEE	
0	1	3	7	7	3	0	7	6	7	6	2	0	8	1	4	0	8	0	0	6	0	0	0	3	0	4	0	1	1	3	0	0	0	0	0	0	0	X
0	1	1	0	0	0	0	0	0	0	0	1	0	0	5	0	0	0	0	0	0	1	1	0	2	0	0	2	0	0	0	0	0	0	0	0	0	0	S
0	3	1	1	0	0	5	0	0	1	0	1	0	0	2	0	4	0	0	0	0	4	1	1	2	3	0	1	0	1	0	0	0	0	0	0	0	0	U

Total Goals

BEVAN	R HOLMES	BONNER	D HOLMES	O'LOUGHLIN	MURPHY	GREEN	DEMPSEY	RICKETTS	MORGAN-SMITH	DUNCUM	GRAHAM	DOUGLAS	WATERFALL	BURGE	WHITE	CASKEY	LOWSON	FAIRCLOUGH	ELEY	BEECROFT	HARRIS	WEIR-DALEY	DOYLE	HOOKS	COOMBES	MITCHELL	PALMER	MENDES	WATTS	PRENDERGAST	SHORT	GODDEN	COLEMAN	ZOOMERS	GHAICHEM	RODNEY	LEE	
0	0	1	3	2	0	0	3	7	16	3	3	0	2	1	1	0	0	0	0	0	0	0	0	0	0	0	0	0	3	0	0	1	0	0	1	2	1	Lge
0	0	0	0	1	0	0	2	3	3	1	2	0	0	1	0	0	0	0	0	0	0	0	0	0	0	0	0	0	0	0	0	0	0	0	0	0	0	Cup

ILKESTON TOWN

CURRENT SQUAD AS OF BEGINING OF 2010-11 SEASON

GOALKEEPERS	HT	WT	D.O.B	AGE	P.O.B	CAREER	APPS	GOA
Dan Lowson			4/2/88	22		Gretna, Newcastle Blue Star, Ilkeston 7/09	34	0
DEFENDERS								
Tom Bonner	6'00"	11 06	6/2/88	22	Camden	Northampton Rel 1/07, Bedford (SL) 2/06, Nuneaton (L) 8/06, Rushden & D 1/07 Rel 8/07, Bedford (L) 2/07, Heybridge (L) 3/07, Corby T 8/07, Hinckley U 1/08, Solihull Moors 2/09, Corby T 6/09, Ilkeston 8/09	32	1
Sam Clare	5'11"	11'05"	7/10/91	18	Derby	Chesterfield, Ilkeston 6/10		
Ryan Clarke			22/1/84	26		Notts County (Scholar), Boston U 7/03, Kings Lynn (L) 10/04, Leigh RMI (L) 12/04 Perm 3/05, Alfreton 7/05, Worcester 6/07, Boston U 5/08, Grantham 7/09, Eastwood T 8/09 Rel 11/09, Northwich 12/09, Ilkeston 5/10		
Paul Dempsey	5'11"	12 00	3/12/81	28	Birkenhead	Sheff Utd, Northampton 3/01 Rel c/s 02, Aukland Kingz (NZ) 4/02, Scarborough 1/03 Rel c/s 03, RKSV Leonidas Rotterdam (Holl) 5/03, Worksop 8/04, Hucknall 6/06, Worksop 6/08, Wakefield 2/09, Ilkeston 6/09	32	3
Charlie O'Loughlin	6'01"	13 02	17/3/89	21	Birmingham	Port Vale Rel 4/08, Nantwich (L) 11/07, Hinckley U (L) 1/08, Nantwich 6/08, Ilkeston 6/09	36	2
MIDFIELDERS								
Josh Burge			29/6/90	20		Grimsby (Scholar) Rel c/s 08, Aston Villa (Trial) 1/07, Appalachian State University (USA) c/s 08, Ilkeston 6/09	25	1
Darren Caskey			21/8/74	36		Tottenham, Watford (L) 10/95, Reading 2/96, Notts County 7/01, Bristol C 3/04, Hornchurch 6/04, Peterborough 11/04, Bath C 1/05, Havant & W 1/05, Virginia Beach Mariners 3/05, Rushden & D 1/06, Kettering 7/06, Halesowen T (3ML) 10/07 (Pl/Coach) 1/08, Ilkeston (Pl/Coach) 8/09	7	0
Liam Green	5'09"	10 00	17/3/88	22	Grimsby	Doncaster Rel c/s 07, Guiseley (L) 12/06, Boston U 7/07, Ilkeston 7/09	27	0
Dan Holmes	6'00"	12 00	17/11/86	23	Burton	Port Vale Rel c/s 06, Burton 7/06 Rel 5/09, Ilkeston 7/09	33	3
Callum Lloyd	5'09"	11 04	1/1/86	24	Nottingham	Mansfield Rel 5/07, Alfreton (L) 11/05, Kettering 5/07 Rel 11/07, Hinckley U (L) 10/07, Hinckley U 11/07, Kings Lynn 6/09, Ilkeston 2/10		
Joe Maguire			23/9/91	18	Sheffield	Scunthorpe Rel c/s 10, Ilkeston 6/10		
Jack Watts	5'11"	11 08	1/6/91	19	Australia	Barnsley (Scholar) Rel c/s 09, Ilkeston 10/09	18	3
Laurie Wilson	5'10"	11 03	5/12/84	25	Brighton	Sheff Wed Rel c/s 04, Burton 7/04 Rel 4/05, Gresley (L) 12/04, Grantham (L) 1/05, Belper T (L) 2/05, Kidderminster 6/05, Hucknall 3/06, Alfreton 7/07, Hucknall 6/08, Ilkeston 5/10		
FORWARDS								
Chukki Eribenne	5'10"	11 12	2/11/80	29	Westminster	Coventry Rel c/s 00, Bournemouth 7/00 Rel c/s 03, Hereford (L) 10/02, Northampton (Trial) 5/03, Havant & W 8/03, Weymouth 7/04, Aldershot (L) 12/04, Farnborough (L) 1/05, Grays 1/07 Rel 5/07, Gravesend (SL) 3/07, Ebbsfleet 5/07 Rel 5/08, Sutton U 8/08, Hinckley U 8/09, Ilkeston T 6/10		
David Graham	5'10"	11 05	6/10/78	31	Edinburgh	Rangers, Dunfermline 11/98, Inverness Caledonian (2ML) 1/01, Lincoln C, Sheffield FC 3/09, Torquay 3/01, Wigan 6/04, Sheff Wed 8/05, Huddersfield (SL) 1/06, Bradford C (5ML) 7/06, Torquay (SL) 3/07, Gillingham 8/07 Rel 1/08, Lincoln C 7/08 Rel 12/08, Sheffield FC 3/09, Ilkeston T 8/09	14	3
Joe Harris	6'03"	13 04	13/7/91	19		Swansea (Scholar) Rel c/s 09, Ilkeston 7/09, Shepshed D (L) 1/10	5	0
Ian Holmes	6'00"	12 05	29/6/85	25	Ellesmere Port	University Football, Matlock c/s 06, Mansfield Undisc 8/07 Rel 5/08, AFC Telford (SL) 3/08, Eastwood T 7/08 Rel 5/10, Ilkeston 6/10		
Jason Lee	6'03"	13 08	9/5/71	39	Forest Gate	Charlton, Fisher (L) 8/89, Stockport (L) 2/91, Lincoln C £35,000 3/91, Southend (L) 8/93 £150,000 9/93, N.Forest £200,000 3/94, Charlton (2ML) 2/97, Grimsby (L) 3/97, Watford £200,000 6/97, Chesterfield £250,000 8/98, Peterborough (2ML) 1/00 £50,000 3/00 Rel c/s 03, Scarborough (Trial) 7/03, Falkirk 8/03, Boston U 8/04, Northampton 1/06 Rel c/s 06, Notts County 6/06 Rel c/s 08, Mansfield 7/08, Kettering 1/09, Corby 3/09, Ilkeston 3/10	7	1
Amari Morgan-Smith	6'00"	13 06	3/4/89	21	Wolverhampton	Wolves (Yth), Crewe (Scholar), Alsager T (WE) 3/07, Stockport 8/07 Rel c/s 08, Ilkeston 6/08	39	16
Gary Ricketts			13/7/75	35	Nottingham	Notts Forest (Yth), Heanor, Arnold, Hinckley U c/s 99, Cambridge U (Trial) 1/00, Hucknall £1,500 3/01, Nuneaton 5/07, Hucknall 9/07, Tamworth 3/09, Ilkeston 6/09	31	7

Loanees	HT	WT	DOB	AGE	POB	From - To	APPS	GOA
(G)David Bevan	6'02"	13 00	24/6/89	21	Cork	Aston Villa 8/09 - Solihull Moors (L) 12/09	4	0
(F)Ben Fairclough	5'06"	09 10	18/4/89	21	Nottingham	Notts County 8/09 -	4	0
(G)Ed Eley	6'02"		1/3/91	19		Grimsby 8/09 - Mansfield (L) 9/09, Mansfield (2ML) 11/09, Eastwood T 1/10 Rel 5/10	0	0
(M)Jake Beecroft			4/9/89	20		Rushden & D (3ML) 9/09 - St Albans (2ML) 1/10, Rel 5/10	11	0
(D)Aaron Mitchell	6'05"		5/2/90	20		Notts Forest (2ML) 10/09 - Rel 1/10, Burton, Hucknall 3/10, Tamworth 3/10	5	0
(D)Rory Coleman	6'00"	11 09	22/12/90	19	Rotherham	Scunthorpe (SL) 1/10 -	9	0
(M)Matt Godden			29/7/91	19	Canterbury	Scunthorpe (SL) 1/10 -	10	1
(F)Nialle Rodney			28/2/91	19		Notts Forest 3/10 -	9	2

Departures	HT	WT	DOB	AGE	POB	From - To	APPS	GOA
(M)Mitchell Griffiths			22/10/90	19		Boston U 7/09 - Rel 8/09, Deeping R 8/09		
(F)Jon Douglas			24/5/84	26	Coventry	Lincoln U 1/08 - Rel 9/09, Solihull Moors 9/09 Rel 11/09, Oxford C 11/09, Wealdstone 6/10	7	0
(F)Spencer Weir-Daly	5'09"	10 11	5/9/85	24	Leicester	ex Notts County 9/09 - Boston U 10/09	0	0
(D)James Dudgeon	6'02"	12 04	19/3/81	29	Newcastle	Wakefield 6/09 - Rel 1/10, Frickley (L) 9/09, Goole AFC (L) 10/09		
(F)Mark Doyle			25/9/88	21		Cyprus 9/09 - Rel 10/09	0	0
(F)Junior Mendes	5'10"	11 00	15/9/76	33	Balham	Aldershot 11/09 - Rel 11/09	0	0
(M)Rory Prendergast	5'08"	12 00	6/4/78	32	Pontefract	Goole AFC 11/09 - Rel 1/10, Goole AFC 3/10	2	0
(F)Jermaine Palmer			28/8/86	24	Nottingham	Boston T 10/09 - Rel 1/10	2	0
(M)Chris Davies	5'10"	11 10	8/4/84	26	Rotherham	Frickley 6/09 - Frickley (L) 9/09, Frickley 2/10		
(M)Neal Hooks			3/7/87	23	Hexham	Sunshine George Cross (Aust) 9/09 - Blyth 2/10	8	0
(M)Sam Duncum	5'09"	11 02	18/2/87	23	Sheffield	Rotherham 5/08 - Eastwood T Undisc 2/10	20	3
(D)Kieran Murphy	5'11"	11 00	21/12/87	22	Kingston	MK Dons c/s 08 - Boston U 5/10	24	0
(D)Luke Waterfall	6'02"	12 11	30/7/90	20	Sheffield	Tranmere 8/09 - Gainsborough 5/10	35	2
(D)Richie Holmes	6'01"	13 00	1/10/90	19		Chesterfield 6/09 - Hucknall 6/10	3	0
(G)David Coombes			8/3/87	23		Loughborough University 10/09 - Rel c/s 10	2	0
(D)Alex White			28/8/88	22		Tow Law 6/09 - Rel c/s 10	20	1
(M)Jimmy Ghaichem			11/4/84	26		Harrogate T 3/10 - Rel c/s 10	9	1
(M)Oscar Short			11/4/92	18		Yth - Buxton (L) 2/10	0	0
(M)Tobin Zoomers						Bulli FC (Aust) 3/10 -	1	0

NUNEATON TOWN

Chairman: Ian Neale

Secretary: Ian Brown (T) 07976 375292 (E) ian.brown@nuneatontownfc.com

Additional Committee Members:
Kirk Stephens, Neil Hodgson, Dawn Towers

Manager: Kevin Wilkin

Programme Editor: Club (E) ian.brown@nuneatontownfc.com

Club Factfile

Founded: 2008 **Nickname:** The Boro

Previous Names: Nuneaton Borough 1937-2008

Previous Leagues: Central Amateur 1937-38, Birmingham Combination 1938-52, West Midlands 1952-58, Southern 1958-79 81-82, 88-90, 2003-04, 08-10, Conference 1979-81, 82-88, 99-03, 04-08

Club Colours (change): Blue & white halves/blue/blue (Pink/white/black)

Ground: Liberty Way, Nuneaton, Warwickshire CV11 6RR (T) 02476 385 738

Capacity: **Seats:** **Covered:** **Clubhouse:** **Shop:**

Previous Grounds: Manor Park

Simple Directions
From the South, West and North West, exit the M6 at Junction 3 and follow the A444 into Nuneaton. At the Coton Arches roundabout turn right into Avenue Road which is the A4254 signposted for Hinckley. Continue along the A4254 following the road into Garrett Street, then Eastboro Way, then turn left into Townsend Drive. Follow the road round before turning left into Liberty Way for the ground. From the North, exit the M1 at Junction 21 and follow the M69. Exit at Junction 1 and take the 4th exit at roundabout onto A5 (Tamworth, Nuneaton). At Longshoot Junction turn left onto A47, continue to roundabout and take the 1st exit onto A4254, Eastboro Way. Turn right at next roundabout into Townsend Drive, then right again into Liberty Way, CV11 6RR.

Record Attendance: 22,114 v Rotherham United - FA Cup 3rd Round 1967 (At Manor Park)

Record Victory: 11-1 - 1945-46 and 1955-56

Record Defeat: 1-8 - 1955-56 and 1968-69

Record Goalscorer: Paul Culpin - 201 (55 during season 1992-93)

Record Appearances: Alan Jones - 545 (1962-74)

Additional Records: Paid £35,000 to Forest green Rovers for Marc McGregor 2000
Received £80,000 from Kidderminster Harriers for Andy Ducros 2000

Senior Honours: Southern League Midland Division 1981-82, 92-93, Premier Division 1988-99, Premier Division Play-offs 2009-10. Birmingham Senior Cup x7.

10 YEAR RECORD

00-01	01-02	02-03	03-04	04-05	05-06	06-07	07-08	08-09	09-10
Conf 13	Conf 10	Conf 20	SthP 4	Conf N 2	Conf N 3	Conf N 10	Conf N 7	SthE 2	SthP 2

NUNEATON TOWN

No.	Date	Comp	H/A	Opponents	Att:	Result	Goalscorers	Pos
1	Aug 15	Zamaretto P.	A	Chippenham Town	530	L 1 - 2	Oddy 16	15
2	18		H	Halesowen Town	901	D 1 - 1	Connor 62 (og)	16
3	22		H	Oxford City	765	W 3 - 1	Armson 43 48 Murphy 90	11
4	25		A	Evesham United	258	W 2 - 1	Storer 45 (pen) Dillon 53	7
5	29		A	Cambridge City	412	D 1 - 1	Armson 87	8
6	31		H	Hednesford Town	944	W 3 - 1	Armson 43 88 Oddy 70	
7	Sept 5		A	Merthyr Tydfil	413	W 3 - 1	Oddy 17 (pen) Moore 31 Forsdick 67	7
8	**12**	**F.A.C 1Q**	**A**	**Brigg Town**	**239**	**W 5 - 0**	**Dillon 13 Spacey 36 Oddy 55 90 Marsden 88**	
9	19		H	Hemel Hempstead	815	W 3 - 1	Dean 40 Oddy 60 Dillon 63	3
10	**26**	**F.A.C 2Q**	**H**	**Carlton Town**	**903**	**D 1 - 1**	**Spacey 36**	
11	**29**	**F.A.C.2Qr**	**A**	**Carlton Town**	**254**	**W 3 - 0**	**Marsden 12 Noon 35 Forsdick 50**	
12	Oct 4		H	Brackley Town	785	D 2 - 2	Noon 68 Dean 73	4
13	6		A	Bedford Town	380	L 1 - 2	Dillon 27	7
14	**10**	**F.A.C. 3Q**	**H**	**Gainsborough Trinity**	**930**	**W 1 - 0**	**Marsden 34**	
15	**17**	**F.A.T 1Q**	**H**	**Hucknall Town**	**660**	**D 1 - 1**	**Spacey 59**	
16	**20**	**F.A.T 1Q**	**A**	**Hucknall Town**	**100**	**W 3 - 0**	**Moore 56 Marsden 68 Murphy 88**	
17	**24**	**F.A.C 4Q**	**H**	**Kendal Town**	**1103**	**W 1 - 0**	**Foster 86**	
18	**31**	**F.A.T 2Q**	**A**	**Willenhall Town**	**335**	**W 6 - 0**	**Walker 29 Nisevic 60 Spacey 79 Foster 82 90 Dillon 89**	
19	**Nov 7**	**F.A.C. 1R**	**H**	**Exeter City**	**2452**	**L 0 - 4**		
20	11		A	Swindon Supermarine	193	W 4 - 2	Dillon 52 71 Pierpoint 66 Walker 60	
21	14		A	Banbury United	488	L 1 - 2	Dillon 44	
22	17		H	Truro City	731	W 4 - 0	Armson 14 Dillon 28 Moore 38 Oddy 66	
23	**21**	**F.A.T 3Q**	**A**	**Hyde United**	**328**	**D 3 - 3**	**Pierpoint 22 Spacey 30 Oddy 63 (pen)**	
24	**23**	**F.A.T. 3Qr**	**H**	**Hyde United**	**464**	**W 1 - 0**	**Marsdon 84**	
25	28		H	Clevedon Town	734	W 4 - 2	Dean 18 Armson 31 Walker 49 Oddy 90 (pen)	4
26	Dec 5		A	Farnborough	1180	W 2 - 0	Moore 13 Marsden 68	4
27	8		H	Stourbridge	708	D 0 - 0		
28	**12**	**F.A.T 1R**	**A**	**Workington**	**319**	**L 1 - 2**	**Oddy 27 (pen)**	
29	23		A	Hemel Hempstead	348	W 3 - 1	Armson 19 Oddy 41 Dillon 85	4
30	Jan 26		H	Rugby Town	882	D 1 - 1	Oddy 47	
31	30		H	Merthgyr TYdfil	833	W 3 - 1	Dillon 23 Marsden 58 Nisevic 72	4
32	Feb 2		A	Bashley	223	L 1 - 2	Armson 36	
33	6		A	Rugby Town	612	W 3 - 0	Armson 13 75 Foster 90	3
34	12		H	Banbury United	702	W 5 - 0	Dean 29 38 Dillon 43 79 Armson 68	3
35	23		A	Halesowen Town	350	L 2 - 3	Dillon 58 Moore 90	
36	March 2		A	Didcot Town	226	D 1 - 1	Dillon 23	
37	6		H	Evesham United	844	W 2 - 0	Moore 50 Dillon 62	5
38	9		H	Bedford Town	659	W 4 - 0	Storer 44 Peirpoint 45 Dean 51 Noore 80	
39	13		A	Brackley Town	426	D 0 - 0		
40	16		A	Hednesford Town	459	W 3 - 0	Storer 33 Oddy 43 Moore 61	
41	20		H	Swindon Supermarine	736	W 1 - 0	Oddy 78 (pen)	2
42	24		A	Tiverton Town	236	W 2 - 1	Hadland 15 Moore 13	
43	27		A	Truro Town	558	W 2 - 0	Armson 27 Dillon 58	2
44	30		A	Stourbridge	382	W 2 - 1	Moore 37 Marsden 89	
45	April 3		H	Tiverton Town	803	W 1 - 0	Oddy 45 (pen)	2
46	5		A	Leamington	1251	W 2 - 0	Dillon 45 63	2
47	7		H	Cambridge City	826	D 1 - 1	Marsden 89	
48	10		H	Farnborough	1765	D 1 - 1	Storer 71	2
49	15		H	Leamington	938	D 1 - 1	Oddy 35	
50	17		A	Clevedon Town	226	W 3 - 0	Spacey 25 Marsden 82 Moore 90	2
51	18		H	Chippenham Town	651	L 0 - 1		2
52	20		H	Didcot Town	555	W 2 - 0	Forsdick 2 Foster 74	
53	22		A	Oxford CIty	315	W 4 - 1	Forsdick 23 Moore 23 Marsden 30 Noon 83	
54	24		H	Bashley	715	W 5 - 2	FOSTER 3 (13 50 82) Oddy 18 Armson 44	2
55	**27**	**Play Off S-F**	**H**	**Brackley Town**	**1639**	**W 6 - 0**	**Forsdick 41 Moore 54 Dillon 56 Deane 63 Armson 69 Nisevic 88**	
56	**28**	**Play-Off F**	**H**	**Chippenham Town**	**3018**	**W 2 - 1**	**Dillon 74 Nisevic 105**	
					Goals	124 49		

Home Attendances:

Highest:	1765 v Farnborough
Lowest:	555 v Didcot Town
Average:	785

Top Goalscorer: Dillon - 21 (League 17, FAC 1, FAT 1, Play-off 2)

NUNEATON TOWN

CURRENT SQUAD AS OF BEGINING OF 2010-11 SEASON

GOALKEEPERS	HT	WT	D.O.B	AGE	P.O.B	CAREER	APPS	GOA
Darren Acton			19/5/73	37	Wolverhampton	Telford, Burton c/s 94, Bloxwich 7/98, Kidderminster 8/98, Tamworth 6/99, Nuneaton B/T 6/03		
DEFENDERS								
Gareth Dean	6'02"		25/1/90	20	Nuneaton	Nuneaton T		
Guy Hadland	6'01"	12 11	23/1/79	31	Nuneaton	Aston Villa Rel c/s 98, Injured, Hinckley U 1/00, Evesham (L) 10/01, Bedworth 10/03, Solihull B 8/04, Bedworth 12/04, Evesham 8/05, Brackley 11/05, Nuneaton 6/08		
Ed Matthews						Luton (Yth), Derby (Yth), S&L c/s 08, Nuneaton T 8/09		
Eddie Nisevic						Nuneaton T, Shepshed D (L) 9/09		
Rob Oddy			13/11/85	24	Coventry	Coventry (Scholar) Rel c/s 04, Nuneaton (SL) 3/04, Nuneaton 8/04, Rugby T (L) 3/08		
Stuart Pierpoint					Halesowen	Oldbury U, Sutton Coldfield, Halesowen T 8/05, Stafford R 7/08, Nuneaton T 6/09		
MIDFIELDERS								
James Armson							Nuneaton T	
Matthew Collins	5'10"	12 00	10/2/82	28	Hitchin	West Brom Rel c/s 03, Nuneaton B/T 5/03, Notts County (Trial) 2/04		
Simon Forsdick			27/4/83	27	Cambridge	Coventry (Ass Sch), Stratford, Loughborough Univ, Shepshed D, Halesowen T 1/04, Hednesford T 7/07, AFC Telford 9/07, Nuneaton T (L) 8/08, Bloxwich U (L) 8/08, Rushall O (Dual) 2/09, Stratford T (Dual) 3/09, Nuneaton T (L) 3/09 Perm 6/09		
Mark Noon	5'10"	12 04	23/9/83	26	Leamington Spa	Coventry, Tamworth 3/04 (03/04 7,0) Nuneaton B/T 7/04		
Kyle Storer			30/4/87	23	Nuneaton	Leicester (Jun), Bedworth 7/02, Tamworth 6/04, Hinckley U (L) 1/06, Hinckley U 9/07, Atherstone 8/08, Nuneaton T 2/09		
Adam Walker	5'06"	09 00	22/1/91	19	Coventry	Coventry Rel 4/10, Nuneaton T (3ML) 10/09, Nuneaton T 4/10		
FORWARDS								
Tom Berwick						Daventry T, Nuneaton T 6/10		
Chris Dillon	6'00"		13/1/84	26	Middlesbrough	Luton, Enfield 11/02, Grays 12/02, Hitchin 3/03, Bedford T 12/03, Hitchin 5/06, Histon Undisc 3/07, Hemel Hempstead (3ML) 10/07 Perm 1/08, Nuneaton T 5/09		
Justin Marsden			7/3/84	26	Coventry	Rugby U, Solihull B 7/05, AFC Telford 5/06, Bedworth U (L) 2/08, Leamington (L) 3/08, Brackley 6/08, Nuneaton T 9/08		
Aiden Moore	6'00"	11 00	18/3/92	18	Nuneaton	Doncaster Rel c/s 10, Nuneaton T 6/10		
Lee Moore			9/11/85	24	Bathgate	Coventry (Jun), Bedworth 7/02, Tamworth 7/06, AFC Telford (3ML) 9/06 £5,000 12/06, Nuneaton T 6/09		
Danny Spencer						St Andrews, Atherstone U, St Andrews, Rothwell 1/04, Barwell, Brackley, Redditch 11/07, Brackley 2/08, Kings Lynn 9/09, Oadby T 11/09, Nuneaton T 3/10		

Do you remember when...

Nuneaton Boro'

Playing as Nuneaton Borough this squad had celebrated winning the Southern League Championship and was preparing for Conference football in the 1999-2000 season.

Back Row, left to right: Ian King, Jon Gittens, Krystof Kotylo, Andy Thackeray, Alex Sykes, Wayne Simpson, Mark Taylor and Lee Charles.
Middle Row: Brian Clarke (Kitman), Shaun Wray, Nathan Thompson, Carl Bacon, Chris Mackenzie, Barry Williams, Ryan Young, Bobby Stevenson, Karl Brennan, Simon Weaver and Kevin Shoemake.
Front Row: Richie Norman (Physio), Terry Angus, Richard Mitchell, Delton Francis, Brendan Phillips (Manager) , Steve Burr (Coach), Marc McGregor, Michael Love, David Crowley and Paul Egan (Physio).

REDDITCH UNITED

Chairman: Ken Rae
Secretary: Tim Delaney (T) 07827 963 212
(E) sec.rufc@yahoo.co.uk
Additional Committee Members:
KEn Rae, Dave Chatwin, Claire Lane, Tim Delaney, Dave Jones
Manager: Matt Gardiner
Programme Editor: Tracey Rae (E) programmeeditor.reds@yahoo.com

Club Factfile

Founded: 1891 **Nickname:** The Reds
Previous Names: Redditch Town
Previous Leagues: Birmingham combination 1905-21, 29-39, 46-53, West Midlands 1921-29, 53-72, Southern 1972-79, 81-2004, Alliance 1979-80

Club Colours (change): All red (White/blue/blue)

Ground: Valley Stadium, Bromsgrove Road, Redditch B97 4RN (T) 01527 67450
Capacity: 5,000 **Seats:** 400 **Covered:** 2,000 **Clubhouse:** Yes **Shop:** Yes
Previous Grounds: HDA Sports Ground, Millsborough Road
Simple Directions
M42 J2, at island first exit onto the A441 for 2 miles, next island first exit onto Birmingham Road A441 for 1.2 miles then at island third exit onto Middlehouse Lane B4184 for 0.3 miles. At traffic lights (next to the fire station) turn left onto Birmingham Road for 0.2 miles then turn right into Clive Road for 0.3 miles. At island take first exit onto Hewell Road for 0.2 miles then at 'T' junction right onto Windsor Street for 0.1 miles. At traffic lights (next to bus station) continue straight ahead onto Bromsgrove Road for 0.3 miles and at the brow of the hill, turn right into the ground's entrance.

Record Attendance: 5,500 v Bromsgrove Rovers - Wets Midlands League 1954-55
Record Victory: Not known
Record Defeat: Not known
Record Goalscorer: Not known
Record Appearances: Not known
Additional Records: Paid £3,000 to Halesowen Town for Paul Joinson
Received £40,000 from Aston Villa for David Farrell

Senior Honours: Worcestershire Senior Cup 1893-94, 29-30, 74-75, 76-76, 2007-08.
Birmingham Senior Cup 1924-25, 31-32, 38-39, 76-77, 2004-05.
Southern League Division 1 North 1975-76, Western Division 2003-04. Staffordshire Senior Cup 1990-91.

10 YEAR RECORD

00-01	01-02	02-03	03-04	04-05	05-06	06-07	07-08	08-09	09-10
SthW 7	SthW 18	SthW 7	SthW 1	Conf N 9	Conf N 20	Conf N 19	Conf N 13	Conf N 14	Conf N 19

REDDITCH UNITED

No.	Date	Comp	H/A	Opponents	Att:	Result	Goalscorers	Pos
1	8/8/09	BSN	H	Stalybridge Celtic	349	L 1-4	Byrne 69	19
2	11/8/09	BSN	A	Ilkeston Town	310	L 2-3	Spittle 8, Og (D Holmes) 69	19
3	15/8/09	BSN	A	Blyth Spartans	458	L 0-1		19
4	18/8/09	BSN	H	Stafford Rangers	294	L 1-2	Sheldon 19	19
5	22/8/09	BSN	A	Northwich Victoria	483	W 2-0	L Francis 44, Hay 83	19
6	29/8/09	BSN	H	Alfreton Town	291	W 3-0	Oliver 32, Bridgwater pen 52, Hay 72	13
7	31/8/09	BSN	A	Hinckley United	413	L 1-5	Charlton 16	17
8	5/9/09	BSN	H	Fleetwood Town	230	D 0-0		17
9	8/9/09	BSN	H	Gainsborough Trinity	246	L 0-3		19
10	12/9/09	BSN	A	Harrogate Town	233	L 2-3	Bridgwater 6, Ducros 68	20
11	19/9/09	BSN	H	Workington	275	W 2-1	Dance 29, Bridgwater 85	18
12	3/10/09	BSN	A	Stalybridge Celtic	474	L 0-3		20
13	31/10/09	BSN	H	Harrogate Town	365	W 2-0	Byrne 27, Semper 82	19
14	7/11/09	BSN	A	Corby Town	505	D 2-2	Spittle 28, Byrne 52	19
15	10/11/09	BSN	A	Southport	611	L 0-2		19
16	14/11/09	BSN	A	Fleetwood Town	1167	L 0-8		20
17	24/11/09	BSN	A	Solihull Moors	266	W 2-1	Sheldon 12, Byrne 14	15
18	28/11/09	BSN	H	Blyth Sprtans	270	D 2-2	Birch 17, Murray 76	17
19	15/12/09	BSN	H	AFC Telford	343	W 3-0	Byrne 4, L Francis 34, Ducros 50	16
20	26/12/09	BSN	H	Gloucester City	428	W 4-1	Ducros 4, Blair 8, Sheldon 2 (68, 85)	12
21	1/1/10	BSN	A	Gloucester City	378	L 0-2		13
22	19/1/10	BSN	H	Eastwood Town	174	L 1-2	Blair 1	16
23	23/1/10	BSN	A	Eastwood Town	457	L 1-3	Sheldon 12	16
24	30/1/10	BSN	A	Vauxhall Motors	186	W 5-0	Jakab 3 (25, 45, 59), Carter 36, L Francis 50	16
25	6/2/10	BSN	H	Hyde United	266	D 0-0		17
26	9/2/10	BSN	H	Northwich Victoria	206	D 1-1	Byrne 27	16
27	13/2/10	BSN	A	AFC Telford	1522	L 0-3		16
28	20/2/10	BSN	H	Solihull Moors	347	L 1-4	Charlton 75	18
29	27/2/10	BSN	A	Workington	316	L 0-1		19
30	2/3/10	BSN	A	Stafford Rangers	353	W 1-0	Clarke pen 88	17
31	6/3/10	BSN	H	Ilkeston Town	316	D 2-2	Benjamin 2 (pen 54, 69)	18
32	13/3/10	BSN	H	Southport	344	D 2-2	Adaggio 55, Campion 70	16
33	20/3/10	BSN	A	Gainsborough Trinity	312	L 0-3		18
34	23/3/10	BSN	H	Droylsden	148	L 1-3	Benjamin 60	18
35	27/3/10	BSN	H	Corby Town	301	W 1-0	Adaggio 50	16
36	3/4/10	BSN	A	Alfreton Town	477	L 0-3		18
37	5/4/10	BSN	H	Hinckley United	428	L 0-2		19
38	10/4/10	BSN	A	Hyde United	301	L 2-3	Benjamin 38, Hadley 41	19
39	17/4/10	BSN	H	Vauxhall Motors	348	D 1-1	Clarke 45	19
40	24/4/10	BSN	A	Droylsden	367	L 1-6	Carter 37	19
	Farsley Celtic record expunged 12/03							
13	17/10/09	BSN	H	Farsley Celtic	288	L 1-2	Bridgwater 6	21
20	5/12/09	BSN	A	Farsley Celtic	302	L 3-4	Ducros 38, L Francis 2 (48, 72)	19
	Cups							
1	26/9/09	FAC 2Q	H	Stratford Town	361	D 1-1	L Francis 40	
2	29/9/09	FAC 2QR	A	Stratford Town	481	W 2-0	Hay 2 (80, 84)	
3	10/10/09	FAC 3Q	A	Solihull Moors	490	W 2-0	L Francis 34, Byrne 54	
4	24/10/09	FAC 4Q	A	Kettering Town	1403	D 1-1	Dance 38	
5	27/10/09	FAC 4QR	H	Kettering Town	1101	L 0-1 aet		
6	21/11/09	FAT 3Q	A	Leigh Genesis	283	W 1-0	Oliver 80	
7	12/12/09	FAT 1	A	Guiseley	245	L 0-1		

Home Attendances:	
Highest:	428 v Hinckley United
Lowest:	148 v Droylsden
Average (08-09):	298 (294)
Top Goalscorer:	Byrne - 7 (6 League, 1 Cup) in 36 appearances - 19% strike rate
Most Appearances:	Lewis - 47 (40 League, 7 Cup)

LEWIS	SPITTLE	CHARLTON	DICKINSON	L FRANCIS	BYRNE	BRIDGWATER	HAY	CLARKE	COOPER	BALL	DUCROS	BULLIMORE	SHELDON	STREET	HEGARTY	OLIVER	DANCE	BIRCH	HANDS	GILL	ASHTON	SEMPER	MORAKA	JAKAB	BLAIR	CARTER	MURRAY	MCGRATH	TURNER	BARLONE	JACKSON	SCHEPPEL	MORAN	MUNDAY	CAMPION	ADAGGIO	GARDINER	BENJAMIN	HAYWARD	HADLEY	RAVENHILL	
X	X	X	X	X	X	X	X	X	X	S	S	S	U																													1
X	X	X	X	X	X	X	X	X		S	X	U	S	X																												2
X	X	X	X	X	X	X	X	X		X	U	U	S	X	U																											3
X	X	X	X	X	X	X	X	X	S	X		U	X	U	U																											4
X	X	X	X	X	X	X	X		X		S	S	S		U	X	X																									5
X	X	X	S	X	X	X	X	X	U		S		S	U		X	X	X																								6
X	X	X	U	X		X	X	X	X		S	U	S	S		X	X	X																								7
X	X	X	U	X	X	X	X	S	U		U			U			X	X																								8
X	X	X	X	X	X	X	X	S	U		S		S	U			X	X																								9
X	X	X	U	X	X	X		X	U	X	S		U				X	X	S																							10
X		X	S	X	X	X		S	S				X			X	X	X	X	X	U																					11
X	U	X	S	X	X			X			U		X			X	X	X	X	X	S	S																				12
X	X	X		X	X	S	X	X			X	U	U			X	X			X		S	S																			13
X	X	X	U	X	X	X		X			U	U	S			X	X			X		X	S																			14
X	X	X	U	X	X	X	X	X			S		X			S	X			X		S	U																			15
X	X	X	U	X	X	X	X	X			X		S			X		U		X		S																				16
X	U	X		X	X			X			X		X		U			X		X		X	U	S	X	S																17
X	U	X			X			X			X		X					X		X		S	U	X	X	U	X	S														18
X		X		X	X	S		X			X		X							X		U		U	X	S	X	S		X												19
X		X		X	X	S		X			X		X							X		S			X	U		S		X												20
X				X	X	U		X			X		X					X		X		S		U	X			X	U	X												21
X		X		X	X	X		X			X									X		S	U	S	X	U		X		X												22
X		X		X	X	S		X			X		X					X		X		S		U	X			U		S												23
X		X		X	X	X		X				X			U			U				X	S	X	X	X			U		S											24
X		X		X	X	X		X				X										X	S	X	X	X		U	U		U											25
X		X		X	X	X		X				X										S	U	X	X	X		X	U		U											26
X		X			X	X		X				X						U				X	S	X	X	S		X	U		S	X										27
X		X			X	X		X				U										U	U	X	X	S		X			U	X										28
X		X			X	X		X							U							X	S		U	X		X	U		S	X	X	X								29
X		X			X			X														S	U	S	X	U		X				X	X	X	X	X	U					30
X		X				X		X														U		U	X	U		X				S	X	X	X	X	U	X				31
X		X				X		X														U			X	U		X	U			S	X	X	X	X	U	X				32
X		X				X		X														U	U			X		X	U		S	X	X	X		X	S	X				33
X		X				X		X																		S		X	U		U	S	X	X		X	U	X	X	X		34
X		X				S																				U		X	U		U	X	X	X	X	X	S	X	X	X		35
X		X				X									U								U			X		X	U		S	X	X	X			X			X	X	36
X		X				X																				X		S			U	X	X	X			X	X	X	X	S	37
X		X				X		X															S			S			U		U	X	X				X	X	X	X	X	38
X								X															U			X		X			U	X	X	X	X		X		U	X	X	39
X		X				X		U							U								X			X		X	S		S	X	X	X			X			X		40
X	S	X	S	X	X	X	X	X			X		U				X	X		X		S	U																			
X		X		X				X			X		X					X		X		S	U	X	X	U	X	S	U													
X		X		X	X	X		X	U			U	X				X	X	X	X	U	S	S																			1
X	U	X		X	X	X	X	X	S			U	S				X	X	S	X	U	X	U																			2
X	U	X	S	X	X	X	X	X			X	U	S				X	X		X	U	S	U																			3
X	X	X		X	X	X	X	X			X	U	S				X			X	S	U	U																			4
X	X	X		X	X	S	X	X			X	U	U		U		X		X	X	U	U	U																			5
X	U	X		X	X	X	X	X			S		S			X		X		X		X	U	S																		6
X		X		X	X	S		X			X		X							X		X	U	X		S	X	S	U													7
Total League Appearances																																										
40	14	38	6	25	29	29	12	32	3	3	10	4	10	2	0	8	11	11	2	13	0	6	1	6	15	9	2	15	0	4	0	11	12	11	5	6	5	7	4	7	3	X
0	0	0	3	0	0	5	0	3	2	2	7	2	8	1	0	1	0	0	1	0	1	11	7	3	0	6	0	4	1	1	6	3	0	0	0	0	2	0	0	0	1	S
0	3	0	6	0	0	1	0	1	4	0	4	7	3	4	8	0	0	3	0	0	1	5	10	4	1	7	0	2	12	0	8	0	0	0	0	0	4	0	1	0	0	U
Total Cup Appearances																																										
7	2	7	0	7	7	5	5	7	0	0	4	0	2	0	0	1	5	4	2	7	0	3	0	1	0	0	1	0	0	0	0	0	0	0	0	0	0	0	0	0	0	X
0	0	0	1	0	0	2	0	0	1	0	1	0	4	0	0	0	0	0	1	0	1	2	1	1	0	1	0	1	0	0	0	0	0	0	0	0	0	0	0	0	0	S
0	3	0	0	0	0	0	0	0	1	0	0	5	1	0	1	0	0	0	0	0	4	2	6	0	0	0	0	0	1	0	0	0	0	0	0	0	0	0	0	0	0	U
Total Goals																																										
0	2	2	0	3	6	3	2	2	0	0	3	0	5	0	0	1	1	1	0	0	0	1	0	3	2	2	1	0	0	0	0	0	0	0	1	2	0	4	0	1	0	Lge
0	0	0	0	2	1	0	2	0	0	0	0	0	0	0	0	1	1	0	0	0	0	0	0	0	0	0	0	0	0	0	0	0	0	0	0	0	0	0	0	0	0	Cup

Also played: F FRANCIS X(1)U(2). WEYMAN U(1,2). DANIELS S(3,4)U(5). BROWN X(8,10). GREEN X(8,9) U(11). GORTON U(16). ROWE X(20). BENBOW U(20)S(21,22). HEGGS X(23),S(25). WALTERS U(26). PITHAM X(28). MARSDEN X(28). WARD S(36) U(37,39). WATSON S(37,40) U(38,39).

CURRENT SQUAD AS OF BEGINING OF 2010-11 SEASON

GOALKEEPERS	HT	WT	D.O.B	AGE	P.O.B	CAREER	APPS	GOA
Jake Meredith			9/12/87	22		Aston Villa (Yth), Birmingham (Yth), Team Bath c/s 07, Worcester 5/09 Rel 5/10, Redditch 6/10		
Tom Turner			17/12/92	18		Redditch	1	0
DEFENDERS								
Bradley Bullimore			19/1/91	19		Redditch	6	0
Darren Campion	5'11"	11 00	17/10/88	21	Birmingham	Birmingham Rel c/s07, Shrewsbury(Trial), Hereford(Trial), Carlisle 9/07 Rel 1/09, Solihull M 10/09, Redditch 3/10	5	1
Chris Dickinson			22/11/89	20		Redditch	9	0
Matt Gardiner	5'04"	10 10	28/3/74	36	Birmingham	Torquay Rel c/s 93, Moor Green c/s 93, Stourbridge 6/94, Halesowen T, Hereford 6/00 Rel c/s 01, Worcester 6/01, Hereford 9/01, Hednesford 11/01, Evesham 8/02 Rel 1/03, Redditch 1/03, Bromsgrove (L) 12/04, Worcester 1/05, Bromsgrove 3/05, Stourport, Boldmere St Michaels 8/06, Bromsgrove, Redditch 3/10 (Pl/Man) 5/10	7	0
Andy Jones						Bridgnorth, Stourport 7/04, AFC Telford 10/05 Rel 8/07, Malvern (L) 1/07, Malvern 8/07, Bromsgrove 12/07, Hednesford 6/08, Stourport 10/08 Redditch 6/10		
Gary Moran			24/10/82	27		Rugby U (Yth), Grimsby (Scholar) Rel c/s 02, Gresley R 8/02, Rugby U 9/02, Solihull B c/s 05, Woodford U, Bedworth 10/07, Stratford 6/08, Bedworth, Rushall O 12/09, Redditch 2/10	12	0
MIDFIELDERS								
Chris Cornes	5'08"	14 02	20/12/86	23	Worcester	Wolves Rel 9/06, Port Vale (3ML) 8/05, Worcester 10/06, AFC Telford (SL) 3/07, AFC Telford 5/07, Bromsgrove 1/08, Stourport 10/08, Worcester 8/09, Stourport. Redditch 6/10		
Jordan Fitzpatrick	6'00"	12 00	15/6/88	22	Stourbridge	Wolves (Scholar), Hereford 9/06 Rel c/s 08, Bromsgrove (L) 3/08, Worcester 8/08 Rel 2/10, Redditch 7/10		
Will Gayton						Evesham, Stourport, Redditch 6/10		
Nathan Jukes			10/4/79	31	Worcester	Portsmouth (Yth), Dorchester, Worcester 2/99, Evesham, Stourport 12/03, Malvern 1/04, Evesham 5/06, Cinderford 9/06, Stourport 12/07, Redditch 6/10		
Luke Keen						Tamworth Rel c/s 08, Atherstone T c/s 08, Highgate U (L), Coalville T 12/08, Atherstone T, Redditch 7/10		
Michael McGrath			4/9/85	24		Kidderminster Rel 1/09, Bromsgrove (L), Redditch (7ML) 8/05, Worcester (L) 9/08, Oxford U (Trial) 1/09, Galway U 2/09, Sligo 7/09, Redditch 12/09	19	0
Danny Scheppel			27/4/81	29		Birmingham, Worcester, Moor Green 7/01, Bromsgrove 8/03, Redditch 8/04, Hednesford 11/05, Redditch 1/06, Evesham c/s 07, Bromsgrove 9/09, Redditch 2/10	14	0
Kevin Spencer			22/7/89	21		WBA (Yth), Tamworth, Kettering 6/07 Rel 8/08, Halesowen T (L) 10/07, Worcester (L) 11/07, Solihull Moors 8/08 Rel 10/08, Stratford T, Worcester 3/09 Rel 2/10, Evesham 2/10, Redditch 7/10		
Marlon Walters			24/12/83	26	Birmingham	Wolves Rel, Worcester (Trial) 3/04, Hednesford 10/04, Willenhall, Bromsgrove 3/07, Willenhall 10/07, Chasetown 3/08, Cradley T 6/08, Bromsgrove 6/09, Hednesford 3/10, Highgate U 3/10, Redditch 6/10		
Alex Woodhouse						Worcester, Shifnal T, Bromsgrove 11/09, Redditch 7/10		
FORWARDS								
Marco Adaggio	5'08"	12 04	6/10/87	22	Malaga, Sp	Shrewsbury, AFC Telford (L) 1/06, Bangor C 1/07, Stafford R 8/07 Rel c/s 08, Worcester 8/08 Rel 4/10, Redditch (L) 3/10, Redditch 7/10	6	2
Shane Benjamin			30/1/81	29	Birmingham	Castle Vale, Grosvenor Park 8/03, Hednesford, Studley, Evesham 1/06, Shepshed D, Stourbridge 2/09, Redditch 6/09, Rushall O 8/09, Shepshed D 11/09, Redditch 3/10	7	4
Danny Campbell			12/8/85	25	Dudley	Stockport, Mossley 12/05, Woodley Sports (L), Cincinnati Kings (USA), Worcester, Halesowen T 11/08, Bromsgrove 3/09, Tividale, Redditch 6/10		
Dan Carter			2/9/91	18		Redditch	15	2
Dexter Ravenhill			16/12/89	20	Dudley	Crewe (Yth), Walsall, Chasetown (L) 2/08, Bromsgrove 8/09, Evesham, Redditch 3/10	4	0
Matt Smith						USA University, Redditch 7/10		
Loanees	**HT**	**WT**	**DOB**	**AGE**	**POB**	**From - To**	**APPS**	**GOA**
(D)Jacob Rowe			9/12/90	19		Birmingham 12/09 -	1	0
(F)Luke Benbow			21/8/91	19		Birmingham (2ML) 12/09 - Weymouth (SL) 2/10	2	0
(D)Danny Pitham			25/1/86	24		Nuneaton T (2WL) 2/10 - Bedworth 2/10, Hinckley U 3/10, Corby T 6/10	1	0
(F)Justin Marsden			7/3/84	26		Nuneaton T 2/10 -	1	0
(M)Nathan Hayward	5'08"	12 01	8/11/91	28	Kidderminster	Kidderminster (SL) 3/10 -	4	0
(F)Kyle Hadley	5'08"	11 07	27/11/86	23		Kidderminster (SL) 3/10 -	7	1
Departures	**HT**	**WT**	**DOB**	**AGE**	**POB**	**From - To**	**APPS**	**GOA**
(F)Francino Francis	6'02"	14 03	18/1/87	23	Jamaica	Barwell 8/09 - Barwell 8/09	1	0
(D)Jordan Street	6'01"	12 08	3/12/89	20	Southampton	Yeovil 8/09 - Bromsgrove 9/09	3	0
(F)Richard Ball			25/11/80	29	Birmingham	Evesham 4 fig 2/07 - Evesham (L) 8/09, Evesham 9/09, Sutton Coldfield 10/09	5	0
(D)Mark Hands			27/10/86	23		Evesham 1/09 - Evesham	3	0
(D)Aaron Brown	6'04"	14 07	23/6/83	27	Birmingham	Yeovil 9/09 - Burton 9/09, Mansfield (Trial) 1/10, AFC Telford 1/10, Truro C 2/10, Aldershot 3/10	2	0
(M)James Dance			15/3/87	23		Rushall 8/09 - Kettering 11/09	11	1
(D)Jamie Oliver			12/3/86	24		Dudley Town 1/09 - Kings Lynn (L) 9/09, Kings Lynn 11/09, Stourbridge 12/09	9	1
(F)Gary Hay			5/9/76	33	Birmingham	Hednesford 3/09 - Chasetown 12/09	12	2
(M)Lucan Spittle	6'03"		16/2/81	29		Chasetown 12/08 - Stratford T (L) 12/09 Perm 1/10, Stourbridge 3/10	14	2
(D)Liam Murray	6'03"	11 00	1/8/85	25	Stafford	Kings Lynn 12/09 - Solihull Moors 12/09, AFC Telford 6/10	2	1
(D)Jerry Gill	5'11"	12 00	8/9/70	39	Clevedon	ex Forest Green 9/09 - Weymouth (Pl/Man) 1/10 Resigned 3/10, Solihull Moors 3/10, Bristol R (Coach) 6/10	13	0
(F)Jamie Sheldon	5'11"	11 05	14/8/91	19		Birmingham (Scholar) c/s 09 - NK Interbloc (Slo) 1/10	18	5
(M)Andy Ducros	5'04"	9 08	16/8/77	32	Evesham	Barwell 8/09 - Evesham 2/10	17	3
(F)Carl Heggs			11/10/70	39		Kings Lynn (Man) 1/10 - Hinckley U 2/10	2	0
(D)Liam Francis			27/9/89	20	Birmingham	Stratford T 8/09 - Hednesford 2/10	25	3
(M)Jack Byrne			20/7/89	21		Stratford T 1/09 - Kidderminster 3/10	29	6
(M)Matt Blair			21/6/89	21		Bedworth 11/09 - AFC Telford 3/10	15	2
(F)Myron Semper			10/7/88	22		GSA 9/09 - Stratford T 3/10	17	1
(G)Danny Lewis	6'01"	14 00	18/6/82	28	Redditch	Moor Green 6/07 - Kidderminster 5/10	40	0
(D)Asa Charlton	5'11"	12 00	7/12/77	32	Cosford	AFC Telford 10/08 - Corby T 5/10	38	2
(M)David Bridgwater	6'00"	12 07	27/9/80	29	Stourbridge	Stourbridge 8/09 - Nuneaton T (Dual) 3/10, Hednesford 6/10	34	3
(D)Richard Munday			24/8/87	23		Romulus 2/10 - Hinckley U 6/10	11	0
(M)Joe Clarke			28/7/88	22		Yth - Sollihull Moors 7/10	35	2
(D)Tom Birch			29/9/87	22		Bradford PA 8/09 -	11	1
(F)Curtis Walters			1/9/90	19		Yth -	0	0
(F)Aaron Daniels			26/6/89	21		Highgate U 1/09 -	2	0
(F)Karl Gorton			15/12/85	24		Enville Ath 11/09 -	0	0
(F)Jozsef Jakab			31/10/83	26		Stratford T 11/09 -	9	3
(F)Graham Ashton			16/8/82	28		Dudley T - Alvechurch (L) 12/09	1	0
(F)Luke Barlone			8/1/88	22		Shepshed D 12/09 -	5	0
(M)James Cooper	5'09"	11 02	4/1/90	20		Lincoln C (Scholar)8/09 -	5	0
(M)Phil Green			10/3/88	22		Kings Lynn 9/09 -	2	0
(M)Michael Hegarty			9/6/91	19		Yth -	0	0
(M)Steven Jackson			31/12/91	18		Yth -	6	0
(M)Godwill Moraka			8/10/88	21		Bangor C 9/09 -	8	0
(M)James Ward			6/11/92	17		Yth -	1	0
(M)Mat Weyman			20/12/91	18		Dudley T c/s 09 -	0	0
Watson						Yth -	2	0

SOLIHULL MOORS

Chairman: Nigel Collins
Secretary: Robin Lamb (T) 07976 752 493
(E) robin.lamb5@btinternet.com
Additional Committee Members: Graham Davison, Margaret Smith, Trevor Stevens, Geoff Hood, Ray Bird, Danny Thomas, Father Ronald Crane
Manager: Bob Faulkner
Programme Editor: James Newbold (E) info@thedesignery.co.uk

no up-to-date image available

Club Factfile

Founded: 2007 **Nickname:**
Previous Names: Today's club was formed after the amalgamation of Solihull Borough and Moor Green in 2007
Previous Leagues: None

Club Colours (change): White/black/white (Yellow/royal blue/royal blue)

Ground: Damson Park, Damson Parkway, Solihull B91 2PP (T) 0121 705 6770
Capacity: 3,050 **Seats:** 280 **Covered:** 1,000 **Clubhouse:** Yes **Shop:** Yes
Previous Grounds: None
Simple Directions
M42 junction 6 take the A45 towards Birmingham after approx 1.5 miles take the left filter lane at the traffic lights onto Damson Parkway. Ground approx 1 mile on the right.

Record Attendance: 1,076 v Rushden & Diamonds - FA Cup 4th Qualifying Round 27/10/2007
Record Victory: 4-1 v Southport - Conference South 05/04/2008
Record Defeat: 1-6 v Kettering Town - Conference South 01/01/2008
Record Goalscorer: Not known
Record Appearances: Carl Motteram - 71 (2007-09)
Additional Records:

Senior Honours: None

10 YEAR RECORD

00-01	01-02	02-03	03-04	04-05	05-06	06-07	07-08	08-09	09-10
							Conf N 17	Conf N 16	Conf N 17

SOLIHULL MOORS

No.	Date	Comp	H/A	Opponents	Att:	Result	Goalscorers	Pos
1	8/8/09	BSN	H	Fleetwood Town	279	L 1-2	English 62	15
2	11/8/09	BSN	A	Alfreton Town	453	L 0-3		20
3	15/8/09	BSN	A	Northwich Victoria	485	L 0-2		20
4	18/8/09	BSN	H	Gloucester City	239	L 0-1		20
5	22/8/09	BSN	A	Harrogate Town	272	W 1-0	Dempster 78	20
6	29/8/09	BSN	H	Stalybridge Celtic	220	D 2-2	Gould 55, Daly 77	20
7	31/8/09	BSN	A	Stafford Rangers	583	W 3-2	Edwards 2 (10, 14), Daly 81	16
8	5/9/09	BSN	H	Gainsborough Trinity	239	L 0-1		19
9	8/9/09	BSN	H	Ilkeston Town	246	L 0-3		20
10	12/9/09	BSN	A	Blyth Spartans	556	L 0-2		21
11	19/9/09	BSN	A	Vauxhall Motors	187	W 2-0	Mills 55, McPike 90	19
12	3/10/09	BSN	H	Southport	338	D 1-1	Mills 12	18
13	17/10/09	BSN	A	Gainsborough Trinity	320	D 0-0		18
14	24/10/09	BSN	H	Harrogate Town	204	W 1-0	Beswick 89	13
15	31/10/09	BSN	A	Droylsden	293	L 3-5	Og (Sorvel) 30, McPike 55, English 87	17
16	3/11/09	BSN	H	AFC Telford	404	L 0-1		16
17	7/11/09	BSN	H	Blyth Spartans	212	D 1-1	Lea 30	14
18	24/11/09	BSN	H	Redditch United	266	L 1-2	Mills pen 85	19
19	28/11/09	BSN	H	Vauxhall Motors	186	W 4-0	Khela 17, McPike 57, Edwards 72, Gardner 80	14
20	5/12/09	BSN	A	Southport	733	L 0-3		17
21	26/12/09	BSN	H	Hinckley United	400	L 2-4	Beswick 37, Gardner 90	18
22	19/1/10	BSN	H	Alfreton Town	161	D 1-1	Khela 90	18
23	23/1/10	BSN	A	Corby Town	369	W 2-1	Streete 71, Stapleton 85	17
24	2/2/10	BSN	A	Gloucester City	215	L 0-1		18
25	6/2/10	BSN	A	Workington	368	L 0-1		18
26	13/2/10	BSN	H	Corby Town	249	W 3-0	Beswick 2 (41, 67), English 54	18
27	15/2/10	BSN	A	Hinckley United	471	W 3-0	Gould 53, Price 58, English 84	16
28	20/2/10	BSN	A	Redditch United	347	W 4-1	Price 33, S Johnson 2 (46, 55), Dempster pen 78	15
29	27/2/10	BSN	H	Eastwood Town	256	W 2-1	Edwards 79, Lea 89	14
30	2/3/10	BSN	H	Hyde United	167	W 3-0	Gould 15, S Johnson 2 (25, 73)	13
31	6/3/10	BSN	A	AFC Telford	1525	D 0-0		12
32	13/3/10	BSN	A	Fleetwood Town	1451	L 0-3		13
33	20/3/10	BSN	H	Northwich Victoria	246	D 1-1	Edwards 70	13
34	27/3/10	BSN	H	Droylsden	208	L 1-2	English 33	14
35	3/4/10	BSN	A	Stalybridge Celtic	414	L 1-3	Beswick 50	15
36	5/4/10	BSN	H	Stafford Rangers	236	D 1-1	Edwards pen 60	15
37	10/4/10	BSN	A	Eastwood Town	304	L 1-2	Edwards 69	17
38	13/4/10	BSN	A	Ilkeston Town	251	L 0-1		17
39	17/4/10	BSN	H	Workington	205	L 1-2	Gardner 53	18
40	24/4/10	BSN	A	Hyde United	340	D 1-1	Lee 67	17
	Farsley Celtic record expunged 12/03							
18	14/11/09	BSN	A	Farsley Celtic	285	L 0-1		16
25	30/1/10	BSN	H	Farsley Celtic	215	L 1-2	Gardner 53	18
	Cups							
1	26/9/09	FAC 2Q	A	Mickleover Sports	240	W 4-3	Price 28, Mills 2 (29, 54), Douglas 64	
2	10/10/09	FAC 3Q	H	Redditch United	490	L 0-2		
3	1/12/09	FAT 3Q	A	Workington	188	D 1-1	Mills 25	
4	8/12/09	FAT 3QR	H	Workington	117	L 2-4	McPike 11, Streete 80	

Home Attendances:	
Highest:	404 v AFC Telford
Lowest:	161 v Alfreton Town
Average (08-09):	239 (234)
Top Goalscorer:	Edwards - 6 (6 League, 0 Cup) in 36 appearances - 17% strike rate
Most Appearances:	Crane - 42 (38 League, 4 Cup)
	Streete - 42 (37+1 League, 4 Cup)

CRANE	KHELA	M JOHNSON	STREETE	DALY	GOULD	ENGLISH	DOWNES	EDWARDS	LEA	BROWN	LEWIS	FAULDS	GARDNER	RECCI	C DAVIES	MIDWORTH	PUGH	STAPLETON	DEMPSTER	PRICE	RACHEL	MCPIKE	MILLS	DOUGLAS	CAMPION	BESWICK	RICHARDSON	BEVAN	R DAVIES	MURRAY	AMOO	S JOHNSON	FARRELL	MILEY	ATKINS	
X	X	X	X	X	X	X	X	X	X	X	S	S	S	U	U																					1
X	X	X	X	X	X	X	X	S	X	X	X	U	S	U	S																					2
X	X	U	X	X	X	X	X	S	X	X	X	U	S		S	X																				3
X			X	X	X	X	X	S	X	X	X	U	S	X	S	X	U																			4
X	X			X	X	X	X	X	X			U	X		U	X	S	X	S	S																5
X			X	X	X	X	X		X	X		S	X		U	X	S	X	S	U																6
X			X	X	X	X	X	X		S		X			U	X	U	X	X	S	U															7
X			X	X	X	X	X	X				X			S	X	U	X	S	S	U	X														8
X		X	X	X	S	X	X	X				U	S		X		S	X	U	X		X														9
X			X	X	X	X	X	X				X	U		S		S	X	S	U		X	X													10
X			X	X		X	X	S				U	U		S	X	X	X		S		X	X	X												11
X	U		X	X		X	X	S				U	U			X		X		X		X	X	X	S											12
X	X		X			X	X		S			X	X			X	U	X	S	U		X		S		X										13
X	X			X		X		U	S			X	X				X	X	S	X		X		S	U	X										14
X	X		S	X		X	X		U			X	S				X	X		X		X		S	U	X										15
X	X		X	X		X	X		U			X	S				U	X	S			X		X	X	S										16
X	X		X	X		X	X	S	X			X	S				U	X	U					X	X	S										17
X	X		X			X	X	X	U				S			U			S	U		X	X		X	X	X									18
X	X		X			X	X	X	S				S					U	U	S		X	X		X	X	X									19
	X		X			X	X	S	U				U					X		S		X	X		X	S	X	X	X							20
U	U		X				X	X					S			X		S	S			X	X		X	X		X	X	X						21
X	X		X				X	S	S				X			X		X	U	S	U	X				X			X	X						22
X	X		X				X	S	S				X			X		X	U	S		X			U	X			X	X						23
X			X			X	X	S					X			X		X	S	S	U	X			U	X			X	X						24
X	X		X		S		X	X					X			X		X	S							X			X	X						25
X			X		X	X		X	S				S			X		X	U	S	U					X				X	X	X				26
X	U		X		X	X		X	S				S			X				X	U					X				X	X	X				27
X			X		X	X	U	X	S				S			X			S	X	U					X				X	X	X				28
X	U		X		X	X	U	X	S				U			X			U	X						X				X	X	X				29
X	U	S	X		X	X	U		X				U			X			S	X						X				X	X	X				30
X	S		X		X	X	U	U	X				S			X			U	X										X	X	X	X			31
X	U		X		X	X		X	X				S			X			U	S										X	X	X	X	S		32
X	X		X		X	X	S	X	X				U			X			S	X						S				X			X	U		33
X	X		X		X	X	U	X	X				S			X			U	X						X				X				S	U	34
X	U		X		X	X	S	X	X				S			X			S	X						X				X				X	U	35
X	U		X		X	X	S	X	S				S			X			X	X										X	X			X	U	36
X	U		X		X	X	U	X	S				S			X			X	X										X	X			X	U	37
X	U		X		X	X	S	X	S				S			X				X						X				X	X			X	U	38
X	U		X		X	X	U	X	S				X			X			S	X						X				X	X				U	39
X	U		X		X	X	U	X	S				X			X			S	X						X				X				X	U	40
X			X	X		X		S	X				U			U	X	X	S	S		X			X	X	X									
X	X		X			U	X	S	S				X			X		X		S		X			U	X			X	X						
X	S		X	X		X	X	U				S	S		U	X		X	U	X	U	X	X	X												1
X			X	X		X	X	X					S			X		X		X		X	X	S												2
X			X			X	X	X	S			U	S					X	U	U		X	X		X	X	X									3
X	X		X			X	X	X										S	S			X	X		X	X	X									4
Total League Appearances																																				
38	17	3	37	16	24	36	24	23	13	5	3	8	10	1	1	29	3	19	3	17	0	16	7	4	6	20	3	2	6	20	11	7	3	5	0	X
0	1	1	1	0	2	0	4	10	14	1	1	2	21	0	6	0	4	1	17	11	0	0	0	3	1	4	0	0	0	0	0	0	0	2	0	S
1	12	1	0	0	0	0	8	2	4	0	0	7	7	2	4	1	6	1	10	4	7	0	0	0	4	0	0	0	0	0	0	0	0	1	7	U
Total Cup Appearances																																				
4	1	0	4	2	0	4	4	3	0	0	0	0	0	0	0	2	0	3	0	2	0	4	4	1	2	2	2	0	0	0	0	0	0	0	0	X
0	1	0	0	0	0	0	0	0	1	0	0	1	3	0	0	0	0	1	1	0	0	0	0	1	0	0	0	0	0	0	0	0	0	0	0	S
0	0	0	0	0	0	0	0	1	0	0	0	1	0	0	1	0	0	0	2	1	1	0	0	0	0	0	0	0	0	0	0	0	0	0	0	U
Total Goals																																				
0	2	0	1	2	3	5	0	6	2	0	0	0	3	0	0	0	0	1	2	2	0	3	3	0	0	5	0	0	0	0	0	4	0	0	0	Lge
0	0	0	1	0	0	0	0	0	0	0	0	0	0	0	0	0	0	0	0	1	0	1	3	1	0	0	0	0	0	0	0	0	0	0	0	Cup

SOLIHULL MOORS

CURRENT SQUAD AS OF BEGINING OF 2010-11 SEASON

GOALKEEPERS	HT	WT	D.O.B	AGE	P.O.B	CAREER	APPS	GOA
Jasbir Singh	6'02"	13 05	12/3/90	20		Shrewsbury Rel c/s 09, Bridgnorth (L) 8/08, Hinckley U (L) 10/08, Sutton Coldfield (L) 1/09, Kidderminster 8/09 Rel 5/10, Solihull Moors 7/10		
DEFENDERS								
Indy Khela	6'00"	12 06	6/10/83	26	Birmingham	Bedworth, Coventry Marconi, Kidderminster 8/02, Evesham (L) (02/03), Evesham 6/03, Willenhall, AFC Telford 2/06 Rel 5/09, Solihull Moors 6/09	18	2
Phil Midworth			17/5/85	25		WBA (Sch), Burton 2/05, Moor Green/Solihull Moors 3/05. Bromsgrove (L) 3/09	29	0
Danny Miley						Aston Villa, Tamworth, Halesowen T 12/06, Bedworth, Crewe (Trial) 2/10, Solihull B 3/10	7	0
Darren Stapleton			19/3/87	23	Dublin	Cherry Orchard, Reading, Kildare County, Shamrock 11/07 Rel 2/09, Solihull Moors 8/09	20	1
Theo Streete	6'01"	12 06	23/11/87	22	Birmingham	Derby, Doncaster (4ML) 9/06, Bristol R (Trial) 1/07, Grimsby (Trial) 1/07, Rotherham 1/07, Solihull Moors 1/07	38	1
Colm Tiernan						Alvechurch, Worcester, Romulus, Solihull Moors 7/10		
MIDFIELDERS								
Ryan Beswick			12/1/88	22	Walton-on-Thames	Leicester, Redditch (SL) 1/09, Kettering 5/09, Kings Lynn (2ML) 8/09, Solihull Moors 10/09	24	5
Joe Clarke			28/7/88	22		Redditch, Sollihull Moors 7/10		
Junior English			8/10/85	24		Moor Green/Solihull Moors	36	5
Tim Gould			11/6/86	24		Boldmere St M, Solihull Moors 7/07, Australia 9/09, Solihull Moors 2/10	26	3
Dean Lea			15/11/89	20		Tamworth Rel 5/09, Solihull Moors 6/09	27	2
Alex Price			15/4/91	19		Solihull Moors, Stratford T (L) 3/09	28	2
FORWARDS								
Adam Cunnington			7/10/87	22		Coventry (Yth), Barton R, Leighton T, Hitchin 3/07, Aylesbury 10/07, Barton R 11/07, Rothwell T 2/08, Stamford 7/08, Barwell (L), Barwell c/s 09, Solihull Moors 7/10		
Ross Dempster			2/12/90	19		Solihull Moors	20	2
Aaron Farrell	6'00"	12 06	24/4/86	24		Kidderminster (Yth), Solihull B 8/04, Evesham 12/04, Bedworth 2/05, Sutton Coldfield 2/06, Solihull B 8/06, Halesowen T 3/07, Rushall O 11/07, Stratford T 12/07, Sutton Coldfield 8/08, Kidderminster 7/09 Rel 2/10, Worcester 2/10 Rel 2/10, Sollihull Moors	3	0
Mark Gardner			30/12/82	27		Birmingham, Highgate U, Stafford R (Trial) 10/08, Solihull Moors 11/08	31	3
Matt West			11/3/90	20		Coventry (Scholar), Hinckley U 7/09, Solihull Moors 6/10		

Loanees	HT	WT	DOB	AGE	POB	From - To	APPS	GOA
(M)Greg Mills			18/9/90	19		Derby 9/09, (6WL) 11/09 - Macclesfield (L) 1/10	7	3
(M)Richard Davies	5'11"	11 05	15/5/90	20	Willenhall	Walsall (2ML) 12/09 -	6	0
(G)David Bevan	6'02"	13 00	24/6/89	21	Cork	Aston Villa 12/09 -	2	0

Departures	HT	WT	DOB	AGE	POB	From - To	APPS	GOA
(F)Matty Lewis	6'02"	12 02	20/3/84	26	Coventry	AFC Telford 6/09 - Atherstone T, Nuneaton T 11/09, Leamington 12/09	4	0
(D)Loyiso Recci			19/1/91	19		Yth - Shepshed D 10/09	1	0
(F)Jon Douglas			24/5/84	26	Coventry	Ilkeston 9/09 - Rel 11/09, Oxford C 11/09, Wealdstone 6/10	7	0
(D)Liam Daly	6'06"		28/8/87	23		Redditch 10/08 - Halesowen T 11/09, Leamington 6/10	16	2
(M)James Pugh			16/9/90	19		Birmingham 8/09 - Bromsgrove, Romulus 6/10	7	0
(M)Peter Faulds	5'07"	10 00	26/8/82	28	Birmingham	Kidderminster 8/02 - Leamington 12/09	10	0
(F)James McPike	5'10"	11 02	4/10/88	21	Birmingham	Kettering 9/09 - Rel 2/10, Leamington 2/10 Rel c/s 10	16	3
(M)Charlton Davies			24/1/89	21	Coleshill	Walsall 8/09 - Leamington 2/10, Rushall O (L) 3/10	7	0
(D)Darren Campion	5'11"	11 00	17/10/88	21	Birmingham	ex Carlisle 10/09 - Redditch 3/10	7	0
(F)Simon Johnson	5'09"	11 09	9/3/83	27	West Bromwich	Halesowen T 2/10 - Guiseley 3/10	7	4
(F)Marvin Johnson			1/12/90	19		Yth - Rushall O 3/10	4	0
(F)Jake Edwards	6'01"	12 08	11/5/76	34	Prestwich	Burton 8/08 - Retired 4/10	33	6
(G)Daniel Crane	6'03"	14 11	27/5/84	26	Birmingham	Corby 1/08 - Hednesford 5/10	38	0
(M)Lee Downes	6'00"	12 00	27/2/83	27	Dudley	Redditch 2/09 - Leamington 5/10	28	0
(D)Liam Murray	6'03"	11 00	1/8/85	25	Stafford	Redditch 12/09 - AFC Telford 6/10	20	0
(D)Jerry Gill	5'11"	12 00	8/9/70	39	Clevedon	Weymouth 3/10 - Bristol R (Coach) 6/10		
(G)Jamie Atkins			29/8/88	22		Cadbury Ath 10/09 -	0	0
(G)Adam Rachel	5'11"	12 08	10/12/76	33	Birmingham	Blackpool 7/01 -	0	0
(D)Jon Richardson	6'01"	12 02	29/8/75	35	Nottingham	Worcester 11/09 -	3	0
(F)Junior Brown			28/12/84	25			6	0
(M)Ryan Amoo			11/10/83	26		Thurnby R 2/10 -	11	0

STAFFORD RANGERS

Chairman: TBA
Secretary: Mike Hughes **(T)** 07850 996 386
(E) mike.hughes@staffordrangersfc.co.uk
Additional Committee Members:
Reg Bates, Jon Downing, Roly Tonge, Cliff Went, Rod Woodward, Lorna Beeby
Manager: Chris Brindley
Programme Editor: Ken Hunt **(E)** ken.hunt.15@btinternet.com

Back row (L-R): Andre Francis, John Patrick, Niall Maguire, Joe Rogers, Fabrice Kasiama, Chris Sterling.
Middle Row: Mark Dudley, Nick Wellecomme, Lee Evans, Ben Mills, Tom Harrison, Ross Davidson, Ollie Parker.
Front Row: Alex Forde, Craig McAughtrie (Capt) Chris Brindley (Manager) Steve Wynn (Asst Manager), Jermaine Johnson, Tom Moss.

Club Factfile

Founded: 1876 **Nickname:** Rangers
Previous Names:
Previous Leagues: Shropshire 1891-93, Birmingham 1893-96, N. Staffs. 1896-1900, Cheshire 1900-01, Birmingham Comb. 1900-12, 46-52, Cheshire County 1952-69, N.P.L. 1969-79, 83-85, Alliance 1979-83, Conf. 1985-95
Club Colours (change): Black & white stripes/black/black (All red)

Ground: Marston Road, Stafford ST16 3BX **(T)** 01785 602 430
Capacity: 6,000 **Seats:** 4,264 **Covered:** 3,500 **Clubhouse:** Yes **Shop:** Yes
Previous Grounds:
Simple Directions
M6 Junction 14. Follow signs for Uttoxeter and Stone. Straight over at 1st and 2nd (A34) islands, 3rd right sign posted Common Road and Astonfields Road Ind. Estate. The ground is straight ahead after three quarters of a mile. The route from the Motorway is highlighted by the standard football road signs.

Record Attendance: 8,536 v Rotherham United - FA Cup 3rd Round 1975
Record Victory: 14-0 v Kidsgrove Athletic - Staffordshire Senior Cup 2003
Record Defeat: 0-12 v Burton Town - Birmingham League 1930
Record Goalscorer: M. Cullerton - 176
Record Appearances: Jim Sargent
Additional Records: Paid £13,000 to VS rugby for S. Butterworth
Received £100,000 from Crystal Palace for Stan Collymore
Senior Honours: Northern Premier League 1971-72, 84-85. FA trophy 1971-72.
Staffordshire Senior Cup x7

10 YEAR RECORD

00-01	01-02	02-03	03-04	04-05	05-06	06-07	07-08	08-09	09-10
SthP 7	SthP 9	SthP 2	SthP 3	Conf N 8	Conf N 2	Conf 20	Conf 23	Conf N 18	Conf N 16

STAFFORD RANGERS

No.	Date	Comp	H/A	Opponents	Att:	Result	Goalscorers	Pos
1	8/8/09	BSN	A	Hyde United	401	L 0-1		16
2	11/8/09	BSN	H	Corby Town	531	L 0-2		18
3	15/8/09	BSN	H	Workington	452	W 2-0	Mills 18, Kasiama 82	14
4	18/8/09	BSN	A	Redditch United	294	W 2-1	Thorley 22, Og (Dickinson) 50	9
5	29/8/09	BSN	A	Vauxhall Motors	195	D 2-2	Wellecomme 2 (17, 51)	10
6	31/8/09	BSN	H	Solihull Moors	583	L 2-3	Wilson 4, Mills 27	13
7	5/9/09	BSN	A	Droylsden	419	L 1-7	Wellecomme 78	14
8	8/9/09	BSN	A	Southport	606	L 2-4	Wilson 18, Thompson 28	16
9	12/9/09	BSN	H	Eastwood Town	507	D 3-3	Thompson 18, Wellecomme 34, Owens 39	17
10	19/9/09	BSN	A	Harrogate Town	339	W 4-1	Wellecomme 32, Johnson 2 (62, 90), Wilson 64	13
11	3/10/09	BSN	H	Hinckley United	501	L 2-3	Wellecomme 23, E Francis 84	16
12	17/10/09	BSN	H	Stalybridge Celtic	667	L 0-2		17
13	24/10/09	BSN	A	Corby Town	475	L 2-3	Mills 80, Reid 89	18
14	27/10/09	BSN	A	Ilkeston Town	395	W 3-2	Mills 2, Moult 36, Wilson 71	14
15	31/10/09	BSN	H	Northwich Victoria	627	D 2-2	Thorley 21, Mills 26	13
16	7/11/09	BSN	A	Alfreton Town	462	L 1-3	Mills 53	13
17	14/11/09	BSN	H	Gloucester City	547	W 1-0	Moult 8	13
18	28/11/09	BSN	A	Hinckley United	515	L 1-3	Ojamaa 28	15
19	5/12/09	BSN	H	Blyth Spartans	483	D 1-1	Thorley pen 87	15
20	12/12/09	BSN	H	Droylsden	363	D 2-2	Reid 38, Kasiama 89	15
21	19/12/09	BSN	A	Fleetwood Town	1120	L 1-2	Wilson 12	15
22	26/12/09	BSN	A	AFC Telford	2200	L 1-2	Reid 4	16
23	16/1/10	BSN	A	Gainsborough Trinity	334	W 3-1	Reid 41, W Alexander 2 (70, 72)	14
24	19/1/10	BSN	H	AFC Telford	670	W 2-0	W Alexander 64, Wellecomme 75	11
25	23/1/10	BSN	H	Harrogate Town	525	W 1-0	Thorley 76	10
26	30/1/10	BSN	H	Southport	635	L 1-2	Wellecomme 41	11
27	6/2/10	BSN	A	Stalybridge Celtic	456	D 2-2	Kasiama 54, Thorley 80	12
28	13/2/10	BSN	A	Blyth Spartans	466	D 2-2	Wellecomme 19, Dinning 60	13
29	20/2/10	BSN	H	Hyde United	507	D 1-1	Dinning 13	14
30	27/2/10	BSN	H	Alfreton Town	466	D 1-1	Dinning pen 72	16
31	2/3/10	BSN	H	Redditch United	353	L 0-1		16
32	6/3/10	BSN	A	Eastwood Town	442	D 0-0		15
33	13/3/10	BSN	A	Northwich Victoria	630	D 2-2	McAughtrie 44, Merella 58	15
34	20/3/10	BSN	H	Ilkeston Town	434	L 0-1		16
35	27/3/10	BSN	H	Fleetwood Town	580	D 2-2	Reid 13, Wellecomme 54	18
36	3/4/10	BSN	H	Vauxhall Motors	463	W 3-1	Glover 1, Goodhead 16, Merella 37	16
37	5/4/10	BSN	A	Solihull Moors	236	D 1-1	Merella 59	16
38	10/4/10	BSN	A	Gloucester City	340	L 0-2		18
39	17/4/10	BSN	H	Gainsborough Trinity	506	W 2-1	Wellecomme 83, Reid 87	16
40	24/4/10	BSN	A	Workington	656	D 1-1	Wellecomme 28	16
	Farsley Celtic record expunged 12/03							
5	22/8/09	BSN	H	Farsley Celtic	515	D 2-2	Kasiama 6, Wellecomme 27	10
	Cups							
1	26/9/09	FAC 2Q	A	Coventry Sphinx	312	D 2-2	Thorley pen 49, Og (McAteer) 55	
2	29/9/09	FAC 2QR	H	Coventry Sphinx	465	L 2-3	Kasiama 77, Thorley pen 84	
3	21/11/09	FAT 3Q	A	Blyth Spartans	442	L 0-2		

Home Attendances:	
Highest:	670 v AFC Telford
Lowest:	353 v Redditch United
Average (08-09):	507 (598)
Top Goalscorer:	Wellecomme - 11 (11 League, 0 Cup) in 37 appearances - 30% strike rate
Most Appearances:	Thorley - 42 (39 League, 3 Cup)

HARRISON	A FRANCIS	KASIAMA	THORLEY	WILSON	OWENS	MORGAN	MOULT	MILLS	DAVIDSON	AMOS	WELLECOMME	PROFFITT	HULME	ROGERS	ALLEN	BRINDLEY	VAULS	E FRANCIS	D ALEXANDER	PATRICK	BRUNT	EVANS	REID	THOMPSON	JOHNSON	LUMLEY	UDOJI	WOOLISCROFT	SAMBA	WHITEHOUSE	OJAMAA	W ALEXANDER	WILLIAMS	DINNING	HOLLAND	MCAUGHTRIE	BURNS	GOODHEAD	MERELLA	DAVIS	GLOVER	
X	X	X	X	X	X	X	X	X	X	X	S	S	U	U	U																											1
X	X	X	X	X		X	X	X	X	X	X	S	U	U	U	U																										2
X	X	S	X	X	X	X	X	X	X		X		U	U	U		X	S																								3
X	X	X	X	X			X	X	X		X		U	U	S	U	X	U	X																							4
	X	X	X	X			X	X	X		X		U	U	X		X		X	U	S	U																				5
	X	X	X	X			X	X			X		S	U	X		X		X	U	S	U	X																			6
	X	X	X	X			X				X		S	U	U		X		X	S	S	X	X	X																		7
	X	X	X	X			X				X			U	U		X		S	S	U	X	X	X	X																	8
	X	X	X	X	X						X		U	U	X	U		U	U	X			X	X	X																	9
U		X	X	X				X			X		S	U			U	U		X			X	X	X	X	X															10
U	U	X	X	X	X	X	S	X			X		S					S		X			X		X	X																11
U	X	X		X	S		X	X			X		X	U			U	S		X			X			X	X															12
U	X	X	X	X	X		X	S			X		U				U	U				X	X				X	X														13
U	X	X	X	X			X	X			X		U	U		U	X	U				X					X	X														14
	X		X	X			X	X			X		U	U		U	X	S				X	X				X	X														15
	X	U	X	X			X	X			X		U	U		U	X	U				X	X				X	X														16
	X	S	X	X			X	X			X			U			X	U				X	X				X	X														17
	X	S	X	X			X							U				S		X		X	X		X			X	U	U	X	X										18
	X	X	X	X														S		X		X			U			X	S	U	X	X	X	X								19
	S	S	X				X				X							S		X		X	X		X			X	U	U	X		X	X								20
	X	X	X	X			X				X			U		U				X		X	X		X				U	U	X											21
	S	U	X	X			X				X							S		X		X	X		X			X		U	X	S	X									22
		X	X	X		S					X			U		U				X		X	X		X		X			U		X	X									23
		X	X	X		S					X			U				S		X		X	X		X		X			U		X	X		S							24
		X	X			S					X			U				X		X		X	X				X			U			X	U	U	X	X					25
	X	X	X			U					X			U						X		X	X				X			U		X		U	U	X	X					26
	X	X	X								X			U		U				X		X	X				X			U		X		S	U	X	X					27
	X	X	X								X			U			S			X		X	X				X			U				X		X	X	U				28
	X	X	X								X			U			X					X	X				X			U				X	U	X	X	U				29
U	X	X	X														X					X	X				X					S		X	U	X	X	S	X			30
U	X	X	X											U			X					X	X									X		X	S	X	X	X	S			31
U		X	X											U		U	X					X	X				X	X				U		X	U		X	X	X			32
U		S	X								X			U		U	X					X	X					X						X		X	X	X	X	S		33
U		X	X								X			U		U						X	X					X						X		X	X	X	X	S		34
U	S	X	X						X		X			U								X	X					X						U		X		X	X	U	X	35
U	S	X	X						X		X			U						U		X	X					X								X		X	X	U	X	36
U	X	X	X						X					U		U				S		X	X					X								X		X	X	U	X	37
U	X	X	X						X		X			S		U				X		X						X										X	X	S	X	38
U	S	X	X						X		X			U						S		X	X					X								X		X	X	U	X	39
U	S	X	X						X		X			U						U		X	X					X								X		X	X	U	X	40
	X	X	X	X	X		X	X	X		X		S	U	X		X	S	S	U																						

HARRISON	A FRANCIS	KASIAMA	THORLEY	WILSON	OWENS	MORGAN	MOULT	MILLS	DAVIDSON	AMOS	WELLECOMME	PROFFITT	HULME	ROGERS	ALLEN	BRINDLEY	VAULS	E FRANCIS	D ALEXANDER	PATRICK	BRUNT	EVANS	REID	THOMPSON	JOHNSON	LUMLEY	UDOJI	WOOLISCROFT	SAMBA	WHITEHOUSE	OJAMAA	W ALEXANDER	WILLIAMS	DINNING	HOLLAND	MCAUGHTRIE	BURNS	GOODHEAD	MERELLA	DAVIS	GLOVER	
U		X	X	X	X	S	X	X			X			U		U	X			U					X	X	X															1
U		X	X	X	X	S	X	X			X		S			U	X			S			X		X	X																2
	X	X	X	X			X				X			U			X	S		S		X	X		X			X	S	U												3

Total League Appearances

HARRISON	A FRANCIS	KASIAMA	THORLEY	WILSON	OWENS	MORGAN	MOULT	MILLS	DAVIDSON	AMOS	WELLECOMME	PROFFITT	HULME	ROGERS	ALLEN	BRINDLEY	VAULS	E FRANCIS	D ALEXANDER	PATRICK	BRUNT	EVANS	REID	THOMPSON	JOHNSON	LUMLEY	UDOJI	WOOLISCROFT	SAMBA	WHITEHOUSE	OJAMAA	W ALEXANDER	WILLIAMS	DINNING	HOLLAND	MCAUGHTRIE	BURNS	GOODHEAD	MERELLA	DAVIS	GLOVER	
4	26	32	39	23	5	4	18	13	11	2	33	0	1	0	3	0	15	1	4	16	0	30	32	4	10	3	16	18	0	0	5	7	6	9	0	14	10	10	10	0	6	**X**
0	6	5	0	0	1	3	1	1	0	0	1	2	4	1	1	0	1	9	1	4	3	0	0	0	0	0	0	0	1	0	0	2	0	1	2	0	0	1	1	3	0	**S**
16	1	2	0	0	0	1	0	0	0	0	0	0	10	33	5	14	3	7	1	4	1	2	0	0	1	0	0	0	3	12	0	1	0	3	6	0	0	2	0	5	0	**U**

Total Cup Appearances

HARRISON	A FRANCIS	KASIAMA	THORLEY	WILSON	OWENS	MORGAN	MOULT	MILLS	DAVIDSON	AMOS	WELLECOMME	PROFFITT	HULME	ROGERS	ALLEN	BRINDLEY	VAULS	E FRANCIS	D ALEXANDER	PATRICK	BRUNT	EVANS	REID	THOMPSON	JOHNSON	LUMLEY	UDOJI	WOOLISCROFT	SAMBA	WHITEHOUSE	OJAMAA	W ALEXANDER	WILLIAMS	DINNING	HOLLAND	MCAUGHTRIE	BURNS	GOODHEAD	MERELLA	DAVIS	GLOVER	
0	1	3	3	3	2	0	3	2	0	0	3	0	0	0	0	0	3	0	0	0	0	1	2	0	3	2	1	1	0	0	0	0	0	0	0	0	0	0	0	0	0	**X**
0	0	0	0	0	0	2	0	0	0	0	0	0	1	0	0	0	0	1	0	2	0	0	0	0	0	0	0	0	1	0	0	0	0	0	0	0	0	0	0	0	0	**S**
2	0	0	0	0	0	0	0	0	0	0	0	0	0	2	0	2	0	0	0	1	0	0	0	0	0	0	0	0	0	1	0	0	0	0	0	0	0	0	0	0	0	**U**

Total Goals

HARRISON	A FRANCIS	KASIAMA	THORLEY	WILSON	OWENS	MORGAN	MOULT	MILLS	DAVIDSON	AMOS	WELLECOMME	PROFFITT	HULME	ROGERS	ALLEN	BRINDLEY	VAULS	E FRANCIS	D ALEXANDER	PATRICK	BRUNT	EVANS	REID	THOMPSON	JOHNSON	LUMLEY	UDOJI	WOOLISCROFT	SAMBA	WHITEHOUSE	OJAMAA	W ALEXANDER	WILLIAMS	DINNING	HOLLAND	MCAUGHTRIE	BURNS	GOODHEAD	MERELLA	DAVIS	GLOVER	
0	0	3	5	5	1	0	2	6	0	0	11	0	0	0	0	0	0	1	0	0	0	0	6	2	1	0	0	0	0	0	1	3	0	3	0	1	0	1	3	0	1	**Lge**
0	0	1	2	0	0	0	0	0	0	0	0	0	0	0	0	0	0	0	0	0	0	0	0	0	0	0	0	0	0	0	0	0	0	0	0	0	0	0	0	0	0	**Cup**

Also Played: LUNN U(15,17). LYCETT U(17) S(19). MASADE U(28). LLOYD S(29,31) U(30).

STAFFORD RANGERS

CURRENT SQUAD AS OF BEGINING OF 2010-11 SEASON

GOALKEEPERS	HT	WT	D.O.B	AGE	P.O.B	CAREER	Apps	Gls
Lee Evans			24/5/83	27	Sutton Coldfield	Ilkeston, Stourport 6/03, Willenhall, Bedworth 8/04, Bromsgrove c/s 05, Chasetown 5/06, Gresley R (L) 10/08, Stafford R 6/09	30	0
Tom Harrison	6'00"	13 07	11/11/90	19		Stoke (Scholar) Rel c/s 09, Stafford R 8/09	4	0
Adam Whitehouse			7/6/92	18		Stafford R 0	0	
DEFENDERS								
Chris Brindley			5/7/69	41		Stafford R (Man) 12/08	0	0
Andre Francis			25/4/85	25	Birmingham	Stafford R, Rushall O, Halesowen T 6/07, Romulus 1/08, Stafford R 7/08	32	0
Grant Goodhead			22/2/85	25		Hednesford (Yth), Heath Hayes, Goodrich 1/06, Cradley T, Market Drayton c/s 07, Hednesford 10/09, Stafford R 2/10	11	1
Craig McAughtrie	6'04"	13 10	3/3/81	29	Burton	Sheff Utd Rel c/s 00, Carlisle 8/00 Rel c/s 02, Stafford R 7/02, Tamworth Undisc 9/07 Rel 5/09, Kings Lynn 6/09, Eastwood T 9/09 Rel 4/10, Stafford R (SL) 1/10, Stafford R 5/10	14	1
Jonathan Patrick			24/5/91	19	Wolverhampton	Walsall Rel 3/09, Stafford R 3/09	20	0
Joe Rogers			20/2/92	18	Stafford	Stafford R 1	0	
MIDFIELDERS								
Fabrice Kasiama			2/10/90	19		Wolves (Scholar), Gillingham (Trial) 4/09, Stafford R 8/09	37	3
Levi Reid	5'05"	11 04	19/1/83	27	Stafford	Port Vale Rel c/s 05, Grimsby (Trial) 7/05, Stafford R 8/05, Hinckley U 7/06, Port Vale (Reserves), Stafford R 1/07 Rel c/s 07, Macclesfield 8/07 Rel c/s 08, Oxford U 8/08 Rel 9/08, Mansfield (Trial) 1/09, Stafford R 8/09	32	6
FORWARDS								
James Davis			1/11/90	19		Wolves, Glen Hoddle Academy (Spa), Stafford R 3/10	3	0
Dominic Merella			31/12/89	20	Chorley	Blackpool, Burscough 3/09, Weymouth 3/09, Burscough c/s 09, Glen Hoddle Academy (Spa), Stafford R 2/10	11	3
Ben Mills			29/3/89	21	Stoke	Leek T, Newcastle T 7/07, Leek T 9/08, Stafford R 7/09, Alfreton 11/09, Stafford R 6/1014		6
Nick Wellecomme			31/5/84	26	Stafford	Brocton, Newcastle T 7/06, Stafford R 3/08, Corby T 6/10, Stafford R 6/10	34	11

Loanees	HT	WT	DOB	AGE	POB	From - To	APPS	GOA
(M)Ross Davidson	6'02"	11 05	6/9/89	20	Burton	Port Vale (2ML) 8/09 - Nantwich T (L) 12/09, Stafford R (L) 3/10, Rel c/s 10	11	0
(F)Steve Thompson	5'07"	11 01	15/4/89	21	Peterlee	Port Vale 9/09 - Rel 10/09, AFC Telford 10/09	4	2
(D)Jermaine Johnson			2/10/90	19		Derby 9/09, 11/09 -	10	1
(F)Henrik Ojamaa			20/5/91	19		Derby 11/09 - 5	1	
(F)Warwick Alexander			8/11/91	18		Stoke 11/09 -	9	3
(M)Michael Burns	5'10"	11 07	4/10/88	21	Huyton	Carlisle (2ML) 1/10 -	10	0
(F)Aaron Lloyd			13/3/92	18		Shrewsbury 2/10 -	2	0
(M)Danny Glover	20	6'00"	11 02	24/10/89	20	Crewe Port Vale 3/10 - Rel c/s 10	6	1

Departures	HT	WT	DOB	AGE	POB	From - To	APPS	GOA
(F)Dorryl Proffitt			2/5/85	25	Stafford	Newcastle T 8/09 - Buxton 8/09, Hednesford 1/10	2	0
(D)Nick Amos			23/7/75	36	Ilford	Halesowen T 6/08 - Hednesford (Dual) 8/09, Bloxwich U, Rushall O 11/09	2	0
(D)Andy Owens	6'03"	13 05	15/10/89	20		Glen Hoddle Soccer Academy 8/09 - Altrincham 11/09	6	1
(G)Billy Lumley	6'05"	14 13	28/12/89	20	Loughton	Grays 9/09 - Rel 11/09, Northampton 12/09, Eastleigh 3/10	3	0
(D)Scott Lycett	6'00"	11 11	5/9/87	22	Stoke	Hednesford 11/09 - Leamington (L) 11/09, Leamington 12/09	1	0
(F)Darren Alexander			15/9/83	26		USA 8/09 - Hednesford 12/09	5	0
(F)Bobby Wilson			11/8/88	22	Harlow	Gainsborough NC 3/09 - Stirling Lions (Aust) 1/10	23	5
(M)Jake Moult	5'10"	10 05	10/2/89	21	Stoke	Leek T 10/08 - Alfreton 1/10	19	2
(M)Luke Morgan	5'08"	10 02	26/10/88	21	Leeds	Glen Hoddle Soccer Academy (Spa) 7/09 - Curzon Ashton 2/10	7	0
(F)Eugene Francis			25/2/86	24	Nottingham	Gedling T 8/09 - Hucknall 3/10	10	1
(D)Emmanuel Udoji	6'00"	13 05	9/1/89	21		Glen Hoddle Soccer Academy 9/09 - Bromley 3/10	16	0
(D)Ashley Wooliscroft	5'10"	11 02	28/12/79	30	Stoke	Fleetwood 3/10 - Leek T (Dual) 3/10, AFC Telford 6/10	18	0
(M)Tom Thorley	5'10"	11 08	5/4/90	20	Stafford	Stoke (SL) 1/09, Perm 7/09 - Worcester 6/10	39	5
(G)Danny Allen			13/9/90	19	Stafford	Yth -	4	0
(G)Ashley Lunn			27/2/89	21		Yth -	0	0
(D)Craig Holland			20/7/82	28	Tittensor	Stafford T 1/10 -	2	0
(D)Curtley Williams	6'00"	13 05	19/3/90	20		Glen Hoddle Soccer Academy 12/09 -	6	0
(M)Darren Brunt	5'10"	11 00	23/12/89	20		Stoke (Scholar) 8/09 -	3	0
(M)Tony Dinning	6'00"	13 05	12/4/75	35	Wallsend	Hednesford 12/09 -	10	3
(M)Craig Hulme			8/5/89	21	Stafford	Stafford T 7/09 -	5	0
(D)Richard Vauls	5'11"	11 08	23/9/90	19		Stoke (Scholar) 7/09 -	16	0
(M)Ebenezer Masade			8/9/88	21		Tonbridge A 2/10 -	0	0
(F)Saul Otobo			17/9/87	22		Eastleigh 2/10 -		
(F)Patrick Samba			1/9/82	27		Glapwell 11/09 -	1	0

STALYBRIDGE CELTIC

Chairman: Rob Gorski
Secretary: Martyn Torr **(T)** 07860 841 765
(E) office@stalybridgeceltic.co.uk
Additional Committee Members: Syd White, Gerald Crossley, Dorothy Norton, Gordon Greenwood, Bill McCallum, John Dillon, Les Taylor, Mark Hagan, John Hall
Manager: Jim Harvey
Programme Editor: Nick Shaw **(E)** nick@newimage.co.uk

Back row (L-R): Mark Storah, kit manager; Joe Paladino, goalkeeping coach; Kristian Platt; Craig Hobson; Lloyd Ellams; Kieran Gonzalez; Will Jones; Nathan Finnigan; Laquan Esdaille; Joel Bembo-Leta; Dave Pover, Sports Therapist; Stacey Arthern, assistant physio.
Front row: Phil Marsh; Jack Rea; Callum Warburton; Connor Jennings; Graeme Law; Jim Harvey, manager; Tim Ryan, assistant manager; Steve Woods; Jody Banim; Glen Rule; Lee Elam; Greg Wilkinson.

Club Factfile

Founded: 1909 **Nickname:** Celtic
Previous Names:
Previous Leagues: Lancashire Combination 1911-12, Central League 1912-21, Southern 1914-15, Football League 1921-23, Cheshire Co. 1923-82, North West Co. 1982-87, N.P.L. 1987-92, 98-2001, Conference 1992-98, 01-02

Club Colours (change): Royal blue/white/royal blue (All yellow)

Ground: Bower Fold, Mottram Road, Stalybridge, Cheshire SK15 2RT **(T)** 0161 338 2828
Capacity: 6,108 **Seats:** 1,200 **Covered:** 2,400 **Clubhouse:** Yes **Shop:** Yes
Previous Grounds:

Simple Directions
Leave the M6 at junction 19 (Northwich). At the roundabout at the end of the slip road turn right (exit 3 of 4) to join the A556 towards Altrincham. Stay on the A556 for 5 miles to a roundabout with the M56. Turn right at the roundabout (exit 3 of 4) onto the M56. Stay on the M56 for 6 1/2 miles to junction 3 (M60 signposted Sheffield, M67) Stay on the M60 for 7 miles to junction 24 (M67, Denton) At the roundabout turn right (exit 4 of 5) to join the M67. Stay on the M67 to the very end, Junction 4. At the roundabout turn left (exit 1 of 4) onto the A57 (Hyde Road). After 1/2 a mile you will reach a set of traffic lights (signposted Stalybridge). Turn left onto B6174 (Stalybridge Road). Almost immediately, there is a mini roundabout. Turn left (exit 1 of 5) onto Roe Cross Road (A6018). Follow this road for 1 3/4 miles passing the Roe Cross Inn on the right and through the cutting (the road is now called Mottram Road). When you pass the Dog and Partridge on the right, you will be almost there. Bower Fold is on the left opposite a sharp right turn next to the Hare and Hounds pub. If the car park is full (it usually is), parking can be found on the streets on the right of Mottram Road.

Record Attendance: 9,753 v West Bromwich Albion - FA Cup replay 1922-23
Record Victory: 16-2 v Manchester NE - 01/05/1926 and v Nantwich - 22/10/1932
Record Defeat: 1-10 v Wellington Town - 09/03/1946
Record Goalscorer: Harry Dennison - 215
Record Appearances: Kevan Keelan - 395
Additional Records: Cecil Smith scored 77 goals during the 1931-32 season
Paid £15,000 to Kettering Town for Ian Arnold 1995. Received £16,000 from Southport for Lee Trundle.
Senior Honours: Manchester Senior Cup 1922-23.
Northern Premier League Premier Division 1991-92, 2000-01.
Cheshire Senior Cup x2.

10 YEAR RECORD

00-01	01-02	02-03	03-04	04-05	05-06	06-07	07-08	08-09	09-10
NP P 1	Conf 21	NP P 4	NP P 11	Conf N 19	Conf N 7	Conf N 18	Conf N 2	Conf N 6	Conf N 9

STALYBRIDGE CELTIC

No.	Date	Comp	H/A	Opponents	Att:	Result	Goalscorers	Pos
1	8/8/09	BSN	A	Redditch United	349	W 4-1	Hankin 21, Barlow 2 (28, 74), Og (Spittle) 45	1
2	11/8/09	BSN	H	AFC Telford	587	L 0-3		10
3	15/8/09	BSN	H	Corby Town	449	L 1-3	O'Neill 79	15
4	18/8/09	BSN	A	Southport	764	L 1-2	Briggs 70	18
5	22/8/09	BSN	H	Workington	393	D 2-2	Briggs 54, O'Neill 75	16
6	29/8/09	BSN	A	Solihull Moors	220	D 2-2	Barlow 2 (15, 53)	16
7	31/8/09	BSN	H	Vauxhall Motors	483	W 3-1	Jennings 16, Wilkinson 25, Og (Moogan) 29	12
8	8/9/09	BSN	A	Eastwood Town	575	W 3-1	O'Neill 24, Jennings 53, Hankin 73	9
9	12/9/09	BSN	H	Droylsden	803	D 2-2	Peyton 5, Hardiker 10	8
10	19/9/09	BSN	A	Alfreton Town	537	W 5-3	Peyton 38, Barlow 39, O'Neill 2 (54, 82), Hobson 89	8
11	3/10/09	BSN	H	Redditch United	474	W 3-0	Jennings 8, O'Neill 34, Hankin 88	5
12	17/10/09	BSN	A	Stafford Rangers	667	W 2-0	Barlow 13, Jennings 46	4
13	24/10/09	BSN	A	Gainsborough Trinity	381	W 3-1	Peyton 45, O'Neill 2 (57, 87)	1
14	31/10/09	BSN	A	Hinckley United	573	D 0-0		4
15	5/12/09	BSN	H	Ilkeston Town	474	W 1-0	Briggs 4	7
16	8/12/09	BSN	H	Gloucester City	352	W 4-1	Barlow 37, Hankin 65, O'Neill 71, Hardiker 81	4
17	23/1/10	BSN	H	Hinckley United	470	D 0-0		7
18	26/1/10	BSN	A	Blyth Spartans	393	L 1-4	Carr 61	7
19	2/2/10	BSN	H	Blyth Spartans	269	L 0-1		7
20	6/2/10	BSN	H	Stafford Rangers	456	D 2-2	Briggs 16, Jennings 38	8
21	9/2/10	BSN	A	Workington	267	L 0-1		8
22	13/2/10	BSN	A	Ilkeston Town	435	L 2-3	O'Neill 47, Smart 86	9
23	20/2/10	BSN	A	Gloucester City	323	W 2-1	O'Neill 80, Peyton pen 90	8
24	27/2/10	BSN	H	Gainsborough Trinity	423	W 3-2	O'Neill 23, Banim 25, Jennings 90	8
25	6/3/10	BSN	A	Harrogate Town	365	W 4-0	Banim 2 (38, 75), Dodgson 47, Carr 64	8
26	9/3/10	BSN	H	Southport	471	L 0-1		8
27	13/3/10	BSN	H	Harrogate Town	454	W 3-0	Banim 15, Jennings 2 (76, 83)	8
28	16/3/10	BSN	H	Hyde United	632	L 2-4	Banim 6, Woods 43	8
29	20/3/10	BSN	A	AFC Telford	1508	W 1-0	Og (Killock) 21	6
30	22/3/10	BSN	A	Hyde United	706	L 1-2	Peyton pen 24	6
31	25/3/10	BSN	H	Fleetwood Town	587	L 2-3	O'Neill 2 (67, 76)	6
32	27/3/10	BSN	H	Alfreton Town	530	L 0-1		8
33	29/3/10	BSN	A	Droylsden	508	L 2-3	Banim 2 (63, 90)	8
34	3/4/10	BSN	H	Solihull Moors	414	W 4-1	Briggs 42, Banim 51, Barlow 57, Jennings 88	7
35	5/4/10	BSN	A	Vauxhall Motors	265	L 2-3	Briggs 62, Peyton pen 89	7
36	10/4/10	BSN	A	Corby Town	260	L 1-5	Banim 24	8
37	13/4/10	BSN	H	Northwich Victoria	326	D 1-1	Barlow 21	10
38	17/4/10	BSN	H	Eastwood Town	384	W 1-0	O'Neill 78	8
39	20/4/10	BSN	A	Northwich Victoria	440	L 1-2	Jennings 69	9
40	24/4/10	BSN	A	Fleetwood Town	3011	L 0-2		9
	Farsley Celtic record expunged 12/03							
8	5/9/09	BSN	A	Farsley Celtic	500	W 2-1	Hardiker 29, Woods 51	9
24	16/2/10	BSN	H	Farsley Celtic	264	L 0-1		9
	Cups							
1	26/9/09	FAC 2Q	A	Stocksbridge Park Steels	352	W 7-2	O'Neill 35, Barlow 2 (pen 55, 65), Briggs 2 (56, 87), Jennings 59, Hobson 76	
2	11/10/09	FAC 3Q	A	FC United of Manchester	2819	D 3-3	Barlow 39, O'Neill 2 (55, pen 69)	
3	13/10/09	FAC 3QR	H	FC United of Manchester	1923	L 0-1		
4	21/11/09	FAT 3Q	H	AFC Telford	422	D 1-1	Briggs 33	
5	24/11/09	FAT 3QR	A	AFC Telford	938	W 2-1	Briggs 20, O'Neill 47	
6	12/12/09	FAT 1	A	Nantwich Town	581	W 3-0	Barlow 31, O'Neill 70, Briggs 74	
7	20/1/10	FAT 2	H	Corby Town	253	L 1-2	Hankin 9	

Home Attendances:	
Highest:	803 v Droylsden
Lowest:	269 v Blyth Spartans
Average (08-09):	463 (503)
Top Goalscorer:	O'Neill - 20 (15 League, 5 Cup) in 44 appearances - 45% strike rate
Most Appearances:	O'Neill - 44 (34+3 League, 7 Cup)

PHILLIPS	BATTERSBY	SMART	WOODS	CARR	HARDIKER	HANKIN	BRIGGS	O'NEILL	BARLOW	PEYTON	KEELING	JENNINGS	LAW	WILKINSON	MOSS	OJAPAH	ENNIS	HOBSON	ABADAKI	CARNELL	BANIM	DODGSON	ADAMS	TWISS	RYAN	BEMBO-LETA	BELL	CHADWICK	
X	X	X	X	X	X	X	X	X	X	X	S	S	S	U	U														1
X	X	X	X	X	X	X	X	X	X	X	U	S	U	S	U														2
X	X	X	X	X	X	X	X	X	X	X	S	S	S		U														3
X	X	X		X	X	X	X	X	X	X	X	S	S	S	U														4
X	X	X		X	X	S	X	X	X	X	X	S	X	S	U														5
X	X	X	X	X	X	S	X	X	X	S		X	X	U	U														6
X	X	S	X	S	X	X	X	X		X		X	X	X	U	S													7
X	X	U	X	S	X	X	X	X	X	X		X	X	U			S	S											8
X	X	S	X	U	X	X	X	X	X	X		X	X	U			S	S											9
X		X	X	S	X	X	X	X	X	X		X	X	U	U			S	S										10
X	S	X	X	U	X	X	X	X	X	X		X	X		U		S	S											11
X	X	S		X	X	X	X	X	X	X		X	X	U	U		S	S											12
X	X	S	X	S	X		X	X	X	X		S	X	U	U		X	X											13
X	X	U	X	S	X	S	X	X	X	X		S	X		U		X	X											14
	S	X	X	X	X	X	X	X	X	X		S	X		U			S	U	X									15
	S	X	X	X	X	X	X	X	X	X		S	X		U			U	S	X									16
	U	X	X	X	X	X	X	X		X	U	S	X		U			X	U	X									17
	X	X	X	X	X	X	X	X	X		U	U	X		U			U	U	X									18
	S	X	X	X	X	X	X	X	X	X	S	S	X		U			U		X									19
	X	X	X	U		X	X	X	X	X	X	X	S		U			U		X	S								20
	X	X	X	S	X	X	X	X	X	X	U	X	S					U		X	S								21
	X	X	X	S	X	X	X	X	X	X	U	S	U					S		X	X								22
	X	X	X	X	X	X		X		X	S	S	X	U				S	U	X	X								23
	X	X		X	X	X		X		X	X	S	U	S				S	U	X	X	X							24
	X	X		X	X	X		X	S	X	X	S	U	U				S		X	X	X							25
	X	X		X		X	S	X	S	X		U	X	U						X	X	S	X	X					26
	X	U	X	S	X	X	X	X	S	X		S	U							X	X		X	X					27
	U		X		X	X	X	S	X		U	X	X	S						X	X	S	X	X					28
	S	S	X		X	X	X	X	U		X	U								X	X	S	X	X	X				29
	X	X	X		X	X	X	S	U	X		S								X	X	S	U	X	X				30
	X		X			X	X	X	X	X		U	S	U						X	S	S	X	X	X				31
		S	X						X	X	S	X	X	S	U					X	X	X	X	X	X				32
		X	X						X	X	X	S	U	S	U					X	X	X	X	X	X	S			33
		X	X			X	X	S	X	X	X	S		U			S			X	X			X	X		U		34
	X	X	X	S		X	X	X	X	X	S	S								X	X		U		X		U		35
		X	X	U				U	X	X	X	X		X			S			X	X			X	X	S		S	36
		X	X	X				X	X	U	X	X		X			S	U		X	X				X		U	U	37
		X	X	X			X	X	X	S	X	X	X	X			S	U		X							U	S	38
		X	X	X			U	X	X	S	X	X	X	X			S	U		X						X		S	39
		X	X	X			U	X	X	S		X	X	X			U			X	S				X	S		X	40
X	X	U	X	U	X	X	X	X	X	X		X	X	U			S	U											
	X	X	X	X	X	S	X	X		X	U	X	S	U				S		X	X								
X	U	X	X	S	X	X	X	X	X	X		X	X		U		S	S	U										1
X	S	X	X	U	X	X	X	X	X	X		X	X	U	U		S	S	U										2
X	X	U	X	S	X	X	X	X	X	X		X	X	U	U		S	S	U										3
	X	U	X	X	X	X	X	X	X	X		S	X	U	U			U		X									4
	U	X	X	X	X	X	X	X	X	X		S	X	U	U			U		X									5
	U	X	X	X	X	X	X	X	X	X		S	X		U			S	S	X									6
	X	X	X	X	X	X		X		X	U		X	U	U			X	S	X									7
Total League Appearances																													
14	24	29	34	20	28	29	30	34	31	32	12	16	22	6	0	0	2	3	0	26	15	4	7	10	10	1	0	1	X
0	5	6	0	9	0	3	1	3	3	4	6	20	6	7	0	1	9	10	2	0	4	5	0	0	0	3	0	3	S
0	2	3	0	4	0	0	2	1	2	1	6	4	6	12	20	0	1	8	5	0	0	0	2	0	0	0	4	1	U
Total Cup Appearances																													
3	3	5	7	4	7	7	6	7	6	7	0	3	7	0	0	0	0	1	0	4	0	0	0	0	0	0	0	0	X
0	1	0	0	2	0	0	0	0	0	0	0	3	0	0	0	0	3	4	2	0	0	0	0	0	0	0	0	0	S
0	3	2	0	1	0	0	0	0	0	0	1	0	0	5	7	0	0	2	3	0	0	0	0	0	0	0	0	0	U
Total Goals																													
0	0	1	1	2	2	4	6	15	9	6	0	10	0	1	0	0	0	1	0	0	9	1	0	0	0	0	0	0	Lge
0	0	0	0	0	0	1	5	5	4	0	0	1	0	0	0	0	0	1	0	0	0	0	0	0	0	0	0	0	Cup

STALYBRIDGE CELTIC

CURRENT SQUAD AS OF BEGINING OF 2010-11 SEASON

GOALKEEPERS	HT	WT	D.O.B	AGE	P.O.B	CAREER	Apps	Gls
Josh Bell	6'01"	13 03	22/1/90	20	Stockport	Farsley Celtic (Yth), Oldham Rel c/s 09, Farsley Celtic 8/09 Rel 3/10, Stalybridge 3/10	0	0
Dave Carnell			18/4/85	25		Man Utd (Yth), Oldham T, Hyde c/s 06, Curzon Ashton (L) Perm, Stalybridge 11/09	26	0
DEFENDERS								
John Hardiker	5'11"	11 01	7/7/82	28	Preston	Morecambe, Stockport £150,000 1/02 Rel c/s 05, Bury 7/05, Morecambe (3ML) 10/05 Perm 1/06, Fleetwood 7/06, Forest Green (L) 11/06 Perm 12/06 Rel 3/09, Stalybridge 3/09	28	2
Graeme Law	5'10"	10 10	6/10/84	25	Kirkcaldy	York, Dundee 2/06, Tamworth 7/06, Farsley Celtic 7/07, Tamworth (L) 10/07 Perm 11/07 Rel c/s 09, Stalybridge 8/09	28	0
Tim Ryan	6'00"	11 07	10/12/74	35	Stockport	Scunthorpe, Buxton 11/94, Doncaster 8/96 Rel c/s 97, Altrincham (2ML) 3/97, Southport 8/97, Doncaster 5/00 Rel 1/06, Peterborough 3/06 Rel c/s 06, Boston U 7/06, Darlington Undisc 1/07 Rel c/s 09, Harrogate T (L) 8/08, Chester 7/09 Rel 3/10, Stalybridge 3	10	0
Steve Woods	5'11"	11 13	15/12/76	33	Davenham	Stoke, Plymouth (SL) 3/98, Chesterfield 7/99 Rel c/s 01, Darlington (Trial) 11/00, Darlington (Trial) 7/01,Torquay 8/01 Rel 4/09, Stalybridge 8/09	34	1
MIDFIELDERS								
Michael Carr	5'08"	10 07	6/12/83	26	Crewe	Macclesfield, Northwich 1/05, Morecambe 5/08 Rel 1/09, Northwich (L) 9/08, Kidderminster 2/09 Rel 5/09, Stalybridge 7/09	29	2
Matthew Chadwick			27/10/92	17		Stalybridge	4	0
Greg Wilkinson			3/10/89	20		East Manchester, Stalybridge 2/08	13	1
FORWARDS								
Jody Banim	5'08"	13 01	1/4/78	32	Manchester	Man Utd (Trainee), Trafford, Altrincham, Flixton, Hyde, Rossendale, Radcliffe B c/s 01, Shrewsbury £20,000 + 12/03, Accrington (L) 8/04, Droylsden Undisc 9/04, Stalybridge 9/05. Droylsden Undisc 5/06, Torquay (SL) 2/08, Burton 5/08 Rel 4/09, Altrincham (L) 1/09, Droylsden (SL) 3/09, Real Maryland Monarchs (USA) 4/09, Salford C 7/09, Droylsden 9/09, Radcliffe B 9/09, Salford C 1/10, Stalybridge 1/10	19	9
Matty Barlow	5'11"	10 02	25/6/87	23	Oldham	Oldham Rel c/s 07, Stafford R (L) 11/06, Stalybridge (L) 1/07, Stalybridge 7/07	34	9
Joel Bembo-Leta			15/2/92	18		Oldham (Yth), Stalybridge	4	0
Paul Ennis	5'06"	11 02	1/2/90	20	Stockport	Stockport Rel c/s 09, Salford C (L) 9/08, Wrexham (Trial) 7/09, Stalybridge 9/09 Rel 11/09, Bala T 1/10, Stalybridge 3/10	11	0
Craig Hobson			25/2/88	22		Kendal T, Stalybridge 9/09	13	1
Conner Jennings						Stalybridge	36	10

Loanees	HT	WT	DOB	AGE	POB	From - To	APPS	GOA
(D)Philip Ojapah			31/12/89	20		Oldham 8/09 - Rhyl (SL) 1/10	1	0

Departures	HT	WT	DOB	AGE	POB	From - To	APPS	GOA
(D)Jonathan Jackson						Yth - Mossley 8/09		
(G)Paul Phillips			15/11/78	31	Manchester	Droylsden 5/08 - Droylsden 11/09	14	0
(M)Barrie Keeling			19/8/78	32	Oldham	Radcliffe B 6/03 - Radcliffe B (L) 8/07, Radcliffe B 11/09	18	0
(M)Osebi Abadaki			22/4/91	19		Altrincham (Yth) 8/09 - Ashton U 3/10	2	0
(M)Lee Dodgson			24/3/84	26	Lancaster	Fleetwood 2/10 - Rel 3/10	9	1
(G)Ryan Moss	6'00"	12 06	5/3/91	29		Macclesfield (Scholar) 8/09 - Rel 3/10	0	0
(D)Danny Adams	5'08"	13 08	3/1/76	34	Manchester	Morecambe 3/10 - Rel 4/10	7	0
(M)Dave Hankin	6'03"		25/3/85	25		Clitheroe 6/09 - Rel 4/10, Kidderminster 6/10	32	4
(F)Michael Twiss	5'11"	13 03	28/12/77	32	Salford	Morecambe 3/10 - Rel 4/10, Altrincham 5/10	10	0
(M)Keith Briggs			11/12/81	28	Glossop	Mansfield 7/08 - Kidderminster 5/10	31	6
(F)Joe O'Neill	6'00"	10 05	28/10/82	27	Blackburn	Altrincham 6/09 - Guiseley 6/10	37	15
(M)Warren Peyton	5'09"	11 03	13/12/79	30	Manchester	Altrincham 6/09 - Guiseley 6/10	36	6
(D)Andrew Smart	6'01"	14 00	17/3/86	24	Wythenshawe	Macclesfield 6/07 - Hyde U 7/10	35	1
(D)Tony Barras			29/3/71	39		FC Halifax 10/09 -		
(D)Richard Battersby	5'08"	10 03	13/6/79	31	York	Radcliffe B 10/08 -	29	0

VAUXHALL MOTORS

Chairman: Alan Bartlam
Secretary: Carole Paisey **(T)** 07789 235 647
(E) stephen.mcinerney3@ntlworld.com
Additional Committee Members: Stephen McInerney, A Woodley, L Jones, D Mathers, Mrs L Bartlam, M Harper, N Kelly, PJarvis, T Marley, Mrs L Edmunds, Miss M Jones, Mrs C Mathers, C Wheelwright, Mrs T Wheelwright
Manager: Carl Macauley
Programme Editor: Mike Harper **(E)** mike.harper@sky.com

Archive photo

Club Factfile

Founded: 1963 **Nickname:** The Motormen
Previous Names: Vauxhall Motors 1963-87, Vauxhall GM 1995-99
Previous Leagues: Ellesmere Port, Wirral Combination, West Cheshire 1966-87, 92-95, North West Co. 1987-92, 95-2000, Northern Premier 2000-04

Club Colours (change): White/cobalt blue/white (Electricity yellow/black/black)

Ground: Rivacre Park, Rivacre Road, Ellesmere Port, South Wirrall CH66 1NJ **(T)** 0151 328 1114 (Club) 327 2294 (Social)
Capacity: 3,500 **Seats:** 266 **Covered:** 1,000 **Clubhouse:** Yes **Shop:** Yes
Previous Grounds:
Simple Directions
Leave M53 at junction 5 and take A41 towards North Wales. At first set of traffic lights (Hooton Crossroads) turn left into Hooton Green. At 'T' junction turn left into Hooton Lane. At next 'T' junction turn right into Rivacre Road. Ground is 200 yards on right.

Record Attendance: 1,500 - FA XI fixture for the opening of Rivacre Park 1987
Record Victory: Not known
Record Defeat: Not known
Record Goalscorer: Terry Fearns - 111
Record Appearances: Carl Jesbitt - 509
Additional Records:

Senior Honours: North West Counties League Division 2 1988-89, 95-96, Division 1 1999-2000.
Wirral Senior Cup 1987.

10 YEAR RECORD

00-01	01-02	02-03	03-04	04-05	05-06	06-07	07-08	08-09	09-10
NP 1 2	NP P 2	NP P 3	NP P 9	Conf N 15	Conf N 18	Conf N 15	Conf N 21	Conf N 11	Conf N 20

VAUXHALL MOTORS

No.	Date	Comp	H/A	Opponents	Att:	Result	Goalscorers	Pos
1	8/8/09	BSN	H	Gainsborough Trinity	260	D 2-2	Griffiths 2 (pen 28, pen 59)	10
2	11/8/09	BSN	A	Harrogate Town	327	L 0-3		15
3	15/8/09	BSN	A	Alfreton Town	410	D 2-2	Noon 8, Wilson 10	17
4	18/8/09	BSN	H	Fleetwood Town	224	W 2-1	Noon 34, Og (Taylor 58)	12
5	22/8/09	BSN	A	Hinckley United	243	D 1-1	Furlong 70	12
6	29/8/09	BSN	H	Stafford Rangers	195	D 2-2	Booth 21, Noon 45	12
7	31/8/09	BSN	A	Stalybridge Celtic	483	L 1-3	Furlong 84	15
8	5/9/09	BSN	H	Gloucester City	206	D 0-0		13
9	8/9/09	BSN	H	Blyth Spartans	176	D 1-1	Noone 4	14
10	12/9/09	BSN	A	Ilkeston Town	429	L 0-4		16
11	19/9/09	BSN	H	Solihull Moors	187	L 0-2		21
12	3/10/09	BSN	A	Workington	327	L 0-1		21
13	17/10/09	BSN	H	Eastwood Town	197	W 3-2	Wilson 57, Grice 60, Hine 62	19
14	27/10/09	BSN	H	Southport	323	L 1-3	Moogan 13	20
15	31/10/09	BSN	A	Hyde United	308	D 2-2	Noon 38, Moogan pen 90	20
16	7/11/09	BSN	H	Droylsden	193	L 1-2	Wilson 51	21
17	28/11/09	BSN	A	Solihull Moors	186	L 0-4		21
18	5/12/09	BSN	H	Corby Town	178	L 2-4	Wilson 8, Noon 70	21
19	28/12/09	BSN	A	Fleetwood Town	1170	L 2-4	Furlong 58, Wilson pen 84	22
20	16/1/10	BSN	A	Blyth Spartans	384	L 2-3	Furlong 20, Noon 90	22
21	23/1/10	BSN	H	Alfreton Town	158	D 1-1	Wilson 21	22
22	26/1/10	BSN	H	Workington	184	D 1-1	Wilson 35	22
23	30/1/10	BSN	H	Redditch United	186	L 0-5		22
24	2/2/10	BSN	A	AFC Telford	1169	L 1-5	Wilson 23	22
25	6/2/10	BSN	A	Eastwood Town	372	D 0-0		22
26	9/2/10	BSN	H	Ilkeston Town	184	W 4-2	Furlong 2 (27, 45), Wilson 34, Noon 85	21
27	13/2/10	BSN	H	Hinckley United	200	D 1-1	Furlong 7	21
28	16/2/10	BSN	H	Harrogate Town	178	L 1-2	J Macauley 68	22
29	20/2/10	BSN	A	Droylsden	340	D 1-1	Lane 34	22
30	23/2/10	BSN	A	Gainsborough Trinity	229	L 0-2		22
31	27/2/10	BSN	H	Hyde United	249	W 1-0	Wilson 76	21
32	2/3/10	BSN	H	Northwich Victoria	378	W 1-0	Moogan pen 35	20
33	6/3/10	BSN	A	Corby Town	261	L 1-4	J Macauley 46	21
34	13/3/10	BSN	A	Gloucester City	301	L 0-1		20
35	16/3/10	BSN	A	Northwich Victoria	353	D 0-0		20
36	27/3/10	BSN	A	Southport	826	L 0-3		20
37	3/4/10	BSN	A	Stafford Rangers	463	L 1-3	Moogan pen 5	20
38	5/4/10	BSN	H	Stalybridge Celtic	265	W 3-2	Egerton 29, Noon 2 (37, 86)	20
39	17/4/10	BSN	A	Redditch United	348	D 1-1	Noon 56	20
40	24/4/10	BSN	H	AFC Telford	387	W 3-1	Moogan 49, Brown 2 (52, 88)	20
	Farsley Celtic record expunged 12/03							
14	24/10/09	BSN	A	Farsley Celtic	285	L 0-1		20
	Cups							
1	26/9/09	FAC 2Q	A	Whitby Town	286	W 5-0	Furlong 4 (48, 70, 81, 84), Noone 71	
2	10/10/09	FAC 3Q	A	Fleetwood Town	951	L 2-3	Furlong 2 (4, 20)	
3	21/11/09	FAT 3Q	A	Quorn	175	W 3-2	Moogan pen 1, Wilson 55, Hine 62	
4	12/12/09	FAT 1	H	Kings Lynn		walkover		
5	19/1/10	FAT 2	A	Stevenage Borough	578	L 0-6		

Home Attendances:	
Highest:	387 v AFC Telford
Lowest:	158 v Alfreton Town
Average (08-09):	198 (203)
Top Goalscorer:	Furlong - 12 (7 League, 5 Cup) in 34 appearances - 35% strike rate
Most Appearances:	Lane - 43 (39 League, 4 Cup)

ST LOUIS-HAMILTON	LANE	DAMES	HOLMES	GRIFFITHS	HOLDEN	WILSON	DAVIES	NOON	HINE	NOONE	FURLONG	HANNIGAN	K SMITH	EGERTON	F SMITH	MUSTAFA	BOOTH	OWENS	MOOGAN	WRIGHT	SWASH	WADE	GRICE	C MACAULEY	EVANS	BATHURST	RICHARDS	COATES	DODGSON	J MACAULEY	WINTERS	BROWN	
X	X	X	X	X	X	X	X	X	X	X	S	S	S	U	U																		1
X	X	X	X	X	X	X	X	X	X	X	S	S		U	S	U																	2
X	X	X	X	X	X	X	U	X	X	X	U	U		S		U	X																3
X	X	X		X	X		U	X	X	X	S	S		X	U		X	X	S														4
X	X	X	X		X		S	X	X	X	S			X	S	U	X		X	U													5
X	X	X	X		X	S	S	X	X	X	S		U	X			X		X		U												6
X	X		X		X	X	S	X	X	X	S		S	X	U		X		X	U													7
X	X	X	U		U	X	X	X	X	S		X	S	X			X		X	S													8
X	X	X			U	X	U	X	S	X	X	X	U	X			X		X	S													9
X	X	X			U	X	U	X	S	X	X	X	S	X			X		X	S													10
X	X	X				X		X	S	X	X	X	X	X					X	S		S											11
X	X	X	S		X	X			S	X	X	X	X	S		U	X		X			U											12
X	X		X		X	X		X	S	X	X		X	U		U			X	U			X										13
X	X		X		X	X		X	X	X				X					X	S			X										14
X	X		X		X	X		X	X	X		S	S	X					X	S			X										15
X	X	S	X			X		X	X	X		X	U	X		U		U	X	S			X										16
X	X	X	X			X		X	X	X	S	S		X				S	X	U			X	U									17
X	X	X	U			X		X		X	X	X	U					U	X	U			X		X	S							18
X	X		U	U		X		X		X	X	X	U	X				S	X				X		X		S						19
	X	X	U	X		X		X		X	X	X	S	U				X	X	U			S					X					20
	X	U	X			X		X		X	X		S	S				X	X	U			X		X		U	X					21
	X	S	X			X		X		X	X	U	S	S				X	X	U			X		X			X					22
	X		X			X		X		X	X	S		S				X	X	S			X		X			X					23
	X					X		S			X	X	X	X		U		U	X	S			X	U	X			X	X				24
	X					X		X			X	X	X			U		U	X	U			X	U	X		U	X	X				25
	X					X		X			X	X	X	S		U		S	X	U			X		X		U	X	X				26
	X	U				X				U	X	X	X	U				U	X	S			X		X			X	X	X			27
	X	S				X		X		S		X	X	S				U	X	U			X		X			X	X	X			28
	X	S				X		X		S		X	X	S		U		U	X				X		X			X	X	X			29
	X	X				X		X		X		X	U	X		U		U	X	U			X	U				X		X			30
	X	X				X		S		X		X	S	X		U		U	X	U			X					X		X	X		31
	X	X				X		X		U		X	U	X		U		U	X	U			X					X		X	X		32
	X	X				X		X		S	S	X	U	X		U		U	X				X					X		X	X		33
	X	X				X		X		X	S	X		X		U		S	S	U			X					X		X	X		34
	X	X				X		U		X	X	X	U	X		U		U		U			X					X		X	X		35
		X				X		S		S	X	X	U	U		U		X	X				X					X		X	X	X	36
	X	X				X		S		X	S		S	X		U		X	X	U			X					X		X		X	37
	X	X						X		X	S		X	X		U		X	X	U			S	U				X		X		X	38
	X					X		X		X	X	X	X	X		U			X	S			U					X		U	S	X	39
	X					X		X		X	X	X	X	X					X	S				U				X			S	X	40
X	X	X	X		X	X		S	S	X	X		X	S		U			X	U			X										
X	X	X	S		X	X		X	S	X	X	X	X	U			X			U		S											1
X	X	X	S		X	X			S	X	X	X	X	U		U	X		X	U													2
X	X		X			X		X	X	X	S	U	X	X				S	X	U			X										3
																																	4
X	X	X	S		X		X		U	X		X					S	X	U			X				U	X						5
Total League Appearances																																	
19	39	23	14	5	11	36	3	33	12	30	19	24	12	24	0	0	9	8	34	0	0	0	24	0	11	0	0	21	6	12	6	5	X
0	0	4	1	0	0	1	3	4	5	5	11	6	10	8	2	0	0	4	2	12	0	1	2	0	0	1	1	0	0	0	2	0	S
0	0	2	4	1	3	0	4	1	0	2	1	2	10	6	3	20	0	12	0	18	1	1	1	6	0	0	3	0	0	1	0	0	U
Total Cup Appearances																																	
3	4	3	2	0	2	4	0	3	1	3	3	2	4	1	0	0	2	0	3	0	0	0	2	0	0	0	0	1	0	0	0	0	X
0	0	0	2	1	0	0	0	0	2	0	1	0	0	0	0	0	0	2	0	0	0	1	0	0	0	0	0	0	0	0	0	0	S
0	0	0	0	0	0	0	0	0	0	1	0	1	0	2	0	1	0	0	0	4	0	0	0	0	0	0	1	0	0	0	0	0	U
Total Goals																																	
0	1	0	0	2	0	10	0	10	1	1	7	0	0	1	0	0	1	0	5	0	0	0	1	0	0	0	0	0	0	2	0	2	Lge
0	0	0	0	0	0	1	0	1	1	1	5	0	0	0	0	0	0	0	1	0	0	0	0	0	0	0	0	0	0	0	0	0	Cup

VAUXHALL MOTORS

CURRENT SQUAD AS OF BEGINING OF 2010-11 SEASON

GOALKEEPERS	HT	WT	D.O.B	AGE	P.O.B	CAREER	Apps	Gls
James Coates			22/2/85	25		Man City (Jun), Mansfield (Sch) Rel c/s 04, Worcester 10/04, Burton 3/05, Moor Green 7/05, Leigh RMI 2/06, Worcester c/s 06, Bromsgrove (L) 11/06, Hucknall 2/07, Kidsgrove A (L) 3/07, Kidsgrove A c/s 07, Altrincham (Trial) c/s 08, Vauxhall Motors 8/08, Northwich 7/09, Rhyl (4ML) 8/09, Vauxhall Motors 1/10	21	0
Zharir Mustaffa			24/7/87	23		Vauxhall Motors	0	0
DEFENDERS								
Lee Dames			21/1/86	24	Liverpool	Tranmere (Yth), Burscough, Vauxhall Motors 6/06	27	0
Jonathan Egerton			19/9/88	21		Vauxhall Motors	32	1
Gareth Evans	6'01"	12 12	10/1/87	23	Wrexham	Newi Cefn Druids, Wrexham (Yth c/s 04) (Pro) 8/06 Rel 1/09, Northwich (L) 9/07, Tamworth (L) 1/08, Austin Aztecs (USA), Vauxhall Motors 11/09	11	0
Chris Lane	6'00"	12 10	24/5/79	31	Liverpool	Everton Rel c/s 98, Hereford 6/98, Southport 1/01, Morecambe 5/03, Leigh RMI 1/04, Chester 2/04, Leigh RMI 6/04, Southport 5/05 Rel 5/07, Altrincham 6/07 Rel 5/09, Vauxhall Motors 7/09	39	1
Brian Moogan			4/9/84	25		Everton Rel c/s 04, Macclesfield (Trial), Lancaster 11/04, Vauxhall Motors 3/05, Burscough 10/07, Vauxhall Motors 6/09	36	5
Lee Owens			29/6/86	24		Wigan (Scholar), Chester (Trial) c/s 05, Vauxhall Motors (07/08)	12	0
MIDFIELDERS								
Paul Brown	5'11"	12 00	10/9/84	25	Liverpool	Tranmere Rel c/s 06, Accrington (L) 8/05, Barrow 7/06, Kingston City (Aus) 2/07, Barrow 8/07 Rel 5/09, Droylsden 6/09 Rel 3/10, Witton 3/10, Vauxhall Motors 3/10	5	2
Tom Grice			2/2/90	20		Everton (Yth), Burscough, Cavecanen, Caernarfon 7/08, Marine c/s 09, Vauxhall Motors 10/09	26	1
Tom Hannigan			30/6/88	22		Vauxhall Motors	30	0
Sean Richards			21/6/91	19		Vauxhall Motors	1	0
Keith Smith			21/8/81	29		Vauxhall Motors, Caernarfon 9/08, Burscough 2/09, Vauxhall Motors 8/09	22	0
Josh Wilson			5/7/88	22	Liverpool	Stoke (Scholar) Rel 6/06, Abroad, Northwich 7/07 Rel 5/08, Leigh RMI/Leigh Genesis 5/08, Burscough 11/08, Vauxhall Motors 8/09	37	10
FORWARDS								
Lee Furlong			9/8/79	31		Southport, Burscough 6/01, Marine 1/03, Witton 9/03, Newton, Runcorn 8/05, Vauxhall Motors 3/06, Caernarfon 7/08, Vauxhall Motors 1/09	30	7
Carl Macauley			29/10/70	39		Vauxhall Motors Man	0	0
Karl Noon			15/9/86	23		Tranmere (Yth), Liverpool (Scholar) Rel c/s 05, Chester (Reserves), Prescot Cables, Bamber Bridge, Marine 12/06, Southport c/s 07, Bangor C (L) 1/08 Perm, Vauxhall Motors 8/08	37	10
Chris Noone	6'02"	12 00	25/10/84	25	Liverpool	Everton, Vauxhall Motors, La Nucia (Spa), Caernarfon c/s 07 Rel 9/07, Banned, Vauxhall Motors c/s 08	35	1
Anthony Wright	5'11"	11 00	6/3/78	32	Liverpool	Wrexham, Barrow, Droylsden 9/98, TNS, Aberystwyth, Hyde (L) 8/03, Vauxhall Motors 8/04, Colwyn Bay 1/08, Vauxhall Motors 5/08	12	0

Loanees	HT	WT	DOB	AGE	POB	From - To	APPS	GOA
(G)Danzelle St Louis-Hamilton	6'04"	12 13	7/5/90	20	Stevenage	Stoke (5ML) 7/09 - Worcester (L) 2/10	19	0
(M)Robbie Booth	5'07"	11 08	30/12/85	24	Liverpool	Southport (2ML) 8/09 -	9	1
(M)Lee Dodgson			24/3/84	26	Lancaster	Fleetwood 2/10 - Stalybridge 2/10	6	0
(F)Josh Macauley	6'00"	12 00	2/3/91	19	Liverpool	Tranmere 2/10 -	12	2
(D)Rory Winters			16/2/90	20		Morecambe 2/10 - Rel 5/10	8	0

Departures	HT	WT	DOB	AGE	POB	From - To	APPS	GOA
(F)Ryan Wade			22/1/88	22		Burscough 9/09 - Skelmersdale 10/09	1	0
(M)James Holden			16/10/86	23		Bala T 7/09 - Rel 11/09, FCUM 1/10	11	0
(F)Jonathan Bathurst			29/7/89	21		Southport 12/09 - Burscough 1/10	1	0
(M)Craig Davies			21/12/88	21		Burscough c/s 09 -	6	0
(M)Alan Griffiths			24/2/85	26		Tranmere c/s 03 -	5	2
(M)Jordan Holmes			12/1/88	22		Lancaster 8/07 -	15	0
(M)Fran Smith			23/9/87	22			2	0
(M)Matty Swash			2/8/89	21			0	0
(F)Josh Hine			4/3/91	19		Burscough 7/09 -	17	1

WORCESTER CITY

Chairman: Anthony Hampson
Secretary: Joe Murphy (T) 07837 086 205
(E) joemurphy77@yahoo.co.uk
Additional Committee Members:
Jim Painter, Colin Layland, Andrew Watson, Mike Davis, Philip Williamson
Manager: Carl Heeley
Programme Editor: Rob Bazley (E) programme@worcestercityfc.co.uk

Back Row (L-R): Ernie North (Kitman), Simon Richman, Shabir Khan, RobElvins, Danny Glover, Kevin O'Connor, Jamie Price, MartinObrey (Assistant Therapist) Middle Row : Kevin Gardiner (Kit Manager), Pete O'Connell (Chiropodist), Jason Pike, Dan Polan, Mark Wright, Brad Birch, Gary Walker, Mark Owen (First Team Coach), Steve Ball (Head Therapist)
Front Row : Marc McGregor, Mark Danks, Carl Heeley (Manager), Mark Clyde (Assistant Manager), Graham Ward (Captain), Tom Thorley

Club Factfile

Founded: 1902 **Nickname:** City
Previous Names:
Previous Leagues: West Midlands, Birmingham, Southern 1938-79, 85-2004, Alliance 1979-85

Club Colours (change): Blue & white stripes/royal blue/white (Sky blue/navy/sky)

Ground: St George's Lane, Barbourne, Worcester WR1 1QT (T) 01905 23003
Capacity: 4,004 **Seats:** 1,125 **Covered:** 2,000 **Clubhouse:** Yes **Shop:** Yes
Previous Grounds: Severn Terrace, Thorneloe, Flagge Meadow
Simple Directions
Leave the M5 at Junction 6 (Worcester North) and take the A449 dual-carriageway towards Kidderminster. At the first island take the 2nd exit towards Worcester. After around 3 miles, at traffic lights/T-junction turn right towards Worcester City Centre. Take the 3rd turning on the left - St. George's Lane North. Ground on the left.

Record Attendance: 17,042 v Sheffield United - FA Cup 4th Round 24/01/1959
Record Victory: 18-1 v Bilston - Birmingham League 21/11/1931
Record Defeat: 0-10 v Wellington - Birmingham League 29/08/1920
Record Goalscorer: John Inglis - 189 (1970-77)
Record Appearances: Bobby McEwan - 596 (1959-75)
Additional Records: Paid £8,500 to Telford United for Jim Williams 1981
Received £27,000 from Everton for John Barton

Senior Honours: Birmingham League 1913-14, 24-25, 28-29, 29-30.
Southern League Cup 1939-40, 2000-01, Division 1 1967-68, 76-77, Premier 1978-79.
Birmingham Senior Cup 1975-76. Worcestershire Senior Cup x26 (last win 1996-97)

10 YEAR RECORD

00-01	01-02	02-03	03-04	04-05	05-06	06-07	07-08	08-09	09-10
SthP 8	SthP 8	SthP 6	SthP 5	Conf N 7	Conf N 8	Conf N 9	Conf N 12	Conf S 16	Conf S 20

WORCESTER CITY

No.	Date	Comp	H/A	Opponents	Att:	Result	Goalscorers	Pos
1	8/8/09	BSS	H	Bromley	645	L 1-2	Elvins 4	19
2	11/8/09	BSS	A	St Albans City	318	L 0-2		22
3	15/8/09	BSS	A	Woking	1120	L 0-1		22
4	17/8/09	BSS	H	Basingstoke Town	620	D 1-1	Wilding 87	19
5	22/8/09	BSS	A	Weymouth	603	L 1-2	Adaggio pen 67	22
6	29/8/09	BSS	H	Staines Town	555	D 0-0		22
7	31/8/09	BSS	A	Bath City	620	D 1-1	Bridges 40	22
8	5/9/09	BSS	H	Dorchester Town	502	W 4-0	Carter 3, Dinsmore 2 (4, 24), Elvins 39	16
9	8/9/09	BSS	A	Weston-Super-Mare	270	L 1-3	Ward 65	19
10	12/9/09	BSS	A	Braintree Town	473	D 0-0		20
11	19/9/09	BSS	H	Thurrock	577	L 1-2	Wilding pen 83	20
12	3/10/09	BSS	H	Dover Athletic	737	W 1-0	Clyde 34	19
13	17/10/09	BSS	A	Hampton & Richmond B.	486	D 2-2	Adaggio 47, Bridges 79	17
14	26/10/09	BSS	H	Weston-Super-Mare	823	W 4-1	McGregor 18, Wilding 22, Elvins 51, Daniel 67	16
15	31/10/09	BSS	A	Eastleigh	501	L 1-4	Brown 26	18
16	7/11/09	BSS	H	Welling United	708	L 0-1		19
17	9/11/09	BSS	H	Chelmsford City	516	L 1-2	Davies 44	19
18	14/11/09	BSS	A	Dorchester Town	419	D 1-1	Wilding 53	19
19	28/11/09	BSS	H	Bishops Stortford	518	D 1-1	Adaggio 54	19
20	5/12/09	BSS	A	Welling United	474	L 0-1		19
21	15/12/09	BSS	A	Thurrock	221	L 1-2	Wilding 8	19
22	28/12/09	BSS	A	Basingstoke Town	395	W 1-0	McGregor 81	19
23	1/1/10	BSS	A	Newport County	2525	L 0-1		19
24	16/1/10	BSS	A	Bishops Stortford	302	L 1-2	McGregor 48	19
25	23/1/10	BSS	H	Weymouth	646	W 3-1	Adaggio 2 (45, 86), Kemp 83	18
26	6/2/10	BSS	A	Havant & Waterlooville	784	L 2-3	Clyde 67, Carter 89	19
27	13/2/10	BSS	H	Woking	607	W 3-2	Elvins 2 (33, 67), Carter 74	19
28	15/2/10	BSS	H	Braintree Town	525	L 2-3	Farrell 20, Emery 50	19
29	20/2/10	BSS	H	Havant & Waterlooville	543	L 0-2		19
30	22/2/10	BSS	H	Newport County	1017	L 1-4	Dinsmore 87	19
31	27/2/10	BSS	A	Lewes	501	D 3-3	Ward 73, McGregor 2 (75, 90)	19
32	1/3/10	BSS	H	Maidenhead United	501	W 1-0	Wilding 32	18
33	6/3/10	BSS	H	Hampton & Richmond B.	646	L 0-1		19
34	9/3/10	BSS	A	Dover Athletic	655	W 2-0	McGregor 62, Elvins 85	19
35	13/3/10	BSS	A	Bromley	414	L 0-2		19
36	20/3/10	BSS	H	St Albans City	605	D 0-0		19
37	27/3/10	BSS	A	Maidenhead United	379	D 1-1	Quaynor 75	19
38	2/4/10	BSS	A	Staines Town	471	W 1-0	Carter 17	19
39	5/4/10	BSS	H	Bath City	832	L 0-2		19
40	10/4/10	BSS	H	Lewes	779	L 1-2	Dinsmore 75	19
41	17/4/10	BSS	A	Chelmsford City	963	L 0-1		20
42	24/4/10	BSS	H	Eastleigh	752	W 4-1	Adaggio pen 8, Clyde 42, Elvins 2 (75, 83)	20
	Cups							
1	26/9/09	FAC 2Q	H	Bourne Town	555	W 3-0	Bridges 27, Davies 81, Adaggio 88	
2	10/10/09	FAC 3Q	A	AFC Telford	1459	D 0-0		
3	12/10/09	FAC 3QR	H	AFC Telford	1062	L 0-1		
4	21/11/09	FAT 3Q	H	Burnham	377	W 2-1	Birley 56, Wilding 77	
5	12/12/09	FAT 1	H	Grays Athletic	545	W 3-1	Elvins 16, Carter 24, Wilding 90	
6	18/1/10	FAT 2	H	Carshalton Athletic	468	D 1-1	Adaggio 58	
7	26/1/10	FAT 2R	A	Carshalton Athletic	259	W 4-0	McGregor 2 (31, 62), Adaggio 69, Davies 90	
8	1/2/10	FAT 3	H	Kidderminster Harriers	1653	L 0-1		

Home Attendances:	
Highest:	1017 v Newport County
Lowest:	501 v Maidenhead United
Average (08-09):	620 (721)
Top Goalscorer:	Adaggio - 9 (6 League, 3 Cup) in 36 appearances - 25% strike rate
	Elvins - 9 (8 League, 1 Cup) in 40 appearances - 23% strike rate
Most Appearances:	Wilding - 45 (35+2 League, 8 Cup)

MACE	SPENCER	KHAN	CLYDE	DANIEL	KEMP	FITZPATRICK	ELVINS	BUTLER	ADAGGIO	MOSES-GARVEY	WILDING	WARD	DINSMORE	WALKER	BRIDGES	HEELEY	HINCHLIFFE	CARTER	EMERY	LEDGISTER	WARDLE	CONNOLLY	DAVIES	MEREDITH	BIRLEY	MCGREGOR	BROWN	CAREY-BERTRAM	DURRANT	FARRELL	ST LOUIS-HAMILTON	BEAHON	PRICE	OWEN	BURGE	PIKE	QUAYNOR	LEE	
X	X	X	X	X	X	X	X	X	X	X	S	S	S	U	U																								1
X	S	X	X	X	X	X	X	X	S	X		X	U	X	U	U																							2
X	U	X	X	X	X	U	X	X	X	S	X		X	X	U	U																							3
U	X			X	X	U		X	X	X	X	S	X	X		U	X	X	S																				4
	X		S	X	X		S	X	X	X	X	U	X	X		U	X	X	S																				5
U			X	X	X		X	U	X		X	X		U	X		X	X	X	S	U																		6
U			X	X	X		X		X		X	X		S	X		X	X	X	S	S	U																	7
U			X	X	X	S	X		S		X	X	X	X	X	U	X	X		S																			8
U			X		X	S	X		X		X	X	X	X	X	U	X	X		U			S																9
	U		X		X		X		S		X	X	X	X	X		X	X	X	S			U	U															10
	S	S	X		X		X				X	X	X	U	X		X	X	X				S	U	X														11
	X	X	X	U	X		X		S		X	X	X	S	X		X						S	U	X														12
	X	X	S	X	X		X		X		X	U	X	S	S		X						X	U	X														13
	X	X	X	X			X		S		X	S	X	U				S					X		X	X													14
	X		X	X	X						X		X				X						X		X	X	X												15
	X	X	X	S	X						X	X	S	S			X	X					U	U	X	X	X												16
	X	X		X	X				X		X	U	X	X			X	S					S	U	X	X	S												17
	X	X	X	X			X		X		X		X	X	U			S					U	X	X	U	U												18
	U		U	X	X	U	X		X		X	X	X	X	S			X					S	X	X														19
	S		X	X	X	U			X		X	X		U	S			X					U	X	X	X		X											20
	U		X	X	X		X				X	X	S	X	U			X					X	X	S	X		S											21
	U	X	X	X	X		X				X	X	U	U				X					S	X	X	S		X											22
	S	X	X	X	X	U			S			X		U	U			X					X	X	X	X		X											23
	S		X	X	X	U	X		S		X	X	S	U				X					X	X	X	X													24
	U		X	X	X	U	S		X		X	X	S	S				X					X	X	X	X													25
	U	X	X	X	X	U	S		X		X	X		X	U	U		X					X	X															26
		X	X	X	U		X		U		U	X	U	X				X	X				S	X					X	X									27
		X	X	X			X		U		U	X	U	X	U			X	X				S	X					X	X									28
		X	X	X			X		S		S	X	U	X		U		X	X				S	X					X	X									29
		X		X			X		X		X	X	X	X	U	U			X				S	X		U			X	S									30
		X	X	S	X		X				X	X	X	X				X	X					U	S	S			U		X								31
		X		X	X		X		U		X	X	X	X					X					U	S	U			U		X	X							32
		X		X	X		X				X	X	X	X				S	X				S	U		S			U		X	X							33
				X			X				X	X	S	X		S			X			S	X	U		X					X		X	X					34
				X			X				X	X	X	X		U		S	X			S	X	U							X		X		X				35
			X	X							X	X		X		U		X				U	X	S	S	X					X		X			X	S		36
			X	X							X	X		X	U	U		X				S	X	X		X							X	U		X	S		37
		X	X	X					X		X	X	S	X				X				U	X	X	U								X			U	U		38
		X		X					X		X	X	X	X		U						U	X	X	S								X			S	U	X	39
		X	X	X			X		S		U	X	X	X									S	X	X	S							X			X	U		40
		X	X	X			X		X		X	X	S	X								U		X	X	S							X			U	U		41
		X	X	X			X		X		X			X					U				X	X	X	U							X	U		U	S		42

MACE	SPENCER	KHAN	CLYDE	DANIEL	KEMP	FITZPATRICK	ELVINS	BUTLER	ADAGGIO	MOSES-GARVEY	WILDING	WARD	DINSMORE	WALKER	BRIDGES	HEELEY	HINCHLIFFE	CARTER	EMERY	LEDGISTER	WARDLE	CONNOLLY	DAVIES	MEREDITH	BIRLEY	MCGREGOR	BROWN	CAREY-BERTRAM	DURRANT	FARRELL	ST LOUIS-HAMILTON	BEAHON	PRICE	OWEN	BURGE	PIKE	QUAYNOR	LEE	
	X	X	X		X	X	X		S		X	X	X	S	X	U	X			U		U	S	U															1
	X	X	X	U	X		X		S		X	X	X	X	S		X			U		U	X	U															2
	X	X	U	X	X		X		X		X	X	X	X	U		X			U		U	S	U															3
	X		X	X		U	X		X		X	S	X	X	U			X					U	X	X	S													4
	U		X	X	X	U	X		S		X	X	S	X	U			X					X	X		X													5
	X		X	X		S	S		X		X	X	S	U	U			X					X	X	X	X													6
	U	X		X	X	U	X		X		X	X	S		U	U		X					X	X		X													7
	U	X	S	X	X	U	X		X		X	X	S	S				X					X	X		X													8

Total League Appearances

3	10	24	31	36	27	2	29	5	19	4	35	32	21	28	7	0	13	24	13	0	0	0	15	19	17	12	2	3	4	3	6	2	9	1	1	3	0	1	X
0	5	1	2	2	0	2	3	0	9	1	2	3	8	5	3	1	0	5	2	4	1	3	12	1	5	5	1	1	0	1	0	0	0	0	0	1	3	0	S
5	7	0	1	1	1	8	0	1	3	0	3	3	5	8	10	13	0	0	1	1	1	5	4	11	1	4	1	0	3	0	0	0	0	2	0	3	4	0	U

Total Cup Appearances

0	5	5	5	6	6	1	7	0	5	0	8	7	4	4	1	0	3	5	0	0	0	0	5	5	2	4	0	0	0	0	0	0	0	0	0	0	0	0	X
0	0	0	1	0	0	1	1	0	3	0	0	1	4	2	1	0	0	0	0	0	0	0	2	0	0	1	0	0	0	0	0	0	0	0	0	0	0	0	S
0	3	0	1	1	0	4	0	0	0	0	0	0	0	1	5	2	0	0	0	3	0	3	1	3	0	0	0	0	0	0	0	0	0	0	0	0	0	0	U

Total Goals

0	0	0	3	1	1	0	8	0	6	0	6	2	4	0	2	0	0	4	1	0	0	0	1	0	0	5	1	0	0	1	0	0	0	0	0	0	1	0	Lge
0	0	0	0	0	0	0	1	0	3	0	2	0	0	0	1	0	0	1	0	0	0	0	2	0	1	2	0	0	0	0	0	0	0	0	0	0	0	0	Cup

WORCESTER CITY

CURRENT SQUAD AS OF BEGINING OF 2010-11 SEASON

GOALKEEPERS	HT	WT	D.O.B	AGE	P.O.B	CAREER	Apps	Gls
Tim Sandercombe	6'04"	13 12	15/6/89	21	Plymouth	QPR (Yth), Plymouth (Scholar) Rel c/s 07, Tiverton (L) 11/06, Notts County 7/07 Rel c/s 08, Torquay (Trial), Stafford R 9/08, Mansfield 5/09, Weymouth 2/10, Worcester 7/10		
DEFENDERS								
Mark Clyde	6'01"	12 00	27/12/82	27	Limavady, NI	Wolves Retired 2/07, Kidderminster (L) 9/02, Worcester 7/09 (Pl/Ass Man)	33	3
Carl Heeley			17/10/69	40		Worcester (Pl/Man)	1	0
Shabir Khan			10/11/85	24		Worcester	25	0
Jamie Price	5'07"	11 00	22/7/88	22	Hereford	Cheltenham (Yth), Birmingham Rel c/s 07, Tamworth (L) 1/07, Gloucester 8/07, Worcester 11/07 Rel 4/09, Stourport c/s 09, Worcester (SL) 3/10, Worcester 5/10	9	0
MIDFIELDERS								
Matt Birley	5'08"	11 01	26/7/86	24	Bromsgrove	Birmingham Rel c/s 07, Lincoln C (L) 11/06, Bournemouth (Trial) 5/07, Bromsgrove c/s 07, Tamworth 10/08, Kings Lynn 6/09 Rel 9/09, Worcester 9/09	22	0
Kevin O'Connor	5'11"	12 02	19/10/85	24	Dublin	Wolves Rel c/s 08, Stockport (L) 3/06, Port Vale (Trial) 9/08, Injured, AFC Telford NC 1/10, Worcester 6/10		
Jason Pike						Bridgnorth, Worcester 3/10	4	0
Tom Thorley	5'10"	11 08	5/4/90	20	Stafford	Stoke Rel 6/09, Stafford R (3ML) 7/08, Burscough (L) 10/08, Stafford R (SL) 1/09, Stafford R 7/09, Worcester 6/10		
Gary Walker			10/2/88	22		Walsall, Worcester, Malvern (L) 3/07, Evesham (Dual) 9/07	33	0
Graham Ward	5'08"	11 09	25/2/83	27	Dublin	Wolves, Cambridge U (Trial) 3/03, Bournemouth (Trial) 4/03, Kidderminster Free 8/03 Rel c/s 04, Cheltenham 8/04, Rel c/s 05, Burton (L) 3/05, Tamworth 5/05, Worcester (L) 10/06 Perm	35	2
FORWARDS								
Mark Danks	5'09"	10 08	8/2/84	26	Worley	Wolves (Scholar), Bradford City 7/02, Halesowen T (SL) 3/03, Hednesford 7/03. Aberystwyth 5/04, Forest Green 8/04, Stafford R (2ML) 9/04, Kettering (L) 3/05, Bromsgrove (L), Cirencester (L) 1/06, Worcester 1/06, Halesowen T 5/08, AFC Telford 2/09 Rel 5/09, Northwich 7/09, Worcester 6/10		
Rob Elvins	6'02"	12 04	17/9/86	23	Alvechurch	West Brom, Cheltenham (L) 9/06, York C (2ML) 1/07, Aldershot 6/07 Rel c/s 09, Woking (2ML) 2/09, Worcester 7/09	32	8
Marc McGregor	5'09"	11 10	30/4/78	32	Southend	Oxford U Rel c/s 97, Endsleigh c/s 97, Forest Green 8/98, Cirencester (L) 10/98, Nuneaton £35,000 6/00, Weston Super-Mare (L) 8/02, Macclesfield (Trial) 1/03, Tamworth 8/03, Chippenham (L) 9/03, Weston-Super-Mare (L) 10/03, Weston-Super-Mare (L) 12/03, Weston-Super-Mare 3/04, Hinckley U 5/05, Weston-Super-Mare 5/06, Worcester 10/09	17	5

Loanees	HT	WT	DOB	AGE	POB	From - To	APPS	GOA
(M)Josh Emery	5'06"	10 10	30/9/90	19	Ledbury	Cheltenham 8/09 - Oxford C (WE) 11/09, Worcester (L) 2/10	15	1
(F)Marvin Brown	5'09"	11 01	16/7/83	26	Bristol	Weston-Super-Mare 10/09 - Rel 1/10, Turo C 1/10	3	1
(F)Danny Carey-Bertram	5'11"	13 00	14/6/84	25	Birmingham	AFC Telford 12/09 -	4	0
(M)Jack Durrant	6'00"	11 03	6/5/91	19	Bristol	Cheltenham 2/10 - Weston-Super-Mare 7/10	4	0
(G)Danzelle St Louis-Hamilton	6'04"	12 13	7/5/90	19	Stevenage	Stoke 2/10 -	6	0
(F)Jake Lee						Cheltenham 3/10 -	1	0

Departures	HT	WT	DOB	AGE	POB	From - To	APPS	GOA
(F)Aaron Moses-Garvey	5'08"	11 13	6/9/89	19	Birmingham	Birmingham 7/09 - Rel 8/09	5	0
(F)Martin Butler	5'11"	11 09	15/9/74	34	Wordsley	Burton 7/09 - Rel 8/09	5	0
(G)Richard Mace			5/8/91	19		Cambridge U (Yth) 7/09 - Evesham (Dual) 8/09, Evesham 10/09, Cradley T 12/09	3	0
(G)Ben Hinchliffe	5'10"	11 07	9/10/88	19	Preston	Oxford U 8/09 - Kendal T 11/09, Bamber Bridge 1/10	13	0
(M)Jordan Fitzpatrick	6'00"	12 00	15/6/88	21	Stourbridge	Hereford 8/08 - Rel 2/10, Redditch 7/10	4	0
(D)Kevin Spencer			22/7/89	21		Stratford T 3/09 - Rel 2/10, Evesham 2/10, Redditch 7/10	15	0
(F)Aaron Farrell	6'00"	12 06	24/4/86	23		Kidderminster 2/10 - Rel 2/10, Sollihull Moors 3/10	4	1
(F)Craig Wilding	5'10"	11 11	30/10/81	27	Birmingham	Redditch 6/06 - Rel 4/10, Leamington 5/10	37	6
(D)Wayne Daniel			12/12/76	32	Birmingham	Stafford R 6/09 - Rel 4/10, Nuneaton T (Trial) 7/10	38	1
(F)Marco Adaggio	5'08"	12 04	6/10/87	21	Malaga, Sp	Stafford R 8/08 - Rel 4/10, Redditch (L) 3/10, Redditch 7/10	28	6
(D)Tom Kemp	6'03"		16/1/87	22	Ashby	Halesowen T 11/08 - Rel 4/10, Brackley T 6/10	27	1
(F)Alfie Carter			13/8/80	30	Birmingham	TNS NC 8/09 - Rel 4/10, Hednesford 6/10	29	4
(M)Louis Bridges			10/8/91	19		Yth - Rel 4/10	10	2
(M)Jack Connolly			26/11/90	19		Yth - Rel 4/10	3	0
(F)Matthew Dinsmore			22/1/90	19		Yth - Rel 4/10	29	4
(G)Jake Meredith			9/12/87	21		Team Bath 5/09 - Rel 5/10, Redditch 6/10	20	0
(M)George Clegg	5'10"	12 00	16/11/80	29	Manchester	ex Hinckley U 6/10 - Northwich 7/10		
(M)Rob Davies	5'09"	11 03	24/3/87	21	Tywyn	Oxford U 9/08 - Rel 7/10	27	1
(M)Tom Beahon			18/9/89	20		Glen Hoddle Soccer Academy 3/10 -	2	0
(M)Ryan Burge			12/10/88	21		Glen Hoddle Soccer Academy 3/10 -	1	0
(M)Aaron Ledgister	5'10"	11 07	15/11/88	21	Homg Kong	Cheltenham 8/09 -	4	0
(M)Mike Wardle			22/10/90	19		Yth -	1	0
(F)Mark Owen						Evesham 3/10 -	1	0
(D)Josh Quaynor			16/11/91	18		Cheltenham (Scholar) 3/10 -	3	1

WORKINGTON

Chairman: Humphrey Dobie
Secretary: Steve Durham (T) 07899 938 156
(E) sbj.durham@btinternet.com
Additional Committee Members: Jos Taylor, Stafford Lloyd, Paul Armstrong, Colin Doorbar Alec Graham, Thex Johnston, Jos Taylor, Dave Wilson, Les Smallwood
Manager: Darren Edmondson
Programme Editor: Paul Armstrong (E) paul@workingtonafc.com

Archive photo

Club Factfile

Founded: 1884 **Nickname:** Reds
Previous Names:
Previous Leagues: Cumberland Assoc. 1890-94, Cumberland Senior 1894-1901, 03-04. Lancashire 1901-03, Lancashire Comb. 1904-10, North Eastern 1910-11, 21-51, Football League 1951-77, N.P.L. 1977-2005
Club Colours (change): Red/white/red (Sky blue/navy/sky blue)

Ground: Borough Park, Workington, Cumbria CA14 2DT (T) 01900 602 871
Capacity: 2,500 **Seats:** 500 **Covered:** 1,000 **Clubhouse:** Yes **Shop:** Yes
Previous Grounds: Various 1884-1921, Lonsdale Park 1921-37
Simple Directions
A66 into Workington. At traffic lights at bottom of hill (HSBC opposite), turn left towards town centre. Approach traffic lights in centre lane (Washington Central Hotel on your right) and turn right. Continue on this road, passing over a mini roundabout, a pedestrian crossing and a further set of traffic lights. You will come to the Railway Station (facing you), carry on through the junction and bear right, passing the Derwent Park Stadium (Rugby League/speedway), then left and Borough Park becomes visible ahead of you.

Record Attendance: 21,000 v Manchester United - FA Cup 3rd round 04/01/1958
Record Victory: 17-1 v Cockermouth Crusaders - Cumberland Senior League 19/01/1901
Record Defeat: 0-9 v Chorley (A) - Northern Premier League 10/11/1987
Record Goalscorer: Billy Charlton - 193
Record Appearances: Bobby Brown - 419
Additional Records: Paid £6,000 to Sunderland for Ken Chisolm 1956
Received £33,000 from Liverpool for Ian McDonald 1974
Senior Honours: North West Counties League 1998-99
Cumberland County Cup x23

10 YEAR RECORD

00-01	01-02	02-03	03-04	04-05	05-06	06-07	07-08	08-09	09-10
NP 1 14	NP 1 16	NP 1 10	NP 1 7	NP P 2	Conf N 13	Conf N 3	Conf N 14	Conf N 12	Conf N 4

WORKINGTON

No.	Date	Comp	H/A	Opponents	Att:	Result	Goalscorers	Pos
1	8/8/09	BSN	H	Hinckley United	462	L 0-1		17
2	11/8/09	BSN	A	Gainsborough Trinity	419	W 1-0	Hardman 61	12
3	15/8/09	BSN	A	Stafford Rangers	452	L 0-2		16
4	18/8/09	BSN	H	Harrogate Town	410	D 1-1	Hopper 59	16
5	22/8/09	BSN	A	Stalybridge Celtic	393	D 2-2	A Wright 59, Arnison pen 73	13
6	29/8/09	BSN	H	Northwich Victoria	471	L 0-1		17
7	31/8/09	BSN	A	Fleetwood Town	1079	L 0-4		19
8	5/9/09	BSN	H	Ilkeston Town	355	D 0-0		20
9	8/9/09	BSN	H	Alfreton Town	337	D 1-1	A Wright 31	17
10	12/9/09	BSN	A	Gloucester City	331	W 2-0	Arnison 2 (21, 53)	14
11	19/9/09	BSN	A	Redditch United	275	L 1-2	J Wright 71	16
12	3/10/09	BSN	H	Vauxhall Motors	327	W 1-0	Aldred 81	14
13	17/10/09	BSN	A	Droylsden	381	W 1-0	Arnison 7	12
14	31/10/09	BSN	A	AFC Telford	1535	L 0-1		12
15	7/11/09	BSN	H	Southport	427	L 0-2		12
16	14/11/09	BSN	A	Corby Town	342	W 2-0	Arnison 64, J Wright 75	11
17	28/11/09	BSN	H	Eastwood Town	296	W 1-0	Arnison pen 35	10
18	5/12/09	BSN	H	Gainsborough Trinity	293	D 1-1	A Wright 70	11
19	23/1/10	BSN	H	Gloucester City	304	W 2-0	Arnison 2 (pen 78, 84)	13
20	26/1/10	BSN	A	Vauxhall Motors	184	D 1-1	McLuckie 90	13
21	6/2/10	BSN	H	Solihull Moors	368	W 1-0	Arnison 41	11
22	9/2/10	BSN	H	Stalybridge Celtic	267	W 1-0	J Wright 1	10
23	13/2/10	BSN	H	Droylsden	383	L 0-1		12
24	16/2/10	BSN	A	Alfreton Town	296	L 0-2		12
25	27/2/10	BSN	H	Redditch United	316	W 1-0	Bowman 4	12
26	2/3/10	BSN	H	Blyth Spartans	314	W 3-1	J Wright 2 (15, 57), Arnison 78	10
27	9/3/10	BSN	A	Blyth Spartans	414	D 0-0		11
28	13/3/10	BSN	H	Corby Town	470	D 1-1	Arnison 68	9
29	16/3/10	BSN	A	Southport	709	L 0-2		11
30	20/3/10	BSN	A	Eastwood Town	342	W 2-1	Bowman 81, Arnison 89	11
31	23/3/10	BSN	A	Harrogate Town	201	W 2-1	McLuckie 35, Arnison 44	10
32	27/3/10	BSN	A	Hinckley United	395	W 2-1	Arnison 2 (34, 77)	7
33	3/4/10	BSN	A	Northwich Victoria	430	W 3-2	May 2 (30, 90), J Wright 90	6
34	5/4/10	BSN	H	Fleetwood Town	731	W 1-0	McLuckie 14	6
35	7/4/10	BSN	A	Ilkeston Town	316	W 3-1	McLuckie 34, Arnison 66, Hopper 86	5
36	10/4/10	BSN	H	AFC Telford	619	W 2-1	Vipond 41, Hopper 59	4
37	13/4/10	BSN	H	Hyde United	493	D 2-2	J Wright pen 52, May 63	4
38	17/4/10	BSN	A	Solihull Moors	205	W 2-1	McLuckie 61, Shannon 86	4
39	19/4/10	BSN	A	Hyde United	325	W 2-0	Rowntree 5, A Wright 90	3
40	24/4/10	BSN	H	Stafford Rangers	656	D 1-1	A Wright 61	4
	Farsley Celtic record expunged 12/03							
14	27/10/09	BSN	H	Farsley Celtic	324	D 2-2	Ruttledge 63, J Wright 70	11
	Cups							
1	26/9/09	FAC 2Q	H	Cammell Laird	302	W 4-1	Arnison 44, J Wright 3 (46, 48, 87)	
2	10/10/09	FAC 3Q	H	Radcliffe Borough	318	W 3-0	Arnison 12, Hardman 39, J Wright 55	
3	24/10/09	FAC 4Q	H	Rushden & Diamonds	724	L 0-3		
4	1/12/09	FAT 3Q	H	Solihull Moors	188	D 1-1	Arnison 27	
5	8/12/09	FAT 3QR	A	Solihull Moors	117	W 4-2	Hardman 10, J Wright 12, Arnison 2 (pen 57, 80)	
6	12/12/09	FAT 1	H	Nuneaton Town	319	W 2-1	Arnison 13, McLuckie 85	
7	19/1/10	FAT 2	H	Rushden & Diamonds	252	W 2-1	Og (Downer) 24, Hardman 46	
8	30/1/10	FAT 3	A	AFC Wimbledon	2301	W 3-2	J Wright 2 (31, 81), Vipond 86	
9	20/2/10	FAT 4	A	Stevenage Borough	1510	L 1-2	McLuckie 25	
10	28/4/10	PO SF1	H	Alfreton Town	1483	L 0-1		
11	2/5/10	PO SF2	A	Alfreton Town	1575	L 1-3	Arnison 13 (L 1-4 agg)	

Home Attendances:	
Highest:	731 v Fleetwood Town
Lowest:	267 v Stalybridge Celtic
Average (08-09):	376 (344)
Top Goalscorer:	Arnison - 23 (16 League, 7 Cup) in 43 appearances - 53% strike rate
Most Appearances:	Langford - 51 (40 League, 11 Cup)

CAIG	LANGFORD	ROWNTREE	MAY	ANDREWS	HARDMAN	HENNEY	HOPPER	J WRIGHT	ARNISON	A WRIGHT	SHANNON	RUTTLEDGE	ROBINSON	CASSON	TAYLOR	EDMONDSON	VIPOND	MCLUCKIE	COOK	ALDRED	LLOYD	HEWSON	HINDMARCH	MAIN	BOWMAN	TINNION	BLAKE	
X	X	X	X	X	X	X	X	X	X	X	S	U	U	U	U													1
X	X	X	X	X	X	X	X		X	X	X	S	S	U	U	U												2
X	X	X		X	X	X	X		U	X	X	S	S	X	U	U	X											3
X	X	X		X	S	X	X	X		X	X	S		S	U	U	X	X										4
X	X	X	X	X	S	X	X	X	S	X	X	U			U		X	S										5
X	X	X	X	X	S	X	X		X	X		S		U	U		X	S	X									6
X	X	X	X	X	S	X	X		X	X	S	U				U	X	S	X									7
X	X	X	X	X	S	X	X	X	X	X	S	U					X	U	S									8
X	X	X		X	U	X	X		X	X	S	S				U	X	U	X	X								9
X	X	X	X		S	X		X	X	X	S	S						X	X	X								10
X	X	X	X	U	S	X		X	X	X	S	S				U		X	X	X								11
X	X	S	X	X	U	X	S	X	X	X	S	U					X	X		X								12
X	X	X	X	U	U		X	X	X	X	S	S				U	X	X		X								13
X	X	X	X	U	U		S	X	X	X	S	X				U	X	X		X								14
X	X	X	X	U	U		X	X	X	X	S	S				U	X	X		X								15
X	X	X	X	U	S			X	X	X	S	U			U		X	X		X	X							16
X	X	X	X	S			S	X	X	X		U			U	U	X	X		X	X							17
X	X	X	X	U	U		X	X	X	X		U				U	X	S		X	X							18
X	X	X	X	X	X		X	X	S	X		X			U	U	X	S					S					19
X	X	X	X	X	X		X	X	X	X		S			U	U	X	S					S					20
X	X	X	X	X	S		X	X	X	X		U			U		X	X					S	U				21
X	X	X	X	X	S		X	X	X	X		S			U		S	X					X	U				22
X	X	X	X	X	S		X		X			S			U	U	X	X					X	U	X			23
X	X	X	X	X	S				X		S	X				U	X	X				S	X	U	X			24
X	X	X	X	X	S		X	X		S		U			U		X	X					X		X			25
X	X		X	X	U		X	X	X	X		U			U		X	X				U	X		S			26
X	X	X	X	X	U		X	X	X	X					U		X	X				U	U		S			27
X	X	X	X	X	S		X	X	X			U			U		X	X				U	S		X			28
X	X	X	X	X	U		X	X	X	X		U					X	X				S	U		S			29
X	X	X	X	X	U		X	X	X	X					U		X	X				S	U		S			30
X	X	X	X	X			X	X	X	S		U			U		X	X				S	U		X			31
X	X	X	X	X				X	X	X		S			U	U	X	X				X	S	S				32
X	X	X	X	X			X	X	X	X		U			U		X	X				S	S			S		33
X	X	X	X	X			X	S	X			X			U		S	X				X	X			S	U	34
X	X		X	X			X	S	X		U	X				U	X	X				X	X			S	S	35
X	X	X	X	X			X	X		S	S	X			U		X					X	X			S	U	36
X	X	X	X	U			U	X		X	S				U		X	X				X	X			X	U	37
X	X	X	X				X	X		X	S	S			U		X	X				X	X			S	U	38
U	X	X	X				U	U		X	X	X			X	U	X	X				X	S	X				39
U	X	X	X					S	X	X	X				X		U	S				X	X	X		S	X	40
X	X	X	X	U	S	S		X	X	X	S	X			U		X	X		X								
X	X	X	X	X	S	X		X	X	X	S	X			U	U	S	X										1
X	X	X	X		X	S	X	X	X		S	S			U	U	X	X		X								2
X	X	X	X	U	U		X	X	X	X	S	S			U	U	X	X		X								3
X	X	X	X	U	S		S	X	X	X		S				U	X	X		X	X							4
X	X	X	X	X	X			X	X	X		S				U	X	X			S	U						5
X	X	X	X	X	X		S	X	X	X	U	U			U	U	X	X										6
X	X	X	X	X	X		X	X		X	S	X			U	U	X						S	U				7
X	X	X	X	X	S		X	X	X	X		S			U		X	X					U	U				8
X	X	X	X	X	U		X	X	X	X					S		X	X				U	S		S			9
X	X	X	X	X			X	X	X	S		U			U		X	X				X	U			U		10
X	X	X	X	X			X	X	X		S	U			U		X	X				X	S			U		11
Total League Appearances																												
38	40	37	37	28	5	12	29	29	31	32	6	7	0	1	2	0	33	27	5	10	3	8	11	2	5	1	1	X
0	0	1	0	1	14	0	3	3	2	3	15	14	2	1	0	0	2	7	1	0	0	5	7	1	4	6	1	S
2	0	0	0	7	10	0	2	1	1	0	1	15	1	3	25	18	1	2	0	0	0	3	4	4	0	0	4	U
Total Cup Appearances																												
11	11	11	11	8	4	1	7	11	10	8	0	2	0	0	0	0	10	10	0	3	1	2	0	0	0	0	0	X
0	0	0	0	0	3	1	2	0	0	1	5	5	0	0	1	0	1	0	0	0	1	0	3	0	1	0	0	S
0	0	0	0	2	2	0	0	0	0	0	1	3	0	0	8	7	0	0	0	0	0	2	2	2	0	2	0	U
Total Goals																												
0	0	1	3	0	1	0	3	7	16	5	1	0	0	0	0	0	1	5	0	1	0	0	0	0	2	0	0	Lge
0	0	0	0	0	3	0	0	7	7	0	0	0	0	0	0	0	1	2	0	0	0	0	0	0	0	0	0	Cup

WORKINGTON

CURRENT SQUAD AS OF BEGINING OF 2010-11 SEASON

GOALKEEPERS	HT	WT	D.O.B	AGE	P.O.B	CAREER	Apps	Gls
Tony Caig	6'01"	13 04	11/4/74	36	Cleator Moor	Carlisle, Blackpool £40,000 3/99, Charlton (2ML) 11/00 Perm 1/01 Rel c/s 01, Hibernian 7/01, Newcastle 1/03, Barnsley (L) 1/04, Vancouver Whitecaps (Can) 4/06 Rel 9/07, Gretna 10/07 Rel 1/08, Houston Dynamos (USA) 4/08 Rel 12/08, Chesterfield 3/09 Rel c/s	38	0
Aaron Taylor			20/11/86	23		Annan Ath, Penrith, Workington c/s 07, Barrow 7/08 Rel 9/08, Penrith, Workington (Trial) 2/09, Workington 3/09	2	0
DEFENDERS								
Lee Andrews	6'00"	11 06	23/4/83	27	Carlisle	Carlisle Rel 5/06, Rochdale (L) 2/03, York (2ML) 11/05, Torquay (L) 3/06, Torquay 5/06 Rel c/s 07, Newcastle Blue Star 9/07, Workington 1/08	29	0
Darren Edmondson	6'00"	12 12	4/11/71	38	Coniston	Carlisle, Huddersfield 3/97, Plymouth (L) 9/98, York C 3/00 Rel c/s 04, Chester 8/04 Rel c/s 05, Barrow 8/05, Workington 1/06	0	0
Andrew Langford	5'11"	12 05	3/7/88	22	Manchester	Morecambe Rel c/s 08, Leek T (L) 11/07, Workington 12/08	40	0
Kyle May			7/9/82	27	Doncaster	Carlisle Rel c/s 02, Gretna 8/02, Workington (5ML) 8/04, Workington 1/05	37	3
Phil McLuckie			13/4/89	21		Morecambe, Workington (3ML) 12/07 Perm 3/08	34	5
Gari Rowntree			5/10/86	23		Carlisle (Yth), Blackburn, Workington 3/07	38	1
MIDFIELDERS								
Jonny Blake	5'08"	11 00	4/2/91	19	Carlisle	Carlisle, Workington 3/10	2	0
David Hewson			5/5/83	27		Gretna, Workington, Harraby CC (L)	13	0
Tony Hopper	5'11"	12 08	31/5/76	34	Carlisle	Carlisle Rel c/s 00, Barrow (L) 3/93, Bohemians 8/00, Workington 1/01, Carlisle 2/01 Rel c/s 02, Barrow 8/02, Workington 10/02	32	3
Adam Main			16/1/92	18		Workington	3	0
Conor Tinnion			4/3/91	19		Carlisle, Workington 3/10	7	0
Shaun Vipond	5'11"	11 04	25/12/88	21	Hexham	Carlisle, Workington (3ML) 8/08 Perm 11/08, Hamilton (Trial) 1/09, Sweden 3/09 Rel 5/09, Workington 8/09	35	1
Anthony Wright			13/4/86	24		Penrith, Workington 6/06	35	5
FORWARDS								
Gareth Arnison			18/9/86	23		Morecambe, Workington 8/05, Kendal (L) 12/06 Perm 1/07, Workington 8/08	33	16
Andrew Hardman			6/2/89	21		Carlisle, Workington 2/08	19	1
Stephen Hindmarch	5'10"	11 11	16/11/89	20	Penrith	Carlisle Rel c/s 08, Shrewsbury 7/08 Rel c/s 09, Workington 6/09	18	0
Callum Ruttledge			20/1/88	22		Morecambe (Yth), Workington 3/09	21	0
Dan Shannon			26/8/87	23		Local, Workington 8/09, Rossendale (L) 3/10	21	1
Johnny Wright			31/10/85	24		Whitehaven Amateurs, Workington 8/07	32	7

Loanees	HT	WT	DOB	AGE	POB	From - To	APPS	GOA
(F)Andy Cook	6'01"	11 04	18/10/90	19	Bishop Auckland	Carlisle 8/09 - Barrow (L) 10/09	6	0
(D)Tom Aldred	6'02"	13 02	11/9/90	19	Bolton	Carlisle (2ML) 9/09 -	10	1
(M)Paul Lloyd	5'09"	10 11	26/3/87	23	Preston	Forest Green 11/09 - Rel 2/10, Bamber Bridge 6/10	3	0
(F)Ryan Bowman			30/11/91	18		Carlisle (SL) 2/10 -	9	2

Departures	HT	WT	DOB	AGE	POB	From - To	APPS	GOA
(M)Matt Henney	6'00"	11 08	9/8/76	34	Carlisle	Barrow 5/09 - Rel 11/09	12	0
(D)Darren Casson			22/1/88	22		South Shields 8/09 - Rel 2/10	2	0
(F)Dan Robinson	5'10"	10 10	21/5/89	21	Penrith	Gretna 6/08 - Rel 2/10	2	0
(D)Kevin Gray	6'00"	14 00	7/1/72	38	Sheffield	Chesterfield 7/08 -		

BASINGSTOKE TOWN

Chairman: Rafi Razzak
Secretary: Richard Trodd (T) 07887 507 447
(E) richard.trodd@ntlworld.com
Additional Committee Members: Ian Halloway, David Knight, Sarah Parsons, Geoff Yates, David Partridge, John Gaston
Manager: Frank Gray
Programme Editor: David Partridge (E) dave.partridge@btfc.co.uk

Basingstoke Town Football Club 2009-2010 Season
Blue Square South

Back row (left to right): Adam Aimiable, Phil Ruggles, Matt Finlay, Joe Dolan (Captain), Ross Kitteridge (GK), Lewis Christon, Craig Smith, Rob Watkins, Jide Ogunbote

Front row (left to right): Robbie Rice, Matt Warner, Tom Williamson, Sean Hankin, David Pratt, Ryan Stevens, Jahson Downes, Tom Walsh, Ian Jones

Club Factfile

Founded: 1896 **Nickname:** Dragons
Previous Names:
Previous Leagues: Hampshire 1900-40, 45-71, Southern 1971-87, Isthmian 1987-2004

Club Colours (change): Royal blue and yellow/royal blue/yellow (Red/red/black)

Ground: Camrose Road, Western Way, Basingstoke RG22 6EZ (T) 01256 327 575
Capacity: 6,000 **Seats:** 651 **Covered:** 2,000 **Clubhouse:** Yes **Shop:** Yes
Previous Grounds: Castle Field 1896-1947
Simple Directions
Leave M3 at junction 6 and turn left onto South Ringway which is the A30. Straight over first roundabout. At second roundabout turn left into Winchester Road. Proceed past ground on right to roundabout. Take fifth exit into Western Way. Ground on right.

Record Attendance: 5,085 v Wycombe Wanderers - FA Cup 1st Round replay 1997-98
Record Victory: 10-1 v Chichester City (H) - FA Cup 1st Qualifying Round 1976
Record Defeat: 0-8 v Aylesbury United - Southern League April 1979
Record Goalscorer: Paul Coombs - 159 (1991-99)
Record Appearances: Billy Coomb
Additional Records: Paid £4,750 to Gosport Borough for Steve Ingham

Senior Honours: Hampshire League 1967-68, 69-70, 70-71. Southern League Southern Division 1984-85.
Hampshire Senior Cup 1970-71, 89-90, 95-96, 2007-08.

10 YEAR RECORD

00-01	01-02	02-03	03-04	04-05	05-06	06-07	07-08	08-09	09-10
Isth P 3	Isth P 18	Isth P 5	Isth P 14	Conf S 6	Conf S 19	Conf S 19	Conf S 15	Conf S 18	Conf S 15

BASINGSTOKE TOWN

No.	Date	Comp	H/A	Opponents	Att:	Result	Goalscorers	Pos
1	8/8/09	BSS	A	Hampton & Richmond B.	534	W 1-0	Pratt 72	6
2	11/8/09	BSS	H	Weston-Super-Mare	355	W 2-1	Ruggles pen 21, Pratt 49	4
3	15/8/09	BSS	H	Chelmsford City	522	W 2-1	Warner 36, Rice 52	2
4	17/8/09	BSS	A	Worcester City	620	D 1-1	Williamson 34	1
5	22/8/09	BSS	H	Maidenhead United	657	D 0-0		4
6	29/8/09	BSS	A	Havant & Waterlooville	1156	W 2-0	Ogunbote 29, Pratt 89	2
7	31/8/09	BSS	H	Dorchester Town	578	W 2-1	Pratt pen 70, Ogunbote 84	2
8	5/9/09	BSS	A	Lewes	396	D 0-0		2
9	8/9/09	BSS	H	Woking	942	L 1-2	Hankin 46	5
10	12/9/09	BSS	H	Bishops Stortford	452	L 0-2		7
11	19/9/09	BSS	A	Braintree Town	437	W 2-1	Laidler 6, Downes 51	5
12	3/10/09	BSS	H	Thurrock	429	L 0-4		6
13	17/10/09	BSS	A	Bath City	685	L 3-4	Downes 2 (8, 31), Mitchell 74	8
14	20/10/09	BSS	A	Dover Athletic	1060	W 3-2	Finlay 11, Og (Schulz) 20, Pratt 78	6
15	24/10/09	BSS	H	Weymouth	426	W 2-1	Franks 15, Ruggles pen 45	4
16	27/10/09	BSS	A	Bromley	481	L 0-2		5
17	31/10/09	BSS	A	Newport County	1241	L 0-1		6
18	7/11/09	BSS	H	St Albans City	424	D 1-1	Warner pen 33	5
19	14/11/09	BSS	A	Maidenhead United	288	L 2-3	Frewen pen 80, Franks 85	5
20	28/11/09	BSS	H	Welling United	429	D 1-1	Warner pen 20	5
21	1/12/09	BSS	A	St Albans City	205	L 0-2		6
22	5/12/09	BSS	A	Staines Town	483	W 1-0	Ogunbote 63	6
23	26/12/09	BSS	A	Eastleigh	623	L 0-6		11
24	28/12/09	BSS	H	Worcester City	395	L 0-1		11
25	19/1/10	BSS	H	Bromley	293	L 2-3	Williamson 42, Frewen 77	14
26	23/1/10	BSS	A	Chelmsford City	1109	W 2-1	Bryant 50, Pratt 80	12
27	2/2/10	BSS	A	Bishops Stortford	265	W 2-0	Pratt 50, Hankin 64	12
28	6/2/10	BSS	H	Hampton & Richmond B.	403	L 1-2	Frewen pen 7	12
29	13/2/10	BSS	A	Weymouth	588	W 6-0	Bryant 6 (4, 26, 42, 53, 62, 73)	12
30	20/2/10	BSS	A	Weston-Super-Mare	211	D 1-1	Downes 80	13
31	23/2/10	BSS	H	Eastleigh	335	L 0-1		13
32	2/3/10	BSS	A	Newport County	646	L 1-5	Rice 41	14
33	6/3/10	BSS	H	Lewes	457	D 1-1	Ogunbote 49	14
34	13/3/10	BSS	H	Dover Athletic	418	L 1-3	Frewen 57	14
35	20/3/10	BSS	A	Woking	958	L 2-4	Warner 32, Downes 49	14
36	23/3/10	BSS	H	Staines Town	306	L 0-1		14
37	27/3/10	BSS	H	Bath City	524	W 1-0	Webb 86	14
38	3/4/10	BSS	H	Havant & Waterlooville	410	D 1-1	Warner 25	14
39	5/4/10	BSS	A	Dorchester Town	502	L 1-6	Akwuegbu 3	14
40	10/4/10	BSS	A	Thurrock	219	D 0-0		14
41	17/4/10	BSS	H	Braintree Town	477	L 0-1		15
42	24/4/10	BSS	A	Welling United	507	D 1-1	Pratt pen 55	15
	Cups							
1	26/9/09	FAC 2Q	A	Brackley Town	326	W 1-0	Pratt 81	
2	10/10/09	FAC 3Q	A	Eastleigh	681	L 0-2		
3	21/11/09	FAT 3Q	A	Northwood	178	L 1-2	Rice 9	

Home Attendances:	
Highest:	942 v Woking
Lowest:	293 v Bromley
Average (08-09):	429 (425)

Top Goalscorer:	Pratt - 9 (8 League, 1 Cup) in 44 appearances - 21% strike rate
Most Appearances:	Downes - 44 (32+9 League, 2+1 Cup)
	Pratt - 44 (41 League, 3 Cup)

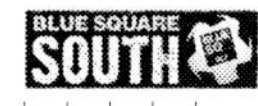

KITTERIDGE	RICE	WATKINS	AIMABLE	DOLAN	FINLAY	OGUNBOTE	WILLIAMSON	PRATT	DOWNES	RUGGLES	STEPHENS	JONES	SMITH	LUMSDEN	ATKINSON	CHRISTON	WARNER	FREWEN	HANKIN	LAIDLER	FRANKS	WALSH	POWELL	MITCHELL	ROWE	WHITE	BRYANT	AKWUEGBU	BARNARD	MITCHELL-COOP	ALLEN	WEBB	FOYLE	
X	X	X	X	X	X	X	X	X	X	X	S	U	U	U	U																			1
X	X	X	U	X	X	X	X	X	X	X		U		U		X	S	U																2
X	X	X	X	X	X	S	X	X	X	X	U	U					X	U	S															3
X	X	X		X	X	X	X	X	X	X	S	U				S	S	U	X															4
X	X	X			X	X	X	X	X	S		U	U	S		X		S	X	X														5
X	X	U		X		X	X	X	X	S		U		U	U	X		X	X	X														6
X	X	U		X		X	X	X	X	U		U		U	U	X		X	X	X														7
X	X	X		X	S	X	X	X	X	U		U		S	U	X		X		X														8
X	X	U		X	S	X	X	X	X	S		U		U		X		X	X	X														9
X	X	S	S	X	X	X	X	X	X	S	U	U		X					X	X														10
X	X	X		X	X	X	U	X	X	S	S	S		X	U					X	X													11
X	X	X			X	X	X	X	X	S	S	U		S		U			X	X	X													12
X	X				X	X	X	X	X	X		U		S	U				X	X	X		U	S										13
X	X		U		X	X	X	X		X		S		U	U				X	X	X	U		X										14
X	X				X	X	X	X	S	X		X	U		U					X	X	U	S	X										15
X					X	X	X	X	X	X		S			U				X	X	X	U	S	X										16
	X				X	X		X	X	S		S	U		X					X	X		U	X	X	X								17
X	X				U	X		X	X	U	S	X			U	X	X	S		X	X			X										18
X	X				S	X		X	X	U	S	X				X	X	S	X	X	X			U										19
U	X				X	X	X	X	S		X	U			X	X	X	S		X	X			U										20
U	X				X	X	X	X	S		X	U			X	X	X		S	X	X			S										21
X	X				X	X	X	X	S		U	S					S		X	X	X			X			X	U						22
X			X		X	X	X	X	S			S			U	X	U	S	X	X				X			X							23
X	X				X	S	X	X	X			U				X	X	S	X	X			U	U			X							24
U	X				S		X	X	S		S	U				X	X	X	X	X							X		X	X				25
U	X				X		X	X	S		S						X	X	X	X		U	U				X		X	X				26
U							X	X	X		U					U	X	X	X	X		S		X			X		X	X				27
U					S	S	X	X	X		S					U	X	X	X	X				X			X		X	X				28
U	X				X	X		X	S		S					X	S	X	X	X				U			X		X	X				29
U	X				X	X	X	X	X		S					X	X	X		U		U					X		X					30
U	X				X	S	X	X	X		U						S	X	X	X			U	X			X		X					31
X	X				X	S	X	X	S		U					X	X	X	S	X				U			X			X				32
X	X					X	X	X	X		S					X	X	X	X	X			U	U			S			U				33
X	X				X	X	X	X	X		U						X	S		X			U	X						X	U			34
X	X				X	X	X	X	X		S					X	X	X		X				U			S				U	S		35
X	X				X		X		X		U					X	X	X		X		U		X			S	X			U	S		36
X	X				X	X	X	X	X		U					X	X		U	X				X				S			U	S		37
X	X				X	X	X	X	X		U					X	X		U	X				X			S	U				S		38
X					X	X	X	X	X		S					X	X		S				S					X		X	U	X	U	39
X					X	X	X	X	X		U					X	X	U	X	X				U			U	U				X		40
X					X	X	X	X	X		S					X	X	X	X				U	U				S			U	X		41
X	X				X	X	X	X	X		U					X	X	S	X				S	S				U				X		42
X	X	X				X	X	X	X	X	S	U	U	S	U				X	X	X	U	U											1
X	X				X	X	X	X	S	X	S	U	U	S	U	X			X	X	X		U											2
X	X				X		S	X	X	S	S	X			U	X	X	U		X	X			X										3
Total League Appearances																																		
32	35	8	3	10	32	33	37	41	32	8	2	3	0	2	3	25	22	16	24	34	12	0	0	14	1	1	11	2	7	8	0	4	0	X
0	0	1	1	0	5	5	0	0	9	7	15	6	0	4	0	1	5	8	4	0	0	1	4	3	0	0	4	2	0	0	0	4	0	S
9	0	3	2	0	1	0	1	0	0	4	12	16	4	6	11	3	1	4	2	1	0	6	8	9	0	0	1	4	0	1	6	0	1	U
Total Cup Appearances																																		
3	3	1	0	0	2	2	2	3	2	2	0	1	0	0	0	2	1	0	2	3	3	0	0	1	0	0	0	0	0	0	0	0	0	X
0	0	0	0	0	0	0	1	0	1	1	3	0	0	2	0	0	0	0	0	0	0	0	0	0	0	0	0	0	0	0	0	0	0	S
0	0	0	0	0	0	0	0	0	0	0	0	2	2	0	3	0	0	1	0	0	0	1	2	0	0	0	0	0	0	0	0	0	0	U
Total Goals																																		
0	2	0	0	0	1	4	2	8	5	2	0	0	0	0	0	0	5	4	2	1	2	0	0	1	0	0	7	1	0	0	0	1	0	Lge
0	1	0	0	0	0	0	0	1	0	0	0	0	0	0	0	0	0	0	0	0	0	0	0	0	0	0	0	0	0	0	0	0	0	Cup

BASINGSTOKE TOWN

CURRENT SQUAD AS OF BEGINING OF 2010-11 SEASON

GOALKEEPERS	HT	WT	D.O.B	AGE	P.O.B	CAREER	Apps	Gls
Lee Allen			6/6/91	19		Basingstoke	0	0
Chris Tardif	5'11"	12 07	20/6/81	29	Guernsey	Portsmouth Rel c/s 04, Newport IOW (L) 3/00, Bournemouth (SL) 8/02, Havant & W (L) 10/03, Wycombe (Trial) 3/04, Oxford U 7/04 Rel 9/07, Eastleigh 10/07 Rel 10/07, Basingstoke 12/07 Rel 3/08, Maidenhead 3/08, Farnborough 5/08, Bognor Regis 8/08 Rel 2/09, Winchester 3/09, Worcester (Dual) 3/09, Maidenhead 6/09, Basingstoke 5/10		
DEFENDERS								
Ross Adams	5'11"	12 04	11/3/83	27	Birmingham	Swindon (Sch), Highworth T, Chippenham 7/05, Basingstoke 5/10		
Lewis Christon	6'00"	12 02	24/1/89	21	Milton Keynes	Wycombe Rel 1/09, Woking (L) 1/08, AFC Wimbledon (SL) 3/08, Oxford C (L) 11/08, Basingstoke NC 3/09	26	0
Jay Gasson			29/12/84	25		Fulham (Yth), Croydon A, Whyteleafe 10/03, Croydon A 2/04, Corinthian Casuals 7/04, Farnborough 6/05, Woking 6/07 Rel 5/08, Havant & W 5/08, Basingstoke 5/10		
Robert Rice	5'08"	11 11	23/2/89	21	Hendon	Fulham (Yth), Wycombe Rel c/s 09, Wealdstone (L) 1/08, Basingstoke 6/09	35	2
MIDFIELDERS								
Matt Finlay	6'02"	12 00	25/1/90	20	Salisbury	Bournemouth (Trainee) Rel c/s 08, Salisbury (Trial) c/s 08, Bashley 8/08, Basingstoke NC 6/09	37	1
Chris Foyle			7/9/91	18		Basingstoke	0	0
Gary Frewen			21/11/90	19		Reading Rel c/s 09, Basingstoke 8/09	24	4
Sean Hankin	5'11"	12 04	28/2/81	29	Camberley	C.Palace, Torquay (2ML) 10/01 £20,000 12/01, Margate 10/03, Northwich 11/03, Crawley 1/04 Rel 5/05, Lewes 7/05, St Albans 10/05, Farnborough 12/05, Basingstoke 5/07	28	2
Steve Laidler			10/10/83	26	Reading	Reading (Scholar) Rel c/s 03, Basingstoke 8/03, Farnborough 11/03, Dorking 1/04, Dumbarton 3/04 Rel c/s 04, Year Out, Farnborough 7/05, Woking (Trial) c/s 06, Basingstoke 5/07, Farnborough 5/08 Rel 9/09, Basingstoke (L) 8/09 Perm 9/09	34	1
Stuart Lake			17/11/79	30	London	Wimbledon, Walton & Hersham, Farnborough 10/98, Northwood 3/99, Yeading, Northwood, Marlow 2/03, Uxbridge 7/04, Ashford T (Middx), Hampton & R 2/07, Basingstoke 6/10		
Jide Ogunbote			17/8/88	22		Woking, Corinthian C (L) 9/07, Basingstoke 8/08	38	4
Matt Pattison			24/3/84	26	Surrey	Camberley, Farnborough 7/03, Woking 6/07 Rel 5/09, Rushden & D 6/09 Rel 5/10, Basingstoke 5/10		
Matt Warner			12/5/85	25	Farnham	Wycombe, Baingstoke (2ML) 10/03, Team Bath, Farnborough 6/05, Basingstoke 7/06	27	5
Tom Williamson	5'09"	10 02	24/12/84	25	Leicester	Leicester Rel c/s 04, Canvey Island 10/04 Rel 4/05, Grays 7/05, Bishops Stortford 8/07 Rel 5/08, Basingstoke 7/08	37	2
FORWARDS								
Jahson Downes			3/11/90	19		Reading Rel c/s 09, Bognor Regis (SL) 1/09, Basingstoke 6/09	41	5
Ross Montague	6'00"	12 11	1/11/88	21	Twickenham	Brentford Rel c/s 09, Sutton U (6WL) 8/07, Welling (L) 9/07, Basingstoke (L) 10/08, AFC Wimbledon 8/09 Rel 4/10, Basingstoke 5/10		
Grant Powell			11/9/91	18	Basingstoke	Basingstoke, Whitchurch U (SL) 6/10	4	0
David Pratt			1/8/87	23		Swindon Supermarine, Chippenham 6/07, Basingstoke 5/09	41	8

Loanees	HT	WT	DOB	AGE	POB	From - To	APPS	GOA
(D)Fraser Franks	6'00"	10 12	22/11/90	19		Brentford (3ML) 9/09 -	12	2
(M)James Rowe			21/10/91	18		Reading 10/09 - Oxford C (L) 2/10	1	0
(F)Andy White			1/9/91	18		Reading 10/09 - Havant & W (2WL) 1/10, Staines (L) 3/10, Gillingham 6/10	1	0
(F)Mitchell Bryant			22/11/90	19		Reading (3ML) 12/09 - Rel 5/10	15	7

Departures	HT	WT	DOB	AGE	POB	From - To	APPS	GOA
(D)Joe Dolan	6'03"	13 05	27/5/80	30	Harrow	Canvey Island 7/06 - Rel 10/09, Carshalton, Croydon Ath 3/10	10	0
(D)Robbie Watkins	5'10"		14/10/85	24	Carshalton	Fulham 5/08 - Rel 10/09	9	0
(M)Jordan Lumsden	5'10"	10 02	3/2/91	19		Wycombe (Scholar) 8/09 - Rel 10/09	6	0
(F)Phil Ruggles			26/10/82	27	Surrey	Walton & H 7/08 - Rel 11/09, Bromley 12/09, Cray W (L) 3/10, Met Police 3/10 Rel c/s 10	15	2
(M)Ian Jones			13/9/89	20	Basingstoke	Southampton (Scholar) c/s 08 - AFC Totton 1/10, Gosport 6/10	9	0
(G)Ross Kitteridge			28/12/89	20	Reading	Reading (Scholar) (SL) 7/08 Perm 7/09 - Rel 5/10	32	0
(M)Ashley Mitchell			18/9/90	19		Reading (Scholar) NC 10/09 - Rel 5/10	17	1
(D)Miles Mitchell-Coop			20/10/89	20		Waltham Abbey 12/09 - Rel 5/10	8	0
(M)Tom Walsh			8/5/87	23	Basingstoke	Yth -	1	0
(D)Craig Smith			5/7/90	20		Yth -	0	0
(F)Ryan Stephens			4/8/86	24	Basingstoke	Injured 12/08 - Rel 5/10	17	0
(F)Benedict Akwuegbu			3/11/74	35		ex Lens 11/09 - Rel 5/10	4	1
(M)Josh Webb			23/1/90	20		Eastleigh 3/10 - Rel 5/10	8	1
(G)Craig Atkinson			21/10/86	23		Whitchurch U 8/08 -	3	0
(G)Richard Barnard	6'01"	12 13	27/12/80	29	Frimley	Farnborough 1/10 -	7	0
(D)Adam Aimable			1/11/87	22	Basingstoke	Yth -	4	0

BISHOP'S STORTFORD

Chairman: Luigu Del Basso
Secretary: Ian Kettridge **(T)** 07904 169 017
(E) ianket@aol.com

Additional Committee Members:
Franco Del Basso, John Turner

Manager: Mark Simpson
Programme Editor: John Allington **(E)** j.allington@bsfc.co.uk

Archive photo

Club Factfile

Founded: 1874 **Nickname:** Blues or Bishops
Previous Names:
Previous Leagues: East Herts 1896-97, 1902-06, 19-21, Stansted & District 1906-19, Herts County 1921-25, 27-29, Herts & Essex Border 1925-27, Spartan 1929-51, Delphian 1951-63, Athenian 1963-73, Isthmian 1974-2004

Club Colours (change): All blue (All red)

Ground: Woodside Park, Dunmow Road, Bishop's Stortford, Herts CM23 5RG **(T)** 08700 339 930
Capacity: 4,000 **Seats:** 298 **Covered:** 700 **Clubhouse:** Yes **Shop:** Yes
Previous Grounds:

Simple Directions
Woodside Park is situated 1/4 mile from Junction 8 of M11. Follow A1250 towards Bishop's Stortford Town Centre, entrance to ground is signposted through Woodside Park Industrial Estate.

Record Attendance: 6,000 v Peterborough Town - FA Cup 2nd Round 1972-73 and v Middlesbrough - FA Cup 3rd Round replay 1982-83
Record Victory: 11-0 v Nettleswell & Buntwill - Herts Junior Cup 1911
Record Defeat: 0-13 v Cheshunt (H) - Herts Senior Cup 1926
Record Goalscorer: Post 1929 Jimmy Badcock - 123
Record Appearances: Phil Hopkins - 543
Additional Records:

Senior Honours: Athenian League 1969-70. FA Amateur Cup 1973-74. Isthmian League Division 1 1980-81. FA Trophy 1980-81. London Senior Cup 1973-74. Premier Inter League Cup 1989-90. Herts Senior Cup x9.

10 YEAR RECORD

00-01	01-02	02-03	03-04	04-05	05-06	06-07	07-08	08-09	09-10
Isth1 4	Isth1 2	Isth P 13	Isth P 11	Conf S 10	Conf S 15	Conf S 5	Conf S 10	Conf S 9	Conf S 18

BISHOP'S STORTFORD

No.	Date	Comp	H/A	Opponents	Att:	Result	Goalscorers	Pos
1	8/8/09	BSS	H	Newport County	704	D 0-0		12
2	11/8/09	BSS	A	Dover Athletic	1210	L 0-2		16
3	15/8/09	BSS	A	Weymouth	623	W 6-2	Harris 4, Sheringham 5 (10, 23, 52, 86, 90)	12
4	18/8/09	BSS	H	Staines Town	387	D 2-2	Jackman 19, Nicholls 67	13
5	22/8/09	BSS	A	Woking	1090	L 0-1		15
6	29/8/09	BSS	H	St Albans City	461	W 2-0	Smith 11, Harris 41	10
7	31/8/09	BSS	A	Thurrock	368	D 2-2	Patterson pen 23, Bowditch 42	11
8	5/9/09	BSS	H	Bath City	467	L 1-5	Sheringham 38	13
9	8/9/09	BSS	A	Hampton & Richmond B.	391	W 3-1	Sheringham 3 (14, 24, 77)	12
10	12/9/09	BSS	A	Basingstoke Town	452	W 2-0	Nicholls 27, Jackman 61	10
11	19/9/09	BSS	H	Dorchester Town	401	W 2-0	Sheringham 26, Jackman 80	8
12	3/10/09	BSS	A	Welling United	507	W 2-0	Sheringham 2 (23, 45)	5
13	17/10/09	BSS	H	Havant & Waterlooville	449	W 1-0	Sheringham pen 22	4
14	24/10/09	BSS	A	Lewes	246	L 1-2	Southam 31	5
15	27/10/09	BSS	H	Chelmsford City	809	L 0-1		7
16	31/10/09	BSS	A	Weston-Super-Mare	250	W 3-1	Sheringham 57, Nicholls 70, Sulaiman 90	5
17	14/11/09	BSS	H	Weymouth	507	L 0-1		6
18	28/11/09	BSS	A	Worcester City	518	D 1-1	Smith 23	6
19	5/12/09	BSS	H	Woking	507	L 0-3		10
20	8/12/09	BSS	H	Eastleigh	282	L 0-1		11
21	26/12/09	BSS	H	Braintree Town	613	D 0-0		13
22	28/12/09	BSS	A	Staines Town	382	D 2-2	Riddle 18, Brayley 59	14
23	1/1/10	BSS	A	Braintree Town	994	L 0-2		14
24	16/1/10	BSS	H	Worcester City	302	W 2-1	Sheringham 71, Southam 75	12
25	23/1/10	BSS	A	Bath City	558	D 2-2	Sheringham 2 (62, 78)	13
26	30/1/10	BSS	H	Welling United	407	L 0-4		13
27	2/2/10	BSS	H	Basingstoke Town	265	L 0-2		13
28	6/2/10	BSS	A	Maidenhead United	263	L 0-4		15
29	8/2/10	BSS	A	Havant & Waterlooville	601	L 1-2	Shulton pen 29	15
30	13/2/10	BSS	H	Hampton & Richmond B.	337	L 0-1		15
31	20/2/10	BSS	A	Dorchester Town	432	L 0-2		16
32	23/2/10	BSS	H	Bromley	248	W 3-0	Shulton 2 (5, 47), Lettejallow 70	15
33	6/3/10	BSS	A	Chelmsford City	982	L 0-3		15
34	12/3/10	BSS	A	Newport County	3084	L 0-1		16
35	16/3/10	BSS	H	Dover Athletic	302	L 0-2		17
36	20/3/10	BSS	H	Lewes	337	D 0-0		18
37	27/3/10	BSS	A	Bromley	432	D 1-1	Shulton 62	18
38	3/4/10	BSS	A	St Albans City	402	W 4-2	D Morgan 2 (19, 74), Duncan 39, Antoine 43	16
39	5/4/10	BSS	H	Thurrock	368	D 0-0		16
40	10/4/10	BSS	H	Maidenhead United	309	L 1-2	Shulton 57	18
41	17/4/10	BSS	A	Eastleigh	481	D 1-1	D Morgan 87	18
42	24/4/10	BSS	H	Weston-Super-Mare	401	W 3-0	Sellears 27, Jackman 28, Shulton 88	18
	Cups							
1	26/9/09	FAC 2Q	H	Thurrock	425	L 2-3	Patterson 10, Jackman 12	
2	21/11/09	FAT 3Q	A	Ramsgate	298	W 3-0	Nicholls 28, Sulaiman 41, Riddle 81	
3	12/12/09	FAT 1	H	Maidenhead United	245	L 1-2	Smith 83	

Home Attendances:

Highest:	809 v Chelmsford City
Lowest:	248 v Bromley
Average (08-09):	387 (454)

Top Goalscorer:	Sheringham - 17 (17 League, 0 Cup) in 30 appearances - 57% strike rate
Most Appearances:	M Jones - 31 (29+1 League, 1 Cup)

EYRE	M JONES	WRIGHT	LETTEJALLOW	GOODACRE	ANGUS	HARRIS	BOWDITCH	JACKMAN	SHERINGHAM	NICHOLLS	R JONES	CHAMPION	ESSANDOH	PATTERSON	COOPER	SMITH	BRAYLEY	NUNN	RIDDLE	SULAIMAN	SOUTHAM	LLEWELLYN	SHULTON	QUERRY	SARGENT	GREENWOOD	ABDULLAHI	LATHROPE	HAHN	BENTLEY	DOCKER	CHICK	BOYLE-RENNER	D MORGAN	SACKEY	DUNCAN	N MORGAN	MUIR	ANTOINE	SIMPSON	PRESTEDGE	
X	X	X	X	X	X	X	X	X	X	X	U	U																														1
X	X	X	S	X	X	X	X		X	X	U	U	S																													2
X	X	X	S	X	X	X	X	S	X	X	U	S		X																												3
X	X	X	S	X		X	X	X	X	X	U	X		X	U																											4
X	X	X	S	X		X	X	S	X	X	X	X		X	U																											5
X		X	X	X		X	X	S	S	U	U	X		X	X	X	X																									6
X		X	X	X		X	X	S	S	U		X		X	X	X	X	U																								7
	U	X	X	X		X	X	S	X	S		X		X	X		X																									8
X	X	U		X		X	X	S	X	X		X	S	X	X		X	S																								9
X				X	U	X	X	S	X	X	U	X	S	X	X		X	X																								10
X		U		X	S	X	X	S	X	X		X		X	X	S	X	X																								11
X	U			X	U	X	X		X	X		X	S	X	X	X	S	X																								12
X	U				X				X	X	U	X	S	X	X	X	X	X	S	X																						13
X	X				X				X	S	U	X	S		X	X	S	X	X	X	X																					14
X	S				X				X	X	U	X	S		X	X	S	X	X	X	X	U																				15
X	X				X				X	X		X	S			X		X		X	X		X	U	U	U																16
X	X				X				X	X		X	S	X		X				X	X		X		U	U	S															17
X	X				X				X	X		X	S	X		X		X	S	U	X		X				U	S														18
X	X				X				X			X	U			X		X	S	X	X		X		U		S	X														19
X	X								X		X	X	S			X		X	X	X	X			U	U	U	X	S														20
X			X		X				S		X	X	X			X	S		X	U	X		U					S	X													21
X			X		X				X		X	X					X	X	X	X	X	U	S				U	S														22
X	U		X		X				X		U	X	S				X	X	X	U	X		S					X														23
X	X				X				X		X		S				X	X			X		X				U	X	S	X	S											24
X	X		S		X				X		X						X	X			X		X				U	X	S	X	U	S										25
X	X		X		X				X		X		U				X	X	S		X		U					X	S	X												26
	X		X						X		X		X				X	X				U	X	S	S		U						X									27
	X		X						X				X				X	X					X	U	S		S			X			U									28
	X		X								S							X				S	X	S	X		X			X	X		X	X	S							29
			X		X												X	X					X	S		U	X			X	S		X	X	U	X						30
	U		X		X												X	X					X		U		X			X	X		S	X	S	X	X	S				31
	X		X		X												X	X					X				S			U	S		U		X	X	X	S	X			32
	X		X															X					X		U		U			X	S		U		X	X	X	X	X	S		33
	X		X		X													X					X		U		S				X			U	S	X	X	X	X			34
	X		X		X													X					X		U		S				X			S	U	X	X	S	X			35
	X				X			X			S							X					X				X				X		S		U	X	X	U			X	36
	X				X						X											X	X		U		X								U	X	X	S	X	U	X	37
	X				X						X											X	X						X		S	S		X	S	X	X		X	U	X	38
	X				X						X		S									X	S		S				X		X	U		X		X	X		X	U	X	39
	X										X											X	X		X		X		S		S	S		X		X	X		X	U	X	40
	X				X			X			X											S	X				U		X		S	X		S		X	X			X	X	41
	X				X			X			X											X	X			X			S		S	U			U	X			S	X	X	42
X		U		X	U	X	X	X		X	U	X	S	X	X		X	X	S																							1
X	X				X				X	X		X	S	X		S		X	S	X	X		X			U	U															2
X					X				X		X		S			X		X	X	S	X		X		U	U	S	X														3
Total League Appearances																																										
25	29	8	17	12	27	12	12	5	25	14	14	20	3	13	10	12	17	25	6	8	13	5	21	0	2	1	7	5	4	8	6	1	3	6	2	13	11	2	8	2	7	**X**
0	1	0	5	0	1	0	0	8	3	2	2	1	14	0	0	1	4	1	4	0	0	2	3	3	3	0	6	4	5	0	8	3	2	2	4	0	0	4	1	1	0	**S**
0	5	2	0	0	2	0	0	0	0	2	10	2	2	0	2	0	0	1	0	3	0	3	2	3	9	4	7	0	0	1	1	2	3	1	5	0	0	1	0	4	0	**U**
Total Cup Appearances																																										
3	1	0	0	1	2	1	1	1	2	2	1	2	0	2	1	1	1	3	1	1	2	0	2	0	0	0	0	1	0	0	0	0	0	0	0	0	0	0	0	0	0	**X**
0	0	0	0	0	0	0	0	0	0	0	0	0	3	0	0	1	0	0	2	1	0	0	0	0	0	0	1	0	0	0	0	0	0	0	0	0	0	0	0	0	0	**S**
0	0	1	0	0	1	0	0	0	0	0	1	0	0	0	0	0	0	0	0	0	0	0	0	0	1	2	1	0	0	0	0	0	0	0	0	0	0	0	0	0	0	**U**
Total Goals																																										
0	0	0	1	0	0	2	1	4	17	3	0	0	0	1	0	2	1	0	1	1	2	0	6	0	0	0	0	0	0	0	0	0	0	3	0	1	0	0	1	0	0	**Lge**
0	0	0	0	0	0	0	0	1	0	1	0	0	0	1	0	1	0	0	1	1	0	0	0	0	0	0	0	0	0	0	0	0	0	0	0	0	0	0	0	0	0	**Cup**

Also Played: HILL S(1,2). MCKENZIE S(1,4,5)X(2,3). TAYLOR-FORBES S(1,4)X(2),U(3,5). DAYTON S(6,7,8)U(9). THOMPSON X(8). HUSSAIN U(8). GREEN S(10,12)U(11)S(Cup1). AKINNAWO S(13)U(14). TRAVELLER U(16). CRASTON U(17). PALMER S(19)X(21,23,Cup3). MASON U(22,24). STONE U(26,27,Cup1). MEHMET X(27,28,29,30). WAPPETT X(27). AZZOPARDI X(28),S(29),U(30). YEARWOOD U(28). ERSKINE X(32,33,34,35,36). PAVETT S(34,36)X(35,37). SELLEARS U(38,40,41)X(42).

BISHOP'S STORTFORD

CURRENT SQUAD AS OF BEGINING OF 2010-11 SEASON

GOALKEEPERS	HT	WT	D.O.B	AGE	P.O.B	CAREER	Apps	Gls
Bert Greenwood			28/4/92	18		Bishop's Stortford	1	0
DEFENDERS								
Stevland Angus	6'00"	12 00	16/9/80	29	Westminster	West Ham, Bournemouth (2ML) 8/00, Cambridge U 7/01 Rel c/s 05, Hull C (6WL) 12/04, Scunthorpe (SL) 1/05, Shrewsbury (Trial) 7/05, Southend (Trial) 8/05, Grays 8/05 Rel 5/06, Barnet (SL) 1/06, Torquay 7/06, Grimsby (Trial) 7/07,Barnet 8/07, Fisher 10/07 Rel, Braintree 8/08, Concord R 9/08, Bishop's Stortford 2/09	28	0
David Chick			27/2/85	25	Norwich	Norwich (Sch), Kings Lynn 1/04, Boston U (Trial) 2/04, Cheltenham (Trial) 2/04, Cambridge U 7/05 Rel 2/06, Peterborough (Trial) 10/06, Cambridge C 3/07 Rel 5/07, Boston U 9/07, Cambridge C 10/07 Rel 11/07, Bishop's Stortford 10/08 Rel 8/09, AFC Sudbury (L) 12/08, Bishop's Stortford 1/10	4	0
Matt Jones			4/3/85	25		Havant T, Waterlooville, BAT, Havant & W, Eastleigh, Bashley, St Albans, Bashley, Salisbury, Bishop's Stortford	30	0
Ritchie Jones			6/3/90	20		Northampton Rel 11/08, Cheshunt 12/08, Gillingham (Trial) 3/09, Dag & Red (Trial), Bishop's Stortford 3/09	16	0
Ted Llewellyn			14/1/92	18		Bishop's Stortford, Waltham Abbey (L)	7	0
Aiden Palmer	5'08"	10 10	2/1/87	23	Enfield	L.Orient Rel c/s 09, Dag & Red (L) 1/09, Prison, Bishop's Stortford 12/09, Cambridge U 1/10 Rel 4/10, Bishop's Stortford 7/10	3	0
Chris Sargent			10/10/91	18		Bishop's Stortford	5	0
Mark Wright			20/1/87	23	London	Norwich (Jun), Tottenham (Scholar), Charlton (Scholar), Southend, Lewes (L) 12/05, Grays 8/06, Crawley (2ML) 11/06, St Albans (L) 2/07, Rushden & D (L) 3/07, Bishop's Stortford 7/07 Rel 12/07, Fisher 12/07, Thurrock 9/08, Bishop's Stortford 2/09	8	0
MIDFIELDERS								
Ali Abdullahi			19/5/91	19		Dulwich H, Bishop's Stortford 11/09	13	0
Jon Docker			12/2/86	24	London	Sheff Wed Rel c/s 04, RKC Waalwijk (Holl) 7/04 Rel c/s 05, Northampton 9/05 Rel 12/05, Fisher 1/06, Chesham 2/06, Dorchester 7/07 Rel 4/08, Thurrock 8/08, Welling 10/08 Rel 11/08, Hitchin 2/09, Billericay 3/09, St Neots, Bishop's Stortford 12/09	14	0
Mitch Hahn			9/7/86	24		Bolton (Yth), Southend (Yth), Wealdstone 3/04, Redbridge, Enfield T 6/08, Aveley 12/08, Brentwood (L) 1/09, Bishop's Stortford 12/09	9	0
Baimass Lettejallow	5'09"	10 12	16/4/84	26	London	Barnet, Braintree 10/03, Harlow 1/04, Dag & Red 1/05, Aveley (L) 2/07, Thurrock (SL) 9/07, Thurrock (3ML) 8/08, Bishop's Stortford (SL) 1/09, Bishop's Stortford c/s 09	22	1
Nick Muir			19/1/88	22		Billericay, Heybridge 9/09, Bishop's Stortford 2/10	6	0
Reece Prestedge			25/12/85	24		Bishop's Stortford, Dag & Red, Brimsdown, Cheshunt 6/08, Bishop's Stortford 2/09, Thurrock 10/09, AFC Hornchurch 10/09, Billericay 12/09, Bishop's Stortford 3/10	7	0
Tom Querry			6/3/92	18		Bishop's Stortford	3	0
Scott Shulton			31/1/90	20		Watford (Yth), Wycombe Rel 5/09, Hendon (WE) 11/07, Basingstoke (L) 9/08, Hendon (L) 12/08, Ebbsfleet 8/09, Bishop's Stortford (L) 10/09 Perm 11/09, Southampton (Trial) 7/10	24	6
Charlie Simpson			6/8/89	21		Bishop's Stortford, Aveley (L) 11/07, Cheshunt (L) 2/09, Harlow (Dual) 8/09	3	0
FORWARDS								
Leon Antoine			30/4/85	25		Maldon T, Aveley 12/06, Tilbury 3/07, Boreham Wood, Redbridge, Canvey Island 7/08, Braintree c/s 09, AFC Hornchurch 9/09, Billericay 10/09, Heybridge (L) 11/09, Bishop Stortford 2/10	9	1
Duane Jackman			5/9/85	24		St Albans (Jun), Bishop's Stortford, Brimsdown 8/06, St Albans 9/06 (06/07 6,1), Rel 10/06, Brimsdown 11/06, Aveley 12/06, Potters Bar c/s 07, Cheshunt 8/08, Bishop's Stortford 11/08, AFC Hornchurch 10/09 Rel 2/10, Bishop's Stortford 3/10	13	4
Sheldon Sellears						Bishop's Stortford	1	1
Scott Traveller			21/9/92	17		Bishop's Stortford	0	0
George Wappett			26/12/91	18		Bishop's Stortford	1	0
Roraigh Yearwood			21/12/92	17		Bishop's Stortford	0	0
Loanees	**HT**	**WT**	**DOB**	**AGE**	**POB**	**From - To**	**APPS**	**GOA**
(M)Damon Lathrope	5'08"	10 02	28/10/89	20	Stevenage	Norwich 11/09 - Rel 5/10	9	0
(D)Alex Bentley			17/9/90	19		Dag & Red 1/10 - Rel 6/10	8	0
(G)Deniz Mehmet			19/9/92	17		West Ham 2/10 -	4	0
(F)Jacob Erskine	6'01"	13 06	13/1/89	21	London	Gillingham 2/10 - Croydon Ath (SL) 3/10	5	0
(G)Nick Morgan	6'07"		11/1/86	24		Braintree (SL) 2/10 -	11	0
(D)Lynvall Duncan			22/7/82	28		Braintree (SL) 2/10 -	13	1
(F)Jordan Pavett			16/12/91	18		Colchester 3/10 -	4	0
Departures	**HT**	**WT**	**DOB**	**AGE**	**POB**	**From - To**	**APPS**	**GOA**
(D)Narada Bernard	5'02"	10 05	30/1/81	29	Bristol	Maidenhead (L) 1/09 Perm 2/09 - Margate 8/09		
(D)Richard Howell			29/8/82	28	Hitchin	Stevenage 5/03 - Hitchin 8/09		
(F)Leon McKenzie			18/10/84	25		ex Grays 6/09 - Thurrock 9/09	5	0
(F)Ashley Taylor-Forbes			20/10/86	23		Cheshunt 3/09 - Harlow 9/09	3	0
(M)James Dayton	5'08"	10 01	12/12/88	21	Enfield	C.Palace NC 8/09 - Bromley 9/09	3	0
(G)Ed Thompson	5'10"	12 12	8/1/83	27	Finchley	Dag & Red 2/09 - Wingate & F, Potters Bar 10/09, Newport Pagnell 11/09	1	0
(D)Paul Goodacre			15/7/84	26		Maldon T 6/06 - Rel 10/09, Braintree 10/09, Dartford 5/10	12	0
(M)Danny (DJ) Green			4/8/90	20		St Albans 9/09 - Billericay 10/09, Dag & Red 4/10	2	0
(M)Marlon Patterson	5'09"	11 10	24/6/83	27	London	Histon 8/09 - Chelmsford 12/09 Rel c/s 10	13	1
(D)Grant Cooper	6'02"		16/9/77	32	London	Maidenhead 1/09 - Rel 12/09, Chelmsford 12/09 Rel 2/10, Margate 3/10	10	0
(F)Lewis Smith			27/10/89	20		Fulham 12/08 - Chelmsford 1/10 Rel 2/10, Thurrock 2/10	13	2
(D)Tom Champion			15/5/86	24	London	Barnet 7/05 - Braintree 1/10, Dartford 5/10	21	0
(M)Glen Southam	5'07"	11 10	27/8/80	30	Enfield	Hereford 10/09 - Histon 2/10 Rel 4/10, Barnet 6/10	13	2
(G)Nick Eyre	5'10"	10 10	7/9/85	24	Braintree	St Albans 7/08 - Rel 3/10, Chelmsford 3/10	25	0
(M)Bert Brayley	5'09"	12 07	5/9/81	28	Basildon	Chelmsford 8/09 - Rel 3/10, Braintree 3/10 Rel c/s 10, Concord R 7/10	21	1
(M)Ashley Nicholls	5'11"	11 11	30/10/81	28	Ipswich	Maidenhead 5/09 - Newport C (2ML) 12/09, Eastleigh 3/10, Maidenhead 6/10	16	3
(D)Ben Nunn			25/10/89	20		Cambridge C c/s 09 - Chelmsford 3/10	26	0
(F)Charlie Sheringham	6'01"	11 06	17/4/88	22	Chingford	Welling £6,500 5/09 - Histon (SL) 2/10, Dartford 6/10	28	17
(M)Louis Riddle	5'11"	12 00	29/8/82	28	Harlow	Braintree 5/09 - Braintree 6/10	10	1
(G)Nedjet Hussain			16/10/83	26		Thurrock c/s 09 -	0	0
(G)Ben Stone			21/12/89	20		Yth -	0	0
(D)Victor Boyle-Renner			18/4/79	31		Waltham Forest 2/10 -	5	0
(D)Michael Marin			5/6/85	25		Eton Manor 2/10 -		
(D)Emmanuel Sackey			1/2/86	24		Hampton & R 2/10 -	6	0
(D)Brian Suchley			26/10/81	28				
(D)Hassan Sulaiman			26/9/85	24	London	St Albans 10/09 -	8	1
(M)Ola Akinnawo			10/6/87	23		Cheshunt 7/09 - Harlow (Dual) 8/09	1	0
(M)Nick Azzopardi			6/10/92	17		Yth -	2	0
(M)Ben Bowditch	5'10"	12 00	19/2/84	26	Bishop's Stortford	ex St Albans 7/09 -	12	1
(M)Howard Craston			25/11/91	18		Yth -	0	0
(M)Danny Harris			7/7/86	24	Newnham	East Thurrock 12/07 - Dartford (Dual) 10/09 Perm	12	2
(M)Rory Hill			28/3/90	20	Lewisham	Gillingham 3/09 -	2	0
(M)Dean Mason			28/2/89	21	Islington	Maidenhead 12/09 -	0	0
(M)Daryl Sydes			20/11/90	19		L.Orient 1/10 -		
(F)Danny Morgan			4/11/84	25		St Albans 2/10 -	8	3
(F)Ellis Remy			13/2/84	26		ex Enfield T 8/09 - Potters Bar (L) 9/09		
(F)Roy Essandoh	6'00"	12 04	17/2/76	33	Belfast	Cambridge C 8/08 -	17	0

BOREHAM WOOD

Chairman: Danny Hunter
Secretary: Dell Ward (T) 07867 661 592
(E) ddelldell@aol.com
Additional Committee Members:
Bill Hunter, Matthew Hunter, John Gill
Manager: Ian Allinson
Programme Editor: John Gill (E) johndgill2002@yahoo.co.uk

Back Row (L-R): Ryan Kirby, Marc Charles-Smith, Jon Wordsworth, Simon Overland, Anthony Anstead, Kevin Stephens, Greg Morgan, Curtis Ujah, Sean Sonner, Laura Dalby (Physiotherapist).
Front Row: Raphael Sylvester, Billy Hawes, Jon Clements, Joe Reynolds, Paul Burrows (First Team Coach), Wes Daly (Club Captain), Ian Allinson (Team Manager), Mario Noto, Lewis Cook, Lee Allinson.

Club Factfile

Founded: 1948 **Nickname:** The Wood
Previous Names: Boreham Wood Rovers and Royal Retournez amalgamated in 1948 to form today's club
Previous Leagues: Mid Herts 1948-52, Parthenon 1952-57, Spartan 1956-66, Athenian 1966-74, Isthmian 1974-2004, Southern 2004-10

Club Colours (change): White/black/black (Sky blue/white/white)

Ground: Meadow Park, Broughinge Road, Boreham Wood WD6 5AL (T) 0208 953 5097
Capacity: 4,502 **Seats:** 600 **Covered:** 1,568 **Clubhouse:** Yes **Shop:** Yes
Previous Grounds: Eldon Avenue 1948-63
Simple Directions
Leave A1 at A5135 and follow A5135 towards Borehamwood. Cross two mini roundabouts then at large roundabout turn right (second exit) into Brook Road then take first right after car park for Broughinge Road.

Record Attendance: 4,030 v Arsenal - Friendly 13/07/2001
Record Victory: Not known
Record Defeat: Not known
Record Goalscorer: Mickey Jackson
Record Appearances: Dave Hatchett - 714
Additional Records: Received £5,000 from Dagenham & Redbridge for Steve Heffer

Senior Honours: Athenian League 1973-74. Isthmian League Division 2 1976-77, Division 1 1994-95, 2000-01.
Southern League East 2005-06, Premier Division Play-off 2009-10.
Herts Senior cup 1971-72, 98-99, 2001-02. London Challenge Cup 1997-98.

10 YEAR RECORD

00-01	01-02	02-03	03-04	04-05	05-06	06-07	07-08	08-09	09-10
Isth1 1	Isth P 15	Isth P 22	Isth1N 9	SthE 7	SthE 1	Isth P 7	Isth P 19	Isth P 18	Isth P 4

BOREHAM WOOD

No.	Date	Comp	H/A	Opponents	Att:	Result	Goalscorers	Pos
1	Aug 15	Ryman P.	H	Hastings United	159	D 0 - 0		12
2	18		A	AFC Hornchurch	242	L 1 - 2	Allinson 58	
3	22		A	Margate	345	L 1 - 2	Hunter 15	17
4	25		H	Wealdstone	235	L 0 - 1		20
5	29		A	Ashford United	100	W 2 - 0	Yao 36 75	18
6	31		H	Billericay Town	237	W 2 - 0	Yao 22 (pen) Morgan 44	
7	Sept 5		A	Sutton United	504	W 1 - 0	Green 80	8
8	**12**	**F.A.C.1Q**	**H**	**Waltham Forest**	**81**	**W 1 - 0**	**Allinson 90**	
9	19		H	Maidstone United	187	L 0 - 2		12
10	22		H	Carshalton Athletic	101	W 3 - 1	Hunter 35 Allinson (pen) 40 Noto 71	9
11	Oct 3		A	Horsham	286	W 3 - 1	Watters 9 16 Noto 62	6
12	10		H	Bognor Regis Town	191	W 1 - 0	Hunter 66	5
13	13		A	Cray Wanderers	133	D 1 - 1	Green 24	
14	24		H	Tonbridge Angels	172	W 2 - 0	Watters 33 Richards 80	2
15	**31**	**F.A.T 2Q**	**H**	**Slough Town**	**167**	**W 3 - 2**	**RICHARDS 3 (28 53 69)**	
16	Nov 17		H	Kingstonian	185	L 0 - 1		
17	**21**	**F.A.T 3Q**	**H**	**Hungerford Town**	**89**	**W 1 - 2**	**Allinson 61 (pen)**	**11**
18	23		A	Harrow Borough		L 0 - 2		
19	28		A	Billericay Town	305	L 0 - 2		11
20	Dec 5		H	Ashford Town	103	D 3 - 3	Hunter 9 75 Richards 81	10
21	12	F.A.T 1R	A	AFC Wimbledon	1306	L 1 - 2	Hunter 53	
22	19		A	Hastings United	306	L 1 - 2	Hunter 66	
23	26		H	Waltham Abbey	111	W 3 - 0	Richards 37 Green 89 90	10
24	Jan 18		A	Tooting & Mitcham	147	W 2 - 0	Richards 41 Watters 90	
25	23		A	Maidstone United	233	W 1 - 0	Noy 20	7
26	26		H	Aveley	83	W 3 - 2	Allinson 45 Clements 65 Morgan 69	
27	30		H	Horsham	144	W 4 - 0	Noto 24 (pen) Richards 35 Hunter 88 Watters 90	3
28	Feb 6		A	Carshalton Athletic	259	D 0 - 0		4
29	9		H	Canvey Island	113	L 1 - 3	Watters 58	
30	13		H	Cray Wanderers	128	L 2 - 4	Braithwaite 58 Clements 90	5
31	16		H	Hendon	135	W 2 - 1	Noto 47 (pen) Parker 72 (og)	
32	20		A	Bognor Regis Town	319	W 1 - 0	Morgan 4	3
33	27		H	Dartford	385	L 0 - 1		3
34	March 2		H	Sutton United	123	L 1 - 2	Effiong 83	
35	7		A	Kingstonian	351	L 1 - 4	Morgan 25	
36	13		H	Harrow Borough	113	W 1 - 0	Morgan 22	5
37	16		A	Dartford	726	W 2 - 1	Moran 45 Morgan 71	
38	20		A	Aveley	331	L 0 - 2		5
39	23		A	Waltham Abbey	87	D 1 - 1	Richards 53	
40	27		H	Margate	148	D 1 - 1	Hunter 43	4
41	April 3		A	Canvey Island	252	W 1 - 0	Seanla 55	4
42	6		A	Hendon	169	W 1 - 0	Noto 60 (pen)	4
43	10		A	Wealdstone	406	D 0 - 0		4
44	13		H	AFC Hornchurch	151	D 0 - 0		
45	17		A	Tonbridge Angels	587	W 2 - 0	Noto 64 Seanla 70	4
46	24		H	Tooting & Mitcham	311	W 3 - 2	Noto 14 18 (pen) Seanla 53	4
47	26	Play Off	A	Aveley		W 1 - 0	Seanla 78	
					Goals	61 50		

Home Attendances:	
Highest:	385 v Dartford
Lowest:	83 v Aveley
Average (08-09):	148 (162)
Top Goalscorer:	Hunter - 9 (League 8, FAT 1)

BOREHAM WOOD

CURRENT SQUAD AS OF BEGINING OF 2010-11 SEASON

GOALKEEPERS	HT	WT	D.O.B	AGE	P.O.B	CAREER	Apps	Gls
DEFENDERS								
Daniel Braithwaite			16/10/81	28	London	Enfield, Chesham, Boreham Wood 8/03, Dover c/s 04, Ashford T 7/07, Harrow, Ashford T 8/08, Boreham Wood c/s 09		
Bradley Fraser						Boreham Wood		
Luke Garrard	5'10"	10 09	22/9/85	23	Barnet	Tottenham (Scholar), Swindon 7/02 Rel c/s 05, Bishop's Stortford 7/05, Boreham Wood 10/05, Northwood 11/05, AFC Wimbledon 3/06, Boreham Wood (3ML) 10/09 Perm 1/10		
Ryan Kirby	5'11"	12 00	6/9/74	35	Chingford	Arsenal, Doncaster 7/04 Rel c/s 06, Preston 7/06, Crewe 8/96, Wigan 8/96, Northampton 9/96, Stevenage 11/96 Rel 3/01, Aldershot (L) 1/01, Aldershot T 3/01, Harlow 6/02, Thurrock 8/04 Rel 3/05, Fisher 3/05, Harlow 1/06 (Pl/Man) 11/06 Rel 12/08, AFC Hornchurch 1/09, Boreham Wood 2/09		
Ryan Moran			31/3/82	28		Luton, St Albans 3/00, Boreham Wood 8/03, Braintree 2/08, Boreham Wood 11/09		
Kevin Stephens	5'10"	12 05	28/7/84	26	Enfield	L.Orient Rel 2/04, Billericay (L) 9/03, Cambridge U (Trial) 12/03, Hornchurch (L) 1/04, Chesham, Redbridge c/s 04, Billericay 12/04, Redbridge 3/05, Ilford, Enfield T 12/05, Dag & Red (Trial) 12/06, Chelmsford 12/06, Enfield Town 1/07, Redbridge 12/07, Newport C 6/08, Enfield T 9/08, Boreham Wood 10/08, Newport C 1/09 Rel 3/09, Boreham Wood 3/09		
Curtis Ujah	6'00"		22/7/88	22	Sheffield	Reading, Slough (L) 9/06, Tamworth 3/07, Yeovil 7/07 Rel 12/07, Crawley (L) 8/07, Weston-Super-Mare 12/07 Rel 5/08, Dag & Red (Trial) c/s 08, Halesowen T 9/08 Rel 9/08, Dover (Trial), Hednesford 10/08, Boreham Wood 2/09		
MIDFIELDERS								
Lee Allinson						Watford (Yth), Barton R, Edgware, Boreham Wood, Stotfold, Potters Bar 7/05, Enfield 9/05, Boreham Wood, Stotfold, Boreham Wood 6/08		
Bobby Highton			10/12/80	29	Barnet	Stevenage, Aylesbury U 12/99, Boreham Wood 12/00 Rel 2/01, Bracknell, Hayes 7/01, Hemel Hempstead 12/01, Cheshunt 11/04, Harrow 2/07, Boreham Wood 6/09		
Leon Hunter	5'07"	11 06	27/8/81	29	London	Southend, Chelmsford (L) 1/01, Grays (L) 1/02 Perm, Heybridge 8/02, Billericay 7/03 Rel c/s 09, Boreham Wood 6/09		
Greg Morgan						Boreham Wood		
Mario Noto			24/10/84	25	Enfield	Tottenham (Scholar), Reading (Scholar), Wycombe (Trial) 2/04, Southend (Trial) 4/04, C.Palace (Trial) c/s 04, Darlington (Trial) 12/04, Canvey Island 1/05, Chelmsford 7/06 Rel 7/08, Boreham Wood c/s 08		
FORWARDS								
Jay Brett						Boreham Wood		
Dewayne Clarke			9/11/78	31		Arlesey, Boreham Wood, Farnborough 9/03 Rel 11/03, Waltham Forest 11/03, Cheshunt c/s 05, Thurrock 12/06, Cheshunt 1/07, Boston U 7/07, Harrow, Cheshunt, Waltham Forest 12/07, Dulwich H 1/08, Cheshunt 7/08, Harrow 9/08, Harringey (Dual) 1/10, Boreham Wood 3/10		
Jon Clements						Boreham Wood		
Claude Seanla	5'09"	11 11	2/6/88	22	Abidjan. IvC	Tottenham (Scholar), Watford 6/06 Rel 2/07, Kettering 3/07 Rel 5/07, Barnet 7/07 Rel 4/08, St Albans (L) 11/07, Wivenhoe (L) 3/08, Ashford T 9/08, Horsham 1/09, Boreham Wood 3/10		
Sherwin Stanley						Boreham Wood, Edgware (Dual) 2/05, Enfield T, Enfield 1893, Brentwood, Aveley 8/09, Boreham Wood 7/10		

BRAINTREE TOWN

Chairman: Lee Harding
Secretary: Tom Woodley (T) 07950 537 179
(E) tawoodley@talktalk.net
Additional Committee Members: Barry Shepherd, Bird Luckin, Kim Cowell, Vic Dixon, Terry Thorogood, Alan Stuckey, Andy Green,
Manager: Rod Stringer
Programme Editor: Lee Harding (E) braintreetfc@aol.com

Archive photo

Club Factfile

Founded: 1898 **Nickname:** The Iron
Previous Names: Crittall Athletic > 1968, Braintree and Crittall Athletic > 1981, Braintree > 1983
Previous Leagues: N.Essex 1898-1925, Essex & Suffolk Border 1925-29, 55-64, Spartan 1928-35, Eastern Co. 1935-37, 38-39, 52-55, 70-91, Essex Co. 1937-38, London 1945-52, Gt London 1964-66, Met 1966-70, Southern 1991-96, Isthmian 1996-2006

Club Colours (change): Orange/blue/orange (Blue/white/blue)

Ground: The Cressing Road Stadium, Clockhouse Way, Braintree CM7 3RD (T) 01376 345 617
Capacity: 4,000 **Seats:** 550 **Covered:** 1,769 **Clubhouse:** Yes **Shop:** Yes
Previous Grounds: The Fiar Field 1898-1903, Spalding Meadow and Panfield Lane

Simple Directions
Leave M11 at junction 8A (for Stansted Airport) and follow A120 towards Braintree and Colchester for 17 miles. At Gallows Corner roundabout (with WestDrive Kia on your right) take first exit into Cressing Road. Clockhouse Way and the entrance to the ground are three quarters of a mile on the left and are clearly sign-posted.

Record Attendance: 4,000 v Tottenham Hotspur - Testimonial May 1952
Record Victory: 12-0 v Thetford - Eastern Counties League 1935-36
Record Defeat: 0-14 v Chelmsford City (A) - North Essex League 1923
Record Goalscorer: Chris Guy - 211 (1963-90)
Record Appearances: Paul Young - 524 (1966-77)
Additional Records: Gary Bennett scored 57 goals during season 1997-98
Received £10,000 from Brentford for Matt Metcalf and from Colchester United for John Cheesewright

Senior Honours: Eastern Counties League 1983-84, 84-85, Essex Senior Cup 1995-96. Isthmian League Premier Division 2005-06.
East Anglian Cup x3

10 YEAR RECORD

00-01	01-02	02-03	03-04	04-05	05-06	06-07	07-08	08-09	09-10
Isth1 3	Isth P 4	Isth P 16	Isth P 23	Isth P 4	Isth P 1	Conf S 3	Conf S 5	Conf S 14	Conf S 7

BRAINTREE

No.	Date	Comp	H/A	Opponents	Att:	Result	Goalscorers	Pos
1	8/8/09	BSS	A	Eastleigh	436	W 2-1	Purcell 8, Marks 88	3
2	11/8/09	BSS	H	Lewes	430	W 3-0	Purcell 2 (15, 74), Marks 65	1
3	15/8/09	BSS	H	Maidenhead United	507	W 2-0	Marks 14, Tejan-Sie 54	1
4	18/8/09	BSS	A	Hampton & Richmond B.	355	D 2-2	Game 69, Keeling 83	1
5	22/8/09	BSS	H	Havant & Waterlooville	527	L 0-2		5
6	29/8/09	BSS	A	Welling United	534	D 0-0		6
7	31/8/09	BSS	H	Chelmsford City	1260	W 2-1	Bailey-Dennis 11, Game 20	4
8	5/9/09	BSS	A	Weston-Super-Mare	262	W 2-1	Purcell 2 (43, 80)	4
9	8/9/09	BSS	A	Bromley	455	D 1-1	Marks 16	4
10	12/9/09	BSS	H	Worcester City	473	D 0-0		4
11	19/9/09	BSS	H	Basingstoke Town	437	L 1-2	Purcell 59	6
12	3/10/09	BSS	A	Dorchester Town	459	L 0-5		8
13	17/10/09	BSS	H	Staines Town	453	W 2-0	Mingle 69, Goodacre 90	6
14	27/10/09	BSS	H	Thurrock	580	W 3-1	Mingle 27, Duncan 41, Marks pen 66	6
15	31/10/09	BSS	A	Woking	1418	D 0-0		7
16	14/11/09	BSS	A	St Albans City	344	D 1-1	Jones 85	7
17	28/11/09	BSS	H	Eastleigh	454	D 1-1	Power 74	7
18	5/12/09	BSS	H	Weymouth	431	W 3-2	Purcell 2 (2, 44), Marks 21	7
19	8/12/09	BSS	H	Bath City	434	W 2-0	Purcell 2 (22, 42)	4
20	26/12/09	BSS	A	Bishop's Stortford	613	D 0-0		6
21	28/12/09	BSS	H	Hampton & Richmond B.	503	D 1-1	Power 77	6
22	1/1/10	BSS	H	Bishop's Stortford	994	W 2-0	Power 29, Marks 39	5
23	30/1/10	BSS	H	Woking	654	W 1-0	Purcell 68	6
24	6/2/10	BSS	A	Lewes	424	D 2-2	Marks 6, Purcell 27	7
25	9/2/10	BSS	H	Weston-Super-Mare	402	W 1-0	Game 15	3
26	13/2/10	BSS	H	Dover Athletic	718	L 1-2	Game 30	6
27	15/2/10	BSS	A	Worcester City	525	W 3-2	Mingle 13, Calver 73, Marks 90	2
28	20/2/10	BSS	H	Bromley	578	D 1-1	Game 34	5
29	23/2/10	BSS	A	Weymouth	1222	D 1-1	Purcell 72	3
30	27/2/10	BSS	A	Newport County	2117	L 0-1		4
31	6/3/10	BSS	A	Dover Athletic	1007	D 0-0		6
32	9/3/10	BSS	A	Thurrock	315	W 2-1	Marks 27, Purcell 65	4
33	13/3/10	BSS	H	Dorchester Town	508	W 2-0	Bruce 57, Purcell 72	3
34	16/3/10	BSS	A	Maidenhead United	155	D 0-0		3
35	20/3/10	BSS	A	Bath City	619	W 4-2	Purcell 2 (16, 90), Marks 2 (40, 44)	3
36	22/3/10	BSS	A	Havant & Waterlooville	594	D 1-1	Quinton pen 64	3
37	27/3/10	BSS	A	Staines Town	426	L 1-2	Purcell 30	4
38	2/4/10	BSS	H	Welling United	799	W 1-0	Purcell 14	4
39	5/4/10	BSS	A	Chelmsford City	1685	D 1-1	Purcell 2	4
40	10/4/10	BSS	H	St Albans City	500	D 2-2	Mingle 14, Quinton pen 25	4
41	17/4/10	BSS	A	Basingstoke Town	477	W 1-0	Marks 20	4
42	24/4/10	BSS	H	Newport County	1187	L 1-2	Quinton pen 55	7
	Cups							
1	26/9/09	FAC 2Q	H	Hampton & Richmond B.	327	D 0-0		
2	29/9/09	FAC 2QR	A	Hampton & Richmond B.	216	L 1-4	Purcell 8	
3	21/11/09	FAT 3Q	A	Newport County	684	L 1-2	Purcell 51	

Home Attendances:	
Highest:	1260 v Chelmsford City
Lowest:	430 v Lewes
Average (08-09):	503 (560)

Top Goalscorer:	Purcell - 22 (20 League, 2 Cup) in 44 appearances - 50% strike rate
Most Appearances:	Purcell - 44 (40+1 League, 3 Cup)

MORGAN	PETERS	BAILEY-DENNIS	BRUCE	MORAN	QUINTON	MINGLE	GAME	PURCELL	MARKS	TEJAN-SIE	HOWELL	STARKEY	DUNCAN	ANTOINE	MCDONALD	SMITH	DEAN	KEELING	BRUNO	JONES	ROACHE	MCMAHON	POWER	BLACKMORE	GOODACRE	EMMANUEL	RHODES	CALLISTE	HUGHES	HARRIS	HOLLOWAY	CHAMPION	CALVER	BURBRIDGE	DUMAS	MARTIN	BRAYLEY	
X	X	X	X	X	X	X	X	X	X	X	S	S	S	U	U																							1
X	X	X	X		X	X	X	X	X	X	X	S	S	S	U	U																						2
X	X	X	X		X	X	X	X	X	X	X	S	S	S	U	U																						3
X		X	X		X		X	X		X	X	X	S	X	U		X	S	U	U																		4
X		S	X		X		X	X		X	X	X	X	X	U		X	S	S	U																		5
X	X	X	X		X	X	X	X	X	U		S		S	U		X	S		X																		6
X	X	X	X		X	X	X	S	X	S		U		S	U		X	X		X																		7
X	X	X	X		X	X	X	X	X	X		U			U		S	S		X	S																	8
X	X	X	X		X		X	X	X		U	S			U		X	X	U	X	S																	9
X	X	X	X		X		X	X	X			S	U		U		X	X	S	X	S																	10
X	X	X	X	S			X	X			X	X	U		S	U	X	X	S		X																	11
U	X	X	X	X			X	X	X				S		X		X	X	X	S	U		S															12
	X	U				X	X	X	X			S	X		U			X	X	X			S	X	X	U												13
	X	U	S			X	X	X	X			U	X		U			X	X	X			S	X	X													14
	X	U	S			X	X	X	X			U	X		U			X	X	X			S	X	X													15
	X		X			X	X	X	S			X	S		U				S	X			X	X	X		X	U										16
			X			X	X	X	X			S	X		U			X	X	X			S	X		U	X		U									17
	X		U			X	X	X	X			S	X		U				X	X			S	X	X		X			S								18
	X		U		S	X	X	X	X			U	X						X	X			S	U	X					X	X							19
	X		X		S	X	X	X	X				X		U				U	X			S		X		S			X	X							20
	X		X		S	X	X	X	S			S	X		U				U				X		X		X			X	X							21
	X		X		X	X	X	X	X				U		U				S	X			X		X		S			S	X							22
	X		U		X	X	X	X	X				U		U				S	X			X		X					S	X	X						23
	X		U		X	X	X	X	X				U		U				S	X			S		X					X	X	X						24
	X		X		X	X	X	X	X				S		U				U	X										X	X	X	S	U				25
	X		X		X	S	X	X	X						U				U	X					X					X	X	X	S		U			26
	X		X		S	X	X	X	X										U	X					X					X	X	X	S	U	S			27
	X		X		S	X	X	X	X										U	X					X					X	X	X	S	S	U			28
	S		X		X	X	X	X	X						X					X					X					X	U	X	U	S	S			29
	X		X		X	X	X	X	X						U				S	X										X	X	X	U		S	S		30
	X		X		X	X	X	X	X						U				U	X										X	X	X	S		U	S		31
	X		X		X	X	X	X	X						U				U	X										S	X	X			U	X	S	32
	X		X			X	X	X	X						U				S	X					U					X	X	X			S	X	S	33
	X		X			X	X	X	X						U				S	X					U						X	X		S	U	X	X	34
	X		X		X	X	X	X	X						U				S	X					X						X			X	U	S	S	35
	X		X		X	X		X	X										U	X					X					S	X	X		X	S	S	U	36
	X		X		X	X		X	S										S	X					X					X	X	X		X	U	U	S	37
	X		U		X	X		X	S										S	X					X					X	X	X		X	U	X	S	38
	X		X		X	X		X	S										U	X					X					X	X	X		X	S	U	S	39
	X		X		X	X			X						U				S	X			U		X						X	X		S	S	X	X	40
	X		X		X	X		X	X						U				U	X			S		X					S	X	X		X		U		41
			X		X	X		X	X						U				S	X			S		X					X	X	X			S	X	U	42
	X	U	X	X			X	X	X		U	X	S		U	U	X	X	S	X	S	X																1
	X	U	X	X			X	X	X		S	X	S		U	U	X	X	S	X	U	X																2
	X		X			X	X	X	X			U	U		U				X	X			S	X	X	U	X											3

Total League Appearances

11	37	11	34	2	27	35	35	40	34	6	5	4	9	2	2	0	8	9	7	34	1	0	4	6	23	0	4	0	0	16	23	19	0	6	0	6	2	X
0	1	1	2	1	5	1	0	1	5	1	1	10	7	4	1	0	1	4	15	1	3	0	11	0	0	0	2	0	0	6	0	0	5	4	8	4	6	S
1	0	3	5	0	0	0	0	0	0	1	1	5	5	1	32	3	0	0	13	2	1	0	1	1	2	2	0	1	1	0	1	0	2	2	8	3	2	U

Total Cup Appearances

0	3	0	3	2	0	1	3	3	3	0	0	2	0	0	0	0	2	2	1	3	0	2	0	1	1	0	1	0	0	0	0	0	0	0	0	0	0	X
0	0	0	0	0	0	0	0	0	0	0	1	0	2	0	0	0	0	0	2	0	1	0	1	0	0	0	0	0	0	0	0	0	0	0	0	0	0	S
0	0	2	0	0	0	0	0	0	0	0	1	1	1	0	3	2	0	0	0	0	1	0	0	0	0	1	0	0	0	0	0	0	0	0	0	0	0	U

Total Goals

0	0	1	1	0	0	0	0	20	13	1	0	0	1	0	0	0	1	0	0	1	0	0	3	0	1	0	0	0	0	0	0	0	1	0	0	0	0	Lge
0	0	0	0	0	0	0	0	2	0	0	0	0	0	0	0	0	0	0	0	0	0	0	0	0	0	0	0	0	0	0	0	0	0	0	0	0	0	Cup

BRAINTREE TOWN

CURRENT SQUAD AS OF BEGINING OF 2010-11 SEASON

GOALKEEPERS	HT	WT	D.O.B	AGE	P.O.B	CAREER	Apps	Gls
Nathan McDonald			16/5/91	19		Braintree	3	0
Ollie Morris-Sanders	6'04"					Stanway R, Wivenhoe, Rio Grande Uni (USA) c/s 00, Wivenhoe 6/04, Heybridge 8/07, Aveley 11/09, Braintree 6/10		
DEFENDERS								
Michael Alaile	6'00"	12 09	23/11/88	21		Dag & Red Rel c/s 09, Aveley (SL) 2/07, Potters Bar (L) 9/07, Billericay (SL) 12/07, Fisher (L) 9/08, Bishop's Stortford (L) 10/08, Witham T (L) 12/08, Billericay (2ML) 2/09, Chelmsford (Trial) c/s 09, Aveley 8/09, Braintree 6/10		
Adam Bailey-Dennis			18/9/90	19		Colchester, Felixstowe & W (WE) 1/09, Braintree 5/09, Billericay (L) 11/09, Great Wakering (L) 1/10, Aveley (L) 3/10	12	1
Kenny Davis	5'07"	11 02	17/4/88	22	London	Chelsea (Yth), Redbridge 3/05, Harlow c/s 05, Grays 8/08, Braintree 6/10		
Ryan Doyle	6'02"					Barking, Aveley 12/07, Braintree 6/10		
Sam Holloway						AFC Hornchurch, Redbridge, Tilbury 9/07, Aveley 12/07, Braintree 6/10		
Mark Jones			6/8/79	31		Burnham Ramblers, Billericay, Romford, Braintree 2/00	35	1
Matthew Paine	6'01"	12 12	22/12/87	22	Bexley	Colchester, Thurrock (SL) 1/07, Thurrock c/s 07, Braintree 6/10		
Bradley Thomas	6'02"	13 00	29/3/84	26	Forest Gate	Peterborough, Aldershot (L) 12/03, Heybridge (L) 3/04, Sutton U (L) 8/04, Welling (L) 10/04, Weymouth (L) 1/05 Perm 2/05, Eastleigh 9/05, Yeovil Undisc 1/06, Tamworth (2ML) 8/06, Tamworth (L) 10/06, Crawley 6/07, Kings Lynn (SL) 10/08, St Albans 8/09, Billericay 8/09, Sutton U 8/09, Hendon 11/09, Braintree 7/10		
MIDFIELDERS								
Tom Bruno			9/6/92	18		Harlow, Braintree 8/09	22	0
Reece Harris			12/12/91	18		Stanway R, Heybridge 10/09, Braintree 12/09	22	0
Robbie Martin			29/12/84	25		Watford, Hornchurch (L) 3/04, Braintree 5/04, Havant & W 10/08 Rel 2/10, Braintree 2/10	10	0
Bradley Quinton			7/9/78	31		Hornchurch, Aveley, Romford, Bishop's Stortford, Braintree 1/00 Temp Man 10/07	32	0
Louis Riddle	5'11"	12 00	29/8/82	28	Harlow	West Ham, Stevenage (L) 2/02, Stevenage 10/02, Braintree (L) 2/03, Braintree 5/03, Cambridge C 8/03, Braintree 6/04 Rel 5/09, Bishop Stortford 5/09, Braintree 6/10		
Phil Starkey	6'00"	12 06	10/9/87	22	Dartford	C.Palace Rel c/s 07, Ebbsfleet 8/07, Tonbridge A (L) 1/08 Perm, Ebbsfleet (Trial) 7/09, Braintree 8/09	14	0
Nicky Symons						Maldon T, Tilbury 11/06, Maldon T, Redbridge 10/07, Brentwood c/s 08, Aveley, Braintree 6/10		
FORWARDS								
Jamie Guy	6'01"	13 00	1/8/87	23	Barking	Colchester, Gravesend (L) 10/05, Staines (2ML) 10/05, Staines (L) 1/06, Cambridge U (SL) 2/06, Oxford U (SL) 7/08, Dag & Red (L) 3/09, Port Vale (L) 10/09, Grays 1/10 Rel 5/10, Braintree 7/10		
Justin Hazell	5'09"	11 06	15/1/92	18	Leigh-on-Sea	Southend, Braintree 6/10		
Sean Marks			25/11/85	24	Essex	Heybridge, Braintree £1,000 5/08	39	13
Michael Power			8/1/83	27	Kent	Thamesmead, Cray W c/s 04, Bromley 6/06 Rel 8/06, Tonbridge A 8/06, Cray W 2/07, Margate 8/08, Carshalton 11/08, Cray W 3/09, Braintree 10/09	15	3
Martin Tuohy						Barking, East Thurrock, Aveley (L) 8/06 Perm, Great Wakering 1/07, East Thurrock 6/08, Aveley c/s 09, Braintree 6/10		
Loanees	**HT**	**WT**	**DOB**	**AGE**	**POB**	**From - To**	**APPS**	**GOA**
(M)Tommy Tejan-Sie	5'06"	11 08	23/11/88	21	London	Dag & Red 7/09 -	7	1
(M)Harlee Dean	6'00"	11 10	26/7/91	19	Basingstoke	Dag & Red (2ML) 8/09 - Grays (L) 11/09, Southampton (Trial) c/s 10	9	1
(F)Craig Calver	5'10"		20/1/91	19	Cambridge	Southend 2/10 - AFC Sudbury (L) 3/10	5	1
Departures	**HT**	**WT**	**DOB**	**AGE**	**POB**	**From - To**	**APPS**	**GOA**
(F)Leon Antoine			30/4/88	22		Canvey Island c/s 09 - AFC Hornchurch 9/09, Billericay 10/09, Heybridge (L) 11/09, Bishop Stortford 2/10	6	0
(D)Ryan Moran			31/3/82	28		Boreham Wood 2/08 - Boreham Wood 11/09	3	0
(D)Andrew Howell	5'11"	12 01	18/3/89	21	Great Yarmouth	Tooting & M 6/09 - Rel 11/09	6	0
(F)Ramon Calliste			16/12/85	24		Cambridge C 10/09 - Bromley 12/09, Cambridge C 2/10	0	0
(M)Daniel Emmanuel			17/11/91	18		West Ham 10/09 - AFC Sudbury 12/09	0	0
(M)Alex Rhodes	5'09"	10 04	23/1/82	28	Cambridge	Oxford U 11/09 - Grays 1/10 Rel 5/10	6	0
(F)Lee Roache	5'09"	11 00	30/4/84	26	Leytonstone	Histon 9/09 - Eastleigh 2/10, Bath C 3/10, Hemel Hempstead 3/10	4	0
(D)Lynvall Duncan			22/7/82	28		Billericay 5/09 - Bishop's Stortford (SL) 2/10, Rel c/s 10	16	1
(D)Paul Goodacre			15/7/84	26		Bishop's Stortford 10/09 - Dartford 5/10	23	1
(D)Tom Champion			15/5/86	24	London	Bishop's Stortford 1/10 - Dartford 5/10	19	0
(M)Jacob Mingle			28/1/86	24		Eastbourne B 6/09 - Rel 5/10, Tonbridge A 6/10	36	0
(D)Ashley Dumas			15/8/87	23		Billericay 2/10 - Canvey Island 6/10	8	0
(D)Ryan Peters			21/8/87	23		Margate 5/09 - Staines 6/10	38	0
(D)Joe Bruce	6'00"	12 00	5/7/83	27	London	Cambridge C 7/08 - Dartford 6/10	36	1
(M)Matt Game			24/3/85	25	Upney	Billericay 5/09 - Canvey Island 6/10	35	0
(M)George Purcell	5'11"	11 09	8/4/88	22	Gravesend	Ebbsfleet 5/09 - York C Undisc 7/10	41	20
(G)Craig Holloway			10/8/84	26	Blackheath	Chelmsford 12/09 - Bromley 7/10	23	0
(G)David Blackmore	6'06"	13 00	23/3/89	21	Chelmsford	Margate 10/09 - Rel c/s 10	6	0
(G)Billy McMahon			11/7/83	27		AFC Hornchurch 9/09 - Rel	0	0
(M)Bert Brayley	5'09"	12 07	5/9/81	28	Basildon	Bishop's Stortford 3/10 - Rel c/s 10, Concord R 7/10	8	0
(M)Lee Hodges			2/3/78	32		Tilbury 2/10 -		
(M)Scott Smith			20/7/90	20		Yth -	0	0
(F)Rikki Burbridge			12/12/78	31		Brimsdown 2/10 - Rel c/s 10, AFC Hornchurch c/s 10	10	0
(F)Andy Hughes			7/6/89	21		ex Haverhill 11/09 - AFC Sudbury 12/09, Braintree 2/10 Rel c/s 10	0	0
(G)Nick Morgan	6'07"		11/1/86	24		Crawley 2/09 - Farnborough (2ML) 11/09, Croydon Ath (L) 1/10, Bishop's Stortford (SL) 2/10 Rel c/s 10	11	0
(M)Jon Keeling			6/6/76	34	Essex	Chelmsford 8/09 -	13	0

BROMLEY

Chairman: Paul Greenwood
Secretary: Colin Russell (T) 07970 031 511
(E) colin@bromleyfc.co.uk

Additional Committee Members:
Jeremy Dolke, Jeff Hutton
Manager: Mark Goldberg
Programme Editor: Jeff Hutton (E) info@bromleyfc.net

Photo: edboydenphotos.co.uk (Archive photo)

Club Factfile

Founded: 1892 **Nickname:** The Lillywhites
Previous Names:
Previous Leagues: South London, Southern, London, West Kent, South Surburban, Kent, Spartan 1907-08, Isthmian 1908-11, 52-2007, Athenian 1919-1952

Club Colours (change): White/black/black (All red)

Ground: The Stadium, Hayes Lane, Bromley, Kent BR2 9EF **(T)** 020 8460 5291
Capacity: 5,000 **Seats:** 1,300 **Covered:** 2,500 **Clubhouse:** Yes **Shop:** Yes
Previous Grounds:

Simple Directions
From M25 Motorway: Leaving the M25 at Junction 4, follow the A21 to Bromley and London, for approximately 4 miles and then fork left onto the A232 signposted Croydon/Sutton. At the 2nd set of traffic lights turn right into Baston Road (B265), following it for about 2 miles as it becomes Hayes Street and then Hayes Lane. Bromley FC is on right hand side of road just after a mini roundabout. From the Croydon/Surrey areas use the A232, turn left into Baston Road (B265), following it for about 2 miles as it becomes Hayes Street and then Hayes Lane. From West London use the South Circular Road as far as West Dulwich and then via Crystal Palace, Penge, Beckenham and Bromley South areas. From North and East London use the Blackwall Tunnel and then the A20 road as far as Sidcup. Then use the A232 to Keston Common, turn right into Baston Road (B265), following it for about 2 miles as it becomes Hayes Street and then Hayes Lane.

Record Attendance: 10,798 v Nigeria - 1950
Record Victory: 13-1 v Redhill - Athenian League 1945-46
Record Defeat: 1-11 v Barking - Athenian League 1933-34
Record Goalscorer: George Brown - 570 (1938-61)
Record Appearances: George Brown
Additional Records: Received £50,000 from Millwall for John Goodman

Senior Honours: Isthmian League 1908-10, 53-54, 60-61. Athenian League 1922-23, 48-49, 50-51.
Kent Senior Cup x5. Kent Amateur Cup x12. London Senior Cup x4

10 YEAR RECORD

00-01	01-02	02-03	03-04	04-05	05-06	06-07	07-08	08-09	09-10
Isth1 18	Isth1 19	Isth1S 6	Isth1S 8	Isth1 4	Isth P 11	Isth P 2	Conf S 11	Conf S 13	Conf S 12

BROMLEY

No.	Date	Comp	H/A	Opponents	Att:	Result	Goalscorers	Pos
1	8/8/09	BSS	A	Worcester City	645	W 2-1	I'Anson 20, McBean 90	4
2	11/8/09	BSS	H	Havant & Waterlooville	510	L 0-2		12
3	15/8/09	BSS	H	Hampton & Richmond B.	387	L 1-2	O'Sullivan 19	14
4	18/8/09	BSS	A	Eastleigh	607	L 1-6	G A Williams 23	17
5	22/8/09	BSS	H	Dorchester Town	297	W 3-1	McBean 2 (4, 32), Hall 90	14
6	29/8/09	BSS	A	Chelmsford City	1070	W 2-1	G A Williams 16, Hall pen 45	9
7	31/8/09	BSS	H	Lewes	603	W 3-0	Dalhouse 2 (28, 89), McBean 66	8
8	5/9/09	BSS	A	Weymouth	792	W 5-1	Dolby 2 (36, 53), G A Williams 40, McBean 2 (55, 60)	8
9	8/9/09	BSS	H	Braintree Town	455	D 1-1	Dunk 46	8
10	12/9/09	BSS	H	Weston-Super-Mare	424	D 1-1	McBean 52	8
11	19/9/09	BSS	A	Staines Town	366	D 2-2	G A Williams 15, Gillman 32	9
12	3/10/09	BSS	A	Maidenhead United	276	L 0-4		9
13	17/10/09	BSS	H	Woking	710	W 3-1	McBean 9, Hall 35, I'Anson 84	7
14	27/10/09	BSS	H	Basingstoke Town	481	W 2-0	Greene 61, I'Anson 63	8
15	31/10/09	BSS	A	Bath City	585	D 0-0		8
16	15/11/09	BSS	A	Newport County	2026	L 0-2		11
17	28/11/09	BSS	H	St Albans City	307	W 2-0	G A Williams 33, Corneille 76	8
18	5/12/09	BSS	H	Dover Athletic	703	D 2-2	Gillman 17, I'Anson 29	8
19	12/12/09	BSS	A	St Albans City	312	L 0-2		9
20	26/12/09	BSS	A	Welling United	841	W 2-0	Dolby 37, McBean 43	9
21	28/12/09	BSS	H	Eastleigh	637	W 3-0	McBean 63, Carew pen 79, Cassius 85	8
22	1/1/10	BSS	H	Welling United	1093	L 0-1		8
23	16/1/10	BSS	H	Maidenhead United	399	L 1-2	Ruggles 81	9
24	19/1/10	BSS	A	Basingstoke Town	293	W 3-2	Gillman 15, Butler 2 (37, 87)	7
25	23/1/10	BSS	A	Hampton & Richmond B.	470	W 2-0	Ruggles 54, McBean 64	6
26	25/1/10	BSS	A	Havant & Waterlooville	580	L 1-2	McBean 26	7
27	30/1/10	BSS	H	Newport County	817	L 2-3	Hall 62, McBean 65	8
28	6/2/10	BSS	A	Dorchester Town	461	D 0-0		10
29	13/2/10	BSS	H	Staines Town	426	L 0-2		10
30	20/2/10	BSS	A	Braintree Town	578	D 1-1	Og (Jones) 21	12
31	23/2/10	BSS	A	Bishop's Stortford	248	L 0-3		12
32	27/2/10	BSS	H	Weymouth	549	W 4-0	Carew pen 4, Gillman 22, Butler 64, McBean 71	9
33	2/3/10	BSS	A	Weston-Super-Mare	168	D 3-3	Carew pen 73, McBean 77, Hall 83	9
34	13/3/10	BSS	H	Worcester City	414	W 2-0	McBean 2 (41, 56)	11
35	20/3/10	BSS	A	Dover Athletic	1027	L 0-1		13
36	27/3/10	BSS	H	Bishop's Stortford	432	D 1-1	McBean 90	13
37	30/3/10	BSS	H	Thurrock	201	L 2-3	Ferguson 4, Butler 60	13
38	3/4/10	BSS	H	Chelmsford City	626	D 3-3	Hall 21, Gillman 27, Sobers 90	12
39	5/4/10	BSS	A	Lewes	426	L 0-1		12
40	10/4/10	BSS	A	Woking	1216	L 1-2	Ferguson 40	13
41	17/4/10	BSS	H	Bath City	508	L 1-2	Og (Holland) 30	13
42	24/4/10	BSS	A	Thurrock	313	W 6-3	Daly 15, Carew pen 25, Ferguson 52, Dunk 78, Butler 2 (87, 90)	12
	Cups							
1	26/9/09	FAC 2Q	H	Flackwell Heath	442	W 2-0	McBean 47, Corneille 50	
2	10/10/09	FAC 3Q	A	Tonbridge Angels	944	W 2-0	Hall 38, O'Sullivan 87	
3	24/10/09	FAC 4Q	H	Ebbsfleet United	1133	W 3-0	Erskine 6, McBean 2 (20, 49)	
4	7/11/09	FAC 1	H	Colchester United	4242	L 0-4		
5	21/11/09	FAT 3Q	H	Maidstone United	655	L 0-1		

Home Attendances:	
Highest:	1093 v Welling United
Lowest:	201 v Thurrock
Average (08-09):	481 (519)
Top Goalscorer:	McBean - 21 (18 League, 3 Cup) in 36 appearances - 58% strike rate
Most Appearances:	Carew - 42 (33+4 League, 4+1 Cup)

	G I WILLIAMS	FRAY	DUNK	CORNEILLE	HENRIQUES	GILLMAN	CAREW	I'ANSON	MCBEAN	HALL	DALHOUSE	CASSIUS	IBRAHIMA	O'SULLIVAN	DOLBY	NORVAL	SOBERS	G A WILLIAMS	GACHERU	KEMBER	GREENE	SHAW	LEE	STEPHEN	CHABAAN	CARTER	DAYTON	MANNING	ERSKINE	HARDING	AGU	READ	STONE	CALLISTE	DALY	RUGGLES	BUTLER	FERGUSON	FARRAR	FODERINGHAM	UDOJI	SMITH
1	X	X	X	X	X	X	X	X	X	X	X	S	S	S	U	U																										
2	X	X	X	X	X	X	X	X	X	X	X	S	S	S	U	U																										
3	X	X	X		X	X	X	X	X	X	X	S	S	X	S	U	U																									
4	X		X		X	X	X	X	X	X	X	S	S	X	U	S		X	U																							
5	X		X	X	X	X			X	X		S		S	X	X		X	U	X	S	U																				
6	X		X			X			X	X			S	X	X	X		X	U	X		S	X	U	U																	
7	X	X	X	X			S		X	X	X		X	X	X			X	U					S	S	U																
8	X		X	X		U		S	X	X	X		S	X	X	X		X		U			X			S																
9	X		X	X		U	S	S		X	X	X	U	X	X	X		X		U			X																			
10	X		X	X		X	X		X	X		S	U	X	S	X		X		S	U		X																			
11	X	S	X	X	U	X	X		X	X	X	S	S		U			X		X			X																			
12	X	X		X	U	X	U	X	X	X	X	S		S	S		X	X					X																			
13	X			X	X		X	X	X	X	U		U	X	X		X	U			U						U		X													
14	X	U		X	X	X	X	X	X		X	U	S	X				S		U	X								X													
15	X		X	X	X	X	X	X	X		U	S	U	X				S		U	X								X													
16	X	X	X	X	X	X	X	X			U	S		X	X			X		U	U											U										
17	X	X	X	X	X	X	X	X	X			S	S	S	U			X			X												U									
18	X	X		X	X	X	X	X	X	X		S	S		X		U	X			U												U									
19	X	X	X	X	X	X	X	X	X	X		S			S		U	X			U													S								
20	X	X	X		X	X	X	X	X			S	S		X		S													U			U		X	X						
21	X		X		X		X	X	X			S	X		X		X	U			X									S			S		U	X						
22	X		X	X	X		X	X	X			S	X		X		X				U									S			S		U	X						
23	X		X	S	X	X	X		X				X		U		X				U													S	X	S	X	X				
24	X		X	X	S	X	X		U				X		S		X				U													S	X	X	X	X				
25	X		X	X	X		X	U	S				X		U		X				U													S	X	X	X	X				
26	X		X	X	X	U	X	S	X				X		U		X				U													S	X	X		X				
27	X		X	X	U	X	X	S	X	X			X		U		X																	S	X	S		X				
28	X		X		U	X	X	S	X	X			X		S		X				X														X	S		X				
29	X				U	X	X	U	X	X			X		X		X				X														X	S	X	S				
30	X	X		X	U	X	S	X		X			X				X				X														U	S	X	X	S			
31	X	X		X	X	X	S	X	S	X			X								U														S	X	X	X	U			
32	X			X	U	X	X	S	X	X			X				X				S			U											X	S	X	X				
33	X	U		X	S	X	X	X	X	X							X				U														X	U	X	X	U			
34		X	X		X	X	X		X	X		U	S								U							U							X		X	X	S	X		
35		X	X		U	X	X		X			S	X		S		X				U														X		X	X		X	U	
36		X			S	X	X		X			S	X		X		X				U														X		X	X	U	X	U	
37		X	X		X	X	X			X		S									S			U											X		X	X	S	X	U	X
38		X			U	X				X		S	X		X		X				S														X		X	X	S	X	U	X
39		X				X	X			X		X			X		U				S			S											X			X	X	X	X	S
40		X	U		U	X	X			X			X				X				U														X		X	X	S	X	X	S
41			X		S	X	X					S			X		X				X														X		X	X	S	X	X	U
42			X		X	X	X					U			X		X				U			S											X		X	X		X	X	
Cup 1	X		X	X	X	X	X		X	X	S	S	U		X		U	X			U		X				S	U														
Cup 2	X			X	X	S	X	X	X	X	X	S	U	X	X		X	U			U						U															
Cup 3	X			X	X	X	X	X	X	X	U	U		S	X		X	S			U								X	S	U											
Cup 4	X		X	X	X	X	X	X	X		S	S	U	X	X			S		U	U							U	X													
Cup 5	X		X	X	X	X	X	X			X	X	S	X	X			S			U												S									
Total League Appearances																																										
X	33	19	29	25	22	34	33	18	30	27	10	2	17	11	17	5	20	13	0	3	8	0	6	0	0	0	0	0	3	0	0	0	0	0	19	7	16	19	1	9	4	2
S	0	1	0	1	4	0	4	6	2	0	0	21	12	5	7	1	1	2	0	1	5	1	0	3	1	1	0	0	0	2	0	0	2	6	1	6	0	1	6	0	0	2
U	0	2	1	0	10	3	1	2	1	0	3	3	4	0	9	3	4	2	4	5	17	1	0	3	1	1	1	1	0	1	0	1	3	0	3	1	0	0	3	0	4	1
Total Cup Appearances																																										
X	5	0	3	5	5	5	4	4	4	3	2	1	0	3	5	0	2	1	0	0	0	0	1	0	0	0	0	0	2	0	0	0	0	0	0	0	0	0	0	0	0	0
S	0	0	0	0	0	0	1	0	0	0	2	3	1	1	0	0	0	3	0	0	0	0	0	0	0	0	1	0	0	1	0	0	1	0	0	0	0	0	0	0	0	0
U	0	0	0	0	0	0	0	0	0	0	1	1	3	0	0	0	1	1	0	1	5	0	0	0	0	0	1	2	0	0	1	0	0	0	0	0	0	0	0	0	0	0
Total Cup Appearances																																										
Lge	0	0	2	1	0	5	4	4	18	6	1	1	0	1	2	0	1	5	0	0	1	0	0	0	0	0	0	0	0	0	0	0	0	0	1	2	6	3	0	0	0	0
Cup	0	0	0	1	0	0	0	0	3	1	0	0	0	1	0	0	0	0	0	0	0	0	0	0	0	0	0	0	1	0	0	0	0	0	0	0	0	0	0	0	0	0

Also Played: DAVIS U(28,29). BYGRAVE U(39,41). GAYLE S(42). BRITNELL S(42). LIBURD U(Cup5).

BROMLEY

CURRENT SQUAD AS OF BEGINING OF 2010-11 SEASON

GOALKEEPERS	HT	WT	D.O.B	AGE	P.O.B	CAREER	Apps	Gls
Paul Agu			31/10/88	21		Bromley	0	0
Craig Holloway			10/8/84	26	Blackheath	Arsenal Rel c/s 04, Farnborough 6/04, Southend (2ML) 1/05, Gravesend 8/05, Injured, Bromley 3/08, Braintree 5/08, Chelmsford 7/09, Braintree 12/09, Bromley 7/10		
DEFENDERS								
Harrison Dunk			25/10/90	19		Bromley	29	2
Arron Fray			1/5/87	23		Bromley Rel 8/09 Re-signed 8/09	20	0
Tutu Henriques			6/6/82	28	Zimbabwe	University of Luton, Carshalton c/s 02, Bromley 7/04	26	0
Donal O'Sullivan			14/11/81	28		Welling, Southall, Ashford T, Southall, Dartford 1/05, Southall, Bromley 2/06, Out Injured, Bromley 7/08 Rel 10/08, Bromley 8/09	16	1
Jerome Sobers	6'02"	13 05	18/4/86	24	London	Ford U, Ipswich 2/04 Rel c/s 05, Brentford (L) 3/05, Chelmsford 7/05, Bromley 10/06, Braintree 7/07 Rel 10/07, Bromley 10/07	21	1
Reiss Stephen			31/7/92	18		Bromley	3	0
MIDFIELDERS								
Ashley Carew	6'00"	11 00	17/12/85	24	Lambeth	Gillingham (Jun), Welling (L) 9/04, Maidstone (L) 10/04, Worthing (L) 11/04, Aveley (L) 8/05 Bromley 12/05 Rel 1/06, Sutton U 2/06, Beckenham 7/06, Fisher 1/07, Beckenham (Dual) 2/07, Barnet 5/07 Rel 3/09, Eastleigh (2ML) 1/09, Eastleigh 3/09, Bromley 6/0	37	4
Wes Daly			7/3/84	26		QPR, Gravesend (L) 10/03, Barnet (Trial) 12/03, Grays (L) 1/04, Raith (L) 8/04, Grays 2/05, AFC Wimbledon c/s 05, Maidenhead 7/07 Rel 5/08, Boreham Wood c/s 08, Carshalton c/s 09, Hendon 10/09, Bromley 12/09	20	1
Ryan Dolby			2/12/89	20		Bromley	24	2
Steve Ferguson	5'11"	11 00	1/4/82	28	Dunfermline	Musselburgh Windsor U18s, East Fife 7/00, Tottenham 9/00 Rel c/s 03, Motherwell (5ML) 8/02 Woking 8/03 Rel 2/07, AFC Wimbledon (L) 1/07 Perm Rel 5/08, Billericay 6/08, Tonbridge A 3/09, Bromley 1/10	20	3
Anthony Finn			27/11/82	27	Manchester	Hayes, Gravesend Rel 2/04, Edgware, Northwood 8/04, Colliers Wood, Met Police 3/06, AFC Wimbledon 6/07 Rel 5/09, Welling U 6/09, Chelmsford 3/10 Rel c/s 10, Bromley 7/10		
Nicky Greene			4/2/83	27		Yeading, Walton & H (L) 10/06, Sutton U 7/07 Rel 6/08, Thurrock 8/08 Rel 9/08, Fisher 10/08, Bromley 8/09	13	1
Salifou Ibrahima			14/10/80	29	Cameroon	SG Dornheim (Ger), TG Darmstadt (Ger), FC Arheilgen (Ger), SV Erzhausen (Ger) FV Bad Vilbel (Ger), SV Buchonia Flieden (Ger) 7/05, SG Rot-Weiß Frankfurt (Ger) 7/06, TSG Worsdorf (Ger) 7/07, SV Viktoria Aschaffenburg (Ger) 8/08 Rel 1/09, Bromley 8/09	29	0
FORWARDS								
Marcus Cassius			6/4/90	19		Erith T, Bromley 8/09, Cray W (2ML) 1/10, Erith & B (SL) 7/10	23	1
Kyle Farrar			17/4/92	18		Bromley	7	0
Warren McBean			13/2/86	24	London	Watford (Jun), Broxbourne B, Barnet 7/04, Waltham Forest (L) 3/05, Farnborough 8/05 Rel 8/06, Braintree 8/06 Rel 10,06, St Albans 10/06 Rel 10/06, Sutton U 10/06, Eastleigh (2ML) 2/08, Bromley 6/08, Chelmsford (SL) 3/10	32	18
Paul Vines						Cray W, Bromley, Dartford 1/04, Kingstonian, Fisher 1/06, Tooting & M c/s 06, Grays (Trial) c/s 09, Bromley 7/10		

Loanees	HT	WT	DOB	AGE	POB	From - To	APPS	GOA
(F)Jacob Erskine	6'01"	13 06	13/1/89	21	London	Gillingham 10/09 - Bishop's Stortford (L) 2/10, Croydon Ath (SL) 3/10	3	0
(D)Charlie Read	6'00"	11 00	26/9/90	19		Ebbsfleet 10/09 - Margate (L) 12/09	0	0
(M)Harry Harding			6/12/91	18		Reading (WE) 12/09 - Oxford C (L) 3/10	2	0
(G)Wes Foderingham			14/1/91	19	Hammersmith	Fulham (SL) 3/10 -	9	0
(G)Danny Bygrave			12/11/91	18		L.Orient 3/10 -	0	0
Departures	**HT**	**WT**	**DOB**	**AGE**	**POB**	**From - To**	**APPS**	**GOA**
(F)Ali Chaaban			16/3/82	28	Lebanon	ex Bromley 8/09 - Staines 9/09	1	0
(M)Curtis Shaw			24/6/87	23	Nottingham	Mansfield 8/09 - Rel 9/09, Kings Lynn 10/09, Alfreton 12/09	1	0
(M)Dwane Lee	6'03"	13 09	26/11/79	30	Hillingdon	AFC Wimbledon 8/09 - Rel 10/09, Boreham Wood 3/10	6	0
(M)Robert Carter			16/1/91	19		Maidstone 8/09 - Maidstone, Thamesmead 11/09, Maidstone 6/10	1	0
(M)Robert Kember			21/8/81	29	Wimbledon	Hampton & R 8/09 - Whyteleafe 11/09, Folkestone I 7/10	4	0
(F)Gareth A Williams	5'10"	11 13	10/9/82	27	Germiston	Braintree 6/09 - Croydon Ath 1/10	15	5
(F)Ramon Calliste			16/12/85	24		Braintree 12/09 - Cambridge C 2/10	6	0
(M)Tom Davis	5'10"	11 07	17/2/84	26	Bromley	Croydon Ath 2/10 - Dorking Wanderers 3/10, Sutton U 5/10	0	0
(G)Gareth I Williams			25/4/86	26		Croydon Ath 2/08 - Rel 3/10	33	0
(M)Luke I'Anson			2/8/88	22		Athletico De Coin (Sp) 11/07 - Kingstonian 3/10, Welling 3/10	24	4
(D)Mark Corneille	5'07"	10 05	31/5/86	24	London	Gillingham c/s 06 - Maidstone 3/10	26	1
(F)Adrian Stone			7/8/82	28		Welling 11/09 - Hastings U (Dual) 1/10, Merstham (L), Maidstone 3/10	2	0
(F)Phil Ruggles			26/10/82	27	Surrey	Basingstoke 12/09 - Cray W (L) 3/10, Met Police 3/10 Rel c/s 10	13	2
(D)Rob Gillman	6'02"	13 08	26/4/84	26	London	Bishop's Stortford 5/08 - Dover 7/10	34	5
(F)Richard Butler			1/5/85	25	Ashford	Staines 1/10 - Rel 7/10, Staines 7/10	16	6
(M)Ryan Hall	5'10"	10 04	4/1/88	22	Dulwich	C.Palace 9/08 - Southend 7/10	27	6
(G)Neale Manning			13/5/89	21		Ashford T c/s 08 -	0	0
(D)Liam Norval			7/10/87	22	Cardiff	ex Thurrock 8/08 -	6	0
(M)Jake Britnell						Yth -	1	0
(M)Aaron Dalhouse			22/9/89	20		C.Palace 2/09 -	10	1
(M)James Dayton	5'08"	10 01	12/12/88	21	Enfield	Bishop's Stortford 9/09 -	0	0
(M)Rowan Liburd			28/2/92	18		Yth -	0	0
(M)Orlando Smith (Mucu)					Jamiaca	Farnborough 3/10 -	4	0
(M)Emmanuel Udoji	6'00"	13 05	9/1/89	21		Stafford R 3/10 -	4	0
(F)Austin Gacheru			1/10/87	22		Croydon Ath c/s 09 -	0	0
(F)Arron Gayle			5/10/91	18		Waltham Abbey 2/10 -	1	0

CHELMSFORD CITY

Chairman: Mansell Wallace
Secretary: Alan Brown **(T)** 07887 642 929
(E) algbrown@blueyonder.co.uk
Additional Committee Members: Paul Hopkins, Trevor Smith, Trevor Wright, Martyn Gard, Martin Bissett, Aaron Desmond, Chris Evans
Manager: Glenn Pennyfather
Programme Editor: Mandy Smith **(E)** mandysmith41@hotmail.com

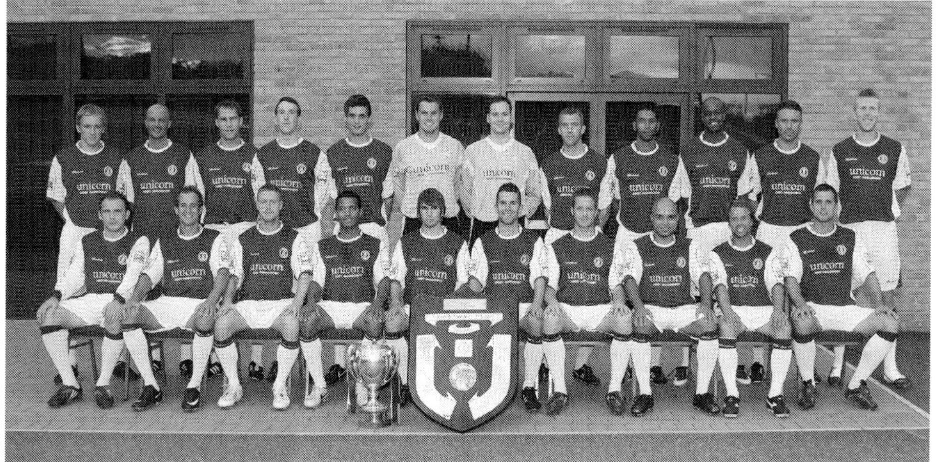

Archive photo

Club Factfile

Founded: 1938 **Nickname:** City or Clarets
Previous Names:
Previous Leagues: Southern League 1938-2004. Isthmian 2004-08

Club Colours (change): Claret/white/white (White/claret/claret)

Ground: Melbourne Park Stadium, Salerno Way, Chelmsford CM1 2EH **(T)** 01245 290 959
Capacity: 3,000 **Seats:** 1,300 **Covered:** 1,300 **Clubhouse:** Yes **Shop:** Yes
Previous Grounds: New Writtle Street 1938-97, Maldon Town 1997-98, Billericay Town 1998-2005
Simple Directions
Leave A12 at J15 and head towards Chelmsford. At the roundabout turn left into Westway. Turn left onto the A1060 signposted Sawbridgeworth. At the second set of traffic lights turn right into Chignal Road. Turn right into Melbourne Avenue. Salerno Way is on your left. At the end of the football pitches and immediately before the block of flats, turn left at the mini roundabout in Salerno Way to enter the Stadium car park.

Record Attendance: 16,807 v Colchester United - Southern League 10/09/1949. Salerno Way: 2,998 v Billericay Town - Isthmian Jan. 2006
Record Victory: 10-1 v Bashley (H) - Southern League 26/04/2000
Record Defeat: 1-10 v Barking (A) - FA Trophy 11/11/1978
Record Goalscorer: Tony Butcher - 287 (1957-71)
Record Appearances: Derek Tiffin - 550 (1950-63)
Additional Records: Paid £10,000 to Dover Athletic for Tony Rogers 1992
Received £50,000 from Peterborough United for David Morrison

Senior Honours: Southern League 1945-46, 67-68, 71-72, Southern Division 1988-89, League Cup 1945-46, 59-60, 90-91.
Essex Professional Cup 1957-58, 69-70, 70-71, 73-74, 74-75. Non-League Champions Cup 1971-72.
Essex Senior Cup 1985-86, 88-89, 92-93, 2002-03. Isthmian League Premier Division 2007-08.

10 YEAR RECORD

00-01		01-02		02-03		03-04		04-05		05-06		06-07		07-08		08-09		09-10	
SthE	2	SthP	18	SthP	9	SthP	18	Isth P	8	Isth P	10	Isth P	3	Isth P	1	Conf S	5	Conf S	3

CHELMSFORD CITY

No.	Date	Comp	H/A	Opponents	Att:	Result	Goalscorers	Pos
1	8/8/09	BSS	H	Bath City	1216	W 4-3	Hockton 10. Hallett 2 (14, 19), Cook 24	2
2	11/8/09	BSS	A	Woking	1508	W 2-1	Hand pen 30, Hallett 58	3
3	15/8/09	BSS	A	Basingstoke Town	522	L 1-2	Hockton 14	7
4	17/8/09	BSS	H	Dover Athletic	1578	D 1-1	Rainford pen 52	7
5	22/8/09	BSS	A	Newport County	1042	L 0-4		12
6	29/8/09	BSS	H	Bromley	1070	L 1-2	Edmans 1	14
7	31/8/09	BSS	A	Braintree Town	1260	L 1-2	Cook 17	15
8	5/9/09	BSS	H	St Albans City	1122	W 2-0	Murray 22, Edmans 86	12
9	7/9/09	BSS	H	Lewes	1137	W 2-1	Cook 14, Hockton 22	9
10	12/9/09	BSS	A	Staines Town	430	W 1-0	Cook 90	9
11	19/9/09	BSS	A	Eastleigh	552	L 1-3	Hockton 2	10
12	3/10/09	BSS	H	Woking	1282	L 0-2		11
13	17/10/09	BSS	H	Welling United	1048	W 3-1	Rainford pen 36, Edmans 57, Murray 90	11
14	27/10/09	BSS	A	Bishop's Stortford	809	W 1-0	Murray 67	9
15	31/10/09	BSS	H	Havant & Waterlooville	1053	D 1-1	Holmes pen 80	9
16	7/11/09	BSS	H	Maidenhead United	1015	D 1-1	Holmes 4	9
17	9/11/09	BSS	A	Worcester City	516	W 2-1	Modeste 35, Holmes 75	7
18	14/11/09	BSS	A	Bath City	543	L 0-1		8
19	28/11/09	BSS	H	Weston-Super-Mare	1072	D 2-2	Holmes 35, Edman 90	9
20	1/12/09	BSS	A	Welling United	500	W 1-0	Holmes 21	5
21	5/12/09	BSS	A	St Albans City	467	W 1-0	Holmes 65	4
22	26/12/09	BSS	H	Thurrock	1077	W 1-0	B Martin 90	3
23	28/12/09	BSS	A	Dover Athletic	1261	W 1-0	Edmans 48	2
24	2/1/10	BSS	A	Thurrock	820	D 1-1	Modeste 85	4
25	16/1/10	BSS	A	Weymouth	519	W 4-1	Holmes 3 (39, 69, 86), Edmans 90	3
26	23/1/10	BSS	H	Basingstoke Town	1109	L 1-2	Smith 85	4
27	25/1/10	BSS	H	Staines Town	844	L 0-1		4
28	6/2/10	BSS	H	Eastleigh	994	D 2-2	Rainford 31, Cook 83	5
29	8/2/10	BSS	H	Dorchester Town	554	W 1-0	J Martin 59	2
30	13/2/10	BSS	H	Newport County	931	D 0-0		2
31	20/2/10	BSS	A	Lewes	579	W 2-0	Edmans 45, Rainford 66	2
32	27/2/10	BSS	A	Maidenhead United	361	W 2-0	Holmes 22, Patterson 85	2
33	6/3/10	BSS	H	Bishop's Stortford	982	W 3-0	Lock 13, Holmes 39, Edmans 71	2
34	13/3/10	BSS	A	Weston-Super-Mare	225	W 2-1	Lock 60, Cook 89	2
35	20/3/10	BSS	H	Weymouth	877	W 2-1	Holmes 47, Cook 51	2
36	27/3/10	BSS	H	Hampton & Richmond B.	1020	W 1-0	Rainford pen 90	2
37	3/4/10	BSS	A	Bromley	626	D 3-3	Rainford 26, McBean 32, Holmes 52	3
38	5/4/10	BSS	H	Braintree Town	1685	D 1-1	Rainford 59	3
39	10/4/10	BSS	A	Dorchester Town	525	W 3-0	McBean 31, Berquez 2 (45, 90)	3
40	13/4/10	BSS	A	Hampton & Richmond B.	510	L 1-2	Holmes 72	3
41	17/4/10	BSS	H	Worcester City	963	W 1-0	McBean 48	2
42	24/4/10	BSS	A	Havant & Waterlooville	1333	L 2-5	McBean 20, Og (Pearce 35)	3
	Cups							
1	26/9/09	FAC 2Q	A	Enfield 1893	406	W 5-0	Cook 2 (54, 89), Modeste 72, Rainford 77, Edmans 85	
2	10/10/09	FAC 3Q	A	Dartford	1830	W 4-1	Murray 2 (18, 90), Holmes 38, Rainford 62	
3	24/10/09	FAC 4Q	H	Stevenage Borough	1762	L 1-2	Edmans 26	
4	21/11/09	FAT 3Q	H	AFC Hornchurch	635	D 4-4	Murray 10, Modeste 26, Lock 38, Holmes 67	
5	24/11/09	FAT 3QR	A	AFC Hornchurch	370	W 2-1	Glover 2 (47, 55)	
6	12/12/09	FAT 1	H	Truro City	701	D 2-2	Holmes 4, Modeste 72	
7	15/12/09	FAT 1R	A	Truro City	322	W 1-0	Rainford 4	
8	18/1/10	FAT 2	H	Crawley Town	715	W 2-1	Cook 42, Rainford pen 59	
9	30/1/10	FAT 3	H	Oxford United	1347	L 1-3	Rainford pen 78	
10	27/4/10	PO SF1	A	Bath City	1425	L 0-2		
11	1/5/10	PO SF2	H	Bath City	1650	L 0-1	(L0-3 agg)	

Home Attendances:	
Highest:	1685 v Braintree Town
Lowest:	554 v Dorchester Town
Average (08-09):	1053 (1474)
Top Goalscorer:	Holmes - 15 (12 League, 3 Cup) in 52 appearances - 29% strike rate
Most Appearances:	Holmes - 52 (41 League, 11 Cup)

HOLLOWAY	LOCK	BUNCE	GLOVER	B MARTIN	HAND	J MARTIN	COOK	HALLETT	HOCKTON	HOLMES	CAROLAN	EDMANS	BRAYLEY	HAINES	OKAY	MODESTE	HARRISON	RAINFORD	WARD	MURRAY	BROWN	R BATCHFORD	HASWELL	SCARLETT	CLARK	BERQUEZ	L BATCHFORD	PATTERSON	ELAD	COOPER	SMITH	HARWOOD	THOMAS	PAVETT	FINN	NUNN	MCBEAN	SINFIELD	EYRE	
X	X	X	X	X	X	X	X	X	X	X	S	S	S	U	U																									1
X	X	X	X		X	X	X	X	X	X	U	S		X	S	S	U																							2
X	X	X	X		X	X		X	X	X		S		X	X	S	U	U	U																					3
X	X				X	X		X		X	U	S		X	X	S	U	X	X	X	U																			4
X	X				X	X	X	S	X	X	S	S			X	U	U	X	X	X																				5
X	X	X			U	X	X			X		X		X		S	U	X	X	X	U																			6
X	X	X			X	X	X			X		X		X		S	U	X	X	S	S	U																		7
X	X	X		X	U	X	X		X	X		S		U		S	U	X	X	X																				8
X	X	X		X	S	X	X		X	X		S		S		U	U	X	X	X																				9
X	X	X			U	X	X		X	X		S		X		S	U	X	X	X	U																			10
X	X			X		X	X		X	X		S		S		S	U	X	X	X	U		X																	11
X	X			X		X	X		X	X		S		X		X	U	X		U			X	S	U															12
X	S		U			X	X			X		X		X		S	S	X	X	X		U	X		X															13
	U		X			X	X		S	X		X		X		S	X		X	X			X		X	U	U													14
U	U		X			X	X		X	X		X		X		S	X		X			U	X		X	S														15
X	X			U		X	X		X	X				X		X	U		X			U	X		X	S														16
X	X			U		X			X	X				X		X	U	X	X			U	X	U	X	S														17
X	X			U		X	S		X	X				X		X	U	X	X	S			X		X	S														18
X	X		X			U	S			X		S		X		X		X	S	X			X		X	X	U													19
	X			U		U	X			X		X		X			X	X	X			U	X	U	X	X	U													20
U	X			U		U	X			X		X		X		U	X	X	X				X		X	X		U												21
	X			X		X				X		S		X		X	X	X	X	X	U					U		X	U	U										22
	X			X		X	X			X		X		X		U	X	X	X	S						U		X	U	U										23
	X			X		X	X			X		X		X		S	X	X	X						U	S		X	U	U										24
				X		X	X			X		S		X		S	X	X	X				X		S	U		X	U		X									25
	X			X		X	X			X				U			X	X	X				S		X	S		X		U	X	U								26
	X			X		X	X			X				X			X				U	U	S		X	X		X		S	X	U								27
	X			X		X	S			X		S					X	X	X				X		X	U		X				U	X	S						28
	X			X		X	X			X		S				S	X	X					X		X	U				X		U	X	U						29
	X			X		X	X			X		S				S	X	X	X				U		X	U		X				U	X							30
	X			X			X			X		X				S	X	X	X		S	U			X	X	U	X						S						31
	X					S	X			X		X		U		X	X	X	X		U	U			X	X	U	X												32
	X			X		S	X			X		X		S		X	X	X	X		U				X	X	U							S						33
	X			X		U	X			X		X		U			X	X	X		U	U			X	X	U	X												34
	X			X		U	X			X		X		U			X	X	X			U			X	X	U	X							S					35
	X			X		S	X			X		X		X			X	X			U				X	X	U	X							S	U				36
	X			U			X			X						S	X	X	X		U				X	X	U	X							S	X	X			37
	X			X			X			X				U		S	X	X			U				X	X	U	X							X	U	X			38
			X	X			U			X		S				X	X	X			U					X	U	X							X	X	X	U		39
	S		X	X			X			X		S				U	X	X			U					X	U	X							X	X	X			40
	S		X			U	X			X		S					X	X							X	X	U	X							X	X	X			41
	X		X			X	X			U		X				S	X				U					X	U	X							X	X	X	S		42
X	X			X		X	X		X	X		S		U		S	U	X	X	X	U		X	S																1
X	U		U			X	X		X	X		S		X		S	U	X	X	X		U	X	U	X															2
	S		X			X	X		U	X		X		X		S	X		X	X		U	X	U	X	S	U													3
X	X		X	S		X				X		U		U		X	U	X	X	X			X		X	S														4
X	X		X	U		U				X		S		X		X	U	X		X		U	X		X	X														5
	X			U		X	X			X		X		X		S	X		X	U	U		X		X	X			U											6
	X			X		X	X			X						S	X	X	X	S	U	U	X		X	X	U													7
	X			X		X	X			X		X				S	X	X	X	S			X		X	U			U	S										8
	X			X		X	X			X		X		U		S	X	X	X			U	X		X					U		U								9
	X		U	X		U	X			X		U				X	X	X	X							X		X							U		X		U	10
	X		U	X		S	X			X		S					X	X	X							X		X					S			X	X		U	11
Total League Appearances																																								
17	35	8	10	22	6	28	34	4	13	41	0	16	0	22	3	9	25	34	29	11	0	0	14	0	23	16	0	19	0	1	3	0	3	0	5	5	6	0	0	X
0	3	0	0	0	1	3	3	1	1	0	2	19	1	3	1	19	1	0	1	3	2	0	2	1	1	6	0	0	0	1	0	0	0	3	3	0	0	1	0	S
2	2	0	1	6	3	6	1	0	0	1	2	0	0	7	1	5	14	1	1	1	15	11	1	2	2	7	15	1	4	4	0	5	0	1	0	2	0	1	0	U
Total Cup Appearances																																								
4	9	0	3	6	0	8	9	0	2	11	0	4	0	4	0	3	7	9	10	5	0	0	9	0	8	5	0	2	0	0	0	0	0	0	0	1	2	0	0	X
0	1	0	0	1	0	1	0	0	0	0	0	4	0	0	0	7	0	0	0	2	0	0	0	1	0	2	0	0	0	1	0	0	1	0	0	0	0	0	0	S
0	1	0	3	2	0	2	0	0	1	0	0	2	0	3	0	0	4	0	0	1	3	5	0	2	0	1	2	0	2	1	0	1	0	0	1	0	0	0	2	U
Total Goals																																								
0	2	0	0	1	1	1	7	3	4	12	0	7	0	0	0	2	0	7	0	3	0	0	0	0	0	0	0	1	0	0	1	0	0	0	0	0	4	0	0	Lge
0	1	0	2	0	0	0	3	0	0	3	0	2	0	0	0	3	0	5	0	3	0	0	0	0	0	0	0	0	0	0	0	0	0	0	0	0	0	0	0	Cup

CHELMSFORD CITY

CURRENT SQUAD AS OF BEGINING OF 2010-11 SEASON

GOALKEEPERS	HT	WT	D.O.B	AGE	P.O.B	CAREER	Apps	Gls
Lewis Batchford			30/9/91	18		Chelmsford	0	0
Nick Eyre	5'10"	10 10	7/9/85	24	Braintree	Tottenham Rel c/s 05, Grays (L) 10/04, Grays 7/05 Rel 7/06, Rushden & D 8/06 Rel 12/06, Histon (Trial), Dag & Red 2/07, St Albans 7/07, Grays (L) 3/08, Bishop's Stortford 7/08 Rel 3/10, Chelmsford 3/10	0	0
James Pullen	6'02"	14 00	18/3/82	28	Chelmsford	Heybridge Swifts, Ipswich 10/99 Rel c/s 03 Re-signed, Blackpool (SL) 8/01, Dag & Red (3ML) 8/03, Peterborough (L) 10/03 Perm 11/03, Heybridge S (2ML) 2/04, Hornchurch (L) 9/04, Welling (L) 10/04, Gravesend 11/04, Fisher 8/05, Dulwich (L) 8/06, Eastleigh 1		
DEFENDERS								
Ryan Batchford			5/11/92	17		Chelmsford	0	0
Josh Brown			29/2/92	18		Chelmsford	2	0
Anthony Cook	5'07"	11 02	10/8/89	21	London	Cardiff (Yth), Croydon Ath, Dag & Red 8/07, Carshalton (L) 10/08, Concord R (L) 12/08 Perm, Braintree (Dual) 3/09, Chelmsford 7/09	37	7
Sami El-Abd			1/1/88	22	Brighton	Crawley, Burgess Hill (2ML) 9/05, Team Bath 8/06, Hayes & Yeading 7/09 Rel 5/10, Lewes (L) 3/10, Chelmsford 7/10		
Mark Haines	6'03"		28/9/89	20		Northampton, Cheshunt (WE) 2/08, Grays (WE) 3/08, Grays 5/08, East Thurrock (L) 9/08, Chelmsford 7/09	25	0
Matt Lock	5'11"	11 04	10/3/84	26	Barnstaple	Exeter Rel c/s 03, Team Bath 8/03, Tiverton 7/04, Mangotsfield (SL) 12/04 Perm 6/05 Rel 9/06, Team Bath 10/06, Newport C (Trial) 6/09, Chelmsford 7/09	38	2
Ben Nunn			25/10/89	20		Boston U, Rushden & D Rel 7/08, Cambridge C 8/08 Rel 6/09, Bishop's Stortford c/s 09, Chelmsford 3/10	5	0
Stephen Reed	5'08"	12 01	18/6/85	25	Barnstaple	Plymouth (Yth), Yeovil Rel 5/06, Forest Green (L) 10/04, Woking (L) 8/05, Aldershot (L) 9/05, Torquay (2ML) 3/06, Torquay 5/06, Tiverton 2/07, Weston-Super-Mare 3/07, Cambridge U 5/07, Weymouth 7/08, Macclesfield 5/09 Rel c/s 10, Grays (L) 11/09, Weymouth (SL) 12/09, Chelmsford 7/10		
Adam Tann	6'00"	12 08	12/5/82	28	Fakenham	Norwich (Yth), Cambridge U Rel c/s 05, Cambridge C (SL) 3/01, Reading (Trial) 7/05, Ipswich (Trial) 8/05, Rushden & D (Trial), Gravesend 10/05, Notts County 11/05, L.Orient 1/06 Rel c/s 07, Notts County 8/07 Rel c/s 09, Histon 7/09, Chelmsford 7/10		
MIDFIELDERS								
Steve Clark	6'01"	12 05	10/2/82	28	London	West Ham, Southend (2ML) 11/01, Southend 1/02 Rel c/s 04, Macclesfield (L) 9/03, Hornchurch c/s 04, Weymouth 12/04, Dag & Red 12/04 (04/05 12,1), Weymouth 3/05, Fisher 5/06 Rel 5/07, Bromley 8/07, Bromley 2/08, Bromley c/s 08 Rel 10/08, Eastleigh 10/08, Chelmsford 10/09	24	0
John Martin	5'05"	10 00	15/7/81	29	Bethnal Green	L.Orient Rel c/s 03, Woking (Trial) 7/03, Farnborough 8/03, Hornchurch 9/03, Grays 11/04, Stevenage 5/07 Rel 5/09, Ebbsfleet (2ML) 2/09, Chelmsford 8/09	31	1
Ricky Modeste			20/2/88	22		Chelmsford	28	2
Marlon Patterson	5'09"	11 10	24/6/83	27	London	Millwall (Trainee), Chelsea (Trainee), Crawley 8/02, Fisher 1/03, Billericay, Fisher 12/03, Carshalton 3/04, Dulwich Hamlet 12/04, Crashalton 7/05, Hayes & Yeading 7/06, Dag & Red NC 8/07, Welling (3ML) 9/07, Grays (SL) 2/08, Bishop's Stortford (L) 11/08, Histon 1/09, Bishop's Stortford (SL) 2/09, Staines (Trial) 8/09, Bishop's Stortford 8/09, Chelmsford 12/09 Rel c/s 10	19	1
Dave Rainford	6'00"	11 11	21/4/79	31	Stepney	Colchester Rel c/s 99, Scarborough (L) 12/98, Slough 6/99, Grays c/s 01, Heybridge S 7/02, Slough 11/02, Ford U 1/03, Bishop's Stortford 3/03, Dag & Red 5/06, Chelmsford 6/08	34	7
FORWARDS								
Rob Edmans			25/1/87	23		Witham T, Chelmsford (L) 8/09 Perm 8/09	35	7
Sam Higgins						Millwall (Yth), Southend (Yth), Bishop's Stortford (WE) 3/08, AFC Hornchurch (WE) 9/08, Fisher (WE) 10/08, Bishop's Stortford 12/08, Brentwood (L) 2/09 Perm, AFC Hornchurch 8/09, East Thurrock 10/09, Chelmsford 6/10		
Tyrone Scarlett			24/11/91	18		Chelmsford	1	0
Simon Thomas	5'06"	12 02	21/7/84	26	Stratford	Redbridge, Boreham Wood 12/06, C.Palace Nominal 7/08 Rel 1/10, Grays (L) 10/08, Rotherham (L) 2/09, Ebbsfleet (L) 8/09, Darlington (2ML) 10/09, Billericay 1/10, Southend (Trial) 2/10, Colchester (Trial) 2/10, Chelmsford 2/10	3	0

Loanees	HT	WT	DOB	AGE	POB	From - To	APPS	GOA
(F)Jordan Pavett			16/12/91	18		Colchester 2/10 - Bishop's Stortford (L) 3/10	3	0
(F)Warren McBean			13/2/86	24	London	Bromley (SL) 3/10 -	6	4
Departures	**HT**	**WT**	**DOB**	**AGE**	**POB**	**From - To**	**APPS**	**GOA**
(F)Bert Brayley	5'09"	12 07	5/9/81	28	Basildon	Eastleigh 3/09 - Rel 8/09, Bishop's Stortford 8/09 Rel 3/10, Braintree 3/10 Rel c/s 10, Concord R 7/10	1	0
(F)Jason Hallett			1/8/86	24	Essex	Canvey Island 7/06 - Rel 8/09, Canvey Island 9/09	5	3
(D)Erkan Okay	5'08"		29/1/85	25	Cambridge	Nuneaton T 1/09 - Rel 9/09, Histon (NC) 9/09	4	0
(M)Ryan Carolan			19/9/89	20	Romford	C.Palace 8/09 - Rel 9/09	2	0
(D)Danny Bunce			30/4/86	24		Woking 7/09 - Rel 9/09, Grays 10/09	8	0
(M)Jamie Hand	6'00"	11 08	7/2/84	26	Uxbridge	Ebbsfleet 2/09 - Rel 9/09, Woking 9/09 Rel 5/10	7	1
(F)Danny Hockton	5'11"	11 11	7/2/79	31	Barking	Braintree 6/09 - Rel 11/09, Maidstone U 11/09	14	4
(G)Craig Holloway			10/8/84	26	Blackheath	Braintree 7/09 - Braintree 12/09, Bromley 7/10	17	0
(M)Antonio Murray	5'08"	11 00	15/9/84	25	Cambridge	Histon 8/09 - Rel 1/10, Cambridge U 2/10 Rel 4/10	14	3
(D)Michael Haswell			23/8/83	27	London	Welling 9/09 - Rel 2/10, Harlow, Billericay 3/10	16	0
(F)Lewis Smith			27/10/89	20		Bishop's Stortford 1/10 - Rel 2/10, Thurrock 2/10	3	1
(D)Grant Cooper	6'02"		16/9/77	32	London	Maidenhead 1/09 - Rel 12/09, Chelmsford 12/09 Rel 2/10, Margate 3/10	2	0
(G)Paul Horwood			24/8/83	27		1/10 - Rel 2/10	0	0
(F)Junior Fatai-Somuyiwa			26/6/89	21		9/09 - Rel 2/10		
(M)Ollie Berquez			24/2/80	30	Essex	Maldon Undisc 11/07 - Rel 5/10, Dartford 6/10	22	0
(F)Ricky Holmes			19/6/87	23		Southend Manor 11/05 - Rel 5/10, Barnet 6/10	41	12
(F)Simon Glover			3/5/82	28		Tonbridge A 7/09 - Maidstone 6/10	10	0
(G)Ashley Harrison			8/6/78	32	Southend	Great Wakering 10/06 - Retired 7/10	26	0
(G)Chris Elad			26/9/80	29		Witham T 12/09 -	0	0
(M)Anthony Finn			27/11/82	27	Manchester	Welling U 3/10 - Rel c/s 10, Bromley 7/10	8	0
(M)Taylor Sinfield						Concord R 3/10 - Rel c/s 10, Concord R c/s 10	1	0
(D)Steve Ward			17/4/71	39		Canvey Island 7/06 - Canvey Island 7/10	30	0
(D)Ben Martin	6'07"	13 08	25/11/82	27	Harpenden	St Albans 7/09 - Rel 7/10	22	1

DARTFORD

Chairman: David Skinner & Bill Archer

Secretary: Peter Martin **(T)** 07976 054 202
(E) peter@martinpe.freeserve.co.uk

Additional Committee Members: Steve Irving, David Boswell, Tony Burman, Norman Grimes, Av Sandhu, Harry Extance, Dave Francis, Jason Outram, Mark Brenland, Jeremy Kite, Nicola Collett

Manager: Tony Burman

Programme Editor: Tony Jaglo **(E)** tonyjaglo@tiscali.co.uk

Back row (L-R): Danny Barber, John Beales, Adam Flanagan, Rob Haworth, James White, Allan Tait. **Middle Row:** Leanne Taylor (Asst Physio); Dave Phillips (Physio), Kiran Dingri, Jamie Day,Lee Burns, Jay May, Den Ibrahim, Andrew Young, Tony Kessell, Elliot Bradbrook, Jamie Coyle, Karl Dent, John Macrae (Goalkeeper Coach). **Front Row:** Adam Burchell, Hussein Isa, Ryan Hayes, Paul Hennessy (ReserveTeanm Manager), Tony Burman (First Team Manager), Paul Sawyer (Asst Manager/Coach), Billy Burgess, Lee Noble, Adam Gross.

Club Factfile

Founded: 1888 **Nickname:** The Darts

Previous Names:

Previous Leagues: Kent League 1894-96, 97-98, 99-1902, 09-14, 21-26, 93-96, Southern 1996-2006

Club Colours (change): White/black/black (Royal blue & red/red/royal blue)

Ground: Princes Park Stadium, Grassbanks, Darenth Road, Dartford DA1 1RT **(T)** 01322 299 990

Capacity: 4,097 **Seats:** 640 **Covered:** Yes **Clubhouse:** Yes **Shop:** Yes

Previous Grounds: The Brent/Westgate House, Potters Meadow, Engleys Meadow, Summers Meadow, Watling Street

Simple Directions

From M25 clockwise leave at Junction 1 B to roundabout controlled by traffic lights. Take third exit onto Princes Road, (A225) then second exit at next roundabout. Continue down hill to traffic lights (ground on your left), turn left into Darenth Road then second turning on your left into Grassbanks leading to car park. From M25 anti-clockwise leave at Junction 2 onto slip road A225 to roundabout, then first exit, second exit at next roundabout then down hill to traffic lights turn left into Darenth Road, then second turning on your left into Grassbanks leading to car park.

Record Attendance: 4,097 v Horsham YMCA - Isthmian Division 1 South 11/11/2006 and v Crystal Palace - Friendly 20/07/2007

Record Victory: Not known

Record Defeat: Not known

Record Goalscorer: Not known

Record Appearances: Steve Robinson - 692

Additional Records: Paid £6,000 to Chelmsford City for John Bartley
Received £25,000 from Redbridge Forest for Andy Hessenthaler

Senior Honours: Southern League Division 2 1896-97, Eastern Section 1930-31, 31-32, Southern Championship 30-31, 31-32, 73-74, 83-84, Southern Division 1980-81, League Cup 1976-77, 87-88, 88-89, Championship Shield 1983-84, 87-88, 88-89.
Isthmian League Division 1 North 2007-08, Premier Division 2009-10. Kent Senior Cup 1929-30, 34-35, 38-39, 69-70.

10 YEAR RECORD

00-01		01-02		02-03		03-04		04-05		05-06		06-07		07-08		08-09		09-10	
SthE	16	SthE	8	SthE	17	SthE	16	SthE	16	SthE	7	Isth1S	7	Isth1N	1	Isth P	8	Isth P	1

DARTFORD

No.	Date	Comp	H/A	Opponents	Att:	Result	Goalscorers	Pos
1	Aug 15	Ryman P.	H	Horsham	968	W 3 - 2	Bradbrook 55 66 Flanagan 63 (pen)	5
2	18		A	Margate	653	W 4 - 0	Day 7 Burns 65 Haworth 63 Tait 74	
3	22		A	Hastings United	717	W 3 - 1	Burns 13 53 Haworth 44	1
4	24		H	Kingstonian	1038	W 5 - 0	Bradbrook 14 BURNS 3 (33 44 84) Hayes 54	1
5	29		H	Wealdstone	1150	D 1 - 1	Burns 64	1
6	31		A	AFC Hornchurch	531	W 2 - 0	Bradbrook 64 Burns 90	
7	Sept 5		H	Hendon	1100	W 5 - 0	Haworth 42 Burns 49 May 78 88 Noble 90	1
8	**12**	**F.A.C. 1Q**	**A**	**Chipstead**	**321**	**W 6 - 1**	**Hayes 1 Burns 7 Burgess 40 White 54 Haworth 89 Gross 90**	
9	19		A	Carshalton Atletic	569	W 4 - 0	Burns 22 Day 38 Haworth 56 Coyle 85	1
10	22		A	Sutton United	648	W 3 - 0	Haworth 56 69 Hawes (o.g.) 60	
11	**26**	**F.A.C. 2Q**	**A**	**Worthing**	**611**	**W 2 - 1**	**Brookfield 40 May 68**	
12	Oct 3		H	Harrow Borough	1326	W 2 - 0	Burns 34 63	1
13	**10**	**F.A.C. 3Q**	**H**	**Chelmsford City**	**1830**	**L 1 - 4**	**Flanagan 83**	
14	13		H	Tonbridge Angels	1228	W 2 - 0	Tait 54 Harris 85	
15	**17**	**F.A.T 1Q**	**A**	**Sittingbourne**	**473**	**W 1 - 0**	**Tait 73**	
16	24		A	Aveley	541	W 4 - 1	Burgess 17 Coyle 47 Harris 67 Hayes 90	1
17	28		A	Ashford Town		W 4 - 1	Noble 37 Hayes 55 Harris 64 May 73	1
18	**31**	**F.A.T 2Q**	**H**	**Chipstead**	**1002**	**W 3 - 0**	**Day 52 Harris 75 Hayes 84**	
19	Nov 7		H	Bognor Regis Town	1295	D 3 - 3	Harris 59 65 Burgess 90	1
20	**21**	**F.A.T 3Q**	**A**	**Dover Athletic**	**1084**	**L 2 - 3**	**May 27 Harris 36**	
21	24		H	Tooting & Mitcham U	871	W 3 - 2	Hayes 35 47 Haworth 83	
22	28		H	AFC Hornchurch	1224	L 0 - 1		1
23	Dec 12		H	Waltham Abbey	959	W 2 - 1	Dafter 18 Haworth 50	
24	26		H	Cray Wanderers	1306	D 1 - 1	Harris 37	1
25	29		A	Canvey Island	442	W 5 - 2	Burns 25 81 Coyle 64 Haworth 73 Harris 77	1
26	Jan 2		A	Cray Wanderers	688	W 2 - 1	Burns 32 White 37	1
27	23		H	Carshalton Athletic	1217	D 1 - 1	Coyle 58	1
28	Feb 2		A	Billericay Town	514	L 0 - 1		1
29	6		H	Sutton United	1180	L 0 - 1		1
30	13		A	Tonbridge Angels	842	W 4 - 1	Johnson 51 Harris 72 Bradbrook 82 Haworth 86	1
31	20		H	Ashford Town	1101	W 3 - 1	Ilesomi 12 (og) Harris 23 Burns 47	1
32	27		A	Boreham Wood	385	W 1 - 0	Bradbrook 18	1
33	Mar 6		H	Billericay Town	1155	L 1 - 4	Burns 21	1
34	9		A	Maidston United	371	W 1 - 0	Burns 10	
35	13		H	Tooting & Mitcham U	515	L 1 - 3	Tait 90	1
36	16		H	Boreham Wood	726	L 1 - 2	Burns 59	
37	18		A	Horsham	332	W 3 - 1	Bradbrook 5 69 Tait 57	
38	20		H	Maidstone UNited	1501	W 3 - 0	Dafter 11 Burns 34 Hayes 82	
39	23		H	Margate	907	L 0 - 1		
40	27		H	Hastings United	1235	W 4 - 3	Hayes 29 Harris 45 66 Bradbrook 89	1
41	April 5		H	Canvey Island	1319	W 2 - 1	Harris 67 Bradbrook 79	
42	10		A	Kingstonian	929	W 6 - 2	Bradbrook 5 48 Hayes 13 70 Harris 38 Burns 79	1
43	13		A	Harrow Borough	209	W 1 - 0	Tait 43	
44	15		A	Waltham Abbey	273	W 4 - 0	White 43 Noble 51 Rooks 85 (pen) Burns 88	1
45	17		H	Aveley	2162	D 2 - 2	Haworth 11 Burgess 37	1
46	20		A	Wealdstone	401	D 1 - 1	Noble 18	
47	22		A	Hendon	200	W 2 - 1	Harris 70 90	
48	24		A	Bognor Regis Town	868	W 2 - 0	Coyle 18 Noble 24	1
					Goals	116 52		

Home Attendances:	
Highest:	2162 v Aveley
Lowest:	726 v Boreham Wood
Average (08-09):	1217 (1118)
Top Goalscorer:	Burns - 23 (League 22, FAC 1 - 1 Hat-trick)

DARTFORD

CURRENT SQUAD AS OF BEGINING OF 2010-11 SEASON

GOALKEEPERS	HT	WT	D.O.B	AGE	P.O.B	CAREER	Apps	Gls
Daren Ibrahim						Gillingham (Trainee), Welling Rel 5/06, Beckenham, Ashford T, Dartford, Sittingbourne (L) 2/10		
Andy Young						Hoddesdon, St Margaretsbury, Bishop's Stortford 7/04 Rel 7/08, Thurrock 7/08, Dartford 9/08		
DEFENDERS								
Joe Bruce	6'00"	12 00	5/7/83	26	London	Luton Rel c/s 02, Wingate & Finchley (SL) 1/02, Molesey, Hitchin 3/03, Grays 8/03 Rel 5/06, Maidenhead (2ML) 1/06, Basingstoke 6/06, Welling 3/07, Cambridge C 6/07, Braintree 7/08, Dartford 6/10		
Billy Burgess						Welling, Braintree 6/04 Rel 5/09, Dartford 6/09		
Tom Champion			15/5/86	23	London	Watford (Yth), Barnet 8/04 Rel c/s 05, Wealdstone (L) 3/05, Bishop's Stortford 7/05, Braintree 1/10, Dartford 5/10		
Paul Goodacre			15/7/84	26		Burnham Ramblers, Maldon T 8/02, Bishop's Stortford 6/06 Rel 10/09, Braintree 10/09, Dartford 5/10		
Adam Gross	6'00"	11 08	16/2/86	24	Thamesmead	Charlton (Scholar) Rel 5/05, Barnet 8/05 Rel 5/07, Grays 5/07 Rel 1/09, Weymouth (L) 1/08, Welling (L) 10/08, Dartford (L) 11/08, Dartford 1/09		
MIDFIELDERS								
Ollie Berquez			24/2/80	30	Essex	Ipswich (Jun), Heybridge S, Chelmsford, St Albans 7/01, Chelmsford, Dag & Red, Braintree 9/02, Canvey Island 12/02, Stevenage 6/05 Rel 5/06, Woking 6/06, Maldon (Pl/Coach) 5/07, Chelmsford Undisc 11/07 Rel 5/10, Dartford 6/10		
Elliott Bradbrook						Maidstone, University (USA), Maidstone c/s 08, Dartford 5/09		
Danny Harris			7/7/86	24	Newnham	Tilbury, East Thurrock 12/04, Bishop's Stortford 12/07, Dartford (Dual) 10/09 Perm		
Ryan Hayes						Slade Green, Dartford 3/05		
Lee Noble						Brentwood, Dartford 6/08		
Michael Shinn						Cambridge C (Yth), Cambridge U (Scholar), St Albans 2/04, Cambridge C 3/04, Heybridge c/s 04, Braintree £1,500 9/07, Billericay 5/09, Dartford 3/10		
James White						Southend (Yth), Tottenham (Yth), Arsenal (Yth), Great Wakering, Dartford 8/08		
FORWARDS								
Adam Burchall	5'10"	10 00	28/11/90	19		Gillingham (Scholar) Rel c/s 09, Welling (WE) 11/08, Dartford (WE) 3/09, Dartford 7/09, Tonbridge A (SL) 2/10		
Lee Burns						East Thurrock, Braintree 10/07, Dartford 6/09		
Danny Crouch			9/4/91	19		West Ham (Yth), Corinthians (Yth), Dartford		
Carl Rook			10/2/83	27		Sittingbourne (Yth), Folkestone I, Sittingbourne, Deal T, Whitstable, Hastings U 9/04, Dover 9/05, Horsham 1/06, Tonbridge A Undisc 12/07, Brighton (Trial) 7/09, Dartford 1/10		
Charlie Sheringham	6'01"	11 06	17/4/88	21	Chingford	Millwall (Yth), Tottenham (Yth), Bournemouth (Trial), Ipswich (Scholar) Rel c/s 05, Charlton, C.Palace Rel 1/08, Crystal Palace Baltimore (USA) (L) 4/07 Cambridge C 3/08, Welling 6/08, Bishop's Stortford £6,500 5/09, Histon (SL) 2/10, Dartford 6/10		

Do you remember when...

Dartford

In 1988-89 Dartford F.C. won the Southern League Cup and finished as Runners-Up in the Premier Division.

A happy post match group during a successful season under Peter Taylor's guidance.
Back row, left to right: Micky Ward (Physio), Jim Cannon,
Terry Harris (Assistant Manager), T.Ragg, Colin Johnson, Gary Harrold,
Keith Hazeldine, Mark Keen, Steve Connor, Gary Britnell and Dave Myers .
Front Row: Terry Skelton (Physio), Colin Sowerby, Steve Robinson,
Peter Taylor (Manager), Tony Mahony and Andy Hessenthaler.

DORCHESTER TOWN

Chairman: Shaun Hearn
Secretary: David Martin (T) 07971 172 795
(E) dave27@gmail.com
Additional Committee Members: David Martin, Adam Robertson, David Diaz, Neal Butterworth, Jon Dickinson, Richard Clark, Keith Kellaway
Manager: Ashley Vickers
Programme Editor: Annie Greenslade (E) anniegreenslade@aol.com

Archive photo

Club Factfile

Founded: 1880 **Nickname:** The Magpies
Previous Names:
Previous Leagues: Dorset, Western 1947-72

Club Colours (change): Black & white/black/black & white (All yellow)

Ground: The Jewson Stadium, Weymouth Avenue, Dorchester DT1 2SP (T) 01305 262 451
Capacity: 5,009 **Seats:** 710 **Covered:** 2,846 **Clubhouse:** Yes **Shop:** Yes
Previous Grounds: Council Recreation Ground, Weymouth Avenue 1908-1929, 1929-90, The Avenue Ground 1929
Simple Directions
The stadium is located at the junction of A35 Dorchester Bypass and the A354 to Weymouth, adjacent to Tesco. There is a coach bay for the team coach at the front of the stadium. Any supporters coach should park on the railway embankment side of the stadium.

Record Attendance: 4,159 v Weymouth - Southern Premier 1999
Record Victory: 7-0 v Canterbury (A) - Southern League Southern Division 1986-87
Record Defeat: 0-13 v Welton Rovers (A) - Western League 1966
Record Goalscorer: Not known
Record Appearances: Derek 'Dinkie' Curtis - 458 (1950-66)
Additional Records: Denis Cheney scored 61 goals in one season. Paid £12,000 to Gloucester City for Chris Townsend 1990. Received £35,000 from Portsmouth for Trevor Sinclair.
Senior Honours: Western League 19954-55. Southern League 1985-86, Division 1 East 2002-03. Dorset Senior Cup x7

10 YEAR RECORD

00-01	01-02	02-03	03-04	04-05	05-06	06-07	07-08	08-09	09-10
SthP 21	SthE 3	SthE 1	SthP 17	Conf S 8	Conf S 11	Conf S 17	Conf S 21	Conf S 19	Conf S 17

DORCHESTER TOWN

No.	Date	Comp	H/A	Opponents	Att:	Result	Goalscorers	Pos
1	8/8/09	BSS	H	St Albans City	450	W 3-0	Forbes 2 (36, 73), Martin 49	1
2	11/8/09	BSS	A	Staines Town	402	L 0-3		10
3	15/8/09	BSS	A	Dover Athletic	1005	L 1-4	Gleeson 38	16
4	18/8/09	BSS	H	Newport County	609	D 0-0		15
5	22/8/09	BSS	A	Bromley	297	L 1-3	Groves 27	19
6	29/8/09	BSS	H	Bath City	507	D 2-2	Martin 20, Walsh 45	17
7	31/8/09	BSS	A	Basingstoke Town	578	L 1-2	Vickers 85	17
8	5/9/09	BSS	A	Worcester City	502	L 0-4		19
9	8/9/09	BSS	H	Havant & Waterlooville	447	W 4-3	Groves 2, Moss 2 (63, 66), Forbes 74	15
10	12/9/09	BSS	H	Welling United	386	L 1-2	Groves 39	19
11	19/9/09	BSS	A	Bishop's Stortford	401	L 0-2		19
12	3/10/09	BSS	H	Braintree Town	459	W 5-0	Jermyn 14, Crittenden 16, Groves 23, Barnes 61, Walsh 67	17
13	17/10/09	BSS	A	Thurrock	237	L 2-5	Groves 2, Walsh 90	20
14	27/10/09	BSS	A	Maidenhead United	304	W 2-1	Devlin 4, Walsh 8	18
15	31/10/09	BSS	H	Dover Athletic	503	L 1-3	McCollin 87	19
16	7/11/09	BSS	A	Havant & Waterlooville	931	W 1-0	Gleeson 78	18
17	10/11/09	BSS	H	Eastleigh	423	L 1-2	Moss 5	18
18	14/11/09	BSS	H	Worcester City	419	D 1-1	Groves 68	18
19	28/11/09	BSS	A	Woking	1269	L 1-3	Jermyn 24	18
20	5/12/09	BSS	H	Hampton & Richmond	427	W 2-1	R Hill 65, Groves 81	17
21	26/12/09	BSS	H	Weymouth	2163	D 0-0		17
22	28/12/09	BSS	A	Newport County	2151	L 0-3		17
23	1/1/10	BSS	A	Weymouth	2392	L 0-2		17
24	23/1/10	BSS	H	Staines Town	418	D 2-2	Crittenden 2 (66, 72)	17
25	26/1/10	BSS	H	Lewes	307	D 1-1	Crittenden 72	17
26	30/1/10	BSS	A	Weston-Super-Mare	258	W 2-0	Moss 10, Emati-Emati 55	17
27	2/2/10	BSS	H	Thurrock	321	W 1-0	Devlin 78	16
28	6/2/10	BSS	H	Bromley	461	D 0-0		17
29	8/2/10	BSS	A	Chelmsford City	554	L 0-1		17
30	13/2/10	BSS	A	Welling United	501	D 1-1	Groves pen 90	17
31	20/2/10	BSS	H	Bishop's Stortford	432	W 2-0	Moss 39, Groves pen 46	15
32	27/2/10	BSS	H	Woking	536	D 1-1	R Hill 88	16
33	2/3/10	BSS	A	St Albans City	240	L 1-2	Groves pen 34	16
34	9/3/10	BSS	A	Hampton & Richmond	306	W 2-1	Llewellyn 14, Moss 29	15
35	13/3/10	BSS	A	Braintree Town	508	L 0-2		16
36	20/3/10	BSS	H	Weston-Super-Mare	425	W 4-2	Moss 29, Groves 35, Og (Ford) 51, Devlin 66	15
37	2/4/10	BSS	A	Bath City	738	L 0-2		16
38	5/4/10	BSS	H	Basingstoke Town	502	W 6-1	Martin 13, Bowles 25, Moss 29, Gleeson 40, Walker 61, R Hill 73	15
39	10/4/10	BSS	H	Chelmsford City	525	L 0-3		17
40	14/4/10	BSS	A	Eastleigh	433	L 0-2		17
41	17/4/10	BSS	A	Lewes	514	L 0-5		17
42	24/4/10	BSS	H	Maidenhead United	648	W 4-2	Groves pen 30, Moss 2 (51, 87), Gleeson 58	17
	Cups							
1	26/9/09	FAC 2Q	H	Hungerford Town	307	W 4-0	Jermyn 3 (7, 10, 22), Gleeson 25	
2	10/10/09	FAC 3Q	H	Gloucester City	498	L 1-2	Crittenden 14	
3	21/11/09	FAT 3Q	A	Weymouth	1032	L 0-3		

Home Attendances:	
Highest:	2163 v Weymouth
Lowest:	307 v Lewes
Average (08-09):	450 (460)
Top Goalscorer:	Groves - 12 (12 League, 0 Cup) in 38 appearances - 32% strike rate
Most Appearances:	Jermyn - 42 (38+1 League, 3 Cup)

NORTHMORE	JERMYN	SMEATON	MITCHELL	BOWLES	K HILL	MARTIN	GLEESON	MOSS	WALSH	FORBES	GROVES	VICKERS	MONTACUTE	FLOOD	COWARD	NODWELL	FILKINS	CRITTENDEN	O'BRIEN	SELLEY	BARNES	COSTA	DEVLIN	SYMES	LAVERS	MCCOLLIN	R HILL	CRITCHELL	SUTTLE	EMATI-EMATI	WALKER	EVANS	COUTTS	CHARLES	BYERLEY	TAYLOR	GILBERT	LLEWELLYN	BRICE	
X	X	X	X	X	X	X	X	X	X	X	S	U	U	U	U																									1
X	X	X	X	X	X	X	X	X	X	X	S	U		U		U	U																							2
X	X	U	X	X	X	X	X		X	X	S	X			U	S		X	U																					3
	X	X	X	X	X	X	X	X	X	U	U	U			X	S		X	U																					4
X	X	S	X	X		X	X	S	X	X	X	X	U		U	S		X																						5
X	X	X	U			X	X	U	X	X	X	X	X		U	U		U		X																				6
X	X	X	X	U		X	S	U	X	X	X	X	X		U	U				X																				7
X	X	X		X		X	X		X	X	X	X	U		S	U			U	X	S																			8
X		U		X		X	X	X	S	X	X	X	U		U	U		X		X	X																			9
X	S	S		X		X	X	X	S	X	X	X	U		U			X		X	X																			10
U	X	X	U	X	U	X	X	X	U		X	X	X		X			X			U																			11
	X	S	U	X	U	X	X		X		X		X		X	S	U	X			X	X																		12
	X	U	U	U	X	X		S					X		X	S				X	X	X																		13
	X	U				X	X	X	X		X	X	X		X	S				X	U	U	X	U																14
	X					X	X	X	X		U	X	U		X					X	U	S	X	U	X	X														15
	X			X		X	X	X	X		S	X	U		X					X	S	U	X		U	X														16
	X			X		X	X	X	X		S	X	U		X	U				X	S		X		U	X														17
	X			X		X	U	X	X		X		U		X	U				X	X		X	U	X	S														18
	X			X		X	X	X	X		S	U	U		X	X				X	S		X	U			X													19
	X	U		S		X	S	X	X		X	X			X	U				X			X				X	X	U											20
	X	U				X		X	X		X	X			X		U	S		X			X				X	X		S	U									21
	X			U		X		X	X		S	X			X	U		X		S			X				X	X		X	U									22
	X			S		X		X	X		S	X			X		U	X		X			X				X	X		S	U									23
	X	X		S	S			X			X	X				U		X					X				U	X		U	X	X	X							24
	X	X		U	U			X			X	X				U		X					X				U	X		U	X	X	X							25
	X	X		S	X	S		X			U					U		X					X					X		X	X	X	X	S						26
	X			X	X	U		X			S					U		X					X				U	X		X	X	X	X	U						27
				X	X	S	X				S				X	U		X					X				S	X		X	X	U	X	X						28
	X			X		X	S				X	U			X	X		U					X				X	X		S	X	U	X							29
	X			X	X	S	X				S				X	U							X				S	X		X	X		X	U	X					30
	X			X	X	U	U	X			X				X			X					X				S	X		S	X		X		S					31
	X				X	U	U	S			X				X	U		X					X				X	X			X		X	U	X					32
	X			U	X	X	X	X			X				X			X					X							S	X		S		X	U	U			33
	X			U	X		U	X			S				X			X					X				X	X			X		X		S			X	S	34
	X			U	X	U	S	X			X				X			X					X				X	X			X		X		S				U	35
	X			U	X	U	U	X			X				X			X					X				X	X			X		X		U				S	36
	X			S	X	S	S	X							X			X					X				X	X			X		X		U			X	U	37
	X			X		X	X	X							X	S		U			U		X				X	X			X				S			X	S	38
	X			X		X	X	X							X	U		S					X				X	X			X		S		U			X	U	39
	X				U	X	X	X			X				X	U		X					X				X				X		S		U			S	X	40
					X	X	S	X			S				X	X		X			X		U					X			S		X		X			U	X	41
	X				X	X	X	X			X				X	U		X					X				X				X		U		U			U	S	42
U	X	X	U	X	U	X	X		X		X	X	X		X	S		U		X	S																			1
	X	U	U	X	S	X	X		X		X		X		X	U	U	X			X	X																		2
	X			X		S		X	X		X	X	U		X	U				X	X		X	S	S	X														3

Total League Appearances

NORTHMORE	JERMYN	SMEATON	MITCHELL	BOWLES	K HILL	MARTIN	GLEESON	MOSS	WALSH	FORBES	GROVES	VICKERS	MONTACUTE	FLOOD	COWARD	NODWELL	FILKINS	CRITTENDEN	O'BRIEN	SELLEY	BARNES	COSTA	DEVLIN	SYMES	LAVERS	MCCOLLIN	R HILL	CRITCHELL	SUTTLE	EMATI-EMATI	WALKER	EVANS	COUTTS	CHARLES	BYERLEY	TAYLOR	GILBERT	LLEWELLYN	BRICE	
9	38	10	6	21	18	30	23	31	19	9	22	18	6	0	29	3	0	24	0	15	6	2	28	0	2	3	15	20	0	5	18	4	14	1	4	0	0	4	2	X
0	1	3	0	5	1	4	6	3	2	0	13	0	0	0	1	7	0	2	0	1	4	1	0	0	0	1	3	0	0	5	1	0	3	1	4	0	0	1	4	S
1	0	6	4	8	4	5	5	2	1	1	3	5	10	2	7	19	4	3	3	0	4	2	1	4	2	0	3	0	1	2	3	2	1	3	5	1	1	2	3	U

Total Cup Appearances

NORTHMORE	JERMYN	SMEATON	MITCHELL	BOWLES	K HILL	MARTIN	GLEESON	MOSS	WALSH	FORBES	GROVES	VICKERS	MONTACUTE	FLOOD	COWARD	NODWELL	FILKINS	CRITTENDEN	O'BRIEN	SELLEY	BARNES	COSTA	DEVLIN	SYMES	LAVERS	MCCOLLIN	R HILL	CRITCHELL	SUTTLE	EMATI-EMATI	WALKER	EVANS	COUTTS	CHARLES	BYERLEY	TAYLOR	GILBERT	LLEWELLYN	BRICE	
0	3	1	0	3	0	2	2	1	3	0	3	2	2	0	3	0	0	1	0	2	2	1	1	0	0	1	0	0	0	0	0	0	0	0	0	0	0	0	0	X
0	0	0	0	0	1	1	0	0	0	0	0	0	0	0	0	1	0	0	0	0	1	0	0	1	1	0	0	0	0	0	0	0	0	0	0	0	0	0	0	S
1	0	1	2	0	1	0	0	0	0	0	0	0	1	0	0	2	1	1	0	0	0	0	0	0	0	0	0	0	0	0	0	0	0	0	0	0	0	0	0	U

Total Goals

NORTHMORE	JERMYN	SMEATON	MITCHELL	BOWLES	K HILL	MARTIN	GLEESON	MOSS	WALSH	FORBES	GROVES	VICKERS	MONTACUTE	FLOOD	COWARD	NODWELL	FILKINS	CRITTENDEN	O'BRIEN	SELLEY	BARNES	COSTA	DEVLIN	SYMES	LAVERS	MCCOLLIN	R HILL	CRITCHELL	SUTTLE	EMATI-EMATI	WALKER	EVANS	COUTTS	CHARLES	BYERLEY	TAYLOR	GILBERT	LLEWELLYN	BRICE	
0	2	0	0	1	0	3	4	10	4	3	12	1	0	0	0	0	0	4	0	0	0	0	3	0	0	1	3	0	0	1	1	0	0	0	0	0	0	1	0	Lge
0	3	0	0	0	0	0	1	0	0	0	0	0	0	0	0	0	0	1	0	0	0	0	0	0	0	0	0	0	0	0	0	0	0	0	0	0	0	0	0	Cup

DORCHESTER TOWN

CURRENT SQUAD AS OF BEGINING OF 2010-11 SEASON

GOALKEEPERS	HT	WT	D.O.B	AGE	P.O.B	CAREER	Apps	Gls
Regan Coward			12/6/90	20		Dorchester, Bridport (Dual) 9/09	30	0
Andy Suttle			6/10/93	16		Dorchester	0	0
DEFENDERS								
Gary Bowles			30/12/88	21		Cardiff (Yth), Yeovil, Dorchester 8/07	26	1
Kyle Critchell	6'00"	12 02	18/1/87	23	Dorchester	Southampton, Torquay (3ML) 10/06, Chesterfield 1/07, Weymouth 6/07, Wrexham 6/08 Rel 6/09, York C (2ML) 1/09, Weymouth (L) 3/09, Weymouth 6/09, Dorchester 11/09	20	0
Jamie Frampton			10/9/91	18		Weymouth, Dorchester 5/10		
Neil Martin			5/4/89	21		Exeter, Hayes & Yeading (L) 8/08 Perm 9/08 Rel 10/08, Salisbury 1/09 Rel c/s 09, Dorchester 8/09	34	3
Jake Smeaton	5'08"	11	9/8/88	21	Yeovil	Yeovil Rel c/s 07, Dorchester 8/07	13	0
Ashley Vickers	6'03"	13 10	14/6/72	38	Sheffield	Sheff Utd, Worcester, Malvern T, 61 Club, Heybridge Swifts, Peterborough £5,000 12/97, St Albans 8/98, Dag & Red 3/00, Weymouth 5/06, Eastleigh 3/08, Newport C (L) 8/08 Perm 9/08, Dorchester (Pl/Coach) 3/09 (Pl/Man) 3/10	18	1
Nathan Walker			3/10/86	23		Weymouth, Portland U (L), Dorchester, Hamworthy U, Wimborne T 1/09, Dorchester 12/09	19	1
MIDFIELDERS								
James Coutts	5'06"	09 07	15/4/87	23	Weymouth	Southampton (Jun), Bournemouth 7/04 Rel 5/07, Grays (L) 11/06, Weymouth (SL) 1/07, Weymouth 7/07, USA (Coaching) c/s 09, Newport C 12/09 Rel 12/09, Dorchester NC 1/10	17	0
Nick Crittenden	5'08"	10 11	11/11/78	31	Ascot	Chelsea Rel 6/00, Plymouth (L) 11/98, Yeovil 8/00 Rel c/s 03 Re-signed, Rel c/s 04, Aldershot 6/04, Weymouth 5/06 Rel 5/08, Dorchester 6/08	26	4
Steve Devlin			3/10/85	24		Liverpool (Yth), Chard T, Southampton (Trial) c/s 03, Frome 1/04, Chard T 7/04, Holt U, Wincanton, Dorchester (Trial) c/s 09, Holt U, Dorchester 10/09	28	3
Connor Flood			19/4/93	17		Dorchester	0	0
Jamie Gleeson	6'00"	12 03	15/1/85	25	Poole	Southampton Rel c/s 04, Kidderminster 7/04 Rel c/s 05, Eastleigh (L) 10/04, Dorchester 8/05	29	4
Kevin Hill	5'08"	10 03	6/3/76	34	Exeter	Torrington, Torquay 8/97, Rel 6/08, Dorchester 6/08	19	0
Ryan Hill			8/10/86	23		Wimbledon (Yth), Millwall (Yth), Weymouth, Dorchester c/s 05 Rel 12/07, Bashley (L) 10/07, Farnborough 1/08, Bognor (Mon) 8/08, Bashley, Dorchester 11/09	18	3
Mark Jermyn	6'00"	11 05	16/4/81	29	Germany	Torquay Rel 2/00, Dorchester 8/00	39	2
Harry Montacute			6/7/91	19		Yeovil (Yth), Dorchester c/s 09, Gillingham T (SL) 1/10	6	0
Harry Nodwell			10/9/90	19		Exeter (Yth), Yeovil (Yth), Dorchester c/s 09	10	0
Adam Taylor			21/5/92	18		Dorchester	0	0
FORWARDS								
Dave Allen			25/11/83	26		Bournemouth Sports, Dorchester 3/05, Lymington & New Milton 2/06, Winchester, Bashley 11/08, Dorchester 5/10		
Warren Byerley			23/4/85	25		Chelsea (Yth), Brighton (Yth), Lewes, Dorchester, Gosport B, Hamworthy (L) 8/07, Dorchester, Bridport (Dual) 1/10	8	0
Matt Groves			17/4/80	30	Poole	Portsmouth, Dorchester 11/98, Lewes 9/07, Eastleigh 5/08 Rel 5/09, Dorchester 6/09	35	12
Josh Llewellyn			27/4/87	23		Derby, Hayes, Team Bath c/s 06, Weston-Super-Mare 5/09, Weymouth 10/09 Rel 3/10, Dorchester 3/10	5	1
Ryan Moss	5'11"	12 04	14/11/86	23	Dorchester	Bournemouth Rel c/s 05, Dorchester 8/05, Bashley 7/06, Dorchester Undisc 6/08 Rel 2/09, Bashley 2/09, Dorchester c/s 09	34	10

Loanees	HT	WT	DOB	AGE	POB	From - To	APPS	GOA
(F)Andre McCollin	5'07"	10 06	26/3/85	25	Lambeth	Yeovil 10/09 - Farnborough (L) 2/10	4	1
(D)Louis Lavers			29/9/90	19		Yeovil 10/09 - Rel 1/10, Bracknell, Wealdstone 2/10	2	0

Departures	HT	WT	DOB	AGE	POB	From - To	APPS	GOA
(F)Ivan Forbes			1/12/86	23	Portimao, Port	Kingsbury London Tigers 8/07 - Rel 10/09, Havant & W 10/09	9	3
(G)Ryan Northmore	6'01"	13 01	5/9/80	29	Plymouth	Weston-Super-Mare 8/09 Rel 10/09 - Weston-Super-Mare 2/10	9	0
(M)Tom Mitchell			21/9/87	22	Poole	Portsmouth 7/07 - Rel 11/09, Gosport (L) 1/09	6	0
(M)Andre Costa			13/5/91	19		Poole T 10/09 - Sutton U, Walton & H (L) 1/10	3	0
(D)Roy O'Brien	6'01"	12 00	27/11/74	35	Cork	Weymouth 6/07 Rel 1/09 - Dorchester 2/09 (Pl/Man) 3/09 Rel 11/09	0	0
(F)Phil Walsh			4/2/84	26	Bristol	Tiverton 3/09 - Dag & Red Small Fee 1/10	21	4
(M)Ian Selley			14/6/74	36		Croydon A 8/09 - Rel 1/10, Havant & W 1/10	16	0
(D)Ollie Barnes			10/3/87	23		Weymouth 9/09 - Clevedon (2ML) 12/09, Gloucester 7/10	10	0
(M)Jamie Symes			17/6/93	17		Bridport 10/09 - Bridport (Dual) 10/09, Blackpool (Trial) 2/10	0	0
(F)Sam Charles			22/3/88	22		Montana State Billings (USA) 1/10 - Bridport (Dual) 2/10	2	0
(F)Jules Emati-Emati			3/4/82	28		Dawlish 12/09 -	10	1
(D)Scott Brice			24/1/87	23		Weymouth 3/10 -	6	0
(D)Steven Gilbert			23/11/84	25		Gosport 1/10 -	0	0
(G)Simon Evans			28/1/88	22		Weymouth 1/10 -	4	0
(G)Sam Filkins			6/9/92	17		Yth -	0	0

DOVER ATHLETIC

Chairman: Jim Parmenter
Secretary: Franke Clarke (T) 01304 822 373
(E) frank.clarke@doverathletic.com

Additional Committee Members:
Roger Knight, Chris Oakley, Scott Rutherford, Andrew Findley, Steve Parmenter

Manager: Martin Hayes
Programme Editor: Chris Collings (E) chris.collings@doverathletic.com

Achive photo

Club Factfile

Founded: 1983 **Nickname:** The Whites
Previous Names: Dover F.C. until club folded in 1983
Previous Leagues: Southern 1983-93, 2002-04, Conference 1993-2002, Isthmian 2004-2009

Club Colours (change): White/black/black (All royal blue)

Ground: Crabble Athletic Ground, Lewisham, Dover, Kent CT17 0PA (T) 01304 822 373
Capacity: 6,500 **Seats:** 1,000 **Covered:** 4,900 **Clubhouse:** Yes **Shop:** Yes
Previous Grounds: None.

Simple Directions
From outside of Kent, find your way to the M25, then take the M2/A2 (following the signs to Canterbury, then from Canterbury follow signs to Dover) as far as the Whitfield roundabout (there is a McDonald's Drive-Thru on the left). Take the fourth exit at this roundabout, down Whitfield Hill. At the bottom of the hill turn left at the roundabout and follow this road until the first set of traffic lights. At the lights turn right (180 degrees down the hill) and follow the road under the railway bridge, the ground is a little further up the road on the left. There is no parking for supporters within the ground, although parking is available in the rugby ground, which is just inside the main entrance - stewards will direct you. If you have to take the M20/A20 leave the A20 in Folkestone (the exit immediately after the tunnel through the hill) and travel through the Alkham Valley (turn left at the roundabout at the end of the slip-road and then left again, following the signs for Alkham) which will eventually take you near Kearsney train station (turn right into Lower Road just before the railway bridge, before you get to the station).

Record Attendance: 4,186 v Oxford United - FA Cup 1st Round November 2002
Record Victory: 7-0 v Weymouth - 03/04/1990
Record Defeat: 1-7 v Poole Town
Record Goalscorer: Lennie Lee - 160
Record Appearances: Jason Bartlett - 359
Additional Records: Paid £50,000 to Farnborough Town for David Lewworthy August 1993
Received £50,000 from Brentford for Ricky Reina 1997

Senior Honours: Southern League Southern Division 1987-88, Premier Division 1989-90, 92-93, Premier Inter League Cup 1990-91. Kent Senior Cup 1990-91. Isthmian League Division 1 South 2007-08, Premier Division 2008-09.

10 YEAR RECORD

00-01	01-02	02-03	03-04	04-05	05-06	06-07	07-08	08-09	09-10
Conf 15	Conf 22	SthP 3	SthP 19	Isth P 21	Isth1 5	Isth1S 3	Isth1S 1	Isth P 1	Conf S 2

DOVER ATHLETIC

No.	Date	Comp	H/A	Opponents	Att:	Result	Goalscorers	Pos
1	8/8/09	BSS	A	Maidenhead United	407	D 0-0		13
2	11/8/09	BSS	H	Bishop's Stortford	1210	W 2-0	Hughes 76, Birchall 79	6
3	15/8/09	BSS	H	Dorchester Town	1005	W 4-1	Birchall 2 (15, 89), Southall 76, Welford 90	3
4	17/8/09	BSS	A	Chelmsford City	1578	D 1-1	Schulz 36	3
5	22/8/09	BSS	H	Weston-Super-Mare	1135	W 5-3	Rogers 15, Brownning 20, Moore 34, Collin pen 45, Welford 63	1
6	29/8/09	BSS	A	Eastleigh	703	W 2-1	Collin 2 (1, 15)	1
7	31/8/09	BSS	H	Welling United	1321	W 2-0	Moore 9, Browning 45	1
8	5/9/09	BSS	A	Havant & Waterlooville	1217	L 1-2	Birchall 66	3
9	8/9/09	BSS	A	Thurrock	534	W 2-0	Birchall 11, Collin 90	1
10	12/9/09	BSS	H	Hampton & Richmond B.	1108	W 4-2	Collin 5, Browning 45, Southall 59, Pugh 72	1
11	19/9/09	BSS	H	Bath City	1069	W 2-1	Birchall 2 (65, 90)	1
12	3/10/09	BSS	A	Worcester City	737	L 0-1		2
13	17/10/09	BSS	A	Weymouth	649	W 2-1	Wallis 10, Welford 27	2
14	20/10/09	BSS	H	Basingstoke Town	1060	L 2-3	Welford 41, Wallis pen 90	2
15	27/10/09	BSS	H	Woking	1218	L 0-2		2
16	31/10/09	BSS	A	Dorchester Town	503	W 3-1	Collin 2 (56, 83), Birchall 58	2
17	7/11/09	BSS	H	Newport County	1680	L 1-2	Welford 59	2
18	14/11/09	BSS	A	Weston-Super-Mare	269	L 1-3	Welford 69	2
19	28/11/09	BSS	H	Thurrock	1008	W 1-0	Southall 90	2
20	1/12/09	BSS	A	Staines Town	473	D 0-0		2
21	5/12/09	BSS	A	Bromley	703	D 2-2	Wallis pen 56, Birchall pen 90	2
22	19/12/09	BSS	H	St Albans City	593	D 1-1	Welford 34	2
23	26/12/09	BSS	A	Lewes	505	L 2-6	Rogers 2, Collin 13	2
24	28/12/09	BSS	H	Chelmsford City	1261	L 0-1		5
25	1/1/10	BSS	H	Lewes	918	W 2-0	Schulz 71, Birchall pen 90	3
26	16/1/10	BSS	H	Havant & Waterlooville	852	W 4-0	Collin 2 (40, 42), Birchall 54, Welford 85	2
27	23/1/10	BSS	A	Woking	1437	L 0-2		3
28	6/2/10	BSS	A	Bath City	667	D 0-0		3
29	13/2/10	BSS	A	Braintree Town	718	W 2-1	Birchall 39, Schulz 79	3
30	20/2/10	BSS	H	Maidenhead United	851	D 1-1	Birchall 2	7
31	6/3/10	BSS	H	Braintree Town	1007	D 0-0		8
32	9/3/10	BSS	H	Worcester City	655	L 0-2		8
33	13/3/10	BSS	A	Basingstoke Town	418	W 3-1	Collin 4, Schulz 27, Welford 34	7
34	16/3/10	BSS	A	Bishop's Stortford	302	W 2-0	Schulz 2 (16, 36)	6
35	20/3/10	BSS	H	Bromley	1027	W 1-0	Moore 90	4
36	27/3/10	BSS	A	St Albans City	577	W 2-1	Birchall 45, Welford 53	5
37	30/3/10	BSS	A	Hampton & Richmond B.	380	W 4-1	Wallis 19, Schulz 3 (45, 75, 90)	3
38	3/4/10	BSS	H	Eastleigh	1127	W 2-1	Birchall 27, Tabiri 80	2
39	5/4/10	BSS	A	Welling United	939	W 1-0	Southall 55	2
40	10/4/10	BSS	H	Weymouth	1022	W 2-0	Southall 9, Moore 90	2
41	17/4/10	BSS	A	Newport County	3201	L 0-3		3
42	24/4/10	BSS	H	Staines Town	1147	D 0-0		2
	Cups							
1	26/9/09	FAC 2Q	H	East Preston	757	W 8-0	Schulz 21, Hill 31, Browning 2 (61, 80), Welford 69, Walder 84, Wallis 2 (86, 87)	
2	10/10/09	FAC 3Q	H	Welling United	1042	W 2-0	Schulz 60, Wallis 77	
3	24/10/09	FAC 4Q	H	Eastleigh	1161	L 3-5	Schulz 26, Browning 63, Birchall pen 90	
4	21/11/09	FAT 3Q	H	Dartford	1084	W 3-2	Birchall 7, Collin 37, Southall 69	
5	12/12/09	FAT 1	A	Havant & Waterlooville	483	W 3-2	Southall 24, Wallis 38, Welford 60	
6	12/1/10	FAT 2	A	Fleetwood Town	871	W 1-0	Birchall 43	
7	30/1/10	FAT 3	A	Stevenage Borough	1203	L 1-4	Welford 28	
8	27/4/10	PO SF1	A	Woking	3080	L 1-2	Schulz 3	
9	1/5/10	PO SF2	H	Woking	2970	D 0-0	(L 1-2 agg)	

Home Attendances:	
Highest:	1680 v Newport County
Lowest:	593 v St Alban's City
Average (08-09):	1060 (1293)
Top Goalscorer:	Andy Brown - 18 (15 League, 3 Cup) in 46 appearances - 39% strike rate
Most Appearances:	Birchall - 46 (33+4 League, 9 Cup)
	Welford - 46 (35+2 League, 9 Cup)

HOOK	WALLIS	ROGERS	HILL	SOUTHALL	MOORE	DAVIS	BIRCHALL	WELFORD	COLLIN	BROWNING	HUGHES	WALDER	KEISTER	GORE	WHITEHOUSE	MARSH	GRANT	SCHULZ	LEBERL	PUGH	ROCASTLE	MILLER	HUMPHREY	WILKINSON	HESSENTHALER	FISH	CLOKE	WYNTER	MAMBO	ADELAKUN	FLITNEY	LEACH	ABNETT	CUMBERS	TABIRI	
X	X	X	X	X	X	X	X	X	X	X	S	S	U	U	U																					1
X	X	X	X	X	X	X	X	X		X	S	U	X	U	U	S																				2
X	X	X	X	X	X	X	X	X		X	S	S	X	S	U		U																			3
X		X	X	X	X	X	X	X	S	X	S		X	S	U		U	X																		4
X		X	X	X	X	X		X	X	X	S	S	X	S	U		U	X																		5
X	X	X	X	X	X	X		X	X	S	U	X	S	S	U			X																		6
X			X	X	X	X	S	X	X	X	S	X	U	X	U	U		X																		7
X	X		X	X	X	U	S	X	X	X	S	X		X	U			X	S																	8
X	X	X	X	X	X	S	X	X	X	U	S			U	U			X	X																	9
X	X	X	X	X	X	U			X	X	S	U		S	U			X	X	X																10
X	X	X	X	X	X	S	S			X	S	X		U	U			X	X	X																11
X	X	X	X	X	X	S		X	S	X	S	X		U				X		X	U															12
X	X	X		X	X	X	X	X		S	S	U						X	X		X	U	U													13
X	X	X	X	X	X	X	X	X		S	S	U						X	X		S		U													14
U	X	X	X	X	S		X		X	S	S	U						X	X					X	X	X										15
U		S	X	X	X	U	X	X	X	U		S						X	X					X		X		X								16
U		X	X	X		X	X	X	X	S	S	U		U					X					X		X		X								17
X		S	X	X	X	X	X	X	X	S		U		S	U				X							X		X								18
U		X	X	X	X		X	X	X	U	S	U		U	X				X							X		X								19
U		X	X	X	X		X	X	X	S	U	S		S	X				X							X		X								20
U	X	X		X	X	S	X	X	X		S	S			X			X	X			U				X										21
U	X	X	X	X	X		X	X	X		S	X			X	U		X	U			U														22
U	X	X	X	X	X		X		X		S	X			X			X	X			U			U		U									23
X	X	X	X	X			X		X			X				S	X	X	X			U	U		S		S									24
X		X	X	X	X		X	X	X						U	S	U	X	X			S				X	S									25
X	X	X		X	X		X	X	X	S		X			S	U	U									X	S			X						26
	X	X		X	X	U	X	X	X	S		X			U		U									X	U			X	X					27
	X	S	X	X	X		X	X	X			X			U			X	U											S	X	X	S			28
	X	U	X	X	X		X	X	X			X			U			X												S	X	X	U	S		29
	X	X	U	X	X		X	X	X			X			U			X												S	X	X	S	S		30
		U	X	X	X		X	X	X						U			X	U							X				S	X	X	S	X		31
		S	X	X	U		X	S	X			U			U			X	X							X				X	X	X		X		32
		X	X	X	S			X	X			X			U			X	S							X				U	X	X		S	X	33
		X	X	X	X		S	X	X						U			X	S							X	U			S	X	X			X	34
		X	X	X	X		X	X							U	U		X	S			U				X	U				X	X			X	35
	X	X		X	X		X	X				U			U			X	U						U	X	S				X	X			X	36
	X	X		X	X		X	X				U			U	S		X	U							X	S				X	X			X	37
	X	X	S	X			X	X				U			U	X		X	U							X	S				X	X			X	38
	X	X	X	X			X	X				U			U	U		X	U							X	S				X	X			X	39
		X	X	X	X		X	X				X			U	S		X	U			U			U		X				X				X	40
	X	X	X	X	X		X	X				X			U			X	U			U			U		S				X				X	41
	X	X	X	X	X		X	S				X			U			X	S						S		X				X				X	42

HOOK	WALLIS	ROGERS	HILL	SOUTHALL	MOORE	DAVIS	BIRCHALL	WELFORD	COLLIN	BROWNING	HUGHES	WALDER	KEISTER	GORE	WHITEHOUSE	MARSH	GRANT	SCHULZ	LEBERL	PUGH	ROCASTLE	MILLER	HUMPHREY	WILKINSON	HESSENTHALER	FISH	CLOKE	WYNTER	MAMBO	ADELAKUN	FLITNEY	LEACH	ABNETT	CUMBERS	TABIRI	
U	X	X	X	X	U	X	X	X		X	S	X			X	U		X			S	S														1
X	X	U	X	X	X	X	X	X	X	U	S	U		U	U			X	X		S															2
U		X		X		X	X	X		X	S	X		U				X	X		X	S		X	S	U	U									3
U		S	X	X	X	S	X	X	X		U	S	X	X					X							X			X							4
U	X	X	U	X	X		X	X	X		S	X			X			X							U	X	U									5
X	X			X			X	X	X	S		X			U	U		X				U			X	X	S			X						6
X	X	X		X	X		X	X	X	S		X						X	U				U			X	U			S						7
		X	X	X			X	X				X			U	U	U	X	X			U				S	X				X				X	8
Total League Appearances												X			U	U	U	X	S							X	X				X				X	9
18	27	34	34	42	35	11	33	35	27	10	0	17	4	2	5	1	1	33	16	3	1	0	0	3	1	19	2	5	0	3	16	12	0	2	10	X
0	0	4	1	0	2	4	4	2	2	9	19	6	1	7	1	5	0	0	5	0	1	1	0	0	2	0	8	0	0	5	0	0	3	3	0	S
Total Cup Appearances												13	2	7	29	5	6	0	9	0	1	8	3	0	4	0	4	0	0	1	0	0	1	0	0	U
3	5	6	5	9	4	3	9	9	5	2	0	7	0	1	3	0	0	8	4	0	1	0	0	1	1	5	2	0	1	1	2	0	0	0	2	X
0	0	1	0	0	1	1	0	0	0	2	4	1	0	0	0	0	0	0	1	0	2	2	0	0	1	1	1	0	0	1	0	0	0	0	0	S
Total Goals												1	0	2	4	4	2	0	1	0	0	2	1	0	1	1	3	0	0	0	0	0	0	0	0	U
0	4	2	0	5	4	0	15	10	11	2	1	0	0	0	0	0	0	9	0	1	0	0	0	0	0	0	0	0	0	0	0	0	0	0	1	Lge
0	4	0	1	2	0	0	3	3	1	3	0	1	0	0	0	0	0	4	0	0	0	0	0	0	0	0	0	0	0	0	0	0	0	0	0	Cup

DOVER ATHLETIC

CURRENT SQUAD AS OF BEGINING OF 2010-11 SEASON

GOALKEEPERS	HT	WT	D.O.B	AGE	P.O.B	CAREER	Apps	Gls
Ross Flitney	6'01"	11 11	1/6/84	26	Hitchin	Arsenal (Yth), Fulham Rel c/s 05, Brighton (2ML) 8/03, Brighton (L) 12/03, Doncaster (L) 1/05, Yeading (L) 3/05, Barnet 8/05 Rel 5/07, Grays 5/07 Rel 1/09, Croydon Ath (2ML) 12/08, Croydon Ath 1/09, Dover Undisc 1/10	16	0
Lee Hook	5'09"	08 11	11/3/79	31	Margate	Wolves (Yth), Exeter, Ramsgate, Whitstable, Sittingbourne 9/02, Eastbourne B 6/03 Rel 5/09, Dover 5/09	18	0
Ben Humphrey			28/11/92	17		Dover	0	0
DEFENDERS								
Matt Fish	6'01"	11 00	5/1/89	21		C.Palace (Scholar) Rel c/s 07, AFC Wimbledon (SL) 3/07, Dover 7/07	19	0
Rob Gillman	6'02"	13 08	26/4/84	26	London	Luton, Enfield (L) 3/03, Ashford T (Middx) 8/03, Bishop's Stortford 7/04, Ashford T (Middx) 7/07, Bishop's Stortford 12/07, Bromley 5/08, Dover 7/10		
Dean Grant			13/7/90	20		Dover	1	0
Dean Hill			14/10/83	26		Dover (Yth), Ashford T, Sittingbourne 2/04, Ramsgate 6/05, Dover 5/08	35	0
Ollie Schulz			25/5/85	25		Ramsgate, Dover 5/08	33	9
Tom Wynter	5'07"	11 11	20/6/90	20	Lewisham	Gillingham, Ramsgate (3ML) 11/08, Dover (2ML) 10/09, Dover 8/10	5	0
MIDFIELDERS								
Sam Cutler			11/2/90	20	Sidcup	Cambridge U, Weymouth 5/08, Grays 8/09, Torquay (Trial), Welling 11/09, Dover 7/10		
James Rogers			9/12/84	25		Dover	38	2
Joe Tabiri	5'09"	11 09	16/10/89	20	Kingsbury	Protec Yth Academy, Barnet 8/07 Rel c/s 10, Staines (L) 12/07, Farnborough (Dual) 1/08, Wingate & F (L) 3/08, Lewes (2ML) 10/08, Grays (L) 1/09, Havant & W (L) 11/09, Havant & W (L) 2/10, Dover (SL) 3/10, Dover 6/10	10	1
Jon Wallis	5'07"	10 08	4/4/86	24	Gravesend	Chelsea (Jun), Gillingham Rel 5/06, Hastings U (3ML) 8/04, Hastings U (L) 9/05 Hereford 6/06 Rel 3/07, Dover (2ML) 11/06, Dag & Red (L) 2/07, Dover 3/07	27	4
FORWARDS								
Adam Birchall	5'07"	11 03	2/12/84	25	Maidstone	Arsenal Rel c/s 05, Wycombe (3ML) 8/04, Mansfield 8/05, Barnet (6WL) 11/06, Barnet Undisc 1/07 Rel c/s 09, Dover 7/09	37	15
Ben Hunt	6'01"	11 00	23/1/90	20	Southwark	West Ham (Scholar), Bristol R c/s 08, Kingstonian (L) 10/09, Gloucester (3ML) 12/09, Newport C (L) 3/10, Dover 7/10		
Jake Marsh			2/3/92	18		Dover	6	0
Andrew Miller			12/12/92	17		Dover	1	0
Shaun Welford			21/5/79	31	Ashington	Corinthian, Dover, Ramsgate 12/04, Dover 10/07	37	10

Loanees	HT	WT	DOB	AGE	POB	From - To	APPS	GOA
(F)Andy Pugh	5'09"	12 02	28/1/89	21	Gravesend	Gillingham 9/09 - Welling (3ML) 11/09, Histon (L) 3/10, Rel c/s 10, Welling 6/10	3	1
(D)Yado Mambo			22/10/91	18	Kilburn	Charlton 11/09 - Staines (L) 12/09	0	0
(D)Hakeem Adelakun			8/1/91	18		C.Palace (10WL) 1/10 -	8	0
(D)Daniel Leach			5/1/86	24		Barnet (2ML) 2/10 -	12	0
(D)Michael Abnett			27/12/90	19		C.Palace 2/10 -	3	0
(M)Luis Cumbers	6'00"	11 10	6/9/88	21	Chelmsford	Gillingham 2/10 - Rel c/s 10, Welling 6/10	5	0

Departures	HT	WT	DOB	AGE	POB	From - To	APPS	GOA
(M)John Keister	5'08"	11 00	11/11/70	39	Manchester	Margate 5/06 - Margate 9/09	5	0
(M)Craig Rocastle	6'01"	13 09	17/8/81	29	Lewisham	Welling 9/09 - Forest Green 10/09	2	0
(G)David Wilkinson	5'11"	12 00	17/4/88	22	Croydon	Truro C 10/09 - Rel 11/09, Forest Green Rovers 12/09	3	0
(M)Jerahl Hughes	5'07"	11 09	10/8/89	21	Brighton	Yeovil 7/08 - Rel 12/09, Eastbourne T, Tonbridge A 2/10	19	1
(M)Tom Davis	5'10"	11 07	17/2/84	26	Bromley	AFC Wimbledon 6/09 - Rel 1/10, Croydon Ath (L) 12/09, Croydon Ath 1/10, Bromley 2/10, Dorking Wanderers 3/10, Sutton U 5/10	15	0
(D)Samuel Gore	5'11"	11 02	29/11/88	21	Dover	Gillingham (Scholar) 6/07 - Rel 2/10	9	0
(F)Lee Browning			6/5/87	23		Sittingbourne 9/07 - Rel 3/10, Tonbridge A 5/10	19	2
(G)John Whitehouse			31/5/77	33		Chatham T 1/08 - Rel 5/10	6	0
(D)Jake Leberl			2/4/77	33	Morden	AFC Wimbledon 6/09 - Rel 5/10	21	0
(D)Danny Walder			3/9/89	20		Ramsgate 8/09 - Rel 5/10, Tonbridge A 5/10	23	0
(F)Francis Collin	5'11"	11 11	20/4/87	23	Chatham	Gillingham 6/07 - Rel 5/10, Tonbridge A 5/10	29	11
(D)Craig Cloke			26/11/84	25		Yth - Ashford (L) 2/10, Margate 5/10	10	0
(M)Andy Hessenthaler			17/8/65	45		Dover (Man) - Gillingham (Man) 5/10	3	0
(M)Nicky Southall	5'10"	12 12	28/1/72	38	Stockton	Gillingham 7/09 - Gillingham (Pl/Coach) 6/10	42	5
(M)Sammy Moore	5'08"	9 00	7/9/87	22	Deal	Stevenage 6/08 - AFC Wimbledon 7/10	37	4

EASTLEIGH

Chairman: Paul Murray

Secretary: Ray Murphy **(T)** 07801 638 158
(E) raymurphy@ntlworld.com

Additional Committee Members: Mike Geddes, Alan Williams, David Malone, John Dunn, Chris Evans, Derik Brooks, Allen Prebble, Mike Andrews, Stuart Deas, Alan Harding, Andrew White, Stephen Brookwell, Peter Vickery, John Russell, Russell Vaughan, Denis Bundy, Malcolm Clarke

Manager: Ian Baird

Programme Editor: Mike Denning **(E)** mike.denning@talk21.com

Achive photo

Club Factfile

Founded: 1946 **Nickname:** The Spitfires

Previous Names: Swaythling Athletic 1946-59, Swaythling 1973-80

Previous Leagues: Southampton Junior & Senior 1946-59, Hampshire 1950-86, Wessex 1986-2003, Southern 2003-04, Isthmian 2004-05

Club Colours (change): White/blue/white (All red)

Ground: Silverlake Stadium 'Ten Acres', Stoneham Lane, Eastleigh SO50 9HT **(T)** 02380 613 361

Capacity: 2,300 **Seats:** 175 **Covered:** 385 **Clubhouse:** Yes **Shop:** Yes

Previous Grounds:

Simple Directions

From junction 13 of M3, turn right into Leigh Road, turn right at Holiday Inn, at mini roundabout take second exit, at the next mini roundabout take second exit, then next mini roundabout take first exit. Then take the first turning right (signposted) ground 200 metres on the left.

Record Attendance: 2,589 v Southampton - Friendly July 2005

Record Victory: 12-1 v Hythe & Dibden (H) - 11/12/1948

Record Defeat: 0-11 v Austin Sports (A) - 01.01.1947

Record Goalscorer: Johnnie Williams - 177

Record Appearances: Ian Knight - 611

Additional Records: Paid £10,000 to Newport (I.O.W.) for Colin Matthews

Senior Honours: Southampton Senior League (West) 1950.
Wessex League Cup 1992,2003, Division One 2002-03.

10 YEAR RECORD

00-01	01-02	02-03	03-04	04-05	05-06	06-07	07-08	08-09	09-10
Wex 7	Wex 13	Wex1 1	SthE 4	Isth P 3	Conf S 8	Conf S 15	Conf S 6	Conf S 3	Conf S 11

EASTLEIGH

No.	Date	Comp	H/A	Opponents	Att:	Result	Goalscorers	Pos
1	8/8/09	BSS	H	Braintree Town	436	L 1-2	Forbes 61	17
2	11/8/09	BSS	A	Weymouth	931	W 5-0	Smith 2 (38, 45), McAuley 43, Forbes 52, Oliver 90	8
3	15/8/09	BSS	A	St Albans City	332	L 1-2	McAuley 66	13
4	18/8/09	BSS	H	Bromley	607	W 6-1	Forbes 2 (9, 54), Brown 39, Jordan 43, Adeniyi 78, Martin 90	10
5	22/8/09	BSS	A	Thurrock	227	L 2-3	Riviere 12, Jordan 38	13
6	29/8/09	BSS	H	Dover Athletic	703	L 1-2	Riviere 16	15
7	31/8/09	BSS	A	Woking	1461	D 0-0		13
8	5/9/09	BSS	H	Staines Town	567	D 0-0		14
9	8/9/09	BSS	A	Bath City	507	W 2-0	Forbes 3, Jordan 18	13
10	12/9/09	BSS	A	Newport County	1316	L 1-5	McAuley 28	13
11	19/9/09	BSS	H	Chelmsford City	552	W 3-1	Jordan 2 (39, 62), Riviere 43	12
12	3/10/09	BSS	A	Havant & Waterlooville	1451	D 2-2	Gillespie 2 (61, 84)	12
13	17/10/09	BSS	H	Maidenhead United	532	L 0-3		15
14	27/10/09	BSS	H	Hampton & Richmond B.	550	D 0-0		15
15	31/10/09	BSS	H	Worcester City	501	W 4-1	Forbes 19, Gillespie 38, Riviere 66, Taggart 79	15
16	10/11/09	BSS	A	Dorchester Town	423	W 2-1	Adeniyi 43, Gillespie 79	11
17	14/11/09	BSS	H	Lewes	465	W 1-0	Og (Manning) 2	9
18	28/11/09	BSS	A	Braintree Town	454	D 1-1	Brown 47	10
19	8/12/09	BSS	A	Bishop's Stortford	282	W 1-0	Riviere 77	8
20	16/12/09	BSS	H	Weston-Super-Mare	253	W 3-1	Taggart 2 (23, 30), Forbes 33	7
21	26/12/09	BSS	H	Basingstoke Town	623	W 6-0	Gillespie 10, Poate 14, Forbes 36, Riviere 63, White 78, Adeniyi 87	5
22	28/12/09	BSS	A	Bromley	637	L 0-3		7
23	23/1/10	BSS	A	Maidenhead United	252	W 3-0	Jordan 4, Forbes 9, Gillespie 18	8
24	30/1/10	BSS	H	Havant & Waterlooville	875	L 0-1		9
25	2/2/10	BSS	H	Weymouth	490	W 4-0	Gillespie 2 (3, 7), Jordan 2 (29, 60)	7
26	6/2/10	BSS	A	Chelmsford City	994	D 2-2	Gillespie 4, Palmer 45	8
27	10/2/10	BSS	H	Newport County	745	L 1-4	Palmer 40	8
28	13/2/10	BSS	A	Weston-Super-Mare	207	D 2-2	Gillespie 55, Forbes 83	9
29	20/2/10	BSS	H	Thurrock	435	L 2-8	Gillespie 51, Adeniyi pen 76	11
30	23/2/10	BSS	A	Basingstoke Town	335	W 1-0	Riviere 74	8
31	27/2/10	BSS	A	Staines Town	509	W 2-1	Butler 13, Og (Mambo) 45	7
32	3/3/10	BSS	A	Lewes	233	W 2-1	Bottomley 6, Wilkinson 40	5
33	6/3/10	BSS	H	St Albans City	479	L 0-1		5
34	13/3/10	BSS	H	Bath City	655	D 1-1	Bottomley 66	6
35	17/3/10	BSS	H	Welling United	354	L 1-3	Gillespie 75	7
36	20/3/10	BSS	A	Hampton & Richmond B.	510	L 1-4	Butler 40	9
37	3/4/10	BSS	A	Dover Athletic	1127	L 1-2	Og (Schulz 67)	11
38	5/4/10	BSS	H	Woking	668	L 0-2		11
39	10/4/10	BSS	A	Welling United	409	W 2-1	Gillespie 13, Bottomley 34	11
40	14/4/10	BSS	H	Dorchester Town	433	W 2-0	Butler 31, Gillespie 45	11
41	17/4/10	BSS	H	Bishop's Stortford	481	D 1-1	Butler 42	11
42	24/4/10	BSS	A	Worcester City	752	L 1-4	Gillespie pen 3	11
	Cups							
1	26/9/09	FAC 2Q	A	Witney United	245	W 6-1	Taylor 9, Gillespie 19, McAuley 20, Poate 2 (26, pen 36), Riviere 80	
2	10/10/09	FAC 3Q	H	Basingstoke Town	681	W 2-0	Gillespie 17, Smith 58	
3	24/10/09	FAC 4Q	A	Dover Athletic	1161	W 5-3	Taggart 2 (11, 32), Jordan 47, Gillespie 60, Forbes 80	
4	7/11/09	FAC 1	A	Barrow	1655	L 1-2	Forbes 85	
5	21/11/09	FAT 3Q	H	Lewes	261	D 1-1	Adeniyi pen 29	
6	24/11/09	FAT 3QR	A	Lewes	211	L 0-1		

Home Attendances:	
Highest:	875 v Havant & Waterlooville
Lowest:	253 v Weston-Super-Mare
Average (08-09):	532 (723)

Top Goalscorer:	Gillespie - 18 (15 League, 3 Cup) in 45 appearances - 40% strike rate
Most Appearances:	Adeniyi - 47 (36+5 League, 5+1 Cup)

MATTHEWS	CLARK	POATE	SMITH	JORDAN	MARTIN	ADENIYI	FORBES	GILLESPIE	TAGGART	MCAULEY	WILLIAMS	HOWELLS	GOODHIND	CHALLIS	OLIVER	BROWN	RIVIERE	TAYLOR	BEAZLEY	ANDY COOK	BAIRD	LOADER	WHITE	ROBINSON	AARON COOK	ARNOLD	S COOK	DAY	WEBB	PALMER	TESSEM	TOOMER	BOTTOMLEY	BUTLER	ROACHE	WILKINSON	LUMLEY	NICHOLLS	EASTON	FOLKES	SHARP	
X	X	X	X	X	X	X	X	X	X	X	S	S	U	U	U																											**1**
X	X	X	X	X	X	X	X	S	X	X	X	U	U	S	S																											**2**
X	X	X	X	X	X	X	X	S	X	X	X	U	U	U	U																											**3**
X	U	S	X	X	X	S	X	S	X	X	U		X	X		X	X																									**4**
X	S	X	X	X	X	X	X				S	U	X	X	U	X	X																									**5**
X	X	X	X	X	X	X	X	S					X	U	U		X	X	U	U																						**6**
X	X	X	X	X	X	X	X	S					X	U	S		X	X	U		U																					**7**
X	X	X	X	X	X	X	X	S	X	S				S	U		X	X	U																							**8**
X	S	X	X	X	X	X	X	S	X	S				X	U		X	X	U																							**9**
X	U	X	X	X	X	X	X	S	X	X		U	U		U		X	X																								**10**
X	S	X	S	X	X	X	X	X	X	X		U	X	S			X	U																								**11**
X		X	X		X	X	S	X	X	X	S		X	U	U		X	X				U																				**12**
X		X	X	X		X	S	X	X	S	S		X	U	U		X	X					X																			**13**
X		X	X	X		X	X	X	X	S			X	U		S	X					U	S		X																	**14**
X		X	X	X		X	X	X	X	S			X	U		S	X	U					S		X																	**15**
		X	X	X		X		X	X	S			X	U		X	X	S				U	S		X	X																**16**
		X	X	X		X	U	X	X	S			X	U		X	X					U	S		X	X																**17**
U		X	X	X		X		S		X			U	U		X	X						X		X	X	X	U														**18**
X		X	X	X		X	X	S	X	X				U		X	X					U	S		X			U														**19**
X		X	X	X		S	X	S	X	X				S		X	X						U		X		X	U														**20**
X		X	X	X		S	X	X	X	X		U		U			X			U			S		X		X															**21**
X		X	X	X		S	S	X	X	X		U				X	X						S		X		X	U														**22**
X				X		X	X	X	X	X		U			X	S	X				U				X		X	S	S													**23**
X			U	X		X	X	X	X	X		U			X	S	X								X		X	U	U													**24**
X			X	X		X	X	X	X	X					X		S										X	X	S													**25**
X			S	X		X		X	X	X					X		X								U		X	X	U	X	S	U										**26**
X			U	X		X	S	X	X	X					X		X										X	X	U	X	S	U										**27**
X			X	X		X	S	X	S	X					X		X								U		X	X		X	S	U										**28**
X		X	X	X		X	X	X							S		X								X			X			X	U	S	S	U							**29**
X			X	X		X	X	X							X		X			U				U	S				S			U	X	X	X							**30**
X			X	X		X	X	X							X		X			U					S				S			U	X	X	S	X						**31**
X		S	X	X		X	X		S	X			S		X		X								U							U	X	X		X						**32**
U		X	X	X			X		X	X			X		S		X								S								X	U	S	X	X					**33**
U		X	X			X		X	X	X			X		U										U								X	S		X	X	X	U			**34**
U		X	X			X		X	X	S			X		S		X								U									S		X	X	X		X		**35**
X		X	X			X		X	X	S					U		X								X									X		X	U	X		S	U	**36**
X		X	U	X		X		X	X	S			X				X								X								X	X			U	U	S			**37**
X		X		X		X		X	X	X			X		U		X								X								X	S			S	U	S			**38**
X		X	S	X		X		X	X	X			X				X															U	X	S				S	U		X	**39**
X		X	X	X		X		X	X						U		X															U	X	X				S	S		X	**40**
U		X	S	X		X		X	X	S					U		X							S								X	X	X				X	X			**41**
		X	X			S		X		U		U	X		S		X															X	X	X				X	X			**42**
X	U	X	X	X		S	U	X	X	X			X	X	X		S	X		U	U	U																				**1**
X		X	X	X	X	X	S	X	S	X				U	S		X	X				U	X	U																		**2**
X		X	X	X	X	X	X	X	X	S			X	U	U		X	S				U	S																			**3**
X		X	X	X		X	X	X	X	S			X	U	U	X	X	S				U	S																			**4**
U		X	X			X	S	X	S	X			X	U		X	X						S		X	X	X															**5**
U			X	X		X	X	X	S	X			S	X		S	X						U		X	X	X															**6**
Total League Appearances																																										
34	6	32	33	37	12	36	24	28	32	23	2	0	18	3	9	8	37	7	0	0	0	0	2	0	15	3	10	5	0	3	1	2	11	8	1	6	3	5	2	1	2	**X**
0	3	2	4	0	0	5	5	11	2	11	4	1	1	4	6	4	1	1	0	0	0	0	7	1	3	0	0	1	4	0	3	0	1	5	2	0	1	2	3	1	0	**S**
5	2	0	3	0	0	0	1	0	0	1	1	10	5	13	14	0	0	2	4	4	2	5	1	1	5	0	0	5	3	0	0	9	0	1	1	0	2	2	2	0	1	**U**
Total Cup Appearances																																										
4	0	5	6	5	2	5	3	6	3	4	0	0	4	2	1	2	5	2	0	0	0	0	1	0	2	2	2	0	0	0	0	0	0	0	0	0	0	0	0	0	0	**X**
0	0	0	0	0	0	1	2	0	3	2	0	0	1	0	1	1	1	2	0	0	0	0	3	0	0	0	0	0	0	0	0	0	0	0	0	0	0	0	0	0	0	**S**
2	1	0	0	0	0	0	1	0	0	0	0	0	0	4	2	0	0	0	0	1	1	4	1	1	0	0	0	0	0	0	0	0	0	0	0	0	0	0	0	0	0	**U**
Total Goals																																										
0	0	1	2	8	1	4	10	15	3	3	0	0	0	0	1	2	7	0	0	0	0	0	1	0	0	0	0	0	0	2	0	0	3	4	0	1	0	0	0	0	0	**Lge**
0	0	2	1	1	0	1	2	3	2	1	0	0	0	0	0	0	1	1	0	0	0	0	0	0	0	0	0	0	0	0	0	0	0	0	0	0	0	0	0	0	0	**Cup**

Also Played: GOSNEY S(5). MULLINS U(Cup2). MORRIS S(25). COLLINS X(42). DONNELLY S(42).

EASTLEIGH

CURRENT SQUAD AS OF BEGINING OF 2010-11 SEASON

GOALKEEPERS	HT	WT	D.O.B	AGE	P.O.B	CAREER	Apps	Gls
Jason Matthews	6'00"	12 02	15/3/75	35	Paulton	Mangotsfield, Welton R, Westbury, Bath C, Paulton, Nuneaton, Taunton 8/98, Exeter 8/99 Rel c/s 00, Aberystwyth c/s 00, Cleveden 6/01, Weymouth 8/02, Eastleigh 3/08	34	0
Fred Toomer			19/2/92	18		Eastleigh, Laverstock & Ford, Eastleigh 2/10	2	0
DEFENDERS								
Warren Goodhind	5'11"	11 06	16/8/77	33	Johannesburg, SA	Barnet, Millwall (Trial) 7/01, Cambridge U £80,000 9/01 Rel c/s 05, Rochdale 9/05, Oxford U (SL) 2/06, Bishop's Stortford 3/07, Dag & Red (Trial) c/s 07, Ebbsfleet 8/07, Eastleigh (L) 11/07 Perm Rel 5/08, Harrow c/s 08, Eastleigh 8/08 Rel 12/09, Spain, Eastleigh 3/10	19	0
Chris Holland	6'00"	10 06	29/8/80	30	Taunton	Bournemouth (Trainee), Bristol C Rel c/s 00, Exeter (L), Team Bath 9/00, Bath C (L) 3/05, Bath C 8/05 Rel 5/10, Weston-Super-Mare (2ML) 11/05, Gloucester (L) 2/06, Eastleigh 5/10		
Tom Jordan	6'04"	12 04	24/5/81	29	Manchester	Bristol C Rel c/s 02, Huddersfield (Trial) 3/02, Carlisle (Trial) 7/02, Exeter (Trial) 7/02, Southend 8/02 Rel c/s 03, Tamworth 8/03, Forest Green 3/04, Havant & W 8/04, Eastleigh 6/08	37	8
Lewis Robinson			26/9/91	18		Eastleigh	1	0
MIDFIELDERS								
Peter Adeniyi			23/1/80	30	London	Erith T, Dulwich H, Lewes 7/03, Beckenham 6/05, Bromley 7/06, Eastleigh 12/07	41	4
Ross Bottomley			11/5/84	26	Ascot	Fareham, Hamble ASSC, Aldershot (Trial) 10/05, AFC Totten, Bashley (2ML) 12/09, Eastleigh 2/10	12	3
Jamie Brown			14/7/81	29	Bournemouth	BAT Sports, Dorchester 7/01, Eastleigh 4 fig 9/06	12	2
Joe Collins	5'09"	10 09	29/10/90	19	Southampton	Portsmouth Rel c/s 09, Dundee U c/s 09 Rel 2/10, Eastleigh 2/10	1	0
Richard Graham	5'10"	11 10	5/8/79	31	Newry	QPR Rel c/s 01, Barnet 7/01, Chesham 9/01, Billericay 7/02 Rel c/s 03, Kettering 8/03, Barnet 7/04 Rel c/s 07, Dag & Red 7/07 Rel c/s 09, Kettering (SL) 1/09, Grays 7/09 Rel 5/10, Eastleigh 7/10		
Chris Mason			11/1/91	19	Southampton	Southampton (Yth), Eastleigh, AFC Totton (L) 9/08, Bashley (Dual) c/s 09		
Shaun McAuley			16/2/87	23		Hayes & Yeading, Hampton & R c/s 07, Walton Casuals (Dual) 10/07, Eastleigh 7/09	34	3
Brett Poate			30/9/83	26	Southampton	Southampton Rel 2/03, Havant & W (2ML) 8/02, QPR (Trial) 2/03, Havant & W 2/03 Rel 4/09, Bognor Regis (L) 1/04, Eastleigh 4/09	34	1
Anthony Riviere			9/11/78	31	Kent	Faversham, Welling 11/98, Fisher 6/04 Rel 5/07, Eastleigh 7/07	38	7
Danny Smith	5'11"	11 04	17/8/82	28	Southampton	Bashley (Yth), Bournemouth Rel c/s 02, Winchester 7/02, Eastleigh 7/04, Bashley (3ML) 12/07, Bashley 3/08, Bognor Regis 7/08, Eastleigh 5/09	37	2
FORWARDS								
Alex Easton			26/4/92	18		Eastleigh	5	0
Richard Gillespie			21/11/84	25		Southampton (Yth), Bashley, Salisbury (SL) 3/05, Eastleigh Undisc 6/09	39	15
Joe Maxwell			28/11/89	20		Eastleigh		
Stafforde Palmer			23/4/88	22		Hayes/Hayes & Yeading, Northwood (L) 12/08, Maidenhead (3ML) 6/09, Eastleigh (SL) 2/10, Eastleigh 7/10	3	2
Jamie Slabber	6'02"	11 10	31/12/84	25	Enfield	Tottenham, AB Copenhagen (L) 3/04, Swindon (L) 12/04, Aldershot 3/05 Rel 5/05, Grays 7/05, Oxford U (L) 11/06, Stevenage 12/06 Rel 5/07, Rushden & D (Trial) 7/07, Havant & W 8/07 Rel 10/08, Grays NC 10/08, Woking 12/09 Rel 5/10, Eastleigh 5/10		
Andy Cook			10/8/69	41		Eastleigh (Coach)	0	0
Matt Gray			18/9/81	28		Eastleigh (Coach)		
Ian Baird			1/4/64	46		Eastleigh (Manager)	0	0

Loanees	HT	WT	DOB	AGE	POB	From - To	APPS	GOA
(M)Mike Gosney			12/2/88	22		AFC Totton 8/09 -	1	0
(F)James Taylor			2/11/76	33		AFC Totton (3ML) 8/09 - Gosport B 6/10	8	0
(F)Jamie White			17/11/89	20		Southampton (2ML) 10/09 -	9	1
(D)Steve Cook	6'01"	12 13	19/4/91	19	Hastings	Brighton 11/09 -	10	0
(D)Luke Wilkinson			27/9/90	19		Portsmouth 2/10 - Dag & red c/s 10	6	1
Departures	**HT**	**WT**	**DOB**	**AGE**	**POB**	**From - To**	**APPS**	**GOA**
(D)Michael Green			12/5/89	21		Christchurch 5/09 - AFC Totton (2ML) 8/09 Undisc 10/09		
(M)Steve Clark	6'01"	12 05	10/2/82	28	London	Bromley 10/08 - Chelmsford 10/09	9	0
(F)Brett Williams			1/12/87	22	Southampton	Winchester 11/08 - AFC Totton (2ML) 8/09 Undisc 10/09	6	0
(D)Aaron Martin	6'02"	11 13	29/9/89	20	Newport, IOW	Yth - Southampton Undisc 11/09, Salisbury (SL) 3/10	12	1
(G)Steve Arnold	6'01"		22/8/89	21	Welham Green	Grays 11/09 - Wycombe (Trial) 12/09 Perm 1/10	3	0
(D)Trevor Challis	5'08"	11 06	23/10/75	34	Paddington	Weymouth 6/08 - Retired 1/10, Eastleigh (Coach)	7	0
(M)Perry Mullins			4/1/91	19		Yth - Wimborne 1/10	0	0
(F)Saul Otobo			17/9/87	22		St Albans 11/09 - Chester (Trial), Stafford R 2/10		
(F)Jo Tessem			28/2/72	38		ex Southampton 2/10 - Rel 2/10	4	0
(D)Matt Day			24/3/87	23		Hungerford 11/09 - Rel 2/10	6	0
(M)Josh Webb			23/1/90	20		ex Farnborough 1/10 - Rel 3/10, Basingstoke 3/10	4	0
(F)Lee Roache	5'09"	11 00	30/4/84	26	Leytonstone	Braintree 2/10 - Bath C 3/10, Hemel Hempstead 3/10	3	0
(M)Tony Taggart			7/10/81	28	London	Havant & W 7/08 - Newport C 5/10	34	3
(F)Andy Forbes			28/5/79	31	Reading	Winchester 8/04 - Rel 5/10, Woking 5/10	29	10
(M)Ashley Nicholls	5'11"	11 11	30/10/81	28	Ipswich	Bishop's Stortford 3/10 - Maidenhead 6/10	7	0
(F)Sam Butler			1/6/88	22		Whyteleafe NC 2/10 - Rel c/s 10	13	4
(D)Aaron Cook	6'01"	11 05	6/12/79	30	Caerphilly	Newport C 10/09 - Gosport B 7/10	18	0
(D)Neil Sharp			9/1/78	32		Cambridge C 3/10 - Chesham 7/10	2	0
(G)Gareth Howells			13/6/70	40	Guildford	Havant & W (Pl/Coach) 10/07 - Rel c/s 10	1	0
(D)Ian Oliver			9/10/85	24	Southampton	Farnborough 6/09 - Rel c/s 10	15	1
(F)Darren Morris			6/9/86	23		-	1	0
(G)Lyall Beazley			22/4/88	22		Farnborough 8/09 -	0	0
(G)Dan Loader			13/9/88	21		Christchurch 8/09 - New Milton (Dual) 10/09	0	0
(G)Billy Lumley	6'05"	14 13	28/12/89	20	Loughton	Northampton 3/10 -	4	0
(D)James Donnelly			12/9/89	20		Yth -	1	0
(D)Sam Doswell			28/2/90	20		Yth -		
(D)Jay Folkes						Glen Hoddle Academy 3/10 -	2	0

EBBSFLEET UNITED

Chairman: Philip Sonsara
Secretary: Peter Danzey (T) 07533 283 431 (E) peter@eufc.co.uk

Additional Committee Members:
Duncan Holt, Cheryl Wanless, Brian Kilcullen, Barry Wickenden, Richard Hills, Charles Webster

Manager: Liam Daish
Programme Editor: Rachel Willett (E) rachel@eufc.co.uk

Back Row (L-R): Kwesi Appiah, Peter Hawkins, John Akinde, Gary MacDonald, Darius Charles, James Smith, Neil Barrett. **Middle**: Ron Hillyard (goalkeeping coach), George Purcell, Ricky Shakes, Michael Gash, Rob French, Lance Cronin, Sam Mott, Kezie Ibe, Mark Ricketts, Luke Moore, Chris Domoney (fitness & conditioning). **Front**: Ian Docker (youth coach), Craig Stone, Dean Pooley, Sacha Opinel, Alan Kimble, Liam Daish, Paul McCarthy, Danny Slatter, Stacy Long, Paul Wilson (sports therapist). Courtesy of EUFC.co.uk (Archive photo)

Club Factfile

Founded: 1946 **Nickname:** The Fleet
Previous Names: Gravesend United and Northfleet United merged in 1946 to form Gravesend and Northfleet > 2007
Previous Leagues: Southern 1946-79, 80-96. Alliance 1979-80, Isthmian 1997-2001

Club Colours (change): Red/white/red (All purple)

Ground: Stonebridge Road, Northfleet, Kent DA11 9GN (T) 01474 533 796
Capacity: 4,184 **Seats:** 500 **Covered:** 3,000 **Clubhouse:** Yes **Shop:** Yes
Previous Grounds: Gravesend United: Central Avenue

Simple Directions
A2 to Ebbsfleet/Eurostar International Junction.
Follow Brown signs to 'The Fleet'.

Record Attendance: 12,036 v Sunderland - FA Cup 4th Round 12/02/1963
Record Victory: 8-1 v Clacton Town - Southern League 1962-63
Record Defeat: 0-9 v Trowbridge Town - Southern League Premier DIvision 1991-92
Record Goalscorer: Steve Portway - 152 (1992-94, 97-2001)
Record Appearances: Ken Burrett - 537
Additional Records: Paid £8,000 to Wokingham Town for Richard Newbery 1996 and to Tonbridge for Craig Williams 1997
Received £35,000 from West Ham United for Jimmy Bullard 1998

Senior Honours: Southern League 1956-57, Division 1 South 1974-75, Southern Division 1994-95. Isthmian League Premier 2001-02.
FA Trophy 2007-08. Kent Senior Cup 1948-49, 52-53, 80-81, 99-00, 00-01, 01-02.

10 YEAR RECORD

00-01	01-02	02-03	03-04	04-05	05-06	06-07	07-08	08-09	09-10
Isth P 6	Isth P 1	Conf 17	Conf 11	Conf 14	Conf 16	Conf 7	Conf 11	Conf 14	Conf 22

EBBSFLEET UNITED

No.	Date	Comp	H/A	Opponents	Att:	Result	Goalscorers	Pos
1	8/8/09	BSP	A	Altrincham	914	D 1-1	Lindie 59	11
2	11/8/09	BSP	H	Cambridge United	1523	L 1-3	Crooks 47	20
3	15/8/09	BSP	H	Kidderminster Harriers	865	D 0-0		18
4	18/8/09	BSP	A	Stevenage Borough	1704	L 0-3		20
5	22/8/09	BSP	A	Mansfield Town	3269	L 0-3		22
6	29/8/09	BSP	H	Hayes & Yeading United	884	L 1-2	Vieira 6	22
7	31/8/09	BSP	A	Eastbourne Borough	1165	W 2-1	Vieira pen 56, Thomas 90	21
8	5/9/09	BSP	H	Oxford United	1468	L 0-2		21
9	8/9/09	BSP	H	Rushden & Diamonds	863	D 0-0		21
10	12/9/09	BSP	A	Forest Green Rovers	762	D 0-0		21
11	19/9/09	BSP	H	AFC Wimbledon	2005	D 2-2	Cumbers 41, Vieira 79	18
12	22/9/09	BSP	A	Histon	647	L 0-1		19
13	26/9/09	BSP	A	Kettering Town	1345	L 0-3		20
14	29/9/09	BSP	H	Salisbury City	792	L 1-2	McCarthy 90	22
15	3/10/09	BSP	H	Crawley Town	987	D 0-0		22
16	10/10/09	BSP	A	Cambridge United	3668	L 0-4		22
17	17/10/09	BSP	A	Barrow	1241	L 0-2		23
18	31/10/09	BSP	H	Wrexham	969	L 0-1		23
19	14/11/09	BSP	A	York City	2629	L 0-1		23
20	21/11/09	BSP	H	Tamworth	867	L 0-1		23
21	24/11/09	BSP	A	AFC Wimbledon	2942	L 0-3		23
22	28/11/09	BSP	H	Mansfield Town	850	W 2-1	Vieira 3, Holmes 57	23
23	1/12/09	BSP	H	Stevenage Borough	836	W 2-1	Bailey 2 (49, 55)	22
24	5/12/09	BSP	A	Oxford United	5188	L 2-4	Vieira 57, Ginty 88	23
25	26/12/09	BSP	H	Grays Athletic	937	W 2-1	Vieira 10, Shakes 79	22
26	28/12/09	BSP	A	Hayes & Yeading United	389	L 2-4	Vieira 84, Ginty 90	22
27	1/1/10	BSP	A	Grays Athletic	793	W 3-0	Holmes 7, Vieira 13, Shakes 42	21
28	16/1/10	BSP	H	Altrincham	875	L 1-2	Ginty 62	22
29	19/1/10	BSP	H	Kettering Town	587	L 1-2	Ashikodi pen 51	22
30	23/1/10	BSP	H	Forest Green Rovers	790	W 4-3	Vieira 2 (19, 55), Bailey 79, Crooks 90	20
31	30/1/10	BSP	A	Luton Town	6658	W 3-2	Vieira 2 (41, 45), Ashikodi 67	19
32	9/2/10	BSP	H	Histon	731	L 0-1		18
33	13/2/10	BSP	H	York City	1226	W 1-0	Ashikodi 52	18
34	20/2/10	BSP	A	Gateshead	533	W 3-1	Shakes 28, Vieira 30, Ashikodi 65	17
35	27/2/10	BSP	H	Barrow	1146	L 1-4	Ashikodi 78	17
36	2/3/10	BSP	A	Kidderminster Harriers	1163	D 2-2	Ashikodi 36, Ginty 69	17
37	6/3/10	BSP	A	Wrexham	2345	D 1-1	Ashikodi 69	18
38	9/3/10	BSP	A	Crawley Town	983	L 1-2	Ashikodi 89	18
39	20/3/10	BSP	H	Luton Town	1923	L 1-6	Og (Kovacs) 24	19
40	2/4/10	BSP	A	Salisbury City	1088	L 1-3	Vieira 46	22
41	5/4/10	BSP	H	Eastbourne Borough	1214	W 3-2	Bailey 7, Ashikodi 2 (63, 65)	22
42	10/4/10	BSP	A	Rushden & Diamonds	1440	L 0-2		22
43	17/4/10	BSP	H	Gateshead	1169	W 2-0	Vieira 2, Stavrinou 89	22
44	24/4/10	BSP	A	Tamworth	1694	W 4-3	Vieira 12, Shakes 38, Ginty 2 (77, 81)	22
	Chester	**record**	**........................**	**...expunged 08/03**				
32	6/2/10	BSP	A	Chester City	460	W 2-1	Vieira 2 (41, 44)	18

No.	Date	Comp	H/A	Opponents	Att:	Result
	Cups					
1	24/10/09	FAC 4Q	A	Bromley	1133	L 0-3
2	12/12/09	FAT 1	A	Stevenage Borough	890	L 0-2

Home League Attendances	
Highest:	2005 v AFC Wimbledon
Lowest:	587 v Kettering Town
Average (08-09):	911 (1203)
Top Goalscorer:	Vieira - 16 (16 League, 0 Cup) in 43 appearances - 37% strike rate
Most Appearances:	Cronin - 46 (44 League, 2 Cup)

CRONIN 1	D CHARLES 24	CROOKS 22	SALMON 2	COLLINS 3	HEEROO 4	FORSHAW 10	SHULTON 15	WELSH 11	VIEIRA 8	SHAKES 16	LINDIE 9	WEST 7	WILLS 14	LAMPRELL 21	POOLEY 5	BAILEY 23	GINTY 12	THOMAS 25	HENRY 17	READ 19	CUMBERS 26	ABBEY 20	MCCARTHY 6	HOLMES 27	E CHARLES 25	EASTON 26	SHERLOCK 28	RILEY 32	SMITH 33	STAVRINOU 15	ASHIKODI 9	HAGAN	
X	X	X	X	X	X	X	X	X	X	X	S	S	S	U	U																		1
X	X	X	X	X	X	S	X	X	X	X	X	S	U	U	U																		2
X	X	X	X	X	X	S	X	X	X	X	X	U	S	U	U																		3
X	X	X	X	X	X	X	S		X	X		X	U	U	U	X	S																4
X	X	X	X	X	X	S	X	X	X			X	S	U	U		S	X															5
X	X	X	X	X	X	S	U	X	X	X				U	X		S	X	U														6
X		X	X	X	X	S	X	X	X	X			S	U	X		S	X		U													7
X	X	X	X	X	X	S	S	X	X	X			S		X		U	X		U													8
X	X	X	U	X	X	S		X	X	S	S		X		X	X	U	X															9
X	X	X	U	X	X			X	X	S	S	S	X		X	X	U	X															10
X	X	X	X		X	S		X	S	S	X		X		X	X		U			X	U											11
X	X	X	X		X	S	U	X	X	S			X		X	X	S				X	U											12
X	X	X	X		S		U	X	X	X			X	U	U	X	S				X		X										13
X	X	X			X	U	U	X	X	X			X	U	U	X	S				X		X										14
X	X	X			X		X	X	S	X		S	X		X	S	U				X	U	X										15
X	X	X	U		X		X	X		X		S	X	U			S				X	S	X	X									16
X	X	X	S		X		X	U	S	S		U	X				X		X				X	X	X								17
X	X	X			X			X	X	S		U	X		S	S	U		X					X	X	X							18
X	X		S		X	S		X	X	X		X	U	U	X	X	S							X					X				19
X	X	X			X	U		X	X	X		X	S	U		X	S							X		S			X				20
X			X		X	S		X	X	X		X	U	U	X	X	U			U				X					X				21
X			X		X			U	X	X		X	U	U	X	X	U			U				X					X	X			22
X	X	X			X			S	X	X		X	S	U	U	X	U							X					X	X			23
X	X	X	U		X			X	X	X		X	S	U	U		S							X					X	X			24
X	X	X	X		U	U		X	X	X			U		X	X	S							X		U				X			25
X	X	X	X			U		X	X	X			S	U	X	X	S							X		S				X			26
X		X	X			U		S	X	X		X	S		X	X	S		U					X		X				X			27
X	S	X	X		U			S	X	X		X	U		X	X	S							X		X				X			28
X	X	X	X		U			S		X		X	S		X	U	S							X		X				X	X		29
X	X	X	X		S			U	X	X		U	U		X	X	S							X						X	X		30
X	X	X	X	U	U				X	X		S	U			X	U							X		X				X	X		31
X	X	X	X		U			U	X	X		S			U	X	S							X		X				X	X		32
X	X	X		S	X			U	X	X		U	U		X	X	S							X		X					X		33
X	X	X	S	X	X				X	X		S	U	U	X	X	S							X							X		34
X	X	X	U	X				S	X	X		U	S		X	X	S							X						X	X		35
X	X	X	S	X	S			U	X	X			U		X	X	S							X						X	X		36
X	X	X	X	X	U			U				U	S		X	X	X							X						X	X		37
X	X	X	S	X	X			S	X	X		U	U		X	X	S													X	X		38
X	X	X	U	X	X			S	X	X		U	U			X	S							X						X	X		39
X	X	X	X		U			U	X	X		S	X		X	S	S							X						X	X		40
X	X	X	X		S			U	X	X			X		X	X	U			U				X						S	X		41
X	X	X	X		X			S	X	X			X	U		X	S			U				X						S	X		42
X	X	X	X		U				X	S		X	U		X	X	S							X						X	X		43
X	X	X	X		U				X	X		X	U		X	X	S			U				X						X			44
X	X	X	X		U			S	X	X		U			U	X	S							X		X				X	X		
X	X	X	U					X	S	X		X	X	U		S	X		X						X	X	U	U					1
X	X	X	X		X	U		X	X	X			U	U	U	X	S							X					X				2
Total League Appearances																																	
44	39	41	27	16	28	2	8	22	38	35	3	13	13	0	27	30	2	6	2	0	6	0	5	28	2	7	0	0	6	19	15		X
0	1	0	5	1	4	11	2	8	3	7	3	9	13	0	1	3	28	0	0	0	0	1	0	0	0	2	0	0	0	2	0		S
0	0	0	6	1	9	5	4	9	0	0	0	9	16	19	10	1	10	1	2	7	0	3	0	0	0	1	0	0	0	0	0		U
Total Cup Appearances																																	
2	2	2	1	0	1	0	0	2	1	2	0	1	1	0	0	1	1	0	1	0	0	0	0	1	1	1	0	0	1	0	0		X
0	0	0	0	0	0	0	0	0	1	0	0	0	0	0	0	1	1	0	0	0	0	0	0	0	0	0	0	0	0	0	0		S
0	0	0	1	0	0	1	0	0	0	0	0	0	1	2	1	0	0	0	0	0	0	0	0	0	0	0	1	1	0	0	0		U
Total Goals																																	
0	0	2	0	0	0	0	0	0	16	4	1	0	0	0	0	4	6	1	0	0	1	0	1	2	0	0	0	0	0	1	10		Lg
0	0	0	0	0	0	0	0	0	0	0	0	0	0	0	0	0	0	0	0	0	0	0	0	0	0	0	0	0	0	0	0		Cp

EBBSFLEET UNITED

CURRENT SQUAD AS OF BEGINING OF 2010-11 SEASON

GOALKEEPERS	HT	WT	D.O.B	AGE	P.O.B	CAREER	Apps	Gls
Joseph Hagan			8/11/91	18		Ebbsfleet	0	0
Matthew Lamprell			26/2/91	19		Millwall, Ebbsfleet 8/09	0	0
DEFENDERS								
Jordan Collins			7/12/88	21		Cambridge U Rel 5/09, Billericay (L) 11/07, Heybridge (SL) 3/08, Weymouth (SL) 11/08, Ebbsfleet 7/09	17	0
Paul Lorraine			12/10/83	26		Welling, Dartford (L) 1/03, Erith & B 3/04, Braintree 5/04, Fisher 5/06, AFC Wimbledon (L) 12/06, Perm 1/07, Woking 5/07, AFC Wimbledon 5/09 Rel 4/10, Ebbsfleet 6/10		
Paul McCarthy	5'10"	13 10	4/8/71	39	Cork	Brighton, Wycombe £100,000 7/96 Rel c/s 03, Oxford U (SL) 3/03, Oxford U 7/03, Rel c/s 04, Hornchurch 6/04, Gravesend/Ebbsfleet 11/04	5	1
Dean Pooley	6'01"	11 02	10/9/86	23	Sidcup	Millwall Rel 12/06, Crawley (L) 3/06, Beckenham (L) 9/06, Bohemians 3/07 Rel 1/08, Ballymena 1/08 Rel 2/08, Ebbsfleet 8/08	28	0
Charlie Read	6'00"	11 00	26/9/90	19		Millwall (Scholar), Ebbsfleet 8/09, Bromley (L) 10/09, Margate (L) 12/09	0	0
Will Salmon			25/11/86	23	Basingstoke	Aldershot Rel c/s 07, Fleet T (SL) c/s 05, Fleet T (SL) 8/06, AFC Wimbledon 6/07 Rel 5/08, Fleet T (L) 2/08, Fleet T c/s 08, Ebbsfleet 8/09	32	0
Steve Springett			31/12/90	19		Ebbsfleet, Ashford T (L) 10/09		
MIDFIELDERS								
Davis Abbey	5'06"		18/3/91	19		Southend (Scholar) Rel 5/09, Ebbsfleet 8/09	1	0
Stefan Bailey	5'11"	12 08	10/11/87	22	Brent	QPR Rel 5/08, Oxford (L) 10/07, Grays 6/08, Farnborough (L) 2/09, Ebbsfleet 8/09	33	4
Leon Crooks	6'00"	11 12	21/11/85	24	Greenwich	Wimbledon/MK Dons, Wycombe Undisc 1/07 Rel 5/09, Ebbsfleet (3ML) 1/09, Ebbsfleet 8/09	41	2
Derek Duncan	5'10"	10 11	23/4/87	23	Newham	L.Orient Rel 5/07, Lewes (L) 9/06, Grays 5/07, Wycombe 7/07, Lewes (2ML) 11/07, Ebbsfleet 1/09, AFC Wimbledon 6/09 Rel 4/10, Ebbsfleet 7/10		
Clint Easton	5'11"	11 00	1/10/77	32	Barking	Watford, Norwich £200,000 6/01 Rel c/s 04, Wycombe 7/04, Gillingham 7/06 Rel c/s 07, Hereford 7/07 Rel 4/09, Mansfield (Trial) 4/09, Ebbsfleet 10/09	9	0
Gavin Heeroo	5'11"	11 07	2/9/84	25	Haringey	C.Palace Rel c/s 04, L.Orient (Trial) 4/04, Billericay c/s 04, Grays 10/04, Farnborough 3/05, Histon (Trial) 9/05, Cambridge U (SL) 11/05, Chelmsford 8/06 Rel 1/07, Fisher 1/07, Sutton U 7/08, Eastleigh 3/09 Rel 5/09, Ebbsfleet 7/09	32	0
Chris Henry			17/5/91	19		Ebbsfleet, Chatham (SL) 2/10	2	0
Rambir Marwa			10/1/80	30	Barkingside	L.Orient (Trainee), Erith & B 2/00, Ilford 7/00, Erith & B 1/01, Australia, L.Orient (Trial) 6/03, Grays 8/03, St Albans 8/04, Dag & Red 5/05, St Albans (L) 1/06 (Perm) 3/06, Hayes & Yeading (L) 11/07 Perm 12/07 Rel 5/10, Ebbsfleet 7/10		
Tom Phipps			3/8/92	18		Ebbsfleet		
Ricky Shakes	5'10"	12 00	26/1/85	25	Brixton	Bolton Rel c/s 05, Bristol R (L) 2/05, Bury (SL) 3/05, Swindon 8/05 Rel c/s 07, Brentford (Trial) 7/07, Brentford 8/07 Rel 5/08, Ebbsfleet 7/08	42	4
Aidan Sherlock			18/2/92	18		Ebbsfleet	0	0
Ishmael Welsh	5'07"	10 10	4/9/87	22	Deptford	West Ham Rel c/s 06, Yeovil 7/06 Rel 5/08, Weymouth (L) 3/07, Torquay (5ML) 8/07, Forest Green (SL) 2/08, Grays 5/08, Ebbsfleet 7/09	30	0
Michael West			9/2/91	19		Ebbsfleet	22	0
Kane Wills	5'09"	10 02	27/2/90	20	Shoreham	Brighton Rel 5/09, Bognor (L) 10/08, Bognor (SL) 1/09, Ebbsfleet 8/09	26	0
FORWARDS								
Scott Ginty	5'08"	11 11	17/5/91	19		Peterborough (Scholar) Rel c/s 09, Stamford (WE) 3/09, Ebbsfleet 8/09	30	6
Callum Willock	6'01"	12 08	29/10/81	28	Waterloo	ADT College, Fulham 7/00, QPR (L) 11/02, Bristol R (L) 8/03, Peterborough (2ML) 10/03 £25,000 12/03, Brentford £50,000 1/06 Rel c/s 07, Port Vale 8/07 Rel 12/07, Stevenage 1/08 Rel 5/09, AFC Wimbledon (Trial) 7/09, Crawley 9/09 Rel 2/10, Cambridge U NC 2/10 Rel 4/10, Ebbsfleet 7/10		

Loanees	HT	WT	DOB	AGE	POB	From - To	APPS	GOA
(F)Simon Thomas	5'06"	12 02	21/7/84	26	Stratford	C.Palace 8/09 - Darlington (2ML) 11/09, Rel 1/10, Billericay 1/10, Colchester (Trial) 2/10, Chelmsford 2/10	6	1
(M)Luis Cumbers	6'00"	11 10	6/9/88	21	Chelmsford	Gillingham 9/09 - AFC Wimbledon (L) 11/09, Dover (L) 2/10 Rel c/s 10, Welling 6/10	6	1
(F)Elliott Charles	6'02"	13 00	23/12/90	19	Enfield	Barnet 10/09 - Havant & W (L) 12/09, Rel 1/10, Kettering 3/10	2	0
(M)Alex Stavinrou	5'08"	10 05	13/9/90	19	Harlow	Charlton (SL) 11/09 -	21	1
Departures	**HT**	**WT**	**DOB**	**AGE**	**POB**	**From - To**	**APPS**	**GOA**
(F)James Lindie			14/11/89	20		Southend 7/09 - Rel 10/09, St Albans 2/10 Rel 4/10	6	1
(F)Chris Riley	5'09"	11 09	2/2/88	22	London	Glen Hoddle Soccer Academy 10/09 - Enfield T, Boreham Wood, Horsham 2/10	0	0
(M)Scott Shulton			31/1/90	19		Wycombe 8/09 - Bishop's Stortford (L) 10/09 Perm 11/09	10	0
(M)Jamie Forshaw	5'08"	11 00	21/11/90	18	Norwich	Southend 7/09 - Rel 2/10, Ashford T (L) 10/09, Lowestoft 2/10	13	0
(D)Ross Smith	6'00"	12 06	4/11/80	29	Guelph (Can)	Rochester Rhinos (USA) 11/09 - Portland Timbers (USA)	6	0
(D)Darius Charles	5'11"	11 10	10/12/87	22	Ealing	Brentford (SL) 6/08 £15,000+ 1/09 - Stevenage Undisc 5/10	40	0
(F)Moses Ashikodi	6'00"	11 09	27/6/87	24	Lagos	Kettering 1/10 - Kettering 6/10	15	10
(F)Magno Vieira	5'09"	11 07	13/2/85	25	Bahia, Bra	Wycombe 8/09 - Fleetwood 7/10	41	16
(G)Lance Cronin	6'01"	13 02	11/9/85	24	Brighton	Shrewsbury 8/06 - Gillingham 7/10	44	0
(M)Peter Holmes	5'11"	11 13	18/11/80	29	Bishop Auckland	Harrogate T 10/09 -	28	2

FARNBOROUGH

Chairman: Simon Hollis
Secretary: (Acting) Brian Berger **(T)** 07717 625 791
(E) farnboroughfc@btinternet.com

Additional Committee Members:
Amanda Hollis, Steve Duly, Vince Williams

Manager: Steve King
Programme Editor: Steve Duly **(E)**

Archive photo

Club Factfile

Founded: 1967 **Nickname:** Boro

Previous Names: Farnborough Town 1967-2007

Previous Leagues: Surrey Senior 1968-72, Spartan 1972-76, Athenian 1976-77, Isthmian 1977-89, 99-2001, Alliance/Conference 1989-90, 91-93, 94-99, Southern 1990-91, 93-94, 2007-10

Club Colours (change): All yellow (All purple)

Ground: Rushmoor Stadium, Cherrywood Road, Farnborough, Hants GU14 8UD **(T)** 01252 541 469

Capacity: 4,163 **Seats:** 627 **Covered:** 1,350 **Clubhouse:** Yes **Shop:** Yes

Previous Grounds: None as Farnborough. Queens Road as Farnborough Town

Simple Directions
Leave the M3 at Junction 4 and take the A331 signed to Farnham, after a few hundred yards exit at the second slip road- signed A325 Farnborough, turn right at the roundabout and cross over the dual carriageway and small roundabout, passing the Farnborough Gate shopping centre on your left hand side, at the next roundabout turn left (first exit) onto the A325. Go over a pelican crossing and at the next set of lights take the right filter into Prospect Avenue. At the end of this road turn rightat the roundabout into Cherrywood Road, the ground is half a mile on the right hand side.

Record Attendance: 2,230 v Corby Town - Southern Premier 21/03/2009
Record Victory: 7-0 v Newport (I.O.W.) (A) - Southern League Division 1 South & West 01/12/2007
Record Defeat: 0-4 v Hednesford Town (A) - Southern League Premier Division 04/03/2010
Record Goalscorer: Dean McDonald - 35 (in 53+3 Appearances 2009-10)
Record Appearances: Nic Ciardini - 147 (2007-10)
Additional Records:

Senior Honours: Southern League Division 1 South & West 2007-08, Premier Division 2009-10.
Farnborough Town: Southern League Premier Division 1990-91, 93-94. Isthmian League Division 1 1984-85, Premier Division 2000-01. Hampshire Senior Cup 1974-75, 81-82, 83-84, 85-86, 90-91, 2003-04.

10 YEAR RECORD

00-01		01-02		02-03		03-04		04-05		05-06		06-07		07-08		08-09		09-10	
Isth P	1	Conf	7	Conf	13	Conf	20	Conf	21	Conf S	3	Conf S	11	SthW	1	SthP	2	SthP	1

FARNBOROUGH

No.	Date	Comp	H/A	Opponents	Att:	Result	Goalscorers	Pos
1	Aug 15	Zamaretto P.	H	Leamington	1009	W 3 - 1	Ibe 55 McDonald 80 Thomas 90	3
2	18		A	Brackley	352	W 3 - 1	Ibe 30 Bubb 50 53	1
3	22		A	Truro City	863	W 3 - 2	Ibe 35 70 Bubb 83	2
4	26		H	Didcot Town	749	W 1 - 0	Bubb 20	
5	29		A	Clevedon Town	216	W 4 - 1	McDonald 3 83 Ibe 40 44	1
6	31		H	Bashley	1024	D 1 - 1	McDonald 43	
7	Sept 5		A	Tiverton Town	377	W 2 - 0	McDonald 40 60	1
8	**12**	**F.A.C 1Q**	**H**	**Hastings United**	**716**	**W 2 - 1**	**King 53 Bubb 61**	
9	19		H	Halesowen Town	1014	W 4 - 0	McDonald 25 85 (pen) J.Smith 37 McMahon 79	1
10	**26**	**F.A.C. 2Q**	**A**	**Windsor & Eton**	**478**	**W 1 - 0**	**McDonald 13**	
11	Oct 4		A	Merthyr TYdfil	464	D 0 - 0		1
12	7		H	Cambridge City	784	D 3 - 3	King 9 McDonald 26 J Smith 79	
13	**10**	**F.A.C. 3Q**	**A**	**Heybridge Swifts**	**295**	**D 0 - 0**		
14	**13**	**F.A.C. 3Qr**	**H**	**Heybridge Swifts**	**567**	**W 3 - 0***	**Bubb 101 McDonald 113 Thomas 116**	
15	**17**	**F.A.T 1Q**	**A**	**Hemel Hempstead**	**316**	**W 1 - 0**	**McMahon 18**	
16	21		H	Rugby Town	702	W 4 - 1	Smith 4 McDonald 50 Ibe 75 Opinel 90	1
17	**24**	**F.A.C 4Q**	**H**	**Salisbury City**	**1247**	**D 0 - 0**		
18	**27**	**F.A.C 4Qr**	**A**	**Salisbury City**	**1200**	**L 2 - 4**	**Ciardini 15 Ruddick 21 (og)**	
19	**31**	**F.A.T. 2Q**	**H**	**Burgess Hill**	**584**	**W 5 - 2**	**Ibe 33 71 McMahon 52 Thomas 55 66**	
20	Nov 7		H	Chippenham	869	W 3 - 1	Holloway 53 Ibe 61 89	1
21	14		A	Evesham United	173	W 2 - 1	Robinson 41 McDonald 90	1
22	**21**	**F.A.T. 3Q**	**H**	**Wealdstone**	**1012**	**W 3 - 0**	**Ibe 2 Robinson 27 Bubb 47**	
23	28		A	Swindon Spermarine	284	W 7 - 0	Bubb 14 57 McDonald 19 (pen) Robinson 27 King 62 68 Thomas 85	1
24	Dec 5		H	Nuneaton Borough	1180	L 0 - 2		1
25	**12**	**F.A.T 1**	**H**	**Newport County**	**805**	**L 1 - 3**	**Holloway 81**	
26	16		H	Oxford City	407	W 2 - 1	Thomas 2 McMahon 22	1
27	26		A	Bashley	525	W 4 - 0	McDONALD 3 (27 30 pen 42) McMahon 90	1
28	Jan 1		H	Hemel Hempstead T	1089	W 3 - 0	Holloway 22 90 Ciardini 82	
29	16		H	Clevedon Town	639	W 2 - 1	McDonald 52 (pen) Ciardini 85	1
30	20		A	Banbury United	252	W 3 - 0	McMahon 23 Ibe 28 Hopkinson 87	1
31	23		A	Halesowen Town	516	D 1 - 1	Bubb 29	1
32	30		H	Tiverton Town	747	W 2 - 1	McDonald 23 McMahon 25	1
33	Feb 2		A	Bedford Town	222	D 2 - 2	Doyle 46 Holloway 60	
34	6		A	Oxford City	376	D 1 - 1	McDonald 61 (pen)	1
35	13		H	Evesham United	674	W 3 - 1	Ibe 45 Dobson 88 Holloway 90 (pen)	1
36	20		A	Leamington	870	W 3 - 2	Wormall 57 Ibe 63 McCollin 89	
37	Mar 4		A	Hednesford Town	327	L 0 - 4		
38	6		A	Didcot Town	384	W 2 - 0	King 53 McCollin 55	1
39	9		A	Cambridge City	292	D 1 - 1	McMahon 675	
40	13		H	Merthyr Tydfil	584	W 3 - 1	McDonald 38 Bubb 64 86	1
41	17		H	Bedford Town	517	W 6 - 1	King 6 Bubb 10 71 Boyle 73 Ibe 76 Holloway 80	
42	20		A	Rugby Town	274	W 4 - 0	McDONALD 3 (27 77 79) Thomas 88	1
43	27		H	Stourbridge	675	L 1 - 2	Doyle 71	
44	April 5		A	Hemel Hempstead	415	D 1 - 1	McDonald 59	1
45	7		H	Truro City	616	W 3 - 1	McDonald 6 (pen) McMahon 26 Bubb 60	1
46	10		A	Nuneaton Town	1765	D 1 - 1	Bubb 9	1
47	12		H	Banbury United	638	W 3 - 0	McDonald 17 Doyle 68 Barratt 79	
48	14		H	Brackley Town	682	W 3 - 0	King 19 McDonald 40 Ibe 49	1
49	17		H	Swindon Supermarine	1372	W 2 - 0	King 20 McDonald 63	1
50	20		A	Stourbridge	294	L 2 - 3	Stevens 69 Thomas 61 (pen)	
51	22		H	Hednesford Town	1039	W 2 - 1	King 2 McDonald 90	1
52	24		A	Chippenham Town	744	L 0 - 2		1
					Goals	118 52		

Home Attendances:	
Highest:	1372 v Swindon Supermarine
Lowest:	407 v Oxford City
Average (08-09):	747 (799)
Top Goalscorer:	McDonald - 30 (League 28, FAC 2 - Hat-trick 2)

FARNBOROUGH

CURRENT SQUAD AS OF BEGINING OF 2010-11 SEASON

GOALKEEPERS	HT	WT	D.O.B	AGE	P.O.B	CAREER	Apps	Gls
Michael Jordan	6'02"	13 02	7/4/86	24	Enfield	Arsenal Rel c/s 06, Yeovil (SL) 3/06, Chesterfield 7/06 Rel 3/08, Lewes 3/08, Stevenage 8/08, Eastbourne B 1/09 Rel 2/10, Farnborough 2/10		
DEFENDERS								
Craig Braham-Barrett			1/9/88	21		Charlton (Yth), Sheff Wed (Yth), Aveley, Dulwich H 7/07, Potters Bar 10/07, Eastleigh, East Thurrock 2/08, Welling 5/08, Peterborough £10,000 + 10/08 Rel 7/09, Kettering (L) 1/09, Grays 8/09 Rel 1/10, Farnborough 1/10		
Adam Doyle						Alton T, Farnborough 10/07, Bisley (Dual) 10/07		
Sacha Opinel	5'09"	11 13	9/4/77	33	Saint Maurice (Fra)	Lille (Fr), Ajaccio GFCO 7/99, Stockport (Trial) 10/99, Raith 12/99, N.County (Trial) 10/00, Plymouth 12/00, Bournemouth (Trial) 1/01, L.Orient 2/01 Rel c/s 01, Billericay 11/01, Casteinau-le-Cres (Fr), Farnborough 7/03, Crawley P/E + Fee 1/05, Gravesend 7/06, Farnborough 6/09, Eastbourne B (L) 2/10		
Steve Robinson			31/1/76	34	Edmonton	Greenwich, Hayes, Islington St Marys, Cheshunt, Edgware c/s 00, Grays 2/01, Lewes 6/05 Rel 5/08, Chelmsford 7/08, Northwich (6WL) 11/08 Perm 1/09, Chelmsford 2/09, Farnborough 8/09		
James Smith	6'01"	13 12	30/8/86	24	London	Cambridge U (Sch), Welling 10/04, Gravesend £3,000 + 6/05, Margate (L) 9/05, Farnborough 6/09		
Jamie Stevens	5'11"	11 04	25/2/89	21	Holbeach	Rushden & D (Yth), Boston U, Crawley 6/07, Ipswich (Trial) 1/08, Northwich 1/09, Ebbsfleet (SL) 3/09, Farnborough c/s 09		
MIDFIELDERS								
Dale Binns			8/7/81	29	London	Hendon, Cambridge C 8/04, Stevenage 6/06 Rel 5/07, Lewes 7/07, Maidenhead 5/08, Hayes & Yeading 2/09 Rel 5/10, Farnborough 6/10		
Nic Ciardini			1/9/88	21		Farnborough (Yth), Southampton (Yth), Swindon (Yth), Bournemouth (Yth), Farnborough		
Gary Holloway			19/3/79	31	Kingston	Walton & Hersham, Hampton & R c/s 00, Farnborough 10/01 (01/02 15,3, 02/03 25,1), Stevenage 2/03 (02/03 9,0, 03/04 22,3), Farnborough 7/04 (04/05 27,1), Aldershot 3/05 (04/05 9,0, 05/06 29,3), Lewes 6/06, Havant & W 5/08, Farnborough 7/09		
Jack King						Didcot, Brackley 6/04, Didcot 11/05, Farnborough 8/09		
Darryl McMahon	5'11"	12 02	10/10/83	26	Dublin	West Ham Rel c/s 04, Torquay (L) 3/04, Port Vale 9/04, L.Orient 11/04, Notts County (2ML) 11/06, Stevenage 1/07, Cambridge U 1/09, Farnborough 7/09		
Owen Price	5'09"	11 13	20/10/86	23	London	Charlton (Yth), Tottenham Rel c/s 05, Lewes c/s 05, GIF Sundsvall (Swe) 1/06, Ljungskile SK (Swe), TPS Turku (Fin), Northwich 12/08 Rel 4/09, GIF Sundsvall (Swe), Farnborough 8/09		
FORWARDS								
Bradley Bubb			20/5/87	23		QPR (Yth), Hendon, Chalfont St Peter c/s 06, Beaconsfield SYCOB c/s 08, Farnborough 7/09		
Kezie Ibe	5'10"	12 00	6/12/82	27	London	Arsenal (Jun), Bournemouth (Jun), Leatherhead 9/01, Hampton & R 12/01, Aylesbury c/s 02, Staines 6/03, Yeovil 8/04, Tiverton (L) 10/04, Exeter (L) 12/04, Weymouth (L) 2/05, St Albans (L) 3/05, Canvey Island 8/05, Chelmsford 8/06 Rel 7/08, Ebbsfleet 8/08, AFC Wimbledon (L) 3/09, Farnborough c/s 09		
Dean McDonald	5'07"	10 12	19/2/86	24	Lambeth	Arsenal (Trainee) Rel c/s 04, Ipswich 2/05 Rel c/s 06, Hartlepool (L) 11/05, Gillingham 7/06, Inverness Caledonian 7/07, Gillingham (Trial) 1/08, Toronto (Trial) 1/08, Rushden & D 7/08 (08/09 3,1), Grays 11/08 Rel 1/09, Northwich 1/09 (08/09 2,1) Rel 2/09, Tooting & M 3/09, Farnborough 5/09		
Anthony Thomas	5'11"	12 08	30/8/82	28	Hammersmith	Ashford T, Edgware 7/04, Hemel Hempstead 7/05, Barnet Undisc 7/07 Rel c/s 08, Cambridge C (L) 10/07, Stevenage 5/08, Hemel Hempstead 12/08, Farnborough 6/09, Hendon (L) 2/10		

Do you remember when...

Farnborough Town

As Farnborough Town F.C., The Beazer Homes (Southern) League Premier Division Championship, The League Championship Match Trophy and the Hampshire Senior Cup had all been won in the 1990-1991 campaign along with Promotion.

This squad led by Manager Ted Pearce finished in a club best 5th place in The Vauxhall Conference in 1991-1992.

Back Row: Ron Manvile (kit/ground manager), Jamie Horton, Jim Wigmore, John Power, Andy Bye, Martin Hanchard, and Paul Coombs.
Middle Row: Ken Ballard (Reserve Team Manager), Gary Stevens, Keith Baker, Brian Broome, Mick Doherty, Danny Holmes, Alan Morris (Remedial Therapist).
Front Row: Simon Read, Andy Rogers, Ted Pearce (Manager), Alan Taylor (Senior Coach), Matthew Lovell and Alan Comfort.

HAMPTON & RICHMOND

Chairman: Steve MCPherson
Secretary: Nick Hornsey (T) 07768 861 446
(E) hrbfcsecretary@gmail.com
Additional Committee Members:
Gerry Jones, Nick Lyon, Chas Milner, Stefan Rance
Manager: Alan Devonshire
Programme Editor: Stefan Rance (E) stef_hrbfc@hotmail.com

Back Row (left to right) Alan Devonshire (Manager), Stuart Lake, Ian Hodges, Orlando Jeffrey, Graham Harper, Matt Lovett, Chico Ramos, Jamie Collins, Craig Tanner, John Scarborough, Steve Tyson, Dean Inman, Keiron Knight, Steve McPherson (Chairman)
Front Row; Dean Wells, Ashley Smith, Dudley Gardner, Leon Yarnie, Francis Quarm, Jon McDonald, Lawrence Yaku, Robbie Kember, Marcello Fernandes, David Tarpey

Hampton & Richmond Borough are sponsored by

1st Express Maintenance

Club Factfile

Founded: 1921 **Nickname:** Beavers or Borough
Previous Names: Hampton > 1999
Previous Leagues: Kingston & District, South West Middlesex, Surrey Senior 1959-64, Spartan 1964-71, Athenian 1971-73, Isthmian 1973-2007

Club Colours (change): Blue with red trim/blue/red (Yellow with blue trim/blue/yellow)

Ground: Beveree Stadium, Beaver Close, Station Road, Hampton TW12 2BX (T) 0208 8979 2456
Capacity: 3,000 **Seats:** 300 **Covered:** 800 **Clubhouse:** Yes **Shop:** Yes
Previous Grounds:
Simple Directions
From M25; Exit M25 at Junction 10 (M3 Richmond). Exit M3 at Junction 1 and take 4th exit (Kempton Park, Kingston). After approximately 3 miles turn left in to High Street, Hampton. Immediately turn left on to Station Road. The entrance to the ground is 200 yards on the right hand side.

Record Attendance: 2,520 v AFC Wimbledon - 11/10/2005
Record Victory: 11-1 v Eastbourne United - Isthmian League Division 2 South 1991-92
Record Defeat: 0-13 v Hounslow Town - Middlesex Senior Cup 1962-63
Record Goalscorer: Peter Allen - 176 (1964-73)
Record Appearances: Tim Hollands - 750 (1977-95)
Additional Records: Paid £3,000 to Chesham United for Matt Flitter June 2000
Received £40,000 from Queens Park Rangers for Leroy Phillips

Senior Honours: Isthmian League Premier Division 2006-07.
Spartan League x4. London Senior Cup x2.

10 YEAR RECORD

00-01	01-02	02-03	03-04	04-05	05-06	06-07	07-08	08-09	09-10
Isth P 9	Isth P 20	Isth P 24	Isth1S 5	Isth P 6	Isth P 5	Isth P 1	Conf S 3	Conf S 2	Conf S 14

HAMPTON & RICHMOND BORO'

No.	Date	Comp	H/A	Opponents	Att:	Result	Goalscorers	Pos
1	8/8/09	BSS	H	Basingstoke Town	534	L 0-1		20
2	11/8/09	BSS	A	Newport County	1185	L 1-3	Wells 83	21
3	15/8/09	BSS	A	Bromley	387	W 2-1	Yaku 27, Dundas 78	15
4	18/8/09	BSS	H	Braintree Town	355	D 2-2	Dundas 43, Lake 90	14
5	22/8/09	BSS	A	Bath City	507	W 3-1	Og (Holland) 20, Matthews pen 42, Yaku 47	9
6	29/8/09	BSS	H	Thurrock	463	D 1-1	Jeffrey 53	11
7	31/8/09	BSS	A	St Albans City	420	W 2-1	Hodges 12, Dundas 20	9
8	5/9/09	BSS	H	Woking	958	L 0-2		11
9	8/9/09	BSS	H	Bishop's Stortford	391	L 1-3	Braithwaite 80	14
10	12/9/09	BSS	A	Dover Athletic	1108	L 2-4	Matthews 13, Jeffrey 50	14
11	19/9/09	BSS	A	Havant & Waterlooville	920	D 1-1	Matthews pen 64	14
12	3/10/09	BSS	H	Weymouth	518	W 3-0	Smith 43, Tanner 70, Dundas 80	13
13	17/10/09	BSS	H	Worcester City	486	D 2-2	Og (Daniel) 3, Lee-Charles 65	14
14	27/10/09	BSS	A	Eastleigh	550	D 0-0		14
15	31/10/09	BSS	H	Maidenhead United	434	W 4-0	Hodges 3 (15, 43, 60), Wells 81	14
16	7/11/09	BSS	A	Lewes	413	L 0-1		14
17	24/11/09	BSS	A	Welling United	375	L 0-2		17
18	5/12/09	BSS	A	Dorchester Town	427	L 1-2	Wells 17	18
19	26/12/09	BSS	H	Staines Town	613	L 1-4	Matthews pen 62	18
20	28/12/09	BSS	A	Braintree Town	503	D 1-1	Beckford 29	18
21	1/1/10	BSS	A	Staines Town	871	L 0-4		18
22	23/1/10	BSS	H	Bromley	470	L 0-2		19
23	6/2/10	BSS	A	Basingstoke Town	403	W 2-1	Yaku 2 (70, 90)	18
24	9/2/10	BSS	H	Welling United	293	D 2-2	Inman 22, Collier 80	18
25	13/2/10	BSS	A	Bishop's Stortford	337	W 1-0	Hodges 70	18
26	20/2/10	BSS	H	Newport County	742	L 0-4		18
27	23/2/10	BSS	A	Weston-Super-Mare	167	D 1-1	Tarpey 72	18
28	2/3/10	BSS	H	Havant & Waterlooville	335	D 1-1	Tarpey 71	18
29	6/3/10	BSS	A	Worcester City	646	W 1-0	Matthews pen 84	18
30	9/3/10	BSS	H	Dorchester Town	306	L 1-2	Hodges 60	18
31	13/3/10	BSS	A	Maidenhead United	285	L 1-2	Matthews pen 3	18
32	16/3/10	BSS	H	Bath City	411	W 3-1	Tarpey 40, Inman 47, Dundas 49	18
33	20/3/10	BSS	H	Eastleigh	510	W 4-1	Dundas 8, Tarpey 2 (pen 25, pen 74), Lake 72	17
34	23/3/10	BSS	A	Woking	803	L 1-3	Yarnie 84	17
35	27/3/10	BSS	A	Chelmsford City	1020	L 0-1		17
36	30/3/10	BSS	H	Dover Athletic	380	L 1-4	Yaku 72	17
37	5/4/10	BSS	H	St Albans City	357	W 3-0	Yaku 9, Tarpey 2 (25, 85)	18
38	10/4/10	BSS	H	Weston-Super-Mare	344	W 2-1	Inman 76, Beadle 80	16
39	13/4/10	BSS	H	Chelmsford City	510	W 2-1	Tarpey 21, Matthews 80	14
40	17/4/10	BSS	A	Weymouth	501	L 0-1		14
41	20/4/10	BSS	A	Thurrock	235	W 2-0	Tarpey 46, Yarnie 89	14
42	24/4/10	BSS	H	Lewes	539	L 1-2	Tarpey 55	14
	Cups							
1	26/9/09	FAC 2Q	A	Braintree Town	327	D 0-0		
2	29/9/09	FAC 2QR	H	Braintree Town	216	W 4-1	Fernandes 34, Dundas 43, Yaku 63, Matthews 76	
3	10/10/09	FAC 3Q	H	Aveley	485	D 1-1	Dundas 80	
4	13/10/09	FAC 3QR	A	Aveley	205	W 2-1	Wells 41, Fernandes 87	
5	24/10/09	FAC 4Q	H	Sutton United	669	L 1-3	Dundas 60	
6	21/11/09	FAT 3Q	H	Concord Rangers	264	W 3-2	Collier 33, Lake 69, Matthews pen 78	
7	12/12/09	FAT 1	H	Lewes	256	D 0-0		

Home Attendances:	
Highest:	958 v Woking
Lowest:	293 v Welling United
Average (08-09):	463 (675)
Top Goalscorer:	Tarpey - 10 (10 League, 0 Cup) in 29 appearances - 34% strike rate
Most Appearances:	Dundas - 48 (41 League, 7 Cup)

DAVIES	HARPER	TANNER	JEFFREY	SCARBOROUGH	WELLS	COLLINS	QUARM	DUNDAS	YAKU	SMITH	TARPEY	MCDONALD	KNIGHT	BRAITHWAITE	LAKE	MATTHEWS	FERNANDES	HODGES	RAMOS	LEE-CHARLES	LOVETT	DAMALI	TYSON	COLLIER	TALBOT	INMAN	QUASHIE	SCHOBURTH	BECKFORD	BEADLE	THOMAS	ROBINSON	COLLEWIJN	GOODMAN	GAISIE	KANJOR	SIMMONDS	DRAKE	ROFFEY	YARNIE	WITHAM	
X	X	X	X	X	X	X	X	X	X	X	S	S	S	U	U																											1
X	X	X	X		X	X	X	X	X	X	S		U	X		S	U																									2
X		X	X		X		X	X	X		S	S	U	X	X	X	X	S																								3
	X	X	X	U			X	X	X		S	S		X	X	X	X	S	X	U																						4
		X	X	X			X	X	X		U	X		S		X	X	S		S	X	X																				5
		X	X	X			X	X	X		S	X		U	X	X	X	S			X	U	U																			6
		X	X	X		S		X	S	X	U	X		U	X	X	X	X			X		U																			7
	S	X		X		X		X	X	X	U	S		X	X	X	X			S	X		U																			8
	X	X	X	U	X	X		X	S	S		S		X	U	X	X			X	X																					9
	X		X	X	X	X		X	X	S		X		U	S	X	X			S	X																					10
		X	X	X	X	X		X	X	S		X		U	S	X	X			U	X																					11
	U	X		X	X			X	S	X		X		U	X	X	X	X		S	X			S																		12
	X	X	X		X	X			S	X	X	S		X		U	S			X	X			X																		13
	X	X	X	X		X		X	X	U		X			U	U	X	S		S	X			X																		14
		X		X	X			X	S	X		X			X	S	X	X		S	X			X	U																	15
		X	X	X	X			X	S	X	S					X	X	X			X			X		U																16
		X	X	X	X			X	X	S	S				X	X	X	S			X			X		U																17
		X	X	X	X			X	X	X	S				X	S	X	U			X			X		U																18
		X	X	X				X	S		S				X	X	X			X	X			X			U	U	X	S												19
		X	X	X				X	U		X				X	X	X			S	X			X			U	S	X	U												20
		X	X	X				X	S						X	X	X			X	X			X		S	S	U	X		U											21
			X		X			X	S		X				X	X		S			X			X		X	S		X		U	X										22
		S	X		X			X	X						X	X		U			X			X		X			X		U	X	S	U								23
		S	X		X			X	X		S				X	X		S			X			X		X	U		X			X	U									24
		X	X		X			X	X						X	X		S			X			X		X						X			S	U						25
		X	X		X			X	X		S				X	X		S			X			X		X			X			U			U	S						26
		X	X		X			X	X		S				X	X		S			X			X	U	X			X			U			U							27
		X	X		X			X	X		X				X	X		S			X			X		X	U		S			S			U							28
		X	X		X			X	X		S					X		X			X					X			X			S				S	X					29
		X	X		X			X	X		X				S	X		X						S		X			S			U				U	X	X				30
		X	X		X			X	X		S				U	X		X			X			S		X			X			U					X		U			31
		X	X		X			X	S		X				X	X		X			X					X			U	U		X				S			U			32
		X	X		X			X	X		X				X			X			X					X	S		S			X				S			U			33
			X		X			X	X		X				X	X		X			X					X	U			S		X				S			U	S		34
			X		X			X	U		X				X	X					X						S		X	X		X	S			X					U	35
			X		X			X	S						X	X		X			X					X	S		U	X		X	U			X			U			36
			X		X			X	X		X				X	X		U			X						U		X	X		X		S		S					S	37
			U		X			X	X		X				X	X		X			X					X	S		X	S		X							U			38
			S		X			X	X		X				X	X		X			X					X	S		U	X		X				U					U	39
			X		X			X	X		X				X	X		X			X					X	U		S	X		U										40
			X		X			X	X		X				X	X		X			X					X	S		U	X			U							S		41
				S	X			X	X		X				X	X		X			X					X	S		X	X									U			4
	S	X	X	X	X	X		X	X	U		X		U	S	X	X				X			S																		1
	U	X	X	X	X	X		X	X	S		X		U	S	X	X			U	X			S	U																	2
	X	X	X	X	X	X		X	X	S		S		U		X	X	S		U	X			U																		3
	X	X	X	X	X	X		X	X	S		U		U		X	X	U		S	X			S																		4
	S	X	X	X	X	X		X	U	X		S		U	U	X	X	S		X	X			U																		5
		X	X	S	X			X	S	X					X	X	X	X			X			X		S																6
			X	X	X			X	S	X					X	X	X	X		S	X			X		S	U	U														7
Total League Appearances																																										
3	7	29	36	16	33	8	6	41	29	9	15	8	0	6	30	35	18	16	1	4	37	1	0	16	0	19	0	0	14	7	0	12	0	0	0	2	3	1	0	0	0	X
0	1	2	1	1	0	1	0	0	11	4	14	6	1	1	3	3	1	12	0	7	0	0	0	3	0	1	9	1	4	3	0	2	2	1	1	6	0	0	0	2	1	S
0	1	0	1	2	0	0	0	0	2	1	3	0	2	6	4	2	1	3	0	2	0	1	3	0	2	3	7	2	4	2	3	5	3	1	3	3	0	0	7	0	2	U
Total Cup Appearances																																										
0	2	6	7	6	7	5	0	7	4	3	0	2	0	0	2	7	7	2	0	1	7	0	0	2	0	0	0	0	0	0	0	0	0	0	0	0	0	0	0	0	0	X
0	2	0	0	1	0	0	0	0	2	3	0	2	0	0	2	0	0	2	0	2	0	0	0	3	0	2	0	0	0	0	0	0	0	0	0	0	0	0	0	0	0	S
0	1	0	0	0	0	0	0	0	1	1	0	1	0	5	1	0	0	1	0	2	0	0	0	2	1	0	1	1	0	0	0	0	0	0	0	0	0	0	0	0	0	U
Total Goals																																										
0	0	1	2	0	3	0	0	6	6	1	10	0	0	1	2	7	0	6	0	1	0	0	0	1	0	3	0	0	1	1	0	0	0	0	0	0	0	0	0	2	0	Lge
0	0	0	0	0	1	0	0	3	1	0	0	0	0	0	1	2	2	0	0	0	0	0	0	1	0	0	0	0	0	0	0	0	0	0	0	0	0	0	0	0	0	Cup

Also Played: SANKEY U(22).

HAMTPON & RICHMOND

CURRENT SQUAD AS OF BEGINING OF 2010-11 SEASON

GOALKEEPERS	HT	WT	D.O.B	AGE	P.O.B	CAREER	Apps	Gls
Matt Lovett			5/9/79	30	Middlesex	Staines, Hampton & R 6/05	37	0
Trevor Roffey			22/7/65	45		Hampton & R (Gk Coach)	0	0
Joe Talbot			24/11/90	19		Hampton & R	0	0
DEFENDERS								
Elliot Braithwaite			2/3/90	20		Wycombe (Yth) Rel c/s 08 QPR (Trial) 3/09, Didcot T, Hampton & R 8/08, Walton Casuals (L) 11/08, Ashford T (L) 12/08	7	1
Blake Goodman			16/6/89	21		Hampton & R	1	0
Dean Inman			25/10/90	19		Hampton & R, Chertsey (3ML) 8/09	20	3
Orlando Jeffrey	6'02"		23/9/77	32	Berkshire	Burnham, Thatcham, Maidenhead, Hampton & R c/s 03, Hayes 5/05, Hampton & R 8/07	37	2
John Scarborough	6'01"		13/3/79	31	Gravesend	Gravesend, Ashford T, Herne Bay, Eastbourne B, Tilbury, Billericay c/s 03, Tilbury 2/04, Chelmsford (Trial) c/s 04, Dover 9/04, Sutton U 9/04, Hampton & R 6/08	17	0
Craig Tanner			13/2/86	24	Surrey	Tooting & Mitcham, Sutton U 10/06, Hampton & R 2/08, Leatherhead (L) 9/08	31	1
Dean Wells	6'01"	13 02	25/3/85	25	Isleworth	Brentford Rel c/s 04, Hampton & R 6/04	33	3
Billy Witham			7/7/93	17		Hampton & R	1	0
MIDFIELDERS								
Louis-Ray Beadle			7/8/90	20		Hampton & R	10	1
Nathan Collier			15/8/85	25		Hampton & R	19	1
Luke Kanjor			6/8/89	21		Hampton & R	8	0
Barrie Matthews	5'09"	10 10	1/2/83	27	Cinderford	Cirencester (Yth), Watford Rel c/s 03, Swindon S (SL) 3/03, Swindon S 8/03, Hornchurch 1/04, Maidenhead 8/04, Hampton & R 9/05	38	7
Ashley Quashie			14/6/89	21		Corinthian Casuals, Hampton & R 11/09	9	0
Chris Robinson			10/12/87	22		Hampton & R (Yth), Staines, Hendon (L), Slough (L), Hampton & R, Walton Casuals (L), Uxbridge 2/09, Hampton & R 1/10	14	0
James Simmonds			3/12/87	22	Hammersmith	Chelsea, Glen Hoddle Academy, Écija Balompié (Spa), Hampton & R 3/10	3	0
Romayne Thomas			18/9/88	21		Hampton & R	0	0
FORWARDS								
Joey Collewijn			24/2/89	21		Hampton & R	2	0
Ian Hodges			18/10/82	27	Cornwall	Porthleven, St Ives, Hayes 8/01, Slough 2/03, Hampton & R 6/06	28	6
David Tarpey			14/11/88	21		C.Palace (Yth), Basingstoke 8/06 Rel 5/09, Hampton & R 7/09, Walton & H (Dual) 9/09	29	10
Lawrence Yaku			19/9/74	35	Nigeria	Wealdstone, Ruislip Manor, Wokingham 7/99, Northwood, Maidenhead 5/02, Hampton & R 5/05	40	6
Leon Yarnie			30/8/84	26		Hampton & R	2	2

Departures	HT	WT	DOB	AGE	POB	From - To	APPS	GOA
(F)Kieran Knight			18/2/81	29	Middlesex	Hayes/Hayes & Yeading 2/09 - Rel 8/09, Maidenhead 8/09	1	0
(M)Jamie Collins	6'03"	12 00	28/9/84	25	Barking	Havant & W 7/09 - Newport C 10/09	9	0
(M)Jamie Beer			17/6/76	34		Kingstonian 10/09 - Walton & H 10/09, Leatherhead 1/10		
(D)Graham Harper			7/8/76	34	London	Whyteleafe 8/04 - Rel 11/09	8	0
(D)Jon McDonald			18/5/85	25	Kingston	Staines 3/09 - Havant & W 11/09	14	0
(M)Ashley Smith			22/12/83	26		Maidenhead 8/09 - Maidenhead 12/09	13	1
(F)Michael Lee-Charles			24/4/87	23		Farnborough 8/09 - Rel 1/10, Walton & H (L) 11/09, Carshalton 1/10, Walton & H 3/10	11	1
(M)Marcello Fernandes			23/7/76	34	Cape Town, SA	Feltham 8/03 - Rel 1/10, Wealdstone (Dual) 3/07	19	0
(M)Francis Quarm			1/8/83	27		Basingstoke - Rel 1/10, Sutton U 1/10, Woking 5/10	6	0
(D)Emmanuel Sackey			1/2/86	24		Eton Manor 1/10 - Bishop's Stortford 2/10	0	0
(F)Steffan Gaisie	5'11"	11 07	29/9/88	21		Chatham 2/10 - Walton Casuals 3/10	1	0
(F)Craig Dundas			16/2/81	29		Sutton U 8/09 - Sutton U 5/10	41	6
(M)Karl Beckford			4/6/85	25		Kingstonian 12/09 - Tooting & M 6/10	18	1
(M)Stuart Lake			17/11/79	30	London	Ashford T (Middx) 2/07 - Basingstoke 6/10	33	2
(G)Kevin Davies			27/8/79	31		Sutton U 8/09 - Sutton U 5/10	3	0
(G)Kieran Drake						-	1	0
(G)Chico Ramos			9/10/83	26	Portugal	ex Dorchester 8/09 -	1	0
(M)Pat Damali			5/12/82	27		Walton Casuals, Hampton & R 8/09	1	0
(M)Sebastian Schoburth			11/1/86	24		-	1	0
(M)Steve Tyson			20/4/88	22		Walton Casuals 8/08 - Rel 8/09, Kingstonian (Dual) 8/09	0	0

HAVANT AND WATERLOOVILLE

Chairman: Derek Pope
Secretary: Trevor Brock **(T)** 07768 271 143
(E) trevor.brock52@yahoo.com
Additional Committee Members:
Adrian Hewett , Ray Jones, Kevin Moore, Michael Jenkins, Adi Aymes
Manager: Shaun Gayle
Programme Editor: Adrian Aymes **(E)** aaymes2125@aol.com

Back row (L-R): Martin Matthews (Kit Manager), Ryan Woodford, Gary MacDonald, Gary Norgate, Nathan Ashmore, Aaron Howe, Jay Gasson, Sam Pearce, Paul Hinshelwood, Stuart Page (Academy Manager). **Centre Row:** Sarah Taylor (Assistant Physio), Robbie Martin, Luke Nightingale, Mustafa Tyriaki, Jake Newton, Ian Simpemba (Club Captain), Shaun Wilkinson, Stephen Hutchings, Conor Geoghegan, Manny Williams, Wes Fogden, Claire Alexandra (Assistant Physio), Ollie Jones (Goalkeeper Coach). **Front Row:** Phil Ashwell (Therapist), John Dyer (Director), John Carter (Director), Adrian Aymes (Fitness Coach), Shaun Gale (Manager), Steve Johnson (Assistant Manager), Kevin Moore (Director), Pat Walsh (Director), Trevor Brock (Secretary/Director).

Club Factfile

Founded: 1998 **Nickname:** Hawks
Previous Names: Havant Town and Waterlooville merged in 1998
Previous Leagues: Southern 1998-2004

Club Colours (change): All white (Yellow/royal blue/yellow)

Ground: Westleigh Park, Martin Road, West Leigh, Havant PO9 5TH **(T)** 02392 787 822
Capacity: 4,800 **Seats:** 562 **Covered:** 3,500 **Clubhouse:** Yes **Shop:** Yes
Previous Grounds:
Simple Directions
Ground is a mile and a half from Havant Town Centre. Take A27 to Havant then turn onto B2149 (Petersfield Road). Turn right at next junction after HERON pub into Bartons Road then take first right into Martin Road.

Record Attendance: 4,400 v Swansea City - FA Cup 3rd Round 05/01/2008
Record Victory: 9-0 v Moneyfields - Hampshire Senior Cup 23/10/2001
Record Defeat: 0-5 v Worcester City - Southern Premier 20/03/2004
Record Goalscorer: James Taylor - 138
Record Appearances: James Taylor - 297
Additional Records: Paid £5,000 to Bashley for John Wilson
Received £15,000 from Peterborough United for Gary McDonald
Senior Honours: Southern League Southern Division 1998-99. Russell Cotes Cup 2003-04

10 YEAR RECORD

00-01	01-02	02-03	03-04	04-05	05-06	06-07	07-08	08-09	09-10
SthP 6	SthP 3	SthP 8	SthP 12	Conf S 13	Conf S 6	Conf 4	Conf S 7	Conf S 15	Conf S 6

HAVANT & WATERLOOVILLE

No.	Date	Comp	H/A	Opponents	Att:	Result	Goalscorers	Pos
1	8/8/09	BSS	H	Thurrock	805	D 1-1	Fogden 52	8
2	11/8/09	BSS	A	Bromley	510	W 2-0	Williams 2 (81, 83)	5
3	15/8/09	BSS	A	Staines Town	396	W 2-1	Tiryaki 26, Williams 41	4
4	17/8/09	BSS	H	Bath City	1181	D 2-2	Williams 2 (7, 90)	4
5	22/8/09	BSS	A	Braintree Town	527	W 2-0	Williams 2 (10, 80)	2
6	29/8/09	BSS	H	Basingstoke Town	1156	L 0-2		7
7	31/8/09	BSS	A	Weymouth	717	W 1-0	Gasson 90	5
8	5/9/09	BSS	H	Dover Athletic	1217	W 2-1	Williams 2 (4, pen 39)	6
9	8/9/09	BSS	A	Dorchester Town	447	L 3-4	Williams 27, Tiryaki 69, Pearce 77	6
10	12/9/09	BSS	A	St Albans City	329	D 1-1	Williams 75	6
11	19/9/09	BSS	H	Hampton & Richmond B.	920	D 1-1	Hutchings 80	7
12	3/10/09	BSS	H	Eastleigh	1451	D 2-2	Tiryaki 30, Nightingale 39	7
13	17/10/09	BSS	A	Bishop's Stortford	449	L 0-1		10
14	26/10/09	BSS	H	Welling United	854	D 2-2	Simpemba 8, Woodford 68	9
15	31/10/09	BSS	A	Chelmsford City	1053	D 1-1	Williams 89	11
16	7/11/09	BSS	H	Dorchester Town	931	L 0-1		12
17	28/11/09	BSS	H	Maidenhead United	681	W 1-0	McDonald 56	12
18	5/12/09	BSS	A	Thurrock	246	D 0-0		14
19	26/12/09	BSS	H	Woking	1007	D 1-1	Simpemba 36	15
20	1/1/10	BSS	A	Woking	1703	L 0-2		15
21	16/1/10	BSS	A	Dover Athletic	852	L 0-4		16
22	25/1/10	BSS	H	Bromley	580	W 2-1	Simpemba 28, Fogden 59	15
23	30/1/10	BSS	A	Eastleigh	875	W 1-0	Walker 63	14
24	6/2/10	BSS	H	Worcester City	784	W 3-2	Williams 3 (pen 30, 52, 79)	13
25	8/2/10	BSS	H	Bishop's Stortford	601	W 2-1	Williams 53, Walker 62	12
26	13/2/10	BSS	H	Lewes	718	D 1-1	MacDonald 32	13
27	16/2/10	BSS	A	Bath City	428	D 1-1	Williams 33	12
28	20/2/10	BSS	A	Worcester City	543	W 2-0	MacDonald 33, Hinshelwood 68	10
29	22/2/10	BSS	H	St Albans City	552	L 0-1		10
30	2/3/10	BSS	A	Hampton & Richmond B.	335	D 1-1	Tiryaki 38	11
31	6/3/10	BSS	A	Welling United	443	L 0-1		13
32	13/3/10	BSS	A	Lewes	447	W 3-0	Tiryaki 67, Simpemba 73, Williams 78	12
33	15/3/10	BSS	A	Newport County	4221	L 0-2		12
34	20/3/10	BSS	H	Staines Town	715	W 1-0	Jusufi 89	11
35	22/3/10	BSS	H	Braintree Town	594	D 1-1	Lopes 84	10
36	27/3/10	BSS	A	Weston-Super-Mare	215	W 2-1	Fogden 24, Tiryaki 72	9
37	3/4/10	BSS	A	Basingstoke Town	410	D 1-1	Tiryaki 40	10
38	5/4/10	BSS	H	Weymouth	820	W 3-1	Tiryaki 3 (8, 44, 81)	10
39	10/4/10	BSS	H	Newport County	1020	W 4-0	Tiryaki 2 (50, 66), Fogden 79, Gasson 87	8
40	13/4/10	BSS	H	Weston-Super-Mare	796	W 6-0	Tiryaki 3, Simpemba 15, Williams pen 34, Fogden 2 (42, 54), Walker 63	7
41	17/4/10	BSS	A	Maidenhead United	336	W 2-0	Walker 46, Tiryaki 90	7
42	24/4/10	BSS	H	Chelmsford City	1333	W 5-2	Fogden 2 (43, 88), Williams 2 (pen 52, pen 75), Simpemba 54	6
	Cups							
1	26/9/09	FAC 2Q	A	Weston-Super-Mare	298	W 1-0	Walker 3	
2	10/10/09	FAC 3Q	H	Chippenham Town	620	L 1-2	Tiryaki 20	
3	21/11/09	FAT 3Q	A	Thurrock	142	W 4-1	Tiryaki 2 (35, 56), Walker 90, Fogden 90	
4	12/12/09	FAT 1	H	Dover Athletic	483	L 2-3	Martin 23, Williams 54	

Home Attendances:	
Highest:	1451 v Eastleigh
Lowest:	552 v St Albans City
Average (08-09):	820 (722)
Top Goalscorer:	Williams - 22 (21 League, 1 Cup) in 41 appearances - 51% strike rate
Most Appearances:	Walker - 45 (35+6 League, 4 Cup)

HOWE	NEWTON	MACDONALD	WALKER	GASSON	SIMPEMBA	FOGDEN	WILKINSON	WILLIAMS	TIRYAKI	MARTIN	PEARCE	HUTCHINGS	NIGHTINGALE	NORGATE	WOODFORD	HINSHELWOOD	ROBSON	ASHMORE	LOPES	FORBES	MCDONALD	TABIRI	CHARLES	SEWELL	GEOGHEGAN	SELLEY	HECTOR	MEDLEY	JUSUFI	HOPKINSON	MELO	
X	X	X	X	X	X	X	X	X	X	X	S	S	S	U	U																	1
X	X		X	X	X	X	X	X	X	U	X		S	S	X	U	U															2
X	X		X	X	X	X	X	X	X	U	X	S	S	U	X	U																3
X	X		X	X		X	X	X	X	U	X	S	U	U	X	X	U															4
X	X		X	X	X	X	X	X	X	U	X	S	S		X	U		U														5
X		U	X	X	X	X	X	X	X	S	X	S	S		X	X		U														6
X	X	U	X	X	X	X	X	X	S	S	X	X	S		X			U														7
X	X	U	X	X	X	X	X	X	S	S	X	X	S		X			U														8
X	X	U	X	X	X	X	X	X	S	U	X	X	S		X			U														9
X	X	X	X	X	X	X	X	X	X	U	U	S	S		X			U														10
X	X	X	X	X	X	X	S	X	S	U	U	X	X		X			U														11
X	X	X	X	X	X	X	S		X	S	U	X	X		X			U	U													12
X	X	X	X	X	X	X	X	X	X	S	U	S	X		S			U														13
X	X	X	X		X			X	X	X	X	U	X		X	S	U	U		S												14
X	X	X	X		X			X	X	X	X	S	X		X	U	U	U		S												15
X	X	X	X		X	S		X	X	X	X	S	X		X	U				S	U											16
X	X	S	X		X	X		X	X	U		S	S		X			U		X	X	X										17
X	X		X		X	X		X	X	U	U		S		X	U		U		X	X	X										18
X	X	X	X		X					X	X	X	X			U		U	S	X	X			S	U							19
X	X	X	X		X			X		X	X	U	X			U		U	S	X	X		S									20
X	S	X	X		X	X		X		U	X	X	U			X		U	S	X	X											21
X	X	X	X		X	X		X	X		S	U				X		U	S		X					X	S					22
X	X	X	X	S	X	X		X	X		U	S				X		U	U		X					X						23
X	X	X	X		X	X		X	X		U	S				X					X	S				X	U	S				24
X	X	X	X	X	X	X		X	X		U	S				X						S				X	U	S				25
X	X	X		U		X		X	X	S	X	S				X			U		X	X				X		S				26
X	X	X	S	X		X		X	X		S	U				X					X	X				X		U	U			27
X	X	X	S	U	X	X		X	X		U					X					X	X				X		S	U			28
X	X	X	S	U	X	X		X	X		U					X					X	X				X		U	S			29
-X		S	X	X	X		X	X		U					X		X			X	X				X		U	U				30
U	X	U	S	X	X	X		X	X							X		X			X	X				X		S	U			31
X	X	X	X	S	X	X		X	X		U					X		U			X			S				X	S			32
X	X		X	X	X	X		X	X		U					S		U			X			S		X		X				33
X	X		X	X		X		X			X					X		U	U		X			S				X	S	X	U	34
X	X		X	X		X					X					X		U	S		X			X	U			X	S	X	S	35
X	X		S	X	X	X			X		X					X		U	U					S		X		X	U	X		36
X	X		X	X	X	X		S	X		X					X		S			U			S		X			U	X		37
U	X		X	U	X	X		X	X		X					S		X			X					X		S	S	X		38
X	X		X	S	X	X		X	X		X					S		U			X			U		X			S	X		39
X	X		X	S	X	X		X	X		X	S				U		U			X					X		S		X		40
	X		X	U	X	X		X	X		X	S				S		X			X					X		S	U	X		41
	X		X	U	X	X		X	X		X	U				S		X			X			S		X		U		X		42

HOWE	NEWTON	MACDONALD	WALKER	GASSON	SIMPEMBA	FOGDEN	WILKINSON	WILLIAMS	TIRYAKI	MARTIN	PEARCE	HUTCHINGS	NIGHTINGALE	NORGATE	WOODFORD	HINSHELWOOD	ROBSON	ASHMORE	LOPES	FORBES	MCDONALD	TABIRI	CHARLES	SEWELL	GEOGHEGAN	SELLEY	HECTOR	MEDLEY	JUSUFI	HOPKINSON	MELO	
X	X	X	X	X	X	X		X	S	S	U	X	X		X	U	U	U	U													1
X	X	X	X	X	X	X	S		X	S	U		X		X	U	U	U	S	X												2
X		X	X			X		X	X	X		S	S		X	X	U	U		S	X	X										3
X	X	X	X		X			X		X	U	S				U	U	U		X	X	X	X									4

Total League Appearances

HOWE	NEWTON	MACDONALD	WALKER	GASSON	SIMPEMBA	FOGDEN	WILKINSON	WILLIAMS	TIRYAKI	MARTIN	PEARCE	HUTCHINGS	NIGHTINGALE	NORGATE	WOODFORD	HINSHELWOOD	ROBSON	ASHMORE	LOPES	FORBES	MCDONALD	TABIRI	CHARLES	SEWELL	GEOGHEGAN	SELLEY	HECTOR	MEDLEY	JUSUFI	HOPKINSON	MELO	
37	40	20	35	22	37	37	11	37	33	6	24	7	8	0	16	18	0	5	0	5	23	8	0	1	0	18	0	5	0	9	0	X
0	1	1	6	4	0	1	2	1	4	6	3	16	11	1	1	6	0	1	5	3	0	2	1	7	0	0	1	8	6	0	1	S
2	0	5	0	6	0	0	0	0	0	10	13	5	2	3	1	9	4	25	5	0	2	0	0	1	2	0	2	4	7	0	1	U

Total Cup Appearances

HOWE	NEWTON	MACDONALD	WALKER	GASSON	SIMPEMBA	FOGDEN	WILKINSON	WILLIAMS	TIRYAKI	MARTIN	PEARCE	HUTCHINGS	NIGHTINGALE	NORGATE	WOODFORD	HINSHELWOOD	ROBSON	ASHMORE	LOPES	FORBES	MCDONALD	TABIRI	CHARLES	SEWELL	GEOGHEGAN	SELLEY	HECTOR	MEDLEY	JUSUFI	HOPKINSON	MELO	
4	3	4	4	2	3	3	0	3	2	2	0	1	2	0	3	1	0	0	0	2	2	2	1	0	0	0	0	0	0	0	0	X
0	0	0	0	0	0	0	1	0	1	2	0	2	1	0	0	0	0	0	1	1	0	0	0	0	0	0	0	0	0	0	0	S
0	0	0	0	0	0	0	0	0	0	0	3	0	0	0	0	3	4	4	1	0	0	0	0	0	0	0	0	0	0	0	0	U

Total Goals

HOWE	NEWTON	MACDONALD	WALKER	GASSON	SIMPEMBA	FOGDEN	WILKINSON	WILLIAMS	TIRYAKI	MARTIN	PEARCE	HUTCHINGS	NIGHTINGALE	NORGATE	WOODFORD	HINSHELWOOD	ROBSON	ASHMORE	LOPES	FORBES	MCDONALD	TABIRI	CHARLES	SEWELL	GEOGHEGAN	SELLEY	HECTOR	MEDLEY	JUSUFI	HOPKINSON	MELO	
0	0	2	4	2	6	8	0	21	14	0	1	1	1	0	1	1	0	0	1	0	1	0	0	0	0	0	0	0	1	0	0	Lge
0	0	0	2	0	0	1	0	1	3	1	0	0	0	0	0	0	0	0	0	0	0	0	0	0	0	0	0	0	0	0	0	Cup

HAVANT & WATERLOOVILLE

CURRENT SQUAD AS OF BEGINING OF 2010-11 SEASON

GOALKEEPERS	HT	WT	D.O.B	AGE	P.O.B	CAREER	Apps	Gls
Nathan Ashmore			22/2/90	20		Havant & W	6	0
Aaron Howe			5/10/87	22		Woking Rel 5/07, Carshalton (L) 2/07, Carshalton c/s 07, Hayes & Yeading 8/08, Havant & W 7/09	37	0
DEFENDERS								
Conor Geoghegan			19/6/91	19		Havant & W	0	0
Paul Hinshelwood	6'02"	14 00	11/10/87	22	Chatham	Brighton Rel c/s 07, Burgess Hill (L) 8/06, Torquay 6/07 Rel 5/08, Tiverton (L) 11/07, Bognor 8/08, Havant & W 1/09	24	1
Jon McDonald			18/5/85	25	Kingston	Staines, Hampton & R 3/09, Havant & W 11/09	23	1
Jake Newton			9/6/84	26	Hammersmith	Hampton & R (Yth), Kingston Academy, Staines c/s 03, Chalfont St Peter (L) 2/04, Bashley 2/05, Staines 7/05, Havant & W 7/09	41	0
Sam Pearce			11/2/87	23	Portsmouth	Havant & W, Fleet T 3/06, South Africa, Bognor Regis 8/08, Salisbury 3/09, Havant & W 6/09	27	1
Ian Simpemba	6'02"	12 08	28/3/83	27	Dublin	Wycombe, Woking (3ML) 10/02, Woking (L) 9/03, Crawley Undisc 7/04, Aldershot (SL) 3/06, Lewes 6/06, Havant & W 5/08	37	6
Ryan Woodford	5'11"	11 08	14/8/91	19		Portsmouth (Scholar) Rel c/s 09, Havant & W 7/09	17	1
MIDFIELDERS								
Bobby Hopkinson	5'08"	13 07	3/7/90	20	Plymouth	Plymouth (Scholar),Tiverton 3/08, Aldershot Undisc 8/09 Rel 3/10, Farnborough (Dual) 1/10, Havant & W 3/10	9	0
Sammy Igoe	5'07"	10 00	30/9/75	34	Spelthorne	Portsmouth, Reading 3/00, Luton (L) 3/03, Swindon 6/03 Rel c/s 05, Millwall 7/05 Rel c/s 06, Bristol R (4ML) 1/06, Bristol R 7/06 Rel c/s 08, Hereford (L) 3/08, Bournemouth 8/08 Rel c/s 10, Havant & W 6/10		
Craig Robson			2/8/91	19		Havant & W	0	0
Ian Selley	5'10"	10 09	14/6/74	36	Chertsey	Arsenal, Southend (L) 12/96, Fulham £500,000 10/97 Rel c/s 00, Wimbledon 8/00 Rel c/s 03, Southend (SL) 2/02, Southend (3ML) 8/02, Woking 8/03 Rel 5/07, Lewes 8/07, Grays (2ML) 11/07 Perm 1/08, Maidstone 3/08, Croydon Ath 12/08, Dorchester 8/09 Rel 1/10,	18	0
Steven Ramsey (was Walker)			23/11/89	20		Portsmouth (Scholar), Rel c/s 08 Havant & W 5/08	41	4
Shaun Wilkinson	5'07"	11 00	12/9/81	28	Portsmouth	Brighton, Havant & W (L) 12/01, Chesterfield (L) 11/02, Havant & W (2ML) 9/03 Perm 11/03, Weymouth £5,000 2/04, Havant & W 12/04, Weymouth, Havant & W 1/07, Lewes (2ML) 1/09	13	0
FORWARDS								
Wesley Fogden	5'08"	10 04	12/4/88	22	Brighton	Brighton Rel 9/08, Dorchester (L) 8/08, Dorchester 9/08, Havant & W 2/09	38	8
Liam Sewell			1/2/91	19		Petersfield, Havant & W 12/09	8	0
Mustafa Tiryaki			2/3/87	23		Turkey, Maidenhead c/s 08, Potters Bar (L) 10/08, Godalming (L) 12/08, Cheltenham (Trial) 5/09, Havant & W 7/09	37	14
Manny Williams			13/11/81	28	London	Notts County (Yth), Millwall (Yth), Concord R, Bowers Utd, Leyton 7/01, Yeading 9/05, Leyton 7/06, Maidenhead 8/07, Woking 5/08 Rel 5/09, Maidenhead (2ML) 11/08, Weston-Super-Mare (3ML) 1/09, Havant & W 6/09	38	21

Loanees	HT	WT	DOB	AGE	POB	From - To	APPS	GOA
(M)Joe Tabiri	5'09"	11 09	16/10/89	20	Kingsbury	Barnet 11/09, 2/10 - Dover (SL) 3/10, Dover 6/10	10	0
(F)Elliott Charles	6'02"	13 00	23/12/90	19	Enfield	Barnet 12/09 - Rel 1/10, Kettering 3/10	1	0
(M)Michael Hector			19/7/92	18		Reading 1/10 -	1	0
(F)Andy White			1/9/91	18		Reading (2WL) 1/10 - Staines (L) 3/10, Gillingham 6/10		
(M)Luke Medley	6'01"	13 03	21/6/89	21	Greenwich	Barnet (SL) 2/10 -	13	0

Departures	HT	WT	DOB	AGE	POB	From - To	APPS	GOA
(F)Gary Norgate			23/5/83	27		Arundel NC 8/09 - Bognor Regis 8/09 Rel 1/10, Arundel 2/10	1	0
(F)Ivan Forbes			1/12/86	23	Portimao, Port	Dorchester 10/09 - Rel 1/10	8	0
(M)Robbie Martin			29/12/84	25		Braintree 10/08 - Rel 2/10, Braintree 2/10	12	0
(D)Jay Gasson			29/12/84	25		Woking 5/08 - Basingstoke 5/10	26	2
(F)Alban Jusufi	5'10"	13 03	7/7/81	29	Angelholm, Swe	Valaznia (Alb) 2/10 - Sweden 5/10	6	1
(F)Luke Nightingale	5'11"	12 03	22/12/80	29	Portsmouth	Bognor 3/08 - Bognor (SL) 1/10, Bognor 7/10	19	1
(D)Gary MacDonald	6'01"	12 12	25/10/79	30	Iselone, Ger	Hayes & Yeading 6/09 -	21	2
(M)Steve Hutchings	6'00"	12 00	13/12/90	19	Portsmouth	Bournemouth 8/09 -	23	1
(M)Joseph Melo						ex Toronto FC 3/10 -	1	0
(F)Jorge Lopes			29/7/89	21		Worthing 8/09 - Horsham (Dual) 11/09	5	1

LEWES

Chairman: Martin Elliott
Secretary: Steve Ibbitson (T) 07704 089 509
(E) steveibbitson@btinternet.com
Additional Committee Members:
David Arnold, Kevin Fingerneissl, Nick Williams, James Boyes
Manager: Steve Ibbitson
Programme Editor: James Boyes (E) james-boyes@lineone.net

Back row, (L-R): Justin Skinner (Coach), Steve King (Manager), Paul Booth, Andrew Drury, Paul Kennett, Ian Simpemba, Steven Williams, Aaron France, Leon Legge, Jay Conroy, Lewis Hamilton, Stephen Robinson, Jean-Michel Sigere, Ray Bugg (Kit man), Bob Childs (physio).
Front: Steven Elliott, Tom Davis, Ross Trevellin, Craig O'Connor, Simon Wormull, Dale Binns, Ian Selley, Gary Holloway, Kirk Watts (Archive photo)

Club Factfile

Founded: 1885 **Nickname:** Rooks
Previous Names:
Previous Leagues: Mid Sussex 1886-1920, Sussex County 1920-65, Athenian 1965-77, Isthmian 1977-2003

Club Colours (change): Red and black/black/black (Sky blue/white/sky blue)

Ground: The Dripping Pan, Mountfield Road, Lewes, East Sussex BN7 2XD (T) 01273 472 100
Capacity: 3,000 **Seats:** 400 **Covered:** 1,400 **Clubhouse:** Yes **Shop:** Yes
Previous Grounds:
Simple Directions
After leaving the M23, follow the A23 to Brighton. On the outskirts of Brighton join the A27 eastbound. Stay on the A27 for about 5 miles. At the roundabout take first exit into Lewes. Follow this road until you reach traffic lights outside Lewes Prison. Turn right at the lights and follow the road down the hill until you reach a mini roundabout outside the Swan public house. Turn left at roundabout into Southover High Street and continue over next mini roundabout outside the Kings Head public house. At the next roundabout go straight over into Mountfield Road. The Dripping Pan is on your right.

Record Attendance: 2,500 v Newhaven - Sussex County League 26/12/1947
Record Victory: Not known
Record Defeat: Not known
Record Goalscorer: 'Pip' Parris - 350
Record Appearances: Terry Parris - 662
Additional Records: Paid £2,000 for Matt Allen
Received £2,500 from Brighton & Hove Albion for Grant Horscroft
Senior Honours: Mid Sussex League 1910-11, 13-14. Sussex County League 1964-65.
Sussex Senior Cup 1964-65, 70-71, 84-85, 2000-01, 05-06. Athenian League Division 2 1967-68, Division 1 1969-70.
Isthmian League Division 2 2001-02, Division 1 South 2003-04. Conference South 2007-08

10 YEAR RECORD

00-01	01-02	02-03	03-04	04-05	05-06	06-07	07-08	08-09	09-10
Isth3 2	Isth2 1	Isth1S 3	Isth1S 1	Conf S 4	Conf S 4	Conf 9	Conf S 1	Conf 24	Conf S 19

LEWES

No.	Date	Comp	H/A	Opponents	Att:	Result	Goalscorers	Pos
1	8/8/09	BSS	H	Weymouth	441	D 1-1	Beck 63	9
2	11/8/09	BSS	A	Braintree Town	430	L 0-3		17
3	15/8/09	BSS	A	Newport County	1201	D 2-2	Crabb 34, Keehan 61	17
4	18/8/09	BSS	H	Thurrock	354	D 1-1	Beck 12	17
5	22/8/09	BSS	A	St Albans City	351	D 1-1	Crabb 68	18
6	29/8/09	BSS	H	Woking	675	L 0-2		20
7	31/8/09	BSS	A	Bromley	603	L 0-3		21
8	5/9/09	BSS	H	Basingstoke Town	396	D 0-0		18
9	7/9/09	BSS	A	Chelmsford City	1137	L 1-2	Wheeler 76	18
10	12/9/09	BSS	A	Bath City	429	D 1-1	Pople 81	21
11	19/9/09	BSS	H	Maidenhead United	206	L 1-2	Wheeler 26	21
12	3/10/09	BSS	H	Staines Town	305	D 1-1	Foreman pen 47	21
13	17/10/09	BSS	A	Weston-Super-Mare	214	L 2-3	Foreman 37, Pearson 85	21
14	24/10/09	BSS	H	Bishop's Stortford	246	W 2-1	Pearson 39, Crabb 62	21
15	31/10/09	BSS	A	Welling United	502	L 0-1		21
16	7/11/09	BSS	H	Hampton & Richmond B.	413	W 1-0	Rivers 43	20
17	14/11/09	BSS	A	Eastleigh	465	L 0-1		21
18	28/11/09	BSS	H	Newport County	521	L 0-3		21
19	5/12/09	BSS	A	Maidenhead United	220	D 1-1	Keehan 58	21
20	26/12/09	BSS	H	Dover Athletic	505	W 6-2	Keehan 3 (18, 61, 66), Brinkhurst 33, Og (Schulz) 41, Wheeler 86	19
21	28/12/09	BSS	A	Thurrock	270	L 1-3	Walder 56	20
22	1/1/10	BSS	A	Dover Athletic	918	L 0-2		20
23	16/1/10	BSS	A	Staines Town	407	L 1-2	Sigere 24	20
24	23/1/10	BSS	H	Weston-Super-Mare	470	W 2-0	Keehan 2 (pen 10, pen 21)	20
25	26/1/10	BSS	A	Dorchester Town	307	D 1-1	Sigere 66	20
26	30/1/10	BSS	A	Weymouth	667	L 1-3	Keehan 22	20
27	6/2/10	BSS	H	Braintree Town	424	D 2-2	Keehan 2 (44, 86)	20
28	13/2/10	BSS	A	Havant & Waterlooville	718	D 1-1	Pearson 90	20
29	20/2/10	BSS	H	Chelmsford City	579	L 0-2		20
30	27/2/10	BSS	H	Worcester City	501	D 3-3	Keehan pen 6, Louis 50, Wheeler 72	20
31	3/3/10	BSS	H	Eastleigh	233	L 1-2	Sigere 32	20
32	6/3/10	BSS	A	Basingstoke Town	457	D 1-1	Keehan 4	20
33	13/3/10	BSS	H	Havant & Waterlooville	447	L 0-3		20
34	20/3/10	BSS	A	Bishop's Stortford	337	D 0-0		20
35	27/3/10	BSS	H	Welling United	421	W 3-1	Keehan 3 (15, 57, pen 76)	20
36	3/4/10	BSS	A	Woking	1128	L 0-2		20
37	5/4/10	BSS	H	Bromley	426	W 1-0	Wheeler 10	20
38	10/4/10	BSS	A	Worcester City	779	W 2-1	Gradwell 21, Brinkhurst 43	20
39	14/4/10	BSS	H	St Albans City	505	D 0-0		20
40	17/4/10	BSS	H	Dorchester Town	514	W 5-0	Keehan 2 (8, 45), Gradwell 52, Breach 55, Sigere 85	19
41	20/4/10	BSS	H	Bath City	603	L 1-2	Wheeler 83	19
42	24/4/10	BSS	A	Hampton & Richmond B.	539	W 2-1	Keehan 48, Gradwell 51	19
	Cups							
1	26/9/09	FAC 2Q	H	Leatherhead	408	D 1-1	Wheeler 48	
2	29/9/09	FAC 2QR	A	Leatherhead	308	W 1-0 aet	Keehan 102	
3	10/10/09	FAC 3Q	A	Wealdstone	530	L 0-3		
4	21/11/09	FAT 3Q	A	Eastleigh	261	D 1-1	Walder 90	
5	25/11/09	FAT 3QR	H	Eastleigh	211	W 1-0	Royce 21	
6	12/12/09	FAT 1	A	Hampton & Richmond B.	256	D 0-0		
7	19/1/10	FAT 2	A	Kidderminster Harriers	654	L 2-3	Hopkinson 79, Pople 84	

Home Attendances:	
Highest:	675 v Woking
Lowest:	206 v Maidenhead United
Average (08-09):	441 (824)
Top Goalscorer:	Keehan - 19 (18 League, 1 Cup) in 44 appearances - 43% strike rate
Most Appearances:	Banks - 49 (42 League, 7 Cup)

BANKS	BARNESS	FISK	CULLIP	PEAUROUX	BREACH	WHEELER	KEEHAN	BECK	CRABB	ROYCE	CHAMBERLAIN	STORRIE	KIRKWOOD	WALDER	PEARSON	SUTTON	FOREMAN	TIMMS	RIVERS	POPLE	HALL	MANNING	HOPKINSON	HIROOKA	ARCHIBALD	BANASCO-ZARAGOZA	CRELLIN	LOUIS	FENELON	BRINKHURST	SIGERE	RAMSAY	HAMILTON	JONES	FRASER	EL-ABD	GRADWELL	
X	X	X	X	X	X	X	X	X	X	X	S	S	S	U	U																							1
X	X	U	X	S	X	X	X	X	X		X	X			X	S	S	U																				2
X	X	X	X	X	X	X	X		X		U		S	X	U	X	U		S																			3
X	X	X		X	X	X	X	X	X	X	U	S	U		X			S	S																			4
X	X	X		X	X	X	X	X	X	S			S	X	X		U	U		S																		5
X	X	U		S	X	X	X		X	X		U	S	X	X		X	X		S																		6
X	X			X	X	X	X		X	S	U	S	S	X	X	X	U	X																				7
X	X					X	X	X	U	S	X	X	X	S	X	X	U	X		S																		8
X				X	X	X		X	X	S	X	X		U	X	X	U	X		S	S																	9
X				S	X	X	X		S	X	X	X			X	X	X			S	X	U	U															10
X	X			S	X	X	X			X	X	X			X	X	X			S		U	U	S														11
X	X			X	X	X	X		U	X	S	U					X			S	X	X			X	U												12
X					X	X			S	X	X	S		X	X	X	X		X	U		X	S				U											13
X	X			U	X	X			X	X	X	S		X	X	X	U		X						U			S										14
X	X			U	X	X	S		X	X	X	X		X	X		U	S							X			S										15
X	X			U	X	X	X			S	S	X		X	X	X	U	S	X									X										16
X				X	X	X	X		U		X					X	X	X	S	U		X	S		X			S										17
X	X			U	X	X	X			X				X	X	X	S	S	X	U								X	S									18
X	X			U	X	X	X			S	S	U		X	X	X	U		X									X		X								19
X	X			X	X	X	X			S				X	X	X	U	U	X									U		X	S							20
X	X				X	X	X			U	X			X	X	X	U	U	X	S										X	S							21
X	X			X	X	X	X			S	U			X	X	X	U	S										S		X	X							22
X	X			X	X	X	X			X				S	X	X		U	U				S					X			X	S						23
X	X				X	X	X			S	S			X	X	X		U	U	S			X					X			X							24
X	X			X	X	X	X			X	S				X	X		U		U			S				S	X			X							25
X	X			X	X	X	X			U	X				X	X		S		S			X				U	S			X							26
X	X				X	X	X				X				X	X		U	U	U			S				U	X			X		X					27
X	X			U	X	X	X			U				U	X	X		U		X			S				X				X		X					28
X	X			S	X	X	X				S			X		X		U		S			X				U				X		X	X				29
X	X				X	X	X				U			X	X	X		U		S			S				S	X			X		X					30
X	X			U	X	X					X			X	X		U	U	X	S							U	X			X		X					31
X	X			U		X	X			U	X			X	X	S		U	X	S								X			X		X					32
X	X			U		X	X			S	S				X	X		U			X						X	S			X		X		X			33
X	X				X	X	S							X	X	X			X			U	U				U	X		X	S				X			34
X	X			S	X	X	X			S				X	X	X				U								U		X					U	X	X	35
X	X			U	X	X	X			U				X	X	X												S		X			S		S	X	X	36
X	X			S	X	X	X			U				X	X					U								U		X			X		S	X	X	37
X	X			U	X	X	X			U					X						S							U		X	S		X		X	X	X	38
X	X			U	X	X	X							X	X					U							S	U		X	S		X		X	X		39
X	X			S	X	X	X							X								U					U	S		X	S		X		X	X	X	40
X	X			S	X	X	X							X		X			U			U	U					S			X		X		X	X		41
X	X			S	X	X	X							X		X						U	U					U			S		X		X	X	X	42
X	X			S	X	X	X	S	S	X	X	X				X	U			U	X	U			X	U												1
X	X			X	X	X	X	X	S	X	U	S				X	U				X	U			X													2
X	X			X	X	X	X		U	X		S		U	X	X	X		S	S		U			X	U												3
X	X			U	X	X	X			X	S	S		X		X		X	X	S		U						X										4
X	X			S	X	X	X			X	U	S		X	X	X	U		X	U								X										5
X	X			U	X	X	X			X	X	U			X	X	X		U	S								U		X								6
X	X			X	X		U			X				X	X	U	X	X	X	S			X				S	S										7

Total League Appearances

BANKS	BARNESS	FISK	CULLIP	PEAUROUX	BREACH	WHEELER	KEEHAN	BECK	CRABB	ROYCE	CHAMBERLAIN	STORRIE	KIRKWOOD	WALDER	PEARSON	SUTTON	FOREMAN	TIMMS	RIVERS	POPLE	HALL	MANNING	HOPKINSON	HIROOKA	ARCHIBALD	BANASCO-ZARAGOZA	CRELLIN	LOUIS	FENELON	BRINKHURST	SIGERE	RAMSAY	HAMILTON	JONES	FRASER	EL-ABD	GRADWELL	
42	38	4	3	13	39	42	36	6	10	12	14	7	1	26	34	29	6	5	10	1	3	3	3	0	3	0	2	11	0	11	13	0	13	1	7	8	6	X
0	0	0	0	10	0	0	2	0	2	11	8	5	5	2	0	2	2	6	3	14	2	0	7	1	0	0	3	9	1	0	7	1	1	0	2	0	0	S
0	0	2	0	12	0	0	0	0	3	7	5	3	1	3	2	0	13	14	4	8	0	6	5	0	1	1	7	6	0	0	0	0	0	0	1	0	0	U

Total Cup Appearances

BANKS	BARNESS	FISK	CULLIP	PEAUROUX	BREACH	WHEELER	KEEHAN	BECK	CRABB	ROYCE	CHAMBERLAIN	STORRIE	KIRKWOOD	WALDER	PEARSON	SUTTON	FOREMAN	TIMMS	RIVERS	POPLE	HALL	MANNING	HOPKINSON	HIROOKA	ARCHIBALD	BANASCO-ZARAGOZA	CRELLIN	LOUIS	FENELON	BRINKHURST	SIGERE	RAMSAY	HAMILTON	JONES	FRASER	EL-ABD	GRADWELL	
7	7	0	0	3	7	6	6	1	0	7	2	1	0	3	4	6	3	2	3	0	2	0	1	0	3	0	0	2	0	1	0	0	0	0	0	0	0	X
0	0	0	0	2	0	0	0	1	2	0	1	4	0	0	0	0	0	0	1	4	0	0	0	0	0	0	1	1	0	0	0	0	0	0	0	0	0	S
0	0	0	0	2	0	0	1	0	1	0	2	1	0	1	0	1	3	0	1	2	0	4	0	0	0	2	0	1	0	0	0	0	0	0	0	0	0	U

Total Goals

BANKS	BARNESS	FISK	CULLIP	PEAUROUX	BREACH	WHEELER	KEEHAN	BECK	CRABB	ROYCE	CHAMBERLAIN	STORRIE	KIRKWOOD	WALDER	PEARSON	SUTTON	FOREMAN	TIMMS	RIVERS	POPLE	HALL	MANNING	HOPKINSON	HIROOKA	ARCHIBALD	BANASCO-ZARAGOZA	CRELLIN	LOUIS	FENELON	BRINKHURST	SIGERE	RAMSAY	HAMILTON	JONES	FRASER	EL-ABD	GRADWELL	
0	0	0	0	0	1	6	18	2	3	0	0	0	0	1	3	0	2	0	1	1	0	0	0	0	0	0	0	1	0	2	4	0	0	0	0	0	3	Lge
0	0	0	0	0	0	1	1	0	0	1	0	0	0	1	0	0	0	0	0	1	0	0	1	0	0	0	0	0	0	0	0	0	0	0	0	0	0	Cup

LEWES

CURRANT SQUAD AS OF BEGINING OF 2010-11 SEASON

GOALKEEPERS	HT	WT	D.O.B	AGE	P.O.B	CAREER	APPS	GOA	
JJ Banasco-Zaragoza			26/9/91	18		Lewes, East Grinstead (L) 3/10		0	0
Chris Winterton	5'10"	12 06	18/11/88	21	Eastbourne	Brighton Rel c/s 08, Burgess Hill (L) 7/07, Horsham YMCA (L) 11/07, Eastbourne B 7/08 Rel 1/09, Worthing (L) 12/08, Lewes 1/09 Rel 3/09, Finland, Burgess Hill 2/10, Lewes 5/10			

DEFENDERS	HT	WT	D.O.B	AGE	P.O.B	CAREER	APPS	GOA	
Anthony Barness	5'11"	12 01	25/3/73	37	Lewisham	Charlton, Chelsea £350,000 9/92, Middlesbrough (2ML) 8/93, Southend (L) 2/96, Charlton £165,000 8/96 Rel c/s 00, Bolton 7/00 Rel c/s 05, Plymouth 7/05 Rel 1/07, Yeovil (Trial) 2/07, Grays 3/07 Rel 5/07, Lewes 8/07		38	0
Chris Breach	5'11"	12 07	19/4/86	24	Brighton	Brighton Rel c/s 07, Bognor (L) 3/06, Bognor (L) 12/06, Bognor 8/07, Lewes 5/08		39	1
Sonny Cobbs	6'01"	13 00	1/12/88	21		Brighton Rel 5/08, Worthing (L) 8/06, Worthing (SL) 12/06, Worthing (3ML) 8/07, Dorchester (L) 11/07, Welling (SL) 1/08, Welling 7/08, Sutton U 6/09, Lewes 6/10			
Lewis Hamilton	6'00"	11 08	21/11/84	25	Derby	Derby (Trainee), QPR 8/04 Rel 8/05, Kingstonian (L) 12/04, AFC Wimbledon (L) 3/05, Aldershot 8/05 Rel 5/06, Lewes 5/06 Rel 5/08, Tonbridge A 7/08 Rel 12/09, Lewes 1/10	14	0	
Scott Manning			17/7/92	18		Eastbourne B (Yth), Lewes		3	0
Andy Pearson	5'11"	13 08	19/9/89	20	Brighton	Brighton Rel 5/09, Worthing (L) 10/08, Lewes (L) 1/09, Bognor Regis (SL) 2/09, Lewes c/s 09	34	3	
Marc Pullan	6'03"	14 06	28/2/74	36	Brighton	Peacehaven, Crawley 7/96 Rel c/s 98, Year Out, Wick 7/99, Crawley 1/00, Worthing 6/04, Eastbourne B 1/06 Rel 5/10, Lewes 6/10			

MIDFIELDERS	HT	WT	D.O.B	AGE	P.O.B	CAREER	APPS	GOA	
Jamie Crellin			17/11/91	18		Lewes	5	0	
Lewis Ide	5'10"	10 10	21/9/90	19	Chichester	Brighton Rel 1/10, Bognor Regis (2ML) 9/09, Bognor Regis 1/10, Lewes 5/10			
George Jones			12/2/93	17		Lewes	1	0	
Ross Sutton			20/7/92	18		Lewes	31	0	
Jack Walder			18/11/89	20		Lewes	28	1	
David Wheeler			4/10/90	19		Lewes	42	6	
Simon Wormull	5'10"	12 03	12/12/76	32	Crawley	Tottenham Rel c/s 97, Brentford 7/97, Brighton 3/98, Dover 9/98, Rushden & D £50,000 3/00, Stevenage 9/01 Rel 4/04, Hornchurch 5/04, Crawley 11/04, Lewes 6/06, Eastbourne B 6/08 Rel 6/09, Farnborough 6/09 Rel 5/10, Lewes 5/10			

FORWARDS	HT	WT	D.O.B	AGE	P.O.B	CAREER	APPS	GOA	
Rob Gradwell	6'02"	13 07	16/12/90	19	Hillingdon	Birmingham (Scholar) Rel c/s 09, Luton (Trial) 4/09, Lincoln C (Trial) 7/09, Hayes & Yeading c/s 09 Rel 5/10, Lewes (L) 3/10, Lewes 5/10		6	3
Tim Rivers			20/5/91	19		Lewes	13	1	

Loanees	HT	WT	DOB	AGE	POB	From - To	APPS	GOA	
(M)Steven Brinkhurst			28/3/91	19	Lewes	Brighton 12/09, 3/10 - Eastbourne B 6/10		11	2
(F)Scott Ramsay			16/10/80	29		Hastings U 12/09 - Rye Utd 1/10		1	0
(D)Sami El-Abd			1/1/88	22	Brighton	Hayes & Yeading 3/10 - Rel 5/10, Chelmsford 7/10		8	0

Departures	HT	WT	DOB	AGE	POB	From - To	APPS	GOA	
(D)Grant Hall			29/10/91	18		Brighton (Yth) - Gillingham (Trial) 8/09, Brighton Nominal 10/09, Bognor Regis (L) 12/09, Lewes (L) 3/10	5	0	
(F)Dan Beck	5'10"	10 11	14/11/83	26	Worthing	Bognor Regis 7/09 - Bognor Regis 11/09		6	2
(M)Scott Kirkwood			4/5/85	25		Worthing 6/09 - Whitehawk		6	0
(F)Ryan Hirooka			18/2/90	20		Bognor Regis 9/09 - Japan (Trial)		1	0
(M)Sam Crabb			25/10/87	22	Eastbourne	Eastbourne B 7/09 - Rel 11/09		12	3
(F)Evan Archibald			19/2/86	24		AC Kajaani (Fin) 9/09 - Rel 11/09, Worthing 11/09, Eastbourne T 6/10		3	0
(M)Ryan Storrie			26/2/91	19		Yth - Southampton (Trial), Rel 12/09, Eastbourne T 1/10		12	0
(D)Danny Cullip	6'01"	12 07	17/9/76	33	Bracknell	Gillingham 7/08 (Pl/Coach) 9/08 - Retired 3/10		3	0
(D)Ryan Timms			11/5/91	19		Southwick - Horsham YMCA 3/10		11	0
(M)Scott Chamberlain	5'09"	10 08	15/1/88	22	Eastbourne	Bognor 7/09 - Eastbourne T 3/10		22	0
(F)Chamal Fenelon			18/6/83	27		ex Seaford 11/09 - Worthing, Dag & Red (Trial) 4/10		1	0
(G)Rikki Banks	6'03"	13 08	13/5/86	24	Brighton	Worthing 6/08 - Wycombe (Trial) 12/09, Eastbourne B 5/10		42	0
(M)Arron Hopkinson			3/2/92	18		Lewes Bridgeview - Eastbourne T (3ML) 11/09, Brighton (Trial) 2/10, Rel 6/10, Cardiff University		10	0
(M)Joe Keehan			7/1/87	23		Worthing 7/08 - Rushden & D 6/10		38	18
(F)James Fraser	5'09"	12 07	26/4/89	21	Brighton	Eastbourne B 3/10 - Rel 6/10		9	0
(F)Jean-Michel Sigere			26/1/77	33		Tonbridge A 12/09 - Rel 6/10		20	4
(M)Dan Royce	5'09"	11 13	26/11/89	20	Chichester	Brighton 7/09 - Rel 7/10		23	0
(F)Kane Louis	5'10"	10 10	21/5/90	20	Brighton	Eastbourne B 10/09 - Ashford T (Middx) 7/10		20	1
(F)Freddie Foreman			30/5/91	19		Brighton (Yth) - Eastbourne T (Dual) 1/10, Eastbourne T c/s 10		8	2
(F)Louis Pople			10/12/91	18		Burgess Hill c/s 09 - Burgess Hill c/s 10		15	1
(M)Sam Fisk			5/2/88	22		Hassocks 1/09 -	4	0	
(M)William Peauroux				15/8/83	27		Horsham 7/09 -	23	0

MAIDENHEAD UNITED

Chairman: Peter Griffin
Secretary: Ken Chandler (T) 07726 351 286
(E) kenneth.chandler@btinternet.com
Additional Committee Members: Robert Hussey, Una Loughrey, Mark Stewart, Steve Jinman, Suzanne Loughrey, Graham Alfred, Mark Smith, Roy Bannister
Manager: Johnson Hippolyte
Programme Editor: Steve Jinman (E) sjinman@hotmail.com

Back Row (L-R): Bradley Quamina, Lewis Ochoa, Reis Stanislaus, Warren Carter, Adam Carpenter, Brandon Martin, Pat Sappleton. **Middle:** Martin Ireland (Coach), Max Bangura (Physio), Kieran Knight, Daniel Brown, Arian Taj, Kieron St. Aimie, Jamal Fyfield, Alex Wall, Nevin Saroya, Mark Nisbet (Captain), James Hamsher, Jake Brooks, Dereck Brown (Assistant Manager), Jon Urry (Kitman). **Seated:** Sam Collins, Luke Barney, Staforde Palmer, Johnson Hippolyte (Manager), Bobby Behzadi, Jack Bradshaw, Dean Mason.

Club Factfile

Founded: 1870 **Nickname:** Magpies
Previous Names: Maidenhead F.C and Maidenhead Norfolkians merged to form today's club
Previous Leagues: Southern 1894-1902, 2006-07, West Berkshire 1902-04, Gr. West Suburban 1904-22, Spartan 1922-39, Gr. West Comb. 1939-45, Corinthian 1945-63, Athenian 1963-73, Isthmian 1973-2004, Conf. 2004-06
Club Colours (change): Black & white stripes/black/red (All red)

Ground: York Road, Maidenhead, Berkshire SL6 1SF (T) 01628 636 314
Capacity: 4,500 **Seats:** 400 **Covered:** 2,000 **Clubhouse:** Yes **Shop:** Yes
Previous Grounds:
Simple Directions
The Ground is in the town centre.
200 yards from the station and two minutes walk from the High Street.
Access from M4 Junctions 7 or 8/9.

Record Attendance: 7,920 v Southall - FA Amateur Cup Quarter final 07/03/1936
Record Victory: 14-1 v Buckingham Town - FA Amateur Cup 06/09/1952
Record Defeat: 0-14 v Chesham United (A) - Spartan League 31/03/1923
Record Goalscorer: George Copas - 270 (1924-35)
Record Appearances: Bert Randall - 532 (1950-64)
Additional Records: Received £5,000 from Norwich City for Alan Cordice 1979

Senior Honours: Corinthian League 1957-58, 60-61, 61-62.
Berks & Bucks Senior Cup x19.

10 YEAR RECORD

00-01	01-02	02-03	03-04	04-05	05-06	06-07	07-08	08-09	09-10
Isth P 16	Isth P 16	Isth P 10	Isth P 12	Conf S 20	Conf S 22	SthP 4	Conf S 17	Conf S 6	Conf S 16

MAIDENHEAD UNITED

No.	Date	Comp	H/A	Opponents	Att:	Result	Goalscorers	Pos
1	8/8/09	BSS	H	Dover Athletic	407	D 0-0		14
2	11/8/09	BSS	A	Bath City	472	L 0-1		15
3	15/8/09	BSS	A	Braintree Town	507	L 0-2		18
4	18/8/09	BSS	H	Weymouth	249	D 1-1	Palmer 68	19
5	22/8/09	BSS	A	Basingstoke Town	657	D 0-0		20
6	29/8/09	BSS	H	Newport County	497	L 1-3	Knight 18	21
7	31/8/09	BSS	A	Staines Town	387	D 1-1	Behzadi 59	20
8	5/9/09	BSS	H	Thurrock	240	L 0-2		22
9	8/9/09	BSS	H	Welling United	187	W 2-0	Quamina 23, Wall 83	17
10	12/9/09	BSS	A	Woking	1427	D 1-1	Knight 25	16
11	19/9/09	BSS	A	Lewes	206	W 2-1	St Aimie 53, Collins 77	15
12	3/10/09	BSS	H	Bromley	276	W 4-0	Nisbet 7, Hendry 56, Brown 85, Wall 87	14
13	10/10/09	BSS	A	Weymouth	571	W 5-0	St Aimie 2 (17, 57), Hendry 25, Palmer 2 (83, 90)	10
14	17/10/09	BSS	A	Eastleigh	532	W 3-0	Hendry 2 (23, 74), Palmer 60	9
15	24/10/09	BSS	H	Weston-Super-Mare	429	D 0-0		8
16	27/10/09	BSS	H	Dorchester Town	304	L 1-2	Hendry 71	10
17	31/10/09	BSS	A	Hampton & Richmond B.	434	L 0-4		12
18	7/11/09	BSS	A	Chelmsford City	1015	D 1-1	Palmer 72	11
19	14/11/09	BSS	H	Basingstoke Town	288	W 3-2	Collins 60, St Aimie 76, Wall 90	10
20	28/11/09	BSS	A	Havant & Waterlooville	681	L 0-1		11
21	5/12/09	BSS	H	Lewes	220	D 1-1	Wall 80	13
22	26/12/09	BSS	H	St Albans City	289	L 0-3		16
23	16/1/10	BSS	A	Bromley	399	W 2-1	Wall 76, Knight 82	15
24	23/1/10	BSS	H	Eastleigh	252	L 0-3		15
25	6/2/10	BSS	H	Bishop's Stortford	263	W 4-0	Collins 34, Wall 2 (45, 74), Quamina 81	16
26	9/2/10	BSS	A	St Albans City	194	L 0-1		16
27	13/2/10	BSS	H	Bath City	250	L 1-2	Knight 63	16
28	20/2/10	BSS	A	Dover Athletic	851	D 1-1	Collins 51	17
29	27/2/10	BSS	H	Chelmsford City	361	L 0-2		17
30	1/3/10	BSS	A	Worcester City	501	L 0-1		17
31	6/3/10	BSS	A	Weston-Super-Mare	207	W 4-1	Behzadi 60, St Aimie 2 (70, 75), Wall 90	16
32	13/3/10	BSS	H	Hampton & Richmond B.	285	W 2-1	Collins 56, Nisbet 75	15
33	16/3/10	BSS	H	Braintree Town	155	D 0-0		15
34	20/3/10	BSS	A	Welling United	461	L 1-3	Og (Clark) 13	16
35	23/3/10	BSS	A	Thurrock	202	D 2-2	Knight 1, Collins 50	16
36	27/3/10	BSS	H	Worcester City	379	D 1-1	Collins 59	15
37	3/4/10	BSS	A	Newport County	1339	L 1-4	Collins 74	15
38	10/4/10	BSS	A	Bishop's Stortford	309	W 2-1	Knight 32, Fyfield 54	15
39	13/4/10	BSS	H	Woking	510	L 1-2	St Aimie pen 29	16
40	17/4/10	BSS	H	Havant & Waterlooville	336	L 0-2		16
41	20/4/10	BSS	H	Staines Town	296	W 2-1	Collins 41, Fyfield 83	15
42	24/4/10	BSS	A	Dorchester Town	648	L 2-4	Collins 37, Wall 73	16
	Cups							
1	26/9/09	FAC 2Q	H	Truro City	313	L 2-5	Og (Gaia) 47, Wall 66	
2	21/11/09	FAT 3Q	H	Bath City	272	W 1-0	St Aimie 69	
3	12/12/09	FAT 1	A	Bishop's Stortford	245	W 2-1	Collins 17, Knight 59	
4	19/1/10	FAT 2	H	Barrow	301	L 0-1		

Home Attendances:	
Highest:	510 v Woking
Lowest:	155 v Braintree Town
Average (08-09):	289 (425)
Top Goalscorer:	Collins - 11 (10 League, 1 Cup) in 45 appearances - 24% strike rate
Most Appearances:	Behzadi - 46 (40+2 League, 4 Cup)

TARDIFF	BRADSHAW	FYFIELD	BROWN	SAROYA	NISBET	BEHZADI	ST AIMIE	STANISLAUS	WALL	BARNES	MASON	PALMER	COLLINS	OCHOA	CARPENTER	TAJBAKHSH	HAMSHER	SAPPLETON	KNIGHT	CARTER	NICOLAU	BARNEY	QUAMINA	HENDRY	BADDELEY	ROSE	CLARKE	MARTIN	JONES	SMITH	DIMITROV	BERNARD	HIPPOLYTE	MUTERO	ROBINSON	CROOK	
X	X	X	X	X	X	X	X	X	X	X	S	S	S	U	U																						1
X	X	X	X	X	X	X		X	S	U	X	X	X	S	U	S																					2
X	X	X	X	X	X	X	X	U	U		X	X		U	S	U	X																				3
X	X	X	X	X	X	X	X	X	S			X	S	U	U	S	X																				4
X	X		X		X	X	X	U	S			X	X	S	U	S	X	X	X																		5
	X	S	X	S	X	X	X		S			X	X	U	X		X	X	X	U																	6
	X	U	S	S	X	X	X		S			X	X		X	X	X	X	X	U																	7
X	X	S	S	X	X	X	X		U			X	X		U	X			X		X	U															8
X	X	X	X	X	X	X	X		S			S	X	U	U	S			X				X														9
X	X	X	X	X	X	X	X		S			S	X	U	U	U			X				X														10
X	X	X	X	X	X	X	X		S				X		U	U		U	X				X	S													11
X	X	X	X	U	X	S	X		S			S	X		U			X	X				X	X													12
X		X	X	S	X	X	X		S			S	X		U			X	X			U	X	X													13
X	S	X	X	U	X	X	X		S			X	X		U			X				S	X	X													14
X	U	X	X	S	X	X	X		S			X	X		U			X	S				X	X													15
X	U	X	X	X	X	X	X		S			X	X		U	U			S				X	X													16
X	S	X	X	S	X	X	X		S			U	X		U			X	X				X	X													17
X	X	X	X	S	X	X	X		S			S	X		U			X	X			U		X													18
X	X		X	X		X	X		S				X		U				X			U	X		X	X	U	U									19
X	X	X	X	X	X	X	X		X				X		U				S			S	X		U	U											20
X	X	X	X	X	X	X	X		S				X	X	U				X						U	S	S										21
X	X			X	X	X	X		X				S			S			X	U		S	X		X	U				X							22
X	X		X	X	X	X	X		X				X			U		U	S	U			X		U					X							23
X	X	S	X	X	X	X	X						X	S		U			X	U			X		X					S							24
X	X	X	X	X	X	X	X		X				X	S					S	U			X			U				S							25
X	S	X	S	X	X	X			X				X	U					X	U			X			X				X	S						26
X	X	X	X	X	X	X			X				X	S					X	U			X								S	S	U				27
X	X	X	S	X	X	X			X				X	U					X	U			X			S				X	S						28
X	X	X		X	X	X			S				X	S					X	U			X			U				X		X		S			29
X	X	X		X	X	X	S		X				X	U					X	U			X			S				X				S			30
X	X	X			X	X	X		S				X	S					X	U		S	X			X			U	X							31
X	X	X	S	S	X	X	X		S				X	U					X	U			X			X				X							32
X	X	X	U	X	X	X	U		X				X	U					X	U			X			S				X							33
X	X	X	U	X	X	X	S		X				X	S					X	U			X			S				X							34
X		X	X		X	X			X				X	S					X	U		U			S	X	X			X			U				35
U		X	X			X							X	S					X	X		X			X	X	X		S	X			S				36
U		X	U			X	X						X	X					X	X		S			X	X						X	U		X	S	37
U		X			X	X	X		S				X	X					X	X		U			X	X				X					S	S	38
U	X	X			X	X	X		X				X	X						X		S			X				U	X		S			U		39
U	X	X			X	X	X		X				X	S						X		U	X		X					X		S			S		40
U		X			X	X	X		S				X	U					S	X		X	X		X	X			S	X							41
U	X	X			X	S	S		S				X	X					X	X			X		U	X				X		X					42
X	X	X	X	X	X	X	X		S			U	X	U	U	S		U	X			S	X														1
X	X			X	S	X	X		S				X		U				X			U	X	X	X	X	S										2
X	X	X		X	X	X	X		X				X			X		S	X	U		S			U				S								3
X	X		X	X	X	X	X		X				X			S		U	S	U		S	X		X												4

Total League Appearances

33	31	34	25	23	39	40	31	3	14	1	2	10	38	5	2	2	5	9	29	7	1	2	27	7	9	10	2	0	0	17	0	3	0	0	1	0	X
0	3	3	5	7	0	2	3	0	23	0	1	6	3	11	1	5	0	0	6	0	0	6	0	1	1	5	1	0	2	2	3	3	1	2	2	2	S
7	2	1	3	2	0	0	1	2	2	1	0	1	0	12	18	6	0	2	0	16	0	7	0	0	4	4	1	1	2	0	0	0	3	0	1	0	U

Total Cup Appearances

4	4	2	2	4	3	4	4	0	2	0	0	0	4	0	0	1	0	0	3	0	0	0	3	1	2	1	0	0	0	0	0	0	0	0	0	0	X
0	0	0	0	0	1	0	0	0	2	0	0	0	0	0	0	2	0	1	1	0	0	3	0	0	0	0	1	0	1	0	0	0	0	0	0	0	S
0	0	0	0	0	0	0	0	0	0	0	0	1	0	1	2	0	0	2	0	2	0	1	0	0	1	0	0	0	0	0	0	0	0	0	0	0	U

Total Cup Appearances

0	0	2	1	0	2	2	7	0	9	0	0	5	10	0	0	0	0	0	6	0	0	0	2	5	0	0	0	0	0	0	0	0	0	0	0	0	Lge
0	0	0	0	0	0	0	1	0	1	0	0	0	1	0	0	0	0	0	1	0	0	0	0	0	0	0	0	0	0	0	0	0	0	0	0	0	Cup

MAIDENHEAD UNITED

CURRENT SQUAD AS OF BEGINING OF 2010-11 SEASON

GOALKEEPERS	HT	WT	D.O.B	AGE	P.O.B	CAREER	Apps	Gls
Adam Carpenter			3/5/89	21		Maidenhead, Chalfont Wasps (L), Bracknell (L)	3	0
Warren Carter			2/8/89	21		Holyport, Maidenhead 8/08, Northwood (L) 3/09	7	0
Steve Williams	6'04"	12 08	21/4/83	27	Oxford	Wycombe, Beaconsfield (WE), Windsor & E (L) 12/02, Forest Green (6ML) 8/06, Lewes 2/07 Rel 5/08, Hayes & Yeading 3/09, Farnborough 7/09, Hastings U (Dual) 1/10, Maidenhead 6/10		
DEFENDERS								
Tom Baddeley			24/2/90	20		Brentford (Scholar), Thatcham (WE) 1/08 Maidenhead 8/08, Bracknell (L) 9/08, Burnham (L) 2/09, Burnham (L) 3/09, Bedfont Green (L)	10	0
Bobby Behzadi			8/2/81	29	London	Stevenage, Wealdstone (L) 1/00, Hayes 3/00, Yeading 8/01, Maidenhead 1/07	42	2
Jack Bradshaw			1/7/89	21		Stevenage Rel 5/09, Tiptree (L) 8/07, Maidenhead (4ML) 1/08, Maidenhead (3ML) 8/08, Ware (L) 12/08, Maidenhead (SL) 2/09, Maidenhead 8/09	34	0
Andrew Fagan						Leighton T, Windsor & E 7/08, Maidenhead 7/10		
Jamal Fyfield			17/3/89	21		L.Orient, Maidenhead 8/07	37	2
Mark Nisbet			29/11/86	23		Flackwell Heath, Maidenhead 7/06	39	2
Marcus Rose			4/6/90	20		QPR (Yth), Barnet (Scholar), Hitchin (2ML) 11/08, Leyton c/s 09, Maidenhead 11/09	15	0
MIDFIELDERS								
Adam Bernard			18/11/88	21		Brentford Rel c/s 07, Welling 8/07 Rel 9/07, Leatherhead, Uxbridge 9/08, Ware 3/09, Hemel Hempstead 3/09, Maidenhead 2/10	6	0
Daniel Brown			28/10/88	21		Northwood, Maidenhead 8/09	30	1
David Clarke			2/9/71	38	Nottingham	Notts County, Eastwood T, Harrow, Dover £5,000 2/98, Chesham (L) 3/01 Kingstonian £10,000 6/01, Yeading c/s 03, Maidenhead (Pl/Coach) 10/06	3	0
Sam Collins	6'00"	12 06	25/6/89	21	London	MK Dons, Maidenhead (L) 11/06, Kettering (3ML) 9/07, Hendon (L) 11/07, Wivenhoe (L) 8/08 Perm, Hendon 12/08, Maidenhead 2/09, Canvey Island (Trial) 6/09, Maidenhead 8/09	41	10
Joseph Crook						Maidenhead	2	0
Ryan Jones			16/9/91	18		Maidenhead	2	0
Ashley Nicholls	5'11"	11 11	30/10/81	28	Ipswich	Ipswich Wan, Ipswich 7/00 Rel c/s 02, Canvey Island (L) 2/02, Hereford (Trial) 7/02, Darlington 8/02, Cambridge U (SL) 2/04, Cambridge U 7/04, Rushden & D (3ML) 8/05, Rushden & D 1/06, Grays 8/06, Boston U 7/07, Maidenhead 4/08 Rel 5/09, Bishop's Stortford 5/09, Newport C (2ML) 12/09, Eastleigh 3/10, Maidenhead 6/10		
Lewis Ochoa	5'10"	11 02	24/6/91	19	London	Brentford (Scholar) Rel c/s 09, Wycombe (Trial) 3/09, Maidenhead 8/09, Hendon (L) 10/09	16	0
Bradley Quamina	5'11"		28/6/85	25		Yeading Rel 8/05, USA Scholarship, Yeading/Hayes & Yeading 1/06, Woking 5/07 Rel 5/09, Maidenhead 6/09	27	2
Ashley Smith			22/12/83	26		Flackwell Heath, Burnham, Flackwell Heath 11/04, Maidenhead c/s 06, Hampton & R 8/09, Maidenhead 12/09	19	0
FORWARDS								
Lee Barney			1/4/92	18		Maidenhead	8	0
Kieran Knight			18/2/81	29	Middlesex	Southall, Chertsey, Southall, Northwood, Aylesbury, Enfield, Northwood 8/02, Hayes/Hayes & Yeading 7/04, Hampton & R 2/09 Rel 8/09, Maidenhead 8/09	35	6
Kieron St Aimie	6'01"	13 00	4/5/89	21	Brent	QPR Rel 1/08, Oxford U (L) 10/07, Barnet 1/08 Rel 2/09, Grays (L) 9/08, Stevenage (L) 11/08, Lewes (L) 1/09, St Albans (Trial), Thurrock 3/09, Hitchin 3/09, Maidenhead 8/09	34	7
Alex Wall			22/9/90	19		Thatcham, Maidenhead 8/09	37	9
Johnson Hippolyte			9/6/64	46		Maidenhead (Man)	1	0

Loanees	HT	WT	DOB	AGE	POB	From - To	APPS	GOA
(F)Stafforde Palmer			23/4/88	22		Hayes & Yeading (3ML) 6/09 - Eastleigh (SL) 2/10	16	5
(M)Trevor Mutero			13/7/93	17		Reading 2/10 -	2	0

Departures	HT	WT	DOB	AGE	POB	From - To	APPS	GOA
(M)Steve Barnes	5'04"	10 09	5/1/76	34	Harrow	Time Out 3/09 - Rel 8/09	1	0
(F)Reis Stanislaus			17/3/89	21		Woking (Yth) 8/09 - Godalming, Leyton 10/09	3	0
(D)Nicky Nicolau	5'08"	10 03	12/10/83	26	Camden	Barnet 8/09 - Woking 9/09	1	0
(M)Will Hendry	5'11"	12 10	10/11/86	23	Slough	Dag & Red 9/09 - AFC Wimbledon 11/09 Rel 4/10, Gabala (Aze) 7/10	8	5
(M)Dean Mason			28/2/89	21	Islington	AFC Wimbledon 8/09 - Cambridge C (Dual) 9/09, Bishop's Stortford 12/09	3	0
(D)Brandon Martin	5'09"	12 01	13/1/91	19		L.Orient (Scholar) 8/09 - Harrow, Godalming 12/09	0	0
(D)Nevin Saroya	6'03"	13 01	15/9/80	29	Hillingdon	Hayes & Yeading 12/08 - Australia 3/10	30	0
(F)Aryan Tajbakhsh			27/10/90	19		Northwood 3/09 - Rel 4/10, Potters Bar (L) 11/09, Godalming (L) 2/10	7	0
(G)Chris Tardif	5'11"	12 07	20/6/81	29	Guernsey	Winchester 6/09 - Basingstoke 5/10	33	0
(D)Pat Sappleton			16/4/82	28	London	Godalming T 11/08 - Aylesbury (Dual) 12/09	9	0
(F)Paul Robinson	5'11"	11 00	20/11/78	31	Sunderland	Consett 3/10 -	3	0
(M)Ivaylo Dimitrov			8/1/89	21		Vihren Sandanski (Bul) 1/10 -	3	0
(M)Jamie Hamsher			13/10/86	23		Northwood -	5	0

ST ALBANS CITY

Chairman: John Gibson
Secretary: Steve Eames (T) 07805 769 083
(E) steveeames@sacfc.co.uk
Additional Committee Members:
Allisdair McMillin, Bill Nicholson, Nick Archer, Daniele Manzi, Karen Gibson
Manager: Steve Castle
Programme Editor: Steve Eames (E) steveeames@sacfc.co.uk

Archive photo

Club Factfile

Founded: 1908 **Nickname:** The Saints
Previous Names:
Previous Leagues: Herts County 1908-10, Spartan 1908-20, Athenian 1920-23, Isthmian 1923-2004

Club Colours (change): Yellow & blue/blue/yellow (All red)

Ground: Clarence Park, York Road, St. Albans, Herts AL1 4PL (T) 01727 864 296
Capacity: 6,000 **Seats:** 904 **Covered:** 1,900 **Clubhouse:** Yes **Shop:** Yes
Previous Grounds: None

Simple Directions
From the M25 (Clockwise) Exit M25 at junction 21A(A405). Follow signs to St. Albans from slip road. At Noke Hotel roundabout (Shell garage will be straight ahead), bear right on A405 and stay on A405 until London Colney rbt (traffic light controlled). Turn left onto A1081. Follow road for approx 1 mile until mini rbt (Great Northern pub on left). Turn right into Alma Road. At traffic lights turn right into Victoria Street and continue to junction with Crown pub. Go straight across into Clarence Road, ground is first on left about 50 yards past junction or take the next turning on the left into York Road, ground entrance is at the end of the road on the left. From the M25 (Counter-clockwise) Exit M25 at juntion 22 (A1081). Follow signs to St. Albans from slip road. At London Colney rbt (traffic light controlled) exit onto A1081. Follow road for approx 1 mile until mini rbt (Great Northern pub on left). Turn right into Alma Road. At traffic lights turn right into Victoria Street and continue to junction with Crown pub. Go straight across into Clarence Road, ground is first on left about 50 yards past junction or take the next turning on the left into York Road, ground entrance is at the end of the road on the left.

Record Attendance: 9,757 v Ferryhill Athletic - FA Amateur Cup 1926
Record Victory: 14-0 v Aylesbury United (H) - Spartan League 19/10/1912
Record Defeat: 0-11 v Wimbledon (H) - Isthmian League 1946
Record Goalscorer: Billy Minter - 356 (Top scorer for 12 consecutive season from 1920-32)
Record Appearances: Phil Wood - 900 (1962-85)
Additional Records: Paid £6,000 to Yeovil Town for Paul Turner August 1957
Received £92,759 from Southend United for Dean Austin 1990

Senior Honours: Athenian League 1920-21, 21-22. Isthmian League 1923-24, 26-27, 27-28.
London Senior Cup 1970-71.

10 YEAR RECORD

00-01	01-02	02-03	03-04	04-05	05-06	06-07	07-08	08-09	09-10
Isth P 14	Isth P 10	Isth P 4	Isth P 19	Conf S 14	Conf S 2	Conf 24	Conf S 19	Conf S 12	Conf S 13

ST ALBANS CITY

No.	Date	Comp	H/A	Opponents	Att:	Result	Goalscorers	Pos
1	8/8/09	BSS	A	Dorchester Town	450	L 0-3		22
2	11/8/09	BSS	H	Worcester City	318	W 2-0	Roberts 59, Green 88	13
3	15/8/09	BSS	H	Eastleigh	332	W 2-1	Roberts 2 (pen 45, pen 81)	10
4	18/8/09	BSS	A	Welling United	445	L 2-3	Quinton 2 (65, pen 76)	12
5	22/8/09	BSS	H	Lewes	351	D 1-1	Peters 90	11
6	29/8/09	BSS	A	Bishop's Stortford	461	L 0-2		13
7	31/8/09	BSS	H	Hampton & Richmond B.	420	L 1-2	Roberts pen 24	14
8	5/9/09	BSS	A	Chelmsford City	1122	L 0-2		15
9	8/9/09	BSS	H	Staines Town	304	L 1-3	J Thurlbourne 73	18
10	12/9/09	BSS	H	Havant & Waterlooville	329	D 1-1	Chillingworth 14	18
11	19/9/09	BSS	A	Weymouth	645	W 2-0	Og (Slocombe) 40, Shields 63	17
12	3/10/09	BSS	A	Weston-Super-Mare	218	W 3-2	L Thurlbourne 21, Cohen 65, Shields 80	15
13	17/10/09	BSS	H	Newport County	581	L 0-1		16
14	31/10/09	BSS	H	Weymouth	377	W 2-1	Poku 35, Roberts pen 37	16
15	7/11/09	BSS	A	Basingstoke Town	424	D 1-1	Roberts 22	16
16	10/11/09	BSS	A	Woking	1008	W 1-0	Sagna 84	15
17	14/11/09	BSS	H	Braintree Town	344	D 1-1	Johnson 74	15
18	28/11/09	BSS	A	Bromley	307	L 0-2		16
19	1/12/09	BSS	H	Basingstoke Town	205	W 2-0	Fisher 29, Cohen 90	15
20	5/12/09	BSS	H	Chelmsford City	467	L 0-1		15
21	12/12/09	BSS	H	Bromley	312	W 2-0	Cohen 28, O'Donnell 85	13
22	19/12/09	BSS	A	Dover Athletic	593	D 1-1	O'Donnell 31	11
23	26/12/09	BSS	A	Maidenhead United	289	W 3-0	McLachlan 4, Roberts 2 (75, 87)	10
24	28/12/09	BSS	H	Welling United	463	L 1-2	Roberts 52	10
25	23/1/10	BSS	A	Newport County	1412	L 0-5		14
26	30/1/10	BSS	H	Bath City	383	L 0-2		15
27	6/2/10	BSS	H	Weston-Super-Mare	279	W 2-1	Dunn 2 (45, 61)	14
28	9/2/10	BSS	H	Maidenhead United	194	W 1-0	Everitt 75	13
29	13/2/10	BSS	A	Thurrock	238	D 0-0		14
30	20/2/10	BSS	A	Staines Town	460	L 3-4	Dunn 28, Peters 32, Cohen 81	14
31	22/2/10	BSS	A	Havant & Waterlooville	552	W 1-0	Roberts 55	14
32	2/3/10	BSS	H	Dorchester Town	240	W 2-1	Roberts 2 (pen 9, 38)	12
33	6/3/10	BSS	A	Eastleigh	479	W 1-0	Roberts 12	9
34	13/3/10	BSS	H	Thurrock	343	W 1-0	Everitt 45	8
35	20/3/10	BSS	A	Worcester City	605	D 0-0		10
36	27/3/10	BSS	H	Dover Athletic	577	L 1-2	Roberts pen 33	12
37	3/4/10	BSS	H	Bishop's Stortford	402	L 2-4	Cohen 49, Dunn 77	13
38	5/4/10	BSS	A	Hampton & Richmond B.	357	L 0-3		13
39	10/4/10	BSS	A	Braintree Town	500	D 2-2	Dunn pen 39, Fisher 47	12
40	14/4/10	BSS	A	Lewes	505	D 0-0		12
41	17/4/10	BSS	H	Woking	752	L 0-1		12
42	24/4/10	BSS	A	Bath City	1030	D 0-0		13
	Cups							
1	26/9/09	FAC 2Q	A	Heybridge Swifts	202	L 0-1		
2	21/11/09	FAT 3Q	A	Woking	823	L 0-6		

Home Attendances:	
Highest:	752 v Woking
Lowest:	194 v Maidenhead United
Average (08-09):	344 (466)

Top Goalscorer:	Roberts - 14 (14 League, 0 Cup) in 34 appearances - 41% strike rate
Most Appearances:	Bastock - 41 (40 League, 1 Cup)

BASTOCK	BAILEY	EVERITT	L THURLBOURNE	MITCHELL	FRATER	SHIELDS	FISHER	COHEN	O'DONOGHUE	GREEN	ROBERTS	QUILTER	CHILLINGWORTH	J THURLBOURNE	QUINTON	HAKIM	PETERS	O'DONNELL	EMERY	CALVER	MORTIMER	GALBRAITH	POKU	CLAYTON	MAXWELL	OTOBO	DEDMAN	JAMES	BAKER	MAGWOOD	SAGNA	JOHNSON	SMITH	MCSWEENEY	MCLACHLAN	SULLIVAN	WHEELER	BEECROFT	ARGENT	DUNN	LINDIE	
X	X	X	X	X	X	X	X	X	X	X	S	S	S	U	U																											1
X	X	X	X		X	X	X	X		S	X	X	S	U	S	X	U																									2
X	X	X	X		X	X	X	X	U	X	X	X	S	U	S		S																									3
X	X	X	X	U	X	X	X	X		X	X	X		S	S	S																										4
X	X				X	X	X	X		X	X	X	S	X	X		S	U	U																							5
X			X		X	X	X	X		X	X	X		X	X		S	U	U	S	S																					6
X	X		X		X	X	X	X		S	X	X		X	U	X	S		U	U																						7
-X	X	X		X		X	X		S	X	X	S	S	U		X		X	X	U																						8
X	X	X	X		X		X	X			X	S	U	S	U	X	X			S		X																				9
X	U	X	X		X		X	X			X	X	X	S			X	U		S	S	X																				10
X	S	X	X		X	X		X			X	X	X				X	S			U	X	S	U																		11
X	X	X	X		X	X	X	X				X	U				S	S	U			X	U	X																		12
X	X	X			X	X	X	X				X	S				S	X					X	X	U	U	U															13
X	X	X			X		X	X			X	X					U	S				X	X	X	S		U	U														14
X	X				X		X	X			X	X					X	X	S				X					U	X	S	U	U										15
X	X				X	X		X			X	X				S	U	X					X	X					U		S	S	X									16
X	X				X	X		X			X	X						X	U				X	X			U		U		S	S	X									17
					X	X	X	S			X	X						X	X		S		X	X			U			S	X	U	X									18
X					X	X	X	X			X	X					U	S	U				X	X			U				X	U	X									19
X		U			X	X	X	X			X	X					X	S			U		X	X							S	S	X									20
X		S			X	X	X	X			X	X				X	S	S					X	X							U	U	X									21
X		X				X	X	X				X					X	X					X	U			U			U	S	S	X		X							22
X		X			X	X	X				X	S				X	S						X	U			X			U		S	X		X							23
X					X		X	X			X	X				X	X						X	U			S			U	S	S	X		X							24
X		X			X		X	X			X	X												S			S			X		X	X	U	U	X	U					25
X		X			X		X	X			X	X						S					X	U			S			U			X			X		X	S			26
X					X	X	X				X	S				X	X						X				U			U			X					X	S	X	S	27
X		X				X	X	S			X	S				X	X						X				U			U			X			S		X			X	28
X						X	X				X	X					X	U					X				S			U			X			U		X	X	X	S	29
X					U	X	X	S			X	X				X	X						X				U			S			X					X		X	S	30
X		X			X	X	X	X			X	S											X				U			U			X			S		X		X	S	31
X		X			X		X	X			X	X					U										S			X			X			S		X		X	S	32
X		X			X		X				X	X					U													X			X			X	U	X			X	33
X		X			X		X				X	X					S										S			X			X	U		X		X		S	X	34
X		X			X		X				X	X					S											U		X		U	X			X	U	X		S	X	35
X		X			X		X	S			X	X					S										S			X		U	X			X		X		U	X	36
X		X			X		X	X								X			U								X	U		X			X			X		X				37
X		X			X		X	X									S										X	U		X		S	X			X	U	X		X		38
X		X			X		X	X									X										X			X		S	X			X	U			X		39
X		X			X		X	X									X		U								X	U		X		S	X			X	U			X		40
X		X			X		X	X									S										X	U		X		S	X			X	U		X	X		41
X		X			X		X	X									X		U								X	S		X			X			X	U			S		42
X		X	X		X	X		X				X	X	U			X	S	U		U	X	X	U	S																	1
	U				X	X	X	X			X	X					U	X	X		U		X	X							S		X	U								2

Total League Appearances

BASTOCK	BAILEY	EVERITT	L THURLBOURNE	MITCHELL	FRATER	SHIELDS	FISHER	COHEN	O'DONOGHUE	GREEN	ROBERTS	QUILTER	CHILLINGWORTH	J THURLBOURNE	QUINTON	HAKIM	PETERS	O'DONNELL	EMERY	CALVER	MORTIMER	GALBRAITH	POKU	CLAYTON	MAXWELL	OTOBO	DEDMAN	JAMES	BAKER	MAGWOOD	SAGNA	JOHNSON	SMITH	MCSWEENEY	MCLACHLAN	SULLIVAN	WHEELER	BEECROFT	ARGENT	DUNN	LINDIE	
40	14	28	11	1	38	23	39	32	1	5	32	30	2	3	2	10	15	6	2	1	0	5	18	9	0	0	7	0	1	12	2	1	27	0	3	12	0	13	2	9	5	X
0	1	1	0	0	0	0	0	4	0	3	1	6	6	4	3	2	13	7	1	3	3	0	1	1	1	0	7	1	0	3	5	10	0	0	0	3	0	0	2	3	5	S
0	1	1	0	1	1	0	0	0	1	0	0	0	2	3	4	0	6	4	9	1	3	0	1	5	1	1	10	7	2	8	2	6	0	2	1	1	8	0	0	1	0	U

Total Cup Appearances

BASTOCK	BAILEY	EVERITT	L THURLBOURNE	MITCHELL	FRATER	SHIELDS	FISHER	COHEN	O'DONOGHUE	GREEN	ROBERTS	QUILTER	CHILLINGWORTH	J THURLBOURNE	QUINTON	HAKIM	PETERS	O'DONNELL	EMERY	CALVER	MORTIMER	GALBRAITH	POKU	CLAYTON	MAXWELL	OTOBO	DEDMAN	JAMES	BAKER	MAGWOOD	SAGNA	JOHNSON	SMITH	MCSWEENEY	MCLACHLAN	SULLIVAN	WHEELER	BEECROFT	ARGENT	DUNN	LINDIE	
1	0	1	1	0	2	2	1	2	0	0	1	2	1	0	0	0	1	1	1	0	0	1	2	1	0	0	0	0	0	0	0	0	1	0	0	0	0	0	0	0	0	X
0	0	0	0	0	0	0	0	0	0	0	0	0	0	0	0	0	0	1	0	0	0	0	0	0	1	0	0	0	0	0	1	0	0	0	0	0	0	0	0	0	0	S
0	1	0	0	0	0	0	0	0	0	0	0	0	0	1	0	0	1	0	1	0	2	0	0	1	0	0	0	0	0	0	0	0	0	1	0	0	0	0	0	0	0	U

Total Cup Appearances

BASTOCK	BAILEY	EVERITT	L THURLBOURNE	MITCHELL	FRATER	SHIELDS	FISHER	COHEN	O'DONOGHUE	GREEN	ROBERTS	QUILTER	CHILLINGWORTH	J THURLBOURNE	QUINTON	HAKIM	PETERS	O'DONNELL	EMERY	CALVER	MORTIMER	GALBRAITH	POKU	CLAYTON	MAXWELL	OTOBO	DEDMAN	JAMES	BAKER	MAGWOOD	SAGNA	JOHNSON	SMITH	MCSWEENEY	MCLACHLAN	SULLIVAN	WHEELER	BEECROFT	ARGENT	DUNN	LINDIE	
0	0	2	1	0	0	2	2	5	0	1	14	0	1	1	2	0	2	2	0	0	0	0	1	0	0	0	0	0	0	0	1	1	0	0	1	0	0	0	0	5	0	Lge
0	0	0	0	0	0	0	0	0	0	0	0	0	0	0	0	0	0	0	0	0	0	0	0	0	0	0	0	0	0	0	0	0	0	0	0	0	0	0	0	0	0	Cup

Also Played: THOMAS U(4),S(5). JACKAMAN X(42). LOKANDO U(32,33,34). ASHCROFT S(39,40,41).

ST ALBANS CITY

CURRENT SQUAD AS OF BEGINING OF 2010-11 SEASON

GOALKEEPERS	HT	WT	D.O.B	AGE	P.O.B	CAREER	Apps	Gls
Paul Bastock	5'11"	14 00	19/5/70	40	Leamington Spa	Coventry (Trainee), Cambridge Utd 3/88, Sabah (Mal) c/s 89, Kettering (L) 3/90, Kettering 7/90, Fisher (L), Boston Utd 8/92, Scarborough 10/04, Dag & Red 10/04, St Albans 11/04 Rel 5/07, Rushden & D 5/07 Rel 2/08, St Albans 2/08	40	0
Adam McWeeney			18/7/93	17		St Albans	0	0
DEFENDERS								
Alex Bailey	5'09"	10 07	21/9/83	26	Newham	Arsenal, Chesterfield Rel 5/07, Halifax NC 10/07, St Albans 9/08 Rel 11/08, St Albans 3/09	15	0
Ross Dedman			22/12/92	17		St Albans	14	0
Adam Everitt			28/6/82	28	Hemel Hempstead	Hemel Hempstead, Harrow c/s 00, Luton, Harrow 10/01, Hayes 6/03 Rel 5/05, Yeading (Trial) c/s 05, Yeading 9/05, Cambridge C 5/07, Eastleigh Undisc 10/07 Rel 5/08, AFC Hornchurch 8/08, Bromley 8/08, St Albans 11/08	29	2
James Fisher			13/4/84	26	London	Chelsea (Yth), Wembley, Wealdstone 8/02, Ruislip Manor, Northwood 12/07, St Albans 2/08	39	2
Ryan Frater			20/1/84	26	Herts	St Albans (Yth), Hitchin, Chelsea (Trial) 3/03, Dunstable 11/04, Bedford T (Trial) c/s 05, Stotfold 8/05, Hitchin 2/06, St Albans 12/07, Welling (Trial) 6/09	38	0
Mark Peters	6'00"	13 03	6/7/72	38	Rhyl	Man City Rel c/s 92, Norwich 9/92 Rel c/s 93, Peterborough 8/93, Mansfield 9/94 Rel c/s 99, Bromsgrove (SL) c/s 96, Rushden & D 7/99, L.Orient 9/03 Rel c/s 05, Aldershot (L) 11/04, Aldershot (Trial) 7/05, Cambridge U 8/05 Rel 5/08, Kings Kynn 7/08, St Albans (Pl/Ass Man) 6/09	28	2
Peter Smith			11/9/85	24		Lymington & New Milton, Winchester, Salisbury, Poole T, St Albans 11/09	27	0
MIDFIELDERS								
Luke Jackaman			26/2/92	18		St Albans	1	0
Tegana James			12/7/88	22		St Albans	1	0
Danny Johnson			31/3/90	20		Maldon T, St Albans 11/09	11	1
Rob Magwood			27/3/92	18		St Albans	15	0
Craig Mortimer			15/11/90	19		St Albans, Northwood (L) 10/08	3	0
Soloman Shields	5'10"	12 00	14/10/89	20	Leyton	L.Orient Rel 5/09, St Albans (2ML) 2/09, Hayes & Yeading (Trial) 7/09, St Albans 8/09	23	2
Harry Wheeler			29/7/88	22		AFC Hornchurch, Potters Bar, Ashford T (Middx), St Albans 1/10	0	0
FORWARDS								
Gary Cohen	5'11"	11 02	20/1/84	26	Leyton	Watford 7/02, Scarborough 2/03 Rel c/s 03, Gretna 8/03, Workington (SL) 8/04, Grimsby (7ML) 7/05 Perm 1/06 Rel c/s 07, St Albans 8/08	36	5
Inih Effiong			2/3/91	19		St Albans, Northwood (L) 10/08, Boreham Wood 8/09, St Albans c/s 10		
Paul Hakim			18/6/82	28	London	Wingate & F, Cheshunt, Slough 11/02, Wingate & F 12/02, Dag & Red (Trial) c/s 04, B.Stortford 8/04, St Albans 7/05, Stevenage 1/07, Woking (L) 9/07, St Albans 1/08	12	0
Sam Perrin						Colney Heath, St Albans 5/10		
Drew Roberts			28/10/83	26	Luton	Leighton Corinthians, AFC Houghton, Leighton T, Barton R, Bedford 3/03, Kettering 7/04, Aylesbury 12/04, Histon 11/05 Rel 5/07, Hemel Hempstead 5/07, Cambridge C 2/08, St Albans 8/09, Brackley 3/10, St Albans c/s 10	33	14
Chris Sullivan			26/9/87	22		Stevenage, Dunstable (L) 3/05, Chesham (3ML) 2/06, Braintree (2ML) 1/07, Braintree 5/07, AFC Wimbledon £3,500 6/08 Rel 5/09, Tooting & M (2ML) 11/08, Billericay c/s 09, Canvey Island 11/09, St Albans 1/10	15	0

Loanees	HT	WT	DOB	AGE	POB	From - To	APPS	GOA
(F)Craig Calver	5'10"		20/1/91	19	Cambridge	Southend 8/09 - Braintree (L) 2/10, AFC Sudbury (L) 3/10	4	0
(M)Jake Beecroft			4/9/89	20		Rushden & D (2ML) 1/10 - Rel 5/10, Tonbridge A 5/10	13	0
(F)Jake Argent			9/12/91	18		L.Orient 1/10 -	4	0

Departures	HT	WT	DOB	AGE	POB	From - To	APPS	GOA
(D)Jason Mitchell			13/4/88	22		Maldon T 8/09 - Rel 8/09	1	0
(F)Jamie-Lee O'Donoghue			2/7/88	22		Brimsdown c/s 09 - Wingate & F 8/09, Brimsdown, Broxbourne B 12/09	1	0
(M)Danny (DJ) Green			4/8/90	20		Bishop's Stortford 8/09 - Rel 9/09, Bishop's Stortford 9/09, Billericay 10/09, Dag & Red 5/10	8	1
(D)Bradley Thomas	6'02"	13 00	29/3/84	26	Forest Gate	Yeovil 8/09 - Billericay 8/09, Sutton U 8/09, Hendon 11/09, Braintree 7/10	1	0
(M)Darren Quinton	5'08"	9 11	28/4/86	24	Romford	Braintree 8/09 - Rel	5	2
(M)Jamie Thurlbourne			7/10/87	22		Newmarket 7/09 - Mildenhall 9/09, Kings Lynn T 6/10	7	1
(M)Luke Thurlbourne			23/3/90	20		Southend 7/09 - Rel 11/09, Mildenhall 11/09, Kings Lynn T 6/10	11	1
(F)Saul Otobo			17/9/87	22		ex Woking 10/09 - Eastleigh 11/09, Chester (Trial), Stafford R 2/10	0	0
(M)Ryan Maxwell			14/6/83	27		Stansted 9/09 - Stansted, Harlow 1/10	1	0
(M)Jonathan O'Donnell			29/10/91	18		Hemel Hempstead 7/09 - Luton (Trial) 12/09, Luton 1/10, St Albans (L) 1/10	13	2
(M)Godfrey Poku			22/7/90	20		Yth - 8/09, Luton (Trial) 12/09, Luton 1/10, St Albans (L) 1/10	19	1
(D)Conner Baker			13/4/92	18		Hemel Hempstead 11/09 - Chesham 1/10	1	0
(F)Babatunde Ayodele			26/11/82	27		Winchester 12/09 - Rel 1/10		
(D)Justin Clayton			29/10/89	20		Southend 9/09 - Rel 1/10	10	0
(F)Lamine Sagna			7/5/88	22		Billericay 11/09 - Welling 3/10	7	1
(M)James Quilter			15/7/83	27		Manford Way 1/08 - Rel 4/10	36	0
(F)James Lindie			14/11/89	20		ex Ebbsfleet 2/10 - Rel 4/10	10	0
(F)Ian Dunn			25/3/81	29	Northampton	Bourne T 2/10 - Rel c/s 10	12	5
(D)Jackson Ohakam			23/11/87	22		Ebbsfleet 8/09 -		
(F)Henry Atu			9/11/89	20		Harlow 10/09 -		
(F)Daniel Chillingworth	6'00"	12 06	13/9/81	28	Cambridge	ex Cambridge U 8/09 -	8	1
(M)Jack Ashcroft			17/11/91	18		London Colney 11/09 -	3	0
(M)David Galbraith	5'08"	11 00	20/12/83	26	Luton	Kings Lynn 9/09 -	5	0
(M)Mbive 'Peggy' Lokando			18/8/89	21	London	Crawley 2/10 -	0	0
(M)Angus McLachlan			8/8/88	22		Cambridge C 12/09 - Cheshunt (Dual) 12/09	3	1
(G)Michael Emery			7/11/90	19		Rushden & D (Scholar) - Skegness (L) 10/09, Spalding (L) 12/09	3	0

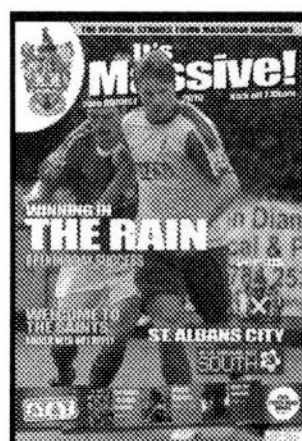

STAINES TOWN

Chairman: Alan Boon
Secretary: Steven Parsons (T) 07876 672 458
(E) catspar57@aol.com
Additional Committee Members: Corinne Boon, Matthew Boon, Chris Boyce, Darren & Vanessa Cox, Hilary Denning, Graham Gould, Glenn Gulyas, John & Maureen Hanson, Mike Holland, Andy Jones, Barbara & Jemm Moss, Sally Payne, Colin Prangley, Jesse Richards, Kim Sherwood, Angie Payne, Stuart Moore, Chris & Kerry Wainw
Manager: Steve Cordery
Programme Editor: S. Moore & S. Parsons (E) catspar57@aol.com

Staines Town FC Squad, August 2010, with the Middlesex Super Cup (George Ruffell Shield) and Middlesex Senior Cup
Back Row (left to right): Craig Maskell (Asst Mgr), Michael Kamara, Danny Gordon, Marc Charles-Smith, Gareth Risbridger, Dominic Sterling James Courtnage, Louis Wells, Richard Orlu, Marien Ifura, Dean Thomas, Darty Brown, Simon Jackson, René Steer, Trent Phillips (Coach).
Front Row: Gareth Workman (Physio'),Ryan Peters, Scott Taylor, Warren Harris, Richard Butler, Alan Boon (Chairman), Steve Cordery (Manag James King, Leroy Griffiths, Ali Chaaban, André Scarlett, Paul Midwinter (Physio').

Club Factfile

Founded: 1892 **Nickname:** The Swans
Previous Names: Staines Albany & St Peters Institute merged in 1895. Staines 1905-18, Staines Lagonda 1918-25, Staines Vale (WWII)
Previous Leagues: Great Western Suburban, Hounslow & District 1919-20, Spartan 1924-35, 58-71, Middlesex Senior 1943-52, Parthenon 1952-53, Hellenic 1953-58, Athenian 1971-73, Isthmian 1973-2009

Club Colours (change): Old gold & blue/blue/blue (White with blue trim/white/white)

Ground: Wheatsheaf Park, Wheatsheaf Lane, Staines TW18 2PD (T) 01784 225 943 / 463 100
Capacity: 3,000 **Seats:** 300 **Covered:** 850 **Clubhouse:** Yes **Shop:** Yes
Previous Grounds:
Simple Directions
Leave M25 at Junction 13. If coming from the North (anticlockwise), bear left onto A30 Staines By-Pass; if coming from the South (clockwise), go round the roundabout and back under M25 to join By-Pass. Follow A30 to Billet Bridge roundabout, which you treat a roundabout, taking last exit, A308, London Road towards Town Centre. At 3rd traffic lights, under iron bridge, turn left into South Street, passing central bus station, as far as Thames Lodge (formerly Packhorse). Turn left here, into Laleham Road, B376, under bridge. After 1km, Wheatsheaf Lane is on the right, by the traffic island. Ground is less than 100 yds on left. Please park on the left

Record Attendance: 2,750 v Banco di Roma - Barassi Cup 1975 (70,000 watched the second leg)
Record Victory: 14-0 v Croydon (A) - Isthmian Division 1 19/03/1994
Record Defeat: 1-18 - Wycombe Wanderers (A) - Great Western Suburban League 27/12/1909
Record Goalscorer: Alan Gregory - 122
Record Appearances: Dickie Watmore - 840
Additional Records:

Senior Honours: Spartan League 1959-60. Athenian League Division 2 1971-72, Division 1 1974-75, 88-89.
Middlesex Senior cup 1975-76, 76-77, 77-78, 88-89, 90-91, 94-95, 97-98, 2009-10. Barassi Cup 1975-76.
Isthmian Full Members Cup 1994-95, Premier Division Play-off 2008-09.

10 YEAR RECORD

00-01		01-02		02-03		03-04		04-05		05-06		06-07		07-08		08-09		09-10	
Isth1	13	Isth1	16	Isth1S	15	Isth1S	6	Isth P	9	Isth P	6	Isth P	12	Isth P	2	Isth P	2	Conf S	8

STAINES TOWN

No.	Date	Comp	H/A	Opponents	Att:	Result	Goalscorers	Pos
1	8/8/09	BSS	A	Weston-Super-Mare	297	W 1-0	Onochie 90	7
2	11/8/09	BSS	H	Dorchester Town	402	W 3-0	Newton 49, Griffiths 85, Bourne 90	2
3	15/8/09	BSS	H	Havant & Waterlooville	396	L 1-2	Onochie 7	6
4	18/8/09	BSS	A	Bishop's Stortford	387	D 2-2	Onochie 26, Newton 62	5
5	22/8/09	BSS	H	Welling United	397	D 1-1	Newton 5	8
6	29/8/09	BSS	A	Worcester City	555	D 0-0		8
7	31/8/09	BSS	H	Maidenhead United	387	D 1-1	Butler 48	10
8	5/9/09	BSS	A	Eastleigh	567	D 0-0		10
9	8/9/09	BSS	A	St Albans City	304	W 3-1	Griffiths pen 5, Newton 30, Bourne 36	9
10	12/9/09	BSS	H	Chelmsford City	430	L 0-1		11
11	19/9/09	BSS	H	Bromley	366	D 2-2	Butler 13, Chaaban pen 90	11
12	3/10/09	BSS	A	Lewes	305	D 1-1	Taylor 5	10
13	17/10/09	BSS	A	Braintree Town	453	L 0-2		12
14	27/10/09	BSS	H	Newport County	621	W 1-0	Chaaban 58	12
15	31/10/09	BSS	A	Thurrock	234	W 2-1	Butler 44, Chaaban pen 45	10
16	10/11/09	BSS	H	Bath City	425	D 1-1	Scarlett 75	10
17	14/11/09	BSS	A	Welling United	452	L 0-3		13
18	1/12/09	BSS	H	Dover Athletic	473	D 0-0		16
19	5/12/09	BSS	H	Basingstoke Town	483	L 0-1		16
20	12/12/09	BSS	H	Weston-Super-Mare	260	W 3-0	Onochie 2 (2, 40), Thomas 37	14
21	19/12/09	BSS	A	Newport County	1460	L 0-1		14
22	26/12/09	BSS	A	Hampton & Richmond B.	613	W 4-1	Chaaban 2 (51, 78), Butler 61, Newton 81	12
23	28/12/09	BSS	H	Bishop's Stortford	382	D 2-2	Butler 53, Chaaban 81	12
24	1/1/10	BSS	H	Hampton & Richmond B.	871	W 4-0	Thomas 18, Chaaban (45, 69, 74)	10
25	16/1/10	BSS	H	Lewes	407	W 2-1	Mambo 52, Newton 53	7
26	23/1/10	BSS	A	Dorchester Town	418	D 2-2	Charles-Smith 2 (45, 65)	9
27	25/1/10	BSS	A	Chelmsford City	844	W 1-0	Charles-Smith 67	6
28	6/2/10	BSS	H	Weymouth	501	W 2-0	Griffiths 11, Newton 20	6
29	13/2/10	BSS	A	Bromley	426	W 2-0	Chaaban 19, Charles-Smith 76	4
30	20/2/10	BSS	H	St Albans City	460	W 4-3	Taylor 2 (21, 35), Ahmad 43, Griffiths 66	3
31	27/2/10	BSS	H	Eastleigh	509	L 1-2	Griffiths pen 83	6
32	2/3/10	BSS	A	Weymouth	365	W 2-1	Newton 2 (32, 45)	3
33	6/3/10	BSS	A	Woking	1419	D 0-0		4
34	13/3/10	BSS	H	Woking	962	W 3-0	White 46, Scarlett 2 (57, 90)	4
35	20/3/10	BSS	A	Havant & Waterlooville	715	L 0-1		5
36	23/3/10	BSS	A	Basingstoke Town	306	W 1-0	Marquis 38	4
37	27/3/10	BSS	H	Braintree Town	426	W 2-1	Newton 71, Marquis 76	3
38	2/4/10	BSS	H	Worcester City	471	L 0-1		5
39	10/4/10	BSS	A	Bath City	762	L 0-2		6
40	17/4/10	BSS	H	Thurrock	439	W 3-0	Marquis 3 (5, 62, pen 86)	8
41	20/4/10	BSS	A	Maidenhead United	296	L 1-2	Marquis 14	8
42	24/4/10	BSS	A	Dover Athletic	1147	D 0-0		8
	Cups							
1	26/9/09	FAC 2Q	A	Sittingborne	196	W 3-2	Sterling 10, Onochie 59, Chaaban 88	
2	10/10/09	FAC 3Q	A	Walton Casuals	238	W 3-0	Thomas 26, Butler 42, Risbridger 45	
3	24/10/09	FAC 4Q	A	Hayes & Yeading United	602	W 1-0	Griffiths 30	
4	7/11/09	FAC 1	A	Shrewsbury Town	3539	W 1-0	Chaaban 21	
5	21/11/09	FAT 3Q	A	Bashley	268	L 1-2	Griffiths 64	
6	28/11/09	FAC 2	H	Millwall	2753	D 1-1	Chaaban pen 79	
7	9/12/09	FAC 2R	A	Millwall	3452	L 0-4		

Home Attendances:	
Highest:	962 v Woking
Lowest:	260 v Weston-Super-Mare
Average (08-09):	430 (296)

Top Goalscorer:	Chaaban - 11 (8 League, 3 Cup) in 28 appearances - 39% strike rate
Most Appearances:	Wells - 49 (42 League, 7 Cup)

WELLS	JACKSON	STERLING	GORDON	IFURA	SCARLETT	NEWTON	RISBRIDGER	TAYLOR	ONOCHIE	GRIFFITHS	CHARLES-SMITH	SARGENT	BOURNE	KERSEY	COURTNAGE	BROWN	BUTLER	KAMARA	THOMAS	WOOZLEY	CHAABAN	CUMBERBATCH	MASON	PHILLIPS	AHMAD	KING	LEE	ARTHUR	ORLU	MAMBO	TUNA	WHITE	GODFREY	MARQUIS	
X	X	X	X	X	X	X	X	X	X	X	S	U	U	U	U																				1
X	X	X	X	X	X	X	X	X	X	X	S	U	S	U		S																			2
X	X	X	X	X	X	X	X	X	X	X	S		S		U	S	U																		3
X		X	X	X	X	X	X	S	X	X	U		U	U		X	U	X																	4
X		X	X	X	X	X	X	X		X	S		U	U		X	S	X	U																5
X	S	X	X	X		X	X	X	X	X			U			X	S	X	U	U															6
X	X	X	X	U	X	X	S	S		X	X		U			X	X	U		X															7
X	X	X	X	X	X	X	X	X		S	S		S			X	X	U	U																8
X	X	X	X	X	X	X	X	U	U	X	S		X				X	U	S																9
X	X	X	X	X	X	X	X	S		X	S		X				X	U	S	U															10
X	X	X	X	X		X		X	S	X	X		S				X	U	X	U	S														11
X	X	X	X	X	X	X		X	X				S				U	X		X	S	U		U											12
X	X	X	X	X	X	X	X	X		X			U			S	X		S	U	S														13
X	X	X	X	X	U	X	X	U	U	X						X	X		S	U	X														14
X	X	X	X	X	X	X	X	S	U	S						X	X		S	U	X														15
X	U		X		X	S	U	X		X			X			X	S	X	X	X	X				S										16
X		X	X		X	U	U	S		X			X			X	X	X	X	X	S				S										17
X	X	X	X	X	X	X	X	S	S	X					U		X	U	U						X										18
X	X	X	X	X	X	X		U	S	X						X	S	U	S		X				X										19
X	X	X	X	X	X	U		X	X	X					U	X	U	S	X						S										20
X	X		X	X	X			X		X	U				U	X	X	X						U	U	X	U								21
X	X	X	X	X	X	X		U		X	S					X	X	S			X				S	U									22
X		X	X	X	X	X		X		X	S					X	X	X			S				S	U		U							23
X		X	X		X	X		S		X	S					X	X	X	X		X				S			U	U						24
X			X		X	X		S		X	U						X	X	X		X				S	U		S		X	X				25
X			X	X	X	X		U		X	X					X		X	X					U	X	U	U	U							26
X			X	X	X	X		S		X	X					X		X	U						U	U		U		X	X				27
X	U		X	X	X	X	S			X	X					X		X	U		S				U					X	X				28
X	X	S	X		X	X	S	S		X	X					X		X	U		X				U					X					29
X	X	S	X	U	X	U	X	X		X	X				U			X	S						X					X					30
X	X	S	X	U	X	S	X	X		X	X				U			X	S						X					X					31
X	X	X	X	U	X	X	X	X		X					U			S	X						U					X					32
X	X	X	X	U	X	X	X	X	U	X					U			S	X						S					X					33
X	X	X	X	U	X	X	X			X						S		U			S				U					X		X	X		34
X	X		X	U	X	X	X	S		X					U	S		X			S									X		X	X		35
X	X	X	X		X	X	X	U	S							X		X			X			U	U		U							X	36
X	X	X		S	X	X	X	U	S	S						X		U			X									X			X	X	37
X	X	X		X	X	X	S	U	S	S						X		U			X									X			X	X	38
X	X	X		X	X	X	X	S		X	S							U			X					U				X			X	S	39
X	X	X	X	U	X	X		S		X	X							S	X					U		S				X				X	40
X	X	X	X	S	X	X		S		X	S					U		U	X		X									X				X	41
X	X	X	X			X	U	S		X	X					X		X	S		U			U		X								X	42
X	X	X		X	X	X		X	X		X		S			U		X		X	S	U	U	U											1
X	X	X	X	X	X		X	X	U	X			S		U	U	X	U	X		S	S													2
X	X	X	X	X	X	X	X	U	S	X			U		U	X	X		S	U	S														3
X	X	X	X	X	S	X	X	S		X			U		U	X	X	U	S	U	X														4
X	X	X		X	X	X	X	U	S	X			X			U	X	U			X				U										5
X	X	X	X	X	U	X	X	U	U	X					U	X	X	U	U		X				U										6
X	X	X	X	X	U	X	X	S	S	X					U	X	X	U	U		X				S										7
Total League Appearances																																			
42	31	32	39	25	38	36	22	17	7	36	10	0	4	0	0	23	15	19	11	4	13	0	0	0	5	2	0	0	0	15	3	2	5	6	X
0	1	3	0	2	0	2	4	15	6	4	12	0	5	0	0	5	4	5	9	0	8	0	0	0	8	1	0	1	0	0	0	0	0	1	S
0	2	0	0	8	1	3	3	8	4	0	3	2	6	4	10	1	4	12	7	6	1	1	0	6	7	6	3	4	1	0	0	0	0	0	U
Total Cup Appearances																																			
7	7	7	5	7	4	6	6	2	1	6	1	0	1	0	0	4	6	1	1	1	4	0	0	0	0	0	0	0	0	0	0	0	0	0	X
0	0	0	0	0	1	0	0	2	3	0	0	0	2	0	0	0	0	0	2	0	3	1	0	0	1	0	0	0	0	0	0	0	0	0	S
0	0	0	0	0	2	0	0	3	2	0	0	0	2	0	5	3	0	5	2	2	0	1	1	1	2	0	0	0	0	0	0	0	0	0	U
Total Goals																																			
0	0	0	0	0	3	9	0	3	5	5	4	0	2	0	0	0	5	0	2	0	8	0	0	0	1	0	0	0	0	1	0	1	0	6	Lge
0	0	1	0	0	0	0	1	0	1	2	0	0	0	0	0	0	1	0	1	0	3	0	0	0	0	0	0	0	0	0	0	0	0	0	Cup

STAINES TOWN

CURRENT SQUAD AS OF BEGINING OF 2010-11 SEASON

GOALKEEPERS	HT	WT	D.O.B	AGE	P.O.B	CAREER	Apps	Gls
Trent Phillips			14/2/71	38	Ashford	Staines (Gk Coach)	0	0
Louis Wells			22/2/82	28		Hayes, Aldershot 6/06, Maidenhead 8/07, Uxbridge 3/08, Staines c/s 08	42	0
DEFENDERS								
Alfie Arthur			20/3/92	18		Staines	1	0
Danny Gordon			20/12/81	28	Aylesbury	Aylesbury, Staines 7/04	39	0
Marien Ifura			7/9/84	25		QPR (Sch) Rel c/s 04, Aylesbury (SL) 3/03, Farnborough (3ML) 9/03, Hendon (L) 1/04, Kingstonian 9/04, Staines 1/05, Studying, Windsor & E 11/06, Staines 3/08	27	0
Simon Jackson			4/4/85	25	Lewisham	Charlton (Sch) Rel 03/04, Woking 8/04 Rel 5/07, Fisher (L) 2/07, Fisher c/s 07, Bognor Regis 8/08, Sutton U 10/08, Staines 8/09	32	0
Michael Kamara			17/5/89	21	Sierra Leone	C.Palace, Bromley (WE) 3/07, Brighton (Trial), Swindon (Trial), Chesterfield (Trial), Colchester (Trial), AFC Wimbledon, St Albans, Bishop's Stortford Rel 10/07, Welling 3/08, Fisher 8/08, Woking 12/08 Rel 5/09, Staines 8/09	24	0
Ryan Peters			21/8/87	23		Brentford (Sch), Windsor & E (2ML) 9/04, Gravesend (L) 12/04, Crawley (L) 11/06, AFC Wimbledon (L) 3/07, Margate 1/08, Braintree 5/09, Staines 6/10		
Dave Sargent			22/12/77	32		Watford (Yth), Wycombe (Yth), Hendon, Hayes, Northwood 10/97, St Albans, AFC Wimbledon c/s 04 Rel c/s 06, Staines 6/06	0	0
Dominic Sterling			8/7/76	34	Isleworth	Wimbledon, Wealdstone, Hayes 7/00, Aldershot 7/02 Rel 6/04, Canvey Island 6/04, Maidenhead 5/06 Rel 5/09, Staines 7/09	35	0
MIDFIELDERS								
Chris Bourne			6/9/85	24		Southend (Yth), Canvey Island, Billericay (L), Welling (L), Brentwood, Heybridge 9/08, Staines 7/09, Croydon Ath (Dual) 12/09	9	2
Darti Brown			10/6/77	33	London	Willesden Constantine, Yeading, Wembley, Harrow, Yeading 3/03, Maidenhead 12/06 Rel 6/08, Staines 7/08	28	0
James King			2/12/90	19		Staines, Harrow (Dual) 2/10	3	0
Gareth Risbridger	5'10"	11 05	31/10/81	28	High Wycombe	Marlow (Yth), Yeovil c/s 98, Southend 7/01 Rel 1/02, Dover (L) 10/01, Salisbury 2/02, Aylesbury 3/02, Staines 12/03	26	0
Andre Scarlett	5'04"	09 06	11/1/80	30	Wembley	Luton Rel c/s 01, Chelmsford 8/01, Boreham Wood, Hemel Hempstead, Stevenage, Wealdstone, Hitchin 3/02, Chesham 7/02, Staines 12/05	38	3
Dean Thomas			20/9/87	22		Staines, Bracknell (L) 8/07	20	2
FORWARDS								
Mazin Ahmad			2/2/85	25	Bucharest, Rom	Woking, Molesey c/s 02, Walton & H 8/03, Hampton & R 10/03, Epsom & E 10/03, Kingstonian 8/04, Aldershot 3/06 (05/06 7,0) Rel c/s 06, Basingstoke 8/06, Kingstonian 9/06, Molesey 12/06, Dulwich H 1/07, Godalming 11/07, Al Ahli (Dubai), Staines 11/09	13	1
Richard Butler			1/5/85	25	Ashford	Ashford T (Middx), AFC Wimbledon 8/04, St Albans 11/07, Staines 2/08, Bromley 1/10 Rel 7/10, Staines 7/10	19	5
Ali Chaaban			16/3/82	28	Lebanon	Dorking, Leatherhead 7/02, Farnborough 6/03 Rel 1/05, Lewes 3/04, Farnborough 8/04, Exeter 2/05 Rel 2/05, Sutton U 8/05 Rel 9/05, Break, Sutton U 12/05, Staines 1/06, Bromley 6/07 Rel, Break, Bromley 1/09 Rel c/s 09, Staines (Dual) 4/09, Gillingham (Trial) c/s 09, Bromley 8/09, Staines 9/09	21	8
Marc Charles-Smith			1/7/84	26		Leatherhead, Staines c/s 07, Boreham Wood (L) 3/09	22	4
Leroy Griffiths	5'11"	13 05	30/12/76	33	London	Sutton U, Banstead, Corinthian C, Hampton & Richmond 2/00, QPR £40,000 5/01 Rel 7/03, Farnborough (L) 8/02, Margate (L) 11/02, Farnborough 8/03, Grays 9/03, Fisher 5/05 Rel 5/07, Aldershot (3ML) 1/06, Grays (SL) 2/07, Havant & W 7/07, Corinthian Casuals 10/07, Lewes 10/07, Gillingham (6WL) 11/07 Perm 1/08 Rel c/s 08, Eastleigh 8/08, Staines 8/08	40	5
Howard Newton			16/3/82	28	Hammersmith	Epsom & E, Hitchin, Wembley, Staines, Hampton & R, Sutton U, Dag & Red, Harrow 9/04, Staines 7/06	38	9
Eliot Onochie			15/3/82	28		Tottenham (Yth), Wimbledon (Yth), Tooting & M, C.Palace (Trial) c/s 04, Croydon A, Kingstonian, Staines 10/04 Harrow 2/05, Boreham Wood 10/07, Staines 3/08	13	5
Scott Taylor	5'10"	11 06	5/5/76	34	Chertsey	Staines, Millwall £15,000 2/95, Bolton £150,000 3/96, Rotherham (2ML) 12/97, Blackpool (L) 3/98, Tranmere £50,000 10/98 Rel c/s 01, Stockport 8/01, Blackpool 1/02, Plymouth £100,000 12/04, MK Dons £100,000 1/06, Brentford (L) 3/07, Rochdale (L) 10/07, Grays 1/08 Rel c/s 08, Lewes 7/08, Staines 11/08	32	3

Loanees	HT	WT	DOB	AGE	POB	From - To	APPS	GOA
(D)Yado Mambo			22/10/91	18	Kilburn	Charlton 12/09 -	15	1
(F)Tamer Tuna	5'08"	11 00	19/10/91	18	Bexley	Charlton 12/09 - Woking (WE) 2/10, Welling (L) 3/10	3	0
(M)Hyum-Jin Lee			8/9/90	19		Halstead T (Dual) 12/09 -	0	0
(M)Elliott Godfrey	5'08"	11 03	22/2/83	27	Toronto, Can	AFC Wimbledon 3/10 - Rel 4/10	5	0
(F)Andy White			1/9/91	18		Reading 3/10 -	2	1
(F)John Marquis			16/5/92	18		Millwall 3/10 -	7	6
Departures	**HT**	**WT**	**DOB**	**AGE**	**POB**	**From - To**		
(D)Lee Kersey	5'09"	11 07	12/8/79	31	Harlow	Maidenhead 8/08 - Boreham Wood, Harlow 10/09, Billericay 11/09	0	0
(D)Marc Cumberbatch			2/8/84	26		Dulwich H 3/09 - Hendon (Dual) 8/09, Tonbridge A 10/09 Rel 6/10	0	0
(D)David Woozley	6'00"	12 10	6/12/79	30	Ascot	Farnborough 6/09 - Windsor & E 3/10	4	0
(F)Charlie Ide			10/5/88	22		Bedfont Green 2/10 - Carshalton, Hayes & Yeading 3/10		
(M)Leigh Mason			24/11/84	25		Marlow U 9/09 -	0	0
(D)Richard Orlu			12/7/88	22		-	0	0
(G)James Courtnage			18/3/84	26		Hendon c/s 05 - Met Police (Dual) 11/09	0	0

THURROCK

Chairman: Tommy Smith
Secretary: Norman Posner (T) 01708 458 301
(E) normpos@aol.com

Additional Committee Members:
Harry South, Gary Reed, Tony Flood

Manager: Hakan Hayrettin
Programme Editor: Tony Flood (E) thurrockfcpressoffice@gmail.com

Club Factfile

Founded: 1985 **Nickname:** Fleet
Previous Names: Purfleet > 2003
Previous Leagues: Essex Senior 1985-89, Isthmian 1989-2004

Club Colours (change): Yellow/green/yellow (Sky blue/claret/claret)

Ground: Thurrock Hotel, Ship Lane, Grays, Essex RM19 1YN (T) 01708 865 492
Capacity: 4,500 **Seats:** 300 **Covered:** 1,000 **Clubhouse:** Yes **Shop:** Yes
Previous Grounds:
Simple Directions
Approaching the ground from the North - along the M25 in a clockwise direction. Leave the motorway at junction 30. At the roundabout take the second exit and stay in the left hand lane. This leads to a large roundabout controlled by traffic lights. The fifth exit is Ship Lane and the ground is approximately 50 yards on the right hand side. Approaching the ground from the South - anti-clockwise on the M25. When going through the Dartford Tunnel take the left hand bore. On coming out of the tunnel take the first exit - junction 31. This leads to a large roundabout controlled by traffic lights. Take the third exit which is Ship Lane. The ground is situated approximately 50 yards on the right hand side.

Record Attendance: 2,572 v West Ham United - Friendly 1998
Record Victory: 10-0 v Stansted (H) - Essex Senior Lge 1986-87 and v East Ham United (A) - Essex Senior Lge 1987-88
Record Defeat: 0-6 v St Leonards Stamco (A) - FA Trophy 1996-97 and v Sutton United (H) - Isthmian League 1997-98
Record Goalscorer: George Georgiou - 106
Record Appearances: Jimmy McFarlane - 632
Additional Records:

Senior Honours: Isthmian League Division 2 1991-92.
Essex Senior Cup 2003-04, 05-06.

10 YEAR RECORD

00-01	01-02	02-03	03-04	04-05	05-06	06-07	07-08	08-09	09-10
Isth P 11	Isth P 5	Isth P 8	Isth P 3	Conf S 3	Conf S 10	Conf S 18	Conf S 12	Conf S 20	Conf S 10

THURROCK

No.	Date	Comp	H/A	Opponents	Att:	Result	Goalscorers	Pos
1	8/8/09	BSS	A	Havant & Waterlooville	805	D 1-1	Bryant 26	10
2	11/8/09	BSS	H	Welling United	378	W 3-2	Orilonishe 22, Bodkin 56, lalite 64	7
3	15/8/09	BSS	H	Weston-Super-Mare	187	W 2-1	Andrews 85, Orilonishe 88	5
4	18/8/09	BSS	A	Lewes	354	D 1-1	Lalite 17	5
5	22/8/09	BSS	H	Eastleigh	227	W 3-2	Bryant 3 (29, 66, 83)	3
6	29/8/09	BSS	A	Hampton & Richmond B.	463	D 1-1	Gilbey 45	5
7	31/8/09	BSS	H	Bishops Stortford	368	D 2-2	Orilonishe 9, Paine 60	7
8	5/9/09	BSS	A	Maidenhead United	240	W 2-0	Bryant 19, McKenzie 84	7
9	8/9/09	BSS	H	Dover Athletic	534	L 0-2		7
10	12/9/09	BSS	H	Weymouth	239	W 2-1	Anderson 64, Paine 75	5
11	19/9/09	BSS	A	Worcester City	577	W 2-1	Olima 36, McKenzie 60	3
12	3/10/09	BSS	A	Basingstoke Town	429	W 4-0	McKenzie 42, Orilonishe 2 (49, 59), Knight 79	3
13	17/10/09	BSS	H	Dorchester Town	237	W 5-2	Orilonishe 4, Bodkin 44, McKenzie 45, Lalite 60, Bryant 73	3
14	27/10/09	BSS	A	Braintree Town	580	L 1-3	Bryant 85	3
15	31/10/09	BSS	H	Staines Town	234	L 1-2	Judge 87	3
16	7/11/09	BSS	A	Weston-Super-Mare	150	W 3-1	McKenzie 27, Orilonishe 34, Bryant 90	3
17	28/11/09	BSS	A	Dover Athletic	1008	L 0-1		4
18	5/12/09	BSS	H	Havant & Waterlooville	246	D 0-0		5
19	9/12/09	BSS	A	Newport County	1603	L 0-5		6
20	15/12/09	BSS	H	Worcester City	221	W 2-1	Bryant 1, Bodkin 55	4
21	26/12/09	BSS	A	Chelmsford City	1077	L 0-1		7
22	28/12/09	BSS	H	Lewes	270	W 3-1	Bodkin 53, McKenzie 2 (60, 89)	4
23	2/1/10	BSS	H	Chelmsford City	826	D 1-1	Swaine 90	6
24	16/1/10	BSS	H	Bath City	275	W 3-1	Clark 21, Mckenzie pen 24, Pope 30	4
25	23/1/10	BSS	A	Welling United	520	D 2-2	McKenzie pen 23, Bodkin 77	5
26	2/2/10	BSS	A	Dorchester Town	321	L 0-1		5
27	6/2/10	BSS	A	Woking	1366	W 1-0	Olima 45	2
28	13/2/10	BSS	H	St Albans City	238	D 0-0		5
29	20/2/10	BSS	A	Eastleigh	435	W 8-2	Og (Poate) 14, Bryant 2 (17, 45), McKenzie 3 (21, pen 29, 37), Bodkin 2 (63, 90)	4
30	6/3/10	BSS	A	Bath City	603	L 0-1		7
31	9/3/10	BSS	H	Braintree Town	315	L 1-2	Olima 30	7
32	13/3/10	BSS	A	St Albans City	343	L 0-1		9
33	16/3/10	BSS	H	Woking	257	D 2-2	Clark 53, Anderson 73	8
34	20/3/10	BSS	H	Newport County	406	W 2-1	Bryant 28, McKenzie 70	8
35	23/3/10	BSS	H	Maidenhead United	202	D 2-2	McKenzie 2 (pen 55, 78)	8
36	27/3/10	BSS	A	Weymouth	364	D 0-0		7
37	30/3/10	BSS	A	Bromley	201	W 3-2	Clark 14, Bryant 57, Mckenzie 71	7
38	5/4/10	BSS	A	Bishops Stortford	368	D 0-0		7
39	10/4/10	BSS	H	Basingstoke Town	219	D 0-0		9
40	17/4/10	BSS	A	Staines Town	439	L 0-3		10
41	20/4/10	BSS	H	Hampton & Richmond B.	235	L 0-2		10
42	24/4/10	BSS	H	Bromley	313	L 3-6	Mckenzie 2 (44, pen 77), Bryant 56	10
	Cups							
1	26/9/09	FAC 2Q	A	Bishops Stortford	425	W 3-2	McKenzie 32, Bodkin 60, Bryant 61	
2	10/10/09	FAC 3Q	H	Potters Bar Town	155	W 4-2	McKenzie 22, Bryant 43, Bodkin 67, Judge pen 83	
3	24/10/09	FAC 4Q	A	Oxford United	3296	L 0-2		
4	21/11/09	FAT 3Q	H	Havant & Waterlooville	142	L 1-4	Bryant 14	

Home Attendances:	
Highest:	826 v Chelmsford City
Lowest:	187 v Weston-Super-Mare
Average (08-09):	246 (341)
Top Goalscorer:	McKenzie - 20 (18 League, 2 Cup) in 39 appearances - 51% strike rate
Most Appearances:	Bodkin - 46 (42 League, 4 Cup)
	Orilonishe - 46 (42 League, 4 Cup)

WOOLLEY	ANDREWS	ANDERSON	SWAINE	CLARK	PAINE	LALITE	BODKIN	BRYANT	OLIMA	ORILONISHE	KNIGHT	GILBEY	LUKE	FLYNN	RAFIS	LEMONIUS	DOYLE	SAUNDERS	MCKENZIE	LIBBY	HOGAN	THOMPSON	JUDGE	OMAND	LINCOLN	STALLEY	POPE	FOSTER	SMITH	O'TOOLE	
X	X	X	X	X	X	X	X	X	X	X	S	U	U	U	U																1
X	X	X		X	X	X	X	X	X	X	U	S	U	X	U	U															2
X	X	X		X	X	X	X	X	X	X	S	S	U	X	U	U															3
X	X	X	S	X	X	X	X	X	X	X	S		U	X	U		U														4
X	S	X	X	X	X	X	X	X	X	X		U	S	X	U		U														5
X	X	X	X		X	X	X	X	X	X	S	X	U		S		U	S													6
X	X	U	X	X	X	X	X	X	X	X	S	U	S	X	U																7
X	X	X	X	X	X	X	X	X	X	X	U	S	S						S	U											8
X	X	X	X	X	X	X	X	X	X	X	S	U	S						S	U											9
	X	S	X	X	X	X	X	X	X	X	S	U	U	X					S		X										10
X	X			X	X	X	X	X	X	X	U	U	S	X					X	U		U									11
X	X	X		X	X	X	X	X	X	X	S	S					U		X			U	S								12
X	X	X		X	X	X	X	X	X	X	U	S		S					X			U	S								13
X	X	X	U	X	X	X	X	X	X	X	S	U		S					X				S								14
X	X	U	U	X	X	X	X	X	X	X	S	S		X					X				S								15
X	U	X		X	X	X	X	X	X	X	U	U		X					X			U	U								16
X	X	X		X	X	X	X		X	X		U							X	U		U	X		S	U					17
X	X	X			X	X	X	X	X	X		U		X					X	U		U	S		U						18
X	X	X	S	X	X	X	X	X	X	X		U					U		X				U		S						19
X		X	S	X	X	X	X	X	X	X		S		X					S					U	U		X				20
X	U	X	U	X		X	X	X		X		X		X			U		X				S			U	X				21
X	U	X	X		S	X	X	X	S	X		X		X					X				S			U	X				22
X	U	X	X	S		X	X	X	S	X		X		X			U		X				S				X				23
X	U	X	X	X	S	X	X	X	S	X		X							X				S				X				24
X	U	X	X	X	S	X	X	X	S	X		X		U					X				S				X				25
X	U	X	X	X	X	X	X	X	S	X				S			U		X				S				X				26
X	U	U	X	X	U	X	X	X	X	X				X			U		X				U				X				27
X	U	U	X	X	S	X	X	X	X	X				X			S		X				S				X				28
X		S	X	X	X	X	X	X	S	X				X					X				S				X	U	U		29
X	U	X	X	X	X	X	X	X	S	X									X				S				X	U	S		30
X		U	X	X	X	X	X	X	X	X		U		X					S				S				X		S		31
X		U	X	X	U	X	X	X	S	X		S		X					X				S				X		X		32
X		S	X	X	U	X	X	X	X	X		U		X					X				U				X		U		33
X		X		X	S	X	X	X	X	X		S		X			U		X				U				X		U		34
X		X		X	S	X	X	X	X	X		U		X			U		X				S				X		S		35
X	X	U	X	X	S	X	X	X	S	X		X					S		X								X		U		36
X	U		X	X	S	X	X	X	S	X		X		X			U		X							U	X				37
X	X		X	X	S	X	X	X	S	X		X					U		X							S	X			U	38
X	S		X		S	X	X	X	X	X		X		X			U		X							U	X		S		39
X	X	U	U		X	X	X	X	X	X				U					X							S	X		X	S	40
X	X	U	U	X	X	X	X	X	S	X							S		X							S			X	X	41
X	X	U		X	X	X	X	X	X	X				U			S		X							S			S	X	42
X	X	S	U	X	X	X	X	X	X	X	U	U		X			U	U	X			U									1
X	X	X	U	X	X	X	X	X	X	X	S	S		U					X			U	S	U							2
X	X	X	U	X	X		X	X	X	X	S	X		S			U		X			U	S	U							3
X	X	X		X	X	X	X	X	X	X		U						U	X	U		S	S								4

Total League Appearances

WOOLLEY	ANDREWS	ANDERSON	SWAINE	CLARK	PAINE	LALITE	BODKIN	BRYANT	OLIMA	ORILONISHE	KNIGHT	GILBEY	LUKE	FLYNN	RAFIS	LEMONIUS	DOYLE	SAUNDERS	MCKENZIE	LIBBY	HOGAN	THOMPSON	JUDGE	OMAND	LINCOLN	STALLEY	POPE	FOSTER	SMITH	O'TOOLE	
41	22	25	23	36	27	42	42	41	29	42	0	10	0	24	0	0	0	0	30	0	1	0	1	0	0	0	21	0	3	2	X
0	2	3	3	1	10	0	0	0	12	0	10	9	5	3	1	0	4	1	5	0	0	0	17	0	2	4	0	0	5	1	S
0	11	10	5	0	3	0	0	0	0	0	5	14	6	4	6	2	14	0	0	5	0	6	5	1	2	5	0	2	4	1	U

Total Cup Appearances

WOOLLEY	ANDREWS	ANDERSON	SWAINE	CLARK	PAINE	LALITE	BODKIN	BRYANT	OLIMA	ORILONISHE	KNIGHT	GILBEY	LUKE	FLYNN	RAFIS	LEMONIUS	DOYLE	SAUNDERS	MCKENZIE	LIBBY	HOGAN	THOMPSON	JUDGE	OMAND	LINCOLN	STALLEY	POPE	FOSTER	SMITH	O'TOOLE	
4	4	3	0	4	4	3	4	4	4	4	0	1	0	1	0	0	0	0	4	0	0	0	0	0	0	0	0	0	0	0	X
0	0	1	0	0	0	0	0	0	0	0	2	1	0	1	0	0	0	0	0	0	0	1	3	0	0	0	0	0	0	0	S
0	0	0	3	0	0	0	0	0	0	0	1	2	0	1	0	0	2	2	0	1	0	3	0	2	0	0	0	0	0	0	U

Total Goals

WOOLLEY	ANDREWS	ANDERSON	SWAINE	CLARK	PAINE	LALITE	BODKIN	BRYANT	OLIMA	ORILONISHE	KNIGHT	GILBEY	LUKE	FLYNN	RAFIS	LEMONIUS	DOYLE	SAUNDERS	MCKENZIE	LIBBY	HOGAN	THOMPSON	JUDGE	OMAND	LINCOLN	STALLEY	POPE	FOSTER	SMITH	O'TOOLE	
0	1	2	1	3	2	3	7	14	3	7	1	1	0	0	0	0	0	0	18	0	0	0	1	0	0	0	1	0	0	0	Lge
0	0	0	0	0	0	0	2	3	0	0	0	0	0	0	0	0	0	0	2	0	0	0	1	0	0	0	0	0	0	0	Cup

THURROCK

CURRENT SQUAD AS OF BEGINING OF 2010-11 SEASON

GOALKEEPERS	HT	WT	D.O.B	AGE	P.O.B	CAREER	Apps	Gls
Joe Woolley			20/9/89	19		Charlton (Yth), Grays c/s 08 Rel 8/08, Thurrock 10/08	41	0
DEFENDERS								
Phil Anderson			1/3/87	22		Southend, Aldershot 7/06 Rel 5/07, Thurrock c/s 07	28	2
Ryan Andrews			29/9/87	22		West Ham (Scholar), Dover, Hastings U 11/07, East Thurrock 1/08, Sittingbourne 2/08, Thurrock c/s 09, Sittingbourne (Dual) 4/10	24	1
Kenny Clark			12/8/88	22		Dag & Red, Heybridge (L) 3/06, Thurrock 6/06	37	3
Lee Flynn	5'09"	11 05	4/9/73	35	Hampstead	Boreham Wood, Wingate & F, Romford, Hendon, Hayes 7/95, Barnet 1/01 £13,500, Stevenage 5/03 Rel 4/04, Dag & Red 5/04, St Albans (L) 10/05, Cambridge C (L) 12/05, St Albans (L) 1/06, St Albans 3/06 Rel 3/07, Thurrock 3/07	27	0
Jamie Libby			30/1/91	18		Thurrock	0	0
Craig Pope	5'10"	11 07	17/9/82	26	Islington	Barnet Rel 5/03, Cambridge C 8/03, Histon 5/07 Rel 12/09, Thurrock 12/09	21	1
Rob Swaine						Billericay, Thurrock 9/07	26	1
MIDFIELDERS								
Matt Bodkin	5'06"	10 11	16/9/86	22	Chatham	Notts Forest Rel c/s 04, Gillingham 8/04, Welling 8/05, Grays 12/06 Rel 2/09, Thurrock (L) 1/07, Dartford (L) 8/07, Thurrock (SL) 9/07, Eastleigh (6ML) 8/08, Dover 2/09 Rel 5/09, Thurrock 5/09	42	7
Reiss Gilbey			8/7/91	19		Thurrock	19	1
Leon Lalite			19/12/80	29		Barnet, Stevenage, Waltham Forest, Harlow 12/03, Thurrock 3/09	42	3
Lamar Lemonius			20/6/92	18		Thurrock	0	0
Ryan Stalley			2/6/92	18		Thurrock	4	0
FORWARDS								
Cliff Akurang	6'02"	12 03	27/2/81	28	Ghana	Chelsea (Jun), Luton (Trainee), Chesham, Hitchin 8/00 Rel 12/01, Purfleet/Thurrock 12/01, Heybridge Swifts 2/05, Dag & Red (L) 11/05 (05/06 3,1), Dag & Red 1/06 (05/06 15,4, 06/07 27,3), Thurrock (SL) 1/07, Histon 5/07 (07/08 19,10), Barnet Undisc 1/08 Rel c/s 10, Weymouth (SL) 3/09 (08/09 8,2), Rushden & D (SL) 7/09, Thurrock 7/10		
David Bryant			9/6/82	27		Dag & Red, Maldon, Aveley, Thurrock 3/07, Braintree 5/08 Rel 8/08, Thurrock 8/08	41	14
Jamie Doyle			18/9/90	19		Redbridge (Yth), Thurrock	4	0
Leon McKenzie			18/10/84	24		L.Orient, Waltham Forest, Thurrock 6/06 Rel 12/08, Luton (Trial) 12/08, Grays 12/08 Rel 1/09, Bishops Stortford 6/09, Thurrock 9/09	35	18
Paul Olima			6/8/86	23	Dublin	St Patricks, Taunton 9/06, Dag & Red, Waltham Forest 8/07, Arlesey 11/07, Ilford 2/08, Walton Casuals, Grays 11/08, Walton Casuals (L) 12/08 Perm, Croydon Ath 1/09, Hitchin 2/09, Thurrock c/s 09	41	3
Lewis Smith			27/10/89	19		Fulham Rel 3/09, Bishops Stortford (SL) 12/08 Perm 3/09 Rel c/s 09, Gillingham (Trial) 3/09, Bournemouth (Trial) 4/09, Bishops Stortford 8/09, Chelmsford 1/10 Rel 2/10, Thurrock 2/10	8	0

Departures	HT	WT	DOB	AGE	POB	From - To	APPS	GOA
(M)Junior Luke			24/5/90	20		Waltham Forest 8/09 - Leyton 9/09, Waltham Forest 11/09, Maldon T, Brentwood 2/10 Rel 5/10	5	0
(G)David Hogan	6'00"	13 10	31/5/89	21	Harlow	Dag & Red 9/09 - Rel 10/09	1	0
(M)Reece Prestedge			25/12/85	24		Bishops Stortford 10/09 - AFC Hornchurch 10/09, Billericay 12/09, Bishops Stortford 3/10		
(G)Adam Rafis			10/5/84	26		Concord R c/s 09 - Rel 10/09	1	0
(F)David Knight			13/9/90	19		Yth - Rel 11/09, Aveley 12/09	10	1
(M)Greg Lincoln	5'09"	10 13	23/3/80	29	Cheshunt	Cambridge C 5/07 - Aveley 12/09	2	0
(M)Chris Saunders			11/9/88	21		Fisher 8/09 - Welling 12/09, Maidstone 3/10, Cray W 6/10	1	0
(F)Leslie Thompson	5'10"	11 02	3/10/88	19	Newham	Havant & W 9/09 - Rel 2/10	0	0
(M)Fola Orilonshe			14/7/86	23		Waltham Forest 8/07 - Sutton U 5/10	42	7
(D)Matthew Paine	6'01"	12 12	22/12/87	21	Bexley	Colchester (SL) 1/07 Perm c/s 07 - Braintree 6/10	37	2
(G)Andre Foster						Enfield T 9/09 -	0	0
(G)Aaron Omand			20/10/87	22		Yth -	0	0
(F)Matthew Judge	6'00"	11 07	18/1/85	24	Barking	ex Ebbsfleet 10/09 -	18	1
(M)Mark O'Toole					Dagenham	Galway 3/10 -	3	0

WELLING UNITED

Chairman: Paul Websdale

Secretary: Barrie Hobbins (T) 07949 180 816 (E) barrie.hobbins@hotmail.com

Additional Committee Members:
Steve Pain, Eric Brackstone, Paul Carter

Manager: Jamie Day

Programme Editor: Paul Carter (E) paul_carter40@yahoo.co.uk

Unfortunately an up-to-date photograph was not available at the time of going to press

Club Factfile

Founded: 1963 **Nickname:** The Wings

Previous Names:

Previous Leagues: Eltham & District 1963-71, London Spartan 1971-77, Athenian 1978-81, Southern 1981-86, 2000-04, Conference 1986-2000

Club Colours (change): All red (All yellow)

Ground: Park View Road Ground, Welling, Kent DA16 1SY (T) 0208 301 1196

Capacity: 4,000 **Seats:** 1,070 **Covered:** 1,500 **Clubhouse:** Yes **Shop:** Yes

Previous Grounds: Butterfly Lane, Eltham 1963-78

Simple Directions
M25 to Dartford then A2 towards London. Take Bexleyheath/Blackfen/Sidcup,turn off (six miles along A2) then follow A207 signed welling, Ground is 1 mile From A2 on main road towards Welling High Street.

Record Attendance: 4,100 v Gillingham - FA Cup
Record Victory: 7-1 v Dorking - 1985-86
Record Defeat: 0-7 v Welwyn Garden City - 1972-73
Record Goalscorer: Not known
Record Appearances: Not known
Additional Records: Paid £30,000 to Enfield for Gary Abbott
Received £95,000 from Birmingham City for Steve Finnan 1995

Senior Honours: Southern League 1985-86. Kent Senior Cup 1985-86, 98-99, 2008-09.
London Senior Cup 1989-90. London Challenge Cup 1991-92.

10 YEAR RECORD

00-01	01-02	02-03	03-04	04-05	05-06	06-07	07-08	08-09	09-10
SthP 4	SthP 15	SthP 15	SthP 9	Conf S 16	Conf S 9	Conf S 8	Conf S 16	Conf S 7	Conf S 9

WELLING UNITED

No.	Date	Comp	H/A	Opponents	Att:	Result	Goalscorers	Pos
1	8/8/09	BSS	H	Woking	844	L 1-2	Cracknell pen 3	18
2	11/8/09	BSS	A	Thurrock	378	L 2-3	Clarke 54, Hobbs 65	20
3	15/8/09	BSS	A	Bath City	479	L 1-2	Hobbs 70	20
4	18/8/09	BSS	H	St Albans City	445	W 3-2	Deane 8, Clarke 18, Sambrook 63	16
5	22/8/09	BSS	A	Staines Town	397	D 1-1	Hobbs 61	17
6	29/8/09	BSS	H	Braintree Town	534	D 0-0		16
7	31/8/09	BSS	A	Dover Athletic	1321	L 0-2		16
8	5/9/09	BSS	H	Newport County	552	L 0-2		17
9	8/9/09	BSS	A	Maidenhead United	187	L 0-2		20
10	12/9/09	BSS	A	Dorchester Town	386	W 2-1	Mambo 9, Whitnell 85	17
11	19/9/09	BSS	H	Weston-Super-Mare	493	W 3-1	Whitnell 73, Parkinson 88, Cracknell 90	16
12	3/10/09	BSS	H	Bishops Stortford	507	L 0-2		18
13	17/10/09	BSS	A	Chelmsford City	1048	L 1-3	Parkinson 4	19
14	26/10/09	BSS	A	Havant & Waterlooville	854	D 2-2	Og (Nightingale) 17, Whitnell 89	19
15	31/10/09	BSS	H	Lewes	502	W 1-0	Fazackerley 83	17
16	7/11/09	BSS	A	Worcester City	708	W 1-0	Parkinson 56	17
17	14/11/09	BSS	H	Staines Town	452	W 3-0	Whitnell 9, Clarke 48, Og (Woozley) 50	16
18	24/11/09	BSS	H	Hampton & Richmond B.	375	W 2-0	Pugh 12, Hobbs 90	13
19	28/11/09	BSS	A	Basingstoke Town	429	D 1-1	Andrews 50	13
20	1/12/09	BSS	H	Chelmsford City	500	L 0-1		14
21	5/12/09	BSS	H	Worcester City	474	W 1-0	Clarke pen 53	11
22	26/12/09	BSS	H	Bromley	841	L 0-2		14
23	28/12/09	BSS	A	St Albans City	463	W 2-1	Pugh 2 (22, 89)	13
24	1/1/10	BSS	A	Bromley	1093	W 1-0	Parkinson 66	11
25	23/1/10	BSS	H	Thurrock	520	D 2-2	Whitnell 43, Cutler 58	11
26	30/1/10	BSS	A	Bishops Stortford	407	W 4-0	Whitnell 4, Clarke pen 49, Pugh 52, Parkinson 81	11
27	6/2/10	BSS	A	Newport County	1449	D 2-2	Whitnell 2 (62, 75)	11
28	9/2/10	BSS	A	Hampton & Richmond B.	293	D 2-2	Whitnell 52, Obersteller 85	11
29	13/2/10	BSS	H	Dorchester Town	501	D 1-1	Clarke pen 17	11
30	20/2/10	BSS	A	Woking	1217	W 5-0	Pugh 3 (38, 55, pen 68), Whitnell 50, Finn 89	9
31	27/2/10	BSS	H	Bath City	572	L 0-2		11
32	6/3/10	BSS	H	Havant & Waterlooville	443	W 1-0	Clarke pen 8	10
33	13/3/10	BSS	A	Weymouth	405	W 3-0	Clarke 2 (49, 90), Cracknell 56	10
34	17/3/10	BSS	A	Eastleigh	354	W 3-1	Parkinson 43, Whitnell 79, Clarke 90	8
35	20/3/10	BSS	H	Maidenhead United	461	W 3-1	Cracknell 3 (45, 83 pen 85)	7
36	23/3/10	BSS	H	Weymouth	427	W 7-1	Hobbs 18, Clarke 2 (30, pen 63), Hurrell 36, Cracknell 83, Healy 84, Fazackerley 89	5
37	27/3/10	BSS	A	Lewes	421	L 1-3	Clarke pen 39	6
38	2/4/10	BSS	A	Braintree Town	799	L 0-1		6
39	5/4/10	BSS	H	Dover Athletic	939	L 0-1		9
40	10/4/10	BSS	H	Eastleigh	409	L 1-2	Clarke 54	10
41	17/4/10	BSS	A	Weston-Super-Mare	201	W 2-1	Clarke 2 (63, 67)	9
42	24/4/10	BSS	H	Basingstoke Town	507	D 1-1	Fazackerley 64	9
	Cups							
1	26/9/09	FAC 2Q	H	East Thurrock United	404	W 2-0	Whitnell 2 (75, 78)	
2	10/10/09	FAC 3Q	A	Dover Athletic	1042	L 0-2		
3	22/11/09	FAT 3Q	H	Tonbridge Angels	510	W 3-2	Pugh 23, Whitnell 2 (36, 77)	
4	12/12/09	FAT 1	H	Eastbourne Borough	437	L 0-1		

Home Attendances:	
Highest:	939 v Dover Athletic
Lowest:	375 v Hampton & Richmond Borough
Average (08-09):	501 (639)

Top Goalscorer:	Clarke - 16 (16 League, 0 Cup) in 36 appearances - 44% strike rate
Most Appearances:	Mitten - 46 (42 League, 4 Cup)

MITTEN	SAMBROOK	DEANE	PARKINSON	KING	ANDREWS	JOHNSON	MINTON	CLARKE	FINN	CRACKNELL	NGAKAM	MENGA	HOBBS	FAZACKERLEY	HURRELL	HASWELL	HUGHES	PROTHEROE	PERKINS	MAMBO	ROCASTLE	WHITNELL	BENNETT	SPILLER	BLACKBURN	HOPKINS	GAISIE	BAKARE	STONE	DAY	PUGH	MULYHILL	OBERSTELLER	CUTLER	JENKINSON	SAUNDERS	SAGNA	OMOGBEHIN	TUNA	HEALY	I'ANSON	
X	X	X	X	X	X	X	X	X	X	X	S	S	S	U	U																											1
X	X	X	X	X		X	X	X		X	U	U	S	X	S	X	S																									2
X	X	S	X	X		X	X	X		X	U	S	X		X	X	S	U																								3
X	X	X	X					X			X	S	X		X	X	X	S	X																							4
X		X	X	X	U			X	S	U		S	X	U	X	X	X	X	X																							5
X		X		U				X	X	X		S	X		X	X	U	U	X	X	X	S																				6
X		X		X				X		X		S	X		X	X		U	X	X	X	S	U																			7
X	X	U		S				S	X	X			X	X	X	X			X	X			U	X	S																	8
X		X		X				X	S	X			X	X	S			X	X	X		S	U		X	U																9
X		X		X				U	X	X			X	U	X			X		X		X			X	S	S	S														10
X	U	X	S	X					X	X			X	U	X			X		X		X			X		S		S													11
X	X	X	X	X	X	X			X				X		S			S				X			U		U	S	X													12
X	X	U	X	X	X	X			X				S	X	X							S			U		S	X	X													13
X	X	X	X	X	X	X			X	X			U	X	S							S					S	U	X													14
X		X	X		X	X		S	X	X			S	X	S			X				X					U	U	X													15
X	S	X	X		X	X		X	X				U	X	S			X				X					S	U	X													16
X	X	X			X			X	X				S	X	S			X				X	U				U	S	X	X												17
X		X	X		X	X		X	X				S	X	X							X						U		S	X		U	U								18
X		X	X		X	X		X	X				S	X	X							X						U		U	X		S	S								19
X	U	X	X		X	X		X					X	X	S								U					S		U	X		X	X								20
X	U	X	X		X	X		X					U	X	X													S		X	X		U	X								21
X	X	X	X		X			X	X				S	X	S							X						S		X	X		U	U								22
X	X	U	X		X			X	X				S	U	X							X						S		X	X		X	U								23
X	X	U	X					X	U	U			S	X	X							X						S		X	X		X	X								24
X		U	X		X				S	U				X	X							X						S		X	X		X	X	X	U						25
X		U	X		X			X	S	U				X	X							X						S		X	X		X	S	X							26
X	U		X		X			X	S	U				X	X							X						U		X	X		X	U	X							27
X	X	U	X		X			X	S	U				X	X							X						S		X	X		X	U								28
X	S	S	X		X			X	U					X	X							X						U		X	X		X	U	X							29
X	U	X	X		X			X		S			U	X	X							X						S		X	X			S	X							30
X	X		X		X			X	X	S			S	X	X							X						U		X				S	X	U						31
X		X	X		X			X	S	X			U	X	X							X						S		X				X	U		S					32
X		X	X		X			X	S	X			S	X	X							X						U		X				X			S	U				33
X		X	X		X			X	S	X			U	X	X							X						U		X				X			U	U				34
X		X	X		X			X		X			U	X	X							X						S		X				X	S			U	S			35
X		X	X		X			X		X			X	X	X													S		X				X						S	S	36
																																										37
X	U	X	X		X			X		X			X	X	X							S						U						X	S					S	X	38
X	X	U	X		X			X		X			S	X	X							X						S		X				X							U	39
X	X	S	X		X			X		X			S	X	X							X						S		X			U	X							U	40
X	X	S	X		X			X					X		S													X		X			X	S	X						X	41
X	X	U			X			X					X	U	X							X						S		X			X	X	U					S	X	42
X	X				X			X					X	X	X							S						U					X	U	X				S	X	X	

MITTEN	SAMBROOK	DEANE	PARKINSON	KING	ANDREWS	JOHNSON	MINTON	CLARKE	FINN	CRACKNELL	NGAKAM	MENGA	HOBBS	FAZACKERLEY	HURRELL	HASWELL	HUGHES	PROTHEROE	PERKINS	MAMBO	ROCASTLE	WHITNELL	BENNETT	SPILLER	BLACKBURN	HOPKINS	GAISIE	BAKARE	STONE	DAY	PUGH	MULYHILL	OBERSTELLER	CUTLER	JENKINSON	SAUNDERS	SAGNA	OMOGBEHIN	TUNA	HEALY	I'ANSON	
X	X	X	S	X	X				X	X			X		X							X	U		X		U	S	S													1
X	S	X	X	X	X	X			X				S		X			X				U	U		S		X		X													2
X	X	X	X		X	X			X				S	X	X							X	U			U		U			X	U										3
X	X	X	X	S	X	X			X				S	X	X													U			X		U	X								4

Total League Appearances

MITTEN	SAMBROOK	DEANE	PARKINSON	KING	ANDREWS	JOHNSON	MINTON	CLARKE	FINN	CRACKNELL	NGAKAM	MENGA	HOBBS	FAZACKERLEY	HURRELL	HASWELL	HUGHES	PROTHEROE	PERKINS	MAMBO	ROCASTLE	WHITNELL	BENNETT	SPILLER	BLACKBURN	HOPKINS	GAISIE	BAKARE	STONE	DAY	PUGH	MULYHILL	OBERSTELLER	CUTLER	JENKINSON	SAUNDERS	SAGNA	OMOGBEHIN	TUNA	HEALY	I'ANSON	
42	19	26	33	11	31	12	3	34	16	19	1	0	16	30	31	7	2	7	6	6	2	25	0	1	3	0	0	2	6	21	13	0	11	13	8	0	0	0	0	1	4	X
0	2	4	1	1	0	0	0	2	9	2	1	6	14	0	10	0	2	2	0	0	0	7	0	0	1	1	5	18	1	1	0	0	1	5	2	0	2	0	2	3	1	S
0	6	9	0	1	1	0	0	1	2	6	2	1	7	6	1	0	1	3	0	0	0	0	5	0	2	1	3	12	0	2	0	0	4	7	2	2	1	3	0	0	2	U

Total Cup Appearances

MITTEN	SAMBROOK	DEANE	PARKINSON	KING	ANDREWS	JOHNSON	MINTON	CLARKE	FINN	CRACKNELL	NGAKAM	MENGA	HOBBS	FAZACKERLEY	HURRELL	HASWELL	HUGHES	PROTHEROE	PERKINS	MAMBO	ROCASTLE	WHITNELL	BENNETT	SPILLER	BLACKBURN	HOPKINS	GAISIE	BAKARE	STONE	DAY	PUGH	MULYHILL	OBERSTELLER	CUTLER	JENKINSON	SAUNDERS	SAGNA	OMOGBEHIN	TUNA	HEALY	I'ANSON	
4	3	4	3	2	4	3	0	0	4	1	0	0	1	2	4	0	0	1	0	0	0	2	0	0	1	0	1	0	1	0	2	0	0	1	0	0	0	0	0	0	0	X
0	1	0	1	1	0	0	0	0	0	0	0	0	3	0	0	0	0	0	0	0	0	0	0	0	1	0	0	1	1	0	0	0	0	0	0	0	0	0	0	0	0	S
0	0	0	0	0	0	0	0	0	0	0	0	0	0	0	0	0	0	0	0	0	0	1	3	0	0	1	1	2	0	0	0	1	1	0	0	0	0	0	0	0	0	U

Total Goals

MITTEN	SAMBROOK	DEANE	PARKINSON	KING	ANDREWS	JOHNSON	MINTON	CLARKE	FINN	CRACKNELL	NGAKAM	MENGA	HOBBS	FAZACKERLEY	HURRELL	HASWELL	HUGHES	PROTHEROE	PERKINS	MAMBO	ROCASTLE	WHITNELL	BENNETT	SPILLER	BLACKBURN	HOPKINS	GAISIE	BAKARE	STONE	DAY	PUGH	MULYHILL	OBERSTELLER	CUTLER	JENKINSON	SAUNDERS	SAGNA	OMOGBEHIN	TUNA	HEALY	I'ANSON	
0	1	1	6	0	1	0	0	16	1	7	0	0	5	3	1	0	0	0	0	1	0	11	0	0	0	0	0	0	0	0	7	0	1	1	0	0	0	0	0	1	0	Lge
0	0	0	0	0	0	0	0	0	0	0	0	0	0	0	0	0	0	0	0	0	0	4	0	0	0	0	0	0	0	0	1	0	0	0	0	0	0	0	0	0	0	Cup

Also Played: GREENHALGH S(4). BILLINGS U(4). MARSH U(38,42).

WELLING UNITED

CURRENT SQUAD AS OF BEGINING OF 2010-11 SEASON

GOALKEEPERS	HT	WT	D.O.B	AGE	P.O.B	CAREER	Apps	Gls
Matthew Bennett			1/7/91	19		Welling	0	0
Jamie Billings			22/9/90	19		Welling	0	0
Charlie Mitten	6'02"	12 07	9/10/74	35	Woolwich	Thamesmead T, Dover 3/96, Margate (3ML) 9/96, Gillingham 10/99 Rel c/s 01, Margate 7/01, Gravesend NC 2/04 Rel 11/04 Welling 11/04 Rel 5/05, Margate 7/05, Folkestone I c/s 07, Welling 1/09	42	0
DEFENDERS								
Graeme Andrews			7/8/84	26		Bearsted, Dover, Welling 7/08	31	1
Jamie Coyle			31/5/83	27	Lewisham	Gravesend Rel 1/03, Sittingbourne (L) 12/01, Sittingbourne (L) 9/02, Sittingbourne 1/03, Dulwich H 7/05, Dartford 5/07, Welling 6/10		
Jack Obersteller	6'02"	13 00	10/10/88	21	Newham	Millwall, Crawley (L) 3/07, Wycombe 7/07 Rel 5/08, Grays (SL) 10/07, Exeter 5/08, Grays NC 8/09, Welling 11/09	12	1
Femi Omogbehin			3/1/90	20		Watford (Yth), Thamesmead, Dulwich H 10/08 Rel 12/08, Welling 3/10	0	0
Andrew Sambrook	5'10"	11 09	13/7/79	31	Chatham	Gillingham (AS), USA Scholarship (Hartwick College) c/s 97, Gillingham 3/01 Rel 6/01, Rushden & D 8/01 Rel c/s 05, Grays 7/05, Fisher 7/08, Thurrock 11/08, AFC Wimbledon 1/09, Welling 5/09	21	1
MIDFIELDERS								
Dean Cracknell	5'10"	12 04	12/10/83	26	Hitchin	Watford (Ass Sch), Northampton Rel 2/04, Stevenage 3/04 Rel c/s 04, Aylesbury 7/04, Barnet 1/05, B.Stortford 2/05, St Albans 5/05 Hemel Hempstead 5/07, St Albans 1/08, Cambridge C 3/08, Brackley 6/08, Welling 7/09	21	7
Jamie Day	5'10"	11 04	13/9/79	30	Bexley	Arsenal, Bournemouth £20,000 3/99 Rel c/s 01, Dover 7/01, Welling 5/04, Grays 5/07, Eastbourne (L) 9/07, Havant & W (SL) 3/08, Dartford 8/08, Welling (Pl/Man) 11/09	22	0
Louis Fazackerley			24/7/84	26	Winchester	Fulham Rel c/s 04, Northampton (Trial) c/s 04, Farnborough (Trial) c/s 04, Sutton U 8/04, Eastbourne B 11/04, Leyton 7/06, Bishops Stortford 8/07, Bromley 5/08, Welling 10/08	30	3
Jack Parkinson			23/7/89	21		Tonbridge A (Yth), VCD Ath, Welling 7/08, Margate (L) 10/08, Bournemouth (Trial) 3/10	34	6
Loick Pires	6'03"	13 02	20/11/89	20	Lisbon, Port	Stoke (Yth), L.Orient Rel c/s 10, Welling 7/10		
FORWARDS								
Michale Bakare			1/12/86	23		Maidenhead, Edgware, Welwyn Garden, Hertford, Waltham Forest, Haringey, Leyton, Welling 9/09,	20	0
Lee Clarke	5'11"	10 08	28/7/83	27	Peterborough	Yaxley, Peterborough Undisc 10/01, Kettering (SL) 3/03, Kettering (2ML) 8/03, St Albans (SL) 1/04, St Albans 7/04 Rel 4/09, Welling 5/09, Cambridge C (L) 9/09	36	16
Luis Cumbers	6'00"	11 10	6/9/88	21	Chelmsford	Gillingham Rel c/s 10, Maidstone (L) 9/07, Grays (L) 11/07, AFC Wimbledon (SL) 3/08, Ebbsfleet (L) 3/09, Ebbsfleet (L) 9/09, AFC Wimbledon (2ML) 11/09, Dover (L) 2/10, Welling 7/10		
Joe Healy	6'00"	12 04	26/12/86	23	Sidcup	Millwall, Crawley (L) 2/05, Walton & H (L) 2/06, Fisher 8/06, Yeading (SL) 3/07, Beckenham c/s 07, Welling 7/08 Rel 10/08, Beckenham 10/08, Margate 12/08 Rel 2/10, Welling 3/10	4	1
James Lawson	5'09"	10 03	21/1/87	23	Basildon	Southend Rel c/s 07, Grimsby (L) 9/06, Bournemouth (L) 1/07, Dag & Red (L) 2/07, Grays 8/07, Chelmsford (3ML) 10/07 Perm 1/08, Welling 6/09		
Adam Marsh			22/1/91	19		Welling	0	0
Andy Pugh	5'09"	12 02	28/1/89	21	Gravesend	Gillingham Rel c/s 10, Welling (L) 10/07, Maidstone (L) 2/08, Folkestone I (L) 8/08, Grays (SL) 1/09, Dover (L) 9/09, Welling (2ML) 11/09, Histon (L) 3/10, Welling 7/10	13	7
Tom Whitnell			12/10/88	21		Millwall (Scholar), Cray W, Welling 8/09	32	11

Loanees	HT	WT	DOB	AGE	POB	From - To	APPS	GOA
(D)Yado Mambo			22/10/91	18	Kilburn	Charlton 8/09 - Dover (L) 11/09, Staines (L) 12/09	6	1
(D)Carl Jenkinson			8/2/92	18		Charlton 12/09 -	10	0
(F)Tamer Tuna	5'08"	11 00	19/10/91	18	Bexley	Charlton 3/10 -	2	0
Departures	**HT**	**WT**	**DOB**	**AGE**	**POB**	**From - To**		
(M)Jeff Minton	5'06"	11 10	28/12/73	36	Hackney	Chelmsford 7/09 - Rel 8/09	3	0
(D)Cedric Ngakam			20/12/85	24		Dulwich Hamlet 8/09 - Rel 8/09, Concord R, Leyton 10/09, Chatham 12/09	2	0
(M)Craig Rocastle	6'01"	13 09	17/8/81	29	Lewisham	Thrasyvoulos (Gre) 8/09 - Rel 9/09, Dover 9/09, Forest Green 10/09	2	0
(F)Lheureux Menga			27/5/86	24	Angola	Shepshed D 8/09 - Rel 9/09	6	0
(M)Danny Spiller	5'08"	11 00	10/10/81	28	Maidstone	Wycombe 9/09 - Dag & Red 9/09	1	0
(M)Steve Perkins			25/4/76	34	Southport	Hayes & Yeading 8/09 - Rel 9/09, Sutton U Rel c/s 10	6	0
(D)Michael Haswell			23/8/83	27	London	Grays 8/09 - Rel 9/09, Chelmsford 9/09 Rel 2/10, Harlow, Billericay 3/10	7	0
(M)Lee Blackburn	5'08"	10 05	1/10/85	23	Romford	Aveley 9/09 - Rel 10/09, Met Police 10/09, Maldon & Tiptree 5/10	4	0
(F)Steffan Gaisie	5'11"	11 07	29/9/88	21		ex Bognor Regis 9/09 - Chatham, Hampton & R 2/10, Walton Casuals 3/10	5	0
(D)Lee Protheroe			5/11/75	34		St Albans 11/08 (Pl/Ass Man) 5/09 - Rel 11/09, Wealdstone 12/09 Rel 12/09, Harlow 2/10	9	0
(F)Adrian Stone			7/8/82	28		Carshalton 9/09 - Rel 11/09, Bromley 11/09	7	0
(D)Ryan Johnson			15/1/87	23	Dartford	Slade Green 8/08 - Rel 12/09, Sittingbourne (L) 8/08	12	0
(D)Steve King			29/5/84	26		Bishops Stortford 7/09 - Rel 12/09, Brentwood, Concord R 12/09	12	0
(M)Chris Saunders			11/9/88	21		Thurrock 12/09 - Maidstone 3/10, Cray W 6/10	0	0
(M)Anthony Finn			27/11/82	27	Manchester	AFC Wimbledon 6/09 - Chelmsford 3/10 Rel c/s 10, Bromley 7/10	25	1
(M)Sam Hurrell			13/7/88	22	Hillingdon	St Albans 2/09 - Woking 5/10	41	1
(D)Michael Deane			31/10/84	25		7/09 - Maldon & Tiptree 6/10	30	1
(M)Sam Cutler			11/2/90	20	Sidcup	Grays 11/09 - Dover 7/10	18	1
(D)Tom Hopkins			1/10/89	20		Thamesmead 9/09 -	1	0
(D)Ciaran Mulyhill			30/1/91	19		Yth -	0	0
(M)Ben Greenhalgh			16/4/92	18		Yth -	1	0
(M)Rob Hughes	5'08"	11 10	6/9/80	29	Sutton	ex Sutton U 8/09 -	4	0
(F)Jake Hobbs	5'10"		10/2/91	19		Blackpool (Scholar) 7/09 - Sittingbourne (L), Chatham (Dual) 2/10	30	5
(F)Luke I'Anson			2/8/88	22		Kingstonian 3/10 -	5	0
(F)Lamine Sagna			7/5/88	22		St Albans 3/10 -	2	0

WESTON-SUPER-MARE

Chairman: Paul Bliss

Secretary: Richard Sloane (T) 0771 107 8589 (E) wsmsecretary@hotmail.co.uk

Additional Committee Members:
Dennis Usher, Oliver Bliss, Paul Macey, Phil Sheridan

Manager: Craig Laird

Programme Editor: Phil Sheridan (E) phil.sheridan29@btopenworld.com

Back Row (L-R): Amy Callow(Sports Therapist), Ryan Northmore (Youth team Manager, 1st team Coach), Danny Wring, Jack Durrant*, Bradley Middleton, Kane Ingram, Nat Pepperell, Matt Villis, Lloyd Irish (GoalKeeper), Steven Orchard, Dayle Grubb, Jake Mawford, Jamie Laird, Paul Kendall, Jak Martin, Jon Haile (Assistant Manager), Front Row: Alan Bull(Goalkeeper Coach), Craig Laird Jnr, Nabia Diablo*, Brett Trowbridge, Marcus Duharty, Dean Grubb, Craig Laird (Manager), Craig Rand (Team Captain), Simon Gilbert, Ben Kirk, Rhys Farmer, Sahr Kabba, Martin Slocombe, Dave Williams Jnr (Kitman) (*no longer with Club)

Club Factfile

Founded: 1899 **Nickname:** Seagulls

Previous Names: Borough or Weston-super-Mare

Previous Leagues: Somerset Senior, Western League

Club Colours (change): White/black/black (All royal blue)

Ground: Woodspring Stadium, Winterstoke Road, Weston-super-Mare BS24 9AA (T) 01934 621 618

Capacity: 3,000 **Seats:** 278 **Covered:** 2,000 **Clubhouse:** Yes **Shop:** Yes

Previous Grounds: Langford Road, Winterstoke Road

Simple Directions

Leave the M5 at Junction 21, take the dual carriageway A370 and continue straight until the 4th roundabout with ASDA on the right. Turn left into Winterstoke Road, bypassing a mini roundabout and continue for 1/2 mile. Woodspring Stadium is on the right.

Record Attendance: 2,623 v Woking - FA Cup 1st Round replay 23/11/1993 (At Winterstoke Road)

Record Victory: 11-0 v Paulton Rovers

Record Defeat: 1-12 v Yeovil Town Reserves

Record Goalscorer: Matt Lazenby - 180

Record Appearances: Harry Thomas - 740

Additional Records: Received £20,000 from Sheffield Wednesday for Stuart Jones

Senior Honours: Somerset Senior Cup 1923-24, 26-67.
Western League 1991-92.

10 YEAR RECORD

00-01	01-02	02-03	03-04	04-05	05-06	06-07	07-08	08-09	09-10
SthW 8	SthW 3	SthW 2	SthP 10	Conf S 11	Conf S 14	Conf S 21	Conf S 20	Conf S 17	Conf S 21

WESTON-SUPER-MARE

No.	Date	Comp	H/A	Opponents	Att:	Result	Goalscorers	Pos
1	8/8/09	BSS	H	Staines Town	297	L 0-1		21
2	11/8/09	BSS	A	Basingstoke Town	355	L 1-2	Holgate 59	21
3	15/8/09	BSS	A	Thurrock	187	L 1-2	Fortune 90	21
4	18/8/09	BSS	H	Woking	319	D 1-1	Holgate 47	21
5	22/8/09	BSS	A	Dover Athletic	1135	L 3-5	A Harris 8, Llewellyn 46, Mullings 52	21
6	28/8/09	BSS	H	Weymouth	341	W 3-0	Fortune 37, McGregor 2 (80, 85)	17
7	31/8/09	BSS	A	Newport County	1404	L 0-2		19
8	5/9/09	BSS	H	Braintree Town	262	L 1-2	Mullings 35	21
9	8/9/09	BSS	H	Worcester City	270	W 3-1	Mullings 37, McGregor 2 (67, 88)	16
10	12/9/09	BSS	A	Bromley	424	D 1-1	Holgate 20	15
11	19/9/09	BSS	A	Welling United	493	L 1-3	Compton 80	18
12	3/10/09	BSS	H	St Albans City	218	L 2-3	Compton 30, Og (Quilter) 87	20
13	17/10/09	BSS	H	Lewes	214	W 3-2	Gilroy 3 (14, 48, 53)	18
14	24/10/09	BSS	A	Maidenhead United	429	D 0-0		17
15	26/10/09	BSS	A	Worcester City	823	L 1-4	Joyce 77	18
16	31/10/09	BSS	H	Bishops Stortford	250	L 1-3	Gilroy 53	20
17	7/11/09	BSS	H	Thurrock	150	L 1-3	Gilroy 52	21
18	14/11/09	BSS	H	Dover Athletic	269	W 3-1	Compton 21, Gilroy 2 (52, 62)	20
19	28/11/09	BSS	A	Chelmsford City	1072	D 2-2	Cleverley 2 (5, 37)	20
20	12/12/09	BSS	A	Staines Town	260	L 0-3		20
21	16/12/09	BSS	A	Eastleigh	253	L 1-3	Klein-Davies 67	20
22	26/12/09	BSS	H	Bath City	659	L 0-2		21
23	28/12/09	BSS	A	Woking	1299	L 1-2	Og (Sam-Yorke) 19	21
24	23/1/10	BSS	A	Lewes	470	L 0-2		21
25	30/1/10	BSS	H	Dorchester Town	258	L 0-2		22
26	2/2/10	BSS	A	Bath City	548	L 0-1		22
27	6/2/10	BSS	A	St Albans City	279	L 1-2	Cleverley 43	22
28	9/2/10	BSS	A	Braintree Town	402	L 0-1		22
29	13/2/10	BSS	H	Eastleigh	207	D 2-2	Og (Oliver) 69, Gurney 80	21
30	20/2/10	BSS	H	Basingstoke Town	211	D 1-1	Mullings 8	21
31	23/2/10	BSS	H	Hampton & Richmond B.	167	D 1-1	Cleverley 44	21
32	2/3/10	BSS	H	Bromley	168	D 3-3	Burnell 2 (4, 70), R Evans 61	21
33	6/3/10	BSS	H	Maidenhead United	207	L 1-4	Burnell pen 9	21
34	13/3/10	BSS	H	Chelmsford City	225	L 1-2	Clarke 31	21
35	20/3/10	BSS	A	Dorchester Town	425	L 2-4	Klein-Davies 44, Fortune 62	21
36	27/3/10	BSS	H	Havant & Waterlooville	215	L 1-2	Klein-Davies 75	21
37	3/4/10	BSS	A	Weymouth	502	W 2-1	Clarke 2 (78, 88)	21
38	6/4/10	BSS	H	Newport County	810	L 1-4	J Harris 55	21
39	10/4/10	BSS	A	Hampton & Richmond B.	344	L 1-2	Clarke 51	21
40	13/4/10	BSS	A	Havant & Waterlooville	796	L 0-6		21
41	17/4/10	BSS	H	Welling United	201	L 1-2	Cleverley 56	21
42	24/4/10	BSS	A	Bishops Stortford	401	L 0-3		21
	Cups							
1	26/9/09	FAC 2Q	H	Havant & Waterlooville	298	L 0-1		
2	21/11/09	FAT 3Q	H	Carshalton Athletic	199	D 1-1	Fortune 87	
3	24/11/09	FAT 3QR	A	Carshalton Athletic	214	L 1-3	Compton 70	

Home Attendances:

Highest:	810 v Newport County
Lowest:	150 v Thurrock
Average (08-09):	225 (339)
Top Goalscorer:	Gilroy - 7 (7 League, 0 Cup) in 6 appearances - 116% strike rate
Most Appearances:	Sawyer - 44 (42 League, 2 Cup)

SAWYER	GREEN	PARRINELLO	A HARRIS	RAND	FORTUNE	WELLS	MULLINGS	LLEWELLYN	HOLGATE	BARTLETT	COMPTON	JEANNE	MCGREGOR	BROWN	KLEIN-DAVIES	LABORIEUX	GURNEY	BEST	T EVANS	DAYLE GRUBB	HODREIN	J EVANS	PURNELL	JOYCE	STEARN	GILROY	CLEVERLEY	HART	FARMER	SHEPHARD	OSMAN	J HARRIS	CLARKE	DEAN GRUBB	FORD	R EVANS	NORTHMORE	BURNELL	MAWFORD	GARDNER	
X	X	X	X	X	X	X	X	X	X	X	S	S	S	U	U																										1
X		X	X	X	X	S	X	X	X	X	X	U	S	S	X	U																									2
X		X	X	X	X	U	X	S	X	X	X	S	X	X	U	U																									3
X	X		X	X		S	X	S	X	X	X	U	X	X	S	X	U																								4
X	X	S	X			S	X	X	X	X	X		X	X	S	X	U	U																							5
X	X	X	X	X	X	U	X	X	X	S	X		S	X	S				U																						6
X	X	X	X	X	X	S	X	X	X	S	X		S	X				U	U																						7
X	X	X	X	X	X	S	X	X	X	X	S		S	X			U		U																						8
X	X	X	X	X		U	X	S	X	X	X		X	S			U		X	U																					9
X	X	X	X	X	X	S	X	S	X	X	X		X	S				U	U																						10
X	X	X	X	X	X	S	X	X	X	X	X			S					S	U																					11
X	X	X	X		X	S	X	S	X	X	X		U	U					X					X	S																12
X	X	X	X	X	X	X	U			X	X			U	U				S	S				X		X															13
X	X	X	X	X	U	X	S			X	X			U	S				X	U				X		X															14
X	X	X	X	X	X	X	S			X	X			U	S				U	S				X		X															15
X	X	X		X	X	U	X			X	X				S		U		U	S				X		X	X														16
X	X	X	X	X	X		X			U	X				S				U	U				X		X	X	U													17
X	X		X	X	X	U	U			X	X				U				X	U				X		X	X	U													18
X	X	S	X		X	S	U			X	X			X	U				X	X							X	X		U											19
X	X			S	X	U	X			X				X	S				X	X							X	X		X	U	U									20
X	X			X	X	U	X			X				X	S					S							X	X		X	X	S									21
X	X			X	X	X	X			X				S	X				S								X	X		S	U	U	X								22
X	X		X	X	X		U			X				S	X				X	U							X	X		U		U	X								23
X		U		X	X		X			X					X				X	S		X					X	X				U	X	S	U						24
X	X	X		X	X		U			X					S				S	S				X			X						X	X	U	X					25
X	X	X		X			X								X		S		X	X							X	U				S	X	X	S		U				26
X	X	X		X			X								X		U										X	U				S	X	X	X	X	U				27
X	X	X					X								X		U										X	X				S	S	X	X	X		X			28
X	X	X					X								X		S										X	X				U	X	S	X	X	U	X			29
X	X	X			S		X										S				U			S			X	X				U	X	X	X	X		X			30
X	X	X		X	U		X										U			S				U			X	X				U	X	X		X		X			31
X	X	X		X	U		X													S				S			X	X				U	X	X	U	X		X			32
X	X	X		X	U		X								S					S				S			X	X					X	X	U	X		X			33
X	X	X		X	X		X								S					U				U			X	X					X	X	S	S		X			34
X		X		X	X		X								X				X	S				U			X	S					X	U	X	X		S			35
X		X		X	X		X								X		U		X	X							X	X					S		S	X	U	S			36
X	X	X		X	X		X												X	S							X	X				S	X		S			X	U	U	37
X	X			X	X		X										U		X	X	U						X	X				S	X		S			S	X		38
X	X			X	X		X								S		U		X	X	S						X		U			X	X		X				S		39
X	X			X	X		X								X		X		X	X							X					S			X		U		S	S	40
X	X			X	U		X								S				U	X		S					X	X	X			X			S				X	X	41
X		S		X	U		X								S				X	X	S	U					X	X	X			X							X	X	42
X	X	X		X		X	X	S	S	X	X		X	X					X	S	U	U	U																		1
X	X	U	X	X	X	S	X			X	X				X				X	X								S	U												2
	X		X	X	X	U	X			X	X				X				X	X			X					S	S												3

Total League Appearances

SAWYER	GREEN	PARRINELLO	A HARRIS	RAND	FORTUNE	WELLS	MULLINGS	LLEWELLYN	HOLGATE	BARTLETT	COMPTON	JEANNE	MCGREGOR	BROWN	KLEIN-DAVIES	LABORIEUX	GURNEY	BEST	T EVANS	DAYLE GRUBB	HODREIN	J EVANS	PURNELL	JOYCE	STEARN	GILROY	CLEVERLEY	HART	FARMER	SHEPHARD	OSMAN	J HARRIS	CLARKE	DEAN GRUBB	FORD	R EVANS	NORTHMORE	BURNELL	MAWFORD	GARDNER	
42	36	28	19	35	28	5	35	7	12	22	17	0	5	9	11	2	1	0	16	9	0	1	0	8	0	6	27	18	2	2	1	3	16	9	7	10	0	8	3	2	X
0	0	3	0	1	1	9	2	5	0	2	2	2	5	6	15	0	3	0	4	11	2	1	0	3	1	0	0	1	0	1	0	7	2	2	6	1	0	3	2	1	S
0	0	1	0	0	6	7	5	0	0	1	0	2	1	5	5	2	11	3	8	7	2	1	0	3	0	0	0	4	1	2	2	8	0	1	4	0	5	0	1	1	U

Total Cup Appearances

SAWYER	GREEN	PARRINELLO	A HARRIS	RAND	FORTUNE	WELLS	MULLINGS	LLEWELLYN	HOLGATE	BARTLETT	COMPTON	JEANNE	MCGREGOR	BROWN	KLEIN-DAVIES	LABORIEUX	GURNEY	BEST	T EVANS	DAYLE GRUBB	HODREIN	J EVANS	PURNELL	JOYCE	STEARN	GILROY	CLEVERLEY	HART	FARMER	SHEPHARD	OSMAN	J HARRIS	CLARKE	DEAN GRUBB	FORD	R EVANS	NORTHMORE	BURNELL	MAWFORD	GARDNER	
2	3	1	2	3	2	1	3	0	0	3	3	0	1	1	2	0	0	0	3	2	0	0	1	0	0	0	0	0	0	0	0	0	0	0	0	0	0	0	0	0	X
0	0	0	0	0	0	1	0	1	1	0	0	0	0	0	0	0	0	0	0	1	0	0	0	0	0	0	0	2	1	0	0	0	0	0	0	0	0	0	0	0	S
0	0	1	0	0	0	1	0	0	0	0	0	0	0	0	0	0	0	0	0	0	1	1	1	0	0	0	0	0	1	0	0	0	0	0	0	0	0	0	0	0	U

Total Goals

SAWYER	GREEN	PARRINELLO	A HARRIS	RAND	FORTUNE	WELLS	MULLINGS	LLEWELLYN	HOLGATE	BARTLETT	COMPTON	JEANNE	MCGREGOR	BROWN	KLEIN-DAVIES	LABORIEUX	GURNEY	BEST	T EVANS	DAYLE GRUBB	HODREIN	J EVANS	PURNELL	JOYCE	STEARN	GILROY	CLEVERLEY	HART	FARMER	SHEPHARD	OSMAN	J HARRIS	CLARKE	DEAN GRUBB	FORD	R EVANS	NORTHMORE	BURNELL	MAWFORD	GARDNER	
0	0	0	1	0	3	0	4	1	3	0	3	0	4	0	3	0	1	0	0	0	0	0	0	1	0	7	5	0	0	0	0	0	4	0	0	1	0	3	0	0	Lge
0	0	0	0	0	1	0	0	0	0	0	1	0	0	0	0	0	0	0	0	0	0	0	0	0	0	0	0	0	0	0	0	0	0	0	0	0	0	0	0	0	Cup

WESTON-SUPER-MARE

CURRENT SQUAD AS OF BEGINING OF 2010-11 SEASON

GOALKEEPERS	HT	WT	D.O.B	AGE	P.O.B	CAREER	Apps	Gls
Lloyd Irish						Yeovil Rel 10/09, Chard T (Dual) c/s 07, Taunton (Dual) c/s 08, Bridgwater, Weston-Super-Mare 7/10		
DEFENDERS								
Rhys Farmer			25/3/91	19		Weston-Super-Mare	2	0
Jamie Laird			18/6/89	21		Plymouth (Yth) Rel c/s 07, Ange IF (Swe), Bridgwater 10/07, Teramo Calcio (Ita) (Trial) 11/07, Bath C NC 4/08 Rel c/s 08, Bridgwater 11/08, Weston-Super-Mare 7/10		
Craig Rand	6'01"	11 00	24/6/82	28	Bishop Auckland	Sheff Wed, Whitby 3/02, Stocksbridge PS 12/02, Spennymoor 5/03, Thornaby 10/03, Durham 8/04, Team Bath 10/05, Weston-Super-Mare 11/05	36	0
MIDFIELDERS								
Jack Durrant	6'00"	11 03	6/5/91	19	Bristol	Cheltenham Rel c/s 10, Mangotsfield (L) 11/08, Worcester (L) 2/10, Weston-Super-Mare 7/10		
Mason Gardner			7/12/90	19		Weston-Super-Mare	3	0
Scott Gilbert						Larkhall, Chippenham, Bath C, Almondsbury T, Weston-Super-Mare 7/10		
Dayle Grubb			24/7/91	19		Weston-Super-Mare	20	0
Dean Grubb	5'09"	11 11	4/10/87	22	Weston-Super-Mare	Bristol C Rel c/s 07, Weston-Super-Mare 8/07, Gloucester 3/09, Weymouth 5/09 Rel 8/09, Tiverton (Trial) 8/09, Newport C 9/09 Rel 9/09, Cheddar FC, Wellington FC, Weston-Super-Mare 12/09	11	0
Kane Ingram						Bristol C (Yth), Bath C, Almondsbury T, Paulton 10/09, Cinderford 1/10, Weston-Super-Mare 7/10		
Ben Kirk			30/9/84	25		Bridgwater, Chippenham 8/04, Weston-Super-Mare 6/06, Bridgwater Undisc 8/06, Weston-Super-Mare 7/10		
Jake Mawford			7/6/93	17		Weston-Super-Mare	5	0
Steve Orchard			18/2/85	25		Weymouth, Bideford 7/04, Bridgwater, Weston-Super-Mare 7/10		
Danny Wring	5'10"	10 03	26/10/86	23	Portishead	Bristol C Rel c/s 07, Torquay 8/07 Rel 1/08, Team Bath 1/08, Newport C 8/08, Mangotsfield 8/08, Clevedon T 11/08 Rel 1/10, Chippenham 1/10, Weston-Super-Mare 7/10		
FORWARDS								
Marcus Duharty			22/2/86	24		Cadbury Heath, Mangotsfield 9/08, Bridgwater T 1/09, Weston-Super-Mare 7/10		
Sahr Kabba						Bristol R (Yth), Almondsbury T, Weston-Super-Mare 7/10		
Graham Mercieca			11/9/89	20		Bishops Lydeard, Bridgwater 7/08, Weston-Super-Mare 7/10		

Loanees	HT	WT	DOB	AGE	POB	From - To	APPS	GOA
(F)Ben Joyce	5'08"	11 04	9/9/89	20	Plymouth	Torquay 10/09 - Forest Green (L) 11/09, Weston-Super-Mare (SL) 1/10, Rel 5/10	11	1
(F)Dave Gilroy	5'11"	11 05	23/12/82	27	Yeovil	Newport C 10/09 - Rel 5/10, Woking 6/10	6	7
(M)Chris Shephard	6'03"	13 03	25/12/88	21	Exeter	Exeter 11/09 - Salisbury (L) 3/10	3	0
(M)Richard Evans	5'09"	11 08	19/6/83	27	Cardiff	Bath C (3ML) 1/10 - Rel 5/10, Haverfordwest 6/10	11	1
(F)Danny Burnell			8/3/88	22		Chesham (2ML) 2/10 - Wealdstone 6/10	11	3
Departures	**HT**	**WT**	**DOB**	**AGE**	**POB**	**From - To**		
(M)Mark McKeever	5'11"	11 08	16/11/78	31	Derry	Bath C 3/08 - Retired 8/09		
(M)Leon Jeanne	5'08"	11 01	17/11/80	29	Cardiff	Carpenter Arms 7/09 - Rel 9/09, Maesteg Park (L) 8/09	2	0
(D)Eric Laborieux			24/7/84	26		Fairford T 8/09 - Frome T 10/09	2	0
(F)Ashan Holgate	6'02"	12 00	9/11/86	23	Swindon	Eastleigh 3/08 - Newport C 10/09 Rel 1/10, Swindon Supermarine 3/10	12	3
(F)Josh Llewellyn			27/4/87	23		Team Bath 5/09 - Weymouth 10/09 Rel 3/10, Dorchester 3/10	12	1
(F)Marc McGregor	5'09"	11 10	30/4/78	32	Southend	Hinckley U 5/06 - Worcester 10/09	10	4
(F)Ross Stearn	5'06"	10 07	17/9/90	19	Bristol	Forest Green 9/09 - Almonsbury T 10/09	1	0
(M)Jack Compton	5'08"	10 07	2/9/88	21	Portsmouth	Havant & W 2/09 - Falkirk Undisc 1/10	19	3
(M)Adie Harris			21/2/81	29		Newport C 4 fig 1/09 - Rel 1/10, Bath C 1/10	19	1
(D)Charlie Comyn-Platt	6'02"	12 00	2/10/85	24	Manchester	ECU Joondalup (Aust) 12/09 - Australia 1/10		
(M)Ben Osman	5'10"	10 13	24/9/90	19	Southampton	ex Salisbury 12/09 - Forest Green Rovers 1/10, Frome T 2/10	1	0
(F)Marvin Brown	5'09"	11 01	16/7/83	27	Bristol	Salisbury 7/08 - Rel 1/10, Worcester (L) 10/09, Turo C 1/10	15	0
(D)Scott Bartlett			30/5/79	31	Salisbury	Salisbury 2/09 - Bath C 2/10 Rel 6/10, Forest Green 6/10	24	0
(M)Andy Gurney	5'10"	11 06	25/1/74	36	Bristol	Newport C (Pl/Ass Man) 5/08 Manager - Rel 4/10	4	1
(D)Mike Green	5'09"	11 04	18/12/84	25	Gloucester	Bath C 12/07 - Gloucester 6/10	36	0
(M)Ben Cleverley			12/9/81	28		Tiverton 10/09 - Paulton 6/10	27	5
(G)Kevin Sawyer			14/4/80	30	Swindon	Gloucester 5/09 - Gloucester 6/10	42	0
(D)Tomaso Parrinello			10/7/89	21		Bristol R (2ML) 12/08 Perm 2/09 - Gloucester 6/10	31	0
(M)Ben Wells	5'09"	10 07	26/3/88	22	Basingstoke	Basingstoke 7/08 - Swindon Supermarine 6/10	14	0
(M)Darren Mullings	6'01"	12 00	3/3/87	23	Bristol	Torquay 8/08 - Gloucester 7/10	37	4
(G)Ryan Northmore	6'01"	13 01	5/9/80	29	Plymouth	Dorchester 2/10 -	0	0
(G)Luke Purnell			1/6/90	20		Weston St Johns -	0	0
(D)Josh Evans			1/9/90	19		Yth -	2	0
(D)Tom Evans	6'01"	12 00	20/6/90	20	Surrey	Swindon 8/09 -	20	0
(D)Clayton Fortune	6'03"	13 10	10/11/82	27	Forest Gate	Darlington 7/09 -	29	3
(D)Josh Ford			28/6/90	20	Bristol	Tiverton 1/10 -	13	0
(D)Callum Hart	6'00"	11 00	21/12/85	24	Cardiff	Bath C 10/09 -	19	0
(F)Reeko Best			13/7/92	18		Bristol R -	0	0
(F)Jermaine Clarke			10/12/83	26		Evesham 12/09 -	18	4
(F)Jake Harris			28/10/90	19		Yth -	10	0
(F)Ryan Hodrein			4/9/91	18		Yth -	2	0
(F)Josh Klein-Davies	5'11"	13 09	6/7/89	21	Bristol	Weymouth 10/09 -	26	3

WOKING

Chairman: Shahid Azeem
Secretary: Derek Powell (T) 01483 772 470
(E) derek.powell@wokingfc.co.uk
Additional Committee Members:
Peter Jordan, David Taylor, Jane Spong, Peter Sheppard, Barry Hitchcock
Manager: Graham Baker
Programme Editor: Jane Spong/Martin Townsend (E) programme@wokingfc.co.uk

Club Factfile

Founded: 1889 **Nickname:** The Cards
Previous Names: None
Previous Leagues: Isthmian 1911-92

Club Colours (change): Red and white/black/white (All yellow)

Ground: Kingfield Stadium, Kingfield Road, Woking, Surrey GU22 9AA (T) 01483 772 470
Capacity: 6,000 **Seats:** 2,500 **Covered:** 3,900 **Clubhouse:** Yes **Shop:** Yes
Previous Grounds: Wheatsheaf, Ive Lane (pre 1923)
Simple Directions
Exit M25 Junction 10 and follow A3 towards Guildford. Leave at next junction onto B2215 through Ripley and join A247 to Woking. Alternatively exit M25 junction 11 and follow A320 to Woking Town Centre. The ground is on the outskirts of Woking opposite the Leisure Centre.

Record Attendance: 6,000 v Swansea City - FA Cup 1978-79 and v Coventry City - FA Cup 1996-97
Record Victory: 17-4 v Farnham - 1912-13
Record Defeat: 0-16 v New Crusaders - 1905-06
Record Goalscorer: Charlie Mortimore - 331 (1953-65)
Record Appearances: Brian Finn - 564 (1962-74)
Additional Records: Paid £60,000 to Crystal Palace for Chris Sharpling
Received £150,000 from Bristol Rovers for Steve Foster

Senior Honours: Surrey Senior Cup 1912-13, 26-27, 55-56, 56-57, 71-72, 90-91, 93-94, 95-96, 99-2000, 2003-04. FA Amateur Cup 1957-58.
Isthmian League Cup 1990-91, Premier Division 1991-92. FA Trophy 1993-94, 94-95, 96-97.
Vauxhall Championship Shield 1994-95. GLS Conference Cup 2004-05.

10 YEAR RECORD

00-01	01-02	02-03	03-04	04-05	05-06	06-07	07-08	08-09	09-10
Conf 14	Conf 19	Conf 19	Conf 9	Conf 8	Conf 11	Conf 15	Conf 17	Conf 21	Conf S 5

WOKING

No.	Date	Comp	H/A	Opponents	Att:	Result	Goalscorers	Pos
1	8/8/09	BSS	A	Welling United	844	W 2-1	Thomas 76, Sole pen 80	5
2	11/8/09	BSS	H	Chelmsford City	1508	L 1-2	Medley 23	11
3	15/8/09	BSS	H	Worcester City	1120	W 1-0	Ademola 62	9
4	18/8/09	BSS	A	Weston-Super-Mare	319	D 1-1	Arter 80	9
5	22/8/09	BSS	H	Bishops Stortford	1090	W 1-0	Sole pen 83	6
6	29/8/09	BSS	A	Lewes	675	W 2-0	Anane 44, Moone 90	3
7	31/8/09	BSS	H	Eastleigh	1461	D 0-0		6
8	5/9/09	BSS	A	Hampton & Richmond B.	958	W 2-0	Sloma 25, Sam-Yorke 56	5
9	8/9/09	BSS	A	Basingstoke Town	942	W 2-1	Sam-Yorke 4, Ademola 51	2
10	12/9/09	BSS	H	Maidenhead United	1427	D 1-1	Medley 12	3
11	19/9/09	BSS	H	Newport County	1862	L 0-1		4
12	3/10/09	BSS	A	Chelmsford City	1282	W 2-0	Domoraud 37, Sloma 70	4
13	17/10/09	BSS	A	Bromley	710	L 1-3	Arter 56	5
14	27/10/09	BSS	A	Dover Athletic	1218	W 2-0	Sole 2 (pen 33, 67)	4
15	31/10/09	BSS	H	Braintree Town	1418	D 0-0		4
16	10/11/09	BSS	H	St Albans City	1008	L 0-1		4
17	17/11/09	BSS	A	Weymouth	544	D 0-0		4
18	28/11/09	BSS	H	Dorchester Town	1269	W 3-1	Ademola 44, Arter 76, Pinney 81	3
19	1/12/09	BSS	A	Bath City	447	L 0-5		3
20	5/12/09	BSS	A	Bishops Stortford	507	W 3-0	Wright 32, Ademola 65, Sole pen 73	3
21	19/12/09	BSS	H	Bath City	1190	L 1-3	Ricketts 67	4
22	26/12/09	BSS	A	Havant & Waterlooville	1007	D 1-1	Sole pen 64	4
23	28/12/09	BSS	H	Weston-Super-Mare	1299	W 2-1	Wright 2 (2, 75)	3
24	1/1/10	BSS	H	Havant & Waterlooville	1703	W 2-0	Wright 13, Sole 60	2
25	23/1/10	BSS	H	Dover Athletic	1437	W 2-0	Thomas 35, Sam-Yorke 85	2
26	30/1/10	BSS	A	Braintree Town	654	L 0-1		2
27	6/2/10	BSS	H	Thurrock	1366	L 0-1		4
28	13/2/10	BSS	A	Worcester City	607	L 2-3	Pinney 10, Sole 17	8
29	20/2/10	BSS	H	Welling United	1217	L 0-5		8
30	27/2/10	BSS	A	Dorchester Town	536	D 1-1	Pinney 83	10
31	6/3/10	BSS	H	Staines Town	1419	D 0-0		12
32	13/3/10	BSS	A	Staines Town	962	L 0-3		13
33	16/3/10	BSS	A	Thurrock	257	D 2-2	Faulconbridge 17, Arter 58	13
34	20/3/10	BSS	H	Basingstoke Town	958	W 4-2	Faulconbridge 1, Sole 2 (45, 79), Pinney 60	12
35	23/3/10	BSS	H	Hampton & Richmond B.	803	W 3-1	Faulconbridge 38, Moone 75, Pinney 89	9
36	27/3/10	BSS	A	Newport County	1742	L 0-1		10
37	3/4/10	BSS	H	Lewes	1128	W 2-0	Faulconbridge 2 (20, 60)	9
38	5/4/10	BSS	A	Eastleigh	668	W 2-0	Sole 41, Pinney pen 77	8
39	10/4/10	BSS	H	Bromley	1216	W 2-1	Sole 18, Ricketts 75	7
40	13/4/10	BSS	A	Maidenhead United	510	W 2-1	Og (Baddeley) 74, Sole pen 82	5
41	17/4/10	BSS	A	St Albans City	752	W 1-0	Arter 44	5
42	24/4/10	BSS	H	Weymouth	2137	W 4-0	Faulconbridge 4, Sole 13, Nicolau 77, Ademola 90	5
	Cups							
1	26/9/09	FAC 2Q	A	Hythe Town	557	D 2-2	Anane 71, Sole pen 78	
2	29/9/09	FAC 2QR	H	Hythe Town	761	W 5-1	Sole 2 (pen 10, 49), Sogbanmu 2 (82, 85), Sloma 90	
3	10/10/09	FAC 3Q	H	Maidstone United	1434	W 2-0	Domoraud 9, Medley 90	
4	24/10/09	FAC 4Q	A	Hendon	528	W 5-0	Sole 2 (2, 20), Arter 3 (45, 48, 85)	
5	7/11/09	FAC 1	A	Swindon Town	4805	L 0-1		
6	21/11/09	FAT 3Q	H	St Albans City	823	W 6-0	Og 2 (Quilter 19, Frater 61), Ademola 44, Anane 46, Arter 67, Sole 90	
7	12/12/09	FAT 1	H	Forest Green Rovers	956	W 1-0	Pinney 15	
8	19/1/10	FAT 2	A	Oxford United	1581	L 0-1		
9	27/4/10	PO SF1	H	Dover Athletic	3080	W 2-1	Ademola 17, Wright 40	
10	1/5/10	PO SF2	A	Dover Athletic	2970	D 0-0	(W 2-1 agg)	
11	9/5/10	PO Final	A	Bath City	4865	L 0-1		

Home Attendances:	
Highest:	2137 v Weymouth
Lowest:	803 v Hampton & Richmond Borough
Average (08-09):	1299 (1728)
Top Goalscorer:	Sole - 20 (14 League, 6 Cup) in 50 appearances - 40% strike rate
Most Appearances:	Worner - 51 (41 League, 10 Cup)

WORNER	ANANE	THOMAS	RICKETTS	SINTIM	SINCLAIR	MEDLEY	ARTER	ADEMOLA	SOLE	SLOMA	SAM-YORKE	HUSSEY	MOONE	PEGLER	MCNERNEY	HUTCHINSON	WATKINS	MALEDON	NICOLAU	ONIBUJE	BLACKMORE	HAND	COUSINS	SOGBANMU	DOMORAUD	BOARDMAN	CARR	TOPHAM	BRYANT	BENJAMIN	WRIGHT	PINNEY	SLABBER	TUNA	FAULCONBRIDGE	
X	X	X	X	X	X	X	X	X	X	X	S	S	S	U	U																					1
X	X	X	X	U	X	X	X	X	X	X	S		S	U	S	X																				2
X	X	X	X	U	X	X	X	X	X	X	S		U			X	S	U																		3
X	X	X	X	S	X	S	X	X	X	X	S	U		U		X	X																			4
X	X		X	U	X	X	X	X	X	X	S		U		U	X	X	S																		5
X	X	X	X	U	X	S	X	X	X	X	S		S	U		X	X																			6
X	X	X	X	U	X	S	X	X	X	X	S		S	U		X	X																			7
X	X	X	X	U	X	S	X	X	S	X	X		S		U	X	X																			8
X	X	X	X	U	X	X	X	X	S	X	X		U	S	S	X																				9
X	X		X	U	X	X	X	X	X	X	X		S	U	S	X	S																			10
X	X		X		X	S	X	X	U	X	X			U	S	X	X		X	S																11
X	X	X	X	U					X	X				U	X	X	X	S		S		X		S	X											12
X	X	X	X		X	S	X		U	X	S				U	X	X		S			X			X											13
X	X	X	X		U	S	X		X	S	X				U	X		S	X			X				X										14
X	X	X	X		S	U	X		X	S	X					X		U	X			X				X			S							15
X	X	X	U		X	X	S	S	S	X						X		X	U			X				X			X							16
X	X		X	U	X	S	X	X	X	X	X		S						X			U				X			S							17
X	X	U	X		X		X	X	X	U						X			X			X							S	X	S	S				18
X	X	S	X		X		X	X	X	U						X			X			X				U				X	S	S				19
X		X	X		X	S	X	X	X	S			U		S	X						U				X					X	X				20
X	S	X	X		X	S	X	X	X	S				U		X			U							X					X	X				21
X	S	X	X		X	S	X	X	X		U					X			U			X				X					X	S				22
X	S	X	X		X	U	X	X	X	S	U					X		S								X					X	X				23
X	U	X	X		X	S	X	X	X	S						X		U								X					X	X	S			24
X	U	X	X		X		X	X	X	S	S				U	X		S	X							X					X					25
X	U	X	X		X		X	X	X	U	S					X		S	X							X					X		S			26
X	S	X			X		X	S	X		S	U			U	X		X	X							X					X		X			27
X	S	X			X		X	X	X	U	S					X		X	U			U				X					X	X				28
X	X	X	X		X			X	X		U				S	X		S	U			X									X	X		S		29
X		X	X		X			S	X	X	X				U	X		U	U			X				X					S	X				30
-	X	X		X		X	U	U	X	S			X		X			U			X				X					X	X		S			31
X	U	X	X		X		X	U	S	X						X			S			X				X					X	X			S	32
X	X	X	X		X		X	X	X			U	U			X		S	S							X						S			X	33
X	X	X	X	X	X		X	X	X			U	S			X		S	U													S			X	34
X	X	X	X	X	X		X	X	X			U	S			X		S	U													S			X	35
X	X	X	X	U	X			X	X			S		U		X		X	S												S	X			X	36
X	X	X			X			X	X			U	S			X		X	X							S					S	X			X	37
X	X	X			X		S	X	X				U	U		X		X	X							S					S	X			X	38
X	X	X	S		X		X	X	X				S	U		X		X	X							U					S				X	39
X	X	X	X		X		S	X	X			U	U			X		X	S							X					S				X	40
X	X	X	X		X		X	X	X			U	U		S	X			X							U					S				X	41
X	X	X	X		X			X	X		S		S		U	X		S	X							U					X				X	42

WORNER	ANANE	THOMAS	RICKETTS	SINTIM	SINCLAIR	MEDLEY	ARTER	ADEMOLA	SOLE	SLOMA	SAM-YORKE	HUSSEY	MOONE	PEGLER	MCNERNEY	HUTCHINSON	WATKINS	MALEDON	NICOLAU	ONIBUJE	BLACKMORE	HAND	COUSINS	SOGBANMU	DOMORAUD	BOARDMAN	CARR	TOPHAM	BRYANT	BENJAMIN	WRIGHT	PINNEY	SLABBER	TUNA	FAULCONBRIDGE	
	X		X	X			S	X	X	X	S			U	X	X	S	U		X	X	X														1
X	X	U	X	U			X		X	X	X			U	X	X	X	U		X		S	S	S												2
X	X	X	S	U		S	X		X	X	U			U	X	X	X	U	S			X			X											3
X	X	X	X			S	X		X	S	X			U	S	X		U	X			X				X	U	U								4
X	X	S	X		X	U	X	S	X	U	X			U		X		U	X			S				X			X							5
X	X	S	X		X	S	X	X	X	U				U		X			X			X							S	X						6
X	S	X	X		X	X	X	X	X	S						X			U			U		S		X						X				7
X	X	X	X		X		X	X	X	S	S			U	S			X	X							X										8
X	X	X	X		X			X	X				S	U	S	X		X	X							U					S				X	9
X	X	X	X		X			X	X				S	U	S	X		X	X							U					S				X	10
X	X	X	X		X			X	X				U	U	S	X		X	X							U					S				X	11

Total League Appearances

WORNER	ANANE	THOMAS	RICKETTS	SINTIM	SINCLAIR	MEDLEY	ARTER	ADEMOLA	SOLE	SLOMA	SAM-YORKE	HUSSEY	MOONE	PEGLER	MCNERNEY	HUTCHINSON	WATKINS	MALEDON	NICOLAU	ONIBUJE	BLACKMORE	HAND	COUSINS	SOGBANMU	DOMORAUD	BOARDMAN	CARR	TOPHAM	BRYANT	BENJAMIN	WRIGHT	PINNEY	SLABBER	TUNA	FAULCONBRIDGE	
41	30	36	36	3	39	7	33	33	35	18	8	0	0	1	1	40	8	8	14	0	0	12	0	0	2	18	0	0	1	2	13	12	1	0	10	X
0	5	1	1	1	1	12	3	3	4	7	14	2	12	1	7	0	2	11	5	2	0	0	0	1	0	2	0	0	3	0	9	6	2	2	1	S
0	4	1	1	11	1	2	0	2	3	4	3	8	8	12	9	0	0	4	9	0	0	3	0	0	0	4	0	0	0	0	0	0	0	0	0	U

Total Cup Appearances

WORNER	ANANE	THOMAS	RICKETTS	SINTIM	SINCLAIR	MEDLEY	ARTER	ADEMOLA	SOLE	SLOMA	SAM-YORKE	HUSSEY	MOONE	PEGLER	MCNERNEY	HUTCHINSON	WATKINS	MALEDON	NICOLAU	ONIBUJE	BLACKMORE	HAND	COUSINS	SOGBANMU	DOMORAUD	BOARDMAN	CARR	TOPHAM	BRYANT	BENJAMIN	WRIGHT	PINNEY	SLABBER	TUNA	FAULCONBRIDGE	
10	10	7	10	1	7	1	7	7	11	3	3	0	0	0	3	10	2	4	7	2	1	4	0	0	1	4	0	0	1	1	0	1	0	0	3	X
0	1	2	1	0	0	3	1	1	0	3	2	0	2	0	5	0	1	0	1	0	0	2	1	2	0	0	0	0	1	0	3	0	0	0	0	S
0	0	1	0	2	0	1	0	0	0	2	1	0	1	10	0	0	0	5	1	0	0	1	0	0	0	3	1	1	0	0	0	0	0	0	0	U

Total Goals

WORNER	ANANE	THOMAS	RICKETTS	SINTIM	SINCLAIR	MEDLEY	ARTER	ADEMOLA	SOLE	SLOMA	SAM-YORKE	HUSSEY	MOONE	PEGLER	MCNERNEY	HUTCHINSON	WATKINS	MALEDON	NICOLAU	ONIBUJE	BLACKMORE	HAND	COUSINS	SOGBANMU	DOMORAUD	BOARDMAN	CARR	TOPHAM	BRYANT	BENJAMIN	WRIGHT	PINNEY	SLABBER	TUNA	FAULCONBRIDGE	
0	1	2	2	0	0	2	5	5	14	2	3	0	2	0	0	0	0	0	1	0	0	0	0	0	1	0	0	0	0	0	4	6	0	0	6	Lge
0	2	0	0	0	0	1	4	2	6	1	0	0	0	0	0	0	0	0	0	0	0	0	0	2	1	0	0	0	0	0	1	1	0	0	0	Cup

WOKING

CURRENT SQUAD AS OF BEGINING OF 2010-11 SEASON

GOALKEEPERS	HT	WT	D.O.B	AGE	P.O.B	CAREER	Apps	Gls
Matt Pegler			12/8/91	19		Aldershot (Yth), Woking c/s 09	2	0
Ross Worner			3/10/89	20		Woking	41	0
DEFENDERS								
Ricky Anane	5'08"	11 02	18/2/89	20	Manchester	Bradford C (Yth), Bury Rel c/s 09, Workington (L) 2/09, Fleetwood (SL) 3/09, Woking 7/09	35	1
Luke Baker			2/2/90	20		Woking		
Joseph McNerney			24/1/90	20		Woking, Corinthian Casuals (L) 10/09	8	0
Nicky Nicolau	5'08"	10 03	12/10/83	26	Camden	Arsenal, Southend (SL) 3/04, Southend 5/04 Rel c/s 05, Swindon 7/05 Rel 5/06, Hereford (3ML) 1/06, Barnet 7/06 Rel c/s 08, Weymouth (Trial) 7/08, Brighton (Trial) 7/08, Grimsby (Trial) 8/08, Barnet 9/08 Rel c/s 09, Maidenhead 8/09, Woking 9/09	19	1
Daniel Sintim			19/5/91	18		Woking, Godalming T (2ML) 10/09, Croydon Ath (L) 1/10	4	0
Aswad Thomas	5'10"	11 06	9/8/89	20	Westminster	Charlton Rel c/s 09, Accrington (SL) 1/08, Barnet (L) 8/08, Lewes (3ML) 9/08, Woking 6/09	37	2
MIDFIELDERS								
Matt Ferdinando			10/8/90	20		Woking		
Sam Hurrell			13/7/88	21	Hillingdon	North Greenford, Chelsea Rel c/s 07, L.Orient (Trial), Bradford C (Trial), Chelsea (Youngsters Coach) 2/08, St Albans 10/08, Welling 2/09, Woking 5/10		
Alan Inns			5/6/82	27	Reading	Oxford C (Jun), Wokingham, Hampton & R 9/02, AFC Wimbledon 5/08 Rel 4/10, Woking 5/10		
Jerome Maledon			24/2/88	21		Woking Rel 8/08, Basingstoke (L) 3/06, Carshalton (SL) 1/07, Basingstoke 10/08, Woking 6/09, Cray W (L) 11/09	19	0
Matthew Powell			10/2/90	20		Woking		
Francis Quarm			1/8/83	26		Dulwich H (Yth), Tooting & M (Yth), Dulwich H 7/01, Hampton & R 7/05, Basingstoke 7/06, Hampton & R 12/06 Rel 1/10, Windsor & E (Dual) 9/07, Sutton U 1/10, Woking 5/10		
Mark Ricketts	6'00"	11 02	7/10/84	24	Sidcup	Charlton Rel c/s 06, MK Dons (3ML) 11/05, Gravesend/Ebbsfleet 8/06, Woking 6/09	37	2
FORWARDS								
Moses Ademola	5'06"	10 08	18/7/89	20	Bermondsey	Cray W (Yth), Croydon A, Brentford Undisc 7/08, Welling (L) 11/08 Recalled 1 day, Welling (L) 12/08, Welling (2ML) 2/09, Woking (6ML) 7/09, Woking 1/10	36	5
Craig Faulconbridge	6'01"	13 00	20/4/78	32	Nuneaton	Coventry, Dunfermline (SL) 3/98, Dunfermline (3ML) 7/98, Hull C (3ML) 12/98, Wrexham 8/99, Wycombe 5/02 Rel c/s 05, Wingate & F 7/06, Oxford C 7/07, Carshalton 7/09, Woking 3/10	11	6
Andy Forbes			28/5/79	30	Reading	Reading, Basingstoke, Andover, Winchester 8/02, Eastleigh 8/04 Rel 5/10, Woking 5/10		
Dave Gilroy	5'11"	11 05	23/12/82	26	Yeovil	Bristol R Rel 1/04, Clevedon (L) 1/02, Bath C (6WL) 2/02, Forest Green (L) 8/03, Clevedon (L) 9/03, Weston-Super-Mare 1/04, Chippenham (L) 11/04, Chippenham £1,000 2/05, Bath C 5/07, Newport C 4/09 Rel 5/10, Weston-Super-Mare (L) 10/09, Bath C (6WL) 2/10, Woking 6/10		
Ola Sogbanmu			6/3/92	18		Woking	1	0
Rob Carr						Woking	0	0
Tom Topham						Woking	0	0

Loanees	HT	WT	DOB	AGE	POB	From - To	APPS	GOA
(M)Luke Medley	6'01"	13 03	21/6/89	20	Greenwich	Barnet (6ML) 7/09 - Havant & W (SL) 2/10	19	2
(F)Mitchell Bryant			22/11/90	19		Reading 10/09 - Basingstoke (L) 12/09	4	0
(F)Nathaniel Pinney	6'00"	12 05	16/11/90	19	South Norwood	C.Palace (5WL) 11/09, (2ML) 2/10 -	18	6
(F)Matthew Wright			13/4/91	19		C.Palace (5WL) 11/09, (SL) 1/10 -	22	4
(F)Tamer Tuna	5'08"	11 00	19/10/91	18	Bexley	Charlton 2/10 - Welling (L) 3/10	2	0
Departures	**HT**	**WT**	**DOB**	**AGE**	**POB**	**From - To**		
(G)David Blackmore	6'06"	13 00	23/3/89	20	Chelmsford	Thurrock NC 9/09 - Margate 10/09, Braintree 10/09	0	0
(F)Fola Onibuje	6'05"	14 09	25/9/84	25	Lagos, Ghana	ex Weymouth 9/09 - Rel 10/09, Grays 10/09 Rel 1/10, Southport 3/10	2	0
(F)Craig Watkins			4/5/86	23	Croydon	Havant & W 8/09 - Rel 10/09, Hayes & Yeading 11/09 Rel 5/10, Met Police 6/10	10	0
(F)Anson Cousins			22/11/91	18		Yth - Godalming (L) 11/09 Perm 11/09	0	0
(M)Harry Arter	5'09"	11 07	23/12/89	19	Sidcup	Charlton 6/09 - Bournemouth Undisc 5/10	36	5
(F)Giuseppe Sole			8/1/88	21		Yth - Newport C 5/10	39	14
(D)Tom Hutchinson	6'01"	12 06	23/2/82	27	Kingston	Dundee 1/06 - Rel 5/10	40	0
(D)Jon Boardman	6'02"	13 11	27/1/81	28	Reading	Dag & Red 6/09 - Rel 5/10, Kingstonian 6/10	20	0
(M)Jamie Hand	6'00"	11 08	7/2/84	25	Uxbridge	Chelmsford 9/09 - Rel 5/10, Hemel Hempstead (L) 3/10	12	0
(M)Billy Hussey			6/7/89	21		Yth - Rel 5/10	2	0
(M)Charlie Moone			14/11/88	20		Yth - Rel 5/10, Walton & H (L) 9/09	12	2
(F)Delano Sam-Yorke			20/1/89	20		Yth - Rel 5/10 Cray W (L) 11/09	22	3
(F)Jamie Slabber	6'02"	11 10	31/12/84	24	Enfield	Grays 12/09 - Rel 5/10, Eastleigh 5/10	3	0
(M)Sam Sloma	5'08"	11 06	29/10/82	26	London	Chelmsford 6/09 - Rel 5/10, AFC Hornchurch (L) 3/10, Wingate & Finchley 7/10	25	2
(D)Tony Sinclair			5/3/85	24		Welling 6/09 - Gillingham 7/10	40	0
(F)Trevor Benjamin	6'02"	13 07	8/2/79	30	Kettering	Harrogate T 11/09 -	2	0
(F)Wilfried Domoraud	6'00"	13 10	18/8/88	20	Maisons-Alfort (Fra)	ex Woking 10/09 -	2	1

Witton Albion's Stuart Rudd scores goal number three against Spalding. Photo: Keith Clayton

Another goal being scored, this time by Heler of Witton against Sheffield. Photo: Keith Clayton.

Pritchard's (Witton) overhead kick hits the crossbar and crosses the line, giving Sheffield's Walker, in goal, no chance. Photo: Keith Clayton.

WIN NEXT YEAR'S NON-LEAGUE CLUB DIRECTORY

(AND HAVE A BIT OF FUN AT THE SAME TIME!)

NON-LEAGUE CLUB DIRECTORY PREDICTION COMPETITION

This year we have decided to re-introduce a popular competition that was run by the Cherry Red Non-League Newsdesk Annual for a number of years.

Entrants predict the 2010-11 champions of the top competitions, and the contestant with the most correct tips is the champion and receives next year's Directory FREE. Could not be simpler!

To enter, list your prediction for the champions of all three divisions of each of the Blue Square Conference, Ryman Isthmian, Zamaretto Southern and the Evo-stik Northern Premier Leagues PLUS the top divisions of each of 14 feeder leagues: Baker Joiner Midland Alliance, Cherry Red Combined Counties League, Essex Senior League, Hereward United Counties League, Koolsport Northern Counties League, Molten Spartan South Midlands League, Ridgeons Eastern Counties League, Safety Net Kent League, Skilltraining Northern League, Sussex County League, Sydenhams Wessex League, Toolstation Western League, Uhlsport Hellenic League League, Vodkat Northern West Counties League.

Entries should be emailed to james.m.wright.t21@btinternet.com or posted to Prediction Competition, 6 Harp Chase, Taunton TA1 3RY.

Rules:

By entering you agree that..

1) All entries must be received BEFORE November 1st 2010.
2) The number of second (or even third or fourth) places will be used as a tie-breaker if necessary.
3) The contact details of all entrants will be stored electronically and may be used to publicise future competitions or products of TW Publications (under no circumstances will they ever be divulged to any third party).
4) Participants' names and scores may be published in the Non-League Club Directory 2012, or on the Directory's website.
5) In the unlikely event that the Non-League Club Directory is not published in 2011, the winner will be entitled to a cash prize equivalent to the cover price of the current edition.
6) In the event of any dispute, the decision of the publisher is final.

ENTRY IS FREE, SO GIVE IT A GO. GOOD LUCK!

President:

N White F.S.C.A.

Chairman:

M Harris

Vice Chairman:

K Brown

Secretary

& Press Officer:

P Bradley

7 Guest Road,

Prestwich,

Manchester M25 7DJ

Tel: 0161 798 5198

Fax: 0161 773 0930

NORTHERN PREMIER LEAGUE

Premier Division		P	W	D	L	F	A	GD	Pts
1	Guiseley	38	25	4	9	73	41	32	79
2	Bradford Park Avenue	38	24	6	8	94	51	43	78
3	Boston United	38	23	8	7	90	34	56	77
4	North Ferriby United	38	22	9	7	70	38	32	75
5	Kendal Town	38	21	8	9	75	47	28	71
6	Retford United	38	18	11	9	73	46	27	65
7	Matlock Town	38	17	9	12	72	49	23	60
8	Buxton	38	16	12	10	66	43	23	60
9	Marine	38	17	6	15	60	55	5	57
10	Nantwich Town	38	16	6	16	64	69	-5	54
11	Stocksbridge Park Steels	38	15	7	16	80	68	12	52
12	Ashton United	38	15	6	17	48	63	-15	51
13	FC United of Manchester	38	13	8	17	62	65	-3	47
14	Whitby Town	38	12	10	16	56	62	-6	46
15	Frickley Athletic	38	12	9	17	50	66	-16	45
16	Burscough	38	13	5	20	55	65	-10	44
17	Hucknall Town	38	12	8	18	65	81	-16	44
18	Worksop Town	38	7	9	22	45	68	-23	30
19	Ossett Town	38	6	7	25	46	92	-46	25
20	Durham City (-6)	38	2	0	36	27	168	-141	0
21	Kings Lynn - did not finish - results expunged.								
22	Newcastle Blue Star - did not start.								

PROMOTION PLAY-OFFS

SF **Bradford Park Avenue** 2 Kendal Town 1 26/04/10 Att: 608

SF **Boston United** 2 North Ferriby United 1 27/04/10 Att: 2165

F Bradford Park Avenue 1 **Boston United** 2 aet 01/05/10 Att: 2208

	1	2	3	4	5	6	7	8	9	10	11	12	13	14	15	16	17	18	19	20
1 Ashton United	-	0-2	3-2	1-1	1-2	1-0	2-2	1-3	3-2	1-2	2-3	0-2	0-2	3-2	0-1	2-0	1-0	0-1	2-2	2-1
2 Boston United	3-0	-	0-1	3-3	2-1	10-0	4-1	4-2	2-1	2-2	0-0	2-1	1-1	5-0	3-1	7-0	0-1	3-2	0-0	2-0
3 Bradford Park Avenue	0-1	2-2	-	1-3	0-0	7-1	3-2	3-1	2-4	2-0	3-2	2-0	5-2	3-2	1-2	4-2	0-1	2-0	1-0	1-0
4 Burscough	1-2	3-1	0-2	-	0-1	8-0	1-0	1-0	0-4	2-0	3-0	1-2	0-2	1-0	0-1	5-1	0-4	0-1	2-2	3-0
5 Buxton	2-0	0-1	1-1	2-2	-	6-2	3-0	4-1	3-1	2-0	1-2	2-2	1-1	0-0	1-1	2-2	0-2	3-1	0-2	1-0
6 Durham City	0-1	1-4	0-7	2-3	0-7	-	1-2	2-3	2-3	0-2	0-7	1-5	0-4	0-2	0-2	1-2	1-4	1-5	4-3	0-5
7 FC United of Manchester	2-3	1-2	1-5	2-0	0-1	1-2	-	0-0	1-2	2-0	1-4	3-0	1-0	4-0	3-3	2-1	2-4	4-3	1-1	2-0
8 Frickley Athletic	1-2	0-1	2-2	1-0	1-0	3-1	0-2	-	1-2	4-2	0-0	0-1	1-0	2-0	2-1	1-1	1-2	1-0	1-1	1-1
9 Guiseley	2-0	1-3	2-1	2-1	3-1	2-0	2-0	0-0	-	3-0	1-0	0-2	2-0	1-0	2-3	1-1	1-1	3-1	3-1	1-2
10 Hucknall Town	1-2	1-4	0-5	5-2	3-1	7-1	2-3	2-2	0-1	-	4-2	0-0	2-2	1-1	1-4	3-0	1-4	4-3	2-0	3-1
11 Kendal Town	0-0	1-0	1-1	3-2	0-2	5-0	1-0	3-1	2-1	3-1	-	4-1	1-1	1-2	2-0	2-2	2-1	1-1	2-0	4-1
12 Marine	3-4	0-0	1-3	2-1	1-1	7-2	1-1	2-0	0-1	2-1	4-3	-	2-1	0-2	1-3	2-0	1-2	2-1	2-0	1-1
13 Matlock Town	5-0	1-0	1-3	1-0	1-1	6-0	4-3	2-2	2-1	5-1	3-0	3-0	-	1-3	0-1	0-1	0-1	2-2	3-1	4-3
14 Nantwich Town	2-0	0-4	0-1	1-1	0-3	6-1	1-6	3-1	0-2	4-1	2-3	3-2	2-1	-	4-2	2-0	2-3	2-2	3-2	3-2
15 North Ferriby United	4-0	0-0	4-2	1-0	1-1	7-0	1-0	5-1	1-1	2-2	0-2	0-1	2-0	5-3	-	3-1	0-0	1-0	0-2	1-0
16 Ossett Town	0-3	0-5	4-6	1-2	3-1	3-0	1-2	4-1	1-4	2-2	3-2	1-4	0-1	0-1	0-1	-	1-2	2-4	1-3	0-2
17 Retford United	3-2	1-2	1-1	6-1	1-2	6-1	1-1	3-5	0-2	1-2	1-1	0-1	1-1	0-0	1-1	2-2	-	1-1	5-0	2-1
18 Stocksbridge Park Steels	2-1	2-1	2-3	4-1	3-1	6-0	1-1	4-1	2-4	2-3	0-2	4-2	3-4	5-3	1-1	3-1	1-2	-	2-0	2-2
19 Whitby Town	1-1	2-0	2-3	4-0	1-5	2-0	2-2	3-1	1-2	3-1	2-3	1-0	2-2	0-3	0-2	1-1	2-0	2-1	-	1-1
20 Worksop Town	1-1	1-5	1-3	0-1	1-1	4-0	3-1	1-2	1-3	1-1	0-1	1-0	0-3	0-0	0-2	3-1	3-3	1-2	0-4	-

NORTHERN PREMIER LEAGUE DIVISION ONE NORTH

		P	W	D	L	F	A	GD	Pts
1	FC Halifax Town	42	30	10	2	108	38	70	100
2	Lancaster City	42	31	3	8	95	45	50	96
3	Curzon Ashton (-6)	42	23	12	7	93	50	43	75
4	Colwyn Bay	42	23	6	13	77	57	20	75
5	Skelmersdale United	42	22	8	12	80	56	24	74
6	Leigh Genesis	42	21	8	13	81	51	30	71
7	Mossley	42	18	11	13	73	67	6	65
8	Clitheroe	42	18	8	16	72	66	6	62
9	Warrington Town	42	18	6	18	65	69	-4	60
10	Radcliffe Borough	42	17	6	19	65	78	-13	57
11	Salford City	42	16	8	18	63	74	-11	56
12	Trafford	42	15	8	19	79	73	6	53
13	AFC Fylde	42	15	8	19	67	79	-12	53
14	Bamber Bridge	42	14	10	18	58	67	-9	52
15	Prescot Cables	42	13	11	18	51	68	-17	50
16	Chorley	42	13	10	19	56	76	-20	49
17	Harrogate Railway Athletic (-3)	42	15	7	20	58	79	-21	49
18	Wakefield	42	12	12	18	49	58	-9	48
19	Woodley Sports	42	10	15	17	53	67	-14	45
20	Garforth Town	42	11	7	24	64	94	-30	40
21	Ossett Albion	42	7	7	28	52	91	-39	28
22	Rossendale United	42	6	7	29	38	94	-56	25

PROMOTION PLAY-OFFS

SF Curzon Ashton 1 **Colwyn Bay** 2 27/04/10 Att: 364

SF **Lancaster City** 2 Skelmersdale United 0 27/04/10 Att: 386

F Lancaster City 0 **Colwyn Bay** 1 01/05/10 Att: 667

DIVISION 1 NORTH	1	2	3	4	5	6	7	8	9	10	11	12	13	14	15	16	17	18	19	20	21	22
1 AFC Fylde	-	1-1	2-1	0-3	5-2	0-0	2-2	3-1	2-2	1-2	2-1	0-0	2-0	0-3	1-1	1-0	0-1	0-4	0-3	2-3	1-2	2-1
2 Bamber Bridge	2-4	-	2-1	1-0	1-2	1-2	0-2	3-1	4-0	2-1	3-1	1-2	1-1	0-0	0-1	0-0	4-3	1-4	3-2	0-1	1-0	2-2
3 Chorley	3-2	1-1	-	2-2	1-2	2-5	3-3	3-1	1-1	1-2	1-5	3-2	3-2	1-1	1-0	0-0	3-2	0-4	4-2	0-0	1-2	0-0
4 Clitheroe	7-1	3-0	2-3	-	2-1	4-4	1-2	2-1	4-2	1-3	1-2	0-0	2-1	1-2	2-1	2-1	2-0	1-1	1-4	2-1	2-1	1-0
5 Colwyn Bay	1-2	1-0	3-1	0-0	-	0-1	0-3	3-1	2-0	0-2	1-0	3-1	4-2	3-1	1-4	4-0	3-2	1-2	2-2	1-1	2-3	1-0
6 Curzon Ashton	3-1	0-0	5-0	4-1	1-1	-	0-5	6-2	2-0	0-0	2-1	2-3	1-1	2-1	5-1	1-0	5-1	1-1	5-1	4-0	1-2	2-2
7 FC Halifax T.	3-0	4-1	1-0	2-2	3-0	1-0	-	1-0	3-0	4-0	3-1	4-2	5-0	3-0	2-1	2-0	6-1	1-1	2-0	1-1	4-1	2-1
8 Garforth Town	3-2	3-3	1-1	2-2	2-4	1-3	3-4	-	1-4	2-3	0-5	0-1	4-3	0-5	4-2	2-1	0-1	1-3	1-1	0-3	5-3	1-1
9 Harrogate R.A.	2-1	3-1	0-2	2-3	1-3	2-0	1-2	2-1	-	3-1	2-1	0-3	1-0	0-3	2-2	2-0	0-1	0-1	3-2	0-1	2-1	3-1
10 Lancaster City	2-0	3-1	3-0	2-1	1-1	1-1	0-1	0-3	3-0	-	2-0	2-1	4-2	5-0	4-0	4-0	4-1	4-2	2-1	3-1	4-1	7-1
11 Leigh Genesis	4-1	0-3	0-2	2-0	3-1	0-0	1-1	2-1	5-1	0-2	-	1-1	1-0	6-0	1-2	4-3	2-1	0-1	2-0	2-0	3-2	2-0
12 Mossley	4-2	1-0	2-2	4-2	1-4	1-4	3-3	5-2	3-2	0-2	1-1	-	2-1	1-1	1-0	4-1	0-1	1-1	2-0	1-1	5-0	2-0
13 Ossett Albion	0-2	0-1	2-1	1-5	0-2	2-4	2-4	2-1	0-1	1-4	2-4	2-0	-	2-2	4-2	1-1	2-4	1-3	1-3	0-1	1-1	0-0
14 Prescot Cables	1-2	0-2	1-0	2-0	0-1	0-1	1-0	3-2	2-2	0-2	0-4	0-0	2-1	-	3-3	2-2	1-3	2-1	1-1	3-1	1-2	1-1
15 Radcliffe Boro'	1-1	4-2	1-0	0-2	0-7	1-3	3-2	0-2	2-4	0-1	2-1	0-1	1-0	1-2	-	3-2	1-3	2-1	4-2	3-1	0-2	2-1
16 Rossendale U.	2-1	2-2	1-2	2-0	1-4	3-1	0-3	0-2	0-2	2-4	1-3	1-2	0-2	1-0	1-3	-	1-1	0-2	1-8	1-0	1-3	1-2
17 Salford City	3-1	1-2	3-0	1-1	2-1	0-3	0-3	0-0	1-1	1-2	3-3	4-1	1-2	0-2	1-2	0-2	-	2-0	2-1	1-1	1-1	3-1
18 Skelmersdale U.	1-4	3-1	2-0	3-1	0-1	2-2	2-2	1-3	4-3	1-2	0-2	5-2	1-1	2-0	0-4	2-1	3-1	-	4-0	1-2	2-1	2-2
19 Trafford	2-2	3-2	3-1	0-2	1-2	2-3	0-3	0-2	0-0	2-0	0-2	3-3	5-2	3-0	1-1	5-0	5-1	0-1	-	1-1	1-2	2-0
20 Wakefield	1-3	0-1	1-4	2-0	1-1	0-3	1-1	1-1	6-0	2-0	2-2	2-3	2-1	1-1	0-0	2-0	0-1	1-2	1-2	-	1-2	1-0
21 Warrington T.	1-4	1-1	2-0	0-1	0-1	3-1	1-3	2-0	3-1	0-1	0-0	2-0	2-1	3-0	1-2	5-1	1-3	1-4	0-2	1-0	-	1-1
22 Woodley Sports	0-4	3-1	0-1	3-1	3-0	0-0	2-2	0-1	1-1	4-1	1-1	2-1	1-3	2-1	3-2	1-1	1-1	1-0	2-3	3-1	3-3	-

NORTHERN PREMIER DIVISION ONE NORTH DATES & GATES	AFC Fylde	Bamber Bridge	Chorley	Clitheroe	Colwyn Bay	Curzon Ashton	FC Halifax Town	Garforth Town	Harrogate Railway Ath.	Lancaster City	Leigh Genesis	Mossley	Ossett Albion	Prescot Cables	Radcliffe Borough	Rossendale United	Salford City	Skelmersdale United	Trafford	Wakefield	Warrington Town	Woodley Sports
AFC Fylde		7 Nov *295*	13 Feb *323*	9 Mar *221*	14 Nov *268*	24 Oct *203*	20 Mar *741*	12 Dec *203*	27 Mar *215*	28 Nov *362*	3 Oct *202*	25 Aug *240*	27 Feb *215*	5 Apr *207*	15 Aug *262*	19 Sep *228*	17 Apr *244*	3 Nov *190*	6 Oct *190*	5 Sep *235*	30 Jan *241*	16 Jan *196*
Bamber Bridge	6 Mar *259*		2 Feb *231*	15 Sep *194*	6 Feb *181*	2 Apr *160*	23 Jan *486*	18 Aug *158*	21 Nov *187*	23 Mar *185*	1 Dec *125*	2 Mar *117*	31 Oct *128*	24 Apr *148*	20 Feb *183*	10 Oct *237*	20 Mar *125*	16 Feb *148*	8 Apr *89*	13 Mar *121*	22 Aug *201*	20 Oct *109*
Chorley	20 Oct *251*	5 Apr *409*		7 Apr *152*	31 Oct *241*	28 Nov *265*	25 Aug *675*	23 Jan *211*	19 Sep *222*	20 Feb *438*	27 Feb *260*	23 Mar *179*	12 Dec *206*	24 Nov *153*	27 Mar *265*	13 Mar *164*	5 Sep *274*	27 Oct *261*	14 Nov *310*	15 Aug *232*	17 Apr *268*	6 Mar *259*
Clitheroe	23 Mar *236*	28 Nov *311*	18 Aug *250*		22 Apr *161*	12 Dec *244*	16 Mar *654*	2 Apr *265*	10 Nov *152*	5 Apr *351*	20 Oct *151*	10 Oct *256*	24 Apr *182*	23 Jan *300*	6 Feb *260*	20 Feb *300*	6 Mar *187*	22 Aug *232*	19 Sep *180*	21 Nov *194*	2 Mar *167*	27 Oct *160*
Colwyn Bay	24 Apr *393*	24 Oct *325*	20 Mar *247*	5 Sep *313*		13 Feb *350*	15 Aug *854*	19 Sep *302*	30 Jan *374*	9 Mar *262*	15 Sep *227*	13 Apr *245*	7 Nov *328*	25 Aug *308*	1 Jan *346*	12 Dec *244*	29 Sep *224*	27 Feb *307*	17 Oct *367*	27 Mar *237*	16 Mar *185*	5 Apr *356*
Curzon Ashton	6 Feb *130*	24 Aug *232*	14 Sep *194*	26 Sep *188*	10 Apr *154*		12 Apr *803*	14 Nov *147*	15 Aug *135*	1 Mar *174*	17 Aug *196*	5 Apr *277*	7 Apr *60*	27 Feb *121*	31 Oct *166*	7 Nov *103*	27 Mar *164*	23 Jan *163*	17 Apr *141*	10 Mar *71*	5 Dec *179*	20 Mar *117*
FC Halifax Town	10 Nov *1045*	19 Jan *917*	2 Apr *1508*	20 Apr *1932*	13 Mar *1388*	29 Sep *1504*		31 Aug *1554*	13 Feb *1271*	10 Apr *3152*	19 Sep *1292*	20 Feb *1267*	2 Mar *935*	6 Mar *1322*	15 Apr *1589*	23 Feb *801*	12 Dec *1242*	24 Apr *2939*	22 Aug *1359*	15 Dec *966*	18 Aug *1253*	28 Nov *1249*
Garforth Town	16 Mar *80*	9 Feb *72*	6 Oct *92*	25 Aug *105*	5 Dec *107*	24 Apr *111*	7 Apr *642*		5 Apr *177*	24 Oct *155*	27 Mar *190*	15 Aug *122*	20 Feb *141*	9 Mar *82*	15 Sep *97*	21 Nov *135*	13 Feb *118*	7 Nov *120*	30 Jan *129*	22 Apr *129*	20 Mar *135*	5 Sep *118*
Harrogate Railway	22 Aug *128*	17 Apr *88*	5 Dec *132*	15 Feb *96*	10 Oct *101*	19 Apr *70*	19 Oct *636*	4 Mar *96*		6 Mar *131*	23 Jan *102*	26 Sep *136*	2 Apr *140*	31 Oct *125*	14 Nov *105*	17 Aug *125*	7 Apr *76*	10 Apr *92*	13 Mar *109*	14 Sep *117*	22 Mar *76*	6 Feb *85*
Lancaster City	15 Sep *278*	1 Jan *395*	17 Nov *239*	2 Feb *203*	17 Apr *238*	22 Apr *172*	5 Sep *698*	6 Feb *203*	27 Feb *181*		25 Aug *252*	27 Mar *168*	23 Jan *184*	15 Aug *228*	16 Feb *154*	15 Dec *162*	16 Jan *262*	26 Sep *235*	20 Mar *184*	5 Dec *204*	14 Nov *195*	10 Oct *203*
Leigh Genesis	19 Dec *173*	10 Apr *164*	6 Feb *187*	13 Feb *166*	28 Nov *193*	24 Mar *110*	5 Dec *618*	22 Aug *186*	18 Nov *84*	2 Apr *233*		24 Oct *235*	20 Mar *196*	26 Sep *178*	8 Apr *107*	17 Feb *61*	21 Apr *95*	24 Feb *122*	7 Nov *151*	24 Apr *136*	1 Sep *101*	13 Mar *185*
Mossley	2 Apr *209*	12 Dec *182*	31 Aug *246*	27 Feb *126*	18 Aug *182*	15 Apr *174*	2 Feb *419*	20 Apr *90*	20 Mar *174*	22 Aug *194*	12 Sep *163*		13 Mar *165*	6 Feb *149*	10 Apr *220*	24 Apr *164*	19 Sep *162*	22 Apr *117*	29 Sep *158*	7 Nov *161*	16 Feb *127*	8 Apr *104*
Ossett Albion	26 Jan *79*	15 Aug *121*	10 Apr *106*	14 Nov *127*	6 Mar *105*	10 Oct *114*	17 Apr *1170*	20 Oct *103*	16 Mar *94*	6 Oct *77*	5 Sep *143*	15 Sep *86*		27 Mar *126*	30 Mar *80*	10 Nov *84*	24 Oct *118*	5 Dec *127*	13 Feb *107*	5 Apr *163*	20 Apr *99*	25 Aug *100*
Prescot Cables	13 Apr *155*	19 Sep *180*	24 Oct *234*	13 Mar *216*	2 Apr *225*	12 Sep *167*	7 Nov *614*	29 Sep *135*	12 Dec *183*	16 Mar *150*	14 Nov *247*	13 Feb *206*	22 Aug *147*		17 Apr *192*	10 Apr *174*	2 Mar *161*	31 Aug *243*	18 Aug *137*	20 Mar *159*	3 Nov *216*	17 Oct *150*
Radcliffe Borough	2 Mar *104*	16 Mar *85*	22 Aug *185*	24 Oct *164*	31 Aug *212*	5 Sep *175*	27 Feb *566*	13 Mar *104*	24 Apr *130*	20 Apr *106*	12 Dec *174*	9 Mar *130*	18 Aug *112*	21 Nov *109*		2 Apr *179*	13 Apr *104*	20 Mar *160*	23 Feb *72*	13 Feb *120*	7 Nov *128*	19 Sep *108*
Rossendale United	5 Dec *117*	9 Mar *55*	9 Feb *101*	20 Mar *111*	26 Sep *114*	6 Mar *95*	5 Apr *745*	17 Apr *69*	30 Mar *79*	7 Apr *113*	15 Aug *136*	14 Nov *138*	17 Oct *121*	5 Sep *135*	25 Aug *146*		16 Mar *96*	15 Sep *81*	27 Feb *92*	20 Apr *74*	24 Oct *75*	27 Mar *94*
Salford City	2 Feb *91*	27 Feb *121*	15 Apr *118*	7 Nov *135*	23 Mar *126*	22 Aug *171*	15 Sep *544*	3 Oct *115*	9 Mar *98*	18 Aug *145*	30 Mar *106*	15 Dec *118*	9 Feb *74*	5 Dec *116*	23 Jan *132*	6 Feb *112*		2 Apr *135*	10 Apr *126*	16 Feb *72*	13 Mar *109*	24 Apr *177*
Skelmersdale Utd	20 Feb *265*	26 Jan *220*	20 Apr *216*	27 Mar *261*	12 Sep *255*	6 Oct *195*	14 Nov *927*	6 Mar *301*	5 Sep *206*	12 Dec *361*	5 Apr *249*	17 Apr *212*	19 Sep *221*	19 Jan *200*	9 Feb *201*	28 Nov *257*	25 Aug *246*		24 Oct *225*	13 Apr *195*	13 Feb *280*	15 Aug *229*
Trafford	23 Jan *105*	5 Sep *138*	24 Apr *121*	5 Dec *122*	20 Feb *117*	21 Nov *110*	27 Mar *512*	10 Oct *156*	25 Aug *127*	13 Apr *136*	6 Mar *124*	16 Mar *106*	12 Sep *127*	9 Feb *73*	5 Apr *145*	31 Oct *119*	15 Aug *214*	6 Feb *119*		26 Sep *128*	15 Sep *118*	2 Mar *76*
Wakefield	10 Apr *88*	14 Nov *84*	16 Mar *77*	17 Apr *95*	22 Aug *108*	17 Oct *106*	6 Feb *659*	31 Oct *121*	28 Nov *119*	19 Sep *105*	20 Feb *110*	6 Mar *95*	23 Mar *104*	10 Oct *137*	26 Oct *129*	23 Jan *92*	9 Nov *82*	17 Aug *127*	12 Dec *86*		2 Apr *113*	28 Sep *80*
Warrington Town	10 Oct *184*	27 Mar *153*	21 Nov *166*	15 Aug *161*	23 Jan *175*	19 Sep *131*	9 Mar *505*	10 Apr *104*	13 Apr *101*	24 Apr *266*	26 Jan *111*	4 Sep *151*	6 Feb *116*	20 Feb *164*	6 Mar *191*	2 Feb *103*	5 Apr *168*	20 Oct *122*	28 Nov *155*	25 Aug *83*		12 Dec *136*
Woodley Sports	18 Aug *105*	13 Feb *108*	7 Nov *109*	10 Apr *116*	9 Feb *121*	20 Feb *152*	30 Mar *514*	26 Sep *110*	24 Oct *121*	30 Jan *207*	17 Apr *82*	1 Dec *176*	21 Nov *85*	15 Sep *138*	5 Dec *98*	22 Aug *92*	14 Nov *132*	9 Mar *101*	2 Apr *156*	19 Dec *98*	27 Feb *94*	

NORTHERN PREMIER LEAGUE DIVISION ONE SOUTH

		P	W	D	L	F	A	GD	Pts
1	Mickleover Sports	42	28	5	9	93	51	42	89
2	Chasetown	42	24	10	8	78	42	36	82
3	Glapwell	42	23	12	7	73	42	31	81
4	Kidsgrove Athletic	42	22	12	8	93	50	43	78
5	Sheffield FC	42	21	10	11	74	50	24	73
6	Belper Town	42	21	8	13	83	55	28	71
7	Witton Albion	42	20	7	15	76	53	23	67
8	Leek Town	42	18	13	11	68	61	7	67
9	Carlton Town	42	19	9	14	74	68	6	66
10	Stamford	42	18	10	14	77	54	23	64
11	Grantham Town	42	17	11	14	62	56	6	62
12	Rushall Olympic	42	16	11	15	68	61	7	59
13	Market Drayton Town	42	16	5	21	71	81	-10	53
14	Loughborough Dynamo	42	15	8	19	70	80	-10	53
15	Brigg Town	42	15	7	20	60	77	-17	52
16	Cammell Laird	42	13	11	18	51	66	-15	50
17	Shepshed Dynamo	42	10	18	14	44	55	-11	48
18	Goole AFC	42	12	10	20	70	84	-14	46
19	Lincoln United	42	13	5	24	57	67	-10	44
20	Quorn	42	9	13	20	55	78	-23	40
21	Spalding United	42	5	5	32	33	111	-78	20
22	Willenhall Town (-10)	42	5	4	33	21	109	-88	9

PROMOTION PLAY-OFFS

SF **Chasetown** 3 Sheffield 2 27/04/10 Att: 657

SF **Glapwell** 1 Kidsgrove Athletic 0 27/04/10 Att: 253

F **Chasetown** 1 Glapwell 0 01/05/10 Att: 1265

DIVISION 1 SOUTH	1	2	3	4	5	6	7	8	9	10	11	12	13	14	15	16	17	18	19	20	21	22
1 Belper Town	2-0	3-0	2-0	0-2	1-1	2-2	1-1	3-2	1-1	0-1	7-1	4-1	1-0	2-1	1-3	2-2	1-1	4-0	3-3	3-0	3-2	
2 Brigg Town	3-0		1-0	2-4	0-1	2-4	1-3	1-1	1-3	2-3	2-1	4-2	1-5	0-1	2-2	2-2	0-2	1-1	1-1	3-2	5-0	1-0
3 Cammell Laird	1-3	3-1		1-1	0-2	0-0	2-2	1-1	0-2	2-0	2-1	3-3	3-0	1-2	1-0	3-2	2-0	1-1	0-1	0-2	1-0	1-1
4 Carlton Town	2-4	1-2	3-0		0-2	0-1	2-0	0-3	1-1	5-2	4-3	3-3	5-3	2-3	1-0	1-0	2-0	2-1	3-1	1-1	0-2	4-1
5 Chasetown	0-1	3-0	2-1	1-1		2-1	4-3	1-1	1-1	1-0	2-2	1-1	0-2	2-1	6-2	1-2	3-1	1-1	4-0	0-0	2-0	1-0
6 Glapwell	2-1	3-2	4-1	3-2	1-0		3-0	0-2	1-1	2-1	2-0	3-1	1-3	0-0	0-0	2-0	1-1	1-0	2-0	1-0	1-0	1-1
7 Goole	1-2	1-3	0-1	1-1	0-5	2-2		1-2	3-4	0-2	2-1	4-1	3-0	1-4	2-0	4-0	2-2	4-1	4-0	1-1	4-1	0-1
8 Grantham Town	4-2	3-4	4-0	0-1	1-3	1-1	1-3		0-4	0-1	1-0	0-2	2-0	3-1	1-1	2-2	0-2	1-0	2-0	1-2	4-1	0-1
9 Kidsgrove Athletic	2-1	3-1	4-2	0-2	1-3	0-1	2-1	2-2		5-2	3-0	1-0	3-3	2-2	2-1	2-1	1-1	2-0	5-0	2-0	7-0	0-1
10 Leek Town	2-1	5-1	4-2	3-1	1-3	2-2	1-1	0-1	2-1		2-2	3-3	1-1	3-2	2-2	1-1	2-2	1-1	1-0	1-0	5-1	1-1
11 Lincoln United	1-2	2-0	0-2	2-0	0-1	1-4	1-2	0-2	3-3	0-1		1-2	2-0	0-2	4-0	2-1	0-1	3-1	4-0	1-2	3-1	0-1
12 Loughborough Dyn.	2-1	1-1	2-0	0-3	2-2	1-4	3-1	1-2	1-4	0-2	1-0		0-1	3-1	3-3	1-0	3-2	2-3	5-3	2-1	5-0	2-4
13 Market Drayton Tn	2-1	2-0	0-3	1-2	1-0	2-1	1-2	1-5	1-3	0-2	1-2	0-2		1-3	4-2	1-2	1-5	2-1	6-0	3-1	7-1	2-1
14 Mickleover Sports	2-1	2-1	1-1	4-0	3-0	3-0	3-2	4-1	1-0	2-0	2-0	3-2	1-0		2-1	3-2	4-2	2-1	4-0	1-1	3-3	2-1
15 Quorn	1-3	1-2	2-2	3-3	1-1	3-1	3-1	2-1	1-1	2-0	4-2	2-1	1-1	0-3		1-2	1-0	1-1	2-2	0-1	0-2	1-4
16 Rushall Olympic	0-3	0-0	2-2	4-1	4-2	2-1	5-0	2-2	1-1	2-2	1-4	2-1	4-0	3-1	1-0		1-1	0-1	3-0	1-2	3-2	0-1
17 Sheffield	2-6	0-1	3-1	5-1	2-0	0-0	3-0	1-1	0-3	1-2	2-0	1-0	3-1	4-2	2-0	1-1		4-1	3-1	0-0	1-0	1-0
18 Shepshed Dynamo	1-1	1-0	2-0	0-0	0-0	1-1	3-3	2-0	1-1	1-1	1-1	1-0	0-0	0-4	1-2	2-0	0-4		4-0	1-1	0-0	2-1
19 Spalding United	1-0	0-2	0-1	2-2	1-7	0-2	1-1	0-1	0-2	3-0	1-2	0-2	3-4	0-5	3-0	1-1	1-3	2-3		1-3	2-0	1-6
20 Stamford	2-1	1-2	3-0	1-3	2-3	1-7	2-2	4-0	3-3	2-0	4-1	2-1	1-1	3-1	3-1	1-2	0-1	2-1	3-1		9-0	4-1
21 Willenhall Town	0-2	0-2	0-3	0-1	0-1	1-7	1-0	0-1	0-3	1-2	0-0	0-1	0-3	1-2	0-3	0-2	0-3	0-0	1-0	1-0		0-3
22 Witton Albion	0-1	3-0	1-1	0-3	1-2	1-3	6-0	1-1	2-1	0-1	2-4	1-1	4-2	2-1	2-2	2-1	3-0	2-0	3-0	3-1	5-1	

NORTHERN PREMIER DIVISION ONE SOUTH DATES & GATES	Belper Town	Brigg Town	Cammell Laird	Carlton Town	Chasetown	Glapwell	Goole	Grantham Town	Kidsgrove Athletic	Leek Town	Lincoln United	Loughboro. Dynamo	Mkt Drayton Town	Mickleover Sports	Quorn	Rushall Olympic	Sheffield	Shepshed Dynamo	Spalding United	Stamford	Willenhall Town	Witton Albion
Belper Town		20 Oct *162*	24 Apr *154*	5 Sep *198*	5 Apr *263*	16 Mar *161*	28 Nov *205*	25 Aug *180*	6 Feb *224*	1 Dec *167*	12 Dec *225*	21 Nov *221*	20 Feb *203*	23 Mar *430*	23 Jan *205*	6 Mar *194*	19 Sep *256*	29 Sep *180*	10 Oct *207*	10 Nov *196*	15 Aug *201*	27 Mar *192*
Brigg Town	23 Feb *88*		27 Feb *115*	28 Nov *114*	12 Dec *117*	24 Apr *129*	19 Jan *83*	20 Mar *135*	21 Nov *122*	2 Apr *138*	31 Aug *132*	7 Nov *126*	10 Apr *120*	30 Jan *133*	29 Sep *107*	24 Oct *117*	3 Nov *125*	22 Aug *129*	18 Aug *98*	6 Oct *112*	19 Sep *134*	13 Feb *135*
Cammell Laird	13 Feb *103*	15 Aug *104*		27 Mar *68*	10 Oct *123*	23 Jan *107*	12 Dec *104*	5 Sep *74*	20 Apr *67*	17 Nov *103*	19 Sep *128*	25 Aug *78*	1 Dec *72*	2 Mar *107*	20 Feb *99*	9 Mar *65*	29 Sep *117*	6 Feb *106*	17 Apr *50*	31 Oct *103*	23 Mar *62*	5 Apr *132*
Carlton Town	10 Apr *81*	15 Sep *72*	22 Aug *67*		20 Mar *92*	5 Dec *109*	13 Mar *67*	24 Nov *112*	30 Mar *67*	24 Oct *89*	3 Nov *74*	30 Jan *80*	17 Apr *56*	1 Dec *63*	18 Aug *64*	13 Feb *61*	31 Aug *101*	23 Mar *68*	2 Apr *68*	9 Feb *71*	14 Nov *73*	7 Nov *85*
Chasetown	26 Jan *319*	26 Sep *361*	30 Jan *374*	10 Nov *302*		6 Mar *413*	21 Nov *307*	13 Mar *318*	24 Apr *402*	7 Apr *340*	13 Feb *376*	24 Oct *309*	23 Mar *322*	13 Apr *580*	22 Aug *362*	5 Dec *378*	2 Apr *371*	18 Aug *416*	10 Apr *355*	12 Sep *365*	1 Dec *316*	6 Oct *410*
Glapwell	18 Aug *129*	14 Nov *113*	7 Apr *72*	19 Sep *86*	7 Nov *108*		31 Aug *101*	27 Feb *118*	12 Dec *126*	13 Feb *122*	28 Nov *74*	20 Apr *89*	22 Aug *95*	24 Oct *88*	10 Apr *81*	13 Mar *109*	23 Mar *141*	2 Apr *131*	29 Sep *65*	30 Jan *126*	17 Apr *95*	2 Mar *82*
Goole	12 Sep *129*	5 Apr *174*	5 Dec *152*	15 Aug *164*	17 Apr *183*	26 Jan *116*		2 Mar *149*	5 Sep *152*	30 Jan *173*	16 Mar *94*	13 Feb *156*	6 Mar *131*	20 Feb *149*	15 Dec *119*	3 Oct *149*	31 Oct *236*	26 Sep *162*	14 Nov *167*	25 Aug *140*	27 Mar *144*	24 Oct *184*
Grantham Town	2 Apr *192*	10 Nov *141*	10 Apr *152*	23 Jan *180*	31 Oct *246*	19 Jan *91*	18 Aug *202*		10 Oct *173*	14 Nov *206*	26 Dec *156*	5 Dec *180*	13 Feb *151*	15 Sep *139*	6 Mar *173*	23 Mar *106*	22 Aug *232*	17 Apr *193*	12 Sep *205*	26 Jan *155*	6 Feb *146*	26 Sep *206*
Kidsgrove Athletic	24 Oct *162*	17 Apr *160*	31 Aug *170*	19 Jan *90*	14 Nov *242*	26 Sep *134*	10 Apr *145*	13 Apr *153*		2 Mar *237*	2 Apr *173*	16 Mar *121*	15 Sep *152*	6 Oct *116*	13 Feb *116*	10 Nov *161*	18 Aug *151*	6 Mar *154*	22 Aug *124*	5 Dec *138*	20 Feb *131*	26 Jan *173*
Leek Town	27 Feb *315*	25 Aug *216*	20 Mar *261*	6 Feb *236*	22 Apr *306*	9 Mar *161*	10 Oct *342*	24 Apr *255*	5 Apr *472*		29 Sep *201*	15 Aug *229*	23 Jan *251*	22 Aug *229*	12 Dec *205*	21 Nov *289*	7 Nov *307*	28 Nov *240*	19 Sep *276*	5 Sep *272*	13 Mar *235*	9 Feb *229*
Lincoln United	19 Jan *60*	9 Feb *98*	13 Mar *75*	9 Mar *99*	15 Aug *190*	13 Apr *82*	20 Oct *58*	5 Apr *202*	25 Aug *82*	23 Mar *80*		27 Mar *98*	14 Nov *85*	5 Dec *110*	6 Feb *130*	31 Oct *76*	17 Apr *140*	10 Nov *81*	23 Jan *102*	16 Jan *115*	6 Mar *101*	5 Sep *86*
Loughboro. Dyn.	17 Apr *125*	6 Mar *116*	2 Apr *110*	10 Oct *156*	6 Feb *202*	10 Nov *90*	29 Sep *113*	19 Sep *200*	20 Oct *80*	16 Feb *75*	22 Aug *103*		18 Aug *101*	31 Oct *142*	26 Dec *238*	10 Apr *125*	12 Dec *136*	31 Aug *256*	28 Nov *115*	20 Feb *176*	23 Jan *128*	14 Nov *121*
Market Drayton T.	3 Nov *93*	5 Sep *95*	9 Feb *66*	21 Nov *68*	29 Sep *214*	27 Mar *97*	7 Nov *88*	15 Aug *163*	28 Nov *149*	15 Dec *105*	24 Apr *83*	13 Mar *85*		5 Apr *158*	19 Sep *121*	30 Jan *113*	20 Mar *71*	12 Dec *115*	27 Feb *74*	24 Oct *85*	2 Feb *65*	25 Aug *229*
Mickleover Sports	17 Oct *356*	10 Oct *202*	19 Aug *179*	12 Dec *147*	19 Sep *220*	6 Feb *225*	11 Nov *157*	28 Nov *167*	23 Jan *195*	27 Mar *229*	7 Nov *216*	27 Feb *213*	26 Dec *244*		10 Mar *147*	2 Apr *274*	10 Apr *384*	13 Feb *204*	21 Oct *136*	24 Apr *475*	30 Sep *141*	20 Mar *71*
Quorn	9 Feb *96*	13 Mar *108*	7 Nov *110*	16 Mar *82*	27 Mar *149*	5 Sep *152*	27 Feb *103*	16 Feb *119*	15 Aug *119*	26 Sep *122*	1 Dec *77*	5 Apr *192*	5 Dec *123*	17 Apr *191*		15 Sep *107*	26 Jan *74*	14 Nov *210*	20 Mar *97*	20 Apr *106*	25 Aug *98*	30 Jan *129*
Rushall Olympic	7 Nov *133*	6 Feb *142*	3 Nov *97*	20 Oct *98*	20 Apr *398*	15 Aug *138*	19 Sep *116*	29 Sep *127*	20 Mar *119*	17 Apr *134*	27 Feb *91*	5 Sep *118*	10 Oct *127*	25 Aug *128*	28 Nov *114*		14 Nov *104*	23 Jan *139*	12 Dec *101*	27 Mar *129*	5 Apr *114*	16 Mar *132*
Sheffield	5 Dec *345*	20 Apr *269*	16 Feb *195*	13 Apr *261*	25 Aug *330*	5 Apr *348*	23 Jan *243*	27 Mar *763*	13 Mar *240*	6 Mar *362*	21 Nov *215*	26 Sep *272*	17 Oct *249*	5 Sep *263*	2 Mar *255*	24 Apr *441*		1 Dec *192*	6 Feb *229*	15 Aug *315*	10 Oct *475*	15 Sep *254*
Shepshed Dynamo	9 Mar *104*	27 Mar *134*	24 Oct *131*	5 Apr *133*	16 Mar *147*	25 Aug *144*	20 Mar *112*	21 Nov *167*	7 Nov *157*	12 Sep *141*	30 Jan *138*	26 Jan *189*	13 Apr *117*	15 Aug *187*	24 Apr *162*	6 Oct *157*	30 Mar *115*		3 Nov *101*	16 Feb *98*	5 Sep *144*	5 Dec *167*
Spalding United	30 Jan *80*	16 Mar *65*	21 Nov *80*	25 Aug *95*	5 Sep *108*	9 Feb *60*	24 Apr *71*	1 Jan *219*	27 Mar *83*	5 Dec *73*	6 Oct *99*	15 Sep *74*	31 Oct *78*	6 Mar *66*	3 Oct *84*	26 Sep *70*	24 Oct *90*	2 Mar *55*		5 Apr *174*	7 Nov *85*	15 Aug *120*
Stamford	20 Mar *213*	23 Jan *205*	6 Mar *161*	15 Dec *125*	28 Nov *218*	10 Oct *240*	2 Apr *250*	7 Nov *469*	19 Sep *228*	10 Apr *182*	19 Aug *245*	3 Nov *192*	6 Feb *166*	14 Nov *179*	2 Feb *170*	22 Aug *214*	13 Feb *194*	20 Oct *185*	19 Jan *145*		12 Dec *193*	17 Apr *284*
Willenhall Town	30 Mar *45*	5 Dec *53*	23 Feb *48*	24 Apr *44*	27 Feb *190*	21 Nov *53*	22 Aug *73*	24 Oct *73*	13 Oct *72*	18 Aug *92*	20 Mar *45*	3 Oct *59*	10 Nov *57*	9 Feb *52*	2 Apr *36*	19 Jan *71*	30 Jan *78*	10 Apr *62*	13 Feb *63*	26 Sep *72*		3 Nov *81*
Witton Albion	22 Aug *259*	23 Mar *186*	19 Jan *176*	6 Mar *220*	23 Jan *263*	20 Feb *228*	6 Feb *203*	12 Dec *219*	29 Sep *179*	31 Aug *236*	10 Apr *241*	24 Apr *200*	2 Apr *273*	30 Mar *234*	10 Oct *285*	18 Aug *260*	28 Nov *285*	19 Sep *210*	13 Mar *195*	27 Feb *189*	12 Sep *190*	

UNIBOND LEAGUE CHALLENGE CUP

FIRST ROUND

AFC Fylde 2 Bamber Bridge 1 *(Sep 22)* Att: 181
Brigg Town 0 **Harrogate Railway Ath.** 3 *(Sep 22)* Att: 69
Cammell Laird 3 Chorley 0 *(Sep 22)* Att: 62
Chasetown 1 Kidsgrove Athletic 0 *(Sep 22)* Att: 169
Curzon Ashton 2 Woodley Sports 0 *(Sep 21)* Att: 88
Garforth Town 0 **FC Halifax Town** 1 *(Sep 22)* Att: 152
Glapwell 1 **Leek Town** 3 *(Sep 22)* Att: 46
Grantham Town 3 **Quorn** 5 *(Sep 22)* Att: 98
Lancaster City 3 Skelmersdale Utd 0 *(Sep 22)* Att: 102
Leigh Genesis 6 Warrington Town 1 *(Sep 23)* Att: 139
Lincoln United 5 Loughborough Dyn. 1 *(Sep 22)* Att: 57
Mickleover Sports 2 Belper Town 1 *(Sep 23)* Att: 111
Mossley 1 Radcliffe Borough 0 *aet (Sep 22)* Att: 142
Prescot Cables 3 Colwyn Bay 1 *(Sep 22)* Att: 91
Rossendale United 2 Clitheroe 1 *(Sep 22)* Att: 110
Rushall Olympic 1 **Market Drayton** 3 *(Sep 22)* Att: 71
Sheffield 7 Goole 1 *(Sep 22)* Att: 134
Shepshed Dynamo 1 Carlton Town 0 *(Sep 22)* Att: 83
Stamford 2 Spalding United 0 *(Sep 22)* Att: 142
Trafford 5 Salford City 1 *(Sep 22)* Att: 122
Wakefield 1 **Ossett Albion** 3 *aet (Sep 21)* Att: 112
Witton Albion 2 Willenhall Town 1 *(Sep 22)* Att: 112

SECOND ROUND

FC Halifax Town 2 Ossett Albion 0 *(Oct 27)* Att: 401
Lancaster City 1 Prescot Cables 0 *(Oct 27)* Att: 121
Leek Town 2 Chasetown 1 *(Oct 27)* Att: 203
Lincoln United 1 **Shepshed Dynamo** 3 *(Oct 27)* Att: 56
Market Drayton T. 2 **Mickleover Spts** 3 *(Oct 27)* Att: 69
Mossley 4 Leigh Genesis 0 *(Oct 27)* Att: 131
Rossendale United 0 **Curzon Ashton** 2 *(Oct 27)* Att: 106
Sheffield 4 Harrogate Railway Athletic 3 *(Oct 27)* Att: 153
Stamford 1 **Quorn** 3 *(Oct 27)* Att: 125
Trafford 1 **AFC Fylde** 2 *aet (Oct 27)* Att: 98
Witton Albion 1 **Cammell Laird** 2 *(Oct 27)* Att: 138

THIRD ROUND

Ashton United 4 AFC Fylde 0 *(Dec 14)* Att: 75
Boston United 2 Hucknall Town 1 *(Nov 24)* Att: 607
Burscough 4 Cammell Laird 2 *(Nov 24)* Att: 118
Durham City 2 **FC Halifax Town** 4 *(Nov 24)* Att: 125
FC United 1 **Kendal Town** 2 (at Kendal) *(Dec 8)* Att: 181
Frickley Ath 4 **North Ferriby** 4 *aet* (2-3p) *(Dec 1)* Att: 78
King's Lynn 1 **Retford United** 2 *(Nov 24)* Att: 463
Lancaster City 3 Mossley 0 *(Dec 8)* Att: 92
Marine 2 **Curzon Ashton** 3 *(Dec 1)* Att: 72
Mickleover Sports 5 Buxton 3 *(Nov 25)* Att: 158
Nantwich Town 2 Matlock Town 0 *(Jan 20)* Att: 131
Ossett Town 0 **Sheffield** 1 *(Nov 24)* Att: 81
Quorn 1 **Shepshed Dyn.** 1 *aet* (3-4p) *(Nov 24)* Att: 114
Stocksbridge PS 2 Bradford PA 1 *(Nov 25)* Att: 108
Whitby Town 0 Guiseley 0 *aet* (4-3p) *(Nov 25)* Att: 121
Worksop Town 1 **Leek Town** 2 *(Nov 25)* Att: 240

FOURTH ROUND

Boston United 2 Sheffield 0 *(Jan 16)* Att: 538
Burscough 0 **Kendal Town** 2 *(Jan 19)* Att: 88
FC Halifax T. 0 N. Ferriby 0 *aet* (3-1p) *(Jan 26)* Att: 387
Lancaster City 2 Ashton United 0 *(Jan 26)* Att: 113
Leek Town 2 **Curzon Ashton** 4 *(Jan 27)* Att: 75
Mickleover Sports 0 **Nantwich Town** 2 *(Jan 27)* Att: 82
Shepshed Dynamo 2 **Retford United** 6 *(Jan 19)* Att: 83
Stocksbridge Park Steels 4 Whitby 0 *(Jan 26)* Att: 69

QUARTER-FINALS

Boston United 5 FC Halifax Town 2 *(Feb 9)* Att: 559
Kendal Town 3 Lancaster City 1 *(Feb 9)* Att: 185
Nantwich Town 1 **Curzon Ashton** 3 *(Feb 9)* Att: 171
Retford United 2 Stocksbridge PS 0 *(Feb 9)* Att: 125

SEMI-FINALS

Curzon Ashton 0 **Boston United** 2 *(Mar 13)* Att: 223
Retford United 1 Kendal Town 0 *(Mar 13)* Att: 198

FINAL *(April 21st at Lincoln United)*

Boston United 2 Retford United 0 Att: 503

UNIBOND LEAGUE PRESIDENT'S CUP *(First Division teams)*

PRELIMINARY ROUND

Cammell Laird 2 Colwyn Bay 1 *(Sep 8)* Att: 86
Chorley 0 **Prescot Cables** 1 *(Sep 8)* Att: 163
Clitheroe 2 Radcliffe Borough 0 *(Sep 8)* Att: 149
Curzon Ashton 3 Trafford 0 *(Sep 7)* Att: 111
FC Halifax Town 1 Wakefield 0 *aet (Sep 8)* Att: 422
Glapwell 2 **Belper Town** 2 *aet* (3-4p) *(Sep 8)* Att: 108
Goole 4 **Brigg Town** 6 *(Sep 8)* Att: 98
Loughborough Dyn. 4 Shepshed 3 *aet (Sep 8)* Att: 137
Market Drayton Town 3 Kidsgrove 2 *(Sep 8)* Att: 92
Spalding United 2 Lincoln United 0 *(Sep 8)* Att: 57
Willenhall Town 0 **Chasetown** 1 *aet (Sep 8)* Att: 157

FIRST ROUND

Belper Town 3 Sheffield 3 *aet* (3-1p) *(Oct 13)* Att: 135
Cammell Laird 0 **Warrington Town** 2 *(Oct 13)* Att: 72
Carlton Town 2 Mickleover Sports 1 *(Oct 13)* Att: 64
Chasetown 2 Rushall Olympic 1 *(Oct 13)* Att: 403
Curzon Ashton 4 Clitheroe 2 *aet (Oct 12)* Att: 89
FC Halifax Town 3 Ossett Albion 1 *(Oct 13)* Att: 439
Garforth Town 3 Harrogate Railway A. 2 *(Oct 13)* Att: 75
Leek Town 2 **Market Drayton Town** 3 *(Oct 20)* Att: 128
Loughborough Dyn. 0 **Grantham Town** 2 *(Oct 13)* Att: 88
Mossley 4 Lancaster City 1 *(Oct 13)* Att: 128
Prescot Cables 1 **Witton Albion** 2 *(Oct 13)* Att: 154
Quorn 3 Spalding United 0 *(Oct 13)* Att: 83
Salford City 1 **AFC Fylde** 5 *(Nov 17)* Att: 79
Skelmersdale Utd 3 Rossendale Utd 0 *(Oct 13)* Att: 116
Stamford 2 Brigg Town 2 *aet* (4-1p) *(Oct 13)* Att: 103
Woodley Sports 2 Leigh Genesis 1 *(Oct 13)* Att: 72

SECOND ROUND

AFC Fylde 3 Warrington Town 2 *(Dec 1)* Att: 77
Belper Town 2 Chasetown 0 *(Nov 24)* Att: 136
Carlton Town 1 **Stamford** 3 *(Nov 17)* Att: 82
Curzon Ashton 3 Garforth Town 1 *(Nov 16)* Att: 74
FC Halifax Town 2 Mossley 1 *(Nov 17)* Att: 420
Quorn 1 **Grantham Town** 3 *(Nov 17)* Att: 118
Skelmersdale Utd 5 Woodley Sports 2 *(Nov 17)* Att: 113
Witton Albion 2 Market Drayton T. 0 *(Nov 17)* Att: 112

QUARTER-FINALS

AFC Fylde 4 Witton Albion 1 *(Dec 8)* Att: 120
Belper Town 4 Grantham Town 0 *(Dec 8)* Att: 141
Curzon Ashton 2 **Skelmersdale Utd** 3 *(Dec 14)* Att: 100
Stamford 2 FC Halifax Town 1 *(Dec 8)* Att: 168

SEMI-FINALS

Skelmersdale United 2 **Belper Town** 3 *(Mar 13)* Att: 174
Stamford 1 AFC Fylde 0 *(Mar 13)* Att: 219

FINAL *(April 14th at Quorn)*

Belper Town 3 Stamford 1 Att: 286

PETER SWALES SHIELD CUP

(Prem Div champions v Chairman's Cup holders)

(May 1st at Guiseley)

Guiseley 1 Mickleover Sports 1 (5-3p) Att: 259

CHAIRMAN'S CUP

(Div One North v Div One South champions)

(April 28th at FC Halifax Town)

FC Halifax Town 2 **Mickleover Sports** 2 (1-3p) Att: 427

Northern Premier League Premier Division
Season's Stats 2009-2010

	Lg Pos	F.A. Cup	F.A. T	Av. Lg. Att.	Best Att.	Opponents	No of Goalscorers + own goals	Goalscorers with at least 10 goals	
Ashton United	12	2Q	1Q	163	258	v Bradford P.A.	17+ 3		-
Boston United	3	2Q	2Q	1314	2533	v F.C.United	15 + 0	Newsham	23
								Weir-Daley	18
								Davidson	16
Bradford P.A.	2	3Q	1Q	446	1150	v F.C.United	17+ 4	Hall	19
								Savory	19
								O'Brien	11
Burscough	16	3Q	1Q	218	675	v F. C.United	18+ 1	Byers	17
								Roberts	11
Buxton	8	3Q	2Q	348	1232	v F.C.Buxton	16 + 1	Reed	26
								Knight	13
								Lugsden	10
Durham City	20	1Q	1Q	176	606	v F.C.United	13 + 0	-	
F.C.United	13	3Q	3Q	1739	2871	v Matlock Town	14 + 1	Roca	13
								Marsh	11
Frickley Athletic	15	3Q	2Q	230	701	v F.C.United	16 + 0	-	
Guiseley	1	3Q	2Rd	330	841	v F.C.United	22 + 3	Walshaw	30
								Needham	10
Hucknall Town	17	3Q	1Q	229	573	v F.C.United	22 + 3	Nightingale	17
Kendall Town	5	4Q	1Q	246	1117	v F.C.United	22 + 1	Taylor	17
								Walmsley	17
Marine	9	1Q	1Q	355	1367	v Boston United	18 + 1	Rainford	16
Matlock Town	7	2Q	1Q	297	562	v F.C.United	16 + 0	Hannah	32
Nantwich Town	10	1Q	1Rd	444	1171	v F.C.United	16 + 1	Lennon	17
North Ferriby Utd	4	2Q	3Q	227	423	v Boston United	18 + 1	Bradshaw	24
								Davidson	17
Ossett Town	19	2Q	1Q	168	801	v F.C.United	19 + 0	-	
Retford Town	6	1Q	1Q	311	664	v Boston United	13 + 3	Harvey	14
								Thomas	14
								Godber	11
								Marrison	11
Stocksbridge P.S.	11	2Q	1Q	225	761	v F.C.United	20 + 1	Vardy	16
								Ring	15
								Ward	11
Whitby Town	14	2Q	2Q	294	636	v F.C.United	14+1	Beadle	15
								Hackworth	11
Worksop Town	18	1Q	1Q	174	398	v Boston United	15 + 1	Tomlinson	10

Statistics are compiled from League and Play-Off matches plus FA Cup and F.A.Trophy ties, with cup runs being shown by 1Q = First Round Qualifying and 1Rd = First Round Proper of the F.A.Cup and F.A.Trophy competitions.

The clubs scoring most penalties in the season were:
Guiseley: 13. James Walshaw 11 (including eight in the last fourteen games) plus Tony Lloyd 2.
Frickley Athletic: 9 Danny Walsh 6, Lee Morris 2 and Chris White.
Buxton's Mark Reed scored in eight consecutive games from 2nd March to 2nd April inclusively.

Champions Guiseley only failed to score in two of their 46 matches and scored twice as many goals as they conceded (90-45).

ASHTON UNITED

Chairman: David Aspinall
Secretary: Bryan Marshall **(T)** 07944 032 362
(E) bmarshall.aufc@btinternet.com
Additional Committee Members: Tony Collins, John Milne,Terry Hollis, Eric Stafford,Jackie Tierney Michael Cummings, Denise Pinder, Jim Pnder, Tony Robinson, Ronnie Thomasson, Jan Sutherland
Manager: Danny Johnson
Programme Editor: Ken Lee **(E)** kenlee1947@hotmail.co.uk

Club Factfile

Founded: 1878 **Nickname:** Robins
Previous Names: Hurst 1878-1947
Previous Leagues: Manchester, Lancashire Combination 1912-33, 48-64, 66-68, Midland 1964-66, Cheshire County 1923-48, 68-82, North West Counties 1982-92

Club Colours (change): Red and white halves/black/red (Navy and sky stripes/navy/sky)

Ground: Hurst Cross, Surrey Street, Ashton-u-Lyne OL6 8DY **(T)** 0161 339 4158 (Club) 330 1511 (Social)
Capacity: 4,500 **Seats:** 250 **Covered:** 750 **Clubhouse:** Yes **Shop:** Yes
Previous Grounds: Rose HIll 1878-1912

Simple Directions
From the M62 (approx 7.5 miles) Exit at Junction 20, take A627M to Oldham exit (2.5 miles) Take A627 towards Oldham town centre At King Street Roundabout take Park Road Continue straight onto B6194 Abbey Hills Road Follow B6194 onto Lees Road Turn right at the stone cross memorial and 1st right into the ground. From the M60 (approx 2.5 miles); Exit at Junction 23, take A635 for Ashton town centre Follow by-pass to B6194 Mossley Road. At traffic lights turn left into Queens Road Continue onto B6194 Lees Road Turn left at the stone cross memorial and 1st right into the ground.

Record Attendance: 11,000 v Halifax Town - FA Cup 1st Round 1952
Record Victory: 11-3 v Stalybridge Celtic - Manchester Intermediate Cup 1955
Record Defeat: 1-11 v Wellington Town - Cheshire League 1946-47
Record Goalscorer: Not known
Record Appearances: Micky Boyle - 462
Additional Records: Paid £9,000 to Netherfield for Andy Whittaker 1994
Received £15,000 from Rotherham United for Karl Marginson 1993

Senior Honours: Manchester Challenge Shield 1992-93. Northern Premier League Division 1 Cup 1994-95.
Manchester Senior Cup x4. Manchester Premier Cup x5, Manchester Junior Cup x3.

10 YEAR RECORD

00-01		01-02		02-03		03-04		04-05		05-06		06-07		07-08		08-09		09-10	
NP 1	3	NP 1	3	NP P	16	NP P	14	Conf N	21	NP P	15	NP P	18	NP P	10	NP P	9	NP P	12

ASHTON UNITED

No.	Date	Comp	H/A	Opponents	Att:	Result	Goalscorers	Pos
1	Aug 15	Unibond P.	A	Durham City	180	W 1 - 0	Smith 46	7
2	17		H	Kendal Town	142	L 2 - 3	Smith 22 Hallam 70 (og)	10
3	22		H	Guiseley	123	W 3 - 2	Howard 30 (pen) Piana 52 McFadden 85	6
4	29		A	Hucknall Town	231	W 2 - 1	Piana 42 46	4
5	31		H	Buxton	259	L 1 - 2	Silcox 3 (og)	
6	Sept 5		A	Bradford P.A.	310	W 1 - 0	Bennett 57	4
7	7		H	Burscough	139	D 1 - 1	Moore 9	4
8	**12**	**F.A.C 1Q**	**A**	**Lancaster City**	**191**	**W 3 - 0**	**McFadden 11Howard 40 Flanagan 86**	
9	15		A	Marine	218	W 4 - 3	Moore 32 Smith 61 Richards 84 Bennett 86	
10	19		H	Retford United	164	W 1 - 0	Bennett 61	2
11	22		A	NantwichTown	470	L 0 - 2		4
12	**26**	**F.A.C. 2Q**	**A**	**Chorley**	**294**	**L 0 - 2**		
13	Oct 3		H	Ossett Town	126	W 2 - 0	McFadden 30 Bennett 72	
14	5		H	Worksop Town	91	W 2 - 1	Howard 87 Jones 90 (og)	1
15	10		A	Boton United	1259	L 0 - 3		1
16	12		H	Whitby Town	152	D 2 - 2	Howard 57 (pen) Henry 75	1
17	**17**	**F.A.T 1Q**	**H**	**F.C.United**	**729**	**L 1 - 3**	**O'Neill 44**	
18	24		A	North Ferriby United	123	L 0 - 4		2
19	27		A	Frickley Athletic	213	W 2 - 1	Weston 45 Richards 81	
20	31		A	Burscough	174	W 2 - 1	Bennett 41 Richards 90	1
21	Nov 7		H	Stocksbridge Park Steels	152	L 0 - 1		1
22	14		A	Matlock Town	295	L 0 - 5		3
23	21		H	Hucknall Town	105	L 1 - 2	Richards 85	3
24	28		H	North Ferriby United	136	L 0 - 1		4
25	Dec 5		A	Retford United	295	L 2 - 3	Ferguson 34 Rchards 37	4
26	12		H	Marine	130	L 0 - 2		6
27	Jan 23		A	Ossett Town	98	W 3 - 0	Moore 5 Bennett 5 Flanagan 33	5
28	Feb 6		A	Worksop Town	137	D 1 - 1	O.Neill 78	7
29	13		H	Boston United	227	L 0 - 2		8
30	27		H	Nantwich Town	136	W 3 - 2	Howard 24 (pen) Bennett 69 Robinson 88	8
31	Mar 1		H	Matlock Town	148	L 0 - 2		
32	6		A	Stocksbridge P.S.	118	L 1 - 2	Egan 19	11
33	13		A	Whitby Town	239	D 1 - 1	Howard 82	
34	20		H	Frickley Athletic	122	L 1 - 3	Howard 83	13
35	27		H	Bradford P.A.	258	W 3 - 2	O'Neill 6 32 Robinson 22	11
36	April 5		H	F.C. United	707	D 2 - 2	O'Neill 53 Morning 58	
37	10		A	Buxton	312	L 0 - 2		15
38	15		A	Kendal Town	179	D 0 - 0		
39	17		H	Durham City	108	W 1 - 0	Smith 87	12
40	21		A	F.C.United	1624	W 3 - 2	Howard 28 (pen) Dawson 37 Robinson 46	
41	24		A	Guiseley	485	L 0 - 2		12
					Goals	52 68		

Home Attendances:	
Highest:	707 v F.C. United
Lowest:	105 v Hucknall Town
Average (08-09):	184 (242)
Top Goalscorer:	Howard - 8 (League 7, FAC 1)

BRADFORD PARK AVENUE

Chairman: Dr. John Dean
Secretary: Trevor Jowett (T) 07863 180 787
(E) tjj@21thirlmere.freeserve.co.uk
Additional Committee Members: Robert Blackburn, Kevin Hainsworth

Manager: Simon Collins
Programme Editor: Tim Parker (E) timparker79@yahoo.co.uk

Club Factfile

Founded: 1907 **Nickname:** Avenue
Previous Names: Reformed in 1988
Previous Leagues: Southern 1907-08, Football League 1908-70, Northern Premier 1970-74, West Riding Co.Am. 1988-89, Central Midlands 1989-90, North West Counties 1990-95

Club Colours (change): Green and white/green/green (Yellow/black/black)

Ground: Horsfall Stadium, Cemetery Road, Bradford, West Yorkshire BD6 2NG (T) 01274 604 578
Capacity: 5,000 **Seats:** 1,247 **Covered:** 2,000 **Clubhouse:** Yes **Shop:** Yes
Previous Grounds: Park Ave. 1907-73, Valley Parade 1973-74, Manningham Mills 1988-89, McLaren Field 1985-93, Batley 1993-96
Simple Directions
M62 to junction 26. Join M606 leave at second junction. At the roundabout take 2nd exit (A6036 signposted Halifax) and pass Odsal Stadium on the left hand side. At next roundabout take the 3rd exit (A6036 Halifax, Horsfall Stadium is signposted). After approximately one mile turn left down Cemetery Road immediately before the Kings Head Public House. Ground is 150 yards on the left.

Record Attendance: 2,100 v Bristol City - FA Cup 1st Round 2003
Record Victory: 11-0 v Derby Dale - FA Cup 1908
Record Defeat: 0-7 v Barnsley - 1911
Record Goalscorer: Len Shackleton - 171 (1940-46)
Record Appearances: Tommy Farr - 542 (1934-50)
Additional Records: Paid £24,500 to Derby County for Leon Leuty 1950
Received £34,000 from Derby County for Kevin Hector 1966

Senior Honours: Football League Division 3 North 1928.
North West Counties League 1994-95. Northern Premier League Division 1 2000-01, Division 1 North 2007-08.
West Riding Senior Cup x9. West Riding County Cup x2.

10 YEAR RECORD

00-01	01-02	02-03	03-04	04-05	05-06	06-07	07-08	08-09	09-10
NP 1 1	NP P 10	NP P 7	NP P 17	Conf N 22	NP P 21	NP 1 4	NP1N 1	NP P 7	NP P 2

BRADFORD PARK AVENUE

No.	Date	Comp	H/A	Opponents	Att:	Result	Goalscorers	Pos
1	Aug 15	Unibond P.	A	Buxton	421	D 1 - 1	Campbell 88	11
2	17		H	F.C.United	1150	W 3 - 2	Knowles 14 Savory 21 Hall 37	2
3	22		H	Hucknall Town	442	W 2 - 0	Hall 26 Baldry 68	4
4	25		A	Kendal Town	306	D 1 - 1	Hall 38	3
5	31		H	North Ferriby United	465	L 1 - 2	Bett 27 (pen)	
6	Sept 5		H	Ashton United	310	L 0 - 1		15
7	**12**	**F.A.C. 1Q**	**H**	**Bishop Auckland**	**248**	**W 4 - 1**	**Bett 19 Savoury 31 45 Ainge 56**	
8	14		H	Boston United	455	D 2 - 2	Baldry 52 Gibson 90	
9	22		A	Marine	223	W 3 - 1	Gibson 10 83 Savory 58	13
10	**26**	**F.A.C 2Q**	**H**	**Harrogate Town**	**375**	**W 4 - 0**	**Hall 12 GIBSON 3 (26 36 82)**	
11	Oct 3		H	Matlock Town	350	W 5 - 2	Brough 27 (og) Hall 45 46 O.Brien 67 88	11
12	5		H	Burscough	340	L 1 - 3	Savory 26	16
13	**10**	**F.A.C 3Q**	**A**	**Buxton**	**533**	**D 2 - 2**	**Savory 35 (pen) 56**	
14	**12**	**F.A.C. 3Qr**	**H**	**Buxton**	**375**	**L 0 - 1**		
15	**17**	**F.A.T. 1Q**	**H**	**Clitheroe**	**310**	**L 0 - 1**		
16	24		A	Stocksbridge Park Steels	224	W 3 - 2	Hall 34 65 Downes 73 (pen)	13
17	28		A	Whitby Town	346	W 3 - 2	Savory 5 37 Gibson 78	
18	31		H	Durham City	275	W 7 - 1	Ayre 3 (og) Baldry 35 Savory 36 54 O'Brien 82 Hall 84 90	
19	Nov 7		H	Retford United	343	L 0 - 1		
20	14		A	Worksop Town	168	W 3 - 1	James 16 Hall 24 Downes 70 (pen)	7
21	21		H	Frickley Athletic	319	W 3 - 1	Baldry 27 O'Brien 77 Price 81	5
22	28		A	Nantwich Town	516	W 1 - 0	Hume 82	3
23	Dec 5		H	Nantwich Town	325	W 3 - 2	Baldry 26 Savory 32 Hume 52	3
24	12		A	Boston United	1212	W 1 - 0	Downes 44 (pen)	2
25	23		A	Matlock Town	309	W 3 - 1	O'Brien 22 Savory 40 78	3
26	30		H	Marine	481	W 2 - 0	Price 20 Hall 26	1
27	Jan 6		A	Burscough	254	W 2 - 0	Baldry 13 Gibson 90	1
28	13		H	Ossett Town	484	W 4 - 2	James 1 O'Brien 53 Hume 66 Savory 67	1
29	16		A	North Ferriby United		L 2 - 4	James 3 Hall 13	
30	20		A	Durham City	208	W 7 - 0	Tiani 16 Downes 26 90 HALL 3 (33 40 85) Ovington 52	1
31	27		H	Stocksbridge P.S.	403	W 2 - 0	Tiani 50 Baldry 62	1
32	Mar 6		A	Retford United	547	D 1 - 1	Simpkins 25 (og)	1
33	13		H	Worksop Town	475	W 1 - 0	O'Brien 57	
34	24		A	F.C.United	1891	W 5 - 1	Baldry 33 HUME 3 (43 73 77) Savory 83	1
35	27		A	Ashton United	258	L 2 - 3	Baldry 43 Hall 75	
36	April 2		H	Kendal Town	526	W 3 - 2	Hall 45 52 Reeves 78	
37	5		A	Guiseley	1299	L 1 - 2	Tiani 6	
38	7		H	Guiseley	909	L 2 - 4	Elam 42 87	3
39	10		A	Ossett Town	252	W 6 - 4	Reeves 9 88 O'Brien 45 (pen) 67 Elam 54 Tiani 76	3
40	12		H	Buxton	535	D 0 - 0		
41	17		A	Frickley Athletic	309	D 2 - 2	Savory 45 O'Brien 90 (pen)	3
42	19		H	Whitby Town	406	W 1 - 0	Elam 90	
43	24		A	Hucknall Town	340	W 5 - 0	Reeves 17 71 Savory 46 James 73 Smith 75 (og)	2
44	**27**	**Play Off S-F**	**H**	**Kendal Town**	**608**	**W 2 - 1**	**Savory 10 O'Brien 45 (pen)**	
45	**May 1**	**Play Off Final**	**H**	**Boston United**	**2327**	**L 1 - 2**	**Reeves 34**	
					Goals	107 59		

Home Attendances:

Highest:	1150 v F.C. United
Lowest:	275 v Durham City
Average (08-09):	472 (499)
Top Goalscorer:	Hall - 19 (League 18, FAC 1)

BURSCOUGH

Chairman: Frank Parr
Secretary: Stan Petheridge (T) 07787 331 854
(E) stanpeth@fsmail.net
Additional Committee Members: Gary Wright, Richard Aindow, David Hughes

Manager: Andy Gray
Programme Editor: Stan Petheridge (E) stanpeth@fsmail.net

Unfortunately an up-to-date photograph was not available at the time of going to press

Club Factfile

Founded: 1946 **Nickname:** Linnets
Previous Names:
Previous Leagues: Liverpool County Combination 1946-53, Lancashire Combination 1953-70, Cheshire County 1970-82, North West Counties 1982-98, Northern Premier League 1998-2007, Conference 2007-09
Club Colours (change): All green (All pale blue)

Ground: Victoria Park, Bobby Langton Way, Mart Lane, Burscough L40 0SD (T) 01704 893 237
Capacity: 2,500 **Seats:** 270 **Covered:** 1,000 **Clubhouse:** Yes **Shop:** Yes
Previous Grounds:
Simple Directions
M6 to J27. Follow signs for 'Parbold' (A5209), carry on through Newburgh into Burscough passing Briars Hall Hotel on left. Turn right at second mini-roundabout into Junction Lane (signposted 'Burscough & Martin Mere') into village, over canal. Take second left into Mart Lane to ground at end.

Record Attendance: 4,798 v Wigan Athletic - FA Cup 3rd Qualifying Round 1950-51
Record Victory: 10-0 v Cromptons Rec - 1947 and v Nelson - 1948-49 both Lancashire Combination
Record Defeat: 0-9 v Earltown - Liverpool County Combination 1948-49
Record Goalscorer: Wes Bridge - 188
Record Appearances: Not known
Additional Records: Johnny Vincent scored 60 goals during the 1953-64 season
Louis Bimpson scored 7 goals in one game.
Senior Honours: North West Counties League Division 1 1982-83. FA Trophy 2002-03. Northern Premier League Premier Division 2006-07. Liverpool Challenge Cup x3. Liverpool Non-League Senior Cup x2.

10 YEAR RECORD

00-01	01-02	02-03	03-04	04-05	05-06	06-07	07-08	08-09	09-10
NP P 15	NP P 18	NP P 18	NP P 19	NP P 6	NP P 7	NP P 1	Conf N 8	Conf N 21	NP P 16

BURSCOUGH

No.	Date	Comp	H/A	Opponents	Att:	Result	Goalscorers	Pos
1	Aug 15	Unibond P.	A	Frickley Athletic	159	L 0 - 1		16
2	18		H	Hucknall Town	185	W 2 - 0	Byers 68 70	9
3	25		A	Nantwich Town	472	D 1 - 1	Byers 20	17
4	29		A	F.C.United	1879	L 0 - 2		21
5	31		H	Durham City	261	W 8 - 0	Roberts 5 Brookfield 28 Byers 40 Kay 45 Merella 60 O'Donnell 76 90 Taylor 86	
6	Sept 5		H	Boston United	280	W 3 - 1	Roberts 53 Byers 59 Brookfield 60	7
7	7		A	Ashton United	139	D 1 - 1	Parry 29	6
8	**13**	**F.A.C. 1Q**	**A**	**Hallam**	**102**	**W 4 - 0**	**Byers 65 82 McCulloch 87 Bayliss 90**	
9	15		H	Stocksbridge PS	175	L 0 - 1		
10	19		A	Ossett Town	158	W 2 - 1	Roberts 38 73	4
11	22		H	Guiseley	209	L 0 - 4		9
12	**26**	**F.A.C 2Q**	**A**	**Horden C.W.**	**86**	**W 4 - 1**	**Parry 34 88 McCulloch 59 Thomas 82 (og)**	
13	Oct 5		A	Bradford (P.A.)	340	W 3 - 1	Byers 18 Moore 58 Wilson 71	7
14	**10**	**F.A.C 3Q**	**A**	**F.C. Halifax**	**1459**	**L 0 - 1**		
15	13		H	Marine	319	L 1 - 2	Moore 48	9
16	**17**	**F.A.T 1Q**	**A**	**Brigg Town**	**105**	**L 2 - 3**	**McEvatt 68 Roberts 85**	
17	24		H	Worksop Town	203	W 3 - 0	Roberts 13 Baylis 47 Moore 61 (pen)	12
18	26		A	Buxton	253	D 2 - 2	Byers 47 Parry 83	
19	31		H	Ashton United	174	L 1 - 2	McCulloch 70	
20	Nov 7		H	Whitby Town	295	D 2 - 2	Roberts 55 88	12
21	14		A	North Ferriby United	226	L 0 - 1		14
22	21		H	Buxton	229	L 0 - 1		15
23	28		A	Boston United	1256	D 3 - 3	Byers 19 Hanley 39 Bayliss 90	14
24	Dec 12		A	Stocksbridge Park Steels	121	L 1 - 4	Roberts 38	
25	16		A	Hucknall Town	171	L 2 - 5	Field 423 Byers 50	15
26	23		H	Kendal Town	182	W 3 - 0	McEVATT 3 (20 44 89)	14
27	Feb 6		H	Bradford PA	254	L 0 - 2		15
28	13		A	Retford United	210	L 1 - 6	Byers 30	16
29	16		H	Nantwich Town	139	W 1 - 0	Byers 39	
30	20		A	Marine	404	L 1 - 2	McEvatt 7	
31	23		A	Kendal Town	164	L 2 - 3	Roberts 43 Mahon 86	
32	27		H	Retford United	225	L 0 - 4		16
33	Mar 6		A	Whitby Town	291	L 0 - 4		18
34	9		A	Guiseley	239	L 1 - 2	MacDermott 57	
35	20		H	Matlock Town	160	L 0 - 2		18
36	27		H	Ossett Town	191	W 5 - 1	McEvatt 33 88 Byers 64 90 Roberts 71	
37	April 2		H	North Ferriby United	214	L 0 - 1		18
38	5		A	Durham City	125	W 3 - 2	Byers 11 74 Moore 69	
39	10		H	F.C.United	675	W 1 - 0	Mahon 27	17
40	17		A	Matlock Town	271	L 0 - 1		17
41	21		A	Worksop Town		W 1 - 0	Foster 29	
42	24		H	Frickley Athletic	218	W 1 - 0	McEvatt 71	16
					Goals	65 70		

Home Attendances:	
Highest:	675 v F.C. United
Lowest:	139 v Nantwich Town
Average (08-09):	242 (408)
Top Goalscorer:	Byers - 17 (League 15, FAC 2)

BUXTON

Chairman: Tony Tomlinson
Secretary: Don Roberts (T) 07967 822 448
(E) admin@buxtonfc.co.uk
Additional Committee Members: C Brindley, B Goodwin, G Taylor, D Belfield, J Yates, P Timmins
Manager: John Reed
Programme Editor: Mike Barton (E) mike@buxtonfc.co.uk

Club Factfile

Founded: 1877 **Nickname:** The Bucks
Previous Names:
Previous Leagues: Combination 1891-99, Manchester 1899-1932, Cheshire County 1932-40, 46-73, Northern Premier 1973-98, Northern Counties East 1998-2006

Club Colours (change): All royal blue (White/black/black)

Ground: The Silverlands, Buxton, Derbyshire SK17 6QH (T) 01298 231 197
Capacity: 4,000 **Seats:** 490 **Covered:** 2,500 **Clubhouse:** Yes **Shop:** Yes
Previous Grounds:
Simple Directions
FROM STOCKPORT (A6): Turn left at first roundabout after dropping down the hill into the town, turn right at next roundabout, right at traffic lights (London Road pub) to Buxton Market Place. After two sets of pedestrian lights turn right at Royles shop then turn immediate left and follow road approx 500 metres to ground (opposite police station.) FROM BAKEWELL (A6): Turn left at roundabout on to Dale Road and follow road to traffic lights then as above. FROM MACCLESFIELD/CONGLETON/LEEK: Follow road to Burbage traffic lights and take right fork in the road at the Duke of York pub (Macclesfield Road.) Then at next traffic lights turn left (London Road pub) and follow as above. FROM ASHBOURNE (A515): Go straight on at first traffic lights (London Road pub) and follow directions as above.

Record Attendance: 6,000 v Barrow - FA Cup 1st Round 1961-62
Record Victory: Not known
Record Defeat: Not known
Record Goalscorer: Mark Reed - 164 (in 265 appearances 2002-07, 2009-)
Record Appearances: David Bainbridge - 642
Additional Records: Paid £5,000 to Hyde United for Gary Walker 1989
Received £16,500 from Rotherham for Ally Pickering 1989
Senior Honours: Manchester League 1931-32, Lge cup 1925-26, 26-27. Cheshire Co. League 1972-73, Lge Cup 1956-57, 57-58, 68-69. N.C.E. League 2005-06, Presidents Cup 2004-05, 05-06. N.P.L. Division 1 2006-07, President's Cup 1981-82, 2006-07. Derbyshire Senior Cup 1938-39, 45-46, 56-57, 59-60, 71-72, 80-81, 85-86, 86-87, 2008-09.

10 YEAR RECORD

00-01	01-02	02-03	03-04	04-05	05-06	06-07	07-08	08-09	09-10
NCEP 12	NCEP 19	NCEP 4	NCEP 7	NCEP 9	NCEP 1	NP 1 1	NP P 5	NP P 14	NP P 8

BUXTON

No.	Date	Comp	H/A	Opponents	Att:	Result	Goalscorers	Pos
1	Aug 15	Unibond P.	H	Bradford P.A.	421	D 1 - 1	Knight 87	12
2	18		A	Marine	305	D 1 - 1	Lugsden 88	13
3	23		A	Worksop Town	296	D 1 - 1	Knight 48	
4	25		H	Stocksbridge Park Steels	308	W 3 - 1	Towey 49 Ridley 70 Schofield 36 (og)	8
5	29		H	Retford United	352	L 0 - 2		15
6	31		A	Ashton United	259	W 2 - 1	Reed 50 McGraw 77	15
7	Sept 7		A	Hucknall Town	267	L 1 - 3	Lugsden 73	15
8	**12**	**F.A.C 1Q**	**H**	**Winterton Rangers**	**258**	**W 2 - 1**	**Reed 55 Knight 85**	
9	19		A	Frickey Athletic	287	L 0 - 1		10
10	22		A	Ossettt Town	144	L 1 - 3	Agus 10	16
11	**26**	**F.A.C. 2Q**	**H**	**Fylde**	**292**	**W 5 - 0**	**Lugsden 32 KNIGHT 3 (36 45 71) Millar 41**	
12	Oct 3		H	Nantwich Town	403	D 0 - 0		18
13	5		H	Boston United	352	L 0 - 1		20
14	**10**	**F.A.C. 3Q**	**H**	**Bradford P.A.**	**533**	**D 2 - 2**	**Lugsdon 57 74**	
15	**12**	**F.A.C. 3Qr**	**A**	**Buxton**	**375**	**W 1 - 0**	**Agus 89 (pen)**	
16	**17**	**F.A.T 1Q**	**H**	**Hednesford Town**	**352**	**W 1 - 0**	**Wilcox 43**	
17	**24**	**F.A.C. 4Q**	**H**	**Stourbridge**	**793**	**L 0 - 4**		
18	26		H	Burscough	253	D 2 - 2	Knight 67 Reed 74	20
19	**31**	**F.A.T 2Q**	**H**	**Stourbridge**	**262**	**L 0 - 1**		
20	Nov 7		A	F.C.United	2147	W 1 - 0	Knight 43	
21	14		A	Durham City	159	W 7 - 0	REED 4 (2 44 67 83) Millar 5 Knight 79 Ridley 87	17
22	21		A	Burscough	229	W 1 - 0	Knight 45	12
23	Dec 5		H	Hucknall Town	321	W 2 - 0	Reed 38 Knight 70	10
24	Jan 23		A	Nantwich Town	406	W 3 - 0	Knight 7 47 Ridley 22	13
25	26		A	Guiseley	236	L 1 - 3	Schofield 49	
26	Feb 6		A	Boston United	1151	L 1 - 2	Wilcox 85	14
27	9		H	Frickley Athletic	204	W 4 - 1	Black 47 Hanley 55 Reed 90 90	
28	13		H	Whitby Town	339	L 0 - 2		15
29	20		H	Guiseley	312	W 3 - 1	Morris 13 Reed 60 (pen) Lugsden 90	14
30	27		A	Kendal Town	250	W 2 - 0	Lugsden 52 Morris 81	12
31	Mar 2		H	Marine	236	D 2 - 2	Reed 6 Morris 62	
32	6		H	F.C.United	1232	W 3 - 0	Lugsden 17 Morris 26 Reed 83	9
33	9		A	Matlock Town	477	D 1 - 1	Reed 24	
34	13		H	North Ferriby United	315	D 1 - 1	Reed 84	
35	17		H	Ossett Town	222	D 2 - 2	Reed 22 40	
36	20		A	North Ferriby United	236	D 1 - 1	Reed 34	8
37	23		A	Retford United	205	W 2 - 1	Reed 14 Stevens 69	
38	27		H	Worksop Town	342	W 1 - 0	Reed 90 (pen)	7
39	April 2		A	Stocksbridge Park Steels	313	L 1 - 3	Reed 55	
40	5		H	Matlock Town	512	D 1 - 1	Stevens 64	
41	10		H	Ashton United	312	W 2 - 0	Reed 62 Morris 90	8
42	12		A	Bradford P.A.	535	D 0 - 0		
43	17		A	Whitby Town	331	W 5 - 1	Reed 16 Maxfield 40 Anderson 52 Morris 70 Stevens 79	8
44	19		H	Kendal Town		L 1 - 2	Reed 81 (pen)	
45	24		H	Durham City	307	W 6 - 2	Lugsden 11 89 Reed 24 55 Morris 44 Ridley 66	8
					Goals	77 51		

Home Attendances:	
Highest:	1273 v F.C. United
Lowest:	204 v Frickley Athletic
Average (08-09):	367 (442)
Top Goalscorer:	Reed - 26 (League 25, FAC 1, Hat-trick 1)

CHASETOWN

Chairman: John Donnelly
Secretary: John Richards **(T)** 07866 902 093
(E) john.goddard200@ntlworld.com
Additional Committee Members: Michael Joiner, Alan Smith, Janice Brooks, John Goddard, Steve Maden, Mark Prince, Dave Goddard, Robert Brookes
Manager: Charlie Blakemore
Programme Editor: Russell Brown **(E)** rwbcfc@googlemail.com

Club Factfile

Founded: 1954 **Nickname:** The Scholars
Previous Names: Chase Terrace Old Scholars 1954-72
Previous Leagues: Cannock Youth 1954-58, Lichfield & District 1958-61, Staffordshire County 1961-72, West Midlands 1972-94, Midland Alliance 1994-2006, Southern 2006-09

Club Colours (change): Royal blue/royal blue/white (Bright red/bright red/white)

Ground: The Scholars, Church Street, Chasetown, Walsall WS7 8QL **(T)** 01543 682 222
Capacity: 2,000 **Seats:** 151 **Covered:** 220 **Clubhouse:** Yes **Shop:** Yes
Previous Grounds: Burntwood Recreation
Simple Directions
From the M42 junction10 towards Tamworth or from the M6 Junction 11 or 12 towards Cannock or the A38 southbound from Derby - follow signs for A5 towards Brownhills, At the traffic lights at the Terrace Restaurant turn towards Burntwood onto the A5195. Straight over first island towards Chasetown and Hammerwich, over toll road and at second island turn left into Haney Hay Road which leads into Highfields Road signposted Chasetown, up the hill to mini island, then straight on into Church Street past the church on left and school on right. Ground is on the left at end of road. If using M6 Toll exit at junction T6 Burntwood - turn left out of Toll booths and left at second island and follow over toll road as above.

Record Attendance: 2,420 v Cardiff City - FA Cup 3rd Round January 2008
Record Victory: 14-1 v Hanford - Walsall Senior Cup 1991-92
Record Defeat: 1-8 v Telford United Reserves - West Midlands League
Record Goalscorer: Tony Dixon - 197
Record Appearances: Not known
Additional Records:

Senior Honours: West Midlands League 1978, League Cup x2.
Midland Alliance 2005-06.
Walsall Senior Cup x2.

10 YEAR RECORD

00-01	01-02	02-03	03-04	04-05	05-06	06-07	07-08	08-09	09-10
MidAl 10	MidAl 18	MidAl 9	MidAl 7	MidAl 2	MidAl 1	SthM	SthM 7	SthM 4	NP1S 2

COLWYN BAY

Chairman: Geoff Cartwight
Secretary: Grant McIndoe (T) 07769 538 012
(E) egmcindoe@yahoo.co.uk
Additional Committee Members: Roger Skinner, Darren Cartwright, Martin Cartwright, Mark Williams
Manager: David Challinor
Programme Editor: Mark Williams (E) mark_williams_cbfc@hotmail.co.uk

Unfortunately an up-to-date photograph was not available at the time of going to press

Club Factfile

Founded: 1885 **Nickname:** Seagulls
Previous Names:
Previous Leagues: North Wales Coast 1901-21, 33-35, Welsh National 1921-30, North Wales Combination 1930-31, Welsh League (North) 1945-84, North West Counties 1984-91
Club Colours (change): Sky blue and claret/sky blue/sky blue (All white)

Ground: Llanelian Road, Old Colwyn, North Wales LL29 8UN (T) 01492 514 581
Capacity: 2,500 **Seats:** 250 **Covered:** 700 **Clubhouse:** Yes **Shop:** Yes
Previous Grounds: Eirias Park
Simple Directions
From Queensferry take the A55 and exit at Junction 22 signposted Old Colwyn at end of slip road turn left, up the hill to the mini roundabout, straight across onto Llanelian Road, ground is approx half mile on the right.

Record Attendance: 5,000 v Borough United at Eirias Park 1964
Record Victory: Not known
Record Defeat: Not known
Record Goalscorer: Peter Donnelly
Record Appearances: Bryn A Jones
Additional Records:

Senior Honours: Northern League Division 1 1991-92, Division 1 Play-off 2009-10

10 YEAR RECORD

00-01		01-02		02-03		03-04		04-05		05-06		06-07		07-08		08-09		09-10	
NP P	19	NP P	20	NP P	22	NP 1	16	NP 1	13	NP 1	12	NP 1	5	NP1S	7	NP1N	4	NP1N	4

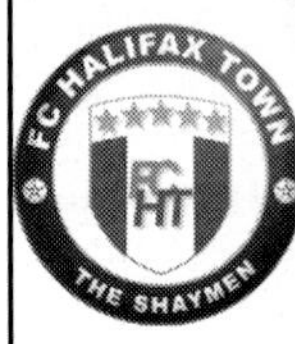

F.C. HALIFAX TOWN

Chairman: David Bosmworth

Secretary: Hayley Horne **(T)** 01422 341 222 **(E)** hayleyhorne@halifaxafc.co.uk

Additional Committee Members: Bobby Ham, Stuart Peacock

Manager: Neil Aspin

Programme Editor: Greg Stainton **(E)** marketing@sandal.bmw-net.co.uk

Back Row: Dan Codman, Nicky Gray, James Riley, Phil Senior, Jonathan Hedge, Steve Payne, Paul Sykes, Sam Jerome

Middle Row: Trevor Storton Assistant Manager, James Dean, Mark Whitehouse, Luke Smith, Neil Ross, Ross Clegg, Alan Russell-Cox Physio, Kevin Gillespie Fitness Coach

Front Row: Richard Marshall, Aaron Hardy, Daniel Lowe, Ryan Crossley, Neil Aspin Manager, Tom Baker, Scott Phelan, Mark Peers, Mark Hotte

Club Factfile

Founded: 1911 **Nickname:** Shaymen

Previous Names: Halifax Town 1911-2008 then reformed as F.C. Halifax Town

Previous Leagues: Yorkshire Combination 1911-12, Midland 1912-21, Football League 1921-93, 98-2002, Conference 1993-98, 2002-08

Club Colours (change): All blue (Lime green/black/lime green and black)

Ground: The Shay Stadium, Shay Syke, Halifax HX1 2YT **(T)** 01422 341 222

Capacity: 6,561 **Seats:** 2,330 **Covered:** 4,231 **Clubhouse:** Yes **Shop:** Yes

Previous Grounds: Sandhall Lane 1911-15, Exley 1919-20

Simple Directions
M62, junction 24, head towards Halifax on A629 and the Town Centre. After 3-4 miles, ground is on the right (Shaw Hill) sign posted The Shay.

Record Attendance: 36,885 v Tottenham Hotspur - FA Cup 5th Round 14/02/1953

Record Victory: 12-0 v West Vale Ramblers - FA Cup 1st Qualifying Road 1913-14

Record Defeat: 0-13 v Stockport County - Division 3 North 1933-34

Record Goalscorer: Albert Valentine

Record Appearances: John Pickering

Additional Records:

Senior Honours: Conference 1997-98. Northern Premier League Division 1 North 2009-10.

10 YEAR RECORD

00-01		01-02		02-03		03-04		04-05		05-06		06-07		07-08		08-09		09-10	
FL 3	23	FL 3	24	Conf	8	Conf	19	Conf	9	Conf	4	Conf	16	Conf	20	NP1N	8	NP1N	1

Do you remember when...

Halifax Town

Halifax Town experienced their first spell in The Conference in 1993-1994 when they finished thirteenth, and this group started the following campaign and achieved an improvement of five places.

Back row, left to right: William Griffiths, Andrew Heningway, Chris Horsfall, Damian Place and Paul Hand.
Middle row: Darren Heyes, Danny Megson, Noel Homer, Lee Ludlow, Michael Midwood, Paul Stoneman, Michael Trotter, Gary Worthington, Elliot Beddard and Andy Woods.
Front row: Alan Russell-Cox (Physio), Simon Johnson, Lee Wilson, Simon Thompson, John Bird (Manager), Jon Brown, Steve Prindiville, Kieran O'Regan, George Mulhall (Assistant Manager).

F.C. UNITED OF MANCHESTER

Chairman: Andy Walsh (General Manager)
Secretary: Lindsey Robertson (T) 0161 273 8950
(E) lindsey@fc-utd.co.uk
Additional Committee Members: Adam Brown, Scott Fletcher, Alan Hargreave, Helen Lambert, John Manning, Martin Morris, Steve Pagnam, Phil Sheeran, Mike Sherrard, Jules Spencer, Alison Watt
Manager: Karl Marginson
Programme Editor: Lindsey Robertson (E) lindsey@fc-utd.co.uk

Club Factfile

Founded: 2005 **Nickname:** F.C.
Previous Names: None
Previous Leagues: North West Counties 2005-07

Club Colours (change): Red/white/black (White/black/white)

Ground: Bury F.C., Gigg Lane, Bury B19 9HR (T) 0161 273 8950 / 764 4881
Capacity: 11,840 **Seats:** **Covered:** **Clubhouse:** Yes **Shop:** Yes
Previous Grounds:
Simple Directions
Exit M60 at junction 17 (s/p A56 Whitefield, Salford). At roundabout follow signs to Whitfield A56, Radcliffe (A665), Bury A56 onto the A56. After 0.3 miles go straight over double traffic lights passing McDonalds on LHS (s/p Bury A56, Radcliffe A665). At lights after 0.8 miles (just after the Bulls Head pub) bear right (s/p Bury A56). Straight on at lights after 1.0 miles (s/p Town Centre). After 1.0 miles turn right (s/p Football Ground) into Gigg Lane. Ground is on RHS after 0.1 miles. From North and East (via M66): Exit M66 at junction 2 and follow signs to Bury A58, Football Ground onto the A58 Rochdale Road. After 0.5 miles turn left at traffic lights by the Crown Hotel (s/p Football Ground) onto Heywood Street. After 0.4 miles turn right at second mini-roundabout (s/p Football Ground, Manchester, Salford B6219) into Wellington Road. At next mini-roundabout turn left into Market Street. Straight on over mini-roundabout after 0.1 miles and right at T-junction after 0.2 miles into Gigg Lane.

Record Attendance: 6,023 v Great Harwood Town - 22/04/2006
Record Victory: 10-2 v Castleton Gabriels - 10/12/2005
Record Defeat: 1-5 v Bradford Park Avenue - 24/03/2010
Record Goalscorer: Rory Patterson - 99 (2005-08)
Record Appearances: Simon Carden - 199 (2005-10)
Additional Records: Simon Carden scored 5 goals against Castleton Gabriels 10/12/2005

Senior Honours: North West Counties League Division 2 2005-06, Division 1 2006-07.
Northern Premier League Division 1 North Play-off 2007-08.

10 YEAR RECORD

00-01	01-02	02-03	03-04	04-05	05-06	06-07	07-08	08-09	09-10
					NWC2 1	NWC1 1	NP1N 2	NP P 6	NP P 13

F.C. UNITED OF MANCHESTER

No.	Date	Comp	H/A	Opponents	Att:	Result	Goalscorers	Pos
1	Aug 15	Northern P.	H	Boston United	2482	L 1 - 2	Tong 80	15
2	17		A	Bradford P.A.	1150	L 2 - 3	Carden 68 85	18
3	22		A	Retford Town	613	D 1 - 1	Tong 57	19
4	29		H	Burscough	1879	W 2 - 0	Wright 44 Mann 58	8
5	26		H	Marine	1884	W 3 - 0	Nugent 7 Deegan 47 Mack 90	
6	31		A	Ossett Town	801	W 2 - 1	Deegan 59 Chadwick 90	
7	Sept 5		A	Kendal Town	1117	L 0 - 1		8
8	9		H	Whitby Town	1716	D 1 - 1	Wright 90	
9	**12**	**F.A.C 1Q**	**A**	**Sheffield F.C.**	**1208**	**W 3 - 1**	**Deegan 31 Roca 39 (pen) 45**	
10	19		H	Guiseley	2108	L 1 - 2	Wright 36	12
11	23		A	Worksop Town	345	L 1 - 3	Tong 81	18
12	**26**	**F.A.C. 2Q**	**A**	**North Ferriby United**	**838**	**W 1 - 0**	**Deegan 66**	
13	Oct 3		H	Stocksbridge Park Steels	1888	W 4 - 3	Roca 6 (pen) 90 Deegan 51 Wright 77	13
14	7		H	Nantwich Town	1650	W 4 - 0	MARSH 3 (23 31 63) Mack 84	9
15	**11**	**F.A.C 3Q**	**H**	**Stalybridge Celtic**	**2819**	**D 3 - 3**	**Roca 13 Marsh 35 Chadwick 50**	
16	**13**	**F.A.C.3Qr**	**A**	**Stalybridge celtic**	**1923**	**W 1 - 0**	**Wright 35**	
17	**17**	**F.A.T 1Q**	**A**	**Ashton UNited**	**729**	**W 3 - 1**	**Marsh 22 Tong 43 Roca 70**	
18	**24**	**F.A.C 4Q**	**A**	**Northwich Victoria**	**2615**	**L 0 - 3**		
19	27		A	North Ferriby United	412	L 0 - 1		17
20	**31**	**F.A.T 2Q**	**A**	**Lancaster City**	**743**	**D 3 - 3**	**Yoffe 15 21 Roca 75**	
21	**Nov 4**	**F.A.T. 2Qr**	**H**	**Lancaster City**	**756**	**W 1 - 0**	**Deegan 95**	
22	7		H	Buxton	2147	L 0 - 1		18
23	14		A	Hucknall Town	573	W 3 - 2	Marsh 8 45 Cottrell 27	16
24	**21**	**F.A.T 3Q**	**H**	**Harrogate Town**	**1166**	**L 2 - 3**	**Carden 64 85**	
25	Dec 5		A	Whitby Town	636	D 2 - 2	Leeson 39 (og) Yoffe 47	19
26	12		H	Retford United	1920	L 2 - 4	Roca 41 Carden 61	
27	Jan 23		A	Stocksbridge Park Steels	761	D 1 - 1	Roca 59	17
28	27		H	Frickley Athletic	1468	D 0 - 0		
29	30		A	Durham City	606	W 2 - 1	Yoffe 50 Marsh 77	15
30	Feb 6		A	Nantwich Town	1171	W 6 - 1	WILSON 3 (5 23 79) Carden 37 Deegan 47 Wright 72	
31	13		H	Worksop Town	2137	W 2 - 0	Carden 43 55	10
32	20		A	Frickley Athletic	701	W 2 - 0	Deegan 1 Wilson 66	9
33	27		H	North Ferriby United	2121	D 3 - 3	Deegan 59 79 (pen) Chadwick 65	
34	Mar 3		H	Ossettt Town	1681	W 2 - 1	Wright 11 Deegan 90	
35	6		A	Buxton	1232	L 0 - 3		10
36	13		A	Durham City	2164	L 1 - 2	Roca 9	
37	16		A	Matlock Town	562	L 3 - 4	Chadwick 15 Marsh 48 Wright 68	
38	20		H	Hucknall Town	2016	W 2 - 0	Roca 10 Chadwick 75	10
39	24		H	Bradford P.A.	1891	L 1 - 5	Marsh 48	
40	27		A	Guiseley	841	L 0 - 2		13
41	April 2		A	Marine	1093	D 1 - 1	Chadwick 45	
42	5		A	Ashton United	707	D 2 - 2	Roca 10 (pen) 11	
43	7		H	Kendal Town	1585	L 1 - 4	Mack 85	
44	10		A	Buxton	312	L 0 - 2		13
45	17		A	Boston United	2533	L 1 - 4	Wright 4	15
46	21		H	Aashton United	1624	L 2 - 3	Marsh 20 Deegan 73	
47	24		H	Matlock Town	2871	W 1 - 0	Wright 83	13
					Goals	79 80		

Home Attendances:	
Highest:	2871 v Matlock Town
Lowest:	1468 v Frickley Athletic
Average (08-09):	1954 (2195)
Top Goalscorer:	Roca - 13 (League 8, FAC 3, Hat-trick 2)

FRICKLEY ATHLETIC

Chairman: Peter Bywater
Secretary: Steve Pennock (T) 07985 291 074
(E) steve@pennocks.freeserve.co.uk
Additional Committee Members: Gareth Dando, Steve Shorthouse, Barry Johnson, Colin Theedom
Manager: Billy Heath
Programme Editor: Darren Haynes (E) Darren_haynes@live.co.uk

Unfortunately an up-to-date photograph was not available at the time of going to press

Club Factfile

Founded: 1910 **Nickname:** The Blues
Previous Names: Frickley Colliery
Previous Leagues: Sheffield, Yorkshire 1922-24, Midland Counties 1924-33, 34-60, 70-76, Cheshire County 1960-70, Northern Premier 1976-80, Conference 1980-87
Club Colours (change): Blue and white stripes/blue/blue (White/black/black)

Ground: Tech5 Stadium, Westfield Lane, South Elmsall, Pontefract WF9 2EQ **(T)** 01977 642 460
Capacity: 2,087 **Seats:** 490 **Covered:** 700 **Clubhouse:** Yes **Shop:** Yes
Previous Grounds: Not known
Simple Directions
From North : Leave A1 to join A639, go over flyover to junction. Turn left and immediately right, signed South Elmsall. Continue to roundabout and take 2nd exit to traffic lights and turn left onto Mill Lane (B6474). Turn right at the T-junction and continue down hill to next T-junction. Turn right and immediately left up Westfield Lane. The ground is signposted to the left after about half a mile.

From South : Exit M18 at J2 onto A1 (North). Leave A1 for A638 towards Wakefield. Continue on A638, going straight on at the first roundabout and turn left at next roundabout to traffic lights. Continue as above from traffic lights.

Record Attendance: 6,500 v Rotherham United - FA Cup 1st Round 1971
Record Victory: Not known
Record Defeat: Not known
Record Goalscorer: K Whiteley
Record Appearances: Not known
Additional Records: Received £12,500 from Boston United for Paul Shirtliff and from Northampton Town for Russ Wilcox

Senior Honours: Hallamshire Senior Cup x10

10 YEAR RECORD

00-01	01-02	02-03	03-04	04-05	05-06	06-07	07-08	08-09	09-10
NP P 20	NP P 13	NP P 20	NP P 22	NP P 18	NP P 2	NP P 16	NP P 14	NP P 11	NP P 15

FRICKLEY ATHLETIC

No.	Date	Comp	H/A	Opponents	Att:	Result	Goalscorers	Pos
1	Aug 15	Unibond P.	H	Burscough	159	W 1 - 0	Walsh 67	8
2	18		A	Ossett Town	184	L 1 - 4	Morris 12	12
3	22		A	Whitby Town	267	L 1 - 3	Holt 90	16
4	25		H	Boston United	338	L 0 - 1		19
5	29		H	Worksop Town	203	D 1 - 1	Daly 52	20
6	31		A	Stocksbridge Park Steels	375	L 1 - 4	White 16	
7	Sept 5		A	Marine	253	L 0 - 2		20
8	8		H	Durham City	193	W 3 - 1	Towler 53 Morris 74 (pen) Lindley 77	19
9	**13**	**F.A.C. 1Q**	**A**	**Worksop Town**	**178**	**D 1 - 1**	**Towler 75**	
10	**16**	**F.A.C. 1Qr**	**H**	**Worksop Town**	**228**	**W 2 - 1**	**Davies 18 Morris 63**	
11	19		H	Buxton	287	W 1 - 0	Walsh 22	18
12	22		A	Matlock Town	333	D 2 - 2	Davies 25 Towler 71	19
13	**16**	**F.A.C. 2Q**	**A**	**Congleton Town**	**294**	**W 1 - 0**	**Towler 55**	
14	Oct 3		H	North Ferriby United	215	W 2 - 1	Morris 74 White 80	17
15	**10**	**F.A.C 3Q**	**A**	**Lincoln United**	**273**	**D 1 - 1**	**Booth 38**	
16	**13**	**F.A.C.3Qr**	**H**	**Lincoln United**	**274**	**D 1 - 1**	**Towler 64 Lincoln United won 3-1 on penalties**	
17	**17**	**F.A.T. 1Q**	**H**	**Bamber Bridge**	**171**	**W 2 - 1**	**Morris 16 Towler 75**	
18	24		H	Hucknall Town	187	W 4 - 2	Morris 31 61 (pen) Walsh 82 Towler 84	16
19	27		H	Ashton United	213	L 1 - 2	Groome 68	
20	**31**	**F.A.T 2Q**	**H**	**Guiseley**	**254**	**L 0 - 3**		
21	Nov 7		A	Guiseley	360	D 0 - 0		16
22	21		A	Bradford P.A.	319	L 1 - 3	White 21 (pen)	19
23	Dec 5		A	Durhan City	133	W 3 - 2	Morris 37 Lindley 39 Clarke 65	17
24	12		H	Kendal Town	212	D 0 - 0		18
25	Jan 23		A	North Ferriby United	256	L 1 - 5	Morris 53	18
26	27		A	F.C.United	1468	D 0 - 0		
27	Feb 6		H	Marine	162	L 0 - 1		18
28	9		A	Buxton	204	L 1 - 4	Groome 44	
29	13		A	Nantwich Town	318	L 1 - 3	Towler 63	
30	16		A	Worksop Town	137	W 2 - 1	White 31 Lee 90	17
31	20		H	F.C.United	701	L 0 - 2		17
32	27		A	Hucknall Town	206	D 2 - 2	Lee 18 56	17
33	Mar 6		H	Matlock Town	199	W 1 - 0	Walsh 82 (pen)	16
34	12		H	Ossett Town	191	D 1 - 1	Lee 7	
35	16		H	Nantwich Town	143	W 2 - 0	White 32 Goddard 85	
36	20		A	Ashton United	122	W 3 - 1	White 36 Clarke 74 Lindley 86	16
37	27		A	Retford United	297	W 5 - 3	Walsh 41 (pen) 43 (pen) LEE 3 (62 85 90)	
38	April 2		A	Boston United	1417	L 2 - 4	Chapman 22 Clarke 39	
39	5		H	Retford UNited	325	L 1 - 2	Walsh 82 (pen)	15
40	7		H	Whitby Town	153	D 1 - 1	Walsh 35 (pen)	
41	10		H	Stocksbridge PS	182	W 1 - 0	Wood 47	14
42	13		A	Kendal Town	195	L 1 - 3	Catton 67	
43	17		H	Bradford P.A.	309	D 2 - 2	Walsh 39 (pen) Clarke 66	14
44	20		H	Guiseley	292	L 1 - 2	White 66	
45	24		A	Buxton	218	L 0 - 1		15
					Goals	58 74		

Home Attendances:	
Highest:	701 v F.C. United
Lowest:	143 v Nantwich Town
Average (08-09):	246 (286)
Top Goalscorer:	Walsh - 9 (League 9)

HUCKNALL TOWN

Chairman: David Gamble
Secretary: Tony Knowles (T) 07775 001 266
(E) tony.knowles@ntlworld.com
Additional Committee Members: John Coleman, Peter Chapman, Dave Green, Geoff Gospel, Andy Johnson, Lynne Taylor, Andy Graves
Manager: Tommy Brooklands
Programme Editor: Terry Brumpton (E) terrybrumpton@yahoo.co.uk

Club Factfile

Founded: 1987 **Nickname:** The Town
Previous Names: Not known
Previous Leagues: Bulwell & District 1946-59, 60-65, Central Alliance 1959-60 Notts Spartan 1965-70, Central Midlands 1989-92
Club Colours (change): Yellow/black/yellow (All white)

Ground: Watnall Road, Hucknall, Notts NG15 6EY (T) 0115 963 0206 (Club) 956 1253 (Social)
Capacity: 3,013 **Seats:** 500 **Covered:** 900 **Clubhouse:** Yes **Shop:** Yes
Previous Grounds: Not known
Simple Directions
Exit the M1 at Junction 27 and take the A608 towards Hucknall. Turn right onto the A611 to Hucknall then take the Hucknall bypass. At the second roundabout join Watnall Road (B6009) and the ground is 100 yards on the right.

Record Attendance: 1,841 v Bishop's Stortford - FA Trophy Semi-final 2004-05
Record Victory: 12-1 v Teversal - Notts Senior Cup 1989-90
Record Defeat: Not known
Record Goalscorer: Maurice Palethorpe - 400 approx. (1980-90)
Record Appearances: Dave McCarthy - 282
Additional Records: Received £10,000 from Brentford for Stuart Nelson 2003-04

Senior Honours: Central Midlands League 1989-90, 90-91, League Cup x3. Northern Counties East 1997-98, League Cup x3.
Northern Premier League Premier Division 2003-04.
Notts Senior Cup x5.

10 YEAR RECORD

00-01	01-02	02-03	03-04	04-05	05-06	06-07	07-08	08-09	09-10
NP P 10	NP P 16	NP P 8	NP P 1	Conf N 10	Conf N 12	Conf N 13	Conf N 20	Conf N 22	NP P 17

HUCKNALL TOWN

No.	Date	Comp	H/A	Opponents	Att:	Result	Goalscorers	Pos
1	Aug 15	Northern P.	H	Ossett Town	233	W 3 - 0	NIGHTINGALE 3 (11 58 82)	2
2	18		A	Burscough	185	L 0 - 2		6
3	22		A	Bradford P.A.	442	L 0 - 2		13
4	25		H	Matlock Town	291	D 2 - 2	Whittington 26 Bonnick 79	14
5	29		H	Ashton United	231	L 1 - 2	Meikle 24	16
6	31		A	Boston United	1471	D 2 - 2	Whittington 48 Wilson 76 (pen)	16
7	Sept 5		A	Durham City	153	W 2 - 0	Smith 79 Shiels 80	16
8	8		H	Buxton	267	W 3 - 1	Shiels 7 Walters 9 Meikle 63	7
9	**12**	**F.A.C. 1Q**	**A**	**Blackstones**	**85**	**W 4 - 2**	**Jones 6 (og) Gover 54 (og) Nightingale 60 Hawkridge 67**	
10	19		H	Kendal Town	204	W 4 - 2	Nightingale 23 Wilson 56 60 Frost 82	6
11	22		A	King's Lynn	674	L 0 - 3		10
12	**26**	**F.A.C 2Q**	**A**	**Rugby Town**	**224**	**W 3 - 1**	**Nightingale 32 Liburd 38 Kelly 90**	
13	Oct 3		H	Whitby Town	237	W 2 - 0	McCormick 60 Wiggin-Thomas 86	9
14	6		H	Stocksbridge Park Steels	196	W 4 - 3	Nightingale 13 Whittington 15 Meikle 75 Kelly 76	9
15	**10**	**F.A.C. 3Q**	**A**	**Stourbridge**	**384**	**D 0 - 0**		
16	**13**	**F.A.C. 3Qr**	**H**	**Stourbridge**	**324**	**L 1 - 6**	**Wilson 14**	
17	**17**	**F.A.T 1Q**	**A**	**Nuneaton Town**	**660**	**D 1 - 1**	**Thomas 10**	
18	**20**	**F.A.T. 1Qr**	**H**	**Nuneaton Town**	**215**	**L 0 - 3**		
19	24		A	Frickley Atheltic	187	L 2 - 4	Whittington 6 Wilson 24	13
20	27		H	Retford United	283	L 1 - 4	Whittington 24	13
21	Nov 7		H	Nantwich Town	167	D 1 - 1	Whittington 86	13
22	10		A	Retford Town	226	W 2 - 1	Ellender 4 (og) Wilson 87 (pen)	
23	14		H	F.C.United	573	L 2 - 3	Bonnick 67 Nightingale 87	
24	21		A	Ashton United	105	W 2 - 1	Smedley 35 Bonnick 90 (pen)	8
25	28		H	Durham City	198	W 7 - 1	Smedley 32 43 Nightingale 47 55 Hawkridge 51 Bonnick 75 89	7
26	Dec 5		A	Buxton	321	L 0 - 2		7
27	12		H	North Ferriby United	150	L 1 - 4	Nightingale 46	
28	Jan 16		H	Burscough	171	W 5 - 2	Nightingale 1 90 Hawes 47 Bonnick 57 Wiggins-Thomas 61	5
29	23		A	Whitby Town	221	L 1 - 3	Boafo 45	6
30	Feb 6		A	Stocksbridge P.S.	134	W 3 - 2	Nightingale 67 81 O'Brien 88	6
31	9		H	Worksop Town	227	W 3 - 1	Meikle 14 Nightingale 44 Hawes 79	
32	13		H	Marine	97	D 0 - 0		5
33	20		A	North Ferriby United	241	D 2 - 2	Nightingale 13 Wilson 36	6
34	27		H	Frickley Athletic	206	D 2 - 2	Nightingale 14 Smith 62	7
35	Mar 6		A	Marine	315	L 1 - 2	Lathem 62 (og)	7
36	13		H	Guiseley	228	L 0 - 1		
37	20		A	F.C. United	2016	L 0 - 2		12
38	27		A	Kendal Town	196	L 1 - 3	Wilson 18	14
39	April 2		A	Matlock Town	335	L 1 - 5	Hopkinson 26	
40	5		H	Boston United	501	L 1 - 4	Hawes 7	
41	11		A	Worksop Town	237	D 1 - 1	Garner 46	
42	17		A	Nantwich Town	503	L 1 - 4	Wiggins-Thomas 58	16
43	20		A	Ossett Town	78	D 2 - 2	Williams 40 Hawkridge 87	
44	24		H	Bradford P.A.	340	L 0 - 5		17
					Goals	74 94		

Home Attendances:	
Highest:	573 v F.C. United
Lowest:	150 v North Ferriby United
Average (08-09):	257 (294)
Top Goalscorer:	Nightingale - 17 (League 15, FAC 2 - Hat-trick 1)

KENDAL TOWN

Chairman: Haydon Munslow

Secretary: Craig Campbell (T) 07980 660 428
(E) craig_campbell1@sky.com

Additional Committee Members: Roy Nicholson, Graham O'Callaghan, Brett Munslow, Steve Dixon, Meril Tummey

Manager: Lee Ashcroft

Programme Editor: (E)

Club Factfile

Founded: 1919 **Nickname:** Town

Previous Names: Netherfield

Previous Leagues: Westmorland, North Lancashire Combination 1945-68, Northern Premier 1968-83, North West Counties 1983-87

Club Colours (change): Black and white stripes/white/white (All red)

Ground: Lakelands Radio Stadium, Parkside Road, Kendal, Cumbria LA9 7BL (T) 01539 727 472 / 722 469

Capacity: 2,490 **Seats:** 450 **Covered:** 1000 **Clubhouse:** Yes **Shop:** Yes

Previous Grounds: Not known

Simple Directions
M6 junction 36, via A590/591/A6 to Kendal (South). At first traffic lights turn right, left at roundabout, right into Parkside Road. Ground on right over brow of hill.

Record Attendance: 5,184 v Grimsby Town - FA Cup 1st Round 1955
Record Victory: 11-0 v Great Harwood - 22/03/1947
Record Defeat: 0-10 v Stalybridge Celtic - 01/09/1984
Record Goalscorer: Tom Brownlee
Record Appearances: Not known
Additional Records: Received £10,250 from Manchester City for Andy Milner 1995

Senior Honours: Westmorlands Senior Cup x12. Lancashire Senior Cup 2002-03.

10 YEAR RECORD

00-01	01-02	02-03	03-04	04-05	05-06	06-07	07-08	08-09	09-10
NP 1 18	NP 1 21	NP 1 12	NP 1 21	NP 1 5	NP 1 3	NP P 19	NP P 11	NP P 5	NP P 5

KENDAL TOWN

No.	Date	Comp	H/A	Opponents	Att:	Result	Goalscorers	Pos
1	Aug 15	Northern P.	H	Worksop Town	205	W 4 - 0	Wisdom 4 Walmsley 39 (pen) Foster 43 Taylor 57	1
2	17		A	Ashton United	142	W 3 - 2	Hallam 7 Walmsley 51 78	1
3	22		A	Boston United	1512	D 0 - 0		3
4	25		H	Bradford P.A.	306	D 1 - 1	Beattie 75	2
5	29		H	Marine	181	W 4 - 1	Beattie 21 Robson 26 Walmsley 37 71	1
6	31		A	Whitby Town	303	W 3 - 2	Taylor 11 Hobson 45 Walmsley 90	
7	Sept 5		H	F.C.United	1117	W 1 - 0	Wane 44	1
8	8		A	Ossett Town	233	L 2 - 3	Wane 30 Steel 77	1
9	**12**	**F.A.C. 1Q**	**H**	**Guiseborough Town**	**161**	**W 9 - 1**	**TAYLOR 3 (5 33 50) OSMAN 3 (45 46 76) Wane 64 73 Mulvaney 90**	
10	19		A	Hucknall Town	204	L 2 - 4	Walmsley 37 Taylor 41	3
11	22		A	Stocksbridge Park Steels	253	W 2 - 0	Hallam 31 Walmsley43	1
12	**26**	**F.A.C 2Q**	**H**	**Ossett Town**	**183**	**W 2 - 0**	**Walmsley 72 Mulvaney 81**	
13	**10**	**F.A.C 3Q**	**A**	**Guiseley**	**405**	**D 1 - 1**	**Salmon 18**	
14	**13**	**F.A.C. 3Qr**	**H**	**Guiseley**	**333**	**W 1 - 0**	**Osman 78**	
15	**17**	**F.A.T 1Q**	**A**	**Leek Town**	**316**	**L 1 - 2**	**Taylor 85**	
16	**24**	**F.A.C. 4Q**	**A**	**Nuneaton Town**	**1103**	**L 0 - 1**		
17	27		A	Durham City	134	W 7 - 0	Foster 3 Wisdom10 Taylor 13 Walmsley18 Steel 74 Osman 82 Ayers 19 (og)	6
18	31		H	Stocksbridge Park Steels	205	D 1 - 1	Taylor 4	6
19	Nov 14		H	Guiseley	277	W 2 - 1	Taylor 29 40	6
20	21		A	Retford United	261	D 1 - 1	Winters 90	7
21	Dec 5		H	Ossett Town	203	D 2 - 2	Bell 26 Winters 59	8
22	12		A	Frickley Athletic	212	D 0 - 0		8
23	Jan 23		A	Burscough	182	L 0 - 3		9
24	30		H	Boston United	293	W 1 - 0	Foster 34	7
25	Feb 6		A	Matlock Town	240	L 0 - 3		8
26	13		H	North Ferriby United	200	W 2 - 0	Walmsley 21 90	7
27	20		A	Nantwich Town	323	W 3 - 2	Steel 30 Kilford 45 Osman 70	
28	23		H	Burscough	164	W 3 - 2	Osman 14 83 Connolly 18	
29	27		H	Buxton	250	L 0 - 2		6
30	Mar 3		A	Guiseley	275	L 0 - 1		
31	6		A	North Ferriby United	295	W 2 - 0	Steel 6 Taylor 90	6
32	9		H	Nantwich Town	169	L 1 - 2	Taylor 68	
33	20		H	Durhan City	189	W 5 - 0	Taylor 68 Wisdom 36 Walmsley 63 (pen) 81 (pen)	
34	23		A	Marine	254	L 3 - 4	Stopforth 43 Walmsley 53 (pen) 90 (pen)	
35	27		H	Hucknall Town	196	W 3 - 1	Taylor 43 Wright 75 Stopforth 78	6
36	April 2		A	Bradford PA	526	L 2 - 3	Wisdom 21 Steel 28	
37	7		A	F.C.United	1585	W 4 - 1	Wright 28 Walmsley 30 (pen) Osman 47 Taylor50	
38	10		H	Matlock Town	233	D 1 - 1	Wisdom 45	6
39	13		H	Frickley Athletic	195	W 3 - 1	Wright 8 73 Taylor 69	
40	15		H	Ashton United	179	D 0 - 0		
41	17		H	Retford Town	284	W 2 - 1	Wisdom 9 Kilford 38	6
42	19		A	Buxton	227	W 2 - 1	Mulvaney 50 Warburton 60	
43	21		H	Whitby Town	327	W 2 - 0	Wisdom 7 Green 33	
44	24		A	Worksop Town	125	W 1 - 0	Green 87	5
45	**27**	**Play Off**	**A**	**Bradford P.A.**	**608**	**L 1 - 2**	**Wisdom 16**	
					Goals	90 53		

Home Attendances:

Highest:	1117 v F.C. United
Lowest:	164 v Burscough
Average (08-09):	272 (260)
Top Goalscorer:	Taylor - 17 (League 13, FAC 3, FAT 1 - Hat-trick 1)
	Walmsley - 17 (League 16 (6 Penalties), FAC 1)

MARINE

Chairman: Paul Leary
Secretary: Richard Cross (T) 07762 711 714
(E) richard@marinefc.com
Additional Committee Members: Brian Lawlor, Jean-Pierre Hall, Geoff Kewlsey, Mark Prescott, Dave Rannard, Paul Eustace, Peter McCormick, Dave McMillan, Martin Bates
Manager: Kevin Lynch
Programme Editor: Dave Rannard (E) drannard@blueyonder.co.uk

Back Row (L-R): Steve (Kit Man), Peter McCormack, Barry Godfrey, Brian Lawlor (V. Chair.), Jean-Pierre Hall (President), Paul Leary (Chairman), Dave Rannard, Paul Eustace, Richard Cross (Secretary), Geoff Kewley, Mark Prescott & Phil Brazier (Asst Man.) Middle Row: Neil Coomber (Sports Therapist), Steven Hussey, Jonathan Goulding, Kevin Leadbetter, Shaun Callacher, Joe Doyle, Ryan McMahon, Lee Parle, Ian Latham, Joe McMahon, Tony Davies, Nick McCarthy (Sports Therapist) & Peter Cumiskey (Coach) Front Row: Liam Rushton, John Cass, Paul Parle, Stephen Johnson, Joe Fowler, Kevin Lynch (Manager), Jamie Rainford, Chris Butler, Sean Doherty & John Shaw. Photo: Raymond Farley Photography

Club Factfile

Founded: 1894 **Nickname:** Mariners
Previous Names: Not known
Previous Leagues: Liverpool Zingari, Liverpool County Combination, Lancashire Combination 1935-39, 46-69, Cheshire County 1969-79

Club Colours (change): White/black/black (Yellow/green/green)

Ground: Arriva Stadium, College Road, Crosby, Liverpool L23 3AS (T) 0151 924 1743
Capacity: 3,185 **Seats:** 400 **Covered:** 1,400 **Clubhouse:** Yes **Shop:** Yes
Previous Grounds: Waterloo Park 1894-1903

Simple Directions
From the East & South: Leave the M62 at junction 6 and take the M57 to Switch Island at the end. At the end of the M57 take the A5036 (signposted Bootle & Docks). At the roundabout, at the end of the road (by Docks), turn right onto the A565 following signs for 'Crosby' and 'Marine AFC' and follow this road for 1 mile. After passing the Tesco Express on your right, turn left at the traffic lights (by Merchant Taylors' School) into College Road. The ground is half a mile on your left
From the North: Leave the M6 at junction 26 and join the M58. Travel along the M58 to Switch Island at the end. Take the A5036 (signposted Bootle & Docks) and follow directions above.

Record Attendance: 4,000 v Nigeria - Friendly 1949
Record Victory: 14-0 v Sandhurst - FA Cup 1st Qualifying Round 01/10/1938
Record Defeat: 2-11 v Shrewsbury Town - FA Cup 1st Round 1995
Record Goalscorer: Paul Meachin - 200
Record Appearances: Peter Smith 952
Additional Records: Paid £6,000 to Southport for Jon Penman October 1985
Received £20,000 from Crewe Alexandra for Richard Norris 1996

Senior Honours: Northern Premier League Premier Division 1993-94, 84-95.
Lancashire Junior Cup 1978-79, Lancashire Trophy x3. Lancashire Amateur Cup x5. Lancashire Senior Cup x6.
Liverpool Non-League Cup x3. Liverpool Challenge Cup x3.

10 YEAR RECORD

00-01	01-02	02-03	03-04	04-05	05-06	06-07	07-08	08-09	09-10
NP P 18	NP P 17	NP P 11	NP P 16	NP P 15	NP P 3	NP P 4	NP P 7	NP P 13	NP P 9

MARINE

No.	Date	Comp	H/A	Opponents	Att:	Result	Goalscorers	Pos
1	Aug 15	Northern P.	A	North Ferriby United	162	W 1 - 0	Rainford 90	9
2	18		H	Buxton	305	D 1 - 1	Jackson 34	4
3	22		H	Durham City	292	W 7 - 2	Prince 13 Black 17 86 Cumiskey 40 Parle 45 Rainford 85 88	2
4	26		A	F.C.United	1884	L 0 - 3		
5	29		A	Kendal Town	181	L 1 - 4	Rainford 30	5
6	31		H	Guiseley	307	L 0 - 1		
7	Sept 5		H	Frickley Athletic	253	W 2 - 0	Prince 63 Rainford 86	10
8	8		A	Stocksbridge Park Steels	312	L 2 - 4	Johnson 40 Hussey 68	12
9	**12**	**F.A.C. 1Q**	**A**	**Salford City**	**159**	**L 1 - 2**	**Cumiskey 86**	
10	15		H	Ashton United	218	L 3 - 4	Rainford 6 19 Fowler 90	
11	19		A	Worksop Town	131	L 0 - 1		20
12	22		H	Bradford P.A.	223	L 1 - 3	Rainford 16	20
13	26		A	Durham City	121	W 5 - 1	RAINFORD 3 (18 48 72) Fowler 35 Johnson 90	
14	Oct 3		A	Retford United	233	W 1 - 0	Burton 55	
15	10		A	Whitby Town	332	L 0 - 1		15
16	13		A	Burscough	319	W 2 - 1	Crewe 47 Jackson 65	
17	**17**	**F.A.T 1Q**	**H**	**King's Lynn**	**240**	**L 0 - 1**		
18	31		H	Ossett Town	262	W 2 - 0	Hussey 69 (pen) Hay 83 (og)	11
19	Nov 7		A	Matlock Town	314	L 0 - 3		11
20	14		A	Boston United	1150	L 1 - 2	Rushton 33	12
21	Dec 5		H	Stocksbridge P.S.	306	W 2 - 1	Cumiskey 13 Hussey 26	12
22	12		A	Ashton United	130	W 2 - 0	Cumiskey 44 Rainford 66	
23	26		H	Nantwich Town	369	L 0 - 2		10
24	Jan 23		H	Retford United	292	L 1 - 2	Moore 82	12
25	30		A	Bradford P.A.	481	L 0 - 2		12
26	Feb 6		A	Frickley Atletic	162	W 1 - 0	McEvilly 23	11
27	13		A	Hucknall Street	197	D 0 - 0		11
28	20		H	Burscough	404	W 2 - 1	Hussey 53 Davies 90	11
29	27		H	Worksop Town	355	D 1 - 1	McEvilly 53	10
30	Mar 2		A	Buxton	236	D 2 - 2	Cumiskey 18 Fowler 77	
31	6		H	Hucknall Town	315	W 2 - 1	Hussey 69 (pen) Moore 87	8
32	13		H	Matlock Town	290	W 2 - 1	Shaw 21 Doherty 63	
33	23		H	Kendal Town	254	W 4 - 3	Hussey 10 (pen) Fowler 18 Taylor 86 (og) Lathem 90	
34	27		H	Whitby Town	305	W 2 - 0	Fowler 58 Hussey 64	8
35	April 2		H	F.C.United	1093	D 1 - 1	Rushton 90	
36	5		A	Nantwich Town	421	L 2 - 3	McMahon 50 Goulding 67	
37	7		A	Ossett Town	48	W 4 - 1	Hussey 18 pen Rushton 46 Rainford 58 Johnson 82	8
38	10		H	North Ferriby United	255	L 1 - 3	Rainford 16 (pen)	
39	17		A	Guiseley	557	W 2 - 0	Rainford 45 58	9
40	24		H	Boston United	1367	D 0 - 0		9
					Goals	61 58		

Home Attendances:

Highest: 1367 v Boston United

Lowest: 218 v Ashton United

Average (08-09): 393 (356)

Top Goalscorer: Rainford - 16 (League 16)

MATLOCK TOWN

Chairman: Tom Wright

Secretary: Keith Brown (T) 07831 311 427 (E) keith61brown@yahoo.co.uk

Additional Committee Members: S Baker, P Bates, J Beaumont, S Else, Mrs C Else, P Eyre, S Greenhough, D Reynolds, I Richardson, A Smith, G Tomlinson, Mrs LH West, T Weston

Manager: Mark Atkins

Programme Editor: Mike Tomlinson (E) clubshop@matlocktownf.co.uk

Club Factfile

Founded: 1885 **Nickname:** The Gladiators

Previous Names: Not known

Previous Leagues: Midland Combination 1894-96, Matlock and District, Derbyshire Senior, Central Alliance 1924-25, 47-61, Central Combination 1934-35, Chesterfield & District 1946-47, Midland Counties 1961-69

Club Colours (change): All royal blue (All yellow)

Ground: Causeway Lane, Matlock, Derbyshire DE4 3AR (T) 01629 583 866

Capacity: 5,500 **Seats:** 560 **Covered:** 1,200 **Clubhouse:** Yes **Shop:** Yes

Previous Grounds: Not known

Simple Directions
On A615, ground is 500 yards from Town Centre and Matlock BR.

Record Attendance: 5,123 v Burton Albion - FA Trophy 1975

Record Victory: 10-0 v Lancaster City (A) - 1974

Record Defeat: 0-8 v Chorley (A) - 1971

Record Goalscorer: Peter Scott

Record Appearances: Mick Fenoughty

Additional Records: Paid £2,000 for Kenny Clark 1996
Received £10,000 from York City for Ian Helliwell

Senior Honours: FA Trophy 1974-75. Anglo Italian Non-League Cup 1979.
Derbyshire Senior Cup x7.

10 YEAR RECORD

00-01	01-02	02-03	03-04	04-05	05-06	06-07	07-08	08-09	09-10
NP 1 12	NP 1 14	NP 1 8	NP 1 2	NP P 11	NP P 9	NP P 5	NP P 16	NP P 15	NP P 7

MATLOCK TOWN

No.	Date	Comp	H/A	Opponents	Att:	Result	Goalscorers	Pos
1	Aug 15	Northern P.	A	Guiseley	305	L 0 - 2		20
2	22		H	North Ferriby United	264	L 0 - 1		14
3	25		A	Hucknall Town	291	D 2 - 2	Haran 6 Hannah 21 (pen)	15
4	29		A	Durham City	170	W 4 - 0	Hannah 7 70 Lukic 36 Algar 90	9
5	31		H	Nantwich Town	399	L 1 - 3	Algar 47	
6	Sept 5		H	Ossett Town	214	L 0 - 1		17
7	8		A	Boston United	1216	D 1 - 1	Cropper 4	18
8	**12**	**F.A.C 1Q**	**H**	**Sleaford Town**	**380**	**D 1 - 1**	**Jackson 60**	
9	**15**	**F.A.C. 1Qr**	**A**	**Sleaford Town**	**421**	**W 2 - 1**	**Lukic 25 Hannah 56 (pen)**	
10	19		A	Stocksbridge P.S.	276	W 4 - 3	HANNAH 3 (5 75 78) Benger 55	14
11	22		H	Frickley Athletic	333	D 2 - 2	King 16 Hannah 73	14
12	**26**	**F.A.C 2Q**	**H**	**Bury Town**	**341**	**D 2 - 2**	**King 33 Cropper 41**	
13	**29**	**F.A.C. 2Qr**	**A**	**Bury Town**	**518**	**L 0 - 1**	**after extra time**	
14	Oct 3		A	Bradford P.A.	1350	L 2 - 5	Warne 54 Hannah 85	19
15	13		H	Retford Town	348	L 0 - 1		
16	**17**	**F.A.T 1Q**	**H**	**Loughborough Dynamo**	**236**	**W 2 - 1**	**Benger 33 Davies 75**	
17	24		A	Whitby Town	318	D 2 - 2	Warne 49 73	20
18	27		A	Worksop Town	253	W 3 - 0	Benger 32 Hannah 37 Cropper 84	
19	**31**	**F.A.T 2Q**	**A**	**Cambridge City**	**276**	**W 1 - 0**	**Davies 66**	
20	Nov 7		H	Marine	314	W 3 - 0	Warne 44 Davies 48 Cropper 76	15
21	14		H	Ashton United	295	W 5 - 0	Sturdy 25 Hannah 30 54 Warne 41 Benger 77	
22	**21**	**F.A.T 3Q**	**A**	**Witton Albion**	**254**	**D 1 - 1**	**Haran 86**	
23	Dec 5		H	Boston United	409	W 1 - 0	Joynes 60	13
24	**12**	**F.A.T 1**	**H**	**Kidderminster Harriers**	**460**	**L 0 - 2**		
25	Jan 1		A	Nantwich Town	707	L 1 - 2	Hannah 63	
26	16		A	Matlock Town	225	L 0 - 2		16
27	23		H	Bradford P.A.	309	L 1 - 3	Featherstone 45	16
28	Feb 6		H	Kendal Town	240	W 3 - 0	Warne 26 Joynes 40 Hannah 69	16
29	9		A	Ossett Town	116	W 1 - 0	Joynes 4	
30	13		H	Durham City	283	W 6 - 0	Warne 38 Hannah 47 49 Joynes 69 Wood 76 Yates 90	12
31	20		A	Retford Town	221	D 1 - 1	Hannah 90	13
32	27		H	Whitby Town	302	W 3 - 1	King 32 Lukic 44 Hannah 90	11
33	Mar 1		A	Ashton United	148	W 2 - 0	Hannah 76 89	
34	6		A	Frickley Athletic	199	L 0 - 1		12
35	9		H	Buxton	477	D 1 - 1	Hannah 61	
36	13		A	Marine	290	L 1 - 2	Benger 8	
37	16		H	F.C.United	562	W 4 - 3	HANNAH 3 (41 56 78 pen) Warne 54	11
38	20		A	Burscough	160	W 2 - 0	Hannah 15 Cropper 28	7
39	27		H	Stocksbridge Park Steels	312	D 2 - 2	Cropper 88 :Likic 90	9
40	April 2		H	Hucknall Town	335	W 5 - 1	Cropper 6 King 33 HANNAH 3 (41 43 76)	
41	5		A	Buxton	512	D 1 - 1	Benger 18	
42	7		H	Worksop Town	270	W 4 - 3	King 2 Joynes 22 Hannah 81 (pen) Joynes 92	
43	10		A	Kendal Town	233	D 1 - 1	Joynes 1	7
44	13		H	Guiseley	304	W 2 - 1	Hannah 63 82	
45	17		H	Burscough	271	W 1 - 0	Hannah 79 (pen)	7
46	24		A	F.C.United	2871	L 0 - 1		7
					Goals	81 58		

Home Attendances:

Highest:	562 v F.C. United
Lowest:	214 v Ossett Town
Average (08-09):	328 (322)

Top Goalscorer: Hannah - 32 (League 31, FAC 1)

MICKLEOVER SPORTS

Chairman: Johnathan Green
Secretary: Tony Shaw (T) 07966 197 246
(E) tony@warren-shaw.co.uk
Additional Committee Members: Keith Jenkinson, Roger Lee, Alan Baines, Alan Brown, J. Edge, Kevin Haddon, Charles Divers, Ken Blackshaw, Stuart Clarke, Richard Pratley, Maurice Searcey
Manager: Richard Pratley
Programme Editor: James Edge (E) edgemeister1@hotmail.com

Club Factfile

Founded: 1948 **Nickname:** Sports
Previous Names: Not known
Previous Leagues: Central Midlands 1993-99, Northern Counties East 1999-2009

Club Colours (change): Red and black stripes/black/red (All blue)

Ground: Mickleover Sports Club, Station Road, Mickleover Derby DE3 9FB (T) 01332 512 826
Capacity: 1,500 **Seats:** 280 **Covered:** 500 **Clubhouse:** Yes **Shop:** Yes
Previous Grounds: Not known
Simple Directions
M1 NORTH - J28. A38 to Derby. At Markeaton Island right A52 Ashbourne, 2nd left Radbourne Lane, 3rd Left Station Road 50 yds.

M1 SOUTH – J25. A52 to Derby. Follow signs for Ashbourne, pick up A52 at Markeaton Island (MacDonalds) then as above.

FROM STOKE A50 – Derby. A516 to A38 then as above.

Record Attendance: Not known
Record Victory: Not known
Record Defeat: Not known
Record Goalscorer: Not known
Record Appearances: Not known
Additional Records: Won 16 consecutive League matches in 2009-10 - a Northern Premier League record

Senior Honours: Central Midlands Supreme Division 1998-99. Northern Counties East Division 1 2002-03, Premier Division 2008-09. Northern Premier League Division 1 South 2009-10.

10 YEAR RECORD

00-01		01-02		02-03		03-04		04-05		05-06		06-07		07-08		08-09		09-10	
NCE1	3	NCE1	5	NCE1	1	NCEP	13	NCEP	7	NCEP	13	NCEP	7	NCEP	14	NCEP	1	NP1S	1

NANTWICH TOWN

Chairman: Clive Jackson
Secretary: Bernard Lycett (T) 07876 230 280
(E) lblycett@btinternet.com
Additional Committee Members: A Pye, N Clarke, P Temmin, J Brydon, P Kelly, J Morris, R Melling, R Tilley, E Beeston, C Thomasson
Manager: Kevin Street and Darren Tinson
Programme Editor: Simon Eaton (E) Gm2s@hotmail.com

Unfortunately an up-to-date photograph was not available at the time of going to press

Club Factfile

Founded: 1884 **Nickname:** Dabbers
Previous Names: Not known
Previous Leagues: Shropshire & Dist. 1891-92, Combination 1892-94, 191-10, Cheshire Junior 1894-95, Crewe & Dist. 1895-97, North Staffs & Dist. 1897-1900, Cheshire 1900-01, Manchester 1910-12, 65-68, Lancs. Com. 1912-14, Cheshire Co. 1919-38, 68-82, Crewe & Dist. 1938-39, 47-48, Crewe Am. Comb. 1946-47, Mid-Cheshire 1948-65, North West Co. 1982-2007
Club Colours (change): All green (Black and amber stripes/black/black)

Ground: Weaver Stadium, Waterlode, Kingsley Fields, Nantwich, CW5 5BS (T) 01270 621 771
Capacity: 3,500 **Seats:** 350 **Covered:** 495 **Clubhouse:** Yes **Shop:** Yes
Previous Grounds: Not known
Simple Directions
M6 Jun 16 A500 towards Nantwich. Over 4 roundabouts onto A51 towards Nantwich Town Centre, through traffic lights and over railway crossing. Over next r/bout then left at next r/bout past Morrisons supermarket on right. Continue over r/bout through traffic lights. Ground on right at next set of traffic lights.

Record Attendance: 5,121 v Winsford United - Cheshire Senior Cup 2nd Round 1920-21
Record Victory: 15-0 v Ashton United - Manchester League 1966-67
Record Defeat: 0-12 v Chirk - FA Cup 2nd Qualifying Round 1889-90
Record Goalscorer: Bobby Jones - 60
Record Appearances: Not known
Additional Records: Gerry Duffy scored 42 during season 1961-62
Received £4,000 from Stafford Rangers for D Dawson

Senior Honours: Cheshire Senior Cup 1975-76.
FA Vase 2005-06

10 YEAR RECORD

00-01	01-02	02-03	03-04	04-05	05-06	06-07	07-08	08-09	09-10
NWC1 16	NWC1 15	NWC1 6	NWC1 13	NWC1 16	NWC1 4	NWC1 3	NP1S 3	NP P 3	NP P 10

NANTWICH TOWN

No.	Date	Comp	H/A	Opponents	Att:	Result	Goalscorers	Pos
1	Aug 15	Northern P.	H	Whitby Town	543	W 3 - 2	Lennon 19 30 (pen) Rhead 68	5
2	19		A	Worksop Town	186	D 0 - 0		
3	22		A	Stocksbridge Park Steels	271	L 3 - 5	Lennon 63 Rhead 69 Mahmoud 90	9
4	25		H	Burscough	472	D 1 - 1	Carter 10	11
5	29		H	Ossett Town	502	W 2 - 0	McPherson 35 Carter 55	7
6	31		A	Matlock Town	399	W 3 - 1	Whittaker 7 Lennon 50 McPherson 52	
7	Sept 5		A	North Ferriby United	206	L 3 - 5	Backhurst 15 White 48 (og) Southern 77	6
8	**12**	**F.A.C. 1Q**	**A**	**Warrington Town**	**204**	**L 0 - 1**		
9	15		A	Guiseley	233	L 0 - 1		
10	20		H	Durham City	395	W 6 - 1	RHEAD 3 (40 75 90) Carter 44 Lennon 65 84	6
11	22		H	Ashton United	470	W 2 - 0	Tinson 58 Sedgemore 84	
12	Oct 3		A	Buxton	403	D 0 - 0		2
13	7		A	F.C.United		L 0 - 4		
14	10		H	North Ferriby United	603	W 4 - 2	Sedgemore 15 Flynn 32 Lennon 39 69	
15	**17**	**F.A.T 1Q**	**A**	**Retford United**	**222**	**W 1 - 0**	**Ells 68 (og)**	
16	24		H	Boston United	693	L 0 - 4		5
17	**31**	**F.A.T. 2Q**	**H**	**Leek Town**	**579**	**W 4 - 1**	**Flynn 35 Lennon 70 Whittaker 80 Blackhurst 89**	
18	Nov 7		A	Hucknall Town	167	D 1 - 1	Whittaker 14	7
19	14		H	Retford United	364	L 2 - 3	Rhead 23 (pen) 84	
20	**21**	**F.A.T 3Q**	**A**	**Eastwood Town**	**312**	**W 3 - 0**	**Lennon 11 Dawson 23 Madeley 40**	
21	28		H	Bradford P.A.	516	L 0 - 1		11
22	Dec 5		A	Bradford P.A.	325	L 2 - 3	McPherson 31 Sedgemore 85	14
23	**12**	**F.A.T 1**	**H**	**Stalybridge Celtic**	**581**	**L 0 - 3**		
24	26		A	Marine	369	W 2 - 0	Robinson 42 90	
25	Jan 1		H	Matlock Town	707	W 2 - 1	McPherson 77 Robinson 83	
26	23		H	Buxton	406	L 0 - 3		11
27	Feb 6		H	F.C.United	1171	L 1 - 6	Robinson 10	13
28	13		H	Frickley Athletic	318	W 3 - 1	Robinson 43 70 Carter 57	14
29	16		A	Burscough	139	L 0 - 1		
30	20		H	Kendal Town	323	L 2 - 3	Sedgemore 80 Lennon 83	16
31	27		A	Ashton United	139	L 2 - 3	McPherson 37 Sedgemore 78 (pen)	15
32	Mar 2		H	Worksop Town	270	W 3 - 2	LENNON 3 (5 16 39)	
33	6		H	Guiseley	331	L 0 - 2		15
34	9		A	Kendal Town	169	W 2 - 1	Flynn 34 Lennon 81	
35	13		H	Stocksbridge Park Steels	307	D 2 - 2	Tickle 33 Robinson 43	
36	16		A	Frickley Athletic	143	L 0 - 2		
37	20		A	Boston United	1378	L 0 - 5		15
38	27		A	Durham City	163	W 2 - 0	Tinson 11 Sedgemore 28	
39	April 2		A	Whitby Town	317	W 3 - 0	Sedgemore 71 Sutton 77 Mahmood 90	
40	5		H	Marine	421	W 3 - 2	Blackhurst 25 Flynn 57 90	
41	10		A	Retford Town	250	D 0 - 0		10
42	17		H	Hucknall Town	503	W 4 - 1	Lennon 38 52 Sedgemore 62 (pen) Robinson 89	
43	24		A	Ossett Town	144	W 1 - 0	Mahmood 90	10
					Goals	72 74		

Home Attendances:	
Highest:	1171 v F.C. United
Lowest:	270 v Worksop Town
Average (08-09):	490 (664)
Top Goalscorer:	Lennon - 17 (League 15, FAT 2 - Hat-trick 1)

NORTH FERRIBY UNITED

Chairman: Les Hare
Secretary: Steve Tather (T) 07845 378 512
(E) tather@tather39.karoo.co.uk
Additional Committee Members: Colin Wicks, Mike Bonewell, Alan Sage, Steve Turtle, Richard Hodgkinson, Jim White, Phil Wither, Chris Holbrough
Manager: Neil Allison
Programme Editor: Richard Watts (E) richard@wattsshyngle.karoo.co.uk

Unfortunately an up-to-date photograph was not available
at the time of going to press

Club Factfile

Founded: 1934 **Nickname:** United
Previous Names: Not known
Previous Leagues: East Riding Church, East Riding Amateur, Yorkshire 1969-82, Northern Counties East 1982-2000

Club Colours (change): Green/white/green (Yellow/black/yellow)

Ground: Grange Lane, Church Road, North Ferriby, East Yorkshire HU14 3AA (T) 01482 634 601 / 633 089
Capacity: 3,000 **Seats:** 250 **Covered:** 1,000 **Clubhouse:** Yes **Shop:** Yes
Previous Grounds: Not known
Simple Directions
Main Leeds to Hull road A63 or M62. North Ferriby is approx. 8 miles west of Hull. Proceed through village past the Duke of Cumberland Hotel. Turn right down Church Road. Ground mile down on left.

Record Attendance: 1,927 v Hull City - Charity game 2005
Record Victory: 9-0 v Hatfield Main - Northern Counties East 1997-98
Record Defeat: 1-7 v North Shields - Northern Counties East 1991
Record Goalscorer: Mark Tennison - 161
Record Appearances: Paul Sharp - 497 (1996-2006)
Additional Records: Andy Flounders scored 50 during season 1998-99
Received £60,000 from Hull City for Dean Windass

Senior Honours: Northern Counties East 1999-2000. Northern Premier League Division 1 2004-05.
East Riding Senior Cup x11.

10 YEAR RECORD

00-01		01-02		02-03		03-04		04-05		05-06		06-07		07-08		08-09		09-10	
NP 1	13	NP 1	12	NP 1	4	NP 1	17	NP 1	1	NP P	5	NP P	13	NP P	15	NP P	10	NP P	4

NORTH FERRIBY UNITED

No.	Date	Comp	H/A	Opponents	Att:	Result	Goalscorers	Pos
1	Aug 15	Northern P.	H	Marine	162	L 0 - 1		18
2	18		A	Retford United	162	D 1 - 1	Bradshaw 12	17
3	22		A	Matlock Town	264	W 1 - 0	Pell 56	8
4	25		H	Whitby Town	185	L 0 - 2		
5	29		H	Stocksbridge Park Steels	169	W 1 - 0	Bolder 90	13
6	31		A	Bradford Park Avenue	465	W 2 - 1	Bird 11 Bradshaw 69 (pen)	
7	Sept 5		H	Nantwich Town	206	W 5 - 3	Hunter 8 58 Bradshaw 35 61 Cooke 90	3
8	**12**	**F.A.C. 1Q**	**H**	**Harrogate R.A.**	**121**	**W 2 - 1**	**Hunter 9 Morley 71**	
9	22		H	Durham City	178	W 7 - 0	Pell 1 Bolder 13 Matthews 16 Bradshaw 18 Davidson 51 Morley 76 Foot 80	5
10	**26**	**F.A.C 2Q**	**H**	**F.C.United**	**838**	**L 0 - 1**		
11	Oct 3		A	Frickley Atletic	215	L 1 - 2	Bradshaw 68	
12	10		A	Nantwich Town	603	L 2 - 4	Bradshaw 65 (pen) Matthews 90	11
13	**17**	**F.A.T 1Q**	**H**	**Worksop Town**	**222**	**D 1 - 1**	**Hunter 52**	
14	**21**	**F.A.T. 1Qr**	**A**	**Worksop Town**	**127**	**D 4 - 4***	**BRADSHAW 3 (8 10 96) Hunter 36 Won 5-4 on pens**	
15	24		H	Ashton United	123	W 4 - 0	Fry 12 Cooke 37 Chapman 42 Davidson 55	8
16	27		H	F.C.United	412	W 1 - 0	Foot 2	
17	**31**	**F.A.T 2Q**	**A**	**Carlton Town**	**92**	**W 3 - 0**	**Bradshaw 13 43 Fry 58**	
18	Nov 7		A	Boston United	1235	L 1 - 3	Davidson 10	10
19	14		H	Burscough	364	W 1 - 0	Bradshaw 33	8
20	**21**	**F.A.T 3Q**	**H**	**Gainsborough Trinity**	**176**	**D 2 - 2**	**Cooke 81 Davidson 90**	
21	**24**	**F.A.T. 3Qr**	**A**	**Gainsborough Trinity**	**226**	**D 2 - 2***	**Bradshaw 86 (pen) Larvin 90 Lost 2-3 after pens**	
22	28		A	Ashton Uited	136	W 1 - 0	Bradshaw 21	8
23	Dec 8		A	Guiseley	172	W 3 - 2	Denton 59 61 Davidson 84	
24	12		A	Hucknall Town	150	W 4 - 1	BRADSHAW 3 (14 65 87) Davidson 90	4
25	Jan 16		H	Matlock Town	225	W 2 - 0	Denton 48 Fry 84	4
26	23		H	Frickley Atheltic	256	W 5 - 1	Davidson 6 BRADSHAW 3 (13 18 24) Cooke 30	4
27	Feb 6		H	Guiseley	195	D 1 - 1	Bradshaw 79 (pen)	4
28	13		A	Kendal Town	200	L 0 - 2		4
29	16		H	Bradford P.A.	288	W 4 - 2	Davidson 14 Bradshaw 19 Whitehouse 59 Bolder 76	
30	20		H	Hucknall Town	241	D 2 - 2	Fry 70 Davidson 85	4
31	27		A	F.C.United	2021	D 3 - 3	Quistin 5 (og) Whitehouse 43 Bolder 71	4
32	Mar 3		A	Stocksbridge P.S.	137	D 1 - 1	Bradshaw 43 (pen)	
33	6		H	Kendal Town	295	L 0 - 2		5
34	10		A	Whitby Town	181	W 2 - 0	Davidson 54 Turner 69	
35	13		A	Buxton	315	D 1 - 1	Hunter 50	
36	20		H	Buxton	236	D 1 - 1	Davidson 57	6
37	24		A	Worksop Town	120	W 2 - 0	Davidson 44 88	
38	27		H	Boston United	423	D 0 - 0		4
39	April 2		A	Burscough	214	W 1 - 0	Hunter 59	
40	5		H	Ossett Town	267	W 3 - 1	Bolder 32 Fry 36 Barnwell 61	4
41	10		A	Marine	255	W 3 - 1	Denton 7 Davidson 13 69	4
42	13		A	Ossett Town	90	W 1 - 0	Bolder 48	
43	17		H	Worksop Town	323	W 1 - 0	Barnwell 80	4
44	20		A	Durham City	142	W 2 - 0	Barnwell 49 Davidson 62	
45	24		H	Retford United	224	D 0 - 0		4
46	**27**	**Play Off**	**A**	**Boston United**	**2165**	**L 1 - 2**	**Foot 78**	
					Goals	85 51		

Home Attendances:	
Highest:	423 v Boston United
Lowest:	123 v Ashton United
Average (08-09):	244 (228)
Top Goalscorer:	Bradshaw - 24 (League 18, FAT 6 - Hat-trick 3)

NORTHWICH VICTORIA

Chairman: James Rushe
Secretary: Derek Nuttall (T) 07787 345 082
(E) drnuttall@aol.com
Additional Committee Members: Martin Rushe, Howard Roberts

Manager: Andy Preece
Programme Editor: David Thomas (E) david.thomas@northwichvics.co.uk

Unfortunately an up-to-date photograph was not available at the time of going to press

Club Factfile

Founded: 1874 **Nickname:** Vics, Greens or Trickies
Previous Names: Not known
Previous Leagues: The Combination 1890-92, 1894-98, Football League 1892-94, Cheshire 1898-1900, Manchester 1900-12 Lancashire 1912-19, Cheshire County 1919-68, Northern Premier 1968-79, Conference 1979-2010
Club Colours (change): Green and white/white/white (Yellow/blue/blue)

Ground: Victoria Stadium, Wincham Avenue, Northwich, Cheshire CW9 6GB (T) 01606 815 200
Capacity: 5,300 **Seats:** 1,180 **Covered:** 3,700 **Clubhouse:** Yes **Shop:** Yes
Previous Grounds: The Drill Field
Simple Directions
From M6, leave at Junction 19. Follow A556 towards Northwich for approx 3 miles. Turn right onto the A559 towards Lostock Gralam. (at the point where A556 becomes dual carriageway) Turn right at traffic lights before "Slow & Easy" Public House. Follow brown signs to "Victoria Stadium" (Distance 1.5 miles)

Record Attendance: 11,290 v Witton Albion - Cheshire League Good Friday 1949
Record Victory: 17-0 v Marple Association 1883
Record Defeat: 3-10 v Port Vale - 1931
Record Goalscorer: Peter Burns - 160 (1955-65)
Record Appearances: Ken Jones - 970 (1969-85)
Additional Records: Paid £12,000 to Hyde United for Malcolm O'Connor August 1988. Received £50,000 from Leyton Orient for Gary Fletcher June 1921 and from Chester City for Neil Morton October 1990.
Senior Honours: FA Trophy 1983-84.
Conference North 2005-06.
Cheshire Senior Cup x15. Staffordshire Senior Cup x3.

10 YEAR RECORD

00-01	01-02	02-03	03-04	04-05	05-06	06-07	07-08	08-09	09-10
Conf 17	Conf 13	Conf 14	Conf 22	Conf 19	Conf N 1	Conf 13	Conf 19	Conf 22	Conf N 12

NORTHWICH VICTORIA

No.	Date	Comp	H/A	Opponents	Att:	Result	Goalscorers	Pos
1	8/8/09	BSN	A	Eastwood Town	768	D 1-1	Grand 82	21
2	15/8/09	BSN	H	Solihull Moors	485	W 2-0	Elam 78, Allan 89	21
3	17/8/09	BSN	A	Droylsden	568	L 1-5	Grand 51	21
4	22/8/09	BSN	H	Redditch United	483	L 0-2		22
5	29/8/09	BSN	A	Workington	471	W 1-0	Grand 66	22
6	31/8/09	BSN	H	Southport	724	D 1-1	Connor 38	21
7	5/9/09	BSN	A	Corby Town	404	L 0-1		21
8	8/9/09	BSN	A	AFC Telford	1557	W 2-1	Danks 7, Allan 54	21
9	12/9/09	BSN	H	Hyde United	481	W 3-1	Allan 17, Bailey 39, Danks 50	19
10	19/9/09	BSN	A	Gainsborough Trinity	416	W 4-1	Allan 2 (18, pen 47), Danks 40, Bailey 85	15
11	3/10/09	BSN	H	Harrogate Town	536	W 3-2	Bailey 21, Danks 33, Riley 86	13
12	17/10/09	BSN	A	Ilkeston Town	547	D 1-1	Danks pen 52	14
13	31/10/09	BSN	A	Stafford Rangers	627	D 2-2	Newby 6, Danks 8	15
14	15/11/09	BSN	A	Hyde United	718	D 1-1	Allan 3	15
15	1/12/09	BSN	H	Hinckley United	451	L 0-1		19
16	5/12/09	BSN	A	Gloucester City	316	W 1-0	J Brown 86	16
17	15/12/09	BSN	H	Fleetwood Town	489	L 0-3		17
18	16/1/10	BSN	H	Eastwood Town	530	W 4-3	Riley 2 (24, 52), Dutton 38, Bailey 56	17
19	19/1/10	BSN	H	Blyth Spartans	357	W 5-1	Herring 2 (2, 58), Aspin 25, Brown 80, James Spencer 85	12
20	3/2/10	BSN	H	Droylsden	372	L 2-5	Danks 48, Bailey 90	13
21	6/2/10	BSN	A	Hinckley United	486	D 1-1	Riley 23	15
22	9/2/10	BSN	A	Redditch United	206	D 1-1	Riley 90	14
23	13/2/10	BSN	H	Alfreton Town	481	D 1-1	Dutton 10	14
24	20/2/10	BSN	H	Ilkeston Town	476	W 4-1	Kerr 51, Vermiglio 58, Herring pen 77, Riley 83	11
25	23/2/10	BSN	H	AFC Telford	539	W 2-0	Danks 30, Riley 45	10
26	27/2/10	BSN	A	Fleetwood Town	1271	W 3-0	Danks 44, Dutton 69, Elam 78	9
27	2/3/10	BSN	A	Vauxhall Motors	378	L 0-1		9
28	6/3/10	BSN	A	Blyth Spartans	483	W 1-0	Vermiglio 51	9
29	9/3/10	BSN	H	Corby Town	359	D 2-2	Riley 9, Connor 75	9
30	13/3/10	BSN	H	Stafford Rangers	630	D 2-2	Dutton 11, Danks 68	12
31	16/3/10	BSN	H	Vauxhall Motors	353	D 0-0		12
32	20/3/10	BSN	A	Solihull Moors	246	D 1-1	Danks pen 58	12
33	27/3/10	BSN	H	Gainsborough Trinity	495	L 0-1		13
34	3/4/10	BSN	H	Workington	430	L 2-3	Og (Hopper) 9, Riley 33	14
35	5/4/10	BSN	A	Southport	1107	L 1-2	Danks 27	14
36	10/4/10	BSN	A	Alfreton Town	500	L 2-3	Danks pen 13, Riley 51	15
37	13/4/10	BSN	A	Stalybridge Celtic	326	D 1-1	Riley 47	15
38	17/4/10	BSN	H	Gloucester City	421	W 1-0	Riley 88	13
39	20/4/10	BSN	H	Stalybridge Celtic	440	W 2-1	Newby 39, Dutton 59	12
40	24/4/10	BSN	A	Harrogate Town	247	L 1-2	Connor 27	12
	Farsley Celtic record expunged 12/03							
2	11/8/09	BSN	H	Farsley Celtic	520	W 2-1	Riley 62, Connor 63	21
21	23/1/10	BSN	A	Farsley Celtic	370	W 3-2	Bailey 52, Og (Syers) 66, Dutton 80	11
	Cups							
1	26/9/09	FAC 2Q	H	Bardon Hill Sports	502	W 8-0	Danks 5 (pen 10, 18, 63, 88, 90), Grand 2 (33, 76), Bailey 49	
2	10/10/09	FAC 3Q	H	Chorley	617	W 4-1	Danks 3 (13, 17, 70), Connor 61	
3	24/10/09	FAC 4Q	H	FC United Of Manchester	2615	W 3-0	Danks pen 56, Og (Tong) 85, Riley 90	
4	8/11/09	FAC 1	H	Charlton Athletic	2153	W 1-0	Riley 81	
5	21/11/09	FAT 3Q	A	Fleetwood Town	847	L 0-2		
6	28/11/09	FAC 2	H	Lincoln City	3544	L 1-3	Bailey 47	

Home Attendances:	
Highest:	724 v Southport
Lowest:	353 v Vauxhall Motors
Average (08-09):	481 (787)
Top Goalscorer:	Danks - 22 (13 League, 9 Cup) in 39 appearances - 56% strike rate
Most Appearances:	Riley - 44 (28+10 League, 2+4 Cup)

OSSETT TOWN

Chairman: Graham Firth
Secretary: Simon Turfrey (T) 07773 649 251
(E) simonturfrey@aol.com
Additional Committee Members: Martin Voakes, Bruce Saul, Justin Fozard

Manager: Philip Sharp
Programme Editor: Bruce Saul (E) jimmers1664@aol.com

Unfortunately an up-to-date photograph was not available at the time of going to press

Club Factfile

Founded: 1936 **Nickname:** Town
Previous Names: Not known
Previous Leagues: Leeds 1936-39, Yorkshire 1945-82, Northern Counties East 1983-99

Club Colours (change): All red (All blue)

Ground: Ingfield, Prospect Road, Ossett, Wakefield WF5 9HA (T) 01924 280 028 / 272 960
Capacity: 4,000 **Seats:** 360 **Covered:** 1,000 **Clubhouse:** Yes **Shop:** Yes
Previous Grounds: Not known
Simple Directions
From M1 Junction 40: Take A638 signposted Ossett Town Centre. Take first left off A638 onto Wakefield Road, sixth left turn into Dale Street (B6120) to traffic lights. Turn left at lights. The Ground is in front of you opposite the bus station. The entrance to the Ground is just before the Esso petrol station.

Record Attendance: 2,600 v Manchester United - Friendly 1989
Record Victory: 10-1 v Harrogate RA (H) - Northern Counties East 27/04/1993
Record Defeat: 0-7 v Easington Colliery - FA Vase 08/10/1983
Record Goalscorer: Dave Leadbitter
Record Appearances: Steve Worsfold
Additional Records: Received £1,350 from Swansea Town for Dereck Blackburn

Senior Honours: West Riding County Cup 1958-59, 81-82

10 YEAR RECORD

00-01	01-02	02-03	03-04	04-05	05-06	06-07	07-08	08-09	09-10
NP 1 8	NP 1 2	NP 1 20	NP 1 14	NP P 16	NP P 11	NP P 10	NP P 18	NP P 12	NP P 19

OSSETT TOWN

No.	Date	Comp	H/A	Opponents	Att:	Result	Goalscorers	Pos
1	Aug 15	Northern P.	A	Hucknall Town	233	L 0 - 3		22
2	18		H	Frickley Athletic	184	W 4 - 1	McGuire 39 Clayton 45 Douglas 62 Tonks 88	9
3	25		A	Guiseley	240	D 1 - 1	Clayton 41	13
4	29		A	Nantwich Town	502	L 0 - 2		19
5	31		H	F.C.United	801	L 1 - 2	Lee 8	
6	Sept 5		A	Matlock Town	214	W 1 - 0	Clayton 90	18
7	8		H	Kendal Town	233	W 3 - 2	Hardaker 19 Lee 56 Hollindrake 71	14
8	**12**	**F.A.C 1Q**	**A**	**Morpeth Town**	**38**	**W 1 - 0**	**Lee 60**	
9	16		A	Whitby Town	436	D 1 - 1	Clayton 59	
10	19		H	Burscough	158	L 1 - 2	Hall 40	16
11	22		H	Buxton	144	W 3 - 1	Clayton 14 26 Lee 46	12
12	**26**	**F.A.C. 2Q**	**A**	**Kendal Town**	**183**	**L 0 - 2**		
13	Oct 3		A	Ashton United	126	L 0 - 2		16
14	6		A	Durham City	98	W 2 - 1	Clayton 45 Hollindrake68	
15	10		H	Retford United	163	L 1 - 2	Hall 16	
16	13		H	Stocksbridge Park S		L 2 - 4	Clayton 60 Forrest 69	
17	**17**	**F.A.T 1Q**	**H**	**Willenhall**	**91**	**L 1 - 2**	**Hollindrake 82**	
18	20		A	Retford Town	227	D 2 - 2	Hardaker 30 Lee 79	
19	31		A	Marine	262	L 0 - 2		16
20	Nov 7		H	Worksop Town	219	L 0 - 2		17
21	21		H	Boston United	246	L 0 - 5		19
22	Dec 5		A	Kendal Town	203	D 2 - 2	Nettleton 8 Clayton 48	
23	12		H	Whitby Town	182	L 1 - 3	Lee 18	19
24	Jan 23		H	Ashton United	98	L 0 - 3		19
25	Feb 6		H	Durham City	113	W 3 - 0	Sykes 22 McGuire 44 Mohammed 87	19
26	9		H	Matlock Town	116	L 0 - 1		
27	13		A	Bradford P.A.	464	L 2 - 4	Cotton 77 Malcher 82	19
28	27		A	Boston United	1250	L 0 - 7		19
29	Mar 2		A	F.C.United	1281	L 1 - 2	Cotton 77	
30	6		A	Worksop Town	143	L 1 - 3	Malcher 65	19
31	12		A	Frickley Athltic	191	D 1 - 1	McGuire 3	
32	17		A	Buxton	222	D 2 - 2	Sheriffe 33 Malcher 54	
33	27		A	Burscough	191	L 1 - 5	McGuire 44	
34	April 2		H	Guiseley	265	L 1 - 4	Sheriffe 45	
35	5		A	North Ferriby United	267	L 1 - 3	Leister 58 (pen)	
36	7		H	Marine	48	L 1 - 4	Bordman 6	
37	10		H	Bradford P.A.	252	L 4 - 6	McGuire 6 Bordman 16 33 Harris 21	19
38	13		H	North Ferriby United	90	L 0 - 1		
39	17		A	Stocksbridge P.S.	118	L 1 - 3	Cyrus 83	19
40	20		H	Hucknall Town	78	D 2 - 2	Sheriffe 60 86	
41	24		H	Nantwich Town	144	L 0 - 1		19
					Goals	48 96		

Home Attendances:	
Highest:	801 v F.C. United
Lowest:	48 v Marine
Average (08-09):	194 (199)
Top Goalscorer:	Clayton - 9 (League 9)

RETFORD UNITED

Chairman: Bill Wyles
Secretary: Annie Knight **(T)** 07825 047 799
(E) annierufc@sky.com
Additional Committee Members: S Payling, G Brittian, A Legg, J Lewis

Manager: David Lloyd
Programme Editor: Jon Knight **(E)** jondknight@sky.com

Archive photo

Club Factfile

Founded: 1987 **Nickname:** Badgers
Previous Names: Not known
Previous Leagues: Gainsborough & District, Nottinghamshire Football Alliance > 2001, Central Midlands 2001-04, Northern Counties East 2004-07
Club Colours (change): Black and white stripes/black/black (All yellow)

Ground: Cannon Park, Leverton Road, Retford, Notts DN22 6QF **(T)** 01777 869 468 / 710 300
Capacity: 2,000 **Seats:** 150 **Covered:** 300 **Clubhouse:** Yes **Shop:** Yes
Previous Grounds: Not known
Simple Directions
Leave the A1 at Ranby and follow the A620 towards Retford. Go past Ranby prison and go straight on at the next 2 mini roundabouts. At the 3rd roundabout take the 3rd exit signposted Gainsborough. Passing Morrisons on the left, go through the traffic lights and move into the right hand lane. Turn right at the traffic lights. Turn left at the traffic lights by the Broken Wheel Public House into Leverton Road. Go past the Masons Arms Public House and go over 2 hump backed bridges. The ground is signposted and is on the right.

Record Attendance: 1,527 v Doncaster Rovers - Friendly July 2006
Record Victory: Not known
Record Defeat: Not known
Record Goalscorer: Andy Powell - 126 (1990-95)
Record Appearances: Steve Hardy - 272 (1987-96)
Additional Records:

Senior Honours: Notts Alliance Division 1 2000-01. Central Midlands League Division 1 2001-02, Supreme Division 2003-04, League Cup 01-02, 03-04, Floodlit Cup 03-04. Northern Counties East Premier Division 2006-07, Presidents Cup 06-07. Northern Premier Division 1 South 2007-08, 08-09, Chairmans Cup 2007-08. Notts Senior cup 2008-09.

10 YEAR RECORD

00-01	01-02	02-03	03-04	04-05	05-06	06-07	07-08	08-09	09-10
NAl 1 1	CM P 1	CM Su 4	CM Su 1	NCE1 8	NCE1 2	NCEP 1	NP1S 1	NP1S 1	NP P 6

RETFORD UNITED

No.	Date	Comp	H/A	Opponents	Att:	Result	Goalscorers	Pos
1	Aug 18	Northern P.	H	North Ferriby United	162	D 1 - 1	Godber 56	14
2	22		H	F.C.United	613	D 1 - 1	Bettney 52	18
3	25		A	Durham City	207	W 4 - 1	Thomas 23 Godber 45 50 Ellender 90	10
4	29		A	Buxton	352	W 2 - 0	Bettney 2 34	5
5	Sept 5		H	Stocksbridge Park Steels	369	W 1 - 1	Godber 90	8
6	9		A	Worksop Town	214	D 3 - 3	Marrison 45 Ludlam 64 Godber 82	9
7	**12**	**F.A.C 1Q**	**H**	**Lincoln United**	**258**	**D 1 - 1**	**Marrison 7**	
8	**15**	**F.A.C. 1Qr**	**A**	**Lincoln United**	**182**	**L 1 - 2**	**Ford 36**	
9	19		A	Ashton United	164	L 0 - 1		11
10	22		A	Boston United	1008	W 1 - 0	Wood (og) 82	8
11	26		H	Worksop Town	576	W 2 - 1	Barwick 15 Marrison 63	7
12	Oct 3		H	Marine	233	L 0 - 1		8
13	10		A	Ossett Town	163	W 2 - 1	Godber 28 85	5
14	13		A	Matlock Town	348	W 1 - 0	Bettney 11	
15	**17**	**F.A.T 1Q**	**H**	**Nantwich Town**	**222**	**L 0 - 1**		
16	24		H	Ossett Town	227	D 2 - 2	Ludlam 45 Godber 58 (pen)	
17	27		H	Guiseley	281	L 0 - 2		
18	31		A	Hucknall Town	283	W 4 - 1	Harvey 22 Marrison 34 Godber 38 56	2
19	Nov 7		A	Bradford P.A.	343	W 1 - 0	Ellis 45	2
20	10		H	Hucknall Town	226	L 1 - 2	Ellis 49	
21	14		A	Nantwich Town	364	W 3 - 2	Thomas 50 Harvey 63 81	1
22	21		H	Kendal Town	261	D 1 - 1	Harvey 55	2
23	28		A	Stocksbridge Park Steels	235	W 2 - 1	Thomas 18 Riordon 61 (og)	1
24	Dec 5		H	Ashton United	295	W 3 - 2	Harvey 8 9 Smith 29	1
25	12		A	F.C. United	1920	W 3 - 1	Thomas 3 24 Marrison 18	1
26	Jan 23		A	Marine	292	W 2 - 1	Morrison 12 Harvey 69	1
27	Feb 6		A	Whitby Town	307	L 0 - 2		3
28	13		H	Burscough	210	W 6 - 1	THOMAS 3 (5 20 53) Marrison 12 (pen) 55 (pen) Harvey 23	
29	20		H	Matlock Town	221	D 1 - 1	Bettney 50	
30	27		A	Burscough	225	W 4 - 0	Harvey 12 64 Thomas 70 84	2
31	Mar 6		H	Bradford P.A.	547	D 1 - 1	Harvey 7	3
32	9		H	Boston United	664	L 1 - 2	Bettney 41	
33	20		A	Guiseley	421	D 1 - 1	Smith 34	4
34	23		H	Buxton	205	L 1 - 2	Marrison 28 (pen)	
35	27		H	Frickley Athletic	297	L 3 - 5	Marrison 5 Smith 18 Harvey 39	5
36	April 2		H	Durham City	318	W 6 - 1	Marrison 12 Thomas 22 72 Godber 35 Ellender 44 Leggitt 84	
37	5		A	Frickley Athletic	325	W 2 - 1	Smith 4 Heath 14 (og)	
38	10		H	Nantwich Town	250	D 0 - 0		5
39	13		H	Whitby Town	215	W 5 - 0	Thomas 25 37 Harvey 28 Bettney 55 Simpkins 58	
40	17		A	Kendal Town	284	L 1 - 2	Harvey 58	5
41	24		A	North Ferriby United	224	D 0 - 0		6
					Goals	74 49		

Home Attendances:	
Highest:	664 v Boston United
Lowest:	162 v North Ferriby United
Average:	325
Top Goalscorer:	Harvey - 14 (League 14)
	Thomas - 14 (League 14 - Hat-trick 1)

STOCKSBRIDGE PARK STEELS

Chairman: Allen Bethel
Secretary: Michael Grimmer (T) 07801 626 725
(E) mickgrimmer@gmail.com
Additional Committee Members: A Horsley, P Kenny, M Kenny, R Sellers, J Newton, P Birkinshaw, W Fieldsend, T Grayson, W Cefferty
Manager: Gary Marrow
Programme Editor: Edwin O'Sullivan (E) sheffprint@aol.com

Unfortunately an up-to-date photograph was not available at the time of going to press

Club Factfile

Founded: 1986 **Nickname:** Steels
Previous Names: Stocksbridge Works and Oxley Park merged in 1986
Previous Leagues: Northern Counties East 1986-96

Club Colours (change): Yellow/royal blue/yellow (All red)

Ground: Look Loacl Stadium, Bracken Moor Lane, Stocksbridge, Sheffield **(T)** 0114 288 8305 / 288 2045
Capacity: 3,500 **Seats:** 400 **Covered:** 1,500 **Clubhouse:** Yes **Shop:** Yes
Previous Grounds: Stonemoor 1949-51, 52-53
Simple Directions
From West onto A616. Immediately you reach the Stocksbridge bypass turn Right signed (Stocksbridge West), then continue until you reach the shopping centre approx 1.5 miles. 300 yards past the centre you will see Gordons Autos on your left. Turn right directly opposite signed (Nanny Hill) and continue up the hill for Approx 500 yds, Ground is on the Left.
From M1- From North Junction 36 on to A61 Sheffield to McDonalds Roundabout. From South Junction 35a on to A616 Manchester to McDonalds Roundabout. From McDonalds roundabout on A616 Manchester for approx 6 miles then take Stocksbridge West exit, then continue until you reach the shopping centre approx 1.5 miles. 300yds past the centre you will see Gordons Autos on your Left. Turn right directly opposite signed (Nanny Hill) and continue up the hill for Approx 500yds, ground on Left.

Record Attendance: 2,050 v Sheffield Wednesday - opening of floodlights October 1991
Record Victory: 17-1 v Oldham Town - FA Cup 2002-03
Record Defeat: 0-6 v Shildon
Record Goalscorer: Trevor Jones - 145
Record Appearances: Not known
Additional Records: Paul Jackson scored 10 v Oldham Town in the 2002-03 FA Cup - a FA Cup record
Received £15,000 from Wolverhampton Wanderers for Lee Mills

Senior Honours: Northern Counties East Division 1 1991-92, Premier Division 1993-94, League Cup 1994-95.
Sheffield Senior Cup 1951-52, 92-93, 95-96, 98-99

10 YEAR RECORD

00-01	01-02	02-03	03-04	04-05	05-06	06-07	07-08	08-09	09-10
NP 1 4	NP 1 20	NP 1 17	NP 1 19	NP 1 14	NP 1 6	NP 1 6	NP1S 5	NP1S 3	NP P 11

STOCKSBRIDGE PARK STEELS

No.	Date	Comp	H/A	Opponents	Att:	Result	Goalscorers	Pos
1	Aug 18	Northern P.	H	Durham City	188	W 6 - 0	RILEY 3 (14 16pen 53 pen) Ward 51 Telling 76 Vardy 89	1
2	22		H	Nantwich Town	271	W 5 - 3	VARDY 3 (9 64 88) Cusworth 17 Green 59	1
3	25		A	Buxton	308	L 1 - 3	Vardy 80	1
4	29		A	North Ferriby United	169	L 0 - 1		3
5	31		H	Frickley Athletic	375	W 4 - 1	Vardy 28 82 Ring 30 Ward 61 (pen)	
6	Sept 5		A	Retford Town	369	D 1 - 1	Telling 51	2
7	8		H	Marine	312	W 4 - 2	Lovell 23 Ward 30 Cusworth 48 Ring 51	2
8	**12**	**F.A.C 1Q**	**A**	**Clitheroe**	**201**	**W 2 - 0**	**Clarke 63 Joyce 81**	
9	15		A	Burscough	176	W 1 - 0	Cusworth 62	
10	19		H	Matlock Town	276	L 3 - 4	Cusworth 13 Ward 37 63	1
11	22		H	Kendal Town	253	L 0 - 2		2
12	**26**	**F.A.C. 2Q**	**H**	**Stalybridge Celtic**	**352**	**L 2 - 7**	**Vardy 29 70**	
13	Oct 3		A	F.C.United	1888	L 3 - 4	Vardy 27 Ward 41 Ring 47	4
14	6		A	Hucknall Town	196	L 3 - 4	Ring 2 56 Darker 64	
15	13		A	Ossett Town	156	W 4 - 2	Cusworth 4 Ring 53 Ward 78 Tracey 90	5
16	**17**	**F.A.T 1Q**	**H**	**Glapwell**	**110**	**L 1 - 2**	**Ward 81**	
17	24		H	Bradford P.A.	224	L 2 - 3	Collery 69 Ward 79	6
18	27		H	Boston United	362	W 2 - 1	Darker 38 Ring 40	
19	31		A	Kendall	205	D 1 - 1	Tracey 90	3
20	Nov 7		A	Ashton United	152	W 1 - 0	Stirrup 45	4
21	14		A	Whitby Town	308	L 1 - 2	Ward 60	5
22	21		H	Worksop Town	229	D 2 - 2	Callery 10 Stirrup 52	6
23	28		H	Retford Town	235	L 1 - 2	Ward 36	6
24	Dec 5		A	Marine	306	L 1 - 2	Stacey 90	6
25	12		H	Burscough	121	W 4 - 1	Stirrup 23 Vardy 34 45 Tracey 78	
26	26		A	Boston United	1365	L 2 - 3	Ring 81 Pearson 83 (og)	7
27	Jan 23		H	F.C.United	761	D 1 - 1	Ring 87	8
28	Feb 6		H	Hucknall Town	134	L 2 - 3	Stirrup 31 Riordan 81	10
29	13		A	Guiseley	305	L 1 - 3	Claisse 83	13
30	16		A	Durham City	87	W 5 - 1	Vardy 15 80 Lovell 33 90 Callery 51	
31	27		A	Bradford P.A.	403	L 0 - 2		14
32	Mar 2		H	North Ferriby United	137	D 1 - 1	Callery 38	
33	6		H	Ashton United	118	W 2 - 1	Callery 22 Ring 57	14
34	13		A	Nantwich Town	307	D 2 - 2	Clayton 58 Ring 90	
35	20		A	Worksop	166	W 2 - 1	Lovell 49 Clayton 69	11
36	23		H	Guiseley	178	L 2 - 4	Tracey 8 Claisse 12	
37	27		A	Matlock Town	312	D 2 - 2	Tracey 28 Ring 49 (pen)	10
38	April 2		H	Buxton	313	W 3 - 1	Hall 16 Stirrup 57 Ring 69	
39	10		A	Frickley Athletic	182	L 0 - 1		11
40	17		H	Ossett Town	118	W 3 - 1	Vardy 7 90 Ring 67	11
41	24		H	Whitby Town	128	W 2 - 0	Schofield 76 Ring 79	11
					Goals	85 77		

Home Attendances:	
Highest:	761 v F.C. United
Lowest:	118 v Ossett Town
Average:	229
Top Goalscorer:	Vardy - 16 (League 14, FAC 2 - Hat-trick 1)

WHITBY TOWN

Chairman: Anthony Graham Manser
Secretary: John Tyreman (T) 01947 605 153
(E) agm_wtfc@hotmail.com
Additional Committee Members: P J Tyreman, A J Spenceley, M Agar, J Nellist, B Lonsdale, G Osbourne, M Osbourne, C Bone, D Griffiths, J Smith, M Green
Manager: Harry Dunn
Programme Editor: Lee West (E) guitarhero202@ntlworld.com

Club Factfile

Founded: 1926 **Nickname:** Seasiders
Previous Names: Whitby United (pre 1950)
Previous Leagues: Northern League 1926-97

Club Colours (change): All royal blue (All white)

Ground: Turnbull Ground, Upgang Lane, Whitby, North Yorks YO21 3HZ (T) 01947 604 847 / 603 193
Capacity: 2,680 **Seats:** 622 **Covered:** 1,372 **Clubhouse:** Yes **Shop:** Yes
Previous Grounds: Not known
Simple Directions
On entering Whitby from both the A169 and A171 roads, take the first fork and follow signs for the "West Cliff". Then turn left at the Spa Shop and Garage, along Love Lane to junction of the A174. Turn right and the ground is 600 yards on the left.

Record Attendance: 4,000 v Scarborough - North Riding Cup 18/04/1965
Record Victory: 11-2 v Cargo Fleet Works - 1950
Record Defeat: 3-13 v Willington - 24/03/1928
Record Goalscorer: Paul Pitman - 382
Record Appearances: Paul Pitman - 468
Additional Records: Paid £2,500 to Newcastle Blue Star for John Grady 1990
Received £5,000 from Gateshead for Graham Robinson 1997
Senior Honours: Rothmans National Cup 1975-76, 77-78. Northern League 1992-93. FA Vase 1996-97.
Northern Premier League Division 1 1997-98.
North Riding Senior Cup x5.

10 YEAR RECORD

00-01	01-02	02-03	03-04	04-05	05-06	06-07	07-08	08-09	09-10
NP P 17	NP P 15	NP P 10	NP P 15	NP P 4	NP P 6	NP P 11	NP P 12	NP P 19	NP P 14

WHITBY TOWN

No.	Date	Comp	H/A	Opponents	Att:	Result	Goalscorers	Pos
1	Aug 15	Northern P.	A	Nantwich Town	543	L 2 - 3	Hockworth 10 (pen) Blott 43	14
2	22		H	Frickley Athletic	267	W 3 - 1	Hassan 13 Charlton 34 90	11
3	19		H	Guiseley	361	L 1 - 2	Charlton 11	
4	25		A	North Ferriby United	185	W 2 - 2	Blott 16 Charlton 45	7
5	31		H	Kendal Town	303	L 2 - 3	Hackworth 23 Beadle 69	
6	Sept 5		H	Worksop Town	304	D 1 - 1	Tymon 7	14
7	9		A	F.C.United	1716	D 1 - 1	Beadle 67	14
8	**12**	**F.A.C 1Q**	**A**	**Bridlington Town**	**370**	**W 1 - 0**	**I.Gildea**	
9	16		H	Ossett Town	436	D 1 - 1	Beadle 65	13
10	19		A	Boston United	1048	D 0 - 0		17
11	**26**	**F.A.C 2Q**	**H**	**Vauxhall Motors**	**286**	**L 0 - 5**		
12	Oct 3		A	Hucknall Town	237	L 0 - 2		20
13	10		H	Marine	332	W 1 - 0	Beadle 18	18
14	12		A	Ashton United	152	D 2 - 2	Brunskill 76 Scott 81	
15	**17**	**F.A.T 1Q**	**H**	**Warrington Town**	**274**	**W 5 - 2**	**Hackworth 21 Lyth 34 Beadle 51 56 Brunskill 57**	
16	24		H	Matlock Town	318	D 2 - 2	Dalton 28 Hackworth 80	18
17	27		H	Bradford P.A.	346	L 2 - 3	Beadle 15 90	
18	**31**	**F.A.T 2Q**	**H**	**King's Lynn**	**251**	**L 0 - 2**		
19	Nov 7		A	Burscough	295	D 2 - 2	Beadle 60 69	19
20	14		H	Stocksbrdge Park Steels	308	W 2 - 1	Gildea 69 Campbell 90	18
21	28		A	Worksop Town	140	W 4 - 0	Lyth 45 Campbell 52 Hackworth 56 76	13
22	Dec 5		H	F.C.United	636	W 2 - 2	Cambpell 34 Hackworth 40	
23	12		A	Ossett Town	182	W 2 - 1	Campbell 12 Leeson 61 Dalton 75	
24	Jan 23		H	Hucknall Town	221	W 3 - 1	Hackworth 14 Dalton 66 Campbell 80	10
25	Feb 6		H	Retford Town	307	W 2 - 0	Scott 10 Leeson 45	
26	13		A	Buxton	339	W 2 - 0	Hackworth 45 70	9
27	16		A	Guiseley	190	L 1 - 3	Campbell 56 (pen)	
28	27		A	Matlock Town	302	L 1 - 3	Campbell 15	
29	Mar 6		H	Burscough	281	W 4 - 0	Hackwood 8 Dalton 21 Leeson 23 Beadle 39	13
30	10		H	North Ferriby United	181	L 0 - 2		
31	13		H	Ashton United	238	D 1 - 1	Leeson 48	
32	16		A	Durham City	166	L 3 - 4	Beadle 38 87 Leeson 85	
33	24		H	Boston United	275	W 2 - 0	Beadle 29 49 (pen)	13
34	27		A	Marine	305	L 0 - 2		12
35	April 2		H	Nantwich Town	317	L 0 - 3		
36	7		A	Frickley Athletic	153	D 1 - 1	Leeson 38	
37	10		H	Durham City	407	W 2 - 0	Charlton 32 Robinson 47	12
38	13		A	Retford Town	215	L 0 - 5		
39	17		H	Buxton	331	L 1 - 5	Campbell 66	11
40	19		A	Bradford P.A.	406	L 0 - 1		
41	21		A	Kendal Town	327	L 0 - 2		
42	24		A	Stocksbridge Park Steels	128	L 0 - 2		14
					Goals	61 73		

Home Attendances:	
Highest:	636 v F.C. United
Lowest:	181 v North Ferriby United
Average (08-09):	325 (333)
Top Goalscorer:	Beadle - 15 (League 13, FAT 2)

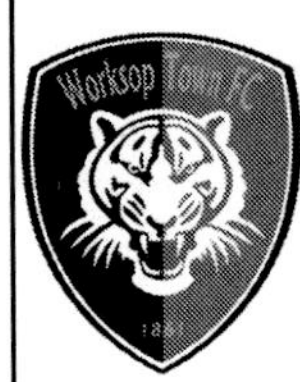

WORKSOP TOWN

Chairman: Jason Clark
Secretary: Keith Ilett (T) 07734 144 961
(E) k.ilett@sky.com
Additional Committee Members: Chris Smith, I Smith, A Richards

Manager: Peter Rinkcavage
Programme Editor: Steve Jarvis (E) mstephenjarvis@yahoo.co.uk

Club Factfile

Founded: 1861 **Nickname:** Tigers
Previous Names: Not known
Previous Leagues: Midland Co. 1896-98, 1900-30, 49-60, 61-68, 69-74, Sheffield Amateur 1898-99, 1931-33, Central Combination 1933-35, Yorkshire 1935-39, Central Alliance1947-49, 60-61, Northern Premier 1968-69, 74-2004, Conference 2004-07
Club Colours (change): Amber and black/black/amber (Light blue and white stripes/navy/blue and white)

Ground: Retford Utd FC, Cannon Park, Leverton Road, Retford, Notts. DN22 6QF **(T)** 01777 869 468
Capacity: 2,000 **Seats:** 150 **Covered:** 300 **Clubhouse:** Yes **Shop:** Yes
Previous Grounds: Central Avenue, Sandy Lane, shared with Ilkeston Town (New Manor Ground)
Simple Directions
Leave the A1 at Ranby and follow the A620 towards Retford. Go past Ranby prison and go straight on at the next 2 mini roundabouts. At the 3rd roundabout take the 3rd exit signposted Gainsborough. Passing Morrisons on the left, go through the traffic lights and move into the right hand lane. Turn right at the traffic lights. Turn left at the traffic lights by the Broken Wheel Public House into Leverton Road. Go past the Masons Arms Public House and go over 2 hump backed bridges. The ground is signposted and is on the right.

Record Attendance: 8,171 v Chesterfield - FA Cup 1925 (Central Avenue)
Record Victory: 20-0 v Staveley - 01/09/1984
Record Defeat: 1-11 v Hull City Reserves - 1955-56
Record Goalscorer: Kenny Clark - 287
Record Appearances: Kenny Clark - 347
Additional Records: Paid £5,000 to Grantham Town for Kirk Jackson
Received £47,000 from Sunderland for Jon Kennedy 2000
Senior Honours: Sheffield Senior Cup 1923-24, 52-53, 54-55, 65-66, 69-70,72-73, 81-82, 84-85, 94-95, 96-97, 2002-03.
Northern Premier League President's Cup 1985-86, 96-97, Chairman's Cup 2001-02.

10 YEAR RECORD

00-01	01-02	02-03	03-04	04-05	05-06	06-07	07-08	08-09	09-10
NP P 5	NP P 4	NP P 5	NP P 7	Conf N 17	Conf N 9	Conf N 21	NP P 9	NP P 17	NP P 18

WORKSOP TOWN

No.	Date	Comp	H/A	Opponents	Att:	Result	Goalscorers	Pos
1	Aug 15	Northern P.	A	Kendal Town	205	L 1 - 4	Bacon 28	21
2	19		H	Nantwich Town	186	D 0 - 0		
3	23		H	Buxton	296	D 1 - 1	Callery 25	19
4	29		A	Frickley Athletic	203	D 1 - 1	Sanasy	19
5	Sept 5		A	Whitby Town	304	D 1 - 1	Bacon 42	19
6	9		H	Retford United	214	D 3 - 3	Sanasy 55 Townsend 66 70	19
7	**13**	**F.A.C. 1Q**	**H**	**Frickley Athletic**	**178**	**D 1 - 1**	**Sanasy 31**	
8	**16**	**F.A.C. 1Qr**	**A**	**Frickley Athletic**	**114**	**L 1 - 2**	**Potter 75 after extra time**	
9	19		H	Marine	131	W 1 - 0	Townsend 23	20
10	22		H	F.C.United	345	W 3 - 1	Bacon 26 74 Tomlinson 61	15
11	26		A	Retford United	576	L 1 - 2	Simpkins 63 (og)	16
12	Oct 3		A	Guiseley	276	W 2 - 1	Glass 90 Jones 90	12
13	5		A	Ashton United	178	L 1 - 2	Tomlinson 27	
14	10		A	Durham City	135	W 5 - 0	Bacon 37 Bowler 45 Tomlinson 69 Townsend 88 Hindley 90	
15	13		A	Boston United	1137	L 0 - 2		13
16	**17**	**F.A.T 1Q**	**A**	**North Ferriby United**	**202**	**D 1 - 1**	**Townsend 64**	
17	**21**	**F.A.T. 1Qr**	**H**	**North Ferriby United**	**127**	**D 4 - 4**	**Hindley 59 Bacon 68 Jones 80 Glass 120 Lost 4-5 on pens.**	
18	24		A	Burscough	203	L 0 - 3		14
19	27		H	Matlock Town	253	L 0 - 3		
20	Nov 7		A	Ossett Town	219	W 2 - 0	Townsend 21 Wankiewitcz 45	14
21	14		H	Bradfpod P.A.	168	L 1 - 3	Bacon 68	15
22	21		A	Stocksbridge P.S.	229	D 2 - 2	Austin 13 Tomlinson 28	
23	28		H	Whitby Town	140	L 0 - 4		17
24	Dec 12		H	Durham City	145	W 4 - 0	Burley 50 (pen) White 55 83 Glass 74	
25	Jan 23		H	Guiseley	184	L 1 - 3	Townsend 39	15
26	Feb 6		H	Ashton United	137	D 1 - 1	Tomlinson 46	
27	9		A	Hucknall Town	227	L 1 - 3	Tomlinson 70	
28	13		A	F.C.United	2137	L 0 - 2		17
29	16		H	Frickley Athletic	137	L 1 - 2	Tomlinson 52	
30	27		A	Marine	355	D 1 - 1	Tomlinson 32	18
31	Mar 2		A	Nantwich Town	270	L 2 - 3	Bacon 13 Tomlinson 45	
32	6		H	Osett Town	143	W 3 - 1	Austin 26 Townsend 46 Mallon 61	17
33	13		A	Bradford PA	475	L 0 - 1		
34	20		H	Stocksbridge P.S.	166	L 1 - 3	Austin 75	17
35	24		H	North Ferriby United	120	L 0 - 2		
31	27		A	Buxton	342	L 0 - 1		18
37	April 7		A	Matlock Town	270	L 3 - 4	SANASAY 3 (4 29 38 pen)	
38	11		H	Hucknall	238	D 1 - 1	Mallon 28	
39	14		H	Boston United	398	L 1 - 5	Tomlinson 90 (pen)	
40	17		A	North Ferriby United	323	L 0 - 1		18
41	21		H	Burscough	131	L 0 - 1		
42	24		H	Kendal Town	125	L 0 - 1		18
					Goals	52 77		

Home Attendances:	
Highest:	398 v Boston United
Lowest:	120 v North Ferriby United
Average (08-09):	192 (213)
Top Goalscorer:	Tomlinson - 10 (League 10)

A.F.C. FYLDE

Chairman: Dai Davies
Secretary: Martin Benson **(T)** 07545 735 154
(E) clubsecretary@afcfylde.co.uk
Additional Committee Members: David Haythornthwaite, Stuart King, Martin Booker

Manager: Kelham O'Hanlon
Programme Editor: Martin Booker **(E)** martin@afcfylde.co.uk

Unfortunately an up-to-date photograph was not available at the time of going to press

Club Factfile

Founded: 1988 **Nickname:**
Previous Names: Wesham FC and Kirkham Town amalgamated in 1988 to form Kirkham & Wesham > 2008
Previous Leagues: West Lancashire, North West Counties 2007-09

Club Colours (change): All white (red and blue stripes/blue/blue)

Ground: Kellamergh Park, Bryning Lane, Warton, Preston PR4 1TN **(T)** 01772 635 880. 07525 323 775 (MD)
Capacity: 1,426 **Seats:** 282 **Covered:** 282 **Clubhouse:** Yes **Shop:** Yes
Previous Grounds: Coronation Road > 2006

Simple Directions
EXIT via Junction 3 M55 (signposted A585 Fleetwood/Kirkham). Up approach and turn left towards signs for Kirkham.In around 3/4 mile you will approach a roundabout. Then follow the signs for Wrea Green and Lytham St. Annes (2nd exit) B5259.After another 500 yards you will approach a new roundabout (go straight on) and 1/4 mile you will go over main Preston/Blackpool railway bridge and drop down almost immediately to a small mini roundabout (pub on left called Kingfisher). Carry on straight over this and up to main roundabout (another 200 yards) at junction of main Preston/Blackpool A583. Go straight over roundabout and drive on into Wrea Green Village.At 2nd mini roundabout in the centre of the village (Church on right l) take left turn into Bryning Lane, signposted on The Green (small white signpost) to Warton (2 miles).The Green will now be on your right as you exit out of the village and in around 1.8 miles you will come to the Birley Arms Pub on your left. Turn immediately left into The Birley Arms Pub Car park and continue to drive through the car park TO BOTTOM LEFT CORNER until you reach access road and park in the Main Club Car Park located behind the Main Stand. Approximate mileage from motorway to the ground is 5 miles and will take around 10 minutes to travel in a car.

Record Attendance: 1,217 v New Mills - North West Counties 09/05/2009
Record Victory: Not known
Record Defeat: Not known
Record Goalscorer: Not known
Record Appearances: Not known
Additional Records:

Senior Honours: West Lancashire League 1999-2000, 00-01, 01-02, 03-04, 04-05, 05-06, 06-07.
FA Vase 2007-08.
North West Counties League 2008-09

10 YEAR RECORD

00-01	01-02	02-03	03-04	04-05	05-06	06-07	07-08	08-09	09-10
WYkP 1	WYkP 1	WYkP 2	WYkP 1	WYkP 1	WYkP 1	WYkP 1	NWC2 2	NWCP 1	NP1N 13

BAMBER BRIDGE

Chairman: Terry Gammans
Secretary: George Halliwell (T) 07970 042 954
(E) geohalli@blueyonder.co.uk
Additional Committee Members: Dennis Allen, Dave Spencer, Geoff Wright, Gerry Lawson
Manager: Tony Greenwood
Programme Editor: Dave Rowland (E) rowland@live.co.uk

Club Factfile

Founded: 1952 **Nickname:** Brig
Previous Names: Not known
Previous Leagues: Preston & District 1952-90, North West Counties 1990-93

Club Colours (change): White/black/black (All red)

Ground: QED Stadium, Irongate, Brownedge Road, Bamber Bridge PR5 6UX **(T)** 01772 909 690 / 909 695
Capacity: 3,000 **Seats:** 554 **Covered:** 800 **Clubhouse:** Yes **Shop:** Yes
Previous Grounds: King George V, Higher Wallton 1952-86
Simple Directions
Junction 29, A6 (Bamber Bridge by-pass)onto London Way. First roundabout take 3rd exit Brownedge Road (East) then take first right. Ground on left at the bottom of the road.

Record Attendance: 2,300 v Czech Republic - Pre Euro '96 friendly
Record Victory: 8-0 v Curzon Ashton - North West Counties 1994-95
Record Defeat: Not known
Record Goalscorer: Not known
Record Appearances: Not known
Additional Records: Paid £10,000 to Horwich RMI for Mark Edwards
Received £15,000 from Wigan Athletic for Tony Black 1995
Senior Honours: ATDC Lancashire Trophy 1994-95.
Northern Premier League Premier Division 1995-96, Challenge Cup 1995-96.

10 YEAR RECORD

00-01	01-02	02-03	03-04	04-05	05-06	06-07	07-08	08-09	09-10
NP P 12	NP P 23	NP 1 13	NP 1 10	NP P 21	NP 1 13	NP 1 13	NP1N 5	NP1N 11	NP1N 14

LAIRDS

CAMMELL LAIRD FC

CAMMELL LAIRD

Chairman: John Lynch

Secretary: Anthony R Wood (T) 07931 761 429 (E) toddywood@hotmail.com

Additional Committee Members: George Higham, Paul Connelly, Larry Embra, Ray Steele

Manager: Alex Hay

Programme Editor: Debbie Smaje (E) jockey_one@hotmail.com

Unfortunately an up-to-date photograph was not available at the time of going to press

Club Factfile

Founded: 1907 **Nickname:** Lairds

Previous Names: Not known

Previous Leagues: West Cheshire, North West Counties

Club Colours (change): All royal blue (Red and black stripes/black/red)

Ground: Kirklands, St Peter's Road, Rock Ferry, Birkenhead CH42 1PY (T) 0151 645 3132 / 645 5991

Capacity: 2,000 **Seats:** 150 **Covered:** Yes **Clubhouse:** Yes **Shop:** Yes

Previous Grounds: Not known

Simple Directions

FROM CHESTER: M53, leave at Junction 5, take third exit on to A41 and travel towards Birkenhead. At New Ferry signpost take B5136 towards New Ferry. After approx 1 mile at sign for Lairds Sports Club, turn right down Proctor Road, ground on the left. FROM LIVERPOOL: Take the Birkenhead Tunnel then A41 signposted North Wales for approx 1 mile. At large roundabout take B5136 signposted New Ferry, Rock Ferry. Follow until 2nd set of traffic lights at Abbotsford pub. Turn left then first right into St Peters Road. Ground at bottom of road on right.

Record Attendance: 1,700 v Harwich & Parkeston - FA Vase 5th Round 1990-91

Record Victory: Not known

Record Defeat: Not known

Record Goalscorer: Not known

Record Appearances: Not known

Additional Records:

Senior Honours: North West Counties League Division 2, League Cup and Trophy 2004-05, Division 1 2005-06.
West Cheshire League x19 (Most recently 2000-01). Cheshire Amateur Cup x11.
Wirral Senior Cup.

10 YEAR RECORD

00-01	01-02	02-03	03-04	04-05	05-06	06-07	07-08	08-09	09-10
WCh1 1	WCh1 2	WCh1 3	WCh1 2	NWC2 1	NWC1 1	NP 1 2	NP1S 2	NP P 18	NP1S 16

CHESTER

Chairman: Chris Pilsbury

Secretary: John Davies **(T)** 07720 764 000 **(E)** jhdaviesref@btinternet.com

Additional Committee Members: Steve Ashton, Mike Vickers, Mark Howell, Campbell Smith, Jane Hipkiss, Jim Green, Richard Wightman, David Evans, Jeff Banks

Manager: Neil Young

Programme Editor: Rob Ashcroft **(E)** rob.ashcroft@chesterfc.com

Club Factfile

Founded: 1885 **Nickname:** Blues

Previous Names: Chester > 1983, Chester City 1983-2010

Previous Leagues: Cheshire 1919-31, Football League 1931-2000, 2004-09, Conference 2000-04, 09-10 (Did not finish the season)

Club Colours (change): Blue and white/black/blue and white hoops (Purple/white/white)

Ground: Deva Stadium, Bumpers Lane, Chester. CH1 4LT **(T)** 01244 371376

Capacity: 6,012 **Seats:** 3,284 **Covered:** Yes **Clubhouse:** Yes **Shop:** Yes

Previous Grounds: Faulkner Street 1885-98, The Old Showground 98-99, Whipcord Lane 1901-06, Sealand Road 06-90, Macclesfield FC 90-92

Simple Directions

Stay on the M56 until you reach a roundabout at the end of the motorway. Follow the signs to North Wales & Queensferry A5117. After around one and a half miles you will reach a set of traffic lights where you need to bear left on to the A550 (signposted North Wales & Queensferry). Then from the A550, take the A548 towards Chester. Head straight through the first set of traffic lights and after passing a Vauxhall and then a Renault garage on your left, turn right at the next lights into Sovereign Way. Continue to the end of Sovereign Way and then turn right into Bumpers Lane and the entrance to the Club car park is just down on the right.

Record Attendance: 20,378 v Chelsea - FA Cup 3rd Round replay 16/01/1952

Record Victory: 12-0 v York City - 01/02/1936

Record Defeat: Not known

Record Goalscorer: Stuart Rimmer - 135

Record Appearances: Ray Gill - 406 (1951-62)

Additional Records: Paid £100,000 to Rotherham for Gregg Blundell.
Received £300,000 from Liverpool for Ian Rush

Senior Honours: Conference 2003-04.
Cheshire Senior Cup 1894-95, 96-97, 1903-04, 07-08, 08-09, 30-31, 31-32. Herefordshire Senior Cup 1991-92 (shared).
Welsh Cup 1907-08, 32-33, 46-47.

10 YEAR RECORD

00-01	01-02	02-03	03-04	04-05	05-06	06-07	07-08	08-09	09-10
Conf 8	Conf 14	Conf 4	Conf 1	FL 2 20	FL 2 15	FL 2 18	FL 2 22	FL 2 23	Conf dnf

CHORLEY

Chairman: Ken Wright
Secretary: Harold Taylor **(T)** 07749 643 310
(E) harold@harold7.wanadoo.co.uk
Additional Committee Members: Brian Pilkington, Tony Garner, Geoff Haslam, Peter Hardcastle, Brian Haslam
Manager: Gary Flitcroft
Programme Editor: John Newman **(E)** john.newman2@homecall.co.uk

Club Factfile

Founded: 1883 **Nickname:** Magpies
Previous Names: Not known
Previous Leagues: Lancashire Alliance 1890-94, Lancashire 1894-1903, Lancashire Combination 1903-68, 69-70, Northern Premier 1968-69, 70-72, 82-88, Cheshire County 1970-82, Conference 1988-90
Club Colours (change): Black and white stripes/black/black (All sky blue)

Ground: Victory Park, Duke Street, Chorley, Lancs PR7 3DU **(T)** 01257 263 406 / 275 662
Capacity: 4,100 **Seats:** 2,800 **Covered:** 900 **Clubhouse:** Yes **Shop:** Yes
Previous Grounds: Dole Lane 1883-1901, Rangletts Park 1901-05, St George's Park 1905-20
Simple Directions
M61 leave at junction 6, follow A6 to Chorley, going past the Yarrow Bridge Hotel on Bolton Road. Turn left at first set of traffic lights into Pilling Lane, first right into Ashley St. Ground 2nd entrance on left.

M6 junction 27, follow Chorley, turn left at lights, A49 continue for 2 ½ miles, turn right onto B5251. Drive through Coppull and into Chorley for about 2 miles. On entering Chorley turn right into Duke Street 200 yards past Plough Hotel. Turn right into Ashby Street after Duke Street school, and first right into Ground.

Record Attendance: 9,679 v Darwen - FA Cup 1931-32
Record Victory: Not known
Record Defeat: Not known
Record Goalscorer: Peter Watson - 371 (158-66)
Record Appearances: Not known
Additional Records: Received £30,000 from Newcastle United for David Eatock 1996

Senior Honours: Lancashire Alliance 1892-93. Lancashire League 1896-97, 98-99. Lancashire Combination x11. Cheshire County League 1975-76, 76-77, 81-82. Northern Premier League 1987-88. Lancashire FA Trophy x14. Lancashire Combination League cup x3.

10 YEAR RECORD

00-01	01-02	02-03	03-04	04-05	05-06	06-07	07-08	08-09	09-10
NP 1 10	NP 1 13	NP 1 5	NP 1 18	NP 1 16	NP 1 18	NP 1 23	NP1N 14	NP1N 14	NP1N 16

CLITHEROE

Chairman: Carl Garner
Secretary: Colin Wilson (T) 07949 031 039
(E) wilsoncfc424370@aol.com
Additional Committee Members: Anne Barker, Andrew Jackson

Manager: Peter Smith
Programme Editor: Chris Musson (E) chris.musson1964@googlemail.com

Club Factfile

Founded: 1877 **Nickname:** The Blues
Previous Names: Not known
Previous Leagues: Blackburn & District, Lancashire Combination 1903-04, 05-10, 25-82, North West Counties 1982-85

Club Colours (change): Royal blue/royal blue/red (Pink/black/black)

Ground: Shawbridge, off Pendle Road, Clitheroe, Lancashire BB7 1DZ (T) 01200 444 487
Capacity: 2,400 **Seats:** 250 **Covered:** 1,400 **Clubhouse:** Yes **Shop:**
Previous Grounds: Not known
Simple Directions
M6 junction 31, A59 to Clitheroe (17 miles) at 5th roundabout turn left after half a mile at Pendle Road. Ground is one mile behind Bridge Inn on the right.

Record Attendance: 2,050 v Mangotsfield - FA Vase Semi-final 1995-96
Record Victory: Not known
Record Defeat: Not known
Record Goalscorer: Don Francis
Record Appearances: Lindsey Wallace - 670
Additional Records: Received £45,000 from Crystal Palace for Carlo Nash

Senior Honours: North West Counties League 1984-85, 2003-04.
Lancashire Challenge Trophy 1984-85. East Lancashire Floodlit Trophy 1994-95.

10 YEAR RECORD

00-01	01-02	02-03	03-04	04-05	05-06	06-07	07-08	08-09	09-10
NWC1 2	NWC1 6	NWC1 2	NWC1 1	NP 1 19	NP 1 16	NP 1 16	NP1N 13	NP1N 12	NP1N 8

CURZON ASHTON

Chairman: Harry Galloway
Secretary: Robert Hurst (T) 07713 252 310
(E) rob@curzon-ashton.co.uk
Additional Committee Members: Harry Twamley, Ronnie Capstick, Simon Shuttleworth, Paul Price, James Newall, David Jones, Steve Ball, Ian Seymour, Ron Walber, Wayne Salkeld.
Manager: Gary Lowe
Programme Editor: Ian Seymour (E) curzon70@ntlworld.com

Club Factfile

Founded: 1963 **Nickname:**
Previous Names: None
Previous Leagues: Manchester Amateur, Manchester > 1978, Cheshire County 1978-82, North West Counties 1982-87, 98-2007, Northern Premier 1987-97, Northern Counties East 1997-98,

Club Colours (change): All royal blue (All red)

Ground: Tameside Stadium, Richmond Street, Ashton-u-Lyme OL7 9HG (T) 0161 330 6033
Capacity: 5,000 **Seats:** 504 **Covered:** Yes **Clubhouse:** Yes **Shop:** Yes
Previous Grounds: Katherine Street > 204, Stalybridge Celtic FC 2004-06

Simple Directions
From Stockport (south) direction Leave the M60 at junc 23 (Ashton-U-Lyne). Turn left at the top of the slip road, go straight through the next set of lights, and bear right (onto Lord Sheldon Way) at the next set. Continue on this road until you come to a set of traffic lights with the Cineworld Cinema on your right. Turn left here onto Richmond St. Over the bridge, across the mini-roundabout and then first left down to the ground. From Oldham (north) direction Leave the M60 at junc 23 (Ashton-U-Lyne) and turn right at the top of the slip road signposted A635 Manchester. Turn right at the second set of traffic lights, sign posted Ashton Moss, and then follow directions as from the south.

Record Attendance: 1,826 v Stamford - FA Vase Semi-final
Record Victory: 7-0 v Ashton United
Record Defeat: 0-8 v Bamber Bridge
Record Goalscorer: Alan Sykes
Record Appearances: Alan Sykes
Additional Records:

Senior Honours: Manchester Premier Cup x5

10 YEAR RECORD

00-01	01-02	02-03	03-04	04-05	05-06	06-07	07-08	08-09	09-10
NWC1 11	NWC1 13	NWC1 18	NWC1 7	NWC1 4	NWC1 7	NWC1 2	NP1N 4	NP1N 4	NP1N 3

DURHAM CITY

Chairman: Ian Walker
Secretary: Ian Ward (T) 07827 842 903
(E) ianaward53@btinternet.com
Additional Committee Members: Austin Carney, Terry Brown, Simon Carey

Manager: Lee Collings
Programme Editor: Kevin Hewitt (E) hewittkd@fsmail.net

Club Factfile

Founded: 1949 **Nickname:** City
Previous Names: Original club founded in 1918 disbanded in 1938 and reformed in 1949
Previous Leagues: Victory 1918-19, North Eastern 1919-21, 28-38, Football League 1921-28, Wearside 1938-39, 50-51, Northern 1951-2008

Club Colours (change): Yellow/blue/blue (Red and black stripes/black/black)

Ground: Arnott Stadium, Belmont Industrial Estate, Durham DH1 1GG (T) 0191 386 9616
Capacity: 2,700 **Seats:** 270 **Covered:** 750 **Clubhouse:** Yes **Shop:** No
Previous Grounds: Holiday Park 1921-38, Ferens Park 1949-94
Simple Directions
Leave the A1M at J62 (signed Durham City) At the top of the slip road turn left. After about 1/2 mile bear left (signed Belmont + Dragonville). At the top of the slip road turn left. At traffic lights turn left then take the 2nd left, the stadium is on your right.

Record Attendance: 2,750 v Whitley Bay - FA Vase Semi-final 2001-02
Record Victory: Not known
Record Defeat: Not known
Record Goalscorer: Not known
Record Appearances: Joe Raine - 552
Additional Records: Lee Ludlow scored 45 goals in one season

Senior Honours: Northern League 1994-95, 2007-08. Northern Premier League Division 1 North 2008-09, Chairman's Cup 2008-09.

10 YEAR RECORD

00-01	01-02	02-03	03-04	04-05	05-06	06-07	07-08	08-09	09-10
NL 1 4	NL 1 6	NL 1 5	NL 1 2	NL 1 6	NL 1 11	NL 1 8	NL 1 1	NP1N 1	NP P 20

GARFORTH TOWN

Chairman: Tom Murray
Secretary: Steve Nichol (T) 07984 786 782
(E) s.nichol@icfds.com
Additional Committee Members: Norman Hebbron, Simon Clifford, Gillian Clifford, Jane Close, George Williams
Manager: Steve Nichol
Programme Editor: George Williams (E) g.williams@garforthtown.com

Club Factfile

Founded: 1964 **Nickname:** The Miners
Previous Names: Garforth Miners 1964-85
Previous Leagues: Leeds Sunday Combination 1964-72, West Yorkshire 1972-78, Yorkshire 1978-83, Northern Counties East 1983-2007

Club Colours (change): Yellow/blue/white (Blue and white stripe/white/blue)

Ground: Genix Healthcare Stadium, Cedar Ridge, Garforth, Leeds LS25 2PF **(T)** 0113 287 7145
Capacity: 3,000 **Seats:** **Covered:** 200 **Clubhouse:** Yes **Shop:** Yes
Previous Grounds: Not known
Simple Directions
From North: travel south on A1 and join M1. Turn off at 1st junc (47). From South: M1 to junc 47. From Leeds area: join M1 at junc 44 or 46 and turn off at junc 47. From West: M62 to junc 29, join M1 and off at junc 47. From junc 47: take turning signe 'Garforth' (A642). Approx. 200 yds turn left into housing estate opposite White House. (Cedar Ridge). Stadium at end of lane. From the South (alternative): A1, turn off on to A63 signposted 'Leeds' immediately after 'Boot & Shoe' Public House. At 1st roundabout turn right on to A656 and follow to next roundabout. Take 1st left on to A642 (Garforth) and follow from M1 junc 47.

Record Attendance: 1,385 v Tadcaster Albion - Socrates debut - Northern Counties East League record
Record Victory: Not known
Record Defeat: Not known
Record Goalscorer: Simeon Bambrook - 67
Record Appearances: Philip Matthews - 1982-93
Additional Records:

Senior Honours: Northern Counties East Division 1 1997-98

10 YEAR RECORD

00-01	01-02	02-03	03-04	04-05	05-06	06-07	07-08	08-09	09-10
NCEP 17	NCEP 20	NCEP 20	NCE1 6	NCE1 2	NCEP 10	NP1N 4	NP1N 10	NP1N 16	NP1N 20

HARROGATE RAILWAY ATHLETIC

Chairman: Mick Gray
Secretary: David Shepherd (T) 07816 986 799
(E) mail4rail@ntlworld.com
Additional Committee Members: Paddy Hall, David Greenwood

Manager: Nigel Danby
Programme Editor: David Shepherd (E) mail4rail@ntlworld.com

Club Factfile

Founded: 1935 **Nickname:** The Rail
Previous Names: Not known
Previous Leagues: West Yorkshire, Harrogate & District, Yorkshire 1955-73, 80-82, Northern Counties East 1982-2006

Club Colours (change): Red/green/red (White/black/white)

Ground: Station View, Starbeck, Harrogate, North Yorkshire HG2 7JA (T) 01423 883 104
Capacity: 3,500 **Seats:** 800 **Covered:** 600 **Clubhouse:** Yes **Shop:** No
Previous Grounds: Not known

Simple Directions
From All Areas I would suggest using the M1 A1 Link Road heading North. Once on the A1 North stay on it until Junction 47. Exit at Junction 47 and take the 1st Exit at the Roundabout A59 heading towards Knaresborough and Harrogate. At the next Roundabout take the 3rd exit A59 Knaresborough. Stay on the A59 through Knaresborough and on towards Harrogate, after approx 1 mile from Knaresborough you will enter Starbeck. Proceed through Starbeck over the Railway Crossing. Station View is the 1st Right after the Railway Crossing. The Ground is at the far end of Station View. If you are coming from Harrogate towards Knaresborough on the A59 turn left immediately prior to pelican crossing just before the Railway Crossing. The Ground is at the far end of Station View.

Record Attendance: 3,500 v Bristol City - FA Cup 2nd Round 2002-03
Record Victory: Not known
Record Defeat: Not known
Record Goalscorer: Not known
Record Appearances: Not known
Additional Records: Received £1,000 from Guiseley for Colin Hunter

Senior Honours: Northern Counties East Division 2 North & League cup 1983-84, Division 1 1989-99.

10 YEAR RECORD

00-01	01-02	02-03	03-04	04-05	05-06	06-07	07-08	08-09	09-10
NCEP 13	NCEP 5	NCEP 10	NCEP 12	NCEP 3	NCEP 3	NP 1 12	NP1N 12	NP1N 18	NP1N 17

LANCASTER CITY

Chairman: Mick Hoyle
Secretary: Barry Newsham **(T)** 07759 530 901
(E) barry.newsham@lancastercityfc.com
Additional Committee Members: Stuart Houghton, Ian Sharp, David Needham, John Bagguley, Norman Wilson, Steve Ball, Eric Williams
Manager: Tony Hesketh
Programme Editor: Barry Newsham **(E)** barry.newsham@lancastercityfc.com

Club Factfile

Founded: 1905 **Nickname:** Dolly Blues
Previous Names: Not known
Previous Leagues: Lancashire Combination 1905-70, Northern Premier League 1970-82, 87-2004, North West Counties 1982-87, Conference 2004-07
Club Colours (change): Blue/white/blue (White/black/white)

Ground: Giant Axe, West Road, Lancaster LA1 5PE **(T)** 01524 382 238 / 843 500
Capacity: 3,064 **Seats:** 513 **Covered:** 900 **Clubhouse:** Yes **Shop:** Yes
Previous Grounds: Not known
Simple Directions
From the South: Exit M6 at Junction 33. At roundabout take the second exit onto the A6, pass through Galgate and then Lancaster University on the right until the next roundabout. Take the second main exit into Lancaster and follow signs for the railway station. At the traffic lights by Waterstones Bookshop turn immediately left. Take the second right onto Station Road and follow downhill on West Road and take the first right into the ground. From the North: Exit M6 at Junction 34 and turn left onto the A683. Follow signs for railway station into City around the one way system. Move over to the right hand side lane at the police station and through traffic lights. Manoeuvre into the left-hand lane until traffic lights at Waterstones Bookshop. Follow directions as from the south.

Record Attendance: 7,500 v Carlisle United - FA Cup 1936
Record Victory: 8-0 v Leyland Motors (A) - 1983-84
Record Defeat: 0-10 v Matlock Town - Northern Premier League Division 1 1973-74
Record Goalscorer: David Barnes - 130
Record Appearances: Edgar J Parkinson - 591
Additional Records: Paid £6,000 to Droylsden for Jamie Tandy
Received £25,000 from Birmingham City for Chris Ward

Senior Honours: Lancashire Junior Cup (ATS Challenge Trophy) 1927-28, 28-29, 30-31, 33-34, 51-52, 74-75.
Northern Premier League Division 1 1995-96.

10 YEAR RECORD

00-01	01-02	02-03	03-04	04-05	05-06	06-07	07-08	08-09	09-10
NP P 4	NP P 3	NP P 17	NP P 8	Conf N 13	Conf N 15	Conf N 24	NP1N 11	NP1N 7	NP1N 2

LEIGH GENESIS

Chairman: Alan Leach
Secretary: Mary Croasdale **(T)** 07800 874 831
(E) mary.croasdale@leighgenesis.com
Additional Committee Members: Gary Culshaw, Stan Walker, Matt Lawton, Andy Walsh Rob Atherton, Andy Healy, Gary Burke
Manager: Mark Maddox
Programme Editor: Stan Walker **(E)** info@leighgenesis.com

Club Factfile

Founded: 1896 **Nickname:** Railwaymen
Previous Names: Horwich RMI 1896-1994, Leigh RMI 1994-2008
Previous Leagues: Lancashire Alliance 1891-97, Lancashire 1897-1900, Lancashire Combination 1917-18, 19-39, 46-68, Cheshire Co. 1968-82, North West Counties 1982-83, Northern Premier 1983-2000, Conference 2000-06
Club Colours (change): White/black/black (All blue)

Ground: Atherton LR FC, Crilly Park, Spa Road, Atherton, Lancashire M46 9XG **(T)** 0800 634 2878
Capacity: **Seats:** **Covered:** **Clubhouse:** **Shop:**
Previous Grounds: Grundy Hill 1896-1994, Leigh RLFC, Leigh Sports Village Stadium > 2010
Simple Directions

Record Attendance: 8,500 v Wigan Athletic - Lancashire Junior Cup 1954
Record Victory: 19-1 v Nelson - Lancashire Combination 1964
Record Defeat: 1-9 v Brandon United - FA Cup
Record Goalscorer: Neil McLachlan
Record Appearances: Neil McLachlan
Additional Records: Paid £6,000 to Prescot Cables for Peter Cumiskey
Received £75,000 from Crewe Alexandra for Steve Jones
Senior Honours: Lancashire FA Cup 1984-85. Northern Premier League and League Cup 1999-2000.
Lancashire Trophy 2002-03.

10 YEAR RECORD

00-01	01-02	02-03	03-04	04-05	05-06	06-07	07-08	08-09	09-10
Conf 5	Conf 16	Conf 18	Conf 21	Conf N 22	Conf N 21	Conf N 17	Conf N 22	NP P 21	NP1N 6

MOSSLEY

Chairman: Vacant at time of going to press

Secretary: Harry Hulmes **(T)** 07944 856 343 **(E)** harry.hulmes@btinternet.com

Additional Committee Members: Steve Burgess, Colin Fielding, Mark Griffin, John Lamer, Gary Threlkeld, Steve Tague, J. Cawthorne, Joanne Blackshaw, Elaine Field, John Hughes, Linda Hughes, Marie Phillips, Michelle Freeman.

Manager: Shaun Higgins

Programme Editor: John Cawthorne **(E)** mossleyweb@hotmail.com

Club Factfile

Founded: 1903 **Nickname:** Lilywhites

Previous Names: Park Villa 1903-04, Mossley Juniors

Previous Leagues: Ashton, South East Lancashire, Lancashire Combination 1918-19, Cheshire County 1919-72, Northern Premier 1972-95, North West Counties 1995-2004

Club Colours (change): All white (Orange/black/black)

Ground: Seel Park, Market Street, Mossley, Lancashire OL5 0ES **(T)** 01457 832 369 / 836 104

Capacity: 4,500 **Seats:** 200 **Covered:** 1,500 **Clubhouse:** Yes **Shop:** Yes

Previous Grounds: Not known

Simple Directions

Exit M60 Junction 23 following A635 Ashton-under-Lyne. Take 3rd exit off roundabout then 3rd exit off next roundabout (Asda) and then 3rd exit off next roundabout signed Mossley A670. At junction turn right on to Mossley Rd through traffic lights. After approx 2.5 miles drop down hill entering Mossley town centre. Passing supermarket on left turn right before next traffic lights. Continue up the hill and left into Market Street. Ground is approx 200 yards on the left.

Record Attendance: 7,000 v Stalybridge Celtic 1950

Record Victory: Not known

Record Defeat: Not known

Record Goalscorer: David Moore - 235 (1974-84)

Record Appearances: Jimmy O'Connor - 613 (1972-87)

Additional Records: Paid £2,300 to Altrincham for Phil Wilson
Received £25,000 from Everton for Eamonn O'Keefe

Senior Honours: Northern Premier League 1978-79, 79-80, Challenge Cup 78-79, Division 1 2005-06

10 YEAR RECORD

00-01	01-02	02-03	03-04	04-05	05-06	06-07	07-08	08-09	09-10
NWC1 10	NWC1 8	NWC1 3	NWC1 2	NP 1 7	NP 1 1	NP P 20	NP1N 15	NP1N 10	NP1N 7

OSSETT ALBION

Chairman: Eric Gilchrist
Secretary: Andrew Lightfoot (T) 07711 309 923
(E) andrew.jl@sky.com
Additional Committee Members: S Chambers, S Garside, Miss L Burns, Miss G Patterson, K Fletcher, A Nash, J Shaw, S Wilkinson, Mrs S Langdale, N Yarrow, P Young, B Haddington
Manager: Eric Gilchrist
Programme Editor: Neville Wigglesworth (E) ossettalbion@hotmail.com

Unfortunately an up-to-date photograph was not available at the time of going to press

Club Factfile

Founded: 1944 **Nickname:** Albion
Previous Names: Not known
Previous Leagues: Heavy Woollen Area 1944-49, West Riding County Amateur 1949-50, West Yorkshire 1950-57, Yorkshire 1957-82, Northern Counties East 1982-2004
Club Colours (change): Old gold/black/black (All white)

Ground: The Warehouse Systems Stadium, Dimple Wells, Ossett, Yorkshire (T) 01924 273 746 / 273 618
Capacity: 3,000 **Seats:** Yes **Covered:** 750 **Clubhouse:** Yes **Shop:** Yes
Previous Grounds: Fearn House
Simple Directions
From M1 Junction 40: Follow Wakefield signs for 200 yards. Turn right at traffic lights (Holiday Inn on the corner). At the end of Queens Drive turn right and then 2nd left onto Southdale Road. At the end of Southdale Road turn right then immediately left onto Dimple Wells Road, the ground is facing. NOTE: There is a weight limit on Southdale Road. Coaches will need to continue on Station Road to the end, turn left, then at the end left again. Take 1st right onto Priory Road following for 200 yards turning left twice.

Record Attendance: 1,200 v Leeds United - Opening of floodlights 1986
Record Victory: 12-0 v British Ropes (H) - Yorkshire League Division 2 06/05/1959
Record Defeat: 2-11 v Swillington (A) - West Yorkshire League Division 1 25/04/1956
Record Goalscorer: John Balmer
Record Appearances: Peter Eaton - 800+ (22 years)
Additional Records:

Senior Honours: Northern Counties East League Division 1 1986-87, Premier Division 1998-99, 2003-04, League Cup 1983-84, 2002-03. West Riding County Cup x4.

10 YEAR RECORD

00-01	01-02	02-03	03-04	04-05	05-06	06-07	07-08	08-09	09-10
NCEP 2	NP 1 22	NCEP 5	NCEP 1	NP 1 12	NP 1 14	NP 1 11	NP1N 6	NP1N 6	NP1N 21

PRESCOT CABLES

Chairman: Tony Zeverona

Secretary: Doug Lace **(T)** 07753 143 273 **(E)** doug.lace@hotmail.com

Additional Committee Members: D Bellairs, P Kneale, K Derbyshire, M Flaherty, N Parr, B Banawich, M Byron, N Arnold, G Conway, I Sedden

Manager: Joe Gibiliru

Programme Editor: Brian Banawich **(E)** b.banawich@sky.com

Club Factfile

Founded: 1884 **Nickname:** Tigers

Previous Names: Prescot > 1995

Previous Leagues: Liverpool County Combination, Lancashire Combination 1897-98, 1918-20, 27-33, 36-76, Mid Cheshire 1976-78, Cheshire County 1978-82, North West Counties 1982-2003

Club Colours (change): Amber/black/black (All red)

Ground: Valerie Park, Eaton Street, Prescot L34 6HD **(T)** 0151 430 0507

Capacity: 3,000 **Seats:** 500 **Covered:** 600 **Clubhouse:** Yes **Shop:** Yes

Previous Grounds: Not known

Simple Directions

From North: M6 to Junction 26, onto M58 to Junction 3. Follow A570 to junction with A580 (East Lancs Road). (Approach junction in right hand lane of the two lanes going straight on). Cross A580 and take first road on right (Bleak Hill Road). Follow this road through to Prescot (2 miles). At traffic lights turn right, straight on at large roundabout (do not follow route onto Prescot by-pass) and right at next lights. 100 yards turn right at Hope and Anchor pub into Hope Street. Club will be in sight at bottom of road. **From South:** M6 to Junction 21a (M62 junction 10). Follow M62 towards Liverpool, to junction 7. Follow A57 to Rainhill and Prescot. Through traffic lights at Fusilier pub, 100 yards turn right at Hope and Anchor pub (as above). **From East:** Follow M62 as described in 'From South' or A580 East Lancs Road to Junction with A570 (Rainford by-pass), turn left and take first right. Follow route as 'From North'.

Record Attendance: 8,122 v Ashton National - 1932

Record Victory: 18-3 v Great Harwood - 1954-55

Record Defeat: 1-12 v Morecambe - 1936-37

Record Goalscorer: Freddie Crampton

Record Appearances: Harry Grisedale

Additional Records:

Senior Honours: Lancashire Combination 1956-57. North West Counties League 2002-03. Liverpool Non-League Cup x4. Liverpool Challenge Cup x6.

10 YEAR RECORD

00-01		01-02		02-03		03-04		04-05		05-06		06-07		07-08		08-09		09-10	
NWC1	8	NWC1	2	NWC1	1	NP 1	12	NP P	5	NP P	13	NP P	14	NP P	13	NP P	22	NP1N	15

RADCLIFFE BOROUGH

Chairman: David Chalmers (MD)
Secretary: Gerry Luczka **(T)** 07872 329 970
(E) rbfc@hotmail.co.uk
Additional Committee Members: David Murgatroyd, Graham Fielding

Manager: Gerry Luczka
Programme Editor: Dave Chalmers **(E)** rbfc@hotmail.co.uk

Unfortunately an up-to-date photograph was not available at the time of going to press

Club Factfile

Founded: 1949 **Nickname:** Boro
Previous Names: Not known
Previous Leagues: South East Lancashire, Manchester 1953-63, Lancashire Combination 1963-71, Cheshire County 1971-82, North West Counties 1982-97
Club Colours (change): All blue (Red and black stripes/black/white)

Ground: Stainton Park, Pilkington Road, Radcliffe, Lancashire M26 3PE **(T)** 0161 724 8346 / 724 5937
Capacity: 3,000 **Seats:** 350 **Covered:** 1,000 **Clubhouse:** Yes **Shop:** Yes
Previous Grounds: Not known
Simple Directions
M62 junction 17 – follow signs for 'Whitefield' and 'Bury'. Take A665 to Radcliffe via by-pass to Bolton Road. Signposted to turn right into Unsworth Street opposite Turf Hotel. The Stadium is on the left approximately half a mile turning Colshaw Close East.

Record Attendance: 2,495 v York City - FA Cup 1st Round 2000-01
Record Victory: Not known
Record Defeat: Not known
Record Goalscorer: Ian Lunt - 147
Record Appearances: David Bean - 401
Additional Records: Paid £5,000 to Buxton for Gary Walker 1991
Received £20,000 from Shrewsbury Town for Jody Banim 2003
Senior Honours: North West Counties 19984-85. Northern Premier League Division 1 1996-97.

10 YEAR RECORD

00-01	01-02	02-03	03-04	04-05	05-06	06-07	07-08	08-09	09-10
NP 1 9	NP 1 5	NP 1 3	NP P 20	NP P 9	NP P 18	NP P 21	NP1N 16	NP1N 16	NP1N 10

SALFORD CITY

Chairman: Darren Quick
Secretary: Andrew Giblin **(T)** 07867 823 713
(E) andrewgiblin@aol.com
Additional Committee Members: D.Brent, P Byram, G Carter, L Flint, B Gaskill, M George, Jolley, I Malone, F McCauley, P Raven, G Russell, J Simpson, B Taylor, D Taylor.
Manager: Darren Quick
Programme Editor: **(E)**

Back row (L-R): Jamie Tandy, Dean Cooper, Billy McCartney, Andy Robertson, Rhodri Giggs, Steve Foster
Front row: Darren Hockenhull, Alex Mortimer (c), Matt Cross, Gareth Thomas, Ashley Kelly

Club Factfile

Founded: 1940 **Nickname:** Ammies
Previous Names: Salford Central 1940-63, Salford Amateurs 1963 until merger with Anson Villa, Salford F.C. > 1990
Previous Leagues: Manchester 1963-80, Cheshire County 1980-82, North West Counties 1982-2008

Club Colours (change): Tangerine/black/tangerine (Green and white stripes/green/green)

Ground: Moor Lane, Kersal, Salford, Manchester M7 3PZ **(T)** 0161 792 6287
Capacity: 8,000 **Seats:** 260 **Covered:** 600 **Clubhouse:** Yes **Shop:** No
Previous Grounds: Not known
Simple Directions
M62 to Junction 17 (Prestwich, Whitefield). Take A56 Bury New Road towards Manchester. Continue through four sets of traffic lights. Turn right into Moor Lane. Ground 500 yards on left. Take first left after ground (Oaklands Road), first left again into Nevile Road and follow along to main entrance.

Record Attendance: 3,000 v Whickham - FA Vase 1980
Record Victory: Not known
Record Defeat: Not known
Record Goalscorer: Not known
Record Appearances: Not known
Additional Records:

Senior Honours: Manchester League Premier Division 1975, 76, 77, 79. North West Counties League Cup 2006.

10 YEAR RECORD

00-01	01-02	02-03	03-04	04-05	05-06	06-07	07-08	08-09	09-10
NWC1 7	NWC1 3	NWC1 9	NWC1 15	NWC1 18	NWC1 5	NWC1 4	NWC1 2	NP1N 20	NP1N 11

SKELMERSDALE UNITED

Chairman: Frank Hughes
Secretary: Bryn Jones (T) 07904 911 234
(E) skemsaint@sky.com
Additional Committee Members: Mrs L Boardman, Mr W Boardman, Mr D Bolderston, Mr A Gore, Mr T Garner, Mr P Griffiths, Mr F Hughes, Mr B Jones, Mr P McGee, Mr J Sewell, Mr M Sewell.
Manager: Tommy Lawson
Programme Editor: Frank Hughes (E) frankhughes@skelmersdaleutdfc.com

Club Factfile

Founded: 1882 **Nickname:** Skem
Previous Names: Not known
Previous Leagues: Liverpool County Combination, Lancashire Combination 1891-93, 1903-07, 21-24, 55-56, 76-78, Cheshire County 1968-71, 78-82, Northern Premier 1971-76, North West Counties 1983-2006

Club Colours (change): All royal blue (All red)

Ground: Skelmersdale & Ormskirk College Stadium, Stanley Ind. Est. WN8 8EF (T) 01695 722 123
Capacity: 2,300 **Seats:** 240 **Covered:** 500 **Clubhouse:** Yes **Shop:** Yes
Previous Grounds: Not known
Simple Directions
Exit M58 J4 (signposted Skelmersdale), carry straight on at next roundabout (Hope Island) into Glenburn Road, left at next roundabout (Half Mile Island) into Neverstitch Road (signposted Stanley Industrial Estate). Immediately right at next roundabout into Staveley Road and then left into Statham Road. Ground is 500 yards on left in Selby Place.

Record Attendance: 7,000 v Slough Town - FA Amateur Cup Semi-final 1967
Record Victory: Not known
Record Defeat: Not known
Record Goalscorer: Stuart Rudd - 230
Record Appearances: Robbie Holcroft - 422 including 398 consecutively
Additional Records: Paid £2,000 for Stuart Rudd
Received £4,000 for Stuart Rudd
Senior Honours: FA Amateur Cup 1970-71. Barassi Anglo-Italian Cup 1970-71.
Lancashire Junior Cup x2. Lancashire Non-League Cup x2.

10 YEAR RECORD

00-01	01-02	02-03	03-04	04-05	05-06	06-07	07-08	08-09	09-10
NWC1 12	NWC1 9	NWC1 5	NWC1 8	NWC1 6	NWC1 2	NP 1 15	NP1N 3	NP1N 2	NP1N 5

TRAFFORD

Chairman: Howard Nelson
Secretary: Graham Foxall **(T)** 07796 864 151
(E) foxxytfc@talktalk.net
Additional Committee Members: D Brown, D Law, D Murray, T Walmsley, B Whitten, M.Brown, N.Brown, B Griffin, A Heathcote, L.Knights, H Nelson, P Thomas, J Williams.
Manager: Garry Vaughan
Programme Editor: Dave Murray **(E)** davem@traffordfc.co.uk

Back Row L-R): G. Vaughan (Manager), K. Coppin, K. Harrop, T. Bailey, C. Lawton, N. Bayunu, T. Read, A. Lundy, L. Hargreaves, T. Smith, S. Woodford, T. Turner, R. Marley, J. McComb (Ass. Manager), J. McDermott (Coach)
Front Row: S. Gallanders, P. Ashton, D. White, M. Keddie, J. Shaw, W. Collier, N. Papargiris, S. Barlow.

Club Factfile

Founded: 1990 **Nickname:** The North
Previous Names: North Trafford 1990-94
Previous Leagues: Mid Cheshire 1990-92, North West Counties 1992-97, 2003-08, Northern Premier 1997-2003

Club Colours (change): All white (All yellow)

Ground: Shawe View, Pennybridge Lane, Flixton Urmston M41 5DL **(T)** 0161 747 1727
Capacity: 2,500 **Seats:** 292 **Covered:** 740 **Clubhouse:** Yes **Shop:** Yes
Previous Grounds: Not known
Simple Directions
Anti-Clockwise exit at J10 (Trafford Centre) and turn right towards Urmston B5214. Straight across two roundabouts. First lights turn right into Moorside Road, at next roundabout take second exit in to Bowfell Road. At next lights turn sharp left then immediately right in to Pennybridge Lane next to Bird In Hand Pub, parking on left 100 yards.
Or Leave M60 at J8, taking A6144 towards Lymm, Partington, Carrington. At second set of traffic lights turn right on B5158 towards Flixton. Remain on B5158 crossing railway bridge at Flixton Station and turn right at next set of traffic lights. Passing Bird in Hand Pub take immediate right in to Pennybridge Lane. Parking on left 100 yards.

Record Attendance: 803 v Flixton - Northern Premier League Division 1 1997-98
Record Victory: Not known
Record Defeat: Not known
Record Goalscorer: Garry Vaughan - 88
Record Appearances: Garry Vaughan - 293
Additional Records:

Senior Honours: North West Counties Division 1 1996-97, 2007-08.
Manchester Challenge Trophy 2004-05. Northern Premier President's Cup 2008-09.

10 YEAR RECORD

00-01		01-02		02-03		03-04		04-05		05-06		06-07		07-08		08-09		09-10	
NP 1	5	NP 1	15	NP 1	22	NWC1	16	NWC1	12	NWC1	15	NWC1	5	NWC1	1	NP1N	15	NP1N	12

WAKEFIELD

Chairman: Vacant at time of going to press
Secretary: Peter Matthews (T) 0794 382 9818
(E) peter.matthews@wakefieldfc.com
Additional Committee Members: Marcus Pound, Pete Belvis, Daniel Brownhill,

Manager: Ronnie Glavin
Programme Editor: Dan Brownhill (E) daniel.brownhill@wakefieldfc.com

Photo courtesy of Wakefield Express.

Club Factfile

Founded: 1903 **Nickname:** The Bears
Previous Names: Emley AFC 1903-2002, Wakefield & Emley AFC 2002-04, 2004-06 Wakefield - Emley AFC
Previous Leagues: Huddersfield > 1969, Yorkshire 1969-82, Northern Counties East 1982-89

Club Colours (change): All nike royal blue (All nike hooped volt (Fluo Yellow) and black/black/black)

Ground: Wakefield Sports Club, Eastmoor Road, Wakefield WF1 3RR (T) 01924 365 007 / 372 038
Capacity: 2,500 **Seats:** 460 **Covered:** 700 **Clubhouse:** Yes **Shop:** Yes
Previous Grounds: Welfare Ground 1903-2000, Belle Vue 2000-06
Simple Directions
Junction 41 M1 take the A650 towards Wakefield at the third roundabout follow A642 Garforth at the third roundabout turn right A642 to Wakefield, passed the hospital on your right second set of lights which does not include pelican crossing turn right into Eastmoor Road the ground is 500 yards on your left. Coaches park round the back of the ground, coach turns left before the ground then first right park on the street. There is an entrance also from here.

Record Attendance: 5,134 v Barking - FA Amateur Cup 3rd Round 01/02/1969 at Welfare Ground
Record Victory: 12-0 v Ecclesfield Red Rose - Sheffield & Hallamshire Senior Challenge Cup 2nd Round 10/12/1996
Record Defeat: 1-7 v Altrincham - Northern Premier League Premier Division 25/04/1998
Record Goalscorer: Mick Pamment - 305
Record Appearances: Ray Dennis - 762
Additional Records: Received £60,000 from Ayr United for Michael Reynolds 1998

Senior Honours: Yorkshire League 1975-76, 77-78, 79-80, 81-82, League Cup 1969-70, 78-79, 81-82.
Northern Counties East 1987-88, 88-89.
Sheffield & Hallamshire Senior Cup 1975-76, 79-80, 80-81, 83-84, 88-89, 90-91, 91-92, 97-98.

10 YEAR RECORD

00-01	01-02	02-03	03-04	04-05	05-06	06-07	07-08	08-09	09-10
NP P 2	NP P 5	NP P 12	NP P 23	NP P 13	NP P 20	NP 1 21	NP1N 7	NP1N 9	NP1N 18

WARRINGTON TOWN

Chairman: Gary Skeltenbury
Secretary: Geoff Bell (T) 07805 015 126
(E) Bell199@btinternet.com
Additional Committee Members: Richard Sutton, Toby McCormac, Kevin Read, David Mowat MP, Bill Carr, David Hughes, Jeff Greenwood, Martin Simcock, Ken Lacey.
Manager: Joey Dunn
Programme Editor: Paul Roach (E) roach.paul@lineone.net

Club Factfile

Founded: 1948 **Nickname:** The Town
Previous Names: Stockton Heath 1949-62
Previous Leagues: Warrington & District 1949-52, Mid Cheshire 1952-78, Cheshire County 1978-82, North West Counties 1982-90 Northern Premier 1990-97
Club Colours (change): Yellow and blue/blue/blue (All red)

Ground: Cantilever Park, Common Lane, Latchford, Warrington WA4 2RS (T) 01925 631 932 / 653 044
Capacity: 2,000 **Seats:** 350 **Covered:** 650 **Clubhouse:** Yes **Shop:** Yes
Previous Grounds: Not known
Simple Directions
From M62 Junction 9 Warrington Town Centre: Travel 1 mile south on A49, turn left at traffic lights into Loushers Lane, ground ½ mile on right hand side. From M6 North or South Junction 20: Follow A50 (Warrington signs) for 2 miles, cross Latchford Swingbridge, turn immediate left into Station Road, ground on left.

Record Attendance: 2,600 v Halesowen Town - FA Vase Semi-final 1st leg 1985-86
Record Victory: Not known
Record Defeat: Not known
Record Goalscorer: Steve Hughes - 167
Record Appearances: Neil Whalley
Additional Records: Paid £50,000 to Preston North End for Liam Watson
Received £60,000 from Preston North End for Liam Watson
Senior Honours: North West Counties 1989-90, Division 2 2000-01, League Cup 1985-86, 87-88, 88-89

10 YEAR RECORD

00-01	01-02	02-03	03-04	04-05	05-06	06-07	07-08	08-09	09-10
NWC2 1	NWC1 11	NWC1 16	NWC1 5	NP 1 20	NP 1 19	NP 1 22	NP1S 13	NP1N 19	NP1N 9

WITTON ALBION

Chairman: Mark Harris
Secretary: Graham Shuttleworth **(T)** 07966 289 434
(E) graham@shuttleworth7.orangehome.co.uk
Additional Committee Members: Reg Hardingham, Clodagh Buckley, Ernest Fryer, Graham Pickering, Paul Worthington.
Manager: Paul Ogden
Programme Editor: Stewart Cain **(E)** stewart.cain@murraysmith.com

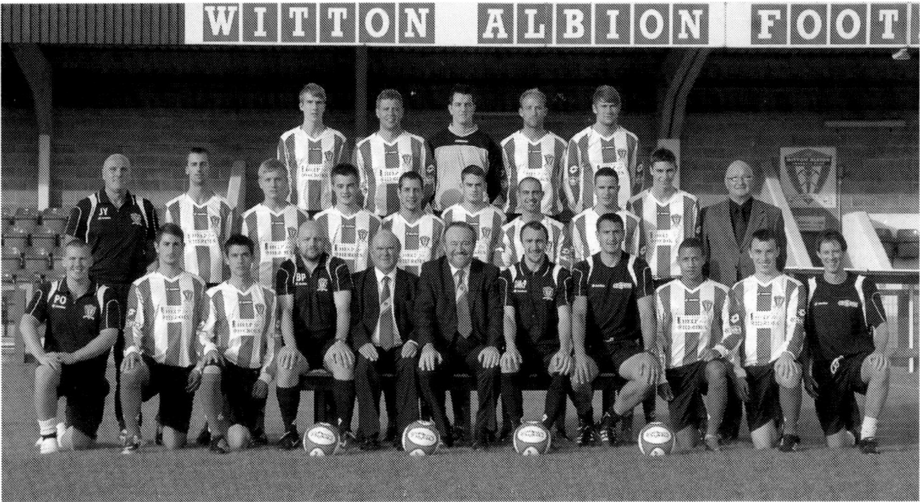

Club Factfile

Founded: 1887 **Nickname:** The Albion
Previous Names: Not known
Previous Leagues: Lancashire Combination, Cheshire County > 1979, Northern Premier 1979-91, Conference 1991-94

Club Colours (change): Red & white stripes/black/red (Yellow and black stripes/yellow/yellow)

Ground: Wincham Park, Chapel Street, Wincham, Northwich CW9 6DA **(T)** 01606 430 08
Capacity: 4,500 **Seats:** 650 **Covered:** 2,300 **Clubhouse:** Yes **Shop:** Yes
Previous Grounds: Not known
Simple Directions
M6 Junction 19: Follow A556 for Northwich for three miles, through two sets of traffic lights. Turn right at the beginning of the dual carriageway onto A559. After ¾ mile turn right at traffic lights by Slow & Easy Public House, still following A559. After a further ¾ mile turn left a Black Greyhound Public House (signposted). Follow the road through the industrial estate for about ½ mile. Turn left immediately after crossing the canal bridge (signposted) **From M56 Junction 10:** Follow the A558 (Northwich Road) towards Northwich for approximately 6 miles. Turn right at the crossroads by the Black Greyhound Public House (signposted). Follow the road through the industrial estate for about ½ mile. Turn left immediately after crossing the canal bridge (signposted)

Record Attendance: 3,940 v Kidderminster Harries - FA Trophy Semi-final 13/04/1991
Record Victory: 13-0 v Middlewich (H)
Record Defeat: 0-9 v Macclesfield Town (A) - 18/09/1965
Record Goalscorer: Frank Fidler - 175 (1947-50)
Record Appearances: Alf Ashley - 556 (1946-58)
Additional Records: Paid £12,500 to Hyde United for Jim McCluskie 1991
Received £11,500 from Chester City for Peter Henderson
Senior Honours: Northern Premier League 1990-91. Cheshire Senior Cup x7.

10 YEAR RECORD

00-01	01-02	02-03	03-04	04-05	05-06	06-07	07-08	08-09	09-10
NP P 7	NP P 10	NP P 7	NP P 5	NP 1 8	NP 1 8	NP P 2	NP P 2	NP P 20	NP1S 7

WOODLEY SPORTS

Chairman: Tony Whiteside
Secretary: Rod Haslem (T) 07772 223 115
(E) rhaslam@woodleysportsfc.co.uk
Additional Committee Members: Dave Parsonage, John Rourke, Darrin Whittaker, Peter Ross, Matt Reeves
Manager: Gareth McClelland
Programme Editor: Matt Reeves (E) info@woodleysportsfc.co.uk

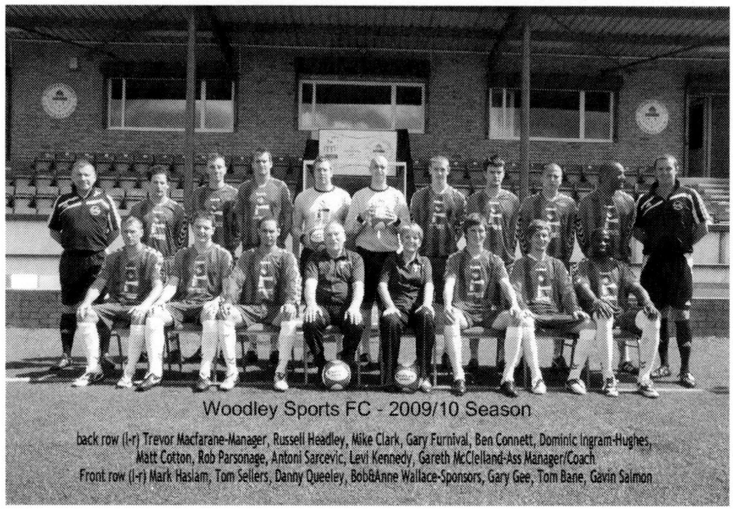

Woodley Sports FC - 2009/10 Season
back row (l-r) Trevor Macfarane-Manager, Russell Headley, Mike Clark, Gary Furnival, Ben Connett, Dominic Ingram-Hughes, Matt Cotton, Rob Parsonage, Antoni Sarcevic, Levi Kennedy, Gareth McClelland-Ass Manager/Coach
Front row (l-r) Mark Haslam, Tom Sellers, Danny Queeley, Bob&Anne Wallace-Sponsors, Gary Gee, Tom Bane, Gavin Salmon

Club Factfile

Founded: 1970 **Nickname:** The Steelmen
Previous Names: Woodley Athletic
Previous Leagues: Lancashire and Cheshire, Manchester, North West Counties

Club Colours (change): Red and blue/blue/blue (Orange/orange/black and orange)

Ground: The Neil Rourke, Lambeth Stadium, Lambeth Grove, Woodley SK6 1QX **(T)** 0161 406 6896 / 494 6429
Capacity: 2,300 **Seats:** 300 **Covered:** Yes **Clubhouse:** Yes **Shop:**
Previous Grounds: None

Simple Directions
Woodley Sports Football Club is located in Woodley, a suburb of Stockport in the North West of England. The ground lies a short distance from the new Manchester Ring Road, the M60. To reach us from the motorway, you should leave at Junction 25, which is signposted for Bredbury. Follow signs from here for the A560 towards Bredbury and Sheffield. Just after passing the McDonalds Drive-Thru, take a left at the traffic lights and proceed down Stockport Road towards Woodley, passing under the railway bridge at Bredbury Railway Station. Having passed St Mark's Church on the right, you reach a set of traffic lights. Immediately after the lights, at The Lowes Arms and before the Waggon & Horses Pub, turn left onto Mill Street. Proceed over the bridge on Mill Lane and then follow the signs to the ground.

Record Attendance: 1,500 v Stockport County
Record Victory: Not known
Record Defeat: Not known
Record Goalscorer: Not known
Record Appearances: Not known
Additional Records:

Senior Honours: North West Counties League Division 2 1999-2000.
Cheshire Senior Cup 2003-04.

10 YEAR RECORD

00-01	01-02	02-03	03-04	04-05	05-06	06-07	07-08	08-09	09-10
NWC1 13	NWC1 10	NWC1 17	NWC1 4	NP 1 11	NP 1 4	NP 1 10	NP1N 17	NP1N 13	NP1N 19

BARWELL

Chairman: David Laing
Secretary: Mrs Shirley Brown **(T)** 07961 905 141
(E) shirley.brown16@ntlworld.com
Additional Committee Members: Colin Burton, Derek Withers, Bob Gee, Geoff Hines, Viv Coleman, Steve Brown, Neil French. Mandy French, Keith Powell, Steve Greenhill, Gary Williams, Dave Langhor, Julie Laing, Lynda Dawson, Merv Nash
Manager: Marcus Law
Programme Editor: Dave Richardson **(E)** daverichardson@cleartherm.com

Unfortunately an up-to-date photograph was not available at the time of going to press

Club Factfile

Founded: 1992 **Nickname:** Kirkby Roaders
Previous Names: Barwell Athletic FC and Hinckley FC amalgamated in 1992.
Previous Leagues: Midland Alliance 1992-2010

Club Colours (change): Yellow with green trim/green with yellow trim/yellow (White with royal blue trim/royal/white & royal)

Ground: Kirkby Road Sports Ground, Kirkby Road, Barwell LE9 8FQ **(T)** 01455 843 067
Capacity: 2,500 **Seats:** 256 **Covered:** 750 **Clubhouse:** Yes **Shop:** No
Previous Grounds: Not known

Simple Directions
FROM M6 NORTH/M42/A5 NORTH: From M6 North join M42 heading towards Tamworth/Lichfield, leave M42 at Junction 10(Tamworth Services) and turn right onto A5 signposted Nuneaton. Remain on A5 for approx 11 miles, straight on at traffic lights at Longshoot Motel then at next roundabout take first exit signposted A47 Earl Shilton. In about 3 miles at traffic lights go straight on and in 1 mile at roundabout take first exit signposted Barwell. In about 1.5 miles, centre of village, go straight over mini roundabout and then in 20 metres turn right into Kirkby Road. Entrance to complex is 400 metres on right opposite park. **FROM M1 SOUTH:** From M1 South Take M69)Signposted Coventry) Take Junction 2 Off M69 (Signposted Hinckley) Follow signs to Hinckley . Go straight on at traffic lights with Holywell Pub on the right. The road bears to the right at next traffic lights turn right signposted Earl Shilton/Leicester. Keep on this road past golf club on right at Hinckley United Ground on left and at large roundabout take second exit signposted Barwell. In about 1.5 miles, centre of village, go straight over mini roundabout and then in 20 metres turn right into Kirkby Road. Entrance to complex is 400 metres on right opposite park.

Record Attendance: Not known
Record Victory: Not known
Record Defeat: Not known
Record Goalscorer: Andy Lucas
Record Appearances: Adrian Baker
Additional Records:

Senior Honours: Midland Alliance League Cup 2005-06, Champions 2009-10

10 YEAR RECORD

00-01	01-02	02-03	03-04	04-05	05-06	06-07	07-08	08-09	09-10
MidAl 3	MidAl 8	MidAl 12	MidAl 18	MidAl 13	MidAl 9	MidAl 6	MidAl 10	MidAl 2	MidAl 1

BELPER TOWN

Chairman: Phil Varney
Secretary: David Laughlin **(T)** 07768 010 604
(E) dave.laughlin@btinternet.com
Additional Committee Members: Stephen Boxall, Christopher Balls, Rex Baker, Alan Benfield, Graham Boot, Andrew Carter, David Winterbottom
Manager: Andy Carney and Danny Hudson
Programme Editor: David Laughlin **(E)** dave.laughlin@btinternet.com

Back Row (L-R): Gary Middleton (Assistant Manager), Mark Barnard (Assistant Manager), Harry Lord, Justin Jenkins, Matt Plant, Richard Adams, Alessandro Barcherini, Simon Mirfin, Nathan Benger, Chris Wood, Simon Harrison, Rob Paling, Aaron Pride, Paul Bennett (Kit Manager), Lucy Sawer (Physiotherapist)
Front: Ruben Wiggins-Thomas, Russell Peel, Andy Rushbury, Jon Froggatt, Andy Carney (Manager), Lee Thompson, Ryan Booker, Leigh Warriner, Luke Fedorenko

Club Factfile

Founded: 1883 **Nickname:** Nailers
Previous Names: Not known
Previous Leagues: Central Alliance 1957-61, Midland Counties 1961-82, Northern Counties East 1982-97

Club Colours (change): Yellow/black/black (All white)

Ground: Christchurch Meadow, Bridge Street, Belper DE56 1BA **(T)** 01773 825 549
Capacity: 2,650 **Seats:** 500 **Covered:** 850 **Clubhouse:** Yes **Shop:** Yes
Previous Grounds: Acorn Ground > 1951

Simple Directions
From North: Exit M1: Exit junction 28 onto A38 towards Derby. Turn off at A610 (signposted 'Ripley/Nottingham') 4th exit at roundabout towards Ambergate. At junction with A6 (Hurt Arms Hotel) turn left to Belper. Ground on right just past first set of traffic lights. Access to the ground is by the lane next to the church.
From South: Follow A6 north from Derby towards Matlock. Follow A6 through Belper until junction with A517. Ground on left just before traffic lights at this junction. Access to the ground is by the lane next to the church.
NB. Please do not attempt to bring coaches into the ground – these can be parked outside

Record Attendance: 3,200 v Ilkeston Town - 1955
Record Victory: 15-2 v Nottingham Forest 'A' - 1956
Record Defeat: 0-12 v Goole Town - 1965
Record Goalscorer: Mick Lakin - 231
Record Appearances: Craig Smithurst - 678
Additional Records: Paid £2,000 to Ilkeston Town for Jamie Eaton 2001
Received £2,000 from Hinckley United for Craig Smith

Senior Honours: Central Alliance League 1958-59, Derbyshire Senior Cup 1958-59, 60-61, 62-63, 79-80.
Midland Counties 1979-80. Northern Counties East 1984-85.

10 YEAR RECORD

00-01	01-02	02-03	03-04	04-05	05-06	06-07	07-08	08-09	09-10
NP 1 6	NP 1 18	NP 1 6	NP 1 20	NP 1 17	NP 1 9	NP 1 19	NP 1 8	NP1S 2	NP1S 6

BRIGG TOWN

Chairman: Kye Brown
Secretary: Martin North (T) 07891 122 242
(E) martinnorthfc@yahoo.co.uk
Additional Committee Members: John Martin, Bob Taylor, Jack Dunderdale, Mark Cawkwell, Carl Atkinson, Mike Smith, Simon Harris, Tim Harris, Kenny Bowers, Carolyn Smith
Manager: Steve Housham
Programme Editor: Michael Harker (E) mharker@blueyonder.co.uk

BACK L - R: Andy Holt, Phil Jackman, Jason Maxwell, Gregg Archer, Ryan Paczkowski, Scott Hellewell, Paul Metcalfe, Andy Pettinger, Rob Zand, Lee Roy Cochrane, Adam Holtham, Ollie Chappell, Danny Buttle, Lewis Walden.

FRONT L -R: Scott Raworth, Jamie Steel, Anthony Bowsley, Paul Grimes, Dave Andrews, Daniel Barrett, Stev Housham, Tommy Spall, Alan Lamb, Leigh Hutchinson, Stefan Melin, Sam West.

Club Factfile

Founded: 1864 **Nickname:** Zebras
Previous Names: Not known
Previous Leagues: Lincolnshire 1948-76, Midland Counties 1976-82, Northern Counties East 1982-2004

Club Colours (change): Black and white stripes/black/red (All green)

Ground: The Hawthorns, Hawthorn Avenue, Brigg DN20 8PG* **(T)** 01652 652 767 / 651 605
Capacity: 2,500 **Seats:** 370 **Covered:** Yes **Clubhouse:** Yes **Shop:** Yes
Previous Grounds: Old Manor House Convent, Station Road > 1939, Brocklesby 1939-59
Simple Directions
From M180 (Exit 4 - Scunthorpe East) A18 to Brigg. Leave Town via Wrawby Road, following signs for Airport and Grimsby. 100 metres after Sir John Nelthorpe Lower School, and immediately after bus stop/shelter, turn left into Recreation ground (signposted "Football Ground") and follow road into club car park.

*SAT NAV postcode DN20 8DT

Record Attendance: 2,000 v Boston United - 1953
Record Victory: Not known
Record Defeat: Not known
Record Goalscorer: Not known
Record Appearances: Not known
Additional Records:

Senior Honours: Midland Counties League 1977-78. FA Vase 1995-96, 2002-03. Northern Counties East Premier Division 2000-01. Lincolnshire League x8, League Cup x5. Lincolnshire 'A' Senior Cup x4. Lincolnshire 'B' Senior Cup x5.

10 YEAR RECORD

00-01	01-02	02-03	03-04	04-05	05-06	06-07	07-08	08-09	09-10
NCEP 1	NCEP 2	NCEP 2	NCEP 3	NP 1 8	NP 1 8	NP 1 17	NP 1 16	NP1S 20	NP1S 15

CARLTON TOWN

Chairman: Michael Garton

Secretary: Paul Shelton (T) 07854 586 875 (E) paul.shelton1@btopenworld.com

Additional Committee Members: Terry Fowler, Roger Smith, Mark Steggles, Jenny Shaw, Bob Sharpe, Tim Bee, Ian White, Brian Dennett

Manager: Les McJannet

Programme Editor: Ashley Winfield (E) info@msrnews.co.uk

Archive photo

Club Factfile

Founded: 1904 **Nickname:** Town

Previous Names: Sneinton

Previous Leagues: Notts Alliance, Central Midlands, Northern Counties East

Club Colours (change): Yellow with blue trim/royal blue/yellow and royal blue (Green with white trim/green/green)

Ground: Bill Stokeld Stadium, Stoek Lane, Gedling, Nottingham NG4 2QP (T) 0115 940 3192 / 940 2531

Capacity: 1,000 **Seats:** 164 **Covered:** 100 **Clubhouse:** Yes **Shop:** No

Previous Grounds: Not known

Simple Directions

From M1 J26 take A610 to Nottingham Ring Road. Follow signs for Mansfield (A60) for approx 4 miles via 2 roundabouts until reaching junction with A60 at Arnold. Take right turn at Vale Hotel on to Thackerays Lane. Proceed to roundabout and take 3rd exit on to Arno Vale Road. Proceed through traffic lights to top of hill and continue straight on at next lights on to Arnold Lane. Continue past golf course, the old Gedling Colliery and church to mini roundabout. Continue straight on to the old junction with A612. (Southwell) must turn right here and at next set of lights turn left and follow the loop road to the next junction. Take left turn on to the new A612 Gedling By Pass and follow to the next set of traffic lights at Severn Trent Works. Turn left on to Stoke Lane. Entrance to Carlton Town is immediate right. **[Ground must be accessed via the new A612 between Netherfield and Burton Joyce. Otherwise you may run into trouble with the local police]**

Record Attendance: 1,000 - Radio Trent Charity Match

Record Victory: Not known

Record Defeat: Not known

Record Goalscorer: Not known

Record Appearances: Not known

Additional Records:

Senior Honours: Notts Alliance League Division 2 1984-85, Division 1 1992-93. Central Midlands Supreme Division 2002-03. Northern Counties East Division 1 2005-06

10 YEAR RECORD

00-01	01-02	02-03	03-04	04-05	05-06	06-07	07-08	08-09	09-10
		CM Su 1	NCE1 9	NCE1 3	NCE1 1	NCEP 3	NP 1 10	NP1S 4	NP1S 9

GLAPWELL

Chairman: Dr Colin Hancock

Secretary: Malc Holmes **(T)** 07792 113 376 **(E)** malcholmesglapwellfc@hotmail.co.uk

Additional Committee Members: Gary Brown, David Brunt, Debbie Davies, Phil Davies, Paul Harrison, Brian Hepworth, Brian Smith, Bill Taylor, Bernard Wale

Manager: John Gaunt

Programme Editor: Brian Smith **(E)** brian_c_smith@btopenworld.com

Archive photo

Club Factfile

Founded: 1985 **Nickname:** The Well

Previous Names: Not known

Previous Leagues: Sutton and Skegby 1985-89, Central Midlands 1989-96, Northern Counties East 1996-2008

Club Colours (change): Black and white stripes/black/black (Yellow/blue/yellow)

Ground: Mansfield Town FC, Field Mill, Quarry Lane, Mansfield, NG18 5DA **(T)** 01623 482 482

Capacity: 9,899 **Seats:** Yes **Covered:** Yes **Clubhouse:** Yes **Shop:** Yes

Previous Grounds: Not known

Simple Directions

FROM THE NORTH: Take the M1 exiting at junction 29, then join the A617 to Mansfield, after around 6 miles turn right into Rosemary Street, then proceed to Quarry Lane where you should turn right into the ground.

FROM THE SOUTH & WEST: Take the M1 exiting at junction 28, then take the A38 to Mansfield, after around 6 miles turn right into Belvedere Street (at crossroads), then after a quarter of a mile turn right into Quarry Lane.

FROM THE EAST: Take the A617 to Rainworth, at the crossroads turn left, after 3 miles turn right into Nottingham Road, a left turn will take you into Quarry Lane where you will find the ground.

Record Attendance: Not known

Record Victory: Not known

Record Defeat: Not known

Record Goalscorer: Not known

Record Appearances: Not known

Additional Records:

Senior Honours: Central Midlands Division 1 1989-90, Supreme Division 1993-94.
Derbyshire Senior Cup 1997-98.

10 YEAR RECORD

00-01		01-02		02-03		03-04		04-05		05-06		06-07		07-08		08-09		09-10	
NCEP	10	NCEP	14	NCEP	11	NCEP	10	NCEP	13	NCEP	2	NCEP	6	NCEP	2	NP1S	6	NP1S	3

GOOLE

Chairman: Chris Hoff
Secretary: Mrs Ann Smith (T) 07837 607 233
(E) asmith1940@hotmail.co.uk
Additional Committee Members: Phil Jones

Manager: Karl Rose
Programme Editor: Malcolm Robinson (E) malrob01@tiscali.co.uk

Club Factfile

Founded: 1997 **Nickname:** The Badgers
Previous Names: Not known
Previous Leagues: Central Midlands 1997-98, Northern Counties East 2000-04

Club Colours (change): Red and white/red/red (All yellow)

Ground: Victoria Pleasure Gardens, Marcus Road, Goole DN14 6WW (T) 01405 762 794
Capacity: 3,000 **Seats:** 200 **Covered:** 800 **Clubhouse:** Yes **Shop:** Yes
Previous Grounds: Not known

Simple Directions
Leave the M62 at Junction 36 and follow signs to Goole Town Centre. Turn right at the 2nd set of traffic lights into Boothferry Road. Turn right again after 300 yards into Carter Street. The Victoria Pleasure Grounds is at the end of the road. 366 Metres from Goole Railway Station.

Record Attendance: 976 v Leeds United - 1999
Record Victory: Not known
Record Defeat: Not known
Record Goalscorer: Kevin Severn (1997-2001)
Record Appearances: Phil Dobson - 187 (1999-2001)
Additional Records:

Senior Honours: Central Midlands 1997-98. Northern Counties East Division 1 1999-2000, Premier Division 2003-04.

10 YEAR RECORD

00-01	01-02	02-03	03-04	04-05	05-06	06-07	07-08	08-09	09-10
NCEP 4	NCEP 12	NCEP 3	NCEP 6	NCEP 1	NP 1 21	NP 1 7	NP 1 9	NP1S 18	NP1S 18

GRANTHAM TOWN

Chairman: Steve Boam
Secretary: Patrick Nixon (T) 07747 136 033
(E) psnixon@hotmail.com
Additional Committee Members: Roger Booth, Barry Palmer, Peter Railton, D Quinn

Manager: Wayne Hallcro and Jimmy Albans
Programme Editor: Mike Koranski (E) mike.koranski@ntlworld.com

Club Factfile

Founded: 1874 **Nickname:** Gingerbreads
Previous Names: Not known
Previous Leagues: Midland Amateur Alliance, Central Alliance 1911-25, 59-61, Midland Counties 1925-59, 61-72, Southern 1972-79, 85-2006, Northern Premier 1979-85

Club Colours (change): Black and white/black/black (Red and black/red/red)

Ground: South Kesteven Sports Stadium, Trent Road, Gratham NG31 7XQ (T) 01476 402 224
Capacity: 7,500 **Seats:** 750 **Covered:** 1,950 **Clubhouse:** Yes **Shop:** Yes
Previous Grounds: London Road

Simple Directions
FROM A1 NORTH Leave A1 At A607 Melton Mowbray exit. Turn left at island on slip road into Swingbridge Lane. At T junction turn left into Trent Road ground is 100yds on right.
FROM A52 NOTTINGHAM. Pass over A1 and at first island turn right into housing estate & Barrowby Gate. Through housing estate to T junction. Turn right and then immediately left into Trent road ground is 100 yards on the left.
FROM A607 MELTON MOWBRAY. Pass under A1 and take next left A1 South slip road. At island turn right into Swingbridge Road then as for A1 North above. From all directions follow brown signs for Sports Complex, which is immediately behind the stadium.

Record Attendance: 3,695 v Southport - FA Trophy 1997-98
Record Victory: 13-0 v Rufford Colliery (H) - FA Cup 15/09/1934
Record Defeat: 0-16 v Notts County Rovers (A) - Midland Amateur Alliance 22/10/1892
Record Goalscorer: Jack McCartney - 416
Record Appearances: Chris Gardner - 664
Additional Records: Received £20,000 from Nottingham Forest for Gary Crosby

Senior Honours: Southern League Midland Division 1997-98. Lincolnshire Senior Cup x20. Lincolnshire County Senior Cup x2.

10 YEAR RECORD

00-01		01-02		02-03		03-04		04-05		05-06		06-07		07-08		08-09		09-10	
SthE	3	SthE	2	SthP	16	SthP	22	SthP	13	SthP	11	NP P	22	NP 1	6	NP1S	13	NP1S	11

KIDSGROVE ATHLETIC

Chairman: Michael Fitzjohn
Secretary: Samuel Brotherton (T) 01782 810 745
(E) samthepen@hotmail.com
Additional Committee Members: David James, Ernie Langford, John Rowley,

Manager: Peter Ward
Programme Editor: Steve Green (E) james.accountancy@live.co.uk.

Club Factfile

Founded: 1952 **Nickname:** The Grove
Previous Names: Not Known
Previous Leagues: Buslem and Tunstall 1953-63, Staffordshire County 1963-66, Mid Cheshire 1966-90, North West Counties 1990-2002

Club Colours (change): All blue (All green)

Ground: The Seddon Stadium, Hollinwood Road, Kidsgrove, Staffs ST7 1DQ (T) 01782 782 412
Capacity: 4,500 **Seats:** 1,000 **Covered:** 800 **Clubhouse:** Yes **Shop:** Yes
Previous Grounds: Vickers and Goodwin 1953-60
Simple Directions
Leave the M6 at Junction 16, join the A500 towards Stoke-on-Trent. Take the 2nd exit signposted Newcastle & Kidsgrove. Top of the slip road, turn left onto A34 Kidsgrove/Congleton. Straight over at roundabout. At 1st set of traffic lights (by Caudwell Arms pub) turn right onto A34. Continue to next set of lights, turn right into Cedar Avenue. Continue then take 2nd right into Lower Ash Road. Take 3rd left into Hollinwood Road, Ground on left at top.

Record Attendance: 1,903 v Tiverton Town - FA Vase Semi-final 1998
Record Victory: 23-0 v Cross Heath W.M.C. - Staffordshire Cup 1965
Record Defeat: 0-15 v Stafford Rangers - Staffordshire Senior Cup 20/11/2001
Record Goalscorer: Scott Dundas - 53 (1997-98)
Record Appearances: Not known
Additional Records: Paid £10,000 to Stevenage Borough for Steve Walters
Received £3,000 for Ryan Baker 2003-04

Senior Honours: Mid Cheshire League x4, League Cup x3.
North West Counties Division 1 1997-98, 2001-02, Challenge Cup 1997-98.

10 YEAR RECORD

00-01	01-02	02-03	03-04	04-05	05-06	06-07	07-08	08-09	09-10
NWC1 6	NWC1 1	NP 1 19	NP 1 22	NP 1 10	NP 1 17	NP 1 8	NP 1 17	NP1S 15	NP1S 4

LEEK TOWN

Chairman: Andrew Wain

Secretary: Brain Wain **(T)** 07967 204 470 **(E)** b.wain@tiscali.co.uk

Additional Committee Members: A Reeves, Mrs T Reynolds, S Reynolds, M Howson, C Hermiston

Manager: Wayne Johnson

Programme Editor: Steve & Tracy Reynolds **(E)** stevepreynolds@hotmail.com

Back Row (L-R): Ken Ashford (Kit Man/Physio), Ashley Miller, Wayne Corden, Leon Ashman, Matt Bradbury, John Ritchie, Paul Heeps, Pete Johnson, Rob Hawthorne, Paul Rutter, Dean Crowe, Chris Hermiston (Groundsman/Director)
Front Row: Joe Wolliscroft, Dan Cope, Mitch Shenton, Bobby Gee, Wayne Johnson (Manager), Andy Wain (Chairman), Paul Macari (Asst Manager), Matt Johnson, Luke Robinson, Andy Taylor, Tom France

Club Factfile

Founded: 1946 **Nickname:** The Blues

Previous Names: Not known

Previous Leagues: Staffordshire Co., Manchester 1951-54, 57-73, West Midlands (B'ham) 1954-56,Cheshire Co. 1973-82, North West Counties 1982-87, N.P.L. 1987-94, 95-97, Southern 1994-95, Conference 1997-99

Club Colours (change): All blue (Red and black stripes/black/black)

Ground: Harrison Park, Macclesfield Road, Leek, Cheshire ST13 8LD **(T)** 01538 399 278

Capacity: 3,600 **Seats:** 625 **Covered:** 2,675 **Clubhouse:** Yes **Shop:** Yes

Previous Grounds: Not known

Simple Directions

From the South: Leave M6 at J15, over roundabout on to the A500, go over the flyover, up the slip road, onto the A50 and follow the signs to Leek. Go straight over the roundabout (Britannia Building on the left) to large set of lights. Go straight across St. Georges Street to top of road to junction, turn left, go down the hill for about a half a mile. The Ground is on the left. **From the North:** Leave M6 at J19. Take Macclesfield signs. Follow into Macclesfield then take A523 Leek/Buxton signs. Follow these to Leek. Ground is situated on the right as you come into Leek. From West Midlands: M6 J15. A500 towards Stoke, over flyover, take A50 past Brittania Stadium. After approx 3 miles join A53 signposted Leek. On entering the town, straight ahead up St Edwards St. (Remainder as above)

Record Attendance: 5,312 v Macclesfield Town - FA Cup 1973-74

Record Victory: Not known

Record Defeat: Not known

Record Goalscorer: Dave Sutton - 144

Record Appearances: Gary Pearce - 447

Additional Records: Paid £2,000 to Sutton Town for Simon Snow
Received £30,000 from Barnsley for Tony Bullock

Senior Honours: Northern Premier League 1996-97. Staffordshire Senior Cup 1995-96.

10 YEAR RECORD

00-01	01-02	02-03	03-04	04-05	05-06	06-07	07-08	08-09	09-10
NP P 22	NP 1 6	NP 1 9	NP 1 8	NP P 7	NP P 12	NP P 17	NP P 19	NP1S 9	NP1S 8

LINCOLN UNITED

Chairman: Chris Geeson
Secretary: John Wilkinson (T) 07773 284 017
(E) johnwilk@live.co.uk
Additional Committee Members: C Bestford, A Adams, J J Dolan, G Chapman

Manager: John Wilkinson
Programme Editor: John Wilkinson (E) johnwilk@live.co.uk

Unfortunately an up-to-date photograph was not available at the time of going to press

Club Factfile

Founded: 1938 **Nickname:** United
Previous Names: Lincoln Amateurs > 1954
Previous Leagues: Lincolnshire 1945-46, 60-67, Lincoln 1946-60, Yorkshire 1967-82, Northern Counties East 1982-86, 92-95, Central Midlands 1982-92

Club Colours (change): White/red/red (Red/black/black and red)

Ground: Ashby Avenue, Hartsholme, Lincoln LN6 0DY (T) 01522 696 400 / 690 674
Capacity: 2,714 **Seats:** 400 **Covered:** 1,084 **Clubhouse:** Yes **Shop:** Yes
Previous Grounds: Skew Bridge 1940s, Co-op Sports Ground > 1960s, Hartsholme Cricket Club > 1982
Simple Directions
Along Lincoln Relief Road (A46) until reaching roundabout with exit for Birchwood. Take this exit which is Skellingthorpe Road for approximately 1 mile, at 30 mph sign turn right into Ashby Avenue. Entrance to ground is 200 yards on right.

Record Attendance: 2,000 v Crook Town - FA Amateur Cup 1st Round 1968
Record Victory: 12-0 v Pontefract Colliery - 1995
Record Defeat: 0-7 v Huddersfield Town - FA Cup 1st Round 16/11/1991
Record Goalscorer: Tony Simmons - 215
Record Appearances: Steve Carter - 447
Additional Records: Paid £1,000 to Hucknall Town for Paul Tomlinson December 2000
Received £3,000 from Charlton Athletic for Dean Dye July 1991

Senior Honours: Northern Counties East Division 1 1985-86, 92-93, Premier Division 1994-95.

10 YEAR RECORD

00-01	01-02	02-03	03-04	04-05	05-06	06-07	07-08	08-09	09-10
NP 1 15	NP 1 19	NP 1 16	NP 1 4	NP P 14	NP P 19	NP P 15	NP P 20	NP1S 10	NP1S 19

LOUGHBOROUGH DYNAMO

Chairman: Frank Fall
Secretary: Brian Pugh (T) 07775 825 321
(E) brian.pugh1@btinternet.com
Additional Committee Members: Keith Hawes, Greg Blood

Manager: Ian Blyth
Programme Editor: Rob Smith (E) lufbrafox@ntlworld.com

Club Factfile

Founded: 1955 **Nickname:** Dynamo
Previous Names: Not known
Previous Leagues: Loughborough Alliance 1957-66, Leicestershire & District 1966-71, East Midlands 1971-72, Central Alliance 1972-89, Leicestershire Senior 1989-2004, Midland Alliance 2004-08
Club Colours (change): Gold/black/gold (Green and white hoops/white/green and white hoops)

Ground: Nanpantan Sports Ground, Nanpantan Road, Loughborough LE11 3YE (T) 01509 237 148
Capacity: 1,500 **Seats:** 250 **Covered:** Yes **Clubhouse:** Yes **Shop:** No
Previous Grounds: Not known
Simple Directions
From M1: At Junction 23 turn towards Loughborough (A512). At 1st set of traffic lights turn right on to Snells Nook Lane.. At 1st crossroads ("Priory" pub on left) turn left on to Nanpantan Rd. Turn (1st) right after 0.75 miles on to Watermead Lane. The ground is at the end of the lane. **From Leicester (A6):** Turn left at 3rd roundabout on Epinal Way (Ring Road) on to Forest Road. After 2 miles turn (5th) left on to Watermead Lane. **From Nottingham (A60):** Turn right at 1st set of traffic lights in Loughborough. Go through next 4 sets of traffic lights. Turn left at the first roundabout on to Epinal Way straight on at next roundabout and then take the third exit at following roundabout on to Forest Road. After 2 miles turn (5th) left on to Watermead Lane.

Record Attendance: Not known
Record Victory: Not known
Record Defeat: Not known
Record Goalscorer: Not known
Record Appearances: Not known
Additional Records:

Senior Honours: Leicestershire Senior League Division 1 2001-02, Premier Division 2003-04.
Leicestershire Senior Cup 2002-03, 03-04.

10 YEAR RECORD

00-01		01-02		02-03		03-04		04-05		05-06		06-07		07-08		08-09		09-10	
LeicS1	17	LeicS1	1	LeicS	4	LeicS	1	MidAl	14	MidAl	13	MidAl	9	MidAl	2	NP1S	14	NP1S	14

MARKET DRAYTON TOWN

Chairman: Julian Parton
Secretary: Brian Garratt **(T)** 07854 725 957
(E) julian@halessawmills.co.uk
Additional Committee Members: Stuart Holloway, Clive Jones, Frank Hodgkiss, Ron Ebrey, Graham Machin, Alex Mutch, Mark Paton, Nick Alsop, Gary Burns.
Manager: Simon Line
Programme Editor: Stuart Holloway **(E)** jsholloway@morris-lubricants.co.uk

Club Factfile

Founded: 1969 **Nickname:**
Previous Names: Little Drayton Rangers > 2003
Previous Leagues: West Midlands (Regional) 1969-2006, Midland Alliance 2006-09

Club Colours (change): All red (All navy blue)

Ground: Greenfields Sports Ground, Greenfields Lane, Market Drayton TF9 3SI **(T)** 01630 655 088
Capacity: **Seats:** **Covered:** **Clubhouse:** Yes **Shop:**
Previous Grounds: Not known
Simple Directions
Take the A41 to Ternhill Island, turn right on A53 for Newcastle-under-Lyne. Straight on at first island (by Muller factory). At next island turn right to town centre (by Gingerbread Inn). Approx 200yds take 2nd right into Greenfields Lane. Ground 150 yards on right, car park opposite.

From Stoke-on-Trent take A53 for Shrewsbury, at Gingerbread Inn turn left for town centre then as above.

Record Attendance: Not known
Record Victory: Not known
Record Defeat: Not known
Record Goalscorer: Not known
Record Appearances: Not known
Additional Records:

Senior Honours: West Midlands (Regional) League 2005-06. Midland Alliance 2008-09.

10 YEAR RECORD

00-01	01-02	02-03	03-04	04-05	05-06	06-07	07-08	08-09	09-10
WMP 3	WMP 4	WMP 4	WMP 7	WMP 2	WMP 1	MidAl 13	MidAl 3	MidAl 1	NP1S 13

NEWCASTLE TOWN

Chairman: Paul Ratcliffe

Secretary: Ray Tatton (T) 07792 292 849 (E) rftatton@tiscali.co.uk

Additional Committee Members: Carl Birchall, Michael Pagett, Geoff Eccleston, Ken Walshaw, Les Morris, Colin Spencer.

Manager: Greg Clowes

Programme Editor: Ray Tatton (E) rftatton@tiscali.co.uk

Left to Right Back Row Dorian Garner Ass Manager, Ian Willis, Andy Nicholls, Ryan Dicker, Mike Douglas, Greg Smith, Danny Read, Chris Budrys, Karl Espley, John Sheldon, Jordan Johnson.
Front Row Mathew Bell, Kyle Diskin, Louis James, Alan Nagington, Paul Donnelly (Capt), Michael Morton, Dan Skelton.

Club Factfile

Founded: 1964 **Nickname:** Castle

Previous Names: Parkway Hanley, Clayton Park & Parkway Clayton. Merged as NTFC 86

Previous Leagues: Newcatle & District, Staffs Co & Mid Cheshire, North West Counties

Club Colours (change): Royal blue/royal blue/white (All white)

Ground: Lyme Valley Parkway Stadium, Buckmaster Avenue, Clayton, ST5 3BX **(T)** 01782 662 351

Capacity: 4,000 **Seats:** 300 **Covered:** 1,000 **Clubhouse:** Yes **Shop:** Yes

Previous Grounds: Not known

Simple Directions

FROM M6: Leave the M6 at Junction 15 and immediately turn left up the bank (signposted A519 Newcastle.) Go to the second roundabout and turn right into Stafford Avenue. Take the first left into Tittensor Road (signposted Newcastle Town FC.) Go to the end and the ground is below in the parkway. (Entrance through the gateway signposted Newcastle Town FC.) **FROM A50 DERBY:** Follow the A50 to the end and join the A500 (signposted M6 South) just past Stoke City Football Ground. Follow the A500 to the Motorway and at the roundabout turn right up the bank (A519 Newcastle.) Go to the second roundabout and turn right into Stafford Avenue. Take the first left into Tittensor Road (signposted Newcastle Town FC.) Go to the end and the ground is below in the parkway. (Entrance through the gateway signposted Newcastle Town FC.)

Record Attendance: 3,948 v Notts County - FA Cup 1996

Record Victory: Not known

Record Defeat: Not known

Record Goalscorer: Andy Bott - 149

Record Appearances: Dean Gillick - 632

Additional Records:

Senior Honours: Mid Cheshire League 1985-86. Walsall Senior Cup 1993-94, 94-95.

10 YEAR RECORD

00-01	01-02	02-03	03-04	04-05	05-06	06-07	07-08	08-09	09-10
NWC1 9	NWC1 5	NWC1 4	NWC1 6	NWC1 2	NWC1 6	NWC1 12	NWC1 3	NWCP 3	NWCP 1

QUORN

Chairman: Stuart Turner
Secretary: Reg Molloy **(T)** 07729 173 333
(E) k.molloy@ntlworld.com
Additional Committee Members: Les Caunt, Stewart Warrington, John Unwin, Jake Nooney, Mavis Turner, Margaret Berry, Peter Clarke, Terry Brookes, Ivan Kirk, Andrew Webb, Hilary Simpson, Jane Penny, Jim Simpson
Manager: Dougie Keast
Programme Editor: Stewart Warrington **(E)** stewart.warrington@ntlworld.com

Club Factfile

Founded: 1924 **Nickname:** Reds
Previous Names: Quorn Methodists
Previous Leagues: Leicestershire Senior, Midland Alliance

Club Colours (change): All red (Yellow/blue/white)

Ground: Farley Way Stadium, Farley Way, Quorn, Leicestershire LE12 8RB **(T)** 01509 620 232
Capacity: 1,550 **Seats:** 350 **Covered:** 250 **Clubhouse:** Yes **Shop:**
Previous Grounds: Not known
Simple Directions
Exit Junction 24 M1 Southbound on A6 through Kegworth, continue on A6 signposted Leicester/Loughborough bypass. Through Loughborough and at first roundabout take 2nd exit signposted Quorn. Turn left at traffic lights 200 yards from island and the ground is situated just inside on the left.

Record Attendance: Not known
Record Victory: Not known
Record Defeat: Not known
Record Goalscorer: Not known
Record Appearances: Not known
Additional Records:

Senior Honours: Leicestershire Senior Cup 1940, 1952, 1954.
Leicestershire Senior League 2000-01

10 YEAR RECORD

00-01		01-02		02-03		03-04		04-05		05-06		06-07		07-08		08-09		09-10	
LeicS1	1	MidAl	7	MidAl	5	MidAl	4	MidAl	4	MidAl	7	MidAl	3	NP 1	12	NP1S	12	NP1S	20

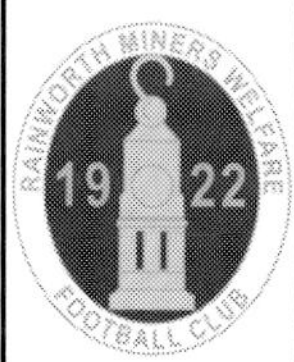

RAINWORTH MINERS WELFARE

Chairman: Derek Blow
Secretary: Leslie Lee (T) 07740 576 958
(E) leslie.lee7@ntlworld.com
Additional Committee Members: Brian Reece, Derek Bentley, Gordon Foster, Brian Martin, Sue Funk, Dick Draper
Manager: Rudy Funk
Programme Editor: Gordon Foster (E) gord@rainworth.fsnet.co.uk

Club Factfile

Founded: 1922 **Nickname:** The Wrens
Previous Names: Rufford Colliery
Previous Leagues: Notts Alliance 1922-03, Central Midlands League 2003-07, Northern Counties East 2007-10

Club Colours (change): All White (All Royal Blue).

Ground: Welfare Ground, Kirklington Road, Rainworth, Mansfield NG21 0JY (T) 01623 792 495
Capacity: 2,000 **Seats:** 221 **Covered:** 350 **Clubhouse:** Yes **Shop:** No
Previous Grounds: Not known
Simple Directions
From M1 (Junction 29) – take A617. At Pleasley turn right onto the new Mansfield Bypass road which is still the A617 and follow to Rainworth. At roundabout with B6020 Rainworth is off to the right, but it is better to go straight over onto the new Rainworth Bypass and then right at the next roundabout (the ground can be seen on the way along the Bypass) At mini roundabout, turn right onto Kirklington Road and go down the hill for ¼ mile – ground and car park on the right
Alternatively you can reach the new A617 Bypass from the A38 via Junction 28 on the M1. From A614 at roundabout, take the A617 to Rainworth for 1 mile. Left at 1st roundabout into village. At mini roundabout right into Kirklington road – ¼ mile down hill as above.

Record Attendance: 5,071 v Barton Rovers FA Vase SF 2nd Leg, 1982.
Record Victory: Not known
Record Defeat: Not known
Record Goalscorer: Not known
Record Appearances: Not known
Additional Records:

Senior Honours: Notts Senior Cup Winners 1981-82

10 YEAR RECORD

00-01	01-02	02-03	03-04	04-05	05-06	06-07	07-08	08-09	09-10
NottS 2	NottS 8	NottS 5	CM P 3	CM Su 20	CM Su 9	CM Su 3	NCE1 4	NCE1 2	NCEP 2

ROMULUS

Chairman: Richard Evans
Secretary: Peter Lowe (T) 07738 604 391
(E) peterwloweuk@yahoo.co.uk
Additional Committee Members: Andy Fitchett, Peter Morgan, Roger Evans, Phillip Hobson, Paul Dockerill, Craig Seaman, Keith Brown, Andy Mitchell, Tom Clarke, Mark Taylor, Graham Morris, Keith Higham.
Manager: Richard Evans and Keith Brown
Programme Editor: Paul Dockerill (E) paul-dockerill@btconnect.com

Unfortunately an up-to-date photograph was not available at the time of going to press

Club Factfile

Founded: 1979 **Nickname:** The Roms
Previous Names: Not known
Previous Leagues: Midland Combination 1999-2004, Midland Alliance 2004-07, Southern 2007-2010

Club Colours (change): Red and white stripes/red/red (Black and green stripes/black/black)

Ground: Sutton Coldfield FC, Central Ground,Coles Lane B72 1NL (T) 0121 354 2997
Capacity: 4,500 **Seats:** 200 **Covered:** 500 **Clubhouse:** Yes **Shop:** Yes
Previous Grounds: Not known
Simple Directions
From M42 Junc 9, take A4097 (Minworth sign). At island, follow signs to Walmley Village. At traffic lights turn right (B4148). After shops turn left at traffic lights into Wylde Green Road. Over railway bridge turn right into East View Road, which becomes Coles Lane.

Record Attendance: Not known
Record Victory: Not known
Record Defeat: Not known
Record Goalscorer: Not known
Record Appearances: Not known
Additional Records:

Senior Honours: Midland Combination 2003-04

10 YEAR RECORD

00-01		01-02		02-03		03-04		04-05		05-06		06-07		07-08		08-09		09-10	
MCmP	3	MCmP	4	MCmP	5	MCmP	1	MidAl	12	MidAl	4	MidAl	2	SthM	10	SthM	11	SthM	8

RUSHALL OLYMPIC

Chairman: John C Allen

Secretary: Peter Athersmith **(T)** 07909 792 422 **(E)** rushallolympic@yahoo.co.uk

Additional Committee Members: Nick Allen, Brian Greenwood, Ray Barrow, Edwin Venables, Ray Jones, Bob Thomas, Simon Haynes, Raymond Jones

Manager: Neil Kitching

Programme Editor: Darren Stockall **(E)** darren@stockall.fslife.co.uk

Club Factfile

Founded: 1951 **Nickname:** The Pics

Previous Names: Not known

Previous Leagues: Walsall Amateur 1952-55, Staffordshire County (South) 1956-78, West Midlands 1978-94, Midland Alliance 1994-2005, Southern 2005-08

Club Colours (change): Black and gold/black/black (Red and white stripes/red/red)

Ground: Dales Lane off Daw End Lane, Rushall, Nr Walsall WS4 1LJ **(T)** 01922 641 021

Capacity: 2,500 **Seats:** 200 **Covered:** 200 **Clubhouse:** Yes **Shop:** Yes

Previous Grounds: Rowley Place 1951-75, Aston University 1976-79

Simple Directions

M6 J10 follow signs for Walsall stay on this dual carriage way for about four miles until you come to the Walsall Arboretum and turn left following signs for Lichfield A461. Go under the bridge and you will come to McDonald's on your right, turn right into Daw End Lane. Go over the canal bridge and turn right opposite the Royal Oak Public House and the ground is on the right.

Alternative: From the A38 to it's junction with the A5 (Muckley Corner Hotel) take the A461 to Walsall after about five miles you will reach some traffic lights in Rushall by Mcdonald's, turn left into Daw End Lane go over the canal bridge and turn right opposite The Royal Oak Public House the ground is on the right.

Record Attendance: 2,000 v Leeds United Ex players

Record Victory: Not known

Record Defeat: Not known

Record Goalscorer: Graham Wiggin

Record Appearances: Alan Dawson - 400+

Additional Records:

Senior Honours: West Midlands League 1979-80. Midland Alliance 2004-05.

10 YEAR RECORD

00-01	01-02	02-03	03-04	04-05	05-06	06-07	07-08	08-09	09-10
MidAl 2	MidAl 5	MidAl 2	MidAl 14	MidAl 1	SthW 10	SthM 15	SthM 5	NP1S 5	NP1S 12

SHEFFIELD

Chairman: Richard Tims
Secretary: Stephen Hall **(T)** 07761 207 447
(E) steve@sheffieldfc.com
Additional Committee Members: I Cameron, R Dyson, P. Hancock, J. Harrison, A. Methley, J Ball, P. Bowden, I. Feeley, N. Hughes,D. Risely, W. Towning, M. Turnidge, L Walshaw, C. Williamson, Mrs. D. Risely, Mrs. J. Towning
Manager: Christopher Dolby
Programme Editor: Craig Williamson **(E)** craig4271@blueyonder.co.uk

Club Factfile

Founded: 1857 **Nickname:** Not known
Previous Names: None
Previous Leagues: Yorkshire 1949-82

Club Colours (change): Red/black/red (All blue)

Ground: The BT Local Business Stadium, Sheffield Road, Dronfield S18 2GD **(T)** 01246 292 622 / 413 269
Capacity: 1,456 **Seats:** 250 **Covered:** 500 **Clubhouse:** Yes **Shop:** Yes
Previous Grounds: Abbeydale Park, Dore 1956-89, Sheffield Amateur Sports Stadium, Hillsborough Park 1989-91, Don Valley Stadium 1991-97

Simple Directions
From the South – M1 to Junc 29, A617 into Chesterfield. At Roundabout follow A61 Sheffield. This is a dual carriageway passing over 2 roundabouts. At the 3rd roundabout take the 3rd exit signposted Dronfield. The Coach and Horses Public House is at the bottom of the hill on the right and the BT Local Business Stadium directly behind it. Entrance to the ground is by turning right at the traffic lights and immediate right into the Club Car Park. **From the East** - M18 to M1 north to Junc 33 (Sheffield). Turn towards Sheffield and take the 3rd exit from dual carriageway signposted' Ring Road / Chesterfield'. Go straight on at traffic island so that you are travelling alongside dual carriageway for a short period. At the junction turn left onto A61 Chesterfield. This is a dual carriageway passing through numerous traffic lights and two traffic islands. Follow Chesterfield sign at all times. After passing Graves Tennis centre on your left, turn left at next traffic island (still signposted Chesterfield). At next traffic island take 2nd exit signposted Dronfield The Coach and Horses Public House is at the bottom of the hill on the right and the BT Local Business Stadium directly behind it. Entrance to the ground is by turning right at the traffic lights and immediate right into the Club Car Park.

Record Attendance: 2,000 v Barton Rovers - FA Vase Semi-final 1976-77
Record Victory: Not known
Record Defeat: Not known
Record Goalscorer: Not known
Record Appearances: Not known
Additional Records: Paid £1,000 to Arnold Town for David Wilkins. Received £1,000 from Alfreton for Mick Godber 2002. World's first ever Football Club.

Senior Honours: FA Amateur Cup 1902-03. Northern Counties East Division 1 1988-89, 90-91, League Cup 2000-01, 04-05. Sheffield and Hallamshire Senior Cup 1993-94, 2004-05, 05-06.

10 YEAR RECORD

00-01	01-02	02-03	03-04	04-05	05-06	06-07	07-08	08-09	09-10
NCEP 7	NCEP 9	NCEP 7	NCEP 4	NCEP 4	NCEP 4	NCEP 2	NP 1 4	NP1S 11	NP1S 5

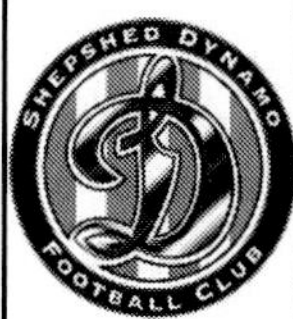

SHEPSHED DYNAMO

Chairman: Peter Bull

Secretary: Dave Wheatley **(T)** 07725 302 287 **(E)** davidwheatley9@aol.com

Additional Committee Members: Elaine Hunt, Ben Reed, John Sharples, Danny Pole, Mick Voce, N.Attwal, S.Attwal, S.Straw, A.Gibson, J.Croson. P.Bailey, M.Bailey, S.Bailey, P.Robinson, M.Widdowson, S.Baker, S.Gardener.

Manager: Barry Baker

Programme Editor: Ben Reed **(E)** ben@shepsheddynamo.co.uk

Club Factfile

Founded: 1994 **Nickname:** Dynamo

Previous Names: Shepshed Albion/Charterhouse > 1994

Previous Leagues: Leicestershire Senior 1907-16, 19-27, 46-50, 51-81, Midland Counties 1981-82, N.C.E. 1982-83, Southern 1983-88, 96-2004, N.P.L. 1988-93, Midland Combination 1993-94, Midland Alliance 1994-95

Club Colours (change): Black and white stripes/black/black (All yellow)

Ground: The Dovecote, Butt Hole Lane, Shepshed, Leicestershire LE12 9BN **(T)** 01509 650 992

Capacity: 2,050 **Seats:** 570 **Covered:** 400 **Clubhouse:** Yes **Shop:** Yes

Previous Grounds: Not known

Simple Directions

From M1: Leave at Junction 23 and take A512 (Ashby). At first traffic lights turn right into Leicester Road and continue to garage on right. Turn right at mini roundabout into Forest Street and continue to Black Swan pub on left. Turn right into Butt Hole Lane, ground 100 yards. **From M6:** Leave at Junction 15 (Stoke-on-Trent) and take A50 to join M1 at Junction 24 South. At Junction 23 leave M1 and continue as above.

Record Attendance: 2,500 v Leicester City - Friendly 1996-97

Record Victory: Not known

Record Defeat: Not known

Record Goalscorer: Lee McGlinchey - 107

Record Appearances: Lee McGlinchey - 255

Additional Records:

Senior Honours: Midland Counties League 1981-82, League Cup 81-82. Northern Counties East 1982-83, League Cup 82-83. Midland Alliance 1995-96. Leicestershire Senior Cup x7

10 YEAR RECORD

00-01	01-02	02-03	03-04	04-05	05-06	06-07	07-08	08-09	09-10
SthW 15	SthW 16	SthW 17	SthW 21	NP 1 15	NP 1 10	NP 1 20	NP 1 15	NP1S 8	NP1S 17

SPALDING UNITED

Chairman: Chris Toynton
Secretary: Audrey Fletcher (T) 07778 411 916
(E) tulips@uk2.net
Additional Committee Members: Graham Chappell, Ray Tucker, Rodney Sadd

Manager: Richard Scott
Programme Editor: Ray Tucker (E) ray.tucker@talktalk.net

Club Factfile

Founded: 1921 **Nickname:** Tulips
Previous Names: Not known
Previous Leagues: Peterborough, United Counties 1931-55, 68-78, 86-88, 91-99, 2003-04, Eastern Counties 1955-60, Central All. 1960-61, Midland Co. 1961-68, N.C.E. 1982-86, Southern 1988-91, 99-2003

Club Colours (change): All royal blue (Orange/black/black)

Ground: Sir Halley Stewart Playing Fields, Winfrey Avenue, Spalding PE11 1DA (T) 01775 712 047
Capacity: 2,700 **Seats:** 300 **Covered:** 500 **Clubhouse:** Yes **Shop:** Yes
Previous Grounds: Not known
Simple Directions
From the North follow the A52 and pick up the A16 south, as you near Spalding follow A16 By-pass past the New Power Station (on right). Carry on the by-pass to Springfields Roundabout, (McDonalds is on the left) turn right. Follow signs to Spalding Town Centre over Fulney Bridge on the Holbeach Road and travel approx ¾ mile from by-pass. Turn right over second bridge forming the roundabout then straight over into West Elloe Avenue. Continue down to traffic lights (Approx 400 yards). Turn left into Pinchbeck Road. After approx 300 yards turn right at the traffic lights. Turn left at the next set of traffic lights into Winfrey Avenue. The Ground is on the left.

Record Attendance: 6,972 v Peterborough - FA Cup 1982
Record Victory: Not known
Record Defeat: Not known
Record Goalscorer: Not known
Record Appearances: Not known
Additional Records:

Senior Honours: United Counties League 1954-55, 75-75, 87-88, 98-99, 2003-04. Northern Counties East 1983-84. Lincolnshire Senior Cup 1952-53.

10 YEAR RECORD

00-01	01-02	02-03	03-04	04-05	05-06	06-07	07-08	08-09	09-10
SthE 22	SthE 18	SthE 21	UCL P 1	NP 1 18	NP 1 20	SthM 19	NP 1 18	NP1S 17	NP1S 21

STAMFORD

Chairman: Kenneth Joynson
Secretary: Phil Bee (T) 07772 646 776
(E) phil.bee@queen-eleanor.lincs.sch.uk
Additional Committee Members: Guy Walton, John Burrows, John Drewnicki, Bob Feetham, Dave Salisbury, Roger Twiddy, Jeremy Biggs
Manager: Simon Clark
Programme Editor: John Burrows (E) john.burrows35@yahoo.co.uk

Back row (L-R): Luke Weston (coach), Becky Moss (physio), Ross Watson, Tony Battersby, Lee Beeson, Chris Wright, Miles Chamberlain (Captain), Richard Stainsby, Ben Sedgemore (assistant manager), Andy Toyne, Paul Malone, Stuart King, Simon Clark (manager).
Front row (L-R): Ricky Miller, David Sheridan, Craig Rook, Liam Hook, Dan Cotton, Adam Weston, Nick Jackson, Callum Reed, Simon Mowbray.

Club Factfile

Founded: 1894 **Nickname:** The Daniels
Previous Names: Stamford Town and Rutland Ironworks amalgamated in 1894 to form Rutland Ironworks > 1896
Previous Leagues: Peterborough, Northants (UCL) 1908-55, Central Alliance 1955-61, Midland counties 1961-72, United Counties 1972-98, Southern 1998-2007
Club Colours (change): Red/black/red (All navy blue)

Ground: Vic Couzens Stadium, Kettering Road, Stamford, Lincs PE9 2JS (T) 01780 763 079
Capacity: 2,000 **Seats:** 250 **Covered:** 1,250 **Clubhouse:** Yes **Shop:** Yes
Previous Grounds: None
Simple Directions
Travel on A1 Southbound. Leave A1 by A43 slip road. At junction turn left. Ground is one mile on the left.

Record Attendance: 4,200 v Kettering Town - FA Cup 3rd Qualifying Round 1953
Record Victory: 13-0 v Peterborough Reserves - Northants League 1929-30
Record Defeat: 0-17 v Rothwell - FA Cup 1927-28
Record Goalscorer: Bert Knighton - 248
Record Appearances: Dick Kwiatkowski - 462
Additional Records:

Senior Honours: FA Vase 1979-80. United Counties League x7. Lincolnshire Senior Cup, Senior Shield. Lincolnshire Senior 'A' Cup x3.

10 YEAR RECORD

00-01		01-02		02-03		03-04		04-05		05-06		06-07		07-08		08-09		09-10	
SthE	7	SthE	5	SthE	3	SthE	7	SthE	21	SthE	4	SthP	8	NP P	20	NP1S	7	NP1S	10

SUTTON COLDFIELD TOWN

Chairman: Tom Keogh
Secretary: Bill Worship (T) 07837 375 369
(E) billandpatworship@tiscali.co.uk
Additional Committee Members: Bernard Bent, Bernard Cheek, Ken Hawkins, Chris Rogers, Andy Taylor, Neil Murrall, Nick Thurston
Manager: Chris Keogh
Programme Editor: Lyn Coley (E) lyncoley@blueyonder.co.uk

Founded: 1897 **Nickname:** Royals
Previous Names: Sutton Coldfield F.C. 1879-1921
Previous Leagues: Central Birmingham, Walsall Senior, Staffordshire County, Birmingham Combination 1950-54, West Midlands (Regional) 1954-65, 79-82, Midlands Combination 1965-79

Club Colours (change): All blue (All yellow)

Ground: Central Ground, Coles Lane, Sutton Coldfield B72 1NL (T) 0121 354 2997
Capacity: 4,500 **Seats:** 200 **Covered:** 500 **Clubhouse:** Yes **Shop:** Yes
Previous Grounds: Meadow Plat 1879-89, Coles Lane 1890-1919
Simple Directions
From M42 Junc 9, take A4097 [Minworth sign]. At island, follow signs to Walmley Village. At traffic lights turn right [B4148]. After shops turn left at traffic lights into Wylde Green Road. Over railway bridge turn right into East View Road, which becomes Coles Lane.

Record Attendance: 2,029 v Doncaster Rovers - FA Cup 1980-81
Record Victory: Not known
Record Defeat: Not known
Record Goalscorer: Eddie Hewitt - 288
Record Appearances: Andy Ling - 550
Additional Records: Paid £1,500 to Gloucester for Lance Morrison, to Burton Albion for Micky Clarke and to Atherstone United for Steve Farmer 1991. Received £25,000 from West Bromwich Albion for Barry Cowdrill 1979

Senior Honours: West Midlands League 1979-80. Midland Combination x2.

10 YEAR RECORD

00-01	01-02	02-03	03-04	04-05	05-06	06-07	07-08	08-09	09-10
SthW 20	SthW 6	SthW 11	SthW 8	SthW 18	SthW 7	SthM 12	SthM 4	SthM 6	SthM 6

Founded: 1894

Chairman:
Ken Turner

Secretary:
Jason Mills
secretary@southern-football-league.co.uk

SOUTHERN LEAGUE

Premier Division		P	W	D	L	F	A	GD	Pts
1	Farnborough	42	28	9	5	100	44	56	93
2	Nuneaton Town	42	26	10	6	90	37	53	88
3	Chippenham Town	42	21	11	10	67	43	24	74
4	Hednesford Town	42	20	13	9	79	51	28	73
5	Brackley Town	42	21	9	12	83	61	22	72
6	Cambridge City	42	18	17	7	73	44	29	71
7	Bashley	42	20	11	11	79	61	18	71
8	Halesowen Town	42	21	17	4	84	53	31	70
9	Stourbridge	42	19	13	10	80	65	15	70
10	Leamington	42	19	8	15	84	75	9	65
11	Truro City	42	17	11	14	78	65	13	62
12	Banbury United	42	14	13	15	53	67	-14	55
13	Oxford City	42	13	15	14	65	67	-2	54
14	Swindon Supermarine	42	10	14	18	48	76	-28	44
15	Didcot Town	42	10	11	21	56	70	-14	41
16	Evesham United	42	9	14	19	35	52	-17	41
17	Merthyr Tydfil (-10 pts)	42	12	11	19	62	73	-11	37
18	Bedford Town	42	9	10	23	50	88	-38	37
19	Tiverton Town	42	8	12	22	35	61	-26	36
20	Hemel Hempstead Town	42	8	10	24	50	81	-31	34
21	Clevedon Town	42	6	11	25	48	92	-44	29
22	Rugby Town	42	4	8	30	41	114	-73	20

PROMOTION PLAY-OFFS

SF **Chippenham Town** 2 Hednesford Town 0 27/04/10 Att: 811

SF **Nuneaton Town** 6 Brackley Town 0 27/04/10 Att: 1639

F **Nuneaton Town** 2 Chippenham Town 1 01/05/10 Att: 3018

	1	2	3	4	5	6	7	8	9	10	11	12	13	14	15	16	17	18	19	20	21	22
1 Banbury United	-	1-1	0-0	0-3	1-0	0-0	4-3	1-0	0-1	0-3	2-1	3-2	1-1	1-2	3-1	2-1	1-1	2-1	3-3	3-1	0-1	0-0
2 Bashley	1-0	-	1-2	5-2	0-2	0-1	3-2	3-2	2-1	0-4	1-2	0-4	3-0	1-1	3-2	2-1	3-2	4-0	4-4	3-0	0-1	2-0
3 Bedford Town	1-1	0-4	-	2-2	0-2	1-2	3-1	1-5	1-2	2-2	1-1	3-2	5-0	0-2	2-4	2-1	1-1	3-1	0-1	1-2	2-0	0-2
4 Brackley Town	5-1	2-3	3-0	-	0-0	0-1	2-1	2-2	3-1	1-3	2-1	0-1	2-0	1-0	1-0	0-0	1-2	3-1	3-2	1-2	2-0	4-3
5 Cambridge City	2-1	2-2	4-2	5-0	-	1-0	4-1	4-1	1-1	1-1	1-1	0-3	1-1	2-2	1-1	1-1	2-0	1-0	6-1	5-0	1-1	0-3
6 Chippenham T.	5-0	1-2	3-0	2-3	2-1	-	2-0	2-0	2-1	2-0	1-1	0-1	6-1	4-2	1-5	2-1	2-0	1-0	2-2	0-1	4-2	2-1
7 Clevedon Town	1-2	0-2	0-3	0-3	0-1	0-0	-	1-1	1-4	1-4	3-3	0-3	1-0	1-3	1-1	0-3	1-2	1-3	4-1	2-6	0-1	0-3
8 Didcot Town	0-0	1-1	2-2	0-1	0-3	0-2	0-1	-	0-2	1-2	1-2	0-1	2-1	4-2	3-0	1-1	4-4	3-1	0-1	0-2	1-1	1-1
9 Evesham United	3-2	0-0	0-0	1-3	3-1	0-0	0-0	0-1	-	1-2	0-0	0-0	0-2	0-1	1-1	1-2	0-0	1-0	1-1	0-1	2-2	0-2
10 Farnborough	3-0	1-1	6-1	3-0	3-3	3-1	2-1	1-0	3-1	-	4-1	2-1	3-0	3-1	3-1	0-2	2-1	4-1	1-2	2-0	2-1	3-1
11 Halesowen T.	0-2	3-2	4-1	1-1	1-1	2-0	2-2	3-1	1-0	1-1	-	2-2	1-0	3-0	1-1	3-2	3-3	5-1	2-1	2-0	1-1	3-2
12 Hednesford T.	0-0	1-0	2-1	1-4	2-2	1-1	0-0	1-2	2-1	4-0	2-2	-	4-3	4-2	1-1	0-3	4-2	6-0	1-1	0-0	2-1	2-3
13 Hemel H. Town	2-3	0-1	5-1	1-1	2-3	0-1	1-1	1-2	2-0	1-1	3-5	2-2	-	0-2	3-1	1-3	2-1	1-0	2-2	3-1	0-2	0-2
14 Leamington	3-3	0-1	2-0	2-1	1-0	4-4	0-1	3-5	4-1	2-3	2-2	1-3	3-1	-	5-3	0-2	1-2	2-1	2-1	3-1	5-0	1-3
15 Merthyr Tydfil	3-2	2-1	0-0	2-1	0-1	2-1	2-3	4-2	2-1	0-0	0-2	1-2	1-2	2-3	-	1-3	2-3	1-1	2-1	1-0	1-1	1-2
16 Nuneaton Town	5-0	5-2	4-0	2-2	1-1	0-1	4-2	2-0	2-0	1-1	1-1	3-1	3-1	1-1	3-1	-	3-1	1-1	0-0	1-0	1-0	4-0
17 Oxford City	1-1	1-1	4-1	2-3	0-1	0-0	1-2	1-1	3-0	1-1	2-2	2-0	2-2	1-1	2-2	1-4	-	3-0	1-3	2-1	1-0	2-2
18 Rugby Town	0-2	2-3	1-4	1-4	0-3	0-0	4-4	4-3	0-0	0-4	0-3	1-6	2-2	1-4	1-4	0-3	4-0	-	1-2	0-0	3-2	1-1
19 Stourbridge	2-1	2-2	2-0	4-2	3-1	1-0	4-1	1-0	0-0	3-2	1-4	1-1	2-0	2-1	2-0	1-2	0-2	6-0	-	0-0	2-1	7-2
20 Swindon Sup.	1-2	3-3	0-0	1-7	1-1	1-1	3-2	1-1	1-1	0-7	1-2	0-0	1-0	2-3	1-1	2-4	2-4	5-1	2-2	-	2-1	0-4
21 Tiverton Town	2-1	0-5	2-0	1-1	0-0	0-0	0-0	1-2	0-1	0-2	0-2	0-2	0-0	2-3	0-1	1-2	1-0	3-1	2-2	0-0	-	1-2
22 Truro City	1-1	1-1	5-1	1-1	1-1	3-5	2-2	2-1	1-2	2-3	1-2	1-2	3-1	2-2	3-1	0-2	0-1	4-1	4-1	0-0	2-0	-

DIVISION ONE MIDLANDS

		P	W	D	L	F	A	GD	Pts
1	Bury Town	42	32	6	4	115	40	75	102
2	Hitchin Town	42	31	7	4	91	36	55	100
3	Burnham	42	26	9	7	67	43	24	87
4	Chesham United	42	24	8	10	76	41	35	80
5	Slough Town	42	23	8	11	87	54	33	77
6	Sutton Coldfield Town	42	22	11	9	93	61	32	77
7	Woodford United	42	18	8	16	70	68	2	62
8	Romulus	42	16	13	13	66	48	18	61
9	Arlesey Town	42	17	10	15	58	48	10	61
10	Leighton Town	42	18	6	18	63	66	-3	60
11	Soham Town Rangers	42	17	7	18	73	80	-7	58
12	Biggleswade Town	42	14	13	15	56	63	-7	55
13	Atherstone Town	42	15	9	18	65	82	-17	54
14	AFC Sudbury	42	13	12	17	55	54	1	51
15	Marlow	42	12	14	16	64	65	-1	50
16	Bedworth United	42	12	11	19	59	72	-13	47
17	Stourport Swifts	42	11	10	21	63	69	-6	43
18	Rothwell Town	42	11	8	23	53	80	-27	41
19	Beaconsfield SYCOB	42	8	8	26	46	96	-50	32
20	Bromsgrove Rovers (-10)	42	8	15	19	45	68	-23	29
21	Barton Rovers	42	6	9	27	49	95	-46	27
22	Aylesbury United	42	4	6	32	48	133	-85	18

PROMOTION PLAY-OFFS

SF Burnham 0 **Chesham United** 1 27/04/10 Att: 541

SF Hitchin Town 1 **Slough Town** 2 27/04/10 Att: 541

F **Chesham United** 4 Slough Town 0 01/05/10 Att: 1115

	1	2	3	4	5	6	7	8	9	10	11	12	13	14	15	16	17	18	19	20	21	22
1 AFC Sudbury	-	2-0	1-1	5-2	0-1	0-2	0-0	0-1	3-0	1-2	0-2	4-1	0-2	0-0	2-3	1-1	0-0	1-2	2-2	2-1	1-2	1-1
2 Arlesey Town	1-1	-	2-0	4-1	5-0	3-0	0-0	1-0	0-0	0-1	1-0	1-3	1-2	2-0	0-2	2-0	4-0	1-2	3-1	1-0	1-4	1-1
3 Atherstone Tn	0-2	2-4	-	2-2	2-1	1-2	1-0	1-1	2-0	1-3	3-6	3-3	1-2	0-1	0-3	1-5	4-2	2-0	3-2	3-2	2-0	0-1
4 Aylesbury Utd	0-4	2-1	3-4	-	0-1	3-3	1-2	1-3	1-0	1-2	0-4	0-1	3-4	1-3	2-2	1-2	2-5	2-5	0-4	1-1	0-4	0-4
5 Barton Rovers	2-0	1-1	2-3	1-1	-	1-2	5-2	2-2	2-2	0-1	1-3	0-2	3-6	2-1	1-1	0-2	1-2	3-3	1-2	0-4	2-5	1-2
6 Beaconsfield	0-0	1-2	4-0	1-2	2-5	-	4-0	0-2	2-2	1-4	1-2	1-4	1-1	2-0	1-0	1-4	0-2	1-4	0-4	0-6	0-2	0-2
7 Bedworth Utd	2-2	1-3	4-0	2-2	2-0	1-0	-	4-0	1-1	0-1	2-2	2-1	1-1	1-2	4-1	0-1	1-3	2-4	2-5	4-0	2-4	3-1
8 Biggleswade T.	0-0	3-2	1-0	3-1	2-1	1-1	1-0	-	1-1	2-1	0-3	1-1	0-3	1-0	2-3	0-1	0-4	1-0	1-0	2-2	3-3	3-1
9 Bromsgrove R.	2-3	1-2	1-1	5-0	1-0	3-1	1-1	1-1	-	2-2	0-4	0-0	0-1	0-4	2-0	2-2	1-0	1-1	0-2	2-1	0-1	1-2
10 Burnham	1-2	0-0	2-2	1-0	2-1	2-0	2-0	2-1	3-0	-	1-2	2-1	0-0	1-1	2-2	0-0	2-0	1-1	3-0	2-1	1-5	1-0
11 Bury Town	3-1	3-1	3-1	6-2	8-2	5-1	6-0	2-1	1-0	2-3	-	1-1	0-0	5-0	3-0	5-0	3-1	1-0	2-1	3-1	2-2	4-5
12 Chesham Utd	3-2	0-0	3-0	2-0	3-0	1-0	0-1	3-0	2-0	0-1	1-1	-	2-0	1-2	3-2	0-3	3-0	1-0	2-3	3-0	4-1	3-0
13 Hitchin Town	1-0	4-1	2-1	5-1	3-0	4-1	1-0	1-0	1-1	4-0	1-0	1-2	-	3-0	3-0	2-0	4-0	3-2	1-2	2-1	3-2	3-0
14 Leighton Town	6-4	2-1	1-1	2-1	3-0	1-1	2-0	3-1	1-2	3-0	0-2	2-1	2-2	-	1-2	1-0	2-1	0-1	4-4	2-1	1-2	2-4
15 Marlow	2-0	1-1	1-1	4-0	1-0	3-0	3-3	0-0	2-4	0-1	1-2	1-1	1-1	0-2	-	1-2	1-0	0-1	6-1	2-2	2-4	0-1
16 Romulus	0-1	0-0	1-2	5-0	0-0	7-1	2-0	1-1	2-1	0-1	1-2	0-1	2-3	4-0	0-0	-	1-1	1-4	1-0	0-0	2-3	0-0
17 Rothwell Town	1-0	1-0	2-3	5-0	2-2	2-2	0-1	0-7	2-0	1-2	0-0	1-2	0-1	0-1	3-3	1-3	-	1-3	4-2	0-3	0-3	0-0
18 Slough Town	0-1	1-2	3-3	5-1	5-1	3-1	2-0	4-2	3-2	0-2	0-1	1-3	0-1	3-1	1-1	2-2	4-1	-	2-0	3-2	2-2	1-0
19 Soham Town R.	0-1	2-0	1-3	5-1	3-2	2-3	2-2	3-2	0-0	1-1	0-3	1-4	3-2	2-1	2-1	0-0	4-2	0-2	-	1-0	0-1	4-4
20 Stourport Swifts	1-1	0-1	1-3	5-4	2-0	0-0	2-0	0-0	5-1	1-4	1-2	1-1	0-1	2-0	2-1	2-4	1-1	1-4	1-2	-	1-0	3-4
21 Sutton Coldfield	0-2	1-0	1-2	0-2	1-1	2-1	1-1	5-2	1-1	3-1	3-4	2-1	1-3	3-2	2-2	2-2	3-0	2-2	6-0	1-1	-	2-1
22 Woodford Utd	3-2	2-2	1-0	6-1	1-0	3-1	2-5	1-1	4-1	1-3	0-2	0-2	1-3	2-1	2-3	3-2	1-2	0-1	1-0	1-2	1-1	-

SOUTHERN DIVISION ONE MIDS DATES & GATES	AFC Sudbury	Arlesey Town	Atherstone Town	Aylesbury United	Barton Rovers	Beaconsfield SYCOB	Bedworth United	Biggleswade Town	Bromsgrove Rovers	Burnham	Bury Town	Chesham United	Hitchin Town	Leighton Town	Marlow	Romulus	Rothwell Town	Slough Town	Soham Town Rangers	Stourport Swifts	Sutton Coldfield	Woodford United
AFC Sudbury		13 Oct 154	6 Mar 204	6 Feb 179	28 Nov 196	22 Aug 174	16 Mar 116	8 Dec 137	10 Apr 182	5 Sep 206	3 Apr 545	2 Jan 195	18 Aug 205	13 Apr 170	10 Oct 213	23 Jan 188	11 Mar 106	1 Dec 163	9 Mar 147	27 Mar 192	26 Jan 121	24 Apr 405
Arlesey Town	30 Jan 160		22 Aug 140	14 Nov 113	24 Oct 190	6 Mar 107	3 Nov 121	15 Apr 125	5 Sep 123	20 Feb 127	4 Mar 121	10 Apr 152	3 Apr 492	24 Apr 106	16 Feb 80	10 Oct 121	9 Mar 67	8 Dec 141	18 Aug 133	28 Nov 119	13 Feb 113	27 Mar 92
Atherstone Town	19 Sep 213	27 Feb 231		13 Mar 207	13 Feb 215	24 Oct 167	5 Apr 305	12 Sep 214	2 Mar 188	10 Nov 156	15 Aug 203	24 Apr 210	27 Mar 236	3 Nov 157	28 Nov 168	15 Apr 180	26 Dec 205	14 Nov 203	16 Feb 202	25 Aug 163	30 Jan 208	10 Apr 205
Aylesbury United	16 Dec 87	20 Mar 142	5 Sep 158		24 Apr 128	30 Jan 107	2 Dec 104	20 Feb 136	6 Mar 112	10 Mar 112	18 Nov 95	3 Apr 232	10 Apr 276	17 Feb 129	9 Dec 98	17 Mar 110	9 Sep 86	28 Nov 181	22 Aug 167	13 Feb 110	7 Nov 119	27 Jan 82
Barton Rovers	17 Apr 105	23 Jan 116	17 Nov 64	12 Dec 114		7 Nov 60	19 Sep 102	10 Oct 154	13 Apr 67	16 Mar 55	30 Mar 90	20 Apr 112	2 Feb 190	22 Apr 61	25 Aug 48	5 Dec 64	15 Apr 60	23 Mar 82	13 Oct 77	15 Aug 61	20 Mar 70	13 Mar 194
Beaconsf'd SYCOB	27 Feb 90	19 Sep 52	23 Jan 85	12 Oct 130	27 Mar 65		14 Dec 90	10 Apr 47	19 Apr 48	5 Apr 101	13 Mar 72	24 Aug 257	28 Nov 112	7 Dec 67	8 Apr 70	31 Oct 66	1 Mar 71	15 Feb 200	6 Feb 72	14 Nov 45	24 Apr 86	15 Aug 75
Bedworth United	20 Mar 123	6 Feb 140	26 Jan 273	23 Jan 139	6 Mar 102	23 Mar 91		24 Apr 136	18 Aug 208	22 Aug 198	31 Oct 179	28 Nov 150	19 Jan 147	10 Apr 96	7 Nov 149	13 Oct 176	5 Sep 227	2 Feb 139	8 Apr 111	17 Oct 157	9 Mar 102	3 Apr 120
Biggleswade Town	22 Apr 95	5 Apr 180	21 Nov 145	15 Aug 150	8 Apr 90	16 Mar 61	12 Dec 125		20 Mar 82	30 Jan 121	18 Mar 141	7 Nov 161	13 Feb 315	24 Oct 121	19 Sep 101	17 Apr 76	26 Sep 115	13 Mar 172	26 Dec 131	11 Mar 52	3 Nov 112	25 Aug 90
Bromsgrove Rov.	5 Dec 281	16 Mar 169	30 Mar 152	19 Sep 307	26 Sep 270	21 Nov 180	23 Feb 119	14 Nov 255		15 Dec 140	17 Apr 353	15 Aug 367	24 Oct 272	13 Feb 100	27 Feb 181	25 Aug 282	12 Dec 242	15 Apr 161	27 Mar 124	26 Jan 188	5 Apr 177	30 Jan 251
Burnham	13 Mar 137	15 Aug 135	23 Mar 117	25 Aug 163	16 Feb 102	9 Feb 151	27 Feb 153	13 Oct 117	6 Feb 147		20 Mar 223	8 Dec 245	24 Apr 361	7 Nov 153	3 Apr 181	19 Sep 147	26 Jan 95	13 Apr 507	23 Jan 103	10 Apr 112	28 Nov 109	10 Oct 123
Bury Town	26 Dec 781	13 Apr 439	20 Feb 427	2 Mar 310	8 Dec 234	5 Sep 267	13 Feb 373	18 Aug 249	28 Nov 319	14 Nov 303		3 Nov 252	23 Mar 662	30 Jan 307	24 Apr 1550	27 Mar 418	6 Mar 430	10 Apr 605	5 Apr 640	16 Mar 255	22 Aug 254	15 Dec 274
Chesham United	5 Apr 245	5 Dec 226	12 Dec 206	2 Feb 255	18 Aug 241	9 Mar 186	17 Apr 249	27 Mar 274	20 Feb 264	30 Mar 224	6 Feb 261		6 Mar 378	22 Aug 263	13 Oct 272	21 Nov 239	23 Jan 219	10 Nov 310	31 Oct 279	16 Feb 203	5 Sep 219	14 Nov 223
Hitchin Town	15 Apr 326	26 Dec 510	7 Nov 353	5 Dec 327	5 Apr 405	17 Apr 562	2 Mar 220	15 Dec 303	23 Jan 300	12 Dec 277	25 Aug 330	19 Sep 432		20 Mar 325	15 Aug 303	6 Feb 356	9 Feb 191	13 Oct 295	30 Mar 238	13 Mar 370	17 Nov 244	27 Feb 341
Leighton Town	26 Sep 164	2 Feb 65	6 Feb 112	5 Apr 283	2 Mar 98	30 Mar 52	5 Dec 112	23 Jan 114	31 Oct 108	27 Mar 99	1 Dec 95	27 Feb 209	14 Nov 192		13 Mar 103	15 Aug 100	17 Apr 104	25 Aug 164	21 Nov 113	19 Sep 135	16 Mar 59	23 Feb 58
Marlow	2 Mar 101	16 Mar 81	17 Apr 154	30 Mar 104	9 Mar 74	18 Aug 98	27 Mar 106	6 Mar 114	22 Aug 125	2 Feb 106	12 Dec 118	13 Apr 172	20 Feb 158	5 Sep 101		14 Nov 81	5 Dec 81	5 Apr 239	26 Sep 105	3 Nov 105	24 Oct 139	13 Feb 101
Romulus	24 Oct 102	20 Apr 52	18 Aug 152	20 Oct 117	10 Apr 85	13 Feb 81	21 Apr 78	28 Nov 124	9 Mar 119	6 Mar 121	7 Nov 135	23 Mar 101	3 Nov 114	1 Apr 81	20 Mar 71		22 Aug 85	24 Apr 186	5 Sep 73	5 Apr 95	9 Feb 155	8 Dec 88
Rothwell Town	15 Aug 168	25 Aug 147	21 Apr 91	31 Oct 121	21 Nov 76	10 Oct 142	13 Mar 92	13 Apr 92	24 Apr 104	13 Feb 85	19 Sep 168	24 Oct 128	22 Apr 111	26 Apr 110	10 Apr 87	25 Mar 131		27 Mar 113	17 Nov 91	20 Apr 61	8 Apr 124	23 Mar 34
Slough Town	13 Feb 238	30 Mar 182	20 Mar 200	17 Apr 261	22 Aug 226	3 Apr 283	21 Nov 241	5 Sep 252	17 Nov 209	18 Aug 337	5 Dec 276	2 Mar 286	20 Apr 307	9 Mar 182	9 Feb 234	12 Dec 229	7 Nov 245		6 Mar 227	24 Oct 244	20 Feb 254	3 Nov 206
Soham Town Rges	25 Aug 200	11 Mar 81	10 Oct 120	13 Apr 100	30 Jan 114	12 Sep 100	15 Aug 145	2 Mar 75	7 Nov 137	24 Oct 108	2 Jan 410	13 Feb 138	8 Dec 120	20 Apr 80	23 Mar 81	13 Mar 110	20 Mar 100	19 Sep 168		24 Apr 122	10 Apr 116	28 Nov 115
Stourport Swifts	7 Nov 71	17 Apr 54	31 Oct 91	10 Oct 78	20 Feb 58	20 Mar 51	13 Apr 68	22 Aug 88	3 Apr 115	21 Nov 67	21 Nov 63	17 Nov 87	5 Sep 80	6 Mar 65	6 Feb 67	2 Mar 65	5 Sep 69	23 Jan 126	12 Dec 70		18 Aug 76	2 Feb 42
Sutton Coldfield T.	21 Nov 132	1 Mar 112	3 Oct 212	27 Mar 110	14 Nov 102	12 Dec 105	24 Aug 158	6 Feb 115	22 Mar 174	17 Apr 146	15 Apr 138	13 Mar 168	12 Apr 184	14 Dec 124	23 Jan 103	3 Apr 205	19 Apr 112	15 Aug 218	5 Dec 114	22 Feb 122		19 Sep 130
Woodford United	12 Dec 82	7 Nov 98	16 Mar 69	21 Nov 108	5 Sep 69	13 Apr 72	9 Feb 69	9 Mar 52	13 Oct 98	2 Mar 40	20 Apr 121	20 Mar 103	22 Aug 118	18 Aug 72	17 Nov 79	30 Mar 45	5 Apr 57	6 Feb 149	17 Apr 117	26 Sep 77	6 Mar 72	

DIVISION ONE SOUTH & WEST

		P	W	D	L	F	A	GD	Pts
1	Windsor & Eton	42	31	8	3	84	20	64	101
2	AFC Totton	42	32	4	6	105	36	69	100
3	Bridgwater Town	42	26	11	5	83	30	53	89
4	VT FC	42	25	7	10	90	52	38	82
5	Cirencester Town	42	23	9	10	91	46	45	78
6	Frome Town	42	20	15	7	68	44	24	75
7	Paulton Rovers	42	20	10	12	73	58	15	70
8	Gosport Borough (-1)	42	19	10	13	80	59	21	66
9	Mangotsfield United	42	19	5	18	77	67	10	62
10	North Leigh	42	18	7	17	83	72	11	61
11	Bishops Cleeve	42	15	13	14	64	64	0	58
12	Thatcham Town	42	17	6	19	76	72	4	57
13	Yate Town	42	15	10	17	58	64	-6	55
14	Abingdon United	42	15	7	20	65	84	-19	52
15	Uxbridge	42	14	6	22	70	85	-15	48
16	Cinderford Town	42	13	8	21	66	78	-12	47
17	Bedfont Green	42	12	8	22	77	90	-13	44
18	Taunton Town	42	11	7	24	50	85	-35	40
19	Andover	42	9	11	22	54	85	-31	38
20	Hungerford Town (-12)	42	13	6	23	53	68	-15	33
21	AFC Hayes	42	7	4	31	55	105	-50	25
22	Bracknell Town	42	2	0	40	29	187	-158	6

PROMOTION PLAY-OFFS

SF **Bridgwater Town** 3 VTFC 0 28/04/10 Att: 535

SF AFC Totton 2 **Cirencester Town** 3 28/04/10 Att: 411

F Bridgwater Town 3 **Cirencester Town** 4 aet 01/05/10 Att: 771

	1	2	3	4	5	6	7	8	9	10	11	12	13	14	15	16	17	18	19	20	21	22
1 AFC Hayes	-	0-2	1-2	3-1	1-1	4-2	7-1	0-2	4-3	1-6	2-3	0-1	0-4	0-5	4-6	0-1	1-5	1-2	0-4	2-1	1-2	1-4
2 AFC Totton	5-0	-	2-1	2-0	2-1	4-0	9-0	0-0	4-0	2-1	1-0	4-1	3-1	2-1	3-1	0-1	8-1	5-1	2-1	1-3	0-0	3-0
3 Abingdon Utd	2-1	0-4	-	4-1	2-0	1-1	4-0	0-0	1-1	0-1	0-5	0-1	1-4	3-2	3-1	0-1	3-0	2-0	7-4	1-0	0-2	1-2
4 Andover	3-2	1-0	1-2	-	2-1	1-1	5-3	0-1	0-0	0-0	2-2	0-2	0-4	1-2	0-1	2-2	3-0	0-5	2-1	0-3	0-2	1-0
5 Bedfont Green	2-1	1-2	5-3	3-3	-	1-2	8-0	0-4	0-0	2-2	1-4	1-5	3-2	3-1	0-2	1-2	1-3	4-5	2-3	3-4	0-2	2-3
6 Bishops Cleeve	3-1	1-4	2-2	2-2	0-3	-	1-0	2-1	2-2	0-1	0-2	2-2	4-1	3-2	5-2	1-2	1-1	1-0	4-2	0-1	2-0	2-2
7 Bracknell Town	0-7	1-2	0-2	0-3	0-1	0-4	-	2-5	2-7	0-4	2-3	2-3	0-2	0-3	0-9	0-3	2-1	2-6	1-3	2-0	1-5	0-4
8 Bridgwater Tn	3-0	1-3	1-1	3-0	0-1	2-0	5-0	-	2-0	2-3	2-2	2-1	1-0	2-1	1-1	3-1	1-0	2-1	1-0	1-1	2-1	1-0
9 Cinderford Tn	1-1	2-0	2-5	2-1	0-1	3-0	4-1	0-8	-	2-1	1-1	2-2	2-4	3-1	2-1	1-3	0-1	2-0	5-0	2-3	0-1	4-0
10 Cirencester Tn	3-1	0-1	3-2	3-2	5-2	1-2	11-1	0-0	3-1	-	1-0	3-3	3-1	2-2	2-1	1-1	5-0	0-0	1-2	3-2	1-2	2-0
11 Frome Town	3-1	1-1	3-1	1-1	3-1	2-1	4-0	1-3	1-0	3-2	-	1-1	2-1	2-0	2-1	0-0	2-1	1-3	3-1	2-2	1-1	0-0
12 Gosport Boro'	2-1	0-2	4-2	4-0	2-2	1-1	6-0	0-2	4-2	2-0	0-0	-	3-0	4-0	1-2	4-1	2-2	3-0	0-1	0-1	0-0	2-0
13 Hungerford Tn	0-1	0-1	2-2	4-2	0-3	0-0	2-1	0-0	1-0	1-3	0-0	1-1	-	1-2	0-1	1-5	2-1	1-2	2-1	0-1	0-3	4-1
14 Mangotsfield U.	1-0	1-2	0-2	4-3	3-2	2-2	9-0	2-2	3-1	0-3	2-0	3-0	0-2	-	3-1	1-2	4-0	1-0	1-0	0-1	0-4	1-0
15 North Leigh	1-1	0-2	1-1	3-1	1-4	1-3	8-0	0-4	4-2	2-1	4-0	5-1	2-0	2-3	-	3-1	2-0	3-1	1-1	2-2	0-3	2-0
16 Paulton Rovers	3-1	2-3	3-1	2-0	1-2	0-0	5-1	1-1	3-1	0-2	0-1	2-4	1-0	2-2	0-1	-	2-0	4-6	1-3	3-0	0-0	1-1
17 Taunton Town	1-1	3-3	4-0	2-2	2-2	2-1	2-1	0-2	1-0	0-4	0-3	1-0	0-0	0-3	3-1	0-2	-	2-3	3-2	0-4	0-1	0-1
18 Thatcham Town	5-2	1-2	4-0	1-3	1-1	0-2	5-0	1-4	1-0	1-1	1-1	2-3	2-1	0-1	2-2	0-1	2-1	-	3-1	1-3	0-0	3-1
19 Uxbridge	2-0	3-4	5-1	2-0	4-3	0-1	3-1	2-3	0-3	2-1	0-3	3-0	0-1	2-1	1-1	2-2	2-4	0-2	-	4-4	0-1	2-2
20 VTFC	5-0	0-3	7-0	2-2	4-0	3-1	4-1	0-2	2-2	0-0	3-0	2-1	3-1	3-1	2-0	2-4	2-1	2-0	2-0	-	0-3	3-2
21 Windsor & Eton	1-0	1-0	2-0	3-2	1-0	2-1	6-0	1-1	5-0	0-1	0-0	2-1	5-1	1-1	3-1	4-0	2-1	2-1	5-0	1-0	-	2-1
22 Yate Town	1-0	3-2	1-0	1-1	3-3	1-1	2-1	1-0	0-1	0-1	0-0	2-3	2-1	4-2	4-0	2-2	2-1	4-2	1-1	0-3	0-2	-

SOUTHERN DIVISION ONE S & W DATES & GATES	AFC Hayes	AFC Totton	Abingdon United	Andover	Bedfont Green	Bishops Cleeve	Bracknell Town	Bridgwater Town	Cinderford Town	Cirencester Town	Frome Town	Gosport Borough	Hungerford Town	Mangotsfield United	North Leigh	Paulton Rovers	Taunton Town Thatcham	Town Uxbridge	VTFC	Windsor &	Eton Yate	Town
AFC Hayes		17 Apr 104	31 Oct 71	9 Mar 58	11 Mar 66	5 Sep 47	8 Apr 62	12 Dec 70	22 Aug 71	17 Nov 78	23 Jan 52	6 Mar 68	18 Aug 67	16 Mar 50	7 Nov 78	20 Mar 72	13 Apr 61	21 Nov 78	12 Apr 93	6 Feb 75	13 Oct 105	22 Apr 52
AFC Totton	28 Nov 254		13 Oct 280	20 Feb 297	5 Sep 234	6 Mar 386	16 Jan 260	22 Aug 200	23 Jan 338	7 Nov 325	18 Aug 225	16 Feb 200	13 Apr 198	17 Nov 209	18 Mar 158	16 Mar 203	24 Apr 307	20 Mar 263	6 Feb 299	3 Apr 359	10 Apr 470	2 Mar 153
Abingdon United	13 Feb 47	20 Apr 86		20 Mar 91	18 Aug 62	9 Mar 52	3 Apr 66	7 Nov 92	6 Mar 63	10 Apr 82	20 Feb 102	8 Dec 62	23 Mar 68	13 Apr 61	3 Nov 130	22 Aug 85	2 Feb 52	24 Oct 111	5 Sep 81	10 Oct 96	28 Nov 94	24 Apr 101
Andover	25 Aug 100	15 Aug 171	14 Nov 102		12 Dec 105	5 Dec 93	13 Mar 93	21 Nov 110	31 Oct 98	16 Mar 94	10 Oct 147	3 Apr 102	6 Feb 114	17 Apr 125	8 Apr 84	16 Feb 87	13 Oct 95	19 Sep 166	22 Apr 68	6 Apr 114	23 Feb 83	23 Jan 110
Bedfont Green	5 Apr 65	13 Mar 82	15 Apr 35	24 Apr 63		7 Apr 33	25 Aug 75	16 Mar 59	28 Nov 49	19 Sep 71	15 Dec 67	6 Feb 62	9 Feb 38	15 Aug 74	13 Apr 28	17 Oct 62	27 Mar 47	1 Apr 51	13 Oct 78	31 Oct 66	26 Dec 201	2 Feb 51
Bishops Cleeve	13 Mar 40	19 Sep 54	26 Aug 50	10 Apr 55	24 Oct 61		15 Aug 54	27 Jan 48	5 Apr 87	24 Feb 47	24 Mar 65	25 Apr 150	24 Apr 87	30 Jan 66	26 Dec 74	11 Nov 47	4 Mar 50	13 Feb 57	14 Nov 45	18 Mar 36	13 Apr 52	17 Feb 46
Bracknell Town	2 Mar 48	29 Sep 101	9 Feb 48	5 Sep 113	9 Mar 57	22 Apr 28		6 Mar 85	10 Apr 48	28 Nov 73	13 Oct 89	22 Aug 100	16 Mar 41	14 Nov 60	23 Mar 52	2 Feb 75	3 Oct 88	5 Apr 59	18 Aug 73	27 Mar 63	24 Apr 188	6 Feb 52
Bridgwater Town	24 Apr 343	7 Apr 251	27 Mar 331	19 Dec 289	17 Nov 252	15 Apr 303	19 Sep 273		6 Feb 328	25 Aug 277	31 Oct 341	10 Apr 320	19 Jan 232	20 Apr 337	2 Feb 241	3 Apr 348	1 Jan 1016	15 Aug 275	23 Jan 347	23 Mar 302	13 Mar 361	13 Oct 249
Cinderford Town	27 Feb 60	2 Feb 90	19 Sep 110	13 Feb 100	17 Apr 89	16 Mar 97	26 Jan 84	3 Nov 75		30 Jan 125	7 Apr 85	15 Apr 93	10 Oct 120	22 Apr 91	20 Apr 74	17 Nov 70	25 Aug 110	13 Mar 103	3 Oct 70	12 Dec 45	15 Aug 105	13 Apr 81
Cirencester Town	20 Apr 68	27 Mar 154	3 Oct 127	20 Oct 87	6 Mar 82	18 Aug 140	17 Apr 86	9 Mar 101	13 Oct 166		6 Feb 179	5 Sep 110	22 Aug 157	4 Mar 97	5 Apr 151	21 Feb 180	23 Jan 129	12 Dec 137	31 Oct 130	21 Nov 87	14 Nov 118	9 Feb 108
Frome Town	24 Oct 205	24 Feb 172	15 Aug 172	7 Nov 213	20 Mar 162	18 Nov 157	30 Jan 234	13 Feb 303	9 Dec 176	4 Nov 174		24 Apr 235	10 Apr 216	18 Mar 178	19 Sep 202	1 Jan 617	21 Apr 169	26 Aug 156	3 Feb 143	13 Mar 183	17 Feb 240	28 Nov 192
Gosport Borough	19 Sep 156	5 Apr 302	22 Apr 173	26 Dec 209	2 Nov 101	17 Apr 156	27 Feb 257	5 Dec 163	26 Sep 131	13 Mar 243	12 Dec 167		14 Nov 129	21 Nov 140	13 Feb 141	30 Nov 166	15 Aug 142	8 Apr 130	27 Mar 234	22 Feb 284	24 Aug 131	15 Mar 183
Hungerford Town	23 Feb 55	25 Aug 122	5 Apr 65	24 Nov 121	3 Mar 45	12 Dec 73	24 Oct 99	30 Mar 105	16 Feb 59	27 Feb 125	5 Dec 115	20 Mar 74		13 Mar 88	30 Jan 102	13 Feb 93	19 Sep 102	26 Dec 145	17 Apr 89	15 Aug 90	1 Dec 95	7 Nov 89
Mangotsfield Utd	10 Apr 128	23 Mar 117	10 Nov 135	28 Nov 147	20 Feb 157	2 Mar 101	20 Mar 141	18 Aug 146	26 Dec 177	26 Jan 97	22 Aug 179	9 Feb 86	5 Sep 138		24 Apr 186	9 Mar 185	6 Feb 161	7 Nov 131	6 Mar 150	23 Jan 97	31 Oct 137	5 Apr 296
North Leigh	27 Mar 47	21 Nov 54	6 Feb 70	22 Aug 76	26 Sep 72	31 Oct 57	10 Oct 60	17 Apr 98	18 Aug 84	16 Feb 70	6 Mar 82	2 Mar 64	13 Oct 118	12 Dec 66		5 Sep 66	26 Jan 55	15 Apr 50	20 Feb 54	5 Dec 44	23 Jan 96	9 Mar 51
Paulton Rovers	14 Nov 317	29 Mar 249	8 Apr 162	25 Jan 181	5 Dec 198	6 Feb 220	21 Nov 223	8 Feb 279	27 Mar 207	15 Aug 140	5 Apr 571	23 Jan 207	14 Dec 192	24 Aug 345	13 Mar 189		31 Oct 334	17 Apr 210	12 Dec 178	12 Oct 201	19 Sep 119	19 Oct 270
Taunton Town	26 Sep 133	12 Dec 153	16 Feb 106	30 Jan 174	7 Nov 120	30 Mar 113	13 Feb 150	5 Apr 558	9 Mar 152	24 Oct 184	9 Feb 126	20 Feb 164	6 Mar 209	3 Nov 123	20 Mar 153	18 Aug 170		5 Dec 178	22 Aug 188	17 Apr 172	23 Mar 136	5 Sep 225
Thatcham Town	23 Mar 51	14 Nov 122	23 Jan 66	6 Mar 116	22 Aug 113	20 Apr 59	1 Jan 168	20 Feb 116	5 Sep 114	24 Apr 90	9 Mar 65	13 Oct 133	3 Apr 90	27 Mar 51	8 Dec 53	28 Nov 96	10 Apr 71		10 Oct 130	22 Apr 69	6 Feb 155	18 Aug 97
Uxbridge	26 Dec 161	3 Nov 91	13 Mar 85	1 Dec 106	30 Jan 121	20 Mar 101	13 Apr 70	24 Oct 156	9 Feb 60	13 Feb 107	24 Nov 110	7 Nov 111	28 Nov 101	19 Sep 114	15 Aug 84	24 Apr 96	27 Feb 94	16 Mar 71		25 Aug 104	15 Apr 155	10 Apr 92
VTFC	17 Oct 121	26 Dec 100	16 Mar 89	5 Apr 121	13 Feb 76	22 Aug 84	7 Nov 111	17 Apr 214	24 Apr 113	14 Apr 126	5 Sep 98	18 Aug 162	20 Feb 107	8 Apr 96	10 Apr 87	30 Jan 116	28 Nov 148	10 Nov 108	20 Apr 86		2 Feb 196	6 Mar 106
Windsor & Eton	30 Jan 209	5 Dec 237	17 Apr 182	18 Aug 134	22 Apr 151	7 Nov 110	12 Dec 229	5 Sep 152	20 Feb 165	20 Mar 183	21 Nov 153	9 Mar 153	16 Jan 151	13 Feb 155	24 Oct 111	6 Mar 165	10 Oct 149	3 Nov 110	1 Jan 253	26 Apr 405		22 Aug 124
Yate Town	15 Aug 157	13 Feb 147	12 Dec 107	24 Oct 135	20 Apr 105	21 Nov 110	26 Sep 108	30 Jan 161	14 Nov 124	3 Apr 148	17 Apr 153	10 Oct 185	27 Mar 126	1 Jan 460	25 Aug 151	16 Jan 249	13 Mar 138	23 Feb 92	5 Dec 120	19 Sep 146	27 Feb 171	

RED INSURE CUP 2009-10

PRELIMINARY ROUND

Aylesbury Utd 2 Windsor & Eton 1 *(Sep 23)* Att: 83

Bedford Town 2 Rothwell Town 1 *(Sep 22)* Att: 133

FIRST ROUND

Abingdon Utd 0 **Swindon S'marine** 2 *(Oct 27)* Att: 72

AFC Sudbury 5 Soham Town Rgrs 0 *(Oct 27)* Att: 141

Andover 0 **Farnborough** 3 *(Nov 17)* Att: 132

Arlesey 4 Biggleswade Town 2 *aet (Oct 27)* Att: 121

Aylesbury United 3 **AFC Hayes** 5 *(Oct 28)* Att: 87

Barton Rovers 1 **Bedford Town** 2 *(Oct 27)* Att: 117

Beaconsfield SYCOB 0 **Thatcham** 4 *(Oct 26)* Att: 77

Bedfont Green 2 Bracknell Town 0 *(Oct 27)* Att: 39

Bedworth Utd 3 **Atherstone T.** 4 *aet (Oct 27)* Att: 154

Bishops Cleeve 3 Stourbridge 1 *(Oct 28)* Att: 77

Bridgwater Town 1 **Truro City** 2 *(Oct 27)* Att: 257

Bromsgrove R. 0 **Stourport Swifts** 4 *(Oct 27)* Att: 172

Burnham 2 **Leighton Town** 4 *aet (Oct 27)* Att: 53

Bury Town 1 **Cambridge City** 2 *(Oct 27)* Att: 340

Chippenham Town 4 Oxford City 0 *(Oct 27)* Att: 224

Cinderford Town 0 **Evesham Utd 1** *(Oct 27)* Att: 100

Clevedon Town 3 Frome Town 0 *(Oct 27)* Att: 108

Didcot Town 1 **Banbury United** 2 *(Oct 27)* Att: 165

Gosport Borough 3 **AFC Totton** 4 *aet (Oct 26)* Att: 176

Halesowen Town 4 Cirencester T. 0 *(Oct 27)* Att: 195

Hednesford T. 4 Leamington 3 *aet (Oct 27)* Att: 265

Hemel H'stead 0 Hitchin 0 *aet* (8-7p) *(Sep 26)* Att: 200

Hungerford Town 0 **Woodford Utd** 2 *(Oct 27)* Att: 67

Mangotsfield Utd 3 Merthyr Tydfil 1 *(Oct 27)* Att: 127

North Leigh 4 Brackley Town 2 *(Oct 27)* Att: 84

Nuneaton Town 3 Romulus 0 *(Oct 27)* Att: 383

Slough Town 1 **Chesham United** 2 *(Oct 27)* Att: 189

Sutton Coldfield T. 3 Rugby Town 0 *(Oct 26)* Att: 72

Tiverton Town 2 Taunton Town 0 *aet (Oct 28)* Att: 261

Uxbridge 2 **Marlow** 4 *(Oct 27)* Att: 65

VTFC 2 Bashley 0 *(Oct 27)* Att: 116

Yate Town 2 Paulton Rovers 1 *(Oct 27)* Att: 133

SECOND ROUND

AFC Hayes 2 **Chesham United** 5 *(Jan 19)* Att: 60

AFC Sudbury 1 **Cambridge City** 2 *(Nov 24)* Att: 177

AFC Totton 0 **VTFC** 2 *(Nov 24)* Att: 175

Arlesey Town 2 Bedford Town 1 *(Dec 1)* Att: 166

Banbury United 1 **Woodford Utd** 2 *(Nov 24)* Att: 110

Bishops Cleeve 2 Stourport Swifts 1 *(Jan 18)* Att: 37

Chippenham 1 **Clevedon Town** 3 *(Nov 24)* Att: 156

Halesowen Town 1 **Nuneaton Town** 2 *(Dec 2)* Att: 175

Hednesford Town 5 Atherstone 1 *(Nov 24)* Att: 167

Leighton T. 5 Hemel Hempstead 1 *(Nov 24)* Att: 81

Mangotsfield United 0 **Yate Town** 2 *(Dec 1)* Att: 114

Marlow 3 Bedfont Green 0 *(Nov 24)* Att: 61

Sutton Coldfield 3 Evesham United 1 *(Nov 23)* Att: 51

Swindon Supermarine 2 Nth Leigh 1 *(Nov 25)* Att: 77

Thatcham T. 2 **Farnborough** 3 *aet (Nov 24)* Att: 100

Tiverton Town 1 Truro City 0 *(Dec 2)* Att: 190

THIRD ROUND

Arlesey Town 6 Leighton Town 4 *aet (Jan 19)* Att: 79

Farnborough 1 **Chesham United** 3 *(Jan 27)* Att: 202

Hednesford Town 3 Bishops Cleeve 0 *(Feb 3)* Att: 84

Marlow 2 **VTFC** 3 *(Jan 19)* Att: 49

Nuneaton Town 3 Sutton Coldfield 1 *(Jan 19)* Att: 288

Swindon S'marine 5 Clevedon Town 2 *(Feb 3)* Att: 42

Woodford United 3 **Cambridge City** 4 *(Jan 20)* Att: 40

Yate Town 0 **Tiverton Town** 1 *(Jan 19)* Att: 64

QUARTER-FINALS

Cambridge City 2 Arlesey Town 1 *(Feb 9)* Att: 130

Nuneaton T. 1 **Hednesford Town** 2 *(Feb 9)* Att: 281

Swindon Supermarine 1 Tiverton 0 *(Feb 10)* Att: 72

VTFC 2 Chesham United 1 *(Feb 9)* Att: 63

SEMI-FINALS

Cambridge City 2 Hednesford Town 0 *(Mar 2)* Att: 142

VTFC 2 Swindon Supermarine 0 *(Mar 2)* Att: 87

FINAL *(played over two legs)*

VTFC 1 Cambridge City 0 *(Apr 1)* Att: 131

Cambridge City 1 VTFC 0 *aet* (4-2p) *(Apr 12)* Att: 293

CHAMPIONSHIP MATCH

(Premier Division champions v League Cup holders)

(August 1st at Corby)

Corby Town 3 Atherstone Town 2

Southern League Premier Division
Season's Stats 2009-2010

	Lg Pos	F.A. Cup	F.A. T	Av. Lg. Att.	Best Att.	Opponents	No of Goalscorers + own goals	Goalscorers with at least 10 goals	
Banbury United	12	1Q	2Q	312	684	v Leamington	17 + 2	Stone	15
Bashley	7	2Q	1Rd	306	525	v Farnborough	17 + 1	Allen	23
								Gamble	19
Bedford Town	18	3Q	1Q	290	417	v Truro City	20 + 2	Draycott Ian	20
								Daniel	10
Brackley Town	5	2Q	2Q	282	930	v Babury United	16 + 1	Mackey	24
								Winters	18
								Rawle	13
Cambridge City	6	3Q	2Q	355	613	v Hednesford T	16 + 1	Midgeley	12
								Fuller	11
Chippenham Town	3	4Q	2Rd	411	744	v Farnborough	13 + 0	Powell	31
								Highmore	15
								Gullick	10
Clevedon Town	21	1Q	1Q	169	315	v Leamington	20 + 2	-	
Didcot Town	15	2Q	1Q	240	511	v Oxford City	14 + 1	Draycott	15
Evesham United	16	2Q	2Q	165	258	v Nuneaton T.	17 + 2	Palmer	10
Farnborough	1	4Q	1Rd	769	1372	v Swindon Super.	19 + 1	McDonald	30
								Ibe	17
								Bubb	16
Halesowen Town	8	-	-	366	761	v Stourbridge	17 + 1	Moore	35
								Blenkinsopp	10
Hednesford Town	4	1Q	1Q	351	508	v Banbury United	18 +0	Barnett	20
								Durrell	16
								Dyer	16
Hemel Hempstead	20	1Q	1Q	234	415	v Farnborough	25 + 2	-	
Leamington	10	1Q	1Q	646	1251	v Nuneaton T	14 + 2	Bellingham	29
								Corbett	20
Merthyr Tydfil	17	2Q	1Q	310	464	v Farnborough	17 + 1	Griffiths	14
								Belle	13
Nuneaton Town	2	1Rd	1Rd	901	1765	v Farnborough	17 + 1	Dillon	21
								Oddy	17
								Armson	15
								Moore	13
								Marsden	11
Oxford City	13	1Rd	2Q	293	411	v Leamington	14 + 1	Steele	25
Rugby Town	22	2Q	1Q	209	656	v Leamington	17 + 1	Kolodynski	11
Stourbridge	9	4Q	3Q	267	656	v Halesowen T	17 + 1	Rowe	29
Swindon Sup.	14	1Q	1Q	190	289	v Chippenham T	15 + 1	Hopper	11
								Stanley	10
Tiverton Town	19	1Q	1Q	283	533	v Brackley Town	15 + 0	Bushin	10
Truro City	11	3Q	1Rd	456	902	v Tiverton Town	17 + 1	Watkins	25
								Afful	12

BANBURY UNITED

Chairman: Paul Jones
Secretary: Barry Worlsey **(T)** 07941 267 567
(E) bworsley@btinternet.com
Additional Committee Members: David Bennett, Ryan Costello, Richard Cox, Richard Harvey, Ian Jones, Alison Knight, Peter Meadows, Sandra Mold, Nigel Porter, Liz Verrall, David Wyatt.
Manager: Billy Jeffrey
Programme Editor: David Shadbolt **(E)** djshadbolt@tiscali.o.uk

Back Row (left to right): Billy Jeffrey (manager), Anton Sambrook (Coach), Nathan Haisley, Jason Taylor, Adam Learoyd, Joe Murrell, Delroy Gordon, Adam Howarth, Scott Cross, Wally Hastie (coach/physio), Matt Haycocks (coach).
Front Row: David Staff, Nabil Shariff, Declan Benjamin, Joe Coleman, Ollie Stanbridge, Marvin Martin, Ross Oulton, Luke Cray.

Club Factfile

Founded: 1933 **Nickname:** Puritans
Previous Names: Banbury Spencer. Club reformed in 1965 as Banbury United
Previous Leagues: Banbury Junior 1933-34, Oxon Senior 1934-35, Birmingham Combination 1935-54, West Midlands 1954-66, Southern 1966-90, Hellenic 1991-2000

Club Colours (change): Red with gold trim/red/red/ (White/blue/blue)

Ground: Spencer Stadium, off Station Road, Banbury OX16 5TA **(T)** 01295 263 354
Capacity: 6,500 **Seats:** 250 **Covered:** 50 **Clubhouse:** Yes **Shop:** Yes
Previous Grounds: Not known

Simple Directions
From M40, Junction 11, head towards Banbury, over first roundabout, left at next roundabout into Concorde Avenue. Straight on at next roundabout, taking left hand lane, and turn left at traffic lights, turn first right into Station Approach. At station forecourt and car park, take narrow single track road on extreme right and follow to Stadium.(Direct SatNav to OX16 5AB)

Record Attendance: 7,160 v Oxford City - FA Cup 3rd Qualifying Round 30/10/1948
Record Victory: 12-0 v RNAS Culham - Oxon Senior Cup 1945-46
Record Defeat: 2-11 v West Bromwich Albion 'A' - Birmingham Combination 1938-39
Record Goalscorer: Dick Pike and Tony Jacques - 222 (1935-48 and 1965-76 respectively)
Record Appearances: Jody McKay - 576
Additional Records: Paid £2,000 to Oxford United for Phil Emsden
Received £20,000 from Derby County for Kevin Wilson 1979

Senior Honours: Hellenic Premier 1999-2000. Oxford Senior Cup 1978-79, 87-88, 2003-04.

10 YEAR RECORD

00-01	01-02	02-03	03-04	04-05	05-06	06-07	07-08	08-09	09-10
SthE 13	SthE 15	SthE 8	SthE 8	SthP 17	SthP 7	SthP 13	SthP 9	SthP 19	SthP 12

BANBURY UNITED

No.	Date	Comp	H/A	Opponents	Att:	Result	Goalscorers	Pos
1	Aug 15	Zamaretto P.	H	Stourbridge	269	D 3 - 3	Stone 21 66 Tayor 42 (pen)	10
2	17		A	Cambridge City	280	L 1 - 2	Benjamin 10	12
3	22		A	Leamington	766	D 3 - 3	Stone 26 Coleman 45 Farrington 90	16
4	25		H	Bashley	234	D 1 - 1	Stone 42	14
5	29		H	Oxford City	318	D 1 - 1	Taylor 58	15
6	31		A	Swindon Supermarine	223	W 2 - 1	Allen 26 (og) Benjamin 82	
7	Sept 5		H	Truro City	352	D 0 - 0		11
8	**12**	**F.A.C 1Q**	**H**	**Chippenham Town**	**361**	**D 0 - 0**		
9	**15**	**F.A.C. 1Q**	**A**	**Chppenham Town**		**L 2 - 3**	**Taylor 24 Milner 83**	
10	19		A	Rugby Town	257	W 2 - 0	Stone 9 Benjamin 31	10
11	Oct 3		H	Halesowen Town	428	W 2 - 1	Taylor 39 (pen) Benjamin 50	10
12	6		A	Didcot Town	317	D 0 - 0		
13	10		A	Clevedon Town	172	W 2 - 1	Benjamin 68 Fisher 72 (og)	
14	**17**	**F.A.T 1Q**	**H**	**Bridgwater Town**	**247**	**D 2 - 2**	**Haisley 71 Forinton 77**	
15	**20**	**F.A.T. 1Q**	**A**	**Bridgwater Town**	**196**	**W 1 - 0**	**Taylor 67**	
16	24		H	Bedford Town	348	D 0 - 0		5
17	**31**	**F.A.T. 2Q**	**A**	**Godalming**	**188**	**D 1 - 1**	**Taylor 39**	
18	Nov 7		A	Merthyr Tydfil	284	L 2 - 3	Taylor 68 Benjamin 89	6
19	14		H	Nuneaton Town	488	W 2 - 1	Redknapp 65 90	5
20	21		A	Tiverton Town	198	L 1 - 2	Shariff 20	7
21	28		H	Hednesford Town	284	W 3 - 2	Haisley 3 63 Stone 90	6
22	Dec 5		A	Hemel Hempstead	193	W 3 - 2	Walker 2 Learoyd 56 Shariff 59	5
23	15		A	Evesham United	101	L 2 - 3	Stone 63 82 (pen)	
24	Jan 2		A	Brackley Town	930	L 1 - 5	Walker 45	
25	19		H	Farnborough	252	L 0 - 3		
26	23		H	Rugby Town	319	W 2 - 1	Stone 50 53	8
27	26		H	Tiverton Town	160	L 0 - 1		
28	30		A	Truro City	452	D 1 - 1	Stone 44	8
29	Feb 6		H	Merthyr Tydfil	281	W 3 - 1	Redknapp 33 Stone 81 (pen) Stanbridge 89	
30	9		H	Chippenham Town	156	D 0 - 0		
31	12		A	Nuneaton Town	702	L 0 - 5		
32	20		A	Stourbridge	226	L 1 - 2	Benjamin 39	8
33	27		H	Leamington	684	L 1 - 2	Hillard 75	9
34	Mar 6		A	Bashley	316	L 0 - 1		12
35	9		H	Didcot Town	162	W 1 - 0	Coleman 87	
36	13		A	Halesowen Town	435	W 2 - 0	Stone 30 Shariff 65	
37	20		H	ClevedonTown	249	W 4 - 3	Learoyd 43 Stone 64 (pen) Martin 89 Benjamin 90	11
38	23		H	Cambridge City	188	W 1 - 0	Stone 48	
39	27		A	Bedford Town	260	D 1 - 1	Taylor 78 (pen)	11
40	April 3		A	Chippenham Town	419	L 0 - 5		11
41	5		H	Brackley Town	628	L 0 - 3		11
42	10		H	Hemel Hempstead	292	D 1 - 1	Stanbridge 52	12
43	12		A	Farnborough	638	L 0 - 3		
44	15		A	Oxford City	258	D 1 - 1	Stone 43	
45	17		A	Hednesford Town	508	D 0 - 0		12
46	21		H	Swindon Supermarine	131	W 3 - 1	Staff 53 Stone 73 Taylor 81	
47	24		H	Evesham United	321	L 0 - 1		12
					Goals	59 73		

Home Attendances:	
Highest:	684 v Leamington
Lowest:	131 v Swindon Supermarine
Average (08-09):	284 (280)
Top Goalscorer:	Stone - 15 (League 15)

BASHLEY

Chairman: Richard Millbery
Secretary: Dave Grant (T) 07800 800 308
(E) bashdave@hotmail.co.uk

Additional Committee Members:
Pat Bowring, John Bone

Manager: Steve Riley

Programme Editor: Richard Millbery (E) rw_millbery@lineone.net

Archive photo

Club Factfile

Founded: 1947 **Nickname:** The Bash

Previous Names: Not known

Previous Leagues: Bournemouth 1953-83, Hampshire 1983-86, Wessex 1986-89, Southern 1989-2004, Isthmian 2004-06

Club Colours (change): Gold/black/black (White/blue/blue)

Ground: Bashley Road Ground, Bashley Road, New Milton, Hampshire BH25 5RY **(T)** 01425 620 280

Capacity: 4,250 **Seats:** 250 **Covered:** 1,200 **Clubhouse:** Yes **Shop:** Yes

Previous Grounds: Not known

Simple Directions
Take the A35 from Lyndhurst towards Christchurch, turn left onto B3058 towards New Milton. The ground is on the left hand side in Bashley village.

Record Attendance: 3,500 v Emley - FA Vase Semi-final 1st Leg 1987-88
Record Victory: 21-1 v Co-Operative (A) - Bournemouth League 1964
Record Defeat: 2-20 v Air Speed (A) - Bournemouth League 1957
Record Goalscorer: Richard Gillespie - 134
Record Appearances: John Bone - 829
Additional Records: Paid £7,500 to Newport (IOW) for Danny Gibbons and from Dorchester Tn for David Elm. Received £15,000 from Salisbury for Craig Davis, from Eastleigh for Paul Sales and from AFC Bournemouth for Wade Elliott.

Senior Honours: Wessex League 1986-87, 87-88, 88-89. Southern League Southern Division 1989-90, Division 1 South & West 2006-07.

10 YEAR RECORD

00-01	01-02	02-03	03-04	04-05	05-06	06-07	07-08	08-09	09-10
SthE 15	SthE 10	SthE 5	SthE 11	Isth1 14	Isth1 9	Sthsw 1	SthP 5	SthP 14	SthP 7

BASHLEY

No.	Date	Comp	H/A	Opponents	Att:	Result	Goalscorers	Pos
1	Aug 15	Zamaretto P.	A	Merthyr Tydfil	412	L 1 - 2	Middleton 38	14
2	18		H	Swindon Supermarine	245	W 3 - 0	Knight 50 Keeler 65 Allen 81	7
3	22		H	Clevedon Town	250	W 3 - 2	Keeler 41 62 Allen 51	5
4	25		A	Banbury United	234	D 1 - 1	Murrell 71 (og)	6
5	29		H	Evesham United	312	W 2 - 1	Maxwell 89 Kelly 90	6
6	31		A	Farnborough	1024	D 1 - 1	Castle 8	
7	Sept 5		H	Rugby Town	287	W 4 - 0	Knowles 19 38 Kelly 22 Gamble 40	5
8	12	F.A.C 1Q	A	Molesey	92	W 3 - 2	Gazzard 33 Allen 66 (pen) Knight 80	
9	19		A	Stourbridge	211	D 2 - 2	Kelly 45 Allen 79	
10	26	F.A.C. 2Q	H	Gloucester City	287	L 1 - 2	Allen 45	
11	Oct 3		H	Didcot Town	322	W 3 - 2	Maxwell 13 Gamble 72 83	3
12	6		A	Brackley Town	174	W 3 - 2	Gamble 10 Keeler 26 Knight 88	
13	10		A	Tiverton Town	316	W 5 - 0	Hill 31 85 Gamble 45 Tarr 62 McCarthy 89	1
14	17	F.A.T 1Q	A	Beaconsfield SYCOB	78	W 4 - 1	KEELER 3 (43 50 58pen) Kelly 47	
15	24		H	Hednesford Town	349	L 0 - 4		3
16	31	F.A.T. 2Q	H	Marlow	211	W 2 - 1	Knight 1 Kelly 19	
17	Nov 7		H	Cambridge City	379	L 0 - 2		4
18	21	F.A.T 3Q	H	Staines Town	268	W 2 - 1	Mason 10 Gamble 85	
19	28		A	Leamington	527	W 1 - 0	Gamble 45	5
20	Dec 5		H	Halesowen Town	272	L 1 - 2	Allen 40 (pen)	6
21	12	F.A.T 1	H	Crawley Town	335	L 2 - 3	Knight 29 Maxwell 81	
22	15		A	Hemel Hempstead	123	W 1 - 0	Allen 46	
23	26		H	Farnborough	525	L 0 - 4		6
24	Jan 1		A	Oxford City	349	D 1 - 1	Gamble 90	
25	23		H	Stourbridge	274	D 4 - 4	Knowles 15 Allen 41(pen) 89 (pen) Maxwell 90	5
26	26		H	Truro City	215	W 2 - 0	Allen 33 Keeler 88	
27	Feb 2		H	Nuneaton BTown	223	W 2 - 1	Bottomly 4 Middleton 9	
28	6		A	Cambridge City	358	D 2 - 2	Allen 33 56 (pen)	5
29	9		H	Bedford Town	196	L 1 - 2	Maxwell 90	
30	13		H	Hemel Hempstead	247	W 3 - 0	Allen 25 (pen) 45 Gamble 77	4
31	16		A	Truro City	274	D 1 - 1	Knowles 70	
32	20		H	Merthyr Tydfil	319	W 3 - 2	Allen 31 54 Gamble 48	3
33	24		A	Swindon Supermarine	111	D 3 - 3	Kelly 57 Gamble 69 82	
34	27		A	Clevedon Town	146	W 2 - 0	Allen 36 Gamble 90	3
35	Mar 6		H	Banbury United	316	W 1 - 0	Knowles 18	3
36	9		H	Brackley Town	262	W 5 - 2	Maxwell 22 Allen 29 34 Parnell 45 Gamble 74	
37	13		A	Didcot Town	170	D 1 - 1	Gamble 81	
38	16		A	Evesham United	101	D 0 - 0		
39	20		H	Tivertn Town	277	L 0 - 1		3
40	23		A	Rugby Town	128	W 3 - 2	Kelly 22 Cream 80 Allen 90 (pen)	
41	27		A	Hednesford Town	354	L 0 - 1		3
42	April 3		A	Bedford Town	240	W 4 - 0	Knowles 1 GAMBLE 3 (6 45 54)	4
43	5		H	Oxford City	348	W 3 - 2	Knowles 19 Gamble 36 Parnell 90	4
44	8		H	Chippenham Town	316	L 0 - 1		
45	10		A	Halesowen Town	296	L 2 - 3	Allen 8 Knowles 66	4
46	13		A	Chippenham Town	364	W 2 - 1	Parnell 38 Knowles 90	
47	17		H	Leamington	482	D 1 - 1	Allen 71	4
48	24		A	Nuneaton Town	715	L 2 - 5	Allen 87 (pen) Maxwell 90	7
					Goals	93 71		

Home Attendances:	
Highest:	525 v Farnborough
Lowest:	196 v Bedford Town
Average (08-09):	288 (293)
Top Goalscorer:	Allen - 23 (League 21, FAC 2)

BEDFORD TOWN

Chairman: David Howell

Secretary: Dave Swallow (T) 07939 812 965

(E) david.swallow@bedfordeagles.net

Additional Committee Members:

Gerry Edmunds, Dave Redman, Tony Luff, Mick Hooker

Manager: Ady Williams

Programme Editor: Dave Swallow (E) david.swallow@bedfordeagles.net

Back Row (L-R): Chris Gibbons (Physio), Steve Jackman, Graham Clark, Nick Bennion Michael Kavanagh, Gavin Hoyte, Ian Brown, Stuart Wall, Tom Hole, Craig Daniel, Rob Miller.

Front Row: Ian Draycott, Michael McKenzie, Craig Rydeheard, Derwayne Stupple, David Howell (Chairman), Ady Williams (Manager), Phil Draycott, Josh Sozzo, Callum Lewis, Jamie Cole.

Club Factfile

Founded: 1989 **Nickname:** The Eagles

Previous Names: Original Bedford Town founded in 1908 folded in 1982

Previous Leagues: South Midlands 1989-94, Isthmian 1994-2004, Southern 2004-06, Conference 2006-07

Club Colours (change): Blue with white trim/blue/blue (Yellow/navy/yellow or all maroon)

Ground: The Eyrie, Meadow Lane, Cardington, Bedford MK44 3SB (T) 01234 831 558

Capacity: 3,000 **Seats:** 300 **Covered:** 1,000 **Clubhouse:** Yes **Shop:** Yes

Previous Grounds: Allen Park, Queens Park, Bedford Park Pitch 1991-93

Simple Directions

From A1: Take A603 from Sandy to Bedford, go through Willington and ground is a mile and a half on right, signposted Meadow Lane.

From M1: Off at Junction 13, take A421, carry on A421 onto Bedford Bypass and take A603 Sandy turn off. Ground is on left.

Record Attendance: 3,000 v Peterborough United - Ground opening 06/08/1993

Record Victory: 9-0 v Ickleford and v Cardington

Record Defeat: 0-5 v Hendon

Record Goalscorer: Jason Reed

Record Appearances: Eddie Lawley

Additional Records:

Senior Honours: Isthmian League Division 2 1998-99. Bedfordshire Senior Cup 1994-95. Southern League Play-offs 2005-06.

10 YEAR RECORD

00-01	01-02	02-03	03-04	04-05	05-06	06-07	07-08	08-09	09-10
Isth1 2	Isth P 17	Isth P 9	Isth P 15	SthP 5	SthP 5	Conf S 22	SthP 19	SthP 15	SthP 18

BEDFORD TOWN

No.	Date	Comp	H/A	Opponents	Att:	Result	Goalscorers	Pos
1	Aug 15	Zamaretto P.	H	Truro City	417	L 0 - 2		21
2	18		A	Rugby Town	204	W 4 - 1	Woolf 7 Daniel 28 Walker 88 Power 90	10
3	22		A	Stourbridge	178	L 0 - 2		13
4	25		H	Leamington	375	L 0 - 2		16
5	29		A	Merthyr Tydfil	366	D 0 - 0		17
6	31		H	Hemel Hempstead	362	W 5 - 0	Daniel 25 45 Draycott 29 84 Cole 81	
7	Sept 5		A	Halesowen Town	126	L 1 - 4	Cavill 9	15
8	**12**	**F.A.C 1Q**	**H**	**Kingsbury**	**215**	**W 5 - 1**	**Daniel 12 BATTERSBY 3 (14pen 21 49 pen) Draycott 55**	
9	19		H	Didcot Town	353	L 1 - 5	M.Draycott 37	
10	**26**	**F.A.C. 2Q**	**H**	**Romulus**	**283**	**W 2 - 1**	**Cavill 52 Nunez 88**	
11	Oct 4		A	Oxford City	292	L 1 - 4	Lewis 67	16
12	6		H	Nuneaton Town	380	W 2 - 1	Daniel 47 Draycott 65	14
13	**10**	**F.A.C. 3Q**	**A**	**Bury Town**	**1003**	**D 1 - 1**	**Draycott 56**	
14	**13**	**F.A.C. 3Qr**	**H**	**Bury Town**	**481**	**L 3 - 4**	**Battersby 40 (pen) Draycott 63 Darby 67**	
15	**17**	**F.A.T 1Q**	**A**	**Yate Town**	**138**	**L 1 - 2**	**Draycott 76**	
16	24		A	Banbury United	348	D 0 - 0		14
17	Nov 7		A	Swindon Supermarine	139	D 0 - 0		16
18	10		H	Chippenham Town	227	L 1 - 2	Draycott 68 (pen)	
19	14		H	Brackley Town	228	D 2 - 2	Draycott 11(pen) 62	16
20	28		H	Evesham United	276	L 1 - 2	Draycott 74	20
21	Dec 5		A	Clevedon Town	123	W 3 - 0	DRAYCOTT 3 (24 73 87)	17
22	12		A	Tiverton Town	252	L 0 - 2		20
23	15		H	Hednesford Town	198	W 3 - 2	Lawley 35 Daniel 41 Field 57	
24	26		A	Hemel Hempstead	227	L 1 - 5	George 73	17
25	Jan 16		H	Merthyr Tydfil	239	L 2 - 4	Draycott 29 Clark 40	18
26	23		A	Didcot Town	170	D 2 - 2	McDougald 17 Lewis 19	
27	30		H	Halesowen Town	268	D 1 - 1	Lewis 43	18
28	Feb 2		H	Farnborough	222	D 2 - 2	McDougald 22 42	
29	9		A	Bashley	196	W 2 - 1	Daniel 27 Middleton 87 (og)	
30	13		A	Brackley Town	202	L 0 - 3		18
31	20		A	Truro City	347	L 1 - 5	Lewis 3	18
32	Mar 2		H	Rugby Town	180	W 3 - 1	McDougald 44 Wall 62 Daniel 78	
33	6		A	Leamington	614	L 0 - 2		18
34	9		A	Nuneaton Town	659	L 0 - 4		
35	11		H	Stourbridge	156	L 0 - 1		
36	13		H	Oxford City	226	D 1 - 1	Draycott 85	
37	17		A	Farnborough	517	L 1 - 6	Draycott 40	
38	20		A	Chippenham Town	345	L 0 - 3		19
39	22		H	Swindon Supermarine	174	L 1 - 2	McDougald 32	
40	27		H	Banbury United	260	D 1 - 1	Daniel 58	18
41	30		A	Hednesford Town	281	L 1 - 2	Draycott 48	
42	April 3		H	Bashley	240	L 0 - 4		18
43	5		A	Cambridge City	2392	L 2 - 4	Clark 26 Draycott P 78	19
44	10		H	Clevedon Town	251	W 3 - 1	Sozzo 47 I Draycott 74 77	19
45	14		H	Cambridge City	308	L 0 - 2		
46	17		A	Evesham United	119	D 1 - 1		18
47	24		H	Tiverton Town	406	W 2 - 0	Booth 66 (og) Daniel 87	
					Goals	63 98		

Home Attendances:	
Highest:	417 v Truro City
Lowest:	156 v Stourbridge
Average (08-09):	251 (346)
Top Goalscorer:	Ian Draycott - 20 (League 16, FAC 3, FAT 1 - Hat-trick 1)

BRACKLEY TOWN

Chairman: Sara Crannage
Secretary: Pat Ashby (T) 07969 825 636
(E) pat.ashby55@btinternet.com
Additional Committee Members: Phil Hedges, Francis Oliver, Dave Boynton, Phil Crannage Brian Martin, Tim Carroll, Steve Toghill, Jeff Peyton-Bruhl, Nik Phillips, Barry Newbery, Nick Johnson, Gemma Dobbs
Manager: Jon Brady
Programme Editor: Brian Martin (E) brianmartin2905@aol.com

Archive photo

Club Factfile

Founded: 1890 **Nickname:** Saints
Previous Names: Not known
Previous Leagues: Banbury & District, North Buckinghamshire, Hellenic 1977-83, 94-97, 99-2004, United Counties 1983-84, Southern 1997-99
Club Colours (change): Red and white stripes/red/white (All yellow)

Ground: St James Park, Churchill Way, Brackley NN13 7EJ (T) 01280 704 077
Capacity: 3,500 **Seats:** 300 **Covered:** 1,500 **Clubhouse:** Yes **Shop:** Yes
Previous Grounds: Banbury Road, Manor Road, Buckingham Road > 1974
Simple Directions
Take A43 from Northampton or Oxford, or A422 from Banbury to large roundabout south of town. Take exit marked Brackley and follow towards the town (Tesco store on left). Pass the Locomotive public house and take first turning right, signposted Football Club, into Churchill Way - road leads into Club car park.

Record Attendance: 960 v Banbury United - 2005-06
Record Victory: Not known
Record Defeat: Not known
Record Goalscorer: Paul Warrington - 320
Record Appearances: Terry Muckelberg - 350
Additional Records: Received £2,000 from Oxford City for Phil Mason 1998

Senior Honours: Hellenic League Premier Division 1996-97, 2003-04, Division 1 Cup 1982-83. Southern League Division 1 Midlands 2006-07

10 YEAR RECORD

00-01	01-02	02-03	03-04	04-05	05-06	06-07	07-08	08-09	09-10
Hel P 2	Hel P 7	Hel P 7	Hel P 1	SthW 7	SthW 3	SthM 1	SthP 8	SthP 11	SthP 5

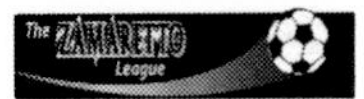

BRACKLEY TOWN

No.	Date	Comp	H/A	Opponents	Att:	Result	Goalscorers	Pos
1	Aug 15	Zamaretto P.	A	Evesham United	167	W 3 - 1	Spencer 36 Mackey 38 40	2
2	18		H	Farnborough	352	L 1 - 3	Sandy 70	11
3	22		H	Halesowen Town	248	W 2 - 1	Rawle 43 Winters 64	8
4	25		A	Hednesford Town	353	W 4 - 1	Anderson 28 Winters 51 88 Rawle 53	4
5	29		A	Hemel Hempstead	211	D 1 - 1	Sandy 62	
6	31		H	Cambridge City	302	D 0 - 0		
7	Sept 5		A	Didcot Town	270	W 1 - 0	Mackey 23	8
8	**12**	**F.A.C. 1Q**	**H**	**Swindon Supermarine**	**180**	**W 1 - 0**	**Sandy 47**	
9	19		H	Clevedon Town	182	W 2 - 1	Sandy 63 Rawle 71	4
10	**26**	**F.A.C. 2Q**	**H**	**Basingstoke Town**	**326**	**L 0 - 1**		
11	Oct 4		A	Nuneaton Town	785	D 2 - 2	Sandy 61 Anderson 83	5
12	6		H	Bashley	174	L 2 - 3	Rawle 76 Burgess O 89	
13	10		A	Swindon Supermarine	148	W 7 - 1	WINTERS 3 (525 60) Rawle 39 Anderson 52 Mackey 55 89	3
14	**17**	**F.A.T.1Q**	**A**	**Clevedon Town**	**108**	**W 4 - 2**	**Mackey 12 (pen) Wilmot 26 Joyce 40 Rawle 80**	
15	20		H	Stourbridge	204	W 3 - 2	Winters 6 McIlwain 36 54	
16	24		A	Leamington	651	L 1 - 2	Mackey 41	2
17	**31**	**F.A.T 2Q**	**H**	**Mossley**	**176**	**D 1 - 1**	**Mackey 67**	
18	Nov 7		H	Tiverton Town	207	W 2 - 0	Winters 24 Mackey 53	2
19	14		A	Bedford Town	228	D 2 - 2	Winters 83 Green 90	2
20	21		H	Swindon Supermarine	192	L 1 - 2	Winters 45	2
21	28		A	Chippenham Town	375	W 3 - 2	Rawle 21 Sandy 26 Burgess 42	2
22	Dec 5		H	Oxford City	268	L 1 - 2	Mackay 46	3
23	8		A	Rugby Town	143	W 4 - 1	Winters 3 Mackey 43 47 Rawle 55	
24	26		A	Cambridge City	369	L 0 - 5		3
25	Jan 1		H	Banbury United	930	W 5 - 1	Green 16 62 Winters 22 Story 47 Mackey 51	
26	23		A	Clevedon Town	141	W 3 - 0	Green 9 Winters 74 Rawle 86	2
27	26		H	Hemel Hempstead	132	W 2 - 0	Rawle 23 Mackey 31	2
28	30		H	Didcot Town	251	D 2 - 2	Story 15 Mackey 80	2
29	Feb 2		H	Truro City	165	W 4 - 3	Story 24 29 Winters 67 85	
30	6		A	Tiverton Town	533	D 1 - 1	Green 90	2
31	13		H	Bedford Town	202	W 3 - 0	Willmott 22 Mackey 60 Story 62	2
32	20		H	Evesham United	228	W 3 - 1	Rawle 73 75 Mackey 83	2
33	27		A	Halesowen Town	411	D 1 - 1	Rawle 5	2
34	Mar 6		H	Hednesford Town	241	L 0 - 1		2
35	9		A	Bashley	262	L 2 - 5	Robinson 47 Winters 68	
36	13		H	Nuneaton Town	426	D 0 - 0		
37	20		A	Stourbridge	217	L 2 - 4	Winters 68 Frew 83	5
38	27		H	Leamington	512	W 1 - 0	Magunda 22	4
39	30		H	Rugby Town	141	W 3 - 1	MACKEY 3 (25 49 54)	
40	April 3		H	Merthyr Tydfil	232	W 1 - 0	Solkhorn 73	3
41	5		A	Banbury United	628	W 3 - 0	Learoyd 23 (og) Winters 47 Mackey 74	3
42	10		A	Oxford City	278	W 3 - 2	MACKEY 3 (5 37 pen 90)	3
43	14		A	Farnborough	682	L 0 - 3		
44	17		H	Chippenham Town	327	L 0 - 1		3
45	20		A	Merthyr Tydfdil	268	L 1 - 2	Storey 17	
46	24		A	Truro City	435	D 1 - 1	Green 72	5
47	**27**	**Play Off S-F**	**A**	**Nuneaton Town**	**1639**	**L 0 - 6**		
					Goals	89 71		

Home Attendances:	
Highest:	930 v Banbury United
Lowest:	132 v Hemel Hempstead
Average (08-09):	232 (249)
Top Goalscorer:	Mackey - 24 (League 22, FAT 2 - Hat-trick 2)

CAMBRIDGE CITY

Chairman: Kevin Satchell
Secretary: Andy Dewey (T) 07720 678 585
(E) andy.dewey@btinternet.com
Additional Committee Members: Terry Dunn,Ken Ledran, Roger de Ste Croix, Gill Wordington
Manager: Gary Roberts
Programme Editor: Chris Farrington (E) ccfc.editor@googlemail.com

Back row (L-R): Gary Roberts, Laurie Stewart, Neil Midgley, Steve Gentle, Zac Barrett, Dave Theobald, Lee Chaffey, James Krause, Joe Miller.
Front Row: Pat Bexfield, Robbie Nightingale, Adrian Cambridge, Ashley Fuller, Craig Radcliffe, Stephen Smith, Tom Pepper.

Club Factfile

Founded: 1908 **Nickname:** Lilywhites
Previous Names: Cambridge Town 1908-51
Previous Leagues: Bury & District 1908-13, 19-20, Anglian 1908-10, Southern Olympian 1911-14, Southern Amateur 1913-35, Spartan 1935-50, Athenian 1950-58, Southern 1958-2004
Club Colours (change): White/black/black (All light blue)

Ground: City Ground, Milton Road, Cambridge CB4 1UY (T) 01223 357 973
Capacity: 2,000 **Seats:** 533 **Covered:** 1,400 **Clubhouse:** Yes **Shop:** Yes
Previous Grounds: Not known
Simple Directions
Take Junction 13 on M11 and head for City Centre. At mini roundabout turn left then straight on at traffic lights. The road then runs parallel with the river. On reaching traffic lights controlling entry to one way system, get into middle lane up beside Staples Office Furniture and follow lane behind Staples where it becomes nearside lane. Stay in this lane until road straightens then take first left. Ground is behind Westbrook Centre.

Record Attendance: 12,058 v Leytonstone - FA Amateur Cup 1st Round 1949-50
Record Victory: Not known
Record Defeat: Not known
Record Goalscorer: Gary Grogan
Record Appearances: Mal Keenan
Additional Records: Paid £8,000 to Rushden & Diamonds for Paul Coe
Received £100,000 from Millwall for Neil Harris 1998
Senior Honours: Southern League 1962-63, Southern Division 1985-86.
Suffolk Senior Cup 1909-10. East Anglian x9.

10 YEAR RECORD

00-01	01-02	02-03	03-04	04-05	05-06	06-07	07-08	08-09	09-10
SthP 16	SthP 14	SthP 18	SthP 8	Conf S 2	Conf S 7	Conf S 13	Conf S 14	SthP 4	SthP 6

CAMBRIDGE CITY

No.	Date	Comp	H/A	Opponents	Att:	Result	Goalscorers	Pos
1	Aug 15	Zamaretto P.	A	Oxford City	327	W 1 - 0	Theobald 33	8
2	17		H	Banbury United	280	W 2 - 1	Gentle 16 Haniver 43	1
3	22		H	Swindon Supermarine	265	W 5 - 0	Midgeley 26 55 Chaffey 53 Frendo 78 90	1
4	26		A	Halesowen Town	140	D 1 - 1	Fuller 22	
5	29		H	Nuneaton Town	412	D 1 - 1	Fuller 15	4
6	31		A	Brackley Town	302	D 0 - 0		
7	Sept 5		H	Chippenham Town	287	W 1 - 0	Frendo 59	3
8	**12**	**F.A.C 1Q**	**H**	**Daventry Town**	**264**	**W 2 - 0**	**Gentle 24 Frendo 60**	
9	19		A	Truro City	627	D 1 - 1	Chaffey 25	5
10	**26**	**F.A.C. 2Q**	**H**	**Northampton Spencer**	**243**	**W 4 - 1**	**Cambridge 28 Stewart 37 Gentle 44 Frendo 60**	
11	Oct 4		H	Tiverton Town	366	D 1 - 1	Frendo 80	6
12	7		A	Farnborough	784	D 3 - 3	Frendo 6 Midgeley 66 Fuller 80	
13	**10**	**F.A.C. 3Q**	**H**	**Hinckley United**	**468**	**L 0 - 5**		
14	**17**	**F.A.T 1Q**	**A**	**Didcot Town**	**195**	**W 1 - 0**	**Stewart 37**	
15	24		H	Clevedon Town	305	W 4 - 1	Fuller 39 51 Midgeley 68 Gentle 81	4
16	**31**	**F.A.T. 2Q**	**H**	**Matlock Town**	**276**	**L 0 - 1**		
17	Nov 7		A	Bashley	379	W 2 - 0	Fuller 17 Krause 24	3
18	14		H	Leamington	378	D 2 - 2	Gentle 37 46	3
19	28		H	Didcot Town	382	W 4 - 1	Nightingale 2 Burke 20 61 Fuller 30	3
20	Dec 1		A	Evesham United	104	L 1 - 3	Chaffey 84	
21	5		A	Merthyr Tydfil	247	W 1 - 0	Cambridge 70	2
22	7		H	Hemel Hempstead	264	D 1 - 1	Gentle 90	
23	12		A	Hedesford United	335	D 2 - 2	Burke 26 Fuller 62	3
24	26		H	Brackley Town	369	W 5 - 0	Cambridge 30 Burke 35 Fuller 51 Midgeley 89 90 (pen)	2
25	Jan 23		H	Truro City	339	L 0 - 3		3
26	26		H	Stourbridge	205	W 6 - 1	Midgeley 13 (pen) 54 Gentle 31 Frendo 72 Theobald 78 83	
27	Feb 2		A	Stourbridge	175	L 1 - 3	Midgeley 27	
28	6		H	Bashley	358	D 2 - 2	Midgeley 22 Barker 54	4
29	13		A	Leamington	575	L 0 - 1		5
30	20		H	Oxford City	317	W 2 - 0	Krause 89 Calliste 90	5
31	Mar 6		H	Halesowen Town	407	D 1 - 1	Kennedy 4	7
32	9		H	Farnborough	292	D 1 - 1	Calliste 25	
33	13		A	Tiverton Town	252	D 0 - 0		
34	16		H	Rugby Town	204	W 1 - 0	Barker 52	
35	18		A	Swindon Supermarine	105	D 1 - 1	Gentle 38	
36	20		H	Evesham United	281	D 1 - 1	Nightingale 26	7
37	23		A	Banbury United	188	L 0 - 1		
38	27		A	ClevedonTown	152	W 1 - 0	Nightingale 90	8
39	April 3		A	Rugby Town	196	W 3 - 0	Theobald 20 Barker 29 Midgeley 35	6
40	5		H	Bedford Town	392	W 4 - 2	Cambridge 2 Lawley 45 (og) Fuller 53 Barker 59	5
41	7		A	Nuneaton Town	826	D 1 - 1	Coulson 70	
42	10		H	Merthyr Tydfil	275	D 1 - 1	Chaffey 60	5
43	14		A	Bedford Town	308	W 2 - 0	Fuller 21 (pen) Barker 84	
44	17		A	Didcot Town	199	W 3 - 0	BARKER 3 (3 63 70 pen)	5
45	20		A	Chippenham Town	387	L 1 - 2	Theobald 44	
46	22		A	Hemel Hempstead	302	W 3 - 2	Burke 6 20 Midgley 71	
47	24	42	H	Hednesford Town	613	L 0 - 3		6
					Goals	80 51		

Home Attendances:

Highest:	613 v Hednesford Town
Lowest:	204 v Rugby Town
Average (08-09):	317 (338)
Top Goalscorer:	Midgeley - 12 (League 12)

CHESHAM UNITED

Chairman: Alan Calder
Secretary: Brian McCarthy **(T)** 07900 376 491
(E) brian_mccarthy@ntlworld.com
Additional Committee Members:
C. Beton, M. Dragisic, D. Jeffrey, B. McCarthy, G. Stevenson, M. Warrick.
Manager: Andy Leese
Programme Editor: Steve Doman **(E)** cufcprogramme@talktalk.net

Unfortunately an up-to-date photograph was not available at the time of going to press

Club Factfile

Founded: 1919 **Nickname:** The Generals
Previous Names: Not known
Previous Leagues: Spartan 1917-47, Corinthian 1947-63, Athenian 1963-73, Isthmian 1973-2004

Club Colours (change): Claret/claret/sky blue (Yellow/black/yellow)

Ground: The Meadow, Amy Lane, Amersham Road, Chesham HP5 1NE **(T)** 01494 783 964
Capacity: 5,000 **Seats:** 284 **Covered:** 2,500 **Clubhouse:** Yes **Shop:** Yes
Previous Grounds: Not known

Simple Directions
From M25 Junction 20 take A41 (Aylesbury), leave A41 at turn-off for Chesham (A416), pass through Ashley Green into Chesham. Follow signs to Amersham, still on A416 pass two petrol stations opposite each other and at next roundabout take third exit into ground.
From M1 Junction 8 follow signs for Hemel Hempstead then joining the A41 for Aylesbury, then as above.

Record Attendance: 5,000 v Cambridge United - FA Cup 3rd Round 05/12/1979
Record Victory: Not known
Record Defeat: Not known
Record Goalscorer: John Willis
Record Appearances: Martin Baguley - 600+
Additional Records: Received £22,000 from Oldham Athletic for Fitz Hall

Senior Honours: Isthmian League 1992-93, Division 1 1986-87, 97-97. Berks & Bucks Senior Cup x12.

10 YEAR RECORD

00-01	01-02	02-03	03-04	04-05	05-06	06-07	07-08	08-09	09-10
Isth P 5	Isth P 7	Isth P 21	Isth1N 4	SthP 12	SthP 22	Sthsw 15	SthM 6	SthM 5	SthM 4

Do you remember when...

Chesham United

Chesham United were Champions of the Isthmian League Division One in 1996-1997.

Back row, left to right: David Stephenson, Ian Hazel, Kevin Mitchell, Richard Pierson and Mike Burgess (Physio).
Middle Row: Andy Thomas (Manager), Tony O'Driscoll (Assistant Manager), John Lawford, Nathan Beckett, Youness Yabil, Trevor Argrave, Andy Reeder, Gary Fisher, Brian Harding (Assistant Physio) and Mickey Stamp (Dressing Room Attendant)
Front Row: Alan Pluckrose, John Caesar, Matthew Howard, Martin Gurney (Captain), Johnson Hyppolyte, Chris McGuire and David Nolan.

CHIPPENHAM TOWN

Chairman: John Applegate
Secretary: Angela Townsley **(T)** 07909 634 875
(E) angelatownsley_chiptownfc@talktalk.net
Additional Committee Members:
Chris Blake, Doug Webb, Simon Eason, Robin Townsley, Ralph Penton
Manager: Adie Mings
Programme Editor: Angela Townsley **(E)** angelatownsley_chiptownfc@talktalk.net

2010-2011 SEASON
Sponsored by Borough Parade Shopping Chippenham

Club Factfile

Founded: 1873 **Nickname:** The Bluebirds
Previous Names: Not known
Previous Leagues: Hellenic, Wiltshire Senior, Wiltshire Premier, Western

Club Colours (change): Royal blue/royal blue/blue (All white)

Ground: Hardenhuish Park, Bristol Road, Chippenham SN14 6LR **(T)** 01249 650 400
Capacity: 3,000 **Seats:** 300 **Covered:** 1,000 **Clubhouse:** Yes **Shop:** Yes
Previous Grounds: Not known
Simple Directions
Exit 17 from M4. Follow A350 towards Chippenham for three miles to first roundabout, take second exit (A350); follow road to third roundabout (junction with A420). Turn left and follow signs to town centre. Ground is 1km on left hand side adjacent to pedestrian controlled traffic lights. Car/Coach park next to traffic lights.

Record Attendance: 4,800 v Chippenham United - Western League 1951
Record Victory: 9-0 v Dawlish Town (H) - Western League
Record Defeat: 0-10 v Tiverton Town (A) - Western League
Record Goalscorer: Dave Ferris
Record Appearances: Ian Monnery
Additional Records:

Senior Honours: Western League 1951-52. Les Phillips Cup 1999-2000. Wiltshire Senior Cup. Wiltshire Senior Shield x4.

10 YEAR RECORD

00-01	01-02	02-03	03-04	04-05	05-06	06-07	07-08	08-09	09-10
WestP 2	SthW 2	SthP 5	SthP 21	SthP 2	SthP 4	SthP 7	SthP 4	SthP 8	SthP 3

CHIPPENHAM TOWN

No.	Date	Comp	H/A	Opponents	Att:	Result	Goalscorers	Pos
1	Aug 15	Zamaretto P.	H	Nuneaton Town	530	W 2 - 1	Highmore 1 Benison 90	5
2	18		A	Didcot Town	268	W 2 - 0	Highmore 5 Powell 21	3
3	22		A	Rugby Town	193	D 0 - 0		3
4	25		H	Hemel Hempstead	416	W 6 - 1	Davies 18 Lamb 28 34 Adams 64 Powell 70 90	1
5	29		A	Leamington	655	D 4 - 4	Powell 26 46 Lamb 39 Highmore 66	
6	31		H	Clevedon Town	537	W 2 - 0	Benison 51 Powell 89	
7	Sept 5		A	Cambridge City	287	L 0 - 1		4
8	**12**	**F.A.C 1Q**	**A**	**Banbury United**	**361**	**D 0 - 0**		
9	**15**	**F.A.C. 1Qr**	**H**	**Banbury United**	**306**	**W 3 - 2**	**Lye 7 Allison 27 Powell 86 (pen)**	
10	19		H	Merthyr Tydfil	490	L 1 - 5	Bassett 66	8
11	**26**	**F.A.C. 2Q**	**H**	**Merthyr Tydfil**	**533**	**W 4 - 1**	**HIGHMORE 3 (13 38 46) Bassett 84**	
12	Oct 4		H	Swindon Supermarine	524	L 0 - 1		7
13	6		A	Truro City	429	W 5 - 3	Adams 3 HIGHMORE 3 (15 45 90) Powell 77	
14	**10**	**F.A.C 3Q**	**A**	**Havant & Waterlooville**	**620**	**W 2 - 1**	**Highmore 35 Powell 71**	
15	**17**	**F.A.T 1Q**	**H**	**Frome Town**	**431**	**W 3 - 1**	**Highmore 22 Benison 48 Allison 85**	
16	**24**	**F.A.C. 4Q**	**A**	**Paulton Rovers**	**931**	**L 0 - 3**		
17	**31**	**F.A.T 2Q**	**H**	**Tooting & Mitcham**	**429**	**W 4 - 1**	**Lye 20 Powell 22 (pen) 58 Lamb77**	
18	Nov 7		A	Farnborough	869	L 1 - 3	Gullick 26	9
19	10		A	Bedford Town	227	W 2 - 1	Gullick 44 Powell 58	
20	14		A	Oxford City	313	D 0 - 0		8
21	17		H	Halesowen Town	381	D 1 - 1	Gullick 69	
22	**22**	**F.A.T 3Q**	**A**	**Kingstonian**	**388**	**W 2 - 0**	**Powell 42 Davies 65**	
23	28		H	Brackley Town	375	L 2 - 3	Powell 8 Griffin 40	7
24	Dec 1		H	Stourbridge	266	D 2 - 2	Griffin 20 Benison 63	
25	5		A	Hednesford Town	340	D 1 - 1	Powell 3 (pen)	7
26	**12**	**F.A.T 1**	**A**	**Arlesey Town**	**221**	**D 1 - 1**	**Brown 23 (og)**	
27	**15**	**F.A.T.1r**	**H**	**Arlesey Town**	**235**	**W 2 - 0**	**Griffin 27 Gullick 55**	
28	**20**	**F.A.T. 2**	**A**	**Gateshead**	**216**	**L 0 - 1**		
29	Jan 23		A	Merthyr Tydfil	288	L 1 - 2	Powell 25	14
30	26		H	Leamington	304	W 4 - 2	Highmore 45 Gullick 75 85 Powell 56	
31	Feb 2		H	Evesham United	294	W 2 - 1	Griffin 84 Powell 89	
32	6		A	Stourbridge	286	L 0 - 1		11
33	9		A	Banbury United	156	D 0 - 0		
34	13		H	Oxford City	374	W 2 - 0	Lamb 12 Powell 24	9
35	23		H	Didcot Town	263	W 2 - 0	Gullick 23 Powell 52	
36	27		H	RugbyTown	379	W 1 - 0	Powell 56	8
37	Mar 2		A	Clevedon Town	135	D 0 - 0		
38	6		A	Hemel Hempstead	242	W 1 - 0	Allison 85	
39	9		H	Truro City	413	W 2 - 1	Kite 78 Powell 82	
40	13		A	Swindon Supermarine	289	D 1 - 1	Gullick 60	8
41	16		H	Tiverton Town	387	W 4 - 2	Powell 42 (pen) 85 Griffin 64 Lye 67	
42	20		H	Bedford Town	345	W 3 - 0	Powell 7 Griffin 13 Gullick 42	6
43	23		A	Evesham United	115	D 0 - 0		
44	30		A	Halesowen Town	352	L 0 - 2		6
45	April 3		H	Banbury United	419	W 5 - 0	Gullick 5 Powell 32 52 Kite 36 Williams 87	5
46	5		A	Tiverton Town	270	D 0 - 0		6
47	8		A	Bashley	316	W 1 - 0	Highmore 90	
48	10		H	Heddnesford Town	434	L 0 - 1		7
49	13		H	Bashley	364	L 1 - 2	Powell 43	
50	17		A	Brackley Town	327	W 1 - 0	Lamb 43 (pen)	8
51	18		A	Nuneaton Borough	651	W 1 - 0	Griffin 34	6
52	20		H	Cambridge City	387	W 2 - 1	Highmore 24 73	
53	24		H	Farnborough	744	W 2 - 0	Davies 37 Powell 72	3
54	**27**	**Play Off S-F**	**H**	**Hednesford Town**	**811**	**W 2 - 0**	**Powell 64 Allison 88**	
55	**May 3**	**Play Off Final**	**A**	**Nuneaton Town**	**3018**	**L 1 - 2**	**Powell 71**	
					Goals	91 56		

Home Attendances:

Highest:	744 v Farnborough
Lowest:	263 v Didcot Town
Average (08-09):	387 (420)
Top Goalscorer:	Powell - 31 (League 24, FAC 2, FAT 3, Play-off 2 - Hat-trick 3)

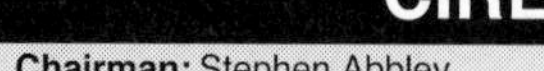

CIRENCESTER TOWN

Chairman: Stephen Abbley

Secretary: Kathie Chambers **(T)** 01285 654 543
(E) kathie.chambers@cirentownfc.plus.com

Additional Committee Members:
Alan Sykes, Ian Stewart, Robert Saunders, Alan Lloyd, David Bougen

Manager: Brian Hughes

Programme Editor: Mark O'Brien **(E)** obrienm2uk@aol.com

Unfortunately an up-to-date photograph was not available at the time of going to press

Club Factfile

Founded: 1889 **Nickname:** Centurions

Previous Names: Not known

Previous Leagues: Hellenic

Club Colours (change): Red and black stripes/black/red (All navy and sky blue)

Ground: The Corinium Stadium, Kingshill Lane, Cirencester GL7 1HS **(T)** 01285 654 543

Capacity: 4,500 **Seats:** 550 **Covered:** 1,250 **Clubhouse:** Yes **Shop:** Yes

Previous Grounds: Smithfield Stadium

Simple Directions
Leave bypass at Burford Road roundabout. Aim for Stow, turn right at traffic lights, then right again at next junction, first left into Kingshill Lane. Ground 500 yards on right.

Record Attendance: 2,600 v Fareham Town - 1969

Record Victory: Not known

Record Defeat: Not known

Record Goalscorer: Not known

Record Appearances: Not known

Additional Records: Paid £4,000 to Gloucester City for Lee Smith

Senior Honours: Hellenic League Premier Division 1995-96.
Gloucestershire Senior Amateur Cup 1989-90. Gloucestershire County Cup 1995-96.

10 YEAR RECORD

00-01		01-02		02-03		03-04		04-05		05-06		06-07		07-08		08-09		09-10	
SthW	11	SthW	13	SthW	14	SthW	3	SthP	7	SthP	18	SthP	21	SthP	21	Sthsw	14	Sthsw	5

Do you remember when...

Cirencester Town

Cirencester Town won promotion from the Southern League Divison One West in 2003-2004

Back row, left to right: Gary Wooton, Gareth Hopkins, Mike Davies, Paul Thompson, Adam Mayo. Kevin Halliday, Nathan Edwards, Alan Bird, Tom Cole, Neil Arndale and the Assistant Coach.
Front Row: Ben Fitch, Stuart Fraser, Shaun Wimble, Scott Griffin, Steve Tapp (Assistant Manager), Brian Hughes (Manager), Darren Robinson (Coach), Adam Hemmings, Nick Stanley and Michael Jackson.

DIDCOT TOWN

Chairman: John Bailey

Secretary: Pat Horsman **(T)** 07882 154 612
(E) didcot@fernring.co.uk

Additional Committee Members: Mick Cox, Steve Clare, Justin Lambourne, Pete Aplin, Dave Warwick, Peter Cox, Mark Roberts, Peter Chalk, Jaquie Chalk, Paul Leach, Mark Buckmaster, Mark Beauchamp, Roger Neal

Manager: Stuart Peace

Programme Editor: Joffy Chinnock **(E)** joffy@hotmail.co.uk

Archive photo

Club Factfile

Founded: 1907 **Nickname:** Railwaymen

Previous Names: Not known

Previous Leagues: Metropolitan 1957-63, Hellenic 1963-2006

Club Colours (change): Red with white sleeves/white/white (Gold/black/black)

Ground: NPower Loop Meadow Stadium, Bowmont Water, Didcot OX11 7GA **(T)** 01235 813 138

Capacity: 5,000 **Seats:** 250 **Covered:** 200 **Clubhouse:** Yes **Shop:** Yes

Previous Grounds: Not known

Simple Directions

From A34 take A4130 towards Didcot. At first roundabout take first exit, at next roundabout take third exit, then straight across next two roundabouts. At fifth roundabout turn right into Avon Way. Follow Avon Way for 1/2 mile till you get to a mini roundabout. Straight across it, ground is on the left after 100 yards, in Bowmont Water.

Record Attendance: 1,512 v Jarrow roofing - FA Vase Semi-final 2005

Record Victory: Not known

Record Defeat: Not known

Record Goalscorer: Ian Concanon

Record Appearances: Not known

Additional Records:

Senior Honours: Hellenic League Premier Division 1953-54, 2005-06, Division 1 1976-77, 87-88, League Cup x6.
FA Vase 2004-05. Berks & Bucks Senior Trophy 2001-02, 02-03, 05-06.

10 YEAR RECORD

00-01	01-02	02-03	03-04	04-05	05-06	06-07	07-08	08-09	09-10
Hel P 4	Hel P 5	Hel P 5	Hel P 5	Hel P 2	Hel P 1	Sthsw 10	Sthsw 3	Sthsw 5	SthP 15

DIDCOT TOWN

No.	Date	Comp	H/A	Opponents	Att:	Result	Goalscorers	Pos
1	Aug 15	Zamaretto P.	A	Clevedon Town	203	D 1 - 1	Hope 17 (pen)	13
2	18		H	Chippenham Town	268	L 0 - 2		17
3	22		H	Hednesford tOwn	286	L 0 - 2		19
4	26		A	Farnborough	749	L 0 - 1		
5	29		H	Stourport	225	L 0 - 1		20
6	31		A	Oxford City	377	D 1 - 1	Draycott 63	
7	Sept 5		H	Brackley Town	270	L 0 - 1		20
8	**12**	**F.A.C 1Q**	**H**	**Shrivenham**	**226**	**W 5 - 0**	**Hope 2 87 Draycott 13 Stanley 45 Bartley 85**	
9	19		A	Bedford Town	353	W 5 - 1	DRAYCOTT 3 (1 60 67) Williams 18 Bridges 79	17
10	**26**	**F.A.C. 2Q**	**H**	**Paulton Rovers**	**225**	**L 0 - 2**		
11	Oct 4		A	Bashley	322	L 2 - 3	Bridges 84 Sampson 86	19
12	6		H	Banbury United	317	D 0 - 0		
13	10		H	Hemel Hempstead	214	W 2 - 1	Draycott 54 75	17
14	**17**	**F.A.T 1Q**	**H**	**Cambridge City**	**195**	**L 0 - 1**		
15	24		A	Merthyr Tydfil	341	L 2 - 4	Sampson 70 79	18
16	31		A	Leamington	551	W 5 - 3	Tabor 25 BARTLEY 3 (27 39 73) Sampson 84	
17	Nov 7		H	Evesham United	230	L 0 - 2		14
18	14		A	Tiverton Town	268	W 2 - 1	Bartley 43 Stanley 66	13
19	28		A	Cambridge City	382	L 1 - 4	John 79	15
20	Dec 5		H	Rugby Town	202	W 3 - 1	Alexis 27 Draycott 76 90	15
21	12		H	Halesowen Town	204	L 1 - 2	Draycott 83	16
22	26		H	Oxford City	511	D 4 - 4	DRAYCOTT 3 (6 10 75) John 90	16
23	Jan 23		H	Bedford Town	170	D 2 - 2	Williams 12 Draycott 90	17
24	30		A	Brackley Town	251	D 2 - 2	Alexis 34 John 60	17
25	Feb 6		A	Evesham United	136	W 1 - 0	John 82	16
26	13		H	Tiverton Town	171	D 1 - 1	Collier 57 (og)	16
27	20		H	Clevedon Town	157	L 0 - 1		16
28	23		A	Chippenham Town	263	L 0 - 2		
29	27		A	Hednesford Town	348	W 2 - 1	Williams 82 Bartley 90	15
30	Mar 2		H	Nuneaton Town	226	D 1 - 1	Sampson 90	
31	6		H	Farnborough	384	L 1 - 2	Mortimer-Jones 63	15
32	9		A	Babury United	162	L 0 - 1		
33	13		H	Bashley	170	D 1 - 1	Mortimer-Jones 9	
34	16		H	Truro City	156	D 1 - 1	Bartley 44	
35	20		A	Hemel Hempstead	188	W 2 - 1	Stanley 2 Brown 57	14
36	24		A	Swindon Supermarine	181	D 1 - 1	Bartley 90	
37	27		H	Merthyr Tydfil	211	W 3 - 0	Williams 16 Huggins 52 Draycott 85	14
38	30		H	Leamington	245	W 4 - 2	Huggins 12 75 Dutton-Black 23 Williams 28	
39	April 5		H	Swindon Supermarine	218	L 0 - 2		14
40	8		A	Stourbridge	187	L 0 - 1		
41	10		A	Rugby Town	184	L 3 - 4	JOHN 3 (18 56 pen 72 pen)	15
42	15		A	Truro City	272	L 1 - 2	Draycott 64	
43	17		H	Cambridge City	199	L 0 - 3		15
44	20		A	Nuneaton Town	555	L 0 - 2		
45	24		A	Halesowen Town	355	L 1 - 3	John 49	15
					Goals	61 74		

Home Attendances:	
Highest:	511 v Oxford City
Lowest:	156 v Truro City
Average:	218
Top Goalscorer:	Draycott - 15 (League 14, FAC 1 - Hat-trick 2)

EVESHAM UNITED

Chairman: Jim Cockerton
Secretary: Mike Peplow (T) 07889 011 539
(E) rwestmacot@aol.com
Additional Committee Members: Steve Lane, Malcolm Davis, Roger Westmacott, David Wright, Bob Prater, Bernard Jordan, Morris Allan, Simon Parry
Manager: Paul West
Programme Editor: Mike Peplow (E) rwestmacot@aol.com

Unfortunately an up-to-date photograph was not available at the time of going to press

Club Factfile

Founded: 1945 **Nickname:** The Robins
Previous Names: Not known
Previous Leagues: Worcester, Birmingham Combination, Midland Combination 1951-55, 65-92, West Midlands (Regional) 1955-62
Club Colours (change): Red and white stripes/white/red (Blue and white stripes/blue/blue)

Ground: Worcester City FC, St George's Lane, Worcester WR1 1QT (T) 01905 23003
Capacity: 2,000 **Seats:** 350 **Covered:** 600 **Clubhouse:** Yes **Shop:** Yes
Previous Grounds: The Crown Meadow > 1968, Common Reed 1968-2006
Simple Directions
Leave M5 at Junction 6 (Worcester North), follow signs for Worcester along the A449. Follow the dual carrigeway until you come to roundabout, take second turning towards Worcester. Stay on this road for about one mile (Ombersley Road) until you reach T-junction and traffic lights. Turn right at lights. St George's Lane is third turning on left between tool hire shop and 'In Toto Kitchen' showrooms. Ground is 500 yards on left.

Record Attendance: 2,338 v West Bromwich Albion - Friendly 18/07/1992
Record Victory: 11-3 v West Heath United
Record Defeat: 1-8 v Ilkeston Town
Record Goalscorer: Sid Brain
Record Appearances: Rob Candy
Additional Records: Paid £1,500 to Hayes for Colin Day 1992
Received £5,000 from Cheltenham Town for Simon Brain
Senior Honours: Midland Combination Premier Division 1991-92, Division 1 1965-66, 67-68, 68-69.
Southern League Division 1 Midlands 2007-08.
Worcestershire Senior Urn x2

10 YEAR RECORD

00-01	01-02	02-03	03-04	04-05	05-06	06-07	07-08	08-09	09-10
SthW 4	SthW 12	SthW 12	SthW 14	SthW 3	SthP 20	SthM 5	SthM 1	SthP 9	SthP 16

EVESHAM UNITED

No.	Date	Comp	H/A	Opponents	Att:	Result	Goalscorers	Pos
1	Aug 15	Zamaretto P.	H	Brackley Town	167	L 1 - 3	Lutz 74	19
2	18		A	Leamington	717	L 1 - 4	Scheppel 18	20
3	22		A	Tiverton Town	280	W 1 - 0	Clarke 74	15
4	25		H	Nuneaton Town	258	L 1 - 2	Clarke 68	18
5	29		A	Bashley	312	L 1 - 2	Ball 8	18
6	31		H	Merthyr Tydfil	192	D 1 - 1	Cole 16	
7	Sept 5		A	Clevedon Town	197	W 4 - 1	Luckett 18 Ball 20 56 Lutz 48	16
8	12	F.A.C. 1Q	H	Tividale	131	D 0 - 0		
9	15	F.A.C. 1Qr	A	Tividale	140	W 2 - 1*	Cornes 41 Darby 116	
10	22		H	Hednesford Town	171	D 0 - 0		14
11	27	F.A.C. 2Q	H	Stourbridge	262	L 0 - 1		
12	Oct 3		A	Stourbridge	242	D 0 - 0		13
13	6		H	Oxford United	119	D 0 - 0		
14	17	F.A.T 1Q	H	Windsor & Eton	85	D 1 - 1	Vaughan 90	
15	20	F.A.T. 1Qr	A	Windsor & Eton	104	W 2 - 0	Clarke 45 52	
16	24		A	Rugby Town	178	D 0 - 0		13
17	27	F.A.T 2Q	A	Northwood	104	D 0 - 0		
18	Nov 7		A	Didcot Town	230	W 2 - 0	Lutz 36 Clarke 38	13
19	14		H	Farnborough	173	L 1 - 2	Cooper 75	14
20	28		A	Bedford Town	276	W 2 - 1	Lennon 87 Palmer 90	13
21	Dec 1		H	Cambridge City	104	W 3 - 1	Fitter 39 Palmer 54 55	
22	5		H	Swindon Supermarine	106	L 0 - 1		14
23	8		A	Truro City	238	W 2 - 1	Rice 13 (og) Hayden 45	
24	15		H	Banbury United	101	W 3 - 2	Palmer 27 87 Luckett 70	
25	Jan 23		A	Hednesford Town	331	L 1 - 2	Palmer 67	11
26	26		A	Merthyr TYdfil	220	L 1 - 2	Palmer 17	
27	Feb 2		A	Chippenham Town	294	L 1 - 2	Lennon 49	
28	6		H	Didcot Town	136	L 0 - 1		14
29	9		H	Halesowen Town	166	D 0 - 0		
30	13		A	Farnborough	674	L 1 - 3	Doyle 12 (og)	
31	20		A	Brackley Town	228	L 1 - 3	Palmer 40	14
32	23		H	Leamington	192	L 0 - 1		
33	29		H	Tiverton Town	126	D 2 - 2	Palmer 37 Hyde 48	16
34	Mar 6		A	Nuneaton Town	644	L 0 - 2		17
35	9		A	Oxford City	106	L 0 - 3		
36	13		H	Stourbridge	178	D 1 - 1	Palmer 21	
37	16		H	Bashley	101	D 0 - 0		
38	20		A	Canbridge City	281	D 1 - 1	Lennon 21	16
39	23		H	Chippenham Town	115	D 0 - 0		
40	27		H	RugbyTown	146	W 1 - 0	Ducros 69	15
41	30		H	Truro City	105	L 0 - 2		
42	April 3		H	Hemel Hempstead	112	L 0 - 2		16
43	5		A	Halesowen Town	411	L 0 - 1		17
44	10		A	Swindon Supermarine	143	D 1 - 1	Fitter 52	18
45	13		H	Clevedon Town	133	D 0 - 0		
46	17		H	Bedford Town	119	D 0 - 0		16
47	20		A	Hemel Hempstead	163	L 0 - 2		
48	24		A	Banbury United	321	W 1 - 0	Spencer 1	16
					Goals	40 54		

Home Attendances:	
Highest:	258 v Nuneaton Town
Lowest:	101 v Banbury United & Bashley
Average (08-09):	133 (164)
Top Goalscorer:	Palmer - 10 (League 10)

HALESOWEN TOWN

Chairman: Graham Ingram

Secretary: Andrew While (T) 07976 769 972 (E) andrew.while@blueyonder.co.uk

Additional Committee Members:

Manager: Rob Elmes & Tony Thorpe

Programme Editor: Bob Pepper (E) robrjp1@btinternet.com

Club Factfile

Founded: 1873 **Nickname:** Yeltz

Previous Names: Not known

Previous Leagues: West Midlands 1892-1905, 06-11, 46-86, Birmingham Combination 1911-39

Club Colours (change): Blue/white/blue (White/blue/white)

Ground: The Grove, Old Hawne Lane, Halesowen B63 3TB (T) 0121 661 9392

Capacity: 3,150 **Seats:** 525 **Covered:** 930 **Clubhouse:** Yes **Shop:** Yes

Previous Grounds: Not known

Simple Directions

Leave M5 at Junction 3, follow A456 Kidderminster to first island and turn right (signposted A459 Dudley). Turn left at next island (signposted A458 Stourbridge). At next island take third exit into Old Hawne Lane. Ground about 400 yards on left.

Record Attendance: 5,000 v Hendon - FA Cup 1st Round Proper 1954

Record Victory: 13-1 v Coventry Amateurs - Birmingham Senior cup 1956

Record Defeat: 0-8 v Bilston - West Midlands League 07/04/1962

Record Goalscorer: Paul Joinson - 369

Record Appearances: Paul Joinson - 608

Additional Records: Paid £7,250 to Gresley Rovers for Stuart Evans
Received £40,000 from Rushden & Diamonds for Jim Rodwell

Senior Honours: FA Vase 1984-85, 85-86 (R-up 1982-83). Southern League Midland Division 1989-90, Western Division 2001-02.
Birmingham Senior Cup 1983-84, 97-98. Staffordshire Senior Cup 1988-89.
Worcestershire Senior Cup 1951-52, 61-62, 2002-03, 04-05.

10 YEAR RECORD

00-01	01-02	02-03	03-04	04-05	05-06	06-07	07-08	08-09	09-10
SthP 22	SthW 1	SthP 19	SthW 4	SthP 9	SthP 8	SthP 6	SthP 3	SthP 10	SthP 8

HALESOWEN TOWN

No.	Date	Comp	H/A	Opponents	Att:	Result	Goalscorers	Pos
1	Aug 15	Zamaretto P.	H	Hemel Hempstead	96	W 1 - 0	Moore 72	9
2	18		A	Nuneaton Town	901	D 1 - 1	Rickards 31	6
3	22		A	Brackley Town	248	L 1 - 2	Moore 9	12
4	26		H	Cambridge City	140	D 1 - 1	Moore 26 (pen)	
5	29		H	Swindon Supermarine	101	W 2 - 0	Moore 40 Bates 74	9
6	31		A	Stourbridge	656	W 4 - 1	Hood 64 Moore 69 90 Rickards 86	
7	Sept 5		H	Bedford Town	126	W 4 - 1	MOORE 3 (16 75 84) Eze 63	6
8	19		A	Farnboorough	1014	L 1 - 4	Moore 39	
9	Oct 4		A	Banbury United	428	L 1 - 2	Moore 68	20
10	7		H	Rugby Town	228	W 5 - 1	Denny 43 Breward 53 Johnson 73 Rickards 75 Moore 85	
11	10		H	Leamington	606	W 3 - 0	Blenkinsopp 54 75 Bates 81	13
12	31		A	Merthyr Tydfil	356	W 2 - 0	Moore 35 61	12
13	Nov 7		H	Hednesford Town	504	D 2 - 2	Moore 6 76	12
14	14		A	Truro City	429	W 2 - 1	Moore 7 (pen) Johnson 64	11
15	17		A	Chippenham Town	381	D 1 - 1	Johnson 87	
16	21		A	Clevedon Town	168	D 3 - 3	Rickards 15 Blenkinsop 22 Moore 29 (pen)	11
17	28		H	TivertonTown	322	D 1 - 1	Edwards 70	10
18	Dec 5		A	Bashley	272	W 2 - 1	Blenkinsopp 10 Moore 26	8
19	9		H	Merthyr Tydfil	291	D 1 - 1	Blenkinsopp 90	
20	12		A	Didcot Town	204	W 2 - 1	Edwards 72 Moore 86	6
21	26		H	Stourbridge	761	W 2 - 1	Edwards 49 Blenkinsopp 79	5
22	Jan 23		H	Farnborough	516	D 1 - 1	Johnson 35	6
23	26		H	ClevedonTown	242	D 2 - 2	Palmer 7 34	
24	30		A	Bedford Town	268	D 1 - 1	Benkinsopp 2	6
25	Feb 6		H	Hednesford Town	504	D 2 - 2	Blenkinsopp 13 Turner 28	7
26	9		A	Evesham United	166	D 0 - 0		
27	13		H	Truro City	385	W 3 - 2	Thorpe 25 Moore 53 69	6
28	20		A	Hemel Hempstead	223	W 5 - 3	MOORE 3 (16 41 74) Rickards 62 Blenkinsopp 68	
29	23		H	Nuneaton Town	350	W 3 - 2	Turner 39 Moore 45 Griffiths 81	
30	27		H	Brackley Town	411	D 1 - 1	Palmer 13	4
31	Mar 6		A	Cambridge City	407	D 1 - 1	Rickards 59	6
32	9		A	Rugby Town	185	W 3 - 0	Blenkinsopp 17 Eze 65 McDermott 87	
33	13		H	Banbury United	435	L 0 - 2		
34	20		A	Leamington	734	D 2 - 2	Moore 33 McDermott 90	8
35	23		H	Oxford City	247	D 3 - 3	Moore 59 85 (pen) Rickards 65	
36	27		H	Chippenham Town	352	W 2 - 0	Turner 9 Moore 43 (pen)	7
37	April 3		A	Oxford City	288	D 2 - 2	Moore 50 Turner 89	9
38	5		H	Evesham United	411	W 1 - 0	Spencer 20 (og)	7
39	10		H	Bashley	296	W 3 - 2	Moore 32 89 (pen) Eze 90	8
40	14		A	Swindon Supermarine	117	W 2 - 1	Moore 5 41(pen)	
41	17		A	Tiverton Town	285	W 2 - 0	Eze 31 Osborne 83	8
42	24		H	Didcot Town	355	W 3 - 1	Cowley 3 42 Griffiths 81	8
					Goals	84 53		

Home Attendances:	
Highest:	761 v Stouridge
Lowest:	96 v Hemel Hempstead
Average (08-09):	350 (444)
Top Goalscorer:	Moore - 35 (League 35 - Hat-trick 1)

HEDNESFORD TOWN

Chairman: Stephen Price
Secretary: Terry McMahon (T) 07901 822 040
(E) mcmahon64@googlemail.com
Additional Committee Members:
Carole Price, Michael Johnson, David Smith
Manager: Bernard McNally
Programme Editor: Michael Johnson (E) bigmickj10@aol.co.uk

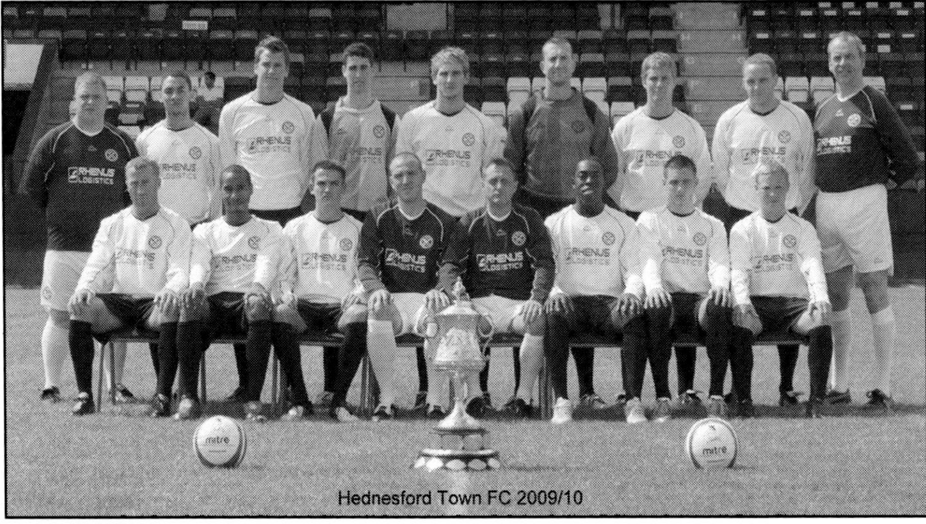
Hednesford Town FC 2009/10

Club Factfile

Founded: 1880 **Nickname:** The Pitmen
Previous Names: Hednesford 1938-74
Previous Leagues: Walsall & District, Birmingham Combination 1906-15, 45-53, West Midlands 1919-39, 53-72, 74-84, Midland Counties 1972-74, Southern 1984-95, 2001-2005, Conference 1995-2001, 05-06, Northern Premier 2006-09

Club Colours (change): White/black/black (All red)

Ground: Keys Park, Park Road, Hednesford, Cannock WS12 2DZ (T) 01543 422 870
Capacity: 6,039 **Seats:** 1,010 **Covered:** 5,334 **Clubhouse:** Yes **Shop:** Yes
Previous Grounds: Not known
Simple Directions
Leave M6 at J11 and follow the signs for Cannock. At the next island take the third exit towards Rugeley (A460). On reaching the A5 at Churchbridge island, rejoin the A460 signposted Rugeley and follow this road over five traffic islands. At the sixth traffic island, by a Texaco petrol station, turn right past a McDonalds restaurant and follow this road to the next island which is 'Cross Keys Island'. Go over this island to the next small island and turn right. Keys Park football ground is on left.

Record Attendance: 3,169 v York City - FA Cup 3rd Round 13/01/1997
Record Victory: 12-1 v Redditch United - Birmingham Combination 1952-53
Record Defeat: 0-15 v Burton - Birmingham Combination 1952-53
Record Goalscorer: Joe O'Connor - 230 in 430 games
Record Appearances: Kevin Foster - 463
Additional Records: Paid £12,000 to Macclesfield Town for Steve Burr
Received £50,000 from Blackpool for Kevin Russell
Senior Honours: Southern League Premier Division 1994-95. FA Trophy 2004-05.
Staffordshire Senior Cup x2. Birmingham Senior Cup 1935-36.

10 YEAR RECORD

00-01	01-02	02-03	03-04	04-05	05-06	06-07	07-08	08-09	09-10
Conf 22	SthP 16	SthP 11	SthP 20	SthP 4	Conf N 22	NP P 7	NP P 8	NP P 8	SthP 4

HEDNESFORD TOWN

No.	Date	Comp	H/A	Opponents	Att:	Result	Goalscorers	Pos
1	Aug 15	Zamaretto P.	H	Tiverton Town	351	W 2 - 1	Bailey 14 Durrell 90	6
2	18		A	Stourbridge	268	D 1 - 1	Rickards 31	5
3	22		A	Brackley Town	248	L 1 - 2	Moore 9	12
4	25		H	Brackley Town	353	L 1 - 4	Walker 86	8
5	29		H	Truro City	359	L 2 - 3	Dinning 29 Durrell 66	11
6	31		A	Nuneaton Town	944	L 1 - 3	Barnett 63	
7	Sept 5		H	Swindon Supermarine	309	D 0 - 0		13
8	**12**	**F.A.C 1Q**	**H**	**Pegasus Juniors**	**274**	**L 1 - 4**	**Barnett 71**	
9	22		A	Evesham United	171	D 0 - 0		
10	26		H	Leamington	475	W 4 - 2	Bailey 4 Barnett 7 Nisbett 33 Dyer 73	10
11	Oct 4		A	Hemel Hempstead	249	D 2 - 2	Dyer 18 Barnett 24	
12	10		H	Merthyr Tydfil	411	D 1 - 1	Dyer 24	11
13	**17**	**F.A.T 1Q**	**A**	**Buxton**	**352**	**L 0 - 1**		
14	24		A	Bashley	349	W 4 - 0	Barnett 8 90 Durrell 58 Bailey 89	9
15	Nov 7		A	Halesowen Town	504	D 2 - 2	Barnett 27 77	8
16	14		H	Clevedon Town	333	D 0 - 0		9
17	21		H	Oxford City	305	W 4 - 2	Dyer 7 (pen) Jagielka 14 Durrell 24 Godhead 76	10
18	28		A	Banbury United	284	L 2 - 3	Dyer 12 55	8
19	Dec 5		H	Chippenham Town	340	D 1 - 1	Barnett 74	10
20	12		H	Cambridge City	335	D 2 - 2	McCullen 16 Dyer 60	
21	15		A	Bedford Town	198	L 2 - 3	Dyer18 Durrell 71	
22	Jan 19		A	Oxford City	142	L 0 - 2		
23	23		H	Evesham United	331	W 2 - 1	Jagielka 21 (pen) Barnett 61	10
24	Feb 6		H	Halesowen Towen	504	D 2 - 2	Barnett 25 Adkins 90	12
25	13		A	Clevedon Town	165	W 3 - 0	BARNETT 3 (52 79 84)	12
26	20		A	Tiverton Town	289	W 2 - 0	Durrell 36 Dyer 80	11
27	27		H	Didcot Town	345	L 1 - 2	Francis 60	
28	Mar 4		H	Farnborough	327	W 4 - 0	DURRELL 3 (12 30 85) Profitt 47	
29	6		A	Brackley	241	W 1 - 0	Dyer R 87	9
30	9		A	Leamington	551	W 3 - 1	Dunkley 2 15 Dyer 90	
31	13		H	Hemel Hempstead	345	W 4 - 3	Francis 23 Durrell 27 Barnett 36 Martin 90	
32	16		H	Nuneaton Town	459	L 0 - 3		
33	23		A	Truro City	259	W 2 - 1	Durrell 74 Dyer R 79	
34	27		H	Bashley	354	W 1 - 0	Profitt 87	10
35	30		H	Bedford Town	281	W 2 - 1	Bailey 6 McGurk 30	
36	April 5		H	Rugby Town	402	W 6 - 0	Durrell 15 BARNETT 3 (39 54 70pen) Dyer 60 90	8
37	7		A	Swindon Supermarine	131	D 0 - 0		
38	10		A	Chippenham Town	434	W 1 - 0	McGurk 90	6
39	13		A	MerthyrTydfil	258	W 2 - 1	Durrell 66 76	
40	15		H	Stourbridge	449	D 1 - 1	Craddock 44	
41	17		H	Banbury United	508	D 0 - 0		7
42	20		A	Rugby Town	198	W 6 - 1	Durrell 36 70 Dyer 51 McGurk 54 Francis 55 Barnett 59	
43	22		A	Farnborough	1039	L 1 - 2	Francis 54	
44	24		A	Cambridge City	613	W 3 - 0	Craddock 58 Barnett 68 82	4
45	**27**	**Play Off S-F**	**A**	**Chippenham Town**	**811**	**L 0 - 2**		
					Goals	80 60		

Home Attendances:	
Highest:	508 v Banbury United
Lowest:	281 v Bedford Town
Average (08-09):	348 (466)
Top Goalscorer:	Barnett - 21 (League 20, FAC 1 - Hat-trick 1)

HEMEL HEMPSTEAD TOWN

Chairman: David Boggins

Secretary: Dean Chance **(T)** 07858 990 550 **(E)** dean.chance@ntlworld.com

Additional Committee Members: Chris Brooks, Brendan Glynn, Laurie McParland, Mick Dorer, Diane Dorer, Mark Slater, Andy Smith, Bev Darvill, John Adams.

Manager: Colin Payne

Programme Editor: Tony Conway **(E)** tonyconway@yahoo.com

Club Factfile

Founded: 1885 **Nickname:** The Tudors

Previous Names: Hemel Hempstead FC

Previous Leagues: Spartan 1922-52, Delphian 1952-63, Athenian 1963-77, Isthmian 1977-2004

Club Colours (change): Red and white quarters/red/red (Claret and blue quarters/claret/claret)

Ground: Vauxhall Road, Adeyfield Road, Hemel Hempstead HP2 4HW **(T)** 01442 259 777

Capacity: 3,152 **Seats:** 300 **Covered:** 900 **Clubhouse:** Yes **Shop:** Yes

Previous Grounds: Crabtree Lane

Simple Directions

Leave M1 at Junction 8 - follow dual carriageway over two roundabouts. Get into outside lane and after 100 yards turn right. Follow road to mini-roundabout turn left, next large roundabout take third exit into ground car park.

Record Attendance: 3,500 v Tooting & Mitcham - Amateur Cup 1962 (Crabtree Lane)

Record Victory: Not known

Record Defeat: Not known

Record Goalscorer: Dai Price

Record Appearances: John Wallace - 1012

Additional Records:

Senior Honours: Isthmian League Division 3 1998-99. Herts Senior Cup x7. Herts Charity Cup x6.

10 YEAR RECORD

00-01	01-02	02-03	03-04	04-05	05-06	06-07	07-08	08-09	09-10
Isth2 6	Isth2 10	Isth1N 3	Isth1N 6	SthP 19	SthW 4	SthP 5	SthP 7	SthP 5	SthP 20

HEMEL HEMPSTEAD TOWN

No.	Date	Comp	H/A	Opponents	Att:	Result	Goalscorers	Pos
1	Aug 15	Zamaretto P.	A	Halesowen Town	96	L 0 - 1		17
2	18		H	Oxford City	230	W 2 - 1	Doyle 11 Peagram 22	12
3	22		H	Merthyr Tydfil	259	W 3 - 1	Hillard 12 (pen) 43 (pen) Webb 75	7
4	25		A	Cheltenham Town	416	L 1 - 4	Gilbert 72	10
5	29		H	Brackley Town	211	D 1 - 1	Hillard 17	12
6	31		A	Bedford Town	362	L 0 - 5		
7	Sept 5		H	Stourbridge	238	D 2 - 2	Bernard 12 Higgins 89	14
8	**12**	**F.A.C. 1Q**	**H**	**Slough Town**	**395**	**D 1 - 1**	**Hillard 78**	
9	**15**	**F.A.C. 1Qr**	**A**	**Slough Town**	**249**	**L 1 - 2**	**McEntegart 48**	
10	19		A	Nuneaton Town	815	L 1 - 3	Hillard 21	
11	Oct 4		H	Hednesford Town	249	D 2 - 2	Black 72 Blake 90	14
12	7		A	Swindon Supermarine	139	L 0 - 1		
13	10		A	Didcot Town	172	L 1 - 2	Williams 57 (og)	
14	**17**	**F.A.T 1Q**	**H**	**Farnborough**	**316**	**L 0 - 1**		
15	24		H	Tiverton Town	178	L 0 - 2		19
16	31		H	Swindon Supermarine	180	W 3 - 1	Blake 25 Akers 31 86	
17	Nov 7		A	Clevedon Town	120	L 0 - 1		17
18	21		H	Rugby Town	230	W 1 - 0	Black 85	
19	Dec 5		H	Banbury United	193	L 2 - 3	Black 4 39	18
20	7		A	Cambridge City	264	D 1 - 1	Hatch 30	
21	12		H	Leamington	270	L 0 - 2		21
22	15		H	Bashley	123	L 0 - 1		
23	26		H	Bedford Town	227	W 5 - 1	Black 2 Ackers 26 EAMES 3 (36 48 58)	18
24	Jan 1		A	Farnborough Town	1089	L 0 - 3		
25	23		H	Nuneaton Town	348	L 1 - 3	Hicks 4	20
26	26		A	Brackley Town	132	L 0 - 2		
27	Feb 6		H	Clevedon Town	182	D 1 - 1	Loxton 73	21
28	9		A	Truro City	247	L 1 - 3	Granville 38	
29	13		A	Bashley	247	L 0 - 3		21
30	16		A	Rugby Town	128	D 2 - 2	Charge 56 McEntegart 67	
31	20		H	Halesowen Town	223	L 3 - 5	Charge 7 Brennan 16 Robson 62	21
32	27		A	Merthyr Tydfil	268	W 2 - 1	Black 75 Hart 84	19
33	Mar 6		H	Chippenham Town	242	L 0 - 1		19
34	13		A	Hednesford Town	345	L 3 - 4	Brennan 9 Black 44 Akers 85	
35	20		H	Didcot Town	188	L 1 - 2	Black 44	21
36	27		A	Tiverton Town	201	D 0 - 0		21
37	April 3		A	Evesham United	112	W 2 - 0	Vemazza 78 Blake 85	
38	5		H	Farnborough	415	D 1 - 1	Judge 62	20
39	7		A	Oxford City	128	D 2 - 2	Berazza 63 Fisher 86	
40	10		A	Banbury United	292	D 1 - 1	Judge 69	20
41	17		H	Truro City	253	L 0 - 2		20
42	20		H	Evesham United	163	W 2 - 0	Judge 11 44 (pen)	
43	22		H	Cambridge City	302	L 2 - 3	Kralisse 9 (og) Roache 85	
44	24		A	Leamington	556	L 1 - 3	Blake 88	20
					Goals	52 81		

Home Attendances:	
Highest:	415 v Farnborough
Lowest:	123 v Bashley
Average (08-09):	230 (282)
Top Goalscorer:	Hillard - 5 (League 4, FAC 1)

LEAMINGTON

Chairman: Jim Scott
Secretary: Richard Edy (T) 07784 718 489
(E) matchsecretary@leamingtonfc.co.uk
Additional Committee Members: Jim Scott, Shaun Brady, Nigel Hodgkins, Nic Sproul, Russell Davis, Graham Moody
Manager: Paul Holleran
Programme Editor: Sally Ellis (E) programme@leamingtonfc.co.uk

(Back row left to right) Richard Beale (coach), Dave Ward (sports therapist), Alex Cowley, Scott Lycett, Lee Downes, Richard Batchelor, Liam Daly, Tony Breeden, Guy Sanders, Matt Lewis, Craig Wilding, Danny Edwards, Luke Corbett, Lee Williams (assistant manager). (Front row Left to right) Darren Stapleton, James Husband, Michael Tuohy, Marcus Jackson, Paul Holleran (manager), Peter Faulds, Chris Murphy, Grant Roscorla, Ron Ainsworth (kit man)

Club Factfile

Founded: 1892 **Nickname:** The Brakes
Previous Names: Leamington Town 1892-1937, Lockheed Borg & Beck 1944-46 , Lockheed Leamington 1946-73, AP Leamington 1973-88
Previous Leagues: Birmingham Combination, Birmingham & District, West Midlands Regional, Midland Counties, Southern, Midland Combination, Midland Alliance
Club Colours (change): Gold and black/black with gold trim/black (Blue with white trim/blue with white trim/blue)

Ground: New Windmill Ground, Harbury Lane, Whitmarsh, Leamington CV33 9JR **(T)** 01926 430 406
Capacity: 5,000 **Seats:** 120 **Covered:** 720 **Clubhouse:** Yes **Shop:** Yes
Previous Grounds: Old Windmill Ground
Simple Directions
From West and North – M40 Southbound – Exit J14 and take A452 towards Leamington. Ahead at 1st island. Next island take 2nd exit A452 (Europa Way). Next island take 4th exit (Harbury Lane) signposted Harbury and Bishops Tachbrook. Next island take 3rd exit (Harbury Lane). At traffic lights continue straight ahead Harbury Lane. Ground is 1.5 miles on left.
From South – M40 northbound – Exit J13. Turn right onto A452 towards Leamington. At 1st island take 3rd exit A452 (Europa Way) and follow as above (Europa Way onwards).

Record Attendance: 1,380 v Retford United - 17/02/2007
Record Victory: Not known
Record Defeat: Not known
Record Goalscorer: Josh Blake - 166
Record Appearances: Josh Blake - 314
Additional Records:

Senior Honours: Birmingham & District 1961-62. West Midlands Regional 1962-63. Midland Counties 1964-65.
Southern League 1982-83, Division 1 Midlands 2008-09.
Midland Combination Division 2 2000-01, Premier Division 2004-05. Midland Alliance 2006-07, League cup 2005-06.

10 YEAR RECORD

00-01	01-02	02-03	03-04	04-05	05-06	06-07	07-08	08-09	09-10
MCm2 1	MCm1 2	MCmP 3	MCmP 2	MCmP 1	MidAl 5	MidAl 1	SthM 2	SthM 1	SthP 10

LEAMINGTON

No.	Date	Comp	H/A	Opponents	Att:	Result	Goalscorers	Pos
1	Aug 15	Zamaretto P.	A	Farnborough	1009	L 1 - 3	Bellingham 30	20
2	18		H	Evesham United	717	W 4 - 1	Bellingham 36 Reynolds 42 Corbett 56 86	8
3	22		H	Banbury United	766	D 3 - 3	Bellingham 15 67 Reynolds 69	10
4	25		A	Bedford Town	375	W 2 - 0	Reynolds 3 Husband 44	5
5	29		H	Chippenham Town	655	D 4 - 4	Lamb 16 (og) Corbett 24 Tuohy 44 Sanders 68	7
6	31		A	Rugby Town	688	W 4 - 1	Bellingham 31 80 Jackson 41 Husband 90	
7	Sept 5		H	Oxford City	721	L 1 - 2	Husband 90	9
8	**12**	**F.A.C 1Q**	**H**	**Market Drayton**	**520**	**L 0 - 2**		
9	19		A	Swindon Supermarine	281	W 3 - 2	BELLINGHAM 3 (44 61 80)	7
10	26		A	Hednesford Town	475	L 2 - 4	Bellingham 45 58 (pen)	9
11	Oct 4		H	Clevedon Town	564	L 0 - 1		9
12	10		A	Halesowen Town	606	L 0 - 3		10
13	**17**	**F.A.T 1Q**	**H**	**Stourbridge**	**615**	**L 1 - 2**	**Bellingham 60**	
14	24		H	Brackley Town	651	W 2 - 1	Corbett 18 Bellingham 20	10
15	31		H	Didcot Town	551	L 3 - 5	BELLINGHAM 3 (18 52 62)	10
16	Nov 7		H	Truro City	640	L 1 - 3	Bellingham 48	10
17	15		A	Cambridge City	378	D 2 - 2	Bellingham 31 Corbett 39	10
18	28		H	Bashley	527	L 0 - 1		12
19	Dec 5		A	Tiverton Town	345	W 3 - 2	Corbett 45 80 (pen) Bellingham 73	12
20	12		A	Hemel Hempstead	270	W 2 - 0	Bellingham 4 43	11
21	Jan 23		H	Swindon Supermarine	565	W 3 - 1	Bellingham 13 Sanders 44 Corbett 90	9
22	26		A	Chippenham Town	304	L 2 - 4	Sanders 62 Bellingham 86	
23	30		A	Oxford City	411	D 1 - 1	Corbett 59	9
24	Feb 2		H	Rugby Town	530	W 2 - 1	Bellingham 29 Corbett 68	
25	6		A	Truro City	430	D 2 - 2	Bellingham 50 Murphy 80	
26	13		H	Cambridge City	575	W 1 - 0	Murphy 89	8
27	16		H	Merthyr Tydfil	419	W 5 - 3	Knight 11 33 Corbett 43 70 Lewis 85	
28	20		H	Farnborough	870	L 2 - 3	Corbett 67 Wormall 80 (og)	7
29	24		A	Evesham United	192	W 1 - 0	Sanders 76	
30	27		A	Banbury United	684	W 2 - 1	Sanders 39 Batchelor 58	6
31	Mar 2		H	Stourbridge	454	W 2 - 1	McPike 53 Husband 69	
32	6		H	Bedford Town	814	W 2 - 0	Batchelor 42 Lewis 62	4
33	9		H	Hednesford Town	551	L 1 - 3	Lycett 80	
34	13		A	Clevedon Town	315	W 3 - 1	Corbett 26 Murphy 31 Faulds 87	
35	16		A	Marthyr Tydfil	269	W 3 - 2	Faulds 48 Corbett 55 (pen) 59 (pen)	
36	20		H	Halesowen Town	734	D 2 - 2	Bellingham 48 60	4
37	27		A	Brackley Town	512	L 0 - 1		5
38	30		A	Didcot Town	245	L 2 - 4	Corbett 25 40 (pen)	
39	April 3		A	Stourbridge	549	L 1 - 2	McPike 54	8
40	5		H	Nuneaton Town	1251	L 0 - 2		10
41	10		H	Tiverton Town	453	W 5 - 0	LEWIS 3 (14 21 68) Sanders 38 McPike 73	9
42	15		A	Nuneaton Town	938	D 1 - 1	Bellingham 10	
43	17		A	Bashley	482	D 1 - 1	Corbett 57	10
44	24		H	Hemel Hempstead	558	W 3 - 1	Corbett 13 Tuohy 69 Bellingham 88	10
					Goals	85 79		

Home Attendances:	
Highest:	1251 v Nuneaton Town
Lowest:	419 v Merthyr Tydfil
Average:	575
Top Goalscorer:	Bellingham - 29 (League 28, FAT 1, Hat-trick 1)

OXFORD CITY

Chairman: Brian Cox
Secretary: John Shepherd (T) 07748 628 911 (E) shepoxf@tiscali.co.uk
Additional Committee Members: Paul Cotterell, Colin Taylor, John Beech, Tina Cotterell, Roy Haley, Claire Hutchins, John Maskell, Ian Rundle, David Scott, Hugh Simpson, Paul Townsend, Richard Lawrence, Andy Cox, Tony Rogers, Peter Burden, Ashby Hope.
Manager: Mike Ford
Programme Editor: Colin Taylor (E) ctoxford@btinternet.com

Unfortunately an up-to-date photograph was not available at the time of going to press

Club Factfile

Founded: 1882 **Nickname:** City
Previous Names: Not known
Previous Leagues: Isthmian 1907-88, 94-2005, South Midlands 1990-93, Spartan South Midlands 2005-06

Club Colours (change): Blue and white hoops/blue/blue (All yellow)

Ground: Court Place Farm, Marsh Lane, Marston, Oxford OX3 0NQ (T) 01865 744 493
Capacity: 3,000 **Seats:** 300 **Covered:** 400 **Clubhouse:** Yes **Shop:** Yes
Previous Grounds: The White House 1882-1988, Cuttleslowe Park 1990-91, Pressed Steel 1991-93
Simple Directions
Ground lies off A40 ring road, northern by-pass. Follow signs for J.R. Hospital in yellow and small green signs to Court Place Farm Stadium.

Record Attendance: 9,500 v Leytonstone - FA Amateur Cup - 1950
Record Victory: Not known
Record Defeat: Not known
Record Goalscorer: John Woodley
Record Appearances: John Woodley
Additional Records: Paid £3,000 to Woking for S Adams
Received £15,000 from Yeovil Town for Howard Forinton

Senior Honours: FA Amateur Cup 1905-06. Oxford Senior Cup x3
Spartan South Midlands League Premier Division 2005-06.

10 YEAR RECORD

00-01	01-02	02-03	03-04	04-05	05-06	06-07	07-08	08-09	09-10
Isth1 10	Isth1 10	Isth1N 15	Isth1N 19	SthW 21	SSM P 1	SthW 12	SthW 4	SthP 6	SthP 13

OXFORD CITY

No.	Date	Comp	H/A	Opponents	Att:	Result	Goalscorers	Pos
1	Agu 15	Zamaretto P.	H	Cambridge City	327	L 0 - 1		18
2	18		A	Hemel Hempstead	230	L 1 - 2	Bell 31	19
3	22		A	Nuneaton Town	765	L 1 - 3	Malone 83	21
4	25		H	Rugby Town	276	W 3 - 0	Bell 12 35 Baird 27	15
5	29		A	Banbury United	318	D 1 - 1	Steele 5	16
6	31		H	Didcot Town	377	D 1 - 1	Steele 5	
7	Sept 5		A	Leamington	721	W 2 - 1	Pond 50 Steele 54	12
8	**12**	**F.A.C. 1Q**	**H**	**Kidlington**	**320**	**W 4 - 2**	**BAIRD 3 (33 76 78) Brooks 48**	
9	19		H	Tiverton Town	201	W 1 - 0	Steele 87	11
10	**26**	**F.A.C. 2Q**	**A**	**VT FC**	**234**	**W 1 - 0**	**Janes 58**	
11	Oct 4		H	Bedford Town	292	W 4 - 1	STEELE 4 (24 29 41 58)	8
12	6		A	Evesham United	119	D 0 - 0		9
13	**10**	**F.A.C. 3Q**	**H**	**Cirencester Town**	**311**	**W 2 - 0**	**Steele 18 72**	
14	**17**	**F.A.T 1Q**	**A**	**Chesham United**	**306**	**D 2 - 2**	**Steele 10 Pond 76**	
15	**20**	**F.A.T. 1Qr**	**H**	**Chesham United**	**213**	**W 2 - 0**	**Brooks 45 Gunn 65**	
16	**24**	**F.A.C 4Q**	**H**	**Bury Town**	**580**	**W 2 - 1**	**Janes 70 Gunn 89**	
17	**31**	**F.A.T 2Q**	**A**	**Arlesey Town**	**170**	**L 1 - 2**	**Baird 9**	
18	**Nov 8**	**F.A.C 1**	**A**	**Burton Albion**	**2207**	**L 2 - 3**	**Alexis 6 Brooks 55**	
19	14		H	Chippenham Town	313	D 0 - 0		12
20	17		H	Swindon Supermarine	231	W 2 - 1	Brooks 6 Bell 74	
21	21		A	Hednesford Town	230	L 2 - 4	Malone 50 Baird 82	
22	28		H	Merthyr Tydfil	243	D 2 - 2	Malone 7 Gunn 74	10
23	Dec 5		A	Brackley Town	268	W 2 - 1	Bell 38 Brookes 82	9
24	8		H	Clevedon Town	174	L 1 - 2	Douglas 46	
25	12		A	Stourbridge	277	W 2 - 0	Lyon 66 Douglas 71	
26	16		A	Farnborough	407	L 1 - 2	Brookes 72	8
27	26		A	Didcot Town	511	D 4 - 4	Douglas 2 Janes 36 Malone 80 Steele 88	
28	Jan 1		H	Bashley	349	D 1 - 1	Savage 12 (pen)	
29	19		H	Hednesford Town	142	W 2 - 0	Steele 24 65	
30	23		A	Tiverton Town	280	L 0 - 1		7
31	30		H	Leamington	411	D 1 - 1	Steele 78	7
32	Feb 6		H	Farnborough	376	D 1 - 1	Steele 54	8
33	13		A	Chippenham Town	374	L 0 - 2		10
34	20		A	Cambridge City	317	L 0 - 2		13
35	Mar 6		A	Rugby Town	243	L 0 - 4		13
36	9		H	Evesham United	106	W 3 - 0	Steele 36 Harding 40 Brookes 70	
37	13		A	Bedford Town	226	D 1 - 1	Steele 64	
38	20		H	Truro City	254	D 2 - 2	Sandy 3 Steele 16	13
39	23		A	Halesowen Town	247	D 3 - 3	Steele 19 Harding 30 Sandy 80	
40	27		A	Swindon Supermarine	183	W 4 - 2	Savage 67 (pen) 75 (pen) Douglas 76 Sandy 90	13
41	April 3		H	Halesowen Town	288	D 2 - 2	Steele 17 Harding 40	13
42	5		A	Bashley	348	L 2 - 3	Bell 70 Sandy 88	13
43	7		H	Hemel Hempstead	128	D 2 - 2	Savage 76 (pen) Douglas 87	
44	10		H	Brackley Town	278	L 2 - 3	Savage 34 Green 68 (og)	13
45	13		A	Truro City	320	W 1 - 0	Elliott 49	
46	15		H	Banbury United	258	D 1 - 1	Sandy 81	
47	17		A	Merthyr Tydfil	306	W 3 - 2	STEELE 3 (55 79 81)	13
48	20		A	Clevedon Town	80	W 2 - 1	Sandy 60 74	
49	22		H	Nuneaton Town	315	L 1 - 4	Savage 88 (pen)	
50	24		H	Stourbridge	278	L 1 - 2	Sandy 70	13
					Goals	81 76		

Home Attendances:	
Highest:	411 v Leamington
Lowest:	106 v Evesham United
Average (08-09):	278 (274)
Top Goalscorer:	Steele - 25 (League 22, FAC 2, FAT 1 - Hat-trick 2)

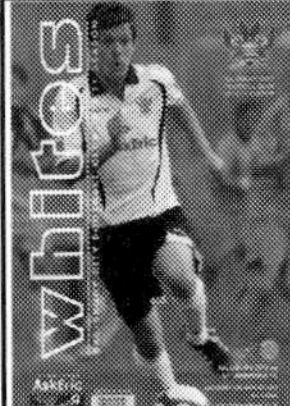

SALISBURY CITY

Chairman: W. Harrison-Allen

Secretary: Alec Hayter (T) 07884 477 168
(E) alechayter@onetel.com or

Additional Committee Members:
Jeff Hooper, Chris Bramall

Manager: TBA

Programme Editor: Paul Osborn (E) info@sarumgraphics.co.uk

Club Factfile

Founded: 1947 **Nickname:** The Whites

Previous Names: Salisbury F.C.

Previous Leagues: Western 1947-68, Southern 1968-2004, Isthmian 2004-05, Conference 2005-10

Club Colours (change): White/black/white (Orange/black/orange)

Ground: Raymond McEnhill Stadium, Partridge Way, Old Sarum SP4 6PU (T) 01722 776 655

Capacity: 5,000 **Seats:** 500 **Covered:** 2,247 **Clubhouse:** Yes **Shop:** Yes

Previous Grounds: Victoria Park

Simple Directions
Situated A345 Salisbury/Amesbury Road.
From North/East/West: Leave A303 at Countess roundabout at Amesbury and take A345 towards Salisbury until Park and Ride roundabout from where the ground is signposted.
From South: Proceed to A345 and then follow directions to Amesbury until Park and Ride roundabout from where the ground is signposted.

Record Attendance: 3,100 v Nottingham Forest - FA Cup 2nd Round 2006
Record Victory: 11-1 v RAF Colerne (H) - Western League Division 2 1948
Record Defeat: 0-7 v Minehead (A) - Southern League 1975
Record Goalscorer: Royston Watts - 180 (1959-65)
Record Appearances: Barry Fitch - 713 (1963-75)
Additional Records: Paid £15,000 to Bashley for Craig Davis
Received £20,000 from Forest Green Rovers for Adrian Randall

Senior Honours: Western League 1957-58, 60-61. Southern League Premier Division 1994-95, 2005-06.

10 YEAR RECORD

00-01	01-02	02-03	03-04	04-05	05-06	06-07	07-08	08-09	09-10
SthP 13	SthP 22	SthE 4	SthE 6	Isth P 12	SthP 1	Conf S 2	Conf 12	Conf 16	Conf 12

SALISBURY CITY

No.	Date	Comp	H/A	Opponents	Att:	Result	Goalscorers	Pos
1	8/8/09	BSP	A	Rushden & Diamonds	1272	W 2-0	Og (Stuart) 47, Flood 90	5
2	11/8/09	BSP	H	Kidderminster Harriers	1034	W 1-0	Webb 52	1
3	15/8/09	BSP	H	Mansfield Town	1147	L 0-1		6
4	18/8/09	BSP	A	AFC Wimbledon	3591	L 0-4		11
5	22/8/09	BSP	A	Histon	684	L 0-2		16
6	29/8/09	BSP	H	Eastbourne Borough	746	D 1-1	Clarke 90	18
7	31/8/09	BSP	A	Hayes & Yeading United	429	W 4-3	Tubbs 3 (44, 49, 84), Flood 51	13
8	5/9/09	BSP	H	Luton Town	2044	D 1-1	Tubbs 43	13
9	8/9/09	BSP	H	Grays Athletic	765	W 2-0	Flood 25, Tubbs 62	10
10	12/9/09	BSP	A	Gateshead	478	L 1-2	Tubbs 54	12
11	19/9/09	BSP	A	Tamworth	1003	L 0-2		22
12	26/9/09	BSP	H	Barrow	876	W 3-0	Tubbs 2 (13, 75), Flood 39	18
13	29/9/09	BSP	A	Ebbsfleet United	792	W 2-1	Flood 88, Sinclair 90	18
14	3/10/09	BSP	A	Wrexham	2556	W 2-1	Anderson 9, Tubbs 18	16
15	10/10/09	BSP	H	York City	1266	W 1-0	Tubbs pen 4	15
16	17/10/09	BSP	A	Stevenage Borough	2009	L 1-3	Flood 53	17
17	31/10/09	BSP	H	Gateshead	1050	L 0-1		17
18	14/11/09	BSP	A	Eastbourne Borough	756	W 1-0	Flood 90	17
19	21/11/09	BSP	H	Rushden & Diamonds	840	L 1-3	Clarke 90	18
20	24/11/09	BSP	A	Crawley Town	603	L 0-2		18
21	28/11/09	BSP	H	Stevenage Borough	851	L 0-1		19
22	1/12/09	BSP	H	AFC Wimbledon	1157	L 0-2		19
23	5/12/09	BSP	A	Kettering Town	1098	W 2-1	Tubbs 36, Anderson 48	18
24	26/12/09	BSP	A	Forest Green Rovers	1079	L 1-3	Tubbs 83	18
25	28/12/09	BSP	H	Oxford United	2677	D 1-1	Gray 89	18
26	23/1/10	BSP	H	Histon	758	W 3-0	Tubbs 2 (37, 75), Adelsbury 63	17
27	6/2/10	BSP	A	Altrincham	777	L 0-5		17
28	13/2/10	BSP	A	Grays Athletic	232	W 2-0	Tubbs 28, Clohessy 90	17
29	16/2/10	BSP	H	Tamworth	586	W 1-0	Cox 2	16
30	27/2/10	BSP	H	Wrexham	948	D 1-1	Tubbs pen 89	16
31	2/3/10	BSP	H	Crawley Town	581	D 2-2	Tubbs 2 (16, 35)	16
32	6/3/10	BSP	A	Mansfield Town	2842	L 2-4	Connolly 39, Adelsbury 90	17
33	9/3/10	BSP	A	York City	1867	W 2-1	Connolly 54, Clarke 65	15
34	16/3/10	BSP	A	Cambridge United	2028	L 1-3	Tubbs 6	16
35	23/3/10	BSP	H	Forest Green Rovers	665	L 1-3	Turley 57	18
36	27/3/10	BSP	A	Kidderminster Harriers	1201	W 1-0	Tubbs 24	16
37	30/3/10	BSP	A	Luton Town	6892	L 0-4		17
38	2/4/10	BSP	H	Ebbsfleet United	1088	W 3-1	Martin 7, Giles 66, Adelsbury 73	16
39	5/4/10	BSP	A	Oxford United	5741	L 0-1		17
40	10/4/10	BSP	H	Cambridge United	1245	W 2-1	Tubbs 2 (60, pen 87)	16
41	13/4/10	BSP	H	Hayes & Yeading United	755	W 3-1	Tubbs 67, Reid 78, Shephard 87	14
42	17/4/10	BSP	A	Barrow	1173	W 1-0	Reid 81	14
43	20/4/10	BSP	H	Altrincham	671	W 4-1	Clohessy 49, Reid 51, Tubbs 2 (52, 57)	13
44	24/4/10	BSP	H	Kettering Town	1123	W 2-0	Shephard 19, Tubbs 85	12
	Chester	**record**	**........................**	**...expunged 08/03**				
12	22/9/09	BSP	H	Chester City	838	D 1-1	Clohessy 82	22
27	19/1/10	BSP	A	Chester City	425	W 1-0	Tubbs pen 86	18
	Cups							
1	24/10/09	FAC 4Q	A	Farnborough	1247	D 0-0		
2	27/10/09	FAC 4QR	H	Farnborough	1200	W 4-2	Tubbs 3 (7, pen 46, 54), Flood 64	
3	7/11/09	FAC 1	A	Accrington Stanley	1379	L 1-2	Tubbs 66	
4	12/12/09	FAT 1	A	Weymouth	642	W 1-0	Flood 90	
5	30/1/10	FAT 2	H	Maidstone United	746	W 2-0	Gray 1, Tubbs 51	
6	2/2/10	FAT 3	A	Cambridge United	1237	D 0-0		
7	9/2/10	FAT 3R	H	Cambridge United	592	W 2-1	Tubbs 18, Sinclair 51	
8	20/2/10	FAT 4	H	Tamworth	1012	W 2-1	Adelsbury 1, Sinclair 35	
9	13/3/10	FAT SF 1	H	Barrow	1782	L 0-1		
10	20/3/10	FAT SF 2	A	Barrow	3070	L 1-2	(Clarke 56) L 1-3 agg)	

Home Attendances:	
Highest:	2677 v Oxford United
Lowest:	581 v Crawley Town
Average (08-09):	912 (1144)
Top Goalscorer:	Tubbs - 32 (26 League, 6 Cup) in 52 appearances - 62% strike rate

STOURBRIDGE

Chairman: Ian Pilkington
Secretary: Nick Pratt **(T)** 07824 328 004
(E) sfcsec@hotmail.co.uk
Additional Committee Members: Andy Pountney, Neil Smith, Nick Pratt, Nigel Gregg, Sharon Hyde, Hugh Clark, Jonathan Martin, Andy Bullingham, Stephen Hyde.
Manager: Gary Hackett
Programme Editor: Nigel Gregg **(E)** ng004f7624@blueyonder.co.uk

Club Factfile

Founded: 1876 **Nickname:** The Glassboys
Previous Names: Not known
Previous Leagues: West Midlands (Birmingham League) 1892-1939, 54-71, Birmingham Combination 1945-53, Southern 1971-2000

Club Colours (change): Red and white stripes/red/red (Yellow/green/yellow)

Ground: War Memorial Athletic Ground, High Street, Amblecote DY8 4HN **(T)** 01384 394 040
Capacity: 2,000 **Seats:** 250 **Covered:** 750 **Clubhouse:** Yes **Shop:** Yes
Previous Grounds: Not known
Simple Directions
From Stourbridge Ring-Road follow signs A491 to Wolverhampton. The ground is on the left within 300 yards immediately beyond the third traffic lights and opposite the Royal Oak public house.

Record Attendance: 5,726 v Cardiff City - Welsh Cup Final 1st Leg 1974
Record Victory: Not known
Record Defeat: Not known
Record Goalscorer: Ron Page - 269
Record Appearances: Ron Page - 427
Additional Records: Received £20,000 from Lincoln City for Tony Cunningham 1979

Senior Honours: Southern League Division 1 North 1973-74, Midland Division 90-91, League Cup 92-93. Midland Alliance 2001-02, 02-03. Worcestershire Junior Cup 1927-28. Hereford Senior Cup 1954-55. Birmingham Senior Cup x3. Worcestershire Senior Cup x9

10 YEAR RECORD

00-01		01-02		02-03		03-04		04-05		05-06		06-07		07-08		08-09		09-10	
MidAl	5	MidAl	1	MidAl	1	MidAl	9	MidAl	8	MidAl	2	SthM	7	SthM	3	SthP	16	SthP	9

STOURBRIDGE

No.	Date	Comp	H/A	Opponents	Att:	Result	Goalscorers	Pos
1	Aug 15	Zamaretto P.	A	Banbury United	269	D 3 - 3	Canavan 49 69 Evans 73	11
2	18		H	Hednesford Town	268	D 1 - 1	Bennett 54	13
3	22		H	Bedford Town	178	W 2 - 0	Billingham 69 Drake 75	9
4	25		A	Clevedon Town	165	L 1 - 4	Rowe 23	12
5	29		A	Didcot Town	225	W 1 - 0	Rowe 62	10
6	31		H	Halesowen Town	656	L 1 - 4	Evans 3	
7	Sept 5		A	Hemel Hempstead	238	D 2 - 2	Dyson 10 Evans 45	10
8	**12**	**F.A.C 1Q**	**A**	**Bromsgrove Rovers**	**485**	**D 1 - 1**	**Collins 48**	
9	**15**	**F.A.C. 1Qr**	**H**	**Bromsgrove Rovers**	**255**	**W 3 - 1**	**Rowe 63 66 Bennett 67**	
10	19		H	Bashley	211	D 2 - 2	Jarrett 45 Rowe 90	12
11	**26**	**F.A.C 2Q**	**A**	**Evesham United**	**262**	**W 1 - 0**	**Rowe 20**	
12	Oct 4		H	Evesham United	242	D 0 - 0		13
13	7		A	Tiverton Town	190	D 2 - 2	Rowe 16 Evans 83	13
14	**10**	**F.A.C.3Q**	**H**	**Hucknall Town**	**384**	**D 0 - 0**		
15	**13**	**F.A.C. 3Qr**	**A**	**Hucknall Town**	**324**	**W 6 - 1**	**EVANS 3 (44 65 73) Rowe 45 Smith 71 Dovey 77**	
16	**17**	**F.A.T 1Q**	**A**	**Leamington**	**615**	**W 2 - 1**	**Drake 12 Evans 40**	
17	20		A	Brackley Town	204	L 2 - 3	Broadhurst 10 Evans 26	15
18	**24**	**F.A.C. 4Q**	**A**	**Buxton**	**793**	**W 4 - 0**	**Rowe 29 38 Evans 44 74**	
19	**31**	**F.A.T 2Q**	**A**	**Buxton**	**262**	**W 1 - 0**	**Drake 74**	
20	Nov 14		H	Swindon Supermarine	235	D 0 - 0		15
21	**21**	**F.A.T 3Q**	**H**	**Southport**	**319**	**D 0 - 0**		
22	**24**	**F.A.T 3Qr**	**A**	**Southport**	**268**	**L 2 - 4**	**Canavan 20 Rowe 60**	
23	28		A	Rugby Town	208	W 2 - 1	Billingham 44 Dovey 90	
24	Dec 1		A	Chippenham Town	266	D 2 - 2	Drake 40 Bennett 76	
25	5		H	Truro City	247	W 7 - 2	Rock 4 ROWE 3 (31 41 76) Dovey 51 86 Billingham 62	
26	8		A	Nuneaton Town	708	D 0 - 0		
27	12		H	Oxford City	277	L 0 - 2		13
28	26		A	Halesowen Town	761	L 1 - 2	Broadhurst 45	13
29	Jan 20		H	Merthyr Tydfil	193	W 2 - 0	Keddle 25 (og) Rowe 44	
30	23		A	Bashley	274	D 4 - 4	Broadhurst 3 64 Rowe 56 74 (pen)	
31	26		A	Cambridge City	205	L 1 - 6	Rowe 64	15
32	Feb 2		H	Cambridge Cty	175	W 3 - 1	Billingham 13 Rock 74 Broadhurst 85	
33	6		H	Chippenham Town	286	W 1 - 0	Rowe 39 (pen)	10
34	13		A	SWindon Supermarine	159	D 2 - 2	Dovey 39 Billingham 70	11
35	20		H	Banbury United	226	W 2 - 1	Bennett 26 Broadhurst 90	9
36	Mar 2		A	Leamington	454	L 1 - 2	Billingham 52	
37	6		H	Clevedon Town	256	W 4 - 1	Bennett 3 Rowe 4 65 Billingham 68	11
38	9		H	Tiverton Town	179	W 2 - 1	Rowe 26 80	
39	11		A	Bedford Town	156	W 1 - 0	Cooper 82	
40	13		A	Evesham United	178	D 1 - 1	Rowe 19	9
41	20		H	Brackley Town	217	W 4 - 2	Rock 11 90 Bennett 54 Rowe 66	
42	23		H	Hemel Hempstead	148	W 2 - 0	Broadhurst 31 Jones 82	
43	27		A	Farnborough	675	W 2 - 1	Rowe 33 Drake 56	9
44	30		H	Nuneaton Town	382	L 1 - 2	Lloyd A 69	
45	April 3		H	Leamington	549	W 2 - 1	Dyson 6 Bennett 39	7
46	5		A	Merthyr Tydfil	302	L 1 - 2	Plinston 76	9
47	8		H	Didcot Town	187	W 1 - 0	Rowe 65	
48	10		A	Truro City	362	L 1 - 4	Plinston 81	
49	15		A	Hednesford Town	449	D 1 - 1	Drake 8	
50	17		H	Rugby Town	206	W 6 - 0	Drake 5 Canavan 25 46 Broadhurst 44 Dovey 72 84	9
51	20		H	Leamington	294	W 3 - 2	Rowe 11 Billingham 29 (pen) 90 (pen)	
52	24		A	Oxford City	278	W 3 - 1	Rock 51 Rowe 54 Bennett 84	
					Goals	100 73		

Home Attendances:	
Highest:	656 v Halesowen Town
Lowest:	148 v Hemel Hempstead
Average (08-09):	235 (251)
Top Goalscorer:	Rowe - 29 (League 22, FAC 6, FAT 1 - Hat-trick 2)

SWINDON SUPERMARINE

Chairman: TBA

Secretary: Judi Moore **(T)** 07785 970 954 **(E)** judimoore6@aol.com

Additional Committee Members: Steve Wheeler, Mark Carter, Keith Yeomans, Marcus Cook, Steve Nicholls, Dave Rideout, Graham Cutler, Steve Gunnett, Frieda Heather, Stuart Jackson, Martin Osman. Roy Heather.

Manager: Mark Collier

Programme Editor: Keith Yeomans **(E)** supermarinefc@aol.com

Club Factfile

Founded: 1992 **Nickname:** Marine

Previous Names: Club formed after the amalgamation of Swindon Athletic and Supermarine

Previous Leagues: Wiltshire, Hellenic > 2001

Club Colours (change): Blue and white/blue/blue (All red)

Ground: The Webbs Stadium, South Marston, Swindon SN3 4SY **(T)** 01793 828 778

Capacity: 3,000 **Seats:** 300 **Covered:** 300 **Clubhouse:** Yes **Shop:** Yes

Previous Grounds: Supermarine: Vickers Airfield > Mid 1960s

Simple Directions

From M5 Junction 11a, take the A417 to Cirencester, then A419 Swindon. At the A361 junction by Honda Factory take road to Highworth. After one mile Club is on 4th roundabout.

From M4 Junction 15, take A419 towards Swindon Cirencester, take A361, then as above .

From A420 Swindon take A419 to Cirencester, near Honda factory take A361, then as above.

Record Attendance: 1,550 v Aston Villa

Record Victory: Not known

Record Defeat: Not known

Record Goalscorer: Damon York - 136 (1990-98)

Record Appearances: Damon York - 314 (1990-98)

Additional Records: Paid £1,000 to Hungerford Town for Lee Hartson

Senior Honours: Hellenic League Premier Division 1997-98, 2000-01, Challenge Cup 97-97, 99-2000.

10 YEAR RECORD

00-01	01-02	02-03	03-04	04-05	05-06	06-07	07-08	08-09	09-10
Hel P 1	SthW 19	SthW 19	SthW 17	SthW 19	SthW 5	Sthsw 4	SthP 12	SthP 13	SthP 14

SWINDON SUPERMARINE

No.	Date	Comp	H/A	Opponents	Att:	Result	Goalscorers	Pos
1	Aug 15	Zamaretto P.	H	Rugby Town	171	W 5 - 1	McKay 37 Barnes M45 Harris 48 (pen) Griffin 50 Taylor 90	1
2	18		A	Bashley	245	L 0 - 3		9
3	22		A	Cambridge City	265	L 0 - 5		14
4	26		H	Truro City	253	L 0 - 4		
5	29		A	Halesowen Town	101	L 0 - 2		19
6	31		H	Banbury United	223	L 1 - 2	Barnes M 88	
7	Sept 5		A	Hednesford Town	309	D 0 - 0		19
8	**12**	**F.A.C 1Q**	**A**	**Brackley Town**	**180**	**L 0 - 1**		
9	19		H	Leamington	281	L 2 - 3	Griffin 41 Moss 51	20
10	Oct 4		A	Chippenham Town	524	W 1 - 0	Edenborough 12	17
11	7		H	Hemel Hempstead	139	W 1 - 0	Edenborough 25	
12	10		H	Brackley Town	148	L 1 - 7	Harris 66	16
13	**17**	**F.A.T 1Q**	**H**	**Fleet Town**	**107**	**L 2 - 4**	**Harris 8 Philpott 90**	
14	31		A	Hemel Hempstead	180	L 1 - 3	Harris 77	
15	Nov 7		H	Bedford Town	139	D 0 - 0		19
16	11		H	Nuneaton Town	193	L 2 - 4	Stanley 81 Henry 85	
17	14		A	Stourbridge	235	D 0 - 0		19
18	17		A	Oxford City	231	L 1 - 2	Hopper 52	
19	21		A	Brackley Town	192	W 2 - 1	Morris 48 72	
20	28		H	Farnborough	284	L 0 - 7		17
21	Dec 5		A	Evesham United	106	W 1 - 0	Hopper 83	16
22	9		H	Tiverton Town	127	W 2 - 1	Cook 2 Harris 90	
23	12		A	Merthyr Tydfil	306	L 0 - 1		15
24	Jan 23		A	Leamington	565	L 1 - 3	Lycett 8 (og)	16
25	Feb 13		H	Stourbridge	159	D 2 - 2	Edenborough 7 Stanley 50 (pen)	19
26	24		H	Bashley	111	D 3 - 3	Stanley 6 26 Hopper 47	
27	Mar 6		A	Truro City	407	D 0 - 0		21
28	11		A	Rugby Town	108	D 0 - 0		
29	13		H	Chippenham Town	289	D 1 - 1	Hopper 49	
30	16		A	ClevedonTown	103	W 6 - 2	Edenborough18 Hopper 24 71 Stanley 31 84 Cook 90	18
31	18		H	Cambridge City	105	D 1 - 1	Henry 65	
32	20		A	Nuneaton Town	738	L 0 - 1		17
33	22		A	Bedford Town	174	W 2 - 1	Stanley 35 49	
34	24		H	Didcot Town	181	D 1 - 1	Hopper 16	
35	27		H	Oxford City	183	L 2 - 4	Hopper 39 Stanley 44 (pen)	
36	April 3		H	Clevedon Town	161	W 3 - 2	HOPPER 3 (8 42 68)	
37	5		A	Didcot Town	218	W 2 - 0	Taylor 19 Hobbs 75	15
38	7		H	Hednesford Town	131	D 0 - 0		
39	10		H	Evesham United	143	D 1 - 1	Fitter 52	14
40	14		H	Halesowen Town	117	L 1 - 2	Edenborough 75	
41	17		A	Farnborough	1372	L 0 - 2		14
42	19		A	Tiverton Town	152	D 0 - 0		
43	21		A	Banbury United	131	L 1 - 3	Stanley 38	
44	24		H	Merthyr Tydfil	269	D 1 - 1	Henry 21	14
					Goals	50 81		

Home Attendances:	
Highest:	289 v Chippenham Town
Lowest:	105 v Cambridge City
Average (08-09):	181 (207)
Top Goalscorer:	Hopper - 11 (League 11)

TIVERTON TOWN

Chairman: David Graham

Secretary: Ramsey Findlay **(T)** 07761 261 990 **(E)** ramsayfindlay@hotmail.co.uk

Additional Committee Members:
David Wright, Kimm Smith, John Smith

Manager: Chris Vinnicombe

Programme Editor: Alan Reidy **(E)** alanreidy@hotmail.com

Archive photo

Club Factfile

Founded: 1920 **Nickname:** Tivvy

Previous Names: None

Previous Leagues: Devon and Exeter, Western

Club Colours (change): All yellow (Pink/black/black)

Ground: Ladysmead, Bolham Road, Tiverton, Devon EX16 6SG **(T)** 01884 252 397

Capacity: 3,500 **Seats:** 520 **Covered:** 2,300 **Clubhouse:** Yes **Shop:** Yes

Previous Grounds: None

Simple Directions
M5 Junction 27, follow A361 to Tiverton's second exit at roundabout, turning left. Continue for about 400 yards, crossing roundabout until reaching mini-roundabout. Carry on straight across. Ground is 200 yards on right.

Record Attendance: 3,000 v Leyton Orient - FA Cup 1st Round Proper 1994-95

Record Victory: 10-0 v Exmouth Town, Devon St Lukes Cup 16/02/1994

Record Defeat: 2-6 v Stafford Rangers (A) - Southern League 2001-02 & Heavitree United, Les Philips Cup 29/11/1997

Record Goalscorer: Phil Everett

Record Appearances: Not known

Additional Records:

Senior Honours: FA Vase 1997-98, 98-99. Western League x5. Southern League Cup 2006-07.
Devon Senior Cup 1955-56, 65-66. East Devon Senior Cup x7.

10 YEAR RECORD

00-01	01-02	02-03	03-04	04-05	05-06	06-07	07-08	08-09	09-10
SthW 2	SthP 6	SthP 4	SthP 15	SthP 8	SthP 12	SthP 15	SthP 17	SthP 12	SthP 19

TIVERTON TOWN

No.	Date	Comp	H/A	Opponents	Att:	Result	Goalscorers	Pos
1	Aug 15	Zamaretto P.	A	Hednesford Town	351	L 1 - 2	Morrissey 53 (pen)	16
2	19		H	Clevedon Town	321	D 0 - 0		
3	22		H	Evesham United	280	L 0 - 1		18
4	25		A	Merthyr Tydfil	376	D 1 - 1	Saunders 53	19
5	29		H	Rugby Town	290	W 3 - 1	Gardner 41 Griffiths 48 Morrissey 53	13
6	31		A	Truro City	902	L 0 - 2		
7	Sept 5		H	Farnborough	377	L 0 - 2		17
8	**12**	**F.A.C 1Q**	**A**	**Paulton Rovers**	**243**	**L 0 - 1**		
9	19		A	Oxford City	201	L 0 - 1		18
10	Oct 4		A	Cambridge City	366	D 1 - 1	A.Faux 5	18
11	7		H	Stourport	190	D 2 - 2	Morrissey 24 Cleverley 69	
12	10		H	Bashley	316	L 0 - 5		20
13	**17**	**F.A.T 1Q**	**H**	**Truro City**	**487**	**L 0 - 4**		
14	24		A	Hemel Hempstead	178	W 2 - 0	Saunders 35 Marshall 73	
15	Nov 7		A	Brackley Town	207	L 0 - 2		20
16	14		H	Didcot Town	268	L 1 - 2	Bushin 77	21
17	21		H	Banbury United	198	W 2 - 1	Bushin 7 83	20
18	28		A	Halesowen Town	322	D 1 - 1	Bushin 82	18
19	Dec 5		H	Leamington	345	L 2 - 3	Ford 28 Marshall 70	19
20	9		A	Swindon Spermarine	127	L 1 - 2	Malsom 45	
21	12		H	Bedford Town	252	W 2 - 1	Marshall 48 (pen) Bushin 58	17
22	Jan 23		H	Oxford City	280	W 1 - 0	Bushin 80	18
23	26		A	Banbury	160	W 1 - 0	Bushin 83	
24	30		A	Farnborough	747	L 1 - 2	Hatch 12	16
25	Feb 6		H	Brackley Town	533	D 1 - 1	Bushin 31	17
26	13		A	Didcot Town	171	D 1 - 1	Saunders 36	17
27	20		H	Hednesford Town	289	L 0 - 2		17
28	23		A	Clevedon Town	114	W 1 - 0	Morimer 85	
29	27		A	Evesham United	126	D 2 - 2	Saunders 84 Booth 90	14
30	Mar 6		H	Merthyr Tydfil	279	L 0 - 1		16
31	9		A	Stourbridge	179	L 1 - 2	Bushin 71	
32	13		H	Cambridge City	252	D 0 - 0		
33	16		A	Chippenham Town	387	L 2 - 4	Head 3 Allison 61	
34	20		A	Bashley	277	W 1 - 0	Saunders 58	15
35	24		H	Nuneaton Town	236	L 1 - 2	Booth 67	
36	27		H	Hemel Hempstead	201	D 0 - 0		16
37	April 3		A	Nuneaton Town	803	L 0 - 1		17
38	5		H	Chippenham Town	270	D 0 - 0		16
39	10		A	Leamington	453	L 0 - 5		17
40	13		A	Rugby Town	108	L 2 - 3	Head 70 Booth 88	
41	17		H	Halesowen Town	285	L 0 - 2		17
42	19		H	Swindon Supermarine	152	D 0 - 0		
43	21		H	Truro City	324	L 1 - 2	Bushin 41	
44	24		A	Bedford Town	406	L 0 - 2		19
					Goals	35 67		

Home Attendances:	
Highest:	533 v Brackley Town
Lowest:	152 v Swindon Supermarine
Average (08-09):	283 (351)
Top Goalscorer:	Bushin - 10 (League 10)

TRURO CITY

Chairman: Kevin Heaney
Secretary: Ian Rennie (T) 07881 498 916
(E) ian-rennie@musikfolk.com

Additional Committee Members:
Chris Webb

Manager: Lee Hodges
Programme Editor: Ian Rennie (E) ian-rennie@musikfolk.com

Unfortunately an up-to-date photograph was not available at the time of going to press

Club Factfile

Founded: 1889 **Nickname:** City
Previous Names: None
Previous Leagues: Cornwall County, Plymouth & District, South Western, Western

Club Colours (change): All white (All royal blue)

Ground: Treyew Road, Truro, Cornwall TR1 2TH (T) 01872 225 400 / 278 853
Capacity: **Seats:** 750 **Covered:** Yes **Clubhouse:** Yes **Shop:**
Previous Grounds: None

Simple Directions
On arriving at Exeter, leave the M5 at junction 31 and join the A30. Travel via Okehampton, Launceston, and Bodmin.. At the end of the dual carriageway (windmills on right hand side) take left hand turning signposted Truro. After approximately 7 miles turn right at traffic lights, travel downhill crossing over three roundabouts, following signs for Redruth. Approximately 500 metres after third roundabout signed 'Arch Hill', ground is situated on left hand side.

Record Attendance: 1,400 v Aldershot - FA Vase
Record Victory: Not known
Record Defeat: Not known
Record Goalscorer: Not known
Record Appearances: Not known
Additional Records:

Senior Honours: South Western League 1960-61, 69-70, 92-93, 95-96, 97-98. Western League Division 1 2006-07, Premier Division 07-08.
FA Vase 2006-07. Southern League Division 1 South & West 2008-09.
Cornwall Senior Cup x15

10 YEAR RECORD

00-01	01-02	02-03	03-04	04-05	05-06	06-07	07-08	08-09	09-10
SWest 14	SWest 17	SWest 16	SWest 15	SWest 6	SWest 2	West1 1	WestP 1	Sthsw 1	SthP 11

TRURO CITY

No.	Date	Comp	H/A	Opponents	Att:	Result	Goalscorers	Pos
1	Aug 15	Zamaretto P.	A	Bedford Town	417	W 2 - 0	Broad 58 Taylor 77	4
2	18		H	Merthyr Tydfil	600	W 3 - 1	Watkins 19 Afful 50 Broad 86	2
3	22		H	Farnborough	863	L 2 - 3	Gala 58 Watkins 87	
4	26		A	Swindon Supermarine	253	W 4 - 0	Afful 28 Broad 30 Watts 44 Watkins 69	2
5	29		A	Hednesford Town	359	W 3 - 2	Watkins 40 85 Afful 43	
6	31		H	Tiverton Town	902	W 2 - 0	McConnell 74 (pen) Watts 83	
7	Sept 5		A	Banbury United	352	D 0 - 0		2
8	**12**	**F.A.C 1Q**	**H**	**Bridport**	**463**	**D 1 - 1**	**Watts 71**	
9	**15**	**F.A.C. 1Qr**	**A**	**Bridport**	**335**	**W 7 - 0**	**Ashe 34 WATKINS 4 (39 59 71 87) Broad 57 Gala 65**	
10	19		H	Cambridge City	627	D 1 - 1	Taylor 5	2
11	**26**	**F.A.C. 2Q**	**A**	**Maidenhead United**	**313**	**W 5 - 2**	**Gala 12 Walker 2 Watts 42 Afful 51 Broad 53**	
12	Oct 4		A	Rugby Town	196	D 1 - 1	Afful 46	2
13	6		H	Chippenham Town	429	L 3 - 5	McConnell 36 (pen) Play 57 Watts 71	
14	**10**	**F.A.C. 3Q**	**H**	**Mangotsfield United**	**574**	**D 1 - 1**	**Yetton 90**	
15	**13**	**F.A.C.3Qr**	**A**	**Mangotsfield Town**	**529**	**D 1 - 1**	**Martin 68 Mangotsfield United won 4-3 on pens**	
16	**17**	**F.A.T 1Q**	**A**	**Tiverton Town**	**487**	**W 4 - 0**	**Pugh 27 Afful 45 85 Grant 90**	
17	**31**	**F.A.T 2Q**	**H**	**Thatcham Town**	**371**	**W 4 - 1**	**Taylor 15 Rea 20 (og) Yetton 29 75**	
18	Nov 7		A	Leamington	640	W 3 - 1	Taylor 2 Afful 8 McConnell 64 (pen)	5
19	14		H	Halesowen Town	429	L 1 - 2	Afful 70	6
20	17		A	Nuneaton Town	731	L 0 - 4		
21	**24**	**F.A.T 3Q**	**H**	**Gloucester City**	**217**	**W 1 - 0**	**Pugh 26**	**9**
22	Dec 5		A	Stourbridge	247	L 2 - 7	Ash 84 Yetton 88	11
23	8		H	Evesham United	238	L 1 - 2	Watkins 3	
24	**12**	**F.A.T 1**	**A**	**Chelmsford City**	**701**	**D 2 - 2**	**Watkins 2 Taylor 89**	
25	**15**	**F.A.T. 1r**	**H**	**Chelmsfrd City**	**322**	**L 0 - 1**		
26	Jan 1		H	Clevedon Town	556	D 2 - 2	Watkins 9 Martin 38	
27	23		A	Cambridge City	339	W 3 - 0	Pelecati 22 McConnell 51(pen) Watkins 75	10
28	26		A	Bashley		L 0 - 2		
29	30		H	Banbury United	452	D 1 - 1	Ash 90	11
30	Feb 2		A	Brackley Town	165	L 3 - 4	Taylor 8 Pugh 31 Yetton 90	
31	6		H	Leamington	430	D 2 - 2	McConnell 1 (pen) Brown M 70	13
32	9		H	Hemel Hempstead	247	W 3 - 1	Watkins 19 Brown M 26 45	
33	13		A	Halesowen Town	385	L 2 - 3	Watkins 56 74	13
34	16		H	Bashley	274	D 1 - 1	Taylor 68	
35	20		H	Bedford Town	347	W 5 - 1	Martin 41 (pen) Watkins 45 75 Watts 53 Yetton 90	12
36	Mar 2		A	Merthyr Tydfil	230	W 2 - 1	E.Brown 55 M.Brown 75	
37	6		H	Swindon Spermarine	407	D 0 - 0		10
38	9		A	Chippenham Town	413	L 1 - 2	Watkins 52	
39	13		H	Rugby Town	336	W 4 - 1	Tayor 29 Ash 33 Afful 58 84	
40	16		A	Didcot Town	156	D 1 - 1	Watkins 45	
41	20		A	Oxford City	254	D 2 - 2	Watkins 2 Martin 66 (pen)	12
42	23		H	Hednesford Town	259	L 1 - 2	Yetton 38	
43	27		H	Nuneaton Town	558	L 0 - 2		12
44	30		A	Evesham United	105	W 2 - 0	Martin 49 Pugh 61	
45	April 5		A	Clevedon Town	392	W 3 - 0	Martin 16 McConnell 44 (pen) Watkins 67	11
46	7		A	Farnborough	615	L 1 - 3	Martin 9	
47	10		H	Stourbridge	382	W 4 - 1	Martin 8 Afful 25 McConnell 62 (pen) Ash 67	11
48	13		H	Oxford City	320	L 0 - 1		
49	15		H	Didcot Town	272	W 2 - 1	Taylor 76 Watkins 90	
50	17		A	Hemel Hempstead	253	W 2 - 0	Watkins 24 McConnell 40	11
51	21		A	Tiverton Town	324	W 2 - 1	McConnell 84 (pen) Broad 86	
52	24		H	Brackley Town	435	D 1 - 1	Watkins 13	11
					Goals	104 74		

Home Attendances:	
Highest:	902 v Tiverton Town
Lowest:	238 v Evesham Town
Average:	444
Top Goalscorer:	Watkins - 25 (League 20, FAC 4, FAT 1 - Hat-trick 1)

WEYMOUTH

Chairman: George Rolls

Secretary: Gary Calder (T) 07733 106505 (E) garycalder1@aol.com

Additional Committee Members: Pranas Preidzius, Bronius Preidzius, Audrius Preidzius, Eugenius Tiskus, Inga Preidziuviene, Lijana Preidziuviene

Manager: Ian Hutchinson

Programme Editor: Hilary Billimore (E) hbillimore@tiscali.co.uk

Photo courtesy of the Dorset Echo.

Club Factfile

Founded: 1890 **Nickname:** The Terras

Previous Names: None

Previous Leagues: Dorset, Western 1907-23, 28-49, Southern 1923-28, 49-79, 89-2005, Alliance/Conference 1979-89, 2005-10

Club Colours (change): All claret with sky blue trim (All white with blue)

Ground: Wessex Stadium, Radipole Lane, Weymouth DT4 9XJ (T) 08721 840 000

Capacity: 6,600 **Seats:** 800 **Covered:** Yes **Clubhouse:** Yes **Shop:** Yes

Previous Grounds: Not known

Simple Directions

Approach Weymouth from Dorchester on the A354. Turn right at first roundabout onto Weymouth Way, continue to the next roundabout then turn right (signposted Football Ground). At the next roundabout take third exit into the ground.

Record Attendance: 4,995 v Manchester United - Ground opening 21/10/97

Record Victory: Not known

Record Defeat: Not known

Record Goalscorer: W 'Farmer' Haynes - 275

Record Appearances: Tony Hobsons - 1,076

Additional Records: Paid £15,000 to Northwich Victoria for Shaun Teale
Received £100,000 from Tottenham Hotspur for Peter Guthrie 1988

Senior Honours: Southern League 1964-65, 65-66. Conference South 2005-06.
Dorset Senior Cup x27

10 YEAR RECORD

00-01	01-02	02-03	03-04	04-05	05-06	06-07	07-08	08-09	09-10
SthP 5	SthP 11	SthP 17	SthP 2	Conf S 7	Conf S 1	Conf 11	Conf 18	Conf 23	Conf S 22

WEYMOUTH

No.	Date	Comp	H/A	Opponents	Att:	Result	Goalscorers	Pos
1	8/8/09	BSS	A	Lewes	441	D 1-1	Cooper 61	11
2	11/8/09	BSS	H	Eastleigh	931	L 0-5		18
3	15/8/09	BSS	H	Bishops Stortford	623	L 2-6	Thorne 31, Reid 73	19
4	18/8/09	BSS	A	Maidenhead United	249	D 1-1	Obaze 89	20
5	22/8/09	BSS	H	Worcester City	603	W 2-1	Reid 10, Cooper 25	16
6	28/8/09	BSS	A	Weston-Super-Mare	341	L 0-3		16
7	31/8/09	BSS	H	Havant & Waterlooville	717	L 0-1		18
8	5/9/09	BSS	H	Bromley	792	L 1-5	Obaze 2	20
9	12/9/09	BSS	A	Thurrock	239	L 1-2	Klein-Davies 15	22
10	16/9/09	BSS	A	Newport County	1509	D 1-1	Reid 70	22
11	19/9/09	BSS	H	St Albans City	645	L 0-2		22
12	3/10/09	BSS	A	Hampton & Richmond B.	518	L 0-3		22
13	10/10/09	BSS	H	Maidenhead United	571	L 0-5		22
14	17/10/09	BSS	H	Dover Athletic	649	L 1-2	Reid 88	22
15	24/10/09	BSS	A	Basingstoke Town	426	L 1-2	Rose 87	22
16	27/10/09	BSS	H	Bath City	675	L 0-2		22
17	31/10/09	BSS	A	St Albans City	377	L 1-2	Obaze 30	22
18	14/11/09	BSS	A	Bishops Stortford	507	W 1-0	Reid 17	22
19	17/11/09	BSS	H	Woking	544	D 0-0		22
20	5/12/09	BSS	A	Braintree Town	431	L 2-3	Llewellyn 54, Reid pen 75	22
21	26/12/09	BSS	A	Dorchester Town	2163	D 0-0		22
22	1/1/10	BSS	H	Dorchester Town	2392	W 2-0	Joseph-Dubois 35, S Bennett 59	22
23	16/1/10	BSS	H	Chelmsford City	519	L 1-4	Brice 30	22
24	23/1/10	BSS	A	Worcester City	646	L 1-3	Farrell 10	22
25	30/1/10	BSS	H	Lewes	667	W 3-1	Llewellyn 17, Reed 58, Reid 78	21
26	2/2/10	BSS	A	Eastleigh	490	L 0-4		21
27	6/2/10	BSS	A	Staines Town	501	L 0-2		21
28	13/2/10	BSS	H	Basingstoke Town	588	L 0-6		22
29	20/2/10	BSS	A	Bath City	656	L 0-2		22
30	23/2/10	BSS	H	Braintree Town	1222	D 1-1	Groves 90	22
31	27/2/10	BSS	A	Bromley	549	L 0-4		22
32	2/3/10	BSS	H	Staines Town	365	L 1-2	Groves 41	22
33	6/3/10	BSS	H	Newport County	1123	L 1-3	Llewellyn 75	22
34	13/3/10	BSS	H	Welling United	405	L 0-3		22
35	20/3/10	BSS	A	Chelmsford City	877	L 1-2	Reed 69	22
36	23/3/10	BSS	A	Welling United	427	L 1-7	Reed 61	22
37	27/3/10	BSS	H	Thurrock	364	D 0-0		22
38	3/4/10	BSS	H	Weston-Super-Mare	502	L 1-2	Richardson 61	Rel
39	5/4/10	BSS	A	Havant & Waterlooville	820	L 1-3	Reed 46	22
40	10/4/10	BSS	A	Dover Athletic	1022	L 0-2		22
41	17/4/10	BSS	H	Hampton & Richmond B.	501	W 1-0	McGuiness 50	22
42	24/4/10	BSS	A	Woking	2137	L 0-4		22
	Cups							
1	26/9/09	FAC 2Q	A	Bishops Cleeve	249	L 0-3		
2	21/11/09	FAT 3Q	H	Dorchester Town	1032	W 3-0	Reid 25, Llewellyn 64, Radcliffe 66	
3	12/12/09	FAT 1	H	Salisbury City	642	L 0-1		

Home Attendances:	
Highest:	2392 v Dorchester Town
Lowest:	364 v Thurrock
Average (08-09):	623 (1213)
Top Goalscorer:	Reid - 8 (7 League, 1 Cup) in 29 appearances - 28% strike rate
Most Appearances:	Radcliffe - 30 (26+2 League, 2 Cup)

WINDSOR & ETON

Chairman: Peter Simpson
Secretary: Steve Rowland (T) 07887 770 630
(E) secretary@wefc.co.uk
Additional Committee Members: Ian Lucas, Brian Whale, Geoff De Feu, Tony Blay, Ian Dawson, Malcolm Williams, Paul Appleyard, Fraser Silvey, Neil Hart, Steve Rowland
Manager: Dave Mudge
Programme Editor: Robert Stevens (E) wefcprogramme@hotmail .co.uk

Unfortunately an up-to-date photograph was not available at the time of going to press

Club Factfile

Founded: 1892 **Nickname:** The Royalists
Previous Names: Not known
Previous Leagues: Southern, West Berks, Great Western, Suburban, Athenian 1922-29, 63-81, Spartan 1929-32, Great Western Comb. Corinthian 1945-50, Metropolitan 1950-60, Delphian 1960-63, Isthmian
Club Colours (change): Red with green trim/red with green trim/red (Yellow with green trim/yellow with green trim/yellow)

Ground: Stag Meadow, St Leonards Road, Windsor, Berks SL4 3DR (T) 01753 860 656
Capacity: 4,500 **Seats:** 400 **Covered:** 550 **Clubhouse:** Yes **Shop:** Yes
Previous Grounds: Ballon Meadow 1892-1912
Simple Directions
Exit M4 at Junction 6, follow dual carriageway (signposted Windsor) to large roundabout at end, take third exit into Imperial Road, turn left at T-junction into St Leonards Road. Ground approx ½ mile on right opposite Stag & Hounds public house.

Record Attendance: 8,500 - Charity Match
Record Victory: Not known
Record Defeat: Not known
Record Goalscorer: Not known
Record Appearances: Kevin Mitchell
Additional Records: Paid £9,000 to Slough Town for Keith White
Received £45,000 from Barnet for Michael Banton and Michael Barnes

Senior Honours: Athenian League 1979-80, 80-81. Isthmian League Division 1 1983-84. Southern League Division 1 South & West 2009-10. Berks & Bucks Senior Cup x11.

10 YEAR RECORD

00-01		01-02		02-03		03-04		04-05		05-06		06-07		07-08		08-09		09-10	
Isth2	2	Isth1	22	Isth1S	13	Isth1S	3	Isth P	15	Isth P	21	Sthsw	14	Sthsw	8	Sthsw	2	Sthsw	1

The ZAMARETTO League

A.F.C. HAYES

Chairman: B Stone
Secretary: Barry Crump (T) 07966 468 029
(E) afchayesfootballsec@hotmail.co.uk
Additional Committee Members: Roger Galloway, Dave Swan, Keith Gavin, Dave Ball, John Handell, Ken Aldridge, P.Squires, P.Betts
Manager: Dave Welch
Programme Editor: Dave Swan (E) daveswan03@hotmail.com

Unfortunately an up-to-date photograph was not available at the time of going to press

Club Factfile

Founded: 1974 **Nickname:** The Brook
Previous Names: Brook House
Previous Leagues: Spartan South Midlands, Isthmian

Club Colours (change): Blue and white stripes/blue/blue (All red)

Ground: Farm Park, Kingshill Avenue, Hayes UB4 8DD (T) 020 8845 0110
Capacity: 2,000 **Seats:** 150 **Covered:** 200 **Clubhouse:** Yes **Shop:** No
Previous Grounds:
Simple Directions
From the A40 McDonalds Target roundabout take A312 south towards Hayes. At White Hart roundabout take third exit into Yeading Lane. Turn right at first traffic lights into Kingshill Avenue. Ground approx one miles on the right-hand side.

Record Attendance: Not known
Record Victory: Not known
Record Defeat: Not known
Record Goalscorer: Not known
Record Appearances: Not known
Additional Records:

Senior Honours: Spartan South Midlands Premier South 1997-98.

10 YEAR RECORD

00-01	01-02	02-03	03-04	04-05	05-06	06-07	07-08	08-09	09-10
Conf 18	Conf 20	Isth P 7	Isth P 8	Conf S 12	Conf S 20	Conf S 20	Sthsw 14	Sthsw 9	Sthsw 21

ARLESEY TOWN

Chairman: Manny Cohen
Secretary: Keith Broughton (T) 07530 860 480
(E) keithbroughton1@ntlworld.com
Additional Committee Members:
Maurice Crouch, Trevor Flint
Manager: Lee Cowley
Programme Editor: Tony Smith (E) cricketfants@sky.com

Archive photo

Club Factfile

Founded: 1891 **Nickname:** The Blues
Previous Names:
Previous Leagues: Biggleswade & Dist., Bedfordshire Co. (South Midlands) 1922-26, 27-28, Parthenon, London 1958-60, United Co. 1933-36, 82-92, Spartan South Mid. 1992-2000, Isthmian 2000-04, 06-08, Southern 2004-07
Club Colours (change): Light and dark blue/dark blue/dark blue (All yellow)

Ground: Armadillo Stadium, Hitchin Road, Arlesey SG15 6RS (T) 01462 734 504
Capacity: 2,920 **Seats:** 150 **Covered:** 600 **Clubhouse:** Yes **Shop:** Yes
Previous Grounds:
Simple Directions
A1 take A507 to Shefford, at third roundabout turn left, fist left follow road through village, ground is 1.5 miles on the left.

Record Attendance: 2,000 v Luton Town Reserves - Bedfordshire Senior Cup 1906
Record Victory: Not known
Record Defeat: Not known
Record Goalscorer: Not known
Record Appearances: Gary Marshall
Additional Records:

Senior Honours: South Midlands Premier Division x5. United Counties Premier Division 1984-85. FA Vase 1994-95.
Isthmian League Division 3 2000-01.
Bedfordshire Senior Cup 1965-66, 78-79, 96-97.

10 YEAR RECORD

00-01	01-02	02-03	03-04	04-05	05-06	06-07	07-08	08-09	09-10
Isth3 1	Isth2 4	Isth1N 16	Isth1N 8	SthE 14	SthE 10	Isth1N 18	Isth1N 15	SthM 18	SthM 9

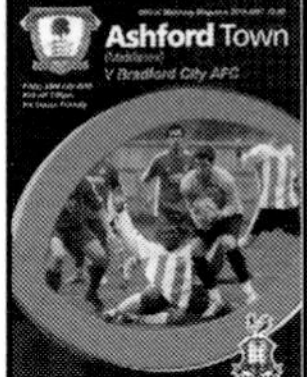

ASHFORD TOWN (MIDDLESEX)

Chairman: Alan Cox
Secretary: Alan Constable (T) 07956 930 719
(E) alanc52@aol.com
Additional Committee Members: Gareth Coates, John Warrington, Mrs. Sue Cox, Bob Parker, Terry Ryan, Mick Tilt, Ben Murray, Sue Cox and Tracey Bessent, Lian Balmer, Dave Baker, Paul Burgess, Dan Butler, Gary Jeffreys, Ed Shaylor, Daryl Watson, Nigel Smith
Manager: Jamie Lawrence
Programme Editor: Gareth Coates (E) garethcoates@hotmail.co.uk

Club Factfile

Founded: 1964 **Nickname:** Tangerines
Previous Names:
Previous Leagues: Hounslow & District 1964-68, Surrey Intermediate 1968-82, Surrey Premier 1982-90, Combined Counties 1990-2000, Isthmian 2000-04, 06-10, Southern 2004-06

Club Colours (change): Tangerine and white stripes/black/white (Blue/white/blue)

Ground: Short Lane Stadium, Stanwell, Staines TW19 7BH (T) 01784 245 908
Capacity: 2,550 **Seats:** 250 **Covered:** 250 **Clubhouse:** Yes **Shop:** No
Previous Grounds: Clockhouse Lane Rec
Simple Directions
M25 junction 13, A30 towards London, third left at footbridge after Ashford Hospital crossroads, ground sign posted after 1/4 mile on the right down Short Lane, two miles from Ashford (BR) and Hatton Cross tube station.

Record Attendance: 992 v AFC Wimbledon - Isthmian League Premier Division 26/09/2006
Record Victory: Not known
Record Defeat: Not known
Record Goalscorer: Andy Smith
Record Appearances: Alan Constable - 650
Additional Records: Received £10,000 from Wycombe Wanderers for Dannie Bulman 1997

Senior Honours: Surrey Premier League 1982-90. Combined Counties League 1994-95, 95-96, 96-97, 97-98. Middlesex Charity Cup 2000-01. Middlesex Premier Cup 2006-07. Isthmian League Cup 2006-07.

10 YEAR RECORD

00-01	01-02	02-03	03-04	04-05	05-06	06-07	07-08	08-09	09-10
Isth3 3	Isth2 12	Isth1S 17	Isth1S 12	SthW 6	SthW 2	Isth P 17	Isth P 6	Isth P 10	Isth P 20

ATHERSTONE TOWN

Chairman: Howard Kerry
Secretary: Geoff Taylor (T) 07999 041 622
(E) taylor_geoff@hotmail.com

Additional Committee Members:
Adrian Burr, Howard Kerry, Graham Reed, Rob Weale

Manager: Dale Belford

Programme Editor: Graham Reed (E) grahamgdr777@aol.com

Front Row (L-R): Jordan Brown, Conor Fulford, Lyndon Weller, Steve Johnson (youth/reserves physio), Shylo Thomas, Stuart Hendrie, Chris Woodhall. **Middle:** John Cole (sports therapist), Kieran Robinson, Will Holyland, Adam Henchcliffe, Nathan Woakes, Dave Clarke, Chris Sturridge-Packer, Grant Roscorla, Giavanni Dainty, Wayne Chapman (youth/reserves coach). **Front:** Mark Grainger (youth/reserves manager), Shawn Boothe, Luke Edwards, Dave Haywood (assistant manager), Daren Fulford (manager), Niki Preston, Tom Weale, Brendan Murphy, Dave Brandon (coach).
Not present for photocall: Marcus Ebdon, Matt Brown, Dean Rathbone, Luke Keen

Club Factfile

Founded: 2004 **Nickname:** The Adders
Previous Names: None
Previous Leagues: Midland Combination 2004-06, Midland Alliance 2006-08

Club Colours (change): Red and white stripes/black/red (All green)

Ground: Sheepy Road, Atherston, Warwickshire CV9 1HD (T) 01827 717 829
Capacity: **Seats:** Yes **Covered:** Yes **Clubhouse:** Yes **Shop:**
Previous Grounds: None

Simple Directions
Take M42 towards Atherstone. Exit at Junction 10. Travel southbound on A5 towards Nuneaton for approximately 4 miles. At third roundabout take first exit to Holly Lane Industrial Estate. Over railway bridge (Aldi HQ on left). At the next roundabout turn right onto Rowlands Way. Ground is 300 yards on the right. Car park and street parking in Rowlands Way.

Record Attendance: Not known
Record Victory: Not known
Record Defeat: Not known
Record Goalscorer: Not known
Record Appearances: Not known
Additional Records:

Senior Honours: Midland Combination Division 1 2004-05, Premier Division 2005-06. Midland Alliance 2007-08.

10 YEAR RECORD

00-01	01-02	02-03	03-04	04-05	05-06	06-07	07-08	08-09	09-10
				MCm1 1	MCmP 1	MidAl 8	MidAl 1	SthM 3	SthM 13

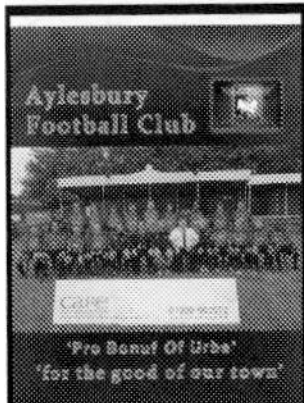

AYLESBURY

Chairman: Danny Martone

Secretary: Ian Brown (T) 07947 338 462 (E) brownzola@aol.com

Additional Committee Members: John Franklin, Warren Sheward, Steve Macdonald, Richard Whitaker, Bill Harrison

Manager: Mark Eaton

Programme Editor: Russell Williams (E) cmartone040@btinternet.com

Club Factfile

Founded: 1897 **Nickname:**

Previous Names: Haywood United > 2004, Haywood FC 2004-05, Aylesbury Vale 2005-09

Previous Leagues: Spartan South Midlands

Club Colours (change): Red with black trim/black/black (Yellow with blue trim/yellow/yellow)

Ground: Haywood Way, Aylesbury, Bucks. HP19 9WZ (T) 01296 42110

Capacity: **Seats:** Yes **Covered:** Yes **Clubhouse:** Yes **Shop:** No

Previous Grounds:

Simple Directions
When entering Aylesbury from all major routes, join the ring road and follow signposts for A41 Bicester and Waddesdon. leave the ring road at the roundabout by the Texaco Garage and Perry dealership. From the Texaco Garage cross straight over four roundabouts. At the fifth roundabout with the Cotton Wheel Pub on the right hand side, turn right into Jackson Road. Take the second left into Haywood Way, club is at the bottom of the road. If entering Aylesbury from Bicester (A41), turn left into Jackson Road by the Cotton Wheel Pub, and then second left into Haywood Way.

Record Attendance: Not known
Record Victory: Not known
Record Defeat: Not known
Record Goalscorer: Not known
Record Appearances: Not known
Additional Records: Not known

Senior Honours: Spartan South Midlands League Division 1 2003-04, Premier Division 2009-10.

10 YEAR RECORD

00-01	01-02	02-03	03-04	04-05	05-06	06-07	07-08	08-09	09-10
SSM1 9	SSM2 2	SSM1 9	SSM1 1	SSM P 3	SSM P 5	SSM P 5	SSM P 9	SSM P 15	SSM P 1

BARTON ROVERS

Chairman: Malcolm Bright
Secretary: Malcolm Aubrey (T) 07718 580 625
(E) malcolm.aubrey@openreach.co.uk
Additional Committee Members: Darron Whilley, Richard Carey, Derek Tripney, John Gray Jnr, Julie Gray, Darrell Thornton, Paul Reardon, Gary Hanley
Manager: Gary Fitzgerald
Programme Editor: Malcolm Aubrey (E) malcolm.aubrey@openreach.co.uk

Club Factfile

Founded: 1898 **Nickname:** Rovers
Previous Names:
Previous Leagues: Luton & district 1947-54, South Midlands 1954-79, Isthmian 1979-2004

Club Colours (change): Royal blue with white trim/royal blue/royal blue (Yellow/Black/yellow)

Ground: Sharpenhoe Road, Barton-le-Clay, Bedford MK45 4SD (T) 01582 707 772
Capacity: 4,000 **Seats:** 160 **Covered:** 1,120 **Clubhouse:** Yes **Shop:** Yes
Previous Grounds:
Simple Directions
Leave M1 at J12 head towards Harlington. Follow signs through Sharpenhoe Village to Barton. At T-junction in village turn right, continue 500 yards and turn right into ground on concrete roadway adjacent to playing fields.

Record Attendance: 1,900 v Nuneaton Borough - FA Cup 4th Qualifying Round 1976
Record Victory: Not known
Record Defeat: Not known
Record Goalscorer: Richard Camp - 152 (1989-98)
Record Appearances: Tony McNally - 598 (1988-2005)
Additional Records: Paid £1,000 to Hitchin Town for B. Baldry 1980
Received £1,000 from Bishop's Stortford for B. Baldry 1981
Senior Honours: South Midlands League x8. Bedfordshire Senior Cup x7. Bedfordshire Premier Cup 1995-96.

10 YEAR RECORD

00-01	01-02	02-03	03-04	04-05	05-06	06-07	07-08	08-09	09-10
Isth1 22	Isth2 14	Isth1N 19	Isth1N 18	SthE 8	SthE 19	SthM 20			SthM 21

BEACONSFIELD SYCOB

Chairman: Fred Deanus
Secretary: Robin Woolman (T) 07778 832 019
(E) robin.woolman@btinternet.com

Additional Committee Members:
Paul Hughes, Mark Hart, Pierre Nayna, Frank Abe, Matthew Grant, Dennis Byatt

Manager: Colin Davis
Programme Editor: Karl McKenzie (E) mandymckenzie71@hotmail.com

Club Factfile

Founded: 1994 **Nickname:** The Rams
Previous Names: Slough YCOB and Beaconsfield United merged in 1994
Previous Leagues: Spartan South Midlands 1004-2004, 07-08, Southern 2004-07

Club Colours (change): Red and white quarters/black/red and white (Yellow/yellow/yellow)

Ground: Holloways Park, Windsor Road, Beaconsfield, Bucks HP9 2SE (T) 01494 676 868
Capacity: **Seats:** **Covered:** **Clubhouse:** Yes **Shop:**
Previous Grounds:
Simple Directions
Leave Junction 2 of M40, take A355 towards Slough, 50 yards off roundabout turn left and at next roundabout turn complete right, coming back towards A355 to continue across A355, then turn right and 150 yards on left is sign to club. Go through gate and clubhouse is 200 yards on right.

Record Attendance: Not known
Record Victory: Not known
Record Defeat: Not known
Record Goalscorer: Allan Arthur
Record Appearances: Allan Arthur
Additional Records:

Senior Honours: Spartan South Midlands 2000-01, 03-04, 07-08. Berks and Bucks Senior Trophy 2003-04

10 YEAR RECORD

00-01	01-02	02-03	03-04	04-05	05-06	06-07	07-08	08-09	09-10
SSM P 1	SSM P 10	SSM P 2	SSM P 1	SthE 14	SthW 13	Sthsw 22	SSM P 1	Sthsw 4	SthM 19

BEDFONT TOWN

Chairman: Doug White
Secretary: Stewart Cook (T) 07946 170 277
(E) stewart.cook@btinternet.com
Additional Committee Members: Les King, Bob Betts, Lawrence Brimicombe, Paul Spencer, Martin Pester, Don Townsend
Manager: Dennis Bainborough
Programme Editor: Stewart Cook (E) stewart.cook@btinternet.com

Club Factfile

Founded: 1965 **Nickname:** The Peacocks
Previous Names: Amalgamated with Bedfont United in 1972 to create today's club
Previous Leagues: West Middlesex Sunday, Hounslow & District, Woking & District 1986-99, Guildford & Woking Alliance 1999-2001, Surrey Intermediate 2001-04, Combined Counties 2004-09

Club Colours (change): Navy/navy/navy (White/red/red & white)

Ground: The Orchard, Hatton Road, Bedfont TW14 9QT (T) 0208 8907 264
Capacity: **Seats:** Yes **Covered:** Yes **Clubhouse:** Yes **Shop:**
Previous Grounds:
Simple Directions
From M4: Leave the M4 at junction 3, then at roundabout take the exit onto the A312 (Heathrow/Staines). Continue to traffic signals connecting to A30 and turn right. At traffic signals turn left into Dick Turpin Way. At traffic signals turn right onto Fagg's Road, turn left onto Hatton Road (signposted Bedfont FC). The ground is on the left opposite the Duke of Wellington Public House.
From M3: Leave the M3 at junction 2, then join the M25 motorway. Leave the M25 at junction 13, at roundabout take the 3rd exit onto the A30. At Crooked Billet continue forward. At Clockhouse Roundabout take the 1st exit onto the A30. At Hatton Cross traffic signals continue to next traffic signals and turn right into Dick Turpin Way. At traffic signals turn right onto Fagg's Road, turn left onto Hatton Road (signposted Bedfont FC). The ground is on the left opposite the Duke of Wellington Public House.

Record Attendance: Not known
Record Victory: Not known
Record Defeat: Not known
Record Goalscorer: Not known
Record Appearances: John Skeen
Additional Records:

Senior Honours: Surrey Intermediate Premier 2003-04. Combined Counties Premier 2008-09.

10 YEAR RECORD

00-01	01-02	02-03	03-04	04-05	05-06	06-07	07-08	08-09	09-10
GWAP 1	SuI3 2	SuI2	SuIP 1	CC1 2	CCP 6	CCP 22	CCP 9	CCP 1	Sthsw 17

BEDWORTH UNITED

Chairman: David Taylor

Secretary: Graham Bloxham **(T)** 07748 640 613 **(E)** graham@greenbacks1.free-online.co.uk

Additional Committee Members:
Steven Collins, David Taylor, Bob Howe, John Roberts, Glen Moran

Manager: Bernie Cope

Programme Editor: David Taylor **(E)** david@sas02.co.uk

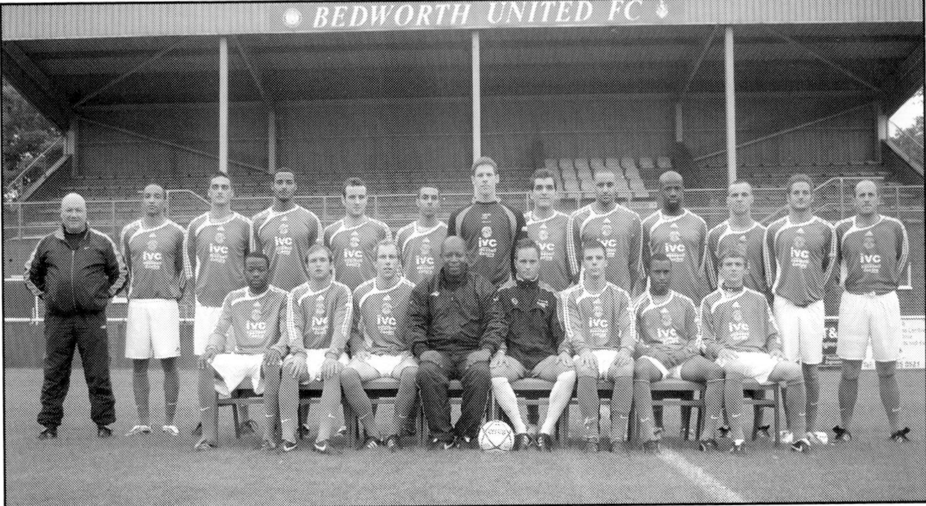

Archive photo

Club Factfile

Founded: 1896 **Nickname:** Greenbacks

Previous Names: Bedworth Town 1947-68

Previous Leagues: Birmingham Combination 1947-54, Birmingham/West Midlands 1954-72

Club Colours (change): All green with white trim (All yellow with white trim)

Ground: The Oval, Coventry Road, Bedworth CV12 8NN **(T)** 02476 314 752

Capacity: 7,000 **Seats:** 300 **Covered:** 300 **Clubhouse:** Yes **Shop:** Yes

Previous Grounds: British Queen Ground 1911-39

Simple Directions
11/2 miles from M6 J3, take B4113 Coventry–Bedworth Road and after third set of traffic lights (Bedworth Leisure Centre). Ground 200 yards on right opposite cemetery. Coaches to park in Leisure Centre.

Record Attendance: 5,127 v Nuneaton Borough - Southern League Midland Division 23/02/1982

Record Victory: Not known

Record Defeat: Not known

Record Goalscorer: Peter Spacey - 1949-69

Record Appearances: Peter Spacey - 1949-69

Additional Records: Paid £1,750 to Hinckley Town for Colin Taylor 1991-92
Received £30,000 from Plymouth Argyle for Richard Landon

Senior Honours: Birmingham Combination x2. Birmingham Senior Cup x3. Midland Floodlit Cup 1981-82, 92-93.

10 YEAR RECORD

00-01	01-02	02-03	03-04	04-05	05-06	06-07	07-08	08-09	09-10
SthW 16	SthW 11	SthW 18	SthW 19	SthW 15	SthW 16	SthM 16	SthM 15	SthM 14	SthM 16

BIGGLESWADE TOWN

Chairman: Maurice Dorrington
Secretary: Andy McDonnell (T) 07879 802 105
(E) andy.mcdonnell@ntlworld.com
Additional Committee Members:
B. Doggett, Annette Dorrington, D. Simpson, M. Draxler
Manager: Chris Nunn
Programme Editor: David Simpson (E) simpson_david@hotmail.co.uk

Unfortunately an up-to-date photograph was not available at the time of going to press

Club Factfile

Founded: 1874 **Nickname:** The Waders
Previous Names:
Previous Leagues: Biggleswade & District, Bedford & District, Spartan South Midlands 1951-55, 80-2009, Eastern Counties 1955-63, United Counties 1963-80

Club Colours (change): Green and white stripes/green/white (Sky blue and white stripes/sky blue/sky blue)

Ground: The Carlsberg Stadium, Langford Road, Biggleswade SG18 9JJ **(T)**
Capacity: **Seats:** **Covered:** **Clubhouse:** Yes **Shop:**
Previous Grounds: Fairfield

Simple Directions
From the south – up the A1, past the first roundabout (Homebase) signposted Biggleswade. At next roundabout (Sainsburys) turn right onto A6001. As you approach the Town Centre, go straight over the mini roundabout following signs for Langford (Teal Road). At traffic lights, turn right (still heading towards Langford). Continue along Hitchin Street over two mini roundabouts and as you pass under the A1, the ground entrance is 200 yards on the right. From the north – exit A1 at the Sainsburys roundabout and follow instructions as above.

Record Attendance: 2,000
Record Victory: Not known
Record Defeat: Not known
Record Goalscorer: Not known
Record Appearances: Not known
Additional Records:

Senior Honours: Spartan South Midlands Premier Division 2008-09. Bedfordshire Premier Cup 2009.

10 YEAR RECORD

00-01	01-02	02-03	03-04	04-05	05-06	06-07	07-08	08-09	09-10
SSM P 14	SSM P 9	SSM P 11	SSM P 15	SSM P 10	SSM P 15	SSM P 18	SSM P 3	SSM P 1	SthM 12

BURNHAM

Chairman: Ian Gould
Secretary: Trevor Saunders (T) 07711 856 780
(E) saunderstrevor@hotmail.com
Additional Committee Members: M. Higton, R. H. Saunders, T. R. Saunders, M. J. Boxall, K. W. Ambrose, B. Breen, G. Breen
Manager: Jamie Jarvis
Programme Editor: Cliff Sparkes (E)

Unfortunately an up-to-date photograph was not available
at the time of going to press

Club Factfile

Founded: 1878 **Nickname:** The Blues
Previous Names: Burnham & Hillingdon 1985-87
Previous Leagues: Hellenic 1971-77, 95-99, Athenian 1977-84, London Spartan 1984-85, Southern 1985-95

Club Colours (change): Blue and white quarters/blue/blue (Red and black quarters/black/red)

Ground: The Gore, Wymers Wood Road, Burnham, Slough SL1 8JG (T) 07771 677 337
Capacity: 2,500 **Seats:** **Covered:** **Clubhouse:** Yes **Shop:** Yes
Previous Grounds: Baldwin Meadow until 1920s
Simple Directions
Approx. 2 miles from M4 junction 7 and 5 miles from M40 junction 2. From M40 take A355 to A4 signposted Maidenhead. From M4 take A4 towards Maidenhead until you reach roundabout with Sainsbury Superstore on left. Turn right into Lent Rise Road and travel approx 11/2 miles over 2 double roundabouts. 100 yards after second double roundabout fork right into Wymers Wood Road. Ground entrance on right.

Record Attendance: 2,380 v Halesowen Town - FA Vase 02/04/1983
Record Victory: 18-0 v High Duty Alloys - 1970-71
Record Defeat: 1-10 v Ernest Turner Sports - 1963-64
Record Goalscorer: Fraser Hughes - 65 (1969-70)
Record Appearances: Not known
Additional Records:

Senior Honours: Hellenic League 1975-76, 98-99, League Cup 1975-76, 98-99, Division 1 Cup 1971-72.

10 YEAR RECORD

00-01	01-02	02-03	03-04	04-05	05-06	06-07	07-08	08-09	09-10
SthE 17	SthE 11	SthE 13	SthE 17	SthW 9	SthW 4	Sthsw 3	Sthsw 10	Sthsw 17	SthM 3

DAVENTRY TOWN

Chairman: Iain Humphrey
Secretary: Matt Hogsden (T) 07855 216 798
(E) dtfcsec@hotmail.co.uk
Additional Committee Members:
Mike Tebbit, Dennis Job, Kurt Shingler, Frank Hobbs, Malcolm Hobbs, Steve Fowler
Manager: Ady Fuller
Programme Editor: Harvey Potter (E) h.potter@shebang.net

Unfortunately an up-to-date photograph was not available at the time of going to press

Club Factfile

Founded: 1886 **Nickname:** The Town
Previous Names:
Previous Leagues: Northampton Town (pre-1987), Central Northways Comb 1987-89, United Counties 1989-2010.

Club Colours (change): Purple/white/white (Yellow/white/white)

Ground: Comm. Park, Browns Rd, Daventry, Northants NN11 4NS (T) 01327 311 239
Capacity: 2,000 **Seats:** 250 **Covered:** 250 **Clubhouse:** Yes **Shop:**
Previous Grounds:
Simple Directions
From Northampton or J.16 of the M1, follow A45 westbound into Daventry, crossing the A5 on the way. At first roundabout bear left along A45 Daventry Bypass. At next roundabout go straight over onto Browns Road. The Club is at the top of this road on the left.

Record Attendance: 850 v Utrecht (Holland) - 1989
Record Victory: Not known
Record Defeat: Not known
Record Goalscorer: Not known
Record Appearances: Not known
Additional Records:

Senior Honours: United Counties League Division 1 1989-90, 90-91, 2000-01, 2007-08, Premier Division 2009-10.

10 YEAR RECORD

00-01	01-02	02-03	03-04	04-05	05-06	06-07	07-08	08-09	09-10
UCL 1 1	UCL P	UCL P	UCL P	UCL P	UCL P	UCL P	UCL 1 1	UCL P 7	UCL P 1

HITCHIN TOWN

Chairman: Terry Barratt
Secretary: Roy Izzard (T) 07803 202 498
(E) roy.izzard@bjca.co.uk
Additional Committee Members: Andy Melvin, Mark Burke, Mrs Chris Morrell, John Morrell, Neil Jenson, Tony Gill, Fred Andrews, Stewart Virgo
Manager: Carl Williams
Programme Editor: Neil Jensen (E) neil.jensen@db.com

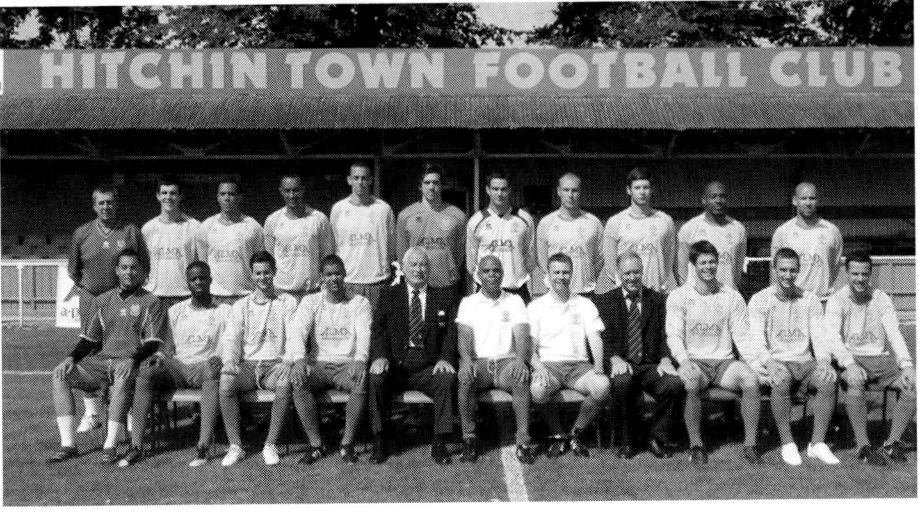

Club Factfile

Founded: 1865 **Nickname:** Canaries
Previous Names: Re-formed in 1928
Previous Leagues: Spartan 1928-39, Herts & Middlesex 1939-45, Athenian 1945-63, Isthmian 1964-2004

Club Colours (change): Yellow/green/green (Green/yellow/yellow)

Ground: Top Field, Fishponds Road, Hitchin SG5 1NJ (T) 01462 459 028 (match days only)
Capacity: 5,000 **Seats:** 500 **Covered:** 1,250 **Clubhouse:** Yes **Shop:** Yes
Previous Grounds:
Simple Directions
From East A1 to J8 onto A602 to Hitchin. At Three Moorhens Pub roundabout, take third exit (A600) towards Bedford, over next roundabout and lights, turn right at next roundabout, turnstiles on left, parking 50 yards on.

Record Attendance: 7,878 v Wycombe Wanderers - FA Amateur Cup 3rd Round 08/02/1956
Record Victory: 13-0 v Cowley and v RAF Uxbridge - both Spartan League 1929-30
Record Defeat: 0-10 v Kingstonian (A) and v Slough Town (A) - 1965-66 and 1979-80 respectively
Record Goalscorer: Paul Giggle - 214 (1968-86)
Record Appearances: Paul Giggle - 769 (1968-86)
Additional Records: Paid £2,000 to Potton United for Ray Seeking
Received £30,000 from Cambridge United for Zema Abbey, January 2000

Senior Honours: AFA Senior Cup 1931-32. London Senior Cup 1969-70. Isthmian League Division 1 1992-93.
Herts Senior Cup x19 (a record)

10 YEAR RECORD

00-01	01-02	02-03	03-04	04-05	05-06	06-07	07-08	08-09	09-10
Isth P 10	Isth P 11	Isth P 14	Isth P 20	SthP 18	SthP 14	SthP 11	SthP 18	SthP 20	SthM 2

LEIGHTON TOWN

Chairman: Iain McGregor

Secretary: Jim Snee (T) 07912 678 038 (E) toptrophies@hotmail.com

Additional Committee Members: Bruce Warner, Roy Parker, Andrew Parker, Alec Irvine, Dave Geddes, Terry Migliori, Jim Snee, Jamie Green, Vicky Janes, Chris Blair

Manager: Sean Downey

Programme Editor: Dave Geddes (E) family.geddes@sky.com

Archive photo

Club Factfile

Founded: 1885 **Nickname:** Reds

Previous Names: Leighton United 1922-63

Previous Leagues: Leighton & District, South Midlands 1922-24, 26-29, 46-54, 55-56, 76-92, Spartan 1922-53, 67-74, United Counties 1974-76, Isthmian

Club Colours (change): Red and white stripes/red/red (Yellow/black/yellow)

Ground: Lake Street, Leighton Buzzard, Beds LU7 1RX (T) 01525 373 311

Capacity: 2,800 **Seats:** 155 **Covered:** 300 **Clubhouse:** Yes **Shop:** No

Previous Grounds: Wayside

Simple Directions

Ground is situated just south of Town Centre on the A4146 Leighton Buzzard to Hemel Hemstead Road. Entrance to car park and ground is opposite Morrisons Supermarket Petrol Station. 1/2 mile south of town centre.

Record Attendance: 1,522 v Aldershot Town - Isthmian League Division 3 30/01/1993

Record Victory: v Met Railway (H) - Spartan League 1925-26

Record Defeat: 0-12 v Headington United (A) - Spartan League 18/10/1947

Record Goalscorer: Not known

Record Appearances: Not known

Additional Records:

Senior Honours: South Midlands League 1966-67, 91-92. Isthmian League Division 2 2003-04. Bedfordshire Senior Cup 1926-27, 67-68, 69-70, 92-93.

10 YEAR RECORD

00-01		01-02		02-03		03-04		04-05		05-06		06-07		07-08		08-09		09-10	
Isth2	21	Isth3	17	Isth2	6	Isth2	1	SthE	10	SthW	8	SthM	18	SthM	9	SthM	8	SthM	10

MARLOW

Chairman: Terry Staines
Secretary: Paul Burdell **(T)** 07961 145 949
(E) marlow.fc@virgin.net

Additional Committee Members:
Ray Frith

Manager: Kevin Stone
Programme Editor: Terry Staines **(E)** terry.staines@ntlworld.com

Archive photo

Club Factfile

Founded: 1870 **Nickname:** The Blues
Previous Names: Great Marlow
Previous Leagues: Reading & District, Spartan 1908-10, 28-65, Great Western Suburban, Athenian 1965-84, Isthmian 1984-2004

Club Colours (change): Royal blue with white trim/royal/royal (Red with white trim/red/red)

Ground: Alfred Davies Memorial Ground, Oak tree Road, Marlow SL7 3ED **(T)** 01628 483 970
Capacity: 3,000 **Seats:** 250 **Covered:** 600 **Clubhouse:** Yes **Shop:**
Previous Grounds: Crown ground 1870-1919, Star Meadow 1919-24

Simple Directions
From M40 (Junction 4 High Wycombe) or M4 (Junction 8/9 Maidenhead) take A404, leave at the A4155 junction signposted Marlow. Follow A4155 towards Marlow then turn right at Esso service station into Maple Rise. At crossroads follow straight ahead into Oak Tree Road. Ground 100 yards on left.

Record Attendance: 3,000 v Oxford United - FA Cup 1st Round 1994
Record Victory: Not known
Record Defeat: Not known
Record Goalscorer: Kevin Stone
Record Appearances: Mick McKeown - 500+
Additional Records: Paid £5,000 to Sutton United for Richard Evans
Received £8,000 from Slough Town for David Lay

Senior Honours: Isthmian League Division 1 1987-88, League Cup 92-93.
Berks & Bucks Senior Cup x11

10 YEAR RECORD

00-01	01-02	02-03	03-04	04-05	05-06	06-07	07-08	08-09	09-10
Isth2 14	Isth2 9	Isth1N 11	Isth1S 16	SthW 13	SthW 6	Sthsw 7	Sthsw 9	SthM 9	SthM 15

NORTH GREENFORD UNITED

Chairman: John Bivens
Secretary: Mrs Barbara Bivens **(T)** 07915 661 580
(E) barbarabivens@talktalk.net
Additional Committee Members: John Chorley, Barbara Bivens, Steve Hawkins, Tony Tuohy, Dave Duffy, Lorraine Chorley, Pat Hillier
Manager: Steve Ringrose
Programme Editor: Pat Hillier **(E)** agneshillier@aol.com

Unfortunately an up-to-date photograph was not available at the time of going to press

Club Factfile

Founded: 1944 **Nickname:** Blues
Previous Names: None
Previous Leagues: London Spartan, Combined Counties 2002-10

Club Colours (change): Blue with white trim/blue with white trim/blue (Yellow with red trim/yellow with red trim/yellow)

Ground: Berkeley Fields, Berkley Avenue, Greenford UB6 0NX **(T)** 0208 422 8923
Capacity: 2,000 **Seats:** 150 **Covered:** 100 **Clubhouse:** Yes **Shop:** No
Previous Grounds:
Simple Directions
A40 going towards London. At the Greenford Flyover come down the slip road, keep in the left hand lane, turn left onto the Greenford Road (A4127). At the third set of traffic lights, turn right into Berkeley Av. Go to the bottom of the road. There is a large car park. We are on the right hand side.

Record Attendance: 985 v AFC Wimbledon
Record Victory: Not known
Record Defeat: Not known
Record Goalscorer: John Hill - 98
Record Appearances: Not known
Additional Records:

Senior Honours: Combined Counties League Premier Division 2009-10

10 YEAR RECORD

00-01	01-02	02-03	03-04	04-05	05-06	06-07	07-08	08-09	09-10
		CC 10	CCP 14	CCP 2	CCP 13	CCP 5	CCP 6	CCP 2	CCP 1

NORTHWOOD

Chairman: Ian Barry
Secretary: Alan Evans (T) 07960 744 349
(E) alan.evansnfc@btopenworld.com
Additional Committee Members: Ken Green, Tino Nannavecchia, Pat Byrne, Peter Barry, Dave Gibbs, Mick Russell, Betty Walley
Manager: Mark Barnham
Programme Editor: Ken Green (E) ken.green01@ntlworld.com

Back row: Mark Barnham (Manager), Sam Sharples, Rodney Hicks, Scott Raper, John Sonuga, Troy Roach, Leon Osei, Andrew Iwediuno, Dean Wallace, Jamie Lindsay, Marie Scott (Physio).
Front row: Kyle Matthews, John Christian, Mark Burgess, Mitch Swain, Ryan Tackley, Wayne Jackson, Scott Orphanou.
Photo: James Brown

Club Factfile

Founded: 1899 **Nickname:** Woods
Previous Names: Northwood Town
Previous Leagues: Harrow & Wembley 1932-69, Middlesex 1969-78, Hellenic 1979-84, London Spartan 1984-93, Isthmian 1993-2005, 2007-10, Southern 2005-07

Club Colours (change): Red/red/red (Yellow with red/blue with yellow trim/blue)

Ground: Northwood Park, Chestnut Avenue, Northwood, Middlesex HA6 1HR (T) 01923 827 148
Capacity: 3,075 **Seats:** 308 **Covered:** 932 **Clubhouse:** Yes **Shop:** No
Previous Grounds:
Simple Directions
M25 Junction 18, take A404 through Rickmansworth to Northwood. After passing under grey railway bridge, take first right into Chestnut Avenue. Ground is in grounds of Northwood Park, entrance is 400 metres on left.
(Ground is 20 minutes from J.18).

Record Attendance: 1,642 v Chlesea - Friendly July 1997
Record Victory: 15-0 v Dateline (H) - Middlesex Intermediate Cup 1973
Record Defeat: 0-8 v Bedfont - Middlesex League 1975
Record Goalscorer: Not known
Record Appearances: Chris Gell - 493+
Additional Records: Lawrence Yaku scored 61 goals during season 1999-2000

Senior Honours: Isthmian League Division 1 North 2002-03, Charity Shield 2002.
Middlesex Premier Cup 1994-95.

10 YEAR RECORD

00-01	01-02	02-03	03-04	04-05	05-06	06-07	07-08	08-09	09-10
Isth1 8	Isth1 5	Isth1N 1	Isth P 21	Isth P 17	SthP 19	SthP 22	Isth1N 10	Isth1N 6	Isth1N 10

RUGBY TOWN

Chairman: Brian Melvin

Secretary: Doug Wilkins (T) 07976 284 614 (E) dougwilkins44@hotmail.com

Additional Committee Members:
Mike Yeats, Les Leeson, Danny Lorden, Lisa Melvin, Darren Knapp, Jim Melvin

Manager: Martin Sockett

Programme Editor: Doug Wilkins (E) dougwilkins44@hotmail.com

Unfortunately an up-to-date photograph was not available at the time of going to press

Club Factfile

Founded: 1956 **Nickname:** The Valley

Previous Names: Valley Sports 1956-71, Valley Sport Rugby 1971-73, VS Rugby 1973-2000, Rugby United 2000-05

Previous Leagues: Rugby & District 1956-62, Coventry & Partnership, North Warwickshire 1963-69, United Counties 1969-75 West Midlands 1975-83

Club Colours (change): Sky blue/white/sky blue (All orange)

Ground: Butlin Road, Rugby, Warwicks CV21 3SD (T) 01788 844 806

Capacity: 6,000 **Seats:** 750 **Covered:** 1,000 **Clubhouse:** Yes **Shop:** Yes

Previous Grounds:

Simple Directions
From M6 J.1 North and South, take A426 signed Rugby at third island turn left into Boughton Road. Continue along Boughton Road after passing under viaduct turn right at traffic lights, B5414 up the hill take second left at mini island into Butlin Road.

Record Attendance: 3,961 v Northampton Town - FA Cup 1984

Record Victory: 10-0 v Ilkeston Town - FA Trophy 04/09/1985

Record Defeat: 1-11 v Ilkeston Town (A) - 18/04/1998

Record Goalscorer: Danny Conway - 124

Record Appearances: Danny Conway - 374

Additional Records: Paid £3,500 for R Smith, I Crawley and G Bradder
Received £15,000 from Northampton Town for Terry Angus

Senior Honours: FA Vase 1982-83. Southern League Midland Division 1986-87. Midland Combination Division 1 2001-02.
Birmingham Senior Cup 1988-89, 91-92

10 YEAR RECORD

00-01	01-02	02-03	03-04	04-05	05-06	06-07	07-08	08-09	09-10
MCm2 2	MCm1 1	MCmP 6	MCmP 3		SthP 15	SthP 17	SthP 15	SthP 17	SthP 22

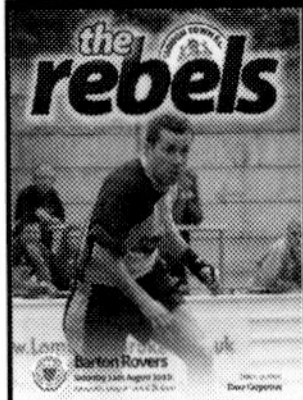

SLOUGH TOWN

Chairman: Steve Easterbrook
Secretary: Gary Thomas (T) 07989 434 371
(E) secretary@sloughtownfc.net
Additional Committee Members: Ray Merryweather, Glen Riley, Alan Harding, Mike Lightfoot, Gary Thomas, Chris Sliski, Kevin Merryweather
Manager: Steve Bateman
Programme Editor: Glen Riley (E) programme@sloughtownfc.net

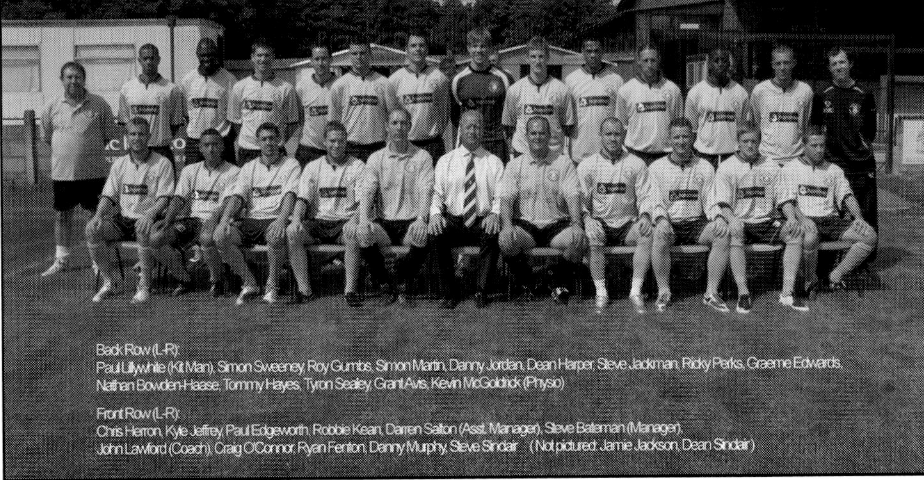

Back Row (L-R):
Paul Lillywhite (Kit Man), Simon Sweeney, Roy Gumbs, Simon Martin, Danny Jordan, Dean Harper, Steve Jackman, Ricky Perks, Graeme Edwards, Nathan Bowden-Haase, Tommy Hayes, Tyron Sealey, Grant Avis, Kevin McGoldrick (Physio)

Front Row (L-R):
Chris Herron, Kyle Jeffrey, Paul Edgeworth, Robbie Kean, Darren Salton (Asst. Manager), Steve Bateman (Manager), John Lawford (Coach), Craig O'Connor, Ryan Fenton, Danny Murphy, Steve Sinclair (Not pictured: Jamie Jackson, Dean Sinclair)

Club Factfile

Founded: 1890 **Nickname:** The Rebels
Previous Names:
Previous Leagues: Southern Alliance 1892-93, Berks & Bucks 1901-05, Gt Western Suburban 1909-19, Spartan 1920-39, Herts & Middx 1940-45, Corinthian 1946-63, Athenian 1963-73, Isthmian 1973-90, 94-95, Conf. 1990-94

Club Colours (change): Amber & navy blue/navy blue/amber (Red and blue shirts/black/red)

Ground: Sharing with Beaconsfield SYCOB, Holloways Park, Slough Rd HP9 2SG (T) 01494 676 868
Capacity: 3,500 **Seats:** 200 **Covered:** Yes **Clubhouse:** Yes **Shop:** Yes
Previous Grounds:
Simple Directions
Leave M40 at Junction 2, take A355 towards Slough, only 50 yards off the roundabout on the A355 is slip road on right with sign giving Club name. Turn right through gate and clubhouse is 200 metres on the right. The ground is 'signposted' from both sides of the carriageway (A355).

Record Attendance: 8,000 v Liverpool - Schoolboys 1976
Record Victory: 17-0 v Railway Clearing House - 1921-22
Record Defeat: 1-11 v Chesham Town - 1909-10
Record Goalscorer: Tony Norris - 84 (1925-26)
Record Appearances: Terry Reardon - 458 (1964-81)
Additional Records: Paid £18,000 to Farnborough Town for Colin Fielder
Received £22,000 from Wycombe Wanderers for Steve Thompson

Senior Honours: Isthmian League 1980-81, 89-90. Athenian League x3. Berks & Bucks Senior Cup x10.

10 YEAR RECORD

00-01	01-02	02-03	03-04	04-05	05-06	06-07	07-08	08-09	09-10
Isth P 20	Isth1 8	Isth1S 4	Isth1S 4	Isth P 13	Isth P 17	Isth P 22	Sthsw 21	Sthsw 16	SthM 5

SOHAM TOWN RANGERS

Chairman: Colin Murfit
Secretary: Karen Prewett (T) 07917 417 516
(E) ladykarenp@btinternet.com
Additional Committee Members: Lisa Moore, Walter Gray, Bill Gray, Graham Eley, Brian Eley, Malcolm Howe, Mark Bailey, Mick Gipp, Dave Thomas, Bett Hornby, Andy Burford, Vince Mallett
Manager: Ian Benjamin
Programme Editor: Fred Parker (E) fred@fredparker.plus.com

Unfortunately an up-to-date photograph was not available at the time of going to press

Club Factfile

Founded: 1947 **Nickname:** Town or Rangers
Previous Names: Soham Town and Soham Rangers merged in 1947
Previous Leagues: Peterborough & District, Eastern Counties 1963-2008

Club Colours (change): Green with white trim/green with white trim/green and white (All royal blue)

Ground: Julius Martin Lane, Soham, Ely, Cambridgeshire CB7 5EQ (T) 01353 720 732
Capacity: 2,000 **Seats:** 250 **Covered:** 1,000 **Clubhouse:** Yes **Shop:** Yes
Previous Grounds:
Simple Directions
Take the turning off the A14 for Soham/Ely. Join the A142 following signs for Ely/Soham. On approaching Soham at the Q8 Petrol Station, continue down the Soham by-pass for approx. 1.5 miles. Turn left after the Bypass Motel, continue bearing left across the Common into Bushel Lane, at end of road, turn right into Hall Street. Julius Martin Lane is 2nd left.

Record Attendance: 3,000 v Pegasus - FA Amateur Cup 1963
Record Victory: Not known
Record Defeat: Not known
Record Goalscorer: Not known
Record Appearances: Not known
Additional Records:

Senior Honours: Eastern Counties League Premier Division 2007-08

10 YEAR RECORD

00-01	01-02	02-03	03-04	04-05	05-06	06-07	07-08	08-09	09-10
ECP 9	ECP 12	ECP 3	ECP 5	ECP 7	ECP 10	ECP	ECP 1	SthM 15	SthM 11

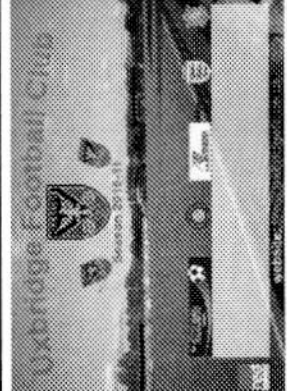

UXBRIDGE

Chairman: Alan Holloway
Secretary: Roger Stevens (T) 07773 513 405
(E) sec@uxbridgefc.co.uk

Additional Committee Members:
A Odell, D Tucker, M Burell, C Rycraft, D Marshall, D Gill, R Turton

Manager: Tony Choules
Programme Editor: Graham Hiseman (E) bbpublications@tiscali.co.uk

Back Row (L-R): Mark Smith, Simon Goodrham, Wayne Carter, Gavin Brown, Rob Fitzgerald
Middle Row: Howard Hall, Craige Tomkins, Michael Howe, Freddie Toomer, Mark Dennison, Matt Burton, Stuart Farrell, Sam Kanani, Tommy Howe
Front Row: Stuart Everly (Physio) Chris Moore, Tom Green, Paolo Cicero, Paul Mills (Assistant Manager), Tony Choules (Manager), Rob Tidbury (Goalkeeping Coach) Jermaine Gumbs, Mohamed Hashi, Kevin Warner, Phil Granville (Reserve Team Manager)

Club Factfile

Founded: 1871 **Nickname:** The Reds
Previous Names: Uxbridge Town 1923-45
Previous Leagues: Southern 1894-99, Gt Western Suburban 1906-19, 20-23, Athenian 1919-20, 24-37, 63-82, Spartan 1937-38, London 1938-46, Gt Western Comb. 1939-45, Corinthian 1946-63, Isthmian

Club Colours (change): Red/white/red (All white)

Ground: Honeycroft Road, West Drayton, Middlesex UB7 8HX (T) 01895 443 557
Capacity: 3,770 **Seats:** 339 **Covered:** 760 **Clubhouse:** Yes **Shop:**
Previous Grounds: RAF Stadium 1923-48, Cleveland Road 1948-78
Simple Directions
M4 to Junction 4 (Heathrow), take A408 towards Uxbridge for 1 mile, turn left into Horton Road. Ground 1/2 mile on right.

Record Attendance: 1,000 v Arsenal - Opening of the floodlights 1981
Record Victory: Not known
Record Defeat: Not known
Record Goalscorer: Phil Duff - 153
Record Appearances: Roger Nicholls - 1,054
Additional Records:

Senior Honours: Middlesex Senior Cup 1893-94, 95-96, 1950-51, 2000-01. London Challenge Cup 1993-94, 96-97, 98-99.

10 YEAR RECORD

00-01	01-02	02-03	03-04	04-05	05-06	06-07	07-08	08-09	09-10
Isth1 7	Isth1 9	Isth1N 5	Isth1N 13	SthE 4	SthE 14	Sthsw 8	Sthsw 5	Sthsw 13	Sthsw 15

WOODFORD UNITED

Chairman: Andrew Worrall

Secretary: David Allen (T) 07889 847 428
(E) allend@wufc.biz

Additional Committee Members:
R Adams, D Allen, D Grogan, Y Worrall, G Allen,

Manager: Phil Mason

Programme Editor: David Allen (E) allend@wufc.biz

Unfortunately an up-to-date photograph was not available at the time of going to press

Club Factfile

Founded: 1946 **Nickname:** Reds

Previous Names:

Previous Leagues: Central Northants Combination 1946-70, United Counties 1971-2006

Club Colours (change): All red (Yellow/black/yellow)

Ground: Byfield Road, Woodford Halse, Daventry, Northants NN11 3QR (T) 01327 263 734

Capacity: 3,000 **Seats:** 252 **Covered:** 252 **Clubhouse:** Yes **Shop:** No

Previous Grounds:

Simple Directions
From M1 J18, M40 J11, take A361 Banbury to Daventry road. Exit A361 in Byfield, follow signs for Woodford Halse. Ground on left 200 yards past industrial estate.

Record Attendance: 1,500 v Stockport County
Record Victory: Not known
Record Defeat: Not known
Record Goalscorer: Not known
Record Appearances: Not known
Additional Records:

Senior Honours: United Counties League Division 2 1973-74, Premier Division 2005-06.

10 YEAR RECORD

00-01	01-02	02-03	03-04	04-05	05-06	06-07	07-08	08-09	09-10
UCL 1 8	UCL 1 3	UCL P 14	UCL P 12	UCL P 7	UCL P 1	SthM 8	SthM 19	SthM 20	SthM 7

A.F.C. TOTTON

Chairman: Phil Shephard
Secretary: Norman Cook **(T)** 02380 669 544
(E) secretary@afctotton.com
Additional Committee Members: Paul Malden, Alf Peckham, Geoffrey Gook, Clive Bratcher, Richard Vowles, John Heskins, Sean McGlead, Ann Dunwell, Ken Dunwell, Valerie Devoy, Angie Cox, Peter Hart, Ted Rose, Bob Coombs, Barbara Piper, Brenda Andrews, Mick Carter, Sheila Benfield, Angie Hales, Malcolm Wort, Derek Hutchings.
Manager: Stuart Ritchie
Programme Editor: Steve Chadwick **(E)** programme@afctotton.com

Archive photo

Club Factfile

Founded: 1886 **Nickname:** Stags
Previous Names: Totton FC until merger with Totton Athletic in 1979
Previous Leagues: Hampshire 1982-86, Wessex 1986-2008

Club Colours (change): All blue (All yellow)

Ground: Testwood Park, Testwood Place, Totton, Southampton SO40 3BE **(T)** 02380 868 981
Capacity: 2,500 **Seats:** 200 **Covered:** 250 **Clubhouse:** Yes **Shop:** Yes
Previous Grounds:
Simple Directions
Leave the M27 at J. 3 and join the M271. At the roundabout take the second exit on to the slip road and join the A35 dual carriageway. Shortly after take the next slip road on to the A36 which takes you under the bypass. Continue until you reach a roundabout. Take the 3rd exit into Library Road, follow this for about 100 yards then turn left in Testwood Lane. Testwood Place is the 2nd turning on the right, approx 150 yards down Testwood Lane.

Record Attendance: 600 v Windsor & Eton - FA Cup 4th Qualifying Round 1982-83
Record Victory: Not known
Record Defeat: Not known
Record Goalscorer: Not known
Record Appearances: James Sherlington
Additional Records:

Senior Honours: Hampshire League 1981-82, 84-85. Wessex League Premier Division 2007-08.

10 YEAR RECORD

00-01	01-02	02-03	03-04	04-05	05-06	06-07	07-08	08-09	09-10
Wex 5	Wex 3	Wex 3	Wex 8	Wex1 8	Wex1 4	WexP 2	WexP 1	Sthsw 3	Sthsw 2

ABINGDON UNITED

Chairman: Mrs Deborah Blackmore

Secretary: John Blackmore (T) 07747 615 691

(E) john.blackmore2@ntlworld.com

Additional Committee Members: Alf White, Pat Evans, Shirley Evans, Bill Fletcher, Doreen White, Darren Edwards, Chris Druce, Chris Janes, Robin Yuill, Derek Turner, Steve Clarkson, Pete Hunt, Andy Slater, Jeff Organ

Manager: Richie Bourne

Programme Editor: Bill Fletcher (E) billfletcher@ntlworld.com

Back Row (L-R): Shane Sherbourne (Goalkeeper Coach), Chris Harper, John McMahon, Luke Carnell, Tom Franklin, Gareth Tucker, Jon Beames, Richard Peirson (Player Coach), Steve Davis, John Mills, Sam Elkins, Andy Lawson (Club Physio)
Front Row: Andy Younie, Anaclet Odhiambo, Tom Melledew, Richie Bourne (Manager), Jim Smith , James Organ, Pablo Haysham

Club Factfile

Founded: 1946 **Nickname:** The U's

Previous Names:

Previous Leagues: North Berkshire 1949-58, Hellenic 1958-2006

Club Colours (change): All yellow (All red)

Ground: The North Court, Northcourt Road, Abingdon OX14 1PL (T) 01235 203 203

Capacity: 2,000 **Seats:** 158 **Covered:** 258 **Clubhouse:** Yes **Shop:**

Previous Grounds:

Simple Directions
From the north – Leave A34 at Abingdon north turning. Ground on right at first set of traffic lights.
From the south – Enter Town Centre, leave north on A4183 (Oxford Road).
Ground on left after one mile.

Record Attendance: 1,500 v Oxford United - Friendly 1994

Record Victory: Not known

Record Defeat: Not known

Record Goalscorer: Not known

Record Appearances: Not known

Additional Records:

Senior Honours: Hellenic League Division 1 1981-82, League Cup 1965-66. Berks & Bucks Senior Trophy x2.

10 YEAR RECORD

00-01	01-02	02-03	03-04	04-05	05-06	06-07	07-08	08-09	09-10
Hel P 5	Hel P 4	Hel P 8	Hel P 11	Hel P 5	Hel P 3	Hel P 18	Sthsw 16	Sthsw 15	Sthsw 14

ALMONDSBURY TOWN

Chairman: Bob Jenkins

Secretary: David Jones (T) 07903 655 723 (E) davidj693@hotmail.co.uk

Additional Committee Members: Steve Martin, Mark Mapstone, John Clift, Fran Jenkins, Lyn Jeffries, Steve Watkins, Roger Perry, John Stewart

Manager: Richard Thompson

Programme Editor: David Jones (E) davidj693@hotmail.co.uk

Unfortunately an up-to-date photograph was not available at the time of going to press

Club Factfile

Founded: 1897 **Nickname:** Almonds

Previous Names: Almondsbury Greenway > 1987. Almondsbury Picksons > 1993.

Previous Leagues: Gloucestershire County, Hellenic > 2009-10

Club Colours (change): Sky blue and white stripes/navy/navy (Yellow/black/black)

Ground: Oakland Park, Almondsbury, Bristol BS32 4AG (T) 01454 612 740

Capacity: 2,000 **Seats:** **Covered:** **Clubhouse:** Yes **Shop:** No

Previous Grounds:

Simple Directions

From M4 (west), leave at J.20 and join M5 (south west). Leave immediately at J16. From slip road take the third exit onto A38 (A38 Thornbury). Take the first left approx. 100 metres from junction signposted 'Gloucestershire FA HQ'. Follow lane straight and turn right for car park. From M5 South, leave at J.16 and follow above.

Record Attendance: 2,100 Newport AFC v Abingdon United - Hellenic League Cup Final 1989-90

Record Victory: Not Known

Record Defeat: Not Known

Record Goalscorer: Not Known

Record Appearances: Not Known

Additional Records:

Senior Honours: Gloucestershire County League 1976-77, 77-78, 78-79, 79-80, 80-81.
Hellenic League 1983-84, 2009-10, Division 1 1988-89, League cup 1983-84, 84-85, 2008-09.

10 YEAR RECORD

00-01	01-02	02-03	03-04	04-05	05-06	06-07	07-08	08-09	09-10
Hel P 19	Hel P 18	Hel P 17	Hel P 21	Hel P 9	Hel P 14	Hel P 5	Hel P 2	Hel P 4	Hel P 1

ANDOVER

Chairman: John Smith
Secretary: Simon Bevis (T) 07775 677 446
(E) simonbevis@btinternet.com
Additional Committee Members:
Ray Emery, Alan Mussell, Martin Mitty, Bob Haynes
Manager: Andy Leader
Programme Editor: TBA (E)

Archive photo

Club Factfile

Founded: 1983 **Nickname:** The Lions
Previous Names:
Previous Leagues: Salisbury & District, Hampshire 1896-98, 1899-1901, 1902-62, Southern 1898-99, 71-93, 98-99, Western 1962-71, Wessex 1993-98, 99-2006
Club Colours (change): Red and black stripes/black/black (Pink/white/white)

Ground: The Portway Stadium, West Portway Ind. Est. Andover SP10 3LF (T) 01264 351 302
Capacity: 3,000 **Seats:** 250 **Covered:** 250 **Clubhouse:** Yes **Shop:** No
Previous Grounds:
Simple Directions
Situated on western outskirts of town. Off A303 follow signs to Portway Industrial Estate. The ground is located on the West Portway Industrial Estate.

Record Attendance: 1,100 v Leicester City - Ground opening
Record Victory: Not known
Record Defeat: Not known
Record Goalscorer: Tommy Muchalls
Record Appearances: Pete Pollard
Additional Records:

Senior Honours: Wessex League 2000-01, 01-02, League Cup 2001-02. Hampshire Senior Cup x5. North Hampshire Senior Cup x6.

10 YEAR RECORD

00-01	01-02	02-03	03-04	04-05	05-06	06-07	07-08	08-09	09-10
Wex 1	Wex 1	Wex 7	Wex 6	Wex1 5	Wex1 3	Sthsw 9	Sthsw 19	Sthsw 19	Sthsw 20

BIDEFORD

Chairman: Roy Portch
Secretary: Kevin Tyrrell (T) 07929 078 613
(E) k.tyrrell@talktalk.net

Additional Committee Members:
Ian Knight

Manager: Sean Joyce
Programme Editor: Ian Knight (E) ianknight160@btinternet.com

Club Factfile

Founded: 1949 **Nickname:** The Robins
Previous Names: Bideford Town
Previous Leagues: Devon & Exeter 1947-49, Western 1949-72, 75-2010, Southern 1972-75

Club Colours (change): All red (All blue)

Ground: The Sports Ground, Kingsley Road, Bideford EX39 2LH (T) 01237 474 974
Capacity: 6,000 **Seats:** 375 **Covered:** 1,000 **Clubhouse:** Yes **Shop:**
Previous Grounds:
Simple Directions
Exit M5 at J.27. A361 to Barnstaple. Turn left onto A39 to Bideford. 9 miles turn left into town. Ground on right hand side as entering town centre.

Record Attendance: 6,000 v Gloucester City - FA Cup 4th Qualifying Round
Record Victory: Not known
Record Defeat: Not known
Record Goalscorer: Tommy Robinson - 259
Record Appearances: Derek May - 527
Additional Records:

Senior Honours: Western LEague 1963-64, 70-71, 71-72, 81-82, 82-83, 2001-02, 03-04, 04-05, 05-06, 09-10, Division 1 1951-52,
Division 3 1949-50.
Devon Senior Cup 1979-80

10 YEAR RECORD

00-01	01-02	02-03	03-04	04-05	05-06	06-07	07-08	08-09	09-10
WestP 5	WestP 1	WestP 3	WestP 1	WestP 1	WestP 1	WestP 4	WestP 6	WestP 6	WestP 1

BISHOP'S CLEEVE

Chairman: David Walker
Secretary: Nigel Green **(T)** 07919 518 880
(E) negreen@tiscali.co.uk
Additional Committee Members: Dave Lewis, Hanif Tai, Bob Weaver, Lyn Weaver, Malcolm Eustace, Paul Price, Hilary Green
Manager: Paul Collicutt
Programme Editor: TBA **(E)**

Unfortunately an up-to-date photograph was not available at the time of going to press

Club Factfile

Founded: 1892 **Nickname:** Villagers
Previous Names:
Previous Leagues: Cheltenham, North Gloucestershire, Hellenic 1983-2006

Club Colours (change): All blue (All white)

Ground: Kayte Lane, Bishop's Cleeve, Cheltenham GL52 3PD **(T)** 01242 676 166
Capacity: 1,500 **Seats:** 50 **Covered:** 50 **Clubhouse:** Yes **Shop:** Yes
Previous Grounds: Stoke Road and ground shared with Moreton Town, Wollen Sports, Highworth Town and Forest Green Rovers
Simple Directions
From Cheltenham take A435 towards Evesham. Pass racecourse, take right at traffic lights then first left into Kayte Lane. Ground 1/2 mile on left.

Record Attendance: 1,300 v Cheltenham Town - July 2006
Record Victory: Not known
Record Defeat: Not known
Record Goalscorer: Kevin Slack
Record Appearances: John Skeen
Additional Records:

Senior Honours: Hellenic League Division 1 1986-87, Premier League Cup 1988.
Gloucestershire Junior Cup North. Gloucestershire Senior Amateur Cup North x3.

10 YEAR RECORD

00-01	01-02	02-03	03-04	04-05	05-06	06-07	07-08	08-09	09-10
Hel1W 2	Hel P 10	Hel P 9	Hel P 3	Hel P 3	Hel P 2	SthM 13	SthM 12	Sthsw 18	Sthsw 11

BRIDGWATER TOWN 1984

Chairman: Alan Hurford
Secretary: Roger Palmer **(T)** 07596 033 277
(E) palmer449@btinternet.com
Additional Committee Members: Keith Setter, Alan Slade, Roland Rich, Eddie Pike, Lin Godfrey, Ian Moore, Shaun Ryall, Winston Davey, Pat Parker, Robin Mobsby, Howard Pike, Ben Norman, Rick Norman, Madeline Davey
Manager: Rob Dray
Programme Editor: Roger Palmer **(E)** palmer449@btinternet.com

Back Row (L-R): Winston Davey (Vice Chairman), Kevin Milsom (Assistant Manager), Carl Tucker, Neil Peek, Josh Turner, Luke Buckingham, Mat Pitcher, Rob Snook, Simon Lyons, Andrew Forward, Leigh Bailey, Josh Ford, Ian Bellinger, Adam Sparks, Becky Bidgood (Physio)
Front Row: Rob Dray (Manager), Eddie Pike (Committee Member), Shane Kingston, Sean Kenny, Andy Robertson, Lee Singleton (from Sponsors TMB), Chris Young (Captain), Mike Mackay, Tom Parsons, Sam Peppin, Keith Setter (President), Steve Perkins (Player/Coach)

Club Factfile

Founded: 1984 **Nickname:** The Robins
Previous Names: Bridgwater Town
Previous Leagues: Somerset Senior, Western

Club Colours (change): Red & white/white/white (Blue and white/white/white)

Ground: Fairfax Park, College Way, Bath Road, Bridgwater, Somerset TA6 4TZ **(T)** 01278 446 899
Capacity: 2,500 **Seats:** 128 **Covered:** 500 **Clubhouse:** Yes **Shop:** Yes
Previous Grounds:
Simple Directions
Southbound from Bristol M5 J.23- enter town on A39 from Glastonbury. Ground is between Bridgwater College and Rugby Ground by railway bridge.
Northbound from Taunton – M5 J.24- enter town on A38, follow signs for Glastonbury (A39). Ground is between Bridgwater College and Rugby Ground as you pass over railway bridge.

Record Attendance: 1,112 v Taunton Town - 26/02/1997
Record Victory: Not Known
Record Defeat: Not Known
Record Goalscorer: Not Known
Record Appearances: Not Known
Additional Records:

Senior Honours: Somerset Senior League x3. Somerset Senior Cup 1993-94, 95-96. Western League Division 1 1995-96.

10 YEAR RECORD

00-01	01-02	02-03	03-04	04-05	05-06	06-07	07-08	08-09	09-10
WestP 15	WestP 8	WestP 6	WestP 6	WestP 6	WestP 11	WestP 2	Sthsw 6	Sthsw 7	Sthsw 3

CINDERFORD TOWN

Chairman: Ashley Saunders
Secretary: Robert Maskell (T) 07835 511 774
(E) maskellbilly@yahoo.co.uk
Additional Committee Members: Ken McNally, Ray Read, Alan Jones, Beryl Reed, Tina Jones, Robert Knight, Chris Warren, Barry Turner, Mike James, Stuart Tait
Manager: Paul Weeks
Programme Editor: Liam Maskell (E) liammaskell@googlemail.com

Archive photo

Club Factfile

Founded: 1922 **Nickname:** The Foresters
Previous Names:
Previous Leagues: Gloucestershire Northern Senior 1922-39, 60-62, Western 1946-59, Warwickshire Combination 1963-64, West Midlands 1965-69, Gloucestershire Co. 1970-73, 85-89, Midland Comb. 1974-84, Hellenic 1990-95
Club Colours (change): Black and white stripes/black/black (Yellow with blue trim/blue/blue)

Ground: The Causeway, Hildene, Cinderford, Gloucestershire GL14 2QH (T) 01594 827 147 / 822 039
Capacity: 3,500 **Seats:** 250 **Covered:** 1,000 **Clubhouse:** Yes **Shop:** Yes
Previous Grounds: Mousel Lane, Royal Oak
Simple Directions
Take A40 west out of Gloucester, then A48 for 8 miles. Turn right at Elton Garage onto A4151 (Forest of Dean). Continue through Littledean, climb steep hill, turn right at crossroads (football ground), then second left into Latimer Road. Or if coming from Severn Bridge take A48 Chepstow through Lydney, Newnham then left at Elton Garage – then as above.

Record Attendance: 4,850 v Minehead - Western League 1955-56
Record Victory: 13-0 v Cam Mills - 1938-39
Record Defeat: 0-10 v Sutton Coldfield - 1978-79
Record Goalscorer: Not known
Record Appearances: Russel Bowles - 528
Additional Records:

Senior Honours: Western League Division 2 1956-57. Midland Combination 1981-82. Hellenic Premier Division 1994-95, League Cup 94-95. Gloucestershire Senior Amateur Cup North x6. Gloucestershire Junior Cup North 1980-81. Gloucestershire Senior Cup 2000-01.

10 YEAR RECORD

00-01	01-02	02-03	03-04	04-05	05-06	06-07	07-08	08-09	09-10
SthW 19	SthW 15	SthW 15	SthW 20	SthW 16	SthW 15	SthM 9	SthM 16	SthM 11	Sthsw 16

CLEVEDON TOWN

Chairman: John Croft

Secretary: Brian Rose (T) 07768 100 632 (E) brian.rose@blueyonder.co.uk

Additional Committee Members:
Russell Conybeare, Matthew Hector

Manager: Micky Bell

Programme Editor: Dave Wright (E) smallwavedave@hotmail.com

Club Factfile

Founded: 1880 **Nickname:** Seasiders

Previous Names: Clevedon FC and Ashtonians merged in 1974

Previous Leagues: Weston & District, Somerset Senior, Bristol Charity, Bristol & District, Bristol Suburban, Western 1974-93

Club Colours (change): Blue & white stripes/blue/blue (All green)

Ground: Hand Stadium, Davis Lane, Clevedon BS21 6TG (T) 01275 871 600

Capacity: 3,500 **Seats:** 300 **Covered:** 1,600 **Clubhouse:** Yes **Shop:** Yes

Previous Grounds: Dial Hill until early 1890s, Teignmouth Road > 1991

Simple Directions
Exit J20 from M5, at bottom of slip road, turn left at roundabout into Central Way. At next roundabout turn left to Kenn Road. Stay on Kenn Road out of town, cross river, take 1st left into Davis Lane, over motorway. Ground 200m on right.

Record Attendance: 2,300 v Billingham Synthonia - FA Amateur Cup 1952-53

Record Victory: 18-0 v Dawlish Town (H) - Western League Premier Division 24/04/1993

Record Defeat: 3-13 v Yate YMCA (A) - Bristol Combination 1967-68

Record Goalscorer: Not known

Record Appearances: Not known

Additional Records:

Senior Honours: Somerset Senior Cup 1901-02, 04-05, 28-29, 2000-01, 01-02. Somerset Premier Cup x4.
Southern League Western Division 1992-93, 2005-06, Midland Division 1998-99.

10 YEAR RECORD

00-01	01-02	02-03	03-04	04-05	05-06	06-07	07-08	08-09	09-10
SthP 19	SthW 10	SthW 13	SthW 11	SthW 4	SthW 1	SthP 18	SthP 11	SthP 18	SthP 21

FROME TOWN

Chairman: Jeremy Alderman

Secretary: Ian Pearce **(T)** 07811 511 222
(E) ian@frometownfc.co.uk

Additional Committee Members: Terry Wolff, Richard Hudson, Gary Collinson, Jon Curle, Jamie Malley, Brian Stevens, Neil Clark, Ivan Carver, Colin Carpenter

Manager: Darren Perrin

Programme Editor: Andrew Meaden **(E)** programmes@amprintcopy.co.uk

Back row (L-R): Ian Pearce (Club Secretary), Derek Graham (Assistant Manager), Shaun Baker (Kit Manager), Terry Wolff (Vice-Chairman), Andrew Crabtree (Manager), Steve Hunt, Dan Harvey, Alex Lapham, Ed Quelch, Josh Payne, Paul Farrell, Greg Lake, Mike Whittington, Matt Cowler, Brian Stevens, Gavin Hares (Chairman), Richard Hudson (Treasurer), Lloyd Chamberlain (Reserve Team Manager).
Front row (L-R): Gavin Eyres, Jamie Cheeseman, Ashley Clarke, Simon Millard, Simeon Allison, Jeremy Alderman (Main Club Sponsor), Roger Smith (Main Club Sponsor), Shaun Percival, Matt Peters, Ian Kennedy.
Picture courtesy of Official Club Photographer: Charlie Hadfield.

Club Factfile

Founded: 1904 **Nickname:** The Robins
Previous Names: None
Previous Leagues: Wiltshire Premier 1904, Somerset Senior 1906-19, Western 1919, 63-2009

Club Colours (change): All red (All blue)

Ground: Aldersmith Stadium, Badgers Hill, Berkley Road, Frome BA11 2EH **(T)** 01373 464 087
Capacity: 2,000 **Seats:** 150 **Covered:** 200 **Clubhouse:** Yes **Shop:**
Previous Grounds:

Simple Directions
From Bath, take A36 and then A361. At third roundabout, follow A361 and at fourth roundabout take A3098. Take first right and ground is one mile on left hand side. From south follow A36 (Warminster) and take A3098 to Frome. At T Junction turn right and take second exit at roundabout. Ground is first right and follow road for one mile on left hand side.

Record Attendance: 8,000 v Leyton Orient - FA Cup 1st Round 1958
Record Victory: Not Known
Record Defeat: Not Known
Record Goalscorer: Not Known
Record Appearances: Not Known
Additional Records:

Senior Honours: Somerset County League 1906-07, 08-09, 10-11.
Western League Division 1 1919-20, 2001-02, Premier Division 1962-63, 78-79.
Somerset Senior Cup 1932-33, 33-34, 50-51 Somerset Premier Cup 1966-67, 68-69 (shared), 82-83, 2008-09.

10 YEAR RECORD

00-01	01-02	02-03	03-04	04-05	05-06	06-07	07-08	08-09	09-10
West1 3	West1 1	WestP 11	WestP 3	WestP 3	WestP 7	WestP 3	WestP 4	WestP 2	Sthsw 6

GOSPORT BOROUGH

Chairman: Mark Hook
Secretary: Brian Cosgrave **(T)** 07984 960 537
(E) brian.cosgrave@hotmail.co.uk
Additional Committee Members: Kevin Blenkinsopp, John Stimpson, Brian Cosgrave, Paul Hook, Barry Mizen, Kevin Mizen, Debbie Blenkinsopp, Glen Reeves, Ian McKiddie, Tracey Dowell.
Manager: Alex Pike
Programme Editor: Nigel Miller **(E)** programme@gosportboroughfc.co.uk

Gosport skipper Craig Davis in action against Taunton Town on the opening day of the 2009/10 season. Photo Keith Fuller

Club Factfile

Founded: 1944 **Nickname:** The 'Boro'
Previous Names: Gosport Borough Athletic
Previous Leagues: Portsmouth 1944-45, Hampshire 1945-78, Southern 1978-92, Wessex 1992-2007

Club Colours (change): Yellow/blue/blue (White/red/red)

Ground: Privett Park, Privett Road, Gosport, Hampshire PO12 0SX **(T)** 023 9250 1042 (Match days only)
Capacity: 4,500 **Seats:** 450 **Covered:** 600 **Clubhouse:** Yes **Shop:** Yes
Previous Grounds:
Simple Directions
Exit M27 at J11. TakeA32 Fareham to Gosport road. After 3 miles take the 3rd exit at Brockhurst r/a, into Military Road. At next r/a take 1st exit into Privett Road. Ground is approx. 400 yards on left.

Record Attendance: 4,770 v Pegasus - FA Amateur Cup 1951
Record Victory: 14-0 v Cunliffe Owen - Hampshire League 1945-46
Record Defeat: 0-9 v Gloucester City - Southern Premier Division 1989-90 and v Lymington & N.M. - Wessex Lge 99-2000
Record Goalscorer: Ritchie Coulbert - 192
Record Appearances: Tony Mahoney - 765
Additional Records:

Senior Honours: Hampshire League 1945-46, 76-77, 77-78. Hampshire Senior Cup 1987-88. Wessex League Cup 1992-93. Wessex League 2006-07.

10 YEAR RECORD

00-01	01-02	02-03	03-04	04-05	05-06	06-07	07-08	08-09	09-10
Wex 8	Wex 4	Wex 2	Wex 3	Wex1 4	Wex1 5	WexP 1	Sthsw 11	Sthsw 12	Sthsw 8

HUNGERFORD TOWN

Chairman: Nigel Warwick
Secretary: Norman Matthews **(T)** 07768 761 795
(E) nmatthews@rhsystems.co.uk
Additional Committee Members: Ken Holmes, Ron Tarry, John Smyth, Mick Butler, John Sopp, Ray Brown, Steve Puffett, Terry Wild, Jim McCafferty, Steve Skipworth, Matt Robinson, Georgie Taylor
Manager: Robert Wilkinson
Programme Editor: John Smyth **(E)** john.smyth@saxon-brands.com

Club Factfile

Founded: 1886 **Nickname:** The Crusaders
Previous Names: None
Previous Leagues: Newbury & District, Swindon & District, Hellenic 1958-78, 2003-09, Isthmian 1978-2003

Club Colours (change): White/blue/white (All blue)

Ground: Bulpitt Lane, Hungerford RG17 0AY **(T)** 01488 682 939
Capacity: 2,500 **Seats:** 170 **Covered:** 400 **Clubhouse:** Yes **Shop:** Yes
Previous Grounds: None
Simple Directions
From M4 Junction, take A338 to Hungerford. First Roundabout turn right on to A4, next roundabout first left, 100 yards roundabout 1st left up High Street, go over three roundabouts, at fourth roundabout turn first left signposted 'Football Club'. Take second left into Bulpitt Lane, go over crossroads, ground on left.

Record Attendance: 1,684 v Sudbury Town - FA Vase Semi-final 1988-89
Record Victory: Not known
Record Defeat: Not known
Record Goalscorer: Ian Farr - 268
Record Appearances: Dean Bailey and Tim North - 400+
Additional Records: Paid £4,000 to Yeovil Town for Joe Scott
Received £3,800 from Barnstaple Town for Joe Scott
Senior Honours: Hellenic Division 1 1970-71, Premier Division 2008-09, League Cup 2006-07, 07-08.
Berks & Bucks Senior Cup 1981-82.
Isthmian representatives in Anglo Italian Cup 1981.

10 YEAR RECORD

00-01	01-02	02-03	03-04	04-05	05-06	06-07	07-08	08-09	09-10
Isth2 17	Isth2 15	Isth2 5	Hel P 6	Hel P 17	Hel P 16	Hel P 3	Hel P 3	Hel P 1	Sthsw 17

MANGOTSFIELD UNITED

Chairman: Mike Richardson
Secretary: Sophie Dyer (T) 07977 585 880
(E) sophie.dyer@filton.ac.uk
Additional Committee Members: Chris Stone, Roger Gray

Manager: Phil Bater
Programme Editor: Bob Smale (E) bob_smale@yahoo.co.uk

Back Row (L-R): Phil Bater (Manager), Pete Brown (Kit Manager), Andy Eisentrager (Assistant Manager), James Pilling, Rob Moore, Karim Rendall, Sam Alexander, Danny Greaves, Mitchell Page, Mike Baker, Jack Pitcher, Michael Meaker, Andy Gurney, James Rowberry (Coach), Sophie Dyer (Football Secretary), Ken Brodie(Welfare Officer).
Front Row: Jack Durrant, Danny Haines, Dan Spill, Geraint Bater, Neil Arndale, Tom Knighton, Harley Purnell, Matt Groves, Joe McClennan.

Club Factfile

Founded: 1950 **Nickname:** The Field
Previous Names: None
Previous Leagues: Bristol & District 1950-67. Avon Premier Combination 1967-72. Western 1972-2000.

Club Colours (change): Sky blue/maroon/sky blue (All orange)

Ground: Cossham Street, Mangotsfield, Bristol BS16 9EN (T) 0117 956 0119
Capacity: 2,500 **Seats:** 300 **Covered:** 800 **Clubhouse:** Yes **Shop:** Yes
Previous Grounds: None
Simple Directions
Exit the M32 at Junction 1 and follow the A4174 towards Downend following signs to Mangotsfield. Turn left into Cossham Street, the ground is approx 300 yards on the right.

Record Attendance: 1,253 v Bath City - F.A. Cup 1974
Record Victory: 17-0 v Hanham Sports (H) - 1953 Bristol & District League
Record Defeat: 3-13 v Bristol City United - Bristol & District League Division 1
Record Goalscorer: John Hill
Record Appearances: John Hill - 600+
Additional Records: In the last 10 matches of the 2003/04 season, the club went 738 minutes (just over 8 games) without scoring and then finished the campaign with 13 goals in the last two, which included a 9-0 away win.

Senior Honours: Gloucestershire Senior Cup 1968-69, 75-76, 2002-03. Somerset Premier Cup 1987-88. Western League 1990-91. Southern League Division One West 2004-05. Gloucestershire F.A. Trophy x6.

10 YEAR RECORD

00-01	01-02	02-03	03-04	04-05	05-06	06-07	07-08	08-09	09-10
SthW 5	SthW 7	SthW 6	SthW 13	SthW 1	SthP 10	SthP 9	SthP 14	SthP 22	Sthsw 9

NORTH LEIGH

Chairman: Peter King
Secretary: Keith Huxley (T) 07775 818 066
(E) keith.huxley08@tiscali.co.uk
Additional Committee Members: Barry Norton, M Burnell, Steve Smith, Phil Horne, Pete Dix, Wayne Reynolds, Stacey McDonough
Manager: Mark Gee
Programme Editor: Mike Burnell (E) michael.burnell1@ntlworld.com

Unfortunately an up-to-date photograph was not available at the time of going to press

Club Factfile

Founded: 1908 **Nickname:** The Millers
Previous Names:
Previous Leagues: Witney & District, Hellenic 1990-2008

Club Colours (change): Yellow/black/yellow (Sky blue/sky blue/white)

Ground: Eynsham Hall Park, North Leigh, Witney, Oxon OX29 6PN (T) 07583 399 577
Capacity: 2,000 **Seats:** 100 **Covered:** 200 **Clubhouse:** Yes **Shop:** No
Previous Grounds:
Simple Directions
Ground is situated off A4095 Witney to Woodstock road, three miles east of Witney. Entrance 300 yards east of main park entrance.

Record Attendance: 426 v Newport County - FA Cup 3rd Qualifying Round 16/10/2004
Record Victory: Not known
Record Defeat: Not known
Record Goalscorer: P Coles
Record Appearances: P King
Additional Records:

Senior Honours: Hellenic Premier Division 2001-02, 02-03, 07-08. Oxon Charity Cup x2.

10 YEAR RECORD

00-01	01-02	02-03	03-04	04-05	05-06	06-07	07-08	08-09	09-10
Hel P 6	Hel P 1	Hel P 1	Hel P 8	Hel P 7	Hel P 4	Hel P 2	Hel P 1	Sthsw 8	Sthsw 10

PAULTON ROVERS

Chairman: David Bissex
Secretary: Andrew Harris (T) 07760 377 302
(E) ahbr23112@blueyonder.co.uk
Additional Committee Members:
Lar Rogers, Paul Rowlands, Les Rogers, Rob Filer, Tim Pow, Andrew Harris
Manager: Andy Jones
Programme Editor: Tracy Curtis (E) tracy.curtis.2000@btinternet.com

Front Row (L-R): Stuart Tovey, Mark Harrington (coach), Callum Hart, Dan Cleverley, Matt Cooper, Chris Lane, Ben Cleverley, Jack Allward, Daine O'Connor, Lee Marshall, Charlie Rich.
Back Row (L-R): Andrew Jones (Manager), Paul Milsom (Asst Manager), Joe Bradley, Ollie Price, Rob Claridge, Josh Jeffries, Ben Lacey, Kyle Phillips, Phil Waters, Craig Loxton, Craig Burchill, Lee Williams (physio), Colin Parsons (kit manager).

Club Factfile

Founded: 1881 **Nickname:** The Robins or Rovers
Previous Names:
Previous Leagues: Wiltshire Premier, Somserset Senior, Western

Club Colours (change): All white (All maroon)

Ground: Athletic Ground, Winterfield Road, Paulton, Bristol BS39 7RF (T) 01761 412 907
Capacity: 5,000 **Seats:** 253 **Covered:** 2,500 **Clubhouse:** Yes **Shop:** Yes
Previous Grounds: Chapel Field, Cricket Ground, Recreation Ground
Simple Directions
From A39 at Farrington Gurney, follow A362 marked Radstock for two miles. Turn left at roundabout, take B3355 to Paulton and ground is on the right.

Record Attendance: 2,000 v Crewe Alexandra - FA Cup 1906-07
Record Victory: Not known
Record Defeat: Not known
Record Goalscorer: Graham Colbourne
Record Appearances: Steve Tovey
Additional Records:

Senior Honours: Somerset Senior Cup x12

10 YEAR RECORD

00-01	01-02	02-03	03-04	04-05	05-06	06-07	07-08	08-09	09-10
WestP 3	WestP 7	WestP 5	WestP 2	SthW 8	SthW 17	Sthsw 2	Sthsw 7	Sthsw 10	Sthsw 7

SHOLING

Chairman: Trevor Lewis
Secretary: Colin Chamberlain (T) 07770 452 660
(E) colinrchamberlain@btinternet.com
Additional Committee Members: Bill Boyle, Arthur Fox, Mrs Chris Lewis, David Diaper, Malcolm Stokes, Kevin Harnelt, Ray Tyrrell, Dave Bell, Mick Brown
Manager: David Diaper
Programme Editor: Mrs Chris Lewis (E) chrislewis@tiscali.co.uk

Club Factfile

Founded: 1916 **Nickname:** The Boatmen
Previous Names: Woolston Works, Thornycrofts (Woolston) 1918-52, Vospers 1960-2003, VT FC 2003-10
Previous Leagues: Hampshire 1991-2004, Wessex 2004-09

Club Colours (change): Red & white stripes/red/red (Yellow and blue/blue/yellow)

Ground: VT Group Sportsground, Portsmouth Road, Sholing, SO19 9PW (T) 02380 403 829
Capacity: **Seats:** Yes **Covered:** Yes **Clubhouse:** Yes **Shop:**
Previous Grounds:

Simple Directions
Leave the M27 at J8 and follow the signs towards Hamble. As you drive up dual carriageway (remain in the L/H lane), you come to Windover roundabout. Take the second exit towards Hamble. Take the R/H lane and carry on straight across the small roundabout. After 200 yards bear right across a second small roundabout (2nd exit). After about 100 yards turn right into Portsmouth Road. Follow straight on for about half mile. VT ground is on right opposite a lorry entrance.

Record Attendance: 150
Record Victory: Not known
Record Defeat: Not known
Record Goalscorer: George Diaper - 100+
Record Appearances: Not known
Additional Records:

Senior Honours: Hampshire Premier Division 2000-01, 03-04

10 YEAR RECORD

00-01	01-02	02-03	03-04	04-05	05-06	06-07	07-08	08-09	09-10
HantP 1			HantP 1	Wex1 12	Wex1 13	WexP 3	WexP 2	WexP 2	Sthsw 4

STOURPORT SWIFTS

Chairman: Chris Reynolds
Secretary: Laura McDonald (T) 07793 768 793
(E) Lmacca65@hotmail.com

Additional Committee Members:
Roy Crowe, Ian Sword, John McDonald, Chris Knight Val Lavery, Martin Goode

Manager: Richard Cowell
Programme Editor: Mike Cooper (E) mike.cooper@allmediapm.co.uk

Club Factfile

Founded: 1882 **Nickname:** Swifts
Previous Names:
Previous Leagues: Kidderminster/Worcestershire/West Midlands (Regional) > 1998, Midland Alliance 1998-2001

Club Colours (change): Black and gold stripes/black/black (All blue)

Ground: Walshes Meadow, Harold Davis Drive, Stourport on Severn DY13 0AA **(T)** 01299 825 188
Capacity: 2,000 **Seats:** 250 **Covered:** 150 **Clubhouse:** Yes **Shop:** Yes
Previous Grounds: Bewdley Road, Moor Hall Park, Feathers Farm, Olive Grove, Hawthorns
Simple Directions
Follow the one way system through Stourport Town Centre signposted 'Sports Centre'. Go over river bridge and turn left into Harold Davies Drive. Ground is at rear of Sports Centre.

Record Attendance: 2,000
Record Victory: 10-0
Record Defeat: 1-7
Record Goalscorer: Gary Crowther
Record Appearances: Ian Johnson
Additional Records:

Senior Honours: Midland Alliance 2000-01

10 YEAR RECORD

00-01	01-02	02-03	03-04	04-05	05-06	06-07	07-08	08-09	09-10
MidAl 1	SthW 8	SthW 16	SthW 18	SthW 14	SthW 20	SthM 22	SthM 17	SthM 16	SthM 17

TAUNTON TOWN

Chairman: Kevin Sturney
Secretary: Martin Dongworth — **(T)** 07791 948 686 **(E)** mpdongworth@somerset.gov.uk

Additional Committee Members:
Stanley Petty, Harold Needs, Andrew Power
Manager: Paul West
Programme Editor: Martin Dongworth — **(E)** mpdongworth@somerset.gov.uk

Club Factfile

Founded: 1947 **Nickname:** The Peacocks
Previous Names: None
Previous Leagues: Western 1954-77, 83-2002, Southern 1977-83

Club Colours (change): Sky blue/maroon/sky blue (All yellow)

Ground: Wordsworth Drive, Taunton, Somerset TA1 2HG **(T)** 01823 278 191
Capacity: 2,500 **Seats:** 300 **Covered:** 1,000 **Clubhouse:** Yes **Shop:** Yes
Previous Grounds:
Simple Directions
From M5 Junction 25 follow signs to Town Centre. Proceed along Toneway then bear left at roundabout into Chritchard Way. At traffic lights proceed into Wordsworth Drive and the ground is on the left.

Record Attendance: 3,284 v Tiverton Town - FA Vase Semi-final 1999
Record Victory: 12-0 v Dawlish Town (A) - FA Cup Preliminary Round 28/08/1993
Record Defeat: 0-8 v Cheltenham Town (A) - FA Cup 2nd Qualifying Round 28/09/1991
Record Goalscorer: Tony Payne
Record Appearances: Tony Payne
Additional Records: Reg Oram scored 67 in one season

Senior Honours: Western League 1968-69, 89-90, 95-96, 98-99, 99-2000, 2000-01. FA Vase 2000-01.
Somerset Premier Cup 2002-03, 05-06.

10 YEAR RECORD

00-01	01-02	02-03	03-04	04-05	05-06	06-07	07-08	08-09	09-10
WestP 1	WestP 2	SthW 10	SthW 15	SthW 17	SthW 18	Sthsw 5	Sthsw 18	Sthsw 20	Sthsw 19

THATCHAM TOWN

Chairman: Eric Bailey
Secretary: Alan Lovegrove **(T)** 07817 723 846
(E) mail@alanlovegrove.wanadoo.co.uk
Additional Committee Members: Peter Woodage, Sylvia Bailey, Steve Berry, Alan Rashbrook, Maurice Brown, Jim Goslin, Charlie Heaver, John Haines, Matthew Lovegrove
Manager: Colin Millard
Programme Editor: Andy Morris **(E)** acmorris@madasafish.com

Archive photo

Club Factfile

Founded: 1895 **Nickname:**
Previous Names:
Previous Leagues: Hellenic 1974-82, Athenian 1982-84, London Spartan 1984-86, Wessex 1986-2006

Club Colours (change): Blue and white stripes/blue/blue (Red/black/red)

Ground: Waterside Park, Crookham Hill, Thatcham, Berks RG19 4PA **(T)** 01635 862 016
Capacity: 3,000 **Seats:** 300 **Covered:** 300 **Clubhouse:** Yes **Shop:** Yes
Previous Grounds: Station Road 1946-52, Lancaster Close 1952-92
Simple Directions
A4 Thatcham at Sony roundabout turn into Pipers Way. At next roundabout turn left, crossing over the railway line. Entrance to Waterside Park 300 metres on left-hand side.

Record Attendance: 1,400 v Aldershot - FA Vase
Record Victory: Not known
Record Defeat: Not known
Record Goalscorer: Not known
Record Appearances: Not known
Additional Records:

Senior Honours: Hellenic League 1974-75. Wessex League 1995-96.

10 YEAR RECORD

00-01	01-02	02-03	03-04	04-05	05-06	06-07	07-08	08-09	09-10
Wex 6	Wex 12	Wex 9	Wex 10	Wex1 3	Wex1 2	Sthsw 6	Sthsw 15	Sthsw 6	Sthsw 12

WIMBORNE TOWN

Chairman: Ken Stewart

Secretary: Peter Barham (T) 07956 833 316

(E) barhamp@tiscali.co.uk

Additional Committee Members: Juliet Piddington, Graham Bell, Ken Fergus, Tony Grant, Brian McIntyre, Paul Miller, Ken Mitchell, Richard Button, Geoff Maxted, Jeff Robbins

Manager: Alex Browne

Programme Editor: Ken Fergus (E) kenfergus@sky.com

Back Row (L-R): Mark Watson (Trainer), John Wyatt, Lee Chudy, Darren Curtis, Jacob Malara, Nick Hutchings, Alan Walker-Harris, Steve Whitcher, Perry Mullins, Jeff Robbins (Kit), Sindre Witzoe (Physio) Middle Row: Ken Mitchell (Director), Brian McIntyre (Director of Football), Tony Grant (Director), James Wilson, Sam Lockyer, Zac Nicholls, Dan Haysom, Gareth Barnes, Karl Yelland, Ross Lloyd, Graham Bell (Director), Ken Fergus (Director), Geoff Maxted (Treasurer) Front Row: Kev James, Alex Browne (Manager), Scott Joyce, Ken Stewart (Chairman), Paul Roast (Captain), Paul Miller (Vice-Chairman), Liam Green, Darren Powell (Assistant Manager), Tom McCormick

Club Factfile

Founded: 1878 **Nickname:** Magpies

Previous Names:

Previous Leagues: Dorset, Dorset Combination, Western 1981-86, Wessex 1986-2010

Club Colours (change): Black and white stripes/black/white (Blue & white/white/blue & white trim)

Ground: The Cuthbury, Cowgrove Road, Wimborne, Dorset, BH21 4EL (T) 01202 884 821

Capacity: 3,250 **Seats:** 275 **Covered:** 425 **Clubhouse:** Yes **Shop:** Yes

Previous Grounds:

Simple Directions

On the Wimborne To Blandford Road (B3082), turn left into Cowgrove Road just past Victoria Hospital.
Postcode for Sat nav is BH21 4EL.

Record Attendance: 3,250 v Bamber Bridge

Record Victory: Not known

Record Defeat: Not known

Record Goalscorer: Jason Lovell

Record Appearances: James Sturgess

Additional Records:

Senior Honours: FA Vase 1991-92. Wessex League 1991-92, 93-94, 99-2000.
Dorset Senior Amateur Cup 1936-37, 63-64.

10 YEAR RECORD

00-01	01-02	02-03	03-04	04-05	05-06	06-07	07-08	08-09	09-10
Wex 3	Wex 8	Wex 4	Wex 2	Wex1 7	Wex1 12	WexP 6	WexP 3	WexP 4	WexP 2

YATE TOWN

Chairman: Peter Jackson
Secretary: Terry Tansley (T) 07875 272 126
(E) admin@yatetownfc.com
Additional Committee Members: Robert Lomas, Peter Crowley, Barry Neal, Colin Pick, John Powell, Michael Powell, Roger Pullin, Malcolm Robinson, Derek Smith, Ian Summers, Roger Berry, Roger Hawkins, Wolston Perks, John Burns, Colin Roddan
Manager: Dave Mogg
Programme Editor: Terry Tansley (E) admin@yatetownfc.com

Back Row (L-R): Kyle Shallcross, Neil Ward*, Scott Thomas, Edd Vahid, Stuart Wood*, Callum Stewart, Jon McAldindon, Jason Burt, Reeko Best*.
Front Row: Mark Reynolds, David Pearse*, Rob Dumphy*, Aron Robins, Aashley Derrick, Marc Hughes, Craig Rimmer*, Tom Warren. * no longer with club. Not in photo: Lee Matthews, Adam White, Sam Duggan, Zayne Simpson. (Archive photo)

Club Factfile

Founded: 1946 **Nickname:** The Bluebells
Previous Names: Yate YMCA 1946-70
Previous Leagues: Bristol Premier Combination > 1968, Gloucestershire County 1968-83, Hellenic 1983-89, 2000-03, Southern 1989-2000

Club Colours (change): White/blue navy/white (Navy blue/white/navy blue)

Ground: Lodge Road, Yate, Bristol BS37 7LE (T) 01454 228 103
Capacity: 2,000 **Seats:** 236 **Covered:** 400 **Clubhouse:** Yes **Shop:** Yes
Previous Grounds:
Simple Directions
From East: leave M4 J18, enter Yate on A432 via Chipping Sodbury bypass. Turn right at first small roundabout (Link Road), straight over next roundabout into Goose Green Way, over more roundabouts and 2 major sets of traffic lights. Turn right at third set of lights (by The Fox), then immediately left into Lodge Road. Ground 200m on right. From North: M5 (South) exit J14, B4509/B4060 into Chipping Sodbury. Turn right into Chipping Sodbury High Street, down Bowling Hill and right at first roundabout into Goose Green Way – then as above. From South: Leave M5 at J15, then join M5. Leave M4 at J19, take second exit onto M32. Leave M32 at J1, at roundabout take first exit onto A4174. Continue on A4174 over traffic lights, then at roundabout take first exit onto A432. Enter Yate on A432, at traffic lights turn left into Stover Road (B4059), then at roundabout take second exit – still on B4059. Left at traffic lights (Fox PH) and immediately left into Lodge Road.

Record Attendance: 2,000 v Bristol Rovers v Bristol Rovers Past XI - Vaughan Jones testimonial 1990
Record Victory: 13-3 v Clevedon - Bristol Premier Combination 1967-68
Record Defeat: Not known
Record Goalscorer: Kevin Thaws
Record Appearances: Gary Hewlett
Additional Records: Paid £2,000 to Chippenham Town for Matt Rawlings 2003
Received £15,000 from Bristol Rovers for Mike Davis

Senior Honours: Hellenic League 1987-88, 88-89. Gloucestershire Senior Cup 2004-05, 05-06.

10 YEAR RECORD

00-01		01-02		02-03		03-04		04-05		05-06		06-07		07-08		08-09		09-10	
Hel P	3	Hel P	3	Hel P	2	SthW	16	SthW	2	SthP	6	SthP	14	SthP	10	SthP	21	Sthsw	13

WIN NEXT YEAR'S NON-LEAGUE CLUB DIRECTORY

(AND HAVE A BIT OF FUN AT THE SAME TIME!)

NON-LEAGUE CLUB DIRECTORY PREDICTION COMPETITION

This year we have decided to re-introduce a popular competition that was run by the *Cherry Red Non-League Newsdesk Annual* for a number of years.

Entrants predict the 2010-11 champions of the top competitions, and the contestant with the most correct tips is the champion and receives next year's Directory FREE. Could not be simpler!

To enter, list your prediction for the champions of all three divisions of each of the Blue Square Conference, Ryman Isthmian, Zamaretto Southern and the Evo-stik Northern Premier Leagues PLUS the top divisions of each of 14 feeder leagues: Baker Joiner Midland Alliance, Cherry Red Combined Counties League, Essex Senior League, Hereward United Counties League, Koolsport Northern Counties League, Molten Spartan South Midlands League, Ridgeons Eastern Counties League, Safety Net Kent League, Skilltraining Northern League, Sussex County League, Sydenhams Wessex League, Toolstation Western League, Uhlsport Hellenic League League, Vodkat Northern West Counties League.

Entries should be emailed to james.m.wright.t21@btinternet.com or posted to Prediction Competition, 6 Harp Chase, Taunton TA1 3RY.

Rules:

By entering you agree that..

1) All entries must be received BEFORE November 1st 2010.
2) The number of second (or even third or fourth) places will be used as a tie-breaker if necessary.
3) The contact details of all entrants will be stored electronically and may be used to publicise future competitions or products of TW Publications (under no circumstances will they ever be divulged to any third party).
4) Participants' names and scores may be published in the Non-League Club Directory 2012, or on the Directory's website.
5) In the unlikely event that the Non-League Club Directory is not published in 2011, the winner will be entitled to a cash prize equivalent to the cover price of the current edition.
6) In the event of any dispute, the decision of the publisher is final.

ENTRY IS FREE, SO GIVE IT A GO. GOOD LUCK!

Ryman
football league

SPONSORED BY:
RYMAN

Founded: 1905

President & Chairman:
Alan C.F. Turvey FCIM

Competition Secretary:
Bruce Badcock
Unit 14-15,
Wisdon Facilities Centre,
42 Hollands Road,
Haverhill, Suffolk CB9 8SA
Telephone: 01440 768840
Mobile: 07921 940784
Fax: 01440 768841
E-mail:
leaguesecretary@isthmian.co.uk

ISTHMIAN LEAGUE

		P	W	D	L	F	A	GD	Pts
1	Dartford	42	29	6	7	101	45	56	93
2	Sutton United	42	22	9	11	65	45	20	75
3	Aveley	42	21	7	14	83	62	21	70
4	Boreham Wood	42	20	8	14	54	44	10	68
5	Kingstonian	42	20	8	14	73	69	4	68
6	Wealdstone	42	17	14	11	65	65	0	65
7	Hastings United	42	18	9	15	68	56	12	63
8	Tonbridge Angels	42	18	8	16	69	67	2	62
9	AFC Hornchurch	42	16	13	13	51	47	4	61
10	Hendon	42	18	6	18	61	59	2	60
11	Horsham	42	16	8	18	65	67	-2	56
12	Tooting & Mitcham United	42	15	10	17	60	64	-4	55
13	Billericay Town	42	14	12	16	44	42	2	54
14	Harrow Borough	42	13	14	15	66	63	3	53
15	Cray Wanderers	42	14	9	19	54	70	-16	51
16	Canvey Island	42	13	11	18	57	62	-5	50
17	Carshalton Athletic	42	12	13	17	58	64	-6	49
18	Maidstone United	42	13	10	19	39	57	-18	49
19	Margate	42	11	12	19	49	71	-22	45
20	Ashford Town (Mx)	42	11	11	20	62	80	-18	44
21	Waltham Abbey	42	12	8	22	49	74	-25	44
22	Bognor Regis Town	42	9	14	19	45	65	-20	41

PROMOTION PLAY-OFFS

SF Aveley 0 **Boreham Wood** 1 26/04/10 Att: 323

SF Sutton United 2 **Kingstonian** 4 27/04/10 Att: 1401

F **Boreham Wood** 2 Kingstonian 0 01/05/10 Att: 1102

	1	2	3	4	5	6	7	8	9	10	11	12	13	14	15	16	17	18	19	20	21	22
1 AFC Hornchurch	-	1-0	2-1	0-0	3-0	2-1	1-0	2-2	0-2	0-2	2-1	1-1	4-4	2-1	1-1	1-0	1-0	1-0	1-1	0-1	4-1	0-0
2 Ashford Tn (Mx)	1-1	-	2-2	3-2	2-2	0-2	1-1	1-2	3-0	1-4	2-6	3-2	1-1	0-2	3-1	0-2	2-2	0-1	3-2	2-1	1-1	3-3
3 Aveley	1-1	2-1	-	1-0	2-0	2-0	4-2	4-0	1-1	1-4	1-2	3-0	1-2	2-1	3-4	2-0	0-3	0-1	2-0	1-2	3-1	2-2
4 Billericay Town	2-0	0-1	2-1	-	1-0	2-0	4-1	0-4	1-1	1-0	1-2	2-0	1-0	1-2	1-5	1-1	1-2	0-1	1-1	0-0	1-1	0-0
5 Bognor Regis T.	4-2	2-0	1-1	1-1	-	0-1	2-2	1-0	1-1	0-2	1-1	0-1	0-3	1-1	3-1	0-0	3-3	1-2	3-1	0-3	1-2	2-2
6 Boreham Wood	0-0	3-3	3-2	2-0	1-0	-	1-3	3-1	2-4	0-1	1-0	0-0	2-1	4-0	0-1	0-2	1-1	1-2	2-0	3-2	3-0	0-1
7 Canvey Island	1-0	2-1	1-4	0-0	0-0	0-1	-	2-2	5-1	2-5	1-1	1-0	2-3	1-2	1-2	0-1	2-0	1-2	1-1	2-1	2-3	1-1
8 Carshalton Ath.	1-0	3-1	0-3	1-0	1-0	0-0	0-0	-	2-0	0-4	2-2	1-3	0-0	1-2	1-2	0-1	1-2	0-0	1-2	4-1	4-1	4-2
9 Cray Wanderers	1-0	1-0	1-2	0-2	0-2	1-1	1-2	3-3	-	1-2	1-3	1-2	2-0	1-1	2-1	1-0	3-2	1-2	1-3	1-0	1-2	1-3
10 Dartford	0-1	3-2	2-2	1-4	3-3	1-2	2-1	1-1	1-1	-	2-0	4-3	5-0	3-2	5-0	3-0	0-1	0-2	2-0	3-2	2-1	1-1
11 Harrow Borough	0-0	1-2	3-3	1-0	1-2	2-0	0-0	3-3	1-1	0-1	-	0-3	0-3	2-2	2-0	2-1	3-0	1-1	1-3	1-1	5-3	3-1
12 Hastings United	1-0	4-4	0-1	1-1	1-2	2-1	1-1	3-1	2-3	1-3	1-1	-	2-1	3-1	0-0	1-2	2-1	1-3	5-1	2-0	2-0	1-0
13 Hendon	3-2	2-1	4-1	1-0	2-0	0-1	2-1	1-0	2-0	1-2	3-1	1-3	-	1-1	0-3	3-0	1-2	1-2	0-0	0-0	0-2	2-3
14 Horsham	2-1	4-1	0-2	0-2	2-1	1-3	1-2	2-2	4-0	1-3	2-0	4-2	3-1	-	0-1	1-0	3-3	1-0	0-3	1-2	2-1	1-3
15 Kingstonian	2-0	1-0	1-6	2-1	1-3	4-1	2-1	1-0	4-1	2-6	3-5	1-2	3-0	2-1	-	1-1	2-0	2-1	2-3	1-1	1-1	3-3
16 Maidstone Utd	0-0	2-0	4-2	1-0	1-0	0-1	0-3	0-2	1-1	0-1	0-3	0-5	0-3	1-1	1-3	-	0-1	2-1	2-2	1-2	2-0	2-3
17 Margate	0-0	1-1	2-3	1-3	1-1	2-1	1-2	1-1	0-1	0-4	2-2	1-0	2-3	1-3	2-1	0-1	-	1-1	0-3	2-1	0-3	1-1
18 Sutton United	4-1	2-4	3-2	2-1	0-0	0-1	1-2	3-0	1-4	0-3	1-0	2-2	3-1	2-1	1-1	0-0	4-0	-	2-1	1-2	0-0	5-0
19 Tonbridge A.	1-2	3-2	3-2	0-1	2-0	0-2	3-1	2-0	3-2	1-4	3-2	2-2	2-1	2-2	1-0	2-1	0-0	1-2	-	1-2	2-0	2-3
20 Tooting & M. Utd	2-3	2-3	1-2	1-1	3-1	0-2	1-3	2-2	0-2	3-1	1-0	1-0	0-2	0-2	2-3	2-2	2-1	1-1	5-3	-	1-1	3-2
21 Waltham Abbey	0-5	0-1	0-2	0-2	4-1	1-1	2-1	2-1	0-1	0-4	1-1	0-1	1-0	2-1	1-0	1-2	3-4	1-2	0-2	1-1	-	1-2
20 Wealdstone	2-3	1-0	0-1	0-0	4-0	0-0	1-0	1-4	3-2	1-1	2-1	1-0	0-2	2-1	2-2	2-2	1-0	2-1	2-1	0-2	2-4	-

ISTHMIAN LEAGUE DIVISION ONE NORTH

		P	W	D	L	F	A	GD	Pts
1	Lowestoft Town	42	32	5	5	115	37	78	101
2	Concord Rangers	42	26	8	8	94	42	52	86
3	Wingate & Finchley	42	24	9	9	88	55	33	81
4	Enfield Town	42	23	11	8	81	47	34	80
5	East Thurrock United	42	23	8	11	102	59	43	77
6	Heybridge Swifts	42	21	8	13	67	56	11	71
7	Thamesmead Town	42	20	7	15	67	56	11	67
8	VCD Athletic	42	19	10	13	61	53	8	67
9	Great Wakering Rovers	42	18	10	14	67	70	-3	64
10	Northwood	42	17	10	15	65	61	4	61
11	Tilbury	42	15	11	16	61	60	1	56
12	Brentwood Town	42	15	7	20	53	53	0	52
13	Romford	42	15	7	20	71	88	-17	52
14	Potters Bar Town	42	14	8	20	51	67	-16	50
15	Cheshunt	42	16	2	24	57	83	-26	50
16	Waltham Forest	42	13	9	20	51	75	-24	48
17	Maldon Town	42	13	6	23	54	74	-20	45
18	Redbridge	42	9	15	18	41	62	-21	42
19	Ware	42	11	9	22	57	84	-27	42
20	Ilford (-9)	42	11	10	21	47	72	-25	34
21	Leyton	42	5	15	22	40	84	-44	30
22	Harlow Town (-10)	42	6	7	29	46	98	-52	15

PROMOTION PLAY-OFFS

SF **Concord Rangers** 1 East Thurrock United 0 27/04/10 Att: 432

SF Wingate & Finchley 2 **Enfield Town** 3 27/04/10 Att: 412

F **Concord Rangers** 3 Enfield Town 1 01/05/10 Att: 751

	1	2	3	4	5	6	7	8	9	10	11	12	13	14	15	16	17	18	19	20	21	22
1 Brentwood Town	-	0-1	2-2	2-0	0-1	0-1	2-0	0-1	1-0	1-2	0-2	0-2	2-3	2-1	2-0	2-2	0-2	0-0	1-1	2-0	0-1	1-2
2 Cheshunt	2-1	-	1-2	4-2	3-1	1-0	2-1	2-3	2-0	0-2	0-3	2-1	1-2	1-2	2-0	2-3	1-5	1-0	0-3	0-1	2-3	1-3
3 Concord R'gers	2-0	2-0	-	1-1	1-1	3-1	3-0	2-2	1-0	1-2	5-0	2-0	1-4	2-1	0-0	5-0	3-1	3-0	1-0	2-0	2-0	3-2
4 East Thurrock U.	1-2	6-1	2-2	-	0-0	1-2	1-1	4-0	5-2	4-1	1-2	3-1	3-2	4-1	3-0	1-0	3-1	5-2	2-2	2-2	2-1	3-0
5 Enfield Town	2-1	4-0	2-1	0-4	-	2-3	2-1	1-0	0-1	3-0	2-2	1-0	2-0	1-1	1-1	2-0	2-0	4-3	1-2	4-2	3-2	0-0
6 Great Wakering	4-3	3-2	0-3	2-0	3-3	-	2-0	0-2	2-0	0-0	0-3	3-1	1-0	0-1	2-2	3-1	1-0	1-1	0-1	4-1	1-3	2-4
7 Harlow Town	0-3	0-2	0-7	1-3	1-3	4-2	-	0-4	1-2	2-2	0-4	1-2	2-4	1-2	3-3	2-0	2-3	0-2	1-2	0-2	1-1	0-2
8 Heybridge Swifts	2-1	3-1	2-1	0-2	1-1	2-3	1-0	-	4-2	0-1	0-3	1-0	1-1	1-1	4-0	3-2	2-0	4-3	1-2	3-1	2-1	1-2
9 Ilford	1-1	1-2	1-2	0-3	0-3	2-2	2-2	2-0	-	2-2	1-3	1-2	1-1	6-1	3-2	1-1	1-1	5-4	0-3	0-0	2-0	1-1
10 Leyton	0-1	1-3	0-4	2-3	0-3	1-2	0-2	0-1	0-1	-	1-1	2-2	1-1	1-2	1-1	0-3	0-1	0-0	1-1	1-3	2-2	1-1
11 Lowestoft Town	1-2	5-1	5-0	4-3	0-0	3-0	3-0	2-0	0-1	8-0	-	4-0	3-0	4-2	2-0	6-1	3-1	3-0	2-0	4-1	2-3	2-1
12 Maldon Town	1-2	0-3	1-4	1-2	0-4	3-1	2-2	1-2	4-0	3-1	0-2	-	1-2	0-4	0-3	0-1	3-3	1-0	4-3	0-1	2-1	2-1
13 Northwood	0-3	2-1	0-1	3-4	2-1	3-3	2-1	2-2	1-0	2-2	1-3	1-1	-	3-2	1-1	1-2	0-1	0-0	2-0	2-1	6-0	0-1
14 Potters Bar Tn	1-2	0-1	0-2	0-3	1-4	1-1	1-0	0-2	0-1	0-1	1-1	1-1	1-0	-	0-2	1-2	1-1	1-1	0-2	3-1	2-1	1-3
15 Redbridge	1-0	1-0	2-0	1-0	1-1	1-2	0-3	0-0	1-2	2-2	0-5	1-3	3-1	0-1	-	2-0	1-2	2-2	1-2	1-0	0-2	0-0
16 Romford	0-4	1-1	3-2	3-2	2-3	4-1	5-4	4-1	0-0	2-2	1-3	2-0	1-2	0-2	1-1	-	1-4	1-2	4-2	3-4	1-2	0-0
17 Thamesmead T.	2-0	7-2	2-1	2-1	0-3	1-2	2-1	2-1	1-0	4-0	0-2	1-5	2-0	2-1	3-0	0-3	-	1-0	2-2	0-1	1-1	1-2
18 Tilbury	3-1	2-2	1-1	2-2	1-0	1-1	4-1	0-2	2-0	2-1	1-2	2-0	0-1	0-1	2-1	4-1	1-0	-	0-1	2-2	3-1	2-1
19 VCD Athletic	1-1	1-0	2-2	4-2	0-1	1-1	1-2	0-2	2-0	4-3	0-2	1-0	4-1	1-1	0-0	0-1	0-0	3-2	-	1-2	1-0	2-1
20 Waltham Forest	1-0	1-3	0-3	0-3	0-4	2-3	1-1	1-1	3-0	1-0	1-2	2-1	0-0	2-3	0-0	1-4	1-4	0-1	2-1	-	1-1	3-4
21 Ware	2-3	1-0	0-3	1-5	3-3	2-1	1-2	2-2	3-2	1-1	2-2	1-3	1-2	1-4	2-2	4-3	1-0	0-1	1-2	1-3	-	0-1
22 Wingate & F.	2-2	4-1	1-6	1-1	4-2	1-2	6-0	3-1	3-0	4-0	4-2	0-0	0-4	3-1	2-1	6-2	1-1	3-2	3-0	2-0	3-1	-

ISTHMIAN DIVISION ONE NORTH DATES & GATES	Brentwood Town	Cheshunt	Concord Rangers	E. Thurrock United	Enfield Town	Gt Wakering Rovers	Harlow Town	Heybridge Swifts	Ilford	Leyton	Lowestoft Town	Maldon Town	Northwood	Potters Bar Town	Redbridge	Romford	Thamesmead Town	Tilbury	VCD Athletic	Waltham Forest	Ware	Wingate & Finchley
Brentwood Town		23 Jan 80	19 Jan 69	9 Feb 75	15 Aug 201	13 Oct 91	20 Feb 109	5 Apr 96	6 Mar 66	5 Sep 97	20 Apr 85	24 Apr 96	26 Sep 90	24 Oct 96	31 Oct 94	24 Nov 122	6 Feb 73	28 Nov 73	25 Aug 85	27 Mar 63	12 Dec 86	20 Mar 65
Cheshunt	19 Sep 126		5 Dec 127	17 Apr 153	16 Mar 249	27 Mar 128	6 Feb 239	20 Feb 161	24 Oct 131	12 Sep 125	25 Aug 195	23 Mar 126	27 Feb 175	13 Oct 195	31 Aug 155	15 Aug 218	7 Nov 125	21 Nov 130	13 Mar 127	12 Dec 129	5 Apr 235	11 Mar 115
Concord Rangers	27 Feb 121	5 Sep 102		5 Apr 225	13 Mar 182	26 Dec 179	28 Nov 117	25 Aug 97	20 Oct 103	24 Oct 101	2 Mar 238	9 Feb 102	23 Jan 121	6 Feb 118	24 Apr 123	13 Oct 148	20 Feb 102	23 Mar 92	10 Oct 138	16 Mar 84	15 Aug 125	12 Dec 85
East Thurrock U.	18 Aug 166	31 Oct 104	30 Mar 183		13 Feb 207	23 Jan 116	22 Sep 97	8 Dec 97	10 Apr 111	26 Jan 82	19 Jan 142	15 Dec 87	2 Feb 76	13 Mar 121	22 Aug 157	5 Sep 133	3 Apr 206	2 Jan 176	30 Jan 136	24 Apr 107	27 Feb 138	10 Oct 137
Enfield Town	11 Mar 172	2 Jan 246	24 Nov 182	24 Oct 224		6 Feb 217	2 Feb 191	20 Mar 217	18 Aug 183	23 Jan 228	14 Nov 255	8 Apr 173	20 Feb 245	5 Sep 208	10 Apr 208	6 Oct 201	6 Mar 206	22 Aug 227	28 Nov 205	15 Dec 138	13 Oct 227	24 Apr 267
Gt Wakering Rov.	30 Jan 85	22 Aug 85	2 Jan 184	19 Sep 105	10 Oct 216		9 Feb 65	17 Apr 85	20 Mar 65	10 Apr 80	6 Mar 175	18 Aug 96	3 Apr 85	7 Nov 115	27 Oct 121	14 Nov 101	24 Nov 84	12 Sep 90	13 Feb 72	22 Sep 90	5 Dec 101	16 Jan 82
Harlow Town	27 Oct 152	10 Oct 221	29 Sep 126	2 Mar 120	5 Apr 297	15 Aug 230		23 Mar 98	7 Nov 162	21 Nov 163	13 Feb 230	30 Mar 93	1 Dec 102	27 Mar 161	19 Sep 144	12 Dec 160	17 Apr 130	13 Mar 156	27 Feb 134	5 Dec 118	26 Dec 193	25 Aug 137
Heybridge Swifts	28 Dec 120	17 Oct 77	10 Apr 129	31 Aug 118	21 Nov 193	31 Oct 147	18 Aug 119		9 Feb 74	22 Aug 110	30 Jan 237	2 Jan 257	13 Mar 89	20 Apr 89	5 Dec 116	24 Apr 138	19 Sep 94	3 Apr 96	1 Dec 87	17 Nov 78	16 Jan 127	13 Feb 123
Ilford	3 Feb 62	13 Feb 43	15 Feb 67	26 Aug 83	3 Mar 101	21 Nov 51	24 Apr 82	15 Aug 56		13 Mar 41	27 Mar 122	31 Aug 82	19 Apr 42	5 Apr 39	10 Oct 57	26 Dec 98	5 Dec 43	27 Feb 50	12 Dec 46	31 Oct 61	19 Sep 65	17 Mar 45
Leyton	5 Dec 46	6 Mar 33	13 Feb 47	15 Aug 68	20 Oct 71	25 Aug 61	20 Mar 67	27 Mar 54	24 Nov 39		31 Aug 130	10 Oct 34	24 Apr 29	12 Dec 45	9 Mar 26	31 Oct 64	2 Mar 46	17 Oct 33	5 Apr 43	30 Jan 79	19 Jan 37	2 Feb 57
Lowestoft Town	9 Mar 542	10 Apr 1139	18 Aug 690	20 Feb 857	13 Apr 771	17 Nov 674	26 Jan 610	29 Sep 492	22 Aug 709	28 Nov 701		5 Apr 827	5 Sep 650	16 Jan 551	3 Apr 776	23 Jan 782	19 Dec 654	24 Apr 1112	21 Nov 712	13 Mar 691	6 Feb 813	31 Oct 642
Maldon Town	7 Nov 108	26 Sep 52	17 Apr 89	6 Mar 81	12 Dec 127	2 Mar 55	13 Oct 95	26 Dec 230	28 Nov 65	6 Feb 68	16 Mar 92		24 Oct 78	20 Feb 66	20 Mar 55	25 Aug 75	14 Nov 38	5 Sep 75	23 Jan 70	15 Aug 82	27 Mar 64	24 Nov 65
Northwood	23 Mar 89	9 Feb 101	19 Sep 142	20 Mar 129	27 Oct 196	26 Jan 117	6 Mar 138	24 Nov 88	17 Apr 115	7 Nov 157	5 Dec 188	13 Feb 103		26 Dec 107	22 Apr 97	27 Mar 127	31 Aug 145	10 Oct 151	15 Aug 127	2 Mar 96	25 Aug 126	5 Apr 141
Potters Bar Town	13 Feb 44	9 Mar 60	2 Feb 68	24 Nov 42	5 Dec 138	24 Apr 45	22 Aug 110	14 Nov 53	13 Apr 42	3 Apr 53	23 Mar 114	27 Oct 81	16 Mar 56		18 Aug 41	20 Mar 81	10 Apr 50	30 Mar 31	31 Oct 65	19 Sep 67	8 Sep 83	6 Mar 83
Redbridge	17 Apr 48	28 Nov 48	7 Nov 67	27 Mar 85	25 Aug 127	20 Apr 58	16 Mar 46	5 Sep 54	23 Mar 50	15 Apr 56	12 Dec 100	21 Nov 31	13 Oct 47	2 Mar 34		5 Apr 131	24 Oct 53	26 Sep 58	11 Mar 65	31 Mar 45	13 Mar 48	15 Aug 31
Romford	13 Mar 105	19 Jan 66	9 Mar 88	5 Dec 114	23 Mar 150	16 Mar 90	20 Apr 88	7 Nov 109	2 Jan 109	17 Apr 85	19 Sep 154	10 Apr 92	22 Aug 97	21 Nov 102	13 Apr 84		18 Aug 79	13 Feb 104	27 Oct 99	10 Oct 92	17 Nov 103	31 Aug 212
Thamesmead T.	10 Oct 58	24 Apr 67	15 Dec 59	12 Dec 53	17 Nov 93	13 Mar 51	31 Oct 59	23 Jan 67	5 Sep 48	26 Sep 51	15 Aug 85	27 Feb 45	28 Nov 51	25 Aug 58	13 Feb 51	2 Feb 52		30 Jan 52	26 Dec 108	5 Apr 49	21 Nov 54	27 Mar 64
Tilbury	31 Aug 82	20 Mar 65	6 Mar 78	26 Dec 102	27 Mar 142	5 Apr 81	24 Nov 87	12 Dec 68	14 Nov 65	20 Feb 55	11 Mar 95	5 Dec 62	6 Feb 55	15 Aug 62	16 Jan 65	24 Oct 92	13 Oct 59		2 Mar 57	25 Aug 56	17 Apr 77	22 Sep 63
VCD Athletic	10 Apr 54	24 Nov 67	22 Aug 93	13 Oct 96	31 Aug 212	24 Oct 108	9 Mar 79	6 Feb 59	3 Apr 95	23 Feb 47	20 Mar 141	19 Sep 91	25 Mar 62	17 Apr 57	6 Mar 57	20 Feb 101	2 Jan 159	18 Aug 98		16 Jan 97	7 Nov 111	5 Dec 70
Waltham Forest	22 Aug 50	3 Apr 36	20 Mar 44	7 Nov 50	17 Apr 107	28 Nov 41	5 Sep 53	6 Mar 40	20 Feb 40	14 Oct 52	25 Nov 59	10 Mar 36	19 Aug 70	23 Jan 33	7 Apr 34	6 Feb 78	10 Feb 34	10 Apr 30	26 Sep 36		24 Oct 36	24 Mar 44
Ware	3 Apr 121	20 Apr 125	26 Jan 78	16 Mar 91	9 Feb 177	5 Sep 146	26 Sep 202	20 Oct 106	23 Jan 108	18 Aug 116	15 Dec 119	22 Aug 143	10 Apr 103	28 Nov 142	24 Nov 91	6 Mar 145	20 Mar 129	31 Oct 123	24 Apr 93	13 Feb 100		27 Oct 128
Wingate/Finchley	21 Nov 82	18 Aug 62	3 Apr 117	6 Feb 103	7 Nov 128	17 Oct 53	10 Apr 102	24 Oct 57	13 Oct 47	2 Jan 110	17 Apr 226	13 Mar 82	29 Dec 65	19 Jan 69	9 Feb 64	28 Nov 82	22 Aug 68	23 Jan 112	5 Sep 75	27 Feb 102	20 Feb 106	

ISTHMIAN LEAGUE DIVISION ONE SOUTH

		P	W	D	L	F	A	GD	Pts
1	Croydon Athletic	42	27	8	7	92	39	53	89
2	Folkestone Invicta (-10)	42	28	8	6	54	23	31	82
3	Worthing	42	25	5	12	83	53	30	80
4	Godalming Town (-3)	42	26	5	11	71	44	27	80
5	Leatherhead	42	22	8	12	78	45	33	74
6	Fleet Town	42	22	6	14	74	49	25	72
7	Burgess Hill Town	42	19	10	13	64	50	14	67
8	Walton & Hersham	42	18	8	16	55	54	1	62
9	Sittingbourne	42	18	7	17	63	48	15	61
10	Metropolitan Police	42	17	9	16	59	50	9	60
11	Horsham YMCA	42	15	14	13	67	61	6	59
12	Dulwich Hamlet	42	14	12	16	57	64	-7	54
13	Corinthian-Casuals	42	17	3	22	66	79	-13	54
14	Ramsgate	42	13	14	15	55	61	-6	53
15	Whyteleafe	42	15	6	21	60	64	-4	51
16	Merstham	42	12	12	18	62	80	-18	48
17	Chatham Town	42	14	4	24	55	75	-20	46
18	Whitstable Town	42	14	3	25	41	85	-44	45
19	Chipstead	42	11	10	21	47	65	-18	43
20	Ashford Town	42	9	11	22	49	90	-41	38
21	Walton Casuals	42	8	10	24	41	66	-25	34
22	Eastbourne Town	42	6	11	25	29	77	-48	29

PROMOTION PLAY-OFFS

SF Folkestone Invicta 2 Leatherhead 2 27/04/10 Att: 437

SF Worthing 1 **Godalming Town** 2 27/04/10 Att: 551

F **Folkestone Invicta** 2 Godalming Town 1 01/05/10 Att: 599

	1	2	3	4	5	6	7	8	9	10	11	12	13	14	15	16	17	18	19	20	21	22
1 Ashford Town	-	0-1	2-1	1-1	4-2	0-6	2-2	2-1	1-4	1-0	2-2	3-2	0-1	0-2	0-1	2-3	2-0	2-2	1-2	0-1	3-2	1-3
2 Burgess Hill Tn	2-2	-	2-1	3-1	2-0	0-0	1-0	3-0	3-2	0-1	1-1	4-0	1-1	1-1	2-1	1-2	1-0	1-1	0-2	0-1	0-0	3-1
3 Chatham Town	0-0	3-2	-	0-1	1-3	1-2	0-2	0-0	1-2	1-2	1-3	1-1	4-3	3-2	3-1	0-1	0-2	0-1	3-0	2-0	2-1	0-1
4 Chipstead	1-0	1-2	1-0	-	1-3	2-2	1-1	4-0	1-2	0-0	0-1	2-0	1-3	0-1	1-4	0-0	0-0	1-1	0-1	3-0	1-4	0-2
5 Corinthian Cas.	5-1	3-1	4-3	3-0	-	2-4	1-3	2-0	2-2	1-2	1-2	2-1	0-2	3-4	2-1	0-3	1-1	3-2	2-1	2-3	1-2	0-4
6 Croydon Athletic	7-0	2-0	3-4	3-0	3-0	-	2-0	3-0	3-2	1-0	3-2	0-0	3-2	1-0	0-2	2-0	2-1	1-0	2-4	3-1	0-2	3-1
7 Dulwich Hamlet	0-1	0-2	3-3	1-1	0-1	1-3	-	1-1	1-0	0-1	1-3	2-2	1-1	3-1	1-1	3-1	0-2	3-1	0-3	4-2	0-2	0-2
8 Eastbourne Town	2-2	1-2	0-1	2-4	2-3	1-1	2-0	-	1-3	1-2	0-2	0-0	0-4	1-1	0-2	0-2	1-0	2-0	1-1	3-1	0-1	3-0
9 Fleet Town	6-2	1-4	4-3	2-0	1-0	1-0	0-1	3-0	-	0-1	3-0	2-0	1-0	6-0	1-1	1-1	0-0	2-1	0-1	3-0	2-1	0-3
10 Folkestone In.	1-0	3-1	2-0	2-1	0-1	0-0	0-0	1-0	2-0	-	0-1	3-0	0-0	2-0	1-0	3-1	3-1	3-2	1-0	1-0	0-1	0-0
11 Godalming Tn	1-1	2-0	3-0	2-1	1-0	0-1	2-0	3-1	2-2	0-2	-	5-3	1-0	3-1	0-1	1-2	2-0	4-2	1-0	0-1	3-2	0-1
12 Horsham YMCA	2-1	1-1	2-0	1-2	4-0	2-5	1-3	9-0	3-2	1-1	0-2	-	4-2	0-0	0-0	1-1	1-1	1-0	1-1	1-0	4-0	1-0
13 Leatherhead	2-0	2-0	3-0	2-1	1-0	0-0	6-1	1-1	1-1	1-2	0-2	2-6	-	3-1	2-0	3-1	4-2	1-1	0-1	7-1	1-2	2-0
14 Merstham	4-0	1-1	2-1	0-3	2-3	1-5	1-1	3-0	0-2	1-1	2-4	2-2	0-0	-	2-2	4-2	0-3	1-1	3-0	3-2	2-2	3-2
15 Met. Police	2-2	2-1	1-3	4-0	1-0	0-0	4-0	1-1	0-2	0-1	3-1	1-2	1-3	2-1	-	1-1	2-1	1-3	1-2	5-0	1-0	1-2
16 Ramsgate	0-0	1-3	2-3	1-1	3-2	1-0	1-3	3-0	1-0	1-2	0-0	1-1	0-2	1-2	1-1	-	1-6	0-0	2-1	0-0	2-2	5-2
17 Sittingbourne	2-1	2-3	4-0	1-2	4-1	2-2	1-2	3-0	2-1	2-0	0-1	0-0	0-3	2-0	3-0	2-1	-	3-1	0-1	2-3	2-1	2-1
18 Walton Casuals	1-4	2-2	0-1	4-1	1-0	2-3	2-2	0-0	0-1	0-1	0-1	0-3	1-0	2-3	1-2	0-2	1-1	-	2-1	0-1	0-1	0-2
19 Walton & H'ham	3-0	1-0	1-2	2-2	2-2	0-3	0-2	0-0	3-2	1-1	2-0	1-2	1-0	2-1	0-1	2-2	1-0	3-0	-	2-0	1-1	2-3
20 Whitstable Tn	3-0	2-1	1-2	1-0	0-1	0-5	1-4	1-0	2-4	1-3	0-3	0-2	1-2	2-1	1-0	1-0	0-1	0-1	2-1	-	1-1	3-3
21 Whyteleafe	2-2	1-2	3-1	0-2	1-4	0-2	1-4	0-1	0-1	0-1	1-2	5-0	1-2	5-2	0-2	1-0	1-2	2-1	3-1	4-1	-	1-4
22 Worthing	5-1	1-4	2-0	3-2	3-0	2-1	1-1	2-0	1-0	1-2	3-2	3-0	1-3	1-1	3-2	2-2	1-0	0-1	5-1	5-0	1-0	-

ISTHMIAN DIVISION ONE SOUTH DATES & GATES	Ashford Town	Burgess Hill Town	Chatham Town	Chipstead	Corinthian Casuals	Croydon Athletic	Dulwich Hamlet	Eastbourne Town	Fleet Town	Folkestone Invicta	Godalming Town	Horsham YMCA	Leatherhead	Merstham	Metropolitan Police	Ramsgate	Sittingbourne	Walton Casuals	Walton & Hersham	Whitstable Town	Whyteleafe	Worthing
Ashford Town		20 Mar 152	24 Apr 188	24 Mar 131	6 Mar 125	7 Apr 164	24 Oct 150	14 Oct 158	3 Feb 90	17 Mar 301	22 Aug 175	20 Feb 122	3 Apr 174	19 Aug 216	12 Apr 115	10 Mar 153	10 Apr 206	27 Jan 83	6 Feb 174	15 Apr 197	19 Sep 177	21 Apr 159
Burgess Hill Town	21 Nov 144		2 Feb 115	27 Mar 164	10 Oct 126	13 Apr 169	13 Mar 200	5 Apr 190	12 Sep 181	31 Aug 187	7 Nov 176	17 Apr 201	13 Feb 185	27 Feb 164	12 Dec 176	5 Dec 169	22 Apr 135	19 Sep 220	25 Aug 188	16 Aug 322	9 Feb 101	26 Dec 265
Chatham Town	7 Nov 198	18 Aug 115		24 Oct 138	14 Nov 118	10 Apr 129	6 Feb 206	30 Mar 94	20 Mar 156	23 Feb 133	16 Mar 90	22 Aug 156	19 Sep 171	16 Jan 129	22 Sep 160	24 Nov 133	2 Mar 244	3 Apr 112	17 Apr 129	13 Oct 193	6 Mar 103	5 Dec 172
Chipstead	27 Feb 101	22 Aug 52	13 Feb 72		9 Mar 70	29 Dec 114	19 Jan 70	24 Apr 87	30 Jan 101	19 Sep 107	13 Mar 72	3 Apr 86	5 Dec 108	2 Jan 163	30 Mar 82	10 Apr 87	18 Aug 79	31 Aug 87	21 Nov 109	8 Dec 74	10 Oct 138	27 Oct 151
Corinthian Casuals	26 Sep 106	6 Feb 93	23 Mar 67	15 Aug 103		20 Feb 107	5 Apr 131	27 Mar 124	25 Aug 115	7 Nov 147	24 Oct 102	13 Oct 91	20 Apr 182	21 Nov 151	26 Dec 92	31 Aug 133	19 Sep 101	5 Dec 123	16 Mar 81	17 Apr 101	12 Dec 71	13 Mar 137
Croydon Athletic	15 Aug 149	6 Mar 136	25 Aug 135	5 Apr 125	27 Oct 127		29 Mar 152	23 Jan 134	24 Nov 104	2 Feb 137	5 Sep 111	28 Nov 106	30 Jan 157	10 Oct 317	27 Mar 126	24 Apr 307	13 Feb 151	20 Mar 151	1 Dec 125	9 Mar 102	26 Jan 143	12 Dec 244
Dulwich Hamlet	13 Feb 176	24 Nov 103	10 Oct 274	17 Apr 177	2 Feb 119	16 Mar 220		17 Oct 149	13 Apr 116	2 Mar 161	18 Aug 165	10 Apr 161	22 Aug 189	3 Apr 188	27 Oct 196	16 Jan 203	6 Mar 172	30 Jan 233	7 Nov 208	5 Dec 186	22 Sep 168	19 Sep 209
Eastbourne Town	30 Jan 221	24 Mar 163	28 Oct 134	7 Nov 105	22 Aug 80	19 Sep 171	21 Nov 141		10 Oct 186	19 Aug 174	17 Apr 143	2 Jan 254	10 Apr 230	5 Dec 139	13 Feb 110	3 Apr 163	17 Mar 110	10 Feb 55	27 Feb 210	13 Mar 86	2 Mar 81	18 Nov 187
Fleet Town	17 Apr 142	20 Feb 121	21 Nov 126	13 Oct 131	10 Apr 151	13 Mar 162	18 Mar 103	6 Feb 127		22 Aug 202	22 Apr 166	24 Oct 142	18 Aug 205	22 Sep 126	19 Sep 201	23 Feb 89	3 Apr 196	19 Jan 63	17 Nov 137	2 Mar 123	5 Dec 118	7 Nov 210
Folkestone Invicta	26 Dec 522	28 Nov 266	5 Apr 314	23 Jan 286	24 Apr 242	20 Apr 2134	15 Aug 264	9 Mar 206	27 Mar 269		26 Sep 248	5 Sep 257	13 Mar 302	30 Mar 225	17 Nov 209	1 Dec 309	27 Oct 304	17 Oct 243	12 Dec 345	25 Aug 338	13 Apr 224	21 Nov 365
Godalming Town	27 Mar 169	24 Apr 113	15 Aug 100	24 Nov 93	13 Feb 92	5 Dec 120	23 Mar 91	1 Dec 74	26 Dec 161	9 Feb 120		6 Mar 94	31 Aug 182	19 Sep 128	10 Oct 229	20 Mar 101	20 Apr 111	27 Oct 137	5 Apr 242	12 Dec 115	25 Aug 115	11 Mar 134
Horsham YMCA	27 Oct 116	15 Dec 114	27 Mar 110	12 Dec 93	30 Jan 131	1 Sep 131	25 Aug 146	26 Dec 86	13 Feb 116	5 Dec 120	17 Nov 82		27 Feb 169	13 Mar 112	11 Mar 81	19 Sep 135	10 Oct 126	9 Mar 66	15 Aug 166	21 Nov 96	24 Apr 164	5 Apr 265
Leatherhead	12 Dec 145	24 Oct 158	23 Jan 164	5 Sep 153	9 Feb 130	13 Oct 201	27 Mar 178	25 Aug 175	16 Mar 131	24 Nov 125	28 Nov 130	19 Jan 94		18 Mar 205	6 Apr 301	6 Mar 158	20 Mar 183	24 Apr 412	13 Apr 310	6 Feb 136	26 Dec 179	15 Aug 226
Merstham	3 Oct 121	19 Jan 100	26 Sep 156	26 Dec 150	20 Mar 101	6 Feb 152	12 Dec 158	5 Sep 108	28 Nov 128	13 Oct 225	23 Jan 134	24 Nov 110	17 Apr 373		15 Aug 116	20 Feb 130	7 Nov 138	6 Mar 122	24 Oct 211	27 Mar 120	5 Apr 220	25 Aug 221
Met Police	5 Sep 126	15 Apr 75	28 Nov 75	26 Sep 126	2 Mar 101	22 Aug 149	20 Feb 103	24 Oct 78	23 Jan 88	6 Mar 171	6 Feb 108	18 Aug 100	8 Apr 178	16 Mar 62		14 Nov 103	26 Jan 62	10 Apr 67	13 Oct 202	7 Nov 101	20 Mar 101	17 Apr 178
Ramsgate	5 Apr 267	5 Sep 190	13 Mar 188	25 Aug 197	28 Nov 177	7 Nov 201	26 Sep 188	12 Dec 183	15 Aug 200	17 Apr 333	13 Apr 202	23 Jan 146	30 Mar 146	12 Sep 171	27 Feb 180		30 Jan 242	2 Mar 110	27 Mar 189	26 Dec 284	16 Feb 97	10 Oct 221
Sittingbourne	25 Aug 179	9 Mar 106	26 Dec 218	14 Apr 84	23 Jan 118	24 Oct 127	17 Nov 126	28 Nov 128	12 Dec 348	20 Feb 210	15 Apr 163	6 Feb 177	21 Nov 131	24 Apr 130	13 Mar 130	13 Oct 144		31 Oct 118	5 Sep 120	6 Apr 169	15 Aug 150	27 Mar 167
Walton Casuals	13 Mar 116	23 Jan 87	12 Dec 103	28 Nov 71	5 Sep 103	21 Nov 106	12 Oct 102	15 Aug 84	5 Apr 109	6 Feb 116	20 Feb 103	30 Nov 92	7 Nov 131	22 Mar 109	24 Aug 157	24 Oct 93	17 Apr 122		26 Dec 227	27 Feb 111	27 Mar 112	15 Mar 154
Walton & Hersham	3 Nov 104	10 Apr 80	31 Oct 114	20 Mar 90	18 Aug 103	23 Mar 90	24 Apr 102	19 Jan 90	6 Mar 108	15 Apr 103	9 Mar 100	2 Feb 93	27 Oct 174	13 Feb 102	4 Mar 90	22 Aug 118	5 Dec 101	23 Feb 128		19 Sep 118	24 Nov 110	29 Sep 157
Whitstable Town	28 Nov 193	20 Apr 96	30 Jan 145	6 Mar 129	31 Oct 133	19 Aug 130	5 Sep 187	24 Nov 100	20 Oct 115	10 Apr 265	3 Apr 285	20 Mar 130	10 Oct 167	22 Aug 125	24 Apr 136	23 Mar 190	16 Feb 116	14 Nov 99	23 Jan 135		27 Oct 146	13 Apr 112
Whyteleafe	23 Jan 129	13 Oct 95	17 Nov 95	6 Feb 145	7 Apr 43	17 Apr 166	28 Nov 140	26 Sep 107	5 Sep 114	24 Oct 115	10 Apr 97	7 Nov 95	9 Mar 124	23 Feb 109	21 Nov 108	18 Aug 114	23 Mar 91	22 Aug 87	13 Mar 118	16 Mar 87		27 Feb 146
Worthing	20 Oct 215	26 Jan 208	5 Sep 237	20 Feb 384	24 Nov 223	3 Apr 429	23 Jan 303	6 Mar 366	24 Apr 341	20 Mar 444	13 Oct 189	2 Mar 212	16 Feb 170	10 Apr 265	31 Oct 292	6 Feb 264	22 Aug 226	18 Aug 232	28 Nov 327	24 Oct 259	14 Nov 241	

CHAMPIONSHIP MANAGER CUP 2009-10

FIRST ROUND

Cheshunt 0 **Northwood** 2 *(Oct 20)*	Att: 96
Godalming Town 4 Merstham 2 *(Oct 20)*	Att: 215

SECOND ROUND

AFC Hornchurch 2 Brentwood T. 1 *(Nov 17)*	Att: 121
Ashford Town 0 **Tilbury** 1 *(Nov 18)*	Att: 61
Canvey Island 1 Gt Wakering R. 0 *(Nov 10)*	Att: 121
Carshalton Athletic 1 **Whyteleafe** 3 *(Nov 10)*	Att: 160
Chatham Town 2 Cray Wanderers 0 *(Nov 10)*	Att: 94
Chipstead 1 **Godalming Town** 2 *(Nov 10)*	Att: 55
Concord Rgrs 3 East Thurrock U. 0 *(Nov 17)*	Att: 110
Croydon Athletic 2 Corinthian Cas. 0 *(Nov 10)*	Att: 81
Eastbourne T. 1 **Horsham YMCA** 3 *(Nov 11)*	Att: 78
Enfield Town 3 Waltham Abbey 1 *(Nov 3)*	Att: 107
Fleet Town 1 Ashford Town (Middx) 0 *(Nov 10)*	Att: 61
Folkestone Invicta 0 **Aveley** 4 *(Nov 10)*	Att: 164
Hastings Utd 4 Tooting/Mitcham 1 *(Nov 10)*	Att: 257
Hendon 3 **Wingate/Fin.** 3 *aet* (3-4p) *(Nov 11)*	Att: 83
Heybridge Swifts 1 **Maldon Town** 3 *(Nov 10)*	Att: 118
Horsham 2 Sutton United 1 *(Nov 10)*	Att: 144
Leatherhead 1 Burgess Hill Town 0 *(Nov 17)*	Att: 58
Leyton 0 **Billericay Town** 2 *(Nov 17)*	Att: 77
Lowestoft Town 3 Ilford 1 *(Nov 10)*	Att: 462
Metropolitan Police 2 Harrow Boro. 1 *(Nov 10)*	Att: 47
Northwood 2 **Potters Bar Town** 3 *(Nov 17)*	Att: 72
Ramsgate 2 **Dartford** 2 *aet* (4-5p) *(Nov 10)*	Att: 177
Redbridge 2 **Harlow Town** 3 *(Nov 17)*	Att: 44
Romford 3 **Maidstone United** 4 *(Nov 10)*	Att: 80
Thamesmead T. 0 **Sittingbourne** 1 *(Nov 10)*	Att: 71
Tonbridge Angels 4 Whitstable T. 1 *(Nov 10)*	Att: 181
VCD Athletic 0 **Margate** 1 *(Nov 10)*	Att: 91
Walton & Hersham 2 Dulwich Ham. 1 *(Nov 10)*	Att: 88
Walton Casuals 4 Kingstonian 3 *(Nov 9)*	Att: 133
Ware 1 **Waltham Forest** 2 *(Nov 3)*	Att: 73
Wealdstone 3 Boreham Wood 1 *(Nov 10)*	Att: 101
Worthing 0 **Bognor Regis Town** 4 *(Nov 10)*	Att: 358

THIRD ROUND

AFC Hornchurch 3 Harlow Town 0 *(Dec 15)*	Att: 104
Concord Rangers v **Billericay Town** (w/o) *(Feb 4)*	
Dartford 4 **Aveley** 5 *(Dec 15)*	Att: 320
Fleet Town 2 Potters Bar Town 0 *(Dec 15)*	Att: 53
Hastings Utd 0 **Croydon Ath.** 1 *(Jan 19)*	Att: 139
Horsham 0 **Horsham YMCA** 2 *(Dec 8)*	Att: 161
Leatherhead 2 Bognor Regis Town 0 *(Jan 26)*	Att: 121
Maidstone Utd 0 **Tilbury** 2 *(at Tilbury) (Feb 2)*	Att: 63
Maldon Town 0 **Lowestoft Town** 3 *(Dec 8)*	Att: 65
Sittingbourne 3 Margate 2 *(Dec 16)*	Att: 130
Tonbridge Angels 2 Chatham T. 0 *(Dec 8)*	Att: 190
Waltham Forest 0 **Canvey Island** 1 *(Dec 9)*	Att: 44
Walton & Hersham 2 Walton Cas. 0 *(Dec 15)*	Att: 110
Wealdstone 2 M. Police 2 *aet* (3-1p) *(Nov 11)*	Att: 101
Whyteleafe 1 **Godalming Town** 2 *(Jan 18)*	Att: 62
Wingate & Finchley 2 Enfield Town 1 *(Dec 1)*	Att: 69

FOURTH ROUND

Aveley 3 AFC Hornchurch 1 *aet (Feb 1)*	Att: 104
Billericay Town 1 **Sittingbourne** 3 *(Mar 4)*	Att: 105
Canvey Island 3 Wingate & Finch. 2 *(Jan 26)*	Att: 97
Fleet Town 3 Horsham YMCA 0 *(Feb 9)*	Att: 55
Godalming Town 0 **Leatherhead** 1 *(Feb 2)*	Att: 90
Lowestoft Town 2 Tilbury 1 *(Feb 9)*	Att: 422
Tonbridge Angels v **Wealdstone** (w/o) *(Feb 4)*	
Walton & Hersham 0 **Croydon Ath.** 1 *(Feb 9)*	Att: 70

QUARTER-FINALS

Aveley 2 Canvey Island 1 *(Mar 2)*	Att: 104
Croydon Athletic 2 Lowestoft Town 1 *(Mar 4)*	Att: 58
Fleet Town 0 **Leatherhead** 3 *(Mar 4)*	Att: 77
Sittingbourne 1 **Wealdstone** 2 *(Mar 11)*	Att: 74

SEMI-FINALS

Leatherhead 1 Aveley 1 *aet* (5-4p) *(Mar 16)*	Att: 105
Wealdstone 1 Croydon Athletic 0 *(Mar 18)*	Att: 113

FINAL

(Mar 25th at Metropolitan Police)

Leatherhead 0 Wealdstone 0 *aet* (4-3p)	Att: 668

Isthmian League Premier Division
Season's Stats 2009-2010

	Lg Pos	F.A. Cup	F.A. T	Av. Lg. Att.	Best Att.	Opponents	No of Goalscorers + own goals	Goalscorers with at least 10 goals	
A.F.C. Hornchurch	9	1Q	3Q	273	531	v Dartford	26 + 3	-	
Ashford Town	20	3Q	1Q	188	354	v Kingstonian	19 + 2	Harrison	17
								Haule	10
Aveley	3	3Q	1Q	213	541	v Dartford	20 + 3	Tuohy	24
								Stanley	14
								Dodson	10
Billericay Town	13	2Q	2Rd	403	616	v AFC Hornchurch	15+1	Bricknell	17
Bognor Regis T.	22	1Q	2Q	361	868	v Dartford	19 + 0	Prior	15
Boreham Wood	4	1Q	1Rd	162	406	v Wealdstone	14 + 1	-	
Canvey Island	16	2Q	1Q	308	450	v Maidstone Utd.	14 + 0	Rowe	22
Carshalton Athletic	17	1Q	2Rd	309	569	v Dartford	19 + 2	Jolly	17
								Faulconbridge	14
Cray Wanderers	15	1Q	1Q	212	1306	v Dartford	17 + 0	Bremner	12
								Luckett	12
Dartford	1	3Q	3Q	1213	2162	v Aveley	18 + 2	Burns	23
								Harris	17
								Bradbrook	12
								Haworth	12
								Hayes	11
Harrow Borough	14	1Q	2Q	191	525	v Wealdstone	17 +1	Baptiste	21
								Clarke	11
Hastings United	7	1Q	1Q	474	717	v Dartford	15 +1	Olorunda A	21
Hendon	10	3Q	2Q	170	331	v Wealdstone	22+ 0	-	
Horsham	11	1Q	1Q	265	441	v Sutton United	16 +1	Harding	24
								Seanla	15
Kingstonian	5	2Q	3Q	400	946	v Sutton United	15 +2	Traynor	34
								Wilson-Denis	11
								Lodge	10
Maidstone United	18	3Q	1Rd	255	447	v Tonbridge	18 + 2	Pinnock	11
Margate	19	1Q	1Q	375	653	v Dartford	18 + 3	Blackman	12
Sutton United	2	1Rd	1Q	642	1027	v Carshalton Ath.	15+ 2	Gargan	15
Tonbridge Angels	8	3Q	3Q	457	842	v Dartford	18 + 0	Booth	18
								Minshull	16
								Rook	16
Tooting & Mitcham	12	1Rd	4Q	312	630	v Sutton United	11 + 3	Vines P	27
								Parker	16
Waltham Abbey	21	1Q	1Q	141	273	v Dartford	15 +1	Holland	12
Wealdstone	6	1RD	3Q	415	735	v Carshalton Ath.	0 +3	Ashe	18
								Martin	10
								Ngoyi	10

Statistics are compiled from League and Play-Off matches plus FA Cup and F.A.Trophy ties, with cup runs being shown by 1Q = First Round Qualifying and 1Rd = First Round Proper of the F.A.Cup and F.A.Trophy competitions.

The clubs scoring most penalties in the season were:

Kingstonian	8 (Traynor 7 and Wilson-Denis 1)
Wealdstone	7 (Ashe 6 and Corcoran 1)
Tonbridge Angels	6 (Rook 6 all scored before the end of October!)

A.F.C. HORNCHURCH

Chairman: Colin McBride
Secretary: Kerry Street **(T)** 0775 834 8244
(E) kelafch@googlemail.com

Additional Committee Members:
Ian Walmsley

Manager: Jim McFarlane
Programme Editor: Peter Butcher **(E)** peter.butcher5@btinternet.com

Unfortunately an up-to-date photograph was not available at the time of going to press

Club Factfile

Founded: 2005 **Nickname:** The Urchins
Previous Names: Formed in 2005 after Hornchurch F.C. folded
Previous Leagues: Hornchurch F.C. Athenian, Isthmian, Conference. Since 2005: Essex Senior

Club Colours (change): Red and white stripes/black/red

Ground: The Stadium, Bridge Avenue, Upminster, Essex RM14 2LX **(T)** 01708 220 080 / 250 501
Capacity: 3,500 **Seats:** 800 **Covered:** 1,400 **Clubhouse:** Yes **Shop:** Yes
Previous Grounds:
Simple Directions
Bridge Avenue is off A124 between Hornchurch and Upminster.

Record Attendance: 3,500 v Tranmere Rovers - FA Cup 2nd Round 2003-04
Record Victory: Not known
Record Defeat: Not known
Record Goalscorer: Not known
Record Appearances: Not known
Additional Records: Won the Essex League with a record 64 points in 2005-06

Senior Honours: Since reformation in 2005: Essex Senior League, League Cup and Memorial Trophy 2005-06.
Isthmian League Division 1 North 2006-07

10 YEAR RECORD

00-01	01-02	02-03	03-04	04-05	05-06	06-07	07-08	08-09	09-10
Isth3 14	Isth3 2	Isth1N 2	Isth P 5	Conf S 17	ESen 1	Isth1N 1	Isth P 4	Isth P 6	Isth P 9

A.F.C. HORNCHURCH

No.	Date	Comp	H/A	Opponents	Att:	Result	Goalscorers	Pos
1	Aug 15	Ryman P.	A	Tonbridge	512	W 2 - 1	Stevens 7 Green 84	6
2	18		H	Boreham Wood	242	W 2 - 1	Shave 29 Stevens 53	
3	22		H	Tooting & Mitcham U	327	L 0 - 1		9
4	25		A	Maidstone United	282	D 0 - 0		8
5	29		A	Sutton United	519	L 1 - 4	Bowes 89	12
6	31		H	Dartford	531	L 0 - 2		
7	Sept 5		A	Bognor Regis Town	276	L 2 - 4	Bowes 47 90	18
8	**12**	**F.A.C 1Q**	**H**	**Billericay Town**	**453**	**L 0 - 3**		
9	19		H	Harrow Borough	234	W 2 - 1	Barnard 30 Gray 65	14
10	22		H	Cray Wanderers	234	L 0 - 2		18
11	26		A	Margate	490	D 0 - 0		
12	Oct 3		A	Carshalton Athletic	241	L 0 - 1		18
13	**18**	**F.A.T. 1Q**	**H**	**Brentwood Town**	**235**	**W 2 - 1**	**Flack 43 Shave 76**	
14	20		H	Wealdstone	223	D 0 - 0		
15	24		A	Waltham Abbey	116	W 5 - 0	Gray 6 34 Hunt 32 (pen) Flack 44 Boyce 83	12
16	**31**	**F.A.T 2Q**	**A**	**Whyteleafe**	**143**	**D 1 - 1**	**Flack 65**	
17	Nov 7		H	Hendon	297	D 4 - 4	Flack 1 Gray 6 Prestedge 57 Janney 71	
18	14		A	Hastings United	367	L 0 - 1		15
19	**21**	**F.A.T 3Q**	**A**	**Chelmsford City**	**635**	**D 4 - 4**	**Hunt 29 83 (pen) Flack 69 Jackman 86**	
20	**24**	**F.A.T. 3Qr**	**H**	**Chelmsford City**	**370**	**L 1 - 2**	**Dormer 78**	
21	28		A	Dartford	1224	W 1 - 0	Coyne 42	15
22	Dec 5		H	Sutton United	293	W 1 - 0	Gray 68	14
23	12		A	Ashford Town	118	D 1 - 1	Dormer 78	
24	26		A	Aveley	247	D 1 - 1	Styles 90	14
25	Jan 2		H	Aveley	371	W 2 - 1	Flack 60 Hunt 88	
26	16		H	Bognor Regis Town	207	W 3 - 0	Hunt 41 65 Janney 84	8
27	23		A	Harrow Borough	180	D 0 - 0		11
28	26		H	Billericay Town	270	D 0 - 0		
29	30		H	Carshalton Athletic	266	D 2 - 2	Hunt 8 Flack 14	10
30	Feb 6		A	Cray Wanderers	201	L 0 - 1		11
31	13		H	Margate	244	W 1 - 0	Flack 17	10
32	20		A	Wealdstone	437	W 3 - 2	Wait 29 Spencer 51 Dormer 55	9
33	27		H	Hastings United	286	D 1 - 1	Hayles 56	9
34	Mar 2		H	Kingstonian	244	D 1 - 1	Dormer 68	
35	6		A	Canvey Island	359	L 0 - 1		11
36	13		H	Horsham	224	W 2 - 1	Page 19 (og) Burbridge 61	9
37	18		H	Canvey Island	271	W 1 - 0	Stuart-Evans 43	
38	20		A	Kingstonian	361	L 0 - 2		10
39	23		A	Horsham	164	L 1 - 2	Tomlinson 84 (pen)	
40	27		A	Tooting & Mitcham U	309	W 3 - 2	York 20 (og) Abraham 76 J.Vines 81 (og)	9
41	April 3		H	Ashford Town	208	W 1 - 0	Styles 90	7
42	5		A	BIllericay Town	616	L 0 - 2		
43	10		H	Maidstone United	260	W 1 - 0	Wall 70	8
44	13		A	Borehamwood	151	D 0 - 0		
45	17		H	Waltham Abbey	209	W 4 - 1	Styles 1 Yao 49 55 Black 86	9
46	20		H	Tonbridge Angels	289	D 1 - 1	Spencer 28	
47	24		A	Hendon	210	L 2 - 3	Styles 29 Williams 90	9
					Goals	**59 58**		

Home Attendances:	
Highest:	531 v Dartford
Lowest:	207 v Bognor Regis Town
Average (08-09):	260 (339)
Top Goalscorer:	Flack - 8

AVELEY

Chairman: Graham Gennings
Secretary: Craig Johnston (T) 0794 643 8540
(E) craigjohnston@aveleyfc.freeserve.co.uk

Additional Committee Members:
Terry King

Manager: Alan Kimble
Programme Editor: Craig Johnston (E) craigjohnston@aveleyfc.freeserve.co.uk

Archive photo

Club Factfile

Founded: 1927 **Nickname:** The Millers
Previous Names:
Previous Leagues: Thurrock Combination 1946-49, London 1949-57, Delphian 1957-63, Athenian 1963-73, Isthmian 1973-2004, Southern 2004-06

Club Colours (change): All royal blue

Ground: Mill Field, Mill Road, Aveley, Essex RM15 4SJ (T) 01708 865 940
Capacity: 4,000 **Seats:** 400 **Covered:** 400 **Clubhouse:** Yes **Shop:** No
Previous Grounds:
Simple Directions
London - Southend A1306, turn into Sandy Lane at Aveley.

Record Attendance: 3,741 v Slough Town - FA Amateur Cup 27/02/1971
Record Victory: 11-1 v Histon - 24/08/1963
Record Defeat: 0-8 v Orient, Essex Thameside Trophy
Record Goalscorer: Jotty Wilks - 214
Record Appearances: Ken Riley - 422
Additional Records:

Senior Honours: Athenian League 1970-71. Isthmian League Division 1 North 2008-09.
Thameside Trophy 1980, 2005, 2007.

10 YEAR RECORD

00-01		01-02		02-03		03-04		04-05		05-06		06-07		07-08		08-09		09-10	
Isth3	6	Isth3	3	Isth1N	6	Isth1N	14	SthE	17	SthE	20	Isth1N	15	Isth1N	11	Isth1N	1	Isth P	3

AVELEY

No.	Date	Comp	H/A	Opponents	Att:	Result	Goalscorers	Pos
1	Aug 15	Ryman P.	H	Cray Wanderers	172	D 1 - 1	Maskell 28	7
2	18		A	Hastings United	417	W 1 - 0	Stanley 88	
3	22		A	Kingstonian	305	W 6 - 1	Hahn 17 TUOHY 3 (12 40 71) Ketchell 56 Stanley 58	3
4	24		H	Margate	243	L 0 - 3		4
5	29		H	Carshalton Athletic	209	W 4 - 0	Stanley 20 Dodson 22 Hahn 31 Doyle 89 (pen)	3
6	31		A	Hendon	225	L 1 - 4	Johnson 2	
7	Sept 5		H	Wealdstone	231	D 2 - 2	Tuohy 45 90	6
8	**12**	**F.A.C. 1Q**	**A**	**London Colney**	**102**	**D 1 - 1**	**Symmons 77**	
9	**15**	**F.A.C. 1Qr**	**H**	**London Colney**	**146**	**W 4 - 1**	**Dodson 60 Lechmere 76 Stanley 85 Luck 90**	
10	19		A	Tooting & Mitcham	248	W 2 - 1	J.Vines 33 (og) Wixon 36	2
11	22		A	Maidstone united	20	L 2 - 4	Johnson 8 Doyle 82	
12	**26**	**F.A.C 2Q**	**A**	**Burnham**	**109**	**D 1 - 1**	**Wixon 87**	
13	**29**	**F.A.C. 2Qr**	**H**	**Burnham**	**116**	**W 3 - 1**	**Johnson 57 Stanley 74 Dodson 90**	
14	Oct 3		H	Sutton United	240	L 0 - 1		10
15	**10**	**F.A.C 3Q**	**A**	**Hampton & Richmond B**	**485**	**D 1 - 1**	**Dodson 73**	
16	**14**	**F.A.C. 3Q**	**H**	**Hampton & Richmond B**	**205**	**L 1 - 2**	**Stanley 45**	
17	**17**	**F.A.T. 1Q**	**H**	**Carshalton Athletic**	**117**	**L 2 - 5**	**Tuohy 20 Stanley 72**	
18	24		H	Dartford	541	L 1 - 4	Dodson 32	13
19	31		H	Canvey Island	200	W 4 - 2	Doyle 29 Stanley 44 Tuohy 45 64	
20	Nov 7		A	Tonbridge Angels	341	L 2 - 3	Johnson 27 Dodson 51	14
21	17		A	Ashford Town (Middx)	118	D 2 - 2	Tuohy 31 Johnson 80	
22	28		H	Hendon	138	L 1 - 2	Tuohy 65	16
23	Dec 5		A	Carshalton Athletic	194	W 3 - 0	Edgar 31 Tuohy 55 Hahn 79	18
24	12		H	Horsham	127	W 2 - 1	Hahn 3 Tuohy 37	
25	26		H	AFC Hornchurch	247	D 1 - 1	Tuohy 51	13
26	Jan 2		A	AFC Hornchurch	371	L 1 - 2	Edgar 80	15
27	19		A	Harrow Borough	102	D 3 - 3	Johnson 45 Stanley 60 Dodson 69	
28	23		H	Tooting & Mitcham U	164	L 1 - 2	Butterworth 68	14
29	26		A	Boreham Wood	83	L 2 - 3	Knight 85 Stadhart 90	
30	30		A	Sutton United	446	L 2 - 3	Symmons 10 Knight 55	15
31	Feb 6		H	Maidstone United	210	W 2 - 0	Doyle 11 Tuohy 63	14
32	8		H	Billericay Town	203	W 1 - 0	Tuohy 15	
33	13		A	Canvey Island	323	W 4 - 1	Doyle 3 Tuohy 45 Edgar 84 Dodson 89	12
34	20		H	Harrow Borough	118	L 1 - 2	Butterworth 85	14
35	Mar 6		H	Ashford Town	112	W 2 - 1	Tuohy 34 Dodson 77	14
36	9		A	Waltham Abbey	102	W 2 - 0	Doyle 25 Stanley 67	
37	13		A	Bognor Regis Town	342	D 1 - 1	Dunk 21 (og)	
38	16		A	Cray Wanderers	118	W 2 - 1	Edgar 49 Butterworth 80	
39	20		H	Boreham Wood	331	W 2 - 0	Butterworth 41 Edgar 63	6
40	27		H	Kingstonian	228	L 3 - 4	Butterworth 29 Stanley 51 Edgar 56	12
41	April 5		H	Waltham Abbey	128	W 3 - 1	Stanley 31 51 Symons 88	
42	8		H	Hastings United	160	W 3 - 0	Dodson 3 Tuohy 4 40	
43	10		A	Margate	356	W 3 - 2	Tuohy 73 Young 90 (og) Gabriel 90	7
44	12		H	Bognor Regis Town	162	W 2 - 0	Tuohy 30 47	
45	15		A	Wealdstone	320	W 1 - 0	Johnson 39	
46	17		A	Dartford	2162	D 2 - 2	Edgar 13 Stanley 83	5
47	20		A	Billericay Town	314	L 1 - 2	Tuohy 80	
48	22		A	Horsham	191	W 2 - 0	Johnson 64 Gabriel 84	
49	24		H	Tonbridge Angels	311	W 2 - 0	Lechmere 30 Tuohy 47	
50	**26**	**Play Off**	**H**	**Boreham Wood**		**L 0 - 1**		
					Goals	96 75		

Home Attendances:

Highest:	541 v Dartford
Lowest:	118 v Harrow Borough
Average:	203

Top Goalscorer:	Tuohy - 24 (League 23, Trophy 1 - 1 Hat-trick)

BILLERICAY TOWN

Chairman: Steve Kent
Secretary: Ian Ansell (T) 0795 897 8154
(E) secretary@billericaytown.co.uk

Additional Committee Members:
Jim Green, Simon Williams

Manager: Craig Edwards
Programme Editor: Gary Clark (E) programme.editor@billericaytown.co.uk

Back Row (L-R): Jamie Dormer, Russell Pond, Harrison Chatting, Jo Flack, Nick Muir, Jack Edwards, Dean Etchells, Luca Frankis. **Middle Row:** Gary Ling (Physio), Fiston Manuella, Spencer Knight, James Baker, Jack West, Andy Walker, Mal Downing (Goalkeeping coach), Danny Fowler, Lawrence Yiga, Ian Wiles, Sam West, Marvin Hamilton. **Front Row:** Dave Wareham, Billy Bricknell, Ashley Dumas, Brian Statham (Manager), Ian Cousins (Captain), Barry Lakin (Assistant Manager), Michael Shinn, Greg Oates, Chris Sullivan.
Not pictured: Wayne Semanshia, Bradley Thomas.

Club Factfile

Founded: 1880 **Nickname:** Town or Blues
Previous Names:
Previous Leagues: Romford & District 1890-1914, Mid Essex 1918-47, South Essex Combination 1947-66, Essex Olympian 1966-71, Essex Senior 1971-77, Athenian 1977-79

Club Colours (change): Royal blue/white/royal blue

Ground: New Lodge, Blunts Wall Road, Billericay CM12 9SA (T) 01277 652 188
Capacity: 3,500 **Seats:** 424 **Covered:** 2,000 **Clubhouse:** Yes **Shop:** Yes
Previous Grounds:
Simple Directions
From the M25 (J29) take the A127 to the Basildon/Billericay (A176) turn-off, (junction after the Old Fortune of War r'about). Take second exit at r'about (Billericay is signposted). Then straight over (2nd exit) at the next roundabout. Continue along that road until you enter Billericay. At the first r'about take the first available exit. At the next r'about (with Billericay School on your left) go straight over (1st exit). At yet another r'about!, turn left into the one-way system. Keep in the left-hand lane and go straight over r'about. At first set of lights, turn left. Blunts Wall Road is the second turning on your right.

Record Attendance: 3,841 v West Ham United - Opening of Floodlights 1977
Record Victory: 11-0 v Stansted (A) - Essex Senior League 05/05/1976
Record Defeat: 3-10 v Chelmsford City (A) - Essex Senior Cup 04/01/1993
Record Goalscorer: Freddie Claydon - 273
Record Appearances: J Pullen - 418
Additional Records: Leon Gutzmore scored 51 goals during the 1997-98 season.
Received £22,500+ from West Ham United for Steve Jones November 1992

Senior Honours: FA Vase 1975-76, 76-77, 78-79. Essex Senior Cup 1975-76. Athenian League 1978-79.
Essex Senior Trophy x2.

10 YEAR RECORD

00-01	01-02	02-03	03-04	04-05	05-06	06-07	07-08	08-09	09-10
Isth P 8	Isth P 9	Isth P 12	Isth P 22	Isth P 2	Isth P 7	Isth P 4	Isth P 10	Isth P 11	Isth P 13

BILLERICAY TOWN

No.	Date	Comp	H/A	Opponents	Att:	Result	Goalscorers	Pos
1	Aug 15	Ryman P.	H	Wealdstone	481	D 0 - 0		11
2	18		A	Hendon	217	L 0 - 1		
3	22		A	Cray Wanderers	280	W 2 - 0	Bicknell 9 Flack 28	11
4	25		H	Waltham Abbey	368	D 1 - 1	Flack 38	12
5	29		H	Tonbridge Angels	424	D 1 - 1	Yiga 54	13
6	31		A	Boreham Wood	237	L 0 - 2		
7	Sept 5		H	Tooting & Mitcham U	418	D 0 - 0		15
8	**12**	**F.A.C. 1Q**	**A**	**AFC Hornchurch**	**453**	**W 3 - 0**	**Flack 48 89 Bricknell 85**	
9	19		A	Hastings United	507	D 1 - 1	Bricknell 77	17
10	22		A	Harrow Borough	138	L 0 - 1		20
11	**26**	**F.A.C. 2Q**	**A**	**Chesham United**	**433**	**L 2 - 4**	**Cousins 33 Flack 40**	
12	Oct 3		H	Ashford Town	401	L 0 - 1		21
13	13		H	Kingstonian	347	L 1 - 5	Baker 90	
14	**17**	**F.A.T 1Q**	**A**	**A.F.C. Sudbury**	**312**	**D 3 - 3**	**Hall 15 Bricknell 26 Baker 52**	
15	**20**	**F.A.T 1Qr**	**H**	**A.F.C. Sudbury**	**252**	**D 2 - 2**	**Ainsley 50 (og) Bricknell 62 Billericay Town won 3-1 on pens.**	
16	24		A	Bognor Regis Town	353	D 1 - 1	Bricknell 15	21
17	**31**	**F.A.T 2Q**	**A**	**Barton Rovers**	**140**	**D 2 - 2**	**Baker 23 Shinn 28**	
18	Nov 7		H	Carshalton Athletic	380	L 0 - 4		22
19	**21**	**F.A.T 3Q**	**H**	**Hitchin Town**	**327**	**D 0 - 0**		
20	**24**	**F.A.T 3Qr**	**A**	**Hitchin Town**	**219**	**W 1 - 0**	**Baker 39**	
21	28		H	Boreham Wood	305	W 2 - 0	Green 37 Bricknell 55 (pen)	21
22	Dec 5		A	Tonbridge Angels	443	W 1 - 0	Kersey 58	21
23	**12**	**F.A.T 1**	**A**	**Rushden & Diamonds**	**596**	**L 0 - 1**		
24	26		H	Canvey Island	547	W 4 - 1	BRICKNELL 3 (33 58 66) Wareham 86	20
25	Jan 16		A	Tooting & Mitcham	291	D 1 - 1	Bricknell 14	20
26	19		H	Horsham	232	L 1 - 2	Bricknell 55	
27	23		H	Hastings United	439	W 2 - 0	Bricknell 10 Thomas 58	20
28	26		A	AFC Hornchurch	270	D 0 - 0		
29	30		A	Ashford Town	212	L 2 - 3	Kersey 1 Green 12	20
30	Feb 2		H	Dartford	514	W 1 - 0	Shinn 46	
31	6		H	Harrow Borough	376	L 1 - 2	Wild 15	18
32	8		A	Aveley	203	L 0 - 1		
33	13		A	Kingstonian	318	L 1 - 2	Kersey 54	19
34	16		A	Margate	232	W 3 - 1	Wareham 16 Cleaver 45 Green 67	
35	20		H	Maidstone United	453	D 1 - 1	Wild 11	18
36	Mar 2		A	Maidstone United	177	L 0 - 1		
37	6		A	Dartford	1155	W 4 - 1	Wareham 24 47 Bricknell 50 Charge 88	
38	9		H	Hendon	205	W 1 - 0	Wild 90	
39	13		H	Margate	391	L 1 - 2	Thomas 67 (pen)	18
40	16		A	Wealdstone	328	D 0 - 0		
41	20		A	Horsham	232	W 2 - 0	Charge 23 36	17
42	23		A	Canvey Island	336	D 0 - 0		
43	27		H	Cray Wanderers	357	D 1 - 1	Bricknell 90	17
44	April 5		H	AFC Hornchurch	616	W 2 - 0	Bricknell 80 90 (pen)	
45	8		A	Carshalton Athletic	188	L 0 - 1		
46	10		A	Waltham Abbey	217	W 2 - 0	Charge 20 Wareham 88	
47	15		H	Sutton United	308	L 0 - 1		
48	17		H	Bognor Regis Town	366	W 1 - 0	Charge 8	13
49	20		H	Aveley	314	W 2 - 1	Russell 8 (og) Green 73	
50	24		A	Sutton United	1014	L 1 - 2	O'Rawe 74	13
					Goals	57 54		

Home Attendances:	
Highest:	616 v AFC Hornchurch
Lowest:	205 v Hendon
Average (08-09):	376 (388)
Top Goalscorer:	Bricknell - 17 (League 14, FAC 1, Trophy 2 - 1 Hat-trick)

BURY TOWN

Chairman: Russell Ward
Secretary: Mrs Wendy Turner **(T)** 07795 661 959
(E) wturner@burytownfc.freeserve.co.uk
Additional Committee Members:
Chris Ward
Manager: Richard Wilkins
Programme Editor: Christopher Ward **(E)** cpward@burytownfc.co.uk

Unfortunately an up-to-date photograph was not available
at the time of going to press

Club Factfile

Founded: 1872 **Nickname:** The Blues
Previous Names: Bury St Edmunds 1895-1902, Bury United 1902-06
Previous Leagues: Norfolk & Suffolk Border, Essex & Suffolk Border, Eastern Counties 1935-64, 76-87, 97-2006, Metropolitan 1964-71, Southern 1971-76, 87-97
Club Colours (change): All blue (All red)

Ground: Ram Meadow, Cotton Lane, Bury St Edmunds IP33 1XP **(T)** 01284 754 721
Capacity: 3,500 **Seats:** 300 **Covered:** 1,500 **Clubhouse:** Yes **Shop:** Yes
Previous Grounds:
Simple Directions
Follow signs to Town Centre from A14. At second roundabout take first left into Northgate Street then left into Mustow Street at T junction at lights and left again into Cotton Lane. Ground is 350 yards on the right.

Record Attendance: 2,500 v Enfield - FA Cup 1986
Record Victory: Not known
Record Defeat: Not known
Record Goalscorer: Doug Tooley
Record Appearances: Doug Tooley
Additional Records: Paid £1,500 to Chelmsford City for Mel Springett
Received £5,500 from Ipswich Town for Simon Milton
Senior Honours: Eastern Counties League 1963-64.
Suffolk Premier Cup x9.

10 YEAR RECORD

00-01	01-02	02-03	03-04	04-05	05-06	06-07	07-08	08-09	09-10
ECP 16	ECP 7	ECP 9	ECP 9	ECP 2	ECP 2	Isth1N 17	Isth1N 7	Isth1N	Isth1N

CANVEY ISLAND

Chairman: George Frost
Secretary: Gary Sutton (T) 0779 002 5828
(E) gary.sutton@sky.com

Additional Committee Members:
Chris Sutton

Manager: John Batch
Programme Editor: Glen Eckett (E) gleneckett@another.com

Back Row (L-R): Tony West (Physio), Kevin Dobinson, Greg Cohen, Chris Moore, Ben Patten, Richard Halle, James Russell, Richard Bastin, Andrew West, Leon Gordon, Reiss Noel, Gabriel Fanibuyan, Jay Curran, John Batch (Manager). **Front Row:** Danny Kerrigan, Ian Luck, Ryan Edgar, Craig Davidson, James Rowe, Nick Reynolds, Stuart Batch, Danny Curran, Jon Edwards, Frank Everett.

Club Factfile

Founded: 1926 **Nickname:** The Gulls
Previous Names:
Previous Leagues: Southend & District, Thurrock & Thames Combination, Parthenon, Metropolitan, Greater London 1964-71, Essex Senior 1971-95, Isthmian 1995-2004, Conference 2004-06

Club Colours (change): Yellow and sky blue/sky blue/yellow and sky blue

Ground: The Brockwell Stadium, Park Lane, Canvey Island, Essex SS8 7PX (T) 01268 682 991
Capacity: 4,100 **Seats:** 500 **Covered:** 827 **Clubhouse:** Yes **Shop:** Yes
Previous Grounds:
Simple Directions
A130 from A13 or A127 at Sadlers Farm roundabout. One mile through Town Centre, first right past old bus garage.

Record Attendance: 3,553 v Aldershot Town - Isthmian League 2002-03
Record Victory: Not Known
Record Defeat: Not Known
Record Goalscorer: Andy Jones
Record Appearances: Steve Ward
Additional Records: Paid £5,000 to Northwich Victoria for Chris Duffy
Received £4,500 from Farnborough Town for Brian Horne

Senior Honours: Isthmian Division 1 1993-94, Premier Division 2003-04.
FA Trophy 2000-01. Essex Senior Cup 1998-99, 2000-01, 2001-02.

10 YEAR RECORD

00-01	01-02	02-03	03-04	04-05	05-06	06-07	07-08	08-09	09-10
Isth P 2	Isth P 2	Isth P 2	Isth P 1	Conf N 18	Conf N 4	Isth1N 6	Isth1N 5	Isth P 12	Isth P 16

CANVEY ISLAND

No.	Date	Comp	H/A	Opponents	Att:	Result	Goalscorers	Pos
1	Aug 15	Ryman P.	A	Harrow Borough	177	D 0 - 0		13
2	18		H	Ashford Town	334	W 2 - 1	Patten 50 Cohen 76	
3	22		H	Bognor Regis T	302	D 0 - 0		10
4	25		A	Sutton United	498	W 2 - 1	Moore 5 Curran 76	3
5	29		A	Horsham	360	W 2 - 0	Haule 29 Davidson 79	2
6	31		H	Maidstone United	450	L 0 - 1		
7	Sept 5		A	Cray Wanderers	214	W 2 - 1	Rowe 17 54	3
8	**12**	**F.A.C. 1Q**	**H**	**Hitchin Town**	**323**	**D 3 - 3**	**Curran 8 Rowe 11 Cohen 41**	
9	**15**	**F.A.C.1Qr**	**A**	**Hitchin Town**	**251**	**W 1 - 0**	**Fanibuyan 74**	
10	19		H	Kingstonian	355	L 1 - 2	Rowe 51	5
11	22		H	Hastings United	267	W 1 - 0	Curran 84	
12	**26**	**F.A.C. 2Q**	**H**	**Tooting & Mitcham**	**376**	**L 0 - 2**		
13	Oct 3		A	Wealdstone	435	L 0 - 1		5
14	10		H	Margate	342	W 2 - 0	Dobinson 22 28	3
15	**17**	**F.A.T 1Q**	**H**	**HItchin Town**	**285**	**L 1 - 2**	**Rowe 62**	
16	31		A	Aveley	200	L 2 - 4	Rowe 11 80	
17	Nov 7		H	Waltham Abbey	286	L 2 - 3	Cohen 21 Hallett 44	8
18	14		H	Carshalton Athletic	240	D 2 - 2	Rowe 62 Gordon 74	7
19	21		A	Tooting & Mitcham United	274	W 3 - 1	Curran 19 Rowe 51 90	
20	24		H	Tonbridge Angels	251	D 1 - 1	Rowe 21	
21	28		A	Maidstone United	301	W 3 - 0	King 32 Rowe 42 75	3
22	Dec 5		H	Horsham	276	L 1 - 2	Curran 47	3
23	26		A	Billericay Town	547	L 1 - 4	Hallett 82	8
24	29		H	Dartford	442	L 2 - 5	Davidson 29 Rowe 88	
25	Jan 16		H	Cray Wanderers	268	W 5 - 1	Rowe 45 89 King 51 Fanibuyan 66 Hallett 76	6
26	23		A	Kingstonian	343	L 1 - 3	Dobinson 45	
27	30		H	Wealdstone	341	D 1 - 1	Davidson 72	11
28	Feb 6		A	Hastings United	431	D 1 - 1	Rowe 48	10
29	9		A	Borehamwood	113	W 3 - 1	Moore 70 Rowe 84 89	
30	13		H	Aveley	323	L 1 - 4	Davidson 36	11
31	20		A	Margate	327	W 2 - 1	Cohen 38 Curran 72	10
32	27		A	Carshalton Athletic	321	D 0 - 0		10
33	Mar 6		H	AFC Hornchurch	359	W 1 - 0	Curran 90	8
34	9		H	Harrow Borough	182	D 1 - 1	Hallett 17	10
35	13		A	Tonbridge Angels	358	L 1 - 3	Rowe 37	10
36	16		A	Hendon	101	L 1 - 2	Edwards 26	
37	18		A	AFC Hornchurch	271	L 0 - 1		
38	20		H	Tooting & Mitcham	283	W 2 - 1	Fanibuyan 61 Halle 90	11
39	23		H	Billericay Town	336	D 0 - 0		
40	27		A	Bognor Regis Town	351	D 2 - 2	King 24 Hallett 90	11
41	April 3		H	Boreham Wood	252	L 0 - 1		11
42	5		A	Darford	1319	L 1 - 2	Cohen 31	
43	10		H	Sutton United	302	L 1 - 2	Halle 51	12
44	17		H	Hendon	278	L 2 - 3	Hallett 45 Rowe 90	15
45	20		A	Ashford Town	126	D 1 - 1	Rowe 78	
46	24		A	Waltham Abbey	131	L 1 - 2	King 89 (pen)	16
					Goals	62 69		

Home Attendances:	
Highest:	450 v Maidstone United
Lowest:	182 v Harrow Borough
Average (08-09):	302 (371)
Top Goalscorer:	Rowe - 22 (League 20, FAC 1, Trophy 1)

CARSHALTON ATHLETIC

Chairman: Alan Walker
Secretary: Frank Thompson (T) 0774 776 4349
(E) frankthompson@carshaltonathletic.co.uk

Additional Committee Members:
Richard Eldridge, Simon Fuller, Paul Williams

Manager: Mark Butler
Programme Editor: Simon Fuller (E) leovialli@hotmail.com

Back Row (L-R): Hayden Bird (manager), Jeff Evans (coach), David Graves, Jamie England, Matt Gray, Adrian Toppin, Richard Stroud, Matt Reed, Liam Harwood, Bashir Alimi, Lewis Gonsalves, Tony Quinton, Micky Reid (physiotherapist), Gerry Wrafter (kit manager). **Front row:** Wes Daly, Charlie Ide, Karl Beckford, Antonio Gonnella, Simon Cooper, Frankie Sawyer, Richard Jolly, Adrian Stone.

Club Factfile

Founded: 1905 **Nickname:** Robins
Previous Names:
Previous Leagues: Southern Suburban > 1911, Surrey Senior 1922-23, London 1923-46, Corinthian 1946-56, Athenian 1956-73, Isthmian 1973-2004, Conference 2004-06

Club Colours (change): All red

Ground: War Memorial Sports Ground, Colston Avenue, Carshalton SM5 2PN **(T)** 0208 642 2551
Capacity: 8,000 **Seats:** 240 **Covered:** 4,500 **Clubhouse:** Yes **Shop:** Yes
Previous Grounds:
Simple Directions
Turn right out of Carshalton Station exit, turn right again and then left into Colston Avenue.

Record Attendance: 7,800 v Wimbledon - London Senior Cup
Record Victory: 13-0 v Worthing - Isthmian League Cup 28/01/1991
Record Defeat: 0-11 v Southall - Athenian League March 1963
Record Goalscorer: Jimmy Bolton - 242
Record Appearances: Jon Warden - 504
Additional Records: Paid £15,000 to Enfield for Curtis Warmington
Received £30,000 from Crystal Palace for Ian Cox

Senior Honours: Isthmian League Division 1 South 2002-03.
Surrey Senior Shield 1975-76. London Challenge Cup 1991-92. Surrey Senior Cup x3.

10 YEAR RECORD

00-01	01-02	02-03	03-04	04-05	05-06	06-07	07-08	08-09	09-10
Isth P 21	Isth1 6	Isth1S 1	Isth P 7	Conf S 19	Conf S 21	Isth P 13	Isth P 18	Isth P 4	Isth P 17

CARSHALTON ATHLETIC

No.	Date	Comp	H/A	Opponents	Att:	Result	Goalscorers	Pos
1	Aug 15	Ryman P.	A	Maidstone United	382	W 2 - 0	Ide16 Toppin 39	4
2	18		H	Bognor Regis T	271	W 1 - 0	Ide 24	
3	22		H	Ashford Town	292	W 3 - 1	Jolly 7 England 22 Ide 60	2
4	25		A	Harrow Borough	166	D 3 - 3	Jolly 64 86 Walters (og) 65	2
5	29		A	Aveley	209	L 0 - 4		5
6	31		H	Kingstonian	502	L 1 - 2	Jolly 13	
7	Sept 5		A	Horsham	406	D 2 - 2	Jolly 18 Gonsalves 25	7
8	**12**	**F.A.C. 1Q**	**A**	**Whitstable Town**	**176**	**L 1 - 2**	**England 59**	
9	19		H	Dartford	569	L 0 - 4		11
10	22		A	Borehamwood	101	L 1 - 3	Faulconbridge	16
11	Oct 3		H	AFC Hornchurch	241	W 1 - 0	Faulconbridge 50 (pen)	12
12	13		H	Waltham Abbey	218	W 4 - 1	Ray 37 Faulconbridge 42 53 Jolly 43	9
13	**17**	**F.A.T 1Q**	**A**	**Aveley**	**1217**	**W 5 - 2**	**Jolly 19 74 Murray 54 65 Faulconbridge 67**	
14	25		A	Cray Wanderers	218	D 3 - 3	Munday 2 Jolly 7 Faulconbridge 58	
15	**31**	**F.A.T 2Q**	**H**	**AFC Totton**	**249**	**W 3 - 1**	**Jolly 54 Faulconbridge 67 87**	
16	Nov 7		A	Billericay Town	360	W 4 - 0	Faulconbridge 24 (pen) Jolly 35 Ray 74 Beaney 87	5
17	14		A	Canvey Island	240	D 2 - 2	Stevens 15 Faulconbridge 83	4
18	17		H	Hastings United	267	L 1 - 3	Kamara 59	
19	**21**	**F.A.T 3Q**	**A**	**Weston-s-Mare**	**199**	**D 1 - 1**	**Ray 18**	
20	**24**	**F.A.T 3Qr**	**H**	**Weston-s-Mare**	**214**	**W 3 - 1**	**Beaney 9 63 Jolly 23**	
21	28		A	Kingstonian	380	L 0 - 1		13
22	Dec 5		H	Aveley	194	L 0 - 3		15
23	**12**	**F.A.T. 1**	**H**	**Northwood**	**231**	**D 1 - 1**	**Ofori 37**	
24	**15**	**F.A.T. 1r**	**A**	**Northwood**	**142**	**W 5 - 0**	**Beaney 17 Amuah 35 Jolly 40 Roberts 70 Woozley 85**	
25	26		A	Sutton United	1027	L 0 - 3		16
26	Jan 2		H	Sutton United	1014	D 0 - 0		17
27	**18**	**F.A.T 2**	**A**	**Worcester City**	**468**	**D 1 - 1**	**Stevens 73**	
28	23		A	Dartford	1217	D 1 - 1	Jolly 45	18
29	**26**	**F.A.T. 2r**	**H**	**Worcester City**	**259**	**L 0 - 4**		
30	30		A	AFC Hornchurch	266	D 2 - 2	Faulconbridge 40 Ray 82	18
31	Feb 2		H	Wealdstone	177	W 4 - 2	FAULCONBRIDGE 3 (14 39 pen 90) Jolly 52	
32	6		H	Boreham Wood	259	D 0 - 0		16
33	11		H	Maidstone United	179	L 0 - 1		
34	13		A	Waltham Abbey	112	L 1 - 2	Bostock 60 (og)	17
35	20		H	Tonbridge Angels	262	L 1 - 2	Ide 82	19
36	27		H	Canvey Island	321	D 0 - 0		19
37	Mar 2		H	Tooting & Mitcham	304	W 4 - 1	Ide 14 Stevens 20 Beaney 40 Jolly 79	
38	6		A	Hastings United	441	L 1 - 3	Ide 46	19
39	9		A	Bognor Regis Town	226	L 0 - 1		
40	13		H	Hendon	227	D 0 - 0		19
41	16		A	Tonbridge Amngels	284	L 0 - 2		
42	20		A	Margate	402	D 1 - 1	Harrison 24	19
43	27		A	Ashford Town	127	W 2 - 1	Ray 32 Toppin 51	19
44	30		H	Margate	201	L 1 - 2	Lampton 41	
45	April 5		A	Tooting & Mitcham	528	D 2 - 2	Stevens 6 Ray 30	
46	8		H	Billericay Town	188	W 1 - 0	Kamara 59	
47	10		H	Harrow Borough	272	D 2 - 2	Harrison 50 Ray 89	17
48	13		H	Horsham	201	L 1 - 2	Gomez 45	
49	15		A	Hendon	129	L 0 - 1		
50	17		H	Cray Wanderers	326	W 2 - 0	Gomez 35 Stevens 71	17
51	24		A	Wealdstone	735	W 4 - 1	HARRISON 3 (6 19 27) Jolly 22	17
					Goals	78 77		

Home Attendances:	
Highest:	1,014 v Sutton United
Lowest:	177 v Wealdstone
Average (08-09):	262 (323)
Top Goalscorer:	Jolly - 17 (League 12, Trophy 5)

CONCORD RANGERS

Chairman: Antony Smith
Secretary: Chris Crerie **(T)** 0790 952 8818
(E) concordrangers@btinternet.com

Additional Committee Members:
Jack Smith junior, Ron Heyfron
Manager: Danny Scopes and Danny Cowley
Programme Editor: Chris Crerie **(E)** concordrangers@btinternet.com

Back Row: Danny Clare(Goalkeeper Coach).Danny Glozier. James Elmes. Harry Elmes. John Easterford. Ashley Miller. Steve King. Lee White. Brad Thomas. James Lawson. Gary Ewers(Kit Manager)
Front Row: Marc Sontag. Liam Hopkins. Tony Stokes. Bertie Brayley. Danny Cowley(Joint Manager). Lamar Johnson. Dale Brightly. Danny Scopes(Joint Manager). Dave Collins. Nicky Cowley. Taylor Sinfield. Kurt Smith.

Club Factfile

Founded: 1967 **Nickname:** Rangers
Previous Names:
Previous Leagues: Southend & District, Southend Alliance, Essex Intermediate 1988-91, Essex Senior 1991-2008

Club Colours (change): Yellow & blue/blue/blue

Ground: Thames Road, Canvey Island, Essex SS8 0HH **(T)** 01268 515 750
Capacity: 1,500 **Seats:** Yes **Covered:** Yes **Clubhouse:** Yes **Shop:**
Previous Grounds: Waterside
Simple Directions
A130 onto Canvey Island. Turn right into Thorney Bay Road. Then right again into Thames Road.

Record Attendance: 1,500 v Lee Chapel North - FA Sunday Cup 1989-90
Record Victory: Not Known
Record Defeat: Not Known
Record Goalscorer: Not Known
Record Appearances: Not Known
Additional Records:

Senior Honours: Essex Intermediate League Division 2 1990-91. Essex Senior League 1997-98, 2003-04, 07-08

10 YEAR RECORD

00-01	01-02	02-03	03-04	04-05	05-06	06-07	07-08	08-09	09-10
ESen 5	ESen 4	ESen 2	ESen 1	ESen 9	ESen 7	ESen 7	ESen 1	Isth1N 5	Isth1N 2

Do you remember when...

Concord Rangers

In season 2003-2004 Concord Rangers won the Essex Senior League with Danny Heale finishing as the leagues' top scorer.

Back row, left to right: Steve Knott, Jamie Gold, Lee Goodwin, Dave Brightley, Brendan Walsh, Dave Cannon and Danny Stanley.
Front Row: Darren Brown, Ian Wastell, Danny Heale and Danny Greaves.

CRAY WANDERERS

Chairman: Gary Hillman

Secretary: John de Palma (T) 0778 603 8822 (E) john.depalma@abbey.com

Additional Committee Members:
Martin Hodson, Jerry Dowlen

Manager: Ian Jenkins

Programme Editor: Greg Mann (E) greg25old@aol.com

Club Factfile

Founded: 1860 **Nickname:** The Wands

Previous Names: None

Previous Leagues: Southern Suburban, Kent x4 most recent 1934-38, West Kent, London, Kent Amateur, S. London All., Aetolian 59-64, Gtr London 64-66, Metropolitan 66-71, London Met. 71-75, London Spartan 75-78.

Club Colours (change): Amber/black/black.

Ground: Bromley FC, Hayes Lane, Bromley, Kent BR2 9EF **(T)** 020 8460 5291

Capacity: 5,000 **Seats:** 1,300 **Covered:** 2,500 **Clubhouse:** Yes **Shop:** Yes

Previous Grounds: Star Lane, Tothills, Twysden, Fordcroft, Grassmeade, St Mary Cray.

Simple Directions
From M25: Leaving the motorway at junction 4, follow the A21 to Bromley and London, for approximately 4 miles and then fork left onto the A232 signposted Croydon/Sutton. At the second set of traffic lights, turn right into Baston Road (B265), following it for about two miles as it becomes Hayes Street and then Hayes Lane. Cray Wanderers FC is on the right hand side of the road just after the mini roundabout. There is ample room for coaches to drive down the driveway, turn round and park.

Record Attendance: 1,523 v Stamford - F.A.Vase 6th Round 1979-80.
Record Victory: 15-0 v Sevenoaks - 1894-95.
Record Defeat: 1-11 v Bromley - 1920-21.
Record Goalscorer: Ken Collishaw - 274.
Record Appearances: John Dorey - 500 (1961-62).
Additional Records:

Senior Honours: Kent League 1901-02, 80-81, 02-03, 03-04. London Spartan League 1976-77, 77-78. Kent League Cup 1983-84, 2002-03. Kent Senior Trophy 1992-93, 2003-04.

10 YEAR RECORD

00-01	01-02	02-03	03-04	04-05	05-06	06-07	07-08	08-09	09-10
Kent P 12	Kent P 5	Kent P 1	Kent P 1	Isth1 6	Isth1 11	Isth1S 12	Isth1S 3	Isth1S 2	Isth P 15

CRAY WANDERERS

No.	Date	Comp	H/A	Opponents	Att:	Result	Goalscorers	Pos
1	Aug 15	Ryman P.	A	Aveley	172	D 1 - 1	Luckett 47	8
2	18		H	Tonbridge Angels	227	L 1 - 3	Power 59	
3	22		H	Billericay Town	280	L 0 - 2		20
4	25		A	Tooting & Mitcham U	228	W 2 - 0	L.Wood 25 J.Wood 28	17
5	29		H	Hastings United	176	L 1 - 2	Bremner 73	20
6	31		A	Margate	423	W 1 - 0	Tyne 33	
7	Sept 5		H	Canvey Island	214	L 1 - 2	Lover 25	17
8	**12**	**F.A.C. 1Q**	**A**	**Walton & Hersham**	**108**	**L 1 - 2**	**Bremner 68**	
9	20		A	Hendon	138	L 0 - 2		
10	22		A	AFC Hornchurch	234	W 2 - 0	Lover 61 Willy 88	17
11	Oct 3		H	Waltham Abbey	137	L 1 - 2	J.Wood 54	20
12	10		A	Kingstonian	359	L 1 - 4	Bremner 79	20
13	13		H	Borehamwood	133	D 1 - 1	Wood L 40	19
14	**18**	**F.A.T 1Q**	**H**	**Burgess Hill**	**101**	**L 1 - 2**	**Sterling 90**	
15	25		H	Carshalton athletic	218	D 3 - 3	Sterling 15 16 J.Wood 34	19
16	Nov 7		A	Horsham	301	L 0 - 4		20
17	17		A	Wealdstone	315	L 2 - 3	Luckett 30 Bremner 76	
18	21		A	Ashford Town	125	L 0 - 3		20
19	24		H	Maidstone United	211	W 1 - 0	Luckett 30	
20	29		H	Margate	179	W 3 - 2	Porter 8 74 S.Yorke 85	
21	Dec 5		A	Hastings United	409	W 3 - 2	Bremner 11 43 Luckett 39 (pen)	
22	12		H	Harrow Borough	143	L 1 - 3	Bremner 10	17
23	15		H	Bognor Regis Town	104	L 0 - 2	Luckett 30	17
24	26		A	Dartford	1306	D 1 - 1	Willey 29	18
25	Jan 2		H	Dartford	688	L 1 - 2	Luckett 62	19
26	16		A	Canvey Island	268	L 1 - 5	Cassius 90	19
27	23		H	Hendon	157	W 2 - 0	Porter 36 Guest 86	16
28	30		A	Waltham Abbey	103	W 1 - 0	Downer 5	14
29	Feb 6		H	AFC Hornchurch	201	W 1 - 0	Luckett 13	13
30	9		A	Tonbridge Angels		L 2 - 3	Bremner 57 Luckett 79 (pen)	
31	13		A	Boreham Wood	128	W 4 - 2	Tyne 10 Porter 19 49 Lover 90	14
32	20		H	Kingstonian	307	W 2 - 1	Bremner 50 Cassius 87	13
33	27		A	Bognor Regis RTown	303	D 1 - 1	Bremner 84	
34	Mar 6		H	Wealdstonme	197	L 1 - 3	Bremner 41	16
35	13		A	Maidstone United	263	D 1 - 1	Porter 24	16
36	16		H	Aveley	118	L 1 - 2	Tyne 78	
37	20		H	Ashford Town	104	W 1 - 0	Quin 67	16
38	27		A	Billericay Town	357	D 1 - 1	Bremner 62	16
39	April 4		A	Sutton United	502	W 4 - 1	Perkin 4 Luckett 34 65 (pen) Porter 60	
40	10		H	Tooting & Mitcham U	233	W 1 - 0	Luckett 50	13
41	17		A	Carshalton Athletic	326	L 0 - 2		16
42	20		H	Sutton United	253	L 1 - 2	Luckett 63	
43	22		A	Harrow Borough	109	D 1 - 1	Cronin 14	
44	24		H	Horsham	169	D 1 - 1	Osborn 90	15
					Goals	56 74		

Home Attendances:

Highest:	688 v Dartford
Lowest:	104 v Ashford Town
Average:	197
Top Goalscorer:	Bremner - 12 (League 11, FAC 1)

CROYDON ATHLETIC

Chairman: Dean Fisher
Secretary: Bob Jenkins (T) 0772 932 1141
(E) bjenkins@crydonathletic.co.uk

Additional Committee Members:
Karen Muir

Manager: Tim O'Shea
Programme Editor: Bob Jenkins (E) bjenkins@croydonathletic.co.uk

Unfortunately an up-to-date photograph was not available at the time of going to press

Club Factfile

Founded: 1947 **Nickname:** The Rams
Previous Names: Norwood FC and Wandsworth FC amalgamated in 1986 to form Wandsworth & Norwood > 1990
Previous Leagues: Wandsworth Parthenon 1960-64, Surrey Senior 1964-77, London Spartan 1977-79

Club Colours (change): Maroon with white flash/maroon/maroon

Ground: The Keith Tucket Stadium, off Maryfield Road, Thornton Heath CR7 6DN **(T)** 020 8664 8343
Capacity: 3,000 **Seats:** 163 **Covered:** 660 **Clubhouse:** Yes **Shop:** Yes
Previous Grounds:

Simple Directions
From M25: Exit at either Junction 6 and then take the A22 to Purley Cross and then join the A23 London Road and then directions below from Purley, or exit at Junction 7 and take the A23 London Road all the way. **From Streatham and Norbury:** Take the A23 London Road to the roundabout at Thornton Heath, continue down the A23 Thornton Road. Then take the 1st on the Right past the No Entry road (Fairlands Avenue), Silverleigh Road, 50 yards, at the fork, keep left (signposted Croydon Athletic FC) into Trafford Road, then Mayfield Road (which is a continuation of Trafford Road) Go to the end of Mayfield Road, then left at the last house. Follow the lane, passed allotments, past an open car park space and continue along the lane to our club car park.

Record Attendance: 1,372 v AFC Wimbledon 2004-05
Record Victory: Not Known
Record Defeat: Not Known
Record Goalscorer: Marc Flemington
Record Appearances: James Gibson - 300
Additional Records:

Senior Honours: London Spartan League 1994-95. Isthmian League Division 3 2001-02, Division 1 South 2009-10.

10 YEAR RECORD

00-01		01-02		02-03		03-04		04-05		05-06		06-07		07-08		08-09		09-10	
Isth3	10	Isth3	1	Isth1S	19	Isth1S	10	Isth1	12	Isth1	8	Isth1S	19	Isth1S	13	Isth1S	10	Isth1S	1

FOLKESTONE INVICTA

Chairman: Lynn Woods
Secretary: Neil Pilcher (T) 07880 745 772
(E) neil.pilcher@xchanging.com

Additional Committee Members:
Elaine Orsbourne, Andy Bowden, Phil Orris
Manager: Neil Cugley
Programme Editor: Richard Murrill (E) richardmurrill@fsmail.net

Unfortunately an up-to-date photograph was not available at the time of going to press

Club Factfile

Founded: 1936 **Nickname:** The Seasiders
Previous Names:
Previous Leagues: Kent 1990-98, Southern 1998-2004

Club Colours (change): Amber with black trim/black with amber trim/black

Ground: The Buzzlines Stadium, The New Pavilion, Cheriton Road CT19 5JU (T) 01303 257 461
Capacity: 6,500 **Seats:** 900 **Covered:** 3,500 **Clubhouse:** Yes **Shop:** Yes
Previous Grounds: South Road Hythe > 1991, County League matches on council pitches
Simple Directions
On the A20 behind Morrisons Supermarket, midway between Folkstone Central and West BR stations

Record Attendance: 7,881 v Margate - Kent Senior Cup 1958
Record Victory: 13-0 v Faversham Town - Kent League Division 1
Record Defeat: 1-7 v Crockenhill - Kent League Division 1
Record Goalscorer: Not Known
Record Appearances: Not Known
Additional Records:

Senior Honours: None

10 YEAR RECORD

00-01	01-02	02-03	03-04	04-05	05-06	06-07	07-08	08-09	09-10
SthP 17	SthP 13	SthP 22	SthE 5	Isth P 13	Isth P 13	Isth P 18	Isth P 21	Isth1S 11	Isth1S 2

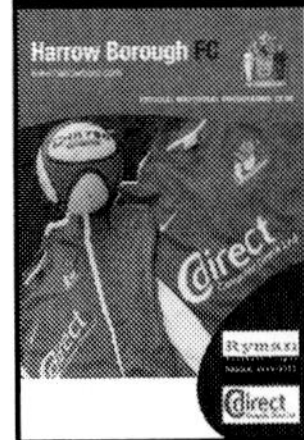

HARROW BOROUGH

Chairman: Peter Rogers
Secretary: Peter Rogers (T) 0795 618 5685
(E) peter@harrowboro.co.uk

Additional Committee Members:
Stuart Hobbs
Manager: David Howell
Programme Editor: Peter Rogers (E) peter@harroboro.co.uk

Club Factfile

Founded: 1933 **Nickname:** Boro
Previous Names: Roxonian 1933-38, Harrow Town 1938-66
Previous Leagues: Harrow & District 1933-34, Spartan 1934-40, 45-58, West Middlesex Combination 1940-41, Middlesex Senior 1941-45, Delphian 1956-63, Athenian 1963-75

Club Colours (change): Red with white/red/red

Ground: Earlsmead, Carlyon Avenue, South Harrow HA2 8SS (T) 0844 561 1347
Capacity: 3,070 **Seats:** 350 **Covered:** 1,000 **Clubhouse:** Yes **Shop:** Yes
Previous Grounds:
Simple Directions
From the M25 junction 16, take the M40 East towards Uxbridge and London. Continue onto A40, passing Northolt Aerodrome on the left hand side. At the Target Roundabout junction (A312) turn left towards Northolt.
Just after passing Northolt Underground Station on the left hand side, turn left at the next set of traffic lights, onto Eastcote Lane, becoming Field End Road.
At next roundabout, turn right onto Eastcote Lane. At a small parade of shops, take the turning on the right into Carlyon Avenue. Earlsmead is the second turning on the right.

Record Attendance: 3,000 v Wealdstone - FA Cup 1st Qualifying Road 1946
Record Victory: 13-0 v Handley Page (A) - 18/10/1941
Record Defeat: 0-8 on five occasions
Record Goalscorer: Dave Pearce - 153
Record Appearances: Les Currell - 582, Colin Payne - 557, Steve Emmanuel - 522
Additional Records:

Senior Honours: Isthmian League 1983-84.
Middlesex Senior Cup 1982-83, 92-93. Middlesex Premier Cup 1981-82.
Middlesex Senior Charity Cup 1979-80, 92-93, 2005-06, 06-07

10 YEAR RECORD

00-01	01-02	02-03	03-04	04-05	05-06	06-07	07-08	08-09	09-10
Isth P 19	Isth P 21	Isth P 18	Isth P 17	Isth P 16	Isth P 16	Isth P 19	Isth P 16	Isth P 14	Isth P 14

HARROW BOROUGH

No.	Date	Comp	H/A	Opponents	Att:	Result	Goalscorers	Pos
1	Aug 15	Ryman P.	H	Canvey Island	177	D 0 - 0		14
2	17		A	Kingstonian	367	W 5 - 3	Fraser 4 10 Fenton 18 Clarke 66 Wassmer 78	1
3	22		A	Horsham	303	L 0 - 2		12
4	25		H	Carshalton Athletic	166	D 3 - 3	Clarke 45 Baptiste 51 68	13
5	29		H	Margate	156	W 3 - 0	Baptiste 20 (pen) Wassmer 22 Hunt 38	
6	31		A	Waltham Abbey	138	D 1 - 1	Constant 8	
7	Sept 5		H	Hastings United	202	L 0 - 3		12
8	**12**	**F.A.C. 1Q**	**A**	**Chesham United**	**286**	**D 1 - 1**	**Baptiste 20 (pen)**	
9	**15**	**F.A.C. 1Qr**	**H**	**Chesham United**	**158**	**L 0 - 2**		
10	19		A	AFC Hornchurch	234	L 1 - 2	Clarke 90	16
11	22		H	Billericay Town	138	W 1 - 0	Clarke 6	13
12	Oct 3		A	Dartford	1326	L 0 - 2		16
13	12		A	Tooting & Mitcham U	245	L 0 - 1		
14	**17**	**F.A.T. 1Q**	**A**	**Soham Town**	**125**	**D 2 - 2**	**R.Baptiste 43 (pen) Walters 62**	
15	**20**	**F.A.T 1Qr**	**H**	**Soham Town**	**91**	**W 5 - 1**	**R Baptiste 10 44 Clarke 69 Leach 72 Constant 74**	
16	**31**	**F.A.T. 2Q**	**H**	**Wealdstone**	**513**	**D 2 - 2**	**R.Baptiste 51 90**	
17	**Nov 3**	**F.A.T 2Qr**	**A**	**Wealdstone**	**315**	**L 1 - 2**	**Lyall 71**	
18	7		H	Ashford Town	178	L 1 - 2	Walters 70	19
19	14		H	Maidstone United	142	W 2 - 1	Fraser 22 R.Baptiste 79	16
20	21		A	Bognor Regis Town	235	D 1 - 1	Jinadu 3	
21	24		H	Boreham Wood	103	W 2 - 0	Clarke 77 88	
22	28		H	Waltham Abbey	131	W 5 - 3	Jinadu 12 60 Watts 52 Nakashima 67 Clarke 84	12
23	Dec 5		A	Margate	353	D 2 - 2	Wilson 75 (og) Constant 85	12
24	12		A	Cray Wanderers	143	W 3 - 1	Watts 11 Clarke 45 Frempong 73	
25	26		H	Hendon	224	L 0 - 3		11
26	28		A	Wealdstone	666	L 1 - 2	Fenton 40	
27	Jan 2		A	Hendon	214	L 1 - 3	Fenton 78	13
28	19		H	Aveley	102	D 3 - 3	Cook 18 Watts 75 Morlese 90	
29	23		H	AFC Hornchurch	180	D 0 - 0		13
30	Feb 6		A	Billericay Town	376	W 2 - 1	R.Baptiste 62 Fenton 74	12
31	9		H	Kingstonian	154	W 2 - 0	R.Baptiste 79 Clarke 90	
32	13		H	Tooting & Mitcham U	177	D 1 - 1	Morlese 77	13
33	20		A	Aveley	118	W 2 - 1	Cook 36 58	12
34	27		A	Maidstone United	202	W 3 - 0	Baptiste 6 Jinadu 87 Clarke 89	
35	Mar 2		A	Hastings UNited	289	D 1 - 1	Baptiste 63	
36	6		H	Bognor Regis Town	389	L 1 - 2	Morlese 87	10
37	9		A	Canvey Island	182	D 1 - 1	Morlese 90	
38	13		A	Boreham Wood	113	L 0 - 1		
39	20		H	Tonbridge Angels	176	L 1 - 3	Morlese 90	13
40	23		A	Sutton United	378	L 0 - 1		
41	27		H	Horsham	135	D 2 - 2	Morlese 12 McGonigle 36	
42	April 5		H	Wealdstone	525	W 3 - 1	R.Baptiste 45 63 McGonigle 80	
43	10		A	Carshalton Athletic	272	D 2 - 2	R.Baptiste 26 54	15
44	13		H	Dartford	209	L 0 - 1		
45	15		A	Tonbridge Angels	397	L 2 - 3	Baptiste 17 Watts 34	
46	17		H	Sutton United	233	D 1 - 1	Jinadu 62	14
47	22		H	Cray Wanderers	109	D 1 - 1	McGonigle 59	
48	24		A	Ashford Town	110	W 6 - 2	Morlese 26 Cooper 32 (og) Cook 44 R.Baptiste 53 79 Nakashima 61	
					Goals	77 73		

Home Attendances:	
Highest:	525 v Wealdstone
Lowest:	102 v Aveley
Average (08-09):	177 (187)
Top Goalscorer:	Baptiste - 21 (League 15, FAC 1, FAT 5)

HASTINGS UNITED

Chairman: David Walters
Secretary: Tony Cosens **(T)** 0771 265 4288
(E) richardcosens@btinternet.com

Additional Committee Members:
Sean Adams, Pat McCrossan

Manager: Tony Dolby
Programme Editor: Simon Rudkins **(E)** simonrudkins@hotmail.com

BackRow (L-R): John Lambert (Manager), Marc Whiteman, Ben Radley, Sam Adams, Scott Ramsay, Chris May, Nathan Russell, Rhys Whyborne, Sam Crabb, Gren Nessling, Mark Stapley (Reserve team assistant manager).
Front Row: Loraine Western (Physio), Antonio Gonnella, Frankie Sawyer, Scott Marshall, Paddy Cody, Danny Spice, Jack Franklin, Matt Maclean, Milton Miltiadou, Paul Nessling, Keith Miles (Reserve team manager).
(Archive photo)

Club Factfile

Founded: 1894 **Nickname:** The Us
Previous Names: Hastings and St Leonards Amateurs, Hastings Town > 2002
Previous Leagues: South Eastern 1904-05, Southern 1905-10, Sussex County 1921-27, 52-85, Southern Amateur 1927-46, Corinthian 1946-48

Club Colours (change): Claret/white/white

Ground: The Pilot Field, Elphinstone Road, Hastings TN34 2AX **(T)** 01424 444 635
Capacity: 4,050 **Seats:** 800 **Covered:** 1,750 **Clubhouse:** Yes **Shop:** Yes
Previous Grounds: Bulverhythe Recreation > 1976
Simple Directions
From A1 turn left at third roundabout into St Helens Road. Then left after one mile into St Helens Park Road leading into Downs Road. Turn left at T-junction at the end of the road. Ground is 200 yards on the right.

Record Attendance: 4,888 v Nottingham Forest - Friendly 23/06/1996
Record Victory: Not Known
Record Defeat: Not Known
Record Goalscorer: Terry White scored 33 during 1999-2000
Record Appearances: Not Known
Additional Records: Paid £8,000 to Ashford Town for Nicky Dent
Received £30,000 from Nottingham Forest for Paul Smith

Senior Honours: Southern League Division 1 1991-92, 2001-01, League Cup 1994-95.

10 YEAR RECORD

00-01		01-02		02-03		03-04		04-05		05-06		06-07		07-08		08-09		09-10	
SthE	6	SthE	1	SthP	20	SthE	18	Isth1	11	Isth1	12	Isth1S	4	Isth P	14	Isth P	17	Isth P	7

HASTINGS UNITED

No.	Date	Comp	H/A	Opponents	Att:	Result	Goalscorers	Pos
1	Aug 15	Ryman P.	A	Boreham Wood	159	D 0 - 0		15
2	18		H	Aveley	417	L 0 - 1		
3	22		H	Dartford	717	L 1 - 3	McLean 61	19
4	25		A	Bognor Regis Town	355	W 1 - 0	Carey 32	18
5	29		A	Cray Wanderers	277	W 2 - 1	A.Olorunda 19 31	11
6	31		H	Horsham	462	W 3 - 1	Phillips 4 Ramsay 53 Adams 79	4
7	Sept 5		A	Harrow Borough	202	W 3 - 0	Adams 76 (pen) A Olorunda 80 Carey 90	3
8	**12**	**F.A.C.1Q**	**A**	**Farnborough**	**716**	**L 1 - 2**	**A.Olorunda72**	
9	19		H	Billericay Town	507	D 1 - 1	T.Olorunda 90	3
10	22		A	Canvey Island		L 0 - 1		7
11	Oct 3		H	Hendon	452	W 2 - 1	A.Olorunda 64 Carey 88	4
12	10		A	Waltham Abbey	171	W 1 - 0	T.Olorundo 22	
13	13		H	Sutton United	492	L 1 - 3	Jirbandey 80	5
14	**17**	**F.A.T 1Q**	**H**	**Merstham**	**358**	**L 1 - 6**	**Upton 28**	
15	24		A	Kingstonian	333	W 2 - 1	A.Olorunda 40 81	3
16	31		H	Ashford Town	372	D 4 - 4	Eldridge 11 Upton 45 A Olorundo 51 T Olorundo 90	
17	Nov 7		H	Margate	517	W 2 - 1	A.Olorunda 64 Eldridge 76	2
18	14		H	AFC Hornchurch	367	W 1 - 0	Eldridge 48	2
19	17		A	Carshalton Athletic	267	W 3 - 1	Phillips 63 A.Olorunda 64 Upton 90	
20	28		A	Horsham	329	L 2 - 4	A.Olorunda 27 Carey 53	
21	Dec 5		H	Cray Wanderers	409	L 2 - 3	A.Olorunda 14 57	2
22	12		A	Tooting & Mitcham U	256	L 0 - 1		2
23	19		H	Boreham Wood	306	W 2 - 1	Ramsay 19 A.Olorundo 51	
24	26		A	Tonbridge Angels	517	D 2 - 2	A.Olorunda 37 Carey 90	2
25	28		H	Maidstone United	631	L 1 - 2	Adams 26	
26	Jan 2		H	Tonbridge Angels	720	W 5 - 1	Eldridge 47 Ray 51 Phillips 61 89 Adams 85	2
27	23		A	Billericay Town	439	L 0 - 2		2
28	Feb 6		H	Canvey Island	431	D 1 - 1	Adams 64 (pen)	3
29	13		A	Sutton United	546	D 2 - 2	Treleaven 20 Pell 85	3
30	20		H	Waltham Abbey	369	W 2 - 0	Treleaven 29 Pell 60	4
31	27		A	AFC Hornchurch	286	D 1 - 1	Pell 50	4
32	Mar 2		H	Harrow Borough	289	D 1 - 1	Treleaven 29	
33	6		H	Carshalton Athletic	441	W 3 - 1	Ray 32 A.Olorunda 61 Pell 90	
34	9		A	Wealdstone	329	L 0 - 1		
35	13		A	Ashford Town	112	L 2 - 3	Adams 55 A.Olorunda 68	4
36	20		H	Wealdtone	429	W 1 - 0	A.Olorunda 45	4
37	27		A	Dartford	1235	L 3 - 4	A.Olorunda 45 65 Bellamy 55	6
38	April 3		H	Tooting & Mitcham	458	W 2 - 0	A.Olorunda 58 Adams 77	5
39	5		A	Maidstone United	308	W 5 - 0	Ulph 24 (og) Treleaven 43 Sterling 51 Ray 55 87	
40	8		A	Aveley	160	L 0 - 3		
41	10		H	Bognor Regis Town	454	L 1 - 2	Adams 66	5
42	13		A	Hendon	135	W 3 - 1	Treleaven 67 82 Sterling 90	
43	17		H	Kingstonian	715	D 0 - 0		6
44	24		A	Margate	435	L 0 - 1		7
					Goals	70 64		

Home Attendances:	
Highest:	720 v Tonbridge Angels
Lowest:	289 v Harrow Borough
Average (08-09):	452 (444)
Top Goalscorer:	A. Olorunda - 21 (League 20, FAC 1)

HENDON

Chairman: Vacant
Secretary: Graham Etchell (T) 0797 369 8552
(E) hendonfc@freenetname.co.uk

Additional Committee Members:
Peter Dean, David Balheimer, Steve Rogers

Manager: Gary McCann

Programme Editor: Graham Etchell (E) hendonfc@freenetname.co.uk

BackRow (L-R): Glenn Garner, Yacine Hamada, Harry Hunt, Casey Maclaren, Peter Dean, Lee O'Leary, James Reading, Berkley Laurencin, Marc Leach, Mark Kirby, Sam Berry, Craig Vargas, Dave Diedhiou, James Bent.
Front Row: James Parker, Wayne O'Sullivan, Jamie Busby, James Burgess, Freddie Hyatt (Assistant Manager), Gary McCann (Manager), Mark Findlay (Sports Therapist), Roy Harwood (Coach), Kevin Maclaren, Wayne Jackson, Lubomir Guentchev, Danny Dyer.

Club Factfile

Founded: 1908 **Nickname:** Dons or Greens
Previous Names: Christ Church Hampstead > 1908, Hampstead Town > 1933, Golders Green > 1946
Previous Leagues: Finchley & District 1908-11, Middlesex 1910-11, London 1911-14, Athenian 1914-63

Club Colours (change): All green & white

Ground: Wembley FC, Vale Farm, Watford Road, Wembley HA0 3HG (T) 020 8908 3553
Capacity: 2,450 **Seats:** 350 **Covered:** 950 **Clubhouse:** Yes **Shop:**
Previous Grounds: Claremont Road
Simple Directions
400 yards from Sudbury Town underground station or 10 minutes walk from North Wembley BR.

Record Attendance: 9,000 v Northampton Town - FA Cup 1st Round 1952
Record Victory: 13-1 v Wingate - Middlesex County Cup 02/02/1957
Record Defeat: 2-11 v Walthamstowe Avenue, Athenian League 09/11/1935
Record Goalscorer: Freddie Evans - 176 (1929-35)
Record Appearances: Bill Fisher - 787 - (1940-64)
Additional Records: Received £30,000 from Luton Town for Iain Dowie

Senior Honours: FA Amateur Cup 1959-60, 64-65, 71-72. Isthmian League 1964-65, 72-73. European Amateur Champions 1972-73. Athenian League x3. London Senior Cup 1963-64, 68-69. Middlesex Senior Cup x14

10 YEAR RECORD

00-01	01-02	02-03	03-04	04-05	05-06	06-07	07-08	08-09	09-10
Isth P 12	Isth P 8	Isth P 3	Isth P 4	Isth P 11	Isth P 19	Isth P 14	Isth P 7	Isth P 16	Isth P 10

HENDON

No.	Date	Comp	H/A	Opponents	Att:	Result	Goalscorers	Pos
1	Aug 15	Ryman P.	A	Bognor Regis Town	404	W 3 - 0	Bent 66 O'Sullivan 81Hunt 89	2
2	18		H	Billericay Town	217	W 1 - 0	O'Sullivan 84	
3	22		H	Sutton United	203	L 1 - 2	Berry 60	7
4	25		A	Ashford Town	270	D 1 - 1	Dean 70	6
5	29		H	Kingstonian	221	L 0 - 3		10
6	31		H	Aveley	225	W 4 - 1	Diedhiou 31 Bent 57 Dyer 85 Dean 90	
7	Sept 5		A	Dartford	1100	L 0 - 5		10
8	**12**	**F.A.C. 1Q**	**A**	**Marlow**	**149**	**W 2 - 0**	**Bent 18 Garner 86**	
9	20		H	Cray Wanderers	138	W 2 - 0	Hamada 43 Busby53	
10	22		H	Margate	159	L 1 - 2	Garner 60	10
11	**26**	**F.A.C. 2Q**	**H**	**Kingstonian**	**226**	**W 2 - 1**	**C.Maclaren 60 Hunt 90**	
12	Oct 3		A	Hastngs United	452	L 1 - 2	Hamada 90	14
13	**10**	**F.A.C 3Q**	**H**	**Ashford Town (Middx)**	**236**	**D 0 - 0**		
14	**13**	**F.A.C. 3Qr**	**A**	**Ashford Town (Middx)**	**226**	**D *2 - 2**	**Ochoa 24 Garner 118 Hendon won 9-8 on pens**	
15	**17**	**F.A.T 1Q**	**H**	**Lowestoft Town**	**174**	**W 2 - 0**	**Guentchev 77 Diedhiou 83**	
16	**24**	**F.A.C. 4Q**	**H**	**Woking**	**528**	**L 0 - 5**		
17	**31**	**F.A.T. 2Q**	**A**	**Kingstonian**	**276**	**L 2 - 4**	**Guentchev 80 Bent 90**	
18	Nov 7		A	AFC Hornchurch	297	D 4 - 4	GUENTCHEV 3 (24 47 89) Bent 84	16
19	17		A	Tonbridge Angels	371	L 1 - 2	Dunn 46	
20	21		A	Waltham Abbey	121	L 0 - 1		19
21	28		A	Aveley	138	W 2 - 1	Cousins 23 Dunn 30	17
22	Dec 1		H	Horsham	116	D 1 - 1	K.Maclaren 39	
23	6		A	Kingstonian		L 0 - 3		19
24	26		A	Harrow Borough	224	W 3 - 0	Parker 43 C.Maclaren 50 Bent 82	
25	Jan 2		H	Harrow Borough	214	W 3 - 1	Cousins 38 51 C.Maclaren 81	16
26	23		A	Cray Wanderers	157	L 0 - 2		17
27	26		H	Tooting & Mitcham U	123	D 0 - 0		
28	Feb 6		A	Margate	297	W 3 - 2	Busby 59 (pen) Bent 75 Dean 88	17
29	9		A	Maidstone United		W 3 - 0	C.Maclaren 6 Bent 8 Busby 27	
30	13		H	Wealdstone	331	L 2 - 3	A.Thomas 6 C Maclaren 73	16
31	16		A	Boreham Wood	135	L 1 - 2	Busby 34 (pen)	
32	20		A	Horsham	280	L 1 - 3	Thomas 90	17
33	27		A	Tooting & Mitcham U	301	W 2 - 0	Thomas 34 Aite-Ouakrim 90	
34	Mar 2		A	Wealdstone	367	W 2 - 0	O'Leary 55 Busby 79 (pen)	
35	6		H	Tonbridge Angels	191	D 0 - 0		15
36	9		A	Billericay Town	205	L 0 - 1		
37	13		A	Carshalton Athletic	227	D 0 - 0		16
38	16		H	Canvey Island	101	W 2 - 1	Guentchev 8 Cousins 89	
39	20		H	Waltham Abbey	118	L 0 - 2		15
40	23		H	Bognor Regis	100	W 2 - 0	Cousins 70 Bent 76	
41	27		A	Sutton United	497	L 1 - 3	Busby 48 (pen)	13
42	April 6		H	Boreham Wood	169	L 0 - 1		
43	10		H	Ashford Town	104	W 2 - 1	Dean 7 C.Maclaren 32	16
44	13		H	Hastings United	135	L 1 - 3	C.Maclaren 66	
45	15		H	Carshalton Athletic	129	W 1 - 0	O'Leary 52	
46	17		A	Canvey Island	278	W 3 - 2	Guentchev 3 72 Thomas 25	12
47	19		H	Maidstoe United	171	W 3 - 0	Busby 64 Dean 69 Burgess 87	
48	22		H	Dartford	200	L 1 - 2	Busby 41 (pen)	
49	24		H	AFC Hornchurch	210	W 3 - 2	Cousins 44 Guentchev 77 Thomas 81	10
					Goals	71 71		

Home Attendances:

Highest:	331 v Wealdstone
Lowest:	100 v Bognor Regis
Average (08-09):	169 (206)
Top Goalscorer:	Bent - 9 (League 7, FAC 1, FAT 1)
	Guentchev - 9 (League 7, FAT 2 - 1 Hat-trick)

HORSHAM

Chairman: Kevin Borrett

Secretary: John Lines (T) 0772 141 8889 (E) linesj@tesco.net

Additional Committee Members:
Annie Raby, Adam Hammond, Tim Hewlett

Manager: John Maggs

Programme Editor: Adam Hammond (E) adam@horshampress.co.uk

HORSHAM FC 2010 - 2011

Back Row L to R: George Magnus, Steve Davies, Tom Graves, Jamal King, Jay Lovett, Alan Tait, Paul Kennett

Middle Row L to R: Darren Etheridge, Steve Elliott, Jack Page, Rob Frankland, Ben Andrews (Capt) Mark Zawadski, Steve Sargent, John Westcott, Chris Copestack, Mark Hawthorne, (Coach)

Front Row L to R: Adam Hutchings, Pat Harding, Dean Wright, John Maggs (Manager) Sam Tucknott, Mark Knee, Gary Charman

Club Factfile

Founded: 1881 **Nickname:** Hornets

Previous Names:

Previous Leagues: West Susses Senior, Sussex County 1926-51, Metropolitan 1951-57, Corinthian 1957-63, Athenian 1963-73

Club Colours (change): Amber and green halves/green/amber

Ground: Horsham YMCA, Gorings Mead, Horsham RH13 5BP (T) 01403 266 888

Capacity: 1,575 **Seats:** 150 **Covered:** 200 **Clubhouse:** Yes **Shop:**

Previous Grounds: Horsham Park, Hurst Park, Springfield Park

Simple Directions
From the east, take A281 (Brighton Road, and the ground is on the left and sign posted opposite Gorings Mead.

Record Attendance: 8,000 v Swindon - FA Cup 1st Round Novmber 1966

Record Victory: 16-1 v Southwick - Sussex County League 1945-46

Record Defeat: 1-11 v Worthing - Sussex Senior Cup 1913-14

Record Goalscorer: Mick Browning

Record Appearances: Mark Stepney

Additional Records:

Senior Honours: Athenian League Division 1 1972-73. Sussex Senior Cup x7

10 YEAR RECORD

00-01	01-02	02-03	03-04	04-05	05-06	06-07	07-08	08-09	09-10
Isth2 7	Isth2 2	Isth1S 8	Isth1S 15	Isth1 3	Isth1 2	Isth1S 9	Isth P 11	Isth P 13	Isth P 11

HORSHAM

No.	Date	Comp	H/A	Opponents	Att:	Result	Goalscorers	Pos
1	Aug 15	Ryman Premier	A	Dartford	968	L 2 - 3	Eldridge 30 Harding 89	17
2	18		H	Sutton United	441	W 1 - 0	Seanla 38	
3	22		H	Harrow Borough	303	W 2 - 0	Seanla 3 Acheampong 65	8
4	25		A	Tonbridge Angels	489	D 2 - 2	Seanla 76 Carney 78	7
5	29		H	Canvey Island	360	L 1 - 2	Andrews 40	9
6	31		A	Hastings United	462	L 1 - 3	Andrews 2	
7	Sept 5		H	Carshalton Athletic	406	D 2 - 2	Nwachukwu 54 Carney 55 (pen)	14
8	**12**	**F.A.C. 1Q**	**A**	**Tooting & Mitcham**	**346**	**L 2 - 4**	**Andrews 30 Harding 58**	
9	19		A	Margate	356	W 3 - 1	Harding 30 71 Haddow 40	
10	21		A	Kingstonian	411	L 1 - 2	Carney	14
11	Oct 3		H	Boreham Wood	286	L 1 - 3	Seanla 60 (pen)	17
12	13		H	Maidstone United	260	W 1 - 0	Lyons	
13	**17**	**F.A.T 1Q**	**H**	**Barton Rovers**	**234**	**D 4 - 4**	**Charman 8 20 Page 10 Seanla 18**	
14	**20**	**F.A.T 1Qr**	**A**	**Barton Rovers**	**88**	**L 3 - 4**	**Harding 12 Seanla 32 Charman 85**	
15	Nov 7		H	Cray Wanderers	301	W 4 - 0	Page 68 Seanla 89 Carney 90 Harding 90	
16	16		A	Tooting & Mitcham United	249	W 2 - 0	Harding 45 Seanla 53	
17	28		H	Hastings United	329	W 4 - 2	Seanla 41 (pen) 49 Harding 45 83	8
18	Dec 1		A	Hendon	116	D 1 - 1	Lyons 67	
19	5		A	Canvey Island	276	W 2 - 1	Seanla 16 Carney 55	5
20	12		A	Aveley	127	L 1 - 2	Harding 29	
21	15		A	Wealdstone	281	L 1 - 2	Harding 1	7
22	26		A	Bognor Regis Town	324	D 1 - 1	Harding 19	7
23	Jan 19		A	Billericay Town	232	W 2 - 1	Harding 66 Haddow 90	
24	23		H	Margate	298	D 3 - 3	Andrews 2 Davis 71 Seanla 80	9
25	26		H	Waltham Abbey	169	W 2 - 1	Seanla 25 Page 60	
26	30		A	Boreham Wood	144	L 0 - 4		9
27	Feb 6		H	Kingstonian	425	L 0 - 1		8
28	9		H	Ashford Town		W 4 - 1	Nwachukwu 10 Hutchings 14 Haddow 35 Harding 64	6
29	20		H	Hendon	280	W 3 - 1	S.Page 58 Harding 66 75	
30	Mar 2		H	Bognor Regis Town	284	W 2 - 1	F.Harding 7 Andrews 74	
31	4		A	Waltham Abbey	81	L 1 - 2	Keepence (og)	
32	6		H	Tooting & Mitcham	323	L 1 - 2	Seanla 45	8
33	9		A	Sutton United	321	L 1 - 2	Harding 81	
34	13		A	AFC Hornchurch	224	L 1 - 2	Knee 36	8
35	16		A	Maidstone United	210	D 1 - 1	Harding 62	
36	18		H	Dartford	332	L 1 - 3	Harding 79	
37	20		H	Billericay Town	232	L 0 - 2		12
38	23		H	AFC Hornchurch	164	W 2 - 1	Harding 47 53	
39	27		A	Harrow Borough	35	D 2 - 2	Nwachukwu 62 Smith 78	10
40	April 5		A	Ashford Town	113	W 2 - 0	Nyane 31 Harding 45	
41	10		H	Tonbridge Angels	353	L 0 - 3		
42	13		A	Carshalton Athletic	201	W 2 - 1	Andrews 45 Harding 52 (pen)	
43	17		H	Wealdstone	343	L 1 - 3	Hardng 60	10
44	22		H	Aveley	191	L 0 - 2		
45	24		A	Cray Wanderers	169	D 1 - 1	Page 16	11
					Goals	74 79		

Home Attendances:	
Highest:	441 v Sutton United
Lowest:	164 v AFC Hornchurch
Average (08-09):	301 (239)
Top Goalscorer:	Harding - 24 (League 22, FAC 1, FAT 1)

KINGSTONIAN

Chairman: Mark Anderson & Malcolm Wainwright
Secretary: Gerry Petit (T) 0785 937 7778
(E) gandjpetit149@tiscali.co.uk

Additional Committee Members:
Ali Kazemi, Clinton Arthur

Manager: Alan Dowson
Programme Editor: Robert Wooldridge (E) floiing@aol.com

Back Row (L-R): Paul Ferrie (backroom), Jamie Street (backroom), Carl Wilson-Denis, Simon Huckle, Francis Duku, Ian Pearce, Neil Lampton, Adam Thompson, Christian Jolley, Mark Francis (backroom), Alan Smith (backroom).
Middle Row: Gerry Petit (secretary), Wayne Finnie, Steve Tyson, Martin Tyler (coach), Josh Willis, Alan Dowson (manager), Luke Garrard, Mark Hams (assistant manager), Rob Sheridan, Max Hustwick, Paul Horsecroft (backroom).
Front Row: Lewis Cook, Luke Pigden, Bobby Traynor, Jon Coke, Tommy Williams, Dean Lodge, Jamie Beer, Tom Dilloway, Liam Collins. (Archive photo)

Club Factfile

Founded: 1885 **Nickname:** The K's
Previous Names: Kingston & Suburban YMCA 1885-87, Saxons 1887-90, Kingston Wanderers 1893-1904, Old Kingstonians 1908-19
Previous Leagues: Kingston & District, West Surrey, Southern Suburban, Athenian 1919-29, Isthmian 1929-98, Conference 1998-2001

Club Colours (change): Red and white hoops/black/red & white

Ground: Kingsmead Stadium, Kingston Road, Kingston KT1 3PB (T) 0208 8547 3528
Capacity: 4,262 **Seats:** 1,080 **Covered:** 2,538 **Clubhouse:** Yes **Shop:** Yes
Previous Grounds: Several > 1921, Richmond Road 1921-89
Simple Directions
Take Cambridge Road from Town Centre (A2043) to Malden Road. From A3 turn off at New Malden and turn left onto A2043. Ground is 1 mile on the left which is half a mile from Norbiton BR.

Record Attendance: 4,582 v Chelsea - Freindly
Record Victory: 15-1 v Delft - 1951
Record Defeat: 0-11 v Ilford - Isthmian League 13/02/1937
Record Goalscorer: Johnnie Wing - 295 (1948-62)
Record Appearances: Micky Preston - 555 (1967-85)
Additional Records: Paid £18,000 to Rushden & Diamonds for David Leworthy 1997
Received £150,000 from West Ham United for Gavin Holligan 1999
Senior Honours: FA Amateur Cup 1932-33. Isthmian League 1933-34, 36-37, 97-98, Division 1 South 2008-09.
FAT Trophy 1998-99, 99-2000. Athenian League x2. London Senior Cup x3. Surrey Senior Cup x3.

10 YEAR RECORD

00-01	01-02	02-03	03-04	04-05	05-06	06-07	07-08	08-09	09-10
Conf 21	Isth P 14	Isth P 11	Isth P 18	Isth P 22	Isth1 7	Isth1S 13	Isth1S 7	Isth1S 1	Isth P 5

KINGSTONIAN

No.	Date	Comp	H/A	Opponents	Att:	Result	Goalscorers	Pos
1	Aug 15	Ryman P.	A	Ashford Town (Middx)	342	L 1 - 3	Cook 48	19
2	17		H	Harrow Borough	367	L 3 - 5	Traynor 1 Wilson-Denis 8 Taylor 22	22
3	22		H	Aveley	305	L 1 - 6	Lodge 28	22
4	25		A	Dartford	1038	L 0 - 5		22
5	29		A	Hendon	221	W 3 - 0	Traynor 41 Beckford 90 Huckle 90	21
6	31		A	Carshalton Athletic	502	W 2 - 1	Traynor 88 90	
7	Sept 5		H	Waltham Abbey	320	D 1 - 1	Traynor 66	20
8	**12**	**F.A.C. 1Q**	**A**	**Bognor Regis Town**	**402**	**W 4 - 1**	**TRAYNOR 3 (45 69 90) Lodge 76**	
9	19		A	Canvey Island	355	W 2 - 1	Gray 25 Huckle 79	15
10	21		H	Horsham	411	W 2 - 1	Huckle 20 Beckford 25	10
11	**26**	**F.A.C. 2Q**	**A**	**Hendon**	**226**	**L 1 - 2**	**Wilson-Dennis 16**	
12	Oct 3		A	Margate	434	L 1 - 2	Gray 10	15
13	10		H	Cray Wanderers	359	W 4 - 1	LODGE 3 (34 53 68) Wilson-Denis 85	8
14	13		A	Billericay Town		W 5 - 1	Traynor 39 (pen) Lodge 67 Huckle 73 Wilson-Denis 75 Beckford 90	
15	**17**	**F.A.T 1Q**	**A**	**Metropolitan Police**	**296**	**W 1 - 0**	**Traynor 64**	
16	24		H	Hastings United	333	L 1 - 2	Traynor 26 (pen)	8
17	**31**	**F.A.T 2Q**	**H**	**Hendon**	**276**	**W 4 - 2**	**Traynor 9 Gray 50 Wilson-Denis 56 Jolly 90**	
18	Nov 7		A	Maidstone Unlted	300	W 3 - 1	Traynor 51(pen) Lodge 79 Jolley 88	
19	14		H	Tonbridge Angels	351	L 2 - 3	Traynor 7 75 (pen)	5
20	17		A	Boreham Wood	165	W 1 - 0	Traynor 80	
21	**22**	**F.A.T 3Q**	**H**	**Chippenham Town**	**388**	**L 0 - 2**		
22	28		H	Carshalton Athletic	380	W 1 - 0	Traynor 87	4
23	Dec 6		H	Hendon	350	W 3 - 0	Wilson-Denis 53 Traynor 77 84	2
24	12		A	Sutton United	731	D 1 - 1	Huckle 69	
25	26		A	Tooting & Mitcham U	440	W 3 - 2	Wilson-Denis 18 Lodge 42 Traynor 45	3
26	28		H	Bognor Regis Town	358	L 1 - 3	Traynor 17	
27	Jan 2		H	Tooting & Mitcham U	480	D 1 - 1	Traynor 78 (pen)	3
28	23		H	Canvey Island	343	W 2 - 1	Traynor 9 Iili 37	3
29	31		H	Margate	347	W 2 - 0	Fletcher 19 Lodge 90	
30	Feb 6		A	Horsham	425	W 1 - 0	Wilson-Denis 31	2
31	9		A	Harrow Borough	154	L 0 - 2		
32	13		H	Billericay Town	318	W 2 - 1	Traynor 27 (pen) Gray 57	2
33	20		A	Cray Wanderers	307	L 1 - 2	Traynor 77	2
34	25		H	Wealdstone	277	D 3 - 3	White 13 Traynor 23 Jolly 50	
35	27		A	Tonbridg e Angels	439	L 0 - 1		2
36	Mar 2		A	AFC Hornchurch	244	D 1 - 1	Lodge 35	3
37	7		H	Boreham Wood	351	W 4 - 1	Traynor 5 Duku 56 Jolley 81 Huckle 89	
38	13		A	Wealdstone	552	D 2 - 2	Wilson-Denis 4 89	3
39	15		H	Ashford Town		W 1 - 0	McNemy 45 (og)	
40	20		H	AFC Hornchurch	361	W 2 - 0	Huckle 17 Fletcher 48	2
41	27		A	Aveley	228	W 4 - 3	Wilson-Denis 45 Traynor 73 (pen) 83 Lodge 90	
42	April 3		H	Sutton United	946	W 2 - 1	Goodliffe 44 (og) Traynor 90	2
43	5		A	Bognor Regis Town	435	L 1 - 3	Traynor 59	
44	7		A	Waltham Abbey	333	L 0 - 1		
45	10		H	Dartford	929	L 2 - 6	Huckle 33 Traynor 56	2
46	17		A	Hastings United	715	D 0 - 0		3
47	24		H	Maidstone United	517	D 1 - 1	Gray 24	5
48	**27**	**Play-off**	**A**	**Sutton United**	**1490**	**W 4 - 2**	**Jolley 10 Thompson 59 Traynor 63 74**	
49	**May 1**	**Play-off**	**A**	**Boreham Wood**	**1102**	**L 0 - 2**		
					Goals	87 80		

Home Attendances:

Highest:	946 v Sutton United
Lowest:	277 v Wealdstone
Average:	354

Top Goalscorer: Traynor - 34 (League 27, FAC 3, FAT 2, Play-off 1 - Hat-trick 1)

LOWESTOFT TOWN

Chairman: Gary Keyzor
Secretary: Terry Lynes (T) 0793 087 2947
(E) terrylynes@fsmail.net

Additional Committee Members:
Simon Reeve

Manager: Micky Chapman and Ady Gallagher
Programme Editor: Terry Lynes (E) terrylynes@fsmail.net

Russell Stock fires at goal during Lowestoft's F.A. Vase final appearance at Wembley stadium back in 2008. Photo: Keith Clayton.

Club Factfile

Founded: 1880 **Nickname:** The Trawler Boys or Blues
Previous Names: Original club merged with Kirkley in 1887 to form Lowestoft and became Lowestoft Town in 1890
Previous Leagues: North Suffolk 1897-35, Eastern Counties 1935-2009

Club Colours (change): All blue

Ground: Crown Meadow, Love Road, Lowestoft NR32 2PA (T) 01502 573 818
Capacity: 3,000 **Seats:** 466 **Covered:** 500 **Clubhouse:** Yes **Shop:** Yes
Previous Grounds:
Simple Directions
Just off A12. Ten minutes from Lowestoft BR.

Record Attendance: 5,000 v Watford - FA Cup 1st Round 1967
Record Victory: Not Known
Record Defeat: Not Known
Record Goalscorer: Not Known
Record Appearances: Not Known
Additional Records:

Senior Honours: Eastern Counties League 1935-36 (shared), 37-38, 62-63, 64-65, 65-66, 66-67, 67-68, 69-70, 70-71, 77-78, 2005-06, 08-09.
Isthmian League Division 1 North 2009-10.
Suffolk Senior Cup 1902-03, 22-23, 25-26, 31-32, 35-36, 46-47, 47-48, 48-49, 55-56.

10 YEAR RECORD

00-01	01-02	02-03	03-04	04-05	05-06	06-07	07-08	08-09	09-10
ECP 3	ECP 3	ECP 4	ECP 8	ECP 4	ECP 1	ECP 3	ECP 11	ECP 1	Isth1N 1

Do you remember when...

Lowestoft Town

Lowestoft Town finished ninth in the Jewson Eastern League in 1990-1991 but won a fine collection of local silverware.

Back row, left to right: Roy Harper (Chairman), Jimmy Campbell (Manager), Mike Quentin-Hick (Physio), Terry Lynes (Secretary), Robert McKechnie, Oscar Harman, Paul Gant, Micky Shade, Sean Trail, Glen High, Stuart Youngman and Karl Sannerude (Trainer)
Front Row: Peter Holland, Matthew Barbrook, Darren Osborne, Gary Tuttle, John Clark, Micky Chapman (Captain), Nigel Jackson and Kevin McGuire.

MAIDSTONE UNITED

Chairman: Paul Bowden-Brown
Secretary: Darren Lovell **(T)** 0777 374 5577
(E) darren.lovell@btinternet.com

Additional Committee Members:
Ian Tucker, Peter Philpot
Manager: Peter Nott
Programme Editor: Ian Tucker **(E)** mufcprogramme@btopenworld.com

Back Row (L-R): Peter Norris (kit man), James Peacock, Peter Hawkins, Jimmy Bottle, Meshach Nugent, Tom Parkinson, Richard Knell, Lynden Rowland, Jamie Turner, Alan Pouton, Roland Edge, Nick Barnes, Jay Saunders, Alan Rogers (goalkeeper coach), Narada Pascal. **Front row:** Nicki Collins (physio), Tim Warden (trainer), Dan Stubbs, Antonio Gonnella, Ashley Ulph, Nathan Paul, Paul Bowden-Brown (chairman), James Pinnock, Dean Hernandez-Bradshaw, Ant Bodle, Ashley Dann, Lloyd Hume (manager).

Club Factfile

Founded: 1992 **Nickname:** The Stones
Previous Names:
Previous Leagues: Kent County, Kent

Club Colours (change): Amber/black/black

Ground: Teh Homelands, Ashford Road, Kingsnorth, Ashford TN26 1NJ **(T)** 01233 611 838
Capacity: 3,200 **Seats:** 500 **Covered:** 1,250 **Clubhouse:** Yes **Shop:** Yes
Previous Grounds: London Road 1992-2001, Central Park (Sittingbourne) 2001-02

Simple Directions
Leave the M20 at Junction 10, follow the signs for Ashford International Station and Brenzett. This will be Bad Munsterieful Road. Follow this road straight over at the first roundabout (McDonalds drivethru and Travel Inn on your right). At the next roundabout take the first exit for Kingsnorth. At the next roundabout go straight over (Tesco on your left). Follow this road for about twomiles, going through Kingsnorth, passing the cricket club on the left. The Homelands is 300 yards on your left.

Record Attendance: 1,589 v Gillingham - Friendly
Record Victory: 12-1 v Aylesford - Kent League 1993-94
Record Defeat: 2-8 v Scott Sports - 1995-96
Record Goalscorer: Richard Sinden - 98
Record Appearances: Aaron Lacy - 187
Additional Records: Paid £2,000 for Steve Jones - 2000

Senior Honours: Kent League 2001-02, 05-06, League cup 05-06. Isthmian Division 1 South 2006-07.
Kent Senior Trophy 2002-03.

10 YEAR RECORD

00-01	01-02	02-03	03-04	04-05	05-06	06-07	07-08	08-09	09-10
	Kent P 1	Kent P 2	Kent P 4	Kent P 4	Kent P 1	Isth1S 1	Isth P 17	Isth P 15	Isth P 18

MAIDSTONE UNITED

No.	Date	Comp	H/A	Opponents	Att:	Result	Goalscorers	Pos
1	Aug 15	Ryman P.	H	Carshalton Athletic	382	L 0 - 2		20
2	18		A	Waltham Abbey	178	W 2 - 1	Gonnella 45 Pinnock77	
3	22		A	Wealdstone	403	D 2 - 2	Saunders 58 82	13
4	25		H	AFC Hornchurch	282	D 0 - 0		14
5	29		H	Tooting & Mitcham U	308	L 1 - 2	Stubbs 41	16
6	31		A	Canvey Island	459	W 1 - 0	Pinnock 40	
7	Sept 5		H	Tonbridge Angels	447	D 2 - 2	Pinnock 71 Paul 90	13
8	**12**	**F.A.C. 1Q**	**H**	**Bedfont**	**294**	**W 2 - 1**	**Saunders 9 Bottle 75**	
9	19		A	Boreham Wood	187	W 2 - 0	Pinnock 45 (pen) Stephens 45 (og)	
10	22		H	Aveley	200	W 4 - 2	Ulph 1 Parkinson 42 Pinnock 66 Barnes 90	9
11	**26**	**F.A.C. 2Q**	**A**	**Harefield United**	**332**	**W 2 - 0**	**Edge 45 Pinnock 87**	
12	Oct 3		A	Bognor Regis Town	421	D 0 - 0		7
13	**10**	**F.A.C. 3Q**	**A**	**Woking**	**1434**	**L 0 - 3**		
14	13		A	Horsham	260	L 0 - 1		10
15	**17**	**F.A.T 1Q**	**A**	**Waltham Forest**	**126**	**W 1 - 0**	**Wright 24**	
16	24		A	Ashford Town	110	W 2 - 0	Pinnock 29 Wright 64	7
17	**31**	**F.A.T 2Q**	**A**	**Bognor Regis Town**	**252**	**W 2 - 0**	**Pinnock 45 O'Donovan 73**	
18	Nov 7		H	Kingstonian	300	L 1 - 3	Pinnock 59 (pen)	10
19	14		A	Harrow Borough	142	L 1 - 2	Pinnock 43	11
20	17		H	Sutton United	216	W 2 - 1	Rowland 33 90	
21	**21**	**F.A.T 3Q**	**A**	**Bromley**	**655**	**W 1 - 0**	**O'Donovan 13**	
22	24		A	Cray Wanderers	211	L 0 - 1		
23	28		H	Canvey Island	301	L 0 - 1		14
24	Dec 5		A	Tooting & Mitcham U	276	D 2 - 2	Kings 33 (og) Hockton 43	
25	26		H	Margate	225	L 0 - 1		15
26	28		A	Hastings United	631	W 2 - 1	Hockton 4 35	
27	Jan 2		A	Margate	568	W 1 - 0	Hockton 63	7
28	20	F.A.T 1	H	Histon	250	L 0 - 3		
29	23		H	Boreham Wood	233	L 0 - 1		12
30	Feb 6		A	Aveley	210	L 0 - 2		15
31	9		H	Hendon	128	L 0 - 3		
32	11		A	Carshalton Athletic	179	W 1 - 0	Pinnock 40	
33	20		A	Billericay Town	453	D 1 - 1	Barnes 50	15
34	27		H	Harrow Borough	202	L 0 - 3		17
35	Mar 2		H	Billericay Town	177	W 1 - 0	Hockton 54	
36	6		A	Sutton United	654	D 0 - 0		17
37	9		H	Dartford	371	L 0 - 1		
38	13		H	Cray Wanderers	263	D 1 - 1	Hawkins 84	17
39	16		H	Horsham	168	D 1 - 1	Stone 53	
40	20		A	Dartford	1501	L 0 - 3		18
41	23		A	Tonbridge Angels	697	L 1 - 2	Stone 16	
42	27		H	Wealdstone	218	L 2 - 3	Peacock 55 Lyall 77	18
43	April 5		H	Hastings United	308	L 0 - 5		
44	10		A	AFC Hornchurch	260	L 0 - 1		21
45	13		H	Waltham Abbey	159	W 2 - 0	Peacock 4 Gonnella 31	
46	17		H	Ashford United	229	W 2 - 0	Hockton 18 Gonnella 78	18
47	19		A	Hendon	171	L 0 - 3		
48	22		H	Gognor Regis Town	246	W 1 - 0	Stone 47	
49	24		A	Kingstonian	517	D 1 - 1	Hockton 68 (pen)	18
					Goals	47 62		

Home Attendances:

Highest:	447 v Tonbridge Angels
Lowest:	128 v Hendon
Average (08-09):	233 (388)
Top Goalscorer:	Pinnock - 11 (League 9, FAC 1, FAT 1)

MARGATE

Chairman: TBA

Secretary: Ken Tomlinson (T) 0771 003 3566 (E) ken.tomlinson@margate-fc.com

Additional Committee Members:
Steve Wells, Peter Cove

Manager: Ian O'Connell

Programme Editor: Don Walker (E) don.walker@margate-fc.com

Archive photo

Club Factfile

Founded: 1896 **Nickname:** The Gate

Previous Names:

Previous Leagues: Kent 1911-23, 24-28, 29-33, 37-38, 46-59. Southern 1933-37, 59-2001, Conference 2001-04

Club Colours (change): All royal blue

Ground: Hartsdown Park, Hartsdown Road, Margate, Kent CT9 5QZ (T) 01843 221 769

Capacity: 3,000 **Seats:** 350 **Covered:** 1,750 **Clubhouse:** Yes **Shop:** Yes

Previous Grounds:

Simple Directions

Record Attendance: 14,500 v Tottenham Hotspur - FA Cup 3rd Round 1973

Record Victory: 8-0 v Tunbridge Wells (H) - 1966-67, v Chatham Town (H) - 1987-88 and v Stalybridge Celtic (H) - 2001-02

Record Defeat: 0-11 v AFC Bournemouth (A) - FA Cup 20/11/1971

Record Goalscorer: Jack Palethorpe scored 66 during 1929-30

Record Appearances: Bob Harrop

Additional Records: Paid £5,000 to Dover Athletic for Steve Cuggy

Senior Honours: Southern League Premier Division 1935-36, 2000-01, Division 1 1962-63, Division 1 South 1977-78.

10 YEAR RECORD

00-01	01-02	02-03	03-04	04-05	05-06	06-07	07-08	08-09	09-10
SthP 1	Conf 8	Conf 10	Conf 16	Conf S 21	Isth P 14	Isth P 6	Isth P 9	Isth P 19	Isth P 19

MARGATE

No.	Date	Comp	H/A	Opponents	Att:	Result	Goalscorers	Pos
1	Aug 15	Ryman P.	A	Sutton United	508	L 0 - 4		22
2	18		H	Dartford	653	L 0 - 4		
3	22		H	Boreham Wood	345	W 2 - 1	Healy 49 Dunn 90	15
4	24		A	Aveley	243	W 3 - 0	Blackman 30 Alaile 33 (og) Wilson 73	10
5	29		A	Harrow Borough	156	L 0 - 3		15
6	31		H	Cray Wanderers	423	L 0 - 1		
7	Sept 5		A	Ashford Town	120	D 2 - 2	Blackman 34 West 23	19
8	**12**	**F.A.C. 1Q**	**H**	**Sutton United**	**402**	**D 2 - 2**	**Cliff 41 Robinson 43**	
9	**15**	**F.A.C. 1Qr**	**A**	**Sutton United**	**301**	**L 2 - 3***	**Wilson 42 Healy 53**	
10	19		H	Horsham	356	L 1 - 3	Healy 87	21
11	22		A	Hendon	159	W 2 - 1	Haveson 68 Blackman 90	17
12	26		H	AFC Hornchurch	490	D 0 - 0		
13	Oct 3		H	Kingstonian	434	W 2 - 1	Edusei 8 Blackman 90	12
14	10		A	Canvey Island	342	L 0 - 2		14
15	**17**	**F.A.T 1Q**	**A**	**Wealdstone**	**265**	**L 1 - 2**	**Stubbs 68**	
16	Nov 7		A	Hastings United	517	L 1 - 2	Blackman 42 (pen)	18
17	17		A	Waltham Abbey	129	W 4 - 3	Healy 31 Cliff 66 J.Elmes 81 (og) Blackman 90 (pen)	
18	24		A	Cray Wanderers	179	L 2 - 3	Robinson 37 Cliff 54	
19	Dec 5		H	Harrow Borough	363	D 2 - 2	Blackman 38 Joseph 63	19
20	12		A	Bognor Regis Town	316	D 3 - 3	Duncan 44 Joseph 81 Clarke 90	
21	26		A	Maidstone United	225	W 1 - 0	Blackman 74	17
22	Jan 2		H	Maidstone Un ited	568	L 0 - 1		18
23	16		H	Ashford Town	280	D 1 - 1	Groombridge 42	18
24	23		A	Horsham	298	D 3 - 3	Wilson 25 Clarke 52 Blackman 90	
25	31		A	Kingstonian	347	L 0 - 2		
26	Feb 6		H	Hendon	297	L 2 - 3	Blackman 6 Stubbs 25	20
27	9		H	Wealdstone	310	D 1 - 1	Healy 70	
28	13		A	AFC Hornchurch	244	L 0 - 1		20
29	16		H	Billericay Town	232	L 1 - 3	Blackman 88	
30	20		H	Canvey Island	327	L 1 - 2	Jones 3	20
31	Mar 2		H	Tonbridge Angels	333	L 0 - 3		
32	6		H	Waltham Abbey	290	L 0 - 3		22
33	9		H	Tooting & Mitcham United	210	W 2 - 1	Jones 11 Huggins 69	21
34	13		A	Billericay Town	391	W 2 - 1	Barnes 48 (pen) Huggins 90	21
35	16		H	Sutton United	302	D 1 - 1	Hugins 39	
36	20		H	Carshalton Athletic	402	D 1 - 1	Jones 73	22
37	23		A	Dartford	907	W 1 - 0	Pinnock 65	
38	27		A	Boreham Wood	148	D 1 - 1	Huggins 28	20
39	30		A	Carshalton Athletic	201	W 2 - 1	Pinnock 29 Saunders 70	
40	April 3		H	Bognor Regis Town	469	D 1 - 1	Pinnock 73	18
41	5		A	Tonbridge Angels	584	D 0 - 0		
42	7		A	Wealdstone	333	L 0 - 1		
43	10		H	Aveley	356	L 2 - 3	Barnes 22 Saunders 86	19
44	17		A	Tooting & Mitcham United	323	L 1 - 2	J.Vines 53 (og)	20
45	24		H	Hastings United	435	W 1 - 0	Blackman 31	
					Goals	54 75		

Home Attendances:

Highest:	653 v Dartford
Lowest:	210 v Tooting & Mitcham United
Average (08-09):	356 (524)
Top Goalscorer:	Blackman - 12 (League 12)

SUTTON UNITED

Chairman: Bruce Elliott
Secretary: Gerard Mills **(T)** 0793 270 2375
(E) honsec@suttonunited.net

Additional Committee Members:
Graham Starns, Tony Dolbear, Dave Farebrother

Manager: Paul Doswell
Programme Editor: Lyall Reynolds **(E)** suttoneditor@hotmail.com

Back Row (L-R): Steve McKimm (Player Coach), Kevin Scriven, Sam Gargan, Karim El-Salahi, Paul Smith, Sonny Cobbs. **Middle row:** Billy Hawes, Anthony Joseph, Sam Stannard, Billy Dunn, Jason Goodliffe (Team Captain), Justyn Roberts, Steffan Payne, Kenny Beaney, Billy Chattaway, Ebenezer Masabe. **Front row:** Alan Bray, Bentley Graham, Danny Phillips, Alan Payne (Assistant Manager), Clive Baxter (Kit Manager), Paul Doswell (Manager), Bob Childs (Physio), Bradley Woods-Garness, James Hawes, Matt Hann.

Club Factfile

Founded: 1898 **Nickname:** The U's
Previous Names:
Previous Leagues: Sutton Junior, Southern Suburban, Athenian 1921-63, Isthmian 1963-86, 91-99, 2000-04, Conference 1999-2000, 04-08

Club Colours (change): Amber and chocolate quarters/amber/amber

Ground: Borough Sports Ground, Gander Green Lane, Sutton, Surrey SM1 2EY **(T)** 0208 644 4440
Capacity: 7,032 **Seats:** 765 **Covered:** 1,250 **Clubhouse:** Yes **Shop:** Yes
Previous Grounds: Western Road, Manor Lane, London Road, The Find
Simple Directions
Travel along the M25 to junction 8. Then north on the A217 for about 15-20 minutes. Ignoring signs for Sutton itself, stay on the A217 to the traffic lights by the Gander Inn (on the left), turn right into Gander Green Lane. The Borough Sports Ground is about 200 yards up this road on the left hand side, if you reach West Sutton station you have gone too far.

Record Attendance: 14,000 v Leeds United - FA Cup 4th Round 24/01/1970
Record Victory: 11-1 v Clapton - 1966 and v Leatherhead - 1982-83 both Isthmian League
Record Defeat: 0-13 v Barking - Athenian League 1925-26
Record Goalscorer: Paul McKinnon - 279
Record Appearances: Larry Pritchard - 781 (1965-84)
Additional Records: Received £100,000 from AFC Bournemouth for Efan Ekoku 1990

Senior Honours: Anglo Italian Cup 1979. Isthmian League x3. Athenian League x3.
London Senior Cup x2. Surrey Senior Cup x2.

10 YEAR RECORD

00-01	01-02	02-03	03-04	04-05	05-06	06-07	07-08	08-09	09-10
Isth P 13	Isth P 12	Isth P 6	Isth P 2	Conf S 15	Conf S 13	Conf S 13	Conf S 22	Isth P 5	Isth P 2

SUTTON UNITED

No.	Date	Comp	H/A	Opponents	Att:	Result	Goalscorers	Pos
1	Aug 15	Ryman P.	H	Margate	508	W 4 - 0	PAYNE 3 (14 53 58 pen) Gargan 31	1
2	18		A	Horsham	441	L 0 - 1		
3	22		A	Hendon	203	W 2 - 1	Gargan 32 90	5
4	25		H	Canvey Island	498	L 1 - 2	Phillips 59	10
5	29		H	AFC Hornchurch	579	W 4 - 1	Joseph 6 Payne 10 56 Shave 32 (og)	6
6	31		A	Wealdstone	480	L 1 - 2	Payne 17	
7	Sept 5		H	Boreham Wood	504	L 0 - 1		11
8	**12**	**F.A.C. 1Q**	**A**	**Margate**	**402**	**D 2 - 2**	**Goodliffe 45 Payne 89**	
9	**15**	**F.A.C 1Qr**	**H**	**Margate**	**301**	**W 3 - 2**	**Hann 20 Phillips 90 Cobbs 113 after extra time**	
10	19		A	Tonbridge Angels	424	W 2 - 1	Gargan 53 Cobbs 90	7
11	22		H	Dartford	648	L 0 - 3		12
12	**26**	**F.A.C. 2Q**	**H**	**Uxbridge**	**365**	**W 3 - 0**	**Goodliffe 20 Gargan 56 Joseph 80**	
13	Oct 3		A	Aveley	240	W 1 - 0	Ketchell 41 (og)	9
14	**10**	**F.A.C. 3Q**	**H**	**Walton & Hersham**	**536**	**W 1 - 0**	**Gargan 86**	
15	13		A	Hastings united	492	W 3 - 1	Gargan 40 Woods-Garner 54 Goodliffe 74	
16	**17**	**F.A.T 1Q**	**H**	**Tonbridge Angels**	**319**	**L 0 - 2**		
17	**24**	**F.A.C. 4Q**	**A**	**Hampton & Richmond**	**669**	**W 3 - 1**	**Hann 22 Gargan 61 Poulton 66 (pen)**	
18	31		H	Waltham Abbey	419	D 0 - 0		7
19	**Nov 7**	**F.A.C 1**	**A**	**Hereford United**	**1713**	**L 0 - 2**		
20	21		A	Bognor Regis Town	402	W 2 - 1	Poulton 26 (pen) Taylor 38	8
21	24		A	Maidstone United	216	L 1 - 2	Perkins 45	
22	28		H	Wealdstone	696	W 5 - 0	Poulton 17 GARGAN 3 (22 48 66) Watts 90	5
23	Dec 1		H	Tooting & Mitcham U	517	L 1 - 2	Watts 85 (pen)	
24	5		A	AFC Hornchurch	293	L 0 - 1		8
25	12		H	Kingstonian	731	D 1 - 1	Norwood 83	
26	26		H	Carshalton Athletic	1027	W 3 - 0	Taylor 23 35 Watts 73 (pen)	6
27	Jan 2		A	Carshalton Athletic	1014	D 0 - 0		6
28	19		H	Ashford Town	383	L 2 - 4	Poulton 21 (pen) Watts 77	
29	23		H	Tonbridge Angels	531	W 2 - 1	Taylor 32 34	6
30	30		H	Aveley	446	W 3 - 2	Taylor 15 Norwood 17 Quarm 41	6
31	Feb 6		A	Dartford	1160	W 2 - 0	Norwod 39 Gargan 79	5
32	13		H	Hastings United	546	D 2 - 2	Cobbs 82 Hann 84	4
33	20		A	Tooting & Mitcham	630	D 1 - 1	Gargan 75	5
34	27		A	Ashford Town	222	W 1 - 0	Watts 46	5
35	Mar 2		A	Boreham Wood	123	W 2 - 1	Gargan 28 Woods-Garness 40	4
36	6		H	Maidstone United	654	D 0 - 0		
37	9		H	Horsham	421	W 2 - 1	Woods-Garner 2 Gargan 12	
38	13		A	Waltham Abbey	179	W 2 - 1	Woods-Garness 56 El Salahi 64	2
39	16		A	Margate	302	D 1 - 1	Perkins 40	
40	20		H	Bognor Regis Town	503	D 0 - 0		3
41	23		H	Harrow Borough	378	W 1 - 0	Taylor 35	
42	27		H	Hendon	497	W 3 - 1	Perkins 5 Joseph 11 Watts 22	
43	April 3		A	Kingstonian	946	L 1 - 2	Taylor 85	3
44	5		H	Cray Wanderers	502	L 1 - 4	Perkins 24	
45	10		A	Canvey Island	302	W 2 - 1	Cobbs 20 Joseph 57	3
46	15		A	Billericay Town	308	W 1 - 0	Cobbs 76	
47	17		A	Harrow Borough	233	D 1 - 1	Phillips 75	2
48	20		A	Cray Wanderers	253	W 2 - 1	Quarm 11 Cobbs 39	
49	24		H	Billericay Town	1014	W 2 - 1	Joseph 19 Hann 33	2
50	**27**	**Play Off**	**H**	**Kingstonian**	**1490**	**L 2 - 4**	**Woods-Garness Perkins**	
					Goals	79 58		

Home Attendances:	
Highest:	1027 v Carshalton Athletic
Lowest:	378 v Harrow Borough
Average (08-09):	508 (566)
Top Goalscorer:	Gargan - 15 (League 12, FAC 3 - 1 Hat-trick)

TONBRIDGE ANGELS

Chairman: Steve Churcher
Secretary: Charlie Cole (T) 0782 570 2412
(E) chcole1063@aol.com

Additional Committee Members:
Mrs Tina Jenner, Andrew Cole

Manager: Tommy Warrilow
Programme Editor: Geoff Curtis (E) curtis.g10@ntlworld.com

Unfortunately an up-to-date photograph was not available at the time of going to press

Club Factfile

Founded: 1948 **Nickname:** Angels
Previous Names: Tonbridge Angels, Tonbridge F.C., Tonbridge A.F.C.
Previous Leagues: Southern 1948-80, 93-2004, Kent 1989-93

Club Colours (change): Blue and white/blue/blue

Ground: Longmead Stadium, Darenth Avenue, Tonbridge, Kent TN10 3JW (T) 01732 352 417
Capacity: 2,500 **Seats:** 707 **Covered:** 1,500 **Clubhouse:** Yes **Shop:** Yes
Previous Grounds: The Angel 1948-80
Simple Directions

Record Attendance: 8,236 v Aldershot - FA Cup 1951
Record Victory: 11-1 v Worthing - FA Cup 1951
Record Defeat: 2-11 v Folkstone - Kent Senior Cup 1949
Record Goalscorer: Jon Main scored 44 goals in one season including seven hat-tricks
Record Appearances: Mark Giham
Additional Records:

Senior Honours: Kent Senior Cup 1964-65, 74-75

10 YEAR RECORD

00-01	01-02	02-03	03-04	04-05	05-06	06-07	07-08	08-09	09-10
SthE 8	SthE 19	SthE 9	SthE 3	Isth P 20	Isth1 3	Isth P 11	Isth P 8	Isth P 3	Isth P 8

TONBRIDGE ANGELS

No.	Date	Comp	H/A	Opponents	Att:	Result	Goalscorers	Pos
1	Aug 15	Ryman P.	H	AFC Hornchurch	512	L 1 - 2	Minshull 11	18
2	18		A	Cray Wanderers	227	W 3 - 1	Cade 1 Booth 4 24	
3	22		A	Waltham Abbey	152	W 2 - 0	Sigere 53 Ferguson 63	6
4	25		H	Horsham	489	D 2 - 2	Booth 12 Rook 90	5
5	29		A	Billericay Town	424	D 1 - 1	Rook 89 (pen)	8
6	31		H	Ashford Town	440	W 3 - 2	Minshull 48 Rook 65 (pen) 90 (pen)	
7	Sept 5		A	Maidstone United	447	D 2 - 2	Rook 24 Minshull 63	5
8	**12**	**F.A.C. 1Q**	**H**	**Metropolitan Police**	**352**	**W 1 - 0**	**Minshull 39**	
9	19		H	Sutton United	424	L 1 - 2	Ferguson 43	8
10	22		H	Bognor Regis Town	348	W 2 - 0	Rook 23 Story 75	4
11	**26**	**F.A.C. 2Q**	**H**	**Horsham YMCA**	**366**	**W 4 - 0**	**Booth 12 Minshull 27 Rook 34 (pen) 72**	
12	Oct 3		A	Tooting & Mitcham United	306	L 3 - 5	ROOK 3 (42 54 55 (pen)	8
13	**10**	**F.A.C 3Q**	**H**	**Bromley**	**944**	**L 0 - 2**		
14	13		A	Dartford	1228	L 0 - 2		
15	**17**	**F.A.T 1Q**	**A**	**Sutton Uited**	**319**	**W 2 - 0**	**Ferguson 45 Booth 66**	
16	24		A	Boreham Wood	172	L 0 - 2		11
17	**31**	**F.A.T 2Q**	**H**	**Merstham**	**388**	**W 6 - 1**	**Booth 2 54 Rook 15 (pen) Cumberbatch 20 Minshull 54 Sigere 88**	
18	Nov 7		H	Aveley	341	W 3 - 2	Bryant 34 Booth 67 Cumberbatch 74	11
19	14		A	Kingstonian	351	W 3 - 2	Harwood 3 Minshull 23 Booth 36	6
20	17		H	Hendon	371	W 2 - 1	Minshull 43 Booth 62	
21	**22**	**F.A.T 3Q**	**A**	**Welling United**	**510**	**L 2 - 3**	**Rook 42 90**	
22	24		A	Canvey Island	251	D 1 - 1	Minshull 75	
23	28		A	Ashford Town	258	L 2 - 3	Harwood 44 Booth 48	
24	Dec 5		H	Billericay Town	443	L 0 - 1		9
25	12		H	Wealdstone	439	W 2 - 3	Rook 47 Minshull 85	
26	26		H	Hastings United	517	D 2 - 2	Minshull 39 41	12
27	Jan 2		A	Hastings United	720	L 1 - 5	Cade 75	14
28	23		A	Sutton United	531	L 1 - 2	Rook 90	15
29	30		H	Tooting & Mitcham U	427	L 1 - 2	Minshull 70	16
30	Feb 6		A	Bognor Regis Town	354	L 1 - 3	Bryant 15	19
31	9		H	Cray Wanderers	220	W 3 - 2	Watts 20 Cumberbatch 45 85	
32	13		H	Dartford	842	L 1 - 4	Booth 18	
33	20		A	Carshalton Athletic	262	W 2 - 1	Hughes 39 Booth 72	16
34	27		H	Kingstonian	439	W 1 - 0	Booth 8	15
35	Mar 2		A	Margate	333	W 3 - 0	Long 11 Booth 85 88	
36	6		A	Hendon	191	D 0 - 0		13
37	13		H	Canvey Island	358	W 3 - 1	Watts 26 Booth 30 Hughes 90	14
38	16		H	Carshalton Athletic	284	W 2 - 0	Burchell 28 Long 53	
39	20		A	Harrow Borough	178	W 3 - 1	Minshull 7 Starkey 45 Burchell 65	8
40	23		H	Maidstone United	697	W 2 - 1	Long 40 Burchell 80	
41	27		H	Waltham Abbey	438	W 2 - 0	Minshull 4 Booth 62	3
42	April 5		H	Margate	584	D 0 - 0		
43	10		A	Horsham	353	W 3 - 0	Storey 7 Long 53 May 90	6
44	15		H	Harrow Borough	397	W 3 - 2	Cade 37 Kinch 52 72	
45	17		H	Boreham Wood	587	L 0 - 2		7
46	20		A	AFC Hornchurch	289	D 1 - 1	Mills 59	
47	22		A	Wealdstone	411	L 1 - 2	Minshull 12	
48	24		A	Aveley	311	L 0 - 2		8
					Goals	84 73		

Home Attendances:	
Highest:	842 v Dartford
Lowest:	220 v Cray Wanderers
Average (08-09):	439 (494)
Top Goalscorer:	Booth - 18 (League 14, FAC 1, FAT 3)

TOOTING & MITCHAM UNITED

Chairman: Steve Adkins
Secretary: Jackie Watkins (T) 0770 271 0400
(E) jackie.watkins@thehubattmufc.co.uk

Additional Committee Members:
Nigel Sarsons, Dave Watters, Lyn Catchpole

Manager: Mark Beard
Programme Editor: Michael Woods (E) michael@mwoods38.freeserves.co.uk

Back row (L-R): Mark Gradosielski, Phil Williams, Craig Vernon, Barry Stevens, Paul Honey, Luke Garrard, Tony Nwanchu, Jason Henry, James Nicholls, Danny Bracken, Aaron Goode, Jon Dollery, Mark Waters, Adam Fletcher, Hasim Deen.
Front row: Nicola Upward, Karl Beckford, Jamie Byatt, Hsang Nyang, Kevin Cooper, Mark Beard, James Evans, Nigel Brake, Lino Gonalves, Nick Tester.

Club Factfile

Founded: 1932 **Nickname:** The Terrors
Previous Names:
Previous Leagues: London 1932-37, Athenian 1937-56

Club Colours (change): Black and white stripes/black/red

Ground: Imperial Fields, Bishopsford Road, Morden, Surrey SM4 6BF (T) 020 8648 3248 / 020 8685 6193
Capacity: 3,50 **Seats:** 600 **Covered:** 1,200 **Clubhouse:** Yes **Shop:** Yes
Previous Grounds: Sandy Lane, Mitcham

Simple Directions
M25 junction 8, take the A217 northbound, this goes through Tadworth and Cheam. It's dual carriageway most of the way, although long stretches have a 40mph speed limit. This leads to a major roundabout with lights (Rose Hill). Take the third exit (Mitcham A217), this is Bishopsford Road and the ground is a mile further on. Go through two sets of lights, the road dips, and the entrance is on the right opposite a petrol station.
From the South: M25 junction 7, M23 then A23 northbound. Turn left onto the A237 after passing under a railway bridge at Coulsdon South station. Through Hackbridge and Beddington, then turn left onto the A239. Turn left again at lights by Mitcham Cricket Green into the A217, the ground is 800 yards on the left.

Record Attendance: 17,500 v Queens Park Rangers - FA Cup 2nd Round 1956-57 (At Sandy Lane)
Record Victory: 11-0 v Welton Rovers - FA Amateur Cup 1962-63
Record Defeat: 1-8 v Kingstonian - Surrey Senior Cup 1966-67
Record Goalscorer: Alan Ives - 92
Record Appearances: Danny Godwin - 470
Additional Records: Paid £9,000 to Enfield for David Flint
Received £10,000 from Luton Town for Herbie Smith

Senior Honours: Athenian League 1949-50, 54-55. Isthmian League 1975-76, 59-60, Division 2 2000-01. Full Members Cup 1992-93. London Senior Cup 1942-43, 48-49, 58-59, 59-60, 2006-07, 07-08. Surrey Senior cup 1937-38, 43-44, 44-45, 52-53, 59-60, 75-76, 76-77, 77-78, 2007-07. Surrey Senior Shield 1951-52, 60-61, 61-62, 65-66. South Thames Cup 1969-70.

10 YEAR RECORD

00-01	01-02	02-03	03-04	04-05	05-06	06-07	07-08	08-09	09-10
Isth2 1	Isth1 12	Isth1S 11	Isth1S 11	Isth1 8	Isth1 6	Isth1S 2	Isth1S 2	Isth P 9	Isth P 12

TOOTING MITCHAM UNITED

No.	Date	Comp	H/A	Opponents	Att:	Result	Goalscorers	Pos
1	Aug 15	Ryman P.	H	Waltham Abbey	246	D 1 - 1	Vines P 67	9
2	18		A	Wealdstone	393	W 2 - 0	Goode 15 Byatt 86	
3	22		A	AFC Hornchurch	327	W 1 - 0	Goode 26	4
4	25		H	Cray Wanderers	228	L 0 - 2		9
5	29		A	Maidstone United	308	W 2 - 1	Vines J 70 Goode 75	4
6	31		H	Bognor Regis Town	285	W 3 - 2	Vines P 8 35 Goode 80	
7	Sept 5		A	Billericay Town	418	D 0 - 0		2
8	**12**	**F.A.C. 1Q**	**H**	**Horsham**	**346**	**W 4 - 2**	**Vines P 5 Parker 60 Yorke 68 (pen) Byatt 90**	
9	19		H	Aveley	248	L 1 - 2	Pitterson 21	4
10	22		A	Ashford Town		L 1 - 3	Yorke 45	8
11	**26**	**F.A.C 2Q**	**A**	**Canvey Island**	**376**	**W 2 - 0**	**Byatt 52 P.Vines 88**	
12	Oct 3		H	Tonbridge Angels	306	W 5 - 3	P VINES 3 (16 42 61) Parker 52 Goode 90	3
13	**10**	**F.A.C. 3Q**	**H**	**Slough Town**	**551**	**W 3 - 2**	**P.Vines 24 Goode 29 Byatt 55**	
14	12		H	Harrow Borough	245	W 1 - 0	P.Vines	2
15	**17**	**F.A.T. 1Q**	**H**	**Walton & Hersham**	**233**	**W 3 - 0**	**Parker 14 P.Vines 38 Cheadle 40 (og)**	
16	**24**	**F.A.C 4Q**	**H**	**Eastbourne Borough**	**687**	**D 3 - 3**	**York 29 P.Vines 87 Parker 89**	
17	**27**	**F.A.C. 4Qr**	**A**	**Eastbourne Borough**	**906**	**W 4 - 3**	**P.Vines 29 Mcleod 43 York 100 103 (pens)**	
18	**Nov 7**	**F.A.C. 1**	**A**	**Stockport County**	**3076**	**L 0 - 5**		
19	16		H	Horsham	249	L 0 - 2		
20	21		H	Canvey Island	274	L 1 - 3	J.Vines 59	13
21	24		A	Dartford	871	L 2 - 3	Byatt 12 P. Vines 24	
22	28		A	Bognor Regis Town	431	W 3 - 0	P.Vines 63 75 Parker 90	9
23	Dec 1		A	Sutton United	517	W 2 - 1	Clayton 6 Parker 29	
24	5		H	Maidstone United	276	D 2 - 2	Parker 40 Clayton 64	
25	12		H	Hastings United	258	W 1 - 0	Parker 34	4
26	26		H	Kingstonian	440	L 2 - 3	Byatt 8 Goode 90	4
27	Jan 2		A	Kingstonian	480	D 1 - 1	Graves 89	5
28	16		H	Billericay Town	291	D 1 - 1	P.Vines 35	5
29	18		H	Boreham Wood	147	L 0 - 2		
30	23		A	Aveley	164	W 2 - 1	Graves 13 Ketchell 61 (og)	4
31	26		A	Hendon	123	D 0 - 0		
32	30		A	Tonbridge Angels	427	W 2 - 1	Goode 1 Minshull 90 (og)	4
33	Feb 6		H	Ashford Town	212	L 2 - 3	Parker 45 65	6
34	13		A	Harrow Borough	177	D 1 - 1	Pitterson 78	6
35	20		H	Sutton United	630	D 1 - 1	Parker 43	7
36	27		H	Hendon	301	L 0 - 2		8
37	Mar 2		A	Carshalton Athletic	304	L 1 - 4	P.Vines 85	
38	6		A	Horsham	323	W 2 - 1	Parker 11 P.Vines 43	7
39	9		A	Margate	210	L 1 - 2	Parker 21	7
40	13		H	Dartford	515	W 3 - 1	Parker 8 P.Vines 81 83	7
41	16		A	Waltham Abbey	102	D 1 - 1	Goode 90	
42	20		A	Canvey Island	283	L 1 - 2	P.Vines 42	9
43	22		H	Wealdstone	242	W 3 - 2	P.Vines 33 37 Parker 90	
44	27		H	AFC Hornchurch	309	L 2 - 3	J.Vines 36 Parker 63	8
45	April 3		A	Hastings United	458	L 0 - 2		9
46	5		H	Carshalton Athletic	528	D 2 - 2	Henry 55 P.Vines 85	
47	10		A	Cray Wanderers	233	L 0 - 1		11
48	17		H	Margate	323	W 2 - 1	P.Vines 45 Yorke 70	11
49	24		A	Boreham Wood	311	L 2 - 3	Henry 25 P.Vines 45	12
					Goals	79 81		

Home Attendances:	
Highest:	630 v Sutton United
Lowest:	147 v Boreham Wood
Average (08-09):	285 (376)
Top Goalscorer:	Paul Vines - 27 (League 21, FAC 5, FAT 1 - Hat-trick 1)

WEALDSTONE

Chairman: Howard Krais

Secretary: Paul Fruin (T) 0779 003 8095 (E) paul@pfruin.orangehome.co.uk

Additional Committee Members:
Alan Couch, Nick Dugard, Peter Worby

Manager: Gordon Bartlett

Programme Editor: Adam Gloor (E) adamgloor@aol.com

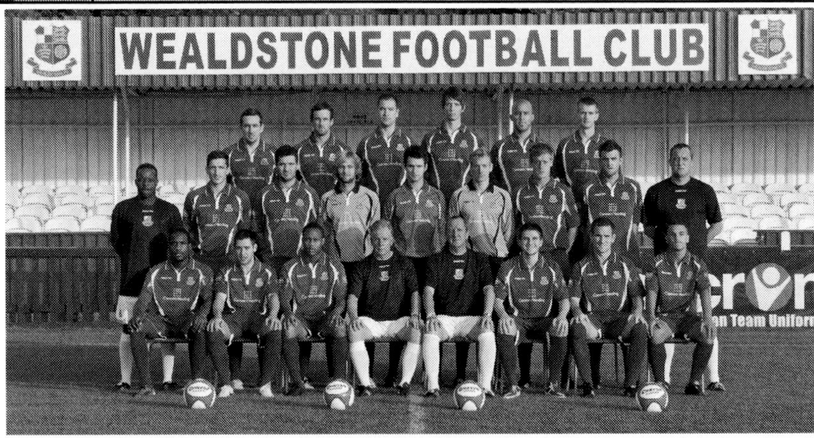

Back Row (L-R): Ryan Ashe, Peter Dean, Scott Fitzgerald, Sean Cronin, Dan Gerrard, Louis Lavers **Middle:** Micky Johnson (coach), Mark E'Beyer, Chris O'Leary, Jonathan North, Sean Thomas, Sam Beagle, Alan Massey, Darren Locke, Mark Gill (coach) **Front:** Kieron Forbes, Danny Burnell, Greg Ngoyi, Gordon Bartlett (Manager), Leo Morris (Assistant Manager), Lee Chappell, Dean Smith, Kurtney Brooks. Not pictured: Danny Spendlove, Wes Parker, Callum Martin, Jon Douglas. Photo: Chertsey of Steve Foster

Club Factfile

Founded: 1899 **Nickname:** The Stones

Previous Names:

Previous Leagues: Willesden & District 1899-1906, 08-13, London 1911-22, Middlesex 1913-22, Spartan 1922-28, Athenian 1928-64, Isthmian 1964-71, 95-2006, Southern 1971-79, 81-82, 88-95, Conference 1979-81, 82-88

Club Colours (change): All blue with white trim

Ground: Grosvenor Vale, Ruislip, Middlesex HA4 6JQ **(T)** 01895 637 487

Capacity: 2,300 **Seats:** 300 **Covered:** 450 **Clubhouse:** Yes **Shop:**

Previous Grounds: Lower Mead Stadium, Watford FC, YEading FC, Northwood FC

Simple Directions

From the M1: Follow Signs for Heathrow Airport on the M25. Come off at Junction 16 onto the A40, come off at The Polish War Memorial junction A4180 sign posted to Ruislip, continue on West End Road, right into Grosvenor Vale after approx 1.5 miles, the ground is at the end of the road.

From the M25: Follow Take Junction 16 Off M25 onto A40. Then come off at The Polish War Memorial junction A4180 sign posted to Ruislip, continue on West End Road, right into Grosvenor Vale after approx 1.5 miles, the ground is at the end of the road.

From the M4: Junction 4B, take the M25 towards Watford, come off Junction 16 and join A40, come off at The Polish War Memorial junction A4180 sign posted to Ruislip, continue on West End Road, right into Grosvenor Vale after approx 1.5 miles, the ground is at the end of the road.

Record Attendance: 13,504 v Leytonstone - FA Amateur Cup 4th Round replay 05/03/1949 (at Lower Mead Stadium)

Record Victory: 22-0 v The 12th London Regiment (The Rangers) - FA Amateur Cup 13/10/1923

Record Defeat: 0-14 v Edgware Town (A) - London Senior Cup 09/12/1944

Record Goalscorer: George Duck - 251

Record Appearances: Charlie Townsend - 514

Additional Records: Paid £15,000 to Barnet for David Gipp
Received £70,000 from Leeds United for Jermaine Beckford

Senior Honours: Athenian League 1951-52. Southern League Division 1 South 1973-74, Southern Division 1981-82. Conference 1984-85. Isthmian League Division 3 1996-97. FA Amateur Cup 1965-66. London Senior Cup 1961-62. FA Trophy 1984-85. Middlesex Senior Cup x11

10 YEAR RECORD

00-01	01-02	02-03	03-04	04-05	05-06	06-07	07-08	08-09	09-10
Isth1 19	Isth1 8	Isth1N 9	Isth1N 7	Isth P 18	Isth P 18	SthP 19	Isth P 13	Isth P 7	Isth P 6

WEALDSTONE

No.	Date	Comp	H/A	Opponents	Att:	Result	Goalscorers	Pos
1	Aug 15	Ryman P.	A	Billericay Town	481	D 0 - 0		16
2	18		H	Tooting & Mitcham U	393	L 0 - 2		
3	22		H	Maidstone United	403	D 2 - 2	Mpi 73 Ashe 81	16
4	25		A	Borham Wood	235	W 1 - 0	Ashe 2 (pen)	15
5	29		A	Dartford	1150	D 1 - 1	O'Leary 1	14
6	31		H	Sutton United	480	W 2 - 1	E'Beyer 74 Spendlove 90	
7	Sept 5		A	Aveley	231	D 2 - 2	Massey 29 McCoy 57	9
8	**12**	**F.A.C. 1Q**	**A**	**Arlesey Town**	**232**	**W 2 - 1**	**Ashe 22 (pen) Ngoyi 65**	
9	19		H	Bognor Regis Town	396	W 4 - 0	Gray 4 Ngoyi 8 60 Ashe 86	6
10	22		A	Waltham Abbey	187	W 2 - 1	Mpi 43 Ngoyi 59	
11	**26**	**F.A.C 2Q**	**A**	**Boreham Wood**	**249**	**W 4 - 2**	**Ashe 5 Chappell 10 44 Massey 72**	
12	Oct 3		H	Canvey Island	435	W 1 - 0	Chappell 45	2
13	**10**	**F.A.C. 3Q**	**H**	**Lewes**	**530**	**W 3 - 0**	**O'Leary 4 Ngoyi 25 Forbes 47**	
14	**17**	**F.A.T 1Q**	**H**	**Margate**	**265**	**W 3 - 1**	**E'Beyer 55 Mpi 63 Lafayette 90**	
15	20		A	AFc Hornchurch		D 0 - 0		4
16	**24**	**F.A.C. 4Q**	**A**	**Aylsbury F.C.**	**682**	**W 4 - 2**	**Ngoyi 26 Ashe 48 78 Forbes 54**	
17	**31**	**F.A.T 2Q**	**A**	**Harrow Borough**	**513**	**D 2 - 2**	**Fitzgerald 7 Chappell 61**	
18	**Nov 3**	**F.A.T. 2nQr**	**H**	**Harrow Borugh**	**315**	**W 2 - 1**	**Ashe 30 Ngoyi 65**	
19	**8**	**F.A.C 1**	**H**	**Rotherham United**	**1638**	**L 2 - 3**	**Ashe 63 90**	
20	17		H	Cray Wanderers	315	W 3 - 2	Spendlove 6 Ashe 52 Lucket 90 (og)	
21	**21**	**F.A.T 3Q**	**A**	**Farnborough**	**1012**	**L 0 - 3**		
22	28		A	Sutton United	698	L 0 - 5		10
23	Dec 12		A	Tonbridge Angels	439	W 3 - 2	Cumberbatch 28 (og) Chappell 31 Ngoyi 62	
24	15		H	Horsham	281	W 2 - 1	Ashe 43 63	5
25	26		A	Ashford Town	265	D 3 - 3	Ashe 16 (pen) Corcoran 22 Mpi 73	5
26	28		H	Harrow Borough	666	W 2 - 1	Corcoran 21(pen) Gibson 51	
27	Jan 23		A	Bognor Regis Town	331	D 2 - 2	Gray 12 Demetriou 57 (og)	5
28	30		A	Canvey Island	341	D 1 - 1	Martin 49	8
29	Feb 2		A	Carshalton Athletic	177	L 2 - 4	Ngoyi 39 Ashe (pen)67	
30	6		H	Waltham Abbey	410	L 2 - 4	E.Beyer 19 Gray 45	9
31	9		A	Margate	310	D 1 - 1	Martin 7	
32	13		A	Hendon	331	W 3 - 2	Locke 15 Martin 16 27	8
33	20		H	AFC Hornchurch	437	L 2 - 3	Ashe 42 (pen) Martin 88	11
34	25		A	Kingstonian	277	D 3 - 3	Martin 32 Spendlove 33 Logie 54	11
35	Mar 2		H	Hendon	367	L 0 - 2		
36	6		A	Cray Wanderers	197	W 3 - 1	Osbourne 68 Spendlove 71 Martin 82	9
37	9		H	Hastings United	329	W 1 - 0	Ashe 34 (pen)	
38	13		H	Kingstonian	552	D 2 - 2	Spendlove 2 O'Leary 3	6
39	16		H	Billericay Town	328	D 0 - 0		
40	20		A	Hastings United	429	L 0 - 1		7
41	22		A	Tooting & Mitcham United	242	L 2 - 3	O'Leary 11 Spendlove 78	
42	27		A	Maidstone United	218	W 3 - 2	Ashe 2 C.Martin 62 84	7
43	April 5		A	Harrow Borough	525	L 1 - 3	Martin 23	
44	7		H	Margate	333	W 1 - 0	Chappell 63	
45	10		H	Boreham Wood	406	D 0 - 0		9
46	13		H	Ashford Town	307	W 1 - 0	E'beyer 61	
47	15		H	Aveley	320	L 0 - 1		
48	17		A	Horsham	343	W 3 - 1	McCLURE 3 (19 55 65)	
49	20		H	Dartford	401	D 1 - 1	Massey 83	8
50	22		H	Tonbriddge Angels	411	W 2 - 1	McClure 24 46	
51	24		H	Carshalton Athletic	735	L 1 - 4	Ngoyi 24	6
					Goals	87 80		

Home Attendances:

Highest:	735 v Carshalton Athletic
Lowest:	281 v Horsham
Average (08-09):	401 (408)
Top Goalscorer:	Ashe - 18 (League 11, FAC 6, FAT 1)

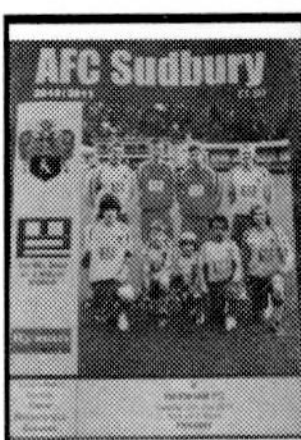

A.F.C. SUDBURY

Chairman: Philip Turner
Secretary: Davis Webb — **(T)** 07885 327 510 **(E)** dave-afc@supanet.com

Additional Committee Members:
Mark Peaman, Danny Crosbie

Manager: Nicky Smith
Programme Editor: Darren Theobald — **(E)** theobaldd@hotmail.co.uk

Club Factfile

Founded: 1999 **Nickname:** Yellows
Previous Names: Sudbury Town (1874) and Sudbury Wanderers (1958) merged in 1999
Previous Leagues: Eastern Counties 1999-2006, Isthmian 2006-08, Southern 2008-10

Club Colours (change): Yellow/blue/yellow

Ground: Kingsmarsh Stadium, Brundon Lane, Sudbury, Suffolk CO10 7HN **(T)** 01787 376 213
Capacity: 2,500 **Seats:** 200 **Covered:** 1,500 **Clubhouse:** Yes **Shop:** Yes
Previous Grounds:
Simple Directions
Follow Halstead/Chelmsford road from Sudbury centre for a mile. First right after bridge at foot of steep hill and first right again after left hand bend.

Record Attendance: 1,800
Record Victory: Not known
Record Defeat: Not known
Record Goalscorer: Gary Bennett - 172
Record Appearances: Paul Betson - 376
Additional Records:

Senior Honours: Eastern Counties League 2000-01, 01-02, 02-03, 03-04, 04-05.
Suffolk Premier Cup 2002, 2003, 2004.

10 YEAR RECORD

00-01	01-02	02-03	03-04	04-05	05-06	06-07	07-08	08-09	09-10
ECP 1	ECP 1	ECP 1	ECP 1	ECP 1	ECP 3	Isth1N 5	Isth1N 2	SthM	SthM 14

BRENTWOOD TOWN

Chairman: Brian Hallett
Secretary: Ray Stevens (T) 0776 800 6370
(E) r.w.stevens@btinternet.com

Additional Committee Members:
Ken Hobbs, John Leyden, Ken Hobbs

Manager: Les Whitton
Programme Editor: Ken Hobbs (E) khobbs1057@aol.com

Archive photo

Club Factfile

Founded: 1955 **Nickname:** Blues
Previous Names: Manor Athletic, Brentwood Athletic, Brentwood F.C.
Previous Leagues: Romford & District, South Essex Combination, London & Essex Border, Olympian, Essex Senior

Club Colours (change): Sky blue/navy/navy

Ground: The Arena, Brentwood Centre, Doddinghurst Road, Brentwood CM15 9NN **(T)** 01708 800 6370
Capacity: 1,000 **Seats:** 50 **Covered:** 250 **Clubhouse:** Yes **Shop:** No
Previous Grounds: King George's Playing Fields (Hartswood), Larkins Playing Fields 1957-93
Simple Directions
From High Street (Wilson's Corner) turn north into Ongar Road. Then at third mini roundabout turn right into Doddinghurst Road.

Record Attendance: 472 v West Ham United - 27/07/2004
Record Victory: Not known
Record Defeat: Not known
Record Goalscorer: Not known
Record Appearances: Not known
Additional Records:

Senior Honours: Essex Senior League 2000-01, 2006-07, League Cup 1975-76, 78-79, 90-91, 2006-07.
Essex Olympian League Cup 1967-68.

10 YEAR RECORD

00-01	01-02	02-03	03-04	04-05	05-06	06-07	07-08	08-09	09-10
ESen 1	ESen 14	ESen 11	ESen 14	ESen 14	ESen 8	ESen 1	Isth1N 6	Isth1N 3	Isth1N 12

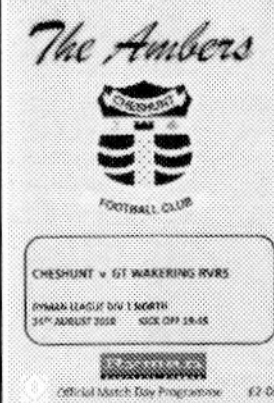

CHESHUNT

Chairman: Vince Sartori
Secretary: Alex Kalinic (T) 0775 483 1800
(E) alex@cheshuntfc.com

Additional Committee Members:
Paul Fletcher

Manager: Bob Dearie
Programme Editor: Alex Kalinic (E) alex@cheshuntfc.com

Back Row L to R – Iain Salt, Billy Haspineall, Nick Mountford, Joe Wright, Tom Dos Anjos, Christiaan Beaupierre, Syrus Gordon, Charie Douse, Darrell Cox. Middle Row L to R - Chris Meikle, Tom Tresadern, Michael Sharman, Graeme Butler, David Hicks, Glen Parry, Matt Thomson, Gary Schillaci, Jimmy Martin, Richard Ashie.
Front Row L to R – Howard Bailey, Adam Norman, Alex Kalinic, Paul Fletcher, Paul Halsey (Assist Manager) Bob Dearie (Manager) Alfie Noarman (Coach) Rebecca Cornish (Physio) Neil Harrison, George Norman, Vince Bates .

Club Factfile

Founded: 1946 **Nickname:** Ambers
Previous Names:
Previous Leagues: London 1947-51, 56-59, Delphian 1952-55, Aetolian 1960-62, Spartan 1963-64, 88-93, Athenian 1965-76, Isthmian 1977-87, 94-2005, Southern 2006-08

Club Colours (change): Amber/black/amber or black

Ground: Cheshunt Stadium, Theobalds Lane, Cheshunt, Herts EN8 8RU **(T)** 01992 633 500
Capacity: 3,500 **Seats:** 424 **Covered:** 600 **Clubhouse:** Yes **Shop:** No
Previous Grounds:
Simple Directions
M25, junction 25 take A10 north towards Hertford. Third exit at roundabout towards Waltham Cross A121. First exit at roundabout towards Cheshunt B176. Under railway bridge then left onto Theobalds Lane. Ground is 800 yard on the right.

Record Attendance: 5,000
Record Victory: v Bromley - FA Amateur Cup 2nd Round 28/01/1950
Record Defeat: 0-10 v Etonn Manor - London League 17/04/1956
Record Goalscorer: Eddie Sedgwick - 148 (1967-72, 1980)
Record Appearances: John Poole - 526 (1970-76, 79-83)
Additional Records: Received £10,000 from Peterborough United for Lloyd Opara

Senior Honours: London League Premier Division 1950, Division 1 1948, 49. Athenian League Premier Division 1976, Division 1 1968.
Spartan League 1963. Isthmian League Division 2 2003.
London Charity Cup 1974. East Anglian Cup 1975. Herts Charity Cup 2006, 2008.

10 YEAR RECORD

00-01		01-02		02-03		03-04		04-05		05-06		06-07		07-08		08-09		09-10	
Isth2	19	Isth2	20	Isth2	1	Isth1N	3	Isth P	19	SthP	16	SthP	16	SthP	22	Isth1N	14	Isth1N	15

EAST THURROCK UNITED

Chairman: Brian Mansbridge
Secretary: Mick Stephens (T) 0797 921 4350
(E) mickygatta@blueyonder.co.uk

Additional Committee Members:
Neil Speight, Peter Lambert

Manager: John Coventry
Programme Editor: Neil Speight (E) speight.n@sky.com

Archive photo

Club Factfile

Founded: 1969 **Nickname:** Rocks
Previous Names: Corringham Social > 1969 (Sunday side)
Previous Leagues: South Essex Combination, Greater London, Metropolitan 1972-75, London Spartan 1975-79, Essex Senior 1979-92, Isthmian 1992-2004, Southern 2004-05

Club Colours (change): Amber/black/black

Ground: Rookery Hill, Corringham, Essex SS17 9LB (T) 01375 644 166
Capacity: 4,000 **Seats:** 160 **Covered:** 1,000 **Clubhouse:** Yes **Shop:** No
Previous Grounds: Billet, Stanford-le-Hope 1970-73, 74-76, Grays Athletic 1973-74, Tilbury FC 1977-82, New Thames Club 1982-84
Simple Directions
From A13 London-Southend road, take A1014 at Stanford-le-Hope for two and half miles. Ground on left.

Record Attendance: 1,215 v Woking FA Cup 2003
Record Victory: 7-0 v Coggeshall (H) - Essex Senior League 1984
Record Defeat: 0-9 v Eton Manor (A) - Essex Senior League 1982
Record Goalscorer: Graham Stewart - 102
Record Appearances: Glen Case - 600+
Additional Records: £22,000 from Leyton Orient for Greg Berry 1990

Senior Honours: Isthmian League Division 3 1999-2000. East Anglian Cup 2002-03.

10 YEAR RECORD

00-01	01-02	02-03	03-04	04-05	05-06	06-07	07-08	08-09	09-10
Isth2 12	Isth2 8	Isth1N 17	Isth1N 12	SthE 2	Isth P 12	Isth P 16	Isth P 20	Isth1N 2	Isth1N 5

ENFIELD TOWN

Chairman: Paul Millington
Secretary: Peter Coath (T) 0794 937 8931
(E) crcl07120@blueyonder.co.uk

Additional Committee Members:
Keith Wortley, Ciaron Glennon, Dave Farenden

Manager: Steve Newing
Programme Editor: Ciaron Glennon (E) ciaron.glennon@btopenworld.com

Archive photo

Club Factfile

Founded: 2001 **Nickname:** ET's or Towners
Previous Names: Broke away from Enfield F.C. in 2001
Previous Leagues: Essex Senior League

Club Colours (change): White/royal blue/white

Ground: Quenn Elizabeth Stadium, Donkey Lane, Enfield EN1 4BT (T) 020 8363 7398
Capacity: **Seats:** **Covered:** **Clubhouse:** **Shop:**
Previous Grounds: Brimsdown Rovers FC 2001-2010
Simple Directions
Turn off A10 at Carterhanger Lane, then turn immediately into Donkey Lane.

Record Attendance: 562 v Enfield - Middlesex Charity Cup 2002-03
Record Victory: 7-0 v Ilford (A) - 29/04/2003
Record Defeat: Not known
Record Goalscorer: Dan Clarke - 68
Record Appearances: Stuart Snowden - 147
Additional Records:

Senior Honours: Essex Senior League 2002-03, 04-05.

10 YEAR RECORD

00-01	01-02	02-03	03-04	04-05	05-06	06-07	07-08	08-09	09-10
	ESen 2	ESen 1	ESen 4	ESen 1	SthE 3	Isth1N 3	Isth1N 12	Isth1N 12	Isth1N 4

GRAYS ATHLETIC

Chairman: John Moncur
Secretary: Val Pepperell (T) 0793 173 1358
(E) vapepp@hotmail.co.uk

Additional Committee Members:
Joel Nathan, Keith Burns

Manager: Julian Dicks

Programme Editor: Tony Packer (E) packerspackers@hotmail.co.uk

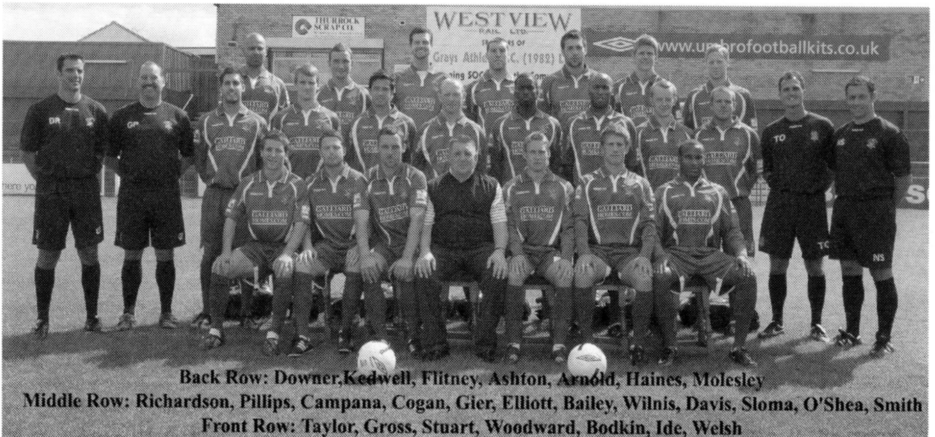

Back Row: Downer, Kedwell, Flitney, Ashton, Arnold, Haines, Molesley
Middle Row: Richardson, Pillips, Campana, Cogan, Gier, Elliott, Bailey, Wilnis, Davis, Sloma, O'Shea, Smith
Front Row: Taylor, Gross, Stuart, Woodward, Bodkin, Ide, Welsh

Archive photo

Club Factfile

Founded: 1890 **Nickname:** The Blues
Previous Names:
Previous Leagues: Athenian 1912-14, 58-83, London 1914-24, 26-39, Kent 1924-26, Corinthian 1945-58, Isthmian 1958-2004, Conference 2004-10
Club Colours (change): All royal blue

Ground: East Thurrock United, Rookery Hill, Corringham, Essex SS17 9LB **(T)** 01375 644 166
Capacity: 4,000 **Seats:** 160 **Covered:** 1,000 **Clubhouse:** Yes **Shop:** No
Previous Grounds: Recreation Ground Bridge Road
Simple Directions
From A13 London-Southend road, take A1014 at Stanford-le-Hope for two and half miles. Ground on left.

Record Attendance: 9,500 v Chelmsford City - FA Cup 4th Qualifying Round 1959
Record Victory: 12-0 v Tooting & Mitcham United - London League 24/02/1923
Record Defeat: 0-12 v Enfield (A) - Athenian League 20/04/1963
Record Goalscorer: Harry Brand - 269 (1944-52)
Record Appearances: Phil Sammons - 673 (1982-97)
Additional Records:

Senior Honours: Conference South 2004-05. FA Trophy 2004-05, 05-06.
Essex Senior Cup x8

10 YEAR RECORD

00-01	01-02	02-03	03-04	04-05	05-06	06-07	07-08	08-09	09-10
Isth P 15	Isth P 6	Isth P 19	Isth P 6	Conf S 1	Conf 3	Conf 19	Conf 10	Conf 19	Conf 23

GREAT WAKERING ROVERS

Chairman: Roy Ketteridge
Secretary: Roger Sampson (T) 0783 785 6482
(E) rogersampson@talktalk.net

Additional Committee Members:
Norman Johnson
Manager: Ryan Wilkinson
Programme Editor: Robert Lilley (E) roblilley@hotmail.co.uk

Back Row (L-R): Jimmy Webb, James Nolan, Ty Benjamin, Stewart Moore, Dan williams, Ben Hudson.
Middle Row: Jack O'Connor, Freskim Rushti, Dominic Binns, Adam Holmes, Louis Godwin-Green, Richard McKinney, Matt Toms, Michael Fox, Danny Heath (Reserve team manager).
Front Row: Billy Johnson, Lewis Sparrow, Cleve Taylor (Physio), Ryan Wilkinson.

Club Factfile

Founded: 1919 **Nickname:** Rovers
Previous Names:
Previous Leagues: Southend & District 1919-81, Southend Alliance 1981-89, Essex Intermediate 1989-92, Essex Senior 1992-99, Isthmian 1999-2004, Southern 2004-05

Club Colours (change): Green and white stripes/white/green

Ground: Burroughs Park, Little Wakering Hall Lane, Gt Wakering SS3 0HH (T) 01702 217 812
Capacity: 2,500 **Seats:** 150 **Covered:** 300 **Clubhouse:** Yes **Shop:** No
Previous Grounds: Great Wakering Rec
Simple Directions
A127 towards Southend and follow signs for Shoeburyness for about four miles. Turn left to Great Wakering on B1017 at Bournes Green. Go down High Street for half a mile and ground is on the left.

Record Attendance: 1,150 v Southend United - Friendly 19/07/2006
Record Victory: 9-0 v Eton Manor - 27/12/1931
Record Defeat: 1-7 v Bowers United - Essex Senior League 01/04/1998
Record Goalscorer: Not known
Record Appearances: Not known
Additional Records:

Senior Honours: Essex Senior League 1994-95. Isthmian League Division 3.

10 YEAR RECORD

00-01	01-02	02-03	03-04	04-05	05-06	06-07	07-08	08-09	09-10
Isth2 9	Isth2 7	Isth1N 14	Isth1N 21	SthE 20	SthE 13	Isth1N 12	Isth1N 13	Isth1N 13	Isth1N 9

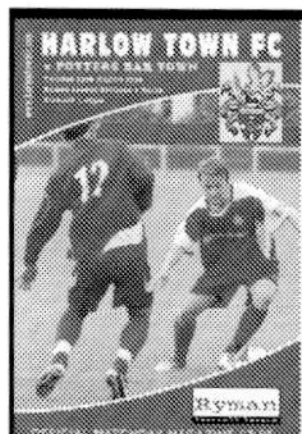

HARLOW TOWN

Chairman: John Barnett
Secretary: John McClelland (T) 0781 639 1892
(E) maccahtfc@hotmail.com

Additional Committee Members:
Ray Dyer, Chris Cain, Steve Clark
Manager: Kevin Warren
Programme Editor: John McClelland (E) maccahtfc@hotmail.com

Back Row (L-R): Paul West-Hook , Ray Dyer, Mark Taylor, Sosthene Yao, Che Stadhart, Jon Stevenson, Rhys Madden, James May, James Hasell, Laurie Stewart, James Bunn, Jeff Hammond, Steven Velandia, Christian Wheeler, Steve Clarke, Danny Chapman
Fornt Row: Sam Taylor, Louis Riddle, Andy Porter, Ben Bradbury, Kevin Warren, John Barnett, Leo Roget, Clark Akers, Shaun Gliddon, Bradley Barnes, Reece Dobson,

Club Factfile

Founded: 1879 **Nickname:** Hawks
Previous Names:
Previous Leagues: East Hertfordshire > 1932, Spartan 1932-39, 46-54, London 1954-61, Delphian 1961-63, Athenian 1963-73, Isthmian 1973-92, Inactive 1992-93, Southern 2004-06

Club Colours (change): All red

Ground: Barrows Farm Std, off Elizabeth Way, The Pinnacles, Harlow CM19 5BE **(T)** 01279 443 196
Capacity: 3,500 **Seats:** 500 **Covered:** 500 **Clubhouse:** Yes **Shop:** Yes
Previous Grounds: Marigolds 1919-22, Green Man Field 1922-60

Simple Directions
Barrows Farm is situated on the western side of town just off of the Roydon Road (A1169) on the Pinnacles Industrial Estate.
If coming into Harlow from the M11 (North or South) exit at Junction 7 and follow the A414 until the first roundabout where you turn left onto the A1169. Follow the A1169 signed for Roydon until you see the ground ahead of you at the Roydon Road roundabout. Go straight over the roundabout and the entrance to the ground is on the left.
If coming into town from the west on the A414 turn right at the first roundabout (the old ground was straight ahead) signed Roydon A1169. Follow the A1169 for approx 1 mile and the entrance to the ground is on the right.

Record Attendance: 9,723 v Leicester City - FA Cup 3rd Round replay 08/01/1980
Record Victory: 14-0 v Bishop's Stortford - 11/04/1925
Record Defeat: 0-11 v Ware (A) - Spartan Division 1 East 06/03/1948
Record Goalscorer: Dick Marshall scored 64 during 1928-29
Record Appearances: Norman Gladwin - 639 (1949-70)
Additional Records:

Senior Honours: Athenian League Division 1 1971-72. Isthmian League Division 1 1978-79, Division 2 North 1988-89.
Essex Senior cup 1978-79

10 YEAR RECORD

00-01	01-02	02-03	03-04	04-05	05-06	06-07	07-08	08-09	09-10
Isth1 11	Isth1 7	Isth1N 10	Isth1N 10	SthE 15	SthE 9	Isth1N 2	Isth P 15	Isth P 20	Isth1N 22

HEYBRIDGE SWIFTS

Chairman: Nick Bowyer
Secretary: Peter Pask (T) 0777 093 0556
(E) admin@heybridgeswifts.com

Additional Committee Members:
Dave Buckingham, Michael Gibson

Manager: Wayne Bond
Programme Editor: Noel Tilbrook (E) noel@steponsafety.co.uk

Archive photo

Club Factfile

Founded: 1880 **Nickname:** Swifts
Previous Names:
Previous Leagues: Essex & Suffolk Border, North Essex, South Essex, Essex Senior 1971-84

Club Colours (change): Black and white stripes/black/black

Ground: Scraley Road, Heybridge, Maldon, Essex CM9 8JA (T) 01621 852 978
Capacity: 3,000 **Seats:** 550 **Covered:** 1,200 **Clubhouse:** Yes **Shop:** Yes
Previous Grounds:
Simple Directions
Leave Maldon on the main road to Colchester, pass through Heybridge then turn right at sign to Tolleshunt Major (Scraley Road). The ground is on the right.

Record Attendance: 2,477 v Woking - FA Trophy 1997
Record Victory: Not known
Record Defeat: Not known
Record Goalscorer: Julian Lamb - 115 (post War)
Record Appearances: Hec Askew - 500+. John Pollard - 496
Additional Records: Paid £1,000 for Dave Rainford and for Lee Kersey
Received £35,000 from Southend United for Simon Royce

Senior Honours: Isthmian League Division 2 North 1989-90, Essex Senior League x3.
Essex Junior Cup 1931-32. East Anglian Cup 1993-94, 94-95.

10 YEAR RECORD

00-01	01-02	02-03	03-04	04-05	05-06	06-07	07-08	08-09	09-10
Isth P 7	Isth P 13	Isth P 20	Isth P 16	Isth P 7	Isth P 2	Isth P 12	Isth P 12	Isth P 21	Isth1N 6

ILFORD

Chairman: Roger Chilvers
Secretary: Roger Chilvers (T) 0771 028 5571
(E) rogerchilvers@aol.com

Additional Committee Members:
Len Llewellyn, Niall Watson

Manager: Colin Walton
Programme Editor: Len Llewellyn (E) exseniorlenl@aol.com

Back Row (L-R): Victor Omogbehin, Jurrel McCarthy, George Dawson, Aaron Scott, Pape Diagne, Derek Hawtin, Callum McGeehan. Middle Row: Richard Pike, Des Gallen, Anton Trice, Junior Konadu, Tony Russell, Harry Chalk, Jason Sam-Franks, Roy Holliwell, Junior Appiah. Front Row: John Hughes, Bradley Drisdale, Neil Matthews, Lucelta Eugeen (Physio), Colin Walton (Asst. Manager), Roger Chilvers (Chairman), Chris Wood (Manager), Michael Thompson (Coach), Jamie Pooley, Michael Noble, John Sparks.

Club Factfile

Founded: 1987 **Nickname:** The Foxes
Previous Names: Reformed as Ilford in 1987 after the original club merged with Leytonstone in 1980.
Previous Leagues: Spartan 1987-94, Essex Senior 1996-2004, Isthmian 2004-05, Southern 2005-06

Club Colours (change): Blue and white hoops/blue/blue

Ground: Cricklefield Stadium, 486 High Road, Ilford, Essex IG1 1UE (T) 020 8514 8352
Capacity: 3,500 **Seats:** 216 **Covered:** Yes **Clubhouse:** Yes **Shop:** No
Previous Grounds:
Simple Directions
Taking the A127, from the east travel towards London before coming to the traffic light controlled junction at Barley Lane, Goodmayes (B177) . Turn Left by taking the slip road and follow Barley Lane to its junction with the traffic light controlled High Road, Goodmayes (A118) (it is the first set of traffic control lights for traffic rather than pedestrians on that road). Turn Right and follow the road past Seven Kings station (which should be on your right) and on towards Ilford. The entrance to the ground is some 400 yards past the station with the Ilford Swimming Baths on the left being the point at which both coaches and those in cars or on foot should turn left into the car parks. Both on Saturday and after 6pm. during the week, the public car park is free of charge.

Record Attendance: Not known
Record Victory: Not known
Record Defeat: Not known
Record Goalscorer: Not known
Record Appearances: Not known
Additional Records:

Senior Honours: Isthmian League Division 2 2004-05.

10 YEAR RECORD

00-01		01-02		02-03		03-04		04-05		05-06		06-07		07-08		08-09		09-10	
ESen	6	ESen	9	ESen	3	ESen	2	Isth2	1	SthE	21	Isth1N	21	Isth1N	21	Isth1N	17	Isth1N	20

LEYTON

Chairman: Tony Hardy
Secretary: Stephen Bellanoff **(T)** 0778 842 1172
(E) leytonfc@btconnect.com

Additional Committee Members:
Barry Abbott

Manager: Wilson Frimpong

Programme Editor: Tony Hardy **(E)** tony.hardy@hsbcpb.com

Unfortunately an up-to-date photograph was not available at the time of going to press

Club Factfile

Founded: 1868 **Nickname:** Lilywhites
Previous Names: Leyton 1891-1973, Leyton Wingate 1976-87
Previous Leagues: Leyton & District Alliance, South Essex, Essex Intermediate, Essex Senior, London Spartan

Club Colours (change): White/royal blue/white

Ground: Leyton Stadium, 282 Lea Bridge Road, Leyton E10 7LD **(T)** 0794 431 3523
Capacity: 2,500 **Seats:** Yes **Covered:** Yes **Clubhouse:** Yes **Shop:** Yes
Previous Grounds:

Simple Directions
Lea Bridge Road is the A104 and the ground is next to the Hare & Hounds Pub. Leyton (Central Line) then bus 58 or 158 to Lea Bridge Road.

Record Attendance: Not known
Record Victory: Not known
Record Defeat: Not known
Record Goalscorer: Not known
Record Appearances: Not known
Additional Records:

Senior Honours: London Senior Cup 1903-04, FA Amateur Cup 1926-27, 27-28. Athenian League 1928-29, 65-66, 66-67.
Isthmian League Division 2 North 1984-85. Essex Senior League 2001-02.

10 YEAR RECORD

00-01	01-02	02-03	03-04	04-05	05-06	06-07	07-08	08-09	09-10
ESen 10	ESen 1	Isth2 2	Isth1N 2	Isth P 5	Isth P 15	Isth P 15	Isth P 22	Isth1N 15	Isth1N 21

MALDON & TIPTREE

Chairman: Alan Brockhouse
Secretary: Phil Robinson (T) 0775 906 6636
(E) robbophil@hotmail.com

Additional Committee Members:
Frazer Snook

Manager: Brad King & Glen Knight
Programme Editor: John Wisbey (E) johnwisbey@btinternet.com

Unfortunately an up-to-date photograph was not available
at the time of going to press

Club Factfile

Founded: 2010 **Nickname:** The Hoops
Previous Names: Maldon Town (1975) and Tiptree United (1933) merged in 2010 to form today's club
Previous Leagues: First season as new club

Club Colours (change): Blue and red stripes/blue/blue

Ground: Wallace Binder Ground, Park Drive, Maldon CM9 6XX (T) 01621 853 762
Capacity: 2,800 **Seats:** 155 **Covered:** 300 **Clubhouse:** Yes **Shop:**
Previous Grounds:
Simple Directions
From M25 junction 28 travel north on A12 until A414 to Maldon. Turn right at Safeways roundabout, then over next two roundabouts. Ground is on the right.

Record Attendance: First season as new club
Record Victory: First season as new club
Record Defeat: First season as new club
Record Goalscorer: First season as new club
Record Appearances: First season as new club
Additional Records:

Senior Honours: First season as new club

10 YEAR RECORD

00-01	01-02	02-03	03-04	04-05	05-06	06-07	07-08	08-09	09-10

NEEDHAM MARKET

Chairman: David Bugg
Secretary: Mark Easlea **(T)** 0779 545 6502
(E) m.easlea@sky.com

Additional Committee Members:
Paul Collier, Alan Jopling, Wendy Hall

Manager: Danny Laws
Programme Editor: Mark Coleman & Bev Dorling **(E)** bev.mark@tesco.net

Club Factfile

Founded: 1919 **Nickname:**
Previous Names: None
Previous Leagues: Suffolk & Ipswich Senior, Eastern Counties

Club Colours (change): Red/black/red

Ground: Bloomfields, Quinton Road, Needham Market IP6 8DA **(T)** 01449 721 000
Capacity: 1,000 **Seats:** 250 **Covered:** 250 **Clubhouse:** Yes **Shop:** Yes
Previous Grounds:
Simple Directions
Quinton Road is off Barretts Lane which in turn is off Needham Market High Street.

Record Attendance: 750 v Ipswich Town - Suffolk Premier Cup 2007
Record Victory: Not known
Record Defeat: Not known
Record Goalscorer: Alvin King
Record Appearances: Not known
Additional Records:

Senior Honours: Suffolk Senior Cup 1989-90, 2004-05. Suffolk & Ipswich Senior League 1995-96. East Anglian Cup 2006-07.
Eastern Counties Premier Division 2009-10.

10 YEAR RECORD

00-01	01-02	02-03	03-04	04-05	05-06	06-07	07-08	08-09	09-10
EC1 4	EC1 5	EC1 11	EC1 14	EC1 2	ECP 6	ECP 4	ECP 2	ECP 3	ECP 1

POTTERS BAR TOWN

Chairman: Peter Waller
Secretary: Alan Evans **(T)** 0783 363 2965
(E) potters_bar_sec@hotmail.co.uk

Additional Committee Members:
Dave Quinlan

Manager: Adam Lee
Programme Editor: Alan Evans **(E)** potters_bar_sec@hotmail.co.uk

Photo: Alan Coomes.

Club Factfile

Founded: 1960 **Nickname:** Grace or Scholars
Previous Names:
Previous Leagues: Barnet & District 1960-65, North London Combination 1965-68, Herts Senior County 1968-91, Spartan South Midlands 1991-2005, Southern 2005-06

Club Colours (change): Maroon/white/white

Ground: The South Mimms Travel Stad., Parkfield, Watkins Rise, Pot.Bar EN6 1QN **(T)** 01707 654 833
Capacity: 2,000 **Seats:** 150 **Covered:** 250 **Clubhouse:** Yes **Shop:** Yes
Previous Grounds:
Simple Directions
M25 junction 24 enter Potters Bar along Southgate Road (A111) turn right into High Street at first lights (A1000) then left into The Walk after half a mile. Ground is 200 yards on the right - opposite Potters Bar Cricket Club.

Record Attendance: 268 v Wealdstone - FA Cup 1998 (4,000 watched a charity match in 1997)
Record Victory: Not known
Record Defeat: Not known
Record Goalscorer: Not known
Record Appearances: Not known
Additional Records:

Senior Honours: Spartan South Midlands League Premier 1996-97, 2004-05.

10 YEAR RECORD

00-01	01-02	02-03	03-04	04-05	05-06	06-07	07-08	08-09	09-10
SSM P 3	SSM P 13	SSM P 3	SSM P 4	SSM P 1	SthE 15	Isth1N 14	Isth1N 17	Isth1N 19	Isth1N 14

REDBRIDGE

Chairman: Jimmy Chapman & Dan Holloway
Secretary: Bob Holloway (T) 0789 069 9907
(E) bobholloway@redbridgefc.com

Additional Committee Members:
John Taylor, Len Cordell, Adam Silver, Tim Ley

Manager: Dave Ross & Kris Taylor
Programme Editor: Adam Silver (E) adammichaelsilver@hotmail.com

Back Row (L-R): Simon Peddie, Ben Turner, Jon Higgs, Fabio Jesus, Mason Durrell, Jake Whincup, Brian Alidjah, Theo Daniels, Carl Bruce. **Middle Row:** Sonny Read, Nathaniel Hibbert, Aaron Hunwicks, Ashley Marsh(coach), Jay Deverux(manager), Dave Ross(coach), Carl Conway,Andy Edmunds, Sonny Adams. **Front Row:** Joel Palmer, Ricki Mackin, Tom Laxton, Mark Nougher, Leon Diaczuk, George Alder.

Club Factfile

Founded: 1959 **Nickname:** Motormen
Previous Names: Ford United 1958-2004
Previous Leagues: Aetolian 1959-64, Greater London 1964-71, Metropolitan 1971-74, Essex Senior 1974-97, Isthmian 1997-2004, Conference 2004-05

Club Colours (change): Blue/blue/white

Ground: Oakside Stadium, Station Road, Barkingside, Ilford IG6 1NB (T) 020 8550 3611
Capacity: 3,000 **Seats:** 316 **Covered:** 1,000 **Clubhouse:** Yes **Shop:** Yes
Previous Grounds: Ford Sports & Social Club > 2000
Simple Directions
A12 from London, turn left off Eastern Avenue into Horns Road, Barkingside (Greengate). Right into Craven Gardens, right again into Carlton Drive and left into Station Road. Go over bridge and ground is on the right.
Adjacent to Barkingside Underground Station (Central Line).

Record Attendance: 58,000 v Bishop Auckland
Record Victory: Not known
Record Defeat: Not known
Record Goalscorer: Jeff Wood - 196
Record Appearances: Roger Bird
Additional Records:

Senior Honours: Aetolian League 1959-60, 61-62. Greater London League 1970-71. Essex Senior League 1991-92, 96-97.
Isthmian League Division 3 1998-99, Division 1 2001-02,

10 YEAR RECORD

00-01	01-02	02-03	03-04	04-05	05-06	06-07	07-08	08-09	09-10
Isth1 6	Isth1 1	Isth P 15	Isth P 13	Conf S 22	Isth P 22	Isth1N 16	Isth1N 3	Isth1N 8	Isth1N 18

ROMFORD

Chairman: Steve Gardener
Secretary: Colin Ewenson **(T)** 0797 371 7074
(E) ewenson@aol.com

Additional Committee Members:

Manager: Paul Martin
Programme Editor: Keith Preston **(E)** prestonruf@aol.com

Club Factfile

Founded: 1876 **Nickname:** Boro
Previous Names: Original club founded in 1876 folded during WW1, Reformed in 1929 folded again in 1978 and reformed in 1992
Previous Leagues: Athenian 1931-39, Isthmian 1945-59, 97-2002, Southern 1959-78, Essex Senior 1992-96, 2002-09

Club Colours (change): Blue and yellow/blue/blue

Ground: Aveley FC, The Mill Field, Mill Road, Aveley RM15 4SJ **(T)** 01708 365 940
Capacity: 4,000 **Seats:** 400 **Covered:** 400 **Clubhouse:** Yes **Shop:**
Previous Grounds:
Simple Directions
London - Southend A1306, turn into Sandy Lane at Aveley.

Record Attendance: 820 v Leatherhead - Isthmian Division 2
Record Victory: Not known
Record Defeat: Not known
Record Goalscorer: Danny Benstock
Record Appearances: S Horne - 234
Additional Records: Essex Senior League 1995-96, 2008-09. Isthmian League Division 2 1996-97.

Senior Honours:

10 YEAR RECORD

00-01	01-02	02-03	03-04	04-05	05-06	06-07	07-08	08-09	09-10
Isth1 21	Isth2 22	ESen 5	ESen 5	ESen 5	ESen 12	ESen 2	ESen 5	ESen 1	Isth1N 13

THAMESMEAD TOWN

Chairman: Mark Lee
Secretary: Miss Kellie Discipline (T) 0781 125 4792
(E) kelliedt@tinyworld.co.uk

Additional Committee Members:
David Joy, Robert Smith
Manager: Keith McMahon
Programme Editor: Robert Smith (E) sladegreen477994@aol.com

Back row (L-R): Alan Martin, Alan Woodward, Pedro Knight, Rikki Cable, Lee Cobourn, Chris Conneally, James Brown, Lew Watts, Richard Dimmock, Keith McMahon, Charlie McCarthy
Front row: Haribingi Grant, Junior Baker, Marc Merridan, Curtis Williams, Scot Mulholland, Nick Smith, Robbie Tarrant, Danny Moore, Peter Smith, Steve Wait. (Archive photo)

Club Factfile

Founded: 1970 **Nickname:** The Mead
Previous Names:
Previous Leagues: Spartan 1987-91, Kent 1991-2008

Club Colours (change): Green and white/green/green

Ground: Bayliss Avenue, Thamesmead, London SE28 8NJ (T) 020 8311 4211
Capacity: 400 **Seats:** 125 **Covered:** 125 **Clubhouse:** Yes **Shop:**
Previous Grounds:
Simple Directions
From the A2 take the A2018 exit toward Dartford/Wilmington, at the roundabout, take the 1st exit onto Shepherd's Ln/A2018. At the roundabout, take the 1st exit onto Rochester Way. Slight right at Swan Ln, continue onto Station Rd. At the roundabout, take the 1st exit onto Crayford Rd/A207, continue to follow A207, slight right to stay on A207, turn left at London Rd/A2000 continue to follow A2000, turn right at Perry St/A2000. At the roundabout, take the 2nd exit onto Northend Rd/A206, continue to follow A206. Go through 1 roundabout. At the roundabout, take the 2nd exit onto Bronze Age Way/A2016, continue to follow A2016. Go through 1 roundabout. At the roundabout, take the 2nd exit onto Eastern Way/A2016. Take the ramp. At the roundabout, take the 3rd exit onto Carlyle Rd/A2041. At the roundabout, take the 3rd exit onto Crossway. Turn right at Bayliss Ave, take the 1st left onto Chadwick Way. Ground will be on the left

Record Attendance: 400 v Wimbledon - Ground opening 1988
Record Victory: 9-0 v Kent Police - Kent League 19/04/1994
Record Defeat: Not known
Record Goalscorer: Delroy D'Oyley
Record Appearances: Not known
Additional Records:

Senior Honours: Kent Senior Trophy 2004-05. Kent Premier 2007-08

10 YEAR RECORD

00-01	01-02	02-03	03-04	04-05	05-06	06-07	07-08	08-09	09-10
Kent P 4	Kent P 4	Kent P 3	Kent P 2	Kent P 8	Kent P 3	Kent P 4	Kent P 1	Isth1N 18	Isth1N 7

TILBURY

Chairman: Robin Nash

Secretary: Lloyd Brown — **(T)** 01375 409 938 **(E)** lloyd55@blueyonder.co.uk

Additional Committee Members:
Craig Gibson, Marcus Hammond, George Hammond

Manager: Paul Vaughan

Programme Editor: Mark Kettlety — **(E)** sundayonly1@aol.com

Archive photo

Club Factfile

Founded: 1900 **Nickname:** The Dockers

Previous Names:

Previous Leagues: Grays & District/South Essex, Kent 1927-31, London, South Essex Combination (Wartime), Corinthian 1950-57, Delphian 1962-63, Athenian 1963-73, Isthmian 1973-2004, Essex Senior 2004-05

Club Colours (change): Black & white/black/red

Ground: Chadfields, St Chads Road, Tilbury, Essex RM18 8NL **(T)** 01375 843 093

Capacity: 4,000 **Seats:** 350 **Covered:** 1,000 **Clubhouse:** Yes **Shop:** No

Previous Grounds:

Simple Directions
A13 Southend bound go left at Chadwell St Mary's turning, then right after 400 metres and right again at roundabout (signed Tilbury). Right into St Chads Road after five miles, first right into Chadfields for ground.

Record Attendance: 5,500 v Gorleston - FA Cup 1949
Record Victory: Not known
Record Defeat: Not known
Record Goalscorer: Ross Livermore - 282 in 305 games
Record Appearances: Nicky Smith - 424 (1975-85)
Additional Records: Received £2,000 from Grays Athletic for Tony Macklin 1990 and from Dartford for Steve Connor 1985

Senior Honours: Athenian League 1968-69. Isthmian League Division 1 1975-76.
Essex Senior Cup x4.

10 YEAR RECORD

00-01	01-02	02-03	03-04	04-05	05-06	06-07	07-08	08-09	09-10
Isth2 10	Isth2 16	Isth1N 20	Isth1N 22	SthE 22	ESen 3	Isth1N 19	Isth1N 20	Isth1N 11	Isth1N 11

WALTHAM ABBEY

Chairman: Joe Collins
Secretary: Derek Bird (T) 0776 583 7246
(E) secretary@wafc.net

Additional Committee Members:

Manager: Paul Wickenden
Programme Editor: Derek Bird (E) secretary@wafc.net

Unfortunately an up-to-date photograph was not available at the time of going to press

Club Factfile

Founded: 1944 **Nickname:** Abbotts
Previous Names: Abbey Sports amalgamated with Beechfield Sports in 1974 to form Beechfields. Club then renamed to Waltham Abbey in 1976
Previous Leagues: Spartan, Essex & Herts Border, Essex Senior

Club Colours (change): Green and white hoops/white/green

Ground: Capershotts, Sewardstone Road, Waltham Abbey, Essex EN9 1LU (T) 01992 711 287
Capacity: 2,000 **Seats:** 300 **Covered:** 500 **Clubhouse:** Yes **Shop:** No
Previous Grounds: Capershotts
Simple Directions
Exit M25 at junction 26 and take 2nd left at roundabout into Honey Lane (A121). At the Sewardstone roundabout, take third right into Sewarstone Road which takes you over the M25. Ground is first right before cemetery.

Record Attendance: Not known
Record Victory: Not known
Record Defeat: Not known
Record Goalscorer: Not known
Record Appearances: Not known
Additional Records:

Senior Honours: London Spartan League Division 1 1977-78, Senior Division 1978-79.
London Senior Cup 1999. Essex Senior Cup 2004-05.

10 YEAR RECORD

00-01	01-02	02-03	03-04	04-05	05-06	06-07	07-08	08-09	09-10
	LonInt 1	ESen 10	ESen 6	ESen 3	ESen 2	Isth1N 10	Isth1N 14	Isth1N 4	Isth1N 21

WALTHAM FOREST

Chairman: Isaac Johnson

Secretary: Andy Perkins (T) 0774 898 3792 (E) andrewpeterperkins@hotmail.co.uk

Additional Committee Members:
Tony Brazier, Steve Howe

Manager: Tony Mercer

Programme Editor: Andy Perkins (E) andrewpeterperkins@hotmail.co.uk

Club Factfile

Founded: 1995 **Nickname:** The Stags

Previous Names: Leyton Pennant formed when Leyton and Walthamstow Pennant merged in 1995. Changed to Waltham Forest in 2003.

Previous Leagues: Isthmian 2003-04, Southern 2004-06

Club Colours (change): White/navy blue/navy blue

Ground: Ilford FC, Cricklefield Stadium, 486 High Road, Ilford, Essex IG1 1UE (T) 0208 514 8352

Capacity: 3,500 **Seats:** 216 **Covered:** Yes **Clubhouse:** Yes **Shop:**

Previous Grounds: Wadham Lodge

Simple Directions

Taking the A127, from the east travel towards London before coming to the traffic light controlled junction at Barley Lane, Goodmayes (B177) . Turn Left by taking the slip road and follow Barley Lane to its junction with the traffic light controlled High Road, Goodmayes (A118) (it is the first set of traffic control lights for traffic rather than pedestrians on that road). Turn Right and follow the road past Seven Kings station (which should be on your right) and on towards Ilford. The entrance to the ground is some 400 yards past the station with the Ilford Swimming Baths on the left being the point at which both coaches and those in cars or on foot should turn left into the car parks. Both on Saturday and after 6pm. during the week, the public car park is free of charge.

Record Attendance: Not known
Record Victory: Not known
Record Defeat: Not known
Record Goalscorer: Not known
Record Appearances: Not known
Additional Records:

Senior Honours: None

10 YEAR RECORD

00-01	01-02	02-03	03-04	04-05	05-06	06-07	07-08	08-09	09-10
Isth2 18	Isth2 6	Isth1N 22	Isth1N 16	SthE 9	SthE 8	Isth1N 8	Isth1N 19	Isth1N 20	Isth1N 16

WARE

Chairman: Aiden Mynott

Secretary: Fred Plume **(T)** 0796 702 2714 **(E)** fredplume@hotmail.co.uk

Additional Committee Members: Billy Shaw, Kieran Mynott

Manager: Tony Faulkner

Programme Editor: Mark Kettlety **(E)** sundayonly1@aol.com

Standing (L-R): Sara Ward (Physio), Barry Mason (Assistant Manager), Ben Andreos, Sam Rose, Steve Horsey, Michael Toner, Matt Turpin, Tom Hodge, Harry Ricketts, Grant Halsey, Ross Price, Kai Ramshaw, Matt Waldron, Dale Archer, Jason Coughlan, James Halsey, Stewart Margolis (Coach), Andy Crawford (Coach)
Sitting: Tamba Ngongou, Claudio Opondo-Mbai, Jimmie Berry, Glenn Harvey, Paul Halsey (Manager), Aiden Mynott (Chairman), Danny Wolf, Paul Abbott, Jermaine Ffolkes, Michael Sharman.

Club Factfile

Founded: 1892 **Nickname:** Blues

Previous Names:

Previous Leagues: East Herts, North Middlesex 1907-08, Herts County 1908-25, Spartan 1925-55, Delphian 1955-63, Athenian 1963-75

Club Colours (change): Blue and white/blue/blue

Ground: Wodson Park, Wadesmill Road, Ware, Herts SG12 0UQ **(T)** 01920 462 064

Capacity: 3,300 **Seats:** 500 **Covered:** 312 **Clubhouse:** Yes **Shop:** Yes

Previous Grounds: Highfields, Canons Park, London Road, Presdales Lower Park 1921-26

Simple Directions
A10 off junction A602 and B1001 turn right at roundabout after 300 yards and follow Ware sign, past Rank factory. Turn left at main road onto A1170 (Wadesmill Road) Stadium is on the right after 3/4 mile.

Record Attendance: 3,800 v Hendon - FA Amateur Cup 1956-57
Record Victory: 10-1 v Wood Green Town
Record Defeat: 0-11 v Barnet
Record Goalscorer: George Dearman scored 98 goals during 1926-27
Record Appearances: Gary Riddle - 654
Additional Records:

Senior Honours: Isthmian League Division 2 2005-06.
East Anglian Cup 1973-74. Herts Senior Cup x5.

10 YEAR RECORD

00-01	01-02	02-03	03-04	04-05	05-06	06-07	07-08	08-09	09-10
Isth3 11	Isth3 13	Isth2 8	Isth2 8	Isth2 10	Isth2 1	Isth1N 7	Isth1N 4	Isth1N 9	Isth1N 19

WINGATE & FINCHLEY

Chairman: Aron Sharpe
Secretary: David Thrilling (T) 0797 700 7746
(E) david.thrilling@soccerkits.com

Additional Committee Members:
Harvey Ackerman, Paul Lerman

Manager: David Norman

Programme Editor: Paul Lerman (E) paullerman@hotmail.com

Club Factfile

Founded: 1991 **Nickname:** Blues

Previous Names: Wingate (founded 1946) and Finchley (founded late 1800s) merged in 1991

Previous Leagues: South Midlands 1991-95, Isthmian 1995-2004, Southern 2004-2006

Club Colours (change): Blue/whiteblue

Ground: Harry Abraham Stadium, Summers Lane, Finchley N12 0PD (T) 020 8446 2217

Capacity: 8,500 **Seats:** 500 **Covered:** 500 **Clubhouse:** Yes **Shop:** No

Previous Grounds:

Simple Directions

The simplest way to get to The Harry Abrahams Stadium is to get on to the A406 North Circular Road.
If coming from the West (eg via M1), go past Henlys Corner (taking the left fork after the traffic lights) and then drive for about 1 mile. The exit to take is the one immediately after a BP garage. Take the slip road and then turn right at the lights onto the A1000.
If coming from the East (eg via A10, M11) take the A1000 turn off. At the end of the slip road turn left at the lights. Go straight over the next set of lights. Then after 100m pass through another set of lights, then at the next set of lights turn right into Summers Lane. The Abrahams Stadium is a few hundred metres down on the right hand side.

Record Attendance: Not known
Record Victory: Not known
Record Defeat: 0-9 v Edgware - Isthmian Division 2 15/01/2000
Record Goalscorer: Not known
Record Appearances: Not known
Additional Records:

Senior Honours: None

10 YEAR RECORD

00-01		01-02		02-03		03-04		04-05		05-06		06-07		07-08		08-09		09-10	
Isth3	15	Isth3	7	Isth1N	18	Isth1N	11	SthE	12	SthE	12	Isth1N	9	Isth1N	18	Isth1N	7	Isth1N	3

BOGNOR REGIS TOWN

Chairman: Dominic Reynolds
Secretary: Simon Cook (T) 07974 229 405 (E) sajcook2@aol.com

Additional Committee Members:
Roger Nash, Peter Martin

Manager: Jamie Howell & Darin Kilpatrick
Programme Editor: Rob Garforth (E) rjgarforth@hotmail.com

Unfortunately an up-to-date photograph was not available at the time of going to press

Club Factfile

Founded: 1883 **Nickname:** The Rocks
Previous Names:
Previous Leagues: West Sussex 1896-1926, Brighton & Hove District 1926-27, Sussex County 1927-72, Southern League 1972-81, Isthmian 1982-2004, Conference 2004-09

Club Colours (change): White with green trim/green/white

Ground: Nyewood Lane, Bognor Regis PO21 2TY (T) 01243 822 325
Capacity: 4,100 **Seats:** 350 **Covered:** 2,600 **Clubhouse:** Yes **Shop:** Yes
Previous Grounds:
Simple Directions
West along sea front from pier past Aldwick shopping centre then turn right into Nyewood Lane.

Record Attendance: 3,642 v Swnsea City - FA Cup 1st Round replay 1984
Record Victory: 24-0 v Littlehampton - West Sussex League 1913-14
Record Defeat: 0-19 v Shoreham - West Sussex League 1906-07
Record Goalscorer: Kevin Clements - 206
Record Appearances: Mick Pullen - 967 (20 seasons)
Additional Records: Paid £2,000 for Guy Rutherford 1995-96. Received £10,500 from Brighton & Hove for John Crumplin and Geoff Cooper, and from Crystal Palace for Simon Rodger.

Senior Honours: Sussex Professional Cup 1973-74. Sussex Senior Cup x9.

10 YEAR RECORD

00-01	01-02	02-03	03-04	04-05	05-06	06-07	07-08	08-09	09-10
Isth1 16	Isth1 4	Isth1S 2	Isth P 10	Conf S 9	Conf S 12	Conf S 12	Conf S 18	Conf S 21	Isth P 22

BURGESS HILL TOWN

Chairman: Kevin Newell
Secretary: Tim Spencer (T) 0781 264 2498
(E) timspencer57@hotmail.com

Additional Committee Members:
Gary Croydon, Allan Turpin

Manager: Gary Croydon
Programme Editor: Peter Ladds (E) peterladds@hotmail.com

Club Factfile

Founded: 1882 **Nickname:** Hillians
Previous Names:
Previous Leagues: Mid Sussex, Sussex County > 2003, Southern 2003-04

Club Colours (change): Yellow and black/black/yellow & black

Ground: Leylands Park, Maple Drive, Burgess Hill, West Sussex RH15 8DL (T) 01444 254 832
Capacity: 2,250 **Seats:** 307 **Covered:** Yes **Clubhouse:** Yes **Shop:** Yes
Previous Grounds:
Simple Directions
Turn east from A273 London Road into Leylands Road, take 4th left sign posted Leyland Park. Nearest station is Wivelsfield.

Record Attendance: 2,005 v AFC Wimbledon - Isthmian League Division 1 2004-05
Record Victory: Not known
Record Defeat: Not known
Record Goalscorer: Ashley Carr - 208
Record Appearances: Paul Williams - 499
Additional Records:

Senior Honours: Sussex County League x6 (Most recently 2001-02, 02-03).
Sussex Senior Cup 1883-84, 84-85, 85-86.

10 YEAR RECORD

00-01	01-02	02-03	03-04	04-05	05-06	06-07	07-08	08-09	09-10
SxC1 2	SxC1 1	SxC1 1	SthE 9	Isth1 10	Isth1 19	Isth1S 14	Isth1S 12	Isth1S 19	Isth1S 7

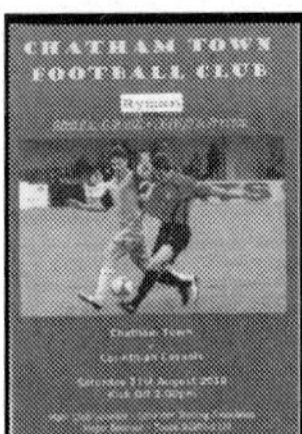

CHATHAM TOWN

Chairman: Jeff Talbot
Secretary: Henry Longhurst (T) 0796 746 5554
(E) h.longhurst@sky.com

Additional Committee Members:
Mike Green

Manager: Paul Foley
Programme Editor: Mike Green (E) mizzieg@live.co.uk

Terry Groom, David Hunt, Brad Potter, Jason Barton, Matt Solly, Nick Hegley, Barry Bell
Jon Hogg, Joe Fuller, Gary Cook, James Tedder GK, Adam Molloy GK, George Mitchell,
Uche Ibemere, Lee Maskell, Anthony Hogg
Ryan Laker, Callum O'Shea, Danny Penny (Capt), Paul Foley (Manager), Kevin Watson (Player Coach), Gary Ward (Vice Capt), Kevin Winchcombe, Ryan Restell

Club Factfile

Founded: 1882 **Nickname:** Chats
Previous Names: Chatham FC 1882-1974, Medway FC 1974-79
Previous Leagues: Southern 1894-1900, 1920-21, 27-29, 83-88, 2001-, Kent 1894-96, 1901-1905, 29-59, 68-83, 88-2001, Aetolian 1959-64, Metropolitan 1964-68

Club Colours (change): Red/black/black

Ground: Maidstone Road Sports Ground, Maidstone Road, Chatham ME4 6LR (T) 01634 812 194
Capacity: 2,000 **Seats:** 600 **Covered:** 600 **Clubhouse:** Yes **Shop:** Yes
Previous Grounds: Great Lines, Chatham 1882-90
Simple Directions
M2, A229 Chatham turn-off, follow signs to Chatham, ground is one and half miles on the right opposite garage. One mile from Chatham BR.

Record Attendance: 5,000 v Gillingham - 1980
Record Victory: Not known
Record Defeat: Not known
Record Goalscorer: Not known
Record Appearances: Not known
Additional Records: Received Transfer fee of £500

Senior Honours: Kent League 1894-95, 1903-04, 04-05, 71-72, 73-74, 75-76, 76-77, 79-80, 2000-01.
Kent Senior Cup 1888-89, 1904-05, 10-11, 18-19. Kent Senior Shield 1919-20.

10 YEAR RECORD

00-01	01-02	02-03	03-04	04-05	05-06	06-07	07-08	08-09	09-10
Kent P 1	SthE 16	SthE 15	SthE 13	SthE 11	SthE 17	Isth1S 16	Isth1S 18	Isth1N 10	Isth1S 17

CHIPSTEAD

Chairman: Neil Scarborough
Secretary: Heather Armstrong (T) 0752 544 3603
(E) armstrongsin35@aol.com

Additional Committee Members:
Terry Tiernan, Keith Harvey
Manager: Mark Tompkins
Programme Editor: Terry Tiernan (E) terry.antell@btopenworld.com

Club Factfile

Founded: 1906 **Nickname:** Chips
Previous Names:
Previous Leagues: Surrey Intermediate 1962-82, Surrey Premier 1982-86, Combined Counties 1986-2007

Club Colours (change): Green and white hoops/black/black

Ground: High Road, Chipstead, Surrey CR5 3SF (T) 01737 553 250
Capacity: 2,000 **Seats:** 150 **Covered:** 200 **Clubhouse:** Yes **Shop:** No
Previous Grounds:
Simple Directions
From the Brighton Road north bound, go left into Church Lane and left into Hogcross Lane. High Road is on the right.

Record Attendance: 1,170
Record Victory: Not known
Record Defeat: Not known
Record Goalscorer: Mick Nolan - 124
Record Appearances: Not known
Additional Records:

Senior Honours: Combined Counties Premier 1989-90, 2006-07.

10 YEAR RECORD

00-01		01-02		02-03		03-04		04-05		05-06		06-07		07-08		08-09		09-10	
CC	5	CC	3	CC	16	CCP	8	CCP	8	CCP	14	CCP	1	Isth1S	15	Isth1S	21	Isth1S	19

CORINTHIAN CASUALS

Chairman: Brian Vandervilt
Secretary: Brian Vandervilt (T) 0773 637 7498
(E) bvandervilt@pearsonmaddin.co.uk

Additional Committee Members:
John Kelvie, Rob Cavallini, Vincent Huggett

Manager: Brian Adamson

Programme Editor: Rob Cavallini (E) rob-cavallini@hotmail.com

Back Row (L-R) : Mark Towse, Jamie Reive, Chris Horwood, Tom Jelley, Richard Price, David Ocquaye, Dan Jackson, Byron Brown, Martin Dunne, Paul Hunt, Paul Smith.
Front Row: Ryan Hughes, Matt Smith, Jason Haniff, Tyrone Myton, Dale Hennessey, Russell Banyard, Colin Harris. (Archive photo)

Club Factfile

Founded: 1939 **Nickname:** Casuals
Previous Names: Casuals and Corinthians merged in 1939
Previous Leagues: Isthmian 1939-84, Spartan 1984-96, Combined Counties 1996-97

Club Colours (change): Chocolate and pink halves/navy blue/navy blue

Ground: King George's Field, Queen Mary Close, Hook Rise South, KT6 7NA **(T)** 0208 397 3368
Capacity: 2,000 **Seats:** 161 **Covered:** 700 **Clubhouse:** Yes **Shop:** Yes
Previous Grounds: Kennington Oval, shared with Kingstonian and Dulwich Hamlet

Simple Directions
A3 to Tolworth (Charrington Bowl) roundabout. Hook Rise is the slip road immediately past the Toby Jug Pub. Left under railway bridge after 1/4 mile and ground is on the right. 1/2 mile from Tolworth BR.

Record Attendance: Not known
Record Victory: Not known
Record Defeat: Not known
Record Goalscorer: Cliff West - 219
Record Appearances: Simon Shergold - 526
Additional Records:

Senior Honours: London Spartan League Senior Division 1985-86.

10 YEAR RECORD

00-01		01-02		02-03		03-04		04-05		05-06		06-07		07-08		08-09		09-10	
Isth3	5	Isth3	10	Isth1S	21	Isth1S	23	Isth1	13	Isth1	23	Isth1S	22	Isth1S	20	Isth1S	20	Isth1S	13

DULWICH HAMLET

Chairman: Jack Payne

Secretary: Martin Eede **(T)** 0795 739 5948 **(E)** eede.martin@gmail.com

Additional Committee Members:
John Lawrence

Manager: Gavin Rose

Programme Editor: John Lawrence **(E)** john_lawrence@hotmail.co.uk

Club Factfile

Founded: 1889 **Nickname:** Hamlet

Previous Names:

Previous Leagues: Camberwell 1894-97, Southern Suburban 1897-1900, 01-07, Dulwich 1900-01, Spartan 1907-08

Club Colours (change): Navy blue and pink/navy blue/navy blue

Ground: Champion Hill Stadium, Dog Kennell Hill, Edgar Kail Way SE22 8BD **(T)** 0207 274 8707

Capacity: 3,000 **Seats:** 500 **Covered:** 1,000 **Clubhouse:** Yes **Shop:** Yes

Previous Grounds: Woodwarde Rd 1893-95, College Farm 1895-96, Sunray Ave 1896-1902, Freeman's Gd, Champion Hill 1902-12, Champion Hill (old ground) 1912-92

Simple Directions

East Dulwich station, 200 yards. Denmark Hill station, 10 minutes walk. Herne Hill station then bus 37 stops near ground. Buses 40 & 176 from Elephant & Castle, 185 from Victoria.

Record Attendance: 1,835 v Southport - FA Cup 1998-99

Record Victory: Not known

Record Defeat: Not known

Record Goalscorer: Edgar Kail - 427 (1919-33)

Record Appearances: Reg Merritt - 576 (1950-66)

Additional Records: Received £35,000 from Charlton Athletic for Chris Dickson 2007

Senior Honours: FA Amateur Cup 1919-20, 31-32, 33-34, 36-37.
Isthmian League Premier Division x4, Division 1 1977-78. London Senior Cup x5. Surrey Senior Cup x16.
London Challenge Cup 1998-99.

10 YEAR RECORD

00-01	01-02	02-03	03-04	04-05	05-06	06-07	07-08	08-09	09-10
Isth P 22	Isth1 17	Isth1S 4	Isth1S 7	Isth1 15	Isth1 13	Isth1S 8	Isth1S 6	Isth1S 12	Isth1S 12

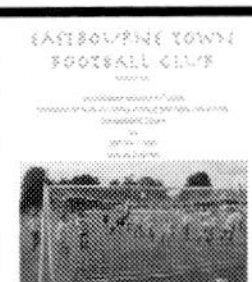

EASTBOURNE TOWN

Chairman: David Jenkins
Secretary: Mark Potter **(T)** 0772 084 6857
(E) markpotter@eastbournera.fsnet.co.uk

Additional Committee Members:
Robert Hylands
Manager: Danny Bloor
Programme Editor: Dave Pelling **(E)** pelling@hc26.freeserve.co.uk

Club Factfile

Founded: 1881 **Nickname:** Town
Previous Names:
Previous Leagues: Southern Amateur 1907-46, Corinthian 1960-63, Athenian 1963-76, Sussex County 1976-2007

Club Colours (change): Yellow/blue/blue

Ground: The Saffrons, Compton Place Road, Eastbourne BN21 1EA **(T)** 01323 723 734
Capacity: 3,000 **Seats:** 200 **Covered:** Yes **Clubhouse:** Yes **Shop:** No
Previous Grounds:
Simple Directions
Turn South West off the A22 into Grove Road.

Record Attendance: 7,378 v Hastings United - 1953
Record Victory: Not known
Record Defeat: Not known
Record Goalscorer: Not known
Record Appearances: Not known
Additional Records:

Senior Honours: Sussex County League 1976-77, Sussex Senior Cup x12.
Sussex RUR Charity Cup x3. AFA Senior Cup x2.

10 YEAR RECORD

00-01	01-02	02-03	03-04	04-05	05-06	06-07	07-08	08-09	09-10
SxC1 19	SxC2 4	SxC2 2	SxC1 5	SxC1 10	SxC1 5	SxC1 1	Isth1S 19	Isth1S 13	Isth1S 22

FAVERSHAM TOWN

Chairman: Bob Mason
Secretary: Mrs Wendy Walker (T) 0778 963 8367
(E) wendy-walker@hotmail.co.uk
Additional Committee Members:
Tony Gray
Manager: Justin Luchford
Programme Editor: Mark Downs (E) lilywhite.editor@googlemail. com

Unfortunately an up-to-date photograph was not available at the time of going to press

Club Factfile

Founded: 1884 **Nickname:** Lillywhites
Previous Names: None
Previous Leagues: Metropolitan, Athenian, Kent

Club Colours (change): White/black/black

Ground: Salters Lane, Faversham Kent ME13 8ND (T) 01795 591 900
Capacity: 2,000 **Seats:** 200 **Covered:** 1,800 **Clubhouse:** Yes **Shop:**
Previous Grounds:
Simple Directions
From the M25 continue onto M26 9.9 miles. Continue onto M20 8.1 miles. Exit onto Slip Road (M20 J7) 0.2 miles. Bear left 0.1 miles. Continue onto Sittingbourne Road A249 0.9 miles. Bear right onto Detling Hill A249 4.6 miles. Bear left 0.1 miles. Continue onto Slip Road (M2 J5) 0.4 miles. Continue onto M2 10.5 miles. Exit onto Slip Road (M2 J6) 0.1 miles. Turn left onto Ashford Road A251 0.5 miles. Turn right onto Canterbury Road A2 0.2 miles. Turn right onto Westwood Place 0.1 miles.

Record Attendance: Not Known
Record Victory: Not Known
Record Defeat: Not Known
Record Goalscorer: Not Known
Record Appearances: Not Known
Additional Records:

Senior Honours: Kent League 1969-70, 70-71, 89-90, 2009-10.

10 YEAR RECORD

00-01	01-02	02-03	03-04	04-05	05-06	06-07	07-08	08-09	09-10
Kent P 16	Kent P 16	Kent P 16				Kent P 12	Kent P 13	Kent P 4	Kent P 1

FLEET TOWN

Chairman: Tony Madden
Secretary: John Goodyear (T) 0796 870 1797
(E) goodyear.john@btinternet.com
Additional Committee Members:
Steve Cantle, Lyn Bevan
Manager: Steve Mellor
Programme Editor: Matt Thorne (E) thornematthew@hotmail.com

Unfortunately an up-to-date photograph was not available
at the time of going to press

Club Factfile

Founded: 1947 **Nickname:** The Blues
Previous Names:
Previous Leagues: Hampshire 1961-77, Athenian, Combined Counties, Chiltonian, Wessex 1989-95, 2000-02, Southern 1995-2000, 02-04, 07-08, Isthmian 2004-07
Club Colours (change): All sky blue and navy

Ground: Calthorpe Park, Crookham Road, Fleet, Hants GU51 5FA (T) 01252 623 804
Capacity: 2,000 **Seats:** 250 **Covered:** 250 **Clubhouse:** Yes **Shop:** Yes
Previous Grounds:
Simple Directions
Leave the M3 at junction 4A. Follow signs to Fleet via A3013. At 5th roundabout (a T-junction) turn left over railway bridge. Carry on past Oatsheaf Pub on the right, ground is a further 1/4 mile on the right.

Record Attendance: 1,336 v AFC Wimbledon - 08/01/2005
Record Victory: 15-0 v Petersfield - 26/12/1994
Record Defeat: 0-7 v Bashley - 12/04/2004
Record Goalscorer: Mark Frampton - 428
Record Appearances: Mark Frampton - 250
Additional Records: Paid £3,000 to Aldershot for Mark Russell

Senior Honours: Wessex League 1994-95.

10 YEAR RECORD

00-01	01-02	02-03	03-04	04-05	05-06	06-07	07-08	08-09	09-10
Wex 4	Wex 2	SthE 20	SthE 22	Isth1 19	Isth1 14	Isth1S 5	Sthsw 2	Isth1S 3	Isth1S 6

GODALMING TOWN

Chairman: Kevin Young
Secretary: Mrs Jane Phillips (T) 0788 993 3512
(E) j.phillips12@ntlworld.com

Additional Committee Members:
Glenn Moulton, Ian Curtis

Manager: Chuck Martini
Programme Editor: Glenn Moulton (E) info@godalmingtownfc.co.uk

Archive photo

Club Factfile

Founded: 1950 **Nickname:** The G's
Previous Names: Godalming & Farncombe United, Godalming & Guildford
Previous Leagues: Combined Counties, Southern 2006-08

Club Colours (change): Yellow/green/yellow

Ground: Wey Court, Mead Row, Guildford, Surrey GU7 3JE (T) 01483 417 520
Capacity: 3,000 **Seats:** 200 **Covered:** 400 **Clubhouse:** Yes **Shop:** Yes
Previous Grounds:

Simple Directions
A3100 from Guildford, pass the Manor Inn on the left and then the petrol station on the right. Wey Court is 50 yards further along the road on the right hand side.
A3100 from Godalming, pass the Three Lions pub on the left and then turn left into Wey Court immediately after the Leathern Bottle pub.
Parking: Please note that the club car park is for players and officials only. Spectators are asked to use the public car park next door to the ground.

Record Attendance: 1,305 v AFC Wimbledon - 2002
Record Victory: Not Known
Record Defeat: Not Known
Record Goalscorer: Not Known
Record Appearances: Not Known
Additional Records:

Senior Honours: Combined Counties League Premier Division 1983-84, 2005-06.

10 YEAR RECORD

00-01	01-02	02-03	03-04	04-05	05-06	06-07	07-08	08-09	09-10
CC 12	CC 17	CC 7	CCP 11	CCP 4	CCP 1	Isth1S 22	Sthsw 12	Isth1S 9	Isth1S 4

HORSHAM YMCA

Chairman: Mick Browning
Secretary: Andy Flack (T) 0777 585 7392
(E) andy.flack@horsham.gov.uk

Additional Committee Members:
Bob Brading, Ron Moulding

Manager: Colin Jenkinson
Programme Editor: Alan Maguire (E) alan.maguire@hotmail.co.uk

Club Factfile

Founded: 1898 **Nickname:** YM's
Previous Names:
Previous Leagues: Horsham & District, Brighton & Hove, Mid Sussex, Sussex County

Club Colours (change): White/black/red

Ground: Gorings Mead, Horsham, West Sussex RH13 5BP (T) 01403 252 689
Capacity: 1,575 **Seats:** 150 **Covered:** 200 **Clubhouse:** Yes **Shop:** No
Previous Grounds:
Simple Directions
From the east, take A281 (Brighton Road) and the ground is on the left and sign posted opposite Gorings Mead.

Record Attendance: 950 v Chelmsford City - FA Cup 2000
Record Victory: 21-1 v Littlehampton - October 2003
Record Defeat: Not Known
Record Goalscorer: Danny Cherryman. Nick Flint scored 10 goals in the clubs record 21-1 win over Littlehampton.
Record Appearances: Gerry Marsh, Peter Durrant and Jason Dumbrill all 500+
Additional Records:

Senior Honours: Sussex League 2004-05, 05-06.
John O'Hara Cup 2001-02.

10 YEAR RECORD

00-01		01-02		02-03		03-04		04-05		05-06		06-07		07-08		08-09		09-10	
SxC1	5	SxC1	10	SxC1	3	SxC1	13	SxC1	1	SxC1	1	Isth1S	9	Isth1S	21	SxC1	3	Isth1S	11

LEATHERHEAD

Chairman: Peter Ashdown
Secretary: Geoff Corner **(T)** 0776 283 1142
(E) gseacorner@btinternet.com

Additional Committee Members:
Richard Wilkinson, John Loveridge

Manager: Mick Sullivan
Programme Editor: Rod Ellis **(E)** rodellis83@hotmail.com

Back row (L-R): Adam Goodwell, Jon Boswell, Dan Dean, Kwabena Agyei, Elliott Thompson, Adrian Jones, Chico Ramos, Antony Russell, Bentley Graham, Gabriel Odunaike, Greg Andrews, Jack Macleod.
Front row: Tom Williams, Kevin Terry, Liam Pestle, Darryl Cooper-Smith, Tommy Hutchings, Mark Simmons, Chris Boulter, Marc Elston, Jon Coke, Steve Barilli, Rob Stevenson, Arnold Okirur.

Club Factfile

Founded: 1946 **Nickname:** The Tanners
Previous Names:
Previous Leagues: Surrey Senior 1946-50, Metropolitan 1950-51, Delphian 1951-58, Corinthian 1958-63, Athenian 1963-72

Club Colours (change): Green/white/green

Ground: Fetcham Grove, Guildford Road, Leatherhead, Surrey KT22 9AS **(T)** 01372 360 151
Capacity: 3,400 **Seats:** 200 **Covered:** 45 **Clubhouse:** Yes **Shop:** Yes
Previous Grounds:
Simple Directions
M25 junction 9 to Leatherhead, follow signs to Leisure Centre, ground adjacent. Half a mile from Leatherhead BR.

Record Attendance: 5,500 v Wimbledon - 1976
Record Victory: 13-1 v Leyland Motors - Surrey Senior League 1946-47
Record Defeat: 1-11 v Sutton United
Record Goalscorer: Steve Lunn scored 46 goals during 1996-97
Record Appearances: P Caswell - 200
Additional Records: Paid £1,500 to Croydon for B Salkeld
Received £1,500 from Croydon for B Salkeld

Senior Honours: Athenian League 1963-64.
Surrey Senior Cup 1968-69. Isthmian League cup 1977-78.

10 YEAR RECORD

00-01	01-02	02-03	03-04	04-05	05-06	06-07	07-08	08-09	09-10
Isth1 20	Isth2 11	Isth1S 14	Isth1S 13	Isth1 7	Isth1 10	Isth1S 11	Isth1S 17	Isth1S 15	Isth1S 5

MERSTHAM

Chairman: Ted Hickman
Secretary: Richard Baxter (T) 0772 029 0027
(E) richardbaxter01@hotmail.com

Additional Committee Members:
Kevin Austen, Mr M Richardson

Manager: Graeme Banyard
Programme Editor: Sarah Fish (E) sarah.fish@ntlworld.com

Club Factfile

Founded: 1905 **Nickname:** Moatsiders
Previous Names:
Previous Leagues: Redhill & District, Surrey Senior 1964-78, London Spartan 1978-84, Combined Counties 1984-2008

Club Colours (change): Amber & black/black/amber

Ground: Moatside Stadium, Weldon Way, Merstham, Surrey RH1 3QB (T) 01737 644 046
Capacity: 2,500 **Seats:** 174 **Covered:** 100 **Clubhouse:** Yes **Shop:** No
Previous Grounds:
Simple Directions
Leave Merstham village (A23) by School Hill, take 5th right (Weldon Way). Clubhouse and car park on the right. Ten minutes walk from Merstham BR.

Record Attendance: 1,587 v AFC Wimbledon - Combined Counties League 09/11/2002
Record Victory: Not Known
Record Defeat: Not Known
Record Goalscorer: Not Known
Record Appearances: Not Known
Additional Records:

Senior Honours: Combined Counties League Premier Division 2007-08.

10 YEAR RECORD

00-01	01-02	02-03	03-04	04-05	05-06	06-07	07-08	08-09	09-10
CC 8	CC 20	CC 17	CCP 12	CCP 16	CCP 2	CCP 2	CCP 1	Isth1S 8	Isth1S 16

METROPOLITAN POLICE

Chairman: Des Flanders
Secretary: Tony Brooking (T) 0796 133 4523
(E) tony.brooking@met.police.uk

Additional Committee Members:
Cliff Travis, Graham Fulcher

Manager: Jim Cooper
Programme Editor: Cliff Travis (E) cliffordtravis@hotmail.com

Back row, left to right: Jamal Carr, Eddie Smith, Craig Watkins, Vernon Francis, Neil Lampton, Rob Smith, Elliot Taylor.
Middle row: Paul Barrowcliff, Steve Noakes, Dominic O'Shea, Adam Broomhead, Mo Maan, Dave Smalley, Daniel Gwyther, James Field, Chris Bourne, Chris MacPherson.
Front row: Craig Brown, Steve Sutherland, Stuart Mackenzie, Gavin MacPherson(assistant manager), Jim Cooper(manager),John Nicholson, Nicky Humphrey, Tyron Smith.

Club Factfile

Founded: 1919 **Nickname:** The Blues
Previous Names:
Previous Leagues: Spartan 1928-60, Metropolitan 1960-71, Southern 1971-78

Club Colours (change): All blue

Ground: Imber Court, Ember Lane, East Molesey, Surrey KT8 0BT (T) 0208 398 7358
Capacity: 3,000 **Seats:** 297 **Covered:** 1,800 **Clubhouse:** Yes **Shop:** No
Previous Grounds:
Simple Directions
From London A3 take A309 towards Scilly Isles roundabout then right into Hampton Court Way. Left at first roundabout into Imber Court Road. Ground is in 300 yards.

Record Attendance: 4,500 v Kingstonian - FA Cup 1934
Record Victory: 10-1 v Tilbury - 1995
Record Defeat: 1-11 v Wimbledon - 1956
Record Goalscorer: Mario Russo
Record Appearances: Pat Robert
Additional Records:

Senior Honours: Spartan League x7.
Middlesex Senior Cup 1927-28, Surrey Senior Cup 1932-33. London Senior Cup 2009-10.

10 YEAR RECORD

00-01	01-02	02-03	03-04	04-05	05-06	06-07	07-08	08-09	09-10
Isth2 13	Isth2 13	Isth1S 23	Isth1S 20	Isth1 5	Isth1 4	Isth1S 6	Isth1S 4	Isth1S 4	Isth1S 10

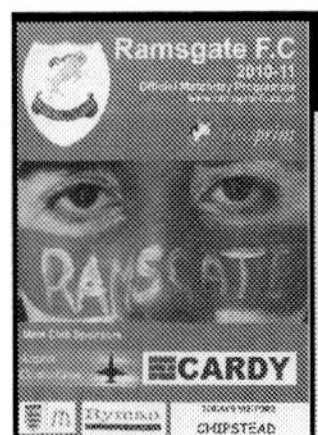

RAMSGATE

Chairman: Richard Lawson
Secretary: Martin Able (T) 0795 899 3959
(E) secretary@ramsgate-fc.co.uk

Additional Committee Members:
Kevin Barham, John Vahid

Manager: Jim Ward
Programme Editor: Martin Able (E) secretary@ramsgate-fc.co.uk

Back Row L-R): Ada Hubbard, Tom Tsangarides, Warren Schulz, Luke Wheatley, Brett Mills, Conor Quinn, Liam Quinn, Gary Lockyer, Richard Langley. (Middle Row: Paul Axon, Ryan Harker, Curtis Winnett, Joe Taylor, Ashley Groombridge, Andy Hadden, Dan Dolton. Front Row: Mark Lovell, Mitchell Sherwood, Ben Laslett, Foy Manoharan-Turner, Richard Lawson, Jim Ward, Ollie Gray, James Gregory, Aaron Beech.

Club Factfile

Founded: 1945 **Nickname:** Rams
Previous Names: Ramsgate Athletic > 1972
Previous Leagues: Kent 1949-59, 1976-2005, Southern 1959-76

Club Colours (change): All red

Ground: Southwood Stadium, Prices Avenue, Ramsgate, Kent CT11 0AN (T) 01843 591 662
Capacity: 5,000 **Seats:** 400 **Covered:** 600 **Clubhouse:** Yes **Shop:** Yes
Previous Grounds:
Simple Directions
Approach Ramsgate via A299 (Canterbury/London) or A256 (Dover/Folkestone) to Lord of Manor roundabout.
Follow the signpost to Ramsgate along Canterbury Road East, counting via 2nd exit of the 1st roundabout.
At the 2nd roundabout, continue towards Ramsgate on London Road (2nd exit).
Take the 3rd turning on the left, into St Mildred's Avenue, then 1st left into Queen Bertha Road.
After the right hand bend, take left into Southwood Road, and 1st left into Prices Ave. The stadium is at the end of Prices Avenue.

Record Attendance: 5,200 v Margate - 1956-57
Record Victory: 11-0 & 12-1 v Canterbury City - Kent League 2000-01
Record Defeat: Not Known
Record Goalscorer: Mick Willimson
Record Appearances: Not Known
Additional Records:

Senior Honours: Kent League Division 1 1949-50, 55-56, 56-57, Premier League 1998-99, 2004-05, Kent League Cup x6.
Isthmian League Division 1 2005-06, League Cup 2007-08.
Kent Senior Cup 1963-64, Kent Senior Trophy x3.

10 YEAR RECORD

00-01	01-02	02-03	03-04	04-05	05-06	06-07	07-08	08-09	09-10
Kent P 5	Kent P 6	Kent P 5	Kent P 9	Kent P 1	Isth1 1	Isth P 8	Isth P 5	Isth P 22	Isth1S 14

SITTINGBOURNE

Chairman: Andy Spice
Secretary: John Pitts (T) 0750 513 4135
(E) johncp49@hotmail.com

Additional Committee Members:
Peter Pitts

Manager: Gary Abbott
Programme Editor: Lee Richardson (E)

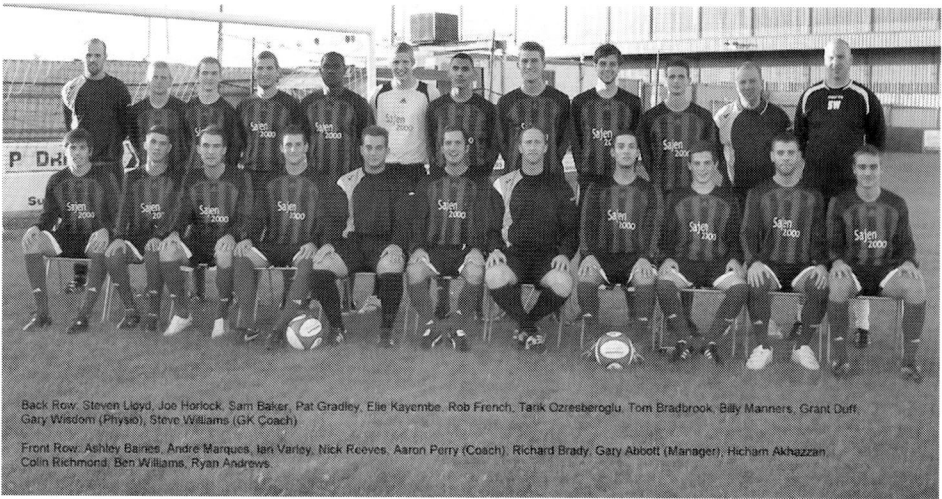

Back Row: Steven Lloyd, Joe Horlock, Sam Baker, Pat Gradley, Elie Kayembe, Rob French, Tarik Ozresberoglu, Tom Bradbrook, Billy Manners, Grant Duff, Gary Wisdom (Physio), Steve Williams (GK Coach).

Front Row: Ashley Baines, Andre Marques, Ian Varley, Nick Reeves, Aaron Perry (Coach), Richard Brady, Gary Abbott (Manager), Hicham Akhazzan, Colin Richmond, Ben Williams, Ryan Andrews.

Club Factfile

Founded: 1886 **Nickname:** Brickies
Previous Names: Sittingbourne United 1881-86
Previous Leagues: Kent 1894-1905, 1909-27, 30-39, 45-59, 68-91, South Eastern 1905-09, Southern 1927-30, 59-67

Club Colours (change): Red with black stripes/black/black

Ground: Bourne Park, Central Park Stadium, Eurolink, Sittingbourne ME10 3SB (T) 01795 435 077
Capacity: 3,000 **Seats:** 300 **Covered:** 600 **Clubhouse:** Yes **Shop:** Yes
Previous Grounds: Sittingbourne Rec. Ground 1881-90, Gore Court Cricket Grd 1890-92, The Bull Ground 1892-1990

Simple Directions
Through Sittingbourne on the main A2, club sign posted clearly and regularly from both east and west. One mile from Sittingbourne BR station.

Record Attendance: 5,951 v Tottenham Hotspur - Friendly 26/01/1993
Record Victory: Not Known
Record Defeat: Not Known
Record Goalscorer: Not Known
Record Appearances: Not Known
Additional Records: Paid £20,000 to Ashford Town for Lee McRobert 1993
Received £210,000 from Millwall for Neil Emblem and Michael Harle 1993

Senior Honours: Southern League Southern Division 1992-93, 95-96. Kent League x7, League cup x4.
Kent Senior Cup 1901-02, 28-29, 29-30, 57-58.

10 YEAR RECORD

00-01	01-02	02-03	03-04	04-05	05-06	06-07	07-08	08-09	09-10
SthE 21	SthE 17	SthE 12	SthE 10	SthE 19	SthE 18	Isth1S 10	Isth1S 9	Isth1S 6	Isth1S 9

WALTON & HERSHAM

Chairman: Alan Smith
Secretary: Michael Groom (T) 0771 023 0694 (E) mhgroom@aol.com
Additional Committee Members:
Mervyn Rees, Steve Hudd, John Crawford, Mark Massingham
Manager: John Crumplin
Programme Editor: Mark Massingham (E) mark@waltonfc.freeserve.co.uk

Archive photo

Club Factfile

Founded: 1896 **Nickname:** Swans
Previous Names:
Previous Leagues: Surrey Senior, Corinthian 1945-50, Athenian 1950-71

Club Colours (change): All red

Ground: Sports Ground, Stompond Lane, Walton-on-Thames KT12 1HF (T) 01932 245 263
Capacity: 5,000 **Seats:** 400 **Covered:** 2,500 **Clubhouse:** Yes **Shop:** Yes
Previous Grounds:
Simple Directions
From Walton Bridge go over and along New Zealand Avenue, down one way street and up A244 Hersham Road. Ground is second on the right.

Record Attendance: 10,000 v Crook Town - FA Amateur Cup 6th Round 1951-52
Record Victory: 10-0 v Clevedon - FA Amateur Cup 1960
Record Defeat: 3-11 v Kingstonian - Surrey Shield 1958
Record Goalscorer: Reg Sentance - 220 (During 11 seasons)
Record Appearances: Terry Keen - 449 (During 11 seasons)
Additional Records: Paid £6,000. Received £150,000 from Bristol Rovers for Nathan Ellington 1999.

Senior Honours: Athenian League 1968-69.
FA Amateur Cup 1972-73. Barassi Cup 1973-74.
Surrey Senior Cup x6. London Senior Cup.

10 YEAR RECORD

00-01	01-02	02-03	03-04	04-05	05-06	06-07	07-08	08-09	09-10
Isth1 17	Isth1 13	Isth1S 7	Isth1S 9	Isth1 2	Isth P 9	Isth P 19	Isth1S 10	Isth1S 14	Isth1S 8

WALTON CASUALS

Chairman: Graham James
Secretary: Gus Schofield (T) 0782 469 6705
(E) g.schofield1@ntlworld.com

Additional Committee Members:
Stuart Roberts, David Symonds

Manager: Neil Shipperley
Programme Editor: Stuart Roberts (E) sroberts@cattronuk.com

Archive photo

Club Factfile

Founded: 1948 **Nickname:** The Stags
Previous Names:
Previous Leagues: Surrey Intermediate, Surrey Senior, Suburban, Surrey Premier, Combined Counties

Club Colours (change): Tangerine/black/black

Ground: Franklyn Road Sports Ground, Waterside Drive, Walton KT12 2JP **(T)** 01932 787 749
Capacity: 2,000 **Seats:** 153 **Covered:** 403 **Clubhouse:** Yes **Shop:** Yes
Previous Grounds:
Simple Directions
Left off Terrace Road at first major roundabout out of Walton centre. Ground is next to The Xcel Leisure Centre.

Record Attendance: 1,748 v AFC Wimbledon - Combined Counties League 12/04/2004
Record Victory: Not Known
Record Defeat: Not Known
Record Goalscorer: Greg Ball - 77
Record Appearances: Craig Carley - 234
Additional Records:

Senior Honours: Combined Counties League Premier Division 2004-05, League Cup 1999-2000.

10 YEAR RECORD

00-01	01-02	02-03	03-04	04-05	05-06	06-07	07-08	08-09	09-10
CC 7	CC 9	CC 18	CCP 7	CCP 1	Isth1 15	Isth1S 17	Isth1S 16	Isth1S 17	Isth1S 21

WHITEHAWK

Chairman: Wally Sweetman
Secretary: John Rosenblatt (T) 07724 519 370
(E) lee.brace@bracsoakley.co.uk

Additional Committee Members:
Lee Brace, Drew Swinston, Keith Fowler

Manager: Darren Freeman
Programme Editor: Drew Swainston (E) drew.swainston@hotmail.com

Unfortunately an up-to-date photograph was not available at the time of going to press

Club Factfile

Founded: 1945 **Nickname:** Hawks
Previous Names: Whitehawk & Manor Farm Old Boys untill 1958
Previous Leagues: Brighton & Hove District, Sussex County > 2010

Club Colours (change): All red (All blue)

Ground: Enclosed Ground, East Brighton Park, Wilson Avenue, Brighton BN2 5TS **(T)** 01273 609 736
Capacity: 3,000 **Seats:** **Covered:** 500 **Clubhouse:** Yes **Shop:** No
Previous Grounds:
Simple Directions
From N (London) on M23/A23 – after passing Brighton boundary sign & twin pillars join A27 (sp Lewes); immediately after passing Sussex University (on L) leave A27 via slip rd at sp B2123, Falmer, Rottingdean; at roundabout at top of slip rd turn R onto B2123 (sp Falmer, Rottingdean); in 2m at traffic lights in Woodingdean turn R by Downs Hotel into Warren Road; in about 1m at traffic lights turn L into Wilson Ave, crossing racecourse; in 1¼m turn L at foot of hill (last turning before traffic lights) into East Brighton Park; follow lane for the ground.

Record Attendance: 2,100 v Bognor Regis Town - FA Cup 1988-89
Record Victory: Not known
Record Defeat: Not known
Record Goalscorer: Billy Ford
Record Appearances: Ken Powell - 1,103
Additional Records:

Senior Honours: Sussex County League Division 1 1961-62, 63-64, 83-84, 2009-10. Division 2 1967-68, 80-81.
Sussex Senior Cup 1950-51, 61-62 Sussex RUR Charity Cup x3.

10 YEAR RECORD

00-01	01-02	02-03	03-04	04-05	05-06	06-07	07-08	08-09	09-10
SxC1 17	SxC1 13	SxC1 2	SxC1 8	SxC1 3	SxC1 3	SxC1 2	SxC1 2	SxC1 13	SxC1 1

WHITSTABLE TOWN

Chairman: Joseph Brownett
Secretary: Alan Gower (T) 0798 086 5637
(E) agower@tiscali.co.uk
Additional Committee Members:
Philip Gurr, Anthony Rouse
Manager: Mark Lane
Programme Editor: Andy Short (E) andy.short2@btinternet.com

Club Factfile

Founded: 1886 **Nickname:** Oystermen or Natives
Previous Names:
Previous Leagues: East Kent 1897-1909, Kent 1909-59, Aetolian 1959-60, Kent Amateur 1960-62, 63-64, South East Anglian 1962-63, Greater London 1964-67, Kent 1967-2007
Club Colours (change): Red and white/white/red and white

Ground: Belmont Ground, Belmont Road, Belmont, Whitstable CT5 1QP (T) 01227 266 012
Capacity: 2,000 **Seats:** 500 **Covered:** 1,000 **Clubhouse:** Yes **Shop:** Yes
Previous Grounds:
Simple Directions
From Thanet Way (A299) turn left at Tesco roundabout and Millstrood Road. Ground at bottom of road, 400 yards from Whitstable BR station.

Record Attendance: 2,500 v Gravesend & Northfleet - FA Cup 19/10/1987
Record Victory: Not known
Record Defeat: Not known
Record Goalscorer: Barry Godfrey
Record Appearances: Frank Cox - 429 (1950-60)
Additional Records:

Senior Honours: Kent Amateur Cup 1928-29.
Kent League 2006-07, League Trophy 2006-07.

10 YEAR RECORD

00-01		01-02		02-03		03-04		04-05		05-06		06-07		07-08		08-09		09-10	
Kent P	8	Kent P	10	Kent P	6	Kent P	5	Kent P	3	Kent P	5	Kent P	10	Isth1S	14	Isth1S	16	Isth1S	18

WHYTELEAFE

Chairman: Mark Coote
Secretary: Edward Lucas — **(T)** 0771 085 9034 **(E)** elucas001@aol.com

Additional Committee Members:
Brian Davis, Graham Douce

Manager: Nicky English
Programme Editor: Chris Layton — **(E)** chris.layton@ntlworld.com

Archive photo

Club Factfile

Founded: 1946 **Nickname:** Leafe
Previous Names:
Previous Leagues: Caterham & Edenbridge, Croydon, Thornton Heath & District, Surrey Intermediate (East) 1954-58, Surrey Senior 1958-75, Spartan 1975-81, Athenian 1981-84

Club Colours (change): Green/black/black

Ground: 15 Church Road, Whyteleafe, Surrey CR3 0AR **(T)** 0208 660 5491
Capacity: 5,000 **Seats:** 400 **Covered:** 600 **Clubhouse:** Yes **Shop:** Yes
Previous Grounds:

Simple Directions
FROM THE M25 AND THE SOUTH: From Junction 6 of the M26 head north along the A22 (signposted to London, Croydon and Caterham). At Wapses Lodge Roundabout, the Ann Summers building is clearly visible opposite, take the third exit. Take the first left adjacent to Whyteleafe South railway station and cross the level crossing. Fork right after 200 yards into Church Road. The ground is a quarter of a mile down the road on the right.
FROM THE NORTH: From Purley Cross (where the A23 crosses the A22), head south signposted to Eastbourne and the M25. Pass 'My Old China' (Chinese restaurant) on your right and continue under a railway bridge. Follow the A22 through Kenley and into Whyteleafe. At the first roundabout (with Whyteleafe Tavern opposite), turn right and cross a level crossing adjacent to Whyteleafe Station. Take first left into Church Road keeping St Luke Church to your right. The ground is a quarter of a mile up the road on the left.

Record Attendance: 2,210 v Chester City - FA Cup 1999-2000
Record Victory: Not known
Record Defeat: Not known
Record Goalscorer: Not known
Record Appearances: Not known
Additional Records: Paid £1,000 to Carshalton Athletic for Gary Bowyer
Received £25,000 for Steve Milton

Senior Honours: Surrey Senior Cup 1968-69.

10 YEAR RECORD

00-01	01-02	02-03	03-04	04-05	05-06	06-07	07-08	08-09	09-10
Isth1 9	Isth1 20	Isth1S 5	Isth1S 17	Isth1 9	Isth1 18	Isth1S 20	Isth1S 11	Isth1S 18	Isth1S 15

WORTHING

Chairman: Dave Agnew & Mrs Deborah McKail

Secretary: Gareth Nicholas (T) 01903 239 575 (E) garethbnicholas@hotmail.co.uk

Additional Committee Members:
Paul Long, Monty Hollis

Manager: Chris White

Programme Editor: Jon Justice (E) jon@worthingfc.com

Unfortunately an up-to-date photograph was not available at the time of going to press

Club Factfile

Founded: 1886 **Nickname:** Rebels

Previous Names:

Previous Leagues: West Sussex 1896-1904, 1905-14, 19-20, Brighton Hove & District 1919-20, Sussex County 1920-40, Corinthian 1948-63, Athenian 1963-77

Club Colours (change): All red

Ground: Woodside Road, Worthing, West Sussex BN14 7HQ (T) 01903 239 575

Capacity: 3,650 **Seats:** 500 **Covered:** 1,500 **Clubhouse:** Yes **Shop:**

Previous Grounds:

Simple Directions
A24 or A27 to Grove Lodge roundabout. A24 (Town Centre exit) and right into South Farm Road. Over five roundabouts take last on right (Pavilion Road) before level crossing. Woodside Road on right, ground on left. 1/2 mile from BR.

Record Attendance: 3,600 v Wimbledon - FA Cup 14/11/1936
Record Victory: 25-0 v Littlehampton (H) - Sussex League 1911-12
Record Defeat: 0-14 v Southwick (A) - Sussex County League 1946-47
Record Goalscorer: Mick Edmonds - 276
Record Appearances: Mark Knee - 414
Additional Records: Received £7,500 from Woking for Tim Read 1990

Senior Honours: Sussex League 1920-21, 21-22, 26-27, 28-29, 30-31, 33-34, 38-39. Sussex League West 1945-46.
Isthmian League Division 2 1981-82, 92-93, Division 1 1982-83.
Sussex Senior Cup x21.

10 YEAR RECORD

00-01	01-02	02-03	03-04	04-05	05-06	06-07	07-08	08-09	09-10
Isth1 12	Isth1 15	Isth1S 12	Isth1S 2	Isth P 10	Isth P 8	Isth P 20	Isth1S 5	Isth1S 5	Isth1S 3

COMBINED COUNTIES LEAGUE

www.combinedcountiesleague.co.uk

Sponsored by:
Cherry Red Records

Founded: 1978

Recent champions:
2005: Walton Casuals
2006: Godalming Town
2007: Chipstead
2008: Merstham
2009: Bedfont Green

Reserve Section		P	W	D	L	F	A	Pts
Worcester Park Res.		32	23	2	7	86	43	71
Bedfont Sports Res.		32	20	6	6	84	38	66
South Park Res.		32	19	8	5	82	40	65
Farnham Town Res.		32	19	6	7	88	46	63
Warlingham Res.	*-3*	32	18	4	10	73	52	55
Eversley Res.		32	14	11	7	64	42	53
Hanworth Villa Res.		32	16	2	14	61	57	50
Westfield Res.		32	14	6	12	59	59	48
Mole Valley SCR Res.		32	13	4	15	54	69	43
Frimley Green Res.		32	12	3	17	51	59	39
Bookham Res.		32	10	5	17	46	59	35
Knaphill Res.		32	10	4	18	57	59	34
Staines Lammas Res.		32	9	7	16	51	66	34
Sheerwater Res.		32	10	3	19	36	92	33
CB Hounslow United Res.		32	8	7	17	47	70	31
Crescent Rovers Res.	*-3*	32	9	5	18	41	84	29
Farleigh Rovers Res.		32	4	5	23	29	74	17

Badshot Lea Res., Chobham Res. - records expunged

Premier Division		P	W	D	L	F	A	Pts
North Greenford United		42	30	8	4	108	42	98
Chertsey Town		42	28	8	6	97	51	92
Camberley Town		42	25	9	8	83	47	84
Egham Town		42	24	5	13	97	62	77
Epsom & Ewell		42	22	5	15	83	58	71
Chessington & Hook Utd		42	20	11	11	64	50	71
Guildford City		42	21	7	14	70	52	70
Molesey	*-1*	42	20	9	13	69	53	68
Sandhurst Town		42	20	8	14	80	67	68
Badshot Lea		42	18	11	13	93	75	65
Ash United		42	19	5	18	76	75	62
Cove		42	16	11	15	72	71	59
Bedfont		42	16	10	16	80	71	58
Horley Town		42	13	14	15	62	70	53
Wembley		42	13	7	22	58	70	46
Croydon		42	9	15	18	55	81	42
Hanworth Villa		42	10	9	23	50	76	39
Raynes Park Vale		42	10	9	23	57	85	39
Colliers Wood United		42	10	8	24	51	79	38
Banstead Athletic		42	8	11	23	50	87	35
Bookham		42	9	5	28	45	99	32
Dorking		42	3	11	28	42	121	20

	Ash United	Badshot Lea	Banstead Athletic	Bedfont	Bookham	Camberley Town	Chertsey Town	Chessington & Hook	Colliers Wood United	Cove	Croydon	Dorking	Egham Town	Epsom & Ewell	Guildford City	Hanworth Villa	Horley Town	Molesey	North Greenford Utd	Raynes Park Vale	Sandhurst Town	Wembley
Ash United		0-6	2-3	1-0	2-0	3-0	1-4	0-1	3-0	3-0	4-0	2-0	1-4	4-1	3-0	1-0	2-1	0-2	2-2	2-1	3-4	2-1
Badshot Lea	1-4		5-3	2-3	1-2	2-0	1-2	3-1	4-0	4-3	1-1	6-5	3-2	4-1	1-0	4-1	3-3	1-1	0-1	2-2	2-2	1-3
Banstead Athletic	1-1	2-2		0-3	0-2	2-3	3-1	0-1	4-0	0-3	4-2	0-0	1-5	0-2	0-2	0-1	0-4	2-3	0-4	1-3	3-1	2-1
Bedfont	6-1	2-1	4-0	***P***	5-3	0-0	0-1	0-0	0-2	1-1	1-0	5-0	1-4	2-4	5-4	1-1	4-1	1-4	2-3	2-1	0-1	3-0
Bookham	3-1	1-4	1-1	0-4	***R***	0-4	0-3	0-0	0-5	1-0	1-3	2-1	0-3	1-3	0-2	0-2	2-3	0-6	0-5	2-0	0-2	1-1
Camberley Town	3-0	0-0	3-0	2-2	5-1	***E***	3-1	1-1	3-1	4-4	2-1	4-2	1-0	1-0	1-0	4-1	2-1	1-1	1-2	3-1	4-1	0-2
Chertsey Town	4-2	1-1	1-1	2-2	3-1	2-1	***M***	0-1	5-1	2-1	4-0	3-0	1-3	3-0	2-2	1-0	1-1	3-2	1-1	2-1	2-1	2-0
Chessington & Hook Utd	0-0	2-1	3-3	2-1	2-1	1-2	3-4	***I***	4-1	0-0	2-0	2-1	2-3	0-0	0-1	3-2	4-0	3-1	0-1	3-2	1-0	1-0
Colliers Wood United	2-3	5-0	1-0	2-3	1-1	0-2	0-3	3-3	***E***	0-2	2-2	6-0	1-0	1-0	0-0	1-4	0-1	0-1	1-3	1-0	1-2	0-2
Cove	2-1	2-1	0-0	3-0	1-0	2-2	2-3	1-3	4-1	***R***	1-1	3-2	0-4	4-3	2-0	2-2	1-1	1-2	0-3	4-1	1-1	2-0
Croydon	3-2	2-3	1-1	3-3	2-4	1-1	1-1	2-3	1-1	0-2		2-2	1-2	1-2	1-0	1-1	1-1	3-2	0-3	3-1	1-5	3-0
Dorking	1-3	1-4	0-2	1-1	2-7	1-1	3-2	1-4	1-1	4-1	0-2	***D***	0-4	0-5	1-1	0-4	1-3	0-1	2-2	1-1	1-3	1-3
Egham Town	0-4	1-3	3-1	2-3	0-0	4-2	2-4	1-0	2-1	2-2	4-1	8-0	***I***	0-1	3-2	4-1	1-2	1-0	2-2	3-1	2-5	3-0
Epsom & Ewell	5-1	2-2	2-0	2-1	1-0	3-2	3-2	3-0	3-1	2-1	1-1	0-0	3-4	***V***	2-0	1-2	2-0	0-1	0-2	0-2	1-2	1-2
Guildford City	1-0	3-0	3-1	4-1	4-1	2-0	0-1	0-2	2-1	3-0	4-0	3-0	3-0	2-1	***I***	1-0	1-1	1-1	3-1	1-2	0-4	3-2
Hanworth Villa	2-1	2-0	2-2	1-1	2-1	0-2	1-3	2-0	0-0	0-3	0-1	2-3	1-1	1-4	3-5	***S***	2-4	0-1	0-4	1-2	0-2	0-2
Horley Town	1-3	0-3	5-1	2-3	2-0	0-1	1-2	1-1	0-1	3-2	1-1	2-2	1-1	0-6	1-1	1-1	***I***	2-2	1-2	2-1	4-1	1-0
Molesey	1-1	2-2	0-0	2-0	3-1	1-4	3-5	0-1	3-1	0-1	2-1	4-0	2-0	0-4	0-1	1-2	3-0	***O***	1-0	4-1	0-0	2-1
North Greenford United	4-0	4-0	0-0	3-1	5-1	0-2	2-2	1-1	4-2	3-1	3-0	3-0	3-2	4-2	5-1	2-1	3-1	2-1	***N***	0-3	3-1	3-1
Raynes Park Vale	2-5	1-4	3-2	1-0	1-2	1-3	0-3	2-2	2-0	2-2	1-1	3-1	0-2	1-1	2-1	1-1	0-0	0-0	1-6		1-2	0-1
Sandhurst Town	1-1	2-5	2-1	3-2	1-0	0-2	0-3	2-0	1-1	2-3	2-2	5-0	1-3	2-3	0-2	2-1	0-1	4-0	2-2	4-2		2-1
Wembley	2-1	0-0	2-3	1-1	3-2	0-1	0-2	3-1	1-2	4-2	1-2	1-1	1-2	1-3	1-1	3-0	2-2	2-3	0-2	5-4	2-2	

RESERVES CUP — **FINAL** *(April 29th at Molesey)* **Eversley Res.** 2 Warlingham Res. 2 *aet* (4-2p)

Division One		P	W	D	L	F	A	Pts
Mole Valley SCR		40	28	7	5	113	44	91
Worcester Park		40	26	10	4	104	35	88
Knaphill		40	26	4	10	98	52	82
Staines Lammas		40	25	6	9	99	46	81
Hartley Wintney		40	22	7	11	95	59	73
South Park		40	22	6	12	89	69	72
Cobham		40	21	8	11	94	56	71
Eversley		40	19	11	10	81	55	68
Bedfont Sports		40	20	8	12	71	48	68
Farleigh Rovers		40	21	3	16	66	57	66
Farnham Town	*-3*	40	20	4	16	88	67	61
Warlingham		40	16	7	17	69	76	55
Frimley Green		40	13	8	19	61	72	47
Croydon Municipal		40	14	5	21	79	97	47
CB Hounslow United		40	11	10	19	58	89	43
Westfield		40	12	4	24	70	92	40
Sheerwater		40	11	4	25	52	100	37
Crescent Rovers		40	7	11	22	60	108	32
Chobham		40	9	4	27	54	104	31
Feltham	*-1*	40	7	7	26	50	107	27
Coulsdon United		40	1	4	35	27	145	7

LEMON RECORDINGS DIVISION ONE CUP

FIRST ROUND
Chobham 1 Warlingham 0
Croydon M. 3 Sheerwater 0
Farnham 4 CB H'slow 3
Mole Valley 2 Farleigh 1
South Park 7 Crescent 0

SECOND ROUND
Bedfont Sports 4 Staines Lammas 4 *aet* (3-1p)
Cobham 2 **Mole Valley SC** 2 *aet* (2-4p)
Eversley 5 Coulsdon United 0
Farnham Town 2 **Croydon Municipal** 2 *aet* (1-4p)
Feltham 1 **Westfield** 4
Frimley Green 1 **Worcester Pk** 1 *aet* (4-5p)
Hartley Wintney 3 Knaphill 0
South Park 5 Chobham 2 *aet*

QUARTER-FINALS
Bedfont Sports 1 **Mole Valley SCR** 2
Eversley 3 South Park 1
Hartley Wintney 1 **Croydon Municipal** 2
Worcester Park 7 Westfield 2

SEMI-FINALS
Eversley 1 **Croydon Municipal** 4
Mole Valley SCR 0 **Worcester Park** 1

FINAL
(May 3rd at Ashford Town (Middx))
Croydon Municipal 1 **Worcester Park** 2

EL RECORDS PREMIER CUP

FIRST ROUND
Banstead Athletic 3 **Raynes Park Vale** 3 *aet* (3-4p)
CB Hounslow United 4 Eversley 1
Chobham 0 **Colliers Wood United** 3
Cobham 0 **Crescent Rovers** 2
Cove 2 Molesey 1
Croydon Municipal 1 Sandhurst Town 0
Dorking 5 Farleigh Rovers 2
Epsom & Ewell 3 Wembley 0
Guildford City 1 Chessington & Hook United 0 *aet*
Mole Valley SCR 2 Bedfont Sports 1
Sheerwater 5 **Camberley Town** 6 *aet*

SECOND ROUND
Bedfont 6 Hartley Wintney 1
Bookham 0 **Chertsey Town** 2
Colliers Wood United 4 Dorking 0
Coulsdon United 0 **South Park** 5
Cove 4 Worcester Park 0
Croydon Municipal 4 Croydon 1
Egham Town 5 Frimley Green 0
Farnham Town 6 CB Hounslow United 1
Feltham 3 Westfield 1
Hanworth Villa 0 **Horley Town** 1
Knaphill 3 **Ash United** 4
Mole Valley SCR 4 Crescent Rovers 2
North Greenford United 1 Epsom & Ewell 0
Raynes Park Vale 1 **Camberley Town** 4
Staines Lammas 1 **Badshot Lea** 3
Warlingham 1 **Guildford City** 5

THIRD ROUND
Bedfont 3 Ash United 2
Camberley Town 3 Egham Town 0
Chertsey Town 3 Feltham 1
Cove 5 Mole Valley SCR 1 *(at Hartley Wintney)*
Croydon Municipal 2 **Badshot Lea** 3
Guildford City 5 North Greenford United 0
Horley Town 1 Colliers Wood United 0 *aet*
South Park 5 Farnham Town 2

QUARTER-FINALS
Chertsey Town 2 **Bedfont** 4
Cove 4 Badshot Lea 2
Horley Town 3 Guildford City 2
South Park 3 **Camberley Town** 4 *aet*

SEMI-FINALS
Bedfont 3 Horley Town 0, Camberley Town 0 **Cove** 4

FINAL *(April 23rd at Staines Town)*
Bedfont 0 **Cove** 2 *aet*

	Bft Sp.	CB Ho	Chob	Cobh	Coul	Cres	Croy	Ever	Farl	Farn	Felt	Frim	Hart	Knap	Mole	Sheer	Sth Pk	Stain	Warl	West	Worc
Bedfont Sports		0-2	0-0	0-1	4-1	9-0	5-1	0-3	2-0	1-1	2-1	2-2	1-0	1-2	0-1	1-2	3-1	0-1	1-1	3-0	0-2
CB Hounslow United	1-3		3-3	2-1	4-0	1-1	3-1	1-1	1-1	2-6	3-2	2-2	1-2	2-4	0-4	1-2	1-2	1-2	3-1	3-2	2-1
Chobham	2-1	0-1		0-3	4-0	3-2	2-0	0-3	1-5	2-3	2-2	1-2	1-2	1-3	0-4	3-1	0-3	0-5	4-1	0-2	0-1
Cobham	0-2	4-1	4-0		2-0	1-1	7-4	1-0	3-1	1-1	4-0	0-0	2-2	1-2	1-5	1-2	3-0	1-0	2-1	3-2	1-1
Coulsdon United	1-2	0-0	2-5	0-7	***D***	1-2	3-3	2-6	0-2	1-2	0-1	0-6	0-4	2-6	0-3	0-1	0-3	0-7	2-4	0-3	1-7
Crescent Rovers	1-1	3-3	4-1	1-4	3-4	***I***	2-1	1-4	2-1	1-2	4-2	0-1	1-1	0-3	2-2	1-3	0-3	0-4	1-2	0-2	1-7
Croydon Municipal	2-3	3-0	3-2	4-1	1-0	4-1	***V***	2-1	2-4	3-1	6-1	3-1	1-2	0-3	0-2	3-1	3-2	0-0	2-3	5-1	1-4
Eversley	1-2	1-2	W-L	4-4	5-1	5-3	2-2	***I***	2-1	1-0	1-1	2-1	2-1	2-1	4-0	1-1	2-0	2-3	1-1	1-2	0-0
Farleigh Rovers	3-1	4-0	1-1	3-2	3-0	2-1	3-2	1-3	***S***	1-0	1-0	2-0	0-2	1-2	0-4	4-2	2-1	1-0	1-2	2-1	2-2
Farnham Town	1-3	5-0	7-2	3-2	3-0	4-1	5-1	1-1	0-1	***I***	8-1	2-0	2-3	2-3	0-4	1-0	0-2	2-1	3-1	3-1	1-0
Feltham	1-3	2-2	8-1	0-4	2-2	1-1	0-2	1-2	3-0	2-5	***O***	2-1	2-2	1-0	0-12	3-1	1-5	0-1	2-0	1-2	0-0
Frimley Green	0-1	3-1	2-1	1-4	5-1	3-1	4-2	1-1	0-3	0-1	4-2	***N***	0-2	1-0	0-3	0-1	1-2	0-0	2-4	2-1	0-0
Hartley Wintney	0-3	5-1	6-1	1-2	6-0	1-0	4-4	2-2	1-0	4-2	4-1	1-0		0-1	0-1	5-1	2-3	0-3	3-0	4-1	1-2
Knaphill	2-0	3-0	3-1	2-2	2-0	1-1	2-1	5-1	3-1	3-0	4-1	1-3	3-5		3-3	4-0	3-5	2-5	4-0	2-0	1-3
Mole Valley SCR	1-1	2-0	4-0	2-1	W-L	6-0	1-1	1-0	2-1	3-0	4-1	4-2	2-5	2-0	***O***	3-0	5-3	2-0	1-3	3-2	1-3
Sheerwater	2-2	1-3	3-2	0-2	1-1	2-3	7-1	1-4	1-0	3-1	2-1	1-2	1-4	1-2	1-4	***N***	0-2	3-8	1-5	1-1	0-3
South Park	1-3	1-1	2-0	2-1	4-0	5-3	1-3	4-3	0-3	2-1	2-0	2-2	2-2	1-1	2-2	3-0	***E***	0-5	1-2	2-1	2-2
Staines Lammas	1-2	4-1	1-2	3-3	2-0	3-3	7-0	3-3	4-0	2-2	1-0	3-2	2-1	1-3	3-2	2-1	2-3		3-0	2-1	0-1
Warlingham	1-1	3-0	2-1	0-2	4-1	1-4	2-1	0-2	1-2	5-1	5-0	2-2	0-0	0-5	0-3	3-0	2-5	1-2		1-0	1-1
Westfield	1-2	3-2	2-3	1-5	8-0	2-2	3-1	2-0	1-2	2-6	1-0	4-2	3-4	0-4	2-2	5-1	1-3	1-2	3-3		0-4
Worcester Park	4-0	1-1	3-2	2-1	8-1	2-2	1-0	0-2	2-1	1-0	3-1	7-1	5-1	1-0	3-3	5-0	3-2	0-1	3-1	6-0	

IN: Mole Valley SCR (P)
OUT: Bedfont (F), North Greenford United (P - Southern League Division One Central)

PREMIER INS & OUTS

ASH UNITED

Founded: 1911 Nickname: United

Secretary: Gareth Watmore **(T)** 07739 188 069 **(E)** garethwatmore@hotmail.com
Chairman: Vaughan Jones **Manager:** Paul Bonner **Prog Ed:** Jake Flockhart
Ground: Youngs Drive off Shawfield Road, Ash, GU12 6RE. **(T)** 01252 320 385 / 345 757
Capacity: 2500 **Seats:** 152 **Covered:** 160 **Midweek Matchday:** Tuesday **Clubhouse:** Yes **Shop:** No

Colours(change): All green.
Previous Names: None
Previous Leagues: Surrey Intermediate
Records: **Att:** 914 v AFC Wimbledon Combined Co 2002-03. **Goals:** Shaun Mitchell (216). **Apps:** Paul Bonner (582).
Senior Honours: Combined Counties Champions 1981-82, 86-87, 98-99.
Aldershot Senior Cup 1998-99, 01-02.

10 YEAR RECORD

00-01	01-02	02-03	03-04	04-05	05-06	06-07	07-08	08-09	09-10
CC 3	CC 2	CC 9	CCP 9	CCP 13	CCP 3	CCP 4	CCP 15	CCP 9	CCP 11

BADSHOT LEA

Founded: 1907 Nickname: Baggies

Secretary: Mrs Nicky Staszkiewicz **(T)** 07921 466 858 **(E)** nstaszkiewicz@ashgatepublishing.com
Chairman: Mark Board **Manager:** David Ford **Prog Ed:** Peter Collison
Ground: Godalming Town FC, Weycourt, Meadow, Farncombe, GU7 3JE **(T)** 01483 417 520
Capacity: 4,163 **Seats:** 620 **Covered:** 1,350 **Midweek Matchday:** Tuesday **Clubhouse:** Yes **Shop:** Yes

Colours(change): Claret/white & sky blue/claret
Previous Names:
Previous Leagues: Surrey Intermediate. Hellenic.
Records: **Att:** 276 v Bisley, 16.04.07.
Senior Honours:

10 YEAR RECORD

00-01	01-02	02-03	03-04	04-05	05-06	06-07	07-08	08-09	09-10
			Hel1E 14	Hel1E 7	Hel1E 12	Hel1E 3	Hel P 11	CCP 7	CCP 10

BANSTEAD ATHLETIC

Founded: 1944 Nickname: A's

Secretary: Terry Parmenter **(T)** 07940 387 041 **(E)** terryparmenter@blueyonder.co.uk
Chairman: Terry Molloy **Manager:** **Prog Ed:** Bob Lockyar
Ground: Merland Rise, Tadworth, Surrey KT20 5JG **(T)** 01737 350 982
Capacity: 3500 **Seats:** 250 **Covered:** 800 **Midweek Matchday:** Tuesday **Clubhouse:** Yes **Shop:** Yes

Colours(change): Amber & black/black/black
Previous Names: None
Previous Leagues: London Spartan League. Athenian League. Isthmian.
Records: **Att:** 1400 v Leytonstone, FA Amateur Cup 1953. **Goals:** Harry Clark. **Apps:** Dennis Wall.
Senior Honours: Surrey Int. Lge 1947-49, Cup 46-47 54-55. Surrey Snr Lge (6) 50-54 56-57 64-65, Lge Cup 57-58.
London Spartan LC 65-67. Athenian LC 80-82.

10 YEAR RECORD

00-01	01-02	02-03	03-04	04-05	05-06	06-07	07-08	08-09	09-10
Isth2 11	Isth2 5	Isth1S 16	Isth1S 18	Isth1S 17	Isth1S 20	CCP 6	CCP 17	CCP 10	CCP 20

BOOKHAM

Founded: 1905 Nickname:

Secretary: Julie Lovegrove **(T)** 07811 441 584 **(E)** jlovegrove21@hotmail.com
Chairman: Simon Butler **Manager:** Andy Taylor **Prog Ed:** Daniel Carnota
Ground: Dorking FC, Mill Lane, Dorking, Surrey RH4 1DX **(T)** 01306 884 112
Capacity: 3000 **Seats:** 200 **Covered:** 600 **Midweek Matchday:** Tuesday **Clubhouse:** **Shop:**

Colours(change): All yellow
Previous Names: None
Previous Leagues: Surrey County Senior League.
Records: **Att:** 81 v AFC Wallingford - 22.10.05.
Senior Honours:

10 YEAR RECORD

00-01	01-02	02-03	03-04	04-05	05-06	06-07	07-08	08-09	09-10
SuCS 8	SuCS 4	SuCS 4	CC1 3	CC1 3	CC1 3	CCP 20	CCP 18	CCP 15	CCP 21

CAMBERLEY TOWN

Founded: 1895 Nickname: Reds or Town

Secretary: Ben Clifford **(T)** 07876 552 210 **(E)** benjaminclifford@ntlworld.com
Chairman: Ronnie Wilson **Manager:** Darren Barnard **Prog Ed:** Andy Vaughan
Ground: Krooner Park, Krooner Road, Camberley, Surrey GU15 2QW **(T)** 01276 65392
Capacity: 2000 **Seats:** 195 **Covered:** 350 **Midweek Matchday:** Tuesday **Clubhouse:** Yes **Shop:** Yes

Colours(change): Red and white stripes/red & blue/red
Previous Names: None
Previous Leagues: Surrey Senior Lge. Spartan Lge. Athenian Lge. Isthmian Lge.
Records: **Att:** 2066 v Aldershot Town, Isthmian Div.2 25/08/90. **Apps:** Brian Ives.
Senior Honours: Surrey Senior Cup 1978-79. Aldershot Senior Cup (x3)

10 YEAR RECORD

00-01	01-02	02-03	03-04	04-05	05-06	06-07	07-08	08-09	09-10
Isth3 20	Isth3 22	Isth2 16	Isth2 10	Isth2 12	Isth2 14	CCP 7	CCP 3	CCP 5	CCP 3

CHERTSEY TOWN

Founded: 1890 Nickname: Curfews

Secretary: Chris Gay **(T)** 07713 473 313 **(E)** chrisegay@googlemail.com
Chairman: Steve Powers **Manager:** Spencer Day **Prog Ed:** Chris Gay
Ground: Alwyns Lane, Chertsey, Surrey KT16 9DW **(T)** 01932 561 774
Capacity: 3,000 **Seats:** 240 **Covered:** 760 **Midweek Matchday:** Tuesday **Clubhouse:** Yes **Shop:** Yes

Colours(change): All white
Previous Names: None
Previous Leagues: Metropolitan. Spartan. Athenian. Isthmian.
Records: **Att:** 2150 v Aldershot Town, Isthmian Div.2 04/12/93. **Goals:** Alan Brown (54) 1962-63.
Senior Honours: Surrey Senior Champions 1959, 61, 62. Isthmian League Cup 1994.

10 YEAR RECORD

00-01	01-02	02-03	03-04	04-05	05-06	06-07	07-08	08-09	09-10
Isth2 8	Isth2 17	Isth1S 24	Isth2 4	Isth2 6	Isth2 6	CCP 8	CCP 8	CCP 3	CCP 2

CHESSINGTON & HOOK UNITED

Founded: 1921 Nickname: Chessey

Secretary: Chris Blackie **(T)** 07748 877 704 **(E)** kandcblackie@googlemail.com
Chairman: Graham Ellis **Manager:** Glyn Stevens **Prog Ed:** Eric Wicks
Ground: Chalky Lane, Chessington, Surrey KT9 2NF **(T)** 01372 745 777
Capacity: 3000 **Seats:** 167 **Covered:** 600 **Midweek Matchday:** Tuesday **Clubhouse:** Yes **Shop:** No

Colours(change): All blue
Previous Names: Chessington United.
Previous Leagues: Surrey Senior Lge. Surrey County Premier Lge.
Records:
Senior Honours:

10 YEAR RECORD

00-01	01-02	02-03	03-04	04-05	05-06	06-07	07-08	08-09	09-10
CC 10	CC 11	CC 14	CCP 10	CCP 3	CCP 8	CCP 11	CCP 11	CCP 19	CCP 6

COLLIERS WOOD UNITED

Founded: 1874 Nickname: The Woods

Secretary: Tony Hurrell **(T)** 07956 983 947 **(E)** collierswoodutd@btconnect.com
Chairman: Tony Eldridge **Manager:** Mark Douglas **Prog Ed:** Chris Clapham
Ground: Wibandune Sports Gd, Lincoln Green, Wimbledon SW20 0AA **(T)** 0208 942 8062
Capacity: 2000 **Seats:** 102 **Covered:** 100 **Midweek Matchday:** Wednesday **Clubhouse:** Yes **Shop:** Yes

Colours(change): Blue & black/black/black
Previous Names: Vandyke Colliers United
Previous Leagues: Surrey County Senior Lge.
Records: 90 v Epsom & Ewell, 14.11.2007.
Senior Honours: Surrey Co Prem Lge Champions 1997-98 (as Vandyke Colliers United)

10 YEAR RECORD

00-01	01-02	02-03	03-04	04-05	05-06	06-07	07-08	08-09	09-10
SuCS 2	SuCS 5	SuCS 2	CC1 2	CCP 14	CCP 4	CCP 13	CCP 7	CCP 14	CCP 19

COVE

Founded: 1897 Nickname:

Secretary: Graham Brown (T) 07713 250 093 (E) covefc1897@aol.com
Chairman: P Wentworth **Manager:** Koo Dumbaya **Prog Ed:** Graham Brown
Ground: Oak Farm Fields, 7 Squirrels Lane, Farnborough GU14 8PB (T) 01252 543 615
Capacity: 2500 **Seats:** 110 **Covered:** 200 **Midweek Matchday:** Tuesday **Clubhouse:** Yes **Shop:** No

Colours(change): Yellow/blue/yellow
Previous Names: None
Previous Leagues: Isthmian League. Hampshire.
Records: **Att:** 1798 v Aldershot Town, Isthmian Div.3 01/05/93.
Senior Honours: Combined Counties Lge Champions 2000-01. Lge Cup 81-82, 00-01.
Aldershot Senior Cup (x5)

10 YEAR RECORD

00-01	01-02	02-03	03-04	04-05	05-06	06-07	07-08	08-09	09-10
CC 1	CC 15	CC 23	CCP 24	CCP 20	CCP 16	CCP 18	CCP 4	CCP 6	CCP 12

CROYDON

Founded: 1953 Nickname: The Trams

Secretary: Antonio Di Natale (T) 07941 576 311 (E) croydonfc@footballfans.co.uk
Chairman: Dickson Gill **Manager:** Dickson Gill **Prog Ed:** Vince Mitchell
Ground: Croydon Sports Arena, Albert Road, South Norwood SE25 4QL (T) 0208 654 8555
Capacity: 6,000 **Seats:** 450 **Covered:** 1,000 **Midweek Matchday:** Wednesday **Clubhouse:** Yes **Shop:** Yes

Colours(change): All sky blue
Previous Names: Croydon Amateurs > 1974.
Previous Leagues: Surrey Senior. Spartan. Athenian. Isthmian. Kent 2006-09.
Records: **Att:** 1,450 v Wycombe Wders, FA Cup 4th Qual. 1975. **Goalscorer:** Alec Jackson - 111. **Apps:** Alec Jackson - 452 (1977-88).
Senior Honours: Isthmian Division 1 1999-00. London Senior Cup 01-02.

10 YEAR RECORD

00-01	01-02	02-03	03-04	04-05	05-06	06-07	07-08	08-09	09-10
Isth P 17	Isth P 22	Isth1S 18	Isth1S 21	Isth1 22	Isth2 10	Kent P 3	Kent P 12	Kent P 9	CCP 16

DORKING

Founded: 1880 Nickname: The Chicks

Secretary: Ray Collins (T) 07710 010 241 (E) dorkingfc@aol.com
Chairman: Jack Collins **Manager:** Anthony Webb **Prog Ed:** Bryan Bletso
Ground: Meadowbank, Mill Lane, Dorking Surrey RH4 1DB (T) 01306 884 112
Capacity: 3500 **Seats:** 200 **Covered:** 800 **Midweek Matchday:** Tuesday **Clubhouse:** Yes **Shop:** Yes

Colours(change): Green & white hoops/green & white/green
Previous Names: Guildford & Dorking (when club merged 1974). Dorking Town 77-82
Previous Leagues: Corinthian Lge. Athenian Lge. Isthmian Lge.
Records: **Att:** 4500 v Folkstone Town FAC 1955 & v Plymouth Argyle FAC 1993. **Goals:** Andy Bushell. **Apps:** Steve Lunn.
Senior Honours: Isthmian Div.2 1988-89.

10 YEAR RECORD

00-01	01-02	02-03	03-04	04-05	05-06	06-07	07-08	08-09	09-10
Isth3 18	Isth3 8	Isth2 14	Isth2 2	Isth1 21	Isth2 9	CCP 16	CCP 22	CC1 3	CCP 22

EGHAM TOWN

Founded: 1886 Nickname: Sarnies

Secretary: Daniel Bennett (T) 07932 612 424 (E) sales@beautiful-bathrooms.co.uk
Chairman: Patrick Bennett **Manager:** Steve Baker **Prog Ed:** Paul Bennett
Ground: Runnymead Stadium, Tempest Road, Egham TW20 8HX (T) 01784 435 226
Capacity: 5500 **Seats:** 262 **Covered:** 3300 **Midweek Matchday:** Tuesday **Clubhouse:** Yes **Shop:** No

Colours(change): All red
Previous Names: Runnymead Rovers 1877-1905. Egham F.C. 05-63.
Previous Leagues: Spartan Lge. Athenian Lge. Isthmian Lge. Southern Lge.
Records: **Att:** 1400 v Wycombe Wanderers, FAC 2nd Qual. 1972-73. **Goals:** Mark Butler (153). **Apps:** Dave Jones (850+).
Senior Honours: Spartan Lge Champions 1971-72. Athenian Lge Div.2 Champions.

10 YEAR RECORD

00-01	01-02	02-03	03-04	04-05	05-06	06-07	07-08	08-09	09-10
Isth3 13	Isth3 6	Isth1S 10	Isth1S 22	SthW 22	Isth2 5	CCP 10	CCP 12	CCP 13	CCP 4

EPSOM & EWELL

Founded: 1918 Nickname: E's

Secretary: Paul Latham (T) 07850 080 493 (E) paul.latham@uk.zurich.com
Chairman: Daniel Nevitt **Manager:** Lyndon Buckwell **Prog Ed:** Gavin Banks
Ground: Eversley Sports Ass. Complex, Chandlers Farm, Eversley, RG27 0NS (T) 0118 973 2400
Capacity: 3400 **Seats:** 174 **Covered:** 800 **Midweek Matchday:** Tuesday **Clubhouse:** Yes **Shop:** No

Colours(change): Yellow & royal blue stripes/royal blue/royal blue
Previous Names: Epsom T (previously Epsom FC) merged with Ewell & Stoneleigh in 1960
Previous Leagues: Corinthian Lge. Athenian Lge. Surrey Senior Lge. Isthmian Lge.
Records: **Att:** 5000 v Kingstonian, FAC 2Q 15/10/49. **Goals:** Tommy Tuite.
Senior Honours: Isthmian Lge Div.2 Champions 1977-78.

10 YEAR RECORD

00-01	01-02	02-03	03-04	04-05	05-06	06-07	07-08	08-09	09-10
Isth3 7	Isth3 5	Isth1S 9	Isth1S 24	Isth2 14	Isth2 15	CCP 17	CCP 10	CCP 4	CCP 5

GUILDFORD CITY

Founded: 1996 Nickname: The City

Secretary: Andrew Masters (T) 07834 956 475 (E) apfmasters@talk21.com
Chairman: Chris Pegman **Manager:** Scott Steele **Prog Ed:** Matt Howell
Ground: Spectrum Leisure Centre, Parkway, Guildford GU1 1UP (T) 01483 443 322
Capacity: 1100 **Seats:** 134 **Covered:** Yes **Midweek Matchday:** Wednesday **Clubhouse:** Yes **Shop:** Yes

Colours(change): Red & white stripes/black/black
Previous Names: AFC Guildford 1996-2005. Guildford United 05-06.
Previous Leagues: Surrey Senior.
Records: **Att:** 211 v Godalming & Guildford, 2004
Senior Honours: Combined Counties Div.1 Champions 2003-04

10 YEAR RECORD

00-01	01-02	02-03	03-04	04-05	05-06	06-07	07-08	08-09	09-10
SuCS 4	SuCS 11	SuCS 9	CC1 1	CCP 12	CCP 17	CCP 21	CCP 2	CCP 20	CCP 7

HANWORTH VILLA

Founded: 1976 Nickname: The Vilans

Secretary: Dave Brown (T) 07971 650 297 (E) brown@park-road.fsnet.co.uk
Chairman: Gary Brunning **Manager:** Tony Buss **Prog Ed:** Gary Brunning
Ground: Rectory Meadows, Park Road, Hanworth TW13 6PN (T) 020 8831 9391
Capacity: 600 **Seats:** 100 **Covered:** **Midweek Matchday:** Tuesday **Clubhouse:** **Shop:**

Colours(change): Red & white/black/black
Previous Names:
Previous Leagues: Hounslow & District Lge. West Middlesex Lge. Middlesex County League.
Records:
Senior Honours: Hounslow & District Div.1 & Premier Division Champions.
West Middlesex Div. 1 & Div. 2 Champions. Middlesex County Champions 2002-03, 04-05.

10 YEAR RECORD

00-01	01-02	02-03	03-04	04-05	05-06	06-07	07-08	08-09	09-10
MidCo 6	MidCo 4	MidCo 1	MidCo 4	MidCo 1	CC1 7	CC1 6	CC1 2	CC1 2	CCP 17

HORLEY TOWN

Founded: 1896 Nickname: The Clarets

Secretary: Jim Betchley (T) 07824 379 184 (E) jimbetchley@btinternet.com
Chairman: Mark Sale **Manager:** Ali Rennie **Prog Ed:** Rob Cortazzi
Ground: The New Defence, Court Lodge Road, Horley RH6 8RS (T) 01293 822 000
Capacity: 1800 **Seats:** 101 **Covered:** Yes **Midweek Matchday:** Tuesday **Clubhouse:** Yes **Shop:** Yes

Colours(change): Claret & sky blue/claret/claret
Previous Names: Horley >1975
Previous Leagues: Surrey Senior, London Spartan, Athenian, Surrey County Senior, Crawley & District
Records: **Att:** 15,00 v AFC Wimbledon, 2003-04. **Goalscorer:** Alan Gates.
Senior Honours: Surrey Senior League Champions 1976-77.

10 YEAR RECORD

00-01	01-02	02-03	03-04	04-05	05-06	06-07	07-08	08-09	09-10
		SuCS 3	CCP 17	CCP 7	CCP 5	CC1 2	CCP 5	CCP 12	CCP 14

MOLE VALLEY SCR

Founded: 1978 Nickname: The Commers

Secretary: Darren Salmon **(T)** 07596 537 933 **(E)** scr1011@live.co.uk
Chairman: Alan Salmon **Manager:** Darren Salmon **Prog Ed:** Michael Bolton
Ground: Cobham FC, Anvil Lane, Downside Bridge Rd, Cobham KT11 1AA **(T)** 01932 866 386
Capacity: 2,500 **Seats:** 112 **Covered:** 212 **Midweek Matchday:** Tuesday **Clubhouse:** Yes **Shop:** Yes

Colours(change): All red
Previous Names: Inrad FC. Centre 21 FC . SCR Plough, SCR Grapes, SRC Litten Tree, SCR Kingfisher
Previous Leagues: South Eastern Combination.
Records:
Senior Honours: Combined Counties League Division 1 2009-10

10 YEAR RECORD

00-01	01-02	02-03	03-04	04-05	05-06	06-07	07-08	08-09	09-10
								CC1 4	CC1 1

MOLESEY

Founded: 1953 Nickname: The Moles

Secretary: Tracey Teague **(T)** 07939 387 277 **(E)** teaguetracy90@yahoo.co.uk
Chairman: Tracy Teague **Manager:** Steve Webb **Prog Ed:**
Ground: 412 Walton Road, West Molesey KT8 2JG. **(T)** 020 8979 4283 (Clubhouse)
Capacity: 4,000 **Seats:** 400 **Covered:** 600 **Midweek Matchday:** Tuesday **Clubhouse:** Yes **Shop:** Yes

Colours(change): White/black/black.
Previous Names: None.
Previous Leagues: Surrey Senior. Spartan. Athethian. Isthmian.
Records: **Att:** 1,255 v Sutton United, Surrey Senior Cup sem-final 1966. **Goalscorer:** Michael Rose (139). **Apps:** Frank Hanley (453).
Senior Honours: Surrey Senior League 1957-58.

10 YEAR RECORD

00-01	01-02	02-03	03-04	04-05	05-06	06-07	07-08	08-09	09-10
Isth2 15	Isth2 19	Isth1S 22	Isth1S 19	Isth1 16	Isth1 17	Isth1S 15	Isth1S 22	CCP 11	CCP 8

RAYNES PARK VALE

Founded: 1995 Nickname: The Vale

Secretary: David Brenen **(T)** 07956 304 566 **(E)** davidbrenen@blueyonder.co.uk
Chairman: Fred Stevens **Manager:** Mark Williams **Prog Ed:** Mike Woods
Ground: Prince George's Playing Field, Raynes Park SW20 9NB **(T)** 0208 540 8843
Capacity: 1500 **Seats:** 120 **Covered:** 100 **Midweek Matchday:** Wednesday **Clubhouse:** Yes **Shop:** No

Colours(change): Yellow/red/yellow
Previous Names: Raynes Park > 1995 until merger with Malden Vale.
Previous Leagues: Surrey County Premier Lge. Isthmian.
Records: **Att:** 1871 v AFC Wimbledon (At Carshalton Athletic).
Senior Honours: Combined Counties Div.1 Champions 2002-03.

10 YEAR RECORD

00-01	01-02	02-03	03-04	04-05	05-06	06-07	07-08	08-09	09-10
CC 16	CC 7	CC 8	CCP 16	CCP 9	CCP 9	CCP 15	CCP 19	CCP 8	CCP 18

SANDHURST TOWN

Founded: 1910 Nickname: Fizzers

Secretary: Mike Ellsmore **(T)** 07986 484 025 **(E)** mike.ellsmore@sky.com
Chairman: Ted Rogers **Manager:** Peter Browning **Prog Ed:** Christine Bell
Ground: Bottom Meadow, Memorial Ground, Yorktown Rd, GU47 9BJ **(T)** 01252 878 768
Capacity: 1000 **Seats:** 102 **Covered:** 100 **Midweek Matchday:** Tuesday **Clubhouse:** Yes **Shop:** No

Colours(change): Red/black/black.
Previous Names: None
Previous Leagues: Reading & Dist. East Berks. Aldershot Senior. Chiltonian Lge.
Records: **Att:** 2,449 v AFC Wimbledon, Combined Counties 17.08.2002.
Senior Honours: Reading & District Premier Champions 1933-34. Division 1 1932-33.
Aldershot FA Senior Invitation Challenge Cup 2000-01, 05-06.

10 YEAR RECORD

00-01	01-02	02-03	03-04	04-05	05-06	06-07	07-08	08-09	09-10
CC 13	CC 13	CC 6	CCP 5	CCP 5	CCP 7	CCP 12	CCP 16	CCP 16	CCP 9

WEMBLEY

Founded: 1946 Nickname: The Lions

Secretary: Mrs Jean Gumm **(T)** 07876 125 784 **(E)** wembleyfc@aol.com
Chairman: Brian Gumm **Manager:** Ian Bates **Prog Ed:** Richard Markiewicz
Ground: Vale Farm, Watford Road, Sudbury, Wembley HA0 3AG. **(T)** 0208 904 8169
Capacity: 2450 **Seats:** 350 **Covered:** 950 **Midweek Matchday:** Tuesday **Clubhouse:** Yes **Shop:** No

Colours(change): Red & white/red/red
Previous Names: None
Previous Leagues: Middlesex Lge. Spartan. Delphian. Corinthian. Athenian. Isthmian.
Records: **Att:** 2654 v Wealdstone, FA Amateur Cup 1952-53. **Goals:** Bill Handraham (105). **Apps:** Spud Murphy (505).
Senior Honours: Middlesex Senior Cup 1983-84, 86-87.

10 YEAR RECORD

00-01		01-02		02-03		03-04		04-05		05-06		06-07		07-08		08-09		09-10	
Isth2	16	Isth2	18	Isth1N	23	Isth2	11	Isth2	13	Isth2	11	CCP	3	CCP	14	CCP	17	CCP	15

Team line up of Bedfont F.C. who finished 13th in the Premier Division in 2009-10, and who unfortunately folded during the close season.
Photo: Alan Coomes.

DIVISION ONE INS & OUTS

IN: Farnborough North End (S - Wessex League Division One), Hayes Gates (P - Middlesex County League Premier Division)
OUT: Coulsdon United (R - Surrey Elite League), Crescent Rovers (W - Surrey Elite League), Croydon Municipal (F), Mole Valley SCR (P)

BEDFONT SPORTS

Founded: 2002 Nickname: The Eagles

Secretary: Terry Reader **(T)** 07967 370 109 **(E)** bedfontsports@yahoo.co.uk
Chairman: David Reader **Manager:** **Prog Ed:** Terry Reader
Ground: Bedfont Sports Club, Hatton Road, Bedfont TW14 9QT **(T)** **Capacity:** 3,000
Colours(change): Red & black hoops/black/red & black hoops

ADDITIONAL INFORMATION:
Previous League: Middlesex County.

CB HOUNSLOW UNITED

Founded: 1989

Secretary: Stephen Hosmer **(T)** 07988 783 019 **(E)** stephen.hosmer@btinternet.com
Chairman: Frank James **Manager:** **Prog Ed:** Stephen Hosmer
Ground: Osterley S.C., Tentelow Lane, Norwood Green UB2 4LW **(T)** 0208 574 7055 **Capacity:** 1,000
Colours(change): All blue

ADDITIONAL INFORMATION:
Previous League: Middlesex County.

CHOBHAM

Founded: 1905

Secretary: Debbie Bexon **(T)** 07875 482 731 **(E)** debbie.bexon@hotmail.com
Chairman: Phil Walker **Manager:** **Prog Ed:** David Walker
Ground: Chobham Rec. Ground, Station Rd, Chobham, Surrey GU24 8AZ **(T)** 01276 857 876 **Capacity:** 100+
Colours(change): Black & white stripes/white/black & white

ADDITIONAL INFORMATION:
Previous Name: Chobham & Ottershaw 1998-2004. **Previous League:** Surrey County Premier.
Honours: Surrey County Premier League 1994-95, 95-96, 98-99.

COBHAM

Founded: 1892 Nickname: Hammers

Secretary: Ken Reed **(T)** 07834 361 724 **(E)** cohamfootballclub@hotmail.com
Chairman: Shaun Russell **Manager:** **Prog Ed:** Shaun Russell
Ground: Leg O'Mutton Field, Anvil Lane, Cobham KT11 1AA **(T)** 01932 866 386 **Capacity:** 2,500
Colours(change): Red & black/black/red

ADDITIONAL INFORMATION: Previous League: Surrey Senior.
Record Att: 2000 - Charity game 1975.
Honours: Combined Counties League Cup 2001-02.

EVERSLEY

Founded: 1910 Wild Boars

Secretary: Paul Latham **(T)** 07850 080 493 **(E)** paul.latham@uk.zurich.com
Chairman: Daniel Nevitt **Manager:** **Prog Ed:** Gavin Banks
Ground: ESA Sports Complex, Fox Lane, Eversley RG27 0NS **(T)** 0118 973 2400 **Capacity:**
Colours(change): Yellow & royal blue stripes/royal blue/royal blue

ADDITIONAL INFORMATION:
Previous League: Surrey Elite Intermediate.
Honours: Surrey Elite Intermediate 2008-09.

FARLEIGH ROVERS

Founded: 1922 Nickname: The Foxes

Secretary: Mark Bassett **(T)** 07921 764 409 **(E)** m.bassett69@btinternet.com
Chairman: David Willcocks **Manager:** **Prog Ed:** Peter Collard
Ground: Parsonage Field, Harrow Road, Warlingham CR6 9EX **(T)** 01883 626 483 **Capacity:** 500
Colours(change): Black & red/black/black

ADDITIONAL INFORMATION:
Previous League: Surrey County Premier.
Honours: Surrey County Premier 1982-83.

FARNBOROUGH NORTH END

Founded: 1967 Nickname: North End

Secretary: Paul Xiberras **(T)** 07733 385 849 **(E)** paul@xiberras.com
Chairman: Paul Xiberras **Manager:** **Prog Ed:** Liam Jones
Ground: Cody Sports & Social Club, Old Ively Rd, Pyestock, Farnborough GU14 0LP **(T)** 01252 543 009 **Capacity:** 1,000
Colours(change): Red/black/black

ADDITIONAL INFORMATION:
Previous Name: Covies. **Previous League:** Wessex > 2010.
Record Goalscorer: Paul Griffiths - 320. **Appearances:** Andy Dermott - 516.

GEDLING TOWN

Secretary: Graham Peck **(T)** 07815 458 196 **(E)** graham@peckgraham.orangehome.co.uk
Chairman: **Manager:** **Prog Ed:** Graham Peck
Ground: Riverside Stadium, Stoke Lane, Stoke Bardolf, Nottingham **(T)** 0115 940 2145 **Capacity:**
Colours(change): Yellow/blue/blue (All red)
ADDITIONAL INFORMATION:

GRAHAM ST. PRIMS

Secretary: Peter Davis **(T)** 07969 160 574 **(E)** j.davis16@sky.com
Chairman: **Manager:** **Prog Ed:** Edward Davis
Ground: Asterdale Sports Centre, Borrowash Road, Spondon, Derbyshire DE21 7PH **(T)** 01332 704 064 **Capacity:**
Colours(change): Red & white/black/black (Blue/red/red)
ADDITIONAL INFORMATION:

GREENWOOD MEADOWS

Secretary: Mark Connors **(T)** 07960 399 812 **(E)** mark@ntextiles.co.uk
Chairman: **Manager:** **Prog Ed:** Martin Asher
Ground: Lenton Lane Ground, Lenton Lane, Nr Clifton Bridge, Nottingham NG7 2SA **(T)** 07712 530 706 **Capacity:**
Colours(change): Green/black/green (Yellow/green/yellow)
ADDITIONAL INFORMATION:

GRESLEY

Secretary: Reg Shorthouse **(T)** 07779 049 847 **(E)** reg.shorthouse@gresleyfc.com
Chairman: **Manager:** **Prog Ed:** Robert Mansfield
Ground: The Moat Ground, Moat Street, Church Gresley, Derbyshire DE11 0PQ **(T)** 01283 216 315 **Capacity:**
Colours(change): Red/white/red (White/red/white)
ADDITIONAL INFORMATION:

HEANOR TOWN

Secretary: Keith Costello **(T)** 07792 691 843 **(E)** ukinfo@jmcengineering.com
Chairman: **Manager:** **Prog Ed:** Stan Wilton
Ground: The Town Ground, Mayfield Avenue, Heanor DE75 7EN **(T)** 01773 713 742 **Capacity:**
Colours(change): White/black/black (Red/white/white)
ADDITIONAL INFORMATION:

HINCKLEY DOWNES

Secretary: Ray Baggott **(T)** 01455 840 088 **(E)** raybaggott@yahoo.co.uk
Chairman: **Manager:** **Prog Ed:**
Ground: Teh Green King Stadium, Leicester Road, Hinckley LE10 3DR **(T)** 01455 840 088 **Capacity:**
Colours(change): All royal blue (All orange)
ADDITIONAL INFORMATION:

HOLBROOK M.W.

Secretary: Chris Sadler **(T)** 07813 680 458 **(E)** chris.sadler@derby-college.ac.uk
Chairman: **Manager:** **Prog Ed:** Chris Sadler
Ground: O'kra Ground, Shaw Lane, Holbrook, Derbyshire DE56 0TG **(T)** 07966 792 011 **Capacity:**
Colours(change): All royal blue (All white)
ADDITIONAL INFORMATION:

HOLWELL SPORTS

Secretary: Chris Parkin **(T)** 07507 322 489 **(E)** chris@parkin007.co.uk
Chairman: **Manager:** **Prog Ed:** Linda Parker
Ground: Welby Road, Asfordby Hill, Melton Mowbray, Leicestershire LE14 3RD **(T)** 07523 427 450 **Capacity:**
Colours(change): Yellow/green/green (Sky blue/black/black)

ADDITIONAL INFORMATION:

IBSTOCK UNITED

Secretary: Arthur Lakin **(T)** 07515 752 772 **(E)** artlakin@ntlworld.com
Chairman: **Manager:** **Prog Ed:** Chris Pallett
Ground: The Welfare Ground, Leicester Road, Ibstock, Leicestershire LE67 6HN **(T)** 01974 657 701 **Capacity:**
Colours(change): Red & white/red/red (Blue & white/white/white)

ADDITIONAL INFORMATION:

RADCLIFFE OLYMPIC

Secretary: Michael Bradley **(T)** 07825 285 024 **(E)** knacks@hotmail.com
Chairman: **Manager:** **Prog Ed:** Brendan Richardson
Ground: The Recreation Grd, Warfe Lane, Radcliffe on Trent, Nottingham NG12 2AN **(T)** 07825 285 024 **Capacity:**
Colours(change): Navy blue & red/navy & red/navy (All red)

ADDITIONAL INFORMATION:

RADFORD

Secretary: Simon Matters **(T)** 07905 678 886 **(E)** swm1288@hotmail.com
Chairman: **Manager:** **Prog Ed:** Howard Bacon
Ground: Selhurst Street, Off Radford Road, Nottingham NG7 5EH **(T)** 0115 942 3250 **Capacity:**
Colours(change): All claret (All light blue)

ADDITIONAL INFORMATION:

ST. ANDREWS

Secretary: Les Botting **(T)** 07793 500 937 **(E)** standrewsfc@btconnect.com
Chairman: **Manager:** **Prog Ed:** Darren Creed
Ground: Canal Street, Aylestone, Leicester LE2 8LA **(T)** 0116 283 9298 **Capacity:**
Colours(change): Black & white stripes/black/red (All blue)

ADDITIONAL INFORMATION:

THURNBY NIRVANA

Secretary: Zak Hajat **(T)** 07811 843 136 **(E)** nirvanafc@hotmail.com
Chairman: **Manager:** **Prog Ed:** Chris Tonge
Ground: Dakyn Road, Thurnby Lodge, Leicester LE5 2ED **(T)** 0116 243 3308 **Capacity:**
Colours(change): All green (Red & black/red & black/black)

ADDITIONAL INFORMATION:

GROUND DIRECTIONS

ASH UNITED - Youngs Drive GU12 6RE - 01252 320 385
FROM M3: Get off the M3 at J4, onto the A331: Take 3rd Exit off to Woking. Up to the roundabout turn left into Shawfields Road, follow road for about 500 yards, Football Ground is on the left, take next turning on your left into Youngs Drive where club is 50yards on. FROM M25: Get onto the A3 heading to Guildford/Portsmouth. Keep on this until you reach the A31(Hog's Back). Then go onto the A31 until you reach the exit for the A331 to Aldershot. Follow the signs for Aldershot, which will be the 1st exit off the A331.When you reach the roundabout take the exit for Woking, which will be the 3rd exit off. Up to the roundabout turn left into Shawfields Road, then as above.

BADSHOT LEA - Farnborough FC GU14 8UG - 01252 541 469
Leave M3 at junction 4, take A331 to Farnham, After a few hundred yards exit at 2nd slip road (A325 to Farnborough). Cross over the dual carriageway and a small roundabout, Pass the Farnborough Gate shopping centre on the left. At the next roundabout turn left onto the A325, Go over pelican crossing and at next set of lights Turn right into Prospect Avenue. At the next roundabout turn right into Cherrywood Road, Ground is half a mile down on the right.

BANSTEAD ATHLETIC - Merland Rise KT20 5JG - 01737 350 982
From M25 junction 8 follow signs to Banstead Sports Centre.

BOOKHAM - Dorking FC, Meadowbank Stadium RH4 1DX- 01306 884 112

CAMBERLEY TOWN - Krooner Park GU15 2QW - 01276 65392
Exit M3 Motorway at Junction 4. At the end of the slip road take the right hand land signposted A331, immediately take the left hand lane signposted Frimley and Hospital (Red H Symbol) and this will lead you up onto the A325. Continue to the roundabout and turn left onto the B3411 (Frimley Road) Continue past Focus DIY store on Left and stay on B3411 for approx 1.5 miles. At the next Mini roundabout turn left into Wilton Road, proceed through industrial estate (past the Peugeot garage) and the entrance to the ground is right at the end.

CHERTSEY TOWN - Alwyns Lane KT16 9DW - 01932 561 774
Alwyns Lane is off Windsor Street at the north end of the town centre close to the parish church of St Peters, a 15 minute walk from the railway station.

CHESSINGTON & HOOK UNITED - Chalky Lane KT9 2NF - 01372 745 777
Chalky Lane is off A243 (Opposite Chessington World of Adventures) which leads to Junction 9 on M25 or Hook Junction on the A3.

COLLIERS WOOD UTD - Wibbandune Sports Ground SW20 0AA - 0208 942 8062
On A3 Southbound 1 mile from Robin Hood Gate.

COVE OAK FARM - Squirrel Lane GU14 8PB - 01252 543 615
From M3 junction 4, follow signs for A325, then follow signs for Cove FC.

DORKING - Meadowbank Stadium RH4 1DX - 01306 884 112

EGHAM TOWN - Runnymede Stadium TW20 8HX - 01784 435 226
From M25 - J13 - Take the A30, heading south. The road runs parallel with the M25 briefly, and sweeps round a sharp left hand bend, under the M25. Stay right, down to the r'about in front of you just the other side of the M25. Go round the r'about and back under the M25.This road is called The Causeway. Carry on down this road, over the small r'about at Sainsbury's and at the bigger r'about turn right (signposted B3376 - Thorpe, Chertsey, Woking). Proceed down Thorpe Rd, over a level crossing, to a mini r'about, go over, and on the left, after the green turn into Pond Road. Left into Wards Place then first right and you will see the entrance to the football ground.

GUILDFORD CITY - Spectrum Arena, Parkway GU1 1UP - 01483 443 322
From Guildford main line station, take no.100 shuttle bus to Spectrum. From London Road Station walk via Stoke Park. From A3, exit at Guildford – follow signs to leisure centre.

HANWORTH VILLA - Rectory Meadows, Park Road TW13 6PN - 0208 831 9391
From M25 and M3 once on the M3 towards London. This becomes the A316, take the A314 (Hounslow Rd) exit signposted Feltham & Hounslow. Turn left onto Hounslow Rd, at the second mini round about (Esso garage on the corner) turn left into Park Rd. Continue down Park Road past the Hanworth Naval Club on the right and Procter's Builders Merchants on the left. Follow the road around the 90 degree bend and continue to the end of the road past the Hanworth Village Hall. Once past the two houses next to the village hall turn left into Rectory Meadows.

HORLEY TOWN - The New Defence RH6 8RS - 07545 697 234
From centre of town go North up Victoria where it meets the A23, straight across to Vicarage Lane, 2nd left into Court Lodge Road follow it through estate and we are behind adult education centre.

MOLE VALLEY SCR - River Lane Sports Ground KT22 0AU - 07757 980 497
Exit M25 (Junction 9); Take first left onto the A224 Oxshott Road stay on it till you come to a Round About take first left into Oaklawn Road follow Road till you reach the "T" junction do a left go straight on you will see a sign post for a sewage works on the right, entrance to the ground is 300 yards on the right by mini roundabout. Ground has its own slip road to do a right hand turn into River Lane.

MOLESEY - 412 Walton Road West KT8 0JG - 0208 979 4283
Take A3 towards Cobham/London & exit at Esher-Sandown turn. 1st exit at roundabout to A244 through Esher to Marquis of Granby Pub. 1st exit A309 at next roundabout. 1st exit at end of road turn right, follow until mini roundabout left into Walton Road after 1 mile ground on left.

RAYNES PARK VALE - Prince Georges Fields SW20 9NB - 0208 540 8843
Exit Raynes Park station into Grand Drive cross Bushey Road at the traffic lights continue up Grand Drive for 400 yards entrance on the left follow drive to clubhouse. From the A3. Onto Bushey Road towards South Wimbledon. Grand Drive on the right, ground in Grand Drive on the left hand side.
SANDHURST TOWN - Bottom Meadow GU47 9BJ - 01252 878 768
Situated on A321 approx 5 miles from Junction 4 on M3, or approx 8 miles from junction 10 on the M4 Park in Council Offices car park and walk down tarmac footpath beside the stream to ground.
WEMBLEY - Vale Farm, Watford Road HA0 3AG - 0208 904 8169
From Sudbury Town Station 400 yards along Watford Road.

DIVISION ONE
BEDFONT SPORTS - Bedfont Sports Club TW14 9QT
From Junction 13, M25 – Staines. At Crooked Billet roundabout turn right onto the A30 Signposted C. London, Hounslow. At Clockhouse Roundabout take the 2nd exit onto the A315 Signposted Bedfont. Turn left onto Hatton Road. Arrive on Hatton Road, Bedfont Sports Club.
CB HOUNSLOW UNITED - Osterley Sports Club UB2 4LW - 0208 574 7055
From the A4 (Great West Road). Turn left at Master Robert, Church Rd. Turn left at Heston Road. Follow for 1 mile. Turn right at Norwood Green (Tentelow Lane). Club is 1 mile on the Right.
CHOBHAM - Chobham Recreation Ground GU24 8AZ - 01276 857 876
Leave M3 At J3. Left At Lights, Follow Road to Roundabout, First Left, Next Roundabout Turn Right. Continue Through Village, Left at Next Roundabout. Ground is on the Right.
COBHAM - Leg of Mutton Field - 07787 383 407
From Cobham High Street, turn right into Downside Bridge Road and turn right into Leg of Mutton Field.
FARLEIGH ROVERS - Parsonage Field, Harrow Road CR6 9EX - 01883 626 483
From M25 junction 6 left at lights up Godstone Hill (Caterham bypass) to roundabout. Take fourth turning off of roundabout. Up Succombs Hill then right into Westhall Rd. Right at the green then second left into Farleigh Rd. Left at mini round about continue still on Farleigh Road. Right at the Harrow Pub. This is Harrow Road. Right at the end of the houses and the ground is behind the houses.
FARNHAM TOWN - Memorial Ground, West St. GU9 7DY - 01252 715 305
Follow A31 to Coxbridge roundabout (passing traffic lights at Hickleys corner. Farnham station to left.) At next roundabout take 3rd exit to Farnham town centre. At the mini roundabout take 2nd exit. The ground is to the left.
FELTHAM - Bedfont FC, Beveree TW14 9QT - 0208 890 7264
Hatton Road runs alongside the A30 at Heathrow. Ground is opposite the Duke of Wellington Public House.
FRIMLEY GREEN - Frimley Green Recreation Groand GU16 6SY - 01252 835 089
Exit M3 at junction 4 and follow the signs to Frimley High Street. At the mini roundabout in front of the White Hart public house turn into Church Road. At the top of the hill by the Church the road bends right and becomes Frimley Green Road. Follow the road for approx of a mile, go over the mini roundabout which is the entrance to Johnson's Wax factory, and the Recreation Ground is the second turning on the left, just past Henley Drive, which is on your right.
HARTLEY WINTNEY - Memorial Playing Fields RG27 8DL - 01252 843 586
On entering Hartley Wintney via the A30 take the turn at the mini roundabout signposted A323 Fleet. Take the 1st right turn, Green Lane, which has St John's Church on the corner. Continue down Green Lane for about 800 metres and turn right into car park, which has a shared access with Greenfields School. Turn left at St John's Church if coming down the A323 from Fleet.
KNAPHILLBROOK - Wood Country Park GU21 2AY - 01483 475 150
From Knaphill High Street turn right at traffic lights into Lower Guildford Road, follow road until you reach the roundabout, take 3rd exit onto Redding Way, take 1st left into Stratchcona Gardens then left again and follow road into the club car park.
SHEERWATER- Sheerwater Recreation Ground GU21 5QJ - 01932 348 192
From M25(J11) take the A320 towards Woking, At Six Cross roundabout take the exit to Monument Road. At the lights turn left into Eve Road for Sheerwater Estate. First left is Blackmore Crescent, Entrance is Quarter of a mile on left.
SOUTH PARK - King George's Field RH2 8LG - 01737 245 963
From junction 8 of the M25, take A217 and follow signs to Gatwick. Follow through the one way system via Reigate town centre and continue on until traffic lights and crossroads by The Angel public house, turn right at these lights, into Prices Lane, and continue on road. After a sharp right bend into Sandcross Lane past Reigate Garden Centre. Take next left after school into Whitehall Lane.
STAINES LAMMAS - Laleham Recreation Ground TW18 1RZ - 01784 465 204
From M25 Junction 13 to Staines. A30 through to A308; right at Fordbridge roundabout; left at mini roundabout to B377 into Laleham; entrance opposite Turks Head Pub.
WARLINGHAM - Verdayne Playing Fields CR6 9RP - 01883 625 718
From Sanderstead take B269 towards Warlingham. Verdayne Gardens is off LImpsfield Road (B269) between Sanderstead and Warlingham.
WESTFIELD - Woking Park, off Elmbridge Lane GU22 7AA - 01483 771 106
Follow signs to Woking Leisure Centre on the A247.
WORCESTER PARK- Skinners Field, Green Lane KT4 8AJ - 0208 337 4995

EAST MIDLAND COUNTIES LEAGUE

www.pitchero.com/football/leagues/east-midlands-counties-league-264

Sponsored by:

No sponsor

Founded: 2008

Recent champions:

2009: Kirby Muxloe SC

LEAGUE CUP

FIRST ROUND

Anstey Nomads 1 **Graham Street Prims** 2
Gedling MW 1 **Radcliffe Olympic** 2 *aet*
Heanor Town 0 **Gedling Town** 2
Radford 0 **Holbrook Miners Welfare** 2

SECOND ROUND

Barrow Town 5 Graham Street Prims 2
Blackwell Miners W. 0 **Gedling Town** 2
Dunkirk 2 Hinckley Downes 1
Ellistown 1 Ibstock United 0
Greenwood Meadows 3 Bardon Hill Spts 1
Holbrook Miners Welfare 4 St Andrews SC 1
Holwell Sports 2 **Borrowash Victoria** 4
Radcliffe Olympic 3 Gresley 3
Replay: **Gresley** 8 Radcliffe Olympic 2

QUARTER-FINALS

Dunkirk 2 Borrowash Victoria 1
Ellistown 3 **Gedling Town** 4 *aet*
Gresley 5 Barrow Town 2
Holbrook Miners Welfare 2 Greenwood Meadows 0

SEMI-FINALS

Dunkirk 2 Holbrook MW 1 *(at Gedling MW)*
Gedling Town 3 Gresley 1 *(at Heanor)*

FINAL

(May 5th at Borrowash Victoria)
Gedling Town 2 Dunkirk 1 *aet*

		P	W	D	L	F	A	Pts
Dunkirk		38	28	6	4	126	38	90
Gresley		38	26	6	6	110	39	84
Holbrook Miners Welfare		38	26	5	7	99	45	83
Bardon Hill Sports		38	26	5	7	113	66	83
Radcliffe Olympic		38	23	7	8	88	49	76
Greenwood Meadows		38	20	8	10	84	53	68
Heanor Town		38	19	8	11	99	70	65
Gedling Miners Welfare		38	20	5	13	69	57	65
Gedling Town	*-3*	38	20	5	13	89	57	62
Hinckley Downes		38	18	4	16	91	81	58
Borrowash Victoria		38	16	6	16	73	70	54
Barrow Town		38	14	5	19	75	81	47
Holwell Sports	*-1*	38	12	8	18	71	72	43
Ibstock United		38	11	9	18	50	78	42
St Andrews SC	*-3*	38	14	3	21	74	117	42
Ellistown		38	8	10	20	62	100	34
Blackwell Miners Welfare		38	7	8	23	56	95	29
Graham Street Prims		38	7	3	28	51	111	24
Radford		38	5	4	29	48	113	19
Anstey Nomads		38	1	3	34	25	161	6

	Anstey N.	Bardon H.	Barrow T.	Blackwell	Borrowash	Dunkirk	Ellistown	G,ling MW	Gedling T.	Graham St	G'wood M.	Gresley	Heanor T.	Hinck. D.	Holbrook	Holwell S.	Ibstock U.	Radcliffe	Radford	St A'drews
Anstey Nomads		0-11	0-3	1-2	1-2	1-10	3-2	1-3	0-1	0-4	1-2	0-6	0-8	0-9	0-1	1-6	1-6	1-1	1-3	2-3
Bardon Hill Sports	5-0		3-2	4-1	4-3	1-5	3-2	0-1	6-4	2-0	1-1	0-5	2-1	6-2	4-2	2-1	5-1	3-3	5-2	5-3
Barrow Town	5-1	1-1		3-1	1-5	2-1	2-3	1-5	2-3	6-1	1-3	1-3	2-3	2-1	2-0	0-2	0-0	3-2	4-3	2-3
Blackwell Miners Welfare	1-0	1-6	0-2		1-1	0-0	0-1	1-2	0-2	5-3	1-3	2-2	2-3	5-2	1-1	1-2	3-3	0-2	1-1	6-4
Borrowash Victoria	7-0	3-4	0-4	3-2		0-1	2-1	1-0	2-2	1-0	0-0	0-2	1-6	3-1	0-3	3-2	2-3	0-2	6-1	2-1
Dunkirk	9-0	1-0	4-0	5-1	4-0		5-4	3-3	5-0	5-0	4-0	4-1	5-1	2-1	1-0	2-2	4-0	1-2	1-0	6-0
Ellistown	3-3	0-3	3-3	2-1	2-4	1-1		1-2	0-4	4-1	0-2	0-4	0-5	0-6	0-3	0-0	2-0	1-5	1-1	1-1
Gedling Miners Welfare	2-0	3-2	1-1	0-0	3-0	3-5	2-2		0-1	5-0	1-0	2-1	1-0	1-2	3-2	2-1	4-0	0-1	1-0	0-3
Gedling Town	7-0	1-1	2-1	3-0	1-1	0-2	2-2	3-0		3-0	2-5	1-2	3-1	2-3	1-4	0-1	1-0	2-0	10-1	4-1
Graham Street Prims	1-0	1-2	1-2	3-4	1-3	1-5	2-1	0-1	0-2		0-4	0-5	1-5	2-0	2-6	2-2	1-1	1-3	1-2	3-5
Greenwood Meadows	3-0	1-1	5-1	7-1	2-2	1-0	5-3	1-0	0-4	0-1		1-3	1-2	6-1	3-1	0-1	1-2	0-1	3-3	1-0
Gresley	5-0	1-0	5-1	3-0	2-1	3-0	2-0	4-1	2-0	6-2	2-1		5-1	2-2	3-4	6-1	4-1	1-1	6-0	1-0
Heanor Town	2-1	4-5	4-3	3-1	1-0	2-2	3-1	3-3	3-1	3-2	3-4	0-0		0-1	0-4	4-1	1-1	1-1	3-2	6-0
Hinckley Downes	2-1	1-2	1-0	6-3	2-2	1-3	5-2	2-3	2-3	5-3	2-4	3-2	4-2		4-0	3-3	2-0	3-6	3-2	2-0
Holbrook Miners Welfare	4-0	2-1	2-2	2-0	1-0	1-1	4-1	1-0	3-1	3-0	1-1	2-0	2-2	2-1		3-2	3-1	4-2	2-1	8-0
Holwell Sports	8-0	0-1	1-3	2-0	1-3	0-2	3-3	4-1	2-2	2-3	1-4	3-3	2-2	0-2	3-1		2-0	0-2	0-2	3-1
Ibstock United	2-1	0-2	1-4	2-2	1-3	2-6	1-1	4-2	2-0	1-0	0-1	0-3	3-3	1-1	0-3	3-1		0-2	1-0	3-2
Radcliffe Olympic	5-0	1-2	2-0	1-3	2-1	1-2	2-3	4-2	2-1	4-4	4-4	1-1	1-0	5-0	1-2	1-0	2-0		4-2	5-0
Radford	3-3	2-3	2-1	3-2	2-4	0-2	1-4	1-3	0-3	1-4	0-2	1-4	0-2	0-3	1-6	0-3	1-2	1-2		0-2
St Andrews SC	4-1	4-5	3-2	2-1	3-2	3-7	4-5	1-3	1-7	2-0	2-2	2-0	2-6	1-0	0-6	4-3	2-2	0-2	5-3	

INS & OUTS

IN: Thurnby Nirvana (P – Leics Senior League Premier Division)
OUT: Dunkirk (P – Midland Alliance). Bardon Hill Sports become Bardon Hill and Holbrook Miners Welfare become Holbrook Sports

ANSTEY NOMADS

Secretary: Chris Hillebrandt **(T)** 0794 685 6430 **(E)** chille1055@hotmail.com
Chairman: Tony Ford **Manager:** Andy Miller **Prog Ed:** Russ&Helen Preston-Hayes
Ground: Cropston Road, Anstey, Leicester LE7 7BP **(T)** 0116 236 4868 **Capacity:**
Colours(change): Red & white stripes/black/red (All green)

ADDITIONAL INFORMATION:
Previous League: Leicestershire Senior

BARDON HILL

Secretary: Adrian Bishop **(T)** 07999 879 841 **(E)** adebishop1@sky.com
Chairman: **Manager:** **Prog Ed:** Terry Gee
Ground: Bardon Close, Coalville, Leicester LE67 4BS **(T)** 01530 815 569 **Capacity:**
Colours(change): All royal blue (All orange)

ADDITIONAL INFORMATION:
Previous League: Leics Senior. **Previous Name:** Bardon Hill Sports

BARROW TOWN

Secretary: Andy Dermott **(T)** 07875 291 365 **(E)** a.dermott514@btinternet.com
Chairman: Michael Bland **Manager:** Dean Martin **Prog Ed:** Andy Dermott
Ground: Riverside Park, Bridge Street, Quorn, Leicestershire LE12 8EN **(T)** 01509 620 650 **Capacity:**
Colours(change): Red & black stripes/black/black (Yellow/blue/blue)

ADDITIONAL INFORMATION:
Previous League: Leicestershire Senior

BLACKWELL MINERS WELFARE

Secretary: Steve Harris **(T)** 07505 366 136 **(E)** steve_harris@bdrmg.co.uk
Chairman: **Manager:** **Prog Ed:** Chris Ryde
Ground: Primrose Hill Sports Ground, Primrose Hill, Blackwell, Alfreton DE55 5JF **(T)** 01773 811 295 **Capacity:**
Colours(change): Red & white stripes/red/red (Purple/black/purple)

ADDITIONAL INFORMATION:
Previous League: Central Midlands

BORROWASH VICTORIA

Secretary: Ian Collins **(T)** 07733 055 212 **(E)** chunkyvics@ntlworld.com
Chairman: Ian Anderson **Manager:** James Fearn **Prog Ed:** Frazer Watson
Ground: Watkinsons Construction Bowl, Borrowash Rd, Spondon, Derby DE21 7PH **(T)** 01332 669 688 **Capacity:**
Colours(change): Red & white stripes/black/black (All blue)

ADDITIONAL INFORMATION:
Previous League: Central Midlands

ELLISTOWN

Secretary: Sue Matthews **(T)** 07881 723 033 **(E)** suematthews7@hotmail.com
Chairman: Andy Roach **Manager:** Danny James **Prog Ed:** Craig Waistell
Ground: Terrace Road, Terrace Road, Ellistown, Leicestershire LE67 1GD **(T)** 01530 230 159 **Capacity:**
Colours(change): Yellow & blue/blue/blue (White & black/black/black)

ADDITIONAL INFORMATION:
Previous League: Leicestershire Senior

GEDLING MINERS WELFARE

Secretary: Norman Hay **(T)** 07748 138 732 **(E)** norman.hay@virginmedia.com
Chairman: Vic Hulme **Manager:** Graham Walker **Prog Ed:** Anthony Hay
Ground: Plains Social Club, Plains Road, Mapperley, Nottingham NG3 5RH **(T)** 0115 926 6300 **Capacity:**
Colours(change): Yellow/blue/yellow (All white)

ADDITIONAL INFORMATION:
Previous League: Central Midlands

GEDLING TOWN

Secretary: Graham Peck **(T)** 07815 458 196 **(E)** graham@peckgraham.orangehome.co.uk
Chairman: Roland Ash **Manager:** **Prog Ed:** Graham Peck
Ground: Riverside Stadium, Stoke Lane, Stoke Bardolf, Nottingham **(T)** 0115 940 2145 **Capacity:**
Colours(change): Yellow/blue/blue (All red)

ADDITIONAL INFORMATION:
Previous League: Northern Counties East

GRAHAM ST. PRIMS

Secretary: Peter Davis **(T)** 07969 160 574 **(E)** j.davis16@sky.com
Chairman: Wayne Harvey-Toon **Manager:** Mark Webster **Prog Ed:** Edward Davis
Ground: Asterdale Sports Centre, Borrowash Road, Spondon, Derbyshire DE21 7PH **(T)** 01332 704 064 **Capacity:**
Colours(change): Red & white/black/black (Blue/red/red)

ADDITIONAL INFORMATION:
Previous League: Central Midlands

GREENWOOD MEADOWS

Secretary: Mark Connors **(T)** 07960 399 812 **(E)** mark@ntextiles.co.uk
Chairman: Mark Burton **Manager:** Neville Silcock **Prog Ed:** Martin Asher
Ground: Lenton Lane Ground, Lenton Lane, Nr Clifton Bridge, Nottingham NG7 2SA **(T)** 07712 530 706 **Capacity:**
Colours(change): Green/black/green (Yellow/green/yellow)

ADDITIONAL INFORMATION:
Previous League: Central Midlands

GRESLEY

Secretary: Reg Shorthouse **(T)** 07779 049 847 **(E)** reg.shorthouse@gresleyfc.com
Chairman: Mark Harrison **Manager:** Gary Norton **Prog Ed:** Robert Mansfield
Ground: The Moat Ground, Moat Street, Church Gresley, Derbyshire DE11 0PQ **(T)** 01283 216 315 **Capacity:**
Colours(change): Red/white/red (White/red/white)

ADDITIONAL INFORMATION:
Previous Name: Gresley Rovers
Previous Leagues: (as Gresley Rovers) West Midlands, Southern

HEANOR TOWN

Secretary: Keith Costello **(T)** 07792 691 843 **(E)** ukinfo@jmcengineering.com
Chairman: **Manager:** Craig Hopkins/Glenn Kirkwood **Prog Ed:** Stan Wilton
Ground: The Town Ground, Mayfield Avenue, Heanor DE75 7EN **(T)** 01773 713 742 **Capacity:**
Colours(change): White/black/black (Red/white/white)

ADDITIONAL INFORMATION:
Previous League: Central Midlands

HINCKLEY

Secretary: Ray Baggott **(T)** 01455 840 088 **(E)** raybaggott@yahoo.co.uk
Chairman: **Manager:** **Prog Ed:**
Ground: Hinckley Utd FC, The Green King Stadium, Leicester Rd, Hinckley LE10 3DR **(T)** 01455 840 088 **Capacity:**
Colours(change): All royal blue (All orange)

ADDITIONAL INFORMATION:
Previous Name: Downes Sports
Previous League: Leicestershire Senior

HOLBROOK SPORTS

Secretary: Chris Sadler **(T)** 07813 680 458 **(E)** chris.sadler@derby-college.ac.uk
Chairman: **Manager:** **Prog Ed:** Chris Sadler
Ground: O'kra Ground, Shaw Lane, Holbrook, Derbyshire DE56 0TG **(T)** 07966 792 011 **Capacity:**
Colours(change): All royal blue (All white)

ADDITIONAL INFORMATION:
Previous Names: Holbrook, Holbrook Miners Welfare
Previous League: Central Midlands

HOLWELL SPORTS

Secretary: Chris Parkin **(T)** 07507 322 489 **(E)** chris@parkin007.co.uk
Chairman: Phil Saddington **Manager:** **Prog Ed:** Linda Parker
Ground: Welby Road, Asfordby Hill, Melton Mowbray, Leicestershire LE14 3RD **(T)** 07523 427 450 **Capacity:**
Colours(change): Yellow/green/green (Sky blue/black/black)

ADDITIONAL INFORMATION:
Previous League: Leicestershire Senior

IBSTOCK UNITED

Secretary: Arthur Lakin **(T)** 07515 752 772 **(E)** artlakin@ntlworld.com
Chairman: Pete Warren **Manager:** **Prog Ed:** Chris Pallett
Ground: The Welfare Ground, Leicester Road, Ibstock, Leicestershire LE67 6HN **(T)** 01974 657 701 **Capacity:**
Colours(change): Red & white/red/red (Blue & white/white/white)

ADDITIONAL INFORMATION:
Previous Name: Ibstock Welfare
Previous League: Leicestershire Senior

RADCLIFFE OLYMPIC

Secretary: Michael Bradley **(T)** 07825 285 024 **(E)** knacks@hotmail.com
Chairman: Nigel Carter **Manager:** **Prog Ed:** Brendan Richardson
Ground: The Rec. Grd, Wharfe Lane, Radcliffe on Trent, Nottingham NG12 2AN **(T)** 07825 285 024 **Capacity:**
Colours(change): Navy blue & red/navy & red/navy (All red)

ADDITIONAL INFORMATION:
Previous Leagues: Notts Alliance, Central Midlands

RADFORD

Secretary: Simon Matters **(T)** 07905 678 886 **(E)** swm1288@hotmail.com
Chairman: Bob Thomas **Manager:** Pete Kelly **Prog Ed:** Howard Bacon
Ground: Selhurst Street, Off Radford Road, Nottingham NG7 5EH **(T)** 0115 942 3250 **Capacity:**
Colours(change): All claret (All light blue)

ADDITIONAL INFORMATION:
Previous League: Central Midlands

ST. ANDREWS

Secretary: Les Botting **(T)** 07793 500 937 **(E)** standrewsfc@btconnect.com
Chairman: Bill Wells **Manager:** **Prog Ed:** Darren Creed
Ground: Canal Street, Aylestone, Leicester LE2 8LA **(T)** 0116 283 9298 **Capacity:**
Colours(change): Black & white stripes/black/red (All blue)

ADDITIONAL INFORMATION:
Previous League: Leicestershire Senior

THURNBY NIRVANA

Secretary: Zak Hajat **(T)** 07811 843 136 **(E)** nirvanafc@hotmail.com
Chairman: **Manager:** **Prog Ed:** Chris Tonge
Ground: Dakyn Road, Thurnby Lodge, Leicester LE5 2ED **(T)** 0116 243 3308 **Capacity:**
Colours(change): All green (Red & black/red & black/black)

ADDITIONAL INFORMATION:
Previous Name: Thurnby Rangers
Previous League: Leicestershire Senior

EASTERN COUNTIES LEAGUE

www.ridgeonsleague.co.uk

Sponsored by: Ridgeons

Founded: 1935

Recent champions:

2005: AFC Sudbury
2006: Lowestoft Town
2007: Wroxham
2008: Soham Town Rangers
2009: Lowestoft Town

Premier Division		P	W	D	L	F	A	Pts
Needham Market		38	27	7	4	83	32	88
CRC		38	27	6	5	96	29	87
Leiston		38	26	4	8	87	38	82
Kirkley & Pakefield		38	22	5	11	76	47	71
Stanway Rovers		38	20	8	10	74	47	68
Mildenhall Town		38	20	6	12	80	59	66
Felixstowe & Walton		38	18	10	10	55	51	64
Wroxham		38	17	8	13	55	51	59
Ely City		38	17	6	15	54	55	57
Dereham Town		38	16	8	14	70	58	56
Wisbech Town	*-2*	38	16	8	14	61	55	54
Haverhill Rovers		38	12	11	15	55	61	47
Walsham-le-Willows		38	13	7	18	53	65	46
Debenham Leis. Cte		38	14	4	20	49	62	46
Norwich United		38	11	10	17	61	67	43
Newmarket Town		38	11	6	21	55	67	39
Histon Res.	*-1*	38	10	5	23	54	84	34
Hadleigh United		38	8	10	20	42	76	34
Woodbridge Town		38	6	2	30	40	102	20
Wivenhoe Town		38	1	5	32	30	124	8

King's Lynn Res., Harwich & Parkeston - records expunged

LEAGUE CUP

PRELIMINARY ROUND

Cornard United 2 **Hadleigh United** 2 *aet* (7-8p)
Ely City 1 King's Lynn Res. 1 *aet* (4-2p)
Godmanchester Rovers 0 **CRC** 1
Kirkley & Pakefield 3 Norwich United 0
Saffron Walden Town 1 Harwich & Parkeston 0 *aet*
Thetford Town 0 **Great Yarmouth Town** 1
Walsham-le-Willows 3 Felixstowe & Walton United 0
Wivenhoe Town 0 **Haverhill Rovers** 3
Woodbridge Town 1 **Needham Market** 3

FIRST ROUND

Dereham 1 **Wroxham** 2 *aet*, Downham 0 **Mildenhall Town** 3
FC Clacton 3 Halstead Town 1
Great Yarmouth Town 3 Gorleston 1 *aet*
Hadleigh United 4 Long Melford 1, **Histon Res.** 8 Ely City 0
Ipswich Wanderers 1 **Walsham-le-Willows** 2
Kirkley & Pakefield 6 Fakenham Town 0, March 0 **CRC** 5
Needham Market 2 Debenham Leisure Centre 0
Newmarket Town 1 Wisbech Town 1 *aet* (3-2p)
Saffron Walden Town 1 **Brantham Athletic** 2
Stanway Rovers 2 **Haverhill Rovers** 3
Stowmarket Town 2 Whitton United 1
Swaffham Town 0 **Diss Town** 1, Team Bury 0 **Leiston** 2

SECOND ROUND

Brantham Athletic 2 **FC Clacton** 4
Great Yarmouth Town 1 **Wroxham** 2 *aet*
Hadleigh United 2 Haverhill Rovers 2 *aet* (3-2p)
Kirkley & Pakefield 2 Diss Town 1 *aet*
Mildenhall Town 3 Histon Res. 2
Newmarket Town 2 CRC 1 *aet*
Stowmarket Town 0 **Needham Market** 3
Walsham-le-Willows 3 Leiston 2

QUARTER-FINALS

FC Clacton 1 **Walsham** 2, Hadleigh Utd 0 **Newmarket Town** 1
Mildenhall 1 **Kirkley** 4, **Needham Market** 1 Wroxham 0

SEMI-FINALS

Kirkley & Pakefield 1 Newmarket Town 0
Walsham-le-Willows 2 **Needham Market** 3

FINAL *(May 3rd at Diss Town)*

Kirkley & Pakefield 1 **Needham Market** 2 *aet*

	CRC	Deb	Der	Ely	Fel	Had	Har	Hav	His	KL	Kir	Lei	Mil	Nee	New	Nor	Sta	Wal	Wis	Wiv	Woo	Wro
CRC		4-2	2-2	3-0	1-1	2-0	n/a	5-0	2-1	1-2	4-1	3-2	3-0	4-1	1-0	2-0	1-1	6-0	1-0	6-0	1-2	2-1
Debenham Leisure Centre	0-2		1-0	2-1	1-2	1-2	6-0	3-3	1-0	4-0	0-1	1-0	0-2	1-2	1-0	0-2	3-1	1-3	2-3	2-0	2-0	0-1
Dereham Town	0-0	2-2		2-3	4-0	0-2	5-1	2-1	2-1	n/a	0-4	1-6	3-0	3-0	3-1	3-0	3-1	1-0	2-4	7-1	6-2	1-3
Ely City	1-4	2-0	1-3	***P***	1-2	1-0	4-2	3-2	1-1	n/a	1-2	1-3	2-0	0-1	3-2	4-2	2-1	0-0	1-0	1-0	1-0	2-1
Felixstowe & Walton Utd	1-1	5-1	1-1	2-0	***R***	1-0	1-0	1-0	4-1	n/a	1-1	0-5	2-2	0-0	2-0	2-1	2-1	2-1	1-0	2-0	5-0	3-0
Hadleigh United	0-2	2-2	2-1	3-3	1-1	***E***	5-1	1-1	1-1	n/a	0-2	0-4	1-3	0-3	0-1	1-4	3-4	0-6	1-1	2-0	3-1	0-1
Harwich & Parkeston	0-6	n/a	n/a	0-5	1-1	0-1	***M***	n/a	n/a	1-0	n/a	0-4	n/a	1-2	1-4	0-4	n/a	n/a	1-6	n/a	0-2	0-2
Haverhill Rovers	2-4	1-0	1-1	1-1	3-0	0-2	n/a	***I***	4-0	n/a	1-1	0-2	2-3	2-2	3-2	1-0	2-0	1-1	1-1	3-2	3-1	0-1
Histon Res.	0-6	0-2	1-0	3-2	1-2	7-2	6-0	0-1	***E***	5-1	1-2	1-6	3-4	0-2	2-2	0-5	0-1	2-3	1-2	5-0	5-0	3-1
King's Lynn Res.	n/a	0-2	n/a	2-1	1-3	n/a	n/a	1-3	1-2	***R***	n/a	n/a	n/a	0-7	3-0	n/a	0-2	2-3	1-1	n/a	0-1	n/a
Kirkley & Pakefield	1-1	3-0	0-3	1-3	4-0	3-2	n/a	2-1	4-0	5-0		2-1	0-2	1-2	3-1	2-1	5-0	0-0	3-2	4-0	3-0	0-2
Leiston	1-0	1-0	3-0	3-2	2-2	2-0	n/a	2-1	2-3	4-0	1-1	***D***	4-1	2-1	2-1	3-1	1-1	0-1	1-2	5-1	2-0	2-1
Mildenhall Town	0-2	2-4	3-3	1-0	0-0	4-0	4-3	0-0	1-1	4-1	3-0	2-1	***I***	1-2	2-0	5-0	2-3	1-0	6-1	9-3	3-0	3-2
Needham Market	3-0	2-1	1-0	2-0	1-1	4-1	2-1	4-2	3-0	n/a	3-2	1-2	5-1	***V***	4-2	1-1	1-0	3-1	5-0	2-0	4-0	0-0
Newmarket Town	1-3	1-1	3-0	0-0	2-0	2-2	5-0	0-1	4-1	n/a	1-2	0-3	2-1	0-1	***I***	2-1	1-1	1-5	2-1	4-1	6-1	1-2
Norwich United	1-3	4-1	1-0	0-2	3-2	1-0	n/a	1-1	1-1	1-0	2-5	1-2	2-3	1-1	4-0	***S***	1-1	3-0	0-0	4-0	0-5	2-2
Stanway Rovers	1-2	1-2	3-0	4-1	5-0	2-0	3-0	0-0	3-0	n/a	2-1	2-0	3-2	1-2	1-0	2-2	***I***	1-0	1-1	2-0	3-1	2-1
Walsham-le-Willows	1-0	0-1	1-1	2-2	1-2	2-3	1-0	3-1	0-1	5-1	0-4	1-4	1-2	2-4	2-1	3-0	1-7	***O***	1-0	4-0	2-1	0-2
Wisbech Town	0-2	5-1	0-2	2-1	1-0	0-0	n/a	4-1	1-0	1-0	3-1	0-1	1-3	0-0	1-1	2-2	1-3	4-1	***N***	5-2	3-0	2-1
Wivenhoe Town	1-5	1-5	1-5	0-1	2-3	0-0	2-0	0-2	1-3	n/a	2-4	1-1	1-1	0-2	4-2	0-3	2-5	2-2	1-4		0-1	0-0
Woodbridge Town	0-6	0-2	1-2	0-2	1-0	1-3	n/a	4-2	1-2	n/a	0-1	1-3	1-2	0-6	0-3	3-3	1-4	0-1	0-2	6-0		3-4
Wroxham	1-0	1-0	1-1	0-2	2-0	2-2	n/a	2-4	5-2	n/a	1-0	1-2	1-0	0-2	2-3	2-1	0-0	1-1	3-2	2-1	2-2	

Division One		P	W	D	L	F	A	Pts
Great Yarmouth Town		36	28	6	2	96	28	90
FC Clacton		36	27	7	2	117	40	88
Brantham Athletic		36	26	6	4	112	34	84
Gorleston		36	25	4	7	67	33	79
Diss Town		36	20	9	7	83	50	69
Halstead Town		36	20	7	9	91	47	67
March Town United		36	20	5	11	71	51	65
Saffron Walden Town		36	16	8	12	66	40	56
Team Bury		36	15	4	17	59	69	49
Whitton United	*-1*	36	13	8	15	51	59	46
Thetford Town		36	11	10	15	51	63	43
Godmanchester Rovers		36	11	9	16	55	70	42
Cornard United		36	10	6	20	51	72	36
Swaffham Town		36	10	5	21	43	84	35
Stowmarket Town		36	9	6	21	46	64	33
Long Melford		36	6	8	22	37	86	26
Ipswich Wanderers		36	7	3	26	39	92	24
Downham Town		36	6	4	26	33	130	22
Fakenham Town		36	2	5	29	28	84	11

DIVISION ONE CUP

PRELIMINARY ROUND

Cornard United 1 **Team Bury** 2

Godmanchester Rovers 5 Thetford Town 0

Swaffham Town 1 **Great Yarmouth Town** 2

FIRST ROUND

FC Clacton 3 Brantham Athletic 0

Godmanchester Rovers 3 March Town United 0

Gorleston 2 Diss Town 1

Great Yarmouth Town 6 Fakenham Town 1

Ipswich Wanderers 1 **Whitton United** 2

Long Melford 0 **Halstead Town** 2

Saffron Walden Town 6 Downham Town 0

Stowmarket Town 4 Team Bury 2

QUARTER-FINALS

FC Clacton 3 Saffron Walden Town 1

Gorleston 2 Stowmarket Town 1

Great Yarmouth Town 0 **Halstead Town** 3

Whitton United 4 Godmanchester Rovers 0

SEMI-FINALS

Gorleston 0 **FC Clacton** 3

Halstead Town 1 Whitton United 1 *aet* (8-7p)

FINAL

(May 7th at Hadleigh United)

FC Clacton 2 Halstead Town 1

	Brantham	Cornard	Diss T.	Downham	FC C'ton	Fak'ham	G'chester	Gorleston	Gt Yarm.	Halstead	I'wich W.	L Melford	March TU	Saff. W.	Stowmkt	Swaffham	T. Bury	Thetford	Whitton
Brantham Athletic		7-0	3-1	9-1	2-3	4-0	7-2	0-2	1-2	2-0	2-0	2-2	2-1	1-0	3-0	5-0	3-2	4-1	2-1
Cornard United	0-2		2-3	5-0	1-5	1-1	1-0	0-2	2-2	1-3	3-0	2-2	1-2	0-3	4-0	1-2	1-0	5-0	0-2
Diss Town	1-1	5-2		6-1	2-0	1-0	1-1	2-2	2-2	0-3	8-1	5-1	2-2	1-0	3-0	0-0	0-0	4-2	2-1
Downham Town	0-6	3-2	1-4	***D***	1-5	2-1	0-5	1-2	0-6	1-3	0-3	1-2	0-3	0-2	2-6	0-5	3-3	1-3	0-0
FC Clacton	0-0	3-0	5-2	9-0	***I***	8-0	3-3	3-2	1-0	3-1	6-3	3-0	3-1	2-2	3-1	6-1	3-1	3-1	5-2
Fakenham Town	0-1	1-2	3-2	1-3	0-4	***V***	0-2	0-1	0-4	1-3	1-2	1-4	1-3	1-6	0-1	3-2	2-4	0-2	0-1
Godmanchester Rovers	0-4	0-3	3-3	1-1	2-2	3-2	***I***	0-1	0-2	5-1	1-1	2-0	3-0	1-3	1-7	1-0	0-1	1-0	1-1
Gorleston	2-5	3-0	1-0	3-1	2-0	1-0	3-0	***S***	0-1	1-2	3-0	4-1	0-0	2-2	2-1	1-0	2-0	4-1	1-0
Great Yarmouth Town	1-1	1-0	3-1	4-0	2-2	2-1	2-1	3-0	***I***	6-0	2-0	3-0	2-1	2-0	2-0	8-0	6-2	3-1	1-0
Halstead Town	1-1	1-1	0-1	9-0	2-2	2-1	2-2	4-1	4-1	***O***	3-1	6-0	2-2	1-0	5-2	4-0	7-0	0-0	1-2
Ipswich Wanderers	0-5	1-1	2-3	4-0	1-5	2-1	1-2	0-2	1-3	0-4	***N***	2-3	1-2	0-3	4-2	1-4	0-4	1-2	2-4
Long Melford	1-3	1-3	1-2	2-2	1-2	2-2	0-4	0-1	0-4	0-4	0-1		0-1	4-2	0-3	2-1	0-1	1-1	1-1
March Town United	3-1	4-2	0-1	4-1	0-2	3-1	2-0	2-0	0-2	1-2	1-0	6-0		1-1	2-1	5-1	4-2	3-1	2-1
Saffron Walden Town	2-2	3-0	0-1	3-0	1-2	2-2	3-2	0-2	1-1	3-0	4-1	0-1	3-0	***O***	1-0	2-1	5-0	2-1	0-1
Stowmarket Town	1-2	0-0	3-0	0-2	0-3	0-0	1-2	1-2	1-2	0-4	2-0	1-1	1-2	3-2	***N***	2-2	1-1	2-1	0-1
Swaffham Town	0-2	3-1	1-3	1-2	1-4	1-0	3-0	0-5	1-2	0-4	3-2	2-0	1-1	1-1	1-3	***E***	4-1	0-2	0-7
Team Bury	0-4	3-1	1-2	5-0	1-2	1-0	4-0	1-2	1-5	2-1	0-1	4-2	4-3	0-0	3-0	0-1		5-3	0-1
Thetford Town	4-8	3-0	1-1	2-1	1-1	1-1	2-1	1-4	1-1	3-1	0-0	3-1	1-2	3-0	0-0	0-0	0-1		0-0
Whitton United	0-5	1-3	1-8	1-2	0-4	1-0	3-3	1-1	2-3	1-1	3-0	1-1	5-2	0-4	1-0	3-0	0-1	1-3	

Reserve Division North		P	W	D	L	F	A	Pts
Lowestoft Town Res.		26	22	2	2	122	22	68
Dereham Town Res.	*+2*	26	21	3	2	84	17	68
Gorleston Res.		26	14	9	3	80	44	51
Walsham-le-Willows Res.		26	14	4	8	71	53	46
Gt Yarmouth Town Res.	*-3*	26	15	0	11	70	54	42
Needham Market Res.	*-3*	26	13	3	10	67	52	39
Woodbridge Town Res.		26	11	3	12	67	64	36
Leiston Res.	*-1*	26	11	3	12	71	70	35
Norwich United Res.		26	9	7	10	46	49	34
Debenham Leis. Cte Res.		26	7	5	14	37	72	26
Stowmarket Town Res.	*-3*	26	7	6	13	50	71	24
Whitton United Res.		26	5	1	20	33	123	16
Thetford Town Res.		26	4	3	19	44	88	15
Diss Town Res.		26	2	5	19	21	84	11

Reserve Division South		P	W	D	L	F	A	Pts
Hadleigh United Res.		26	19	3	4	71	33	60
Braintree Town Res.		26	19	2	5	82	28	59
Witham Town Res.		26	16	3	7	70	45	51
Felixstowe & Walton Res.		26	14	5	7	70	41	47
Brantham Athletic Res.		26	13	6	7	62	46	45
Haverhill Rovers Res.		26	14	2	10	60	40	44
Halstead Town Res.	*-3*	26	14	4	8	48	37	43
Stanway Rovers Res.		26	12	4	10	68	45	40
AFC Sudbury Res.		26	12	4	10	46	38	40
Long Melford Res.		26	10	2	14	38	48	32
Harwich & Parkeston Res.		26	7	7	12	26	49	28
Wivenhoe Town Res.		26	6	0	20	28	66	18
Ipswich Wanderers Res.		26	2	2	22	25	96	8
Cornard United Res.		26	2	0	24	24	106	6

RESERVES CHAMPIONSHIP

(May 11th at Diss Town)

Lowestoft Town Res. 5 Hadleigh United Res. 2

CHELL TROPHY

FINAL *(May 5th at Diss Town)*

Halstead Town Res. 1 Gorleston Res. 1 *aet* (4-3p)

IN: Brantham Athletic (P), FC Clacton (P), Great Yarmouth Town (P)
OUT: Harwich & Parkeston (W/S - Essex & Suffolk Border League Premier Division), King's Lynn Res. (W/S), Needham Market (P – Isthmian League Division One North)

BRANTHAM ATHLETIC

Founded: 1887 Nickname:

Secretary: Andy Powell **(T)** 07919 616 310 **(E)** branthamathfc@hotmail.co.uk
Chairman: Peter Crowhurst **Manager:** Tony Hall and Alan Merchant **Prog Ed:** Andy Powell
Ground: Brantham Leisure Centre, New Village, Brantham CO11 1RZ. **(T)** 01206 392 506
Capacity: 1,200 **Seats:** 200 **Covered:** 200 **Midweek Matchday:** Tuesday **Clubhouse:** Yes **Shop:**

Colours(change): All blue. (Red and black/black/black)
Previous Names: Brantham & Stutton United 1996-98.
Previous Leagues: Eastern Counties. Suffolk & Ipswich.
Records: Att: 1,700 v VS Rugby, FA Vase 5R 1982-83.
Senior Honours: Suffolk & Ipswich Senior League 2007-08

10 YEAR RECORD

00-01	01-02	02-03	03-04	04-05	05-06	06-07	07-08	08-09	09-10
				S&I 1 2	S&I S 14	S&I S 4	S&I S 1	EC1 8	EC1 3

CRC

Founded: Nickname:

Secretary: Jez George **(T)** 07779 099 416 **(E)** jezgeorge@cambridge-united.co.uk
Chairman: Robert Smith **Manager:** Jez George **Prog Ed:** Henry Millward
Ground: Cambridge Utd FC, R Costings Abbey Stad, Newmarket Road CB5 8LN **(T)** 01223 566 500
Capacity: 9,217 **Seats:** 200 **Covered:** Yes **Midweek Matchday:** Wednesday **Clubhouse:** **Shop:** Yes

Colours(change): Amber/black/black (Sky blue and navy stripes/sky blue/sky blue)
Previous Names: None.
Previous Leagues: None
Records:
Senior Honours:

10 YEAR RECORD

00-01	01-02	02-03	03-04	04-05	05-06	06-07	07-08	08-09	09-10
						ECP 17	ECP 13	ECP 2	ECP 2

DEBENHAM LC

Founded: Nickname: The Hornets

Secretary: David Marshall **(T)** 07952 288 298 **(E)** dlmarshall@btinternet.com
Chairman: Stephen Anderson **Manager:** Mel Aldis **Prog Ed:** Ron Raisey
Ground: Debenham Leisure Centre, Gracechurch Street, Debenham IP14 6BL **(T)** 01728 861 101
Capacity: 1,000 **Seats:** 114 **Covered:** 114 **Midweek Matchday:** Wednesday **Clubhouse:** Yes **Shop:** No

Colours(change): Yellow/black/yellow. (All blue).
Previous Names: AFC Debenham.
Previous Leagues: Suffolk & Ipswich.
Records: Att: 400. **Goalscorer:** Lee Briggs. **Apps:** Steve Nelson.
Senior Honours:

10 YEAR RECORD

00-01	01-02	02-03	03-04	04-05	05-06	06-07	07-08	08-09	09-10
	S&I 1 3			S&I S 2	EC1 10	EC1 5	EC1 9	EC1 3	ECP 14

DEREHAM TOWN

Founded: 1884 Nickname: Magpies

Secretary: Ray Bayles **(T)** 07769 644 740 **(E)** ray.bayles@derehamtownfc.co.uk
Chairman: Mike Baldry **Manager:** Matt Henman **Prog Ed:** Barnes Print
Ground: Aldiss Park, Norwich Road, Dereham, Norfolk NR20 3PX **(T)** 01362 690 460
Capacity: 3,000 **Seats:** 50 **Covered:** 500 **Midweek Matchday:** Tuesday **Clubhouse:** Yes **Shop:** Yes

Colours(change): White & black/black/black. (Green & white/green/green)
Previous Names: Dereham and Dereham Hobbies.
Previous Leagues: Norwich District. Dereham & District. Norfolk & Suffolk. Anglian Comb.
Records: Att: 3000 v Norwich City, Friendly, 07/2001.
Senior Honours: Anglian Combination Div.1 Champions 1989-90. Premier 97-98.
Norfolk Senior Cup 2005-06, 06-07.

10 YEAR RECORD

00-01	01-02	02-03	03-04	04-05	05-06	06-07	07-08	08-09	09-10
EC1 2	ECP 13	ECP 19	ECP 18	ECP 15	ECP 12	ECP 6	ECP 4	ECP 4	ECP 10

ELY CITY

Founded: 1885 Nickname: Robins

Secretary: Derek Oakey **(T)** 07720 542 882 **(E)** derek.oakey@tesco.net

Chairman: Robert Button **Manager:** Dennis Lightning **Prog Ed:** Barnes Print

Ground: Unwin Sports Ground, Downham Road, Ely CB6 2SH **(T)** 01353 662 035

Capacity: 1,500 **Seats:** 150 **Covered:** 350 **Midweek Matchday:** Tuesday **Clubhouse:** Yes **Shop:** Yes

Colours(change): All red. (All blue).
Previous Names: None.
Previous Leagues: Peterborough. Central Alliance.
Records: **Att:** 260 v Soham, Eastern Counties Div.1, 12.04.93.
Senior Honours: Cambridgeshire Senior Cup 1947-48. Eastern Counties Div.1 96-97.

10 YEAR RECORD

00-01	01-02	02-03	03-04	04-05	05-06	06-07	07-08	08-09	09-10
ECP 17	ECP 9	ECP 23	EC1 10	EC1 9	EC1 7	EC1 4	EC1 2	ECP 14	ECP 9

FC CLACTON

Founded: 1892 Nickname: The Seasiders

Secretary: Danny Coyle **(T)** 07792 352 187 **(E)** secretary@fcclacton.com

Chairman: David Ballard **Manager:** Steve Pitt **Prog Ed:** Karl Fuller

Ground: Rush Green Bowl, Rush Green Rd, Clacton-on-Sea CO16 7BQ **(T)** 01255 435 051

Capacity: 3,000 **Seats:** 200 **Covered:** Yes **Midweek Matchday:** Tuesday **Clubhouse:** Yes **Shop:** Yes

Colours(change): White/royal blue/royal blue. (Yellow/black/black).
Previous Names: Clacton Town > 2007
Previous Leagues: Eastern Counties. Essex County. Southern League.
Records: **Att:** 3,505 v Romford, FA Cup 1952 at Old Road.
Senior Honours: East Anglian Cup 1953-54, 99-00. Southern League Div.1 59-60.
Eastern Counties Div.1 94-95, 98-99.

10 YEAR RECORD

00-01	01-02	02-03	03-04	04-05	05-06	06-07	07-08	08-09	09-10
ECP 5	ECP 4	ECP 11	ECP 6	ECP 8	ECP 22	ECP 21	EC1 10	EC1 7	EC1 2

FELIXSTOWE & WALTON UNITED

Founded: 2000 Nickname: Seasiders

Secretary: Adrian Hakes **(T)** 07809 391 203 **(E)** Adrian.hakes@btinternet.com

Chairman: Tony Barnes **Manager:** Andy Clarke **Prog Ed:** Phil Griffiths

Ground: Town Ground, Dellwood Avenue, Felixstowe IP11 9HT **(T)** 01394 282 917

Capacity: 2,000 **Seats:** 200 **Covered:** 200 **Midweek Matchday:** Tuesday **Clubhouse:** Yes **Shop:** Yes

Colours(change): Red & white stripes/black/red. (Yellow & blue/yellow/yellow).
Previous Names: Felixstowe Port & Town and Walton United merged in July 2000.
Previous Leagues: None
Records:
Senior Honours:

10 YEAR RECORD

00-01	01-02	02-03	03-04	04-05	05-06	06-07	07-08	08-09	09-10
ECP 18	ECP 21	EC1 16	EC1 15	EC1 17	EC1 2	ECP 13	ECP 8	ECP 12	ECP 7

GREAT YARMOUTH TOWN

Founded: 1897 Nickname:

Secretary: Kevin Smith **(T)** 07914 419 156 **(E)** Kevin.gytfc@yahoo.co.uk

Chairman: Stephen Brierley **Manager:** Paul Tong **Prog Ed:** Gerry Brown

Ground: The Wellesley, Sandown Road, Great Yarmouth NR30 1EY **(T)** 01493 656 099

Capacity: 3,600 **Seats:** 500 **Covered:** 2,100 **Midweek Matchday:** Tuesday **Clubhouse:** Yes **Shop:** Yes

Colours(change): Amber & black stripes/black/black. (All pink).
Previous Names: None
Previous Leagues: Norfolk & Suffolk.
Records: **Att:** 8,944 v Crystal Palace FA Cup R1 52-53. **Goalscorer:** Gordon South - 298 (1927-47). **Apps:** Mark Vincent - 700 (84-05).
Senior Honours: Eastern Counties Champions 1968-69, Division 1 2009-10. Norfolk Senior Cup (x 12)

10 YEAR RECORD

00-01	01-02	02-03	03-04	04-05	05-06	06-07	07-08	08-09	09-10
ECP 8	ECP 17	ECP 8	ECP 16	ECP 22	EC1 13	EC1 13	EC1 11	EC1 5	EC1 1

HADLEIGH UNITED

Founded: 1892 Nickname: Brettsiders

Secretary: Chris Rose **(T)** 07864 828 213 **(E)** chris1rose@btinternet.com

Chairman: Ken Ramsey **Manager:** Stuart Crawford **Prog Ed:** Chris Rose

Ground: Millfield, Tinkers Lane, Duke St, Hadleigh IP7 5NG **(T)** 01473 822 165

Capacity: 3,000 **Seats:** 250 **Covered:** 500 **Midweek Matchday:** Tuesday **Clubhouse:** Yes **Shop:**

Colours(change): White/blue/blue (All red)
Previous Names: None
Previous Leagues: Suffolk & Ipswich.
Records: **Att:** 518 v Halstead Town, FA Vase replay, 17.01.95.
Senior Honours: Suffolk & Ipswich Lge Champions 1953-54, 56-57, 73-74, 76-77, 78-79.
Suffolk Senior Cup 68-69, 71-72, 82-83, 2003-04. Eastern Counties Champions 93-94.

10 YEAR RECORD

00-01	01-02	02-03	03-04	04-05	05-06	06-07	07-08	08-09	09-10
EC1 6	EC1 14	EC1 4	EC1 18	EC1 16	EC1 21	EC1 9	EC1 5	EC1 2	ECP 18

HAVERHILL ROVERS

Founded: 1886 Nickname: Rovers

Secretary: Gary Brown **(T)** 07894 553 267 **(E)** gabrown306@hotmail.com

Chairman: Steve Brown **Manager:** Peter Betts **Prog Ed:** Steven Esdale

Ground: The New Croft, Chalkstone Way, Haverhill, Suffolk CB9 0LD **(T)** 01440 702 137

Capacity: 3,000 **Seats:** 200 **Covered:** 200 **Midweek Matchday:** Tuesday **Clubhouse:** Yes **Shop:**

Colours(change): All red. (White/navy/navy).
Previous Names: None.
Previous Leagues: East Anglian. Essex & Suffolk Border.
Records:
Senior Honours: Essex & Suffolk Border Champions 1947-48, 62-63, 63-64.
Eastern Co. Lge Cup 64-65. Eastern Co. Champions 78-79. Suffolk Sen. Cup 95-96.

10 YEAR RECORD

00-01	01-02	02-03	03-04	04-05	05-06	06-07	07-08	08-09	09-10
EC1 7	EC1 3	EC1 10	EC1 11	EC1 5	EC1 8	EC1 2	ECP 10	ECP 21	ECP 12

HISTON RESERVES

Founded: Nickname:

Secretary: Graham Whiting **(T)** 07879 628 934 **(E)** reserves@histonfc.co.uk

Chairman: (Vice) Angelo Dama **Manager:** TBA **Prog Ed:** Steve Wells

Ground: The Glassworld Stadium, Bridge Road, Impington CB4 9PH **(T)** 01223 237 373 (Matchday only)

Capacity: 3,250 **Seats:** 450 **Covered:** 1,800 **Midweek Matchday:** Wednesday **Clubhouse:** Yes **Shop:** Yes

Colours(change): Red & black stripes/black/black (All royal blue)
Previous Names: None.
Previous Leagues: Cambridgeshire.
Records:
Senior Honours: Cambridgeshire League 1998/99, 00/01

10 YEAR RECORD

00-01	01-02	02-03	03-04	04-05	05-06	06-07	07-08	08-09	09-10
CamP 1	EC1 2	ECP 13	ECP 13	ECP 19	ECP 13	ECP 15	ECP 19	ECP 13	ECP 17

KIRKLEY & PAKEFIELD

Founded: 1886 Nickname: The Kirks

Secretary: Barrie Atkins **(T)** 07970 659 001 **(E)** 2006@tiscali.co.uk

Chairman: Robert Jenkerson **Manager:** Jon Reynolds **Prog Ed:** Ben Atkins

Ground: K. & P. Community Sports & S. Club, Walmer Rd, Lowestoft NR33 7LE **(T)** 01502 513 549

Capacity: 2,000 **Seats:** 150 **Covered:** 150 **Midweek Matchday:** Wednesday **Clubhouse:** Yes **Shop:** Yes

Colours(change): Royal blue & maroon/royal/royal. (All silver).
Previous Names: Kirkley. Kirkley & Waveney 1929-33. Merged with Pakefield in 2007.
Previous Leagues: Norfolk & Suffolk. Anglian Combination.
Records: **Att:** 1,125 v Lowestoft Town. **Goalscorer:** Barry Dale - 241. **Apps:** Barry Dale - 495.
Senior Honours: Suffolk Senior Cup 1900-01, 01-02, 24-25, 00-01, 01-02. Anglian Combination League 2001-02, 02-03.

10 YEAR RECORD

00-01	01-02	02-03	03-04	04-05	05-06	06-07	07-08	08-09	09-10
AngP 3	AngP 1	AngP 1	EC1 5	EC1 3	ECP 14	ECP 7	ECP 6	ECP 6	ECP 4

LEISTON

Founded: 1880 Nickname:

Secretary: David Rees **(T)** 07734 600 414 **(E)** gagrees@aol.com
Chairman: Andrew Crisp **Manager:** Mark Morsley **Prog Ed:** Pat Challis
Ground: LTAA, Victory Road, Leiston IP16 4DQ **(T)** 01728 830 308
Capacity: 2,500 **Seats:** 124 **Covered:** 500 **Midweek Matchday:** Tuesday **Clubhouse:** **Shop:**

Colours(change): All royal blue (Red/white/red)
Previous Names: None
Previous Leagues: Suffolk & Ipswich
Records: **Att:** 271 v AFC Sudbury, 13.11.04. **Goalscorer:** Lee McGlone - 60 (League). **Apps:** Tim Sparkes - 154 (League).
Senior Honours:

10 YEAR RECORD

00-01	01-02	02-03	03-04	04-05	05-06	06-07	07-08	08-09	09-10
S&I S 3	EC1 4	EC1 7	EC1 3	ECP 10	ECP 9	ECP 5	ECP 9	ECP 7	ECP 3

MILDENHALL TOWN

Founded: 1898 Nickname: The Hall

Secretary: Brian Hensby **(T)** 07932 043261 **(E)** bhensby@talktalk.net
Chairman: Martin Tuck **Manager:** Christian Appleford **Prog Ed:** Frank Marshall
Ground: Recreation Way, Mildenhall, Suffolk IP28 7HG **(T)** 01638 713 449
Capacity: 2,00 **Seats:** 50 **Covered:** 200 **Midweek Matchday:** Tuesday **Clubhouse:** Yes **Shop:** Yes

Colours(change): Amber/black/black. (Sky blue & maroon/sky blue & maroon/sky).
Previous Names: None
Previous Leagues: Bury & District. Cambridgeshire. Cambridgeshire Premier.
Records: **Att:** 450 v Derby County, Friendly, July 2001.
Senior Honours:

10 YEAR RECORD

00-01	01-02	02-03	03-04	04-05	05-06	06-07	07-08	08-09	09-10
ECP 15	ECP 11	ECP 10	ECP 12	ECP 6	ECP 5	ECP 2	ECP 5	ECP 11	ECP 6

NEWMARKET TOWN

Founded: 1877 Nickname: The Jockeys

Secretary: Dinah Bugg **(T)** 07775 524 358 **(E)** dinahbugg@talk21.com
Chairman: John Olive **Manager:** Kevin Grainger **Prog Ed:** Dinah Bugg
Ground: Town Ground, Cricket Field Road, Off Cheveley Rd, Newmarket CB8 8BG **(T)** 01638 663 637
Capacity: 2,750 **Seats:** 144 **Covered:** 250 **Midweek Matchday:** Tuesday **Clubhouse:** Yes **Shop:** Yes

Colours(change): Yellow & blue/blue/blue (All red)
Previous Names: None
Previous Leagues: Bury Senior. Ipswich Senior. Essex & Suffolk B. United Counties.
Records: **Att:** 2,701 v Abbey United (now Cambridge Utd) FA Cup, 01.10.49.
Senior Honours: Suffolk Senior Cup 1934-35, 93-94.
Suffolk Premier Cup 93-94, 94-95, 96-97. Eastern Counties Division 1 2008-09.

10 YEAR RECORD

00-01	01-02	02-03	03-04	04-05	05-06	06-07	07-08	08-09	09-10
ECP 20	ECP 19	ECP 18	ECP 10	ECP 13	ECP 17	ECP 12	ECP 21	EC1 1	ECP 16

NORWICH UNITED

Founded: 1903 Nickname: Planters

Secretary: Keith Cutmore **(T)** 07788 437 515 **(E)** secretary.nufc@hotmail.co.uk
Chairman: John Hilditch **Manager:** Paul Chick **Prog Ed:** Barnes Print
Ground: Plantation Park, Blofield, Norwich NR13 4PL **(T)** 01603 716 963
Capacity: 3,000 **Seats:** 100 **Covered:** 1,000 **Midweek Matchday:** Tuesday **Clubhouse:** Yes **Shop:** Yes

Colours(change): Yellow & blue/blue/blue. (All red)
Previous Names: Poringland & District > 1987
Previous Leagues: Norwich & District. Anglian Combination
Records: **Att:** 401 v Wroxham, Eastern Co. Lge, 1991-92. **Goalscorer:** M. Money. **Apps:** Tim Sayer.
Senior Honours: Anglian Combination Senior Cup 1983-84.
Eastern Counties Division 1 1990-91, 01-02.

10 YEAR RECORD

00-01	01-02	02-03	03-04	04-05	05-06	06-07	07-08	08-09	09-10
EC1 10	EC1 1	ECP 16	ECP 11	ECP 14	ECP 20	ECP 16	ECP 15	ECP 19	ECP 15

STANWAY ROVERS

Founded: 1956 Nickname: Rovers

Secretary: Paul Rogers **(T)** 07986 615 481 **(E)** paul.rogers2@ntlworld.com

Chairman: Roy Brett **Manager:** Steve Downey **Prog Ed:** Mike Norfolk

Ground: Hawthorns, New Farm Road, Stanway, Colchester CO3 0PG **(T)** 01206 578 187

Capacity: 1,500 **Seats:** 100 **Covered:** 250 **Midweek Matchday:** Wednesday **Clubhouse:** Yes **Shop:** Yes

Colours(change): Gold & black/black/black. (Light blue/navy/navy).
Previous Names: None.
Previous Leagues: Colchester & East Essex. Essex & Suffolk Border.
Records: **Att:** 210 v Harwich & P, Eastern Co. Lge Div.1, 2004.
Senior Honours: Eastern Counties Div.1 Champions 2005-06. League Cup 2008-09.

10 YEAR RECORD

00-01	01-02	02-03	03-04	04-05	05-06	06-07	07-08	08-09	09-10
EC1 3	EC1 7	EC1 5	EC1 4	EC1 6	EC1 1	ECP 14	ECP 7	ECP 9	ECP 5

WALSHAM-LE-WILLOWS

Founded: 1888 Nickname:

Secretary: Gordon Ross **(T)** 07742 111 892 **(E)** gordonaross@aol.com

Chairman: Mike Powles **Manager:** Christopher Soanes **Prog Ed:** Barnes Print

Ground: Walsham Sports Club, Summer Rd, Walsham-le-Willows IP31 3AH **(T)** 01359 259 298

Capacity: **Seats:** 100 **Covered:** 100 **Midweek Matchday:** Wednesday **Clubhouse:** Yes **Shop:**

Colours(change): Red with yellow trim/red and yellow/red with yellow trim (Royal blue with yellow trim/royal blue/royal blue)
Previous Names: None
Previous Leagues: Bury & District. Suffolk & Ipswich.
Records:
Senior Honours: Suffolk & Ipswich Senior Champions 2001-02, 02-03.
Suffolk Senior Cup 05-06. Eastern Counties Div.1 Champions 06-07.

10 YEAR RECORD

00-01	01-02	02-03	03-04	04-05	05-06	06-07	07-08	08-09	09-10
S&I S 4	S&I S 1	S&I S 1	S&I S 2	EC1 4	EC1 5	EC1 1	ECP 16	ECP 10	ECP 13

WISBECH TOWN

Founded: 1920 Nickname: Fenmen

Secretary: Colin Grant **(T)** 07803 021 699 **(E)** colin@gant5366.freeserve.co.uk

Chairman: Paul Brenchley **Manager:** Steve Appleby **Prog Ed:** Spencer Larham

Ground: The Tom Wood's Fenland Stadium, Lynn Road, Wisbech PE14 7AN **(T)**

Capacity: **Seats:** **Covered:** **Midweek Matchday:** Tuesday **Clubhouse:** **Shop:**

Colours(change): All red. (Yellow/green/yellow).
Previous Names: None
Previous Leagues: East Midlands. Peterborough. United Co. Eastern Co. Midland. Southern.
Records: **Att:** 8,044 v Peterborough Utd, Midland Lge 25/08/1957 **Goalscorer:** Bert Titmarsh - 246 (1931-37) **Apps:** Jamie Brighty - 731
Senior Honours: United Counties Champions 1946-47, 47-48. Southern Lge Div.1 61-62.
Eastern Counties Lge 71-72, 76-77, 90-91. East Anglian Cup 87-88.

10 YEAR RECORD

00-01	01-02	02-03	03-04	04-05	05-06	06-07	07-08	08-09	09-10
SthE 18	SthM 22	ECP 6	ECP 14	ECP 16	ECP 4	ECP 11	ECP 12	ECP 16	ECP 11

WIVENHOE TOWN

Founded: 1925 Nickname: The Dragons

Secretary: Carl Callan **(T)** 07818 596 376 **(E)** carl@nallac.com

Chairman: Carl Callan **Manager:** Mo Osman **Prog Ed:** Richard Charnock

Ground: Broad Lane, Elmstead Road, Wivenhoe CO7 7HA **(T)** 01206 825 380

Capacity: 2876 **Seats:** 161 **Covered:** 1300 **Midweek Matchday:** Tuesday **Clubhouse:** Yes **Shop:** Yes

Colours(change): Blue/white/blue (Yellow/green/yellow)
Previous Names: Wivenhoe Rangers.
Previous Leagues: Brightlingsea & District, Colchester & East Essex. Essex & Suffolk Border, Essex Senior, Isthmian
Records: **Att:** 1,912 v Runcorn, FA Trophy, 1st Round, Feb. 1990. **Goalscorer:** (258 in 350 games). **Apps:** Keith Bain (538).
Senior Honours: Isthmian Div.2 North 1987-88. Div.1 89-90. Essex Senior Trophy 87-88.

10 YEAR RECORD

00-01	01-02	02-03	03-04	04-05	05-06	06-07	07-08	08-09	09-10
Isth2 5	Isth2 21	Isth1N 21	Isth1N 17	SthE 5	SthE 6	Isth1N 11	Isth1N 22	ECP 17	ECP 20

WOODBRIDGE TOWN

Founded: 1885 Nickname: The Woodpeckers

Secretary: Richard Scott **(T)** 07787 980 516 **(E)** richardnscott@btinternet.com
Chairman: John Beecroft **Manager:** Mark Scopes **Prog Ed:** Richard Scott
Ground: Notcutts Park, Fynn Road, Woodbridge IP12 4DA **(T)** 01394 385 308
Capacity: 3,000 **Seats:** 50 **Covered:** 200 **Midweek Matchday:** Wednesday **Clubhouse:** Yes **Shop:** No

Colours(change): Black & white stripes/black/black. (All red).
Previous Names: None.
Previous Leagues: Ipswich & District. Suffolk & Ipswich.
Records: Att: 3,000 v Arsenal, for the opening of the floodlights, 02.10.90.
Senior Honours: Suffolk Senior Cup 1885, 77-78, 92-93, 93-94.
Ipswich & District Senior Champions 1912-13. Suffolk & Ipswich Senior 88-89.

10 YEAR RECORD

00-01	01-02	02-03	03-04	04-05	05-06	06-07	07-08	08-09	09-10
ECP 7	ECP 8	ECP 20	ECP 17	ECP 17	ECP 16	ECP 9	ECP 17	ECP 18	ECP 19

WROXHAM

Founded: 1892 Nickname: Yachtsmen

Secretary: Chris Green **(T)** 07769 783 936 **(E)** secretary@wroxhamfc.com
Chairman: Tom Jarrett **Manager:** David Batch **Prog Ed:** Barnes Print
Ground: Trafford Park, Skinners Lane, Wroxham NR12 8SJ **(T)** 01603 783 538
Capacity: 2,500 **Seats:** 50 **Covered:** 250 **Midweek Matchday:** Tuesday **Clubhouse:** Yes **Shop:** No

Colours(change): Blue & white stripes/blue/blue (All red)
Previous Names: None
Previous Leagues: East Norfolk. Norwich City. East Anglian. Norwich & Dist. Anglian Comb.
Records: Att: 1,011 v Wisbech Town, Eastern Co. Lge, 16.03.93. **Goalscorer:** Matthew Metcalf. **Apps:** Stu Larter.
Senior Honours: Anglian Co. 1981-82, 82-83, 83-84, 84-85, 86-87.
Eastern Co. Div.1 1988-89, Prem 91-92, 92-93, 93-94, 96-97, 97-98, 98-99, 06-07. N'folk Sen'Cup 1992-93, 95-96, 97-98, 99-00, 03-04.

10 YEAR RECORD

00-01	01-02	02-03	03-04	04-05	05-06	06-07	07-08	08-09	09-10
ECP 6	ECP 2	ECP 2	ECP 3	ECP 5	ECP 8	ECP 1	ECP 3	ECP 5	ECP 8

DIVISION 1 INS & OUTS
IN: Cambridge University Press (P - Cambridgeshire County League Premier Division)
OUT: Brantham Athletic (P), FC Clacton (P), Great Yarmouth Town (P)

CAMBRIDGE UNIVERSITY PRESS

Founded: 1893

Secretary: Gary Crick **(T)** 07728 344088 **(E)** gary@cupfc.net
Chairman: Nigel Atkinson **Manager:** Nigel Dixon **Prog Ed:**
Ground: The Cass Centre, Cambridge University Press, Shaftesbury Road, CB2 8BS **(T)** 01223 765129 **Capacity:**
Colours(change): All sky blue (All yellow)

ADDITIONAL INFORMATION: Previous League: Cambridgeshire County > 2010
Honours: Cambridgeshire Senior Cup 1913-14. Cambridgeshire Premier League 1934-35.

CORNARD UNITED

Founded: 1964 Nickname: Ards

Secretary: Chris Symes **(T)** 07811 096832 **(E)** chrissymes@hotmail.com
Chairman: Neil Cottrell **Manager:** Chris Symes **Prog Ed:** Chris Symes
Ground: Blackhouse Lane, Great Cornard, Sudbury, Suffolk CO10 0NL **(T)** 07811 096382 **Capacity:** 2,000
Colours(change): Blue & black stripes/black/blue (Yellow/black/black)

ADDITIONAL INFORMATION: Previous League: Essex & Suffolk Border
Record Att: 400 v Colchester United 1997. **Goalscorer:** Andy Smiles. **Apps:** Keith Featherstone.
Honours: Essex & Suffolk Border League Champions 1988-89. Eastern Counties Div. 1 1989-90. Suffolk Senior Cup 89-90.

DISS TOWN

Founded: 1888 Nickname: Tangerines

Secretary: Steve Flatman **(T)** 07855 531341 **(E)** pam@dissfc.wanadoo.co.uk
Chairman: Richard Upson **Manager:** Robert Taylor **Prog Ed:** Gary Enderby
Ground: Brewers Green Lane, Diss, Norfolk IP22 4QP **(T)** 01379 651223 **Capacity:** 2,500
Colours(change): Tangerine/navy blue/tangerine (Blue/navy/navy)

ADDITIONAL INFORMATION: Previous League: Anglian Combination
Record Att: 1,731 v Atherton LR, FA Vase Semi Final, 19.03.94. **Apps:** Des Tebble.
Honours: Eastern Counties Div.1 Champions 1991-92. FA Vase winners 1993-94.

DOWNHAM TOWN
Founded: 1881 Nickname: Town

Secretary: George Dickson **(T)** 07834 329781 **(E)** george.dickson@britishsugar.com
Chairman: David Green **Manager:** Garth Good **Prog Ed:** Barnes Print
Ground: Memorial Field, Lynn Road, Downham Market PE38 9QE **(T)** 01366 388424 **Capacity:** 1,000
Colours(change): Red/red/red & white (All blue)

ADDITIONAL INFORMATION: Previous League: Peterborough
Record Att: 325 v Wells Town, Norfolk Senior Cup, 1998-99. **Honours:** Peterborough Senior Cup 1962, 63, 67, 72, 87. Peterborough League 1963, 74, 79, 87, 88. Norfolk Senior Cup 1964, 66.

FAKENHAM TOWN
Founded: 1884 Nickname: Ghosts

Secretary: Andrew Mitchell **(T)** 07540 778379 **(E)** andrewmitchell@fakenhamtownfc.co.uk
Chairman: Geoff Saunders **Manager:** Wayne Anderson **Prog Ed:** Paul Wright
Ground: Clipbush Park, Clipbush Lane, Fakenham, Norfolk NR21 8SW **(T)** 01328 855 859 **Capacity:** 3,000
Colours(change): Amber & black stripes/black/amber (Blue & white/blue/blue)

ADDITIONAL INFORMATION: Previous League: Anglian Combination
Record Att: 1,100 v Watford, official opening of new ground.
Honours: Norfolk Senior Cup 1970-71, 72-73, 73-74, 91-92, 93-94, 94-95.

GODMANCHESTER ROVERS
Founded: 1911 Nickname: Goody/Rovers

Secretary: Sue Hurst **(T)** 01480 431659 **(E)** karlsuehurst@hotmail.com
Chairman: Keith Gabb **Manager:** Karl Hurst & David Hurst **Prog Ed:** Sue Hurst
Ground: Bearscroft Lane, Godmanchester, Huntingdon, Cambs PE29 2LQ **(T)** 07774 830507 **Capacity:**
Colours(change): All blue (Red/red/black)

ADDITIONAL INFORMATION: Previous League: Huntingdonshire County
Record Att: 138 v Cambridge City Reserves, Dec. 2003.

GORLESTON
Founded: 1887

Secretary: Ann Santon **(T)** 07597 926329 **(E)** santonmicks@aol.com
Chairman: Jimmy Jones MBE **Manager:** Richard Daniels **Prog Ed:** Jimmy Jones MBE
Ground: Emerald Park, Woodfarm Lane, Gorleston, Norfolk NR31 9AQ **(T)** 01493 602802 **Capacity:** 5,000
Colours(change): Green & white stripes/green/green (Red/black/black)

ADDITIONAL INFORMATION: Previous League: Anglian Combination
Record Att: 4,473 v Orient, FA Cup 1st Round, 29.11.51. **Honours:** Norfolk & Suff. Lge (x 7). Norfolk Senior Cup (x 14). Anglian Comb 1968-69. Eastern Counties Champions 1952-53, 72-73, 79-80, 80-81. Div.1 95-96.

HALSTEAD TOWN
Founded: 1879 Nickname: The Town

Secretary: Steve Webber **(T)** 07763 078563 **(E)** halsteadtownfc@aol.com
Chairman: Jimmy Holder **Manager:** Rob Munro **Prog Ed:** Barnes Print
Ground: Rosemary Lane, Broton Industrial Estate, Halstead, Essex CO9 1HR **(T)** 01787 472082 **Capacity:** 2,000
Colours(change): Black & white stripes/black/black (All blue)

ADDITIONAL INFORMATION: Previous League: Essex Senior
Record Att: 4,000 v Walthamstowe Avenue, Essex Senior Cup 1949.
Honours: Eastern Counties Champions 1994-95, 95-96. Div.1 2002-03. Essex Senior Trophy 1994-95, 96-97.

IPSWICH WANDERERS
Founded: 1983 Nickname: Wanderers

Secretary: Mick Coleman **(T)** 07825 738935 **(E)** mick.coleman4@virgin.net
Chairman: Ed Nicholls **Manager:** Steve Buckle **Prog Ed:** Roger Wosahlo
Ground: SEH Sports Centre, Humber Doucy Lane, Ipswich IP4 3NR **(T)** 01473 728581 **Capacity:** 2,000
Colours(change): Blue & white/blue/blue (All orange)

ADDITIONAL INFORMATION: Previous Name: Lancaster Ipswich
Record Att: 335 v Woodbridge, Eastern Counties League 1993-94.
Honours: Eastern Counties Div.1 Champions 1997-98, 04-05.

LONG MELFORD
Founded: 1868 Nickname: The Villagers

Secretary: Richard Powell **(T)** 07897 751298 **(E)** richard.j.powell@hotmail.co.uk
Chairman: Colin Woodhouse **Manager:** Geoff Cleal **Prog Ed:** Andy Cussans
Ground: Stoneylands Stadium, New Road, Long Melford, Suffolk CO10 9JY **(T)** 01787 312187 **Capacity:**
Colours(change): Black & white stripes/black/black (All white)

ADDITIONAL INFORMATION: Previous League: Essex & Suffolk Border
Honours: Essex & Suffolk Border Champions x5. Suffolk Senior Cup x8.

MARCH TOWN UNITED

Founded: 1885 Nickname: Hares

Secretary: Raymond Bennett (T) 07944 721312 (E) r.bennett639@btinternet.com
Chairman: Philip White **Manager:** Jamie Weston **Prog Ed:** Gary Wesley
Ground: GER Sports Ground, Robin Goodfellow Lane, March, Cambs PE15 8HS (T) 01354 653073 **Capacity:** 4,000
Colours(change): All blue (Tangerine/black/black)

ADDITIONAL INFORMATION: Previous League: United Counties
Record Att: 7,500 v King's Lynn, FA Cup 1956.
Honours: United Counties League 1953-54. Eastern Counties 1987-88.

SAFFRON WALDEN TOWN

Founded: 1872 Nickname: The Bloods

Secretary: Peter Rule (T) 07903 947456 (E) peter.rule@talk21.com
Chairman: John Butchart **Manager:** Marc Das **Prog Ed:** Jim Duvall
Ground: 1 Catons Lane, Saffron Walden, Essex CB10 2DU (T) 01799 522789 **Capacity:** 3,500
Colours(change): Red & black/back/black (Blue & white/blue/white)

ADDITIONAL INFORMATION: Previous League: Essex Senior
Record Goalscorer: Alec Ramsey - 192. **Apps:** Les Page - 538. **Honours:** Essex Senior League 1973-74, 99-00.
Eastern Counties 1982-83. Essex Senior Challenge Trophy 1982-83, 83-84, 84-85.

STOWMARKET TOWN

Founded: 1883

Secretary: Mandy Griffin (T) 01449 614860 (E) footballsecretary@stowmarkettownfc.co.
Chairman: Neil Sharp **Manager:** Steve Jay **Prog Ed:** Nathan Morley
Ground: Greens Meadow, Bury Road, Stowmarket, Suffolk IP14 1JQ (T) 01449 612533 **Capacity:** 2,000
Colours(change): Gold & black/black/black (All red)

ADDITIONAL INFORMATION: Previous Names: Stowuplands Corinthians. Stowmarket Corinthians. Stowmarket FC
Previous League: Essex & Suffolk Border. **Record Att:** 1,200 v Ipswich Town, friendly, July 1994.
Honours: Suffolk Senior Cup x10

SWAFFHAM TOWN

Founded: 1892 Nickname: Pedlars

Secretary: Ray Ewart (T) 07990 526744 (E) rayewart@aol.com
Chairman: Jerome Stockdale **Manager:** Paul Hunt **Prog Ed:** Barnes Print
Ground: Shoemakers Lane, Swaffham, Norfolk PE37 7NT (T) 01760 722700 **Capacity:** 2,000
Colours(change): Black & white stripes/black/black (Tangerine/white/white)

ADDITIONAL INFORMATION: Previous League: Anglian Combination
Record Att: 250 v Downham Town, Eastern Counties League Cup, 03.09.91.
Honours: Eastern Counties Division 1 2000-01.

TEAM BURY

Secretary: Neil Reader (T) 07776 203943 (E) neil.j.reader@wsc.ac.uk
Chairman: Alan Collen **Manager:** TBA **Prog Ed:** Neil Reader
Ground: Bury Town FC, Ram Meadow, Cotton Lane, Bury St Edmunds IP33 1XP (T) 01284 754721 **Capacity:** 3,500
Colours(change): All blue (All red)

ADDITIONAL INFORMATION: Previous League: Essex & Suffolk Border

THETFORD TOWN

Founded: 1883

Secretary: Bob Richards (T) 07795 255160 (E) bobrich60@talktalk.net
Chairman: Michael Bailey **Manager:** Mark Scott **Prog Ed:** Barnes Print
Ground: Recreation Ground, Mundford Road, Thetford, Norfolk IP24 1NB (T) 01842 766120 **Capacity:** 2,000
Colours(change): Claret & blue/claret/claret (White/white/claret)

ADDITIONAL INFORMATION: Previous League: Norfolk & Suffolk
Records Att: 394 v Diss Town, Norfolk Senior Cup, 1991.
Honours: Norfolk Senior Cup 1947-48, 90-91. Norfolk & Suffolk League 1954-55.

WHITTON UNITED

Founded: 1926

Secretary: Phil Pemberton (T) 07848 015638 (E) pemby64@hotmail.com
Chairman: Ruel Fox **Manager:** Ian Brown **Prog Ed:** Phil Pemberton
Ground: King George V Playing Fields, Old Norwich Road, Ipswich IP1 6LE (T) 01473 464030 **Capacity:** 600
Colours(change): Green & white stripes/green/green (Yellow/black/black)

ADDITIONAL INFORMATION: Previous League: Suffolk & Ipswich
Record Att: 528 v Ipswich Town, 29.11.95.
Honours: Suffolk & Ipswich League 1946-47, 47-48, 65-66, 67-68, 91-92, 92-93. Suffolk Senior Cup 1958-59, 62-63, 92-93.

GROUND DIRECTIONS

BRANTHAM ATHLETIC - Brantham Leisure Centre CO11 1RZ - 01206 392 506
Turn off the A12 heading towards East Bergholt, stay on the B1070 through East Bergholt and go straight across the roundabout with the A137. Turn left immediately at the T-junction and follow this road around the sharp curve to the right and turn right immediately before the Village Hall. Follow this road around the sharp left hand turn and the Social Club and the car park are on the right.

CRC - The Trade Recruitment Stadium CB5 8LN - 01223 566 500
Exit the A14 at the fourth junction (situated east of Cambridge), up the slip road to the roundabout (sign posted Stow-Cum-Quy). Turn right onto the A1303, and return westwards towards Cambridge. Go straight over the first roundabout, passing Marshall Airport to the left. Go straight over two sets of traffic lights to a roundabout. The Ground's floodlights can be seen from here and McDonald's is on the right.

DEBENHAM LC - Debenham Leisure Centre IP14 6BL - 01728 861 101
Approach Ipswich along the A14. Turn left at junction 51 onto the A140 signposted towards Norwich. After approx 4 miles turn right towards Mickfield and follow the road into Debenham turning left into Gracechurch Street. Debenham Leisure Centre is approx 1 mile on the right hand side.

DEREHAM TOWN - Aldiss Park, Norwich Road NR20 3PX - 01362 690 460
Take the A47 towards Swaffham & Dereham. Do not take first slip road into Dereham. Carry on along the by-pass and take the second slip road, onto the B1110, sign posted B1147 to Bawdeswell, Swanton Morley and the Dereham Windmill. Follow the slip road round and Aldiss Park is 500 yards on your right.

ELY CITY - Unwin Sports Ground CB6 2SH - 01353 662 035
Follow signs for Kings Lynn/Downham Market as you approach Ely. Don't go into the city centre. After the Little Chef roundabout (junction of A10/A142) continue for approx half a mile until the next roundabout. Turn left for Little Downham (the B1411). There is also a sign for a Golf Course. The Golf Course is part of a Sports Complex which includes the football club. After turning left at the roundabout take another left after only about 50 metres into the Sports Complex entrance. The football club is at the end of the drive past the rugby club and tennis courts.

FC CLACTON - Rush Green Bowl CO16 7BQ - 01255 432 590
Leave the A12 at junction 29, then at roundabout take the 1st exit, then merge onto the A120 (sign posted Clacton, Harwich). Branch left, then merge onto the A133 (sign posted Clacton). Continue along the A133 following signs to Clacton until St Johns Roundabout (tiled Welcome to Clacton sign) take the 4th exit onto St Johns Rd - B1027 (sign posted St Osyth) Entering Clacton On Sea B1027 (fire station on left). B1027 At second mini-roundabout turn left onto Cloes Lane (Budgens on right). Continue down Cloes Lane for about 1/2 mile, passing St.Clares School on your right, at traffic lights, turn right onto Rush Green Rd. Rush Green Bowl will then appear on the right after 1/4 mile.

FELIXSTOWE & WALTON - Town Ground, Dellwood Ave IP11 9HT - 01394 282 917
The A12 meets the A14 (Felixstowe to M1/M6 trunk road) at Copdock interchange, just to the South of Ipswich. For Felixstowe take the A14 heading east over the Orwell Bridge. Follow the A14, for approx. 14 miles until you come to a large roundabout with a large water tower on your right, take the 1st exit off the roundabout, which is straight on. Take the first exit at the next roundabout, straight ahead again. At the next roundabout take the fourth exit onto Beatrice Avenue, take the first left into Dellwood Avenue. The ground is 100 yards down on the left behind tall wooden fencing.

GREAT YARMOUTH TOWN - The Wellesley, Sandown Road NR30 1EY - 01493 656 099
Just off Marine Parade 200 yards north of the Britannia Pier. Half a mile from the BR station.

HADLEIGH UNITED - Millfield, Tinkers Lane IP7 5NG - 01473 822 165
On reaching Hadleigh High Street turn into Duke Street (right next to Library), continue on for approximately 150 metres and take left turn into narrow lane immediately after going over small bridge, continue to end of the lane where you will find the entrance to club car park.

HAVERHILL ROVERS - The New Croft, Chalkstone Way CB9 0LD - 01440 702 137
Take the A143 in to Haverhill and, at the roundabout by Tesco, turn left and then right in the one in front of the store. Carry on over the next roundabout past Aldi on the left and past the Sports Centre, Cricket Club and garage on the left. Just after the Workspace Office Solutions building take a right towards the town centre (towards Parking (South). The drive way into Hamlet Croft is a small turning on the left just after Croft Lane (look for the sign for Tudor Close).

HISTON RESERVES - See Histon

KIRKLEY & PAKEFIELD - K & P Community & Sports Club, Walmer Road, NR33 7LE - 01502 513 549.
From A12 to Lowestoft town centre and go over roundabout at Teamways Garage and past Teamways Pub. Take next left into Walmer Road.

LEISTON - LTAA, Victory Road, Leiston, Suffolk IP16 4DQ - 01728 833 030

MILDENHALL TOWN - Recreation Way, Mildenhall, Suffolk IP28 7HG - 01638 713449 (club)
Next to swimming pool and car park a quarter of a mile from town centre.

NEWMARKET TOWN - Town Ground, Cricket Field Road CB8 8BG - 01638 663 637 (club).
Four hundred yards from Newmarket BR.Turn right into Green Road and right at cross roads into new Cheveley Rd. Ground is at top on left.

NORWICH UNITED - Plantation Park, Blofield, Norwich, Norfolk NR13 4PL - 01603 716963
Off the A47.

STANWAY ROVERS - `Hawthorns', New Farm Road CO3 0PG - 01206 578 187
Leave A12 at Jct 26 to A1124. Turn right(from London)or left from Ipswich onto Essex Yeomanry Way. A1124 towards Colchester 1st right into Villa Rd,then left into Chaple Rd, and left into New Farm Rd. Ground 400 yds on left.Nearest BR station is Colchester North.

WALSHAM LE WILLOWS - Walsham Sports Club, Summer Road IP31 3AH 01359 259 298
From Bury - Diss road (A143) turn off down Summer Lane in Walsham-le-Willows and ground is on the right.

WISBECH TOWN - The Tom Wood's Fenland Stadium, Lynn Road, Wisbech PE14 7AN
The Tom Wood's Bear Fenland Stadium is on the B198 Lynn Road, just on the northern outskirts of Wisbech.

WIVENHOE TOWN - Broad Lane, Elmstead Road CO7 7HA - 01206 825 380
The ground is situated off the B1027 to the north of Wivenhoe.

WOODBRIDGE TOWN - Notcutts Park, Seckford Hall Road IP12 4DA - 01394 385 308
From Lowestoft turn left into Woodbridge at last roundabout (or first roundabout from Ipswich). Take first turning left and first left again. Drive to ground at end of road on left.

WROXHAM - Trafford Park, Skinners Lane NR12 8SJ - 01603 783 538
From Norwich, turn left at former Castle Pub and keep left to ground. Under two miles from Wroxham & Hoveton BR. Buses 722,724 and 717.

DIVISION ONE

CAMBRIDGE UNI. PRESS - Cass Centre, Shaftesbury Road CB2 8BS - 01223 765 129

CORNARD UNITED - Blackhouse Lane CO10 0NL - 07811 096 382
Left off roundabout on A134 coming from Ipswich/Colchester into Sudbury, follow signs for Country Park - ground is immediately opposite along Blackhouse Lane.

DISS TOWN - Brewers Green Lane IP22 4QP - 01379 651 223
Off B1066 Diss -Thetford road near Roydon school. One and a half miles from Diss (BR).

DOWNHAM TOWN - Memorial Field, Lynn Road PE38 9QE - 01366 388 424
One and a quarter miles from Downham Market (BR) - continue to town clock, turn left and ground is three quarters of a mile down Lynn Road.

FAKENHAM TOWN - Clipbush Pk, Clipbush Lane NR21 8SW - 01328 855 859
Corner of A148 & Clipbush Lane.

GODMANCHESTER ROVERS - Bearscroft Lane PE29 2LQ - 07774 830 507
From A14 turn off for Godmanchester. Take A1198 towards Wood Green Animal Shelter, Bearscroft Lane is half mile from A14 on the left.

GORLESTON - Emerald Park, Woodfarm Lane NR31 9AQ - 01493 602 802
On Magdalen Estate follow signs to Crematorium, turn left and follow road to ground.

HALSTEAD TOWN - Rosemary Lane CO9 1HR - 01787 472 082
From A1311 Chelmsford to Braintree road follow signs to Halstead.

IPSWICH WANDERERS - SEH Sports Centre IP4 3NR 01473 728 581

LONG MELFORD - Stoneylands Stadium CO10 9JY - 01787 312 187
Turn down St Catherine Road off Hall St (Bury-Sudbury road) and then turn left into New Road.

MARCH TOWN UNITED - GER Sports Ground PE15 8HS - 01354 653 073
5 mins from town centre, 10 mins from BR station.

SAFFRON WALDEN TOWN - Catons Lane CB10 2DU - 01799 522 789
Into Castle St off Saffron-W High St. Then left at T jct and 1st left by Victory Pub.

STOWMARKET TOWN - Greens Meadow, Bury Road IP14 1JQ - 01449 612 533
About 800 yards from Stowmarket station (BR).Turn right at lights and head out of town over roundabout into Bury Road, Ground is on the right.

SWAFFHAM TOWN - Shoemakers Lane PE37 7NT - 01760 722 700

TEAM BURY - Ram Meadow, Cotton Lane IP33 1XP - 01284 754 721

THETFORD TOWN - Recreation Ground, Munford Road IP24 1NB - 01842 766 120
Off bypass (A11) at A143 junction - ground 800 yards next to sports ground.

WHITTON UNITED - King George V Playing Fields IP1 6LE - 01473 464 030
Turn off A14, junction A1156 approx 3 miles west of A12/A14 junction.

ESSEX SENIOR LEAGUE

essexseniorfootballleague.moonfruit.com

Sponsored by:

No sponsor

Founded: 1971

Recent champions:

2005: Enfield Town

2006: AFC Hornchurch

2007: Brentwood Town

2008: Concord Rgrs

2009: Romford

		P	W	D	L	F	A	Pts
Stansted		34	22	8	4	99	35	74
Witham Town	*-3*	34	22	5	7	81	44	68
Burnham Ramblers		34	20	7	7	86	44	67
Enfield	*-1*	34	19	7	8	63	38	63
Bethnal Green United		34	17	10	7	73	38	61
Southend Manor		34	15	9	10	66	47	54
Barking		34	16	6	12	49	33	54
Takeley	*-3*	34	16	7	11	55	40	52
Barkingside	*-3*	34	15	10	9	62	50	52
Sawbridgeworth Town		34	13	6	15	44	75	45
Hullbridge Sports		34	10	10	14	50	54	40
Basildon United	*-3*	34	12	6	16	47	69	39
London APSA		34	10	7	17	38	55	37
Tiptree United		34	11	1	22	49	82	34
Eton Manor		34	8	9	17	57	71	33
Clapton		34	9	3	22	38	86	30
Bowers & Pitsea		34	8	5	21	48	77	29
Mauritius Spts Assn		34	3	4	27	30	97	13

	Barking	Barkingside	Basildon Utd	Bethnal GU	Bowers & Pit.	Burnham R.	Clapton	Enfield	Eton Manor	Hullbridge S.	London APSA	Mauritius SA	S'bridgeworth	Southend Mnr	Stansted	Takeley	Tiptree Utd	Witham Town
Barking		1-1	0-1	1-0	1-0	0-1	6-0	0-2	1-1	2-1	2-0	3-0	0-1	2-1	0-1	1-0	4-1	1-2
Barkingside	1-3		1-1	0-1	3-2	1-1	1-2	1-1	0-1	5-2	1-2	2-0	1-2	4-2	1-0	2-0	4-0	2-2
Basildon United	1-3	1-2		3-2	2-2	2-2	1-2	2-1	0-4	3-2	1-0	0-0	4-2	0-1	1-3	2-1	3-1	1-2
Bethnal Green United	0-0	1-1	3-2		1-0	0-2	6-0	1-1	2-0	3-1	2-1	3-0	6-1	2-2	0-0	2-0	3-2	1-1
Bowers & Pitsea	1-3	1-3	1-0	2-0		2-2	5-3	0-4	4-2	1-1	1-2	5-1	0-1	1-4	0-4	1-3	1-4	1-3
Burnham Ramblers	1-0	1-1	4-2	1-2	4-1		5-0	2-0	3-3	1-2	2-0	3-3	2-4	2-2	1-2	6-0	2-1	2-3
Clapton	3-1	1-2	3-1	0-3	2-1	0-5		0-5	2-0	0-1	2-2	2-0	0-4	0-3	1-1	0-3	0-1	0-1
Enfield	0-0	2-0	2-1	0-5	4-0	3-2	2-0		1-1	3-2	0-2	4-1	3-0	2-0	2-4	1-0	2-1	0-1
Eton Manor	0-3	2-3	1-3	3-3	3-3	3-4	2-1	0-2		1-1	3-2	4-1	2-0	1-1	1-2	0-4	4-0	1-3
Hullbridge Sports	1-1	4-4	3-1	0-2	1-0	0-1	2-2	1-1	2-1		1-0	4-0	3-0	1-2	3-3	0-1	0-2	3-2
London APSA	0-2	0-2	3-0	1-1	1-1	2-4	1-0	1-1	1-1	2-0		3-2	0-0	1-2	1-3	0-2	1-0	0-1
Mauritius Sports Association	0-2	1-2	1-2	0-6	1-2	1-5	1-0	0-2	1-2	1-0	1-1		2-2	2-3	0-1	2-1	0-1	1-4
Sawbridgeworth Town	0-0	0-4	1-2	0-4	2-1	0-4	2-1	3-1	2-1	2-0	1-2	4-1		1-5	1-4	2-2	3-2	1-1
Southend Manor	3-1	1-1	0-0	3-2	4-0	0-1	1-4	3-1	4-1	1-1	2-1	6-1	0-1		0-0	0-0	6-0	1-2
Stansted	4-2	5-0	0-0	4-1	4-0	3-2	9-2	3-5	3-1	1-1	4-0	5-1	8-0	2-2		0-0	9-0	4-1
Takeley	2-0	0-0	2-3	3-3	0-4	0-2	2-0	0-0	4-3	1-0	6-1	6-1	1-1	3-0	0-2		2-0	1-0
Tiptree United	1-3	5-3	4-1	1-1	1-2	1-3	1-2	1-3	4-3	1-3	1-3	3-1	3-0	3-1	2-1	1-2		0-1
Witham Town	2-0	2-3	10-0	2-1	3-2	0-3	5-3	0-2	1-1	3-3	3-1	4-2	5-0	3-0	3-0	0-3	5-0	

GORDON BRASTED TROPHY

FIRST ROUND

Eton Manor 0 **Bowers & Pitsea** 3

Hullbridge Sports 2 London APSA 2 *aet* (5-4p)

SECOND ROUND

Bethnal Green United 4 Barking 1

Bowers & Pitsea 3 **Sawbridgeworth Town** 4 *aet*

Burnham Ramblers 2 **Basildon United** 3

Clapton 1 **Tiptree United** 2

Southend Manor 2 Enfield 1

Stansted 1 **Barkingside** 3

Takeley 2 Hullbridge Sports 1

Witham Town 2 Mauritius Sports Association 1

QUARTER-FINALS

Barkingside 0 **Bethnal Green United** 2

Basildon United 1 **Southend Manor** 1 *aet* (3-5p)

Takeley 4 Sawbridgeworth Town 0

Tiptree United 1 **Witham Town** 4

SEMI-FINALS

Bethnal Green United (w/o) v Southend Manor

Witham Town 1 **Takeley** 1 aet (2-3p)

FINAL

(April 5th at Burnham Ramblers)

Bethnal Green United 2 Takeley 0

ESSEX SENIOR LEAGUE CUP

GROUP A

	P	W	D	L	F	A	Pts
Burnham Ramblers	4	2	2	0	8	5	8
London APSA	4	2	1	1	7	4	7
Enfield	4	0	1	3	2	8	1

Burnham Ramblers 3 Enfield 1
Burnham Ramblers 3 London APSA 3
Enfield 1 Burnham Ramblers 1
Enfield 0 London APSA 1
London APSA 0 Burnham Ramblers 1
London APSA 3 Enfield 0

GROUP B

	P	W	D	L	F	A	Pts
Takeley	4	3	1	0	9	4	10
Stansted	4	1	1	2	6	7	4
Witham Town	4	0	2	2	5	9	2

Stansted 0 Takeley 3
Stansted 2 Witham Town 2
Takeley 2 Stansted 1
Takeley 1 Witham Town 1
Witham Town 0 Stansted 3
Witham Town 2 Takeley 3

GROUP C

	P	W	D	L	F	A	Pts
Eton Manor	4	2	2	0	9	7	8
Basildon United	4	1	1	2	7	6	4
Clapton	4	1	1	2	4	7	4

Basildon United 3 Clapton 0
Basildon United 2 Eton Manor 3
Clapton 1 Basildon United 0
Clapton 3 Eton Manor 3
Eton Manor 2 Basildon United 2
Eton Manor 1 Clapton 0

GROUP D

	P	W	D	L	F	A	Pts
Barkingside	4	3	1	0	13	5	10
Sawbridgeworth Town	4	1	1	2	7	10	4
Mauritius Sports Ass.	4	0	2	2	5	10	2

Barkingside 4 Mauritius Sports Association 2
Barkingside 4 Sawbridgeworth Town 2
Mauritius Sports Association 1 Barkingside 1
Mauritius Sports Association 1 Sawbridgeworth Town 4
Sawbridgeworth Town 0 Barkingside 4
Sawbridgeworth Town 1 Mauritius Sports Association 1

GROUP E

	P	W	D	L	F	A	Pts
Bowers & Pitsea	4	2	1	1	9	6	7
Tiptree United	4	2	1	1	9	7	7
Hullbridge Sports	4	0	2	2	5	10	2

Bowers & Pitsea 3 Hullbridge Sports 3
Bowers & Pitsea 1 Tiptree United 3
Hullbridge Sports 0 Bowers & Pitsea 1
Hullbridge Sports 0 Tiptree United 4
Tiptree United 0 Bowers & Pitsea 4
Tiptree United 2 Hullbridge Sports 2

GROUP F

	P	W	D	L	F	A	Pts
Bethnal Green United	4	2	1	1	8	5	7
Barking	4	2	0	2	8	12	6
Southend Manor	4	1	1	2	9	8	4

Barking 1 Bethnal Green United 4
Barking 2 Southend Manor 5
Bethnal Green United 1 Barking 2
Bethnal Green United 1 Southend Manor 0
Southend Manor 2 Barking 3
Southend Manor 2 Bethnal Green United 2

QUARTER-FINALS

(played over two legs)

Barkingside 3 Bethnal Green United 3, **Bethnal Green United** 2 Barkingside 1
Bowers & Pitsea 1 Burnham Ramblers 4, **Burnham Ramblers** 4 Bowers & Pitsea 1
Eton Manor 5 Tiptree United 0, Tiptree United 1 **Eton Manor** 4
Takeley 3 London APSA 1, London APSA 0 **Takeley** 1

SEMI-FINALS

(played over two legs)

Eton Manor 1 Burnham Ramblers 2, **Burnham Ramblers** 4 Eton Manor 1
Takeley 1 Bethnal Green United 1, **Bethnal Green United** 1 Takeley 0

FINAL

(May 3rd at Bowers & Pitsea)

Burnham Ramblers 1 **Bethnal Green United** 4

INS & OUTS

OUT: Tiptree United (having merged with Isthmian League Division One club Maldon Town)
Enfield have merged with Brimsdown Rovers

BARKING

Founded: 1880 Nickname: The Blues

Secretary: John Faherty **(T)** 0776 458 7112 **(E)** secretary@barking-fc.co.uk
Chairman: Gillian Faherty **Manager:** Steve Munday **Prog Ed:** Norman Dean
Ground: Mayesbrook Park, Lodge Avenue, Dagenham RM8 2JR **(T)** 0776 458 7112.
Capacity: 2,500 **Seats:** 200 **Covered:** 600 **Midweek Matchday:** Tuesday **Clubhouse:** Yes **Shop:** Yes

Colours(change): All blue. (All yellow).
Previous Names: Barking Rov. Barking Woodville. Barking Working Lads Institute, Barking Institute. Barking T. Barking & East Ham U.
Previous Leagues: South Essex, London, Athenian. Isthmian. Southern.
Records: **Att:** 1,972 v Aldershot, FA Cup 2nd Rnd, 1978. **Goalscorer:** Neville Fox - 241 (65-73). **Apps:** Bob Makin - 566.
Senior Honours: FA Amateur Cup R-Up 1926-27. Athenian League Champions 1934-35. Isthmian League 1978-79.
Essex Senior Cup 1893-94, 95-96, 1919-20, 45-46, 62-63, 69-70, 89-90. London Senior Cup 1911-12, 20-21, 26-27, 78-79.

10 YEAR RECORD

00-01	01-02	02-03	03-04	04-05	05-06	06-07	07-08	08-09	09-10
Isth2 3	Isth1 21	Isth1N 12	Isth1N 23	SthE 6	SthE 5	ESen 6	ESen 9	ESen 12	ESen 8

BARKINGSIDE

Founded: 1898 Nickname:

Secretary: James Flanagan **(T)** 07956 894 194 **(E)** confclothing@aol.com
Chairman: Jimmy Flanagan **Manager:** Tony Fenn **Prog Ed:** Jimmy Flanagan
Ground: Oakside Stadium, Station Road, Barkingside IG6 1NB **(T)** 0208 550 3611
Capacity: 3,000 **Seats:** 350 **Covered:** 850 **Midweek Matchday:** Monday **Clubhouse:** Yes **Shop:** No

Colours(change): Sky blue/navy blue/navy blue. (Pink & black stripes/black/black)
Previous Names: None
Previous Leagues: London. Greater London. Met London. Spartan, South Midlands.
Records: **Att:** 957 v Arsenal Reserves, London League, 1957.
Senior Honours: Greater London League 1964-65. Spartan League 96-97.
London Senior Cup 96-97. Spartan South Midlands Premier 98-99. Essex Senior Cup 2008-09.

10 YEAR RECORD

00-01	01-02	02-03	03-04	04-05	05-06	06-07	07-08	08-09	09-10
ESen 3	ESen 13	ESen 9	ESen 11	ESen 4	ESen 4	ESen 3	ESen 3	ESen 5	ESen 9

BASILDON UNITED

Founded: 1963 Nickname:

Secretary: Richard Mann **(T)** 0796 435 6642 **(E)** rm006e7184@blueyonder.co.uk
Chairman: TBC **Manager:** John Doyle **Prog Ed:** Richard Mann
Ground: The Stadium, Gardiners Close, Basildon SS14 3AW **(T)** 01268 520 268
Capacity: 2,000 **Seats:** 400 **Covered:** 1,000 **Midweek Matchday:** Tuesday **Clubhouse:** Yes **Shop:** No

Colours(change): Amber & black/black/black. (Green & white).
Previous Names: Armada Sports.
Previous Leagues: Grays & Thurrock. Greater London. Essex Senior. Athenian. Isthmian.
Records: **Att:** 4,000 v West Ham, ground opening 11.08.70.
Senior Honours: Essex Senior League Champions 1976-77, 77-78, 78-79, 79-80, 93-94.
Isthmian League Div.2 Champions 83-84.

10 YEAR RECORD

00-01	01-02	02-03	03-04	04-05	05-06	06-07	07-08	08-09	09-10
ESen 8	ESen 10	ESen 13	ESen 7	ESen 7	ESen 11	ESen 10	ESen 16	ESen 8	ESen 12

BETHNAL GREEN UNITED

Founded: 2000 Nickname:

Secretary: Akhtar Ahmed **(T)** 07590 568 422 **(E)** akhtarx@hotmail.com
Chairman: Mohammed Nural Hoque **Manager:** Justin Gardner **Prog Ed:** Akhtar Ahmed
Ground: Mile End Stadium, Rhodeswell Rd, Poplar E14 7TW **(T)** 07958 291 282
Capacity: **Seats:** Yes **Covered:** Yes **Midweek Matchday:** Wednesday **Clubhouse:** **Shop:**

Colours(change): Green & white. (Orange/black/black)
Previous Names: None.
Previous Leagues: Middlesex 2000-09.
Records:
Senior Honours: Middlesex League Champions 2008-09

10 YEAR RECORD

00-01	01-02	02-03	03-04	04-05	05-06	06-07	07-08	08-09	09-10
			Midx1 2	MidxP 7			MidxP 8	MidxP 1	ESen 5

BOWERS & PITSEA

Founded: 1946 Nickname:

Secretary: Lee Stevens **(T)** 07910 626 727 **(E)** lee-stevens@sky.com
Chairman: Barry Hubbard **Manager:** Colin Cook **Prog Ed:** Lee Stevens
Ground: Len Salmon Stadium, Crown Avenue, Pitsea, Basildon SS13 2BE **(T)** 01268 581 977
Capacity: 2,000 **Seats:** 200 **Covered:** 1,000 **Midweek Matchday:** Wednesday **Clubhouse:** Yes **Shop:** Yes

Colours(change): All claret. (All sky blue).
Previous Names: Bowers United > 2004.
Previous Leagues: Thurrock & Thameside Combination. Olympian.
Records: **Att:** 1,800 v Billericay Town, FA Vase.
Senior Honours: Essex Senior Champions 1980-81, 98-99.

10 YEAR RECORD

00-01	01-02	02-03	03-04	04-05	05-06	06-07	07-08	08-09	09-10
ESen 7	ESen 6	ESen 7	ESen 8	ESen 10	ESen 15	ESen 4	ESen 7	ESen 11	ESen 17

BURNHAM RAMBLERS

Founded: 1900 Nickname: Ramblers

Secretary: Shaun Pugh **(T)** 0752 509 9914 **(E)** secretarybrfc@sapugh.gotadsl.co.uk
Chairman: William Hannan **Manager:** Keith Wilson **Prog Ed:** Martin Leno
Ground: Leslie Fields Stadium, Springfield Road CM0 8AU **(T)** 01621 784 383
Capacity: 2,000 **Seats:** 156 **Covered:** 300 **Midweek Matchday:** Tuesday **Clubhouse:** Yes **Shop:** No

Colours(change): Royal blue & black stripes/black/royal blue. (White/blue/white).
Previous Names: None
Previous Leagues: North Essex. Mid-Essex. Olympian. South East Essex.
Records: **Att:** 1,500 v Arsenal, opening of stand.
Senior Honours:

10 YEAR RECORD

00-01	01-02	02-03	03-04	04-05	05-06	06-07	07-08	08-09	09-10
ESen 14	ESen 3	ESen 8	ESen 12	ESen 2	ESen 5	ESen 5	ESen 8	ESen 7	ESen 3

CLAPTON

Founded: 1878 Nickname: Tons

Secretary: Shirley Doyle **(T)** 0798 358 8883 **(E)** shirley.10@hotmail.co.uk
Chairman: Dennis Wright **Manager:** Wilfred Thomas **Prog Ed:** Dennis Wright
Ground: The Old Spotted Dog, Upton Lane, Forest Gate E7 9NU **(T)** 0208 472 0822
Capacity: 2,000 **Seats:** 100 **Covered:** 180 **Midweek Matchday:** Tuesday **Clubhouse:** Yes **Shop:** No

Colours(change): Red & white stripes/black/red (Yellow & blue/blue/blue or Red & black stripes/black/red)
Previous Names: None
Previous Leagues: Southern (founder member). London. Isthmian (founder member).
Records: **Att:** 12,000 v Tottenham Hotspur, FA Cup, 1898-99. First English club to play on the continent, beating a Belgian XI in 1890.
Senior Honours: FA Amateur Cup 1906-07, 08-09, 14-15, 23-24, 24-25.
Isthmian Lge Champions 10-11, 22-23. Div.2 82-83. Essex Senior Cup (x 4).

10 YEAR RECORD

00-01	01-02	02-03	03-04	04-05	05-06	06-07	07-08	08-09	09-10
Isth3 21	Isth3 21	Isth2 9	Isth2 15	Isth2 16	Isth2 16	ESen 14	ESen 11	ESen 16	ESen 16

ENFIELD 1893 FC

Founded: 1893 Nickname:

Secretary: Mark Wiggs **(T)** 0754 593 9791 **(E)** enfieldfc@ntlworld.com
Chairman: Steve Whittington **Manager:** Kevin Lucas & Justin Molesey **Prog Ed:** Mark Kettlety
Ground: Goldsdown Road, Enfield, Middlesex EN3 7RP **(T)** 0795 764 7820
Capacity: 500 **Seats:** 300 **Covered:** Yes **Midweek Matchday:** Wednesday **Clubhouse:** Yes **Shop:**

Colours(change): White/blue/white. (Black & white stripes/black/black).
Previous Names: Enfield Spartans > 1900. Enfield > 2007.
Previous Leagues: Tottenham & District, North Middlesex, London, Athenian, Isthmian, Alliance, Southern
Records: **Att:** 10,000 v Spurs, floodlight opening at Southbury Rd., 10.10.62. **Goals:** Tommy Lawrence - 191 (1959-64). **Apps:** Andy Pape - 643 (85-92 93-99)
Senior Honours: Athenian 1961-62, 62-63. Isthmian 67-68, 68-69, 69-70, 75-76, 76-77,
77-78, 79-80, 94-95. FA Trophy 81-82, 87-88. Alliance 82-83, 85-86. FA Am. C. 66-67, 69-70

10 YEAR RECORD

00-01	01-02	02-03	03-04	04-05	05-06	06-07	07-08	08-09	09-10
Isth P 18	Isth P 19	Isth P 23	Isth1N 24	Isth2 2	SthE 16	Isth1N 13	ESen 2	ESen 2	ESen 4

ETON MANOR

Founded: 1901 Nickname: The Manor

Secretary: John Gibbons (T) 07802 392 897 (E) emfc@hotmail.co.uk
Chairman: Reg Curtis **Manager:** Kevin Durrant **Prog Ed:** John Gibbons
Ground: Barking FC, Mayesbrook Park, Lodge Ave, Dagenham RM8 2JR. (T)
Capacity: 2,500 **Seats:** 200 **Covered:** 600 **Midweek Matchday:** Wednesday **Clubhouse:** Yes **Shop:**

Colours(change): Sky blue & navy. (Black & white stripes/black/black).
Previous Names: Wildernes Leyton.
Previous Leagues: London. Greater London. Metropolitan.
Records: **Att:** 600 v Leyton Orient, opening of floodlights. **Goalscorer:** Dave Sams.
Senior Honours: Essex Senior League Cup 2007-08.

10 YEAR RECORD

00-01	01-02	02-03	03-04	04-05	05-06	06-07	07-08	08-09	09-10
ESen 15	ESen 15	ESen 16	ESen 9	ESen 12	ESen 13	ESen 11	ESen 4	ESen 6	ESen 15

HULLBRIDGE SPORTS

Founded: 1945 Nickname:

Secretary: Mrs Beryl Petre (T) 0776 836 3791 (E) beryl@petre1942.fsnet.co.uk
Chairman: TBC **Manager:** Enrico Tritera **Prog Ed:** Beryl Petre
Ground: Lower Road, Hullbridge, Hockley Essex SS5 6BJ (T) 01702 230 420
Capacity: 1,500 **Seats:** 60 **Covered:** 60 **Midweek Matchday:** Tuesday **Clubhouse:** Yes **Shop:** No

Colours(change): Royal blue & white stripes/royal/royal. (All red).
Previous Names: None
Previous Leagues: Southend & District. Southend Alliance.
Records: **Att:** 800 v Blackburn Rovers, FA Youth Cup 1999-00.
Senior Honours:

10 YEAR RECORD

00-01	01-02	02-03	03-04	04-05	05-06	06-07	07-08	08-09	09-10
ESen 12	ESen 12	ESen 15	ESen 16	ESen 15	ESen 14	ESen 12	ESen 14	ESen 9	ESen 11

LONDON APSA

Founded: 1993 Nickname:

Secretary: Zabir Bashir (T) 07956 660 699 (E) zabirbashir23@hotmail.com
Chairman: Zulfi Ali **Manager:** John Higley **Prog Ed:** Fahim Shah
Ground: Terence McMillian Stadium, Plaistow E13 8SD (T) 0207 511 4477
Capacity: 4,000 **Seats:** 400 **Covered:** 400 **Midweek Matchday:** Tuesday **Clubhouse:** **Shop:**

Colours(change): All blue (Green & white/green & white/green)
Previous Names: Ahle Sunnah
Previous Leagues: Asian League.
Records:
Senior Honours: None

10 YEAR RECORD

00-01	01-02	02-03	03-04	04-05	05-06	06-07	07-08	08-09	09-10
			ESen 15	ESen 13	ESen 9	ESen 13	ESen 17	ESen 14	ESen 13

MAURITIUS SPORTS ASSOCIATION

Founded: Nickname:

Secretary: Sally Chalk (T) 07974 484 525 (E) sallychalk94@aol.com
Chairman: Suresh Taurah **Manager:** Chris Wood **Prog Ed:** Feizal Sobratty
Ground: Wadham Lodge S & S Club, Kitchener Rd E17 4JP (T) 020 8527 2444
Capacity: **Seats:** **Covered:** **Midweek Matchday:** Tuesday **Clubhouse:** Yes **Shop:** No

Colours(change): All white. (All blue).
Previous Names: Mauritius Sports merged with Walthamstow Avenue & Pennant 2007.
Previous Leagues: London Intermediate.
Records:
Senior Honours: None

10 YEAR RECORD

00-01	01-02	02-03	03-04	04-05	05-06	06-07	07-08	08-09	09-10
	LonInt 9	LonInt 8					ESen 13	ESen 15	ESen 18

SAWBRIDGEWORTH TOWN
Founded: 1890 Nickname: Robins

Secretary: Mrs Leslie Atkins **(T)** 07762 553 924 **(E)** sawbosec@hotmail.com
Chairman: Steve Day **Manager:** Pete Wickham **Prog Ed:** Steve Tozer
Ground: Crofters End, West Road, Sawbridgeworth CM21 0DE **(T)** 01279 722 039
Capacity: 2,500 **Seats:** 175 **Covered:** 300 **Midweek Matchday:** Tuesday **Clubhouse:** Yes **Shop:** No

Colours(change): Red & black/black/black. (Green/green/white).
Previous Names: Sawbridgeworth > 1976.
Previous Leagues: Stortford. Spartan. Herts County. Essex Olympian.
Records: Att: 610 v Bishops Stortford.
Senior Honours: Essex Olympian League Champions 1971-72.

10 YEAR RECORD

00-01	01-02	02-03	03-04	04-05	05-06	06-07	07-08	08-09	09-10
ESen 13	ESen 7	ESen 6	ESen 3	ESen 8	ESen 6	ESen 8	ESen 12	ESen 13	ESen 10

SOUTHEND MANOR
Founded: 1955 Nickname: The Manor

Secretary: John Bastin **(T)** 0778 097 7728 **(E)** johnbastin1@gmail.com
Chairman: Robert Westley **Manager:** Russell Faulker **Prog Ed:** Bob Westley
Ground: The Arena, Southchurch Pk, Lifstan Way, Southend SS1 2TH **(T)** 01702 615 577
Capacity: 2,000 **Seats:** 500 **Covered:** 700 **Midweek Matchday:** Tuesday **Clubhouse:** Yes **Shop:** No

Colours(change): Yellow/black/yellow. (White/red/red).
Previous Names: None
Previous Leagues: Southend Borough Combination. Southend & District Alliance.
Records: Att: 1,521 v Southend United, opening floodlights, 22.07.91.
Senior Honours: Essex Senior League Cup 1987-88, 89-90, 2000-01.
Essex Senior League Champions 1990-91. Essex Senior Trophy 92-93.

10 YEAR RECORD

00-01	01-02	02-03	03-04	04-05	05-06	06-07	07-08	08-09	09-10
ESen 4	ESen 5	ESen 4	ESen 10	ESen 6	ESen 10	ESen 9	ESen 6	ESen 4	ESen 7

STANSTED
Founded: 1902 Nickname: Blues

Secretary: Terry Shoebridge **(T)** 0774 304 4824 **(E)** terry.sue.shoebridge@btinternet.com
Chairman: Larry Woods **Manager:** Terry Spillane **Prog Ed:** Andy Taylor
Ground: Hargrave Park, Cambridge Road, Stansted CM24 8DL **(T)** 01279 812 897
Capacity: 2,000 **Seats:** 200 **Covered:** 400 **Midweek Matchday:** Tuesday **Clubhouse:** Yes **Shop:** No

Colours(change): All blue. (All red).
Previous Names: None.
Previous Leagues: Spartan. London. Herts County.
Records: Att: 828 v Whickham, FA Vase, 1983-84.
Senior Honours: FA Vase Winners 1983-84. Essex Senior League 2009-10.

10 YEAR RECORD

00-01	01-02	02-03	03-04	04-05	05-06	06-07	07-08	08-09	09-10
ESen 9	ESen 8	ESen 14	ESen 13	ESen 11	ESen 16	ESen 16	ESen 10	ESen 10	ESen 1

TAKELEY
Founded: 1903 Nickname:

Secretary: Michael Rabey **(T)** 0783 184 5466 **(E)** mcrab@btinternet.com
Chairman: Pat Curran **Manager:** Don Watters **Prog Ed:** David Edwards
Ground: Station Road, Takeley, Bishop's Stortford CM22 6QA **(T)** 01279 870 404
Capacity: **Seats:** **Covered:** **Midweek Matchday:** **Clubhouse:** **Shop:**

Colours(change): All royal blue. (All white).
Previous Names: None.
Previous Leagues: Essex Intermediate/Olympian.
Records:
Senior Honours: Essex Intermediate/Olympian 1987-88, 2001-02.

10 YEAR RECORD

00-01	01-02	02-03	03-04	04-05	05-06	06-07	07-08	08-09	09-10
EssxO 6	EssxO 1	EssxO 2	EssxO 6	EssxO 8	EssxO 9	EssxO 3	EssxO 2	ESen 3	ESen 6

WITHAM TOWN

Founded: 1947 Nickname: Town

Secretary: Mrs Alison Barker **(T)** 01376 324 324 **(E)**

Chairman: Tony Last **Manager:** Danny Greaves **Prog Ed:** David Cobb

Ground: Spicer McColl Stadium, Spa Road, Witham CM8 1UN **(T)** 01376 511 198

Capacity: 2,500 **Seats:** 157 **Covered:** 780 **Midweek Matchday:** Tuesday **Clubhouse:** Yes **Shop:** No

Colours(change): All blue. (All yellow).

Previous Names: None.

Previous Leagues: Mid. Essex. Essex & Suff. B. Essex Senior 1971-87. Isthmian 1987-2009

Records: Att: 800 v Billericay Town, Essex Senior Lge, May 1976. **Goalscorer:** Colin Mitchell. **Appearances:** Keith Dent.

Senior Honours: Essex Senior League Champions 1970-71, 85-86.

10 YEAR RECORD

00-01		01-02		02-03		03-04		04-05		05-06		06-07		07-08		08-09		09-10	
Isth3	8	Isth3	12	Isth2	7	Isth2	6	Isth2	5	Isth2	2	Isth1N	20	Isth1N	20	Isth1N	21	ESen	2

Stansted are the only ever-present founder members of the Essex Senior League and this year they lifted the title for the first time - skipper Andy Oxby does just that, aided by league representative Rob Errington.
Photo: Gordon Whittington.

Stansted FC - Back Row (L-R): Billy Sendall, Jack Dallender, Vinnie Durrant, Lewis Dark, Richard Mann, Jamie Haywood, Ryan Murray, Kevin Vallis, Kieren King.
Front Row: Tommy Spillane, Dwight Gayle, Andy Oxby, Arron Best, John Bricknell, Luke Giddings, Paul Seymour.
Photo: Gordon Whittington.

HELLENIC LEAGUE

www.hellenicleague.co.uk

Sponsored by: Uhlsport

Founded: 1953

Recent champions:

2005: Highworth Town
2006: Didcot Town
2007: Slimbridge
2008: North Leigh
2009: Hungerford Town

Reserve Division One	P	W	D	L	F	A	Pts
Hungerford Town Res.	28	22	3	3	80	41	69
Highworth Town Res.	28	18	3	7	68	37	57
Finchampstead Res.	28	17	4	7	59	39	55
Ardley United Res.	28	12	7	9	53	57	43
Fairford Town Res.	28	13	3	12	55	52	42
Kidlington Res.	28	12	5	11	60	51	41
Henley Town Res.	28	11	5	12	53	47	38
Swindon Supermarine Res.	28	11	4	13	45	51	37
Abingdon Town Res.	28	9	8	11	52	48	35
Wantage Town Res.	28	11	2	15	58	59	35
Abingdon United Res.	28	11	1	16	46	64	34
Binfield Res.	28	10	2	16	51	73	32
Carterton Res.	28	9	3	16	55	73	30
Cheltenham Saracens Res.	28	9	3	16	43	65	30
Wootton Bassett Town Res.	28	6	5	17	36	57	23

Premier Division		P	W	D	L	F	A	Pts
Almondsbury Town		**42**	**30**	**9**	**3**	**111**	**38**	**99**
Shortwood United		**42**	**30**	**5**	**7**	**107**	**46**	**95**
Reading Town		**42**	**27**	**9**	**6**	**95**	**27**	**90**
Flackwell Heath		**42**	**26**	**6**	**10**	**90**	**52**	**84**
Wantage Town		**42**	**24**	**11**	**7**	**92**	**52**	**83**
Witney United		**42**	**23**	**9**	**10**	**92**	**43**	**78**
Ardley United		**42**	**24**	**4**	**14**	**96**	**60**	**76**
Binfield		**42**	**22**	**7**	**13**	**88**	**70**	**73**
Highworth Town		**42**	**22**	**5**	**15**	**93**	**56**	**71**
Oxford City Nomads	***-3***	**42**	**21**	**10**	**11**	**100**	**62**	**70**
Kidlington		**42**	**18**	**9**	**15**	**91**	**74**	**63**
Abingdon Town		**42**	**17**	**8**	**17**	**67**	**58**	**59**
Old Woodstock Town	***-1***	**42**	**15**	**7**	**20**	**59**	**77**	**51**
Pegasus Juniors		**42**	**13**	**11**	**18**	**69**	**78**	**50**
Ascot United		**42**	**13**	**7**	**22**	**66**	**94**	**46**
Shrivenham		**42**	**9**	**11**	**22**	**53**	**86**	**38**
Carterton		**42**	**8**	**11**	**23**	**61**	**89**	**35**
Marlow United		**42**	**9**	**8**	**25**	**55**	**120**	**35**
Malmesbury Victoria		**42**	**8**	**9**	**25**	**48**	**108**	**33**
Fairford Town		**42**	**6**	**11**	**25**	**47**	**95**	**29**
Bicester Town		**42**	**5**	**5**	**32**	**56**	**134**	**20**
Hook Norton		**42**	**3**	**6**	**33**	**37**	**154**	**15**

	Abingdon Town	Almondsbury Town	Ardley United	Ascot United	Bicester Town	Binfield	Carterton	Fairford Town	Flackwell Heath	Highworth Town	Hook Norton	Kidlington	Malmesbury Victoria	Marlow United	Old Woodstock Town	Oxford City Nomads	Pegasus Juniors	Reading Town	Shortwood United	Shrivenham	Wantage Town	Witney United
Abingdon Town		1-1	1-1	4-0	1-0	1-2	0-3	0-1	2-1	3-0	3-0	2-2	8-0	1-2	0-0	2-1	0-0	2-3	1-2	3-0	1-0	1-1
Almondsbury Town	2-0		5-3	6-1	4-1	1-2	2-1	5-0	2-1	2-1	1-0	2-2	3-0	7-0	6-0	0-2	2-1	1-1	4-0	3-0	4-1	1-1
Ardley United	2-1	0-1		3-1	4-1	2-1	3-2	1-1	1-4	0-1	1-0	2-0	1-1	10-0	0-1	3-0	6-0	1-4	1-2	5-1	1-0	1-0
Ascot United	0-3	1-1	4-2	***P***	2-1	0-4	3-1	5-0	5-3	3-1	6-0	1-7	1-1	1-1	0-2	2-2	2-0	0-3	2-3	1-3	0-1	0-1
Bicester Town	0-3	0-5	2-4	0-4	***R***	2-5	3-3	2-3	1-3	0-3	0-2	2-1	1-1	5-0	2-3	2-7	1-3	1-3	1-5	1-2	2-3	0-4
Binfield	3-1	2-2	1-4	0-4	2-1	***E***	0-1	4-2	0-1	2-1	2-1	6-1	1-0	3-0	3-1	4-4	2-1	0-3	3-1	3-1	3-4	2-0
Carterton	3-2	1-3	0-1	3-3	1-1	2-0	***M***	3-0	2-3	1-5	1-1	1-1	3-2	3-1	1-1	0-3	1-1	0-1	2-0	1-3	1-2	1-2
Fairford Town	2-3	3-5	1-2	0-2	6-2	1-2	1-1	***I***	1-1	2-1	1-1	0-0	2-2	2-2	1-1	0-3	0-3	1-1	2-3	2-2	0-1	0-3
Flackwell Heath	1-1	0-1	4-1	2-1	4-1	4-1	2-1	1-0	***E***	1-1	5-1	3-0	2-0	2-0	4-0	3-3	2-1	1-2	0-1	5-1	0-5	1-1
Highworth Town	3-1	0-1	1-1	7-0	5-2	0-1	5-3	5-0	1-0	***R***	6-0	3-1	3-1	5-0	4-0	0-3	1-1	2-4	1-2	5-0	3-0	1-1
Hook Norton	2-3	1-4	0-3	1-6	2-2	3-9	2-2	2-1	1-2	0-2		0-4	0-1	3-3	0-5	2-6	2-2	0-4	1-5	0-3	3-5	0-5
Kidlington	0-1	1-4	2-1	4-0	7-1	4-1	4-1	3-4	3-0	2-1	6-1	***D***	5-2	3-1	2-2	0-3	2-2	2-1	1-1	2-1	1-6	2-2
Malmesbury Victoria	1-2	0-2	2-5	6-1	1-1	1-3	1-1	2-0	0-4	2-1	2-0	0-3	***I***	4-4	2-7	1-4	1-1	0-2	0-7	1-1	1-2	1-3
Marlow United	3-2	0-1	1-6	0-2	2-3	2-2	2-1	2-1	1-3	0-2	5-0	2-0	2-3	***V***	1-0	0-3	1-1	0-0	3-6	1-1	0-3	1-5
Old Woodstock Town	0-1	1-2	2-1	2-0	2-1	1-0	2-0	3-1	2-4	1-2	1-2	1-6	0-1	4-1	***I***	2-0	1-1	0-2	0-3	2-1	2-4	0-5
Oxford City Nomads	3-3	1-2	1-3	2-0	4-1	2-2	5-1	6-1	2-4	3-0	5-1	2-4	3-0	2-1	1-0	***S***	3-0	1-1	1-5	2-2	1-1	0-0
Pegasus Juniors	4-0	0-3	1-2	2-1	1-6	3-1	6-3	2-1	2-0	2-3	6-1	1-2	2-0	6-2	1-2	2-1	***I***	0-1	2-4	1-1	2-2	2-1
Reading Town	3-0	1-1	0-1	5-0	3-0	1-1	4-2	2-0	0-1	0-1	6-0	3-0	6-0	5-1	2-0	2-0	5-0	***O***	0-0	5-0	1-1	1-0
Shortwood United	2-0	2-2	1-0	4-0	6-0	3-0	1-0	3-1	1-2	1-3	4-1	3-0	3-1	5-2	2-1	0-1	0-0	2-0	***N***	6-2	3-1	1-0
Shrivenham	0-2	1-4	1-5	0-0	3-0	2-2	2-2	0-1	0-2	0-0	4-0	0-0	0-3	0-3	1-1	1-2	4-0	0-2	1-2		1-3	5-0
Wantage Town	1-0	2-2	3-1	3-1	1-3	1-1	2-1	1-1	0-0	4-2	8-0	1-0	4-0	3-0	2-2	1-1	2-1	3-1	1-1	1-2		1-1
Witney United	3-1	2-1	5-1	0-0	6-0	0-2	3-0	2-0	2-4	5-1	4-0	3-1	4-0	1-2	4-1	3-1	3-2	1-1	2-1	2-0	1-2	

BLUEFIN INSURANCE BROKERS CUP

(all teams in league)

PRELIMINARY ROUND

Abingdon Town 1 Malmesbury Victoria 0
Ascot Utd 1 Launton Sports 0, Bicester 0 **Trowbridge** 2
Binfield 1 **Slimbridge** 6, Chalfont Wasps 1 **Headington** 5
Cheltenham Saracens 1 Penn & Tylers Green 0
Cirencester United 0 **Pegasus Juniors** 6 *(at Pegasus)*
Clanfield 0 **Cricklade Town** 2, **Eton Wick** 5 Kintbury 0
Fairford Town (w/o) v Hardwicke
Farnborough Res. 2 Chinnor 0
Finchampstead 3 Highworth 1, **Harrow Hill** 1 Milton U. 0
Holyport (w/o) v Nth Leigh Res., **Kidlington** 5 Thame 1
Letcombe 3 Tytherington Rocks 2 *aet*
Marlow United 3 Newbury 1 *aet*
Prestwood 0 **Oxford City Nomads** 10
Purton 1 Winterbourne United 1 *aet* (4-3p)
Reading Town 1 Flackwell Heath 1 *aet* (7-6p)
Shrivenham 2 Henley Town 2 *aet* (4-2p)
South Kilburn 1 **Rayners Lane** 3, **Wantage** 1 Lydney 0
Wokingham & Emmbrook 3 Hook Norton 0
Wootton Bassett Town 0 **Easington Sports** 1

FIRST ROUND

Almondsbury Town 4 Cheltenham Saracens 0
Ardley United (w/o) v Harrow Hill
Ascot Utd 1 **Reading Town** 5, Carterton 1 **Woodley** 2
Pegasus Juniors 5 Cricklade Town 0
Eton Wick 3 Headington Amateurs 1
Finchampstead 4 **Slimbridge** 5 *aet*
Holyport 4 Easington Sports 1
Kidlington 0 **Abingdon Town** 1
Marlow United 3 Farnborough Res. 3 *aet* (4-2p)
Oxford City Nomads 2 Rayners Lane 0 *aet*
Purton 0 **Fairford Town** 2
Shortwood United 4 Trowbridge Town 1
Shrivenham 4 Old Woodstock Town 2
Wantage Town 7 Wokingham & Emmbrook 2
Witney United 8 Letcombe 1

SECOND ROUND

Ardley 3 Fairford Town 1, Eton Wick 0 **Abingdon Town** 3
Holyport 1 **Almondsbury Town** 1 *aet* (4-5p)
Marlow United 1 **Slimbridge** 4
Oxford City Nomads 1 Wantage Town 0
Reading Town 1 Pegasus Juniors 0
Shortwood United 0 **Shrivenham** 2
Witney United 1 **Woodley Town** 1 *aet* (2-4p)

QUARTER-FINALS

Abingdon Town 4 Shrivenham 3 *aet*
Almondsbury Town 4 Oxford City Nomads 0
Ardley United 2 Reading Town 0
Slimbridge 4 Woodley Town 2

SEMI-FINALS

Ardley United 2 Abingdon Town 0
Slimbridge 2 Almondsbury Town 1

FINAL *(May 3rd at Wantage Town)*

Ardley United 2 Slimbridge 0

Division One East	P	W	D	L	F	A	Pts
Thame United	32	24	5	3	72	25	77
Wokingham & Emmbrook	32	21	8	3	77	29	71
Holyport	32	18	4	10	80	52	58
Woodley Town	32	16	9	7	74	41	57
Henley Town	32	16	8	8	58	33	56
South Kilburn	32	16	6	10	43	42	54
Milton United	32	14	7	11	54	54	49
Finchampstead	32	11	11	10	50	51	44
Chalfont Wasps	32	12	6	14	61	76	42
Chinnor	32	10	9	13	49	62	39
Farnborough Res.	32	10	7	15	55	57	37
Rayners Lane	32	8	10	14	55	62	34
Kintbury Rangers	32	10	2	20	49	81	32
Eton Wick	32	9	4	19	47	62	31
Didcot Town Res.	32	9	4	19	48	73	31
Newbury	32	7	5	20	36	72	26
Penn & Tylers Green	32	4	9	19	35	71	21

Prestwood - record expunged

Reserve Division Two East	P	W	D	L	F	A	Pts
Thatcham Town Res.	16	12	1	3	50	15	37
Thame United Res.	16	9	2	5	36	27	29
Holyport Res.	16	9	1	6	31	24	28
Chalfont Wasps Res.	16	8	1	7	31	31	25
Penn & Tylers Green Res.	16	6	4	6	27	26	22
Rayners Lane Res.	16	5	3	8	24	27	18
Ascot United Res.	16	5	3	8	26	37	18
Newbury Res.	16	4	4	8	21	39	16
Chinnor Res.	16	4	1	11	18	38	13

Reserve Division Two West	P	W	D	L	F	A	Pts
Cirencester Town Res.	18	14	1	3	63	23	43
Letcombe Res.	18	11	4	3	40	22	37
Old Woodstock Town Res.	18	10	5	3	37	22	35
Cricklade Town Res.	18	10	2	6	42	38	32
Shrivenham Res.	18	7	3	8	41	30	24
Clanfield Res.	18	7	3	8	33	40	24
Easington Sports Res.	18	7	0	11	34	45	21
Hook Norton Res.	18	5	1	12	27	43	16
Cirencester United Res.	18	5	1	12	27	44	16
Launton Sports Res.	18	4	0	14	18	55	12

	Chal	Chin	Did	EW	Farn	Finc	Hen	Holy	Kint	Milt	New	Pen	Pres	Ray	SK	Tha	Wok	Woo
Chalfont Wasps		0-3	5-1	2-0	1-4	2-2	4-2	0-5	2-3	1-1	2-0	4-3	n/a	1-1	1-1	3-2	2-1	1-4
Chinnor	4-2	***D***	1-1	4-2	3-1	1-2	0-1	1-3	4-1	2-1	1-1	2-2	n/a	3-2	2-1	0-2	1-1	0-4
Didcot Town Res.	0-1	3-0	***I***	2-4	4-1	0-2	2-3	1-4	5-2	3-1	2-3	0-1	13-0	2-0	1-0	0-1	2-2	2-4
Eton Wick	0-3	0-0	4-1	***V***	1-0	1-2	0-2	1-3	2-2	0-2	2-0	1-1	n/a	4-3	1-0	1-2	0-2	1-4
Farnborough Res.	5-2	4-1	1-2	4-2	***I***	0-0	1-3	3-2	5-2	0-1	0-0	2-1	3-0	4-2	0-1	1-5	0-2	1-1
Finchampstead	6-2	3-3	2-2	2-1	2-2	***S***	1-1	1-0	3-1	1-2	1-2	2-1	n/a	1-1	1-1	0-2	1-2	2-2
Henley Town	5-0	1-2	4-0	0-4	1-1	3-0	***I***	2-0	2-0	3-1	4-0	1-0	6-0	2-0	0-1	0-1	1-1	2-1
Holyport	4-3	6-2	4-1	2-1	1-3	4-0	2-2	***O***	3-4	2-1	1-0	0-0	n/a	3-1	2-0	3-3	3-4	1-3
Kintbury Rangers	1-3	3-1	3-1	2-1	2-1	1-1	1-4	2-3	***N***	2-3	2-1	2-1	3-1	1-3	0-2	1-2	0-2	1-6
Milton United	1-0	1-1	2-1	3-2	4-2	3-0	W-L	3-4	3-5		2-0	4-0	5-3	3-3	0-2	1-3	1-1	2-2
Newbury	1-4	2-2	4-1	3-0	0-2	0-4	2-2	0-2	2-0	2-2	***O***	2-0	n/a	0-2	3-4	1-4	1-5	0-2
Penn/Tylers Green	2-2	0-3	0-3	1-5	1-0	0-4	1-1	0-3	3-0	2-2	2-1	***N***	n/a	1-1	2-3	1-2	1-4	2-3
Prestwood	n/a	n/a	n/a	1-4	n/a	0-4	n/a	0-13	n/a	n/a	0-2	0-7	***E***	n/a	2-2	n/a	1-3	1-3
Rayners Lane	2-3	1-1	2-0	1-3	3-3	3-0	1-3	1-4	0-3	5-0	4-0	3-3	9-0		0-0	0-4	3-0	1-1
South Kilburn	2-1	2-0	3-0	3-1	1-1	3-1	1-1	4-3	3-1	1-0	0-5	1-1	8-2	1-3	***E***	1-0	0-4	0-3
Thame United	4-2	1-0	2-2	3-0	3-1	3-0	2-0	1-0	4-0	1-2	3-0	3-2	n/a	2-0	2-0	***A***	0-0	2-0
Wokingham & Em.	4-0	4-0	5-0	2-2	W-L	1-2	2-2	2-1	3-0	2-0	3-0	5-0	1-0	4-1	2-0	2-2	***S***	3-2
Woodley Town	2-2	4-1	2-3	1-0	3-2	1-1	1-0	2-2	2-1	1-2	7-0	2-0	n/a	2-2	0-1	1-1	1-2	***T***

Division One West	P	W	D	L	F	A	Pts
Slimbridge	30	20	7	3	75	20	67
Wootton Bassett Town	30	20	7	3	74	34	67
Headington Amateurs	30	20	4	6	78	42	64
Cheltenham Saracens	30	16	8	6	84	40	56
Purton	30	16	7	7	81	49	55
Easington Sports	30	18	0	12	50	43	54
Letcombe	30	15	5	10	63	48	50
Lydney Town	30	14	4	12	55	48	46
Cricklade Town	30	13	3	14	64	53	42
Clanfield	30	11	4	15	45	57	37
Tytherington Rocks	30	9	7	14	43	49	34
North Leigh Res.	30	9	7	14	42	59	34
Winterbourne United	30	9	2	19	60	61	29
Trowbridge Town	30	6	8	16	43	62	26
Launton Sports	30	4	1	25	25	114	13
Cirencester United	30	1	4	25	24	127	7

Harrow Hill - record expunged

SOCCERKITS PLUS SUPPLEMENTARY CUP

(League Cup Preliminary and First Round losers)

PRELIMINARY ROUND

Binfield 5 Didcot Town Res. 0
Chinnor 1 Lydney Town 2
Cirencester United v Bicester Town
Flackwell Heath 3 Clanfield 2
Launton Sports 0 Thame United 4
Milton United 0 North Leigh Res. 6
Prestwood v Malmesbury Victoria (w/o)
Winterbourne United v South Kilburn

Competition abandoned due to inclement weather

CHAIRMAN'S CUP

FINAL *(May 5th at Kidlington)*
Highworth Town Res. 2 Hungerford Town Res. 1

PRESIDENT'S CUP

FINAL *(May 6th at Old Woodstock Town)*
Holyport Res. 2 Old Woodstock Town Res. 1

A M PRINT & COPY FLOODLIGHT CUP

PRELIMINARY ROUND

Almondsbury Town 4 Harrow Hill 1
Ardley United 2 Wootton Bassett Town 1
Bicester Town 1 **Slimbridge** 4
Didcot Town Res. 0 **Holyport** 5
Malmesbury Victoria 1 **Thatcham Town Res.** 4
Reading Town 3 Oxford City Nomads 1

FIRST ROUND

Abingdon Town 2 **Wantage Town** 5
Abingdon United Res. 3 Cheltenham Saracens 1
Almondsbury Town 4 Marlow United 3
Ascot United 1 **Highworth Town** 2
Binfield 3 Lydney Town 1
Fairford Town 2 **Ardley United** 3
Henley Town 2 Hook Norton 0
Holyport 3 Flackwell Heath 2
Hungerford Town Res. 0 **Shortwood United** 4
Milton United 2 Clanfield 1
North Leigh Res. 1 **Old Woodstock Town** 2
Pegasus Juniors (w/o) v Thatcham Town Res.
Reading Town 0 Shrivenham 0 *aet* (3-1p)
Slimbridge 0 **Kidlington** 0 *aet* (3-4p)
Thame United 6 Swindon Supermarine Res. 0
Witney United 4 Carterton 3

SECOND ROUND

Henley Town 2 Pegasus Juniors 1
Highworth Town 0 **Shortwood United** 1
Holyport 0 **Binfield** 1
Kidlington 12 Almondsbury Town 0
Milton United 0 **Witney United** 3
Old Woodstock Town 3 Ardley United 2
Reading Town 6 Abingdon United Res. 0
Wantage Town 5 Thame United 1

QUARTER-FINALS

Kidlington 0 **Binfield** 2
Reading Town 1 Henley Town 0
Old Woodstock Town 0 **Witney United** 3
Shortwood United 1 Wantage Town 0

SEMI-FINALS

(played over two legs)
Reading Town 1 Binfield 0, Binfield 3 **Reading Town** 3
Shortwood United 2 Witney United 0, Witney United 2 **Shortwood United** 3

FINAL

(played over two legs)
(April 22nd)
Reading Town 3 Shortwood United 0
(May 4th)
Shortwood United 5 Reading Town 0

	Chel	Cire	Clan	Cric	Eas	Harr	Head	Laun	Letc	Lyd	NL	Purt	Slim	Trow	Tyth	Wint	Woo
Cheltenham Saracens	***D***	14-0	2-1	2-3	5-1	n/a	0-1	12-0	0-1	1-1	1-1	2-0	2-2	4-3	2-0	2-2	0-1
Cirencester United	1-3	***I***	1-2	2-3	0-1	1-1	0-5	3-1	2-4	0-5	1-1	0-11	0-4	2-2	0-4	1-5	1-1
Clanfield	3-4	2-0	***V***	2-1	1-3	n/a	2-0	5-0	2-0	4-0	0-4	1-4	0-5	2-2	0-2	3-2	0-3
Cricklade Town	5-5	7-0	2-0	***I***	0-2	n/a	3-0	8-0	1-2	4-2	5-0	1-1	0-3	2-3	1-3	2-2	1-0
Easington Sports	0-2	W-L	2-1	0-2	***S***	4-1	2-3	2-0	4-2	3-4	5-0	0-1	0-2	2-0	2-0	0-5	1-2
Harrow Hill	n/a	n/a	n/a	n/a	n/a	***I***	n/a	4-1	n/a	n/a	n/a	n/a	0-3	n/a	n/a	2-9	1-3
Headington Amateurs	1-3	8-1	4-1	2-0	2-1	5-1	***O***	5-0	3-2	2-1	2-0	2-2	4-3	3-0	2-2	6-2	2-3
Launton Sports	0-2	4-1	0-3	2-1	0-3	n/a	1-4	***N***	4-1	1-2	0-3	0-9	1-4	1-3	2-1	1-4	1-3
Letcombe	1-0	3-2	2-2	1-2	4-0	n/a	2-2	5-0		0-2	1-2	3-4	0-0	1-0	4-1	1-0	1-2
Lydney Town	0-1	2-0	0-1	3-1	0-2	2-0	0-2	5-0	3-4	***O***	6-0	3-0	0-4	2-2	0-3	2-0	2-2
North Leigh Res.	3-5	2-2	1-1	3-2	1-3	n/a	0-2	2-1	1-1	1-2	***N***	2-3	0-3	0-0	3-0	3-0	1-3
Purton	5-1	3-1	2-1	2-1	2-3	n/a	4-4	3-2	2-4	0-1	2-1	***E***	0-4	1-1	2-0	4-2	1-2
Slimbridge	1-1	8-1	4-1	2-0	0-1	n/a	1-0	3-0	1-0	4-0	0-0	2-2		2-1	1-1	2-0	2-0
Trowbridge Town	2-4	4-1	2-0	1-0	0-1	n/a	0-2	2-2	2-4	0-3	0-1	2-3	2-3	***W***	4-4	2-1	1-4
Tytherington Rocks	0-0	6-0	3-1	2-4	0-1	3-1	0-3	3-1	2-4	1-1	0-1	1-1	1-1	1-0	***E***	0-3	0-1
Winterbourne United	0-3	8-0	1-2	5-0	1-3	n/a	0-1	7-0	0-3	0-3	4-3	0-5	0-3	4-0	0-1	***S***	0-1
Wootton Bassett Town	1-1	4-1	1-1	1-2	3-2	n/a	6-1	5-0	2-2	5-0	4-2	2-2	2-1	2-2	4-1	4-2	***T***

PREMIER INS & OUTS

IN: Bracknell Town (R - Southern League Division One South & West), Slimbridge (P – Division One West), Thame United (P – Division One East), Wokingham & Emmbrook (P – Division One East), Wootton Bassett Town (P - Division One West) OUT: Almondsbury Town (P - Southern League Division One South & West), Bicester Town (R – Division One West), Hook Norton (R – Division One West), Malmesbury Victoria (R – Division One West), Marlow United (R – Reading League Premier Division)

ABINGDON TOWN

Founded: 1870 Nickname: The Abbots

Secretary: Wendy Larman **(T)** 01235 763 985 **(E)** thomas.larman@btinternet.com

Chairman: Tom Larman **Manager:** Chris Fontaine **Prog Ed:** Kenny More

Ground: Culham Road, Abingdon OX14 3HP **(T)** 01235 521 684

Capacity: 3,000 **Seats:** 271 **Covered:** 1,771 **Midweek Matchday:** Tuesday **Clubhouse:** Yes **Shop:** Yes

Colours(change): All yellow and green
Previous Names: Abingdon FC (merged with St Michaels in 1899) > 1928.
Previous Leagues: Reading Senior, Reading & District, Oxfordshire Senior, North Berkshire, Spartan, Isthmian
Records: **Att:** 4,000 v Swindon Town, Maurice Owen Benefit, 1950.
Senior Honours: Hellenic League Champions 1956-57, 58-59, 59-60, 86-87. Div.1 75-76.
Berks & Bucks Senior Cup 58-59. Spartan Lge 88-89. Isthmian Lge Div.2 South 90-91.

10 YEAR RECORD

00-01	01-02	02-03	03-04	04-05	05-06	06-07	07-08	08-09	09-10
Isth3 17	Isth3 16	Isth2 4	Isth2 9	Isth2 7	Hel P 18	Hel P 18	Hel P 19	Hel P 19	Hel P 12

ARDLEY UNITED

Founded: 1945 Nickname:

Secretary: Norman Stacey **(T)** 07711 009198 **(E)** ardley.house@virgin.net

Chairman: Norman Stacey **Manager:** Kevin Brock **Prog Ed:** Peter Sawyer

Ground: The Playing Fields, Oxford Road, Ardley OX27 7NZ **(T)** 07711 009 198

Capacity: 1,000 **Seats:** 100 **Covered:** 200 **Midweek Matchday:** Tuesday **Clubhouse:** Yes **Shop:** No

Colours(change): All sky blue.
Previous Names: None
Previous Leagues: Oxford Senior.
Records: **Att:** 278 v Kidlington, 29.08.05.
Senior Honours: Oxfordshire Senior League Champions (x 3).
Hellenic League Div.1 Champions 1996-97, 97-98.

10 YEAR RECORD

00-01	01-02	02-03	03-04	04-05	05-06	06-07	07-08	08-09	09-10
Hel1W 3	Hel1W 3	Hel1W 5	Hel1W 5	Hel P 18	Hel P 10	Hel P 4	Hel P 13	Hel P 5	Hel P 7

ASCOT UNITED

Founded: 1965 Nickname: Yellaman

Secretary: Mark Gittoes **(T)** 07798 701995 **(E)** mark.gittoes@ascotunited.net

Chairman: Mike Harrison **Manager:** Stuart Scammell **Prog Ed:** Michael Cecil

Ground: Ascot Racecourse, Car Park 10, Winkfield Rd, Ascot SL5 7RA **(T)** 07798 701995

Capacity: **Seats:** **Covered:** **Midweek Matchday:** Wednesday **Clubhouse:** Yes **Shop:**

Colours(change): Yellow/blue/yellow
Previous Names: None.
Previous Leagues: Reading Senior.
Records: **Att:**121 v Binfield, 21.08.07.
Senior Honours: Reading Senior Champions 2006-07.

10 YEAR RECORD

00-01	01-02	02-03	03-04	04-05	05-06	06-07	07-08	08-09	09-10
	ReadS 12	ReadS 6	ReadS 6	ReadS 3	ReadS 4	ReadS 1	Hel1E 4	Hel1E 2	Hel P 15

BINFIELD

Founded: 1892 Nickname: Moles

Secretary: Rob Challis **(T)** 07515 336989 **(E)** robchallis@binfieldfc.com

Chairman: Bob Bacon **Manager:** Mark Tallentire **Prog Ed:** Rob Jones

Ground: Stubbs Lane, Binfield RG42 5NR **(T)** 01344 860 822

Capacity: **Seats:** **Covered:** **Midweek Matchday:** Monday **Clubhouse:** Yes **Shop:**

Colours(change): All red.
Previous Names: None.
Previous Leagues: Ascot & District. Great Western Combination. Reading & Dist. Chiltonian.
Records: **Att:** 1000+ Great Western Combination.
Senior Honours: Chiltonian League 1995-96.
Hellenic League Division 1 East 2008-09.

10 YEAR RECORD

00-01	01-02	02-03	03-04	04-05	05-06	06-07	07-08	08-09	09-10
Hel1E 10	Hel1E 14	Hel1E 8	Hel1E 5	Hel1E 5	Hel1E 8	Hel1E 11	Hel1E 9	Hel1E 1	Hel P 8

BRACKNELL TOWN

Founded: 1896 Nickname: The Robins

Secretary: Tony Hardy **(T)** 07920 726 501 **(E)** tony.hardy@bsigroup.com
Chairman: Ian Nugent **Manager:** Richard Whitty **Prog Ed:** Rob Scully
Ground: Larges Lane Bracknell RG12 9AN **(T)** 01344 412305
Capacity: 2,500 **Seats:** 190 **Covered:** 400 **Midweek Matchday:** Tuesday **Clubhouse:** Yes **Shop:** Yes

Colours(change): Red and white/red/red
Previous Names: None
Previous Leagues: Great Western Comb., Surrey Senior 1963-70, London Spartan 1970-75, Isthmian 1984-2004, Southern 2004-10
Records: **Att:** 2,500 v Newquay - FA Amateur Cup 1971. **Goalscorer:** Justin Day. **Apps:** James Woodcock.
Senior Honours: Isthmian League Division 3 1993-94.

10 YEAR RECORD

00-01	01-02	02-03	03-04	04-05	05-06	06-07	07-08	08-09	09-10
Isth3 9	Isth3 4	Isth1S 20	Isth1S 14	SthW 20	SthW 19	Sthsw 19	Sthsw 20	Sthsw	Sthsw 22

CARTERTON

Founded: 1918 Nickname:

Secretary: John McCarthy **(T)** 07835 623 843 **(E)** johnmac277@msn.com
Chairman: Robert King **Manager:** Andy Zoldan **Prog Ed:** Andy Meaden
Ground: Kilkenny Lane, Carterton, Oxfordshire OX18 1DY. Tel: 01993 842 410. **(T)**
Capacity: 1,500 **Seats:** 75 **Covered:** 100 **Midweek Matchday:** Tuesday **Clubhouse:** Yes **Shop:** No

Colours(change): Red with green trim/green/red.
Previous Names: Carterton FC > 1982. Carterton Town > 2004
Previous Leagues: Witney & District.
Records: **Att:** 650 v Swindon Town, July 2001. **Goalscorer:** Phil Rodney.
Senior Honours: Hellenic Div.1 Champions 1989-90, 93-94.

10 YEAR RECORD

00-01	01-02	02-03	03-04	04-05	05-06	06-07	07-08	08-09	09-10
Hel P 10	Hel P 11	Hel P 3	Hel P 7	Hel P 6	Hel P 7	Hel P 12	Hel P 18	Hel P 12	Hel P 17

FAIRFORD TOWN

Founded: 1891 Nickname: Town

Secretary: William Beach **(T)** 07919 940909 **(E)** wbeach007@btinternet.com
Chairman: Andrew Wilson **Manager:** Richard Hadgkiss **Prog Ed:** Andrew Meadon
Ground: Cinder Lane, London Road, Fairford GL7 4AX **(T)** 01285 712 071
Capacity: 2,000 **Seats:** 100 **Covered:** 250 **Midweek Matchday:** Tuesday **Clubhouse:** Yes **Shop:** Yes

Colours(change): Red/white/red.
Previous Names: None.
Previous Leagues: Cirencester & District. Swindon & District.
Records: **Att:** 1,525 v Coventry City, friendly, July 2000. **Goalscorer:** Pat Toomey.
Senior Honours: Hellenic League Div.1 A Champions 1971-72.

10 YEAR RECORD

00-01	01-02	02-03	03-04	04-05	05-06	06-07	07-08	08-09	09-10
Hel P 9	Hel P 6	Hel P 6	Hel P 10	Hel P 8	Hel P 17	Hel P 13	Hel P 20	Hel P 14	Hel P 20

FLACKWELL HEATH

Founded: 1907 Nickname: Heath

Secretary: Brian Kirby **(T)** 01628 528 549 **(E)** blkdavco@aol.com
Chairman: Geoff Turner **Manager:** Matt Flint **Prog Ed:** Geoff Turner
Ground: Wilks Park, Magpie Lane, Heath End Rd, Flackwell Hth HP10 9EA. **(T)** 01628 523 892
Capacity: 2,000 **Seats:** 150 **Covered:** Yes **Midweek Matchday:** Tuesday **Clubhouse:** Yes **Shop:** No

Colours(change): All red.
Previous Names: None.
Previous Leagues: Great Western Combination. Hellenic. Isthmian.
Records: **Att:** 1,500 v Oxford United, charity match, 1966. **Goalscorer:** Tony Wood. **Apps:** Lee Elliott.
Senior Honours: Wycombe Senior Cup Winners (x 12)

10 YEAR RECORD

00-01	01-02	02-03	03-04	04-05	05-06	06-07	07-08	08-09	09-10
Isth3 4	Isth3 20	Isth2 3	Isth2 5	Isth2 9	Isth2 4	Isth1N 22	Hel P 9	Hel P 16	Hel P 4

HIGHWORTH TOWN

Founded: 1893 Nickname: Worthians

Secretary: Claire Haines **(T)** 01793 763 841 **(E)** claire.haines@live.co.uk
Chairman: Darren Robbins **Manager:** Dave Webb **Prog Ed:** Mike Markham
Ground: Elm Recreation Ground, Highworth SN6 7DD **(T)** 01793 766 263
Capacity: 2,000 **Seats:** 150 **Covered:** 250 **Midweek Matchday:** Tuesday **Clubhouse:** Yes **Shop:** No

Colours(change): Red/black/red.
Previous Names: None.
Previous Leagues: Swindon & District. Wiltshire.
Records: **Att:** 2,000 v QPR, opening of floodlights. **Goalscorer:** Kevin Higgs. **Apps:** Rod Haines.
Senior Honours: Wiltshire Senior Cup 1963-64, 72-73, 95-96, 97-98.
Hellenic League Champions 2004-05.

10 YEAR RECORD

00-01	01-02	02-03	03-04	04-05	05-06	06-07	07-08	08-09	09-10
Hel P 8	Hel P 15	Hel P 4	Hel P 9	Hel P 1	Hel P 12	Hel P 15	Hel P 6	Hel P 6	Hel P 9

KIDLINGTON

Founded: 1909 Nickname:

Secretary: David Platt **(T)** 07956 531 185 **(E)** david.platt45@googlemail.com
Chairman: Lloyd Wray **Manager:** Gordon Geary **Prog Ed:** Simon Dickens
Ground: Yarnton Road, Kidlington, Oxford OX5 1AT **(T)** 01865 841 526
Capacity: **Seats:** Yes **Covered:** Yes **Midweek Matchday:** Tuesday **Clubhouse:** Yes **Shop:** No

Colours(change): All green.
Previous Names: None.
Previous Leagues: Oxford Senior.
Records: **Att:** 2,500 v Showbiz XI, 1973.
Senior Honours:

10 YEAR RECORD

00-01	01-02	02-03	03-04	04-05	05-06	06-07	07-08	08-09	09-10
Hel1W 11	Hel1W 10	Hel1W 7	Hel1W 12	Hel1W 3	Hel P 20	Hel P 9	Hel P 15	Hel P 9	Hel P 11

OLD WOODSTOCK TOWN

Founded: Nickname:

Secretary: Louise Jordon **(T)** 07944 418 114 **(E)** louise.jordon@talktalk.net
Chairman: Ted Saxton **Manager:** Simon Lenagan **Prog Ed:** Mark Cain
Ground: North Leigh FC, Eynsham Hall Park North Leigh OX29 6PN **(T)** 07748 152 243
Capacity: 2,000 **Seats:** 100 **Covered:** 200 **Midweek Matchday:** Wednesday **Clubhouse:** Yes **Shop:** No

Colours(change): Royal blue & red/royal/royal.
Previous Names: Old Woodstock and Woodstock Town merged in 1998.
Previous Leagues: Oxfordshire Senior.
Records: **Att:** 258 v Kidlington, 27.08.01.
Senior Honours: Oxfordshire Senior Champions 1998-99.

10 YEAR RECORD

00-01	01-02	02-03	03-04	04-05	05-06	06-07	07-08	08-09	09-10
Hel1W 15	Hel1W 8	Hel1W 6	Hel1W 8	Hel1W 14	Hel1W 7	Hel1W 7	Hel1W 2	Hel P 17	Hel P 13

OXFORD CITY NOMADS

Founded: 1936 Nickname: The Nomads

Secretary: Colin Taylor **(T)** 07817 885 396 **(E)** ctoxford@btinternet.com
Chairman: Richard Lawrence **Manager:** Mark Jones **Prog Ed:** Colin Taylor
Ground: Court Place Farm Stadium, Marsh Lane, Marston OX3 0NQ **(T)** 01865 744 493
Capacity: 3,000 **Seats:** 300 **Covered:** 400 **Midweek Matchday:** Wednesday **Clubhouse:** Yes **Shop:** Yes

Colours(change): Blue & white hoops/blue/blue.
Previous Names: Quarry Nomads > 2005.
Previous Leagues: Chiltonian.
Records: **Att:** 334 v Headington Amateurs, 25.08.03.
Senior Honours: Hellenic Division East Champions 2002-03.

10 YEAR RECORD

00-01	01-02	02-03	03-04	04-05	05-06	06-07	07-08	08-09	09-10
Hel1E 4	Hel1E 11	Hel1E 1	Hel1W 7	Hel1W 15	Hel1E 11	Hel1E 12	Hel1W 9	Hel1W 3	Hel P 10

PEGASUS JUNIORS

Founded: 1955 Nickname: The Redmen

Secretary: Chris Wells **(T)** 07980 465 995 **(E)** cwells@freenetname.co.uk
Chairman: Roger Hesten **Manager:** Steve Griffiths **Prog Ed:** Kevin Bishop
Ground: Old School Lane, Hereford HR1 1EX **(T)** 07980 465 995
Capacity: 1,000 **Seats:** 110 **Covered:** Yes **Midweek Matchday:** Tuesday **Clubhouse:** Yes **Shop:**

Colours(change): All red.
Previous Names: None.
Previous Leagues: Herefordshire.
Records: **Att:** 1,400 v Newport AFC, 1989-90.
Senior Honours: Herefordshire Lge Champions 1963-64. Herefordshire Senior Cup 71-72.
Worcestershire Senior Urn 85-86. Hellenic Div.1 Champions 84-85, 98-99.

10 YEAR RECORD

00-01	01-02	02-03	03-04	04-05	05-06	06-07	07-08	08-09	09-10
Hel P 15	Hel P 13	Hel P 18	Hel P 17	Hel P 16	Hel P 13	Hel P 17	Hel P 17	Hel P 10	Hel P 14

READING TOWN

Founded: 1966 Nickname: Town

Secretary: Richard Grey **(T)** 07762 494 324 **(E)** richardigrey@aol.com
Chairman: Roland Ford **Manager:** Roddy Slater **Prog Ed:** Richard Wickson
Ground: Reading Town Sports Ground, Scours Lane, Reading RG30 6AY **(T)** 0118 945 3555
Capacity: 2000 **Seats:** 120 **Covered:** 200 **Midweek Matchday:** Tuesday **Clubhouse:** Yes **Shop:** No

Colours(change): Red/black/red & black
Previous Names: Lower Burghfield, XI Utd, Vincents Utd, Reading Garage, ITS Reading T.
Previous Leagues: Chiltonian Lge. Combined Counties.
Records: **Att:** 1067 v AFC Wimbledon, Combined Counties 03.05.03.
Senior Honours: Chiltonian League Champions 1994-95.

10 YEAR RECORD

00-01	01-02	02-03	03-04	04-05	05-06	06-07	07-08	08-09	09-10
CC 19	CC 21	CC 15	CCP 3	CCP 19	CCP 10	CCP 9	CCP 13	Hel P 8	Hel P 3

SHORTWOOD UNITED

Founded: 1900 Nickname: The Wood

Secretary: Mark Webb **(T)** 01453 836 233 **(E)** squish.shortwoodfc@live.co.uk
Chairman: Peter Webb **Manager:** John Evans **Prog Ed:** Paul Webb
Ground: Meadowbank, Shortwood, Nailsworth GL6 0SJ **(T)** 01453 833 936
Capacity: 2,000 **Seats:** 50 **Covered:** 150 **Midweek Matchday:** Tuesday **Clubhouse:** Yes **Shop:** No

Colours(change): Red & white/black/white.
Previous Names: None.
Previous Leagues: Gloucestershire County.
Records: **Att:** 1,000 v Forest Green Rovers, FA Vase 5th Rnd 1982. **Goalscorer:** Peter Grant. **Apps:** Peter Grant.
Senior Honours: Gloucestershire Lge Champions 1981-82.
Hellenic Lge Champions 84-85, 91-92. Gloucestershire Senior Cup (x 2).

10 YEAR RECORD

00-01	01-02	02-03	03-04	04-05	05-06	06-07	07-08	08-09	09-10
Hel P 11	Hel P 9	Hel P 13	Hel P 19	Hel P 15	Hel P 15	Hel P 8	Hel P 5	Hel P 2	Hel P 2

SHRIVENHAM

Founded: 1900 Nickname: Shrivy

Secretary: Emma Skilton **(T)** 07845 693 274 **(E)** emma.skilton@nationwide.co.uk
Chairman: Robb Forty **Manager:** Mark Love **Prog Ed:** Matt Hirst
Ground: The Recreation Ground, Shrivenham SN6 8BJ **(T)** 07767 371 414
Capacity: **Seats:** **Covered:** **Midweek Matchday:** Wednesday **Clubhouse:** Yes **Shop:**

Colours(change): Blue & white hoops/white/white.
Previous Names: None.
Previous Leagues: North Berkshire.
Records: **Att:** 800 v Aston Villa, 21.05.2000.
Senior Honours: North Berkshire Champions 1997-98, 00-01.
Hellenic Division 1 West 04-05.

10 YEAR RECORD

00-01	01-02	02-03	03-04	04-05	05-06	06-07	07-08	08-09	09-10
NBk 1 1	Hel1W 9	Hel1W 12	Hel1W 3	Hel1W 1	Hel P 8	Hel P 10	Hel P 8	Hel P 18	Hel P 16

SLIMBRIDGE

Founded: 1899 Nickname: The Swans

Secretary: Keith Sparrow **(T)** 07835 927 226 **(E)** keithjsparrow@hotmail.co.uk
Chairman: Keith Sparrow **Manager:** Leon Sterling **Prog Ed:** Tim Blake
Ground: Wisloe Road, Cambridge, Glos GL2 7AF **(T)** 07835 927 226
Capacity: **Seats:** Yes **Covered:** Yes **Midweek Matchday:** Wednesday **Clubhouse:** Yes **Shop:** Yes

Colours(change): Blue/blue/white.
Previous Names: None
Previous Leagues: Stroud & District. Gloucester Northern. Gloucestershire County.
Records: Since 2002-03. **Att:** 525 v Shortwood United, Hellenic Prem. 24.08.03. **Goals:** Julian Freeman - 79 (from 122 apps.).
Senior Honours: Glos Northern Senior Cup 2000-01. Hellenic League Division 1 West 2002-03, 09-10, Premier 2006-07. Gloucester Northern League 2007-08. Gloucestershire County League 2008-09.

10 YEAR RECORD

00-01	01-02	02-03	03-04	04-05	05-06	06-07	07-08	08-09	09-10
GIN1 2	GICo 2	Hel1W 1	Hel P 4	Hel P 4	Hel P 5	Hel P 1	GIN1 1	GICo 1	Hel1W 1

THAME UNITED

Founded: 1883 Nickname: United

Secretary: Jake Collinge **(T)** 07753 502 955 **(E)** jake@collinge.eclipse.co.uk
Chairman: Jake Collinge **Manager:** Mark West **Prog Ed:** Jake Collinge
Ground: AFC Wallingford, Wallingford Sports Park, Hithercroft Road OX10 9RB **(T)** 01491 835 044
Capacity: 2,500 **Seats:** Yes **Covered:** Yes **Midweek Matchday:** Tuesday **Clubhouse:** Yes **Shop:**

Colours(change): Red & black/black/black.
Previous Names: Thame F.C.
Previous Leagues: Oxon Senior. Hellenic. South Midlands. Isthmian. Southern.
Records: **Att:** 1,035 v Aldershot, Isthmian Div.2, 04.04.94. **Goalscorer:** Not known. **Apps:** Steve Mayhew.
Senior Honours: Hellenic Champions 1961-62, 69-70, Division 1 East 2009-10. South Midlands League 1990-91. Isthmian Division 2 1994-95.

10 YEAR RECORD

00-01	01-02	02-03	03-04	04-05	05-06	06-07	07-08	08-09	09-10
Isth1 5	Isth1 11	Isth1N 8	Isth1N 15	SthW 11	SthW 22	Hel P 20	Hel1E 10	Hel1E 9	Hel1E 1

WANTAGE TOWN

Founded: 1892 Nickname: Alfredians

Secretary: John Culley **(T)** 07921 243 263 **(E)** john_clly@yahoo.co.uk
Chairman: Tony Woodward **Manager:** Andy Wallbridge **Prog Ed:** Tony Woodward
Ground: Alfredian Park, Manor Road, Wantage OX12 8DW **(T)** 01235 764 781
Capacity: 1,500 **Seats:** 50 **Covered:** 300 **Midweek Matchday:** Tuesday **Clubhouse:** Yes **Shop:** No

Colours(change): Green & white/white/white.
Previous Names: None.
Previous Leagues: Swindon & District. North Berkshire. Reading & District.
Records: **Att:** 550 v Oxford United, July 2003.
Senior Honours: Hellenic Division 1 East 1980-81, 03-04. Oxon Senior Cup 82-83.

10 YEAR RECORD

00-01	01-02	02-03	03-04	04-05	05-06	06-07	07-08	08-09	09-10
Hel P 16	Hel P 12	Hel P 21	Hel1E 1	Hel P 10	Hel P 9	Hel P 11	Hel P 12	Hel P 11	Hel P 5

WITNEY UNITED

Founded: 2001 Nickname: The Blanketmen

Secretary: Adrian Bircher **(T)** 07824 999 119 **(E)** adrian1.bircher@ntlworld.com
Chairman: Steve Lake **Manager:** Darren Teggart **Prog Ed:** Gary Walter
Ground: Polythene UK Stadium, Downs Road, Witney OX29 7WT **(T)** 01993 848 558 (Office) or 702 549 (Bar)
Capacity: 3,500 **Seats:** 280 **Covered:** 2,000 **Midweek Matchday:** Tuesday **Clubhouse:** Yes **Shop:** Yes

Colours(change): Yellow/black/yellow.
Previous Names: None.
Previous Leagues: None.
Records: **Att:** 628 v Oxford United, 26.02.08
Senior Honours: None.

10 YEAR RECORD

00-01	01-02	02-03	03-04	04-05	05-06	06-07	07-08	08-09	09-10
		Hel1W 15	Hel1W 4	Hel P 11	Hel P 6	Hel P 6	Hel P 4	Hel P 3	Hel P 6

WOKINGHAM & EMMBROOK

Founded: 2004 Nickname: Satsumas

Secretary: Sally Blee **(T)** 07714 732 790 **(E)** sally.blee@tesco.net

Chairman: Mark Ashwell **Manager:** Wayne Wanklyn **Prog Ed:** Mike Bound

Ground: Bracknell Town FC, Larges Lane, Bracknell RG12 9AN **(T)** 01344 412 305

Capacity: 2,500 **Seats:** 190 **Covered:** 400 **Midweek Matchday:** Tuesday **Clubhouse:** Yes **Shop:**

Colours(change): Orange/black/black.
Previous Names: Club formed when Wokingham Town and Emmbrook Sports merged.
Previous Leagues: Isthmian (Wokingham). Reading (Emmbrook Sports).
Records: **Att:** 305 v Binfield, 25.03.2005.
Senior Honours:

10 YEAR RECORD

00-01	01-02	02-03	03-04	04-05	05-06	06-07	07-08	08-09	09-10
				Hel1E 11	Hel1E 3	Hel1E 8	Hel1E 12	Hel1E 4	Hel1E 2

WOOTTON BASSETT TOWN

Founded: 1882 Nickname:

Secretary: Rod Carter **(T)** 07957 996 283 **(E)** rod.carter63@yahoo.com

Chairman: Paul Harrison **Manager:** Dave Turner **Prog Ed:** Mark Smedley

Ground: Gerard Buxton Sport Ground, Rylands Way SN4 8AW **(T)** 01793 853 880

Capacity: 2,000 **Seats:** None **Covered:** 350 **Midweek Matchday:** Tuesday **Clubhouse:** Yes **Shop:** No

Colours(change): Blue & yellow/blue/yellow.
Previous Names: None.
Previous Leagues: Wiltshire.
Records: **Att:** 2,103 v Swindon Town, July 1991. **Goalscorer:** Brian 'Tony' Ewing. **Apps:** Steve Thomas.
Senior Honours: Wiltshire Champions 1987-88.

10 YEAR RECORD

00-01	01-02	02-03	03-04	04-05	05-06	06-07	07-08	08-09	09-10
Hel P 13	Hel P 19	Hel P 15	Hel P 16	Hel P 21	Hel1W 5	Hel1W 11	Hel1W 15	Hel1W 4	Hel1W 2

CHALFONT WASPS

Founded: 1922 The Stingers

Secretary: Bob Cakeboard **(T)** 07895 094 579 **(E)** robert.cakeboard@btinternet.com
Chairman: Steve Waddington **Manager:** Martin Kenealy **Prog Ed:** Al Yeomans
Ground: Crossleys Bowstridge, Lane Chalfont, St Giles HP8 4QN **(T)** 01494 875 050 **Capacity:**
Colours(change): Yellow and black stripes/black/black

ADDITIONAL INFORMATION: Previous League: Chiltonian (Founder Member)
Record Att: 82 v Didcot Town 17/12/2005.
Honours: Hellenic League Division 1 East 2007-08.

CHINNOR

Founded: 1884

Secretary: Richard Carr **(T)** 07786 115 089 **(E)** richard.carr@eu.sony.com
Chairman: Kevin Avery **Manager:** Richard Carr **Prog Ed:** TBA
Ground: Station Road, Chinnor, Oxon OX39 4PV **(T)** 01844 352 579 **Capacity:** 1,500
Colours(change): All royal blue

ADDITIONAL INFORMATION:
Previous League: Oxfordshire Senior.
Record Att: 306 v Oxford Quarry Nomads, 29.08.2005.

DIDCOT TOWN RESERVES

Founded: 1907 Nickname: Railwaymen

Secretary: Pat Horsman **(T)** 07882 154 612 **(E)** didcot@fernring.co.uk
Chairman: John Bailey **Manager:** Craig Hughes **Prog Ed:** Joffy Chinnock
Ground: NPower Loop Meadow Stadium, Bowmont Water, Didcot OX11 7GA **(T)** 01235 813 138 **Capacity:** 5,000
Colours(change): Red & white/white/red & white

ADDITIONAL INFORMATION:
Previous League: Hellenic Reserves.

FARNBOROUGH RESERVES

Formed: 2009

Secretary: Brian Berger **(T)** 07922 666 621 **(E)** farnboroughfc@btinternet.com
Chairman: Simon Hollis **Manager:** TBA **Prog Ed:** Brian Berger
Ground: Farnborough Elite Centre, Lion Park, Church Lane, Bisley GU24 9ER **(T)** 01252 541 469 **Capacity:**
Colours(change): All yellow

ADDITIONAL INFORMATION: Previous Names: Bisley Sports > 2005, Bisley > 2009. **Previous League:** Surrey County Premier/Senior.
Record Att: 252 v Hounslow Borough, 24.12.2005.
Honours: Hellenic Division 1 East 2006-07.

FINCHAMPSTEAD

Founded: 1952 Nickname: Finches

Secretary: Nick Markman **(T)** 07793 866 324 **(E)** nmarkham@avaya.com
Chairman: Richard Laugharne **Manager:** Steve Cox **Prog Ed:** Nick Markman
Ground: Memorial Park The Village, Finchampstead RG40 4JR **(T)** 0118 9732890 **Capacity:**
Colours(change): Sky blue & white/sky/sky blue

ADDITIONAL INFORMATION: Previous League: Chiltonian.
Record Att: 425 v Sandhurst, 1958-59.
Honours: Chiltonian League 1987-88. Reading Senior Challenge Cup 1986-87. Hellenic League Division 1 East 2001-02.

HENLEY TOWN

Nickname: The Town

Secretary: Tong Kingston **(T)** 07712 139 592 **(E)** tony.kingston1@btinternet.com
Chairman: Barrie Baxter **Manager:** Dave Tuttle **Prog Ed:** Geoff Biggs
Ground: The Triangle Ground, Mill Lane, Henley RG9 4HB **(T)** 01491 411083 **Capacity:** 2,000
Colours(change): White/black/black

ADDITIONAL INFORMATION: Previous League: Chiltonian.
Record Att: 2000+ v Reading, 1922. **Goalscorer:** M. Turner.
Honours: Hellenic League Div.1 1963-64, 67-68, Div.1 East 2000-01. Chiltonian League Division 1 1987-88. Premier 1999-00.

HOLYPORT

Founded: 1934 The Villagers

Secretary: Graham Broom **(T)** 07702 369708 **(E)** grahambroom@btinternet.com
Chairman: Tony Andrews **Manager:** Derek Sweetman **Prog Ed:** Richard Tyrell
Ground: Summerleaze Village SL6 8SP **(T)** 07702 369708 **Capacity:**
Colours(change): Claret/green/claret

ADDITIONAL INFORMATION: Previous League: Hayes & Giles.
Record Att: 218 v Eton Wick, 2006.
Honours: Norfolkian Senior Cup 1999-2000.

DIV.1 EAST INS & OUTS

IN: Hungerford Town Res. (P – Reserve Division One)
OUT: Eton Wick (W – East Berks League Premier Division), Kintbury Rangers (R – North Berks League Division One), Prestwood (WS), Thame United (P), Wokingham & Emmbrook (P)

HUNGERFORD TOWN RESERVES
Founded: 1886 The Crusaders

Secretary: Norman Matthews **(T)** 07768 761 795 **(E)** nmatthews@rhsystems.co.uk
Chairman: Nigel Warrick **Manager:** Gary Cook **Prog Ed:** John Smyth
Ground: Bulpit Lane, Hungerford RG17 0AY **(T)** 01488 682939 **Capacity:** 2,500
Colours(change): White/blue/white

ADDITIONAL INFORMATION:
Previous League: Hellenic Reserves.

MILTON UNITED
Founded: 1909 Nickname: Miltonians

Secretary: Sharon Palmer **(T)** 07774 676 793 **(E)** milton@hellenicleague.co.uk
Chairman: Ron Renton **Manager:** Shaun Smith **Prog Ed:** Ron Renton
Ground: Potash Lane, Milton Heights, OX13 6AG **(T)** 01235 832 999 **Capacity:** 2,000
Colours(change): Claret & sky/claret & sky/claret

ADDITIONAL INFORMATION: Previous League: North Berkshire.
Record Att: 608 Carterton v Didcot Town, League Cup Final, 07.05.05. **Goalscorer:** Nigel Mott.
Honours: Hellenic League 1990-91.

NEWBURY
Founded: 1887

Secretary: Knut Riemann **(T)** 07855 031 000 **(E)** kriemann@yahoo.com
Chairman: Keith Moss **Manager:** Vic Houston **Prog Ed:** Martin Strafford
Ground: Faraday Road, Newbury RG14 2AD **(T)** 01635 41031 **Capacity:**
Colours(change): Amber & black/black/amber & black

ADDITIONAL INFORMATION: Previous Names: Newbury Town, Old London Apprentice, O.L.A. Newbury. **Previous League:** Reading.
Record Att: 246 v Kintbury Rangers 27/12/2008.
Honours: Hellenic League 1978-79, 80-81. Athenian League 1982-83.

PENN & TYLERS GREEN
Founded: 1905

Secretary: Andrea Latta **(T)** 07904 538 868 **(E)** hsvlatta1955@yahoo.co.uk
Chairman: Tony Hurst **Manager:** Matt Miller **Prog Ed:** Fergus Sturrock
Ground: French School Meadows, Elm Road, Penn, Bucks HP10 8LF **(T)** 01494 815 346 **Capacity:**
Colours(change): Blue & white stripes/blue/blue

ADDITIONAL INFORMATION:
Previous League: Chiltonian (Founder member).
Record Att: 125 v Chalfont Wasps, August 2000.

RAYNERS LANE
Nickname: The Lane

Secretary: Tony Pratt **(T)** 01895 233 853 **(E)** richard.mitchell@tesco.net
Chairman: Martin Noblett **Manager:** Dean Gardner **Prog Ed:** TBA
Ground: Tithe Farm Social Club, Rayners Lane, South Harrow HA2 0XH **(T)** 0208 868 8724 **Capacity:**
Colours(change): Yellow/green/yellow

ADDITIONAL INFORMATION: Previous League: Spartan.
Record Att: 550 v Wealdstone 1983.
Honours: Hellenic League Division 1 1982-83.

SOUTH KILBURN

Secretary: Amanda Jennings **(T)** 07595 256 309 **(E)** jenningsmandy@ymail.com
Chairman: Dennis Woolcock **Manager:** Mick Jennings **Prog Ed:** Amanda Jennings
Ground: Vale Farm, Watford Road, North Wembley HA0 3HE **(T)** 0208 908 6545 **Capacity:**
Colours(change): White/black/black

ADDITIONAL INFORMATION:
Previous League: Middlesex County.
Record Att: 65 v Rayners Lane 25/08/2008.

WOODLEY TOWN
Founded: 1904 Nickname: Town

Secretary: John Mailer **(T)** 07883 341 628 **(E)** john_mailer@hotmail.co.uk
Chairman: Mark Rozzier **Manager:** Cyril Fairchild **Prog Ed:** Jim Nightingale
Ground: East Park Farm, Park Lane, Charvil, Berks RG10 9TR **(T)** 07703 474 555 **Capacity:**
Colours(change): All navy blue

ADDITIONAL INFORMATION: Previous League: Reading
Previous League: Reading.
Honours: Reading Football League Senior Division 2008-09. Berkshire Trophy Centre Senior Cup 2008-09.

BICESTER TOWN

Founded: 1876 Nickname: Foxhunters

Secretary: Adrian Marson **(T)** 07880 601 145 **(E)** adrianmarson@btinternet.com
Chairman: John Clutterbuck **Manager:** Chris Hurley **Prog Ed:** Adrian Marson
Ground: Sports Ground, Oxford Road, Bicester OX26 2AD **(T)** 01869 241 036 **Capacity:** 2,000
Colours(change): Red & black/black/black

ADDITIONAL INFORMATION: Previous Name: Slade Banbury Road > 1923. **Previous League:** Oxford Senior.
Record Att: 955 v Portsmouth, opening of floodlights, 01/02/94.
Honours: Hellenic League 1960-61, 79-80, Division 1 1977-78.

CHELTENHAM SARACENS

Founded: 1964 Nickname: Saras

Secretary: Bob Attwood **(T)** 07778 502 539 **(E)** bobattwood@tiscali.co.uk
Chairman: Chris Hawkins **Manager:** Gerry Oldham **Prog Ed:** Bob Attwood
Ground: Petersfield Park, Tewkesbury Road GL51 9DY **(T)** 01242 584 134 **Capacity:**
Colours(change): All navy blue

ADDITIONAL INFORMATION: Previous League: Cheltenham.
Record Att: 327 v Harrow Hill 31/08/2003.
Honours: Glouscestershire Senior Cup 1991-92. Hellenic League Division 1 1999-2000.

CLANFIELD

Founded: 1890 Nickname: Robins

Secretary: John Osborne **(T)** 01993 771 631 **(E)** trevor@cuss.gotadsl.co.uk
Chairman: John Osborne **Manager:** Peter Osborne **Prog Ed:** Trevor Cuss
Ground: Radcot Road, Clanfield OX18 2ST **(T)** 01367 810 314 **Capacity:** 2,000
Colours(change): All red

ADDITIONAL INFORMATION: Previous League: Witney & District.
Record Att: 197 v Kidlington August 2002.
Honours: Hellenic League Division 1 1969-70.

CRICKLADE TOWN

Founded: 1897 Crick

Secretary: Rebecca Ross **(T)** 07970 066 581 **(E)** alisdair.ross@venuesevent.com
Chairman: Alisdair Ross **Manager:** Graham Jackson **Prog Ed:** Alisdair Ross
Ground: Cricklade Leisure Centre, Stones Lane, Cricklade SN6 6JW **(T)** 01793 750 011 **Capacity:**
Colours(change): Green/white/green

ADDITIONAL INFORMATION: Previous League: Wiltshire.
Record Att: 170 v Trowbridge Town 2003-04.
Honours: Wiltshire League 2000-01.

EASINGTON SPORTS

Founded: 1946 Nickname: The Clan

Secretary: Neil Clarke **(T)** 07789 751 488 **(E)** neilclarke@talktalk.net
Chairman: Steve Hill **Manager:** Peter Foley **Prog Ed:** Steve Payton
Ground: Addison Road, Banbury OX16 9DH **(T)** 01295 257 006 **Capacity:** 1,000
Colours(change): Red & white/red & white/red

ADDITIONAL INFORMATION: Previous League: Warwick Combination.
Record Att: 258 v Hook Norton.
Hnours: Oxfordshire Senior League 1957-58, 58-59. Division 1 1965-66. Oxfordshire Senior Ben Turner Trophy 1970-71.

HEADINGTON AMATEURS

Founded: 1949 Nickname: A's

Secretary: Donald Light **(T)** 07764 943 778 **(E)** donald.light@ntlworld.com
Chairman: Donald Light **Manager:** Shaun Pearce **Prog Ed:** Donald Light
Ground: Barton Recreation Ground, Oxford OX3 9LA **(T)** 01865 760 489 **Capacity:**
Colours(change): All red

ADDITIONAL INFORMATION: Previous League: Oxfordshire Senior.
Record Att: 250 v Newport AFC, 1991. **Goalscorer:** Tony Penge. **Apps:** Kent Drackett.
Honours: Oxfordshire Senior League 1972-73, 73-74, 75-76, 76-77, Division 1 1968-69.

HOOK NORTON

Founded: 1898 Nickname: Hooky

Secretary: Michael Barlow **(T)** 07766 554 4980 **(E)** Michael.Barlow@hancocks-legal.co.uk
Chairman: Michael Barlow **Manager:** Mark Boyland **Prog Ed:** Mark Willis
Ground: The Bourne, Hook Norton OX15 5PB **(T)** 01608 737 132 **Capacity:** 500
Colours(change): Royal blue/royal blue/white

ADDITIONAL INFORMATION: Previous League: Oxfordshire Senior.
Record Att: 244 v Banbury United, 12/12/98.
Honours: Oxfordshire Senior League 1999-00, 00-01. Hellenic League Division 1 West 2001-02.

DIV.1 WEST INS & OUTS

IN: Bicester Town (R), Hook Norton (R), Malmesbury Victoria (R)
OUT: Cirencester United (F), Hardwicke (WN), Harrow Hill (WS), Slimbridge (P), Wootton Bassett Town (P)

LAUNTON SPORTS

Founded: 1899

Secretary: Phil Allen **(T)** 07733 156 015 **(E)** philip@bassett38.freeserve.co.uk
Chairman: Dave Smith **Manager:** Jason Allen **Prog Ed:** Alison Simmons
Ground: The Playing Field, Bicester Road, Launton OX26 5DP **(T)** 01869 242 007 **Capacity:**
Colours(change): Yellow/blue/yellow

ADDITIONAL INFORMATION: Previous League: Oxfordshire Senior.
Record Att: 92 v Easington Sports.
Honours: Oxfordshire Senior League Division 1 1992-93.

LETCOMBE

Founded: 1910 Nickname: Brooksiders

Secretary: Des Williams **(T)** 07765 144 985 **(E)** deswilliams45@btinternet.com
Chairman: Dennis Stock **Manager:** Alan Gifford **Prog Ed:** Russell Stock
Ground: Bassett Road, Letcombe Regis OX12 9JU **(T)** 07765 144 985 **Capacity:** 1,500
Colours(change): All purple

ADDITIONAL INFORMATION: Previous League: Chiltonian.
Record Att: 203 v Old Woodstock Town, 29/08/04.
Honours: North Berkshire League Division 1 1989-90. Chiltonian League Division 1 1990-91.

LYDNEY TOWN

Founded: 1911 Nickname: The Town

Secretary: Roger Sansom **(T)** 07887 842 125 **(E)** rsansom@glatfelter.com
Chairman: Peter Elliott **Manager:** Neil Hook **Prog Ed:** Roger Sansom
Ground: Lydney Recreation Ground, Swan Road, Lydney GL15 5RU **(T)** 01594 844 523 **Capacity:**
Colours(change): Black & white stripes/black/black

ADDITIONAL INFORMATION: Previous League: Gloucestershire County.
Record Att: 375 v Ellwood, 05.11.05.
Honours: Gloucestershire County League 2005-06. Hellenic League Division 1 West 2006-07.

MALMESBURY VICTORIA

Nickname: The Vics

Secretary: Sue Neale **(T)** 07885 092 661 **(E)** paul.neale@btconnect.com
Chairman: Paul Neale **Manager:** Ken Turner **Prog Ed:** Andrew Meadon
Ground: Flying Monk Ground, Gloucester Road, SN16 0AJ **(T)** TBA **Capacity:**
Colours(change): Black & white/black/red

ADDITIONAL INFORMATION: Previous League: Wiltshire Premier.
Record Att: 261 v Cirencester United, 25.08.02.
Honours: Wiltshire League 1999-00. Wiltshire Senior Cup 01-02.

PURTON

Founded: 1923 Nickname: The Reds

Secretary: Janice Kuczynski **(T)** 07816 648 949 **(E)** jkuczynski@btinternet.com
Chairman: Alan Eastwood **Manager:** Chris Pethick **Prog Ed:** Alan Eastwood
Ground: The Red House, Purton SN5 4DY **(T)** 01793 770 262 (MD) **Capacity:**
Colours(change): All red

ADDITIONAL INFORMATION: Previous League: Wiltshire County. **Record Att:** 533 v Dorcan April 1987.
Honours: Wiltshire League 1945-46, 46-47, 47-48. Wiltshire County League 1985-86. Hellenic League Division 1 1995-96, Division 1 West 2003-04. Wiltshire Senior Cup 1938-39, 48-49, 50-51, 54-55, 87-88, 88-89, 94-95.

TROWBRIDGE TOWN

Founded: 1880

Secretary: Jodie Arberry **(T)** 07941 776 683 **(E)** bobarberry@blueyonder.co.uk
Chairman: Ralph McCaldon **Manager:** Chris Carr **Prog Ed:** Andy Meaden
Ground: Wood Marsh, Bradley Road, Trowbridge BA14 0SB **(T)** 07545 172 043 **Capacity:** 1,500
Colours(change): Yellow & black/black/yellow

ADDITIONAL INFORMATION: Reformed in 1998. **Previous League:** Wiltshire.
Record Att: 369 v Tytherington Rocs 28/08/2005.
Honours: Wiltshire League 2003-04. Wiltshire Senior Cup 2003-04.

TYTHERINGTON ROCKS

Founded: 1896 Nickname: The Rocks

Secretary: Graham Shipp **(T)** 07811 318 424 **(E)** tramar1618@tiscali.co.uk
Chairman: Ted Travell **Manager:** Barry Granger **Prog Ed:** Mark Brown
Ground: Hardwicke Playing Field, Tytherington Glos GL12 8UJ **(T)** 07837 555 776 **Capacity:** 1,500
Colours(change): Amber & black/black/black

ADDITIONAL INFORMATION:
Previous League: Gloucestershire County.
Record Att: 400 v Thornbury Town, Senior Amateur Cup 1948.

WINTERBOURNE UNITED

Founded: 1911 Nickname: The Bourne

Secretary: Geoff Endicott **(T)** 07778 678 823 **(E)** g.endicott@btopenworld.com
Chairman: Robyn Maggs **Manager:** Nick Tanner **Prog Ed:** Mark Brown
Ground: Parkside Avenue, Winterbourne, Bristol BS36 1LX **(T)** 01454 850 059 **Capacity:**
Colours(change): All red

ADDITIONAL INFORMATION: Previous League: Gloucestershire County.
Record Att: 229 v Malmesbury Victoria, 29/08/2004.
Honours: Gloucestershire County League 2000-01. Hellenic League Division 1 West 2005-06, 07-08.

GROUND DIRECTIONS

ABINGDON TOWN - Culham Road OX14 3HP - 01235 521 684
From Town Centre follow signs for Culham, go over bridge, ground is 300 yards on right.

ARDLEY UNITED - The Playing Fields OX27 7NZ - 07711 009 198
From M40 Junction 10 take B430 towards Middleton Stoney the ground is on the right hand side after mile. From Oxford take B430 through Weston-on-the-Green & Middleton Stoney then on the left hand side after passing Church in village.

ASCOT UNITED - Ascot Racecourse SL5 7RA - 07798 701 995
From Ascot High Street, with Ascot Racecourse on the left, follow the A329 to the mini-roundabout, at the end of the High Street, turn left on Winkfield Rd, go through road underpass and take the first right (signposted Car Park 7&8). Follow the track past the Ascot United welcome sign, through gates into the large car park and the ground is approx. 600m further on.

BINFIELD - Hill Farm Lane RG42 5NR - 01344 860 822
From M4 Junction 10 take A329 signposted Wokingham & Binfield, at roundabout take 1st exit. Go through 1st set of traffic lights, turn left at 2nd set opposite Travel Lodge. Follow road through village over two mini-roundabouts, at 'T' junction with church in front of you turn right. Take left filter road after 150 yards into Stubbs Lane. Ground is on left at end of short lane.

BRACKNELL TOWN - Larges Lane RG12 9AN - 01344 412 305
Leave M4 at J10, take A329M signposted Wokingham & Bracknell. Follow road for 5 miles, over roundabout, pass Southern industrial estate (Waitrose etc.) on right to a 2nd r'about with traffic lights; take 2nd exit and follow signposts for M3. At next r'about take 1st exit. At next r'about take 3rd exit, Church Road dual carriageway. This brings you to another r'about with Bracknell & Wokingham college on right and Old Manor PH on left, take 5th exit for Ascot - A329. Go down hill on dual carriageway, London Road to next r'about take 4th exit back up the dual carriageway, London Road, Larges Lane last left turn before reaching r'about again. Ground 200 yards on right.

CARTERTON - Kilkenny Lane OX18 1DY - 01993 842 410
Leave A40 follow B4477 for Carterton continue along Monahan Way turning right at roundabout, at traffic lights turn right onto Upavon Way. At next set of lights turn right onto B4020 to Burford. Take 2nd right into Swinbrook Road carry onto Kilkenny Lane, a single-track road). Ground & car park 200 metres on left hand side.

FAIRFORD TOWN - Cinder Lane London Road GL7 4AX - 01285 712 071
Take A417 from Lechlade, turn left down Cinder Lane 150 yards after 40 mph sign. From Cirencester take Lechlade Road, turn right down Cinder Lane 400 yards after passing the Railway Inn.

FLACKWELL HEATH - Wilks Park, Magpie Lane HP10 9EA - 01628 523 892
Junction 4 of M40 Follow signs A404 (High Wycombe) Turn right at traffic lights halfway down Marlow Hill, signposted Flackwell Heath. Ground three (3) miles on left.

HIGHWORTH TOWN - Elm Recreation Ground SN6 7DD - 01793 766 263
Enter Town on A361, turn into The Green by Veterinary Surgery, Ground and Car Park 100 yards on left.

KIDLINGTON - Yarnton Road OX5 1AT - 01865 841 526
From Kidlington Roundabout take A4260 into Kidlington. After 3rd set of traffic lights take 2nd left into Yarnton Road. Ground 300 yards on left, just past Morton Avenue.

OLD WOODSTOCK TOWN - Eynsham Hall Park OX29 6PN - 07748 152 243
Ground situated on the A4095 Witney to Woodstock road, some 3 miles East of Witney. The entrance is 300 yards east of the main Eynsham Hall Park entrance. (North Leigh FC)

OXFORD CITY NOMADS - Court Place Farm Stadium OX3 0NQ - 01865 744 493
From South: From Newbury travel along the A34 towards Oxford turn onto Ring Road heading towards London (East). Follow Ring Road over 5 roundabouts to the Green Road roundabout signposted London, M40 East. Go straight over towards Banbury. A fly-over is visible, turn left onto the slip road and follow road to Court Place Farm Stadium on left. From North: At the North Oxford roundabout, travel towards London M40 on the Eastern by-pass, turn off at the flyover, the ground is visible to the left as you go over bridge.

PEGASUS JUNIORS - Old School Lane HR1 1EX - 07980 456 995
Approach City on A4103 (from Worcester) at roundabout on outskirts take 2nd exit (A4103) over railway bridge, traffic light controlled. Take 2nd turning on left into Old School Lane, ground entrance 150 metre's on left.

READING TOWN - Scours Lane RG30 6AY - 0118 945 3555
Leave M4 at junction 12 and take A4 towards Reading. Turn left at 1st lights go through Tilehurst Centre turn right into Norcot Road then left into Oxford Road and 1st right into Scours Lane.

SHORTWOOD UNITED - Meadowbank GL6 0SJ - 01453 833 936
12 miles west of Cirencester head for Cirencester, proceed up Spring Hill for 30 yards turn left through the Car Park, then left at Britannia Inn. Proceed up hill for approx mile to Shortwood. Ground is on the left hand side opposite the Church.

SHRIVENHAM - The Recreation Ground SN6 8BJ - 07767 371 414
Shrivenham village is signposted off A420 Oxford to Swindon road, six miles east of Swindon, four miles west of Faringdon. Drive through village turn into Highworth Road, ground is on right, car park on left.

SLIMBRIDGE - Wisloe Road GL2 7AF - 07835 927 226
From the A38 take the A4135 to Dursley. Ground is 100 yards on the left.

THAME UNITED - Sports Park, Hithercroft Road OX10 9RB - 01491 835 044
Leave Wallingford by-pass at Hithercroft roundabout. Ground is 100 yards on the left.

WANTAGE TOWN - Alfredian Park, Manor Road OX12 8DW - 01235 764 781
Proceed to Market Square. Take road at southeast corner (Newbury Street signposted to Hungerford). Continue for approximately a quarter of a mile take right turning into the ground. Clearly marked 'Wantage Town FC'.

WOKINGHAM & EMMB' - Bracknell Town FC RG12 9AN - 01344 412 305
Leave M4 at J10, take A329M signposted Wokingham & Bracknell. Follow road for 5 miles, over roundabout, pass Southern industrial estate (Waitrose etc.) on right to a 2nd r'about with traffic lights; take 2nd exit and follow sign-posts for M3. At next r'about take 1st exit. At next r'about take 3rd exit, Church Road dual carriageway. This brings you to another r'about with Bracknell & Wokingham college on right and Old Manor PH on left, take 5th exit for Ascot - A329. Go down hill on dual carriageway, London Road to next r'about take 4th exit back up the dual car-riageway, London Road, Larges Lane last left turn before reaching r'about again. Ground 200 yards on right.

WITNEY UNITED - Polythene UK Stadium OX29 7WT - 01993 848 558
From West: A40 towards Oxford. At Minster Lovell roundabout, take the 1st exit to Minster Lovell. Two miles turn right into Downs Road (signposted for Witney Lakes Golf Club), ground half a mile on right. From Witney town cen-tre: go west on Welch Way, at roundabout take 3rd exit into Curbridge Road. Take 3rd exit at roundabout into Deer Park Road, Left at traffic lights into Range Road, then left ground 400 yards on right.

WOOTTON BASSETT - Gerard Buxton Sports Ground SN4 8AW - 01793 853 880
Leave M4 at junction 16 and proceed towards Wootton Bassett Town Centre. Take 1st left after BP Petrol Station in Longleaze. Take 3rd turning on right into Rylands Way. Ground 150 metres on right hand side. Approaching from Calne or Devizes Area - proceed through Wootton Bassett Town Centre, take first right after Shell Garage into Longleaze then follow previous instructions.

DIVISION 1 EAST

CHALFONT WASPS - Crossleys Bowstridge Lane HP8 4QN - 01494 875 050
A413 to Chalfont St Giles, follow signposts for village centre. Bowstridge Lane is 400 yards on left immediately after the shops. Crossleys is 400 yards along Bowstridge Lane on the right. Ground is directly ahead.

CHINNOR - Station Road OX39 4PV - 01844 352 579
Leave M40 at junction 6 and follow B4009 sign posted Princes Risborough. After 3 miles enter Chinnor and turn left at Crown PH roundabout. Ground is 400 yards on right.

DIDCOT TOWN RESERVES - Npower Loop Meadow Stad' OX11 7GA - 01235 813 138
From A34 take A4130 towards Didcot, at first roundabout take first exit, at next roundabout take third exit, then straight across next two roundabouts, at 5th roundabout turn right into Avon Way, ground is on the left. Also foot-path direct from Didcot Railway Station.

FARNBOROUGH RESERVES - Farnborough Elite Centre GU24 9ER - 01252 541 469
Exit M3 at Junction No 3. Head southbound on A322 to Woking/Guilford. In Bisley village centre turn left at round-about by village green, ground is approx 400 yards on left hand side.

FINCHAMPSTEAD - Memorial Park, The Village RG40 4JR - 0118 973 2890
A321 from Wokingham, then fork right onto B3016. At the Greyhound Public House turn right onto the B3348. The ground is 200 yards on the right.

HENLEY TOWN - The Triangle Ground RG9 4HB - 01491 411 083
From Henley Town Centre take the A4155 towards Reading. Mill Lane is approximately one mile from the Town Centre on the left immediately before the Jet Garage. From M4 Junction 11 head towards Reading on the A33 inner distribution road then follow A4155 signed to Henley, turn right into Mill Lane after the Jet Garage. Ground & Car Park on the left over the Railway Bridge.

HOLYPORT - Summerleaze Village SL6 8SP - 07702 369 708
From the A4 Maidenhead take the B4447 towards Cookham after mile turn right into Ray Mill Road West, at the T-junction turn left into Blackamoor Lane. As road bends sharply you will see the entrance to the ground on left, sign-posted Holyport FC. Please observe speed limit down track to the ground.

HUNGERFORD TOWN RESERVES - Bulpit Lane RG17 0AY - 01488 682 939
Leave M4 at junction 14 to A4, right then left at Bear Hotel through town centre, left into Priory Road, 2nd left into Bulpit Lane, over crossroads ground on left.

MILTON UNITED - Potash Lane OX13 6AG - 01235 832 999
Exit A34 at Milton, 10 miles south of Oxford & 12 miles north of junction 13 of M4. Take A4130 towards Wantage approximately 200 metres turn 1st left then right into Milton Hill. Ground 400 metres on the left.

NEWBURY - Faraday Road RG14 2AD - 01635 41031
Leave M4 at junction 13 taking Newbury road. Take A4 towards Thatcham, then take 1st right by 'Topp Tiles' into Faraday Road, ground is at end of road.

PENN & TYLERS GREEN - French School Meadows HP10 8LF - 01494 815 346
From West - 'M40 to High Wycombe leave at J4. Follow A404 to Amersham, via Wycombe. Stay on A404 up the hill past railway station approx. 3 miles at Hazlemere Crossroads turn right onto the B474 signposted to Penn and Beaconsfield. Continue for approx. one mile go past three new houses on left, turn into Elm Road, the ground is on the left. From East -Leave M40 at Junction 2 and take the road signed Beaconsfield. From Beaconsfield follow the road through Penn towards Hazlemere, pass the pond on green and entrance to ground is on the right had side of road before the hill.

RAYNERS LANE - Tithe Farm Social Club HA2 0XH - 0208 868 8724
From A40 Polish War Memorial turn left into A4180 (West End Road), approx. 500 metres turn right into Station Approach, at traffic lights turn right into Victoria Road. At next roundabout continue straight on to traffic lights at junction with Alexandra Avenue (Matrix Bar & Restaurant on left). Continue straight on over traffic lights and take second turning on left into Rayners Lane. Ground is approximately half a mile on the left.

SOUTH KILBURN - Vale Farm, Watford Road HA0 3HE - 0208 908 6545
Leave A40 onto A404, Watford Road, continue along Watford Road, you will see the sign for Vale Farm Sports Ground on right.

WOODLEY TOWN - East Park Farm, Park Lane RG10 9TR - 07703 474 555
Take A4, Bath Road & exit onto A3032 at @Wee Waif' roundabout to Twyford & Charvil. Take right exit at mini-roundabout into Park Lane then 2nd exit at mini-roundabout on Park Lane then left turn into East Park Farm. After-match Hospitality is at the Earley Home Guard Club.

DIVISION 1 WEST

BICESTER TOWN - Sports Ground, Oxford Road OX26 2AD - 01869 241 036
From Oxford, pass Tesco's Superstore on outskirts of Bicester and Ground is on the right. From Aylesbury turn left at first roundabout on outskirts of Bicester onto by-pass. Turn right at next roundabout, pass Tesco's Superstore and ground is on the right.

CHELTENHAM SARACENS - PETERSFIELD PARK GL51 9DY - 01242 584 134
Follow directions into Cheltenham following signs for railway station. At Station roundabout take Gloucester Road, in a Northerly direction for approx 2 miles. Turn left at lights past Tesco entrance onto Tewkesbury Road, follow road past 'The Range' store over railway bridge. Take 1st left and then 1st left again, then left into service road into car park.

CLANFIELD - Radcot Road OX18 2ST - 01367 810 314
Situated on A4095 at southern end of village, 8 miles west of Witney and 4 miles east of Faringdon.

CRICKLADE TOWN - Cricklade Leisure Centre SN6 6JW - 01793 750 011
Cricklade is eight miles North of Swindon signposted off the A419. Leisure Centre is signposted off the B4040 Malmesbury Road.

EASINGTON SPORTS - Addison Road OX16 9DH - 01295 257 006
From North/South M40- Leave M40 at J11, follow A422 to Banbury, 2nd r'about take A4260 to Adderbury. Go through three sets of traffic lights, at top of hill at T-junc' turn left. Take 3rd right into Addison Rd. From South West A361 – Entering Banbury take 1st right turning into Springfield Av after 'The Easington' PH. Follow road, take T-junc' right into Grange Rd, 1st right into Addison Rd. Ground on left at end of road.

HEADINGTON AM' - Barton Recreation Ground OX3 9LA - 01865 760 489
A40 from London take last exit at Headington Roundabout. A40 from Witney take first exit. Take first left after leaving roundabout into North Way. Follow North Way to end where road merges to become Barton Village Road. Ground at bottom of hill on left.

HOOK NORTON - The Bourne OX15 5PB - 01608 737 132
From Oxford – A44 to junction with A361 turn right, take 1st left to a 'T' junction, turn right & enter village, after 30 MPH turn left then 1st right into 'The Bourne', take 1st left into ground.

LAUNTON SPORTS - The Playing Field, Bicester Rd - OX26 5DP- 01869 242 007
Entering Bicester from A34 South, at roundabout take A41 right for Aylesbury, next roundabout take 2nd exit sign posted Launton. At 3rd roundabout take right to Launton. Go through traffic lights over bridge just past church take left turn marked 'Playing Field' & Launton Sports FC.

LETCOMBE - BASSETT ROAD OX12 9JU - 07765 144 985
Take the B4507 from Wantage (Sign posted White Horse). Turn left after half a mile to Letcombe Regis. Ground on Far side of Village, on the right hand side of road.

LYDNEY TOWN - Lydney Recreation Ground GL15 5RU - 01594 844 523
From Gloucester – take Lydney road off A48 down Highfield Hill and into the town centre. Take 1st left into Swan Road after 2nd set of pelican lights. From Chepstow – at by-pass roundabout take Lydney road. Go over railway crossing then take 2nd right into Swan Road.

MALMESBURY VICTORIA - Flying Monk Ground SN16 0AJ
Off A429 signpost Cirencester take B4014 to Tetbury. First left signpost Town Centre Ground on right directly after Somerfield supermarket, narrow right turning into ground behind supermarket.

PURTON - THE RED HOUSE SN5 4DY - 01793 770 262 MD
Red House is near Village Hall Square; Purton is well signposted from all directions, situated on the B4041 Wootton Bassett to Cricklade Road, NW of Swindon.

TROWBRIDGE TOWN - Wood Marsh, Bradley Road BA14 0SB - 07545 172 043
Take the A350 Trowbridge by-pass towards Westbury continue through a set of traffic lights until you reach the Yarnbrook Roundabout, Texaco garage on corner. Take the 3rd exit to Trowbridge Go under a railway bridge, next roundabout take the North Bradley exit. Carry on along this road over a small roundabout and past the 'Mash Tun' PH. Ground is on the left.

TYTHERINGTON ROCKS - Hardwicke Playing Field GL12 8UJ - 07837 555 776
From M5 Junction 14 take A38 for Bristol. Tytherington turn-off is approximately three (3) miles. Enter village, ground is signposted.

WINTERBOURNE UNITED - Parkside Avenue BS36 1LX - 01454 850 059
Leave M4 at Junction 19 sign posted M32. Leave M32 at junction 1, turn left at bottom of slip road and keep in left hand lane turn left again at traffic lights, sign posted Winterbourne & Yate. Keep on road for 2 miles into Winterbourne After Ridings High School turn right into Parkside Avenue entrance to ground is 100 yards on right between houses.

KENT LEAGUE

www.kentleague.com

Sponsored by: Safety Net Associates

Founded: 1966

Recent champions:
2005: Ramsgate
2006: Maidstone United
2007: Whitstable Town
2008: Thamesmead Town
2009: VCD Athletic

	Beck'hm	Cor'thian	Deal T.	Erith T.	Erith & B.	Fav'sham	Fisher	G'wich	Herne B.	Hol'dale	Hythe T.	Lordsw'd	Norton .	Sev'oaks	S Bengal	Tun. W.
Beckenham Town	***P***	2-0	5-1	5-0	2-2	0-1	0-1	2-1	2-4	4-3	0-1	2-2	2-1	2-1	0-0	2-1
Corinthian	0-5	***R***	1-0	1-2	1-3	1-2	2-2	2-1	1-0	0-6	1-2	2-1	0-1	2-3	1-3	3-0
Deal Town	0-1	3-0	***E***	2-1	2-1	0-1	1-0	2-1	1-4	2-1	1-1	0-0	1-4	2-2	7-1	3-1
Erith Town	1-1	2-2	0-1	***M***	2-0	0-1	4-2	2-2	2-2	4-0	3-4	6-1	3-2	2-1	3-0	1-1
Erith & Belvedere	2-1	0-1	3-1	1-0	***I***	3-1	1-3	2-2	0-4	0-0	1-1	1-6	1-3	1-1	2-3	5-1
Faversham Town	1-2	8-0	6-1	3-0	6-1	***E***	0-1	4-0	3-0	4-1	2-1	5-1	3-1	1-0	0-0	6-2
Fisher	1-2	1-2	2-0	1-1	1-2	1-3	***R***	0-3	3-5	0-1	0-4	1-1	0-3	0-1	2-2	2-1
Greenwich Borough	4-1	3-2	2-1	0-1	3-2	3-2	4-0		2-0	1-0	2-2	1-1	1-1	2-2	3-0	0-3
Herne Bay	2-1	1-1	4-2	3-0	1-0	2-4	1-0	1-0	***D***	1-0	1-2	4-2	2-1	0-2	9-0	3-0
Holmesdale	1-2	3-0	4-0	1-2	4-1	0-1	0-3	2-0	1-2	***I***	3-1	2-1	0-1	3-4	3-2	0-2
Hythe Town	3-1	0-1	0-0	3-1	5-2	1-2	6-0	1-1	0-2	4-0	***V***	1-1	1-2	1-0	6-1	0-0
Lordswood	1-2	1-2	0-1	0-4	2-2	1-3	0-3	0-3	0-2	1-2	0-5	***I***	0-1	1-3	4-1	1-1
Norton Sports	1-1	2-1	3-3	2-2	0-1	0-1	1-3	1-2	1-2	1-1	1-1	1-0	***S***	1-2	1-3	1-3
Sevenoaks Town	1-4	3-1	2-4	1-0	0-1	0-3	1-3	1-2	1-5	2-1	4-3	1-1	4-1	***I***	8-1	1-0
Sporting Bengal United	0-2	3-1	6-4	2-1	3-4	0-2	3-3	1-3	1-3	0-3	3-4	1-4	3-0	0-3	***O***	1-3
Tunbridge Wells	2-0	4-0	3-3	4-2	2-1	0-0	3-2	0-0	3-5	1-1	0-3	1-1	1-2	2-1	6-0	***N***

Premier Division	P	W	D	L	F	A	Pts
Faversham Town	**30**	**24**	**2**	**4**	**79**	**23**	**74**
Herne Bay	**30**	**22**	**2**	**6**	**75**	**36**	**68**
Hythe Town	**30**	**15**	**8**	**7**	**67**	**36**	**53**
Beckenham Town	**30**	**16**	**5**	**9**	**56**	**39**	**53**
Greenwich Borough	**30**	**14**	**8**	**8**	**52**	**39**	**50**
Sevenoaks Town	**30**	**14**	**4**	**12**	**56**	**50**	**46**
Tunbridge Wells	**30**	**11**	**8**	**11**	**51**	**50**	**41**
Erith Town	**30**	**11**	**7**	**12**	**52**	**49**	**40**
Deal Town	**30**	**11**	**6**	**13**	**49**	**60**	**39**
Holmesdale	**30**	**11**	**3**	**16**	**47**	**47**	**36**
Norton Sports	**30**	**10**	**6**	**14**	**41**	**48**	**36**
Erith & Belvedere	**30**	**10**	**6**	**14**	**46**	**62**	**36**
Fisher	**30**	**9**	**5**	**16**	**41**	**58**	**32**
Corinthian	**30**	**9**	**3**	**18**	**32**	**67**	**30**
Sporting Bengal Utd	**30**	**7**	**4**	**19**	**44**	**95**	**25**
Lordswood	**30**	**3**	**9**	**18**	**35**	**64**	**18**

CHALLENGE SHIELD

(Prem Div champions v Prem Div cup holders)

(August 1st at VCD Athletic)
VCD Athletic 0 **Croydon** 1

PREMIER DIVISION CUP

FIRST ROUND
(played over two legs)
Corinthian 2 Erith & B'dere 2, **Erith & Belvedere** 1 Corinthian 0
Erith T. 2 Greenwich B. 1, Greenwich Borough 1 **Erith Town** 1
Fisher 0 Faversham Town 2, **Faversham Town** 2 Fisher 2
Holmesdale 1 Herne Bay 2, **Herne Bay** 1 Holmesdale 0
Lordswood 1 Deal Town 2, **Deal Town** 2 Lordswood 2
Sevenoaks Town 1 Norton Sports 2, Norton Sports 1 **Sevenoaks Town** 2 *aet* (2-3p)
Sptg Bengal 1 Beckenham 3, **Beckenham** 6 Sporting Bengal 1
Tunbridge Wells 1 Hythe 3, **Hythe Town** 2 Tunbridge Wells 1

QUARTER-FINALS
(played over two legs)
Beckenham 2 Erith Town 0, Erith Town 2 **Beckenham Town** 3
Faversham 2 Erith & B. 1, Erith & B'dere 1 **Faversham Town** 3
Hythe Town 0 Herne Bay 2, **Herne Bay** 1 Hythe Town 1
Sevenoaks 1 Deal Town 1, Deal Town 3 **Sevenoaks Town** 5

SEMI-FINALS
(played over two legs)
Herne Bay 3 Faversham 1, Faversham Town 1 **Herne Bay** 1
Sevenoaks Town 2 Beckenham Town 2, Beckenham Town 3 **Sevenoaks Town** 3 *aet (Sevenoaks win on away goals)*

FINAL
(May 3rd at Folkestone Invicta)
Herne Bay 3 Sevenoaks Town 2 *aet*

Division One	P	W	D	L	F	A	Pts
Herne Bay Res.	20	13	5	2	47	26	44
Erith & Belvedere Res.	20	11	4	5	40	30	37
Maidstone United Res.	20	10	6	4	35	23	36
Dartford Res.	20	10	2	8	46	30	32
Cray Wanderers Res.	20	7	7	6	45	40	28
Thamesmead Town Res.	20	6	8	6	31	37	26
Ashford Town Res.	20	6	6	8	27	30	24
Chatham Town Res.	20	7	3	10	33	37	24
Whitstable Town Res.	20	5	7	8	43	52	22
Margate Res.	20	6	3	11	24	46	21
Holmesdale Res.	20	2	1	17	28	55	7

Division Two	P	W	D	L	F	A	Pts
Erith Town Res.	18	10	3	5	38	20	33
Beckenham Town Res.	18	9	5	4	41	25	32
Sevenoaks Town Res.	18	9	4	5	39	33	31
VCD Athletic Res.	18	8	4	6	30	25	28
Deal Town Res.	18	8	4	6	32	32	28
Faversham Town Res.	18	6	6	6	28	25	24
Lordswood Res.	18	7	2	9	24	33	23
Folkestone Invicta Res.	18	5	4	9	28	42	19
Hythe Town Res.	18	4	4	10	23	36	16
Ramsgate Res.	18	3	6	9	31	43	15

DIVISION ONE/TWO CUP

FINAL *(May 1st at Welling United)*
Dartford Res. 2 VCD Athletic Res. 1

FLOODLIGHT TROPHY

FINAL *(May 17th at Herne Bay)*
Herne Bay Res. 1 **Dartford Res.** 2

IN: VCD Athletic (R – Isthmian League Division One North)
OUT: Faversham Town (P – Isthmian League Division One South)
Erith Town become Erith & Dartford Town

INS & OUTS

BECKENHAM TOWN

Founded: 1887 Nickname: Reds

Secretary: Peter Palmer **(T)** 07774 728 758 **(E)** secretary@beckenhamtownfc.co.uk
Chairman: Chris McCarthy **Manager:** Jason Huntley **Prog Ed:** Sam Percival
Ground: Eden Park Avenue, Beckenham Kent BR3 1JT **(T)** 07774 728 758
Capacity: 4,000 **Seats:** 120 **Covered:** 120 **Midweek Matchday:** Tuesday **Clubhouse:** Yes **Shop:** Yes

Colours(change): Red/red. (White/blue).
Previous Names: Stanhope Rovers.
Previous Leagues: South East London Amateur. Metropolitan. London Spartan.
Records: **Att:** 720 v Berkhamsted, FA Cup 1994-95. **Goalscorer:** Ricky Bennett. **Apps:** Lee Fabian - 985.
Senior Honours: London League 1927-28.

10 YEAR RECORD

00-01	01-02	02-03	03-04	04-05	05-06	06-07	07-08	08-09	09-10
Kent P 7	Kent P 9	Kent P 10	Kent P 12	Kent P 10	Kent P 2	Kent P 11	Kent P 3	Kent P 15	Kent P 4

CORINTHIAN

Founded: 1972 Nickname:

Secretary: Sue Billings **(T)** 07734 855 554 **(E)** corinthians@billingsgroup.com
Chairman: R J Billings **Manager:** Tony Stitford **Prog Ed:**
Ground: Gay Dawn Farm, Valley Road, Longfield DA3 8LY **(T)** 01474 573 118
Capacity: **Seats:** **Covered:** **Midweek Matchday:** Tuesday **Clubhouse:** Yes **Shop:**

Colours(change): Green & white hoops/white (Yellow/green)
Previous Names: Welling United Reserves
Previous Leagues: Southern 1985-91.
Records:
Senior Honours:

10 YEAR RECORD

00-01	01-02	02-03	03-04	04-05	05-06	06-07	07-08	08-09	09-10
									Kent P 14

DEAL TOWN

Founded: 1908 Nickname: Town

Secretary: Michelle Finn **(T)** 01304 375 574 **(E)**
Chairman: David Reid **Manager:** Derek Hares **Prog Ed:** Colin Adams
Ground: Charles Sports Ground, St Leonards Road, Deal. CT14 9BB **(T)** 01304 375 623
Capacity: 2,500 **Seats:** 180 **Covered:** 180 **Midweek Matchday:** Tuesday **Clubhouse:** Yes **Shop:** Yes

Colours(change): Black & white/black. (Blue/blue).
Previous Names: Deal Cinque Ports FC > 1920
Previous Leagues: Thanet. East Kent. Kent. Aetolian. Southern. Greater London.
Records: **Att:** 2,495 v Newcastle Town, FA Vase S-F, 26.03.2000.
Senior Honours: Kent League 1953-54, 99-00. FA Vase 99-00. Kent Senior Cup (x2).

10 YEAR RECORD

00-01	01-02	02-03	03-04	04-05	05-06	06-07	07-08	08-09	09-10
Kent P 15	Kent P 3	Kent P 4	Kent P 16	Kent P 13	Kent P 9	Kent P 8	Kent P 9	Kent P 12	Kent P 9

ERITH & BELVEDERE

Founded: 1922 Nickname: Deres

Secretary: Frank May **(T)** 07778 987 579 **(E)** frank.may@erithandbelvederefc.co.uk
Chairman: John McFadden **Manager:** Micky Collins **Prog Ed:** Martin Tarrant/Brian Spurrel
Ground: Welling FC, Park View Rd, Welling, DA16 1SY **(T)** 020 8304 0333
Capacity: 4,000 **Seats:** 1,070 **Covered:** 1,000 **Midweek Matchday:** Tuesday **Clubhouse:** Yes **Shop:** Yes

Colours(change): Blue & white quarters/blue. (Red & white quarters/red.
Previous Names: Belvedere & District FC (Formed 1918 restructured 1922)
Previous Leagues: Kent. London. Corinthian. Athenian. Southern.
Records: **Att:** 5,573 v Crook C.W., FA Am. Cup 1949. **Goalscorer:** Colin Johnson - 284 (61-71). **Apps:** Dennis Crawford - 504 (56-71).
Senior Honours: Kent League 1981-82. London Senior Cup 44-45.

10 YEAR RECORD

00-01	01-02	02-03	03-04	04-05	05-06	06-07	07-08	08-09	09-10
SthE 20	SthE 9	SthE 18	SthE 21	SthE 21	Kent P 4	Kent P 7	Kent P 7	Kent P 8	Kent P 12

ERITH & DARTFORD TOWN

Founded: 1959 Nickname: The Dockers

Secretary: Jim Davie **(T)** 07780 712 149 **(E)**
Chairman: Albert Putman **Manager:** Steve O'Boyle **Prog Ed:** Ian Birrell
Ground: Erith Sports Stadium, Avenue Road, Erith DA8 3AT **(T)** 01322 350 271
Capacity: 1,450 **Seats:** 1,006 **Covered:** 1,066 **Midweek Matchday:** Monday **Clubhouse:** Yes **Shop:** No

Colours(change): Red & black/black. (Yellow/white).
Previous Names: Woolwich Town 1959-89 and 1990-97. Erith Town 1997-2010
Previous Leagues: London Metropolitan Sunday. London Spartan.
Records: **Att:** 325 v Charlton Athletic, friendly. **Goalscorer:** Dean Bowey.
Senior Honours:

10 YEAR RECORD

00-01	01-02	02-03	03-04	04-05	05-06	06-07	07-08	08-09	09-10
Kent P 11	Kent P 13	Kent P 15	Kent P 7	Kent P 15	Kent P 14	Kent P 14	Kent P 5	Kent P 7	Kent P 12

FISHER

Founded: 1908 Nickname: The Fish

Secretary: (Acting) Joe Arif **(T)** 07921 149 001 **(E)** joe_fafc@yahoo.co.uk
Chairman: Vacant **Manager:** Gary Lisney **Prog Ed:** Jevon Hall
Ground: Dulwich Hamlet FC, Edgar Kail Way, East Dulwich SE22 8BD **(T)**
Capacity: 3,000 **Seats:** 500 **Covered:** 1,000 **Midweek Matchday:** Monday **Clubhouse:** Yes **Shop:** Yes

Colours(change): Black & white/black. (Red/red).
Previous Names: Fisher Athletic. Reformed as Fisher F.C. in 2009.
Previous Leagues: Parthenon, Kent Amateur, London Spartan, Southern, Isthmian, Conference.
Records: **Att:** 4,283 v Barnet Conference 04/05/1991. **Goalscorer:** Paul Shinners - 205. **Apps:** Dennis Sharp - 720.
Senior Honours: Parthenon League 1961-62. Kent Amateur League 1973-74, 74-75. London Spartan 1980-81, 81-82.
Southern League Southern Division 1982-83, Premier 86-87, Eastern 2004-05. Kent Senior Cup 1983-84. Isthmian League Cup 2005-06.

10 YEAR RECORD

00-01	01-02	02-03	03-04	04-05	05-06	06-07	07-08	08-09	09-10
SthE 20	SthE 6	SthE 14	SthE 14	SthE 1	Isth P 3	Conf S 10	Conf S 4	Conf S 22	Kent P 13

GREENWICH BOROUGH

Founded: 1928 Nickname: Boro

Secretary: Steve Firkins **(T)** 07711 303 936 **(E)** s.firkins@hotmail.com
Chairman: Devon Hanson **Manager:** Steve Firkins/Jim Bajeux **Prog Ed:** TBC
Ground: Holmesdale FC, 68 Oakley Road, Bromley, Kent BR2 8HQ **(T)**
Capacity: **Seats:** **Covered:** **Midweek Matchday:** Tuesday **Clubhouse:** Yes **Shop:** No

Colours(change): All red. (All blue).
Previous Names: Woolwich Borough Council Athletic FC.
Previous Leagues: South London Alliance. Kent Amateur. London Spartan.
Records: **Att:** 2,000 v Charlton Athletic, turning on of floodlights, 1978.
Senior Honours: London Spartan League 1979-80. Kent Senior Trophy 84-85.
Kent League 86-87, 87-88.

10 YEAR RECORD

00-01	01-02	02-03	03-04	04-05	05-06	06-07	07-08	08-09	09-10
Kent P 9	Kent P 15	Kent P 14	Kent P 8	Kent P 9	Kent P 13	Kent P 5	Kent P 8	Kent P 3	Kent P 5

HERNE BAY

Founded: 1886 Nickname: The Bay

Secretary: Tony Day **(T)** 07789 655 768 **(E)** tonyday@hernebayfc.net
Chairman: John Bathurst **Manager:** Simon Halsey **Prog Ed:** John Bathurst
Ground: Winch's Field, Stanley Gardens, Herne Bay CT6 5SG **(T)** 01227 374 156
Capacity: 3,000 **Seats:** 200 **Covered:** 1,500 **Midweek Matchday:** Wednesday **Clubhouse:** Yes **Shop:** Yes

Colours(change): Blue & white strips/blue (Yellow/black/black)
Previous Names: None.
Previous Leagues: East Kent. Faversham & Dist. Cantebury & Dist. Kent Am. Athenian.
Records: **Att:** 2,303 v Margate, FA Cup 4th Qual. 1970-71.
Senior Honours: Kent League 1991-92, 93-94, 96-97, 97-98.

10 YEAR RECORD

00-01	01-02	02-03	03-04	04-05	05-06	06-07	07-08	08-09	09-10
Kent P 2	Kent P 7	Kent P 11	Kent P 10	Kent P 2	Kent P 7	Kent P 9	Kent P 6	Kent P 6	Kent P 2

HOLMESDALE

Founded: 1956 Nickname:

Secretary: Ross Mitchell **(T)** **(E)** secretary@holmesdalefc.co.uk
Chairman: Mark Harris **Manager:** Gary Davies **Prog Ed:** TBC
Ground: Holmesdale Sp.& Soc.Club, 68 Oakley Rd, Bromley BR2 8HQ **(T)** 020 8462 4440
Capacity: **Seats:** **Covered:** **Midweek Matchday:** Tuesday **Clubhouse:** Yes **Shop:** Yes

Colours(change): Green & yellow/green. (All blue).
Previous Names: None.
Previous Leagues: Thornton Heath & Dist. Surrey Inter. Surrey South Eastern. Kent County.
Records: **Goals:** M Barnett - 410 (in 429 apps).
Senior Honours: Kent County League 2006-07

10 YEAR RECORD

00-01	01-02	02-03	03-04	04-05	05-06	06-07	07-08	08-09	09-10
		KC1W 4	KC1W 4	KC1W 8	KC1W 1	KC P 1	Kent P 15	Kent P 5	Kent P 10

HYTHE TOWN

Founded: 1992 Nickname: Town

Secretary: Martin Giles **(T)** 07908 763 101 **(E)** martinrgiles@sky.com
Chairman: Paul Markland **Manager:** Scott Porter **Prog Ed:** Martin Whybrow
Ground: Reachfields Stadium, Fort Road, Hythe CT21 6JS **(T)** 01303 264 932
Capacity: **Seats:** **Covered:** **Midweek Matchday:** Tuesday **Clubhouse:** Yes **Shop:** No

Colours(change): All red (Yellow/blue/yellow)
Previous Names: Hythe Town > 1988. Hythe Town 1988 Ltd > 92. Hythe United 95- 01.
Previous Leagues: Southern.
Records: **Att:** 2,147 v Yeading, FA Vase Semi-Final, 1990.
Senior Honours: Kent League 1988-89.

10 YEAR RECORD

00-01	01-02	02-03	03-04	04-05	05-06	06-07	07-08	08-09	09-10
Kent P 14	Kent P 14	Kent P 8	Kent P 6	Kent P 6	Kent P 12	Kent P 6	Kent P 4	Kent P 2	Kent P 3

LORDSWOOD

Founded: 1968 Nickname: Lords

Secretary: Steve Lewis **(T)** 07775 541 573 **(E)** s.lewis@southernharvesters.co.uk
Chairman: Ron Constantine **Manager:** Jason Lillis **Prog Ed:** Darell Harman
Ground: Martyn Grove, Northdane Way, Walderslade, ME5 8YE **(T)** 01634 669 138
Capacity: 600 **Seats:** 123 **Covered:** 123 **Midweek Matchday:** Tuesday **Clubhouse:** Yes **Shop:** No

Colours(change): Orange & black/black. (Blue & white/blue).
Previous Names: None.
Previous Leagues: Rochester & Dist. Kent County.
Records:
Senior Honours: Kent League 1988-89.

10 YEAR RECORD

00-01	01-02	02-03	03-04	04-05	05-06	06-07	07-08	08-09	09-10
Kent P 10	Kent P 11	Kent P 13	Kent P 13	Kent P 16	Kent P 8	Kent P 13	Kent P 16	Kent P 16	Kent P 16

NORTON SPORTS

Founded: 1927 Nickname:

Secretary: Colin Page **(T)** 07970 549 355 **(E)** c_page@blueyonder.co.uk
Chairman: Kevin James **Manager:** Ben Taylor **Prog Ed:** TBC
Ground: Herne Bay FC, Winch's Field, Herne Bay CT6 5SG **(T)** 01227 374 156
Capacity: 3,000 **Seats:** 200 **Covered:** 1,500 **Midweek Matchday:** Tuesday **Clubhouse:** Yes **Shop:** Yes

Colours(change): Blue & white/black. (All red).
Previous Names: Amalgamated with Teynham & Lynsted in 1998.
Previous Leagues: Kent County.
Records:
Senior Honours: Kent County League 2007-08.

10 YEAR RECORD

00-01	01-02	02-03	03-04	04-05	05-06	06-07	07-08	08-09	09-10
				KC1E 1		KC P 3	KC P 1	Kent P 11	Kent P 11

SEVENOAKS TOWN

Founded: 1883 Nickname: Town

Secretary: Eddie Diplock **(T)** 01732 454 280 **(E)** suesmart53@hotmail.co.uk
Chairman: Tony Smart **Manager:** Keith Levett **Prog Ed:** Vacant
Ground: Greatness Park, Seal Road, Sevenoaks TN14 5BL **(T)** 01732 741 987
Capacity: 2,000 **Seats:** 110 **Covered:** 200 **Midweek Matchday:** Tuesday **Clubhouse:** **Shop:**

Colours(change): Blue stripes/navy. (Green & white/white).
Previous Names: None.
Previous Leagues: Sevenoaks League. Kent Amateur/County.
Records:
Senior Honours: Kent County 1984-85, 95-96, 02-03.

10 YEAR RECORD

00-01	01-02	02-03	03-04	04-05	05-06	06-07	07-08	08-09	09-10
	KC P 2	KC P 1	Kent P 11	Kent P 11	Kent P 16	Kent P 10	Kent P 11	Kent P 14	Kent P 6

SPORTING BENGAL UNITED

Founded: 1996 Nickname: Bengal Tigers

Secretary: Mahbub Hussain **(T)** 07947 161 887 **(E)** bfauk@btconnect.com
Chairman: Suroth Miah **Manager:** Mamun Chowdhury **Prog Ed:** Mahbub Hussain
Ground: Mile End Stadium, Rhodeswell Rd, Off Burdett Rd E14 4TW **(T)** 020 8980 1885
Capacity: **Seats:** Yes **Covered:** **Midweek Matchday:** Wednesday **Clubhouse:** **Shop:**

Colours(change): Blue/blue. (Yellow & orange/orange).
Previous Names: None.
Previous Leagues: Asian League. London Intermediate.
Records: **Att:** 4,235 v Touring Phalco Mohammedan S.C.
Senior Honours: None.

10 YEAR RECORD

00-01	01-02	02-03	03-04	04-05	05-06	06-07	07-08	08-09	09-10
LonInt 6	LonInt 7		Kent P 17	Kent P 14	Kent P 15	Kent P 17	Kent P 17	Kent P 17	Kent P 15

TUNBRIDGE WELLS

Founded: 1886 Nickname: The Wells

Secretary: Phill Allcorn **(T)** 07900 243 508 **(E)** secretary@twfcexec.com
Chairman: Joe Croker **Manager:** Martin Larkin **Prog Ed:** TBC
Ground: Culverden Stadium, Culverden Down, Tunbridge Wells TN4 9SG **(T)** 01892 520 517
Capacity: 3,750 **Seats:** 250 **Covered:** 1,000 **Midweek Matchday:** Tuesday **Clubhouse:** Yes **Shop:** No

Colours(change): Red/red (Blue/blue)
Previous Names: None.
Previous Leagues: Isthminan. London Spartan.
Records: **Att:** 967 v Maidstone United, FA Cup 1969. **Goalscorer:** John Wingate - 151. **Apps:** Tony Atkins - 410.
Senior Honours: Kent League 1984-85.

10 YEAR RECORD

00-01	01-02	02-03	03-04	04-05	05-06	06-07	07-08	08-09	09-10
Kent P 6	Kent P 8	Kent P 12	Kent P 14	Kent P 7	Kent P 10	Kent P 15	Kent P 10	Kent P 10	Kent P 7

VICKERS CRAYFORD DARTFORD ATHLETIC

Founded: 1916 Nickname: The Vickers

Secretary: Chris Dudley **(T)** **(E)** chris.dudley@ntlworld.com
Chairman: Gary Rump **Manager:** Ricky Bennett **Prog Ed:**
Ground: VCD Athletic Club, Old Road, Crayford DA1 4DN **(T)** 01322 524 262
Capacity: **Seats:** Yes **Covered:** Yes **Midweek Matchday:** Tuesday **Clubhouse:** Yes **Shop:** No

Colours(change): Green & white/white (Blue/black)
Previous Names: Vickers (Erith). Vickers (Crayford)
Previous Leagues: Dartford & District. Kent County. Isthmian
Records:
Senior Honours: Kent County League 1996-97. Kent League 2008-09.

10 YEAR RECORD

00-01	01-02	02-03	03-04	04-05	05-06	06-07	07-08	08-09	09-10
Kent P 3	Kent P 2	Kent P 7	Kent P 3	Kent P 5	Kent P 6	Kent P 2	Kent P 2	Kent P 1	Isth1N 8

GREENWICH BOROUGH F.C.
Photo: Alan Coomes.

ORPINGTON F.C.
Photo: Alan Coomes.

ERITH & BELVEDERE F.C.
Photo: Alan Coomes.

Team
Photos

SNODLAND F.C.
Photo: Alan Coomes.

CRAY VALLEY F.C.
Photo: Alan Coomes.

LORDSWOOD F.C.
Photo: Alan Coomes.

MIDLAND COMBINATION

www.midcomb.com

Sponsored by:
ImoSports

Founded: 1927

Recent champions:

2005: Leamington

2006: Atherstone Town

2007: Coventry Sphinx

2008: Coleshill Town

2009: Loughborough University

Premier Division		P	W	D	L	F	A	Pts
Heath Hayes		42	29	4	9	128	60	91
Heather St John		42	26	10	6	119	42	88
Pilkington XXX	*-3*	42	26	5	11	95	73	80
Castle Vale		42	23	10	9	98	55	79
Coventry Copsewood		42	22	11	9	81	55	77
Walsall Wood		42	21	8	13	79	76	71
Brocton		42	20	6	16	94	65	66
Dosthill Colts		42	17	13	12	77	62	64
GSA Sports		42	18	9	15	97	80	63
Bartley Green		42	19	5	18	99	63	62
Knowle		42	18	6	18	59	57	60
Nuneaton Griff		42	15	12	15	74	64	57
Massey-Ferguson		42	16	8	18	72	88	56
Continental Star		42	15	9	18	81	84	54
Southam United		42	13	14	15	77	82	53
Castle Vale JKS		42	13	10	19	83	82	49
Pelsall Villa		42	14	7	21	70	97	49
Bolehall Swifts		42	12	8	22	65	91	44
Cadbury Athletic		42	10	11	21	63	109	41
Pershore Town		42	9	8	25	45	98	35
Meir KA		42	9	5	28	46	105	32
Racing Club Warwick		42	7	1	34	44	158	22

TONY ALLDEN MEMORIAL CUP

(Prem Div champions v Challenge Cup holders)

(October 13th at Castle Vale)

Loughborough University 0 **Castle Vale** 2

	Bartley Green	Bolehall Swifts	Brocton	Cadbury Athletic	Castle Vale	Castle Vale JKS	Continental Star	Coventry Copsewood	Dosthill Colts	GSA Sports	Heath Hayes	Heather St John	Knowle	Massey-Ferguson	Meir KA	Nuneaton Griff	Pelsall Villa	Pershore Town	Pilkington XXX	Racing Club Warwick	Southam United	Walsall Wood
Bartley Green		4-2	1-2	3-1	1-2	1-2	1-0	2-3	2-2	3-2	1-3	1-4	0-0	4-0	5-1	2-3	1-3	3-0	5-0	8-1	3-0	3-0
Bolehall Swifts	1-0		0-6	1-1	0-3	0-1	0-0	0-1	2-2	0-4	3-6	0-6	0-0	4-5	5-0	0-1	3-3	4-0	1-2	3-1	4-2	2-3
Brocton	2-1	1-2		2-2	1-2	1-0	0-1	0-1	4-2	5-2	6-1	1-5	3-2	1-0	2-0	4-2	3-0	4-1	2-4	3-0	2-2	1-1
Cadbury Athletic	0-3	0-3	1-4	***P***	3-2	0-2	2-2	5-0	0-4	2-5	2-2	0-7	4-0	4-1	1-1	5-1	1-0	0-1	4-2	2-3	2-2	0-4
Castle Vale	2-6	4-0	2-2	5-1	***R***	3-2	0-1	3-1	1-0	1-1	3-3	0-2	0-1	1-0	1-1	1-1	3-0	3-0	3-0	6-0	4-4	2-3
Castle Vale JKS	1-1	2-1	0-6	2-0	1-2	***E***	3-1	1-2	1-1	2-4	0-1	3-1	2-2	3-3	4-1	1-5	2-2	1-2	2-3	10-0	6-1	2-2
Continental Star	2-2	2-2	2-0	0-0	3-3	3-2	***M***	0-1	2-1	1-3	3-2	0-4	0-1	1-3	2-3	4-2	5-3	3-0	2-3	7-0	4-3	1-2
Coventry Copsewood	2-4	2-4	3-0	6-0	2-2	2-1	2-2	***I***	1-1	1-1	2-2	2-1	3-0	3-1	3-0	0-0	3-1	4-0	1-3	2-1	4-1	0-1
Dosthill Colts	1-0	2-0	3-0	2-1	3-4	0-0	3-0	2-2	***E***	0-2	0-3	1-3	0-1	1-3	3-1	1-5	1-0	6-0	2-0	1-0	2-2	2-1
GSA Sports	3-2	0-3	2-1	4-4	0-1	1-4	7-2	0-2	2-2	***R***	0-5	0-3	0-2	0-2	4-0	6-0	1-2	0-0	5-5	5-2	2-2	3-2
Heath Hayes	3-1	5-1	2-0	8-0	2-1	4-2	4-2	1-2	2-1	2-2		1-2	3-0	4-1	2-0	3-1	4-0	9-1	0-2	6-0	3-0	7-0
Heather St John	3-2	5-0	2-0	2-2	0-3	0-0	4-1	3-1	0-0	4-1	4-0	***D***	1-1	3-0	5-2	1-1	4-0	0-0	5-0	4-1	1-1	9-1
Knowle	0-2	2-0	3-1	5-0	0-2	3-2	1-3	2-1	0-1	0-2	1-2	1-2	***I***	2-1	2-0	2-0	2-0	3-0	1-2	2-0	0-3	1-2
Massey-Ferguson	1-0	3-3	2-1	1-2	2-1	3-3	4-4	1-1	3-3	0-3	3-2	1-3	1-3	***V***	2-1	1-4	2-2	2-4	2-2	3-2	1-0	1-3
Meir KA	2-0	3-1	0-5	0-2	0-3	2-3	0-5	1-3	1-1	3-2	1-4	1-4	2-2	1-3	***I***	1-0	2-1	3-0	2-1	0-0	3-4	1-2
Nuneaton Griff	0-4	0-1	1-1	1-1	0-1	1-1	1-2	1-2	1-1	2-2	6-0	2-1	1-1	4-1	4-2	***S***	2-0	2-2	1-2	7-0	1-1	1-1
Pelsall Villa	2-5	1-3	1-0	2-2	2-2	4-3	1-0	2-2	1-8	3-7	0-3	4-3	2-0	0-1	3-1	0-2	***I***	1-2	4-1	3-2	3-1	2-2
Pershore Town	2-3	0-1	3-3	4-1	1-3	2-1	2-1	0-0	1-2	0-2	0-2	1-1	1-0	0-1	1-2	0-2	2-3	***O***	1-3	5-1	2-2	1-4
Pilkington XXX	2-0	2-1	4-3	5-1	1-1	2-1	6-1	0-2	4-0	1-4	1-2	2-1	3-1	2-1	2-0	1-2	3-2	1-1	***N***	3-2	2-2	3-0
Racing Club Warwick	0-8	2-1	0-4	1-0	1-9	1-2	1-5	1-4	1-3	0-2	3-7	1-3	2-4	0-2	2-1	2-1	1-5	4-1	1-3		3-1	0-5
Southam United	2-0	2-2	1-2	1-2	2-1	5-2	1-1	1-1	2-3	2-0	1-3	2-2	2-1	2-1	4-0	2-1	0-1	3-1	1-4	3-0		4-2
Walsall Wood	1-1	2-1	1-5	5-2	1-2	3-0	1-0	3-1	3-3	2-1	1-0	1-1	1-4	1-3	2-0	0-1	2-1	4-0	0-3	4-1	0-0	

Division One		P	W	D	L	F	A	Pts
Stockingford AA		32	22	7	3	104	38	73
Earlswood Town		32	21	6	5	95	37	69
Alveston		32	21	5	6	80	43	68
Fairfield Villa		32	20	7	5	74	37	67
Archdale		32	20	4	8	81	42	64
Northfield Town		32	17	10	5	69	31	61
West Midlands Police		32	16	4	12	73	59	52
Littleton		32	15	6	11	51	37	51
Castle Vale Res.		32	14	8	10	56	50	50
Shirley Town		32	14	2	16	77	69	44
Phoenix United		32	11	7	14	67	74	40
Brereton Social		32	11	5	16	53	74	38
Coton Green		32	8	4	20	53	71	28
Droitwich Spa		32	7	5	20	44	77	26
Burntwood Town		32	5	2	25	28	115	17
Newhall United	*-3*	32	4	3	25	47	116	12
Mile Oak Rovers		32	2	3	27	19	101	9

PRESIDENT'S CUP

FIRST ROUND

Alveston 6 Brereton Social 1

SECOND ROUND

Archdale 2 Stockingford AA 1
Droitwich Spa 0 **Coton Green** 3
Earlswood Town 3 Castle Vale Res. 0
Littleton 4 Mile Oak Rovers 0
Newhall United 2 **Fairfield Villa** 4
Northfield Town 0 **Alveston** 3
Shirley Town 4 Phoenix United 0
West Midlands Police 7 Burntwood Town 3

QUARTER-FINALS

Coton Green 1 **Archdale** 3
Earlswood Town 0 **Littleton** 2
Fairfield Villa 3 West Midlands Police 2 *aet*
Shirley Town 1 **Alveston** 6

SEMI-FINALS

(played over two legs)

Alveston 0 Archdale 0, **Archdale** 2 Alveston 1
Fairfield Villa 2 Littleton 0, Littleton 1 Fairfield Villa 0

FINAL

(May 14th at Bromsgrove Rovers)

Archdale 1 Fairfield Villa 0

ENDSLEIGH CHALLENGE CUP

PRELIMINARY ROUND

AFC Smethwick 6 Burntwood 0, Clements 1 **Kenilworth** 2
Enville 3 Mile Oak Rovers 1, **Greenhill** 4 Newhall Utd 2
Henley F. 4 Droitwich Spa 1, Inkberrow 0 **Hampton** 3
Lichfield C. 3 Perrywood 1, **Phoenix** 7 Coventry Ams 0
Polesworth 2 **Leamington Hibs** 6 (at Leamington Hibs)
Shipston Excelsior 1 **Chelmsley Town** 2 *aet*
Shirley Town 2 **Feckenham** 4, Young W. 1 **Blackwood** 2

FIRST ROUND

Alveston 4 Chelmsley Town 0
Castle Vale JKS 2 **Hampton** 2 *aet* (3-4p)
Coton Green 4 Greenhill 1, Dosthill 1 **AFC Smethwick** 2
Earlswood Town 3 Kenilworth Town KH 2
Feckenham 3 **Brereton Social** 3 *aet* (3-4p)
Henley Forest 4 Leamington Hibernian 3
Littleton 4 Archdale 2 *aet,* Northfield 2 **Blackwood** 3
Phoenix Utd 6 Enville 0, **Stockingford** 2 Fairfield Villa 0
West Midlands Police 3 Lichfield City 0

SECOND ROUND

AFC Smethwick 1 **Heath Hayes** 3
Alveston 5 **Pershore Town** 5 *aet* (9-10p)
Blackwood 0 **WM Police** 4, Bolehall 1 **Walsall Wood** 2
Castle Vale 10 Racing Club Warwick 1
Coton Green 2 **Brocton** 3 *aet,* Earlswood 0 **Knowle** 3
GSA Sports 0 **Bartley Green** 2, **Hampton** 2 Cadbury 1
Heather St John 4 Continental Star 0
Littleton 2 **Stockingford AA** 3, Meir 0 **Brereton Social** 1
Nuneaton Griff 0 **Coventry Copsewood** 1
Phoenix United 8 Henley Forest 0
Pilkington XXX 4 Massey-Ferg. 2, Southam 0 **Pelsall** 1

THIRD ROUND

Bartley Green 6 Hampton 1
Castle Vale 3 Pilkington XXX 0
Coventry Copsewood 2 Brereton Social 1
Heath Hayes 5 Walsall Wood 2
Pelsall Villa 0 **Heather St John** 1
Pershore Town 2 Knowle 1
Stockingford AA 2 **Brocton** 2 *aet* (6-7p)
West Midlands Police 2 Phoenix United 1

QUARTER-FINALS

Brocton 0 **Coventry Copsewood** 2
Heather St John 6 Heath Hayes 2
Pershore Town 0 **Castle Vale** 7
West Midlands Police 1 **Bartley Green** 4

SEMI-FINALS

(played over two legs)

Bartley G. 1 Heather SJ 1, **Heather SJ** 2 Bartley Green 1
Coventry Copsewood 1 Castle Vale 1, Castle Vale 1
Coventry Copsewood 2

FINAL

(May 10th at Walsall)

Coventry Copsewood 0 **Heather St John** 4

	Alve	Arch	Brer	Burn	Cast	Cot	Droi	Earl	Fair	Litt	MO	New	Nort	Pho	Shir	Stoc	WM
Alveston	***D***	5-1	3-2	1-2	1-1	1-1	3-0	1-3	2-2	2-0	6-0	5-0	3-1	3-1	1-3	0-1	4-1
Archdale	2-3	***I***	4-0	4-0	4-1	4-1	3-1	0-2	2-1	2-2	5-0	4-0	2-1	2-1	4-2	2-3	0-1
Brereton Social	4-4	0-2	***V***	5-1	0-2	3-3	5-3	2-1	0-3	0-3	2-0	0-0	3-2	4-1	3-1	1-2	1-3
Burntwood Town	0-1	0-2	2-1	***I***	1-2	0-4	1-3	0-7	0-3	0-3	1-1	5-3	0-4	3-0	1-7	0-3	0-6
Castle Vale Res.	1-3	0-2	2-1	0-0	***S***	4-3	4-0	1-4	0-0	1-0	4-2	5-2	0-1	0-3	0-2	1-1	2-1
Coton Green	1-2	2-5	2-3	2-0	2-2	***I***	0-1	2-3	2-3	3-1	1-0	4-2	2-1	4-4	1-2	0-2	4-0
Droitwich Spa	0-1	0-5	0-3	3-2	0-1	2-1	***O***	1-4	1-2	1-0	1-1	4-1	1-3	1-3	1-4	2-4	4-5
Earlswood Town	2-0	2-1	5-0	3-0	3-3	5-0	2-1	***N***	2-2	4-0	9-0	6-0	1-1	5-0	5-4	0-2	2-2
Fairfield Villa	1-3	0-0	1-0	7-1	3-2	4-1	1-1	2-3		4-1	6-1	2-1	1-1	3-2	2-1	4-3	4-2
Littleton	0-2	0-1	5-0	4-1	2-0	2-0	2-1	2-1	0-0		W-L	5-3	0-0	0-0	0-0	1-2	2-0
Mile Oak Rovers	2-3	0-3	0-4	1-2	0-4	0-3	1-2	0-1	0-2	0-3		3-2	0-2	0-3	0-9	0-0	1-3
Newhall United	3-5	1-3	1-1	4-1	0-4	3-0	3-2	2-5	0-1	2-5	4-5		1-8	2-3	0-4	0-5	1-5
Northfield Town	2-2	2-2	1-2	6-0	5-1	1-0	3-3	0-0	3-2	2-0	1-0	0-0		1-0	2-0	2-0	1-0
Phoenix United	1-5	2-2	1-1	7-1	1-1	3-1	3-1	3-2	0-2	1-2	5-0	4-3	0-5		5-4	4-4	1-2
Shirley Town	0-1	3-5	7-0	4-3	0-2	3-1	4-1	0-0	2-1	1-4	3-1	0-2	1-3	2-1	***O***	1-7	1-5
Stockingford AA	3-1	2-1	6-2	11-0	3-3	3-1	1-1	4-1	0-1	1-1	2-0	9-1	2-2	5-1	4-1	***N***	5-2
West Midlands Police	2-3	4-2	3-0	3-0	0-2	2-1	1-1	1-2	0-4	2-1	5-0	3-0	2-2	3-3	3-1	1-4	***E***

Division Two		P	W	D	L	F	A	Pts
Hampton		**28**	**22**	**2**	**4**	**68**	**23**	**68**
Kenilworth Town KH		**28**	**20**	**5**	**3**	**82**	**35**	**65**
Lichfield City		**28**	**18**	**5**	**5**	**80**	**37**	**59**
Feckenham		**28**	**16**	**1**	**11**	**51**	**38**	**49**
Knowle Res.		**28**	**13**	**4**	**11**	**43**	**48**	**43**
Perrywood		**28**	**11**	**6**	**11**	**60**	**62**	**39**
Cadbury Athletic Res.		**28**	**11**	**6**	**11**	**52**	**67**	**39**
Continental Star Res.		**28**	**12**	**2**	**14**	**56**	**51**	**38**
Henley Forest		**28**	**11**	**4**	**13**	**60**	**59**	**37**
AFC Smethwick	*-3*	**28**	**12**	**3**	**13**	**52**	**52**	**36**
Leamington Hibernian		**28**	**10**	**3**	**15**	**46**	**52**	**33**
Enville Athletic		**28**	**8**	**4**	**16**	**39**	**61**	**28**
Chelmsley Town		**28**	**6**	**4**	**18**	**34**	**58**	**22**
Droitwich Spa Res.		**28**	**5**	**7**	**16**	**30**	**65**	**22**
Greenhill		**28**	**6**	**2**	**20**	**26**	**71**	**20**

Racing Club Warwick Res. - record expunged

Reserve Division		P	W	D	L	F	A	Pts
Quorn Res.		22	16	2	4	66	28	50
Chasetown Res.		22	16	2	4	62	26	50
Boldmere St Michaels Res.		22	14	4	4	62	25	46
Oadby Town Res.		22	12	4	6	51	49	40
Barwell Res.		22	12	3	7	46	36	39
Gresley Res.		22	8	4	10	35	38	28
Heather St John Res.		22	7	5	10	39	41	26
Highgate United Res.		22	6	7	9	37	51	25
Walsall Wood Res.		22	7	2	13	33	52	23
Banbury United Res.		22	5	4	13	26	50	19
Brocton Res.		22	4	2	16	33	68	14
Bromsgrove Rov. Res.	*-10*	22	4	3	15	45	71	5

CHALLENGE TROPHY FINAL *(May 6th at Barwell)*

Barwell Res. 1 **Boldmere St Michaels Res.** 3

CHALLENGE BOWL FINAL *(April 24th at Boldmere)*

Boldmere St Michaels Res. 2 Quorn Res. 1

CHALLENGE VASE

FIRST ROUND

AFC Smethwick 0 **Feckenham** 4

Cadbury Athletic Res. 4 **Continental Star Res.** 7

Chelmsley Town 1 Kenilworth Town KH 0

Enville Athletic 6 Henley Forest 5

Hampton 2 Lichfield City 1

Knowle Res. 3 Perrywood 1

Leamington Hibernian 1 Greenhill 0

Racing Club Warwick Res. 1 **Droitwich Spa Res.** 2

QUARTER-FINALS

Chelmsley Town 1 **Feckenham** 4

Continental Star Res. 0 **Knowle Res.** 2

Enville Athletic 4 Droitwich Spa Res. 2 *aet*

Hampton 5 Leamington Hibernian 0

SEMI-FINALS

(played over two legs)

Enville Athletic 1 Hampton 2,

Hampton 6 Enville Athletic 0

Feckenham 3 Knowle Res. 1,

Knowle Res. 1 Feckenham 1

FINAL *(May 11th at Boldmere St Michaels)*

Hampton 2 **Feckenham** 3

	AFC	Cad	Che	Con	Droi	Env	Fec	Gre	Ham	Hen	Ken	Kno	Lea	Lic	Per	Rac
AFC Smethwick		1-2	2-1	1-3	0-2	2-1	5-1	1-3	2-1	4-2	0-5	7-0	3-5	0-2	4-4	8-1
Cadbury Athletic Res.	2-2		3-1	1-5	4-2	1-0	1-0	5-4	0-5	3-4	2-2	3-3	4-1	1-6	3-6	4-3
Chelmsley Town	1-0	3-0	***D***	0-4	1-2	1-2	1-3	2-0	0-1	3-1	1-3	1-0	2-3	2-4	0-0	7-1
Continental Star Res.	1-2	6-4	4-0	***I***	1-1	1-0	0-3	2-3	1-2	4-2	2-0	2-3	1-0	1-1	3-1	6-2
Droitwich Spa Res.	0-2	1-1	0-0	1-5	***V***	1-1	0-3	2-0	0-4	1-2	1-4	1-2	1-1	0-3	1-2	n/a
Enville Athletic	0-3	1-3	4-1	2-0	2-2	***I***	0-3	2-3	1-0	2-5	1-4	2-0	2-4	2-4	2-2	2-2
Feckenham	2-0	1-0	2-0	2-1	2-0	2-3	***S***	6-0	1-2	1-0	2-5	1-3	4-2	1-4	2-0	3-1
Greenhill	0-1	1-0	0-2	1-3	0-4	1-3	1-2	***I***	0-4	0-1	0-3	1-0	1-0	0-2	2-2	0-1
Hampton	3-1	4-0	3-2	1-0	3-2	1-0	1-0	4-1	***O***	5-0	4-2	3-1	2-1	0-1	3-0	n/a
Henley Forest	2-1	0-1	4-2	5-1	7-0	1-1	1-2	1-1	3-3	***N***	3-3	5-2	2-3	0-4	2-1	5-1
Kenilworth Town KH	1-1	4-0	1-1	4-2	6-0	1-0	2-1	5-1	1-1	4-0		3-1	2-0	4-2	5-0	n/a
Knowle Res.	1-0	0-3	1-0	3-0	1-0	5-1	1-1	4-1	0-2	1-0	0-1	***T***	3-2	1-3	1-1	3-1
Leamington Hibernian	3-0	1-2	1-1	3-1	2-3	1-2	1-0	3-0	0-1	2-1	0-3	1-2	***W***	3-2	1-2	5-1
Lichfield City	2-4	1-1	7-3	3-1	1-1	6-1	3-0	4-0	1-0	0-4	6-0	2-2	1-1	***O***	3-1	4-0
Perrywood	2-3	2-2	3-2	2-1	5-1	3-1	1-3	3-1	2-5	4-2	3-4	1-2	4-1	3-2		n/a
Racing Club Warwick Res.	n/a	n/a	n/a	0-3	n/a	6-1	n/a	n/a	n/a	n/a	0-7	n/a	n/a	3-4	n/a	

MIDLAND COMBINATION DIVISION TWO CONSTITUTION 2010-11

BLACKWOOD . . . . Hampton Sports Ground, Field Lane, Solihull B91 2RT . . . . None

BROMSGROVE SPORTING . . . . Studley FC, The Beehive, Abbeyfields Drive, Studley B80 7BF. 01527 853087

CADBURY ATHLETIC RES. . Cadbury Recreation Ground, Bournville Lane, Bournville, Birmingham B30 1LA 0121 454 4264

CHELMSLEY TOWN. . . . . The Pavilion, Coleshill Road, Marston Green, Birmingham B37 7HW. 0121 779 5400

CLEMENTS. . . . . Sedgemere Sports & Social Club, Sedgemere Road, Yardley, Birmingham B26 2AX. 0121 783 0888

CONTINENTAL STAR RES. . . Chelmsley Town FC, The Pavilion, Coleshill Road, Marston Green B37 7HW 0121 779 5400

DROITWICH SPA RES. . . . . Droitwich Spa Leisure Centre, Briar Mill, Droitwich WR9 0RZ 01905 771212

ENVILLE ATHLETIC. . . . . Enville Athletic Club, Hall Drive, Enville, Stourbridge DY7 5HB. 01384 872368

FECKENHAM . . . . Studley Sports & Social Club, Eldorado Close, Studley B80 7HP 01527 852671

GREENHILL. . . . . Dudley Sports FC, Dudley Sports & Social Club, Hillcrest Avenue, Brierley Hill DY5 3QH 01384 826420

HENLEY FOREST. . . . . . . Henley-in-Arden Sports & Social Ground, Stratford Road, Henley-in-Arden B95 6AD 01564 792022

KNOWLE RES.. . . . . Hampton Road, Knowle, Solihull B93 0NX 01564 779807

LEAMINGTON HIBERNIAN . . . . Ajax Park, Hampton Road, Warwick CV35 8HA 01926 495786

LICHFIELD CITY . . . . Brownsfield Park, Brownsfield Road, off Eastern Avenue, Lichfield WS13 6AY. . . . . None

PERRYWOOD . . . . Neel Park, Droitwich Road, Perdiswell, Worcester WR3 7SN 07808 768222

YOUNG WARRIORS . . . . Coventry Sphinx FC, Sphinx Drive, Siddeley Avenue, Coventry CV3 1WA. 024 7645 1361

IN: Blackwood (P), Clements (P), Bromsgrove Sporting (N), Young Warriors (P)

OUT: AFC Smethwick (S - West Midlands League Division Two), Hampton (P), Kenilworth Town KH (P), Racing Club Warwick Res. (WS)

Division Three		P	W	D	L	F	A	Pts
Blackwood		30	26	2	2	94	24	80
Clements '83		30	20	6	4	82	28	66
Young Warriors		30	18	6	6	96	59	60
Earlswood Town Res.		30	16	4	10	85	55	52
Stratford Town A		30	16	4	10	91	64	52
Dosthill Colts Res.		30	16	3	11	75	56	51
Archdale Res.		30	13	5	12	73	68	44
Inkberrow	*-3*	30	14	4	12	75	68	43
Northfield Town Res.		30	12	6	12	52	57	42
Shipston Excelsior		30	8	11	11	44	55	35
Polesworth		30	10	2	18	54	65	32
Littleton Res.		30	9	3	18	56	84	30
Pershore Town Res.		30	8	6	16	45	77	30
Coton Green Res.		30	6	6	18	41	87	24
Coventry Amateurs		30	5	4	21	42	91	19
Chelmsley Town Res.		30	5	4	21	58	125	19

CHALLENGE URN

FIRST ROUND
Chelmsley Town Res. 0 **Littleton Res.** 3
Coventry Amateurs 4 Coton Green Res. 3
Earlswood Town Res. 2 Archdale Res. 1 *aet*
Inkberrow 0 **Dosthill Res.** 3
Northfield Town Res. 0 **Blackwood** 3
Pershore Town Res. 3 Clements 3 *aet* (4-2p)
Polesworth 3 **Stratford A** 5
Shipston 1 **Young Warriors** 3

QUARTER-FINALS
Coventry Ams 1 **Stratford Town A 3** *(at Stratford)*
Dosthill Colts Res. 3 Pershore Town Res. 2
Earlswood Town Res. 1 Littleton Res. 0
Young W. 0 **Blackwood** 5

SEMI-FINALS
(played over two legs)
Dosthill Colts Res. 5 Earlswood Town Res. 0,
Earlswood Town Res. 2 **Dosthill Colts Res.** 0
Stratford A 4 Blackwood 1,
Blackwood 5 Stratford A 1

FINAL
(May 12th at Pilkington)
Blackwood 5 Dosthill Colts Res. 2 *aet*

	Arc	Bla	Che	Cle	Cot	Cov	Dos	Ear	Ink	Litt	Nor	Per	Pol	Shi	Str	You
Archdale Res.		1-4	6-3	0-2	2-0	9-1	1-0	3-4	3-3	4-0	2-1	6-0	3-3	9-1	1-1	0-4
Blackwood	3-0	***D***	6-1	2-0	3-0	1-2	1-0	3-0	2-2	6-0	1-0	5-1	2-1	3-0	4-2	3-2
Chelmsley Town Res.	2-3	1-10	***I***	0-5	1-1	1-0	2-5	5-2	5-5	5-1	4-5	4-3	0-4	0-1	3-9	1-7
Clements '83	8-0	0-0	4-0	***V***	2-1	3-0	0-1	1-2	3-2	3-0	7-0	3-1	5-0	4-3	4-2	2-2
Coton Green Res.	2-6	3-7	2-2	0-3	***I***	2-2	2-4	1-3	2-4	2-1	2-1	1-0	2-1	0-0	2-3	1-4
Coventry Amateurs	6-1	1-2	1-2	1-3	1-0	***S***	2-2	4-3	0-1	3-6	0-2	1-3	1-2	0-6	1-3	3-3
Dosthill Colts Res.	0-2	2-4	4-2	0-2	1-3	8-2	***I***	3-2	4-2	5-2	3-1	0-0	3-1	1-2	2-1	4-2
Earlswood Town Res.	2-2	0-1	4-0	1-1	3-1	5-1	4-1	***O***	1-3	4-1	1-2	8-0	2-1	2-0	4-1	14-1
Inkberrow	2-3	0-5	5-2	0-1	7-0	4-0	1-3	1-1	***N***	1-5	0-3	6-3	1-0	1-0	3-1	2-3
Littleton Res.	3-0	0-1	4-2	2-1	1-4	3-1	2-2	7-1	4-3		1-1	1-2	3-6	1-3	2-3	0-1
Northfield Town Res.	5-1	0-1	2-1	3-3	2-0	3-2	0-1	1-1	2-3	3-2	***T***	0-2	1-0	1-1	3-0	1-1
Pershore Town Res.	0-0	0-1	5-1	0-3	2-2	4-0	1-5	0-2	3-6	3-0	1-4	***H***	0-0	2-2	0-2	3-2
Polesworth	2-1	1-3	7-4	1-2	4-1	2-3	0-5	1-3	0-1	0-1	4-3	2-0	***R***	1-3	1-2	4-2
Shipston Excelsior	1-0	0-4	1-1	1-1	1-1	1-1	6-4	2-0	1-2	1-1	1-1	1-2	1-2	***E***	2-2	0-0
Stratford Town A	2-3	1-5	4-2	2-5	12-3	4-1	4-1	5-0	5-2	6-2	5-0	3-3	1-0	3-2	***E***	1-1
Young Warriors	3-1	3-1	9-1	1-1	4-0	2-1	2-1	2-6	3-2	7-0	6-1	6-1	6-3	5-0	2-1	

JACK MOULD TROPHY

(Division Two and Three clubs)

FIRST ROUND
Blackwood 2 **Feckenham** 3 **aet**
Cadbury Athletic Res. 4 Leamington Hibernian 2 *(at Leamington Hibernian)*
Chelmsley Town 1 Knowle Res. 0
Cont. Star Res. 12 Chelmsley Res. 1
Coton Green Res. 0 **Lichfield City** 4
Coventry Amateurs 1 **Clements '83** 4
Dosthill Colts Res. 1 AFC Smethwick 0
Earlswood Town Res. 0 **Racing Club Warwick Res.** 1
Hampton 2 Droitwich Spa Res. 0
Inkberrow 2 **Stratford Town A** 3
Kenilworth Town KH 4 Archdale Res. 1
Littleton Res. 6 Enville Athletic 1
Northfield Town Res. 1 **Greenhill** 2
Perrywood 0 **Henley Forest** 6
Shipston Excelsior 0 **Pershore Res.** 2
Young Warriors 5 Polesworth 5 *aet* (5-4p)

SECOND ROUND
Chelmsley Town 10 Littleton Res. 1
Clements '83 3 Continental Star Res. 3 *aet* (4-2p)
Feckenham 0 **Lichfield City** 3
Hampton 3 Dosthill Colts 0
Henley Forest 0 **Cadbury Ath. Res.** 4
Pershore Res. 2 **Young Warriors** 3
RC Warwick Res. 3 Greenhill 3 *aet* (6-5p)
Stratford Town A 0 **Kenilworth T. KH** 3

QUARTER-FINALS
Clements 2 **Chelmsley Town** 4
Hampton 4 Young Warriors 4 *aet* (6-5p) *(at Coventry Sphinx)*
Kenilworth Town KH 6 Lichfield City 0
RC Warwick Res. v **Cadbury Res.** (w/o)

SEMI-FINALS
(played over two legs)
Hampton 0 Chelmsley Town 2,
Chelmsley Town 1 Hampton 2
Kenilworth 2 Cadbury Athletic Res. 0,
Cadbury Res. 0 **Kenilworth Town KH** 5

FINAL *(May 13th at Alveston)*
Kenilworth Town KH 2 Chelmsley Town 1

MIDLAND COMBINATION DIVISION THREE CONSTITUTION 2010-11

ALVESTON RES. . . . . Home Guard Club, Main Street, Tiddington, Stratford-upon-Avon CV37 7AY 01789 297718
ARCHDALE RES. . . . . County Sports Ground, Claines Lane, Worcester WR3 7SS 07736 309670
ASTON . . . . Moor Lane Pavilion, Moor Lane, Perry Barr, Birmingham B6 7AA 0121 331 6515
COTON GREEN RES. . . . . New Mill Lane, Fazeley, Tamworth B78 3RX . . . . None
COVENTRY AMATEURS . . David Sinclair Sports, Westwood Heath Rd, Westwood Heath, Coventry CV4 8GP . . . . None
DOSTHILL COLTS RES. . . . . . Mile Oak Community Ground, Price Avenue, Mile Oak, Tamworth B78 3NL. 01827 289614
FUTURE LEGENDS . . . . Moat House Leisure Centre, Winston Avenue, Coventry CV2 1EA. 024 7684 1720
INKBERROW. . . . . Sands Road, Inkberrow, Worcester WR7 4HJ . . . . None
JDG ALLIANCE . . . . Moor Lane Pavilion, Moor Lane, Perry Barr, Birmingham B6 7AA 0121 331 6515
LICHFIELD CITY RES. . . . . . Brownsfield Park, Brownsfield Road, off Eastern Avenue, Lichfield WS13 6AY. None
LITTLETON RES. . . . . Five Acres, Pebworth Road, North Littleton, Evesham WR11 8QL 07966 297971
NORTHFIELD TOWN RES. . . Shenley Lane Comm. Centre, Shenley Lane, Selly Oak, Birmingham B29 4HZ. 0121 475 3870
POLESWORTH. . . . . North Warwickshire Sports & Social, Hermitage Hill, Polesworth, Tamworth B78 1HS. 01827 892482
STRATFORD TOWN A . . . . Knights Lane, Tiddington, Stratford-on-Avon CV37 7BZ 01789 269336
WALSALL WOOD RES. . . . . Oak Park, Lichfield Road, Walsall Wood WS9 9NP 01543 361084

IN: Alveston Res. (N), Aston (P - Birmingham AFA Premier Division), Future Legends (P - youth football), JDG Alliance (N), Lichfield City Res. (P - Burton & District League Premier Division), Walsall Wood Res. (P - Reserve Division)
OUT: Blackwood (P), Chelmsley Town Res. (W), Clements (P), Earlswood Town Res. (W), Pershore Town Res. (W), Shipston Excelsior (R - Stratford Alliance Division One), Young Warriors (P)

ALVESTON
Founded: 1927

Secretary: Julie Edwards **(T)** 07884 034 465 **(E)** julesedwards1@hotmail.co.uk
Chairman: Martin Beese **Manager:** **Prog Ed:**
Ground: The Home Guard Club, Main St, Tiddington, Stratford-u-Avon CV37 7AY **(T)** **Capacity:**
Colours(change): All maroon & sky blue

ADDITIONAL INFORMATION:

BARTLEY GREEN
Founded: 1959

Secretary: Mark Wigley **(T)** 07967 630 644 **(E)** mark.wigley@draka.com
Chairman: David Shepherd **Manager:** **Prog Ed:**
Ground: Illey Lane, Halesowen, Birmingham, West Midlands B62 0HE **(T)** **Capacity:**
Colours(change): Amber/black/black

ADDITIONAL INFORMATION:
Honours: Midland Combination Division 2 2005-06, Division 1 2006-07.

BOLEHILL SWIFTS
Founded: 1953

Secretary: James Latham **(T)** 07802 856 168 **(E)** jiml2009@live.co.uk
Chairman: Geoffrey Mulvey **Manager:** **Prog Ed:**
Ground: Rene Road, Bolehall, Tamworth, Staffordshire B77 3NN **(T)** **Capacity:**
Colours(change): Yellow/green/green

ADDITIONAL INFORMATION:
Honours: Midland Combination Division 2 1984-85.

BROCTON
Founded: 1937

Secretary: Terry Homer **(T)** 07791 841 774 **(E)** terryhomer@yahoo.co.uk
Chairman: Brian Townsend **Manager:** Brian Chandler **Prog Ed:**
Ground: Silkmore Lane Sports Grd, Silkmore Lane, Stafford, Staffordshire ST17 4JH **(T)** **Capacity:**
Colours(change): Green & white/white/green

ADDITIONAL INFORMATION:

CADBURY ATHLETIC
Founded: 1994

Secretary: Ron Thorn **(T)** 07905 358 477 **(E)** ronald_thorn@wragge.com
Chairman: John Peckham **Manager:** Darren Barnwell **Prog Ed:**
Ground: Alvechurch FC, Lye Meadow, Redditch Road, Alvechurch, Worcs B48 7RS **(T)** **Capacity:**
Colours(change): Purple with black & white trim/black/purple with white & black hoops

ADDITIONAL INFORMATION:

CASTLE VALE
Founded: 1964

Secretary: Shane Godwood **(T)** 07787 804 153 **(E)** shanegodwood@msn.com
Chairman: Gary Higgins **Manager:** **Prog Ed:**
Ground: Vale Stadium, Farnborough Road, Castle Vale, Birmingham B35 7DA **(T)** **Capacity:**
Colours(change): All red

ADDITIONAL INFORMATION:
Previous Names: Kings Heath > 2002, Castle Vale K.H. > 2005.

CASTLE VALE JKS
Founded: 1998

Secretary: Pamela Crocker **(T)** 07717 175 361 **(E)** castlevalejks@hotmail.co.uk
Chairman: Graham Crocker **Manager:** **Prog Ed:**
Ground: Vale Stadium, Farnborough Road, Castle Vale, Birmingham B35 7DA **(T)** **Capacity:**
Colours(change): All yellow & blue

ADDITIONAL INFORMATION:
Honours: Midland Combination Division 1 2008-09.

PREMIER INS & OUTS
IN: Alveston (P)
OUT: GSA Sports (F), Heath Hayes (P - Midland Alliance), Knowle (R), Meir KA (W)

CONTINENTAL STAR
Founded: 1975

Secretary: Keith John **(T)** 07956 429 046 **(E)** keith.john6@hotmail.co.uk
Chairman: Keith John **Manager:** Lincoln Moses **Prog Ed:**
Ground: Rushall Olympic FC, Dales Lane, Rushall, Walsall, West Midlands WS4 1LJ **(T)** **Capacity:**
Colours(change): Yellow & blue/blue/blue

ADDITIONAL INFORMATION:
Previous Name: Handsworth Continental Star 2001-02.
Honours: Midland Combination Division 2 1995-96.

COVENTRY COPSEWOOD
Founded: 1923

Secretary: David Wilson **(T)** 07807 969 327 **(E)** copsewoodfc@btopenworld.com
Chairman: Robert Abercrombie **Manager:** Carl Nolan & Darren Dickson **Prog Ed:**
Ground: Copsewood Sports & Social Club, Allard Way, Binley, Coventry CV3 1HQ **(T)** **Capacity:**
Colours(change): All blue

ADDITIONAL INFORMATION:
Previous Names: G.P.T. Coventry > 2000, Coventry Marconi > 2005.
Honours: Midland Combination Challenge Cup 2006-07.

DOSTHILL COLTS
Founded: 1990

Secretary: David Brown **(T)** 07799 075 828 **(E)** davidbrown13@btinternet.com
Chairman: Paul Billing **Manager:** **Prog Ed:**
Ground: Coleshill Town FC, Pack Meadow, Packington Lane, Coleshill B46 3JQ **(T)** **Capacity:**
Colours(change): White/blue/red

ADDITIONAL INFORMATION:

HEATHER ST. JOHN'S
Founded: 1949

Secretary: Adrian Rock **(T)** 07952 633 331 **(E)** adrianrock@hotmail.co.uk
Chairman: Adrian McDowell **Manager:** Maz Warriner & Andy Gray **Prog Ed:**
Ground: St. John's Park, Ravenstone Road, Heather, Leicestershire LE67 2QJ **(T)** **Capacity:**
Colours(change): All royal blue

ADDITIONAL INFORMATION:

MASSEY FERGUSON
Founded: 1956

Secretary: Terry Borras **(T)** 07791 553 031 **(E)** tgborras@hotmail.com
Chairman: Lindsey Bailey **Manager:** Kevin Kingham **Prog Ed:**
Ground: Bannerbrook Park, Off Banner Lane, Tile Hill, Coventry CV4 9GT **(T)** **Capacity:**
Colours(change): Red & white stripes/black/red

ADDITIONAL INFORMATION:
Honours: Midland Combination Division 2 1993-94, Division 1 1994-95.

NUNEATON GRIFF
Founded: 1974

Secretary: Peter Kemp **(T)** 07931 297 935 **(E)** nuneatongriff@talktalk.net
Chairman: John Gore **Manager:** Paul Brassington **Prog Ed:**
Ground: The Pingles Stadium, Avenue Road, Nuneaton, Warwickshire CV11 4LX **(T)** **Capacity:**
Colours(change): Blue & white/blue/blue

ADDITIONAL INFORMATION:
Honours: Midland Combination Premier Division 1999-2000, 00-01.

PELSALL VILLA
Founded: 1898

Secretary: Shaun Mason **(T)** 07779 111 023 **(E)** shaunmason1967@yahoo.co.uk
Chairman: Shaun Mason **Manager:** Mark Bentley **Prog Ed:**
Ground: The Bush Ground, Walsall Road, Walsall, West Midlands WS3 4BP **(T)** **Capacity:**
Colours(change): Red & black stripes/black/black

ADDITIONAL INFORMATION:

PERSHORE TOWN
Founded: 1988

Secretary: Alan Barnett **(T)** 01386 860 243 **(E)**
Chairman: Damien Rourke **Manager:** Neil Hunt **Prog Ed:**
Ground: King George V Playing Field, King George's Way, Pershore WR10 1AA **(T)** **Capacity:**
Colours(change): Blue & white stripes/blue/blue

ADDITIONAL INFORMATION: Previous Names: Merged with Pershure United, Pershore Recreation Rovers, Pershore Bullets 1988.
Previous League: Midland Alliance (Founder members).
Honours: Midland Combination Division 2 1989-90, Premier 1993-94.

PILKINGTON XXX
Founded: 2002

Secretary: Stephen McGinn **(T)** 07855 741 696 **(E)** stephen.mcginn@primecare.uk.net
Chairman: Saul Gray **Manager:** **Prog Ed:**
Ground: Triplex Sports, Eckersall Road, Kings Norton, Birmingham B38 8SR **(T)** **Capacity:**
Colours(change): Green/black/green

ADDITIONAL INFORMATION:
Previous Name: Burman Hi-Ton > 2002.
Honours: Midland Combination Division 2 2001-02.

RACING CLUB WARWICK
Founded: 1919 Nickname: Racers

Secretary: Bob Cranton **(T)** 07517 988 070 **(E)** bobcranton@hotmail.com
Chairman: Bob Dhillon **Manager:** Ryan Cranton **Prog Ed:**
Ground: Hampton Road, Warwick, Warwickshire CV34 6JP **(T)** 01926 495 786 **Capacity:** 1,280
Colours(change): Gold/black/black

ADDITIONAL INFORMATION: Previous Name: Saltisford Rovers > 1968. **Previous League:** Midland Alliance.
Record Att: 1,280 v Leamington FC, Midland All.26/12/2005. **Goalscorer:** Steve Edgington - 200. **Apps:** Steve Cooper - 600+
Honours: Midland Combination Premier Division 1987-88.

SOUTHAM UNITED
Founded: 1905

Secretary: Charles Hill **(T)** 07802 949 781 **(E)** charles@southamunitedfc.com
Chairman: Charles Hill **Manager:** Luke Fogarty **Prog Ed:**
Ground: Banbury Road, Southam, Warwickshire CV47 2BJ **(T)** **Capacity:**
Colours(change): Yellow/blue/blue

ADDITIONAL INFORMATION:
Honours: Midland Combination Division 3 1980-81.

WALSALL WOOD
Founded: 1919

Secretary: John Rogers **(T)** 07504 981 141 **(E)** erogers@blueyonder.co.uk
Chairman: Roger Merrick **Manager:** Rob Masefield **Prog Ed:**
Ground: Oak Park, Lichfield Road, Walsall Wood, Walsall WS9 9NP **(T)** **Capacity:**
Colours(change): All red

ADDITIONAL INFORMATION: Previous Names: Walsall Borough - formed when Walsall Wood & Walsall Sportsco merged in 1982.
Previous League: West Midlands (Regional).
Honours: Worcestershire/Midland Combination 1951-52.

MIDLAND COMBINATION DIVISION ONE CONSTITUTION 2010-11

ARCHDALE '73.............................County Groud Sports Ground, Claines Lane, Worcester WR3 7SS................................01905 27866
BRERETON SOCIAL.........Red Lion Ground, Armitage Lane, Brereton , Rugeley , Staffordshire , WS15 1ED.................07970 016 662
BURNTWOOD TOWN...Long Lane Park, Long Lane, Essington , Wolverhampton , West Midlands , WV11 2AA 07771 551 244
COTON GREEN................................New Mill Lane, Fazeley , Tamworth , Staffordshire , B78 3RX................................07917 206 163
DROITWICH SPA................Droitwich Spa Leisure Centre, Briar Mill , Droitwich , Worcestershire , WR9 0RZ..................07860 591 091
EARLSWOOD TOWN.........The Pavilions, Malthouse Lane, Earlswood , Solihull , West Midlands , B94 5DX..................07866 122 254
FAIRFIELD VILLA........Recreation Ground, Stourbridge Road, Fairfield , Bromsgrove , Worcestershire , B61 9LZ 07880 77 673
FC GLADES SPORTING................The Glades, Lugtrout Lane , Solihull , West Midlands , B91 2RX.............................07790 583 693
HAMPTON................................Hampton Sports Club, Field Lane , Solihull , West Midlands , B91 2RT 07881 503 342
KENILWORTH TOWN K.H........................Gypsy Lane , Kenilworth , Warwickshire , CV8 1FN...07946 144 831
KNOWLE..Hampton Road, Knowle , Solihull , West Midlands , B93 0NX...07798 713 982
LITTLETON.....................Five Acres, Pebworth Road, North Littleton , Evesham , Worcestershire , WR11 8QL 01386 832 906
NORTHFIELD TOWN ...Shenley Lane Community Association, Shenley Lane, Selly Oak , Birmingham B29 4HZ............07976 543 218
PHOENIX UNITED.............The Pavilions, Malthouse Lane, Earlswood , Solihull , West Midlands , B94 5DX..................07961 140 810
SHIRLEY TOWN................................Tilehouse Lane, Shirley , Solihull , West Midlands , B90 1PH 07889 124 991
STRETTON EAGLES....Shobnall Sports Gound, Shobnall Road , Burton-upon-Trent , Staffordshire , DE14 2BB 07730 735 831
WEST MIDLANDS POLICE....Tally Ho Training Centre, Pershore Road, Edgbaston , Birmingham B5 7RD 07771 920 801

IN: Hampton (P), Kenilworth Town KH (P), Knowle (R), Stretton Eagles (S - Staffordshire County Premier League Premier Division)
OUT: Alveston (P), Mile Oak Rovers (F), Newhall United (R - Leicestershire Senior League Division One), Stockingford AA (W)
Castle Vale Res. become Glades.

GROUND DIRECTIONS

ALVESTON - Ground: The Home Guard Club, Main Street, Tiddington , Stratford-upon-Avon , Warwickshire , CV37 7AY
M40 junction 15, take A429 towards Stow/Wellesbourne. From the Wellesbourne by-pass turn right into the Stratford Road (B4086) at the 2nd Island. Continue for 4 miles and past the Alveston village turns on your right, to Tiddington where the ground is on your left before you enter the village.

BARTLEY GREEN - Ground: Illey Lane, Halesowen , Birmingham , West Midlands , B62 0HE
From M5 junctions 3, follow the A456 for Halesowen/Kidderminster for approx 1.5 miles to Grange Island. Turn left along the B4551 Bromsgrove Road for approx 400 yards, take the 1st left into Illey Lane and the ground is approximately 1 mile on the left hand side.
Exit M42 at Junction 10, take A5 towards Tamworth, exit A5 at 2nd exit (Glascote & Amington Industrial Estate). Turn right onto Marlborough Way, at next island turn left (B5000), turn right into Argyle Street (opposite chip shop). At T-junction, turn left into Amington Road, drive over the canal bridge, and turn 2nd right into Leedham Avenue. Take right fork into Rene Road. Club is situated 150 yards on right immediately after school.

BROCTON - Ground: Silkmore Lane Sports Ground, Silkmore Lane , Stafford , Staffordshire , ST17 4JH
From M6 J13 take A449 towards Stafford for 1.5 miles until reaching traffic lights by Esso petrol station. Turn right at lights into Rickescote Road, follow road round over railway bridge to mini island, at island bear left into Silkmore Lane. At next mini island take 4th exit for entrance to ground. From Lichfield/Rugeley. After passing Staffs Police HQ at Baswick go downhill past BMW garage and pub to large island, take 1st exit into Silkmore Lane, at next mini island take 2nd exit into ground entrance. Do not turn into Lancaster Road or Silkmore Crescent as directed by Sat Navs.

CADBURY ATHLETIC - Ground: Lye Meadow, Redditch Road , Alvechurch , Worcestershire , B48 7RS
M42 Junction 2, Follow signs for Redditch, taking dual carriageway. At 1st island turn right (Signposted Alvechurch), ground approximately 1km on right. Car Park entrance before ground.

CASTLE VALE - Ground: Vale Stadium, Farnborough Road, Castle Vale , Birmingham , West Midlands , B35 7DA
From M6 Junction 5 turn right at the island onto the A452 to island with Spitfire sculpture, turn right into Tangmere Drive, then right into Farnborough Road. Ground is on the right hand side after approximately 1/2 mile.

CASTLE VALE JKS - Ground: Vale Stadium, Farnborough Road, Castle Vale , Birmingham , West Midlands , B35 7DA
See Castle Vale above.

CONTINENTAL STAR - Ground: Dales Lane, Rushall , Walsall , West Midlands , WS4 1LJ
From M6: Leave at Junction 10 and follow signs for Walsall on A454 (Wolverhampton Road). Keep in the left hand lane and at the 1st set of traffic lights turn left into Bloxwich Lane. Progress through a set of traffic lights, keeping in the right hand lane and at the island bear left continuing along Bloxwich Lane. At the 3rd set of lights turn into Leamore Lane (at T-junction). Continue along Leamore Lane over the 1st island (A34 Somerfield Road-Green Lane) and pass through traffic lights on B4210 Bloxwich Road into Harden Road, continue along Harden Road and go straight over a mini island, at the next island take the 2nd exit continuing along Harden Road progressing into Station Road. At the set of traffic lights at the staggered junction with the A461 Lichfield Road, turn right and then left ono the B4154 (Daw End Lane) towards Aldridge, with McDonalds on your right. Continue up Daw End Lane and over the canal bridge, Dales Lane is the next on the right opposite the Royal Oak Public House. The ground entrance is sign posted.

COVENTRY COPSEWOOD - Ground: Copsewood Sports & Social Club, Allard Way, Binley , Coventry , West Midlands , CV3 1HQ
M6 South: Leave at junction 2 and follow A4600 signs for City Centre. Go over 3 roundabouts and past 1 set of traffic lights, on reaching the 2nd set of traffic lights with Coventry Oak pub on left, turn left down Hipswell Highway. Follow road for 1 mile and reach another set of lights (Fire Station is on left and Mill Pool pub is on right). Go over lights and the ground is 300 yards on the left. From M40: Follow A46 signs to Coventry and Leicester, stay on this road until very end, you then reach a roundabout with a flyover, go round the roundabout following M69 signs. This road takes you past Asda and you reach a set of traffic lights with a roundabout. Take 2nd left turn off the roundabout, again following M69 signs, This is Allard Way and takes you past Matalan on left, Go under railway bridge and ground is 400 yards on the right. A45 from Birmingham Direction: Follow A45 until reaching a slip road signposted A46, this slip road has the Festival Pub on left side of it. It is after a roundabout with big Peugeot car showroom on left. Go down slip road and take 2nd exit. , this is another slip road leading to A46, signposted B4114 Coventry. Follow road until reaching roundabout with a flyover, and then follow as M40 directions above.

DOSTHILL COLTS - Ground: Pack Meadow, Packington Lane , Coleshill , Warwickshire , B46 3JQ
Exit M6 at Junction 4, take A446 signposted Lichfield, turn right across dual carriageway onto B4117 to Coleshill. After school on right, turn right into Packington Lane, ground is 1/2 mile of the left.

HEATHER ST. JOHN'S - Ground: St. John's Park, Ravenstone Road , Heather , Leicestershire , LE67 2QJ
From Birmingham take M42, A42 north to Ashby De La Zouch, exit at junction 13, take the 5th exit, A511 to Coalville for 3 miles, at the roundabout take the 4th exit A447 for 3 miles. At the double mini island take 3rd exit to Heather, 1 mile at the mini island take 3rd exit, ground is 200 yards on the left. From Coventry/Warwick. A46 to M69 exit junction 1, to the A5 take the 2nd exit, then follow signs for Ibstock A447. At the mini island in Ibstock take 1st exit to Heather, 1 mile at the mini island take 3rd exit ground 200yards on the left.

MASSEY FERGUSON - Ground: Bannerbrook Park, Off Banner Lane, Tile Hill , Coventry , West Midlands , CV4 9GT
M42 or M6 take A45 to Coventry from Birmingham direction. At 1st set of lights bear right into Broad Lane. Travel down Broad Lane until you reach the Vauxhall dealers on your right. Turn left opposite onto Banner Lane. Travel for 1/4 mile until you reach the brick wall sign (Bannerbrook Park) on your right hand side. This is the entrance to Massey Fergusuon F.C. Follow the road, which will take you into the ground. (Please dive slowly through the new housing estate, as there are speed bumps).

NUNEATON GRIFF - Ground: The Pingles Stadium, Avenue Road , Nuneaton , Warwickshire , CV11 4LX
From M5, M42 & M6: Take M6 south to junction 3 and leave by turning left onto A444 (Nuneaton). Stay on A444 through Bermuda Park, McDonalds and George Eliot Hospital roundabouts until reaching large roundabout with footbridge over road. Carry straight on (2nd exit) and downhill, taking right hand lane. At bottom of hill you reach Coton Arches Island, take 2nd exit (A4252 Avenue Road) and travel 1/2 mile to Cedar Tree Pub traffic lights, turn left into Stadium car park service road. It is unsuitable for coaches to turn around in. From A5: Travel south following signs for Nuneaton. After passing through Atherstone travel for 2 1/2 miles until junction with A444. At this junction (Royal Red Gate Pub) turn right at staggered junction and continue on A444 through Caldecote and Weddington into Nuneaton. Join one-way system at Graziers Arms by turning left and immediately take right hand lane for 300 yards and follow A444 for Coventry. At Third Island turn left on to dual carriageway (Coton Road) for 1/2 mile and turn left at Coton Arches island on to A4252 (Avenue Road) then as above.

PELSALL VILLA - Ground: The Bush Ground, Walsall Road , Walsall , West Midlands , WS3 4BP
Leave M6 at junction 7 sign-posted A34 Birmingham. Take A34 towards Walsall to 1st Island, turn right (marked Ring Road) across 3 islands. At large island at the bottom of the hill, take last exit marked Lichfield. Up hill and across next island to traffic lights, continue to next set of lights and turn left (B4154 Pelsall). Go over Railway Bridge to Old Bush Public House, the ground is next to the public house signposted Pelsall Cricket Club. From Birmingham East: Follow A452 from Spitfire Island then follow signs towards Brownhills. At the traffic lights at the Shire Oak P.H, turn left onto A461 (Walsall) and pass the entrance to Walsall Wood FC. At the traffic lights in Shelfield (The Spring Cottage PH) turn right (signposted Pelsall). At the next set of traffic lights turn left, the Bush is approx 400 yards on left. From: Coventry: Take A45 to Stonebridge Island, turn right onto A452 but then keep to the right following A446 (signposted Lichfield). Follow the A446 to Bassett's Pole Island. Take the 3rd exit onto A38 (Lichfield). Leave the A38 at sliproad for the A5 and take the 2nd exit at the island. Follow the A5 over next 2 islands and at Muckley Corner turn left (inside lane) to join A461. Go straight on at the traffic lights and follow directions as above.

PERSHORE TOWN - Ground: King George V Playing Field, King George's Way , Pershore , Worcestershire , WR10 1AA
M5 Junction 7, take B4080 (formerly A44) to Pershore. On entering the town turn left at 2nd set of traffic lights (signposted Leisure Centre). The ground is 300 yards on the left hand side.

PILKINGTON XXX - Ground: Triplex Sports, Eckersall Road, Kings Norton , Birmingham , West Midlands , B38 8SR
From Cotteridge A441 through and past Kings Norton Station, 150 yards turn right across dual carriageway at petrol station, approximately 300 yards there is a sharp bend, turn right. Ground is on right.

RACING CLUB WARWICK - Ground: Hampton Road , Warwick , Warwickshire , CV34 6JP
M40 Junction 15, signposted Warwick. At roundabout with traffic lights take A429 to Warwick. Follow this road for 1/2 mile and you will come to houses on your left. Take the 2nd turn on the left into Shakespeare Avenue. Follow to T-junction. Turn right into Hampton Road. Entrance to ground is 50 yards on left.

SOUTHAM UNITED - Ground: Banbury Road , Southam , Warwickshire , CV47 2BJ
From Birmingham: M40 Junction 12, exit to A4451 to Southam. Approximately 6 1/2 miles to an island in Southam, turn right, at 2nd island turn right again, ground is 100 yards on right. From Coventry: take A423 Banbury Road; the ground is approximately 12 1/2 miles from Coventry.

WALSALL WOOD - Ground: Oak Park, Lichfield Road, Walsall Wood , Walsall , West Midlands , WS9 9NP
From North using M6 motorway: M6 south to junction 12. Take A5 until big island just outside Brownhills (next island after the Turn pub on left). Take A452 Chester Road North through Brownhills High Street to traffic lights at Shire Oak (pub at junction on right hand side). Turn right on to A461 for Walsall, go to next set of traffic lights, cross over and turn right immediately on to Oak Park Leisure Centre car park (rear of Kentucky Fried Chicken). Proceed diagonally over car park and follow road round to ground entrance. From South using M5/M6 motorways: M5 North past junction 1 on to M6 north. Leave at junction 9 (Wednesbury turn off). Take A4148 to Walsall. Proceed for about 2 miles over several islands until going down a hill alongside the Arboretum. At big island at bottom, turn right onto A461 for Lichfield. Take A461 for about 4 miles and go through Walsall Wood village (after Barons Court Hotel on right), up the hill after village, Oak Park is on the left opposite Fitness First, turn left and go diagonally across Oak Park Leisure Centre car park, Follow road round to the ground entrance. M5/M6 alternative M5 North and bear left after junction 1 (West Bromwich) onto M6 south. Go to next junction (Junction 7 Great Barr) and follow signs for A34 Birmingham Road to junction with Queslett Road (A4041). Turn left at the junction (traffic lights) and take A4041 past Asda and over several islands to A452 Chester Road. Turn left at this island and travel for about 4 miles to Shire Oak cross-roads (traffic lights with Shire Oak pub opposite). Turn left at the lights onto A461 for Walsall. Go to next lights and cross over, Oak Park is immediately on the right opposite Fitness First. Turn right onto car park and go diagonally across, following road round to the ground entrance.

DIVISION ONE

ARCHDALE '73 - Ground: County Sports Ground, Claines Lane , Worcester , Worcestershire , WR3 7SS
M5 to Junction 6, take A449 (link road) signposted Kidderminster, down to the bottom, at island turn sharp left into Claines Lane, continue past church on right, ground is on the left (about 1/2 mile).

BRERETON SOCIAL - Ground: Red Lion Ground, Armitage Lane, Brereton , Rugeley , Staffordshire , WS15 1ED
From M6 Junction 11 follow A460 to Rugeley, on reaching large roundabout at Rugeley take A51 (signposted Lichfield). At end of dual carriageway in Brereton turn left at traffic lights into Armitage Lane. Entrance is 100 yards on right.

BURNTWOOD TOWN - Ground: Long Lane Park, Long Lane, Essington , Wolverhampton , West Midlands , WV11 2AA
Leave M6 at Junction 11, at the junction island take the A462 towards Willenhall. After approximately 2 miles turn left onto B4210 (Broad Lane). After approx. 300 yards turn left into Long Lane, the ground is 1/2 mile on the left.

COTON GREEN - Ground: New Mill Lane, Fazeley , Tamworth , Staffordshire , B78 3RX
From M42 junction 9, take A446 exit towards The Belfry, at the next island turn right towards Tamworth and Drayton Manor Park (A4091), continue for approximately 4 miles, past entrance to Drayton Mark Park on your left, continue over the canal with 'Debbies Boat Hire' on your right and 'Fazeley Marina' on your left. As you enter Fazeley you need to turn right immediately after the start of the 30mph speed limit, into New Mill Lane (there is a right filter lane). Once in New Mill Lane, follow lane past houses, turn right at the bottom and follow into car park.

DROITWICH SPA - Ground: Droitwich Spa Leisure Centre, Briar Mill , Droitwich , Worcestershire , WR9 0RZ
M5 junction 5, take A38 to Droitwich, At traffic lights by Chateau Impney, go onto dual carriageway, at roundabout take 1st exit (Kidderminster Road), pass Homebase and take next right into Salwarpe Road. Go straight over at next roundabout, next right into Briarmill Road and ground is behind the all weather complex.

EARLSWOOD TOWN - Ground: The Pavilions, Malthouse Lane, Earlswood , Solihull , West Midlands , B94 5DX
From M42 (Junction 3) A435 Evesham to Birmingham Road, at Motorway Island take minor exit to Foreshaw Heath. Follow for 3/4 mile. Turn right into Poolhead Lane. After passing Earlswood Trading Estate (on right) turn first left into Small Lane (no road sign) just before the road crosses the motorway. The ground 1/2 mile on right hand side. From A34 Heading away from Birmingham, leave Shirley. Turn right into Blackford Road (B4102) signposted Earlswood/Redditch. Follow this road for 4 miles. After passing the crossroads at Earlswood (Reservoir Public House) turn next right into Springbrook Lane. Go to the end of Springbrook Lane, Turn left into Malthouse Lane. Ground approximately 1/4 mile on left.

FAIRFIELD VILLA - Ground: Recreation Ground, Stourbridge Road, Fairfield , Bromsgrove , Worcestershire , B61 9LZ
From M42 Junction 1: Take A38 North to junction 4 M5 and then take A491 towards Stourbridge, travel 2 miles to next roundabout, then left onto B4091 up into Fairfield Village. Go past Swan Public House and approximately 200 yards on your left you will see a school warning sign and telephone booth. Turn left here, up drive to ground. From M5 Junction 4: See above From A38 South to M5 junction 4: see above.

FC GLADES SPORTING - Ground: The Glades, Lugtrout Lane , Solihull , West Midlands , B91 2RX
From M42 North or South: Exit motorway at junction 5 (signposted Solihull). Take 1st Exit left (A41). Continue on A41 until you reach 1st set of traffic lights and turn right into Hampton Lane, take the 2nd left (after approx 2 miles) into Lugtrout Lane. Continue on Lugtrout Lane past houses on either side. Entrance to the ground will be on your left (opposite cricket ground).

HAMPTON - Ground: Hampton Sports Club, Field Lane , Solihull , West Midlands , B91 2RT
From M42 North or South: Exit motorway at junction 5 (signposted Solihull). Take 1st Exit left (A41). Continue on A41 until you reach 1st set of traffic lights and turn right into Hampton Lane, after approx 1/2 mile turn left into Field Lane, ground is approx 3/4 mile on the right hand side.

KENILWORTH TOWN K.H. - Ground: Gypsy Lane , Kenilworth , Warwickshire , CV8 1FN
Junction 6 M42 or Junction 4 M6, take A452 to Kenilworth, follow main road to bottom of High Street, take turn for Leek Wooton, turn right into Rouncil Lane. Ground is 150 yards to end of Gypsy Lane. From Coventry take A429 into Kenilworth then as above.

KNOWLE - Ground: Hampton Road, Knowle , Solihull , West Midlands , B93 0NX
Directions: M42 Junction 5, A4140 to Knowle, turn left at Toby Carvery into Hampton Road. Ground is 200 yards on right.

LITTLETON - Ground: Five Acres, Pebworth Road, North Littleton , Evesham , Worcestershire , WR11 8QL
Get on A46 and aim for Bidford-on-Avon, leave A46 at Bidford roundabout and follow signs for B439 (Bidford 0.5 miles). Come to roundabout in Bidford and take exit B4085 (Cleeve Prior), over a very narrow bridge controlled by traffic lights, straight over crossroads following sign to Honeybourne Broadway. Straight on for approximately 3 miles signpost right turn for the Littletons at crossroads, the ground is 1.25 miles on the right.

NORTHFIELD TOWN - Ground: Shenley Lane Community Association, Shenley Lane, Selly Oak , Birmingham , West Midlands , B29 4HZ
From Birmingham City Centre: Take the A38 (Bristol Road) towards Bromsgrove, travel through the districts of Bournbrook and Selly Oak. Once through Selly Oak, the road changes to a dual carriageway, following this until just before the end, where the Royal Orthopaedic Hospital is situated on the left. Turn right across the carriageway at the hospital and proceed down Whitehill Lane. At the bottom turn right across the dual carriageway and 1st right again into the ground. A-Z ref 2A 104. From the M42: From the M6 North join the M42 and head towards Worcester, follow the M42 until the junction A441Redditch/Birmingham is reached. Leave the motorway and head towards Birmingham. As you head towards Birmingham you will go up a hill, at the top of the hill you will come to a mini roundabout. At this island turn left into Longbridge Lane. Follow this all the way to the end, at the end you will come to a dual carriageway, turn right on to this. The dual carriageway is the main A38 heading towards Birmingham. Follow this road until the end when you will come into Northfield centre. As you go through Northfield you will come to a junction controlled by traffic lights, turn left into Bell Lane. As you go down the hill you will join a dual carriageway, at the bottom of the hill, turn across the carriageway and the ground is facing

you. From the M5: Leave the motorway at junction 4 (A38). Follow signs for Birmingham, this is a dual carriageway. After 3 miles you will come to an island, the Rover car plant at Longbridge is directly in front of you. Turn left, still on the A38. Follow this road until the end when you will come into Northfield centre. As you go through Northfield you will come to a junction controlled by traffic lights, turn left into Bell Lane. As you go down the hill you will join a dual carriageway, at the bottom of the hill, turn across the carriageway and the ground is facing you.

PHOENIX UNITED - Ground: The Pavilions, Malthouse Lane, Earlswood , Solihull , West Midlands , B94 5DX

From M42 (Junction 3) A435 Evesham to Birmingham Road, at Motorway Island take minor exit to Foreshaw Heath. Follow for 3/4 mile. Turn right into Poolhead Lane. After passing Earlswood Trading Estate (on right) turn first left into Small Lane (no road sign) just before the road crosses the motorway. The ground 1/2 mile on right hand side. From A34 Heading away from Birmingham, leave Shirley. Turn right into Blackford Road (B4102) signposted Earlswood/Redditch. Follow this road for 4 miles. After passing the crossroads at Earlswood (Reservoir Public House) turn next right into Springbrook Lane. Go to the end of Springbrook Lane, Turn left into Malthouse Lane. Ground approximately 1/4 mile on left.

SHIRLEY TOWN - Ground: Tilehouse Lane, Shirley , Solihull , West Midlands , B90 1PH

Directions: Tanworth Lane after 150yds, turn right into Dickens Heath Road (Chiswick Green Inn on Left). Follow road to island, take 3rd exit and then after 100 yards go right into Tythe Barn Lane. Follow road then approx 3/4 miles at T junction turn right into Tilehouse Lane. Ground 200 yds on Right (opposite Whitlock's End Station car park). From West & M42: Leave @ J3 onto A435 to Birmingham. After 1 1/2 miles (Beckets Island) take 4th Exit (signposted Earlswood) entering Station Road. After 3/4 miles bear right over railway bridge entering Norton Lane. After 1/4 miles turn left into Lowbrook Road. After 1/4 mile at crossroads turn left into Tilehouse lane. After 1 mile approx ground is on right hand side (opposite Whitlock's End Station Car Park).

STRETTON EAGLES - Ground: Shobnall Sports Gound, Shobnall Road , Burton-upon-Trent , Staffordshire , DE14 2BB

Take A38 to Burton on Trent, leave at A5121 and take the 3rd exit towards Burton. At the lights take left hand lane for Burton, go straight through in 200 metres (You will see Bannatynes Leisure on your right). At the roundabout go straight on (A5234 Abbots Bromley). Stay on this road across 3 mini islands, you will then pass the recycling centre before reaching another island. Turn left into Shobnall Road and follow for 400 metres before turning right into Shobnall Leisure Centre. The ground is 200 yards on the right of the driveway.

WEST MIDLANDS POLICE - Ground: Tally Ho Training Centre, Pershore Road, Edgbaston , Birmingham , West Midlands , B5 7RD

Directions: From M5: Exit at junction 3, take A456 Hagley Road to 'Five Ways', turn right on to Islington Row, turn right at traffic lights at Bristol Road. Turn left at next set of traffic lights into Priory Road, then right into Pershore Road. Tally Ho! is on your left. From M6: Exit at junction 6; take Aston Expressway (A38) through Queensway underpasses emerging in Bristol Street/Bristol Road. Turn left at traffic lights at junction with Priory Road. Turn right at next set of traffic lights. Pershore Road and Tally Ho! is on your left (A-Z Reference 3G Page 89).

DIVISION TWO

BLACKWOOD - Ground: Hampton Sports Club, Field Lane , Solihull , West Midlands , B91 2RT

From M42 North or South: Exit motorway at junction 5 (signposted Solihull). Take 1st Exit left (A41). Continue on A41 until you reach 1st set of traffic lights and turn right into Hampton Lane, after approx 1/2 mile turn left into Field Lane, ground is approx 3/4 mile on the right hand side.

BROMSGROVE SPORTING - Ground: The Beehive, Abbeyfields Drive , Studley , Warwickshire , B80 7BF

Leave M42 at junction 3. Take A435 towards Redditch, head south for 5 miles. Abbeyfields Drive is on the left hand side 1/2 mile past 'The Boot' public house, adjacent to a sharp left hand bend.

CADBURY ATHLETIC RESERVES - Ground: Cadbury Recreation Ground, Bournville Lane , Birmingham , West Midlands , B30 1LA

From M5 Junction 4: Take A38 to Birmingham, turn right at Selly Oak lights (A4040), travel 1 mile down Oak Tree Lane/Linden Road to Bournville Lane, turn left, the ground is on the left. From M42 Junction 2: Take A441 to Birmingham through Kings Norton to Cotteridge, take Watford Road (A4040) for 1 mile to Bourneville Lane, and turn right, groud on left. From Birmingham City Centre: Take A38 Bristol Road to Selly Oak Lights, turn left, travel 1 mile down Oak Tree Lane/Linden Road to Bournville Lane, turn left, ground on right. Note: All routes in the South of Birmingham are well signposted for 'Cadbury World'. Following these will lead to our ground.

CHELMSLEY TOWN - Ground: The Pavilion, Coleshill Road, Marston Green , Birmingham , West Midlands , B37 7HW

M6 junction 4, if travelling south, turn left at the motorway island, if travelling north turn right. Turn 1st left into Coleshill Heath Road, straight on at island, 2nd right into Coleshill Road and then 2nd right into ground.

CLEMENTS '83 - Ground: Sedgemere Sports & Social, Sedgemere Road, Yardley , Birmingham , West Midlands , B26 2AX

From M42 Junction 6. Take A45 towards Birmingham, after approximately 4 miles take left exit to Swan Island. At island take A4040 (Church Road), at next island, take the 3rd exit and continue on Church Road then take the 5th right into Queens Road, then take 2nd right. The ground is on the right of Sedgemere Road. From Birmingham City Centre. Take A45 (Coventry Road). After 0.25 miles keep left into Cattell Road, go past Birmingham City ground on B1428, and continue onto Bordesley Green East. After approximately 4 miles turn right into Queens Road, then take the 3rd left into Segdemere Road, the ground is on the right.

CONTINENTAL STAR RESERVES - Ground: The Pavilion, Coleshill Road, Marston Green , Birmingham , West Midlands , B37 7HW

Directions: M6 junction 4, if travelling south, turn left at the motorway island, if travelling north turn right. Turn 1st left into Coleshill Heath Road, straight on at island, 2nd right into Coleshill Road and then 2nd right into ground.

DROITWICH SPA RESERVES - Ground: Droitwich Spa Leisure Centre, Briar Mill , Droitwich , Worcestershire , WR9 0RZ

Directions: See Droitwich Spa - Divison One.

ENVILLE ATHLETIC - Hall Drive, Enville , Stourbridge , West Midlands , DY7 5HB

From Stourbridge take A458 towards Bridgnorth. Cross the A449 at Stourton (formerly the Stewpony and Foley Arms), turn left then immediately right back onto the A458. Proceed for 3 miles to Enville village, at 'The Cat In' public house, turn left onto the car park and follow the private drive to Enville Hall, through the large white gates. The clubhouse and ground are 200 yards along the drive on the left hand side.

FECKENHAM - Ground: Studley Sports & Social Club, Eldorado Close , Studley , Warwickshire , B80 7HP

Leave M42 at junction 3 then, at roundabout, take the 3rd exit onto the A435, signposted Redditch / Evesham. At the next roundabout take the 2nd exit staying on the A435, at the next roundabout, take the 2nd exit onto the B4092, signposted Astwood Bank, then take the 3rd turning on the right into Eldorado Close. Leave the M5 south at junction 4. At the roundabout take the 2nd exit onto the A38, signposted Bromsgrove. Travel for approximately 3 miles then turn onto the A448, signposted Redditch, the A448 will then merge with the A4189. At the next roundabout take the 3rd turning staying on the A4189. At the next roundabout take the 2nd turning still on the A4189, at the next roundabout take the 3rd turning onto the A435 signposted Evesham. At the next roundabout take the 2nd exit, staying on the A435. At the next roundabout take the 2nd exit onto the B4092, signposted Astwood Bank, then take the 3rd turning on the right into Eldorado Close.

GREENHILL - Ground: Dudley Sports & Social Club, Hillcrest Avenue , Brierley Hill , West Midlands , DY5 3QH

The ground is situated in Brierley Hill, just off A461. It can be approached from Stourbridge off the ring road to Amblecote, turning right at the 3rd set of traffic lights or from Dudley passing through Brierley Hill Town Centre. A-Z Ref 4H, page 67.

HENLEY FOREST - Ground: Henley-in-Arden Sports & Social Ground, Stratford Road , Henley-in-Arden , Warwickshire , B95 6AD

Sports & Social Ground is situated on the A3400 about 1/4 mile south of the town centre of Henley in Arden towards Stratford on Avon opposite Warwickshire College.

KNOWLE RESERVES - Ground: Hampton Road, Knowle , Solihull , West Midlands , B93 0NX

See Knowle - Division One.

LEAMINGTON HIBERNIAN - Ground: Ajax Park, Hampton Road , Warwick , Warwickshire , CV35 8HA

From M40: Junction 15, signposted Warwick, at roundabout with traffic lights take A429 to Warwick, follow this road for 1/2 mile, you will come to housed on your left. Take 2nd left into Shakespeare Avenue, follow to the T Junction and turn left into Hampton Road. Carry on past houses on left over the motorway bridge, Ajax Park is on the right hand side.

LICHFIELD CITY - Ground: Brownsfield Park, Brownsfield Road , Lichfield , Staffordshire , WS13 6AY
From M42 J10, follow A5 towards Brownhills, or J9 and follow A446 to Lichfield, then follow signs for A38 Lichfield/Derby. From Swinfen Roundabout take 3rd exit for A38 north and then take next off A38 onto A5192 (Cappers Lane). Follow A5192 through 2 islands onto Eastern Avenue. The Ground is on the right at the top of the hill next to Norgreen factory. From M6 J12, follow A5 towards Lichfield then A38 to Lichfield Derby, then follow instructions as above.

PERRYWOOD - Ground: Neel Park, Droitwich Road, Perdiswell , Worcester , Worcestershire , WR3 7SN
M5 Junction 6, take A449 to Kidderminster, at island take the 1st left signposted to Claines, go to the end of lane to T-junction, take right turn to A38 (Worcester). Go straight on at 1st set of lights, at next set take left turn. Go past Cannons Health Club on left and take the right hand turn as the road bears off left. Go 50 yards and car park and ground are on the left.

YOUNG WARRIORS - Ground: Sphinx Sports & Social Club , Sphinx Drive , off Siddeley Avenue , Coventry , West Midlands , CV3 1WA
From M42/A45: follow A45 towards Coventry. Landmarks to follow: right hand side, large Land Rover dealership (Guy Salmon) and Windmill Village Hotel, left hand side: Quality Hotel. You will then see the Coventry Hill Hotel on your left hand side. Take the slip road by the hotel, which is signposted Coventry City Centre, at the 1st island take the 2nd exit, at the next island, take the 3rd exit on to the Holyhead Road (A4114) The Tollgate Pub will be on your right hand side, stay on this road for approximately 2 1/2 you will then reach the end of this road at the ring road. Turn left to enter onto Coventry ring road at Junction 8. Continue on the ring road until Junction 3 (signposted M69 and Football Stadium). Exit ring road to left. Follow road round to the right to a traffic island; go straight ahead onto Sky Blue Way. Stay on this road following signs for Binley, stay on this road (Binley Road A428), eventually you will see a row of shops on your left and the Bulls Head pub on your right, after the Bulls Head take next right into Biggin Hall Crescent and follow road round until the 5th road on the left (Siddeley Avenue). Approximately 30yards into Siddeley Avenue you will come to a bend where the entrance to the club is situated. Please note that the entrance to the ground is now called Sphinx Drive. From M6: M6 Junction 3, Follow signs for Coventry A444 (Phoenix Way), continue on A444 until you reach the Binley Road Island, Turn left at island into Binley Road (A428), eventually you will see a row of shops on your left and the Bulls Head pub on your right, after the Bulls Head take next right into Biggin Hall Crescent and follow road round until the 5th road on the left (Siddeley Avenue). Approximately 30yards into Siddeley Avenue you will come to a bend where the entrance to the club is situated. Please note that the entrance to the ground is now called Sphinx Drive. From M40/A46 (Warwick Bypass): From M40 take exit signposted Coventry, follow this dual carriageway for approximately 8 miles to the very end, here you will come to a large island. Follow the signs for Stoke and Willenhall. You will then go past an ASDA store before coming to an island, take the exit after the ASDA entrance (signposted Seven Stars Industrial Estate). You are now in Humber Road; you will see a Matalan and Mercedes garage on your right hand side followed by the PSA Citroen (Peugeot factory). At the 2nd set of traffic lights (by a parade of shops) turn right into Bolingbroke Road. At the end of Bolingbroke Road turn right and then 1st left into Bulls Head Lane, take 2nd on right into Siddeley Avenue. Approximately 30yards into Siddeley Avenue you will come to a bend where the entrance to the club is situated. Please note that the entrance to the ground is now called Sphinx Drive.

DIVISION THREE

ALVESTON RESERVES - Ground: The Home Guard Club, Main Street, Tiddington , Stratford-upon-Avon , Warwickshire , CV37 7AY
See Alveston - Premier Division.

ARCHDALE '73 RESERVES - Ground: County Sports Ground, Claines Lane , Worcester , Worcestershire , WR3 7SS
See Archdale '73 - Division One.

ASTON - Ground: Moor Lane Pavilion, Moor Lane , Birmingham , West Midlands , B6 7AA
Exit M6 at junction 7, follow signs for the A34 towards Birmingham. Follow signposts for Birmingham City University, stay in left hand lane for the A453.Stay on the A453 to Sutton Coldfield until you see Moor Lane Sports on your right. Take the 1st right after the sports ground into Moor Lane. The car park entrance is on your right.

Coton Green Reserves - Ground: New Mill Lane, Fazeley , Tamworth , Staffordshire , B78 3RX
See Coton Green - Division Two.

COVENTRY AMATEURS - Ground: David Sinclair Sports Ground, Westwood Heath Road, Westwood Heath , Coventry , West Midlands , CV4 8GP
From Coventry, take A45 towards M45 until at roundabout take the 3rd exit onto Sir Henry Parkes Road (signposted Canley, University), At roundabout take the 2nd exit onto Sir Henry Parkes Road (signposted Cannon Park Shopping Centre), At roundabout take the 2nd exit onto Kirby Corner Road, At roundabout take the 2nd exit onto Westwood Heath Road, ground is approximately 1/2 mile on left hand side.

DOSTHILL COLTS RESERVES - Ground: Mile Oak Community Ground, Price Avenue, Mile Oak , Tamworth , Staffordshire , B78 3NL
Exit M42 at junction 10, take A5 towards Tamworth, exit at 4th exit for Sutton Coldfield (A453), at T-Junction turn left, at traffic lights (garage on right hand side) turn left, take 3rd turning on right into Price Avenue, ground is 400 yards on right hand side.

FUTURE LEGENDS - Ground: Moat House Leisure Centre, Winston Avenue , Coventry , West Midlands , CV2 1EA
Follow A45 towards Coventry. Landmarks to follow: right hand side, large Land Rover dealership (Guy Salmon) and Windmill Village Hotel, left hand side: Quality Hotel. You will then see the Coventry Hill Hotel on your left hand side. Take the slip road by the hotel, which is signposted Coventry City Centre, at the 1st island take the 2nd exit, at the next island, take the 3rd exit on to the Holyhead Road (A4114) The Tollgate Pub will be on your right hand side, stay on this road for approximately 2 1/2 you will then reach the end of this road at the ring road. Turn left to enter onto Coventry ring road at Junction 8. Continue on the ring road until Junction 3 (signposted M69 and Football Stadium). Exit ring road to left. Follow road round to the right to a traffic island; go straight ahead onto Sky Blue Way. Stay on this road following signs for Binley, stay on this road (Binley Road A428. At the roundabout take the 1st exit onto the A444, in 1 1/2 miles take 3rd exit at roundabout onto Bell Green Road. At next roundabout take 3rd exit into Old Church Road, then immediately, at traffic lights, turn right into Hall Green Road, at next traffic lights turn left into Deedmore Road, Winston Avenue is on the right.

INKBERROW - Ground: Sands Road , Inkberrow , Worcestershire , WR7 4PX
Travelling West on A422, turn sharp right immediately on entering village, the car park is 200 yards on the left. Travelling east on A422, continue through the middle of the village and bear left onto Sands Road as the main road bears right out of the village. The car park is 200 yards on the left.

J.D.G. ALLIANCE - Ground: Moor Lane Pavilion, Moor Lane , Birmingham , West Midlands , B6 7AA
Exit M6 at junction 7, follow signs for the A34 towards Birmingham. Follow signposts for Birmingham City University, stay in left hand lane for the A453.Stay on the A453 to Sutton Coldfield until you see Moor Lane Sports on your right. Take the 1st right after the sports ground into Moor Lane. The car park entrance is on your right.

LICHFIELD CITY RESERVES - Ground: Brownsfield Park, Brownsfield Road , Lichfield , Staffordshire , WS13 6AY
See Lichfield City - Division Two.

LITTLETON RESERVES - Ground: Five Acres, Pebworth Road, North Littleton , Evesham , Worcestershire , WR11 8QL
See Littleton - Division One.

NORTHFIELD TOWN RESERVES - Ground: Shenley Lane Community Association, Shenley Lane, Selly Oak , Birmingham , West Midlands , B29 4HZ
See Northfield Town - Division One.

POLESWORTH - Ground: North Warwickshire Sports & Social Club, Armitage Hill, Polesworth , Tamworth , Staffordshire , B78 1HT
Exit M42 at junction 10, take A5 towards Tamworth, exit at 1st exit, take 3rd exit at island over bridge (A5 below). At next island take 1st exit (traffic cameras). Continue until reaching B5000 island, take 3rd exit towards Polesworth, Armitage hill is 3rd exit on right, entrance to ground is directly in front once you have turned into Armitage Hill.

Stratford Town A - Ground: Knights Lane, Tiddington , Stratford-upon-Avon , Warwickshire , CV37 7BZ
From M40 junction 15, take A429 towards Stow/Wellesbourne. From the Wellesbourne by-pass turn right into the Stratford Road (B4086) at the 2nd Island. Continue through the village of Tiddington and on leaving the village turn left into Knights Lane, the ground is past the school on the right.

WALSALL WOOD RESERVES - Ground: Oak Park, Lichfield Road, Walsall Wood , Walsall , West Midlands , WS9 9NP
See Walsall Wood - Premier Division.

MIDLAND ALLIANCE

www.midlandfootballalliance.co.uk

Sponsored by: Baker Joiner

Founded: 1994

Recent champions:

2005: Rushall Olympic
2006: Chasetown
2007: Leamington
2008: Atherstone Town
2009: Market Drayton Town

	P	W	D	L	F	A	Pts
Barwell	42	36	6	0	125	18	114
Coalville Town	42	31	3	8	106	43	96
Stratford Town	42	26	4	12	89	50	82
Tipton Town	42	23	13	6	65	28	82
Westfields	42	23	7	12	82	55	76
Boldmere St Michaels	42	21	7	14	78	51	70
Alvechurch	42	19	9	14	86	64	66
Coleshill Town	41	18	9	14	77	55	63
Coventry Sphinx	42	18	8	16	89	69	62
Kirby Muxloe SC	42	17	11	14	81	62	62
Studley	42	18	8	16	63	62	62
Causeway United	42	17	8	17	61	54	59
Loughborough Univ.	42	16	9	17	51	48	57
Oadby Town	42	16	7	19	70	77	55
Friar Lane & Epworth	41	15	5	21	75	90	50
Rocester	42	14	6	22	63	79	48
Biddulph Victoria	42	12	12	18	56	76	48
Highgate United	42	11	8	23	57	95	41
Malvern Town	42	9	8	25	64	96	35
Bridgnorth Town	42	9	7	26	42	93	34
Shifnal Town	42	7	8	27	39	105	29
Cradley Town	42	0	7	35	29	178	7

Friar Lane & Epworth v Coleshill Town - not played

POLYMAC SERVICES LEAGUE CUP

FIRST ROUND

Alvechurch 2 Malvern Town 1
Barwell 6 Bridgnorth Town 0
Loughborough University 1 Highgate United 0
Rocester 4 Biddulph Victoria 2
Shifnal Town 1 **Friar Lane & Epworth** 3
Stratford Town 1 **Coalville Town** 2

SECOND ROUND

Boldmere St Michaels 1 **Friar Lane & Epworth** 6
Coalville Town 3 Alvechurch 0
Coleshill Town 6 Cradley Town 0
Coventry Sphinx 2 Barwell 1 *aet*
Kirby Muxloe SC 0 **Causeway United** 1
Loughborough University 0 **Studley** 2
Oadby Town 1 **Rocester** 2 *aet*
Tipton Town 2 **Westfields** 3

QUARTER-FINALS

Causeway United 2 Friar Lane & Epworth 0
Coleshill Town 3 Coalville Town 1
Coventry Sphinx 1 Rocester 0
Westfields 3 Studley 2

SEMI-FINALS

(played over two legs)

Coleshill Town 1 Westfields 3,
Westfields 1 Coleshill Town 2
Coventry Sphinx 1 Causeway United 0,
Causeway United 1 **Coventry Sphinx** 1

FINAL

(May 11th at Walsall)

Coventry Sphinx 3 Westfields 1

JOE McGORRIAN CUP

(League champions v League Cup holders)

(July 25th at Market Drayton Town)

Market Drayton Town 0 **Barwell** 4

	Alvechurch	Barwell	Biddulph Vic	Boldmere	Bridgnorth T.	Causeway	Coalville T.	Coleshill T.	Cov. Sphinx	Cradley T.	Friar Lane	Highgate U.	Kirby Mux.	L'boro. Univ	Malvern T.	Oadby Town	Rocester	Shifnal Town	Stratford T.	Studley	Tipton Town	Westfields
Alvechurch		0-7	5-1	0-0	6-1	0-2	2-1	3-3	3-0	2-0	1-0	5-1	4-6	2-3	3-1	0-2	5-0	4-3	3-2	1-0	0-0	1-3
Barwell	2-1		3-1	1-0	6-0	2-1	1-1	3-2	2-0	5-0	2-0	4-1	2-0	1-1	2-0	6-0	2-1	1-0	1-0	5-0	0-0	1-0
Biddulph Victoria	2-1	0-3		0-0	3-1	2-1	3-3	1-5	3-3	1-1	0-2	1-1	1-1	1-0	2-1	1-2	0-2	2-1	0-2	1-1	0-0	2-3
Boldmere St Michaels	0-2	1-3	0-0		1-3	0-2	2-3	2-1	1-0	2-0	3-1	5-0	3-2	2-0	3-1	3-2	0-0	5-0	2-1	2-0	0-1	2-1
Bridgnorth Town	0-4	0-4	1-2	0-3		0-0	0-1	1-2	2-0	2-1	3-2	1-3	2-2	0-0	2-2	2-2	2-1	1-1	1-2	1-2	0-1	0-2
Causeway United	1-1	0-3	0-1	1-1	2-1		0-2	0-0	0-3	3-0	4-2	1-1	1-0	3-0	4-1	1-0	1-5	5-1	0-4	1-2	0-1	0-1
Coalville Town	0-1	0-3	4-2	1-2	6-0	3-2		4-0	0-4	4-2	2-0	7-1	2-1	4-2	3-0	3-0	3-1	5-0	3-0	0-1	0-0	1-0
Coleshill Town	1-1	0-4	3-2	0-2	1-0	2-0	0-1		4-0	8-0	2-1	0-3	2-0	0-0	7-1	2-2	1-2	3-0	1-2	1-0	0-2	1-0
Coventry Sphinx	2-0	1-2	2-2	5-2	5-2	0-0	2-4	1-4		6-0	3-0	4-0	2-2	0-1	2-0	4-4	3-2	0-0	3-1	4-1	1-1	4-3
Cradley Town	0-5	0-5	1-3	0-9	0-2	0-4	1-7	0-3	1-7		0-8	0-0	0-9	0-1	2-2	1-2	2-4	2-2	1-3	2-2	1-5	2-2
Friar Lane & Epworth	2-1	0-6	2-1	1-2	0-2	0-3	2-6	n/a	3-2	6-1		5-3	2-3	2-0	3-3	0-5	0-3	4-0	2-1	3-3	1-0	3-2
Highgate United	0-0	0-3	1-1	0-4	6-0	1-1	0-1	2-1	1-3	4-0	1-4		0-1	2-0	3-3	3-1	1-2	0-0	1-2	2-0	0-1	1-2
Kirby Muxloe SC	3-1	0-2	2-0	2-2	6-1	3-0	1-2	0-0	2-2	2-2	1-0	2-3		0-4	2-1	1-2	2-0	3-3	1-1	3-1	1-1	0-2
Loughborough University	2-2	0-1	0-3	1-0	0-0	2-0	0-4	2-2	1-0	3-1	4-2	6-1	2-1		1-1	2-0	4-0	5-0	0-2	1-2	0-1	0-1
Malvern Town	2-3	2-5	3-1	2-4	1-0	1-4	4-3	2-3	1-3	5-1	1-3	3-1	1-3	0-0		1-2	0-1	1-2	0-2	2-0	1-1	2-1
Oadby Town	3-2	1-3	3-0	2-0	1-2	1-2	0-2	1-1	3-2	5-1	2-1	4-0	0-2	0-2	2-0		3-1	1-2	0-2	1-1	0-2	2-5
Rocester	2-2	0-9	0-3	5-2	2-1	0-3	0-1	1-5	0-1	8-0	4-0	2-1	1-0	2-0	2-3	2-3		0-0	0-2	1-2	2-2	1-1
Shifnal Town	0-4	0-5	0-3	2-1	3-1	1-3	0-2	0-2	0-2	3-0	3-3	0-2	1-2	0-1	1-3	3-2	2-1		1-1	1-3	0-1	1-3
Stratford Town	0-3	0-1	2-0	2-1	2-1	0-2	1-2	4-1	4-2	10-1	2-2	5-0	1-2	1-0	2-1	3-3	2-0	6-1		3-2	0-1	2-1
Studley	3-1	0-0	4-4	1-1	0-1	0-0	0-3	2-1	3-0	8-1	0-1	1-2	0-3	1-0	2-1	3-1	2-1	3-0	1-3		3-2	0-1
Tipton Town	0-0	1-1	3-0	1-3	2-1	3-1	1-2	2-1	2-0	3-1	1-1	5-1	3-2	0-0	2-1	3-0	1-1	4-0	0-1	0-1		3-0
Westfields	3-1	3-3	3-0	1-0	3-1	3-2	1-0	1-1	2-1	3-0	4-1	4-3	2-2	3-0	3-3	0-0	2-0	5-1	2-3	0-2	0-2	

ALVECHURCH

Founded: 1929 Nickname: The Church

Secretary: Stephen Denny **(T)** 07710 012 733 **(E)** alvechurch@btinternet.com
Chairman: Peter Eacock **Manager:** Simon Redhead **Prog Ed:** Alan Deakin
Ground: Lye Meadow, Redditch Road, Alvechurch B48 7RS **(T)** 0121 445 2929
Capacity: 3,000 **Seats:** 100 **Covered:** 300 **Midweek Matchday:** Tuesday **Clubhouse:** Yes **Shop:** No

Colours(change): Gold/black/black. (All blue).
Previous Names: Alvechurch FC >1992. Re-formed in 1994.
Previous Leagues: Midland Combination
Records:
Senior Honours: Since 1994: Midland Combination Premier 2002-03.
Worcestershire Senior Urn 03-04, 04-05.

10 YEAR RECORD

00-01	01-02	02-03	03-04	04-05	05-06	06-07	07-08	08-09	09-10
MCmP 7	MCmP 20	MCmP 1	MidAl 19	MidAl 15	MidAl 14	MidAl 10	MidAl 14	MidAl 10	MidAl 7

BIDDULPH VICTORIA

Founded: 1969 Nickname: The Vics

Secretary: Siobhan Perry **(T)** 07801 028 829 **(E)** siobhan_perry@hotmail.com
Chairman: Terry Greer **Manager:** Karl Wilcox & Mark Bromley **Prog Ed:** John Shenton
Ground: Tunstall Road, Biddulph, Stoke on Trent ST8 7AQ **(T)** 01782 522 737
Capacity: 1,075 **Seats:** 224 **Covered:** 224 **Midweek Matchday:** Tuesday **Clubhouse:** Yes **Shop:** No

Colours(change): Maroon & sky blue/maroon/maroon & sky. (Yellow & navy/navy/navy & yellow).
Previous Names: Knypersley Victoria > 2002.
Previous Leagues: Leek & Moorlands. Staffordshire Co. Staffs Senior. West Midlands (Reg)
Records: **Att:** 1,000 v Port Vale (friendly) 2006. **Goalscorer:** Paul James - 112. **Apps:** Terry Stanway - 682. **Win:** 10-0. **Defeat:** 0-9.
Senior Honours: None

10 YEAR RECORD

00-01	01-02	02-03	03-04	04-05	05-06	06-07	07-08	08-09	09-10
MidAl 20	MidAl 20	MidAl 13	MidAl 16	MidAl 20	MidAl 17	MidAl 21	MidAl 12	MidAl 18	MidAl 17

BOLDMERE ST. MICHAELS

Founded: 1883 Nickname: The Mikes

Secretary: Rob Paterson **(T)** 07528 177 046 **(E)** robb4paterson@btinternet.com
Chairman: Keith Fielding **Manager:** Rob Mallaband **Prog Ed:** Alan Parsons
Ground: Trevor Brown Memorial Gd, Church Rd, Boldmere B73 5RY **(T)** 0121 373 4435
Capacity: 2,500 **Seats:** 230 **Covered:** 400 **Midweek Matchday:** Tuesday **Clubhouse:** Yes **Shop:** No

Colours(change): White/black/black. (Amber/white/amber)
Previous Names: None.
Previous Leagues: West Midlands (Regional). Midland Combination.
Records:
Senior Honours: AFA Senior Cup 1947-48.
Midland Combination Premier 1985-86, 88-89, 89-90.

10 YEAR RECORD

00-01	01-02	02-03	03-04	04-05	05-06	06-07	07-08	08-09	09-10
MidAl 7	MidAl 13	MidAl 14	MidAl 15	MidAl 10	MidAl 10	MidAl 7	MidAl 4	MidAl 4	MidAl 6

BRIDGNORTH TOWN

Founded: 1946 Nickname:

Secretary: Zoe Griffiths **(T)** 07793 281 582 **(E)** zoebtfc@aol.com
Chairman: John Evans **Manager:** **Prog Ed:**
Ground: Crown Meadow, Innage Lane, Bridgnorth WV16 4HS **(T)** 07870 546 726
Capacity: **Seats:** **Covered:** **Midweek Matchday:** Tuesday **Clubhouse:** **Shop:** Yes

Colours(change): All blue. (All white).
Previous Names: None.
Previous Leagues: Worcestershire Combination/Midland Combination. Southern. West Mids.
Records:
Senior Honours: Midland Combination 1979-80, 82-83. West Midlands (Regional) 07-08.

10 YEAR RECORD

00-01	01-02	02-03	03-04	04-05	05-06	06-07	07-08	08-09	09-10
MidAl 9	MidAl 11	MidAl 16	MidAl 10	MidAl 22	MCmP 5	WMP 7	WMP 1	MidAl 12	MidAl 20

INS & OUTS

IN: Heath Hayes (P - Midland Combination Premier Division), Dunkirk (P - East Midlands Counties League), Ellesmere Rangers (P - West Midlands League Premier Division), Willenhall Town (R - Northern Premier League Division One South) OUT: Barwell (P - Northern Premier League Division One South), Cradley Town (R - West Midlands League Premier Division), Shifnal Town (R - West Midlands League Premier Division).

CAUSEWAY UNITED

Founded: 1957 Nickname:

Secretary: Frank Webb (T) 07977 599 847 (E)
Chairman: Edward Russell **Manager:** Carl Burley **Prog Ed:**
Ground: Stourbridge FC, Amblecote, Stourbridge DY8 4HN (T) 01384 394 040
Capacity: **Seats:** **Covered:** **Midweek Matchday:** Tuesday **Clubhouse:** Yes **Shop:**

Colours(change): All blue. (All white).
Previous Names: None.
Previous Leagues: West Midlands (Regional).
Records: **Att:** 150. **Apps:** Malcolm Power - 300+
Senior Honours: West Midlands (Regional) Premier 2001-02.

10 YEAR RECORD

00-01	01-02	02-03	03-04	04-05	05-06	06-07	07-08	08-09	09-10
WMP 5	WMP 1	MidAl 11	Isth P 17	MidAl 16	MidAl 19	MidAl 17	MidAl 6	MidAl 9	MidAl 12

COALVILLE TOWN

Founded: 1994 Nickname: The Ravens

Secretary: Robert Brooks (T) 07983 665 835 (E) rbrooksctfc@hotmail.co.uk
Chairman: Glyn Rennocks **Manager:** Adam Stevens **Prog Ed:**
Ground: Owen Street Sports Ground, Owen St, Coalville LE67 3DA (T) 01530 833 365
Capacity: 2,000 **Seats:** 240 **Covered:** 240 **Midweek Matchday:** Tuesday **Clubhouse:** Yes **Shop:** Yes

Colours(change): Black & white/white/white. (All maroon).
Previous Names: Ravenstoke Miners Ath. 1925-58. Ravenstoke FC 58-95. Coalville 95-98.
Previous Leagues: Coalville & Dist. Amateur. North Leicester. Leicestershire Senior.
Records: **Att:** 1,500. **Apps:** Nigel Simms.
Senior Honours: Leicestershire Senior Cup 1999-00. Leicestershire Senior 01-02, 02-03.

10 YEAR RECORD

00-01	01-02	02-03	03-04	04-05	05-06	06-07	07-08	08-09	09-10
LeicS 7	LeicS 1	LeicS 1	MidAl 8	MidAl 3	MidAl 8	MidAl 18	MidAl 8	MidAl 3	MidAl 2

COLESHILL TOWN

Founded: 1894 Nickname:

Secretary: Vicky Robinson (T) 07968 410 467 (E) vrobinson24@aol.com
Chairman: Paul Woodford **Manager:** Carl Adams **Prog Ed:** As secretary
Ground: Pack Meadow, Packington Lane, Coleshill B46 3JQ (T) 01675 463 259
Capacity: **Seats:** **Covered:** **Midweek Matchday:** Tuesday **Clubhouse:** Yes **Shop:**

Colours(change): Green/black/black (All red)
Previous Names: None.
Previous Leagues: Midland Combination.
Records:
Senior Honours: Midland Combination Div.2 1969-70. Premier 07-08.

10 YEAR RECORD

00-01	01-02	02-03	03-04	04-05	05-06	06-07	07-08	08-09	09-10
MCmP 4	MCmP 10	MCmP 14	MCmP 18	MCmP 9	MCmP 11	MCmP 4	MCmP 1	MidAl 11	MidAl 8

COVENTRY SPHINX

Founded: 1946 Nickname: Sphinx

Secretary: Jackie McGowan (T) 07843 477 799 (E) jackie.mcgowan@coventrysphinx.co.uk
Chairman: Neil Long **Manager:** Danny McSheffrey **Prog Ed:** See chairman
Ground: Sphinx Spts & Social Club, Sphinx Drive, Coventry CV3 1WA (T) 02476 451 361
Capacity: **Seats:** **Covered:** Yes **Midweek Matchday:** Tuesday **Clubhouse:** Yes **Shop:**

Colours(change): Sky blue & white stripes/navy/navy (All red).
Previous Names: Sphinx > 1995.
Previous Leagues: Midland Combination.
Records:
Senior Honours: Midland Combination Premier 2006-07.

10 YEAR RECORD

00-01	01-02	02-03	03-04	04-05	05-06	06-07	07-08	08-09	09-10
MCmP 5	MCmP 2	MCmP 7	MCmP 4	MCmP 2	MCmP 2	MCmP 1	MidAl 19	MidAl 7	MidAl 9

DUNKIRK

Founded: 1946 Nickname: The Boatmen

Secretary: Steve Throssell **(T)** 07903 322 446 **(E)** philallen7@supanet.com
Chairman: Jack Riley **Manager:** Dave Harbottle & Ian Upton **Prog Ed:** Phil Allen & Darren Miller
Ground: Ron Steel Spts Grd, Lenton Lane, Clifton Bridge, Nottingham NG7 2SA **(T)** 0115 985 0803
Capacity: 1,500 **Seats:** 150 **Covered:** 150 **Midweek Matchday:** Tuesday **Clubhouse:** Yes **Shop:**

Colours(change): Red/black/red (White/red/white)
Previous Names: None
Previous Leagues: Notts Amateur 1946-75, Notts Alliance 1975-95, Central Midlands 1995-2008, East Midlands Counties > 2010
Records:
Senior Honours: Notts Amateur League 1973-75. Central Midlands League Supreme Division 2004-05. East Midlands Counties 2009-10

10 YEAR RECORD

00-01	01-02	02-03	03-04	04-05	05-06	06-07	07-08	08-09	09-10
CM Su 10	CM Su 9	CM Su 12	CM Su 6	CM Su 1	CM Su 8	CM Su 6	CM Su 4	EMC 5	EMC 1

ELLESMERE RANGERS

Founded: 1969 Nickname:

Secretary: John Edge **(T)** 07947 864 357 **(E)** john.edge2@homecall.co.uk
Chairman: David Coles **Manager:** Matt Burton **Prog Ed:** Peter Austin
Ground: Beech Grove, Ellesmere, Shropshire SY12 0BT **(T)** 07947 864 357
Capacity: **Seats:** **Covered:** **Midweek Matchday:** Tuesday **Clubhouse:** **Shop:**

Colours(change): Sky blue/navy/sky blue (Yellow/black/yellow)
Previous Names:
Previous Leagues: West Midlands
Records:
Senior Honours: West Midlands League Premier Division 2009-10.

10 YEAR RECORD

00-01	01-02	02-03	03-04	04-05	05-06	06-07	07-08	08-09	09-10
				WM2 4	WM1	WMP 12	WMP 7	WMP 4	WMP 1

FRIAR LANE & EPWORTH

Founded: 2003 Nickname: The Lane

Secretary: Clive Gibbons **(T)** 07834 439 393 **(E)**
Chairman: Clive Gibbons **Manager:** Steve Orme **Prog Ed:**
Ground: Whittier Road, Off Knighton Lane, Aylestone Park LE2 6FT **(T)** 0116 283 3629
Capacity: **Seats:** **Covered:** **Midweek Matchday:** Tuesday **Clubhouse:** Yes **Shop:**

Colours(change): White/black/black (All royal blue)
Previous Names: Friar Lane Old Boys merged with Epworth in 2004.
Previous Leagues: Leicestershire Senior.
Records:
Senior Honours: FLOB: Leicestershire Senior Div.2 1969-70. Prem 70-71, 71-72, 73-74, 74-75, 75-76, 76-77, 77-78. Ep'th: Leics Senior Div.1 02-03. Merged: Leics Sen. Prem 05-06.

10 YEAR RECORD

00-01	01-02	02-03	03-04	04-05	05-06	06-07	07-08	08-09	09-10
LeicS 14	LeicS 2	LeicS 17	LeicS 3	LeicS 9	LeicS 1	MidAl 15	MidAl 16	MidAl 15	MidAl 15

HEATH HAYES

Founded: 1964 Nickname:

Secretary: Kathlyn Davies **(T)** 07969 203 063 **(E)** kathlyndavies@aol.com
Chairman: Paul Mallen **Manager:** Simon Davies **Prog Ed:**
Ground: Coppice Colliery Grd, Newlands Lane, Heath Hayes, Cannock, WS12 3HH **(T)** 07977 239 193
Capacity: **Seats:** **Covered:** **Midweek Matchday:** Tuesday **Clubhouse:** **Shop:**

Colours(change): Blue & white stripes/blue/white (Yellow/black/yellow)
Previous Names:
Previous Leagues: Staffordshire County, West Midlands, Midland Combination 2006-10.
Records:
Senior Honours: Staffordshire County League Division 1 1977-78. West Midlands League Division 1 North 1998-99. Midland Combination Premier Division 2009-10.

10 YEAR RECORD

00-01	01-02	02-03	03-04	04-05	05-06	06-07	07-08	08-09	09-10
WMP 15	WMP 10	WMP 12	WMP 6	WMP 6	WMP 13	MCmP 8	MCmP 10	MCmP 10	MCmP 1

HIGHGATE UNITED
Founded: 1948 Nickname: Red or Gate

Secretary: Paul Davis **(T)** 07527 941 993 **(E)** merryeric@tiscali.co.uk
Chairman: Anthony Clancy **Manager:** Mark Burge **Prog Ed:**
Ground: The Coppice, Tythe Barn Lane, Shirley Solihull B90 1PH **(T)** 0121 744 4194
Capacity: **Seats:** **Covered:** **Midweek Matchday:** Tuesday **Clubhouse:** **Shop:**

Colours(change): All red (White/black/black)
Previous Names: None.
Previous Leagues: Worcestershire/Midland Combination.
Records:
Senior Honours: Midland Combination Premier 1972-73, 73-74, 74-75.

10 YEAR RECORD

00-01	01-02	02-03	03-04	04-05	05-06	06-07	07-08	08-09	09-10
MCmP 18	MCmP 13	MCmP 9	MCmP 12	MCmP 18	MCmP 14	MCmP 3	MCmP 2	MidAl 13	MidAl 18

KIRKBY MUXLOE
Founded: 1910 Nickname:

Secretary: Philip Moloney **(T)** 07775 992 778 **(E)** pmoloney1@hotmail.com
Chairman: Les Warren **Manager:** Gaz Keenan **Prog Ed:**
Ground: Kirby Muxloe Sports Club, Ratby Lane LE9 2AQ **(T)** 0116 239 3201
Capacity: **Seats:** **Covered:** **Midweek Matchday:** Tuesday **Clubhouse:** Yes **Shop:**

Colours(change): All royal blue. (Black & white stripes/white/white)
Previous Names:
Previous Leagues: Leicester Mutual. Leicester City. Leicestershire Senior. East Midlands Co.
Records:
Senior Honours: Leicestershire Co. Cup 2006-07. Leicestershire Senior Champions 07-08.
East Midlands Counties Champions 2008-09.

10 YEAR RECORD

00-01	01-02	02-03	03-04	04-05	05-06	06-07	07-08	08-09	09-10
LeicS 13	LeicS 5	LeicS 7	LeicS 2	LeicS 4	LeicS 8	LeicS 2	LeicS 1	EMC 1	MidAl 10

LOUGHBOROUGH UNIVERSITY
Founded: 1920 Nickname:

Secretary: Margaret Folwell **(T)** 01509226127(Office Hrs) **(E)** M.Folwell@lboro.ac.uk
Chairman: Tom Curtis **Manager:** Tom Curtis **Prog Ed:**
Ground: Nanpantan Sports Ground, Nanpantan Road LE11 3YE **(T)** 01509 237 148
Capacity: **Seats:** **Covered:** **Midweek Matchday:** **Clubhouse:** **Shop:**

Colours(change): All maroon. (All pale blue).
Previous Names: None
Previous Leagues: Leicestershire Senior. Midland Combination.
Records:
Senior Honours: Midland Combination Champions 2008-09.

10 YEAR RECORD

00-01	01-02	02-03	03-04	04-05	05-06	06-07	07-08	08-09	09-10
							MCmP 4	MCmP 1	MidAl 13

MALVERN TOWN
Founded: 1947 Nickname:

Secretary: Marg Scott **(T)** 07944 110 402 **(E)** margicoldicott@ukonline.co.uk
Chairman: Richard Bond **Manager:** Martin Stephens **Prog Ed:** See Secretary
Ground: Langland Stadium, Langland Ave., Malvern WR14 2EQ **(T)** 01684 564 068
Capacity: 2,500 **Seats:** 150 **Covered:** 310 **Midweek Matchday:** Tuesday **Clubhouse:** Yes **Shop:** No

Colours(change): Sky blue/claret/claret (Claret/sky blue/sky blue)
Previous Names: None
Previous Leagues: Worcestershire/Midland Combination. West Mids. Mid. Alliance. Southern.
Records: **Att:** 1,221 v Worcester City F.A. Cup. **Goals:** Graham Buffery. **Apps:** Nick Clayton.
Senior Honours: Worcestershire Senior Urn (x7). Midland Combination Div.1 1955-56.

10 YEAR RECORD

00-01	01-02	02-03	03-04	04-05	05-06	06-07	07-08	08-09	09-10
WMP 7	WMP 9	WMP 6	WMP 1	MidAl 5	MidAl 3	SthM 17	SthM 20	SthM 22	MidAl 19

OADBY TOWN

Founded: 1937 Nickname: The Poachers

Secretary: Ken Farrant **(T)** 07986 359 646 **(E)** oadbytownfc@live.co.uk
Chairman: Vacant **Manager:** **Prog Ed:** Kelly Marie
Ground: Green King Park, Wigston Road, Oadby LE2 5QG **(T)** 07794 088 210
Capacity: 5,000 **Seats:** 224 **Covered:** 224 **Midweek Matchday:** Tuesday **Clubhouse:** Yes **Shop:** Yes

Colours(change): White/red/red (All blue)
Previous Names: Oadby Imperial > 1951.
Previous Leagues: Leicestershire Senior.
Records:
Senior Honours: Leicestershire Senior Div.2 1951-52. Prem 63-64, 67-68, 68-69, 72-73, 94-95, 96-97, 97-98, 98-99. Midland Alliance 99-00.

10 YEAR RECORD

00-01	01-02	02-03	03-04	04-05	05-06	06-07	07-08	08-09	09-10
MidAl 4	MidAl 6	MidAl 4	MidAl 6	MidAl 7	MidAl 18	MidAl 11	MidAl 17	MidAl 19	MidAl 14

ROCESTER

Founded: 1876 Nickname: Romans

Secretary: Barry Smith **(T)** 07770 762 825 **(E)** rocesterfc@btinternet.com
Chairman: Harold Brassington **Manager:** Alan Beaman **Prog Ed:** Barry Smith
Ground: Hillsfield, Mill Street, Rocester, Uttoxeter ST14 5JX **(T)** 01889 590 463
Capacity: 4,000 **Seats:** 230 **Covered:** 500 **Midweek Matchday:** Tuesday **Clubhouse:** Yes **Shop:** Yes

Colours(change): Amber & black/black/black. (All white).
Previous Names: None.
Previous Leagues: Staffs Sen. (Founder Member). W.Mids (Reg). Mid.All (FM) Southern. NPL
Records: **Apps:** Peter Swanwick 1962-82.
Senior Honours: Staffordshire Senior 1985-86, 86-87. West Mids (Regional) Div.1 87-88. Midland Alliance 98-99, 03-04.

10 YEAR RECORD

00-01	01-02	02-03	03-04	04-05	05-06	06-07	07-08	08-09	09-10
SthW 10	SthW 21	SthW 21	MidAl 1	NPL 1 22	MidAl 22	MidAl 12	MidAl 5	MidAl 20	MidAl 16

STRATFORD TOWN

Founded: 1944 Nickname: The Town

Secretary: Brian Rose **(T)** 07833 776 834 **(E)** brian_rose@nfumutual.co.uk
Chairman: Craig Hughes **Manager:** Rod Brown **Prog Ed:** Alan Hawkins
Ground: Knights Lane, Tiddington, Stratford Upon Avon CV37 7BZ **(T)** 01789 269 336
Capacity: **Seats:** Yes **Covered:** Yes **Midweek Matchday:** Tuesday **Clubhouse:** Yes **Shop:** Yes

Colours(change): All blue. (Tangerine/black/tangerine)
Previous Names: Stratford Town Amateurs 1964-70.
Previous Leagues: Worcestershire/Midland Comb. Birmingham & Dist. W.Mid (Reg). Hellenic.
Records: **Att:** 1,078 v Aston Villa, Birmingham Senior Cup, Oct. 1996.
Senior Honours: Worcestershire/Midland Combination 1956-57, 86-87. Birmingham Senior Cup 62-63. Midland Alliance Cup 02-03, 03-04.

10 YEAR RECORD

00-01	01-02	02-03	03-04	04-05	05-06	06-07	07-08	08-09	09-10
MidAl 6	MidAl 4	MidAl 3	MidAl 3	MidAl 11	MidAl 15	MidAl 4	MidAl 7	MidAl 6	MidAl 3

STUDLEY

Founded: 1971 Nickname: Bees

Secretary: Alec James **(T)** 07719 980 091 **(E)** alecjames53@msn.com
Chairman: Barry Cromwell **Manager:** Lee Adams **Prog Ed:**
Ground: The Beehive, Abbeyfields Drive, Studley B80 7BE **(T)** 01527 853 817
Capacity: 1,500 **Seats:** 200 **Covered:** Yes **Midweek Matchday:** Tuesday **Clubhouse:** Yes **Shop:** Yes

Colours(change): Sky blue/navy/navy. (White/blue/white)
Previous Names: Studley BKL > 2002.
Previous Leagues: Redditch & Sth Warwicks Sunday Combination. Midland Combination.
Records: **Att:** 810 v Leamington 2003-04. **Goalscorer:** Brian Powell. **Apps:** Lee Adams - 523.
Senior Honours: Midland Combination Div.1 1991-92. Worcestershire FA Senior Urn 00-01,01-02, 02-03.

10 YEAR RECORD

00-01	01-02	02-03	03-04	04-05	05-06	06-07	07-08	08-09	09-10
MCmP 2	MidAl 9	MidAl 7	MidAl 5	MidAl 18	MidAl 16	MidAl 20	MidAl 13	MidAl 14	MidAl 11

TIPTON TOWN

Founded: 1948 Nickname:

Secretary: Keith Birch **(T)** 07765 141 410 **(E)** birchkeith@yahoo.co.uk

Chairman: Bill Williams **Manager:** **Prog Ed:**

Ground: Tipton Sports Acad., Wednesbury Oak Rd, Tipton DY4 0BS **(T)** 0121 502 5534

Capacity: 1,000 **Seats:** 200 **Covered:** 400 **Midweek Matchday:** Wednesday **Clubhouse:** Yes **Shop:** No

Colours(change): Black & white stripes/black/red. (Orange/white/orange).
Previous Names: None.
Previous Leagues: West Midlands (Regional).
Records: **Att:** 1,100 v Wolves, 01.08.88.
Senior Honours: Wednesbury Senior Cup 1975-76, 76-77, 80-81, 95-96.
West Midlands (Regional) Div.1 83-84. Prem 04-05.

10 YEAR RECORD

00-01	01-02	02-03	03-04	04-05	05-06	06-07	07-08	08-09	09-10
WestP 23	WestP 11	WestP 3	WestP 2	WestP 1	MidAl 11	MidAl 5	MidAl 9	MidAl 5	MidAl 4

WESTFIELDS

Founded: 1966 Nickname: The Fields

Secretary: Andrew Morris **(T)** 07860 410 548 **(E)** admin@andrew-morris.co.uk

Chairman: John Morgan **Manager:** Sean Edwards **Prog Ed:**

Ground: Allpay Park, Widemarsh Common, Hereford HR4 9NP **(T)** 07860 410 548

Capacity: 2,000 **Seats:** 150 **Covered:** 150 **Midweek Matchday:** Tuesday **Clubhouse:** Yes **Shop:** Yes

Colours(change): All Maroon & sky blue/sky blue/sky blue (All white)
Previous Names: None.
Previous Leagues: Herefordshire Sunday. Worcester & Dist. West Midlands (Regional).
Records: **Att:** 518 v Rushden & Daimonds, FA Cup, 1996. **Goalscorer:** Paul Burton. **Apps:** Jon Pugh.
Senior Honours: Hereford Senior Cup 1985-86, 88-89, 91-92, 95-96, 01-02, 02-03, 04-05,
05-06, 07-08. West Midlands (Regional) Premier 2002-03.

10 YEAR RECORD

00-01	01-02	02-03	03-04	04-05	05-06	06-07	07-08	08-09	09-10
WestP 14	WestP 5	WestP 1	MidAl 13	MidAl 6	MidAl 20	MidAl 16	MidAl 11	MidAl 17	MidAl 5

WILLENHALL TOWN

Founded: 1953 Nickname: The Lockmen

Secretary: Chris Blue **(T)** 07878 320 411 **(E)** chrisrobblue@hotmail.co.uk

Chairman: Sean Coughlan **Manager:** **Prog Ed:**

Ground: Noose Lane, Willenhall, West Midlands WV13 3BB **(T)** 01902 636 586

Capacity: 5,000 **Seats:** 324 **Covered:** 500 **Midweek Matchday:** Tuesday **Clubhouse:** Yes **Shop:** Yes

Colours(change): All red (All navy blue)
Previous Names: None
Previous Leagues: Staffs Co, West Mids 1975-78, 91-94, Southern 1982-91, 2005-08, Midland All. 94-2004, N.P.L 2004-05, 08-10
Records: **Att:** 3,454 v Crewe FA Cup 1st Rnd 1981. **Goalscorer & Apps:** Gary Matthews. **Win:** 11-1 v Bridgnorth Town 2001-02.
Senior Honours: Staffs County Premier 1974-75. West Mids Division 1 1975-76, Premier 77-78.
Southern League Midland Division 1983-84.

10 YEAR RECORD

00-01	01-02	02-03	03-04	04-05	05-06	06-07	07-08	08-09	09-10
MidAl 8	MidAl 12	MidAl 6	MidAl 2	NP 1 4	SthW 9	SthM 4	SthM 14	NP1S 16	NP1S 22

NORTH WEST COUNTIES LEAGUE

www.nwcfl.co.uk

Sponsored by:

Vodkat

Founded: 1982

Recent champions:

2005: Fleetwood Town

2006: Cammell Laird

2007: FC United of Manchester

2008: Trafford

2009: AFC Fylde

Premier Division	P	W	D	L	F	A	Pts
Newcastle Town	42	37	3	2	121	21	114
New Mills	42	27	9	6	108	38	90
Bootle	42	26	7	9	92	41	85
Ramsbottom United	42	24	9	9	92	69	81
Congleton Town	42	24	8	10	90	46	80
Maine Road	42	21	7	14	82	59	70
Glossop North End	42	19	12	11	74	49	69
Colne	42	19	10	13	70	65	67
St Helens Town	42	20	6	16	74	75	66
Padiham	42	18	6	18	71	71	60
Runcorn Linnets	42	17	6	19	75	78	57
Bacup Borough	42	15	12	15	63	75	57
Squires Gate	42	15	8	19	61	74	53
Silsden	42	13	7	22	53	75	46
Formby	42	14	3	25	57	81	45
Flixton	42	12	8	22	54	85	44
Nelson	42	12	8	22	47	87	44
Alsager Town	42	11	7	24	60	79	40
Winsford United	42	11	7	24	53	79	40
Atherton LR	42	10	7	25	53	96	37
Ashton Athletic	42	8	8	26	51	101	32
Abbey Hey	42	7	6	29	49	106	27

Reserve Division One		P	W	D	L	F	A	Pt
Bootle Res.		26	20	2	4	79	21	62
Glossop North End Res.		26	19	3	4	74	41	60
Padiham Res.		26	17	4	5	74	32	55
Ashton Town Res.		26	15	5	6	59	38	50
Ashton Athletic Res.		26	16	1	9	64	35	49
Irlam Res.	*-3*	26	13	4	9	49	37	40
AFC Liverpool Res.		26	10	5	11	47	45	35
Cheadle Town Res.		26	10	4	12	54	66	34
Barnoldswick Town Res.		26	9	5	12	45	54	32
Daisy Hill Res.		26	8	5	13	38	60	29
Wigan Robin Park Res.		26	5	6	15	34	73	21
Colne Res.		26	5	5	16	46	72	20
Chadderton Res.	*-1*	26	5	5	16	30	71	19
Atherton LR Res.		26	1	4	21	23	71	7

RESERVES CUP

FINAL *(May 10th at Glossop North End)*

Glossop North End Res. 3 Padiham Res. 1

	Abbey Hey	Alsager T.	Ashton Ath.	Atherton LR	Bacup Boro.	Bootle	Colne	Congleton	Flixton	Formby	Glossop NE	Maine Road	Nelson	New Mills	Newc. Town	Padiham	R'bottom	Runcorn L.	Silsden	Squires G.	St Helens T.	Winsford U.
Abbey Hey		1-0	0-2	1-4	1-1	2-2	1-1	1-5	3-0	1-2	0-1	0-2	1-1	1-7	0-5	1-1	0-2	1-2	3-1	0-1	1-5	1-4
Alsager Town	3-2		2-3	2-0	2-1	0-2	3-1	1-2	3-1	2-0	1-3	2-2	3-0	0-5	0-2	0-2	1-2	2-2	3-2	4-1	1-3	1-2
Ashton Athletic	2-3	0-0		2-1	4-4	0-0	2-1	0-1	2-3	4-3	1-1	0-2	1-1	1-2	1-4	3-4	1-5	0-3	1-2	1-1	4-5	2-3
Atherton LR	3-2	1-8	1-0	***P***	1-1	0-3	0-2	0-2	2-1	0-1	4-1	1-2	2-0	0-6	1-3	1-1	0-4	3-3	1-2	1-1	0-1	0-2
Bacup Borough	2-1	3-2	1-0	1-1	***R***	1-0	2-2	3-6	0-0	3-2	0-0	0-4	2-3	1-1	4-1	2-0	0-3	2-1	0-2	3-1	2-1	2-2
Bootle	5-4	4-0	7-2	3-1	5-1	***E***	0-0	1-0	0-0	4-1	2-0	1-0	5-0	0-2	0-1	3-1	3-6	3-0	2-0	4-0	3-0	3-0
Colne	2-1	2-0	2-0	4-0	2-4	0-2	***M***	1-1	2-1	2-1	1-1	2-4	0-1	0-0	1-2	2-0	1-1	0-3	5-1	3-1	1-2	3-1
Congleton Town	2-0	1-0	6-0	2-2	2-0	2-4	4-1	***I***	1-2	2-2	1-0	5-3	3-0	2-2	2-1	0-1	2-0	3-3	2-0	1-1	2-0	3-0
Flixton	1-4	2-2	5-0	2-1	4-1	0-1	0-1	0-4	***E***	1-5	1-2	0-1	3-2	0-3	0-1	0-2	3-3	1-3	0-0	0-2	0-2	2-2
Formby	1-1	3-0	1-0	1-0	3-0	1-0	2-4	2-6	2-3	***R***	1-1	1-2	1-2	0-1	0-3	1-3	0-2	1-0	3-2	0-1	0-4	5-1
Glossop North End	3-1	1-0	1-1	4-0	0-0	1-0	3-0	0-1	5-0	2-0		4-1	3-1	1-2	0-2	2-2	3-2	1-1	3-1	1-3	5-2	2-2
Maine Road	7-0	2-2	0-1	2-0	0-2	2-2	1-2	1-3	2-1	4-2	2-1	***D***	1-1	2-0	0-2	3-1	2-3	4-2	0-1	0-1	5-0	2-1
Nelson	4-0	2-1	0-2	4-3	2-2	1-3	0-3	0-0	0-1	2-1	2-0	0-3	***I***	0-5	0-2	1-1	0-2	0-2	3-1	2-2	1-2	2-1
New Mills	3-1	4-0	3-1	5-1	2-0	3-2	1-1	3-0	3-3	4-0	0-1	2-2	3-0	***V***	1-1	3-4	5-1	3-5	4-0	0-0	2-1	4-1
Newcastle Town	1-0	4-1	6-0	3-0	3-1	4-1	1-1	2-0	6-0	6-0	1-1	2-1	6-0	2-0	***I***	2-0	5-0	3-0	2-0	5-0	3-0	3-2
Padiham	2-3	3-2	3-0	5-3	2-0	0-2	2-3	1-0	4-1	1-2	0-2	1-0	3-0	2-1	0-2	***S***	1-3	4-1	2-1	1-1	2-4	1-3
Ramsbottom United	1-0	1-2	2-2	3-2	3-1	0-3	0-2	3-3	3-2	0-2	2-2	2-2	3-1	0-0	0-4	4-3	***I***	4-0	3-2	2-2	3-1	1-0
Runcorn Linnets	3-0	2-1	3-0	1-2	2-3	3-1	3-1	2-1	0-2	1-0	3-1	1-2	2-2	0-4	2-3	2-1	2-3	***O***	1-1	5-1	1-2	0-3
Silsden	3-1	2-1	2-0	0-2	0-1	1-1	2-2	1-0	2-3	2-0	1-1	1-3	3-2	0-2	0-2	2-2	1-4	1-2	***N***	1-1	2-3	2-1
Squires Gate	6-0	1-0	2-3	2-3	1-6	1-2	8-1	0-3	1-2	2-1	2-1	3-0	1-2	1-2	0-6	1-0	0-1	1-0	1-2		1-2	1-0
St Helens Town	2-0	1-1	2-0	2-2	3-0	0-0	1-2	2-1	1-2	1-0	1-5	2-2	4-0	0-4	1-3	1-2	3-3	6-3	1-0	0-4		0-0
Winsford United	1-5	1-1	3-2	1-3	0-0	0-3	2-3	0-3	1-1	1-3	1-4	1-2	0-2	0-1	0-1	3-0	0-2	1-0	1-3	3-0	2-0	

Division One		P	W	D	L	F	A	Pts
Stone Dominoes		32	21	6	5	81	37	69
Barnoldswick Town		32	20	7	5	66	27	67
Norton United		32	16	6	10	51	41	54
Chadderton		32	14	8	10	54	46	50
AFC Liverpool		32	15	4	13	60	43	49
Atherton Collieries		32	15	4	13	63	66	49
Holker Old Boys		32	13	8	11	50	50	47
Leek CSOB		32	13	7	12	50	48	46
Eccleshall		32	13	7	12	43	45	46
Irlam		32	12	7	13	52	45	43
Daisy Hill		32	12	7	13	55	60	43
Wigan Robin Park		32	12	5	15	54	60	41
Ashton Town		32	11	7	14	62	73	40
Cheadle Town	*-3*	32	9	9	14	46	57	33
AFC Blackpool		32	9	5	18	50	64	32
Oldham Boro		32	7	8	17	37	57	29
Rochdale Town		32	5	5	22	36	91	20

DIVISION ONE TROPHY

FIRST ROUND

Atherton Collieries 0 **Norton United** 4

SECOND ROUND

AFC Liverpool 3 Holker Old Boys 1 *(at Holker OB)*

Daisy Hill 0 **AFC Blackpool** 5

Eccleshall 1 **Barnoldswick Town** 2

Leek CSOB 0 **Wigan Robin Pk** 2 *(at Wigan RP)*

Norton United 1 **Irlam** 2

Oldham Boro 2 **Cheadle Town** 3

Rochdale Town 0 **Chadderton** 1

Stone Dominoes 3 Ashton Town 1

QUARTER-FINALS

AFC Blackpool 1 Chadderton 0

Irlam 2 **Cheadle Town** 3 *aet*

Stone Dominoes 2 Barnoldswick Town 0

Wigan Robin Park 0 **AFC Liverpool** 4

SEMI-FINALS

AFC Liverpool 3 AFC Blackpool 1

Cheadle Town 2 Stone Dominoes 1

FINAL

(April 27th at Flixton)

AFC Liverpool 2 Cheadle Town 1

CHALLENGE CUP

FIRST ROUND

Ashton Town 1 Barnoldswick Town 0

Atherton Collieries 1 **AFC Blackpool** 2

Chadderton 2 AFC Liverpool 2 *aet*

Replay: **AFC Liverpool** 5 Chadderton 1

Eccleshall 1 **Norton United** 3 *aet*

Holker Old Boys 5 Oldham Boro 1

Leek CSOB 0 **Daisy Hill** 2

Stone Dominoes 1 **Wigan Robin Park** 3

SECOND ROUND

Abbey Hey 2 Rochdale Town 0

AFC Liverpool 3 Alsager Town 2 *aet*

Ashton Athletic 5 Nelson 1

Ashton Town 1 **Wigan Robin Park** 2

Bacup Borough 2 AFC Blackpool 0

Bootle 3 Squires Gate 0

Colne 0 **St Helens Town** 1

Daisy Hill 1 Atherton LR 1 *aet*

Replay: Atherton LR 5 **Daisy Hill** 2

(Atherton LR expelled)

Formby 1 **Newcastle Town** 3 *aet*

Glossop North End 1 Silsden 0

Holker Old Boys 1 **New Mills** 2

Irlam 4 Padiham 3

Norton United 4 Flixton 3 *aet*

Ramsbottom United 4 Congleton Town 3

Runcorn Linnets 4 Cheadle Town 1 *(at Cheadle Town)*

Winsford United 3 Maine Road 2

THIRD ROUND

Abbey Hey 1 Ashton Athletic 0

Daisy Hill 1 **New Mills** 4

Glossop North End 0 AFC Liverpool 0

Replay: AFC Liverpool 0 **Glossop North End** 2

Irlam 0 **Bootle** 3

Norton United 2 **St Helens Town** 5

Ramsbottom United 1 **Newcastle Town** 3

Wigan Robin Park 3 Runcorn Linnets 2

Winsford United 2 Bacup Borough 0

QUARTER-FINALS

Abbey Hey 0 New Mills 3 *(New Mills expelled)*

Bootle 3 Newcastle Town 2

St Helens Town 4 Wigan Robin Park 2 *(at Wigan RP)*

Winsford United 5 Glossop North End 2

SEMI-FINALS

Abbey Hey 1 Bootle 0, **Winsford United** 1 St Helens 0

FINAL

(May 6th at Curzon Ashton)

Abbey Hey 3 Winsford United 0

	AFC Bpl	AFC Liv.	Ashton T	Ath. Colls	Barn'wick	Chad'ton	Cheadle	Daisy H.	Ecc'shall	Holker	Irlam	Leek CS	Norton U.	Oldham	R'dale T.	Stone D	Wigan RP
AFC Blackpool		1-1	2-0	1-3	3-4	1-4	4-0	0-3	1-2	0-2	1-0	2-3	1-1	2-1	3-0	2-4	1-1
AFC Liverpool	3-1		4-0	2-5	2-0	0-1	3-2	1-3	0-2	2-3	1-2	0-1	2-0	2-0	0-1	1-4	0-1
Ashton Town	2-2	2-0	***D***	5-5	2-2	2-1	1-1	2-5	1-0	2-3	2-3	3-2	3-2	4-1	3-0	1-6	2-3
Atherton Collieries	0-2	3-2	1-1	***I***	2-5	1-3	4-1	0-1	2-0	1-2	0-1	2-0	2-1	0-1	2-1	1-0	2-1
Barnoldswick Town	7-1	2-1	4-3	2-0	***V***	0-1	2-1	2-0	0-0	3-0	1-1	2-0	0-0	4-0	6-0	0-0	2-0
Chadderton	2-0	1-1	0-2	1-1	1-2	***I***	2-2	0-0	1-2	2-3	0-0	0-1	1-1	3-1	4-1	2-1	2-1
Cheadle Town	0-3	0-3	3-2	2-3	1-1	2-4	***S***	3-0	1-0	2-2	1-3	3-0	1-1	0-1	2-1	2-2	4-1
Daisy Hill	2-1	0-3	1-3	4-2	1-0	1-1	3-2	***I***	2-2	0-0	3-0	2-3	1-1	2-1	2-2	2-3	1-2
Eccleshall	1-0	2-3	2-1	2-2	0-1	2-3	3-0	3-0	***O***	2-2	1-0	1-1	0-2	2-2	2-1	1-2	2-0
Holker Old Boys	0-3	1-6	3-0	0-2	2-1	1-2	0-0	2-1	6-0	***N***	1-1	1-1	0-1	2-1	0-0	0-2	1-1
Irlam	2-1	3-3	1-1	6-1	0-1	0-3	2-3	1-2	3-0	1-3		0-1	0-1	3-1	4-1	3-3	2-0
Leek CSOB	2-2	1-2	8-1	3-4	2-1	1-3	0-0	6-3	0-1	1-3	1-1		1-3	2-2	2-1	2-0	0-0
Norton United	1-0	0-4	1-0	2-1	1-2	4-2	4-1	3-2	2-0	2-1	2-1	0-1	***O***	2-1	3-1	0-1	1-4
Oldham Boro	2-1	0-0	1-1	2-1	0-2	2-2	0-1	1-3	2-2	3-0	1-3	1-2	3-1	***N***	1-1	2-2	1-3
Rochdale Town	2-3	0-5	0-6	2-4	1-3	2-1	0-0	3-2	1-3	3-5	0-3	2-0	0-6	0-2	***E***	3-5	1-0
Stone Dominoes	5-2	0-1	4-0	7-2	1-1	5-1	2-1	5-1	1-0	2-1	2-0	0-1	3-1	1-0	2-2		2-0
Wigan Robin Park	4-3	1-2	2-4	3-4	0-3	3-0	0-4	2-2	2-3	2-0	3-2	2-1	1-1	3-0	7-3	1-4	

ALSAGER TOWN

Founded: 1968 Nickname: The Bullets

Secretary: Kenneth Stevenson **(T)** 01270 882 336 **(E)**
Chairman: (Vice) Mike Cross **Manager:** Neil Gill **Prog Ed:** Karen Armstrong
Ground: Town Ground, Woodland Court, Alsager ST7 2DP **(T)** 01270 882 336
Capacity: 3,000 **Seats:** 250 **Covered:** 1,000 **Midweek Matchday:** Tuesday **Clubhouse:** Yes **Shop:** Yes

Colours(change): Black & white/black/black. (All red).
Previous Names: Alsager FC (Merger of Alsager Institute & Alsager Utd) in 1965.
Previous Leagues: Crewe. Mid Cheshire. Northern Premier.
Records: Att: 450 v Crewe Alexandra, friendly, 2004. **Goalscorer:** Gareth Rowe. **Apps:** Wayne Brotherton.
Senior Honours: Leek Cup 2002

10 YEAR RECORD

00-01	01-02	02-03	03-04	04-05	05-06	06-07	07-08	08-09	09-10
NWC2 7	NWC2 2	NWC1 11	NWC1 9	NWC1 7	NWC1 3	NP1S 16	NP1S 14	NWCP 7	NWCP 18

ASHTON ATHLETIC

Founded: 1968 Nickname:

Secretary: Alan Greenhalgh **(T)** 01942 716 360 **(E)**
Chairman: Steve Halliwell **Manager:** Chris Brookes **Prog Ed:** Steve Halliwell
Ground: Brockstedes Park, Downall Green, Ashton in Markerfield WN4 0NR **(T)** 01942 716 360
Capacity: 600 **Seats:** 100 **Covered:** 300 **Midweek Matchday:** Tuesday **Clubhouse:** Yes **Shop:** No

Colours(change): All yellow. (Sky Blue/navy/sky blue).
Previous Names: None.
Previous Leagues: Lancashire Combination, Manchester Amateur League
Records: Att: 165 v Runcorn Linnets 2006-07. **Apps:** Steve Rothwell - 50+
Senior Honours: Atherton Charity Cup 2006-07, 07-08, 08-09.

10 YEAR RECORD

00-01	01-02	02-03	03-04	04-05	05-06	06-07	07-08	08-09	09-10
Manc 12	Manc 5	Manc 5	Manc 10	Manc 10	Manc 4	NWC2 16	NWC2 3	NWCP 6	NWCP 21

ATHERTON L.R.

Founded: 1956 Nickname: The Panthers

Secretary: Kylie Wilcock **(T)** 01942 883 950 **(E)**
Chairman: (Acting) Jane Wilcock **Manager:** Dave Hughes **Prog Ed:** Jeff Gorse
Ground: Crilly Park, Spa Road, Atherton, Manchester M46 9XG **(T)** 01942 883 950
Capacity: 3,000 **Seats:** 250 **Covered:** Yes **Midweek Matchday:** Tuesday **Clubhouse:** Yes **Shop:** No

Colours(change): Yellow & blue/royal blue/yellow. (Sky blue/black/black).
Previous Names: Laburnum Rovers
Previous Leagues: Bolton Comb, Cheshire County 80-82, NWCL 82-94 and NPL 94-97
Records: Att: 2,300 v Aldershot Town F.A. Vase Q-Final replay 93-94. **Goalscorer:** Shaun Parker **App:** Jim Evans
Senior Honours: NWCo Champions 1992-93, 93-94. Champs Trophy 1992-93, 93-94.

10 YEAR RECORD

00-01	01-02	02-03	03-04	04-05	05-06	06-07	07-08	08-09	09-10
NWC2 2	NWC1 20	NWC1 14	NWC1 12	NWC1 15	NWC1 20	NWC1 16	NWC1 19	NWCP 12	NWCP 20

BACUP BOROUGH

Founded: 1878 Nickname: The Boro

Secretary: Brent Peters **(T)** 0780 559 3791 **(E)**
Chairman: Paul Fitton **Manager:** Brent Peters **Prog Ed:** TBC
Ground: Brian Boys Stadium, Cowtoot Lane, Blackthorn, Bacup, OL13 8EE **(T)** 01706 878 655
Capacity: 3,000 **Seats:** 500 **Covered:** 1,000 **Midweek Matchday:** Wednesday **Clubhouse:** Yes **Shop:** No

Colours(change): White/black/black. (Tangerine/claret/tangerine).
Previous Names: Bacup FC
Previous Leagues: Lancashire Combination 1903-82
Records: Att: 4,980 v Nelson 1947 **Goalscorer: Jimmy Clarke**
Senior Honours: North West Counties Division Two 2002-03, Challenge Cup 2003-04.

10 YEAR RECORD

00-01	01-02	02-03	03-04	04-05	05-06	06-07	07-08	08-09	09-10
NWC2 14	NWC2 12	NWC2 1	NWC1 14	NWC1 9	NWC1 17	NWC1 15	NWC1 18	NWCP 8	NWCP 12

PREMIER INS & OUTS
IN: Barnoldswick Town (P), Rossendale United (R - Northern Premier League Division One North), Stone Dominoes (P)
OUT: Abbey Hey (R), Nelson (F), Newcastle Town (P - Northern Premier League Division One South)

BARNOLDSWICK TOWN
Founded: 1972 Nickname:

Secretary: Lynn James **(T)** **(E)**
Chairman: Alverley Ashworth **Manager:** B. Hall, S. Airdrie & K. Richardson **Prog Ed:** Peter Naylor
Ground: Silentnight Stadium, West Close Road, Barnoldswick, Colne, BB18 5EW **(T)** 01282 815817
Capacity: **Seats:** **Covered:** **Midweek Matchday:** Tuesday **Clubhouse:** Yes **Shop:**

Colours(change): Yellow & Royal Blue/Royal Blue/Yellow Socks (All red)
Previous Names: Today's club formed after the merger of Barnoldswick United and Barnoldswick Park Rovers in 2003
Previous Leagues: Craven, East Lancashire, West Lancashire.
Records:
Senior Honours: West Lancashire Division 1 1998-99

10 YEAR RECORD

00-01	01-02	02-03	03-04	04-05	05-06	06-07	07-08	08-09	09-10
WLaP 11	WLaP 6	WLaP 9	WLaP 12	WLaP 15	WLaP 15	WLaP 13	WLaP 10	WLaP 6	NWC1 2

BOOTLE
Founded: 1954 Nickname:

Secretary: Joe Doran **(T)** 0151 531 0665 **(E)**
Chairman: Frank Doran **Manager:** Chris O'Bien **Prog Ed:** Ian Porter
Ground: Delta Taxi Stadium, Vestey Rd, Off Bridle Road, Bootle L30 4UN **(T)** 0151 525 4796 or 07852 742790
Capacity: **Seats:** **Covered:** **Midweek Matchday:** Tuesday **Clubhouse:** Yes **Shop:**

Colours(change): All Royal blue. (Yellow/black/black).
Previous Names: Langton Dock 1953 - 1973.
Previous Leagues: Liverpool Shipping. Lancs Comb. Cheshire. Liverpool County Comb.
Records: **Att:** 750 v Casharlton Athletic, FA Trophy 1981.
Senior Honours: Liverpool County Champions 1964-65, 65-66, 67-68, 68-69, 69-70, 70-71, 71-72, 72-73, 73-74. North West Counties Div.1 Champions 2008-09

10 YEAR RECORD

00-01	01-02	02-03	03-04	04-05	05-06	06-07	07-08	08-09	09-10
NWC2 16	NWC2 6	Liv 5	Liv 17	Liv 12	Liv 3	NWC2 10	NWC2 6	NWC1 1	NWCP 3

COLNE
Founded: 1996 Nickname:

Secretary: Edward Lambert **(T)** 01282 862 545 **(E)**
Chairman: David Blacklock **Manager:** Nigel Coates **Prog Ed:** Ray Davies
Ground: The XLCR Stadium, Harrison Drive, Colne, Lancashire. BB8 9SL **(T)** 01282 862 545
Capacity: 1,800 **Seats:** 160 **Covered:** 1,000 **Midweek Matchday:** Wednesday **Clubhouse:** Yes **Shop:** Yes

Colours(change): All Red. (Sky Blue/Navy/Navy).
Previous Names: None
Previous Leagues: None
Records: **Att:** 1,742 v AFC Sudbury F.A. Vase SF 2004 **Goalscorer:** Geoff Payton **App:** Richard Walton
Senior Honours: BEP Cup Winners 96-97 N.W. Co Div 2 Champions 2003-04

10 YEAR RECORD

00-01	01-02	02-03	03-04	04-05	05-06	06-07	07-08	08-09	09-10
NWC2 19	NWC2 14	NWC2 10	NWC2 1	NWC1 10	NWC1 9	NWC1 11	NWC1 5	NWCP 18	NWCP 8

CONGLETON TOWN
Founded: 1901 Nickname: Bears

Secretary: Ken Mead **(T)** 01260 278 152 **(E)**
Chairman: Peter Evans **Manager:** Anthony Buckle & Darren Twigg **Prog Ed:** Ken Mead
Ground: Booth Street, Crescent Road, Congleton, Cheshire CW12 4DG **(T)** 01260 274 460
Capacity: 5,000 **Seats:** 250 **Covered:** 1,200 **Midweek Matchday:** Tuesday **Clubhouse:** Yes **Shop:** Yes

Colours(change): Black & white stripes/black/black. (All yellow).
Previous Names: Congleton Hornets
Previous Leagues: Crew & District, North Staffs, Macclesfield, Cheshire , Mid Cheshire, NW Co, NPL
Records: **Att:** 6,800 v Macclesfield, Cheshire Lge1953-54 **Goalscorer:** Mick Bidde 150+ **App:** Ray Clack 600+ Graham Harrison 600+
Senior Honours: Cheshire Senior Cup 1920-21, 37-38.

10 YEAR RECORD

00-01	01-02	02-03	03-04	04-05	05-06	06-07	07-08	08-09	09-10
NP 1 22	NWC1 16	NWC1 8	NWC1 11	NWC1 19	NWC1 12	NWC1 10	NWC1 9	NWCP 4	NWCP 5

FLIXTON

Founded: 1960 Nickname: Valiants

Secretary: Fintan Doran **(T)** 0161 748 2903 **(E)**

Chairman: Lenny Wood **Manager:** Lloyd Morrison **Prog Ed:** TBC

Ground: Valley Road, Flixton, Manchester M41 8RQ **(T)** 0161 748 2903

Capacity: 2,000 **Seats:** 250 **Covered:** 650 **Midweek Matchday:** Wednesday **Clubhouse:** Yes **Shop:** No

Colours(change): Blue & white Stripes, blue/blue. (All Red).
Previous Names:
Previous Leagues: S. Manc & Wythenshawe 60-63, Lancs & Che 63-73, Manc73-86, NWC 86-96, NPL 97-00
Records: **Att:** 2,050 v FC Utd of Manchester NWC Div.2, 26.12.05.
Senior Honours: NWC Div 2 Champions 1994-95. Div 1 1995-96.

10 YEAR RECORD

00-01	01-02	02-03	03-04	04-05	05-06	06-07	07-08	08-09	09-10
NWC1 20	NWC1 21	NWC1 21	NWC2 5	NWC2 18	NWC2 2	NWC1 13	NWC1 8	NWCP 20	NWCP 16

FORMBY

Founded: 1919 Nickname: Squirrels

Secretary: Leslie Pierce **(T)** 01704 833 615 **(E)**

Chairman: Dave Webster **Manager:** Tony Martin **Prog Ed:** See secretary

Ground: Altcar Road, Formby, Merseyside L37 4EL **(T)** 01704 833 615

Capacity: 2,000 **Seats:** 220 **Covered:** 500 **Midweek Matchday:** Tuesday **Clubhouse:** No **Shop:** Yes

Colours(change): Navy & yellow/navy & yellow/navy. (Green & white/green & white/green)
Previous Names:
Previous Leagues: Liverpool Co. Comb, 1919-68, Lancs Comb. 68-71, Cheshire Co. 71-82
Records: **Att:** 603 v Southport Liverpool Senior Cup 2003-04
Senior Honours: Lancs Co. Am. Cup 1934-35

10 YEAR RECORD

00-01	01-02	02-03	03-04	04-05	05-06	06-07	07-08	08-09	09-10
NWC2 12	NWC2 5	Liv 9	NWC2 3	NWC1 20	NWC1 22	NWC1 21	NWC1 13	NWCP 15	NWCP 15

GLOSSOP NORTH END

Founded: 1886 Nickname: Hillmen

Secretary: Peter Hammond **(T)** 01457 863852 **(E)**

Chairman: David Atkinson **Manager:** Steve Young **Prog Ed:** Neil Rimmer

Ground: Surrey Street, Glossop, Derbys SK13 7AJ **(T)** 01457 855 469

Capacity: 2,374 **Seats:** 209 **Covered:** 509 **Midweek Matchday:** Wednesday **Clubhouse:** Yes **Shop:** Yes

Colours(change): All Royal Blue. (All white).
Previous Names: Glossop North End1886-1896 and Glossop FC 1898-1992
Previous Leagues: The Football League. Cheshire County. Manchester. Lancashire Comb.
Records: **Att:** 10,736 v Preston North End F.A. Cup 1913-1914
Senior Honours: Manchester Champions 1927-28. Derbyshire Senior Cup 2000-01

10 YEAR RECORD

00-01	01-02	02-03	03-04	04-05	05-06	06-07	07-08	08-09	09-10
NWC1 18	NWC1 19	NWC1 20	NWC1 18	NWC1 13	NWC1 16	NWC1 9	NWC1 7	NWCP 5	NWCP 7

MAINE ROAD

Founded: 1955 Nickname: Blues

Secretary: Derek Barber **(T)** 0161 431 8243 **(E)**

Chairman: Ron Meredith **Manager:** Ian Walker **Prog Ed:** Derek Barber

Ground: Brantingham Road, Chorlton-cum-Hardy M21 0TT **(T)** 0161 861 0344

Capacity: 2,000 **Seats:** 200 **Covered:** 700 **Midweek Matchday:** Tuesday **Clubhouse:** Yes **Shop:** No

Colours(change): All sky blue. (Yellow/green/green).
Previous Names:
Previous Leagues: Rusholme Sunday 55-66, Manchester Amateur Sunday 66-72 & Manchester 72-87
Records: **Att:** 3,125 v FC United Manchester, NWC Div.1, 04.11.06, at Stalybridge Celtic.
Senior Honours: Manchester County Champions 1982-83, 83-84, 84-85, 85-86.
NWC Div.2 Champions 1989-90. NWC Challenge Cup 2007-08.

10 YEAR RECORD

00-01	01-02	02-03	03-04	04-05	05-06	06-07	07-08	08-09	09-10
NWC1 15	NWC1 22	NWC2 3	NWC2 2	NWC1 8	NWC1 10	NWC1 6	NWC1 4	NWCP 13	NWCP 6

NEW MILLS

Founded: pre1890 Nickname: The Millers

Secretary: Sue Hyde **(T)** 01663 747 435 **(E)**

Chairman: Ray Coverley **Manager:** Ally Pickering **Prog Ed:** Glyn Jones

Ground: Church Lane, New Mills, SK22 4NP **(T)** 01663 747 435

Capacity: 1,650 **Seats:** 120 **Covered:** 400 **Midweek Matchday:** Monday **Clubhouse:** Yes **Shop:**

Colours(change): Amber & black/amber & black/black. (All sky & navy).
Previous Names: New Mills St Georges until 1919
Previous Leagues: Manchester, North West Counties, Cheshire
Records: Att: 4,500 v Hyde United, September 1921
Senior Honours: Manchester Lge Premier Division 1924, 26, 56, 63, 65, 66, 67, 68, 70, 71
North West Counties Division Two 2007-08. Challenge Cup 2008-09.

10 YEAR RECORD

00-01	01-02	02-03	03-04	04-05	05-06	06-07	07-08	08-09	09-10
Manc1 2	MancP 5	MancP 10	MancP 14	NWC2 9	NWC2 12	NWC2	NWC2 1	NWCP 2	NWCP 2

PADIHAM

Founded: 1878 Nickname: Caldersiders

Secretary: Alan Smith **(T)** 0777 571 7698 **(E)**

Chairman: Frank Heys **Manager:** Craig Chadwick **Prog Ed:** Alan Smith

Ground: Arbories Memories Sports Ground, Well Street, Padiham BB12 8LE **(T)** 01282 773 742

Capacity: 1,688 **Seats:** 159 **Covered:** Yes **Midweek Matchday:** Wednesday **Clubhouse:** Yes **Shop:**

Colours(change): Blue/white/blue. (Red/white/black).
Previous Names: None
Previous Leagues: Lancs Comb. NWC. W.Lancs,.NE Lancs. NE Lancs Comb. E.Lancs Am.
Records: Att: 9,000 v Burnley, Dec.1884 (at Calderside Ground).
Senior Honours: West Lancashire League 1999-00.

10 YEAR RECORD

00-01	01-02	02-03	03-04	04-05	05-06	06-07	07-08	08-09	09-10
NWC2 8	NWC2 13	NWC2 4	NWC2 12	NWC2 4	NWC2 5	NWC2 3	NWC2 12	NWC1 2	NWCP 10

RAMSBOTTOM UNITED

Founded: 1966 Nickname: The Rams

Secretary: Malcolm Holt **(T)** 01204 883085 **(E)**

Chairman: Harry Williams **Manager:** A. Johnson & B. Morley **Prog Ed:** Richard Isaacs

Ground: Riverside Ground, Acre Bottom, Ramsbottom BL0 0BS. **(T)**

Capacity: **Seats:** Yes **Covered:** Yes **Midweek Matchday:** Tuesday **Clubhouse:** Yes **Shop:** No

Colours(change): All blue. (Red/black/red)
Previous Names:
Previous Leagues: Bury Amateur, Bolton Combination & Manchester League
Records: Att:1,653 v FC United of Manchester 07.04.2007. **Goalscorer:** Russell Brierley - 176 (1996-2003).
Senior Honours: North West Counties Division Two 1996-97

10 YEAR RECORD

00-01	01-02	02-03	03-04	04-05	05-06	06-07	07-08	08-09	09-10
NWC1 3	NWC1 12	NWC1 15	NWC1 17	NWC1 5	NWC1 18	NWC1 8	NWC1 16	NWCP 14	NWCP 4

ROSSENDALE UNITED

Founded: 1898 Nickname: The Stags

Secretary: Wendy Ennis **(T)** 07804 362 171 **(E)**

Chairman: Steve Hobson **Manager:** John Hughes **Prog Ed:** Dave Rogan

Ground: Dark Lane, Newchurch, Rossendale, Lancashire BB4 7UA **(T)** 01706 215119

Capacity: 2,500 **Seats:** 500 **Covered:** Yes **Midweek Matchday:** Tuesday **Clubhouse:** Yes **Shop:** Yes

Colours(change): Blue & white stripes/blue/blue (Amber & black/black/amber)
Previous Names:
Previous Leagues: N.E.Lancs. C., Lancs C. 1898-99, 01-70, Cen Lancs 1899-1901, Ches'Co 70-82, N.W.C. 82-89, 93-2001, NPL 01-10
Records: Att: 12,000 v Bolton Wanderers FA Cup 2nd Round 1971. **Goalscorer:** Bob Scott 230. **Apps:** Johnny Clark 770 1947-65.
Senior Honours: North West Counties League Division 1 1988-89, 2000-01.

10 YEAR RECORD

00-01	01-02	02-03	03-04	04-05	05-06	06-07	07-08	08-09	09-10
NWC1 1	NP 1 9	NP 1 18	NP 1 15	NP 1 21	NP 1 15	NP 1 9	NP1N 9	NP1N 21	NP1N 22

RUNCORN LINNETS

Founded: 2006 Nickname: Linnets

Secretary: Lynn Johnston **(T)** 01606 43008 **(E)**
Chairman: Derek Greenwood **Manager:** Steve Wilkes **Prog Ed:** Mark Buckley
Ground: Millbank Linnets Stadium, Murdishaw Ave, Runcorn, Cheshire WA7 6HP **(T)** 07050 801733 (Clubline)
Capacity: **Seats:** **Covered:** **Midweek Matchday:** Tuesday **Clubhouse:** Yes **Shop:**

Colours(change): Yellow & green/green/yellow & green. (Blue & white/blue/blue & white)
Previous Names: None
Previous Leagues: None.
Records: 308 v Winsford United, 2006-07.
Senior Honours: None

10 YEAR RECORD

00-01	01-02	02-03	03-04	04-05	05-06	06-07	07-08	08-09	09-10
						NWC2 2	NWC1 12	NWCP 11	NWCP 11

SILSDEN

Founded: 1904 Nickname:

Secretary: John Barclay **(T)** 01535 656213 **(E)**
Chairman: Sean McNulty **Manager:** Chris Reape **Prog Ed:** Peter Hanson
Ground: Keighley Road, Keighley Road, Silsden, BD20 0EH **(T)** TBC
Capacity: **Seats:** Yes **Covered:** Yes **Midweek Matchday:** Wednesday **Clubhouse:** Yes **Shop:**

Colours(change): Red/black/red (Yellow/green/yellow).
Previous Names: Reformed in 1980.
Previous Leagues: Craven & District. West Riding County Amateur.
Records: **Att:**1,564 v FC United of Manchester- March 2007
Senior Honours:

10 YEAR RECORD

00-01	01-02	02-03	03-04	04-05	05-06	06-07	07-08	08-09	09-10
				NWC2 2	NWC1 14	NWC1 14	NWC1 11	NWCP 9	NWCP 14

SQUIRES GATE

Founded: 1948 Nickname:

Secretary: John Maguire **(T)** 01253 348 512 **(E)**
Chairman: Stuart Hopwood **Manager:** Russ McKenna **Prog Ed:**
Ground: School Road, Marton, Blackpool, Lancs FY4 5DS **(T)** 01253 798 583
Capacity: 1,000 **Seats:** 100 **Covered:** Yes **Midweek Matchday:** Tuesday **Clubhouse:** Yes **Shop:** No

Colours(change): All blue. (All Red)
Previous Names: Squires Gate British Legion FC >1953.
Previous Leagues: Blackpool & District Amateur 1958-61. West Lancashire 1961-91.
Records: **Att:** 600 v Everton, friendly 1995.
Senior Honours:

10 YEAR RECORD

00-01	01-02	02-03	03-04	04-05	05-06	06-07	07-08	08-09	09-10
NWC2 5	NWC2 3	NWC1 12	NWC1 20	NWC1 17	NWC1 13	NWC1 18	NWC1 6	NWCP 10	NWCP 13

ST HELENS TOWN

Founded: 1946 Nickname: Town

Secretary: Jeff Voller **(T)** 0151 222 2963 **(E)**
Chairman: John McKiernan **Manager:** Lee Riley **Prog Ed:** Jeff Voller
Ground: Knowsley Road, St Helens, Merseyside WA10 4AD **(T)** 08707 565 252
Capacity: 19,100 **Seats:** 2,362 **Covered:** 12,408 **Midweek Matchday:** Tuesday **Clubhouse:** Pub **Shop:** Yes

Colours(change): Red & white stripes/red/red. (All blue).
Previous Names: St Helen's Town formed in 1903 folded in 1923.
Previous Leagues: Liverpool Co Comb 1946-49 Lancs Comb 49-75, Chesh Co. 75-82
Records: **Att:** 4,000 v Manchester City 1950. **Goalscorer:** S. Pennington. **App:** Alan Wellens
Senior Honours: Lancs Comb Champions 1971-72 . FA Vase Winners 1986-87.

10 YEAR RECORD

00-01	01-02	02-03	03-04	04-05	05-06	06-07	07-08	08-09	09-10
NWC1 4	NWC1 4	NWC1 7	NWC1 19	NWC1 3	NWC1 8	NWC1 19	NWC1 14	NWCP 16	NWCP 9

STONE DOMINOES

Founded: 1987 Nickname: The Doms

Secretary: Pauline Matthews **(T)** 01785 761 891 **(E)**

Chairman: Chris Haines **Manager:** Shaun Hollinshead **Prog Ed:** Colin Heath

Ground: Motiva Park, Yarnfield Lane, Yarnfield, Stone, Staffs ST15 0NF **(T)** 01785 761 891

Capacity: 1,000 **Seats:** 250 **Covered:** yes **Midweek Matchday:** Wednesday **Clubhouse:** Yes **Shop:**

Colours(change): Red/black/Black (All blue)

Previous Names:

Previous Leagues: Midland League

Records: **Att:** 375 v Port Vale - July 2000

Senior Honours: Midland League 1999-00 North West Counties League Division 1 2009-10.

10 YEAR RECORD

00-01	01-02	02-03	03-04	04-05	05-06	06-07	07-08	08-09	09-10
NWC2 13	NWC2 4	NWC2 2	NWC1 10	NWC1 11	NWC1 21	NWC1 22	NWC2 10	NWC1 3	NWC1 1

WINSFORD UNITED

Founded: 1883 Nickname: Blues

Secretary: Robert Astles **(T)** 01606 558 447 **(E)**

Chairman: Mark Loveless **Manager:** Chris Willcock **Prog Ed:** Robert Astles

Ground: Barton Stadium, Kingsway, Winsford, Cheshire CW7 3AE **(T)** 01606 558 447

Capacity: 6,000 **Seats:** 250 **Covered:** 5,000 **Midweek Matchday:** Tuesday **Clubhouse:** Yes **Shop:** Yes

Colours(change): All royal blue. (Tangerine/black/black).

Previous Names:

Previous Leagues: The Combination 1902-04. Cheshire Co. 1919-40, 47-82. N.P.L. 1987-01

Records: **Att:** 8,000 v Witton Albion, 1947. **Goalscorer:** Graham Smith 66 **Apps:** Edward Harrop 400

Senior Honours: Cheshire League 1920-21, 76-77.

Cheshire Senior Cup 1958-59, 79-80, 92-93. North West Counties League Division 2 2006-07.

10 YEAR RECORD

00-01	01-02	02-03	03-04	04-05	05-06	06-07	07-08	08-09	09-10
NWC1 21	NWC1 7	NWC1 22	NWC2 8	NWC2 3	NWC2 4	NWC2 1	NWC1 10	NWCP 19	NWCP 19

DIVISION ONE INS & OUTS

IN: Abbey Hey (R), AFC Darwen (P - West Lancashire League Premier Division), Runcorn Town (P - West Cheshire League Division One).
OUT: Barnoldswick Town (P), Stone Dominoes (P)

ABBEY HEY

Founded: 1902

Secretary: Tony McAllister **(T)** 0161 231 7147 **(E)**

Chairman: James Whittaker **Manager:** Barry Walker **Prog Ed:** Gordon Lester

Ground: The Abbey Stadium, Goredale Avenue, Gorton, Manchester M18 7HD **(T)** 0161 231 7147 **Capacity:** 1,000

Colours(change): Red/black/red (All blue)

ADDITIONAL INFORMATION: **Previous League:** Manchester.
Record Att: 400 v Manchester City XI, October 1999.
Honours: Manchester League 1981-82, 88-89, 88-89, 91-92, 93-94, 94-95.

AFC BLACKPOOL

Founded: 1947

Secretary: William Singleton **(T)** 01253 761 721 **(E)**

Chairman: Henry Baldwin **Manager:** Stuart Parker **Prog Ed:** David Tebbett

Ground: Mechanics Ground, Jepson Way, Common Edge Road, Blackpool, FY4 5DY **(T)** 01253 761 721 **Capacity:** 2,000

Colours(change): Tangerine/white/tangerine (White/tangerine/tangerine)

ADDITIONAL INFORMATION: **Previous Name:** Blackpool Metal Mechanics. **Previous League:** Lancashire Combination 1962-68.
Previous Ground: Stanley Park 1947-49. **Record Att:** 4,300 v FC United of Manchester, 18/02/2006 at Blackpool FC.
Honours: Lancashire County FA Shield 1957/58, 1960/61. West Lancs Lge 1960/61, 61/62. NWCFL Division 3 1985/86.

AFC DARWEN

Reformed: 2009

Secretary: Derek Slater **(T)** 07989 744 584 **(E)**

Chairman: Derek Slater **Manager:** Kenny Langford **Prog Ed:** Steve Hart

Ground: Anchor Ground, Anchor Road, Darwen, Lancs, BB3 0BB. **(T)** 07989 744 584 **Capacity:**

Colours(change): All red (All navy)

ADDITIONAL INFORMATION: **Previous Name:** Darwen FC > 2009. **Previous League:** West Lancashire.
Record Att: 14,000 v Blackburn Rovers 1882.
Honours: Lancashire League 1902. North West Counties League Cup 1983. North West Alliance Cup 1996.

AFC LIVERPOOL
Founded: 2008

Secretary: Pat Cushion **(T)** 0151 430 0507 **(E)**
Chairman: Chris Stirrup **Manager:** Paul Moore **Prog Ed:** Steven Horton
Ground: Prescot Cables FC, Valerie Pk, Eaton Street, Prescot, Merseyside, L34 6ND **(T)** 0151 430 0507 **Capacity:**
Colours(change): All red (White/black/white)

ADDITIONAL INFORMATION:
Record Att: 604 v Wigan Robin Park 06/09/2008.
Honours: North West Counties Trophy 2008-09, 09-10.

ASHTON TOWN
Founded: 1962

Secretary: Steve Barrett **(T)** 01942 701 483 **(E)**
Chairman: **Manager:** John Carroll **Prog Ed:** Ian Promfrett
Ground: Edge Green Street, Ashton-in-Makerfield, Wigan, WN4 8SL **(T)** 01942 701483 **Capacity:**
Colours(change): Red/black/black (All blue)

ADDITIONAL INFORMATION: Previous Name: Makerfield Hill formed 1953. **Previous League:** Manchester.
Record Att: 1,865 v FC United of Manchester 2007.
Honours: Warrington League Guardian Cup.

ATHERTON COLLIERIES
Founded: 1916 Nickname: The Colts

Secretary: Emil Anderson **(T)** **(E)**
Chairman: Paul Gregory **Manager:** Steve Pilling **Prog Ed:** Emil Anderson
Ground: Alder Street, Atherton, Greater Manchester. M46 9EY. **(T)** 07968 548056 **Capacity:** 2,500
Colours(change): Black & white stripes/black/black (All blue)

ADDITIONAL INFORMATION: Previous League: Cheshire County 1978-82.
Record Att: 3,300 in Lancashire Combination 1920's.
Honours: North West Counties League Division 3 1986-87.

CHADDERTON
Founded: 1947 Nickname: Chaddy

Secretary: Louise Robson **(T)** 0161 624 9733 **(E)**
Chairman: Harry Mayall **Manager:** Paul Buckley **Prog Ed:** Paul Jones
Ground: Andrew Street, Chadderton, Oldham, Greater Manchester. OL9 0JT **(T)** 0161 624 9733 **Capacity:** 2,500
Colours(change): All red (Orange/black/orange)

ADDITIONAL INFORMATION: Previous League: Lancashire Combination.
Record Att: 2,352 v FC United of Manchester 2006.
Honours: Gilgryst Cup 1969-70.

CHEADLE TOWN
Founded: 1961

Secretary: Brian Lindon **(T)** 0161 428 2510 **(E)**
Chairman: Chris Davies **Manager:** Steve Brokenbrow **Prog Ed:** Stuart Crawford
Ground: Park Road Stadium, Cheadle, Cheshire, SK8 2AN **(T)** 0161 428 2510 **Capacity:** 2,500
Colours(change): White/black/white (Sky & white stripes/navy/sky & white)

ADDITIONAL INFORMATION: Previous League: Manchester > 1987.
Record Att: 1,700 v Stockport County August 1994. **Goalscorer:** Peter Tilley. **Apps:** John McArdle.
Honours: Manchester Division 1 1979-80.

DAISY HILL
Founded: 1894

Secretary: Robert Naylor **(T)** 01942 818 544 **(E)**
Chairman: Graham Follows **Manager:** Craig Thomas **Prog Ed:** Simon O'Neill
Ground: New Sirs, St James Street, Westhoughton, Bolton, BL5 2EB **(T)** 01942 818 544 **Capacity:** 2,000
Colours(change): All royal blue (All red)

ADDITIONAL INFORMATION: Previous Name: Westhoughton Town. **Previous League:** Lancashire Combination 1978-82.
Record Att: 2,000 v Horwich RMI, Westhoughton Charity Cup Final 1979-80. **Goalscorer & Apps:** Alan Roscoe 300gls, 450app
Honours: Bolton Combination Premier Division 1962-63, 72-73, 75-76, 77-78.

ECCLESHALL
Founded: 1971

Secretary: Richard Marsh **(T)** 01785 851 351 (MD) **(E)**
Chairman: Andy Mapperson **Manager:** Dave Dale **Prog Ed:** Richard Marsh
Ground: Pershall Park, Chester Road, Eccleshall, ST21 6NE **(T)** 01785-851351 (MD) **Capacity:**
Colours(change): Blue & black stripes/black/black (All yellow)

ADDITIONAL INFORMATION: Previous League: Midland.
Record Att: 2,011 v FC United of Manchester November 2005.
Honours: Midland League 1990, 2002-03.

HOLKER OLD BOYS

Founded: 1936 Nickname: Cobs

Secretary: John Adams **(T)** 01229 828 176 **(E)**
Chairman: Dick John **Manager:** Dave Smith **Prog Ed:** Dick John
Ground: Rakesmoor, Rakesmoor Lane, Hawcoat, Barrow-in-Furness, LA14 4QB **(T)** 01229 828 176 **Capacity:** 1,750
Colours(change): Green & white/green/green & white (All red)

ADDITIONAL INFORMATION: Previous League: West Lancashire 1970-91.
Record Att: 2,303 v FC United of Manchester FA Cup at Craven Park 2005-06. **Goalscorer:** Dave Conlin.
Honours: West Lancashire League 1986-87.

IRLAM

Founded: 1969

Secretary: Warren Dodd **(T)** 07718 756402/07969 946277 **(E)**
Chairman: Ron Parker **Manager:** Ryan Gilligan **Prog Ed:** Warren Dodd
Ground: Silver Street, Irlam, Manchester M44 6HR **(T)** 07718 756402 **Capacity:**
Colours(change): Blue & white/blue/blue (Red/black/black)

ADDITIONAL INFORMATION:
Previous Name: Mitchell Shackleton. **Previous League:** Manchester.
Record Att: 1,600 v Hallam FA Vase.

LEEK C.S.O.B.

Founded: 1945

Secretary: Stan Lockett **(T)** 01538 383734 **(E)**
Chairman: Chris McMullen **Manager:** Brett Barlow **Prog Ed:** Stan Lockett
Ground: Leek Town FC, Harrison Park, Macclesfield Road, Leek, Staffs. ST13 8LD **(T)** 01538 383734 **Capacity:** 3,600
Colours(change): Red & white stripes/black/black (Sky blue & white stripes/navy/navy)

ADDITIONAL INFORMATION: Previous League: Midland.
Record Att: 2,590 v FC United of Manchester August 2005.
Honours: Midland League 1995-96.

NORTON UNITED

Founded: 1989

Secretary: Dennis Vickers **(T)** 01782 838 290 **(E)**
Chairman: Stephen Beaumont **Manager:** Dave Johnson **Prog Ed:** Dennis Vickers
Ground: Norton CC & MWI Community Drive, Smallthorne, Stoke-on-Trent ST6 1QF **(T)** 01782 838 290 **Capacity:**
Colours(change): Black & white/black/black (All claret)

ADDITIONAL INFORMATION: Previous League: Midland > 2001.
Record Att: 1,382 v FC United of Manchester 09/04/2006.
Honours: Midland League 1996-97, 98-99, 2000-01. Staffordshire Senior Vase 1998-99, 2003-04.

OLDHAM BORO

Founded: 1964

Secretary: David Shepherd **(T)** 0161 624 2689 **(E)**
Chairman: Mark Kilgannon **Manager:** Tony Mills **Prog Ed:** David Shepherd
Ground: Whitebank Road, Oldham, Greater Manchester OL8 3JH **(T)** 0161 624 2689 **Capacity:**
Colours(change): Blue/white/red (Cream/black/black)

ADDITIONAL INFORMATION: Previous Name: Oldham Town > 2009. **Previous League:** Lancashire Combination 1981-82.
Record Att: 1,767 v FC United of Manchester 2006.
Honours: North West Counties Division 2 1997-98.

ROCHDALE TOWN

Founded: 1924

Secretary: Jim Picken **(T)** 01706 527103 **(E)**
Chairman: Mark Canning **Manager:** Dean Stokes **Prog Ed:** Bob Sopel
Ground: Mayfield Sports Centre **(T)** 01706 527103 **Capacity:** 1,500
Colours(change): Black & white stripes/black/black (Yellow & green/green/yellow)

ADDITIONAL INFORMATION: Previous Name: Castleton Gabriels. **Previous League:** Manchester 1984-89.
Record Att: 640 v Rochdale, pre-season friendly 1991.
Honours: Manchester Division 1 1986-87.

RUNCORN TOWN

Founded: 2005

Secretary: Martin Fallon **(T)** 01928 590 508 **(E)**
Chairman: Tony Riley **Manager:** Simon Burton **Prog Ed:** Alan Bennett
Ground: Pavilions Sports Complex, Sandy Lane, Weston Point, Runcorn WA7 4EX **(T)** 01928 590 508 **Capacity:**
Colours(change): Sky & navy/navy/sky blue (Yellow & black/black/black)

ADDITIONAL INFORMATION: Previous League: West Cheshire.
Record Att: 113 v Abbey Hey 07/08/2010.
Honours: West Cheshire League Division 2 2006-07. Runcorn Senior Cup 2004-05, 05-06, 07-08.

WIGAN ROBIN PARK

Founded: 2005

Secretary: Taffy Roberts **(T)** 01942 404 950 **(E)**
Chairman: John Neafcy **Manager:** John Neafcy **Prog Ed:** Andrew Vaughan
Ground: Robin Park Arena, Loire Drive, Robin Park, Wigan, WN5 0UH **(T)** 01942 404 950 **Capacity:**
Colours(change): Red & white hoops/black & red/black & red (Orange hoops/navy/navy)

ADDITIONAL INFORMATION:
Previous League: Manchester 2005-08.
Honours: Manchester Premier 2007-08.

GROUND DIRECTIONS

ALSAGER TOWN - The Town Ground, Woodland Court, Alsager, Staffs, ST7 2DP 01270 882336
M6 to Junction16, A500 towards Stoke, leave A500 at 2nd exit (A34 to Congleton) at 2nd set of traffic lights on A34 turn left for Alsager, turn right opposite Caradon/Twyfords Factory (500 Yards), into Moorhouse Ave, West Grove mile on right. No available parking within the ground.

ASHTON ATHLETIC - Brocstedes Park, Downall Green, Ashton in Makerfield. WN4 0NR. 01942 716360
M6 northbound to junction 25, follow the slip road to the island and turn right A49, proceed for approx 0.50 mile turning right into Soughers Lane. At the T junction turn right into Downall Green Road and go over the motorway bridge passing a church on your right. Turn 2nd right into Booths Brow Road and turn 2nd right again into Brocstedes Road which is a narrow street. After 200 yards turn right down a shale road into the car park and ground.
From The North: M6 southbound to junction 24, proceed on to the slip road keeping in the right hand lane, turn right go over the motorway bridge and immediately re-enter the M6 Northbound for approximately 100 yards. Leave at junction 25,Follow the slip road to the island and turn right A49, proceed for approx 0.50 mile turning right into Soughers Lane. At the T junction turn right into Downall Green Road and go over the motorway bridge passing a church on your right. Turn 2nd right into Booths Brow Road and turn 2nd right again into Brocstedes Road which is a narrow street. After 200 yards turn right down a shale road into the car park and ground.

ATHERTON L.R. - Crilly Park, Spa Road, Atherton, Greater Manchester. M46 9XG. 01942 883950
M61 to Junction 5, follow signs for Westhoughton, turn left onto A6, turn right at first lights into Newbrook Road, then turn right into Upton Road, passing Atherton Central Station. Turn left into Springfield Road and left again into Hillside Road into Spa Road and ground.

BACUP BOROUGH - Brian Boys Stadium, Cowtoot Lane, Blackthorn, Bacup, Lancashire. OL13 8EE. 01706 878655
From M62, take M66 onto A681, through Rawtenstall to Bacup Town Centre, turn left onto the A671 towards Burnley, after approx. 300 yards turn right immediately before the Irwell Inn climbing Cooper Street, turn right into Blackthorn Lane, then first left into Cowtoot Lane to ground.

BARNOLDSWICK TOWN - Silentnight Stadium, West Close Road, Barnoldswick, Colne, BB18 5EW. 01282 815817
ravelling from Blackburn to Colne on M65 to end, straight on at roundabout onto Vivary Way onto North Valley Road. Through two sets of traffic lights to roundabout, turn left to Barnoldswick. Straight on till you come to roundabout in Kelbrook turn left to Barnoldswick.On entering Barnoldswick straight ahead at traffic lights, straight ahead at mini roundabout. Travel through built up area past Fosters Arms pub on left set back. Take first right onto Greenberfield Lane, travel 50 yards take middle single track (signposted) travel to bottom of track and bare right to car park at rear of ground.
Travelling from Barrow on A59 from Gisburn towards Skipton turn right at Barnoldswick signpost. Travel approx 2 miles taking 1st left onto Greenberfield Lane, travel 50 yards take middle single track (signposted) travel to bottom of track bare right to car park at rear of ground.
If using a SatNav use postcode BB18 5LJ.

BOOTLE - Delta Taxi Stadium, Vestey Road, off Bridle Road, Bootle, L30 4UN. 0151 525 4796 or 07852 742790
At Liverpool end of M57and M58 follow signs for Liverpool (A59 (S)), for 1 1/2 miles. At Aintree racecourse on left and Aintree Train Station on right ,turn right at lights into Park Lane. Turn left at second set of lights into Bridle Road. After 200 yards turn left at lights into Vestey Estate , ground 200 yards.

COLNE - The XLCR Stadium, Harrison Drive, Colne, Lancashire. BB8 9SL. 01282 862545
Follow M65 to end of motorway. Turn left and follow signs for Skipton and Keighley, continue to roundabout, take 1st left up Harrison Drive, across small roundabout, follow road to ground.

CONGLETON TOWN - Booth Street, off Crescent Road, Congleton, Cheshire, CW12 4DG. 01260 274460
On approach to Congleton from M6, past Waggon & Horses Pub, at 1st roundabout 2nd exit, past fire station, 2nd right into Booth Street. Ground at top of road.

FLIXTON - Valley Road, Flixton, Manchester. M41. 0161 748 2903
Leave M60 junction 10, take the B5214, signposted Urmston, at the second roundabout take third exit, take right only lane on the exit in Davyhulme Road, follow this road to Valley Road, just after the left hand bend after 1 1/2 miles. The ground is at the other end of the road.

FORMBY - Altcar Road, Formby, Merseyside, L37 8DL. 01704 833615
A565 Liverpool to Southport Road. At traffic lights opposite Tesco's superstore, turn right into Altcar Road. The ground is located 350 yards on the right, past Tesco.

GLOSSOP NORTH END - Surrey Street, Glossop, Derbyshire. SK13 7AJ. 01457 855469
A57 to Glossop, turn left at traffic lights (near Tesco sign), Glossopbrook Road. Follow road to top of hill. Ground on right.

MAINE ROAD - Brantingham Road, Chorlton-cum-Hardy, Manchester. M21 0TT. 0161 861 0344
M60 to junction 7, A56 towards Manchester. At traffic island follow signs for Manchester United, Lancs CC, turn right at next set of traffic lights signposted A5145 (Chorlton-cum-Hardy/Stockport), through next set of traffic lights. Take left fork at Y junction (traffic lights) onto A6010 (Wilbraham Road) to Chorlton. Through traffic lights (ignore pedestrian lights) for approx 1 mile. Left at next traffic lights into Withington Road, first left into Brantingham Road. Ground 300 yards on left. From North: M60 clockwise to junction 5 onto A5103 towards Manchester Centre for approx 2 miles, turn left at traffic lights (Wilbraham Road) A6010, then right at 2nd set of lights (Withington Road), first left into Brantingham Road. Ground 300 yards on left.

NEW MILLS - Church Lane, Church Lane, New Mills. SK22 4NP. 01663 747435
From Junction 1 of M60 follow A6 (Buxton) signs to Hazel Grove. Keep on A6 through High Lane and Disley. Follow A6 to traffic lights at the Swan Hotel. Turn left into Albion Road, then through next lights on to Church Road. After Church turn left into Church Lane. The Ground is on the right. Entrance to the Car Park is past the Ground.

PADIHAM - Arbories Memorial Sports Ground, Well Street, Padiham, Lancashire, BB12 8LE. 01282 773742
M65 to Junction 8, then follow A6068 signposted Clitheroe and Padiham. At traffic lights at bottom of hill turn right into Dean Range/Blackburn Road towards Padiham. At next junction turn into Holland Street opposite church, then into Well Street at the side of Hare & Hounds Pub to ground.

RAMSBOTTOM UNITED - Riverside Ground, Acrebottom, Ramsbottom, Bury. BL0 0BS
M66(North) to junction 1, take A56 towards Ramsbottom. After 1 mile turn left at traffic lights down Bury New Road. Turn left after old Mondi Paper Mill (and before the railway crossing) along the road running parallel with East Lancashire Railway. Ground at bottom on the right. From North : Leave M65 at junction 8. Follow A56 to Ramsbottom exit then follow A676 (signposted Bolton) into the centre of Ramsbottom. At the traffic lights in centre of town, turn left into Bridge Street and turn right after the railway crossing.

ROSSENDALE UNITED - Dark Lane, Newchurch, Rossendale, Lancashire BB4 7UA. 01706 215119
Directions From the M62: Take J18 (the M66 towards Bury). Go to the very end of the dual carriageway towards Rawtenstall. At the roundabout take the dual carriageway past the Shell petrol station and the church (left lane) heading towards Burnley. At the 3rd set of traffic lights (pass ASDA on your left) turn right into Newchurch Road (Rams Head pub on the corner). After about one mile turn right into Staghills Road. The ground is about 400 yards on your right.
If you have a SatNav try the postcode BB4 7TY rather than our postal address of BB4 7UA

RUNCORN LINNETS - Millbank Linnets Stadium, Murdishaw Ave, Runcorn, Cheshire. WA7 6HP. 07050 801733 (Clubline)
orth East - M56 junction 12 take A557 Widnes/Northwich. At Roundabout take 1st Exit onto A557 heading Frodsham A56, go through 1 roundabout. Turn left at Chester Rd/A56, turn left at Chester Rd/A533. At the roundabout, take the 2nd exit onto Murdishaw Ave. Destination on the Right.
Head West on M56 towards Exit 11. At junction 11, take the A56 exit to Preston Brook/Daresbury. At the roundabout take the 1st exit onto Chester Rd/A56 heading to Preston Brook/Daresbury. Continue to follow Chester Rd, go through 2 roundabouts.At the roundabout take the 2nd exit onto Murdishaw Ave. Destination on the right.

SILSDEN - Keighley Road, Silsden, BD20 0EH
A629 Skipton to Keighley road, take A6034, ground in on the left after the golf driving range.
SQUIRES GATE - School Road, Marton, Blackpool, FY4 5DS. 01253 798583
From M55: At the end of the M55 (J4), continue along dual carriageway (A5230), and bear left at major roundabout, staying on A5230. At second traffic lights, turn left onto B5261. After passing Shovels pub on left, turn left at lights, and first car park is on left after approx 50 yards. Parking is also available down the lane leading to the Club, on your left, after another 40 yards. If both these are full, parking is also available on the Shovels car park, or on the car park adjacent to the playing fields (turn right at the lights after passing the pub).
ST HELENS TOWN - Knowsley Road, St Helens, Merseyside. WA10 4AD (St Helens RLFC). 08707 565252
M6 South to junction 23 (Haydock), take A580 towards Liverpool, after approx 8 miles turn left at traffic lights onto A570, take first right onto Bleak Hill Road, after approx 1 1/2 miles, when road bends sharply to right, turn left into Mill Brow. Follow to T Junction, turn left onto Knowsley Road at traffic island (Black Bull Public House on right), into Dunriding Lane over bridge, turn right into car park and ground. From south: M6 onto M62 towards Liverpool, exit at junction 7. Take 5th exit on roundabout onto St Helens Linkway, exit Linkway at 3rd roundabout (Sherdley) taking 2nd exit towards Town Centre to next roundabout, take exit following signs for Liverpool and Southport, through traffic lights to next roundabout, take 1st exit off roundabout towards Liverpool. At traffic lights turn right onto Eccleston Street, follow road for approx 1 mile, at Black Bull P/H, turn left over bridge, car park and ground on right. (Note: Follow signs for St Helens RLFC).
STONE DOMINOES - Motiva Park, Yarnfield Lane, Yarnfield, Stone, Staffs, ST15 0NF. 01785 761891
From M6 junction 15, straight on at first roundabout following A500 to Stoke, come to first slip road)before flyover) and turn right at roundabout heading to Stone A34 (5 miles), straight on at next roundabout (Trentham Gardens on your right), through village of Tittensor (take care: cameras - 40mph), at next roundabout straight on (pub in the middle, Darlaston Inn) still on A34, 2 more roundabouts *BP garage on left) get in right hand lane and turn right into Yarnfield Lane (pub on corner called the Wayfarer) football ground is about 1 mile on left before village of Yarnfield.
WINSFORD UNITED - The Barton Stadium, Kingsway, Winsford, Cheshire. CW7 3AE. 01606 558447
From M6 junction 18, follow A54 through Middlewich for approx 3 miles, bear right at roundabout at Winsford Railway Station, follow road for approx 1 mile, turn right into Kingsway, ground is on the right.

DIVISION ONE

ABBEY HEY - The Abbey Stadium, Goredale Avenue, Gorton, Manchester M18 7HD. 0161 231 7147
M60 to junction 24, take A57 to Manchester City Centre for approx 1 mile, at first set of major traffic lights (MacDonalds on right) pass through for approx 300yards, turn left immediatley before overhead railway bridge (A.H.F.C. sign) into Woodland Avenue. Take first right, pass under railway bridge, turn first left into Goredale Avenue.
AFC BLACKPOOL - Mechanics Ground, Jepson Way, Common Edge Road, Blackpool, Lancashire FY4 5DY. 01253 761721
M6 to M55, exit at junction 4. At roundabout turn left along A583 to traffic lights, turn right into Whitehill Road, to traffic lights (2 miles). Go straight across the main road into Jepson Way, ground at top.
AFC DARWEN - Anchor Ground, Anchor Road, Darwen, Lancs, BB3 0BB. 07989-744584
Leave M65 at Junction 4. At traffic lights turn left onto A666 (signposted Darwen). After approx ? mile turn left between Anchor Car Sales and the Anchor Pub. Bare right and ground 200 yards on left.
AFC LIVERPOOL - Valerie Park, Eaton Street, Prescot, Merseyside, L34 6ND. 0151 430 0507
From North: M6 to Junction 26, onto M58 to Junction 3. Follow A570 to junction with A580 (East Lancs Road). (Approach junction in right hand lane of the two lanes going straight on). Cross A580 and take first road on right (Bleak Hill Road). Follow this road through to Prescot (2 miles). At traffic lights turn right, straight on at large roundabout (do not follow route onto Prescot by-pass) and right at next lights. 100 yards turn right at Hope and Anchor pub into Hope Street. Club will be in sight at bottom of road. From South: M6 to Junction 21a (M62 junction 10). Follow M62 towards Liverpool, to junction 7. Follow A57 to Rainhill and Prescot. Through traffic lights at Fusilier pub, 100 yards turn right at Hope and Anchor pub (as above). From East: Follow M62 as described in 'From South' or A580 East Lancs Road to Junction with A570 (Rainford by-pass), turn left and take first right. Follow route as 'From North'
ASHTON TOWN - Edge Green Street, Ashton-in-Makerfield, Wigan, Greater Manchester. WN4 8SL. 01942 701483
M6 to Junction 23, A49 to Ashton-in-Makerfield. Turn right at the traffic lights onto the A58 towards Bolton. After approx. three quarters of a mile, turn right into Golbourne Road. After 200 yards turn right into Edge Green Street. Ground at bottom of street.
ATHERTON COLLIERIES - Alder Street, Atherton, Greater Manchester. M46 9EY. 07968 548056
M61 to junction 5, follow sign for Westhoughton, turn left onto A6, turn right onto A579 (Newbrook Road/Bolton Road) into Atherton. At first set of traffic lights turn left into High Street, then second left into Alder Street to ground.
CHADDERTON - Andrew Street, Chadderton, Oldham, Greater Manchester OL9 0JT. 0161 624 9733
M62 to junction 20, following A627(M) towards Manchester. Motorway becomes a dual carriageway, turn left at first major traffic lights (A699) Middleton Road, then second left into Burnley Street, Andrew Street at the end.
CHEADLE TOWN - Park Road Stadium, Cheadle, Cheshire, SK8 2AN. 0161 428 2510
M60 to junction 2 (formerly M63 junction 11), follow A560 to Cheadle. Go through first main set of traffic lights and then first left after shops into Park Road. Ground at end of road.
DAISY HILL - New Sirs, St James Street, Westhoughton, Bolton, BL5 2EB. 01942 818 544.
M61 to junction 5, A58 (Snydale Way/Park Road) for one and a half mile, left into Leigh Road (B5235) for 1 mile to Daisy Hill. Turn right into village 200 yards after mini roundabout, then left between church and school into St James Street. Ground 250 yards on left.
ECCLESHALL - Pershall Park, Chester Road, Eccleshall, ST21 6NE. 01785-851351 (Match Days Only)
M6 to junction 14 then A5013 to Eccleshall, right at mini-roundabout and then left at next mini-roundabout into High Street B5026, ground 1 mile on right.
M6 to junction 15, then A519 to Eccleshall right at mini-roundabout to High Street B5026, ground 1 mile on right.
HOLKER OLD BOYS - Rakesmoor, Rakesmoor Lane, Hawcoat, Barrow-in-Furness, Cumbria. LA14 4QB. 01229 828176
M6 to junction 36. Take the A590 all the way to Barrow-in-Furness. At the borough boundary continue along the A590. After 1? miles you will pass the Kimberley Clark paper mill on your right. Immediately after passing the paper mill turn left into Bank Lane, signposted "Barrow Golf Club" on the left hand side of the A590 and "Hawcoat yard on the right hand side of the A590. Follow this road to the T- junction at the top of the hill outside the Golf Club. Turn left here into Rakesmoor Lane the ground is 200 yds. down the road on the right. Please be advised that Rakesmoor Lane beyond the ground is a single-track road and as such is unsuitable for coaches. It is not possible to turn a coach into the ground when approaching from that direction.
IRLAM - Irlam Football Club, Silver Street, Irlam, Manchester M44 6HR. 07718 756402/07969 946277
From Peel Green Roundabout (M60 Junction 11), take A57 to Irlam, and then B5320 into Lower Irlam. After passing Morsons Project, turn right into Silver Street, at Nags Head Pub. The ground is situated at the bottom of Silver Street on the right hand side.
LEEK C.S.O.B. - Harrison Park, Macclesfield Road, Leek, Staffs. ST13 8LD (Leek Town FC). 01538 383 734.
M6 to junction 17 - A534 to Congleton - follow signs for Leek (A54) - carry on A54 until junction with A523 - turn right onto A523 - this is road direct to Leek and ground (8 miles) - ground on right just into Leek (Macclesfield Road).
NORTON UNITED - Norton CC & MWI - Community Drive, Smallthorne, Stoke-on-Trent ST6 1QF. 01782 838290
M6 to junction 16, A500 to Burslem/Tunstall, turn off bear right at traffic island to Burslem, through lights to Smallthorne, take 3rd exit on mini-roundabout, turn right by pedestrian crossing into Community Drive, ground 200 metres on left.
OLDHAM BORO - Whitebank Road, Oldham, Greater Manchester OL8 3JH. 0161 624 2689
M60 to Junction 18, join the new M60 motorway to junction 22, Hollinwood, turn left at next set of lights onto Hollins Road (A6104), follow road until you see fire station on right, turn right at fire station, follow road down to next left Whitebank Road. Ground is on your left.
ROCHDALE TOWN - Mayfield Sports Centre, Keswick Street, Castleton, Rochdale. OL11 3AG. 01706 527 103
M62 to junction 20, follow A627M towards Rochdale. Keep right on A627M and turn right at traffic lights at BMW Garage go to next roundabout, take 2nd exit into Queensway towards Castleton and through the Industrial Estate. Turn Right at traffic lights into Manchester Road, A664. Go past Castleton Rail station and turn left at Fairwell Inn, into Keswick St, go through new housing estate to ground --- Rochdale Town FC ground is next to Castlehawk Golf Club.
RUNCORN TOWN - Pavilions Sports Complex, Sandy Lane, Weston Point, Runcorn, Cheshire WA7 4EX. 01928 590 508
M56 J12. Head towards Liverpool. Come off at fourth exit (Runcorn Docks), turn left at the top of slip road, left at T-Junction, then left into Pavilions.
M62 J7. Head towards Runcorn. When crossing Runcorn Bridge, stay in the right hand lane. Follow road around and come off at second exit (Runcorn Docks). Turn right at the top of slip road, left at T-Junction, then left into Pavilions.
WIGAN ROBIN PARK - Robin Park Arena, Loire Drive, Robin Park, Wigan, WN5 0UH. 01942 404 950
M6 J25 take road into Wigan and follow signs for the DW Stadium (Wigan Athletic) Ground is next to stadium, behind Wickes DIY store on the retail park.

NORTHERN COUNTIES EAST LEAGUE

www.ncel.org.uk

Sponsored by:
KoolSport

Founded: 1982

Recent champions:
2005: Goole
2006: Buxton
2007: Retford United
2008: Winterton Rangers
2009: Mickleover Sports

Premier Division	P	W	D	L	F	A	Pts
Bridlington Town	38	30	4	4	123	36	94
Rainworth Miners Welf.	38	26	5	7	98	46	83
Armthorpe Welfare	38	24	7	7	102	48	79
Thackley	38	25	1	12	113	54	76
Scarborough Athletic	38	22	4	12	100	57	70
Winterton Rangers	38	22	3	13	70	43	69
Pickering Town	38	20	5	13	82	58	65
Arnold Town	38	18	7	13	84	69	61
Liversedge	38	17	5	16	89	83	56
Long Eaton United	38	15	8	15	58	52	53
Hall Road Rangers	38	15	6	17	72	80	51
Dinnington Town	38	14	7	17	62	83	49
Selby Town	38	14	6	18	60	84	48
Parkgate	38	13	6	19	83	87	45
Hallam	38	12	6	20	82	93	42
Maltby Main	38	11	9	18	47	70	42
Lincoln Moorlands Rail.	38	10	8	20	57	85	38
Nostell Miners Welfare	38	9	8	21	51	80	35
Shirebrook Town	38	8	3	27	35	95	27
Brodsworth Miners Welf.	38	0	2	36	17	182	2

PRESIDENT'S CUP

(Top eight finishers from Premier and Division One)

FIRST ROUND

AFC Emley 2 Askern Villa 1
Bridlington Town 5 Bottesford Town 0
Dinnington Town 2 Thackley 0
Leeds Carnegie 0 **Selby Town** 3
Long Eaton United 1 **Scarborough Athletic** 0
(Long Eaton United expelled)
Rainworth Miners Welfare 1 **Arnold Town** 2
Staveley Miners Welfare 2 Barton Town Old Boys 1
Winterton Rangers 6 Pickering Town 4

QUARTER-FINALS

Arnold Town 1 Bridlington Town 3
(Bridlington Town expelled)
Scarborough Athletic 1 **Dinnington Town** 2
Selby Town 5 AFC Emley 0
Staveley Miners Welfare 1 **Winterton Rangers** 3

SEMI-FINALS

Arnold Town 2 Selby Town 0
Winterton Rangers 3 Dinnington Town 2

FINAL

(April 20th at Staveley Miners Welfare)
Winterton Rangers 3
Arnold Town 1

	Armthorpe Welfare	Arnold Town	Bridlington Town	Brodsworth MW	Dinnington Town	Hall Road Rangers	Hallam	Lincoln Moor. Rail.	Liversedge	Long Eaton United	Maltby Main	Nostell Miners W.	Parkgate	Pickering Town	Rainworth Miners W.	Scarborough Athletic	Selby Town	Shirebrook Town	Thackley	Winterton Rangers
Armthorpe Welfare		1-1	1-3	5-0	8-1	3-4	3-0	0-1	3-0	1-1	4-1	4-1	1-0	4-0	1-3	3-2	3-0	3-1	1-2	1-0
Arnold Town	3-4		0-7	6-0	1-2	6-3	4-1	2-3	2-3	0-0	4-0	5-3	1-0	1-0	1-2	1-1	1-2	2-0	5-2	3-0
Bridlington Town	2-2	5-1	***P***	8-1	4-0	1-0	4-0	7-0	1-1	1-1	3-1	3-0	2-4	4-1	1-0	1-2	4-1	5-2	4-2	2-0
Brodsworth Miners Welfare	0-10	2-2	0-6	***R***	1-2	0-1	1-9	2-2	0-4	0-3	0-5	0-3	1-4	0-1	0-9	0-1	0-1	1-2	0-5	0-4
Dinnington Town	2-4	2-2	2-2	2-0	***E***	3-1	3-1	4-4	2-2	2-1	2-0	2-0	1-0	1-1	0-2	0-1	1-2	3-1	1-2	3-1
Hall Road Rangers	3-3	3-0	1-4	4-0	1-1	***M***	2-1	1-1	1-0	2-1	1-2	4-2	8-3	1-0	0-3	1-2	5-0	0-1	3-3	2-1
Hallam	1-4	2-3	1-4	9-0	3-0	4-0	***I***	3-1	6-0	1-1	4-0	3-2	1-2	1-3	3-2	4-1	3-3	4-1	2-4	0-5
Lincoln Moorlands Railway	1-2	0-1	1-4	6-2	0-1	4-3	2-1	***E***	0-3	3-3	1-1	3-1	2-2	1-2	0-6	3-1	3-0	1-0	1-2	0-1
Liversedge	1-4	4-2	1-5	9-2	3-2	0-2	7-1	5-4	***R***	1-2	4-0	3-3	3-2	5-1	1-3	0-2	3-4	5-1	0-2	4-1
Long Eaton United	0-1	0-3	2-0	2-0	2-2	2-1	3-2	1-0	1-2		2-0	3-1	2-0	1-4	1-0	1-2	1-1	1-2	0-3	0-0
Maltby Main	1-1	0-3	1-5	3-1	2-3	4-1	2-2	2-0	3-1	1-0	***D***	1-1	1-1	0-0	1-3	1-1	0-1	1-0	2-1	0-2
Nostell Miners Welfare	0-2	0-0	0-1	5-0	1-0	1-2	3-0	1-1	1-1	2-1	1-2	***I***	2-2	1-3	0-4	2-1	3-3	1-0	0-3	0-2
Parkgate	3-4	4-5	0-2	7-0	6-0	4-4	2-2	2-1	2-3	0-1	3-1	1-4	***V***	2-3	1-2	4-3	1-4	0-2	3-2	2-2
Pickering Town	2-0	0-3	0-4	3-1	4-1	4-0	7-1	3-1	7-1	4-6	2-1	1-1	3-1	***I***	2-3	2-1	4-0	5-0	0-1	0-2
Rainworth Miners Welfare	2-2	1-1	3-1	5-0	4-1	3-1	3-3	1-1	3-0	1-0	4-2	2-1	5-1	2-2	***S***	3-0	2-1	1-0	1-5	0-4
Scarborough Athletic	1-1	5-1	0-2	13-0	5-1	3-0	3-0	2-1	5-2	2-0	2-2	6-1	1-3	2-0	2-0	***I***	5-2	6-0	3-2	5-2
Selby Town	1-2	1-4	0-2	6-1	3-2	1-3	1-2	3-0	1-1	0-3	1-1	1-0	1-4	0-5	4-2	3-2	***O***	0-0	0-6	0-2
Shirebrook Town	0-3	0-3	2-3	4-1	1-5	0-0	1-1	1-2	0-4	0-4	2-1	3-1	2-4	0-3	0-4	4-3	1-2	***N***	0-2	1-4
Thackley	3-0	2-0	2-4	7-0	5-1	6-1	4-0	6-1	1-2	4-3	0-1	7-0	1-3	4-0	2-3	4-2	0-5	3-0		2-0
Winterton Rangers	1-3	4-1	0-2	4-0	2-1	3-2	2-0	3-1	1-0	3-2	3-0	0-2	4-0	0-0	0-1	0-1	2-1	3-0	2-1	

Division One		P	W	D	L	F	A	Pts
Tadcaster Albion		34	22	8	4	80	37	74
Brighouse Town		34	23	4	7	80	41	73
Leeds Carnegie	*-3*	34	23	6	5	101	37	72
Staveley Miners Welfare		34	21	5	8	87	46	68
Pontefract Collieries		34	17	8	9	59	49	59
Barton Town Old Boys	*-3*	34	18	6	10	59	55	57
Hemsworth Miners Welf.		34	17	4	13	81	68	55
AFC Emley		34	15	8	11	69	50	53
Bottesford Town		34	13	6	15	62	66	45
Rossington Main		34	11	9	14	52	66	42
Teversal		34	12	5	17	56	66	41
Askern Villa	*-10*	34	14	4	16	63	65	36
Glasshoughton Welfare		34	10	5	19	47	66	35
Yorkshire Amateur		34	10	4	20	48	70	34
Appleby Frodingham		34	10	4	20	48	75	34
Eccleshill United		34	8	4	22	45	96	28
Grimsby Borough		34	6	7	21	36	70	25
Worsbrough Bridge MW		34	5	5	24	36	86	20

WILKINSON SWORD SHIELD

FIRST ROUND

Grimsby Boro. 2 **Teversal** 6

Worsbrough Bridge MW 5 AFC Emley 2

SECOND ROUND

Appleby Frodingham 1 **Leeds Carnegie** 3

Bottesford 7 Eccleshill 2

Brighouse Town 1 **Rossington Main** 2

Glasshoughton Welfare 1 **Askern Villa** 4

Pontefract Collieries 1 **Yorkshire Amateur** 2

Tadcaster Albion 4 Hemsworth MW 2

Teversal 5 Barton Town Old Boys 4

Worsbrough Bridge MW 1 **Staveley Miners Welfare** 2

QUARTER-FINALS

Askern Villa 1 **Leeds Carnegie** 2

Bottesford Town 3 Yorkshire Amateur 0

Staveley Miners Welfare 2 Teversal 0

Tadcaster Albion 3 Rossington Main 3 *aet* (5-4p)

SEMI-FINALS

Leeds Carnegie v **Staveley Miners Welfare** (w/o)

Tadcaster Albion 1 **Bottesford Town** 2

FINAL

(played over two legs)

(April 13th)

Bottesford 2 **Staveley MW** 2

(Bottesford Town expelled)

LEAGUE CUP

FIRST ROUND

AFC Emley 2 Hemsworth Miners Welfare 0

Appleby Frodingham 4 Worsbrough Bridge MW 0

Barton Town Old Boys 2 Bottesford Town 1

Brighouse Town 2 Askern Villa 2 *aet* (4-2p)

Glasshoughton Welfare 1 **Rossington Main** 3

Grimsby Borough 2 Yorkshire Amateur 1

SECOND ROUND

Armthorpe Welfare 9 Eccleshill United 2

Barton Town Old Boys 3 Leeds Carnegie 2

Brighouse Town 2 Liversedge 1

Brodsworth Miners Welfare 1 **AFC Emley** 2

Dinnington Town 2 Hall Road Rangers 1

Grimsby Borough 2 Rainworth Miners Welfare 0

Hallam 3 **Selby Town** 3 *aet* (2-4p)

Lincoln Moorlands Railway 1 **Pickering Town** 2

Long Eaton United 1 Arnold Town 0

Maltby Main 1 **Staveley Miners Welfare** 5

Pontefract Collieries 3 Appleby Frodingham 1

Shirebrook Town 4 Nostell Miners Welfare 0

Tadcaster Albion 2 Rossington Main 1

Teversal 2 Scarborough Athletic 1

Thackley 1 **Bridlington Town** 2

Winterton Rangers 2 **Parkgate** 3

THIRD ROUND

AFC Emley 3 Brighouse Town 3 *aet* (5-4p)

Armthorpe Welfare 4 Bridlington Town 1

Dinnington Town 3 Barton Town Old Boys 2

Grimsby Borough 5 Selby Town 0

Long Eaton United 1 **Tadcaster Albion** 2

Pickering Town 4 Staveley Miners Welfare 2

Pontefract Collieries 2 Teversal 0

Shirebrook Town 2 **Parkgate** 4

QUARTER-FINALS

AFC Emley 0 **Pickering Town** 1

Grimsby Borough 1 Pontefract Collieries 1 *aet* (7-6p)

Parkgate 4 **Dinnington Town** 6

Tadcaster Albion 1 **Armthorpe Welfare** 5

SEMI-FINALS

Armthorpe Welfare 1 Pickering Town 0

Dinnington Town 2 Grimsby Borough 0

FINAL

(May 3rd at Staveley Miners Welfare)

Dinnington Town 5 Armthorpe Welfare 2

	AFC Emley	Appleby Frod.	Askern Villa	Barton T. OB	Bottesford T.	Brighouse T.	Eccleshill Utd	Glasshoughton	Grimsby Boro.	Hemsworth	Leeds Carnegie	Pontefract C.	Rossington M.	Staveley MW	Tadcaster Alb.	Teversal	Worsbrough B.	Yorkshire Amtr
AFC Emley		1-1	4-1	0-1	1-1	2-1	2-2	2-0	6-3	1-2	1-1	1-3	1-1	2-4	1-2	4-0	3-0	0-1
Appleby Frod'gham	1-4		2-4	0-1	1-2	1-2	2-3	1-0	2-2	1-1	2-3	0-3	1-0	0-3	1-2	1-2	1-2	0-1
Askern Villa	1-4	0-2		2-1	3-2	1-2	7-1	2-1	1-1	4-2	0-0	0-1	3-2	0-2	1-1	0-5	1-2	4-0
Barton Town OB	4-2	4-2	1-5	***D***	2-1	1-3	2-1	3-2	1-1	2-3	1-2	2-2	3-0	0-1	2-2	2-1	3-0	4-2
Bottesford Town	1-0	2-0	2-4	2-2	***I***	0-4	7-2	4-3	3-0	0-2	1-3	4-1	4-4	0-1	2-3	1-0	1-0	2-0
Brighouse Town	3-0	1-2	0-1	4-0	2-1	***V***	2-1	1-2	1-0	3-2	3-1	0-1	2-1	3-1	2-1	2-2	1-1	4-1
Eccleshill United	1-1	1-0	1-3	0-1	0-1	2-3	***I***	2-1	4-3	2-3	0-4	0-1	1-1	2-6	0-2	2-0	3-0	1-6
Glasshoughton W.	3-1	3-4	1-3	0-1	3-2	0-2	4-4	***S***	3-0	3-1	3-4	1-3	1-0	1-1	0-1	2-1	0-0	0-3
Grimsby Borough	0-2	2-0	1-0	0-3	2-2	1-2	0-2	1-2	***I***	1-3	2-3	0-1	1-2	1-4	3-1	1-3	1-2	2-0
Hemsworth MW	0-2	2-3	2-1	5-2	2-1	0-5	7-0	6-2	7-0	***O***	2-4	2-0	2-2	3-0	1-4	2-0	7-1	1-3
Leeds Carnegie	2-2	8-0	2-1	1-2	5-2	1-2	8-0	2-0	0-2	5-1	***N***	5-0	9-0	3-1	1-1	3-0	3-1	2-2
Pontefract Collieries	1-3	0-2	5-1	0-1	3-2	2-2	2-0	0-0	4-0	1-1	0-4		1-0	1-1	3-1	1-2	2-2	2-2
Rossington Main	2-4	3-2	4-3	3-0	1-1	4-3	2-1	1-0	0-0	0-2	0-2	1-1	***O***	4-1	1-3	1-1	1-0	3-1
Staveley Miners W.	1-1	3-3	3-1	4-0	4-0	4-3	6-0	1-0	3-0	9-1	0-2	1-2	1-0	***N***	1-4	6-2	2-2	3-1
Tadcaster Albion	2-1	5-0	2-1	2-2	2-2	1-3	4-0	5-0	1-1	2-1	1-1	3-0	4-4	1-0	***E***	2-1	4-0	4-0
Teversal	3-4	3-4	4-1	1-3	2-3	1-1	2-1	3-3	1-0	1-1	2-0	1-3	3-0	1-2	1-2		3-2	2-1
Worsbrough BMW	0-3	2-4	1-1	0-1	0-3	2-6	1-5	1-2	0-3	3-1	1-3	3-5	1-2	1-2	0-3	1-2		2-1
Yorkshire Amateur	1-3	0-2	1-2	1-1	4-0	0-2	2-0	0-1	1-1	0-3	1-4	1-4	3-2	1-5	0-2	4-0	3-2	

ARMTHORPE WELFARE

Founded: 1926 Nickname: Wellie

Secretary: Craig Trewick **(T)** 01302 842 795 **(E)** armthorpe.welfare@hotmail.co.uk
Chairman: Stephen Taylor **Manager:** Des Bennett **Prog Ed:** Martin Turner
Ground: Welfare Ground, Church Street, Armthorpe, Doncaster DN3 3AG **(T)** 01302 842 795 (Match days only)
Capacity: 2,500 **Seats:** 250 **Covered:** 400 **Midweek Matchday:** Tuesday **Clubhouse:** No **Shop:** No

Colours(change): Blue & white quarters/white/white. (Black & grey hoops/black/black)
Previous Names:
Previous Leagues: Doncaster Senior
Records: **Att:** 2,000 v Doncaster R Charity Match 1985-86. **Goalscorer:** Martin Johnson. **App:** Gary Leighton. **Win:** 10-0. **Defeat:** 1-7
Senior Honours: West Riding Challenge Cup 1981-82, 82-83.
Northern Counties East Division 1 Central 1984-85.

10 YEAR RECORD

00-01	01-02	02-03	03-04	04-05	05-06	06-07	07-08	08-09	09-10
NCEP 19	NCEP 6	NCEP 18	NCEP 14	NCEP 18	NCEP 10	NCEP 13	NCEP 9	NCEP 15	NCEP 3

ARNOLD TOWN

Founded: 1989 Nickname: Eagles

Secretary: Roy Francis **(T)** 0115 952 2634 **(E)** mail@arnoldfc.com
Chairman: Roy Francis **Manager:** Chris Freestone (Caretaker) **Prog Ed:** Paul Spencer
Ground: Eagle Valley, Oxton Road, Arnold, Nottingham NG5 8PS **(T)** 0115 965 6000
Capacity: **Seats:** **Covered:** **Midweek Matchday:** Tuesday **Clubhouse:** **Shop:**

Colours(change): All maroon. (Yellow & blue)
Previous Names: Arnold F.C. (founded 1928 as Arnold St. Marys) merged with Arnold Kingswell (1962) in '1989.
Previous Leagues: Central Midland 89-93
Records: **Att:** 3,390 v Bristol Rovers FAC 1-Dec 1967 **Goalscorer:** Peter Fletcher - 100. **App:** Pete Davey - 346. **Win:** 10-1 **Defeat:** 0-7
Senior Honours: Northern Counties East 1985-86. Central Midlands 92-93.
Northern Counties Div.1 93-94.

10 YEAR RECORD

00-01	01-02	02-03	03-04	04-05	05-06	06-07	07-08	08-09	09-10
NCEP 6	NCEP 10	NCEP 15	NCEP 18	NCEP 16	NCEP 5	NCEP 15	NCEP 10	NCEP 6	NCEP 8

BRIDLINGTON TOWN

Founded: 1918 Nickname: Seasiders

Secretary: Gavin Branton **(T)** 07870 865 438 **(E)** gavinbranton@yahoo.co.uk
Chairman: Peter Smurthwaite **Manager:** Gary Allanson **Prog Ed:** Dom Taylor, Gordon Gillot
Ground: Queensgate Lane Rental Stadium, Queensgate, Bridlington YO16 7LN **(T)** 01262 606 879
Capacity: 3,000 **Seats:** 500 **Covered:** 500 **Midweek Matchday:** Tuesday **Clubhouse:** Yes **Shop:** Yes

Colours(change): All red. (White/white/blue).
Previous Names: Original Bridlington Town folded in 1994. Greyhound FC changed to Bridlington Town.
Previous Leagues: Yorkshire 1924-39, 59-82, NCEL 1982-90, 99-2003, Northern Premier 1990-94, 2003-08
Records: **Att:** 1,006 v FC Utd of Manchester, NPLD1N, 03.11.07. **Goalscorer:** Neil Grimson. **Apps:** Neil Grimson - 200+ (1987-97).
Senior Honours: FA Vase 1992-93. Northern Counties East 2002-03, 2009-10, Division 1 1992-93.
ERCFA Senior Cup 1921,22,23,31,53,57,61,65,67,70,72,89,93,05

10 YEAR RECORD

00-01	01-02	02-03	03-04	04-05	05-06	06-07	07-08	08-09	09-10
NCE1 4	NCE1 2	NCEP 1	NP 1 11	NP P 20	NP 1 11	NP 1 24	NP1N 18	NCEP 4	NCEP 1

BRIGHOUSE TOWN

Founded: 1963 Nickname: Town

Secretary: Malcolm Taylor **(T)** **(E)** malctay@blueyonder.co.uk
Chairman: Chris Lister **Manager:** Mark Brier **Prog Ed:** Lauren Brier
Ground: Dual Seal Stadium, St Giles Rd, Hove Edge, Brighouse, HD6 2PL. **(T)**
Capacity: 800 **Seats:** 70 **Covered:** 150 **Midweek Matchday:** Tuesday **Clubhouse:** Yes **Shop:**

Colours(change): Orange/black/orange. (Yellow/green/yellow).
Previous Names:
Previous Leagues: Huddersfield Works. 1963-75. West Riding County Amateur 1975-08.
Records:
Senior Honours: West Riding County Amateur League: Prem Div - 1990/91 1994/95 1995/96 2000/01 2001/02, Prem Cup - 1993/94 1995/96 1998/99 2000/01; Div 1 - 1988/89

10 YEAR RECORD

00-01	01-02	02-03	03-04	04-05	05-06	06-07	07-08	08-09	09-10
WRCP 1	WRCP 1	WRCP 2	WRCP 3	WRCP 4	WRCP 3	WRCP 3	WRCP 8	NCE1 15	NCE1 2

PREMIER INS & OUTS
IN: Brighouse Town (P), Farsley (formerly Farsley Celtic) (WS – Football Conference North), Tadcaster Albion (P)
OUT: Brodsworth Miners Welfare (R), Rainworth Miners Welfare (P – Northern Premier League Division One South), Shirebrook Town (R)

DINNINGTON TOWN

Founded: 2000 Nickname: Dinno

Secretary: Chris Dearns **(T)** 0114 286 4696 **(E)** chris.dearns@gmail.com
Chairman: Vacant **Manager:** Steve Toyne **Prog Ed:** Paul Morris
Ground: 131 Laughton Road, Dinnington, Nr Sheffield S25 2PP **(T)** 01909 518 555
Capacity: 2000 **Seats:** 80 **Covered:** 200 **Midweek Matchday:** Tuesday **Clubhouse:** Yes **Shop:** Yes

Colours(change): Yellow & black/black/yellow. (All white).
Previous Names:
Previous Leagues: Central Midlands League 2000-06
Records:
Senior Honours: Central Midlands League Cup 2002-03, 05-06.
Northern Counties East Division 1 2007-08, League Cup 2009-10.

10 YEAR RECORD

00-01	01-02	02-03	03-04	04-05	05-06	06-07	07-08	08-09	09-10
CM P 6	CM P 3	CM Su 6	CM Su 2	CM Su 2	CM Su 2	NCE1 9	NCE1 1	NCEP 8	NCEP 12

FARSLEY A.F.C.

Founded: 2010 Nickname: The Villagers

Secretary: Joshua Greaves **(T)** 0113 255 7292 **(E)** fcfcsecretary@live.com
Chairman: John Palmer **Manager:** Neil Parsley **Prog Ed:** Phil Morris
Ground: Throstle Nest, Newlands, Pudsey, Leeds, LS28 5BE **(T)** 0113 255 7292
Capacity: 4,000 **Seats:** 300 **Covered:** 1,500 **Midweek Matchday:** Tuesday **Clubhouse:** Yes **Shop:** Yes

Colours(change): Blue/blue/white (White/white/blue)
Previous Names: Farsley Celtic > 2010
Previous Leagues: None
Records: None
Senior Honours: None

10 YEAR RECORD

00-01	01-02	02-03	03-04	04-05	05-06	06-07	07-08	08-09	09-10

HALL ROAD RANGERS

Founded: 1959 Nickname: Rangers

Secretary: Alan Chaplin **(T)** 01482 703 775 **(E)** hallroadrangers@yahoo.co.uk
Chairman: Robert Smailes **Manager:** Martin Thacker **Prog Ed:** Paul Maunoury
Ground: Dene Park, Dene Close, Beverley Road, Dunswell HU6 0AA **(T)** 01482 850 101
Capacity: 1,200 **Seats:** 250 **Covered:** 750 **Midweek Matchday:** Wednesday **Clubhouse:** Yes **Shop:** Yes

Colours(change): Blue & white/blue/blue. (All red & black)
Previous Names:
Previous Leagues: East Riding County, Yorkshire 1968-82.
Records: **App:** 1,200 v Manchester City Aug 93 **Goalscorer:** G James **App:** G James
Senior Honours: East Riding Senior Cup 1972-73, 93-94. N.C.E. Div 2 90-91.

10 YEAR RECORD

00-01	01-02	02-03	03-04	04-05	05-06	06-07	07-08	08-09	09-10
NCE1 6	NCE1 9	NCE1 9	NCE1 14	NCE1 11	NCE1 14	NCE1 10	NCE1 2	NCEP 16	NCEP 11

HALLAM (SECOND OLDEST CLUB IN THE WORLD)

Founded: 1860 Nickname: Countrymen

Secretary: Mark Radford **(T)** 0114 249 7287 **(E)** markradford34@yahoo.com
Chairman: Vacant **Manager:** Kenny Geelan **Prog Ed:** Mark Radford
Ground: Sandygate Road, Crosspool, Sheffield S10 5SE **(T)** 0114 230 9484
Capacity: 1,000 **Seats:** 250 **Covered:** 400 **Midweek Matchday:** Tuesday **Clubhouse:** Yes **Shop:** Yes

Colours(change): All blue. (Red & black).
Previous Names:
Previous Leagues: Yorkshire 1952-82.
Records: **Att:** 2,000 v Hendon F.A. Amateur Cup. **Goalscorer:** A Stainrod 46. **App:** P. Ellis 500+. **Win:** 7-0 x2. **Defeat:** 0-7.
Senior Honours: Sheffield & Hallamshire Senior Cup 1950-51, 61-62, 64-65, 67-68.
Northern Counties East League Cup 2003-04.

10 YEAR RECORD

00-01	01-02	02-03	03-04	04-05	05-06	06-07	07-08	08-09	09-10
NCEP 5	NCEP 3	NCEP 17	NCEP 15	NCEP 15	NCEP 17	NCEP 14	NCEP 6	NCEP 10	NCEP 15

LINCOLN MOORLANDS RAILWAY

Founded: 1989 Nickname: The Moors

Secretary: Ken Rooney **(T)** 07908 809 366 **(E)** kenneth.rooney@ntlworld.com

Chairman: Nicholas Robinson **Manager:** Chris Moyses **Prog Ed:** Ken Rooney

Ground: Moorland Sports Ground, Newark Road, Lincoln LN6 0XJ Tel: 01522 **(T)**

Capacity: 200 **Seats:** 200 **Covered:** **Midweek Matchday:** Wednesday **Clubhouse:** Yes **Shop:** No

Colours(change): Claret & blue/claret/claret. (Royal blue & yellow/royal/royal).
Previous Names:
Previous Leagues: Central Midlands.
Records:
Senior Honours: Central Midlands Supreme 1999-00.
Lincolnshire Senior Cup 2006-07.

10 YEAR RECORD

00-01	01-02	02-03	03-04	04-05	05-06	06-07	07-08	08-09	09-10
CM Su 2	NCE1 4	NCE1 7	NCE1 8	NCE1 4	NCE1 7	NCE1 5	NCEP 19	NCEP 18	NCEP 17

LIVERSEDGE

Founded: 1910 Nickname: Sedge

Secretary: Bryan Oakes **(T)** 01274 683 327 **(E)** bryan@bryanoakes.orangehome.co.uk

Chairman: Alan Durrans **Manager:** Stuart Waddington **Prog Ed:** Alan Dearden

Ground: Clayborn Ground, Quaker Lane, Hightown Road, Cleckheaton WF15 8DF **(T)** 01274 682 108

Capacity: 2,000 **Seats:** 250 **Covered:** 750 **Midweek Matchday:** Tuesday **Clubhouse:** Yes **Shop:** Yes

Colours(change): Sky blue/navy/sky blue. (All red).
Previous Names:
Previous Leagues: Spen Valley, West Riding Co. Amateur 1922-72, Yorkshire 1972-82
Records: **Att:** 986 v Thackley **Goalscorer:** Denis Charlesworth **App:** Barry Palmer
Senior Honours: Northern Counties East League Cup 2005-06.

10 YEAR RECORD

00-01	01-02	02-03	03-04	04-05	05-06	06-07	07-08	08-09	09-10
NCEP 15	NCEP 11	NCEP 9	NCEP 9	NCEP 6	NCEP 2	NCEP 12	NCEP 4	NCEP 14	NCEP 9

LONG EATON UNITED

Founded: 1956 Nickname: Blues

Secretary: Jim Fairley **(T)** 07971 416 444 **(E)** jim@longeatonutd.co.uk

Chairman: Jim Fairley **Manager:** Glyn Stacey **Prog Ed:** Jim Fairley

Ground: Grange Park, Station Rd, Long Eaton, Derbys NG10 2EF **(T)** 0115 973 5700

Capacity: 1,500 **Seats:** 150 **Covered:** 500 **Midweek Matchday:** Tuesday **Clubhouse:** Yes **Shop:** No

Colours(change): All blue. (All yellow).
Previous Names:
Previous Leagues: Central Alliance 1956-61, Mid Co Football Lge 1961-82, NCE 1982-89, Central Midlands 1989-2002
Records: **Att:** 2,019 v Burton Albion FA Cup 1973
Senior Honours: Derbyshire Senior Cup 1964-65, 75-76.
Northern Counties East Div1S 1984-85. League Cup 2008-09.

10 YEAR RECORD

00-01	01-02	02-03	03-04	04-05	05-06	06-07	07-08	08-09	09-10
CM Su 7	CM Su 3	NCE1 3	NCE1 2	NCEP 12	NCEP 19	NCEP 11	NCEP 12	NCEP 2	NCEP 10

MALTBY MAIN

Founded: 1916 Nickname: Miners

Secretary: John Mills **(T)** 01709 813 609 **(E)** john_mills_@hotmail.co.uk

Chairman: Graham McCormick **Manager:** Steve Adams **Prog Ed:** Nick Dunhill

Ground: Muglet Lane, Maltby, Rotherham S66 7JQ. **(T)** 07795 693 683

Capacity: 2,000 **Seats:** 150 **Covered:** 300 **Midweek Matchday:** Wednesday **Clubhouse:** No **Shop:** No

Colours(change): Red/black/black
Previous Names: Maltby Miners Welfare 1970-96
Previous Leagues: Sheffield Co Senior. Yorkshire League 1973-84
Records: **Att:** 1,500 v Sheffield Weds (friendly) 1991-2
Senior Honours: Sheffield & Hallamshire Senior Cup1977-78

10 YEAR RECORD

00-01	01-02	02-03	03-04	04-05	05-06	06-07	07-08	08-09	09-10
NCE1 9	NCE1 6	NCE1 15	NCE1 3	NCEP 19	NCEP 18	NCEP 10	NCEP 18	NCEP 12	NCEP 16

NOSTELL MINERS WELFARE

Founded: 1928 Nickname: The Welfare

Secretary: Granville Marshall **(T)** 01924 864 462 **(E)** nostwellmwfc@hotmail.com

Chairman: Granville Marshall **Manager:** Alan Colquhoun **Prog Ed:** Jeff Dawson

Ground: The Welfare Grd, Crofton Co. Centre, Middle Lane, New Crofton WF4 1LB **(T)** 01924 866 010

Capacity: 1500 **Seats:** 100 **Covered:** 200 **Midweek Matchday:** Tuesday **Clubhouse:** Yes **Shop:** No

Colours(change): Yellow/black/yellow. (All blue).
Previous Names:
Previous Leagues: Wakefield 1950-66, 69-82, West Yorkshire 1966-68, 82-2006
Records:
Senior Honours: West Yorkshire Premier Division 2004-05

10 YEAR RECORD

00-01	01-02	02-03	03-04	04-05	05-06	06-07	07-08	08-09	09-10
WYkP 7	WYkP 8	WYkP 3	WYkP 5	WYkP 1	WYkP 3	NCE1 4	NCE1 5	NCEP 13	NCEP 18

PARKGATE

Founded: 1969 Nickname: The Steelmen

Secretary: Bruce Bickerdike **(T)** 01709 522 305 **(E)** secretary@parkgatefc.co.uk

Chairman: Albert Dudill **Manager:** Doug Shelley **Prog Ed:** Stephen Roberts

Ground: Roundwood Sports Complex, Green Lane, Rawmarsh, S62 6LA **(T)** 01709 826 600

Capacity: 1,000 **Seats:** 300 **Covered:** 300 **Midweek Matchday:** Tuesday **Clubhouse:** Yes **Shop:** No

Colours(change): All Red & White. (All orange).
Previous Names: BSC Parkgate (1982-86) RES Parkgate (pre 1994)
Previous Leagues: BIR County Senior. Yorkshire 1974-82.
Records: **Att:** v Worksop 1982
Senior Honours: N.C.E. Div 1 Champions 2006-07. Wilkinson Sword Trophy 2006-07.

10 YEAR RECORD

00-01	01-02	02-03	03-04	04-05	05-06	06-07	07-08	08-09	09-10
NCE1 7	NCE1 14	NCE1 8	NCE1 10	NCE1 12	NCE1 6	NCE1 1	NCEP 8	NCEP 11	NCEP 14

PICKERING TOWN

Founded: 1888 Nickname: Pikes

Secretary: Keith Usher **(T)** 01751 473 317 **(E)**

Chairman: Keith Usher **Manager:** Mark Wood **Prog Ed:** Alasdair Dinnewell

Ground: Recreation Club, off Mill Lane, Malton Road, Pickering YO18 7DB **(T)** 01751 473 317

Capacity: 2,000 **Seats:** 200 **Covered:** 500 **Midweek Matchday:** Tuesday **Clubhouse:** Yes **Shop:** No

Colours(change): All blue. (All yellow).
Previous Names:
Previous Leagues: Beckett, York & District, Scarborough & District, Yorkshire 1972-1982
Records: **Att:** 1,412 v Notts County (friendly) in August 1991
Senior Honours: N.C.E. Div 2 1987-88. North Riding Cup 1990-91.
Wilkinson Sword Trophy 2000-01

10 YEAR RECORD

00-01	01-02	02-03	03-04	04-05	05-06	06-07	07-08	08-09	09-10
NCE1 2	NCEP 4	NCEP 13	NCEP 5	NCEP 5	NCEP 6	NCEP 9	NCEP 3	NCEP 9	NCEP 7

SCARBOROUGH ATHLETIC

Founded: 2007 Nickname: The Seadogs

Secretary: John Clarke **(T)** 01723 585 150 **(E)** info@scarboroughathletic.com

Chairman: Richard Adamson **Manager:** Brian France **Prog Ed:** James Hunter

Ground: Bridlington FC, Queensgate Stadium, Bridlington, East Yorks YO11 3EP **(T)** 01262 606 879

Capacity: 3000 **Seats:** 500 **Covered:** 1,200 **Midweek Matchday:** Tuesday **Clubhouse:** Yes **Shop:** No

Colours(change): All Red & white (All white & navy blue).
Previous Names: Formed after Scarborough F.C. folded in 2007.
Previous Leagues: N/A
Records: **Att:** 791 v Leeds Carnegie N.C.E. Div.1 - 25.04.09.
Senior Honours: N.C.E. Div.1 Champions 2008-09.

10 YEAR RECORD

00-01	01-02	02-03	03-04	04-05	05-06	06-07	07-08	08-09	09-10
							NCE1 5	NCE1 1	NCEP 5

SELBY TOWN

Founded: 1919 Nickname: The Robins

Secretary: Thomas Arkley **(T)** 01757 700 356 **(E)** toonarkley@yahoo.co.uk
Chairman: Ralph Pearse **Manager:** Michael Gray **Prog Ed:** Thomas Arkley
Ground: Selby Times Stadium, Richard Street, Scott Road, Selby YO8 0DB **(T)** 01757 210 900
Capacity: 5,000 **Seats:** 220 **Covered:** 350 **Midweek Matchday:** Tuesday **Clubhouse:** Yes **Shop:** Yes

Colours(change): All red. (All blue).
Previous Names:
Previous Leagues: Yorkshire 1920-82
Records: **Att:** 7,000 v Bradford PA FA Cup1st Round 1953-54
Senior Honours: Yorkshire League 1934-35, 35-36, 52-53, 53-54. NCE Div.1 95-96.

10 YEAR RECORD

00-01	01-02	02-03	03-04	04-05	05-06	06-07	07-08	08-09	09-10
NCEP 9	NCEP 7	NCEP 16	NCEP 8	NCEP 2	NCEP 8	NCEP 5	NCEP 7	NCEP 3	NCEP 13

TADCASTER ALBION

Founded: 1892 Nickname: The Brewers

Secretary: Howard Clarke **(T)** 01937 835 017 **(E)** sandra.clarke1@tiscali.co.uk
Chairman: Rob Northfield **Manager:** Paul Marshall **Prog Ed:** Kevin Axtell
Ground: The Park, Ings Lane, Tadcaster LS24 9AY **(T)** 01937 834 119
Capacity: 1,500 **Seats:** 150 **Covered:** 400 **Midweek Matchday:** Tuesday **Clubhouse:** Yes **Shop:** No

Colours(change): Yellow/navy/navy (Red/black/black)
Previous Names: None
Previous Leagues: York, Harrogate, Yorkshire (73-82)
Records: **Att:** 1,200 v Winterton FA Vase 4th Round 1996-7
Senior Honours: Northern Counties East Division 1 2009-10.

10 YEAR RECORD

00-01	01-02	02-03	03-04	04-05	05-06	06-07	07-08	08-09	09-10
NCE1 16	NCE1 13	NCE1 16	NCE1 18	NCE1 6	NCE1 3	NCE1 7	NCE1 12	NCE1 17	NCE1 1

THACKLEY

Founded: 1930 Nickname: The Reds

Secretary: Chris Frank **(T)** 01274 615 571 **(E)** chris_thackleyafc@yahoo.co.uk
Chairman: Mike Smith **Manager:** Dave Morgan **Prog Ed:** John McCreery
Ground: Dennyfield, Ainsbury Avenue, Thackley, Bradford BD10 0TL **(T)** 01274 615 571
Capacity: 3000 **Seats:** 300 **Covered:** 600 **Midweek Matchday:** Tuesday **Clubhouse:** Yes **Shop:** Yes

Colours(change): Red/white/red. (White/black/white).
Previous Names: Thackley Wesleyians 1930-39
Previous Leagues: Bradford Am, W. Riding Co. Am., West Yorks, Yorks 1967-82
Records: **Att:** 1,500 v Leeds United 1983
Senior Honours: W. Riding County Cup 1963-64, 66-67, 73-74, 74-75.
Bradford & District Senior Cup (x13).

10 YEAR RECORD

00-01	01-02	02-03	03-04	04-05	05-06	06-07	07-08	08-09	09-10
NCEP 8	NCEP 8	NCEP 6	NCEP 11	NCEP 8	NCEP 9	NCEP 18	NCEP 16	NCEP 7	NCEP 4

WINTERTON RANGERS

Founded: 1930 Nickname: The Reds

Secretary: Mark Fowler **(T)** 01724 733 383 **(E)** wrfc@talktalk.net
Chairman: David Crowder **Manager:** Richard Sennett & Mark Turner **Prog Ed:** Brian Crowder
Ground: West Street, Winterton, Scunthorpe DN15 9QF. Tel: 01724 732 628. **(T)**
Capacity: 3,000 **Seats:** 245 **Covered:** 200 **Midweek Matchday:** Wednesday **Clubhouse:** Yes **Shop:** No

Colours(change): All royal blue. (All yellow).
Previous Names:
Previous Leagues: Scunthorpe & Dist. 1945-65. Lincs 1965-70. Yorkshire 1970-82.
Records: **Att:** 1,200 v Sheffield United, flood lights switch on, October 1978.
Senior Honours: Yorkshire League 1971-72, 76-77, 78-79. NCE Div.2 1989-90.
NCE Premier 07-08.

10 YEAR RECORD

00-01	01-02	02-03	03-04	04-05	05-06	06-07	07-08	08-09	09-10
NCE1 14	NCE1 7	NCE1 10	NCE1 11	NCE1 10	NCE1 5	NCE1 2	NCEP 1	NCEP 5	NCEP 6

A.F.C. EMLEY
Founded: 2005 Nickname: Pewits

Secretary: John Whitehead **(T)** **(E)** afcemley@tiscali.co.uk
Chairman: Graham Roys **Manager:** Darren Bland **Prog Ed:** Rob Dixon
Ground: The Welfare Ground, Off Upper Lane, Emley, nr Huddersfield, HD8 9RE. **(T)** 07702 712 287 **Capacity:** 2000
Colours(change): Sky blue & maroon/sky blue/maroon (All white)

ADDITIONAL INFORMATION:
Previous League: West Yorkshire 2005-06.

APPLEBY FRODINGHAM
Founded: 1990 Nickname: The Steelmen

Secretary: Steve Lumley-Holmes **(T)** **(E)** lumleyholmes@btinternet.com
Chairman: Steve Lumley-Holmes **Manager:** Simon Shorthose/John Simpson **Prog Ed:** Dick Drury
Ground: Brumby Hall Sports Ground, Ashby Road, Scunthorpe, DN16 1AA **(T)** 01724 402134 / 843024 **Capacity:**
Colours(change): Black & red halves/black/black (Royal blue & white halves/royal/royal)

ADDITIONAL INFORMATION:
Previous League: Central Midlands.
Honours: Lincolnshire League: 1962-63, 76-77, 77-98, 93-94; Lincolnshire Challenge Cup: 1962-63, 75-76, 76-77, 77-78, 92-93

ASKERN VILLA
Founded: 1924

Secretary: Dave Hall **(T)** 01302 700 597 **(E)** davidhallgfx@btinternet.com
Chairman: Ted Ellis **Manager:** Brian Johnston **Prog Ed:** Dave Hall
Ground: Askern Villa Sports Ground, Manor Way, Doncaster Road, Askern, DN6 0AJ **(T)** 01302 700597 **Capacity:**
Colours(change): Black & white/red/red (Red & white/red/red)

ADDITIONAL INFORMATION:
Previous League: Central Midlands.
Honours: Central Midlands League 2007-08.

BARTON TOWN OLD BOYS
Founded: 1995 Nickname: Swans

Secretary: Peter Mitchell **(T)** 01652 635 838 **(E)** bartontown@gmail.com
Chairman: Paul Vickers **Manager:** Dave Anderson **Prog Ed:** Phil Hastings
Ground: The Euronics Ground, Marsh Lane, Barton-on-Humber **(T)** 01652 635 838 **Capacity:** 3,000
Colours(change): Sky blue/white/sky blue (All yellow & black)

ADDITIONAL INFORMATION:
Previous League: Central Midlands.

BOTTESFORD TOWN
Founded: 1974 Nickname: The Poachers

Secretary: Victor Jubber **(T)** 01724 871 883 **(E)**
Chairman: Tony Reeve **Manager:** Ian Whyte **Prog Ed:** Liz Gray & Audrey Else
Ground: Birch Park, Ontario Road, Bottesford, Scunthorpe, DN17 2TQ **(T)** 01724 871 883 **Capacity:** 1,000
Colours(change): All blue & yellow (Red & black/black/black)

ADDITIONAL INFORMATION:
Previous League: Central Midlands 2000-07.
Honours: Lincolnshire League 1989-90, 90-91, 91-92. Central Midlands League Supreme Division 2006-07.

BRODSWORTH WELFARE
Founded: 1912 Nickname: Broddy

Secretary: Robert Laws **(T)** 01302 728 380 **(E)**
Chairman: Gordon Jennings **Manager:** Colin Bishop **Prog Ed:** Tony Richardson
Ground: Welfare Ground, Woodlands, Nr. Doncaster, DN6 7PP **(T)** 01302 728 380 **Capacity:** 3,000
Colours(change): All blue (All green)

ADDITIONAL INFORMATION:
Previous Names: Brodsworth Main > 1963, Brodsworth Miners Welfare 1963-2006. **Previous League:** Yorkshire.
Honours: Northern Counties East League Division 1 1998-99.

ECCLESHILL UNITED
Founded: 1948 Nickname: The Eagles

Secretary: David Heaney **(T)** 07501 096945 **(E)** dp.heaney@hotmail.co.uk
Chairman: John Offless **Manager:** Ian Banks **Prog Ed:** Paul Everett
Ground: The Smith Butler Stadium, Kingsway, Wrose, Bradford, BD2 1PN **(T)** 01274 615 739 **Capacity:** 2,225
Colours(change): Navy blue & white/white/navy blue (Yellow & blue/blue/yellow or red/blue/red)

ADDITIONAL INFORMATION: Previous Name: Eccleshill F.C. **Previous League:** West Riding Amateur.
Record Att: 715 v Bradford City 1996-97. **Win:** 10-1. **Defeat:** 0-6.
Honours: Bradford Senior Cup 1985-86. Northern Counties East Division 1 1996-97.

DIVISION ONE INS & OUTS

IN: Brodsworth Miners Welfare (R), Handsworth (P – Sheffield & Hallamshire County Senior League Premier Division), Louth Town (P – Central Midlands League Supreme Division), Shirebrook Town (R)
OUT: Brighouse Town (P), Tadcaster Albion (P)

GLASSHOUGHTON WELFARE

Founded: 1964

Secretary: Frank MacLachlan **(T)** 01977 511 234 **(E)** frank.maclachlan@btinternet.com
Chairman: Phil Riding **Manager:** Craig Elliott **Prog Ed:** Nigel Lea
Ground: Glasshoughton Centre, Leeds Rd, Glasshoughton, Castleford, WF10 4PF **(T)** 01977 511 234 **Capacity:** 2,000
Colours(change): Royal blue & white/royal blue/royal blue & white hoops (All yellow with blue trim)

ADDITIONAL INFORMATION: Previous Name: Anson Sports 1964-76. **Previous League:** West Yorkshire.
Record Att: 300 v Bradford City 1990. **Win:** 8-1. **Defeat:** 0-8.
Honours: West Riding County Cup 1993-94.

GRIMSBY BOROUGH

Founded: 1963 Nickname: The Wilderness Boys

Secretary: Nigel Fanthorpe **(T)** 01472 605 177 **(E)** nigelfanthorpe@hotmail.co.uk
Chairman: Rona Simons **Manager:** Steve Newby **Prog Ed:** Brian Sylvester
Ground: Grimsby Community Stadium, Bradley Road, Grimsby, DN37 0AG **(T)** **Capacity:**
Colours(change): Royal blue/white/royal blue (Yellow/blue/white)

ADDITIONAL INFORMATION:
Previous League: Central Midlands 2004-08.

HANDSWORTH

Founded: 2003

Secretary: Dave Wragg **(T)** **(E)** handsworthjsc@googlemail.com
Chairman: John Ward **Manager:** Russ Eagle **Prog Ed:** John Ward
Ground: Handsworth Junior Sporting Club, Olivers Mount, Handsworth, S9 4PA **(T)** **Capacity:**
Colours(change): Amber & black/black/black (Red & white/white/white)

ADDITIONAL INFORMATION:
Previous League: Sheffield & Hallamshire County Senior 2003-10.
Honours: Sheffield & Hallamshire County Senior League Division 1 2007-08.

HEMSWORTH MINERS WELFARE

Founded: 1981

Secretary: Mark Crapper **(T)** 01977 614 723 **(E)** crapperbruce@aol.com
Chairman: Tony Benson **Manager:** Andrew Cracknell **Prog Ed:** Mark Crapper
Ground: Fitzwilliam Stadium, Wakefield Road, Fitzwilliam, Pontefract, WF9 5AJ **(T)** 01977 614 997 **Capacity:**
Colours(change): All royal blue (All green)

ADDITIONAL INFORMATION:
Previous League: West Riding County Amateur 1995-2008.

LEEDS CARNEGIE

Founded: 1970

Secretary: Sue Watson **(T)** 0113 812 5119 **(E)** j.o.hall@leedsmet.ac.uk
Chairman: Michael Rossiter **Manager:** Graham Potter **Prog Ed:** Joe Rossiter
Ground: Farsley AFC, Throstle Nest, Newlands, Pudsey, Leeds LS28 5BE **(T)** 0113 255 7292 / 812 5119 **Capacity:**
Colours(change): Green/black/green (Purple)

ADDITIONAL INFORMATION:
Previous League: West Yorkshire 2004-07.
Honours: Yorkshire League Division 2 1970-71, Division 1 2004-05, Premier 2005-06.

LOUTH TOWN

Founded: 2007 Nickname: The White Wolves

Secretary: Matt Jones **(T)** **(E)** m.jones255@btinternet.com
Chairman: Eddie Clark **Manager:** Paul Walden **Prog Ed:** Dave Wilson
Ground: The Park Avenue Stadium, Park Avenue, Louth, LN11 8BY **(T)** 07891 965531 **Capacity:**
Colours(change): White/black/black (All blue)

ADDITIONAL INFORMATION:
Previous League: Central Midlands 2007-10.
Honours: Central Midlands League Premier Division 2008-09, Supreme Division 2009-10.

PONTEFRACT COLLIERIES

Founded: 1958 Nickname: Colls

Secretary: Darren Angell **(T)** 07796 136 415 **(E)** darren@pontecolls.co.uk
Chairman: Guy Nottingham **Manager:** Simon Houghton **Prog Ed:** Eddie Fogden
Ground: Skinner Lane, Pontefract, WF8 4QE **(T)** 01977 600 818 **Capacity:** 1,200
Colours(change): Blue/black/blue (Claret & sky blue trim)

ADDITIONAL INFORMATION:
Previous League: Yorkshire 1979-82.
Honours: Northern Counties East League Division 1 1983-84, 95-96.

ROSSINGTON MAIN
Founded: 1919 Nickname: The Colliery

Secretary: Gerald Parsons **(T)** **(E)** g-parsons2@sky.com
Chairman: Carl Stokes **Manager:** Ian Wilson **Prog Ed:** Peter Murden
Ground: Welfare Ground, Oxford Street, Rossington, Doncaster, DN11 0TE **(T)** 01302 865 524 **Capacity:** 2,000
Colours(change): All blue (Orange/black/black)

ADDITIONAL INFORMATION: Previous League: Central Midlands.
Record Att: 1,200 v Leeds United 06/08/1991. **Goalscorer:** Mark Illam. **Apps:** Darren Phipps.
Honours: Central Midlands League Premier Division 1984-85, League Cup 1983-84, 84-85.

SHIREBROOK TOWN
Founded: 1985

Secretary: Aimee Radford **(T)** 01623 742 535 **(E)** aimeeradford@yahoo.co.uk
Chairman: Vacant **Manager:** Dave Rhodes **Prog Ed:** Graham Haworth
Ground: Shirebrook Spts and So C, Langwith Rd, Shirebrook, Mansfield, NG20 8TF **(T)** 01623 742 535 **Capacity:** 2,000
Colours(change): Red/black/red (All white)

ADDITIONAL INFORMATION: Previous Name: Shirebrook Colliery > 1993. **Previous League:** Central Midlands 1985-2002.
Record Goalscorer: Craig Charlesworth - 345.
Honours: Central Midlands League Supreme Division 2000-01, 01-02, Northern Counties East Division 1 2003-04.

STAVELEY MINERS WELFARE
Founded: 1989 Nickname: The Welfare

Secretary: Ele Reaney **(T)** 01246 471 441 **(E)** staveleyed@hotmail.co.uk
Chairman: Terry Damms **Manager:** Billy Fox **Prog Ed:** Ele Reaney
Ground: Inkersall Road, Staveley, Chesterfield, S43 3JL **(T)** 01246 471 441 **Capacity:** 5,000
Colours(change): Blue & white stripes (All orange)

ADDITIONAL INFORMATION: Previous League: County Senior 1991-93.
Record Att: 292 v Scarborough Athletic, NCE Division 1 01/12/2007. **Goalscorer:** Mick Godber. **Apps:** Shane Turner.
Honours: County Senior League Division 3 1991-92, Division 2 1992-93.

TEVERSAL
Founded: 1923 Nickname: Tevie Boys

Secretary: Kevin Newton **(T)** **(E)** enquiries@teversalfc.co.uk
Chairman: John Boden **Manager:** D.Kelk, J.Huson, B.Alberry **Prog Ed:** Kevin Newton
Ground: Teversal Grange Spts and So.Centre, Carnarvon St, Teversal, NG17 3HJ **(T)** 07773 922 539 **Capacity:**
Colours(change): Red/black/black (White/red/red)

ADDITIONAL INFORMATION:
Previous Name: Teversal Grange. **Previous League:** Central Midlands.
Honours: Central Midlands League 2004-05.

WORSBROUGH BRIDGE ATHLETIC
Founded: 1923

Secretary: Charlie Wyatt **(T)** 01226 284 452 **(E)** charlie@worsbroughbridgefc.com
Chairman: John Cooper **Manager:** Ian Shirt & Chris Hilton **Prog Ed:** Charlie Wyatt
Ground: Park Road, Worsbrough Bridge, Barnsley, S70 5LJ **(T)** 01226 284 452 **Capacity:** 2,000
Colours(change): Red/black/red (All blue)

ADDITIONAL INFORMATION: Previous Name: Worsborough M.W. & Athletic 1947-2010. **Previous League:** Yorkshire 1971-82.
Record Att: 1,603 v Blyth Spatans, FA Amateur Cup 1971.
Honours: County Senior League Division 1 1965-66, 69-70.

YORKSHIRE AMATEUR
Founded: 1919 Nickname: Ammers

Secretary: Keith Huggins **(T)** 0113 262 4093 **(E)**
Chairman: Jeni French **Manager:** Paul Lines **Prog Ed:** Keith Huggins
Ground: Bracken Edge, Roxholme Road, Leeds, LS8 4DZ **(T)** 0113 262 4093 **Capacity:** 1,550
Colours(change): White/navy blue/red (All red)

ADDITIONAL INFORMATION: Previous League: Yorkshire 1930-82. **Previous Ground:** Elland Road 1919-20.
Record Att: 4,000 v Wimbledon, FA Amateur Cup Quarter Final 1932.
Honours: Yorkshire League: 1931-32, Div 2 - 1958-59, Div 3 - 1977-78. Leeds & District Senior Cup.

GROUND DIRECTIONS

ARMTHORPE WELFARE - Welfare Ground, Church Street, Armthorpe, Doncaster, DN3 3AG. Tel: (01302) 842795 - Match days only
From the north, turn left at main roundabout in the centre of Doncaster and straight across at next roundabout on to Wheatley Hall Road. Turn right on to Wentworth Road, go to top of hill towards the Hospital on to Armthorpe Road. From the south, take the M18 to J4 on to the A630. At 2nd roundabout, turn left and proceed to next roundabout, then turn right. Ground 400 yards on left behind Netto.

ARNOLD TOWN - Eagle Valley, Oxton Road, Arnold, Nottingham, NG5 8PS. Tel: 0115 965 6000.
From South: From Nottingham, take the A60 Mansfield road. At the first traffic island half a mile north of Arnold, join the A614 towards Doncaster. After 200 yards, go through traffic lights and, after 300 yards, take the next turn right. The ground entrance is 200 yards on the right.
From North: A614 towards Nottingham. As you approach the first set of traffic lights, turn left 300 yards before the lights. The ground entrance is 200 yards on the right.
From M1: Leave at Junction 27. Head towards Hucknall/Nottingham. After one mile, turn right at the first set of traffic lights. One mile, turn first left at island and stay on this road for two miles until junction with A60. Turn right and, at the next island, turn left onto the A614 towards Doncaster. After 200 yards, go through traffic lights and, after 300 yards, take the next right turn. The ground entrance is 200 yards on the right.

BRIDLINGTON TOWN - Queensgate Stadium, Queensgate, Bridlington, East Yorkshire, YO16 7LN. Tel: (01262) 606879
From South (Hull, Beeford, Barmston): Approach Bridlington on the A165, passing golf course on right and Broadacres Pub, Kingsmead Estate on left. Straight through traffic lights to roundabout by B&Q. Turn right. At traffic lights turn left and over the railway bridge. At roundabout bear left and carry on heading north up Quay Road. After traffic lights turn right into Queensgate. Ground is 800 yards up the road on the right.
From South and West (Driffield, Hull, York): Approach Bridlington on A614. (This was formally the A166). Straight on at traffic lights (Hospital on right) and follow the road round the bend. At roundabout straight across to mini roundabout and bear right (second exit). Follow road around to right and to traffic lights. Straight on. At next traffic lights (just after Kwikfit) turn left into Queensgate. Ground is 800 yards up the road on the right.
From North (Scarborough): Approach Bridlington (Esso garage on right) at roundabout turn left then at mini roundabout second exit. Follow road around to right and to traffic lights. Straight on. At next traffic lights (just after Kwikfit) turn left into Queensgate. Ground is 800 yards up the road on the right.

BRIGHOUSE TOWN - Dual Seal Stadium, St Giles Road, Hove Edge, Brighouse, West Yorkshire, HD6 2PL.
M1 to M62 travel westwards to J26 then come off motorway and go on to A58 Halifax to third set of traffic lights at Hipperholme. At lights, turn left onto A644 to Brighouse. Travel approx. one mile passing the Dusty Miller pub, take next left and, within 30-40 metres, turn left on to Spouthouse Lane. Follow this road for approximately 1/4 of a mile until road swings left at this point. Turn right in to car park. Be careful of oncoming traffic on bend.

DINNINGTON TOWN - Phoenix Park, Dinnington Resource Centre, 131 Laughton Road, Dinnington S25 2PP. Tel: (01909) 518555
From M1 J31, follow A57 Worksop Road East for 1 mile. At first traffic lights, turn left onto B6463 Todwick Road then Monks Bridge Road for 2 miles. At petrol station roundabout, take third exit signposted Dinnington and travel half-a-mile, then take first left at Morrell Tyres. Cross mini-roundabout at The Squirrel pub and travel on Laughton Road for 300 yards. Ground is on the left.

FARSLEY A.F.C. - Throstle Nest, Newlands, Pudsey, Leeds, LS28 5BE. Tel: (0113) 255 7292
Farsley is sandwiched between Leeds and Bradford approximately 1 mile from the junction of the Leeds Outer Ring Road (A6110) and the A647 towards Bradford. At the junction, take the B6157 towards Leeds, passing the police station on the left hand side. At New Street (the junction cornered by Go Outdoors) turn left. Newlands is approximately 300 yards on the right. Throstle Nest is situated at the end of Newlands with parking available outside the ground.

HALL ROAD RANGERS - Dene Park, Dene Close, Beverley Road, Dunswell, nr Hull, HU6 0AA. Tel: (01482) 850101
M62 to A63, turn left before Humber Bridge onto A164 to Beverley, after approx. 5 miles turn right onto A1079. In 2 miles, turn left at large roundabout to ground 20 yards on right.

HALLAM - Sandygate, Sandygate Road, Crosspool, Sheffield, S10 5SE. Tel: (0114) 230 9484
A57 Sheffield to Glossop Rd, left at Crosspool shopping area signed Lodge Moor on to Sandygate Rd. Ground half mile on left opposite Plough Inn. 51 bus from Crucible Theatre.

LINCOLN MOORLANDS RAILWAY - Lincoln Moorlands Railway Sports Ground, Newark Road, Lincoln, LN6 8RT. Tel: (01522) 874111
From North: A1 to Markham Moor. Take A57 until Lincoln by-pass. At Carholme Roundabout take 3rd. exit towards Lincoln South. Travel 1.7 miles to Skellingthorpe Roundabout and take 2nd. Exit towards Lincoln South. Travel 1.6 miles to Doddington Roundabout and take 1st. exit B1190 towards Lincoln South. Travel 2.1 miles until T-Junction. Turn left onto A1434 and travel 0.4 mile. Entrance to ground is on left immediately after Chancery Close.
From Newark: A46 to Lincoln by-pass. At roundabout take last exit onto A1434 towards Lincoln. Travel for 3.1 miles, entrance to ground on left immediately after Chancery Close signposted 'Moorlands Railway Club'.

LIVERSEDGE - Clayborn Ground, Quaker Lane, Hightown Road, Cleckheaton, WF15 8DF. Tel: (01274) 682108
M62 J26, A638 into Cleckheaton, right at lights on corner of Memorial Park, through next lights and under railway bridge, first left (Hightown Rd) and Quaker Lane is approx 1/4 mile on left and leads to ground. From M1 J40, A638 thru Dewsbury and Heckmondwike to Cleckheaton, left at Memorial Park lights then as above. Buses 218 & 220 (Leeds - Huddersfield) pass top of Quaker Lane.

LONG EATON UNITED - Grange Park, Station Road, Long Eaton, NG10 2EG. Tel: (0115) 973 5700
M1 Junc 25, take A52 towards Nottingham, to island by Bardills Garden Centre, right onto B6003. Approx 2 miles to end of road to T-junction. At traffic lights, turn right A453 and take 2nd left into Station Road. Entrance on left down un-named road opposite disused car park next to Grange School.

MALTBY MAIN - Muglet Lane, Maltby, Rotherham, S66 7JQ. Tel: (07795) 693683
Exit M18 at Junc 1 with A631. Two miles into Maltby, right at traffic lights at Queens Hotel corner on to B6427 Muglet Lane. Ground 3/4 mile on left.

NOSTELL MINERS WELFARE - The Welfare Ground, Crofton Community Centre, Middle Lane, New Crofton, Wakefield, WF4 1LB. Tel: (01924) 866010
M1 J39, head towards Wakefield (A638), Denby Dale road. Leave Wakefield on the A638 (Doncaster Rd), towards Wakefield Trinity Ground. Continue on this road for another 2 miles, you will pass the Red Beck Motel on your right. Go under the bridge and turn right opposite the Public house 'Crofton Arms'. Follow road through Crofton village (1 1/4 miles). Turn left at 'Slipper' public house, then right onto Middle Lane, follow road round to reach Crofton Community Centre.

PARKGATE - Roundwood Sports Complex, Green Lane, Rawmarsh, Rotherham, S62 6LA. Tel: (01709) 826600
From Rotherham A633 to Rawmarsh. From Doncaster A630 to Conisbrough, then A6023 through Swinton to Rawmarsh. Grd at Green Lane - right from Rotherham, left from Conisbrough at the Crown Inn. Ground 800yds on right.

PICKERING TOWN - Recreation Club, off Mill Lane, Malton Rd, Pickering, YO18 7DB. Tel: (01751) 473317
A169 from Malton. On entering Pickering, take 1st left past Police Station and BP garage into Mill Lane, ground 200 yds on right.

SCARBOROUGH ATHLETIC - Queensgate Stadium, Bridlington, East Yorkshire, YO16 7LN. Tel: (01262) 606879
From South (Hull, Beeford, Barmston): Approach Bridlington on the A165, passing golf course on right and Broadacres Pub, Kingsmead Estate on left. Straight through traffic lights to roundabout by B&Q. Turn right. At traffic lights turn left and over the railway bridge. At roundabout bear left and carry on heading north up Quay Road. After traffic lights turn right into Queensgate. Ground is 800 yards up the road on the right.
From South and West (Driffield, Hull, York): Approach Bridlington on A614. (This was formally the A166). Straight on at traffic lights (Hospital on right) and follow the road round the bend. At roundabout straight across to mini roundabout and bear right (second exit). Follow road around to right and to traffic lights. Straight on. At next traffic lights (just after Kwikfit) turn left into Queensgate. Ground is 800 yards up the road on the right.
From North (Scarborough): Approach Bridlington (Esso garage on right) at roundabout turn left then at mini roundabout second exit. Follow road around to right and to traffic lights. Straight on. At next traffic lights (just after Kwikfit) turn left into Queensgate. Ground is 800 yards up the road on the right.

SELBY TOWN - The Selby Times Stadium, Richard St, Scott Rd, Selby, YO8 4BN. Tel: (01757) 210900
From Leeds, left at main traffic lights in Selby down Scott Rd, then 1st left into Richard St. From Doncaster, go straight across main traffic lights into Scott Rd then 1st left. From York, right at main traffic lights into Scott Rd and 1st left.

TADCASTER ALBION - 2inspire Park, Ings Lane, Tadcaster, LS24 9AY
From West Riding and South Yorks - Turn right off A659 at John Smith's Brewery Clock. From East Riding - Turn left off A659 after passing over river bridge and pelican crossing (New Street).

THACKLEY - Dennyfield, Ainsbury Avenue, Thackley, Bradford, BD10 0TL. Tel: (01274) 615571
On main Leeds/Keighley A657 road, turn off at Thackley corner which is 2 miles from Shipley traffic lights and 1 mile from Greengates lights. Ainsbury Avenue bears to the right 200yds down the hill. Ground is 200yds along Ainsbury Avenue on the right.

WINTERTON RANGERS - West Street, Winterton, Scunthorpe, DN15 9QF. Tel: (01724) 732628
From Scunthorpe - Take A1077 Barton-on-Humber for 5 miles. On entering Winterton take 3rd right (Eastgate), 3rd left (Northlands Rd) and 1st Right (West St). Ground 200 yards on left.

DIVISION ONE

A.F.C. EMLEY - The Welfare Ground, Off Upper Lane, Emley, nr Huddersfield, HD8 9RE. Tel: 01924 849392 or 07702 712287

From M1 J38: Travel on road signposted to Huddersfield through the village of Bretton to the first roundabout. Take first exit off this roundabout signposted Denby Dale. After approximately one mile turn right at road signposted Emley. After 2 miles enter the village of Emley. Entrance to ground is opposite a white bollard in centre of road. (Narrow entrance).

From M1 J39: Travel on road signposted toward Denby Dale. Travel for approximately 3 miles up hill to first roundabout. Take 2nd exit and follow directions as above.

APPLEBY FRODINGHAM - Brumby Hall Sports Ground, Ashby Road, Scunthorpe, DN16 1AA. Tel: 01724 402134 or 01724 843024

From M18, take J5 on to the M180. From M180, take J3 onto the M181 (Scunthorpe West). At the roundabout, turn right onto A18. Straight on at the mini roundabout (McDonalds). At the next large roundabout, take the third exit (A18) up the hill to the next roundabout, turn left and the entrance to the ground is 100 metres on the left.

ASKERN VILLA - Askern Villa Sports Ground, Manor Way, Doncaster Road, Askern, DN6 0AJ. Tel: (01302) 700597

Via A1 - Leave the A1 at Junction A639. Follow Signs Askern/Campsall. At T-Junction turn right towards Sutton. Take left turn at Anne Arms Public House. Take second right on to Manor Way. Car park in grounds of Askern Miners Welfare; Via M62 - Exit Junction 34 follow signs for Doncaster (A19) for about 6 miles take 1st right after "The Askern" Public House. Clubhouse on the left.

BARTON TOWN OLD BOYS - The Euronics Ground, Marsh Lane, Barton-on-Humber. Tel: (01652) 635838

Approaching from the South on A15, Barton is the last exit before the Humber Bridge. Follow the A1077 into the town. Turn right at the mini roundabout at the bottom of the hill into Holydyke. Take second left onto George Street and then into King Street. Marsh Lane is opposite the junction of King Street and High Street. The ground is at the end of Marsh Lane, on the right, immediately after the cricket ground.

BOTTESFORD TOWN - Birch Park, Ontario Road, Bottesford, Scunthorpe, DN17 2TQ. Tel: (01724) 871883

Exit M180 via M181-Scunthorpe. At circle (Berkeley Hotel), turn right into Scotter Road. At circle (Asda) straight ahead, 2nd left into South Park road then on to Sunningdale Road, turn right into Goodwood Road, Birch Park at end (right turn). Please note that Goodwood Road is not suitable for large vehicles. Instead, take 2nd right off Sunningdale Road which is Quebec Road, then 2nd right which is Ontario Road down to the bottom and ground is on the left.

BRODSWORTH WELFARE - Welfare Ground, Woodlands, Nr. Doncaster, DN6 7PP. Tel: (01302) 728380

From A1 take A638 to Doncaster, take left after Woodlands Pub into Welfare Road, ground 50 yards on left.

ECCLESHILL UNITED - The Smith Butler Stadium, Kingsway, Wrose, Bradford, BD2 1PN. Tel: (01274) 615739

M62 J26 onto M606, right onto Bradford Ring Road A6177, left on to A650 for Bradford at 2nd roundabout. A650 Bradford Inner Ring Road onto Canal Rd, branch right at Staples (Dixons Car showrooms on right), fork left after 30mph sign to junction with Wrose Road, across junction - continuation of Kings Rd, first left onto Kingsway. Ground is 200 yards on right.

GLASSHOUGHTON WELFARE - The Glasshoughton Centre, Leeds Rd, Glasshoughton, Castleford, WF10 4PF. Tel: (01977) 511234

Leave the M62 J32, signposted Castleford/Pontefract (A639). At the bottom of the slip road take the A656, taking carer to pick up the middle lane for Castleford. After approx. 1/4 mile, bear left at the first roundabout and, after a further 1/4 mile, left at the next roundabout on to Leeds Road. Ground is then 200 yards on the right.

GRIMSBY BOROUGH - Grimsby Community Stadium, Bradley Road, Grimsby, DN37 0AG

Head South East on the A180 to the Great Coates turn off come back over the A180 and follow for 1/2 mile to the roundabout, take first exit follow over one mini roundabout and through one set of traffic lights until you come to the Trawl Pub roundabout, take the second exit onto Littlecoates road and follow over one mini roundabout to the second roundabout and take the second exit onto Bradley Road. The ground is approx 800 yards on your left with car and coach parking facilities.

HANDSWORTH - Handsworth Junior Sporting Club, Olivers Mount, Handsworth, Sheffield, S9 4PA

From M1 J33 or Sheffield City Centre: Take the A57/A630 Sheffield Parkway. Leave at the slip road showing the B6200 and follow the signs towards Darnall. This is Handsworth Road and should be followed until you pass the White Rose public house. Once through the pelican crossing just below the pub, turn right into Olivers Drive, go down the road and bear right up the hill which is Olivers Mount. The ground is at the top of Olivers Mount.

HEMSWORTH MINERS WELFARE - Fitzwilliam Stadium, Wakefield Road, Fitzwilliam, Pontefract, WF9 5AJ. Tel: (01977) 614997

From East/West: M62 to J32 towards Pontefract then follow A628 towards Hemsworth. At Ackworth roundabout (Stoneacre Suzuki Garage), take a right on to the A638 Wakefield Road. Travel half a mile to next roundabout then take first exit. Travel one mile to crossroads and turn left into Fitzwilliam. Pass a row of shops on your right and turn left after the bus shelter before an iron bridge. To ground.

From North: A1 South to M62 then follow above directions.

From South: A1(M) North to A638 Wakefield Road. Travel to Ackworth Roundabout (Stoneacre Suzuki Garage) and go straight across and follow the A638 to the next roundabout. Take first exit then to crossroads. Turn left into Fitzwilliam and pass row of shops on your right. Turn left after bus shelter before iron bridge and carry on to the ground. Alternative: M1 to J32 then take M18 to A1(M).

LEEDS CARNEGIE - Throstle Nest, Farsley Celtic FC, Newlands, Pudsey, Leeds, LS28 5BE. Tel: (0113) 255 7292 (Matchday), (0113) 812 5119 (Other Times)

Farsley is sandwiched between Leeds and Bradford approximately 1 mile from the junction of the Leeds Outer Ring Road (A6110) and the A647 towards Bradford. At the junction, take the B6157 towards Leeds, passing the police station on the left hand side. At New Street (the junction cornered by Go Outdoors) turn left. Newlands is approximately 300 yards on the right. Throstle Nest is situated at the end of Newlands with parking available outside the ground.

LOUTH TOWN - The Park Avenue Stadium, Park Avenue, Louth, LN11 8BY. Tel: 07891 965531

Enter Louth from the A16 onto North Home Road. Go 1/2 mile and follow the road as it bends to the right to become Newbridge Hill. At the junction, turn right onto Ramsgate. At the mini roundabout next to Morrisons, turn left onto Eastgate. Go 1/2 mile down Eastgate and turn right into Park Avenue just past the fire station.

PONTEFRACT COLLIERIES - Skinner Lane, Pontefract, WF8 4QE. Tel: (01977) 600818

M62 jct32 (Xscape) towards Pontefract. Left at lights after roundabout for park entrance and retail park. Traffic through town should follow racecourse signs through lights to roundabout and back to lights.

ROSSINGTON MAIN - Welfare Ground, Oxford Street, Rossington, Doncaster, DN11 0TE. Tel: (01302) 865524 (Matchdays only)

Enter Rossington and go over the railway crossings. Passing the Welfare Club, Oxford Street is the next road on the right. The ground is at the bottom of Oxford Street.

SHIREBROOK TOWN - Shirebrook Staff Sports and Social Club, Langwith Road, Shirebrook, Mansfield, Notts, NG20 8TF. Tel: (01623) 742535

Depart M1 at Junction 29, at roundabout take A617 towards Mansfield (for 3.5 miles), at next roundabout take 2nd Exit B6407 Common Lane towards Shirebrook (or 1.8 miles), go straight on at next roundabout (for 300 yards), at staggered crossroads turn right onto Main Street (for 1.1 miles), at T Junction turn right (for 100 yards), take the first road on your left (Langwith Road). The ground is 400 yards on the right.

STAVELEY MINERS WELFARE - Inkersall Road, Staveley, Chesterfield, S43 3JL. Tel: (01246) 471441

M1 J30 follow A619 Chesterfield. Staveley is 3 miles from J30. Turn left at GK Garage in Staveley town centre into Inkersall Road. Ground is 200 yards on right at side of Speedwell Rooms.

TEVERSAL - Teversal Grange Sports and Social Centre, Carnarvon Street, Teversal, Sutton-in-Ashfield, NG17 3HJ. Tel: (07773) 922539

From North: Travel South on the M1 to junction 29 take the A6175 to Heath and Holmewood. Travel through Holmewood, and at the roundabout take the B6039 to Hardstaff and Tibshelf. At the T-junction in Tibshelf (pub on your left) turn left onto B6014 travelling over the motorway into Teversal. Follow the road round passing the Carnarvon Arms pub and under a bridge, take 2nd left onto Coppywood Close, travel to the top and following the road round with the ground at the top.

From South: From the M1 junction 28, take the A38 to Mansfield. Travel through a number of sets of traffic lights and after passing the Kings Mill Reservoir you will come to a major junction (King & Miller Pub and McDonalds on your left). Travel straight on taking the A6075 towards Mansfield Woodhouse, at the next set of traffic lights turn left onto the B6014 to Stanton Hill. You will come to a roundabout with a Kwik Save on your left, continue on the B6014 towards Tibshelf. Take the second right onto Coppywood Close, travel to the top and following the road round with the ground at the top.

WORSBOROUGH BRIDGE ATHLETIC - Park Road, Worsbrough Bridge, Barnsley, S70 5LJ. Tel: (01226) 284452

On the A61, Barnsley-Sheffield road two miles south of Barnsley, 2 miles from M1 J36 opposite Blackburns Bridge.

YORKSHIRE AMATEUR - Bracken Edge, Roxholme Road, Leeds, LS8 4DZ. Tel: (0113) 262 4093

From South - M1 to Leeds, then A58 to Wetherby Road to Fforde Green Hotel, left at lights and proceed to Sycamore Avenue (on right). From East - A1 to Boot & Shoe Inn then to Shaftesbury Hotel, turn right into Harehills Lane, then to Sycamore Avenue.

NORTHERN LEAGUE

www.northernleague.org

Sponsored by: Skilltrainingltd

Founded: 1889

Recent champions:

2005: Dunston Federation Brewery

2006: Newcastle Blue Star

2007: Whitley Bay

2008: Durham City

2009: Newcastle Benfield

Division One		P	W	D	L	F	A	Pts
Spennymoor Town		42	31	7	4	118	33	100
Shildon		42	27	6	9	102	60	87
Whitley Bay		42	25	8	9	111	48	83
Dunston UTS		42	24	10	8	96	41	82
Newcastle Benfield		42	23	9	10	89	45	78
Ashington		42	22	8	12	79	59	74
Bedlington Terriers		42	21	8	13	71	51	71
Norton & Stockton Ancients		42	20	7	15	82	84	67
Tow Law Town		42	20	6	16	80	85	66
Consett		42	19	7	16	71	73	64
South Shields		42	19	6	17	83	87	63
Billingham Synthonia		42	17	8	17	76	75	59
Bishop Auckland		42	17	7	18	81	89	58
Penrith	*-3*	42	17	7	18	75	71	55
West Allotment Celtic		42	16	6	20	68	84	54
West Auckland Town		42	15	5	22	83	92	50
Ryton		42	13	5	24	62	86	44
Esh Winning		42	11	6	25	57	94	39
Billingham Town		42	10	5	27	54	110	35
Chester-le-Street Town		42	10	3	29	68	115	33
Morpeth Town		42	7	6	29	49	110	27
Horden Colliery Welfare		42	6	4	32	48	111	22

J R CLEATOR CUP

(League champions v League Cup holders)

(August 1st at Newcastle Benfield)

Newcastle Benfield 5

Consett 0

	Ashington	Bedlington Terriers	Billingham Synthonia	Billingham Town	Bishop Auckland	Chester-le-Street Town	Consett	Dunston UTS	Esh Winning	Horden Colliery Welfare	Morpeth Town	Newcastle Benfield	Norton & Stockton Ancients	Penrith	Ryton	Shildon	South Shields	Spennymoor Town	Tow Law Town	West Allotment Celtic	West Auckland Town	Whitley Bay
Ashington		1-1	1-2	7-1	3-1	2-0	1-2	1-1	4-0	1-1	4-3	0-3	2-1	1-1	1-2	2-1	4-2	0-1	1-3	2-0	4-3	0-0
Bedlington Terriers	0-1		1-0	5-1	3-2	1-1	0-0	0-3	2-1	3-1	3-1	0-0	3-1	1-2	2-0	1-1	2-1	2-1	2-0	1-2	4-0	4-1
Billingham Synthonia	0-2	2-0		0-0	3-1	2-0	1-2	0-3	2-2	5-3	5-2	5-0	2-2	2-2	1-1	1-2	1-2	2-3	2-1	3-2	4-2	1-1
Billingham Town	1-4	0-4	2-3		2-1	2-4	1-5	2-4	3-2	3-2	2-0	0-3	1-0	1-4	0-2	4-0	2-4	0-6	1-2	0-2	1-6	1-6
Bishop Auckland	2-4	2-1	3-0	1-1		3-0	2-0	1-4	2-1	2-3	3-3	1-2	1-1	3-3	2-0	0-1	5-1	2-1	3-4	2-4	0-3	2-7
Chester-le-Street Town	3-4	3-2	0-2	1-5	1-4	***D***	1-3	1-3	1-5	5-4	4-1	1-1	3-0	2-6	3-4	2-2	0-1	0-1	6-4	1-4	5-3	0-3
Consett	1-1	1-0	1-3	2-2	0-3	3-1	***I***	0-2	4-1	2-2	2-2	0-4	0-1	2-2	3-1	1-6	0-2	0-5	1-2	1-0	2-4	1-3
Dunston UTS	1-2	2-0	5-0	4-0	2-2	3-2	0-1	***V***	4-0	3-1	1-1	0-0	0-2	2-0	1-0	2-4	2-0	0-0	5-0	2-2	5-1	3-2
Esh Winning	1-0	1-2	2-2	2-1	1-1	1-2	1-3	1-0	***I***	2-0	2-2	1-2	1-2	0-2	0-2	0-2	2-4	1-4	1-4	0-1	0-3	0-3
Horden Colliery Welfare	2-4	1-3	0-2	0-1	0-2	2-1	2-6	2-2	1-2	***S***	0-1	2-0	2-4	0-1	1-0	0-3	0-2	0-1	3-4	2-1	0-3	0-5
Morpeth Town	1-2	0-3	2-0	0-1	0-5	1-2	0-5	1-4	0-1	3-0	***I***	0-5	1-2	2-1	1-3	2-2	1-2	1-5	0-3	1-2	1-0	0-3
Newcastle Benfield	1-0	1-1	2-1	5-1	1-2	0-1	3-2	0-2	1-1	3-0	4-1	***O***	0-2	3-0	2-2	3-1	2-0	1-3	6-0	7-0	2-0	1-3
Norton/Stockton Ancients	2-4	0-1	3-1	2-0	2-3	3-1	0-2	1-7	2-3	6-0	2-1	1-1	***N***	2-0	2-2	0-3	3-1	2-2	0-3	4-3	3-3	2-1
Penrith	1-1	2-4	1-4	1-0	1-4	4-2	1-3	1-3	4-0	2-1	5-0	0-1	1-2		2-1	0-1	0-1	0-0	2-1	3-1	0-2	2-0
Ryton	0-3	0-3	4-2	1-0	5-1	4-2	1-3	0-2	1-3	3-0	0-3	1-1	2-3	2-0	***O***	0-6	0-2	1-2	1-3	1-2	4-2	2-3
Shildon	5-1	2-0	2-2	2-1	2-1	3-2	1-2	2-1	2-1	4-1	4-2	0-2	5-1	1-4	3-0	***N***	8-1	0-4	4-1	2-1	2-1	3-1
South Shields	0-3	6-1	3-2	5-2	8-1	1-0	0-1	1-0	2-4	2-2	1-1	1-6	3-3	0-1	3-3	4-1	***E***	1-3	2-1	3-1	0-1	3-1
Spennymoor Town	0-0	2-0	4-1	4-1	2-1	3-2	4-1	1-1	6-0	4-2	6-1	4-0	4-1	3-1	5-0	1-2	3-1		2-0	6-0	0-0	1-0
Tow Law Town	2-0	2-4	2-1	1-1	0-1	2-0	0-0	2-2	3-2	1-3	3-1	2-0	2-5	4-3	2-1	1-1	1-1	4-3		0-3	2-1	1-1
West Allotment Celtic	0-1	0-0	0-1	1-0	1-1	3-1	1-2	1-3	2-2	1-0	6-1	0-2	0-4	0-5	2-1	3-3	5-1	1-3	5-4		1-5	1-2
West Auckland Town	3-0	2-0	0-2	1-5	1-2	5-0	5-1	2-2	1-4	4-2	0-3	1-6	2-3	3-3	3-1	1-3	2-2	0-5	3-1	0-2		0-2
Whitley Bay	4-0	1-1	4-1	1-1	7-0	5-1	1-0	1-0	5-2	4-0	2-1	2-2	7-0	5-1	1-3	2-0	6-3	0-0	1-2	1-1	3-1	

Division Two	P	W	D	L	F	A	Pts
Stokesley	38	29	4	5	121	45	91
Sunderland Ryhope CA	38	24	8	6	85	29	80
Jarrow Roofing Boldon CA	38	25	5	8	107	60	80
Marske United	38	22	9	7	77	34	75
Guisborough Town	38	21	9	8	76	43	72
North Shields	38	17	12	9	66	52	63
Whitehaven Amateurs	38	17	9	12	80	60	60
Northallerton Town	38	16	9	13	74	63	57
Newton Aycliffe	38	15	12	11	64	53	57
Whickham *-3*	38	17	7	14	51	51	55
Gillford Park	38	15	5	18	67	74	50
Seaham Red Star	38	15	4	19	70	72	49
Crook Town	38	12	9	17	63	90	45
Team Northumbria	38	12	6	20	58	64	42
Brandon United	38	12	6	20	64	92	42
Hebburn Town	38	11	8	19	61	98	41
Thornaby	38	8	10	20	52	80	34
Washington	38	9	6	23	44	77	33
Darlington Railway Athletic	38	4	8	26	46	115	20
Birtley Town	38	4	4	30	41	115	16

ERNEST ARMSTRONG MEMORIAL CUP

FIRST ROUND

Birtley Town 1 **Jarrow Roofing Boldon CA** 3

Crook 1 **Newton Aycliffe** 2

Stokesley 1 **Gillford Pk** 1 *aet* (3-4p)

Whitehaven 2 Brandon 1

SECOND ROUND

Gillford Park 1 **Team Northumbria** 1 *aet* (1-4p)

Hebburn Town 2 **Sund'land Ryhope CA** 3

Jarrow Roofing BCA 2 Washington 1

Marske United 0 **Guisborough Town** 2

N. Aycliffe 0 **N. Shields** 3

Northallerton Town 3 Whickham 1

Seaham Red Star 2 **Thornaby** 3 *aet*

Whitehaven Amateurs 5 Darlington RA 2 *aet*

QUARTER-FINALS

Sunderland Ryhope CA 0 **North Shields** 4

Team Northumbria 0 **Jarrow Roofing BCA** 3

Thornaby 3 Northallerton 2

Whitehaven Amateurs 3 Guisborough Town 0

SEMI-FINALS

N. Shields 4 **Whitehaven** 5

Thornaby 3 Jarrow R. 2

FINAL

(May 5th at Sund. RCA)

Whitehaven Amateurs 3 Thornaby 1 *aet*

BROOKS MILESON CUP

FIRST ROUND

Bedlington Terriers 3 Darlington Railway Athletic 0

Billingham Town 0 **Tow Law Town** 1

Esh Winning 0 **Dunston UTS** 2

Hebburn Town 1 **Crook Town** 4

Marske United 7 Thornaby 2

Newton Aycliffe 4 North Shields 2

Seaham Red Star 1 **Whickham** 4

Team Northumbria 1 **Guisborough Town** 2

West Allotment Celtic 4 Horden Colliery Welfare 0

Whitehaven Amateurs 0 **Consett** 3

SECOND ROUND

Ashington 2 Northallerton Town 2 *aet* (4-2p)

Bedlington Terriers 3 Marske United 2 *aet*

Billingham Synthonia 1 **West Allotment Celtic** 2

Bishop Auckland 2 Spennymoor Town 1

Dunston 0 **Gillford Park** 1, Guisborough 0 **Penrith** 4

Jarrow Roofing Boldon CA 2 Washington 1 *aet*

Morpeth Town 1 Crook Town 0

Newton Aycliffe 2 West Auckland Town 1

Norton & Stockton Ancients 5 Brandon United 1

Ryton 2 **South Shields** 2 *aet* (4-1p) *(Ryton expelled)*

Stokesley 5 Birtley Town 0

Sunderland Ryhope CA 0 **Shildon** 4

Tow Law Town 0 Consett 0 *aet* (4-3p) *(at Consett)*

Whickham 0 **Chester-le-Street Town** 1

Whitley Bay 4 Newcastle Benfield 3

THIRD ROUND

Ashington 3 Shildon 0

Bishop Auckland 1 **West Allotment Celtic** 2

Jarrow Roofing BCA 1 **Norton & Stockton Ancients** 4

Morpeth Town 0 **Tow Law Town** 2

Newton Aycliffe 2 **Chester-le-Street Town** 4

Penrith 4 Stokesley 1

South Shields 3 Bedlington Terriers 2 *aet*

Whitley Bay 4 Gillford Park 0

QUARTER-FINALS

Chester-le-Street Town 0 **Ashington** 3

Penrith 5 Norton & Stockton Ancients 0

South Shields 1 Tow Law Town 0

Whitley Bay 3 West Allotment Celtic 2 *aet*

SEMI-FINALS

Penrith 0 **Ashington** 1, **South Shields** 2 Whitley Bay 1

FINAL

(May 3rd at Dunston UTS)

South Shields 2 Ashington 2 *aet* (6-5p)

	Birtley	Brand.	Crook	Darl. R	Gillfd P.	Guis.	Hebb.	Jarrow	Mars.	Nwtn A	N Shds	Nthaltn	Seahm	Stoke.	Sund.	Team	Thorn.	Wash.	Whick.	White.
Birtley Town		1-3	2-3	2-2	1-3	0-5	2-0	2-5	2-4	0-1	0-1	0-3	1-6	1-6	0-3	1-2	2-2	2-1	2-5	1-1
Brandon United	3-1		0-0	5-5	1-3	1-2	4-3	2-2	2-1	1-0	2-3	0-4	2-0	2-5	1-4	5-0	3-5	0-1	0-3	0-3
Crook Town	7-1	1-1		3-1	4-0	1-2	0-1	0-5	0-4	1-1	2-2	2-4	2-1	2-2	0-5	0-1	2-1	1-0	1-3	1-1
Darlington Railway Athletic	1-4	1-2	2-1		2-1	1-1	0-1	1-3	1-5	3-5	0-3	1-5	4-4	1-4	1-4	2-2	1-1	2-2	0-2	1-7
Gillford Park	7-1	4-2	2-0	4-1	***D***	1-1	0-5	0-2	2-3	2-2	1-4	2-1	1-1	5-3	1-0	2-0	4-2	0-1	2-0	1-1
Guisborough Town	6-0	2-1	0-0	5-0	3-2	***I***	2-4	4-1	1-2	2-1	0-0	1-0	1-1	1-2	1-1	3-1	3-0	3-1	1-0	1-3
Hebburn Town	3-0	0-3	5-5	2-1	2-1	0-3	***V***	1-3	0-4	1-1	3-3	1-1	1-2	1-3	1-8	2-2	4-1	0-3	0-4	2-1
Jarrow Roofing Boldon CA	2-1	7-2	14-1	7-0	1-0	2-5	2-2	***I***	1-5	3-1	2-1	2-4	3-1	1-4	1-2	2-3	3-2	2-1	0-0	5-0
Marske United	3-1	5-0	3-2	4-1	3-1	2-0	2-0	0-1	***S***	1-0	1-1	1-1	3-1	1-2	0-0	1-0	3-0	1-1	2-0	2-2
Newton Aycliffe	2-1	2-1	10-2	3-2	1-3	0-0	3-2	1-2	1-1	***I***	3-1	3-3	1-4	1-4	1-0	0-0	0-1	3-0	0-1	2-0
North Shields	3-2	3-2	1-2	0-1	2-0	1-1	1-1	0-4	1-0	2-2	***O***	4-1	6-0	1-2	0-0	1-0	2-0	1-0	1-1	1-2
Northallerton Town	3-0	2-2	1-2	2-1	5-0	0-4	3-0	3-4	1-2	3-0	1-2	***N***	1-2	0-4	1-1	2-1	2-2	2-1	0-0	2-2
Seaham Red Star	2-0	1-2	3-1	4-1	1-0	1-2	7-3	0-1	1-0	1-1	0-2	2-3		0-4	1-2	2-1	1-0	1-3	2-0	1-3
Stokesley	3-1	7-1	3-1	3-0	1-0	2-0	1-2	2-2	2-0	1-1	5-1	5-1	1-4	***T***	1-0	3-0	4-2	7-1	3-1	3-1
Sunderland Ryhope CA	3-0	1-0	0-0	5-0	5-2	3-0	8-0	3-3	1-0	0-2	3-1	2-0	1-0	3-2	***W***	0-4	1-0	2-0	3-0	0-0
Team Northumbria	5-2	4-0	4-1	1-2	3-3	1-2	4-0	0-1	3-3	0-2	1-2	0-1	5-2	1-3	0-2	***O***	0-1	1-2	2-1	1-0
Thornaby	1-1	1-1	0-3	2-0	3-0	3-3	2-2	2-3	0-0	2-4	2-2	1-2	3-2	1-5	1-5	1-1		2-0	0-2	2-1
Washington	0-2	1-3	0-4	3-2	2-3	1-2	1-5	0-1	1-1	0-1	2-2	2-2	3-1	1-7	1-2	1-3	2-1		0-1	2-3
Whickham	1-0	1-3	3-2	1-1	2-1	0-1	1-0	2-1	0-2	2-2	1-2	0-1	2-6	1-1	1-0	3-1	3-1	0-0		1-6
Whitehaven Amateurs	4-1	3-1	1-3	2-0	2-3	3-2	6-1	2-3	0-2	0-0	2-2	4-3	2-1	2-1	2-2	3-0	3-1	1-3	1-2	

ASHINGTON

Founded: 1883 Nickname: The Colliers

Secretary: Brian Robinson **(T)** 01670 852 832 **(E)** briansfootie2008@live.co.uk
Chairman: Ian Lavery **Manager:** Gary Middleton **Prog Ed:** Gavin Perry
Ground: Woodhorn Lane, Ashington NE63 9HF **(T)** 01670 811 991
Capacity: **Seats:** **Covered:** **Midweek Matchday:** Tuesday **Clubhouse:** Yes **Shop:** Yes

Colours(change): Black & White stripes/black/black.
Previous Names:
Previous Leagues: Northern Alliance, Football League, N. Eastern, Midland, Northern Counties, Wearside, N.P.L.
Records: **Att:** 13,199 v Rochdale FA Cup 2nd round 1950
Senior Honours: Northern League Div.2 Champions 2000-01, 03-04.

10 YEAR RECORD

00-01	01-02	02-03	03-04	04-05	05-06	06-07	07-08	08-09	09-10
NL 2 1	NL 1 19	NL 2 5	NL 2 1	NL 1 10	NL 1 16	NL 1 19	NL 1 17	NL 1 16	NL 1 6

BEDLINGTON TERRIERS

Founded: 1949 Nickname: Terriers

Secretary: David Collop **(T)** 07853 052 450 **(E)** davidcollop@hotmail.com
Chairman: David Holmes **Manager:** Tony Lowery & Keith Perry **Prog Ed:** Neil Douglass
Ground: Welfare Park, Park Road, Bedlington, NE22 5DA **(T)** 07853 052 450
Capacity: 3,000 **Seats:** 300 **Covered:** 500 **Midweek Matchday:** Wednesday **Clubhouse:** Yes **Shop:**

Colours(change): Red with white trim/red/red.
Previous Names: Bedlington Mechanics 1949-53 Bedlington United 1961-65
Previous Leagues: Northern Alliance
Records: **Att:** 2,400 v Colchester United FA Cup 1st round **Goalscorer:** John Milner
Senior Honours: Northern Lge Div 1: 97-98, 98-99, 99-00, 2000-01, 01-02.
Northumberland Senior Cup 1996-97, 97-98, 2001-02,03-04.

10 YEAR RECORD

00-01	01-02	02-03	03-04	04-05	05-06	06-07	07-08	08-09	09-10
NL 1 1	NL 1 1	NL 1 2	NL 1 3	NL 1 3	NL 1 2	NL 1 20	NL 1 15	NL 1 14	NL 1 7

BILLINGHAM SYNTHONIA

Founded: 1923 Nickname: Synners

Secretary: Graham Craggs **(T)** 07702 530 335 **(E)** graham.craggs@gb.abb.com
Chairman: Stuart Coleby **Manager:** Mickey Watson **Prog Ed:** David Lealman
Ground: The Stadium, Central Ave, Billingham, Cleveland TS23 1LR **(T)** 01642 532 348
Capacity: 1,970 **Seats:** 370 **Covered:** 370 **Midweek Matchday:** Wednesday **Clubhouse:** Yes **Shop:** Yes

Colours(change): Green & white quarters/white/white
Previous Names: Billingham Synthonia Recreation
Previous Leagues: Teesside 1923-the war
Records: **Att:** 4,200 v Bishop Auckland 1958 **Goalscorer:** Tony Hetherington **App:** Andy Harbron
Senior Honours: Northern Lge 1956-57, 88-89, 89-90, 95-96. Div.2 86-87.

10 YEAR RECORD

00-01	01-02	02-03	03-04	04-05	05-06	06-07	07-08	08-09	09-10
NL 1 8	NL 1 11	NL 1 4	NL 1 9	NL 1 2	NL 1 7	NL 1 14	NL 1 9	NL 1 15	NL 1 12

BILLINGHAM TOWN

Founded: 1967 Nickname: Billy Town

Secretary: Glenn Youngman **(T)** 07984 258 608 **(E)** CFS_IFA@hotmail.com
Chairman: Tommy Donnelly **Manager:** Carl Jarrett **Prog Ed:** Peter Martin
Ground: Bedford Terrace, Billingham, Cleveland TS23 4AF **(T)** 01642 560 043
Capacity: 3,000 **Seats:** 176 **Covered:** 600 **Midweek Matchday:** Tuesday **Clubhouse:** Yes **Shop:** No

Colours(change): Blue/blue/white
Previous Names: Billingham Social Club
Previous Leagues: Stockton & District 1968-74 Teesside 1974-82
Records: **Att:** 1,500 v Man City FA Youth Cup 1985 **Goalscorer:** Paul Rowntree 396 **App:** Paul Rowntree 505
Senior Honours: Durham Cup 1976-77, 77-78, 2003-04

10 YEAR RECORD

00-01	01-02	02-03	03-04	04-05	05-06	06-07	07-08	08-09	09-10
NL 1 9	NL 1 10	NL 1 3	NL 1 5	NL 1 7	NL 1 4	NL 1 2	NL 1 10	NL 1 17	NL 1 19

DIVISION ONE INS & OUTS

IN: Jarrow Roofing Boldon CA (P), Stokesley (P), Sunderland Ryhope CA (P)
OUT: Chester-le-Street Town (R), Horden Colliery Welfare (R), Morpeth Town (R)

BISHOP AUCKLAND

Founded: 1886 Nickname:

Secretary: Tony Duffy (T) 07974 286 812 (E) pauline@paulineduffy.wanadoo.co.uk
Chairman: Terry Jackson **Manager:** Colin Myers **Prog Ed:** Dave Strong
Ground: West Auckland FC, Darlington Rd, W.Auckland DL14 9HU (T) 07974 286 812
Capacity: 3,000 **Seats:** 250 **Covered:** 250 **Midweek Matchday:** Wednesday **Clubhouse:** Yes **Shop:** No

Colours(change): Light & dark blue/2 blues/2 blues
Previous Names: Auckland Town 1889-1893
Previous Leagues: Northern Alliance 1890-91, Northern League 1893-1988, Northern Premier 1988-2006
Records: **Att:** 17,000 v Coventry City FA Cup 2nd round 1952 **App:** Bob Hardisty
Senior Honours: Post War: Nth Lge 1949-50, 50-51, 51-52, 53-54, 54-55, 55-56, 66-67, 84-85, 85-86 (18th Nth Lge title).

10 YEAR RECORD

00-01	01-02	02-03	03-04	04-05	05-06	06-07	07-08	08-09	09-10
NP P 3	NP P 21	NP 1 15	NP 1 13	NP P 19	NP 1 22	NL 1 16	NL 1 20	NL 1 18	NL 1 13

CONSETT

Founded: 1899 Nickname: Steelman

Secretary: David Pyke (T) 07889 419 268 (E) david.pyke@trendnetworkservices.com
Chairman: John Hurst **Manager:** Kenny Lindoe **Prog Ed:** Gary Welford
Ground: Belle Vue Park, Ashdale Road, Consett, DH8 6LZ (T) 01207 503 788
Capacity: 4,000 **Seats:** 400 **Covered:** 1000 **Midweek Matchday:** Wednesday **Clubhouse:** Yes **Shop:** No

Colours(change): All Red
Previous Names: None
Previous Leagues: N.All 1919-26, 35-37, N.E.C. 26-35, 37-58, 62-64, Midland 58-60, N.Co. 60-62, Wearside 64-70
Records: **Att:** 7000 v Sunderland Reserves, first match at Belle Vue 1950
Senior Honours: Norh Eastern Lg 39-40 Div 2 26-27, Northern Counties Lg 61-62, Northern Leageu Div.2 1988-89, 05-06.

10 YEAR RECORD

00-01	01-02	02-03	03-04	04-05	05-06	06-07	07-08	08-09	09-10
NL 1 10	NL 1 17	NL 1 20	NL 2 3	NL 1 19	NL 2 1	NL 1 4	NL 1 2	NL 1 2	NL 1 10

DUNSTON UTS

Founded: 1975 Nickname: The Fed

Secretary: Bill Montague (T) 07981 194 756 (E) w.montague@sky.com
Chairman: Malcolm James **Manager:** William Irwin **Prog Ed:** Bill Montague
Ground: UTS Stadium, Wellington Rd, Dunston, Gateshead NE11 9LJ (T) 0191 493 2935
Capacity: 2,000 **Seats:** 120 **Covered:** 400 **Midweek Matchday:** Tuesday **Clubhouse:** Yes **Shop:** No

Colours(change): All Blue with white trim/blue/blue.
Previous Names: Dunston Federation Brewery > 2007. Dunston Federation > 2009.
Previous Leagues: Northern Amateur & Wearside league
Records: **Att:** 1,550 v Sunderland Shipowners Cup Final 01.04.88 **Goalscorer:** Paul King **App:** Paul Dixon
Senior Honours: Wearside League 1988-89, 89-90. Northern League Div.2 92-93. Div.1 2003-04, 04-05.

10 YEAR RECORD

00-01	01-02	02-03	03-04	04-05	05-06	06-07	07-08	08-09	09-10
NL 1 2	NL 1 3	NL 1 8	NL 1 1	NL 1 1	NL 1 3	NL 1 7	NL 1 6	NL 1 6	NL 1 4

ESH WINNING

Founded: 1885 Nickname: Stags

Secretary: David Thompson OBE (T) 07968 909 732 (E) thompsondr@fsmail.net
Chairman: Charles Ryan **Manager:** Adam Furness **Prog Ed:** Simon Bourne
Ground: West Terrace, Waterhouse, Durham DH7 9NQ (T) 0191 373 3872
Capacity: 3,500 **Seats:** 160 **Covered:** 500 **Midweek Matchday:** Tuesday **Clubhouse:** Yes **Shop:** No

Colours(change): Yellow/green/yellow
Previous Names: Esh Albion, Esh Rangers, Esh Pineapple (pre 1982)
Previous Leagues: Northern 1912-35. Durham & Dist. Sunday 1968-81, N. Alliance 1981-82.
Records: **Att:** 5,000 v Newcastle Utd Res. 1910 & Bishop Auckland 1921 **Goalscorer:** Alan Dodsworth 250+ **App:** Neil McLeary - 194
Senior Honours: Northern League Champions 1912-13.

10 YEAR RECORD

00-01	01-02	02-03	03-04	04-05	05-06	06-07	07-08	08-09	09-10
NL 2 5	NL 2 3	NL 1 17	NL 1 15	NL 1 14	NL 1 20	NL 2 16	NL 2 13	NL 2 3	NL 1 18

JARROW ROOFING BOLDON C.A. Founded: 1987 Nickname: Roofing

Secretary: Mark Groves **(T)** 07930 803 387 **(E)** m_groves@sky.com
Chairman: Richard McLoughlin **Manager:** **Prog Ed:** Dave Atkinson
Ground: Boldon CA Sports Ground, New Road, Boldon Colliery NE35 9DZ **(T)** 07930 803 387
Capacity: 3,500 **Seats:** 150 **Covered:** 800 **Midweek Matchday:** Tuesday **Clubhouse:** Yes **Shop:** Yes

Colours(change): Blue with yellow trim/blue/blue
Previous Names:
Previous Leagues: S. Tyneside Senior 1987-88, Tyneside Am. 1988-91, Wearside 1991-96
Records: Att: 500 v South Shields **Goalscorer:** Mick Hales **App:** Paul Chow
Senior Honours:

10 YEAR RECORD

00-01	01-02	02-03	03-04	04-05	05-06	06-07	07-08	08-09	09-10
NL 1 13	NL 1 12	NL 1 9	NL 1 6	NL 1 12	NL 1 15	NL 1 15	NL 1 22	NL 2 16	NL 2 3

NEWCASTLE BENFIELD Founded: 1988 Nickname: The Lions

Secretary: Mark Hedley **(T)** 07973 699 506 **(E)** markhedley3@msn.com
Chairman: Jimmy Rowe **Manager:** **Prog Ed:** Jim Clark
Ground: Sam Smiths Park, Benfield Road, Walkergate NE6 4NU **(T)** 0191 265 9357
Capacity: 2,000 **Seats:** 150 **Covered:** 250 **Midweek Matchday:** Wednesday **Clubhouse:** Yes **Shop:** No

Colours(change): Blue & white hoops/blue/blue
Previous Names: Heaton Corner House. Newcastle Benfield Saints.
Previous Leagues: Northern Alliance 1988-2003
Records:
Senior Honours: Northern Alliance Div 2 Champions 1989-90, Div 1 1994-95, 2002-03
Northern League Cup 2006-07. Northern League Champions 2008-09.

10 YEAR RECORD

00-01	01-02	02-03	03-04	04-05	05-06	06-07	07-08	08-09	09-10
NAl P 7	NAl P 3	NAl P 1	NL 2 2	NL 1 4	NL 1 9	NL 1 5	NL 1 4	NL 1 1	NL 1 5

NORTON & STOCKTON ANCIENTS Founded: 1959 Nickname: Ancients

Secretary: Steven Lawson **(T)** 07871 206 474 **(E)** stevenlawson_16@hotmail.co.uk
Chairman: Michael Mulligan **Manager:** Conrad Hillerby **Prog Ed:** Steven Lawson
Ground: Norton (Teesside) Sports Complex, Station Rd, Norton TS20 1PE **(T)** 01642 530 203
Capacity: 2,000 **Seats:** 200 **Covered:** yes **Midweek Matchday:** Wednesday **Clubhouse:** **Shop:**

Colours(change): Amber & black/black/black.
Previous Names: Norton & Stockton Cricket Club Trust
Previous Leagues: Teesside (pre-1982)
Records: Att: 1,430 v Middlesbrough, Friendly1988.
Senior Honours: Northern League Cup 1982-83.

10 YEAR RECORD

00-01	01-02	02-03	03-04	04-05	05-06	06-07	07-08	08-09	09-10
NL 2 8	NL 2 12	NL 2 18	NL 2 18	NL 2 6	NL 2 7	NL 2 6	NL 2 10	NL 2 2	NL 1 8

PENRITH Founded: 1894 Nickname: Blues

Secretary: Ian White **(T)** 07960 958 367 **(E)** ianwhite77@hotmail.com
Chairman: David Noble **Manager:** **Prog Ed:** Brian Kirkbride
Ground: Frenchfield Park, Frenchfield, Penrith CA11 8UE **(T)** 01768 895 990
Capacity: 4,000 **Seats:** 200 **Covered:** 1,000 **Midweek Matchday:** Tuesday **Clubhouse:** Yes **Shop:** No

Colours(change): Blue/white/blue.
Previous Names: Penrith FC. Penrith Town.
Previous Leagues: Carlisle & Dist. Northern 1942-82. NWC 1982-87, 90-97. NPL 1987-90.
Records: Att: 2,100 v Chester 1981 **Goalscorer:** C Short **App:** Lee Armstrong
Senior Honours: Northern League Division 2 Champions 2002-03, 07-08.

10 YEAR RECORD

00-01	01-02	02-03	03-04	04-05	05-06	06-07	07-08	08-09	09-10
NL 2 7	NL 2 4	NL 2 1	NL 1 21	NL 2 8	NL 2 4	NL 2 7	NL 2 1	NL 1 7	NL 1 14

RYTON

Founded: 1970 Nickname:

Secretary: Ken Rodger **(T)** 07872 839 368 **(E)** kenneth@krodger.fsnet.co.uk

Chairman: Richard Hands **Manager:** Barry Fleming **Prog Ed:** Chris Holt

Ground: Kingsley Park, Stannerford Road, Crawcrook NE40 3SN **(T)** 0191 413 4448

Capacity: 2,000 **Seats:** **Covered:** **Midweek Matchday:** Tuesday **Clubhouse:** Yes **Shop:** No

Colours(change): Blue & black stripes/black/blue

Previous Names:

Previous Leagues: Northern Combination. Northern Alliance

Records: **Att:** 1,100 v Newcastle United 1998

Senior Honours: Northern Alliance Division 1 Champions 1996-97.

10 YEAR RECORD

00-01	01-02	02-03	03-04	04-05	05-06	06-07	07-08	08-09	09-10
NAl P 14	NAl P 13	NAl P 9	NAl P 3	NAl P 2	NAl P 11	NAl P 12	NAl P 3	NL 1 10	NL 1 17

SHILDON

Founded: 1890 Nickname: Railwaymen

Secretary: Gareth Howe **(T)** 07976 822 453 **(E)** gareth.howe3@btopenworld.com

Chairman: Brian Burn **Manager:** Gary Forrest **Prog Ed:** Bob Wake

Ground: Dean Street, Shildon, Co. Durham DL4 1HA **(T)** 01388 773 877

Capacity: 4,000 **Seats:** 480 **Covered:** 1000 **Midweek Matchday:** Wednesday **Clubhouse:** Yes **Shop:** No

Colours(change): All red

Previous Names: Shildon Athletic > 1923.

Previous Leagues: Auckland & Dist 1892-86, Wear Valley 1896-97, Northern 1903-07, North Eastern 1907-32

Records: **Att:** 11,000 v Ferryhill Athletic, Durham Senior Cup 1922 **Goalscorer:** Jack Downing 61 (1936-7) **App:** Bryan Dale

Senior Honours: Durham Amateur Cup 1901-02, 02-03, Durham Challenge Cup 1907-08, 25-26, 71-72,
Northern League Champions 1933-34, 34-35, 35-36,36-37, 39-40, Div 2 2001-02,

10 YEAR RECORD

00-01	01-02	02-03	03-04	04-05	05-06	06-07	07-08	08-09	09-10
NL 2 13	NL 2 1	NL 1 6	NL 1 4	NL 1 11	NL 1 18	NL 1 9	NL 1 5	NL 1 8	NL 1 2

SOUTH SHIELDS

Founded: 1974 Nickname: Mariners

Secretary: Philip Reay **(T)** 07847 173 235 **(E)** philip@sheels.fsnet.co.uk

Chairman: Gary Crutwell **Manager:** Gary Steadman **Prog Ed:** Philip Reay

Ground: Mariners Club, Filtrona Park, Shaftesbury Ave, Jarrow NE32 3UP **(T)** 0191 427 9839

Capacity: 2,500 **Seats:** 150 **Covered:** 400 **Midweek Matchday:** Tuesday **Clubhouse:** Yes **Shop:** Yes

Colours(change): Claret & sky blue/white/white.

Previous Names: South Shields Mariners.

Previous Leagues: Northern Alliance 1974-76, Wearside 1976-95.

Records: **Att:** 1,500 v Spennymoor, Durham Challenge Cup Final 1994-95.

Senior Honours: Northern Alliance 1974-75, 75-76, Wearside League 1976-77, 92-93, 94-95
Monkwearmouth Charity Cup 1986-87.

10 YEAR RECORD

00-01	01-02	02-03	03-04	04-05	05-06	06-07	07-08	08-09	09-10
NL 2 11	NL 2 8	NL 2 8	NL 2 12	NL 2 13	NL 2 18	NL 2 4	NL 2 2	NL 1 19	NL 1 11

SPENNYMOOR TOWN

Founded: 1890 Nickname: Moors

Secretary: David Leitch **(T)** 07530 453 880 **(E)** leitchy1969@btinternet.com

Chairman: Bradley Groves **Manager:** Jason Ainsley **Prog Ed:** Garry Nunn

Ground: Brewery Field, Durham Road, Spennymoor DL16 6JN **(T)**

Capacity: 7,500 **Seats:** 300 **Covered:** 2,000 **Midweek Matchday:** Wednesday **Clubhouse:** Yes **Shop:** Yes

Colours(change): Black & white stripes/white/black

Previous Names: Amalgamation of Evenwood Town & Spennymoor Utd in 2005-06.

Previous Leagues: None

Records:

Senior Honours: Northern League Division 2 2006-07, Division 1 2009-10.

10 YEAR RECORD

00-01	01-02	02-03	03-04	04-05	05-06	06-07	07-08	08-09	09-10
					NL 2 8	NL 2 1	NL 1 12	NL 1 4	NL 1 1

STOKESLEY

Founded: 1920 Nickname:

Secretary: Trevor Wing **(T)** 07860 780 446 **(E)** trevor.wing10@btinternet.com
Chairman: John Passman **Manager:** **Prog Ed:** Trevor Wing
Ground: Lotus Electrical Stadium, Broughton Road, Stokesley TS9 5JQ **(T)** 01642 710 051
Capacity: **Seats:** **Covered:** **Midweek Matchday:** Wednesday **Clubhouse:** **Shop:**

Colours(change): Red & Black/black/black
Previous Names: Stokesley Sports Club > 2009.
Previous Leagues: Langbargh, South Bank, Stokesley & Dist., Teesside, Wearside.
Records:
Senior Honours: Stokesley & District Lge 1975-76. Northern League Division 2 2009-10

10 YEAR RECORD

00-01	01-02	02-03	03-04	04-05	05-06	06-07	07-08	08-09	09-10
Wear 9	Wear 8	Wear 3	Wear 3	Wear 3	Wear 2	NL 2 8	NL 2 9	NL 2 13	NL 2 1

SUNDERLAND RYHOPE C.A.

Founded: 1961 Nickname:

Secretary: Rob Jones **(T)** 07932 951 842 **(E)** Robert.jones10@homecall.co.uk
Chairman: Owen Haley **Manager:** Neil Hixon **Prog Ed:** Rob Jones
Ground: Meadow Park, Beachbrooke, Stockton Rd, Ryhope, Sunderland SR2 0NZ **(T)** 0191 523 6555
Capacity: 2,000 **Seats:** 150 **Covered:** 200 **Midweek Matchday:** Wednesday **Clubhouse:** **Shop:**

Colours(change): Red & white halves/black/red
Previous Names: Ryhope Community Ass. FC
Previous Leagues: S.C. Vaux: Tyne & Wear, NorthEastern Am a Ryhope CA N Alliance.>82
Records:
Senior Honours: Northern Alliance Lge Cup 1981

10 YEAR RECORD

00-01	01-02	02-03	03-04	04-05	05-06	06-07	07-08	08-09	09-10
NL 2 10	NL 2 10	NL 2 11	NL 2 9	NL 2 16	NL 2 17	NL 2 19	NL 2 4	NL 2 4	NL 2 2

TOW LAW TOWN

Founded: 1890 Nickname: Lawyers

Secretary: Steve Moralee **(T)** 07810 238 731 **(E)** stephen.moralee@btinternet.com
Chairman: Sandra Gordon **Manager:** Ian Davison **Prog Ed:** John Dixon
Ground: Ironworks Ground, Tow Law, Bishop Auckland DL13 4EQ **(T)** 01388 731 443
Capacity: 6,000 **Seats:** 200 **Covered:** 300 **Midweek Matchday:** Tuesday **Clubhouse:** Yes **Shop:** Yes

Colours(change): Black & white stripes/black/black
Previous Names: Tow Law.
Previous Leagues: Northern League 1894-1900, South Durham Alliance 1900-05, Crook & District 1905-12
Records: **Att:** 5,500 v Mansfield Town FA Cup 1967.
Senior Honours: Northern League Champions 1923-24, 24-25, 94-95. League Cup 73-74.

10 YEAR RECORD

00-01	01-02	02-03	03-04	04-05	05-06	06-07	07-08	08-09	09-10
NL 1 7	NL 1 2	NL 1 15	NL 1 16	NL 1 16	NL 1 12	NL 1 12	NL 1 7	NL 1 11	NL 1 9

WEST ALLOTMENT CELTIC

Founded: 1928 Nickname:

Secretary: Ted Ilderton **(T)** 07795 246 245 **(E)** tedilderton@o2.co.uk
Chairman: Roland Mather **Manager:** **Prog Ed:** Steve Allott
Ground: Whitley Park, Whitley Road, Benton NE12 9FA **(T)** 0191 270 0885
Capacity: **Seats:** **Covered:** **Midweek Matchday:** Monday **Clubhouse:** **Shop:**

Colours(change): Green & white hoops/green/green & white.
Previous Names:
Previous Leagues: Tynemouth & District. Northern Amateur. Northern Alliance.
Records: **Att:** 510 v Cray Wanderers FA Vase 2004
Senior Honours: Northern Am. 1956-57, 57-58, 58-59, 59-60, 81-82, 82-83, Div 2: 38-39.
Northern Alliance: 1986-87, 90-91, 91-92, 97-98, 98-99, 99-2000, 01-02, 03-04. Northern League Div 2 2004-05

10 YEAR RECORD

00-01	01-02	02-03	03-04	04-05	05-06	06-07	07-08	08-09	09-10
NAl P 2	NAl P 1	NAl P 3	NAl P 1	NL 2 1	NL 1 13	NL 1 18	NL 1 13	NL 1 9	NL 1 15

WEST AUCKLAND TOWN

Founded: 1893 Nickname: West

Secretary: Allen Bayles **(T)** 07894 329 005 **(E)** allenbayles@hotmail.co.uk
Chairman: Jim Palfreyman **Manager:** Peter Dixon **Prog Ed:** Michael Bainbridge
Ground: Darlington Road, West Auckland, Co. Durham DL14 9HU **(T)** 07800 796 630
Capacity: 3,000 **Seats:** 250 **Covered:** 250 **Midweek Matchday:** Tuesday **Clubhouse:** Yes **Shop:** No

Colours(change): All white
Previous Names: Auckland St Helens. St Helens. West Auckland.
Previous Leagues: Auck&D.,Wear Val,Sth D'ham All.Mid D'ham, Nth Lge 1919-20.Palantine 20-24.Sth D'ham 27-28.Gaunless Val 33-34
Records: Att: 6,000 v Dulwich Hamlet FA Amateur Cup 1958-59
Senior Honours: Sir Thomas Lipton Trophy 1909, 1911, Northern Lge 1959-60, 60-61.
Div 2 1990-91. League Cup 1958-59, 62-63, Durham Challenge Cup 1964-65

10 YEAR RECORD

00-01	01-02	02-03	03-04	04-05	05-06	06-07	07-08	08-09	09-10
NL 1 12	NL 1 7	NL 1 13	NL 1 13	NL 1 17	NL 1 5	NL 1 6	NL 1 16	NL 1 20	NL 1 16

WHITLEY BAY

Founded: 1897 Nickname: The Bay

Secretary: Derek Breakwell **(T)** 07889 888 187 **(E)** dbreakwell@hotmail.co.uk
Chairman: Paul McIlduff **Manager:** Ian Chandler **Prog Ed:** Julian Tyley
Ground: Hillheads Park, Rink Way, Whitley Bay, NE25 8HR **(T)** 0191 291 3637
Capacity: 4,500 **Seats:** 450 **Covered:** 650 **Midweek Matchday:** Tuesday **Clubhouse:** Yes **Shop:** Yes

Colours(change): Blue & white stripes/blue/blue
Previous Names: Whitley Bay Athletic 1950-58
Previous Leagues: Tyneside 1909-10, Northern All. 1950-55, N. Eastern 1955-58, Northern 1958-88 N.P.L. 1988-00
Records: 7,301 v Hendon, FA Amateur Cup 1965.
Senior Honours: Northern Alliance 1952-53, 53-54.
Northern League 1964-65, 65-66, 06-07. NPL Div 1 1990-91, FA Vase 2001-02, 08-09.

10 YEAR RECORD

00-01	01-02	02-03	03-04	04-05	05-06	06-07	07-08	08-09	09-10
NL 1 11	NL 1 5	NL 1 10	NL 1 10	NL 1 5	NL 1 10	NL 1 1	NL 1 3	NL 1 3	NL 1 3

DIVISION TWO INS & OUTS
IN: Chester-le-Street Town (R), Horden Colliery Welfare (R), Morpeth Town (R)
OUT: Jarrow Roofing Boldon CA (P), Stokesley (P), Sunderland Ryhope CA (P)

BIRTLEY TOWN

Founded: 1993 Nickname: The Hoops

Secretary: Trevor Armstrong **(T)** 07958540389 **(E)** trevellen@aol.com
Chairman: John Heslington **Manager:** **Prog Ed:** Trevor Armstrong
Ground: Birtley Sports Complex, Durham Road, Birtley DH3 2JH **(T)** 07958540389 **Capacity:**
Colours(change): Green & white hoops/green/green

ADDITIONAL INFORMATION:
Previous League: Wearside 1993-2007.
Honours: Wearside League 2002-03, 06-07, Division 2 1994-95, League Cup 1998, 2002, 2006.

BRANDON UNITED

Founded: 1968 Nickname: United

Secretary: Barry Ross **(T)** 07717 673090 **(E)** barryross430@btinternet.com
Chairman: Bill Fisher **Manager:** **Prog Ed:** Dean Johnson
Ground: Welfare Park, Rear Commercial Street, Brandon DH7 8PL **(T)** 07717 673090 **Capacity:** 3,000
Colours(change): All red

ADDITIONAL INFORMATION: Previous League: Wearside 1981-83. **Record Att:** 2,500 F.A. Sunday Cup Seim-final.
Record: Goalscorer: Tommy Holden. **Apps:** Derek Charlton 1977-86. **Honours:** F.A. Sunday Cup 1975-76.
Northern Alliance Division 2 1977-78, 78-79. Northern League 2002-03, Division 2 1984-85, 99-2000.

CHESTER-LE-STREET TOWN

Founded: 1972 Nickname: Cestrians

Secretary: Lenny Lauchlan **(T)** 07749924318 **(E)** l.w.lauchlan@durham.ac.uk
Chairman: Joe Burlison **Manager:** **Prog Ed:** Keith Greener
Ground: Moor Park, Chester Moor, Chester-le-Street, Co.Durham DH2 3RW **(T)** 07972 419275 **Capacity:** 3,500
Colours(change): Blue & white hoops/white/white

ADDITIONAL INFORMATION: Previous Name: Garden Farm 1972-78. **Previous League:** Wearside 1977-83.
Record Att: 893 v Fleetwood FA Vase 1985 **App:** Colin Wake 361.
Honours: Washington League 1975-6 Wearside League1980-81, Northern League Div 2 1983-84, 97-98.

CROOK TOWN

Founded: 1889 Nickname: Black & ambers

Secretary: Kieron Bennett **(T)** 07838 387 335 **(E)** k.bennett@leybourneurwinltd.co.uk
Chairman: Bill Penman **Manager:** **Prog Ed:** Kieron Bennett
Ground: Millfield Ground, West Road, Crook, Co.Durham DL15 9PW **(T)** 01388 762 959 **Capacity:** 3,500
Colours(change): Amber/black/amber

ADDITIONAL INFORMATION: Previous Name: Crook C.W. **Previous League:** Durham Central 1941-45.
Honours: FA Amateur Cup 1900-01, 53-54, 58-59, 61-62, 63-64. Northern League x5, League Cup x3.
Durham Challenge Cup x4. Durham Benefit Bowl x6. Ernest Armstrong Memorial Trophy 1997.

DARLINGTON R.A.

Founded: 1993

Secretary: Rob Poynter **(T)** 07884 355 513 **(E)** r.poynter@hotmail.co.uk
Chairman: Doug Hawman **Manager:** **Prog Ed:** Chris Griffin
Ground: Brinkburn Road, Darlington, Co. Durham DL3 9LF **(T)** 01325 468 125 **Capacity:** 2,500
Colours(change): All red

ADDITIONAL INFORMATION:
Previous League: Darlington & District 1993-99.
Honours: Auckland & District League 2000-01. Wearside League 2004-05.

GILLFORD PARK

Founded: 2005

Secretary: Jeff Carr **(T)** 07835 795 099 **(E)** donaldfcameron@yahoo.co.uk
Chairman: Donald Cameron **Manager:** **Prog Ed:** Shirley McKaskie
Ground: Gillford Park Railway Club, Off Pettrill Bank Rd, Carlisle, Cumbria CA1 3AF **(T)** 01228 526 449 **Capacity:** 4,000
Colours(change): White/red/red

ADDITIONAL INFORMATION:
Previous Name: Gifford Park Spartans. **Previous League:** Northern Alliance 2005-09.
Honours: Northern Alliance Division 1 2006-07, Premier Division 2008-09, Challenge Cup 2008-09.

GUISBOROUGH TOWN

Founded: 1973 Nickname: Priorymen

Secretary: Daniel Clark **(T)** 07961 819 168 **(E)** danclark8063@hotmail.com
Chairman: Sandy MacKenzie **Manager:** **Prog Ed:** Andrew Willis
Ground: King George V Ground, Howlbeck Road, Guisborough TS14 6LE **(T)** 01287 636 925 **Capacity:** 3,500
Colours(change): White/red/red

ADDITIONAL INFORMATION: Previous League: Northern Counties East 1982-85.
Record Att: 3,112 v Hungerford FA Vase Semi-final. **Goalscorer:** Mark Davis 341. **Apps:** Mark Davis 587.
Honours: Northern Alliance 1979-80. Northern League Cup 1987-88. Nth Riding Sen Cup 1989-90, 90-91, 91-92, 92-93, 94-95

HEBBURN TOWN

Founded: 1912 Nickname: Hornets

Secretary: Tom Derrick **(T)** 07981 456 653 **(E)** tomderrick39@hotmail.com
Chairman: Bill Laffey **Manager:** **Prog Ed:** Steve Newton
Ground: Hebburn Sports & Social, Victoria Rd West, Hebburn, Tyne&Wear NE31 1UN **(T)** 0191 483 5101 **Capacity:** 2,000
Colours(change): Yellow & navy stripes/navy/navy

ADDITIONAL INFORMATION: Previous Names: Reyrolles, Hebburn Reyrolles > 1988, Hebburn 1988-2000.
Previous League: Wearside 1960-89. **Record Att:** 503 v Darwen FA Cup Prelim replay 07/09/1991, **Win:** 10-1. **Defeat:** 3-10.
Honours: Tyneside League 1938-39, Northern Combination 1943-44, Wearside League 1966-67,

HORDEN C.W.

Founded: 1908 Nickname: Colliers

Secretary: John Stubbs **(T)** 07726 694 672 **(E)** johnstubbsuk@btinternet.com
Chairman: Norman Stephens **Manager:** **Prog Ed:** John Stubbs
Ground: Welfare Park, Seventh Street, Horden, Peterlee, Co. Durham SR8 4LX **(T)** **Capacity:** 3,000
Colours(change): Red/black/red

ADDITIONAL INFORMATION: Previous Name: Horden Athletic. **Previous League:** North Eastern 1962-64.
Record Att: 8,000 FA Cup 1937. **Honours:** Wearside League 1911-12, 12-13, 13-14, 33-34, 64-65, 67-68, 69-70, 70-71, 71-72, 72-73. Northern League Division 2 2008-09.

MARSKE UNITED

Founded: 1956 Nickname: The Seasiders

Secretary: Les Holtby **(T)** 07804 150 880 **(E)** marskeunited@ntlworld.com
Chairman: Billy Park **Manager:** **Prog Ed:** Moss Holtby
Ground: GER Stad., Mount Pleasant Avenue, Marske by the Sea, Redcar TS11 7BW **(T)** 01642 471 091 **Capacity:** 2,500
Colours(change): Yellow/blue/blue

ADDITIONAL INFORMATION: Previous League: Wearside 1985-97. **Record Att:** 1,359 v Bedlington Terriers FA Vase. **Win:** 16-0.
Defeat: 3-9. **Goalscorer:** Chris Morgan 169. **Apps:** Mike Kinnair 583. **Honours:** Teeside League 1980-81, 84-85.
Wearside League 1995-96. North Riding Senior Cup 1994-95. North Riding County Cup 1980-81, 85-86.

MORPETH TOWN
Founded: 1909 Nickname: Highwaymen

Secretary: Ken Waterhouse **(T)** 0777 7651 332 **(E)** ken.waterhouse@btinternet.com
Chairman: Jim Smith **Manager:** **Prog Ed:** Ken Waterhouse
Ground: Craik Park, Morpeth Common, Morpeth, Northumberland, NE61 2YX **(T)** **Capacity:**
Colours(change): Yellow/black/yellow

ADDITIONAL INFORMATION:
Previous League: Northern Alliance > 1994.
Honours: Northern Alliance 1983-84, 93-94, Northern League Division 2 1995-96. Northumberland Senior Cup 2006-07.

NEWTON AYCLIFFE
Founded: 1965 Nickname: Aycliffe

Secretary: Stephen Cunliffe **(T)** 07872 985 501 **(E)** stecunliffe@aol.com
Chairman: Gary Farley **Manager:** **Prog Ed:** Paul McGeary
Ground: Moore Lane Park, Moore Lane, Newton Aycliffe, Co. Durham DL5 5AG **(T)** 01325 312 768 **Capacity:**
Colours(change): All blue

ADDITIONAL INFORMATION: Previous League: Wearside.
Record Att: 520 v Teeside Athletic (Sunderland Shipwoners Final) 2008-09.
Honours: Durham Alliance League 2007-08. Wearside League 2008-09.

NORTH SHIELDS
Founded: 1992 Nickname: Robins

Secretary: David Thompson **(T)** 07969 239 476 **(E)** trevorcampbel69@hotmail.com
Chairman: Alan Matthews **Manager:** **Prog Ed:** Mark Scott
Ground: Ralph Gardner Park, West Percy Road, Chirton, North Shields **(T)** 07969 239 476 **Capacity:**
Colours(change): All red

ADDITIONAL INFORMATION:
Previous Names: Preston Colliery > 1928, North Shields Athletic 1995-99. **Previous League:** Wearside.
Honours: FA Amateur Cup 1968-69, N.C.E. Prem Div 91-92, Lge Cup 90-91. Wearside League 1998-99, 01-02, 03-04.

NORTHALLERTON TOWN
Founded: 1994 Nickname: Town

Secretary: Lesley Clark **(T)** 07891 595 267 **(E)** lesleyclark05@yahoo.co.uk
Chairman: Dave Watson **Manager:** **Prog Ed:** Ian Bolland
Ground: RGPS Stadium, Ainderby Road, Northallerton DL7 8HG **(T)** 01609 772 418 **Capacity:**
Colours(change): Black & white/black/black

ADDITIONAL INFORMATION: Previous Name: Northallerton FC 1994. **Previous League:** Harrogate & District.
Record Att: 695 v Farnborough Town FA Trophy 3rd Round 20/02/1993.
Honours: Northern League Division 2 1996-97, League Cup 1993-94.

SEAHAM RED STAR
Founded: 1973 Nickname: The Star

Secretary: Kevin Turns **(T)** 0770 107 684 **(E)** seahamredstarfc@aol.co.uk
Chairman: John McBeth **Manager:** **Prog Ed:** James Smith
Ground: Seaham Town Park, Stockton Road, Seaham. Co.Durham SR7 0HY **(T)** **Capacity:** 4,000
Colours(change): Red & white stripes/black/black

ADDITIONAL INFORMATION: Previous Name: Seaham Colliery Welfare Red Star 1978-87. **Previous League:** Wearside 1979-83.
Record Att: 1,500 v Guisborough. **App:** Michael Whitfield.
Honours: Durham Challenge Cup 1979-80, Wearside League & League Cup 1981-82, Norhtern Lge Cup 1992-93

TEAM NORTHUMBRIA
Founded: 1999

Secretary: Gaz Lee **(T)** 07970 478 723 **(E)** GAZ.LEE@northumbria.ac.uk
Chairman: Ian Elvin **Manager:** **Prog Ed:** Gaz Lee
Ground: Coach Lane, Benton, Newcastle upon Tyne, NE7 7XA **(T)** 0191 215 6575 **Capacity:**
Colours(change): Red/red/red & black

ADDITIONAL INFORMATION:
Previous Name: Northumbria University > 2003. **Previous League:** Northern Alliance 1999-2006.
Honours: Northern Alliance Premier 2005-06.

THORNABY
Founded: 1980

Secretary: Peter Morris **(T)** 07854 152 084 **(E)** thornabyfc@btopenworld.com
Chairman: Lol Lyons **Manager:** **Prog Ed:** Paul Beards
Ground: Teesdale Park, Acklam Road, Thornaby, Stockton on Tees TS17 7JE **(T)** 07833 524 659 **Capacity:** 5,000
Colours(change): Blue with white flash/blue/blue

ADDITIONAL INFORMATION: Previous Names: Stockton Cricket Club 1965-1980, Stockton 1980-99 and Thornaby-on-Tees 1999-2000
Previous League: Wearside 1981-85. **Records Att:** 3,000 v Middlesborough friendly Aug 1986 **App:** Michael Watson
Honours: North Riding County Cup, 1985-86, Northern Lge Div 2 1987-88, 91-92

WASHINGTON

Founded: 1949 Nickname: Mechanics

Secretary: Barry Spendley **(T)** 07810 536 964 **(E)** Derek.Armstrong1@ntlworld.com
Chairman: Derek Armstrong **Manager:** **Prog Ed:** Bob Goodwin
Ground: Nissan Sports Complex, Washington Road Sunderland SR5 3NS **(T)** 0191 4152 354 **Capacity:** 3,000
Colours(change): All red

ADDITIONAL INFORMATION: Previous Names: Washington Mechanics, Washington Ikeda Hoover. **Previous League:** Wearside.
Record Att: 3,800 v Bradford Park Avenue FA Cup 1970.
Honours: Washington Amateur: 1956-57,57-58, 58-59,59-60,61-62,62-63, League Cup: 1955-56, 58-59, 60-61, 64-65.

WHICKHAM

Founded: 1944

Secretary: Paul Nicholson **(T)** 07841 506 694 **(E)** paul-nicholson3@sky.com
Chairman: Brian McCartney **Manager:** **Prog Ed:** Michael Tucker
Ground: Glebe Sports Club, Rectory Lane, Whickham NE16 4NA **(T)** 0191 4200 186 **Capacity:** 4,000
Colours(change): Black & white stripes/black/black

ADDITIONAL INFORMATION: Previous League: Northern Combination 1973-74.
Record Att: 3,165 v Windsor & Eton FA Vase SF 1981. **Honours:** FA Vase 1980-81, Wearside Lge 77-78, 87-88, Sunderland Shipowners Cup 77-78, 80-81, Northern Comb 69-70, 72-73, 73-74 Lge Cup 60-61, 73-74

WHITEHAVEN

Founded: 1994

Secretary: W Robson **(T)** 0759 5276 080 **(E)** whitehavenfc@aol.com
Chairman: S Hocking **Manager:** **Prog Ed:** D J Moors
Ground: Focus Scaffolding Sports Complex, Coach Road, Whitehaven, CA28 9DB **(T)** 01946 692 211 **Capacity:**
Colours(change): Yellow/blue/yellow

ADDITIONAL INFORMATION: Previous League: Wearside 1994-2008
Record Att: 207 v Workington Reds, Cumberland County Cup 13/12/2007.
Honours: Wearside League Division 2 1994-95, Wearside League 2005-06. Monkwearmouth Charity Cup 2006-07.

GROUND DIRECTIONS

ASHINGTON - Leave the A1 at the junction with the A19 north of Newcastle. Go along the A19 eastwards untio the next roundabout . Here take the second left (A189) signposted to Bedlington and Ashington. Continue along A189 until reach Woodhorn roundabout, turn left onto A197. Turn left at first roundabout. Just before the hospital car park entrance, turn right. Ground is on left.

BEDLINGTON TERRIERS - Take the A1068 from the south, and when in the town turn right onto the A193. Turn left at the Northumberland Arms on Front Street in Bedlington town centre. Continue along this road for approx .25 mile, then turn right into Park Road. The ground is 100 yards on right.

BILLINGHAM SYNTHONIA - Leave A19 onto A1027 sign posted towards Billingham. Continue straight ahead over a couple of roundabouts, and you will be on Central Avenue. The ground is on left opposite an empty office block.

BILLINGHAM TOWN - Leave A19 on A1027 signed Billingham. Turn left at third roundabout, into Cowpen Lane. Go over a railway bridge, then first left into Warwick Crescent, then first left again into Bedford Terrace (follow one-way signs) to the ground.

BIRTLEY TOWN - Leave A1(M) at Angel of the North and follow signs to Birtley (A167). Continue along main road through town. Go past Komatsu factory on right and then after approx 200 yards turn right into an unmarked side road. Ground is directly in front of you.

BISHOP AUCKLAND – CURRENTLY GROUNDSHARING AT WEST AUCKLAND - Leave A1 at junction 58 on to the A68. Follow signs to W. Auckland/Corbridge. On entering village, ground is behind factory on left side. Ground is up a track on the left side of road next to Oakley Grange Farm.

BRANDON UNITED - Leave A1 on A690, go through Durham and continue on A690. Once at 'Langley Moor' (you go under a railway bridge), turn right at the "Lord Boyne" pub. After 100 yards take the next left. Go up the road for approx half a mile, and turn right at the newsagents. Take the next left, and Brandon's ground is up a small track.

CHESTER LE STREET - Leave A1M at junction 63 and take the A167 towards Chester Le Street and Durtham. Keep going along this road for a couple of miles. You will go under a railway bridge, and as the road begins to climb, you will see the Chester Moor pub on your left. Turn into the pub and the ground is accessed along a track at the rear of the pub car park.

CONSETT - Take the A692 from the east into Consett. On the edge of the town, the A692 takes a left at a roundabout. Continue along the A692 for approx 100 yards, before turning right into Leadgate Road. Go along here for approx .25 mile, and turn right into Ashdale Road. There is a road sign for the Leisure Centre pointing into Ashdale Road. The ground is approx 200 yards along Ashdale Road on your right.

CROOK TOWN - Leave the A1 at Junction 62, and take the A690 towards Durham. Keep on this road through Durham, Meadowfield, Willington and Helmington Row. When you arrive in Crook town centre keep going straight ahead, as the A690 becomes the A689. The ground is situated on this road on your right, approximately 300 yards from the town centre.

DARLINGTON RAILWAY ATHLETIC - Leave A1(M) at junction 58 and follow the A68 into Darlington. Continue along the road until you see the Brown Trout public house on your right. Turn left at this point into Brinkburn Road, and the ground is 100 yards along on the left.

DUNSTON U.T.S. - From south take Dunston/Whickham exit off A1M. Turn right at top of slip road into Dunston Road and head down the bank. As the road veers left, the road becomes Wellington Road, and the ground is situated on your left.

ESH WINNING - Leave the A1 at Junction 62, and take the A690 towards Durham. Keep on this road through Durham. Once you start to head down a bank on the A690, you will come to a roundabout. Take the right turn onto the B6302, which will be signposted towards Ushaw Moor. Keep on this road though Ushaw Moor (there is a staggered crossroads to negotiate), and carry on the B6302 into Esh Winning. Keep on going as the ground is not in Esh Winning, but the next village along, Waterhouses. When the road takes a sharp left you will see a track continuing straight ahead. The ground is along this track.

GILLFORD PARK - Take junction 42 off the M6 and then the A6 into Carlisle. After 1.75 miles take left turn into Petterill Bank Road (junction is at traffic lights). After half a mile turn right onto track immediately before railway bridge. This leads you to the ground.

GUISBOROUGH TOWN - Turn off the A19 into the A174, then come off at the second junction, turning right onto the A172. Follow this round until roundabout with A1043, take left exit to join the A1043. Take right at next roundabout to join the A171. At second roundabout turn right into Middlesbrough Road (will be signposted towards Guisborough) then take left turning at traffic lights into Park Lane. Take first left into Howlbeck Road, and the ground is at the end of the road.

HEBBURN TOWN - Leave A1M on A194(M) (junction 65) and follow signs for Tyne Tunnel. Continue until fourth roundabout and turn left on to B1306 (Hebburn, Mill Lane). Right at traffic lights into Victoria Road. Ground 200 yards long this road on the left.

HORDEN C.W. - Take A19 to Peterlee turn off (B1320). Follow main road into Peterlee then through on the same road, following signs to Horden (B1320). At T-junction, turn left into Sunderland Road, at lights, (A1086) and then right into South Terrace after ? mile. Ground is at bottom of South Terrace.

JARROW ROOFING - From south take A19 and follow signs for Tyne Tunnel. Turn right at junction marked Boldon Colliery (Testo Roundabout) on to the A184. Turn left at the next roundabout, into the B1293, and head towards Asda. At second roundabout, turn right at end of retail park. At the roundabout at the entrance to Asda, take the "10 to" exit, and you will pass a large brick building on you right, known as The Shack. Turn right into the car park after this building, and at the far end of the car park there is a small lane that leads off left. Roofers ground is at the end of this track.

MARSKE UNITED - Leave A19 and join Parkway (A174) to Marske until Quarry Lane roundabout. Take exit (A1085) into Marske. Take the next right after you pass under a railway bridge, into Meadow Road. Take the next left into Southfield Road and the entrance is on your left shortly before a T-junction.

MORPETH TOWN - From south. Turn off the A1 onto A197, sign posted Morpeth. Turn left at sign pointing Belsay (B6524). Take right turn just before bridge under the A1. Ground is signposted and up a small track is on the right.

NEWCASTLE BENFIELD - Take the A1058 from either the Tyne Tunnel or central Newcastle. Turn off this road at the junction with Benfield Road. Turn south at this junction, and the Crosslings building will be on your left. Ground is around 400 metres on left, by taking the first turning after passing railway bridge. The ground is 100 yards along this road.

NEWTON AYCLIFFE - From North, leave the A1at junction 60, and travel west along the A689 towards Bishop Auckland. At the roundabout, turn left to join A167. Travel along here for a couple of miles, and at first traffic lights and turn right onto B6443 (Central Avenue). At first roundabout (Tesco's) turn left into Shafto Way then 3rd left into Gunn Way then right into Moore Lane.

NORTHALLERTON TOWN - Leave A1 at Leeming Bar (A684) and follow signs to Northallerton. Approaching the town take the left turn B1333, signed Romanby. Ground is on left after 50 yards in Romanby.

NORTH SHIELDS - Continue north on the A19 after Tyne Tunnel. Take right exit at roundabout onto the A1058. At next roundabout take third exit at Billy Mill, signed to North Shields. At roundabout with A193, turn right, then take second left into Silkey's Lane. Ground is 100 yards on left.

NORTON & STOCKTON ANCIENTS - Leave A19 at Stockton/Norton turn off (A1027) and follow signs to Norton. At the roundabout at the top of the bank take a right turn onto the B1274. Take the next right into Station Road. Ground entrance is on left of road in a large sports complex, the entrance to which is just before the railway crossing. The ground a 200 yards along this track.

PENRITH - Turn off M6 at junction 40 then onto dual carriageway to Appleby and Scotch Corner. Take the A686 (signposted Alston), for approximately half a mile. Then take a right turn (opposite Carleton Road), and follow the track running parallel with the A66. Turn left into the sports complex and follow the road to the far end.

RYTON - Leave the A1 at the south side of the River Tyne (A694). At the

roundabout take the A695 (sign posted Blaydon). At Blaydon take the B6317 through Ryton to reach Crawcrook. Turn right at the traffic lights (sign posted Ryton/Clara Vale). Kingsley Park is situated approximately 500 meters on the right.

SEAHAM RED STAR - Leave A19 on B1404 slip road. Follow signs to Seaham/Ryhope. Turn right at traffic lights on to the B1285. Then left at Red Star social club approximately 200 yards after the traffic lights. There is a car park at the next roundabout behid their social club The ground is a short walk at the top of the park.

SHILDON - Leave A1M at junction 58. Follow A68 signed Bishop Auckland, turn right at roundabout onto A6072. At Shildon turn right at second roundabout (onto B6282) , then left into Byerley Rd (still the B6282). Right at Timothy Hackworth pub into Main St., then at the top of the bank, left into Dean Street.

SOUTH SHIELDS - From A1 M take A194 (M) to South Shields. Follow signs for town centre. Turn left at traffic lights (TESCO supermarket) into Shaftesbury Avenue. Ground is at the far end of the road

SPENNYMOOR TOWN - Turn off A1M at J61. Onto A688 towards Spennymoor, turn right at small roundabout & straight on at Thinford roundabout (Still continuing on the A688). Straight over mini roundabout, and take fourth exit from large roundabout (B6288). Continue for approx. ? mile and take left into Durham Road. Ground is on Wood Vue, approx 300 yards on right just off Durham Rd.

STOKESLEY - Turn off A19 onto A174 (Teesport/Redcar). Take third exit onto A172 (Whitby/Stokesley). Turn right and keep on A172 to Stokesley. In Stokesley bear left at first roundabout, still keeping on the A172. At next roundabout go straight across into Broughton Road (Second exit - B1257). Ground is 100 yards on left-hand side.

SUNDERLAND R.C.A. - From the A19, leave at the junction with the A690, but on that roundabout take the B1286 through Doxford Park. Continue along this road for some time (there are number of roundabouts), but there are signposts to Ryhope along this road. You will eventually come to a T-junction at the end of the B1286, and turn right onto the A1018. After 200 yards you will come to another roundabout, here take a right turn. Then take the next right into a new housing estate. There is a board at the entrance pointing you to Meadow Park, the home of R.C.A. The ground is at the far end of the estate.

TEAM NORTHUMBRIA - Take the A1058 from either the A19 or central Newcastle. Turn off this road at the junction with Benfield Road. Turn north at large Crosslings warehouse into Red Hall Drive, this then becomes Coach Lane. The ground is on the right just past Newcastle University halls of residence.

THORNABY - Turn off A19 onto A1130 and head towards Thornaby. Continue along Acklam Road for about half a mile. Ground is signposted from the main road - on the right up a track between houses after half a mile.

TOW LAW TOWN - Leave the A1 at junction 58 and turn on to A68. Follow signs for Tow Law/Corbridge. Ground is at far end of Tow Law on the left side. The ground is situated on Ironworks Road, which is the first left after a sharp left hand bend on the A68 in Tow Law.

WASHINGTON - Leave the A19 on slip road marked "Nissan Offices" as you pass Sunderland travelling north. This is the A1290. Continue to follow "Nissan Offices" signs. Left at traffic lights, then right at roundabout into complex. Ground is at far end of the plant.

WEST ALLOTMENT CELTIC - Continue on the A19 north after Tyne Tunnel until A191 exit. Take left exit marked Gosforth & Newcastle. A191 for three miles. The ground, The Blue Flames Sports Ground is on left.

WEST AUCKLAND TOWN - Leave A1 at junction 58 on to the A68. Follow signs to W. Auckland/Corbridge. On entering village, ground is behind factory on left side. Ground is up a track on the left side of road next to Oakley Grange Farm.

WHICKHAM - From A1M take the A692 junction, and travel in the direction signed to Consett. At top of the back the road forks left towards Consett, but you should take the right fork along the B6317 to Whickham. Follow this road for 1.5 miles, left turn into Rectory Lane (B6316). Take first right into Holme Avenue, and then first left. The ground is at top of lane. More car parking can be found further along Rectory Lane, take the next right. Walk past the cricket pitch to access the football club.

WHITEHAVEN - From the south, on A595, take the turning into Whitehaven at the top of Inkermann Terrace at traffic lights (A5094). Pass the Chase Hotel on left until reach set of traffic lights next to a garage. Turn left into Coach Lane and travel on until see an access to the left indicating a cycleway. Turn in and follow the path until meet the gates to the ground. From the north, it is easier to travel further down the A595, and follow instructions as above. This way you avoid the town centre.

WHITLEY BAY - Leave the A19 on the A191, and turn eastwards towards Whitely Bay. Continue along New York Road (A191) which then becomes Rake Lane (A191). Pass hospital on right & then into Shields Rd. and Hillheads Rd (both A191). Ground is to the right, floodlights can be seen from miles away! It is next to an ice rink.

SOUTH WEST PENINSULA LEAGUE

www.swpleague.co.uk

Sponsored by:
Carlsberg

Founded: 2007

Recent champions:
2008: Bodmin Town
2009: Bodmin Town

CHARITY BOWL

(League champions v League Cup holders)

(August 2nd at Launceston)
Bodmin Town 0
Plymouth Parkway 2

CHARITY VASE

(Division One East champions v Division One West champions)

(August 2nd at Launceston)
Exeter Civil Service 2
Penzance 7

Premier Division	P	W	D	L	F	A	Pts
Buckland Athletic	36	27	6	3	121	46	87
Bodmin Town	36	28	3	5	98	31	87
Falmouth Town	36	23	4	9	87	41	73
St Blazey	36	22	3	11	81	53	69
Tavistock	36	21	3	12	77	52	66
Plymouth Parkway	36	19	7	10	89	53	64
Penzance	36	18	7	11	68	54	61
Torpoint Athletic	36	17	10	9	65	55	61
Saltash United	36	16	10	10	74	49	58
Witheridge	36	17	4	15	83	72	55
Launceston	36	14	5	17	65	67	47
Ivybridge Town	36	11	10	15	57	67	43
Elburton Villa	36	10	11	15	57	78	41
Wadebridge Town	36	10	5	21	53	76	35
Dartmouth	36	10	5	21	48	78	35
Liskeard Athletic	36	7	8	21	54	82	29
Bovey Tracey	36	5	8	23	50	109	23
Cullompton Rangers	36	6	3	27	39	100	21
Holsworthy	36	2	6	28	37	140	12

Clyst Rovers - record expunged

	Bodmin Town	Bovey Tracey	Buckland Athletic	Clyst Rovers	Cullompton Rangers	Dartmouth	Elburton Villa	Falmouth Town	Holsworthy	Ivybridge Town	Launceston	Liskeard Athletic	Penzance	Plymouth Parkway	Saltash United	St Blazey	Tavistock	Torpoint Athletic	Wadebridge Town	Witheridge
Bodmin Town		8-0	2-2	5-0	4-0	0-0	2-0	2-1	5-2	3-1	1-0	4-1	5-0	0-0	1-0	3-0	5-1	2-1	3-2	3-2
Bovey Tracey	1-3		1-1	5-4	2-1	1-2	2-5	0-5	3-0	2-2	2-2	2-2	1-2	1-5	0-3	1-5	4-0	1-3	2-2	0-1
Buckland Athletic	5-0	6-2	***P***	n/a	1-1	4-1	5-2	2-2	7-1	4-1	6-2	1-0	3-1	3-1	2-1	3-1	5-1	3-0	3-0	4-1
Clyst Rovers	n/a	n/a	1-2	***R***	n/a	0-2	0-0	0-0	2-3	n/a	n/a	0-3	4-3	0-3	n/a	1-3	1-2	2-1	1-4	n/a
Cullompton Rangers	0-4	1-3	2-3	n/a	***E***	0-1	3-2	1-5	3-2	0-1	0-5	0-5	1-2	0-5	2-0	1-3	1-5	1-2	3-3	2-1
Dartmouth	1-4	1-1	0-3	1-0	5-2	***M***	1-1	0-5	5-2	1-1	3-1	0-1	1-2	2-1	0-3	0-2	1-3	0-1	3-2	0-4
Elburton Villa	2-8	6-3	0-5	2-0	3-1	2-3	***I***	2-1	2-1	2-2	2-2	3-3	2-1	1-1	2-2	1-2	0-3	0-0	0-4	4-3
Falmouth Town	1-0	7-0	1-3	n/a	4-3	2-0	2-0	***E***	7-0	2-0	1-0	2-0	2-1	1-1	1-0	4-0	2-1	1-3	1-2	3-2
Holsworthy	0-3	1-1	1-6	n/a	2-3	2-1	1-1	0-3	***R***	2-1	0-6	3-3	0-4	1-7	1-3	0-5	0-5	3-3	2-2	1-5
Ivybridge Town	0-1	2-1	3-2	n/a	1-0	0-2	2-2	0-2	3-0		1-2	3-2	2-4	2-2	2-5	2-4	1-2	1-0	1-1	2-1
Launceston	2-0	6-2	2-1	4-1	1-3	4-2	0-1	0-2	3-1	0-0	***D***	1-2	1-4	0-2	2-0	1-3	4-2	0-2	3-0	2-1
Liskeard Athletic	0-5	2-3	1-2	1-0	2-1	1-2	1-2	2-3	3-3	1-5	0-4	***I***	2-3	0-2	3-4	1-4	0-3	0-2	3-1	6-2
Penzance	0-2	1-0	3-0	n/a	3-0	4-0	2-0	3-2	4-2	1-3	2-1	1-1	***V***	3-3	0-0	2-0	0-3	2-2	2-0	1-1
Plymouth Parkway	0-3	4-1	0-2	n/a	4-1	1-0	1-2	3-1	9-0	1-1	4-1	3-3	4-3	***I***	0-1	2-1	2-5	3-2	1-0	4-1
Saltash United	3-1	3-0	3-3	n/a	1-1	4-2	1-1	0-3	6-1	2-2	0-0	4-0	1-1	1-3	***S***	5-1	1-1	3-3	3-2	1-2
St Blazey	1-3	6-1	2-3	n/a	2-0	1-0	1-1	3-1	5-1	4-2	6-0	1-1	0-3	3-0	2-1	***I***	0-1	2-2	2-1	1-0
Tavistock	0-2	2-0	2-4	3-2	1-0	3-3	3-0	1-2	4-1	3-0	5-2	0-0	4-1	0-2	0-1	2-1	***O***	1-2	2-0	3-2
Torpoint Athletic	2-0	2-2	1-8	n/a	3-0	4-1	1-0	2-2	5-0	1-3	1-1	1-0	0-0	1-4	2-1	2-3	1-0	***N***	3-2	1-1
Wadebridge Town	0-3	3-2	1-3	2-1	4-0	3-2	1-0	1-1	3-0	3-2	1-2	0-2	2-1	2-1	2-3	2-3	0-1	1-3		0-4
Witheridge	0-3	4-2	3-3	n/a	5-1	3-2	4-3	3-2	1-0	2-2	4-2	2-0	3-1	4-3	0-4	0-1	2-4	3-1	6-0	

THROGMORTON CUP

FIRST ROUND

Axminster Town 2 **Crediton United** 3
Bickleigh 1 **Budleigh Salterton** 3 *aet*
Callington Town 0 **Alphington** 3
Clyst Rovers 1 **Royal Marines** 2
Dobwalls 1 **Liverton United** 2 *aet*
Exeter University 1 **Exmouth Town** 2
Falmouth Town 3 Perranporth 2 *aet*
Galmpton Utd Torbay Gents 4 Totnes & Dartington SC 1
Godolphin Atlantic 4 Wendron United 0
Hayle 3 Newquay 2
Millbrook 1 **Holsworthy** 4
Okehampton Argyle 1 **Foxhole Stars** 3
Ottery St Mary 0 **Appledore** 2
Penryn Athletic 4 Mousehole 2
Penzance 4 Porthleven 2
Plymstock United 1 **Camelford** 2
St Austell 2 Liskeard Athletic 0
Stoke Gabriel 2 **Launceston** 2 *aet* (6-7p)
Teignmouth 3 Bovey Tracey 0
Truro City Res. 2 **St Blazey** 3 *aet*
Vospers Oak Villa 2 Newton Abbot Spurs 2 *aet* (4-2p)
Wadebridge Town 3 Elburton Villa 1
Witheridge 2 Exeter Civil Service 1

SECOND ROUND

Appledore 3 **Exmouth Town** 3 *aet* (1-3p)
Buckland Athletic 8 Budleigh Salterton 0
Camelford 2 Wadebridge Town 1
Cullompton Rangers 1 **Crediton United** 2 *aet*
Falmouth Town 1 **Bodmin Town** 3 *aet*
Galmpton United & Torbay Gents 2 **Plymouth Parkway** 4
Holsworthy 3 Teignmouth 1
Ivybridge Town 2 Torpoint Athletic 0
Launceston 5 Dartmouth 1
Liverton United 4 Foxhole Stars 2 *aet*
Penryn Athletic 2 **Hayle** 4 *aet*
Royal Marines 3 Witheridge 0
Saltash United 4 Godolphin Atlantic 1
St Austell 2 **Alphington** 3 *aet*
St Blazey 1 **Penzance** 2
Vospers Oak Villa 1 **Tavistock** 3

THIRD ROUND

Alphington 2 Crediton United 1
Bodmin Town 3 Hayle 1
Ivybridge Town 1 **Exmouth Town** 3
Launceston 0 **Buckland Athletic** 5
Liverton United 3 Holsworthy 0
Penzance 1 **Tavistock** 4 *aet*
Plymouth Parkway 2 Camelford 1
Saltash United 1 **Royal Marines** 2

QUARTER-FINALS

Bodmin Town 1 Liverton United 0 *aet*
Exmouth Town 0 **Buckland Athletic** 4
Royal Marines 2 Alphington 1
Tavistock 0 Plymouth Parkway 0 *aet* (5-4p)

SEMI-FINALS

Bodmin Town 1 Tavistock 0 *(at Liskeard Athletic)*
Buckland Athletic 2 Royal Marines 1
aet (at Newton Abbot Spurs)

FINAL

(May 3rd at Cullompton Rangers)
Bodmin Town 1 **Buckland Athletic** 2 *aet*

Division One East	P	W	D	L	F	A	Pts
Royal Marines	34	26	3	5	110	46	81
Stoke Gabriel	34	22	3	9	92	43	69
Liverton United	34	19	8	7	82	47	65
Galmpton U./Torbay Gents	34	18	6	10	83	50	60
Appledore	34	18	3	13	89	69	57
Alphington	34	18	3	13	75	55	57
Totnes & Dartington SC	34	17	5	12	69	50	56
Exmouth Town	34	16	5	13	79	68	53
Budleigh Salterton	34	15	6	13	67	55	51
Exeter Civil Service	34	16	3	15	62	69	51
Teignmouth	34	15	5	14	81	77	50
Exeter University	34	12	5	17	60	68	41
Newton Abbot Spurs	34	12	4	18	64	86	40
Crediton United	34	10	5	19	59	86	35
Axminster Town	34	11	2	21	56	96	35
Okehampton Argyle	34	10	4	20	67	101	34
Ottery St Mary	34	5	7	22	48	127	22
Bickleigh	34	6	3	25	50	100	21

	Alph.	App.	Axm.	Bick.	Bud.	Cred.	Ex. CS	E. Uni	Exm.	Galm.	Liv.	NA Sp.	Oke.	Ottery	Ryl M.	Stoke	T'mth	Totnes
Alphington		2-2	6-0	5-0	4-1	2-0	1-1	0-1	1-2	2-3	0-0	3-0	1-2	5-1	1-2	1-0	2-0	1-3
Appledore	2-3	***D***	5-0	2-3	3-2	7-3	6-1	4-3	3-1	3-2	0-0	1-2	2-3	6-0	1-5	2-1	7-2	4-1
Axminster Town	2-5	5-2	***I***	3-2	2-0	4-1	1-2	0-4	2-0	0-5	1-3	2-3	1-3	3-2	2-4	1-3	4-1	2-2
Bickleigh	2-3	1-3	0-2	***V***	3-6	4-0	0-4	2-3	3-1	0-0	0-2	0-5	1-2	5-8	1-2	0-3	3-2	1-3
Budleigh Salterton	3-1	2-0	1-2	4-1	***I***	6-1	0-1	2-0	3-1	2-4	0-2	4-1	5-0	3-1	2-2	1-0	1-3	4-3
Crediton United	3-1	1-3	3-0	3-3	1-2	***S***	1-0	5-3	3-5	0-1	1-3	1-2	2-2	3-0	1-4	0-3	3-0	1-1
Exeter Civil Service	0-3	0-1	2-4	1-0	1-0	4-5	***I***	2-1	3-3	0-1	2-1	2-0	4-2	1-1	1-5	2-3	1-3	2-1
Exeter University	0-2	2-4	4-0	2-4	3-0	2-1	0-2	***O***	0-2	0-2	2-4	4-1	2-2	3-3	1-4	3-1	1-2	2-1
Exmouth Town	1-2	3-1	4-4	3-0	1-1	2-4	2-1	2-4	***N***	2-1	1-3	2-4	2-2	6-1	3-1	2-0	8-3	1-3
Galmpton Utd/TGs	4-0	2-3	8-1	1-0	2-2	1-2	8-5	2-2	1-2		0-0	4-2	4-0	5-0	3-2	1-4	2-4	3-1
Liverton United	2-1	5-1	5-0	5-0	2-2	3-2	2-0	1-0	2-3	0-0	***O***	3-1	4-1	6-0	0-2	1-1	3-2	0-2
Newton Abbot Spurs	2-3	0-1	2-1	5-2	0-1	2-3	3-4	2-2	2-2	4-2	1-4	***N***	4-3	1-1	3-2	2-4	1-1	0-1
Okehampton Argyle	1-3	1-6	4-3	3-1	2-1	6-1	1-4	2-3	0-2	0-5	4-4	1-3	***E***	2-3	2-3	4-3	4-7	0-4
Ottery St Mary	1-4	1-0	1-0	1-2	1-3	0-0	1-4	1-1	1-4	3-4	1-4	6-0	1-6		2-3	2-2	0-3	1-5
Royal Marines	4-1	4-1	2-0	3-2	2-0	1-1	1-2	2-0	3-1	1-1	4-1	6-1	4-0	8-1	***E***	3-2	8-3	2-1
Stoke Gabriel	3-1	1-1	1-3	5-1	2-0	2-1	6-0	3-0	2-1	2-0	3-2	6-0	3-2	13-0	4-3	***A***	1-2	1-0
Teignmouth	0-4	4-1	4-0	3-3	2-2	4-2	0-3	2-0	4-1	0-1	3-3	1-3	3-0	10-0	1-3	0-1	***S***	2-1
Totnes & Dartington	7-1	3-1	2-1	2-0	1-1	3-0	2-0	1-2	0-3	1-0	6-2	3-2	2-0	2-2	0-5	1-3	0-0	***T***

Division One West	P	W	D	L	F	A	Pts
Perranporth	30	20	4	6	78	35	64
St Austell	30	20	2	8	81	39	62
Hayle	30	18	2	10	68	37	56
Penryn Athletic	30	17	3	10	69	45	54
Newquay	30	16	4	10	79	62	52
Godolphin Atlantic	30	14	7	9	66	51	49
Plymstock United	30	14	7	9	56	41	49
Camelford	30	14	5	11	62	51	47
Dobwalls	30	13	7	10	55	46	46
Callington Town	30	12	7	11	57	50	43
Porthleven	30	11	6	13	64	67	39
Vospers Oak Villa	30	11	4	15	50	62	37
Foxhole Stars	30	7	7	16	41	78	28
Truro City Res.	30	6	4	20	35	73	22
Millbrook	30	6	4	20	34	87	22
Mousehole	30	1	7	22	18	89	10

Wendron United - record expunged

	Callington Town	Camelford	Dobwalls	Foxhole Stars	Godolphin Atlantic	Hayle	Millbrook	Mousehole	Newquay	Penryn Athletic	Perranporth	Plymstock United	Porthleven	St Austell	Truro City Res.	Vospers Oak Villa	Wendron United
Callington Town	***D***	5-1	0-2	2-2	2-4	1-2	5-3	1-1	2-1	4-1	0-0	0-1	3-2	0-1	3-0	2-3	n/a
Camelford	5-2	***I***	2-0	4-2	4-1	1-1	6-0	3-0	0-1	0-2	3-2	2-3	3-1	1-4	1-0	3-2	7-0
Dobwalls	1-1	1-4	***V***	2-0	4-2	1-4	0-3	7-0	0-2	3-3	3-4	2-0	2-0	1-0	0-0	1-1	6-0
Foxhole Stars	2-2	1-4	2-4	***I***	2-2	0-2	3-2	2-0	0-0	1-1	0-2	0-4	4-3	2-1	1-0	2-6	n/a
Godolphin Atlantic	0-2	3-2	0-0	3-0	***S***	1-2	2-0	5-0	5-3	3-2	3-0	5-0	3-3	1-2	2-0	3-1	n/a
Hayle	2-0	2-2	1-2	6-1	3-1	***I***	10-1	6-0	2-4	2-0	1-3	2-1	0-1	0-1	2-0	1-0	n/a
Millbrook	2-5	1-0	1-3	1-1	2-2	0-3	***O***	0-0	0-5	1-2	1-2	0-3	3-2	2-4	0-0	1-4	n/a
Mousehole	2-2	1-2	0-5	2-3	1-3	0-3	0-1	***N***	0-1	1-2	0-5	2-2	0-0	0-2	3-3	0-3	4-0
Newquay	1-2	3-2	5-3	3-1	1-1	1-3	9-3	8-1		2-0	1-1	1-1	3-4	0-3	4-2	3-2	n/a
Penryn Athletic	2-0	3-0	2-0	2-0	1-2	2-1	4-0	9-0	4-1	***O***	2-6	0-4	1-2	0-7	6-0	6-0	n/a
Perranporth	1-2	1-1	1-1	7-2	5-1	4-0	2-0	1-0	1-2	1-0	***N***	2-0	4-1	1-2	6-1	1-2	2-0
Plymstock United	3-3	2-0	1-0	1-1	2-2	2-0	3-1	3-0	4-0	0-2	2-4	***E***	2-2	5-2	0-1	0-1	n/a
Porthleven	3-2	1-1	1-2	2-1	2-2	1-3	4-1	2-2	5-4	1-2	0-3	0-1		3-2	8-1	5-3	n/a
St Austell	2-1	4-1	2-2	6-0	1-0	2-0	1-2	3-0	3-4	2-2	4-5	3-1	3-0	***W***	0-3	4-0	n/a
Truro City Res.	0-1	0-2	1-2	1-3	4-1	1-2	2-1	2-0	6-2	1-5	0-2	1-3	3-4	1-5	***E***	1-1	4-0
Vospers Oak Villa	0-2	2-2	3-1	3-2	0-3	3-2	0-1	0-2	1-4	0-1	0-1	2-2	3-1	1-5	3-0	***S***	6-0
Wendron United	1-3	0-2	0-8	n/a	n/a	n/a	n/a	n/a	n/a	n/a	n/a	0-3	0-4	0-4	0-7	n/a	***T***

BODMIN TOWN

Founded: 1896

Secretary: Nick Giles **(T)** 01208 75794 **(E)**
Chairman: **Manager:** Darren Gilbert **Prog Ed:**
Ground: Priory Park, Bodmin, Cornwall PL31 2AE **(T)** 01208 78165 **Capacity:**
Colours(change): Yellow & black (All white)

ADDITIONAL INFORMATION:
Previous League: South Western.
Honours: South Western League 1990-91, 93-94, 2005-06. South West Peninsula Premier Division 2007-08, 08-09.

BOVEY TRACEY

Founded: 1950 Nickname: Moorlands

Secretary: Steve Cooney **(T)** 07795 373 786 **(E)** c_moon@btinternet.com
Chairman: **Manager:** Cyril Gosling **Prog Ed:**
Ground: Western Counties Roofing (Mill Marsh Pk), Ashburton Rd, Bovey TQ13 9FF **(T)** 01626 832 780 **Capacity:**
Colours(change): All red (All white)

ADDITIONAL INFORMATION: **Previous Names:** Bovey Town and Bovey St John's merged to form Bovey Tracey in 1950.
Previous League: South Devon.
Honours: Herald Cup 1960-61. South Devon League Premier Division 2007-08.

BUCKLAND ATHLETIC

Founded: 1977 Nickname: The Bucks

Secretary: Christine Holmes **(T)** 01626 369 345 **(E)**
Chairman: **Manager:** Steve Massey **Prog Ed:**
Ground: Homers Heath, South Quarry, Kingskerswell Road, Newton Abbot TQ12 5JU **(T)** 01626 361 020 **Capacity:**
Colours(change): All yellow (All blue)

ADDITIONAL INFORMATION:
Previous League: Devon County League 2000-07.
Honours: South West Peninsula League Premier Division 2009-10. Throgmorton Cup 2009-10.

CULLOMPTON RANGERS

Founded: 1945 Nickname: The Cully

Secretary: Marcus Scott **(T)** 07740 168 072 **(E)** scott.marcus@ukgateway.net
Chairman: **Manager:** Peter Buckingham **Prog Ed:**
Ground: Speeds Meadow, Cullompton EX15 1DW **(T)** 01884 33090 **Capacity:**
Colours(change): Red & black (All white)

ADDITIONAL INFORMATION:
Previous League: Devon County 1992-2007.

DARTMOUTH

Founded: 1908 Nickname: The Darts

Secretary: Kathy Greeno **(T)** 01803 832 720 **(E)** kathgreeno@hotmail.com
Chairman: **Manager:** Lance Worthington **Prog Ed:**
Ground: Longcross, Dartmouth TQ5 9LW **(T)** 01803 832 902 **Capacity:**
Colours(change): Red & black (All white)

ADDITIONAL INFORMATION:
Previous League: Devon County 1999-2007.
Honours: Devon County League 2001-02, 02-03, 06-07.

ELBURTON VILLA

Founded: 1982 Nickname: The Villa

Secretary: David Trott **(T)** 01752 217 837 **(E)**
Chairman: **Manager:** Scott Bamford **Prog Ed:**
Ground: Haye Road, Elburton, Plymouth PL9 8NS **(T)** 01752 480 025 **Capacity:**
Colours(change): Red & white stripes/black (White & red)

ADDITIONAL INFORMATION:
Previous League: Devon County 1992-2007.

FALMOUTH TOWN

Founded: 1949 Nickname: The Ambers

Secretary: Stephen Rose **(T)** 07968 515 525 **(E)** stephendrose@aol.com
Chairman: **Manager:** Alan Carey **Prog Ed:**
Ground: Bickland Park, Bickland Water Road, Falmouth TR11 4PB **(T)** 01326 375 156 **Capacity:**
Colours(change): Amber & black (Blue & white)

ADDITIONAL INFORMATION: **Previous League:** South Western 1984-2007.
Honours: South Western League 1961-62, 65-66, 67-68, 70-71, 71-72, 72-73, 73-74, 85-86, 86-87, 88-89, 89-90, 91-92, 96-97, 99-2000. Western League 1974-75, 75-76, 76-77, 77-78. Cornwall Combination 1983-84.

PREMIER DIVISION INS & OUTS
IN: Royal Marines (P – Division One East), St Austell (P – Division One West)
OUT: Clyst Rovers (WS), Holsworthy (R – Division One West)

IVYBRIDGE TOWN
Founded: 1925 Nickname: The Ivys

Secretary: Paul Cocks **(T)** 07967 736 952 **(E)** secretary@ivybridgefc.com
Chairman: **Manager:** Nicky Marker **Prog Ed:**
Ground: Erme Valley, Ermington Road, Ivybridge PL21 9ES **(T)** 01752 896 686 **Capacity:**
Colours(change): Green & black (Blue & white)

ADDITIONAL INFORMATION:
Previous League: Devon County.
Honours: Devon County League 2005-06.

LAUNCESTON
Founded: 1891 Nickname: The Clarets

Secretary: Keith Ellacott **(T)** 07966 497 453 **(E)** launcestonfc@aol.com
Chairman: **Manager:** Joe Davey **Prog Ed:**
Ground: Pennygillam Ind. Est., Launceston PL15 7ED **(T)** 01566 773 279 **Capacity:**
Colours(change): All claret (Sky blue & black)

ADDITIONAL INFORMATION:
Previous League: South Western.
Honours: South Western League 1995-96.

LISKEARD ATHLETIC
Founded: 1889 Nickname: The Blues

Secretary: Brian Olver **(T)** 01579 342 869 **(E)** brianolver25@yahoo.com
Chairman: **Manager:** Leigh Cooper **Prog Ed:**
Ground: Lux Park Sport Association, Coldstyle Rd, Lux Park, Liskeard PL14 2HZ **(T)** 01579 342 665 **Capacity:**
Colours(change): All blue (All yellow)

ADDITIONAL INFORMATION:
Previous League: South Western 1995-2007.
Honours: South Western League 1976-77, 78-79. Western League Premier Division 1987-88.

PENZANCE
Founded: 1818 Nickname: The Magpies

Secretary: John Mead **(T)** 07952 312 906 **(E)** jamead@supanet.com
Chairman: **Manager:** Gary Marks & Wayne Quinn **Prog Ed:**
Ground: Penlee Park, Alexandra Place, Penzance TR18 4NE **(T)** 01736 361 964 **Capacity:**
Colours(change): White & black (Blue & white)

ADDITIONAL INFORMATION: Previous League: South Western 1951-2007.
Honours: South Western League 1955-56, 56-57, 74-75. South West Peninsula Division 1 West 2008-09. Cornwall Charity Cup 2008-09.

PLYMOUTH PARKWAY
Founded: 1988 Nickname: The Parkway

Secretary: Stuart Cadmore **(T)** 07891 476 280 **(E)** ailsastuart@btinternet.com
Chairman: **Manager:** Gez Baggott & Wayne Hillson **Prog Ed:**
Ground: Bolitho Park, St Peters Road, Manadon, Plymouth PL5 3OZ **(T)** **Capacity:**
Colours(change): Yellow & blue (Blue & white)

ADDITIONAL INFORMATION:
Previous Name: Ex-Air Flyers Plymouth.
Previous League: South Western 1998-2007.

ROYAL MARINES
Founded: 2008 Nickname: The Commandos

Secretary: Ian Mullholland **(T)** 07764 983 441 **(E)** rmfa-secretary@hotmail.co.uk
Chairman: **Manager:** Richard Pears & Danny Burwood **Prog Ed:**
Ground: Endurance Park, Heartbreak Lane, Lympstone EX8 5AR **(T)** 01392 414 038 **Capacity:**
Colours(change): All white (Green & white)

ADDITIONAL INFORMATION:
Honours: South West Peninsula League Division 1 East 2009-10.

SALTASH UNITED
Founded: 1945 Nickname: The Ashes

Secretary: Luke Ranford **(T)** 07830 299 555 **(E)** luke.ranford@googlemail.com
Chairman: **Manager:** Kevin Hendy **Prog Ed:**
Ground: Kimberley Stadium, Callington Road, Saltash PL12 6DX **(T)** 01752 845 746 **Capacity:**
Colours(change): Red & white stripes/black (White & black)

ADDITIONAL INFORMATION:
Previous League: South Western 2006-07.
Honours: South Western League 1953-54, 75-76. Western League Division 1 1976-77, Premier 1984-85, 86-87, 88-89.

ST. AUSTELL

Founded: 1890 Nickname: The Lily Whites

Secretary: Peter Beard **(T)** 01726 64138 **(E)**
Chairman: **Manager:** Andy Dingle **Prog Ed:**
Ground: Poltair Park, Trevarthian Road, St Austell PL25 4LR **(T)** 07966 130 158 **Capacity:**
Colours(change): White & black (Red & white)

ADDITIONAL INFORMATION:
Previous League: South Western 1951-2007.

ST. BLAZEY

Founded: 1896 Nickname: The Green & Blacks

Secretary: Simon Tonkin **(T)** 07989 432 467 **(E)** tonki.simon@sky.com
Chairman: **Manager:** Glynn Hooper **Prog Ed:**
Ground: Blaise Park, Station Road, St Blazey PL24 2ND **(T)** 01725 814 110 **Capacity:**
Colours(change): Green & black (Blue & white)

ADDITIONAL INFORMATION:
Previous League: South Western 1951-2007.
Honours: South Western Lge 1954-55, 57-58, 62-63, 63-64, 80-81, 82-83, 98-99, 2000-01, 01-02, 02-03, 03-04, 04-05, 06-07.

TAVISTOCK

Founded: 1888 Nickname: The Lambs

Secretary: Phil Lowe **(T)** 01822 613 715 **(E)** pjlowe442@hotmail.co.uk
Chairman: **Manager:** Ian Southcott **Prog Ed:**
Ground: Langsford Park, Red & Black Club, Crowndale Road, Tavistock PL19 8DD **(T)** 01822 614 447 **Capacity:**
Colours(change): Red & black (All blue)

ADDITIONAL INFORMATION:
Previous League: South Western 1968-2007.

TORPOINT ATHLETIC

Founded: 1887 Nickname: The Point

Secretary: Simon Bell **(T)** 07717 217 700 **(E)** si2bell@yahoo.co.uk
Chairman: **Manager:** Stuart Dudley **Prog Ed:**
Ground: The Mill, Mill Lane, Carbeile Road, Torpoint PL11 2NA **(T)** 01752 812 889 **Capacity:**
Colours(change): Yellow & black (Red & white)

ADDITIONAL INFORMATION:
Previous League: South Western 1962-2007.
Honours: South Western League 1964-65, 66-67.

WADEBRIDGE TOWN

Founded: 1894 Nickname: The Bridgers

Secretary: Bob Steggles **(T)** 07971 973 194 **(E)** bob@steggles.com
Chairman: **Manager:** Robbie Black **Prog Ed:**
Ground: Bodieve Park, Bodieve Road, Wadebridge PL27 7AJ **(T)** 01208 812 537 **Capacity:**
Colours(change): All red (All blue)

ADDITIONAL INFORMATION:
Previous League: South Western 1952-2007.
Honours: South West Peninsula Division 1 West 2007-08.

WITHERIDGE

Founded: 1920 Nickname: The Withy

Secretary: Chris Cole **(T)** 07899 981 396 **(E)** chriscole128@hotmail.com
Chairman: **Manager:** Warren Patmore **Prog Ed:**
Ground: Edge Down Park, Fore Street, Witheridge EX16 8AH **(T)** 01884 861 511 **Capacity:**
Colours(change): Blue with yellow trim (All claret)

ADDITIONAL INFORMATION:
Previous League: Devon County 2006-07.

DIVISION ONE EAST CONSTITUTION 2010-11

ALPHINGTON	The Chronicles EX2 8SW	01392 279 556
APPLEDORE AFC	Marshford EX39 1PA	01237 477 099
AXMINSTER TOWN	Sector Lane EX13 5BP	01297 35890
BICKLEIGH	Happy Meadow EX16 8RJ	01884 855 596
BUDLEIGH SALTERTON	Greenway Lane EX9 6SG	01395 443 850
CREDITON UNITED	Lords Meadow EX17 1ES	01363 774 671
EXETER CIVIL SERVICE	Foxhayes EX4 2BQ	01392 273 976
EXMOUTH TOWN	King George V Playing Field EX8 3EE	01395 263 348
GALMPTON UTD & TORBAY GENTLEMEN	Interline Builders Merchants Ground TQ5 0LP	No number
LIVERTON UNITED	Halford TQ12 6JF	No number
NEWTON ABBOT SPURS	Recreation Ground TQ12 2AR	01626 365 343
OTTERY ST MARY	Washbrook Meadows EX11 1EL	01404 813 539
STOKE GABRIEL	G J Churchward Memorial Ground TQ9 6RR	01803 550 853
TEIGNMOUTH	Coombe Valley TQ14 9EX	01626 776 688
TOTNES & DARTINGTON S.C.	Foxhole Sports Ground	No number
UNIVERSITY OF EXETER	Topsham Sports Ground EX3 0LY	01392 879 542

OUT: Okehampton Argyle (S – Division One West)

DIVISION ONE WEST CONSTITUTION 2010-11

CALLINGTON TOWN	Ginsters Marshfield Parc PL17 7DR	01579 382 647
CAMELFORD	Trefew Park PL32 9TS	07798 918 360
DOBWELLS	Lantoom Park PL14 4LU	07721 689 380
FOXHOLE STARS	Goverseth Park PL26 7UP	01726 824 615
GODOLPHIN ATLANTIC	Godolphin Way TR7 3BU	No number
HAYLE	Trevassack Park TR27 5HT	01736 757 157
HOLSWORTHY	Upcott Field EX22 6HF	01409 254 295
MOUSEHOLE	Trungle Park TR19 6UG	01736 731 518
NEWQUAY	Mount Wise TR7 2BU	01637 872 935
OKEHAMPTON ARGYLE	SIMMONS PARK EX20 1PR	01837 53997
PENRYN ATHLETIC	'Kernick' Kernick Road TR10 8QF	01326 375 182
PERRANPORTH	Ponsmere Valley TR6 0DB	No number
PLYMSTOCK UNITED	Dean Cross PL9 7AZ	01752 406 776
PORTHLEVEN	Gala Parc TR13 9LQ	01326 574 754
TRURO CITY	Treyew Road TR1 2TH	01872 278 853
VOSPERS OAK VILLA	Weston Mill PL2 2EL	01752 363 352

IN: Holsworthy (R), Okehampton Argyle (S – Division One West)
OUT: Millbrook (W – East Cornwall League Division One), St Austell (P)

GROUND DIRECTIONS - PREMIER DIVISION

BODMIN TOWN - Priory Park, Bodmin, Cornwall PL31 2AE. Tel: 01208 781 65.
Situated in Priory Park through main car park. Use football car park on Saturdays.

BOVEY TRACEY - Western Counties Roofing (Mill Marsh Park), Ashburton Road, Bovey Tracey TQ13 9FF. Tel: 01626 832 780.
Coming off the A38 East or Westbound at Drumbridges take the Bovey Tracey turn-off, straight through the lights at Heathfield. Next roundabout take 2nd exit, next roundabout take 3rd exit, then left, 35 yards, follow road to bottom of drive then enter through gate.

BUCKLAND ATHLETIC - Homers Heath, South Quarry, Kingskerswell Road, Newton Abbot TQ12 5JU. Tel: 01626 361 020.
From all areas head for Penn Inn roundabout then take the Newton Abbot turn-off. Keep in left-hand lane and filter left at first set of traffic lights. Go past Sainsbury's and follow road past the Keyberry Hotel. Carry straight on until you see the CLS Laundry then turn right into ground.

CULLOMPTON RANGERS - Speeds Meadow, Cullompton EX15 1DW. Tel: 01884 33090.
Leave M5 at junction 28, left at Town Centre, at Meadow Lane turn left past Sports Centre, at end of road turn right, then in 100 yards turn left into ground at end of lane.

DARTMOUTH - Longross, Dartmouth TQ5 9LW. Tel: 01803 832 902.
From Totnes the ground is on the road into Dartmouth - on the right is a BP garage - take next right (Milton Lane) then first right into ground.

ELBURTON VILLA - Haye Road, Elburton, Plymouth PL9 8NS. Tel: 01752 480 025.
From Plymouth City Centre take A379 Kingsbridge Road. At third roundabout turn left into Haye Road (signposted Saltram House). Ground 50 yards on left.

FALMOUTH TOWN - Bickland Park, Bickland Water Road, Falmouth TR11 4PB. Tel: 01326 375 156.
Take Penryn by-pass from Asda roundabout. Leave by-pass at Hillhead roundabout, take first right and follow industrial estate signs. Ground 1/2 mile on the left.

IVYBRIDGE TOWN - Erme Valley, Ermington Road, Ivybridge. Tel: 01752 896 686.
From Plymouth - leave A38 at Ivybridge and follow signs towards Ermington. Ground is immediately next to South Devon Tennis Centre. From Exeter - leave A38 at Ivybridge. Ground is in front of you at the end of the slip road.

LAUNCESTON - Pennygillam, Pennygillam Ind. Est., Launceston PL15 7ED. Tel: 01566 773 279.
Leave A30 onto Pennygillam roundabout, turn into Pennygillam Industrial Estate. Ground is 400 yards on the left.

LISKEARD ATHLETIC - Lux Park Sport Association, Coldstyle Road, Lux Park, Liskeard PL14 2HZ. Tel: 01579 342 665.
From the Parade (middle of town) turn left at the monument, then first right following signs for Leisure Centre at Lux Park.

PENZANCE - Penlee Park, Alexandra Place, Penzance TR18 4NE. Tel: 01736 361 964.
Follow road along harbour and promenade. Turn right at mini r'about into Alexandra Rd. Take either 1st (Mennaye Rd) 2nd (Alexandra Place) right.

PLYMOUTH PARKWAY - Bolitho Park, St Peters Road, Manadon, Plymouth PL5 3OZ.
From Cornwall/Exeter exit at the Manadon/Tavistock junction off the Plymouth Parkway (A38), off roundabout into St Peters Road. Entrance is one mile on the right.

ROYAL MARINES - Endurance Park, Heartbreak Lane EX8 5AR Tel: 01392 414 038
Take junction 30 off M5 and head towards Exmouth on A376. On approach to CTCRM turn left signposted Kings Squad Parking.

SALTASH UNITED - Ground: Kimberley Stadium, Callington Road, Saltash PL12 6DX. Tel: 01752 845 746.
At the top of Town Centre fork right at mini-roundabout. Ground is situated 400m ahead on the left-hand side next to Leisure Centre and Police Station.

ST AUSTELL - Poltair Park, Trevarthian Road, St Austell PL25 4LR Tel: 07966 130 158
Near Poltair School and St Austell Brewery (5 minutes from St Austell Rail Station).

ST BLAZEY - Blaise Park, Station Road, St Blazey PL24 2ND. Tel: 01725 814 110.
A390 from Lostwithiel to St Austell. At village of St Blazey turn left at traffic lights by Church/Cornish Arms pub into Station Road. Ground is 200 yards on the left.

TAVISTOCK - Langsford Park, Red & Black Club, Crowndale Road, Tavistock PL19 8DD. Tel: 01822 614 447.
From Launceston/Okehampton, stay on A386 trhough town signposted Plymouth, past Drake's statue. Over canal turn right, signposted football ground/recycle centre. Ground is 100 metres past Tavistock college. From Plymouth, stay on A386 pass Morrisons and Texaco garage, over River Tavy, turn left signposted football ground/recycle centre. Then as above.

TORPOINT ATHLETIC - The Mill, Mill Lane, Carbeile Road, Torpoint PL11 2NA. Tel: 01752 812 889.
Take turning at Carbeile Inn onto Carbeille Road and first turning on the right into Mill Lane.

WADEBRIDGE TOWN - Bodieve Park, Bodieve Road, Wadebridge PL27 7AJ. Tel: 01208 812 537.
At the island junction of the A39 & Wadebridge by-pass turn to go into Wadebridge. 200 yards turn right into Bodieve Rd and then 1st right into ground.

WITHERIDGE - Edge Down Park, Fore Street, Witheridge EX16 8AH. Tel: 01884 861 511.
B3137 Tiverton to Witheridge, on entering the village football pitch is on the right-hand side before the Fire Station and School.

SPARTAN SOUTH MIDLANDS LEAGUE

www.ssmfl.org

Sponsored by: Molten

Founded: 1998

Recent champions:
2005: Potters Bar Town
2006: Oxford City
2007: Edgware Town
2008: Beaconsfield SYCOB
2009: Biggleswade Town

Premier Division		P	W	D	L	F	A	Pts
Aylesbury		42	28	8	6	109	41	92
Chalfont St Peter		42	28	4	10	121	52	88
Tring Athletic		42	27	3	12	107	49	84
Royston Town		42	27	3	12	118	67	84
Colney Heath		42	23	7	12	87	68	76
Harefield United		42	23	4	15	81	67	73
Dunstable Town		42	22	6	14	90	58	72
Kingsbury London Tigers		42	21	7	14	86	67	70
Broxbourne Borough V & E		42	21	6	15	84	54	69
Leverstock Green		42	17	10	15	74	64	61
Oxhey Jets		42	17	7	18	83	81	58
Hatfield Town		42	18	4	20	69	71	58
Hanwell Town		42	16	9	17	84	71	57
St Margaretsbury		42	12	13	17	57	76	49
Haringey Borough		42	13	7	22	67	84	46
Hertford Town		42	13	7	22	53	80	46
Kentish Town		42	12	6	24	60	124	42
Hillingdon Borough		42	10	10	22	53	106	40
Langford		42	11	6	25	66	111	39
Biggleswade United		42	11	6	25	48	93	39
Brimsdown Rovers		42	10	8	24	50	84	38
Welwyn Garden City	*-3*	42	9	5	28	51	130	29

PREMIER DIVISION CUP

FIRST ROUND
Aylesbury 3 Oxhey Jets 2
Brimsdown Rovers 2 Leverstock Green 1
Hatfield Town 3 **Colney Heath** 4
Hertford Town 1 Tring Athletic 0
Hillingdon Borough 2 Harefield United 1
Langford 1 **Kingsbury London Tigers** 2

SECOND ROUND
Aylesbury 3 Chalfont St Peter 2
Biggleswade United 0 **St Margaretsbury** 2
Broxbourne Borough V & E 4 Kentish Town 2
Colney Heath 4 Royston Town 3 *aet*
Dunstable Town 1 Hillingdon Borough 0
Hanwell Town 1 Brimsdown Rovers 0
Kingsbury London Tigers 2 Haringey Borough 1
Welwyn Garden City 0 **Hertford Town** 4

QUARTER-FINALS
Aylesbury 1 Dunstable Town 0 *aet*
Broxbourne Borough V&E 1 St Margaretsbury 0
Colney Heath 1 **Kingsbury London Tigers** 1 *aet* (3-4p)
Hertford Town 0 **Hanwell Town** 3

SEMI-FINALS
Broxbourne Borough V & E 2 **Hanwell Town** 4
Kingsbury London Tigers 1 **Aylesbury** 2

FINAL
(April 28th at London Colney)
Aylesbury 2 Hanwell Town 1

	Aylesbury	Big'wade U.	Brimsdown	Broxbourne	Chalfont SP	Colney Hth	Dunstable	Hanwell T.	Harefield U.	Haringey B.	Hatfield T.	Hertford T.	Hillingdon B.	Kentish T.	Kingsb'y LT	Langford	Lev'stock G.	Oxhey Jets	Royston T.	St Marg'bury	Tring Ath.	Welwyn GC
Aylesbury		10-0	3-3	0-0	3-3	2-0	2-0	1-1	0-3	3-1	2-0	2-0	2-0	9-0	1-2	1-2	4-1	3-0	3-2	0-1	2-0	6-1
Biggleswade United	3-2		3-1	2-0	0-2	0-3	0-3	2-2	2-0	0-1	2-1	0-1	2-1	2-2	0-1	0-1	1-3	1-0	1-1	1-1	1-4	2-1
Brimsdown Rovers	0-0	0-3		1-0	1-3	0-1	2-0	0-2	2-1	0-4	0-1	3-2	1-2	2-0	1-2	0-0	0-3	3-4	1-2	0-3	1-4	1-2
Broxbourne Borough V&E	2-2	3-1	4-1	***P***	1-3	3-4	2-2	3-2	5-0	2-1	2-1	3-0	0-0	5-2	2-3	5-1	2-1	2-4	6-1	4-0	0-1	4-0
Chalfont St Peter	0-1	5-1	5-1	1-2	***R***	1-1	3-0	2-1	3-1	4-1	1-0	4-1	5-1	3-0	3-2	1-3	0-2	1-0	1-2	4-2	2-1	4-0
Colney Heath	0-4	4-2	0-2	2-1	0-4	***E***	1-3	1-1	2-1	3-0	0-2	4-0	3-0	5-1	2-2	2-0	1-0	0-1	2-1	3-0	3-0	1-0
Dunstable Town	4-1	3-2	1-1	1-0	1-1	2-4	***M***	0-3	0-2	6-2	1-2	2-0	2-2	4-0	1-2	2-1	3-0	1-0	0-2	1-2	1-0	2-1
Hanwell Town	1-2	1-1	2-1	0-2	0-3	5-0	3-0	***I***	4-1	6-2	1-0	1-1	3-4	5-0	0-3	3-1	1-1	0-1	2-4	1-1	0-6	6-0
Harefield United	0-3	2-0	1-1	3-0	3-2	5-0	2-1	1-1	***E***	2-4	2-1	2-0	4-1	6-2	1-3	1-2	5-2	2-0	0-2	0-2	3-2	3-2
Haringey Borough	1-2	3-0	1-0	0-1	1-1	4-1	1-0	0-7	1-2	***R***	1-2	2-0	8-0	0-2	0-3	3-0	1-0	1-2	1-4	2-0	0-4	1-1
Hatfield Town	0-1	5-2	0-3	1-2	3-2	3-0	1-5	1-2	1-2	2-1		0-1	6-1	1-2	2-0	4-4	3-3	2-2	4-1	1-0	0-1	3-3
Hertford Town	1-1	3-2	2-4	0-0	0-2	3-2	1-3	0-2	4-2	1-3	1-3	***D***	1-0	2-2	1-0	2-0	1-1	3-0	2-1	3-3	2-4	4-0
Hillingdon Borough	1-6	1-2	2-2	2-2	0-6	2-3	1-1	3-0	1-1	0-0	0-4	3-2	***I***	2-2	2-0	1-2	1-1	1-5	0-4	3-2	0-4	0-5
Kentish Town	0-3	2-2	4-2	0-2	1-7	1-1	0-6	3-2	1-3	4-3	1-2	1-0	0-2	***V***	3-2	2-0	1-2	2-0	0-3	3-0	2-5	6-2
Kingsbury London Tigers	0-3	3-1	1-2	2-4	2-3	1-1	1-2	3-2	0-3	2-1	5-1	1-0	1-1	2-0	***I***	2-0	3-1	3-0	4-2	1-1	3-3	5-1
Langford	3-5	2-0	3-0	0-5	1-7	0-7	1-2	2-3	1-2	3-3	0-1	6-0	1-3	1-2	2-3	***S***	0-3	4-4	1-6	1-5	0-2	4-1
Leverstock Green	0-1	2-1	0-2	0-1	1-3	3-3	0-1	2-1	1-1	2-1	6-1	4-0	3-2	4-1	2-2	2-2	***I***	2-5	1-5	3-0	1-1	2-0
Oxhey Jets	1-4	6-0	3-1	3-2	3-1	1-1	4-3	4-1	1-2	2-2	1-2	2-2	2-1	5-1	4-3	2-4	0-0	***O***	1-3	5-2	0-1	1-1
Royston Town	1-2	3-0	3-3	2-0	4-2	0-1	3-4	3-2	3-2	5-2	0-2	3-1	2-1	5-1	3-0	3-1	3-2	6-1	***N***	2-2	0-2	8-0
St Margaretsbury	1-1	1-0	1-1	1-0	1-4	2-4	2-2	1-1	1-3	2-2	1-0	2-0	1-2	1-1	2-2	3-3	0-3	2-0	0-3		0-1	0-2
Tring Athletic	2-4	3-2	4-0	2-0	1-0	3-8	0-2	5-0	0-1	2-0	4-0	0-1	5-0	8-0	2-1	6-0	0-2	3-2	4-2	0-1		6-1
Welwyn Garden City	0-2	0-1	2-0	1-0	2-9	2-3	0-12	0-3	3-0	1-1	2-0	0-4	0-3	3-2	1-5	2-3	0-2	2-1	2-5	3-4	1-1	

Division One		P	W	D	L	F	A	Pts
Holmer Green		40	28	9	3	95	31	93
Hadley		40	28	6	6	90	34	90
London Colney		40	28	5	7	107	40	89
Hoddesdon Town		40	23	9	8	98	46	78
AFC Dunstable		40	24	5	11	108	69	77
New Bradwell St Peter		40	22	6	12	96	70	72
Kings Langley		40	21	7	12	84	60	70
Crawley Green		40	21	5	14	80	59	68
Bedford		40	19	8	13	90	72	65
Bedford Town Res.		40	19	4	17	84	65	61
Cockfosters		40	17	9	14	82	75	60
Harpenden Town		40	15	6	19	65	73	51
Ampthill Town	*-3*	40	15	4	21	61	85	46
Sun Postal Sports		40	12	9	19	70	84	45
Stony Stratford Town		40	11	12	17	67	82	45
Buckingham Athletic		40	12	5	23	58	78	41
Amersham Town		40	10	7	23	49	100	37
Tokyngton Manor	*-3*	40	12	3	25	61	94	36
Cranfield United		40	7	8	25	29	103	29
Sport London E Benfica		40	6	5	29	42	121	23
Brache Sparta		40	1	6	33	27	102	9

DIVISION ONE CUP

FIRST ROUND

Amersham Town 2 Sport London E Benfica 0
Cranfield United 2 **Sun Postal Sports** 3
Harpenden Town 1 **Kings Langley** 3 *aet*
London Colney 1 Holmer Green 0
New Bradwell St Peter 1 **Stony Stratford Town** 4
Tokyngton Manor 2 **Hadley** 6

SECOND ROUND

AFC Dunstable 7 Stony Stratford Town 0
Ampthill Town 2 Bedford Town Res. 1
Brache Sparta 4 Amersham Town 4 *aet* (3-1p)
Cockfosters 3 **Hoddesdon Town** 6
Crawley Green (w/o) v Winslow United
Hadley 0 Bedford 0 *aet* (4-2p)
Kings Langley 4 Buckingham Athletic 1
London Colney 4 Sun Postal Sports 2

QUARTER-FINALS

Ampthill Town 5 AFC Dunstable 1
Crawley Green 3 Brache Sparta 0
Hadley 1 **Hoddesdon Town** 3 *aet*
London Colney 5 Kings Langley 1

SEMI-FINALS

Ampthill Town 0 **London Colney** 2
Crawley Green 1 **Hoddesdon Town** 2

FINAL

(May 8th at Royston Town)
London Colney 1 Hoddesdon Town 0

	AFC Dun.	Amersham	Ampthill	Bedford	Bedfd T Res.	Brache S.	Buck'ham A.	Cockfosters	Cranfield	Crawley G.	Hadley	Harpenden	Hoddesdon	Holmer G.	K. Langley	London C.	N. Bradwell	S. London	Stony Strat.	Sun Postal	Tokyngton
AFC Dunstable		7-1	2-2	3-2	2-0	5-1	4-3	3-1	1-0	2-1	0-3	7-2	1-0	1-2	2-2	4-1	3-4	5-1	2-2	4-0	6-0
Amersham Town	0-3		1-2	0-11	1-3	2-1	1-1	1-6	0-0	0-3	2-3	0-1	0-5	0-1	2-1	1-3	0-1	2-2	3-1	1-1	1-2
Ampthill Town	0-4	1-1		3-4	2-1	3-0	1-1	1-2	0-3	4-5	0-4	0-4	0-1	0-1	1-0	0-7	2-1	1-3	4-0	3-5	2-0
Bedford	4-4	4-3	1-0		1-3	2-1	0-2	5-5	4-2	1-0	1-3	3-0	4-4	0-1	3-2	1-0	7-1	3-0	1-1	3-3	1-3
Bedford Town Res.	5-4	1-3	4-1	1-1	***D***	5-0	4-1	4-0	1-0	1-3	0-1	0-0	0-1	0-2	3-1	1-4	1-1	1-2	1-0	2-3	3-0
Brache Sparta	1-3	0-2	1-1	1-2	0-2	***I***	0-4	1-4	0-2	2-6	0-2	0-1	1-1	0-4	1-4	0-3	1-5	0-2	2-3	1-1	0-1
Buckingham Athletic	1-2	3-1	1-3	1-1	1-0	3-1	***V***	1-2	0-1	1-2	3-0	0-3	0-1	0-3	0-2	0-0	4-1	6-1	1-0	1-0	3-4
Cockfosters	1-1	2-2	4-2	3-1	4-0	3-1	4-1	***I***	3-0	1-1	0-0	3-0	2-3	1-4	2-3	1-1	0-2	3-1	3-1	1-1	2-5
Cranfield United	0-7	0-0	0-5	1-3	0-3	2-1	1-1	0-1	***S***	0-2	0-3	0-4	1-1	0-6	2-4	0-9	2-1	3-0	1-1	0-0	1-0
Crawley Green	4-0	3-1	0-1	2-0	1-2	3-0	3-0	2-3	5-0	***I***	2-1	2-5	1-1	0-2	1-1	2-5	1-3	2-0	3-0	0-2	2-1
Hadley	3-1	2-3	3-0	2-0	3-1	2-0	2-1	3-2	5-1	1-1	***O***	4-1	2-1	0-0	0-0	0-2	3-1	1-0	4-0	1-1	3-1
Harpenden Town	0-1	3-1	3-1	0-3	0-6	1-0	2-1	4-2	3-0	3-2	0-3	***N***	0-1	1-2	1-2	0-2	2-3	6-0	1-1	2-2	0-0
Hoddesdon Town	6-2	8-0	0-1	4-1	2-3	4-0	1-0	3-0	2-2	6-1	2-0	1-0		1-0	1-2	1-1	0-0	4-0	6-3	4-6	5-1
Holmer Green	2-0	7-0	4-0	4-1	4-3	1-0	4-0	0-0	3-0	1-2	3-3	4-0	3-1		2-2	0-3	2-2	4-0	1-1	2-1	2-1
Kings Langley	2-0	3-2	1-3	1-2	3-0	3-1	3-1	2-3	2-0	2-1	1-2	2-2	3-2	1-1	***O***	5-3	1-2	3-0	1-1	5-2	5-1
London Colney	5-0	2-1	5-0	0-1	5-2	2-0	6-1	2-0	3-1	2-2	1-0	3-2	0-2	1-1	2-1	***N***	6-1	2-0	4-0	1-3	5-2
New Bradwell St Peter	0-1	2-0	2-0	3-1	2-6	0-0	5-2	2-0	7-0	1-2	2-3	3-1	3-3	0-1	4-1	3-1	***E***	6-0	2-2	6-1	5-0
Sport London E Benfica	2-5	0-6	0-1	0-1	2-2	1-1	1-2	4-3	5-1	3-1	0-6	0-3	1-4	0-3	0-3	1-2	2-3		0-4	3-3	1-4
Stony Stratford Town	0-6	0-2	1-6	2-2	1-4	4-4	4-0	4-1	0-0	0-2	0-3	4-1	1-1	1-1	0-2	0-2	5-0	4-0		3-1	7-1
Sun Postal Sports	5-0	1-2	1-2	1-0	2-1	0-2	2-5	1-2	4-1	0-1	0-3	1-0	0-4	3-4	3-0	0-1	1-2	3-3	2-3		3-2
Tokyngton Manor	L-W	L-W	4-2	2-4	1-4	3-1	2-1	2-2	3-1	0-3	0-3	3-3	L-W	1-3	1-2	L-W	2-4	4-1	1-2	3-1	

Res. Division One	P	W	D	L	F	A	Pt
Oxhey Jets Res.	30	20	3	7	71	36	63
Lon. Colney Res.	30	17	8	5	67	34	59
Royston T. Res.	30	16	5	9	67	41	53
AFC D'stable Res.	30	16	4	10	73	47	52
Crawley G. Res.	30	15	5	10	62	53	50
Hadley Res.	30	14	3	13	63	57	45
Cockfosters Res.	30	14	2	14	41	48	44
Hoddesdon Res.	30	11	8	11	49	55	41
K. Langley Res. *-1*	30	12	5	13	51	62	40
Langford Res.	30	12	3	15	55	56	39
St Marg'bury Res.	30	13	0	17	49	56	39
Holmer G. Res.	30	10	8	12	41	40	38
Aylesbury Res.	30	9	6	15	61	69	33
Colney Hth Res.	30	8	7	15	39	52	31
Harpenden Res.	30	10	1	19	56	74	31
Tring Corries Res.	30	6	6	18	36	101	24

Res. Division Two	P	W	D	L	F	A	Pt
Cranfield U. Res.	26	19	3	4	68	30	60
Wodson Pk Res.	26	18	5	3	70	26	59
Hatfield T. Res.	26	18	3	5	61	23	57
Ampthill T. Res.	26	16	5	5	47	26	53
The 61 FC Res.	26	14	3	9	72	49	45
Berkhamsted Res.	26	14	2	10	62	41	44
Risborough Res.	26	10	4	12	40	50	34
Totternhoe Res.	26	10	4	12	44	59	34
Toky'ton M. Res.	26	9	4	13	54	50	31
Kent Athletic Res.	26	9	2	15	49	65	29
Sun Postal Res.	26	6	4	16	45	56	22
Old Bradwell Res.	26	6	3	17	36	69	21
Buck'ham A. Res.	26	5	3	18	28	66	18
Bletchley T. Res.	26	4	3	19	20	86	15

Division Two		P	W	D	L	F	A	Pts
Berkhamsted		30	25	3	2	121	34	78
Aston Clinton		30	23	2	5	100	37	71
Padbury United		30	23	2	5	88	33	71
Wodson Park		30	21	2	7	77	43	65
MK Wanderers		30	14	3	13	69	52	45
Tring Corinthians		30	13	5	12	57	49	44
Pitstone & Ivinghoe		30	12	4	14	57	55	40
Totternhoe		30	10	9	11	62	50	39
The 61 FC (Luton)		30	11	6	13	50	52	39
Risborough Rangers		30	10	7	13	53	52	37
Bucks Students Union		30	9	4	17	56	97	31
Caddington		30	6	8	16	53	98	26
Mursley United		30	7	3	20	60	94	24
Kent Athletic		30	5	8	17	37	83	23
Old Bradwell United		30	6	5	19	37	89	23
Bletchley Town	*-3*	30	7	5	18	49	108	23

DIVISION TWO CUP

FIRST ROUND

Aston Clinton 7 Totternhoe 2
Berkhamsted 2 Caddington 0
Kent Athletic 0 **Padbury United** 4
MK Wanderers 5 The 61 FC 2
Old Bradwell United 2 Bucks Student Union 1
Risborough Rangers 1 **Mursley United** 2
Tring Corinthians 2 **Pitstone & Ivinghoe** 2 *aet* (2-4p)
Wodson Park 2 Bletchley Town 1

QUARTER-FINALS

Aston Clinton 4 Padbury United 1
MK Wanderers 3 Wodson Park 1
Old Bradwell United 0 **Mursley United** 1
Pitstone & Ivinghoe 1 **Berkhamsted** 2

SEMI-FINALS

Berkhamsted 1 **Mursley United** 1 *aet* (2-3p)
MK Wanderers 2 **Aston Clinton** 6

FINAL

(May 5th at Berkhamsted)
Mursley United 0 **Aston Clinton** 2

RESERVES CHALLENGE TROPHY

FINAL *(May 4th at Broxbourne Borough V & E)*
St Margaretsbury Res. 2 Royston Town Res. 1

CHALLENGE TROPHY

FIRST ROUND

AFC Dunstable 4 Hanwell Town 3
Amersham Town 3 **Welwyn Garden City** 4
Ampthill Town 2 Sport London E Benfica 0
Aylesbury 5 The 61 FC 4 *aet*, **Bedford** 8 Kent Athletic 1
Bedford Town Res. 6 Bletchley Town 0
Brache Sparta (w/o) v Winslow, **Brimsdown** 2 Tring Corinthians 1
Buckingham Athletic 3 Cranfield United 1
Bucks Student Union 1 **Hadley** 2
Caddington 2 **Kings Langley** 3
Cockfosters 6 Padbury United 3 *aet*
Crawley Green 1 **Colney Heath** 3 aet
Dunstable Town 3 Tring Athletic 1
Harpenden Town 1 **Totternhoe** 3
Hertford Town 2 Haringey Borough 0 *aet*
Kentish Town 0 **Pitstone & Ivinghoe** 4
Kingsbury London Tigers 0 **Broxbourne Borough V & E** 4
Langford 1 **Biggleswade United** 3
MK Wanderers 0 **Aston Clinton** 1
Mursley United 2 **New Bradwell St Peter** 5
Old Bradwell United 1 **Hillingdon Borough** 2
Oxhey Jets 2 **Berkhamsted** 4
Risborough Rangers 0 **Holmer Green** 2
Royston Town 0 **Chalfont St Peter** 1
Sun Postal Sports 0 **St Margaretsbury** 1
Tokyngton Manor 0 **Leverstock Green** 5
Wodson Park 2 Hoddesdon Town 1

SECOND ROUND

AFC Dunstable 6 Stony Stratford Town 1
Aylesbury 3 Ampthill Town 0
Bedford Town Res. 4 Wodson Park 0
Berkhamsted 0 **Brimsdown Rovers** 2
Biggleswade United 3 **Bedford** 5
Broxbourne Borough V & E 8 Totternhoe 0
Chalfont St Peter 1 **Kings Langley** 2
Colney Heath 1 **Welwyn Garden City** 2
Harefield United 0 **Cockfosters** 2
Hatfield Town 2 Leverstock Green 1
Hertford Town 0 **Dunstable Town** 4
Hillingdon Borough 1 **Aston Clinton** 4
Holmer Green 7 Brache Sparta 0
New Bradwell St Peter 0 **London Colney** 3
Pitstone & Ivinghoe 1 **Hadley** 2
St Margaretsbury 7 Buckingham Athletic 1

THIRD ROUND

Aylesbury 1 **Dunstable Town** 3, Bedford 0 **Hadley** 2
Bedford Town Res. 2 Cockfosters 1
Broxbourne Borough V & E 2 AFC Dunstable 1
Hatfield Town 0 **Brimsdown Rovers** 0 *aet* (4-5p)
Holmer Green 1 **London Colney** 2
Kings Langley 3 St Margaretsbury 0
Welwyn Garden City 1 **Aston Clinton** 7

QUARTER-FINALS

Brimsdown Rovers 1 Bedford Town Res. 0
Dunstable Town 2 **Aston Clinton** 3
Kings Langley 1 **Broxbourne Borough V & E** 2
London Colney 3 Hadley 2

SEMI-FINALS

Broxbourne Borough V & E 2 Aston Clinton 0
London Colney 2 Brimsdown Rovers 1

FINAL

(May 11th at Colney Heath)
Broxbourne Borough V & E 0 London Colney 0 *aet* (10-9p)

	AC.	Ber	Ble	Buc	Cad	Ken	MK	Mur	OB	Pad	Pit	Ris	61	Tot	Trin	WP
Aston Clinton	***D***	0-3	5-1	13-1	3-2	3-1	3-1	4-0	10-1	0-1	3-1	6-3	2-0	4-1	3-2	1-0
Berkhamsted	1-1	***I***	3-2	4-0	10-1	10-0	6-2	4-1	0-1	3-0	2-0	4-3	4-4	2-1	2-0	7-1
Bletchley Town	1-9	3-8	***V***	3-1	0-3	1-1	0-6	3-3	2-2	2-7	2-2	3-2	0-1	2-0	1-2	1-2
Bucks Students Union	1-3	0-6	4-0	***I***	3-3	1-5	0-1	3-5	4-1	0-5	4-3	1-2	3-2	3-1	0-3	3-10
Caddington	0-3	0-9	2-4	1-0	***S***	3-3	2-3	5-5	3-1	2-5	2-2	3-2	2-0	1-1	2-4	2-1
Kent Athletic	1-1	1-4	0-3	1-1	2-2	***I***	1-3	3-2	2-5	0-0	1-0	1-4	1-4	5-2	1-1	2-6
MK Wanderers	3-1	1-2	5-0	3-1	5-0	5-1	***O***	2-4	3-1	0-1	0-3	0-0	2-3	2-4	2-3	1-4
Mursley United	1-2	3-10	3-4	1-6	7-4	2-0	2-4	***N***	4-1	1-3	1-2	1-2	1-3	3-2	2-1	0-4
Old Bradwell United	1-4	0-3	4-2	3-4	3-1	0-0	1-1	1-0		0-3	1-7	0-0	2-2	2-4	1-5	0-2
Padbury United	3-0	4-2	6-2	1-2	7-0	7-0	2-1	4-2	6-0		2-1	3-3	2-1	3-1	1-0	0-2
Pitstone & Ivinghoe	2-3	1-2	4-1	0-3	2-2	4-2	2-1	4-1	4-0	0-4		3-2	1-0	2-1	1-2	3-4
Risborough Rangers	1-3	0-3	5-2	6-0	3-0	1-0	0-2	1-1	1-4	1-2	3-0		1-3	1-1	0-2	2-0
The 61 FC (Luton)	1-2	2-3	0-1	3-2	3-0	1-0	0-2	4-3	3-0	0-2	1-1	1-1		1-1	3-2	2-2
Totternhoe	2-1	1-1	10-0	3-3	1-1	3-0	3-3	2-0	5-0	2-1	2-0	0-1	4-1	***T***	1-1	1-2
Tring Corinthians	1-2	0-1	2-2	2-2	3-2	1-2	0-5	4-1	3-1	0-1	3-1	2-1	3-0	2-2	***W***	2-4
Wodson Park	0-5	1-2	6-1	3-0	3-2	3-0	2-0	2-0	1-0	5-2	0-1	1-1	2-1	2-0	2-1	***O***

PREMIER INS & OUTS

IN: Aylesbury United (Southern League Division One Midlands), Hadley (P), Holmer Green (P), Stotfold (S - United Counties League Premier Division)

OUT: Aylesbury (Southern League Division One Central), Brimsdown Rovers (W – merged with Essex Senior League club Enfield), Welwyn Garden City (R)

AYLESBURY UNITED

Founded: 1897 **Nickname:** The Ducks

Secretary: Steve Baker **(T)** 07768 353 265 **(E)** stevepb42@hotmail.com

Chairman: Graham Read **Manager:** Tony Joyce **Prog Ed:** Luke Brown

Ground: Leighton Town FC, Lake Street, Leighton Buzzard, Beds LU7 1RX **(T)** 01525 373311

Capacity: 2,800 **Seats:** 155 **Covered:** 300 **Midweek Matchday:** **Clubhouse:** Yes **Shop:** No

Colours(change): Green & white/green/white (Gold & black/black/gold)

Previous Names: None

Previous Leagues: Post War: Spartan >1951, Delphian 51-63, Athenian 63-76, Southern 76-88, 2004-10, Conf. 88-89, Isthmian 89-2004

Records: **Att:** 6,000 v England 1988. **Goalscorer:** Cliff Hercules - 301. **Apps:** Cliff Hercules 651+18.

Senior Honours: Southern LEague 1987-88. Berks & Bucks Senior Cup x4. Isthmian Cup 1994-95.

10 YEAR RECORD

00-01	01-02	02-03	03-04	04-05	05-06	06-07	07-08	08-09	09-10
Isth1 14	Isth1 3	Isth P 17	Isth P 24	SthP 10	SthP 21	SthM 6	SthM 8	SthM 10	SthM 22

BIGGLESWADE UNITED

Founded: 1929 **Nickname:**

Secretary: Tracey James **(T)** 07714 661 827 **(E)** tracey.james@goeast.gsl.gov.uk

Chairman: Steve Rowland **Manager:** Phil Childs **Prog Ed:** Tracey James

Ground: Second Meadow, Fairfield Rd, Biggleswade, Beds SG18 0BS **(T)** 01767 316 270

Capacity: 2,000 **Seats:** 30 **Covered:** 130 **Midweek Matchday:** Wednesday **Clubhouse:** Yes **Shop:** No

Colours(change): Red/navy/red (Yellow/royal blue/ royal blue)

Previous Names: None

Previous Leagues: Beds & District and Midland. Herts County.

Records: **Att:** 250 v Biggleswade Town

Senior Honours: Spartan South Midlands Div.1 1996-97.

Hunts FA Premier Cup 98-99 and Beds Senior Trophy 03-04, Beds Senior Cup 2001-02

10 YEAR RECORD

00-01	01-02	02-03	03-04	04-05	05-06	06-07	07-08	08-09	09-10
SSM S 3	SSM1 4	SSM1 8	SSM1 8	SSM1 3	SSM P 9	SSM P 14	SSM P 18	SSM P 1	SSM P 20

BROXBOURNE BOROUGH V & E

Founded: 1959 **Nickname:**

Secretary: John Venables **(T)** 07746 239 938 **(E)** venablesjohn@yahoo.co.uk

Chairman: Peter Harris **Manager:** Mark Beels **Prog Ed:** Peter Harris

Ground: Broxbourne Borougn V & E Club, Goffs Lane, Cheshunt, Herts EN7 5QN **(T)** 01992 624 281

Capacity: 500 **Seats:** 300 **Covered:** yes **Midweek Matchday:** Tuesday **Clubhouse:** Yes **Shop:** No

Colours(change): All Blue. (All Red)

Previous Names: Somerset Ambury V & E

Previous Leagues: Herts Senior

Records: **Att:** 120 **Goalscorer:** Wayne Morris **App:** Brian Boehmer

Senior Honours:

10 YEAR RECORD

00-01	01-02	02-03	03-04	04-05	05-06	06-07	07-08	08-09	09-10
SSM P 5	SSM P 11	SSM P 13	SSM P 16	SSM P 9	SSM P 11	SSM P 8	SSM P 12	SSM P 4	SSM P 9

CHALFONT ST PETER

Founded: 1926 **Nickname:** Saints

Secretary: John Carroll **(T)** 07950 981 008 **(E)** jc.chalfontfc@fsmail.net

Chairman: Dennis Mair **Manager:** Danny Edwards **Prog Ed:** Ian Doorbar

Ground: Mill Meadow, Gravel Hill, Amersham Road, Chalfont St Peter SL9 9QX **(T)** 01753 885 797

Capacity: 4,500 **Seats:** 220 **Covered:** 120 **Midweek Matchday:** Tuesday **Clubhouse:** Yes **Shop:** Yes

Colours(change): Red/green/red. (Yellow/blue/yellow).

Previous Names:

Previous Leagues: G W Comb. Parthernon. London. Spartan. L Spartan. Athenian. Isthmian.

Records: **Att:** 2,550 v Watford benefit match 1985 **App:** Colin Davies

Senior Honours: Isthmian Lge Div 2 87-88, Berks & Bucks Intermediate Cup 52-53

10 YEAR RECORD

00-01	01-02	02-03	03-04	04-05	05-06	06-07	07-08	08-09	09-10
Isth3 22	Isth3 14	Isth2 15	Isth2 14	Isth2 11	Isth2 8	SSM P 6	SSM P 2	SSM P 3	SSM P 2

COLNEY HEATH

Founded: 1907 Nickname: Magpies

Secretary: Martin Marlborough **(T)** 07960 155 463 **(E)** m.marlborough@stalbans.gov.uk
Chairman: Martin Marlborough **Manager:** Scott Lacey & Wesley Awad **Prog Ed:** Martin Marlborough
Ground: The Recreation Ground, High St, Colney Heath, St Albans AL4 0NS **(T)** 01727 826 188
Capacity: **Seats:** **Covered:** **Midweek Matchday:** **Clubhouse:** Yes **Shop:**

Colours(change): Black & white stripes/black/black & white. (Red/white/red)
Previous Names:
Previous Leagues: Herts Senior County League 1953-2000
Records:
Senior Honours: Herts County League Div 2 Champions 1953-54 Div 1 A 55-56,
Prem 58-99, 99-00, Div 1 88-89, Spartan South Midlands Div 1 2005-06 , SSML Cup 05-06

10 YEAR RECORD

00-01	01-02	02-03	03-04	04-05	05-06	06-07	07-08	08-09	09-10
SSM S 5	SSM1 3	SSM1 5	SSM1 6	SSM1 5	SSM1 1	SSM P 16	SSM P 15	SSM P 12	SSM P 5

DUNSTABLE TOWN

Founded: 1998 Nickname: The Blues

Secretary: Richard Scott **(T)** 07843 930 189 **(E)** dunstabletown@gmail.com
Chairman: Darren Croft **Manager:** Grant Carney **Prog Ed:** Richard Scott
Ground: Creasey Park Stadium, Brewers Hill Rd, Dunstable LU6 1BB **(T)** 01582 667 555
Capacity: 3,500 **Seats:** 350 **Covered:** 1000 **Midweek Matchday:** Tuesday **Clubhouse:** Yes **Shop:** Yes

Colours(change): Blue & white stripes/blue/blue. (Red & black/black/red)
Previous Names:
Previous Leagues: Spartan South Midlands 1998-2000. Isthmian 2003. Southern 2004-09.
Records:
Senior Honours: Spartan Sth. Midlands Div.1 1999-00. Premier 02-03.
Bedfordshire Senior Cup 03-04, 08-09.

10 YEAR RECORD

00-01	01-02	02-03	03-04	04-05	05-06	06-07	07-08	08-09	09-10
SSM S 2	SSM P 7	SSM P 1	Isth1N 5	SthP 20	SthW 21	SthM 11	SthM 13	SthM 21	SSM P 7

HADLEY

Founded: 1882 Nickname:

Secretary: Bob Henderson **(T)** 07748 267 295 **(E)** gensecretary@hadleyfc.com
Chairman: Guy Slee **Manager:** Ian Gray **Prog Ed:** Mark Bunn
Ground: Potters Bar Town FC, Watkins Rise (off The Walk), Potters Bar EN6 1QB **(T)** 01707 654 833
Capacity: 2,000 **Seats:** 150 **Covered:** 250 **Midweek Matchday:** **Clubhouse:** Yes **Shop:** Yes

Colours(change): Red/black/black (Blue/black/white)
Previous Names:
Previous Leagues: Barnet & Dist. 1922-57, Nth Suburban 57-70, Mid Herts 70-77, Herts Sen. 77-85, 99-2007, Sth Olym. 85-99, W Herts
Records:
Senior Honours: Hertfordshire Senior County League Division 3 1977-78, Division 1 2001-02, Premier 2003-04, 04-05.
West Hertfordshire League 2007-08. Aubrey Cup 2005-06.

10 YEAR RECORD

00-01	01-02	02-03	03-04	04-05	05-06	06-07	07-08	08-09	09-10
Hert1 6	Hert1 1	HertP 8	HertP 1	HertP 1	HertP 3	HertP 2	WHert 1	SSM2 2	SSM1 2

HANWELL TOWN

Founded: 1948 Nickname: Magpies

Secretary: Bob Fisher **(T)** 07730 822 216 **(E)** bob.fisher@hanwelltfc.plus.com
Chairman: Bob Fisher **Manager:** Keith Rowlands **Prog Ed:** Bob Fisher
Ground: Reynolds Field, Preivale Lane, Perivale, Greenford, UB6 8TL **(T)** 0208 998 1701
Capacity: 1,250 **Seats:** 175 **Covered:** 600 **Midweek Matchday:** Tuesday **Clubhouse:** Yes **Shop:** No

Colours(change): Black & white stripes/black/black & white (Yellow/blue/white)
Previous Names:
Previous Leagues: Dauntless. Wembley & Dist. Middlesex. London Spartan. Southern.
Records: **Att:** 600 v Spurs **Goalscorer:** Keith Rowlands. **App:** Phil Player 617 (20 seasons)
Senior Honours: London Spartan Senior Div. 83-84. London Senior Cup 1991-92, 92-93.

10 YEAR RECORD

00-01	01-02	02-03	03-04	04-05	05-06	06-07	07-08	08-09	09-10
SSM P 7	SSM P 3	SSM P 8	SSM P 6	SSM P 2	SSM P 3	SthS 21	SSM P 9	SSM P 7	SSM P 13

HAREFIELD UNITED

Founded: 1868 Nickname: Hares

Secretary: Ray Green **(T)** 07734 771 212 **(E)** rayjgreen1@btinternet.com

Chairman: Keith Ronald **Manager:** Glenn Bellis **Prog Ed:** Keith Ronald

Ground: Preston Park, Breakespeare Road North, Harefield, UB9 6NE **(T)** 01895 823 474

Capacity: 1,200 **Seats:** 150 **Covered:** yes **Midweek Matchday:** Tuesday **Clubhouse:** Yes **Shop:** No

Colours(change): Red/black/red. (White or orange/red or orange/black)
Previous Names:
Previous Leagues: Uxbridge & District, Great Western Comb, Panthernon, Middlesex, Athenian & Isthmian.
Records: **Att:** 430 v Bashley FA Vase
Senior Honours: Middlesex Premier Cup 1985-86

10 YEAR RECORD

00-01	01-02	02-03	03-04	04-05	05-06	06-07	07-08	08-09	09-10
SSM S 5	SSM1 2	SSM P 4	SSM P 5	SSM P 5	SSM P 4	SSM P 2	SSM P 5	SSM P 2	SSM P 6

HARINGEY BOROUGH

Founded: 1907 Nickname: Borough

Secretary: John Bacon **(T)** 07979 050 190 **(E)** clubsecretary@haringeyboroughfc.com

Chairman: Aki Achillea **Manager:** Tom Loizu **Prog Ed:** John Bacon

Ground: Coles Park, White Hart Lane, Tottenham, London N17 7JP **(T)** 0208 889 1415 (Matchday)

Capacity: 2,500 **Seats:** 280 **Covered:** yes **Midweek Matchday:** **Clubhouse:** Yes **Shop:** No

Colours(change): Yellow/green/yellow (Green/black/green)
Previous Names: Tufnell Park 1907
Previous Leagues: London, Isthmian, Spartan, Delphian, Athenian
Records: **Att:** 400
Senior Honours: London Senior Cup 1912-13, 90-91, Athenian League 1913-14

10 YEAR RECORD

00-01	01-02	02-03	03-04	04-05	05-06	06-07	07-08	08-09	09-10
SSM P 18	SSM P 12	SSM P 15	SSM P 18	SSM P 18	SSM P 19	SSM P 21	SSM1 2	SSM P 18	SSM P 15

HATFIELD TOWN

Founded: 1886 Nickname:

Secretary: Phil Knott **(T)** 07768 924 395 **(E)** philip.knott@ntlworld.com

Chairman: Ted Collie **Manager:** Trevor Lloyd **Prog Ed:** Tom Bailey

Ground: Welwyn Garden City FC, Herns Way, Panshanger AL7 1TA **(T)** 01707 384 300

Capacity: 1,500 **Seats:** 40 **Covered:** 120 **Midweek Matchday:** **Clubhouse:** Yes **Shop:** Yes

Colours(change): All blue. (Orange/white/black).
Previous Names: Hatfield FC > 1906. Hatfield Utd > 1922. Hatfield Utd Ath. > 1948
Previous Leagues: Mid. Hertfordshire. Herts County. Parthenon. London. Metropolitan.
Records:
Senior Honours: Herts Senior Champions 2007-08

10 YEAR RECORD

00-01	01-02	02-03	03-04	04-05	05-06	06-07	07-08	08-09	09-10
Hert1 1	HertP 14	Hert1 1	HertP 7	HertP 3	HertP 2	HertP 5	HertP 1	SSM1 3	SSM P 12

HERTFORD TOWN

Founded: 1908 Nickname: The Blues

Secretary: Michael Persighetti **(T)** 07530 056 401 **(E)** m.persighetti@ntlworld.com

Chairman: TBA **Manager:** Scott O'Donoghue **Prog Ed:** TBA

Ground: Hertingfordbury Park, West Street, Hertford, SG13 8EZ **(T)** 01992 583 716

Capacity: 6,500 **Seats:** 200 **Covered:** 1,500 **Midweek Matchday:** Tuesday **Clubhouse:** Yes **Shop:** Yes

Colours(change): Blue/blue/white (Yellow/black/white)
Previous Names:
Previous Leagues: Herts Co. Spartan. Delphian 59-63. Athenian 63-72. Eastern Co 72-73.
Records: **Att:** 5,000 v Kingstonian FA Am Cup 2nd Round 55-56 **App:** Robbie Burns
Senior Honours: Herts Senior Cup 66-67 East Anglian Cup 62-63, 69-70

10 YEAR RECORD

00-01	01-02	02-03	03-04	04-05	05-06	06-07	07-08	08-09	09-10
Isth3 19	Isth3 11	Isth1N 24	Isth2 3	Isth2 4	Isth2 13	SSM P 3	SSM P 4	SSM P 10	SSM P 16

HILLINGDON BOROUGH

Founded: 19190 Nickname: Boro

Secretary: Graham Smith **(T)** 01895 673 181 **(E)** jackieandgraham@talktalk.net
Chairman: Michael Harris **Manager:** Gary Meakin **Prog Ed:** Oliver Chalk
Ground: Middlesex Stadium, Breakspear Rd, Ruislip HA4 7SB **(T)** 01895 639 544
Capacity: 1,500 **Seats:** 150 **Covered:** 150 **Midweek Matchday:** **Clubhouse:** Yes **Shop:**

Colours(change): White/royal blue/royal (Orange/black/black)
Previous Names: Yiewsley. Bromley Park Rangers.
Previous Leagues: Southern 1964-84, 2006-08. South Midlands 1990-2006. Isthmian 2008-09.
Records:
Senior Honours: South Midlands Cup 1996-97.

10 YEAR RECORD

00-01	01-02	02-03	03-04	04-05	05-06	06-07	07-08	08-09	09-10
SSM P 8	SSM P 16	SSM P 12	SSM P 12	SSM P 6	SSM P 2	SthW 16	SthW 13	Isth1N 22	SSM P 18

HOLMER GREEN

Founded: 1908 Nickname:

Secretary: Mike Andrews **(T)** 07885 181186 **(E)** mikesandrews@btinternet.com
Chairman: Frank Francies **Manager:** Chris Allen **Prog Ed:** John Anderson
Ground: Airedale Park, Watchet Lane, Holmer Green, Bucks HP15 6UF **(T)** 01494 711 485
Capacity: 1,000 **Seats:** 25 **Covered:** yes **Midweek Matchday:** Tuesday **Clubhouse:** Yes **Shop:**

Colours(change): Green/white/green (Yellow/white/white)
Previous Names:
Previous Leagues: Chesham 1908-38, Wycombe Combination 1984-95, Chiltonian 1995-98.
Records:
Senior Honours: Spartan South Midlands Senior 1995-96, 98-99, Division 1 2009-10.

10 YEAR RECORD

00-01	01-02	02-03	03-04	04-05	05-06	06-07	07-08	08-09	09-10
SSM P 6	SSM P 15	SSM P 19	SSM P 19	SSM P 13	SSM P 7	SSM P 19	SSM P 20	SSM P 20	SSM1 1

KENTISH TOWN

Founded: 1994 Nickname: Townies

Secretary: James Thompson **(T)** 07866 437 211 **(E)** jamesthompson68@hotmail.com
Chairman: Catherine Dye **Manager:** Rakatahr Hudson **Prog Ed:** Frank Zanre
Ground: Barnet Copthall Stadium, Greenlands Lane, Hendon, London NW4 1RL **(T)** 0208 202 6478
Capacity: **Seats:** **Covered:** **Midweek Matchday:** **Clubhouse:** **Shop:**

Colours(change): All blue (All red)
Previous Names: None
Previous Leagues: Camden & Islington Youth Midweek Lge. Enfield & District Youth.
Records:
Senior Honours: Spartan South Midlands Division One 2007-08.

10 YEAR RECORD

00-01	01-02	02-03	03-04	04-05	05-06	06-07	07-08	08-09	09-10
			SSM2 10	SSM1 9	SSM1 11	SSM1 6	SSM1 1	SSM P 21	SSM P 17

KINGSBURY LONDON TIGERS

Founded: 2006 Nickname: Tigers

Secretary: Valdas Dambrauskas **(T)** 07817 143079 **(E)** valdas@londontigers.org
Chairman: Mesba Ahmed **Manager:** Mesba Ahmed **Prog Ed:** Shalim Uddin
Ground: Silver Jubilee Park, Townsend Lane, London NW9 7NE **(T)** 020 8205 1645
Capacity: **Seats:** **Covered:** **Midweek Matchday:** **Clubhouse:** **Shop:**

Colours(change): Orange/black/black (Yellow/blue/blue)
Previous Names: Kingsbury Town and London Tigers merged in 2006.
Previous Leagues: None
Records:
Senior Honours:

10 YEAR RECORD

00-01	01-02	02-03	03-04	04-05	05-06	06-07	07-08	08-09	09-10
						SSM P 13	SSM P 14	SSM P 5	SSM P 8

LANGFORD

Founded: 1908 Nickname: Reds

Secretary: Keith Albon **(T)** 07711 553 918 **(E)** keith.albon@btinternet.com
Chairman: Ian Chessum **Manager:** Terry Kitchener **Prog Ed:** Kerinda Boswell
Ground: Forde Park, Langford Road, Henlow, Beds SG16 6AG **(T)** 01462 816106
Capacity: 2,000 **Seats:** 109 **Covered:** 100 **Midweek Matchday:** Tuesday **Clubhouse:** Yes **Shop:**

Colours(change): All red. (All blue).
Previous Names:
Previous Leagues:
Records: **Att:** 450 v QPR 75th Anniversary 85
Senior Honours: South Midlands League 1988-89.

10 YEAR RECORD

00-01	01-02	02-03	03-04	04-05	05-06	06-07	07-08	08-09	09-10
SSM S 7	SSM1 6	SSM1 13	SSM1 2	SSM P 17	SSM P 17	SSM P 17	SSM P 6	SSM P 11	SSM P 19

LEVERSTOCK GREEN

Founded: 1895 Nickname: The Green

Secretary: Brian Barter **(T)** 07982 072 783 **(E)** b.barter@btopenworld.com
Chairman: Kate Binns **Manager:** Steve Heath **Prog Ed:** Brian Barter
Ground: Pancake Lane, Leverstock Green, Hemel Hempstead, Herts **(T)** 01442 246280
Capacity: 1,500 **Seats:** 50 **Covered:** 100 **Midweek Matchday:** Tuesday **Clubhouse:** Yes **Shop:** No

Colours(change): White/green/green. (Yellow & blue/blue)
Previous Names: None
Previous Leagues: West Herts (pre 1950) & Herts County 50-91
Records: **Att:** 1,000 **App:** Jonnie Wallace
Senior Honours: South Midlands Senior Division 1996-97.

10 YEAR RECORD

00-01	01-02	02-03	03-04	04-05	05-06	06-07	07-08	08-09	09-10
SSM S 10	SSM1 8	SSM1 4	SSM P 9	SSM P 14	SSM P 6	SSM P 5	SSM P 7	SSM P 6	SSM P 10

OXHEY JETS

Founded: Nickname: Jets

Secretary: David Fuller **(T)** 07786 627 659 **(E)** d.g.fuller@ntlworld.com
Chairman: Phil Andrews **Manager:** Benny Higham **Prog Ed:** David Fuller
Ground: Boundary Stadium, Altham Way, South Oxhey, Watford WD19 6FW **(T)** 020 8421 6277
Capacity: 1,000 **Seats:** 100 **Covered:** 100 **Midweek Matchday:** Wednesday **Clubhouse:** Yes **Shop:** No

Colours(change): All royal blue. (All yellow)
Previous Names:
Previous Leagues: Herts Senior County
Records: **Att:** 257 v Barnet Herts Senior Cup 05-06 **App:** Ian Holdon
Senior Honours: Herts Senior County Premier 2000-01, 01-02, 02-03.
SSML Div 1 Champions 2004-2005, Herts Senior Centenary Trophy 2004-2005

10 YEAR RECORD

00-01	01-02	02-03	03-04	04-05	05-06	06-07	07-08	08-09	09-10
HertP 1	HertP 1	HertP 1	HertP 2	SSM1 1	SSM P 13	SSM P 7	SSM P 19	SSM P 13	SSM P 11

ROYSTON TOWN

Founded: 1872 Nickname:

Secretary: Dave Chappell **(T)** 07795 145249 **(E)** david.chappell2@btinternet.co.uk
Chairman: Steve Jackson **Manager:** Paul Attfield **Prog Ed:** Alan Barlow
Ground: Garden Walk, Royston, Herts, SG8 7HP **(T)** 01763 241 204
Capacity: **Seats:** **Covered:** **Midweek Matchday:** **Clubhouse:** **Shop:**

Colours(change): White/black/black. (All red).
Previous Names: None
Previous Leagues: Cambridgeshire & Herts Co. Isthmian
Records: **Att:** 876 v Aldershot Town, 1993-94.
Senior Honours: Herts County Champions 1976-77. South Midlands Div.1 1978-79, 2008-09.

10 YEAR RECORD

00-01	01-02	02-03	03-04	04-05	05-06	06-07	07-08	08-09	09-10
SSM P 17	SSM P 8	SSM P 16	SSM P 13	SSM P 16	SSM P 18	SSM P 20	SSM1 5	SSM1 1	SSM P 4

ST MARGARETSBURY

Founded: 1894 Nickname: Athletic

Secretary: Philip Hayward **(T)** 07721 415 579 **(E)** philip@niche-direct.com
Chairman: Gary Stock **Manager:** Lee Judges **Prog Ed:** Dave Barker
Ground: Recreation Ground, Station Road, St Margarets SG12 8EH **(T)** 01920 870 473
Capacity: 1,000 **Seats:** 60 **Covered:** 60 **Midweek Matchday:** Tuesday **Clubhouse:** Yes **Shop:** No

Colours(change): Red & black stripes/black/black (All royal blue)
Previous Names: Stanstead Abbots > 1962
Previous Leagues: East Herts, Hertford & District, Waltham & District, 47-48 Herts Co. 48-92
Records: **Att:** 450 v Stafford Rangers FA Cup 2001-02
Senior Honours: Spartan Lg 95-96 Herts Senior Centenary Trophy 92-93,
Herts Charity Shield 97-98

10 YEAR RECORD

00-01	01-02	02-03	03-04	04-05	05-06	06-07	07-08	08-09	09-10
SSM P 13	SSM P 5	SSM P 5	SSM P 3	SSM P 7	SSM P 12	SSM P 15	SSM P 11	SSM P 14	SSM P 14

STOTFOLD

Founded: 1946 Nickname: The Eagles

Secretary: Julie Longhurst **(T)** 07752 430493 **(E)** julie.longhurst@btinternet.com
Chairman: Phil Pateman **Manager:** Gordon Bickerstaff **Prog Ed:** Phil Pateman
Ground: Roker Park, The Green, Stotfold, Hitchin, Herts SG5 4AN **(T)** 01462 730 765
Capacity: 5,000 **Seats:** 300 **Covered:** 300 **Midweek Matchday:** Tuesday **Clubhouse:** Yes **Shop:**

Colours(change): Amber/black/black. (Burgundy or blue & white hoops/burgundy or blue/burgundy or blue).
Previous Names:
Previous Leagues: Biggleswade & Dist, Norths Herts & South Midlands, United Counties >2010
Records: **Att:**1,000 **Goalscorer:** Roy Boon **Apps:** Roy Boon & Dave Chellew
Senior Honours: S. Midlands League 1980-81. Bedfordshire Senior Cup 1964-65, 93-94.
Bedfordshire Premier Cup 1981-82, 98-99. United Counties League 2007-08.

10 YEAR RECORD

00-01	01-02	02-03	03-04	04-05	05-06	06-07	07-08	08-09	09-10
UCL P 15	UCL P 9	UCL P 17	UCL P 10	UCL P 9	UCL P 11	UCL P 19	UCL P 1	UCL P 2	UCL P 7

TRING ATHLETIC

Founded: 1958 Nickname: Athletic

Secretary: Bob Winter **(T)** 07979 816 528 **(E)** robert.winter2007@ntlworld.com
Chairman: Mick Eldridge **Manager:** Phil Casserley **Prog Ed:** Barry Simmons
Ground: Grass Roots Stadium, Pendley Sports Centre, Cow Lane, Tring HP23 5NT **(T)** 01442 891 144
Capacity: 1,233 **Seats:** 150 **Covered:** 100+ **Midweek Matchday:** Tuesday **Clubhouse:** Yes **Shop:** Yes

Colours(change): Red/black/black (Yellow/green/green)
Previous Names: None
Previous Leagues: West Herts 58-88
Records: **Goalscorer:** Andy Humphreys - 209 **App:** Mark Boniface - 642
Senior Honours: Spartan South Midlands Senior Division 1999-00

10 YEAR RECORD

00-01	01-02	02-03	03-04	04-05	05-06	06-07	07-08	08-09	09-10
SSM S 4	SSM1 5	SSM1 3	SSM1 4	SSM P 4	SSM P 10	SSM P 11	SSM P 10	SSM P 8	SSM P 3

AFC DUNSTABLE

Secretary: Craig Renfrew **(T)** 07976 192 530 **(E)** renfrewcraig@aol.com
Chairman: Simon Bullard **Manager:** Alex Butler **Prog Ed:** Craig Renfrew
Ground: Dunstable Town FC, Creasey Pk, Creasey Pk Dr, Brewers Hill Rd, LU6 1BB **(T)** 01582 667555 **Capacity:**
Colours(change): Royal blue/royal blue/white (White/red/red)

ADDITIONAL INFORMATION:

AMERSHAM TOWN

Secretary: Michael Gahagan **(T)** 07979 081827 **(E)** michaelgahagan@ukonline.co.uk
Chairman: Lawrence Lipka **Manager:** Simon Damery **Prog Ed:** Michael Gahagan
Ground: Spratleys Meadow, School Lane, Amersham, Bucks HP7 0EL **(T)** No telephone **Capacity:**
Colours(change): Black & white stripes/black & white/black & white (Yellow & black quarters/black/yellow)

ADDITIONAL INFORMATION:

AMPTHILL TOWN

Secretary: Eric Turner **(T)** 07908 374118 **(E)** ericturner789@btinternet.com
Chairman: Bernie Stuttard **Manager:** Steve Goodridge **Prog Ed:** Eric Turner
Ground: Ampthill Park, Woburn Street, Ampthill MK45 2HX **(T)** 01525 404440 **Capacity:**
Colours(change): Yellow/blue/blue (Light blue/black/black)

ADDITIONAL INFORMATION:

BEDFORD

Founded: 1957

Secretary: Paolo Riccio **(T)** 07930 918290 **(E)** paolo.riccio@ntlworld.com
Chairman: Lui La Mura **Manager:** Luke Capon **Prog Ed:** Paul Warne
Ground: McMullen Park, Meadow Lane, Cardington, Bedford, MK44 3SB **(T)** 01234 831024 **Capacity:** 5,000
Colours(change): Black & white stripes/black/black (All blue)

ADDITIONAL INFORMATION: Previous Names: Printers Diemer-Reynolds > 1972, Bedford Valerio United.
Previous League: United Counties 1970-80.
Record Att: (at Fairhill) 1,500 v Bedford Town-South Mids Div 1 1992 **Apps:** Simon Fordham - 418

BEDFORD TOWN RES.

Nickname: The Eagles

Secretary: Patrick Allen **(T)** 07790 967124 **(E)** pat.allen1@hotmail.co.uk
Chairman: David Howell **Manager:** Steve Rigby **Prog Ed:** Carl Allen
Ground: The Eyrie, Meadow Lane, Cardington, Bedford MK44 3SB **(T)** 01234 831558 **Capacity:** 3,000
Colours(change): All blue (Yellow/navy/yellow)

ADDITIONAL INFORMATION:

BERKHAMSTED

Secretary: Grant Hastie **(T)** 01799 584053 **(E)** gshastie@hotmail.com
Chairman: Rob Allnutt **Manager:** Mick Vipond **Prog Ed:** Grant Hastie
Ground: Broadwater, Lower Kings Road, Berkhamsted HP4 2AL **(T)** 01442 865977 **Capacity:**
Colours(change): Yellow/blue/blue (White/black/black)

ADDITIONAL INFORMATION:
Honours: Spartan South Midlands League Division 1 2009-10.

BUCKINGHAM ATHELTIC

Secretary: Charles Bassano **(T)** 07810 755193 **(E)** charles.bassano@sky.com
Chairman: John Webb **Manager:** Paul Bowley **Prog Ed:** Colin Howkins
Ground: Stratford Fields, Stratford Road, Buckingham MK18 1NY **(T)** 01280 816945 (MD) **Capacity:**
Colours(change): All sky blue (Red/black/black)

ADDITIONAL INFORMATION:

DIVISION ONE INS & OUTS

IN: Berkhamsted (P), London Lions (P - Herts Senior County League Premier Division), St Albans City Res. (P - Capital League Central Division), Welwyn Garden City (R), Wodson Park (P), OUT: Brache Sparta Community (R), Brimsdown Rovers (merged with Essex Senior League club Enfield), Hadley (P), Holmer Green (P), Tokyngton Manor (R – Middlesex County League Premier Division), Winslow United (WS - Division Two)

COCKFOSTERS

Founded: 1921 Nickname: Fosters

Secretary: Graham Bint **(T)** 07729 709926 **(E)** graham.bint@ntlworld.com
Chairman: Dino Ippocratous **Manager:** Neil Ewing **Prog Ed:** Alan Simmons
Ground: Cockfosters Sports Ground, Chalk Lane, Cockfosters, Herts EN4 9JG **(T)** 020 8449 5833 **Capacity:** 1,000
Colours(change): All red (All navy blue)

ADDITIONAL INFORMATION: Previous Name: Cockfosters Athletic > 1968. **Previous League:** Herts Senior County 1966-91.
Record Att: 408 v Saffron Walden.
Honours: London Interim Cup 1970-71, 89. Herts Sen Co Lge 78-79, 80-81. Aubrey Cup 78-79, 84-85. Herts Interm Cup 78-79

CRANFIELD UNITED

Secretary: Larry Corkrey **(T)** 07854 936405 **(E)** larrycor@btinternet.com
Chairman: Tony Beale **Manager:** Lee Bearman **Prog Ed:** Larry Corkrey
Ground: Crawley Road, Cranfield, Beds MK43 0AA **(T)** 01234 751444 **Capacity:**
Colours(change): All red (White/black/white)

ADDITIONAL INFORMATION:

CRAWLEY GREEN

Secretary: Eddie Downey **(T)** 07956 107477 **(E)** eddied@thamesideltd.co.uk
Chairman: Alan Clark **Manager:** Neil Tattersall **Prog Ed:** Alan Clark
Ground: Barton Rovers FC, Sharpenhoe Road, Barton Le Cay, Beds MK45 4SD **(T)** 01582 882398 **Capacity:** 4,000
Colours(change): All maroon (Yellow/blue/blue)

ADDITIONAL INFORMATION:

HARPENDEN TOWN

Founded: 1891 Nickname: Town

Secretary: Les Crabtree **(T)** 07968 120032 **(E)** l.crabtree@colart.co.uk
Chairman: Kelvin Gregory **Manager:** Ryan Thompson **Prog Ed:** Chris Gregory
Ground: Rothamstead Park, Amenbury Lane, Harpenden AL5 2EF **(T)** 07968 120032 **Capacity:** 1,500
Colours(change): Yellow/royal blue/royal blue (Red/red/black)

ADDITIONAL INFORMATION:
Previous Name: Harpenden FC 1891-1908. **Previous League:** Hertfordshire County.
Honours: South Midlands League x2. Hertfordshire Junior Cup x5.

HODDESDON TOWN

Formed: 1879 Nickname: Lilywhites

Secretary: Jane Sinden **(T)** 01767 631 297 & fax **(E)** janedsinden@fsmail.net
Chairman: Roger Merton **Manager:** Andy Crawford **Prog Ed:** Jane Sinden
Ground: The Stewart Edwards Stadium, Lowfield, Park View Hoddesdon EN11 8PX **(T)** 01992 463 133 **Capacity:** 3,500
Colours(change): White/black/black (Blue/blue/yellow)

ADDITIONAL INFORMATION: Previous Name: Hoddesdon F.C. **Previous League:** South Midlands 1984-97
HONOURS (FA Comps & League): FA Vase 1974-75 (1st Winners).
Spartan League Champions 1970-71, Division 1 1935-36, Division 2 'B' 1927-28

KINGS LANGLEY

Secretary: Andy Mackness **(T)** 07976 692801 **(E)** andymackness@yahoo.co.uk
Chairman: Derry Edgar **Manager:** Paul Hobbs **Prog Ed:** Roy Mitchard
Ground: Gaywood Park, Hempstead Road, Kings Langley Herts WD4 8BS **(T)** 07976 692801 **Capacity:**
Colours(change): Black & white stripes/black/black (Red & white stripes/blue/red)

ADDITIONAL INFORMATION:

LONDON COLNEY

Founded: 1907 Nickname: Blueboys

Secretary: Dave Brock **(T)** 07508 035835 **(E)** davebrock42@hotmail.com
Chairman: Tony Clafton **Manager:** Julian Robinson **Prog Ed:** Tony Clafton
Ground: Cotlandswick Playing Fields, London Colney, Herts AL2 1DW **(T)** 01727 822132 **Capacity:** 1,000
Colours(change): All royal blue (Red & black or black & white stripes/black/black)

ADDITIONAL INFORMATION: Previous League: Hertfordshire County 1907-92.
Record Att: 300 v St Albans City Hertfordshire Senior Cup 1998-99.
Honours: Spartan South Midlands Premier Division 2001-02.

LONDON LIONS

Secretary: Basil Wein (T) 07970 661990 (E) basilw@londonlions.com
Chairman: Adam Solomons **Manager:** Tony Gold **Prog Ed:** Basil Wein
Ground: V & E Club, Goffs Lane, Cheshunt, Herts EN7 5QN (T) 01992 624281 **Capacity:** 500
Colours(change): All blue (Yellow/black/black)

ADDITIONAL INFORMATION:

NEW BRADWELL ST PETER

Founded: 1902 Nickname: Peters

Secretary: Ian Rollins (T) 07912 076473 (E) honsecretary@newbradwellstpeter.co.uk
Chairman: John Haynes **Manager:** Gary Flinn **Prog Ed:** Adrian Haynes
Ground: Recreation Ground, Bradwell Road, Bradville, Milton Keynes MK13 7AD (T) 01908 313835 **Capacity:** 2,000
Colours(change): All graphite (Gold/navy blue/purple)

ADDITIONAL INFORMATION:
Honours: South Midlands Division 1 1976-77, 83-84, Senior Division 1997-98. Berks & Berks Senior Trophy 1999-2000.

SPORT LONDON E BENFICA

Secretary: Ninette Fernandes (T) 020 7625 5486 (E) info@sportlondonebenficafc.co.uk
Chairman: John Vitorino **Manager:** Jose Viana **Prog Ed:** Jose Viana
Ground: Harringey Borough FC, Coles Park, White Hart Lane, London N17 7JP (T) 020 8889 1415 (MD) **Capacity:**
Colours(change): Red/white/red (White/black/black)

ADDITIONAL INFORMATION:
Previous League: Middlesex County.

ST ALBANS CITY RES.

Nickname: The Saints

Secretary: Steve Eames (T) 07805 769083 (E) steveeames@safc.co.uk
Chairman: John Gibson **Manager:** Franco Sidoli **Prog Ed:** Steve Eames
Ground: Clarence Park, York Road, St Albans, Herts AL1 4PL (T) 01727 864296 **Capacity:** 6,000
Colours(change): Blue/yellow/blue (Yellow/blue/yellow)

ADDITIONAL INFORMATION:

STONY STRATFORD TOWN

Founded: 1898

Secretary: Steve Sartain (T) 07901 664000 (E) steve.sartain456@btinternet.com
Chairman: Christopher Wise **Manager:** Steve Orchard **Prog Ed:** Annette Way
Ground: Ostlers Lane, Stony Stratford, Milton Keynes MK11 1AR (T) 07914 012709 **Capacity:** 600
Colours(change): Sky blue & navy/navy/navy (Yellow/black/yellow)

ADDITIONAL INFORMATION:
Previous League: Northampton Combination.
Record Att: 476 v Aston Villa U21 1996.

SUN POSTAL SPORTS

Secretary: Maurice Tibbles (T) 07895 066075 (E) tibbles.joe@live.com
Chairman: Andrew Toon **Manager:** Sean Brown **Prog Ed:** Andrew Toon
Ground: Sun Postal Sports Club, Mountwood Avenue, Watford, Herts WD17 3BM (T) 01923 227453 **Capacity:**
Colours(change): Yellow/blue/blue (All Red)

ADDITIONAL INFORMATION:
Previous Names: Sun Postal Sports 2003. Sun Sports 2005.
Previous League: Hertfordshire Senior County > 2003.

WELWYN GARDEN CITY

Founded: 1921 Nickname: Citizens

Secretary: Richard Dunning (T) 07940 125082 (E) richarddunning@ymail.com
Chairman: Gary Bevan **Manager:** Phil Reid **Prog Ed:** TBA
Ground: Herns Way, Welwyn Garden City, Herts AL7 1TA (T) 01707 329358 **Capacity:** 1,500
Colours(change): Sky blue/claret/sky blue (Orange/black/orange)

ADDITIONAL INFORMATION:
Previous League: Metropolitan & Greater London.
Honours: South Midlands League 1973-74, Division 1 1981-82.

WODSON PARK

Secretary: Phil Friend **(T)** 07774 944246 **(E)** phil.friends@sky-mail.net
Chairman: John Murphy **Manager:** Kristian Munt **Prog Ed:** Harminder Tumber
Ground: Ware FC, Wadesmill Road, Herts SG12 0UQ **(T)** 01920 463247 **Capacity:** 3,300
Colours(change): Green & black stripes/black/black (All amber)
ADDITIONAL INFORMATION:

SPARTAN SOUTH MIDLANDS DIVISION TWO CONSTITUTION 2010-11

ASTON CLINTON ....Aston Clinton Park, London Road, Aston Clinton, Bucks. HP22 5HL............................01296 631818
BLETCHLEY TOWN ....The Irish Centre, Manor Fields, Bletchley, Milton Keynes MK2 2HX 01908 375978
BRACHE SPARTA COMMUNITY.........Foxdell Recreation Ground, Dallow Road, Luton LU1 1TG 01582 720751
BUCKS STUDENT UNION.......Amersham Tn FC, Spratleys Meadow, School Lane, Amersham HP7 0EL 01494 727428
CADDINGTON.....................Caddington Recreation Club, Manor Road, Caddington, Luton, Beds LU1 4HH 01582 450151
KENT ATHLETIC ....Tenby Drive, Luton, LU4 9BN 01582 582723
MK WANDERERS.................Kents Hill Pavilion, Frithwood Crescent, Kents Hill, Milton Keynes MK7 6HQ........................No telephone
MURSLEY UNITED ....The Playing Field, Station Road, Mursley MK17 0SA ....No telephone
OLD BRADWELL UNITED...................Abbey Road, Bradwell Village, Milton Keynes, MK13 9AR......................................01908 312355
PADBURY UNITED...........................Springfields Playing Fields, Padbury, Buckingham MK18 2AQ ....No telephone
PITSTONE AND IVINGHOE............Pitstone Recreation Ground, Vicarage Road, Pitstone LU7 9EY ....01296 661271 (match days)
RISBOROUGH RANGERS..........." Windors" Horsenden Lane, Princes Risborough, Bucks HP27 9NE.............................07866 178822
THE 61 FC (LUTON) ....Kingsway Ground, Beverley Road, Luton LU4 8EU 07749 531492
TOTTERNHOE...............................Recreation Ground, Dunstable Road, Totternhoe, Beds LU6 1QP..............................01582 606738
TRING CORINTHIANS ....Tring Corinthians FC, Icknield Way, Tring, Herts HP23 5HJ......................................07886 528214
WINSLOW UNITED.....................The Recreation Ground, Elmfields Gate, Winslow, Bucks MK18 3JG 01296 713057
IN: Brache Sparta Community (R), Winslow United (WS - Division One).
OUT: Berkhamsted (P), Wodson Park (P).

GROUND DIRECTIONS - PREMIER & DIVISION ONE

AFC DUNSTABLE - Creasey Park Stadium, Creasey Park Drive, Brewers Hill Road, Dunstable, Beds LU6 1BB Tel 01582 667555
From the South: When travelling north on the A5, go straight across the lights in the centre of Dunstable. Turn left at the next main set of lights into Brewers Hill Road. You will immediately pass the Fire Station on your left. Carry on until you hit the first roundabout. Go over the roundabout and take the immediate right into Creasey Park Drive. From North: When travelling south on the A5, go through the chalk cutting and over the first set of traffic lights. At the next set of lights turn right into Brewers Hill Road. Go over the roundabout and take the immediate right into Creasey Park Drive. Public Transport: Creasey Park is well served by buses. Arriva and Centrebus services from Luton, Houghton Regis Leighton Buzzard and Aylesbury all stop at the bottom of Brewers Hill Road. Some 24 services stop directly opposite Creasey Park Drive in Weatherby.
AMERSHAM TOWN - Spratleys Meadow, School Lane, Amersham, Bucks HP7 No telephone
From London, take the A413 towards Aylesbury. At the first roundabout in Amersham where the A413 turns left, keep straight on. Then carry on straight over the next four roundabouts to Amersham Old Town. At the western end of the Old Town turn right into right into Mill Lane. At the top of Mill Lane turn left into School Lane. Ground is 100 yards on the left.
AMPTHILL TOWN - Ampthill Park, Woburn Street, Ampthill Tel: 01525 404440.
From the South, leave M1 at junction 12 Toddington. Turn right as signposted until you meet the junction with the Ampthill bypass. Go straight across until you meet a mini-roundabout at the town centre. Turn left into Woburn Street. The ground is about half a mile on the right, just past a lay-by. From the North, leave the M1 at J13 and turn left. At first set of traffic lights, turn right onto A507 Ridgmont bypass. Continue until you see the right-hand turning signposted for Ampthill. Ground is about a mile on the left, opposite the rugby ground.
AYLESBURY UNITED - Leighton Town FC, Lake Street, Leighton Buzzard, Beds LU7 1RX Tel 01525 373311
From Aylesbury: Take the A418 towards Leighton Buzzard and at the bypass turn right onto the A505. Go straight over the first two roundabouts; then turn left at the third onto the A4146. Stay on the A4146 at the next two roundabouts (second exit, first exit), then carry straight on at the next mini-roundabout. The entrance to the ground is about 50 yards after this mini-roundabout on the left. Car parking is on your left as you turn. Travel from the Midlands using the M1: Leave the M1 at junction 15 and take the A508 towards Milton Keynes. After 9 miles you will reach the A5 roundabout. Take the first exit and travel about 8 miles to the roundabout at the end of the dual carriageway. Take the second exit and follow the A5 towards Dunstable. After about 3 miles you will arrive at another roundabout (Flying Fox pub is on your left) take the third exit towards Heath & Reach and Leighton Buzzard. Follow this road for about 4 miles until you arrive at a large roundabout in Leighton Buzzard then take the first exit. At the next roundabout take the second exit, you will then go through 2 sets of lights. The ground and car park is on the right, immediately after the lights and opposite a petrol station.
From the South: Take the M1 to junction 8 (Hemel Hempstead) and head towards the town centre. As you go down the hill into Hemel you will reach a multi-directional roundabout. Turn right and follow the signs for Leighton Buzzard (A4146). Leighton Buzzard is about 16 miles northwest of Hemel Hempstead along this road.
BEDFORD FC - McMullen Park, Meadow Lane, Cardington, Bedford, MK44 3SB. Tel: 01234 831024
From the M1 Junction 13: take the A421 on to the Bedford Bypass, take the third exit onto the A603, the ground is 250 yards on the left. From the A1 at Sandy: take A603 to Bedford. The ground is on the right just before you reach the Bedford Bypass.
BEDFORD TOWN RESERVES - The Eyrie, Meadow Lane, Cardington, Bedford MK44 3SB Tel 01234 831558
From the M1, exit at junction 13, then A421 Bedford Bypass and take the A603 Sandy turn off. Ground is on the left signposted Meadow Lane.
From the A1, take A603 from Sandy to Bedford. Go through Willington. Ground is 1.5 miles on the right signposted Meadow Lane.
BERKHAMSTED - Broadwater, Lower Kings Road, Berkhamsted HP4 2AL Tel 01442 865977
Exit A41 onto A416. Go straight over the town centre traffic lights into Lower Kings Road. Go over the canal bridge and take first left into Broadwater. Follow the road to the left, going parallel to the canal. The ground is on the right hand side, sandwiched between the canal and the railway.
BIGGLESWADE UNITED - Second Meadow, Fairfield Road, Biggleswade SG18 0BS Tel 01767 316270
From A1 south take second roundabout (Sainsbury's NOT Homebase). Cross the river bridge and then take second left into Sun Street then take first left into Fairfield Road and travel to the very end and into lane. From A1 north, take first roundabout (Sainsbury's) and follow previous instructions.
BROXBOURNE BOROUGH V&E - V & E Club, Goffs Lane, Cheshunt, Herts EN7 5QN Tel & Fax 01992 624281
From M25 Junction 25 take A10 towards Cheshunt, at first roundabout turn left onto B198 (Cuffley and Goffs Oak). Go straight over next roundabout. At next roundabout at end of road, turn right into Goffs Lane. Clubhouse is on immediate right.

BUCKINGHAM ATHLETIC - Stratford Fields, Stratford Road, Buckingham MK18 1NY Tel: 01280 816945 (match days & opening hours only)

From Oxford, Aylesbury or Bletchley: take the Buckingham ring road to the roundabout where the A422 from Stony Stratford/Deanshanger meet - turn left, towards town centre. The ground is situated on the left behind fir trees at the bottom of the hill where 30mph begins (opposite a recently-built block of luxury apartments). From Milton Keynes: Up A5 then (A422) to Buckingham - straight across roundabout towards the town centre - ground location as above. From M1: come off at junction 13 and follow A421 straight through, turning right where it meets the Buckingham ring road – then follow as above, turning left at the next-but-one roundabout.

CHALFONT ST. PETER - Mill Meadow, Gravel Hill, Amersham Road, Chalfont St. Peter, Bucks SL9 9QX Tel 01753 885797

The ground is adjacent to the Chalfont Community Centre off the A413 Amersham Road

COCKFOSTERS - Cockfosters Sports Ground, Chalk Lane, Cockfosters, Herts EN4 9JG Tel: 020 8449 5833

Best Route to the Ground: Leaving the M25 motorway at junction 24 (Potters Bar), take the A111 signposted to Cockfosters. The ground is situated approximately 2 miles from the motorway on the right immediately before Cockfosters Underground Station. VEHICLE DRIVERS PLEASE BE AWARE THAT THE YELLOW LINES & PARKING RESTRICTIONS IN CHALK LANE ARE STRICTLY ENFORCED UP TO 6.30PM INCLUDING SATURDAYS. For a restriction-free parking area, drivers are recommended to take the first turning on the right after the Underground Station (Mount Pleasant), drive down about 500 metres and take the first right again (Bevan Road) and then drive up as near to the top of this road as possible. The ground is situated opposite the width restriction barriers at the top of this road.

COLNEY HEATH - The Recreation Ground, High Street, Colney Heath, St Albans, Herts AL4 0NS Tel 01727 826188

From the A1, leave at junction 3 and follow A414 St. Albans. At long roundabout take the left into the village and ground is just past the school on left after 400 yards.

From the M25, leave at junction 22 and follow B556 Colney Heath. On entering the village turn left at Queens Head PH (roundabout) and follow High Street for 1/2 mile. The ground is on the right just before the school. From M1 going south; leave at junction 7. At Park Street roundabout follow A414 Hatfield. Continue on A414 past London Colney. Enter Colney Heath coming round the long roundabout and into village. The ground is past the school on the left after 400 yards.

CRANFIELD UNITED - Crawley Road, Cranfield, Beds MK43 0AA Tel: 01234 751444.

upon entering the village, take the North Crawley/Newport Pagnell road. The ground is on the left hand side just before leaving the speed limit zone.

CRAWLEY GREEN - Barton Rovers FC, Sharpenhoe Road, Barton Le Cay, Beds MK45 4SD Tel 01582 882398

From M1 J12, turn right from South turn left from North, onto the A5120. After approximately 1.5 miles, take the second turning on the right signposted Harlington and Barton. Follow the road through Sharpenhoe to Barton. At mini-roundabout turn right and after about 400 yards, turn right into the ground. Ground entrance is in Luton Road.

DUNSTABLE TOWN - Creasey Park Drive, Brewers Hill Road, Dunstable, Beds LU6 1BB Tel 01582 667555

From the south: When travelling on the A5, go straight across the lights in the centre of Dunstable. Turn left at the next main set of lights into Brewers Hill Road. You will immediately pass the Fire Station on your left. Carry on until you hit the first roundabout, Go over the roundabout and take the immediate right into Creasey Park Drive. From the north: When travelling south on the A5, go through the chalk cutting and over the first set of traffic lights. At the next set of lights, turn right into Brewers Hill Road. Then proceed as above. From the East: Turn right at the traffic lights in the centre of Dunstable. Turn left at the next main set of traffic lights into Brewers Hill Road. Then proceed as above. From the east: When coming into Dunstable, go straight across the first roundabout you come to. Then turn left at the double mini-roundabout into Drovers Way. Follow this road for about 1/2 mile as it bears to the right and becomes Brewers Hill Road. Go over two mini-roundabouts and just before you hit the larger roundabout, turn left into Creasey Park Drive.

Public Transport: Creasey Park is well served by buses. Arriva and Centrebus services from Luton, Houghton Regis, Leighton Buzzard and Aylesbury all stop at the bottom of Brewers Hill Road. Some 24 services stop directly opposite Creasey Park Drive in Weatherby.

HADLEY - Potters Bar Town FC, Parkfield Stadium, Watkins Rise (off The Walk), Potters Bar EN6 1QB Tel 01707 654833

From M25, exit at junction 24 towards Potters Bar along Southgate Road A111. Turn right at first set of traffic lights into High Street A1000. After the petrol station on the left and pedestrian crossing, take the first left into The Walk. After 200 yards, turn right into Watkins Rise. The ground is at the end on the right. Nearest BR Station: Potters Bar. PLEASE NOTE: do not park in the Mayfair Lodge Home car park opposite the ground. Offenders will be clamped.

HANWELL TOWN - Reynolds Field, Perivale Lane, Greenford, Middlesex UB6 8TL Tel 020 8998 1701

From West, junction 16 M25 and follow A40 (M) towards London. Go over the Greenford flyover and get into the nearside lane signposted Ealing & Perivale. Exit and turn right across the A40. The ground is immediately on the left. Turn left into Perivale Lane and the entrance is 200 yards on the left. Nearest railway station is Perivale (London Underground – Central Line).

HAREFIELD UNITED - Preston Park, Breakspear Road North, Harefield, Middlesex, UB9 6NE Tel: 01895 823474.

From the M25 at Junction 16 turn left. At the roundabout turn right towards Denham and at the next roundabout turn left then right at the end of the road. Turn left by the Pub and follow the road over the canal and into the village. Go straight across the roundabout into Breakspear Road and the ground is approximately 800 metres on the right.

HARINGEY BOROUGH - Coles Park, White Hart Lane, Tottenham, London N17 7JP Tel: 020 8889 1415

At junction 25 of the M25 or from the A406 (North Circular Road) turn south onto the A10 (Great Cambridge Road) towards Central London. At the junction of the A10 and White Hart Lane turn right (use slip road at traffic lights) into White Hart Lane and the ground is about 500 yards on the left, some 150 yards after a petrol station. PUBLIC TRANSPORT: Bus W3 from Finsbury Park station to Northumberland Park station via Alexandra Palace station and Wood Green underground station passes ground. In other direction W3 can be boarded at White Hart Lane station).

HARPENDEN TOWN - Rothamstead Park, Amenbury Lane, Harpenden AL5 2EF Tel: 07968 120032

Approaching Harpenden from St. Albans, turn left into Leyton Road at mini-roundabout by the Silver Cup and Fire Station. Coming from Luton, go through the town and as you leave (just past The George) turn right into Leyton Road. Turn left in Amenbury Lane and then left into car park after 300 yards. Entrance to the Club is up the pathway, diagonally across the car park in the far corner from the entrance. This is a pay-and-display car park up to 6.30pm.

HATFIELD TOWN - Gosling Sports Park, Stanborough Road, Welwyn Garden City, Herts AL8 6XE Tel 01707 384300

From A1 (M) junction 4, take A414 towards Hertford/Welwyn Garden City. At the roundabout take the 1st exit onto the A6129, heading to Stanborough/Wheathampstead. At the next roundabout take the 2nd exit onto the A6129 Stanborough Road. At the next roundabout take the 3rd exit into Gosling Sports Park.

HERTFORD TOWN - Hertingfordbury Park, West Street, Hertford, Herts SG13 8EZ Tel 01992 583716

From the A1 follow the A414 to Hertford until you see Gates Ford Dealership on the right. At next roundabout double back and immediately past Gates (now on your left) turn left into West Street. This is a narrow road and when it bears left, turn right and go down the hill and over a bridge to the ground. From the A10 follow the A414 until you see Gates.

HILLINGDON BOROUGH - Middlesex Stadium, Breakspear Road, Ruislip, Middlesex HA4 7SB Tel 01895 639544

From M40/A40 eastbound, leave the A40 at the Swakeleys roundabout, exit is sign-posted Ickenham & Ruislip and take the B467. At the second mini-roundabout turn left into Breakspear Road South. After approx 1 mile, turn right into Breakspear Road by the Breakspear Arms PH. The ground is a further 1/2 mile on the left-hand side.

HODDESDON TOWN - Stewart Edwards Stadium, Lowfield, Park View, Hoddesdon, Herts, EN11 8PU Tel: 01992 463133

For SatNav users, please key in EN11 8PX, which will take you to Park Road, directly opposite the ground

From the A10, take Hoddesdon turnoff (A1170). Follow the slip road to the roundabout at the bottom of the hill and then turn right into Amwell Street. Take the first right, at the church, into Pauls Lane. Follow the road round to left which becomes Taveners Way. At the mini-roundabout opposite the Iceland store, turn right into Brocket Road. At T junction turn left into Park View and the ground is 200 yards on the right.

HOLMER GREEN - Airedale Park, Watchet Lane, Holmer Green, Bucks HP15 6UF Tel 01494 711485

From Amersham on A404 High Wycombe Road. After approx 2 miles turn right into Sheepcote Dell Road. Continue until end of road at Bat & Ball pub. Turn right, then immediately left. Continue approx 1/2 mile until double mini-roundabouts. Turn left in front of the Mandarin Duck restaurant into Airedale Park 150 yards on the right

KENTISH TOWN - Barnet Copthall Stadium, Greenlands Lane, Hendon, London NW4 1RL Tel 020 8202 6478

From the North: take the M1, exiting at junction 4 (Edgware & Harrow.) onto the A41 towards Mill Hill, at the apex of the corner (junction with A1) go straight ahead on the A41. Go over a small roundabout and at the traffic lights (just before the M1 flyover) turn left into Page Street. Travel for about 1/2 mile and turn right into Champions Way. At mini-roundabout turn right into Greenlands Lane and the Stadium complex is on the left. From The South: Follow the A1/A41 towards Mill Hill. At the junction under the M1 flyover, turn right at the traffic lights into Page Street and follow the directions above. Nearest Tube Station is Mill Hill Broadway.

Please note that the service road by the stadium has several small posts which should be avoided.

KINGS LANGLEY - Gaywood Park, Hempstead Road, Kings Langley Herts WD4 8BS Tel: 07976 692801

From M25 leave at junction 20. Take A4251 to Kings Langley. Go through the village. The ground is approximately 1/2 mile on the right.

KINGSBURY LONDON TIGERS - Silver Jubilee Park, Townsend Lane, London NW9 7NE. Tel 020 8205 1645

From Edgware Road A5 NW9, turn into Kingsbury Road (A4006) and up the hill. Townsend Lane is the third turning on the left (McNicholas building on the corner). Follow the road to the bottom of park and drive into the ground on the left.

LANGFORD - Forde Park, Langford Road, Henlow, Beds SG16 6AG Tel: 01462 816106.

From West along A57 to Henlow then north on A6001. Ground at north end of Henlow

From North and East, leave A1 at Langford water tower then into Langford. Turn left at Boot Restaurant. Follow A6001 round to the left. Club is 1/2 mile away.

LEVERSTOCK GREEN - Pancake Lane, Leverstock Green, Hemel Hempstead, Herts Tel: 01442 246280.

From M1 at Junction 8, Follow A414 to second roundabout turn left along Leverstock Green Way. Pancake Lane is on the left 300 yards past the Leather Bottle Public House. Ground is 300 yards on left. All visitors are requested to park inside the ground.

LONDON COLNEY - Cotlandswick Playing Fields, London Colney, Herts AL2 1DW Tel: 01727 822132.

From M25 J22, follow the A1081 signposted to St Albans. At London Colney roundabout take A414, signposted Hemel Hempstead/Watford. There is a hidden turn into the ground after approximately 500 metres (just after lay-by) signposted Sports Ground and London Colney FC. Follow the ground around between the Rugby and Irish clubs to ground entrance.

LONDON LIONS - V & E Club, Goffs Lane, Cheshunt, Herts EN7 5QN Tel & Fax 01992 624281

From M25 Junction 25 take A10 towards Cheshunt, at first roundabout turn left onto B198 (Cuffley and Goffs Oak). Go straight over next roundabout. At next roundabout at end of road, turn right into Goffs Lane. Clubhouse is on immediate right.

NEW BRADWELL ST PETER - Recreation Ground, Bradwell Road, Bradville, Milton Keynes MK13 7AD Tel: 01908 313835.

From M1 J14 go towards Newport Pagnell, turn left at first roundabout into H3 (A422 Monks Way). Go six roundabouts then turn right into V6 (Grafton Street). At first roundabout drive all the way around and then take the first left. At first mini-roundabout, turn left. Go 1/2 mile and straight across next mini-roundabout. Ground is then immediately on the left.

BFrom Bushey Station, take Pinner Road (A4008) and continue along Oxhey Lane (towards Harrow). At the traffic lights turn right into Little Oxhey Lane. Altham Way is on left just after crossing Railway Bridge. Clubhouse is located next to swimming pool. Please park in the Pool/Jets overflow car park to avoid either blocking in cars, or being blocked in yourself.

ROYSTON TOWN - Garden Walk, Royston, Herts SG8 7HP. Tel: 01763 241204.

From A505 (town bypass), take A10 towards town centre. Go straight on at next roundabout. Garden Walk is the second turning on the left. Entrance to ground is approx. 200 metres on left.

SPORT LONDON e BENFICA - Coles Park, White Hart Lane, London N17 7JP Tel: 020 8889 1415 (Match days only)

From Junction 25 on M25 (or from Great Cambridge roundabout on the A406 – North Circular Road) turn south onto A10 and follow it until traffic lights with slip road on right for turning into White Hart Lane (this will be the 2nd traffic lights – ignoring pedestrian only sets – after the Great Cambridge roundabout where it meets the A406 North Circular Road). After turning into White Hart Lane, ground entrance is about 500yds on the left, some 150yds after a petrol station.

By Public Transport: Bus W3 from Finsbury Park station to Northumberland Park station via Alexandra Palace Network Rail station and Wood Green Piccadilly Line underground station passes ground (in other direction W3 can be boarded at Northumberland Park or White Hart Lane Network Rail stations).

ST ALBANS CITY RESERVES - Clarence Park, York Road, St Albans, Herts AL1 4PL Tel 01727 864296

From the North (M1): Take the M10 exit at junction 7 to St Albans. At the end of motorway take 2nd exit at roundabout onto A405. At next roundabout turn left onto A1081. Follow the road for approx 1 mile until mini-roundabout (GREAT NORTHERN PUB ON LEFT). Turn right into Alma Road. At traffic lights turn right into Victoria Street and continue to junction with Crown pub. Go straight across into Clarence Road, ground is first on left about 50 yards past junction or the next turning on the left into York Road, ground entrance is at the end of the road on the left.

From the North (A1M): Come off A1 (M) at junction 3 onto A414 to St Albans. At next major roundabout take A1081 exit to St Albans. Follow road for approx 1 mile until mini-roundabout (GREAT NORTHERN PUB ON LEFT). Then proceed as above.

From the West (A5183/A4147): At Batchwood Hall roundabout go straight on towards St Albans. At next mini-roundabout bear left past petrol station into Catherine Street. Follow road up to roundabout at top of St Peters Street in City centre. Go straight across into Hatfield Road, then straight over another mini-roundabout and over railway line to Crown pub junction. Turn left into Clarence Road, ground is about 50 yards past junction or take next turning on the left into York Road. Ground entrance is at the end of the road on the left.

From the M25 (clockwise): Exit M25 at junction 22 (A1081). Follow signs to St Albans from slip road. At London Colney roundabout (traffic light controlled) exit onto A1081. Follow road for approx 1 mile until mini-roundabout (GREAT NORTHERN PUB ON LEFT). Then proceed as above.

Parking: Ac small amount of parking is available at the Clarence Road entrance, if not, the station car park can be used or surrounding roads, but do not block driveways and be aware of local parking restrictions. Public Transport: St Albans City station is on the Thameslink service from Kings Cross Thameslink (20 minutes). Turn left out of the station into Station Way and cross Hatfield Road into Clarence Park. Follow the path round to the right of the ground until you reach the main entrance.

ST. MARGARETSBURY - Station Road, St. Margarets, Herts SG12 8EH Tel: 01920 870473

A10 to Cambridge. Exit at A414 Harlow & Chelmsford. Proceed 400 yards to Amwell roundabout and take 3rd exit (B181) to Stanstead Abbotts. Ground is 1/2 mile on the right-hand side.

STONY STRATFORD TOWN - Ostlers Lane, Stony Stratford, Milton Keynes MK11 1AR Tel: 07914 012709

From Dunstable on the A5 heading north: On approaching Bletchley continue on the main A5 trunk road signposted to Towcester & Hinckley. Continue to the very end of dual carriageway, where you will meet a main roundabout. This is where the main A5 intersects with the A508 to Northampton. At this roundabout take first exit, this is the old (single carriageway) A5. Follow the main road, straight through the traffic lights, over the river bridge and take the second turning right into Ostlers Lane. The ground is approx 200yds on the right.

From Buckingham on the A422: Continue on the A422, straight on at the first roundabout (pedestrian footbridge overhead). Continue on until you meet the next roundabout and take the last exit (the old single carriageway A5). Then proceed as above.

STOTFOLD - Roker Park, The Green, Stotfold, Hitchin, Herts SG5 4AN Tel 01462 730765

At A1 junction 10, take the A507 to Stotfold and right into town. Proceed along High Street and at traffic lights turn right (from Hitchin – straight over traffic lights) towards Astwick Turn right at the Crown pub into The Green. The ground is set back from The Green on the left.

SUN POSTAL SPORTS - Sun Postal Sports Club, Mountwood Avenue, Watford, Herts WD17 3BM Tel: 01923 227453

From Watford town centre take the A411 (Hempstead Road) away from the Town Hall towards Hemel Hempstead. At 2nd set of traffic lights turn left into Langley Way. At the next roundabout, where there is a parade of shops on the left and the "Essex Arms" on the right, take the third exit into Cassiobury Drive. Then take the first turn left into Bellmountwood Avenue then at the left hand bend turn right into the Club entrance.

TRING ATHLETIC - The Grass Roots Stadium, Pendley Sports Centre, Cow Lane, Tring, Herts HP23 5NT. Tel: 01442 891144

From M25 take A41 to Aylesbury. At roundabout at junction take last exit sign-posted Berkhamsted. Turn next left into Cow Lane. Stadium is on the right at end of Cow Lane.

WODSON PARK - Ware FC, Wadesmill Road, Herts SG12 0UQ Tel 01920 463247

From the South: leave the M25 at junction 25 and take the A10 north past Cheshunt and Hoddesdon. After crossing the Lea Valley with Ware below and to your right, leave the A10 at the junction for the A1170 (signposted for Wadesmill and Thundridge). The slip road comes off the A10 onto a roundabout. Turn left (first exit) onto Wadesmill Road (A1170) and come back over the A10 to a second roundabout. Go straight over and take the first turn on the left into Wodson Park Sports Centre. The football ground is on the far left of the car park. From the North: Leave the A10 at the Ware North turn off (A1170). The slip road takes you to a roundabout. Turn right (3rd exit) into Wadesmill Road and take the first left into Wodson Park Sports Centre.

SUSSEX COUNTY LEAGUE

www.scfl.org.uk

Sponsored by:
No Sponsor

Founded: 1920

Recent champions:
2005: Horsham YMCA
2006: Horsham YMCA
2007: Eastbourne Town
2008: Crowborough Athletic
2009: Eastbourne United Association

Division One		P	W	D	L	F	A	Pts
Whitehawk		38	26	7	5	85	36	85
Peacehaven & Tel.		38	23	9	6	83	42	78
Chichester City		38	21	6	11	87	51	69
Wick		38	19	10	9	80	58	67
Redhill		38	18	11	9	65	49	65
Eastbourne UA		38	16	9	13	70	63	57
Three Bridges		38	16	7	15	78	56	55
Crawley Down		38	14	12	12	71	76	54
Shoreham		38	15	8	15	63	59	53
Lingfield		38	12	16	10	69	67	52
Selsey		38	13	12	13	70	70	51
Arundel		38	12	13	13	74	71	49
Ringmer	*-1*	38	12	14	12	68	71	49
Hassocks		38	12	12	14	51	59	48
East Grinstead Town		38	11	7	20	62	74	40
St Francis Rangers		38	11	7	20	55	76	40
Pagham		38	10	10	18	46	76	40
Crowborough Athletic		38	11	4	23	51	101	37
Hailsham Town		38	9	4	25	50	78	31
Mile Oak		38	6	8	24	36	81	26

JOHN O'HARA CUP

(Division One and Division Two teams)

FIRST ROUND
Arundel 3 Southwick 1
Hailsham Town 3 Rustington 1
Lingfield 1 Rye United 0 *aet*
Mile Oak 2 **Little Common** 3
Ringmer 2 Sidley United 1
Seaford Town 3 Three Bridges 2

SECOND ROUND
Arundel 2 Hailsham Town 1
Chichester City 3 Steyning Town 0
Clymping 2 **Peacehaven & Telscombe** 4
Crawley Down 3 Wealden 2 Crowborough Athletic 1
Storrington 2 East Preston 1 **St Francis Rangers** 2
Hassocks 1 **Seaford Town** 2
Lancing 0 **Whitehawk** 1
Lingfield 3 **Eastbourne United Association** 1
(Lingfield expelled)
Little Common 1 **Ringmer** 2
Midhurst & Easebourne Utd 0 **East Grinstead Town** 1
Pagham 1 **Oakwood** 3
Redhill 5 Littlehampton Town 0
Selsey 2 Worthing United 1
Shoreham 4 Loxwood 0
Westfield 1 **Wick** 3

THIRD ROUND
Chichester City 3 Eastbourne UA 1
Crawley Down 2 Storrington 0
East Grinstead Town 3 Oakwood 0
Peacehaven & Telscombe 2 Selsey 0
Redhill 3 Whitehawk 1
Ringmer 5 **Wick** 7 *aet*
Shoreham 2 **Seaford Town** 3 St Francis Rangers 1 **Arundel** 5

QUARTER-FINALS
Arundel 2 **Peacehaven & Telscombe** 4
Crawley Down 7 East Grinstead Town 0
Redhill 1 Chichester City 0
Seaford Town 0 Wick 0 *aet*
Replay: Wick 1 **Seaford** 3

SEMI-FINALS
Redhill 2 **Peacehaven & Telscombe** 3
(at Three Bridges)
Seaford 1 **Crawley Down** 2
(at Shoreham)

FINAL
(April 2nd at Shoreham)
Crawley Down 0 **Peacehaven & Telscombe** 5

	Arun	Chic	Cra	Crow	EG	Ebne	Hail	Hass	Ling	Mile	Pag	Peac	Red	Ring	Sels	Shor	St F.	Thre	Whit	Wick
Arundel		2-2	4-1	1-2	0-1	6-0	2-1	1-4	3-1	2-0	1-1	2-2	5-2	1-3	1-1	2-2	2-2	3-2	5-2	2-3
Chichester City	4-1		2-2	4-2	7-1	0-2	3-2	1-0	4-0	1-2	4-0	1-3	1-0	1-1	1-0	3-1	2-0	2-0	2-3	1-0
Crawley Down	1-2	2-1		2-3	0-0	5-3	1-0	2-1	0-1	1-1	1-2	1-1	2-5	0-2	3-1	3-0	3-2	1-0	0-0	3-3
Crowborough Athletic	2-1	2-1	4-4		1-4	1-1	3-1	0-0	1-1	2-3	1-2	0-4	0-3	2-1	1-0	0-1	2-3	1-2	2-5	2-4
East Grinstead Town	2-2	1-2	0-2	1-3	***D***	1-1	4-2	0-0	0-1	3-1	0-2	1-1	3-4	2-2	3-2	3-2	1-2	3-7	0-2	2-2
Eastbourne United Assoc.	3-1	0-3	1-1	4-1	1-0	***I***	2-0	2-0	2-2	3-0	3-1	3-1	2-0	2-2	2-1	2-3	0-2	1-2	0-1	6-0
Hailsham Town	0-2	1-3	2-2	5-2	1-5	3-1	***V***	1-3	4-0	1-1	4-1	1-3	0-2	5-0	1-2	1-4	2-4	3-2	0-1	0-1
Hassocks	2-2	2-1	3-3	2-0	1-0	1-3	2-0	***I***	1-1	0-3	4-1	3-3	2-2	3-0	1-2	1-0	1-2	1-1	3-5	1-1
Lingfield	5-2	1-1	2-4	7-1	4-2	3-1	1-2	1-1	***S***	3-3	3-1	0-2	0-0	3-3	1-1	2-0	3-0	0-5	1-1	2-2
Mile Oak	0-0	1-3	0-1	0-1	2-1	2-2	1-0	0-1	0-1	***I***	1-3	1-2	0-3	0-4	1-1	0-3	1-1	1-4	0-5	0-0
Pagham	1-1	0-5	1-2	2-1	0-1	2-2	1-0	1-1	2-3	3-1	***O***	2-0	1-1	1-1	2-1	1-1	2-0	1-4	0-1	0-4
Peacehaven & Telscombe	1-1	2-2	3-3	3-2	2-1	4-2	2-0	2-0	1-1	2-0	4-1	***N***	3-1	4-1	4-2	1-2	0-2	0-2	0-0	2-0
Redhill	4-0	2-0	4-2	0-1	2-1	1-0	3-0	1-0	2-2	2-1	1-1	1-2		1-1	3-3	2-2	2-1	1-0	0-0	2-0
Ringmer	5-4	3-5	2-1	2-1	1-5	1-1	2-3	2-2	3-1	2-0	1-1	0-3	2-2	***O***	1-2	4-1	2-0	1-2	0-2	3-6
Selsey	0-0	1-4	3-3	5-2	3-2	2-0	2-2	2-1	2-1	7-2	4-2	1-7	0-0	0-0	***N***	0-1	4-1	2-2	3-1	1-3
Shoreham	2-1	2-1	1-3	7-0	0-1	1-2	0-1	0-1	3-3	3-1	2-0	0-3	3-0	1-2	3-3	***E***	2-2	0-0	1-2	3-1
St Francis Rangers	1-2	2-5	0-1	3-0	2-1	2-3	3-0	0-1	3-3	2-0	2-1	0-2	1-2	0-5	3-3	2-2		2-3	1-3	1-2
Three Bridges	1-3	3-1	3-2	0-1	2-4	2-2	6-1	6-0	0-3	1-3	0-0	1-2	0-2	2-2	1-2	3-0	4-0		1-2	1-2
Whitehawk	3-2	3-2	8-1	6-1	3-2	2-3	1-0	5-0	2-0	4-2	4-0	1-0	2-0	0-0	2-0	1-2	1-1	0-0		0-1
Wick	2-2	1-1	5-2	6-0	2-0	3-2	0-0	2-1	2-2	3-1	6-3	0-2	5-2	1-1	2-1	1-2	3-0	1-3	0-1	

NORMAN WINGATE TROPHY

(Division One champions v John O'Hara Cup holders)

(August 4th at Eastbourne United Association)

Eastbourne United Association 3 Whitehawk 1

ROY HAYDEN TROPHY

(Division One champions v Sussex Senior Cup holders)

(August 25th at Eastbourne Borough)

Eastbourne Boro. 4 Eastbourne Utd Association 0

Division Two		P	W	D	L	F	A	Pts
Rye United		34	25	1	8	89	41	76
Worthing United		34	22	8	4	73	26	74
Sidley United		34	22	7	5	80	35	73
Little Common		34	22	5	7	88	49	71
Loxwood		34	18	7	9	74	37	61
Clymping		34	16	8	10	77	50	56
Storrington		34	17	1	16	55	65	52
Wealden		34	15	5	14	56	56	50
Oakwood	*-3*	34	15	4	15	65	68	46
Seaford Town		34	14	4	16	61	65	46
Lancing		34	14	3	17	61	82	45
Littlehampton Town		34	12	7	15	61	60	43
Rustington		34	11	9	14	53	64	42
East Preston		34	12	5	17	55	69	41
Westfield		34	11	4	19	46	69	37
Southwick		34	5	7	22	48	72	22
Steyning Town		34	4	7	23	36	86	19
Midhurst & Easebourne		34	4	2	28	31	115	14

DIVISION TWO CUP

FIRST ROUND

Wealden 3 Steyning Town 1

Westfields 7 Midhurst & Easebourne United 0

SECOND ROUND

East Preston 0 **Little Common** 1

Littlehampton Town 4 Rustington 3

Oakwood 1 **Seaford Town** 2

Sidley United 1 **Rye United** 2

Southwick 1 **Loxwood** 2

Storrington 1 **Lancing** 2

Westfields 1 **Clymping** 2

Worthing United 2 Wealden 1

QUARTER-FINALS

Clymping 3 Worthing United 2

Littlehampton Town 2 Little Common 1

Loxwood 1 Lancing 0

Rye United 2 Seaford Town 1

SEMI-FINALS

Littlehampton Town 3 Clymping 0 *(at Wick)*

Loxwood 2 Rye United 0 *(at Ringmer)*

FINAL

(April 2nd at Wick)

Loxwood 4 **Littlehampton Town** 5

	Clymping	East Preston	Lancing	Little Common	Littlehampton Town	Loxwood	Midhurst & Easebourne United	Oakwood	Rustington	Rye United	Seaford Town	Sidley United	Southwick	Steyning Town	Storrington	Wealden	Westfield	Worthing United
Clymping		4-0	3-0	2-2	2-2	3-3	5-0	4-0	3-0	5-1	3-2	2-3	3-1	3-1	0-1	2-2	2-0	1-5
East Preston	1-1		1-0	3-4	1-5	0-3	8-0	2-5	2-3	0-2	2-3	0-3	2-1	2-0	2-1	2-1	0-0	1-4
Lancing	4-4	1-0		2-6	1-3	3-0	2-1	1-0	2-1	2-5	4-4	1-2	2-2	2-1	1-4	0-1	4-3	0-5
Little Common	2-1	1-1	4-2	***D***	3-2	1-1	5-1	4-3	4-0	2-3	7-0	3-2	4-1	2-0	0-1	1-1	5-0	1-1
Littlehampton Town	2-1	1-2	1-2	1-2	***I***	2-1	2-1	3-1	2-3	2-6	2-3	0-7	1-1	3-2	3-0	1-2	0-1	0-0
Loxwood	2-1	5-1	3-0	3-0	2-1	***V***	5-0	4-1	2-1	0-3	3-0	0-1	2-2	8-0	7-1	1-4	5-1	1-0
Midhurst & E'bourne	1-3	2-0	1-4	1-2	1-4	0-2	***I***	0-1	2-0	0-5	2-6	0-2	3-0	0-4	0-4	1-3	2-4	0-3
Oakwood	1-2	0-4	2-5	4-2	1-0	3-1	2-2	***S***	2-1	2-1	7-2	1-2	3-0	2-2	2-1	2-1	2-1	0-1
Rustington	1-1	1-1	2-5	2-3	0-0	0-0	4-0	2-2	***I***	3-1	1-2	1-1	2-1	2-2	0-1	3-0	3-6	1-1
Rye United	0-1	3-0	5-0	0-1	3-0	2-0	4-2	2-6	5-1	***O***	2-0	1-1	4-2	4-1	2-0	3-0	1-2	3-2
Seaford Town	2-0	1-2	1-2	3-2	0-0	2-1	7-0	1-4	0-2	0-1	***N***	1-2	2-1	1-1	1-2	5-1	0-1	1-1
Sidley United	3-2	4-0	2-1	1-2	2-1	2-0	7-0	5-0	1-2	0-3	2-1		4-0	4-1	1-2	0-0	3-2	0-0
Southwick	2-3	1-3	5-1	1-2	3-3	0-0	5-1	2-2	3-2	0-1	2-3	1-2	***T***	0-2	1-2	3-2	1-2	3-1
Steyning Town	2-1	0-5	1-2	0-2	1-3	0-3	2-2	0-4	0-1	0-3	0-2	3-3	0-0	***W***	2-3	1-2	2-1	1-4
Storrington	0-2	2-2	2-3	0-3	0-5	0-3	3-2	3-0	0-2	1-3	3-2	0-2	2-1	3-1	***O***	2-3	4-2	2-0
Wealden	1-1	4-2	3-1	2-4	1-0	1-2	3-0	3-0	1-3	1-3	0-1	3-3	1-0	4-1	0-4		2-1	0-1
Westfield	0-4	1-3	1-0	2-1	3-5	1-1	0-3	2-0	2-2	0-3	0-1	1-3	3-1	1-1	2-1	0-2		0-1
Worthing United	3-2	2-0	3-1	2-1	1-1	0-0	4-0	2-0	6-1	4-1	2-1	0-0	2-1	4-1	5-0	2-1	1-0	

Division Three	P	W	D	L	F	A	Pts
Bosham	28	20	4	4	64	25	64
Bexhill United	28	19	4	5	69	31	61
Haywards Heath Town	28	19	2	7	79	36	59
Dorking Wanderers	28	15	6	7	78	44	51
Ifield Edwards	28	14	5	9	61	43	47
Uckfield Town	28	13	6	9	48	36	45
TD Shipley	28	14	3	11	57	54	45
Saltdean United	28	13	4	11	39	47	43
Newhaven	28	11	3	14	55	50	36
Rottingdean Village	28	10	4	14	44	56	34
Sidlesham	28	10	3	15	38	54	33
Forest	28	8	2	18	38	74	26
Pease Pottage Village	28	7	2	19	30	74	23
Broadbridge Heath	28	6	3	19	31	63	21
Hurstpierpoint	28	3	5	20	34	78	14

TOM STABLER MEMORIAL TROPHY

(October 28th at Three Bridges)

Sussex County League Division Three 0

Kent County League 2

DIVISION THREE CUP

FIRST ROUND

Bosham 1 Rottingdean Village 0

Broadbridge Heath 0 **Bexhill United** 5

Dorking Wanderers 2 Hurstpierpoint 1

Ifield Edwards 4 TD Shipley 4 *aet*

Replay: TD Shipley 0 **Ifield Edwards** 3

Newhaven 2 Sidlesham 0

Saltdean United 3 Forest 1

Uckfield Town 1 **Haywards Heath Town** 2 *aet*

QUARTER-FINALS

Bexhill United 2 **Dorking Wanderers** 3

Bosham 5 Pease Pottage Village 1 *aet*

Haywards Heath Town 1 Ifield Edwards 0 *aet*

Saltdean United 3 **Newhaven** 4

SEMI-FINALS

Dorking Wanderers 0 **Bosham** 2 *(at Wick)*

Newhaven 2 **Haywards Heath Town** 3 *(at Ringmer)*

FINAL

(April 2nd at Storrington)

Haywards Heath Town 0 **Bosham** 1 *aet*

	Bexhill United	Bosham	Broadbridge Heath	Dorking Wanderers	Forest	Haywards Heath Town	Hurstpierpoint	Ifield Edwards	Newhaven	Pease Pottage Village	Rottingdean Village	Saltdean United	Sidlesham	TD Shipley	Uckfield Town
Bexhill United		0-1	2-0	3-2	3-0	5-0	2-2	2-1	2-1	2-0	3-0	5-1	4-1	3-2	2-3
Bosham	2-0		5-1	3-3	1-3	1-4	2-0	2-2	1-0	1-2	2-0	3-0	1-2	4-0	1-0
Broadbridge Heath	3-2	0-2	***D***	1-3	0-2	0-5	2-1	1-2	5-2	0-1	1-2	1-1	3-0	1-1	2-1
Dorking Wanderers	1-1	3-3	4-0	***I***	5-0	1-2	9-1	1-2	1-4	5-0	4-2	3-1	3-2	0-1	2-2
Forest	0-4	0-2	2-0	1-7	***V***	0-1	1-1	0-1	0-4	2-5	2-3	3-2	3-2	2-4	2-1
Haywards Heath Town	4-2	0-1	3-3	3-1	5-1		5-0	2-1	3-1	5-0	6-0	1-2	3-0	4-0	2-0
Hurstpierpoint	2-8	3-5	1-2	0-5	1-1	1-2		1-1	4-0	1-0	1-2	1-2	2-2	2-4	0-1
Ifield Edwards	2-4	0-1	3-0	3-3	5-1	5-2	5-1		2-5	1-0	2-1	8-0	1-3	2-0	3-2
Newhaven	2-3	0-2	5-3	2-0	0-1	2-2	3-0	1-1	***T***	3-1	3-4	0-1	5-0	2-3	1-1
Pease Pottage Village	0-1	0-5	2-0	1-2	2-0	0-5	1-5	2-0	0-5	***H***	3-2	2-2	1-3	1-3	1-1
Rottingdean Village	0-0	0-3	3-1	1-2	3-2	0-2	3-0	2-2	0-1	7-3	***R***	0-0	5-1	0-1	1-0
Saltdean United	0-2	1-1	3-0	0-1	2-1	2-1	2-1	4-2	1-0	2-0	3-0	***E***	2-0	1-0	0-1
Sidlesham	0-1	0-4	1-0	2-3	3-2	0-2	3-0	0-1	0-1	4-0	2-2	1-0	***E***	2-1	1-2
TD Shipley	1-3	1-2	1-0	2-2	2-5	4-3	3-1	2-0	3-2	4-2	4-0	6-2	2-3		2-2
Uckfield Town	0-0	0-3	3-1	1-2	5-1	3-2	2-1	0-3	6-0	3-0	2-1	3-2	0-0	3-0	

Res. Premier Div.	P	W	D	L	F	A	Pt
E'bne UA Res.	30	21	3	6	78	33	66
E'bourne T. Res.	30	20	3	7	94	33	63
Hassocks Res.	30	17	6	7	51	36	57
St Francis Res.	30	17	3	10	69	45	54
Mile Oak Res.	30	15	5	10	64	50	50
Pagham Res.	30	14	8	8	45	33	50
Crawley D. Res.	30	14	5	11	59	56	47
Hailsham T. Res.	30	12	6	12	51	44	42
Selsey Res.	30	12	3	15	32	51	39
Wick Res.	30	12	2	16	58	69	38
Hastings U. Res.	30	11	5	14	44	66	38
Arundel Res.	30	12	1	17	55	67	37
Lingfield Res.	30	9	6	15	49	61	33
Whitehawk Res.	30	9	4	17	35	61	31
Shoreham Res. *-1*	30	5	5	20	42	80	19
Steyning T. Res.	30	4	7	19	27	68	19

Res. Division East	P	W	D	L	F	A	Pt
Peacehaven Res.	24	18	1	5	73	28	55
Haywards H. Res.	24	17	2	5	67	28	53
Wealden Res.	24	15	2	7	65	32	47
Redhill Res.	24	15	2	7	68	38	47
Westfield Res.	24	12	2	10	37	54	38
Seaford T. Res.	24	11	2	11	40	37	35
Newhaven Res.	24	10	4	10	42	40	34
Sidley Utd Res.	24	9	3	12	47	55	30
L. Common Res.	24	8	5	11	35	40	29
Ringmer Res.	24	8	4	12	59	54	28
Bexhill Utd Res.	24	9	1	14	35	55	28
Saltdean Res.	24	8	1	15	51	67	25
Pease PV Res.	24	1	1	22	15	106	4

Res. Division West	P	W	D	L	F	A	Pt
E. Preston Res.	24	18	3	3	58	27	57
Worthing U. Res.	24	18	1	5	80	25	55
Chichester Res.	24	14	5	5	52	29	47
Loxwood Res.	24	12	5	7	59	33	41
Dorking W. Res.	24	12	3	9	64	49	39
Lit'hampton Res.	24	11	4	9	50	43	37
Rustington Res.	24	10	4	10	58	54	34
Southwick Res.	24	10	3	11	52	53	33
Lancing Res.	24	10	1	13	61	48	31
Storrington Res.	24	7	5	12	38	64	26
Bosham Res.	24	8	0	16	43	71	24
Broadbdge H Res.	24	4	2	18	27	69	14
Sidlesham Res.	24	3	2	19	22	99	11

RESERVES CUP

FINAL *(April 21st at Eastbourne Borough)*

Eastbourne UA Res. 2 Eastbourne Town Res. 1

IN: Rye United (P), Sidley United (P)
OUT: Mile Oak (R), Whitehawk (P - Isthmian League Division One South)

ARUNDEL

Founded: 1889 Nickname: Mulletts

Secretary: Kathy Wilson **(T)** 07778 783 294 **(E)** kathy@kathy99.freeserve.co.uk
Chairman: Bob Marchant **Manager:** Gary Wheatcroft **Prog Ed:** Kathy Wilson
Ground: Mill Road, Arundel, W. Sussex BN18 9QQ **(T)** 01903 882 548
Capacity: 2,200 **Seats:** 100 **Covered:** 200 **Midweek Matchday:** Tuesday **Clubhouse:** Yes **Shop:** No

Colours(change): Red/white/red (All Blue)
Previous Names:
Previous Leagues: West Sussex
Records: **Att:** 2,200 v Chichester (League) 1967-68 **Goalscorer:** Paul J Bennett **App:** 537 Paul Bennett (Goalkeeper)
Senior Honours: Sussex County Champions 1957-58, 58-59, 86-87.

10 YEAR RECORD

00-01	01-02	02-03	03-04	04-05	05-06	06-07	07-08	08-09	09-10
SxC1 13	SxC1 9	SxC1 17	SxC1 6	SxC1 9	SxC1 7	SxC1 3	SxC1 3	SxC1 2	SxC1 12

CHICHESTER CITY

Founded: 2000 Nickname: Chi

Secretary: Peter Down **(T)** 07845 105 822 **(E)** peterdown3@btinternet.com
Chairman: John Hutter **Manager:** Mark Poulton **Prog Ed:** soccer@journalist.com
Ground: Oaklands Way, Chichester, W Sussex PO19 6AR **(T)** 07845 105 822
Capacity: 2,000 **Seats:** none **Covered:** 200 **Midweek Matchday:** Tuesday **Clubhouse:** Yes **Shop:** Yes

Colours(change): White/green/green. (Yellow/blue/blue)
Previous Names: Chichester FC (pre 1948), Chichester City 1948-2000. Merged with Portfield in 2000, Chicester City Utd 2000-08
Previous Leagues:
Records:
Senior Honours: Sussex County Division One 2003-04.

10 YEAR RECORD

00-01	01-02	02-03	03-04	04-05	05-06	06-07	07-08	08-09	09-10
SxC1 7	SxC1 3	SxC1 4	SxC1 1	SxC1 16	SxC1 8	SxC1 11	SxC1 16	SxC1 7	SxC1 3

CRAWLEY DOWN

Founded: 1993 Nickname:

Secretary: Jane Suckling **(T)** 07712 814 113 **(E)** b.suckling@btinternet.com
Chairman: Brian Suckling **Manager:** Darren Guirey **Prog Ed:** martinmd@btinternet.com
Ground: The Haven Sportsfield, Hophurst Lane, Crawley Dn RH10 4LJ **(T)** 01342 717 140
Capacity: 1,000 **Seats:** **Covered:** 50 **Midweek Matchday:** **Clubhouse:** **Shop:**

Colours(change): All Red (All white)
Previous Names: Crawley Down United > 1993. Crawley Down Village > 1999.
Previous Leagues: Mid Sussex
Records: **Att:** 404 v East Grinstead Town 96
Senior Honours:

10 YEAR RECORD

00-01	01-02	02-03	03-04	04-05	05-06	06-07	07-08	08-09	09-10
SxC2 16	SxC2 11	SxC2 15	SxC2 11	SxC2 10	SxC2 5	SxC2 16	SxC2 6	SxC2 3	SxC1 8

CROWBOROUGH ATHLETIC

Founded: 1894 Nickname: The Crows

Secretary: Karen Scott **(T)** 07983 676 210 **(E)** kes7@talktalk.net
Chairman: Ken Saunders **Manager:** David Adams **Prog Ed:** Karen Scott
Ground: Crowborough Co. Stadium, Alderbrook Rec, Fermor Rd, TN6 3DJ **(T)** 01892 661 893
Capacity: 2,000 **Seats:** **Covered:** 150 **Midweek Matchday:** **Clubhouse:** **Shop:**

Colours(change): Sky blue & navy blue/navy/navy (All red).
Previous Names:
Previous Leagues: Sussex County 1974-2008. Isthmian 2008-09
Records:
Senior Honours: Sussex County Div. 1 Champions 2007-08. League Cup 2006-07.

10 YEAR RECORD

00-01	01-02	02-03	03-04	04-05	05-06	06-07	07-08	08-09	09-10
SxC2 17	SxC3 4	SxC3 3	SxC3 1	SxC2 1	SxC1 6	SxC1 4	SxC1 1	Isth1S 22	SxC1 18

EAST GRINSTEAD TOWN

Founded: 1890 Nickname: The Wasps

Secretary: Brian McCorquodale **(T)** 07802 528 513 **(E)** brian.mcc@egtfc.co.uk
Chairman: Richard Tramontin **Manager:** Tony Beckingham **Prog Ed:** Bruce Talbot
Ground: The GAC Stadium, East Court, College Lane, East Grinstead RH19 3LS **(T)** 01342 325 885
Capacity: 3,000 **Seats:** none **Covered:** 400 **Midweek Matchday:** **Clubhouse:** Yes **Shop:** No

Colours(change): Gold & black stripes/black/gold & black (Royal blue, yellow & white/royal, yellow & white/royal)
Previous Names: East Grinstead > 1997.
Previous Leagues: Mid Sussex, Sussex County, Souhern Amateur
Records: **Att:** 2,006 v Lancing F A Am Cup **App:** Guy Hill
Senior Honours: Sussex County League Division Two 2007-08.

10 YEAR RECORD

00-01	01-02	02-03	03-04	04-05	05-06	06-07	07-08	08-09	09-10
SxC2 4	SxC2 5	SxC2 3	SxC1 9	SxC1 18	SxC2 7	SxC2 11	SxC2 1	SxC1 17	SxC1 15

EASTBOURNE UNITED ASSOCIATION

Founded: 1894 Nickname: The U's

Secretary: Brian Dowling **(T)** 07507 225 450 **(E)** brian.dowling@btinternet.com
Chairman: Les Aisbitt **Manager:** Brian Dennis **Prog Ed:** Brian Dowling
Ground: The Oval, Channel View Road, Eastbourne, BN22 7LN **(T)** 01323 726 989
Capacity: 3,000 **Seats:** 160 **Covered:** 160 **Midweek Matchday:** Tuesday **Clubhouse:** Yes **Shop:** Yes

Colours(change): Black & white halves/black/white. (Sky blue/sky blue/yellow).
Previous Names: Eastbourne Old Comrades, Eastbourne United (merged with Shinewater Assoc in 2000)
Previous Leagues: Metropolitan 1956-64, Athenian 64-77, Isthmian 77-92
Records: **Att:** 11,000 at Lynchmore
Senior Honours: Sussex County Champions 1954-55, 2008-09, Sussex Senior Cup (5).

10 YEAR RECORD

00-01	01-02	02-03	03-04	04-05	05-06	06-07	07-08	08-09	09-10
SxC1 11	SxC1 19	SxC2 8	SxC2 3	SxC1 5	SxC1 14	SxC1 7	SxC1 11	SxC1 1	SxC1 6

HAILSHAM TOWN

Founded: 1885 Nickname: The Stringers

Secretary: Sue Williams **(T)** 07719 590 268 **(E)** williams.susan8@sky.com
Chairman: Mervyn Walker **Manager:** Dave Shearing **Prog Ed:** Lee Mewett
Ground: The Beaconsfield, Western Road, Hailsham BN27 3DN **(T)** 01323 840 446
Capacity: 2,000 **Seats:** none **Covered:** 100 **Midweek Matchday:** Tuesday **Clubhouse:** Yes **Shop:**

Colours(change): Yellow/green/yellow (All light blue)
Previous Names: Hailsham.
Previous Leagues: East Sussex, Southern Combination
Records: **Att:** 1350 v Hungerford T. FA Vase Feb 89 **Goalscorer:** Howard Stephens 51 **App:** Phil Comber 713
Senior Honours:

10 YEAR RECORD

00-01	01-02	02-03	03-04	04-05	05-06	06-07	07-08	08-09	09-10
SxC2 3	SxC1 6	SxC1 15	SxC1 12	SxC1 12	SxC1 10	SxC1 6	SxC1 13	SxC1 15	SxC1 19

HASSOCKS

Founded: 1902 Nickname: The Robins

Secretary: Dave Knight **(T)** 01273 842 023 **(E)** dw.knight45@googlemail.com
Chairman: (Acting) Bob Preston **Manager:** Mickey Jewell **Prog Ed:** Paul Elphick
Ground: The Beacon, Brighton Road, Hassocks BN6 9NA **(T)** 01273 846 040
Capacity: 1,800 **Seats:** 270 **Covered:** 100 **Midweek Matchday:** Tuesday **Clubhouse:** Yes **Shop:** No

Colours(change): All Red. (All blue)
Previous Names:
Previous Leagues: Mid Sussex, Brighton & Hove & Dist and Southern Counties Comb
Records: **Att:** 610 v Burgess Hill Town **Goalscorer:** Pat Harding 43
Senior Honours:

10 YEAR RECORD

00-01	01-02	02-03	03-04	04-05	05-06	06-07	07-08	08-09	09-10
SxC1 12	SxC1 11	SxC1 8	SxC1 7	SxC1 8	SxC1 9	SxC1 5	SxC1 7	SxC1 16	SxC1 14

LINGFIELD

Founded: 1893 Nickname:

Secretary: Pamela Tomsett **(T)** 07903 428 228 **(E)** pamtomsettlfc@hotmail.co.uk

Chairman: Gary Collis **Manager:** Tony Beckingham **Prog Ed:** See secretary

Ground: Sports Pavillion, Godstone Road, Lingfield, Surrey RH7 6BT **(T)** 01342 834 269

Capacity: 1,000+ **Seats:** Yes **Covered:** Yes **Midweek Matchday:** Tuesday **Clubhouse:** Yes **Shop:** No

Colours(change): Red & Yellow stripes/black/yellow.(Blue & white stripes/white /blue)

Previous Names: None.

Previous Leagues: Redhill. Surrey Intermediate. Combined Counties. Mid Sussex.

Records:

Senior Honours:

10 YEAR RECORD

00-01	01-02	02-03	03-04	04-05	05-06	06-07	07-08	08-09	09-10
SxC2 18	SxC3 16	SxC3 9	SxC3 8	SxC3 3	SxC3 2	SxC2 10	SxC2 2	SxC1 8	SxC1 10

PAGHAM

Founded: 1903 Nickname: The Lions

Secretary: Marc Hilton **(T)** 07771 810 757 **(E)** paghamfc@aol.com

Chairman: Brent Williams **Manager:** Carl Stabler **Prog Ed:** TBA

Ground: Nyetimber Lane, Pagham, W Sussex PO21 3JY **(T)** 01243 266 112

Capacity: 2,000 **Seats:** 200 **Covered:** 200 **Midweek Matchday:** **Clubhouse:** Yes **Shop:** No

Colours(change): White & black/black/red (All red)

Previous Names: None

Previous Leagues: Chichester 1903-50, West Sussex 50-69

Records: **Att:** 1,200 v Bognor 1971 **Goalscorer:** Dick De Luca **App:** Graham Peach

Senior Honours: Sussex County Division Two 1978-79, 86-87, 2006-07.
Division One 80-81, 87-88, 88-89.

10 YEAR RECORD

00-01	01-02	02-03	03-04	04-05	05-06	06-07	07-08	08-09	09-10
SxC1 6	SxC1 8	SxC1 9	SxC1 17	SxC1 19	SxC2 13	SxC2 1	SxC1 9	SxC1 11	SxC1 17

PEACEHAVEN & TELSCOMBE

Founded: 1923 Nickname:

Secretary: Margaret Edwards **(T)** 07766 909 772 **(E)** mejim@edwards2412.fsworld.co.uk

Chairman: Jim Edwards **Manager:** Peter Edwards & Terry Hall **Prog Ed:** Phyllis Parris

Ground: The Sports Park, Piddinghoe Ave, Peacehaven, BN10 8RJ **(T)** 01273 582 471

Capacity: **Seats:** **Covered:** **Midweek Matchday:** **Clubhouse:** **Shop:**

Colours(change): Black & white stripes/white & black/white & black (Luminous yellow/black/black)

Previous Names: Formed when Peacehaven Rangers and Telscombe Tye merged.

Previous Leagues:

Records:

Senior Honours: Sussex County Div.3 2005-06. Div.2 2008-09

10 YEAR RECORD

00-01	01-02	02-03	03-04	04-05	05-06	06-07	07-08	08-09	09-10
SxC2 2	SxC1 12	SxC1 18	SxC2 12	SxC2 17	SxC3 1	SxC2 5	SxC2 4	SxC2 1	SxC1 2

REDHILL

Founded: 1894 Nickname: Reds/Lobsters

Secretary: Phil Whatling **(T)** 07929 742 081 **(E)** phil.whatling@ntlworld.com

Chairman: Andy Wheeler **Manager:** Dean Forbes **Prog Ed:**

Ground: Kiln Brow, Three Arch Road, Redhill, Surrey RH1 5AE **(T)** 01737 762 129

Capacity: 2,000 **Seats:** 150 **Covered:** 150 **Midweek Matchday:** Tuesday **Clubhouse:** Yes **Shop:** Yes

Colours(change): Red & white stripes/red/red. (White/black/white).

Previous Names:

Previous Leagues: E & W Surrey. Spartan. Southern Sub. London. Athenian.

Records: **Att:** 8,000 v Hastings U FA Cup 1956 **Goalscorer:** Steve Turner 119 **App:** Brian Medlicott 766

Senior Honours: Athenian League (2) Surrey Senior cup 28-29, 65-66

10 YEAR RECORD

00-01	01-02	02-03	03-04	04-05	05-06	06-07	07-08	08-09	09-10
SxC1 14	SxC1 15	SxC1 12	SxC1 11	SxC1 13	SxC1 18	SxC1 15	SxC1 8	SxC1 7	SxC1 5

RINGMER

Founded: 1906 Nickname: Blues

Secretary: Michelle Marsh **(T)** 07801 571 803 **(E)** vht.rentals@btopenworld.com
Chairman: Bob Munnery **Manager:** Bob Munnery **Prog Ed:** E Chitty
Ground: Caburn Ground, Anchor Field, Ringmer BN8 5QN **(T)** 01273 812 738
Capacity: 1,000 **Seats:** 100 **Covered:** Yes **Midweek Matchday:** Tuesday **Clubhouse:** Yes **Shop:** Yes

Colours(change): Navy & light blue/navy/navy. (All white).
Previous Names: None.
Previous Leagues: Brighton.
Records: 1,350 v Southwick, Sussex County League, 1970-71.
Senior Honours: Sussex County Division Two 1968-69. Division One 1970-71.
Sussex Senior Cup 1972-73.

10 YEAR RECORD

00-01	01-02	02-03	03-04	04-05	05-06	06-07	07-08	08-09	09-10
SxC1 10	SxC1 2	SxC1 7	SxC1 10	SxC1 6	SxC1 2	SxC1 9	SxC1 10	SxC1 9	SxC1 13

RYE UNITED

Founded: Nickname: United

Secretary: Roger Bond **(T)** 07738 154 685 **(E)** e.r.bond@btinternet.com
Chairman: Clive Taylor **Manager:** Scott Price **Prog Ed:** Roger Bond
Ground: Rye Football & Cricket Salts, Fish Market Rd, Rye TN31 7LU **(T)** 07802 427 013
Capacity: 1,500 **Seats:** **Covered:** 100 **Midweek Matchday:** Tuesday **Clubhouse:** Yes **Shop:** No

Colours(change): Red & black/black/black (All blue)
Previous Names:
Previous Leagues: Sussex County & Kent County until 2000
Records: **Att:** 120 **App:** Scott Price
Senior Honours: Sussex County League Division 3 2000-01, Division 2 1955-56, 2001-02, 02-03, 09-10.

10 YEAR RECORD

00-01	01-02	02-03	03-04	04-05	05-06	06-07	07-08	08-09	09-10
SxC3 1	SxC2 1	SxC2 1	SxC1 2	SxC1 2	SxC1 19	SxC1 19	SxC1 19	SxC2 6	SxC2 1

SELSEY

Founded: 1903 Nickname: Blues

Secretary: Gordon Weller **(T)** 07852 954 042 **(E)** g.weller1@btinternet.com
Chairman: David Lee **Manager:** Gary Block **Prog Ed:** Gordon Weller
Ground: High Street Ground, Selsey, Chichester, PO20 0QG **(T)** 01243 603 420
Capacity: 1,000 **Seats:** 25 **Covered:** 98 **Midweek Matchday:** Tuesday **Clubhouse:** Yes **Shop:** No

Colours(change): All Blue. (All Yellow).
Previous Names:
Previous Leagues: Chichester & District, West Sussex.
Records: **Att:** 750-800 v Chichester or Portfield 1950's
Senior Honours: Sussex County Division Two 1963-64, 75-76.

10 YEAR RECORD

00-01	01-02	02-03	03-04	04-05	05-06	06-07	07-08	08-09	09-10
SxC1 4	SxC1 4	SxC1 11	SxC1 18	SxC2 14	SxC2 2	SxC1 8	SxC1 15	SxC1 10	SxC1 11

SHOREHAM

Founded: 1892 Nickname: Musselmen

Secretary: Gary Millis **(T)** 07801 477 979 **(E)** g.millis@sky.com
Chairman: Matthew Major **Manager:** Mark Burt/Darren Donnelly **Prog Ed:** Gary Millis
Ground: Middle Road, Shoreham-by-Sea, W Sussex, BN43 6LT **(T)** 01273 454 261
Capacity: 1,500 **Seats:** 150 **Covered:** 700 **Midweek Matchday:** **Clubhouse:** Yes **Shop:** No

Colours(change): All Blue. (All red).
Previous Names: None.
Previous Leagues: West Sussex.
Records: **Att:** 1,342 v Wimbledon
Senior Honours: Sussex County Division One 1951-52, 52-53, 77-78.
Division Two 61-62, 76-77, 93-94. John O'Hara League Cup 2007-08.

10 YEAR RECORD

00-01	01-02	02-03	03-04	04-05	05-06	06-07	07-08	08-09	09-10
SxC2 13	SxC2 2	SxC1 16	SxC1 19	SxC2 3	SxC1 13	SxC1 13	SxC1 12	SxC1 6	SxC1 9

SIDLEY UNITED

Founded: 1906 Nickname: Blues

Secretary: Robin Powell **(T)** 07785 703 636 **(E)** rm.powell@sundayfootball.fsnet.co.uk

Chairman: Dickie Day **Manager:** John Lambert & Wayne Farrier **Prog Ed:** Robin Powell

Ground: Gullivers Sports Ground, Glovers Lane, Sidley Bexhill on Sea TN39 5BL **(T)** 01424 217 078

Capacity: 1,500 **Seats:** none **Covered:** 150 **Midweek Matchday:** **Clubhouse:** Yes **Shop:**

Colours(change): All navy blue (Yellow & black/black/yellow)
Previous Names:
Previous Leagues: East Sussex & Hastings & Dist
Records: **Att:** 1,300 in 1959 **App:** Jimmy Watson
Senior Honours: Sussex Division 2 1958-59, 64-65, 98-99, Division 1 2000-01, Sussex Int Cup 1947-48, Sussex Jnr Cup 1924-25

10 YEAR RECORD

00-01	01-02	02-03	03-04	04-05	05-06	06-07	07-08	08-09	09-10
SxC1 1	SxC1 5	SxC1 13	SxC1 16	SxC1 15	SxC1 11	SxC1 14	SxC1 20	SxC2 8	SxC2 3

ST. FRANCIS RANGERS

Founded: 2002 Nickname: Saints/Rangers

Secretary: Mrs Clare Cannon **(T)** 01444 246 723 **(E)** themandus@tesco.net

Chairman: John Goss **Manager:** Roy Staughton **Prog Ed:** Mrs Clare Cannon

Ground: Princess Royal Hospital, Lewes Rd, Haywards Hth RH16 4EX **(T)** 01444 441 881

Capacity: 1,000 **Seats:** None **Covered:** 100 **Midweek Matchday:** Tuesday **Clubhouse:** Yes **Shop:** No

Colours(change): Yellow/black/yellow (All orange)
Previous Names: Formed when Ansty Rangers & St Francis merged 2002.
Previous Leagues: None
Records:
Senior Honours: None

10 YEAR RECORD

00-01	01-02	02-03	03-04	04-05	05-06	06-07	07-08	08-09	09-10
		SxC3 6	SxC3 2	SxC2 4	SxC2 3	SxC2 2	SxC1 14	SxC1 12	SxC1 16

THREE BRIDGES

Founded: 1901 Nickname: Bridges

Secretary: Martin Clarke **(T)** 07885 662 940 **(E)** m-clarke@blueyonder.co.uk

Chairman: Alan Bell **Manager:** Paul Falli **Prog Ed:** Alf Blackler

Ground: Jubilee Field, Three Bridges Rd, Crawley, RH10 1LQ **(T)** 01293 442 000

Capacity: 3,500 **Seats:** 120 **Covered:** 600 **Midweek Matchday:** **Clubhouse:** Yes **Shop:**

Colours(change): Amber & black stripes/black/black. (Blue & white stripes /blue/blue)
Previous Names: Three Bridges Worth 1936-52, Three Bridges Utd 53-64
Previous Leagues: Mid Sussex, E Grinstead, Redhill & Dist 36-52
Records: **Att;** 2,000 v Horsham 1948 **App:** John Malthouse
Senior Honours: Sussex RUR Cup 82-83

10 YEAR RECORD

00-01	01-02	02-03	03-04	04-05	05-06	06-07	07-08	08-09	09-10
SxC1 8	SxC1 7	SxC1 14	SxC1 4	SxC1 7	SxC1 15	SxC1 12	SxC1 6	SxC1 5	SxC1 7

WICK

Founded: 1892 Nickname: Wickers

Secretary: Allan Luckin **(T)** 07816 954 349 **(E)** a_luckin@sky.com

Chairman: Keith Croft **Manager:** Carmelo Danzi **Prog Ed:** upfrontkc@hotmail.com

Ground: Coomes Way, Wick, Littlehampton, W Sussex BN17 7LS **(T)** 01903 713 535

Capacity: 1,000 **Seats:** 100 **Covered:** Yes **Midweek Matchday:** **Clubhouse:** Yes **Shop:** No

Colours(change): Red & black stripes/black with white flash/black with white flash (White/black/black).
Previous Names: Lyminster FC.
Previous Leagues: West Sussex
Records: **Att:** 900
Senior Honours: Sussex County Division One 1989-90, 93-94. Div.2 81-82, 85-86.
Sussex Senior Cup 92-93.

10 YEAR RECORD

00-01	01-02	02-03	03-04	04-05	05-06	06-07	07-08	08-09	09-10
SxC1 3	SxC1 14	SxC1 19	SxC1 4	SxC1 2	SxC1 12	SxC1 16	SxC1 5	SxC1 4	SxC1 4

DIVISION TWO INS & OUTS

IN: Bexhill United (P), Mile Oak (R)
OUT: Rye United (P), Sidley United (P) Wealden become AFC Uckfield

A.F.C. UCKFIELD
Founded: 1988

Secretary: Derek York **(T)** 07847 453 767 **(E)** d-york1@sky.com
Chairman: Tom Parker **Manager:** Simon Rowland **Prog Ed:** Anthony Harvey
Ground: The Oaks, Old Eastbourne Road, Uckfield TN22 5QL **(T)** 07847 662 337 **Capacity:**
Colours(change): Sky & dark blue/dark blue/sky blue (All orange)

ADDITIONAL INFORMATION:
Previous Name: Wealden 1988-2010.
Honours: Sussex County League Division 2 League Cup 2004-05.

BEXHILL UNITED

Secretary: Michael Ottley **(T)** 07841 512 450 **(E)** michaelottley1948@hotmail.com
Chairman: Colin Dunstall **Manager:** Gerad Moyse **Prog Ed:** Michael Ottley
Ground: The Polegrove, Brockley Road, Bexhill on Sea TN39 3EX **(T)** 07815 425 682 **Capacity:**
Colours(change): White/black/black (All blue)

ADDITIONAL INFORMATION:

CLYMPING
Founded: 1947

Secretary: Kay Weller **(T)** 07799 577 993 **(E)** kay.weller@hotmail.co.uk
Chairman: Frank Sumner **Manager:** Darren Prior **Prog Ed:** Anji Sumner
Ground: Clymping Village Hall, Clymping, Littlehampton BN17 5GW **(T)** 07762 498 840 **Capacity:**
Colours(change): Blue/blue/blue & white (All red)

ADDITIONAL INFORMATION:
Previous League: West Sussex 1949-2000.
Honours: Sussex County Division 3 2008-09.

EAST PRESTON
Founded: 1966

Secretary: Keith Freeman **(T)** 07986 596913 **(E)** keweia@btinternet.com
Chairman: Michael Barnes **Manager:** Paul Curtis **Prog Ed:** Keith Freeman
Ground: Roundstone Recreation Ground, Lashmar Road, East Preston BN16 1ES **(T)** 01903 776 026 **Capacity:**
Colours(change): Black & white stripes/black/black (All blue)

ADDITIONAL INFORMATION:

LANCING
Founded: 1941

Secretary: Paul Blann **(T)** 07967 751 281 **(E)** debit@blannayres.fsnet.co.uk
Chairman: (Acting) Brian Hill **Manager:** Martin Gander **Prog Ed:** Brian Hill
Ground: Culver Road, Lancing, West Sussex BN15 9AX **(T)** 01903 767 285 **Capacity:**
Colours(change): Yellow/blue/yellow (All red)

ADDITIONAL INFORMATION:
Previous Name: Lancing Athletic. **Previous League:** Brighton & Hove & District.
Honours: Brighton League 1946-47, 47-48.

LITTLE COMMON
Founded: 1966

Secretary: Mrs Margaret Cherry **(T)** 01424 217 191 **(E)** danieleldridge11@btinternet.com
Chairman: Ken Cherry **Manager:** Mark Linch **Prog Ed:** Dan Eldridge
Ground: Little Common Recreation Ground, Green Lane, Bexhill on Sea TN39 4PH **(T)** 01424 845 861 **Capacity:**
Colours(change): Claret & blue/claret/claret (Yellow/navy/navy)

ADDITIONAL INFORMATION:
Previous Name: Albion United > 1986. **Previous League:** East Sussex 1994-2005.
Honours: East Sussex League 1975-76, 76-77, 2004-05.

LITTLEHAMPTON TOWN
Founded: 1896

Secretary: Alan Barnes **(T)** 07882 460 357 **(E)** truegritagb@aol.com
Chairman: Neil Taylor **Manager:** John Suter **Prog Ed:** Dave Perrett
Ground: Sportsfield, St Flora's Road, Littlehampton BN17 6BD **(T)** 01903 716 390 **Capacity:**
Colours(change): Yellow/black/black (All white)

ADDITIONAL INFORMATION: **Honours:** Sussex County Lge 1958-59 (shared), 75-76, 84-85, 90-91, 96-97. Sussex Sen. Cup 1949, 70.
Lost in the F.A. Cup Preliminary Round v Tunbridge Wells 15-16 on penalties after 40 kicks had been taken - At the time a European record and only one short of the World record.

LOXWOOD

Secretary: George Read **(T)** 07791 766 857 **(E)** thomasread00@btinternet.com
Chairman: Derek Waterman **Manager:** Barry Hunter **Prog Ed:** George Read
Ground: Loxwood Sports Ass., Plaistow Road, Loxwood RH14 0RQ **(T)** 01403 753 185 **Capacity:**
Colours(change): Black & white/black/white (Red/white/red)

ADDITIONAL INFORMATION:
Previous League: West Sussex.
Honours: Sussex County League Division 3 2007-08.

MIDHURST & EASEBOURNE

Secretary: Ted Dummer MBE **(T)** 01730 813 887 **(E)** acs@harrisonrenwick.com
Chairman: Darren Chiverton **Manager:** Trever Waller **Prog Ed:** Ted Dummer MBE
Ground: Rotherfield, Dodsley Lane, Easebourne, Midhurst GU29 9BE **(T)** 01730 816 557 **Capacity:**
Colours(change): Royal blue with black trim/black/royal blue (All red)

ADDITIONAL INFORMATION: Previous Name: Post WW2 Midhurst FC and Easbourne FC amalgamated to form today's club.
Previous League: West Sussex 1999-2002.
Honours: Sussex County League Division 2 Cup 1988-89, Division 3 Cup 2002-03.

MILE OAK

Founded: 1960 Nickname: The Oak

Secretary: Colin Brown **(T)** 07774 754 468 **(E)** colin.d.brown@ntlworld.com
Chairman: Leslie Hamilton **Manager:** Anthony Whittington **Prog Ed:** Colin Brown
Ground: Mile Oak Recreation Ground, Chalky Road, Portslade BN41 2YU **(T)** 01273 423 854 **Capacity:**
Colours(change): Tangerine & black stripes/black/tangerine with black trim (All green)

ADDITIONAL INFORMATION:
Previous League: Brighton & Hove District.
Honours: Brighton & Hove District 1980-81. Sussex County League Division 2.

OAKWOOD

Founded: 1962

Secretary: Kelly Whittaker **(T)** 07973 752 761 **(E)** beccakel@hotmail.com
Chairman: Stuart Lovegrove **Manager:** John Mist **Prog Ed:** Kelly Whittaker
Ground: Tinsley Lane, Three Bridges, Crawley RH10 8AJ **(T)** 01293 515 742 **Capacity:**
Colours(change): Red & black stripes/black/black (Blue/white/blue)

ADDITIONAL INFORMATION:
Previous League: Southern Counties Combination 1980-84.
Honours: Sussex County Division 2 Cup 1989-90.

RUSTINGTON

Secretary: Paul Cox **(T)** 07771 623 224 **(E)** cox121@yahoo.com
Chairman: John Virgoe **Manager:** Brett (Charlie) Torode **Prog Ed:** Paul Cox
Ground: Recreation Ground, Jubilee Avenue, Rustington BN16 3NB **(T)** 01903 770 495 **Capacity:**
Colours(change): Blue/blue/white (Red & black/black/red)

ADDITIONAL INFORMATION:
Honours: Sussex County League Division 3 2006-07.

SEAFORD TOWN

Secretary: John Smith **(T)** 07919 993 751 **(E)** johnsmith@btinternet.com
Chairman: Bob Thomsett **Manager:** Tony Coade **Prog Ed:** John Smith
Ground: The Crouch, Bramber Road, Seaford BN25 1AG **(T)** 01323 892 221 **Capacity:**
Colours(change): All red (White/black/black)

ADDITIONAL INFORMATION:
Honours: Sussex County League Division 2 2005-06.

SOUTHWICK

Founded: 1882

Secretary: Paul Symes **(T)** 07908 289 758 **(E)** p.p.symes@btinternet.com
Chairman: Steve Taylor **Manager:** Roger Feest & Lloyd Suanders **Prog Ed:** Paul Symes
Ground: Old Barn Way, Southwick BN42 4NT **(T)** 01273 701 010 **Capacity:**
Colours(change): Red & black stripes/black/black (Yellow/red/yellow)

ADDITIONAL INFORMATION:
Previous League: Isthmian 1985-92.
Honours: Sussex County League Division 1 x6. Sussex Senior Cup x10.

STEYNING TOWN

Secretary: Mrs Gina Barnes **(T)** 07742 305 847 **(E)** brian.barnes1911@talktalk.net
Chairman: Mrs Gina Barnes **Manager:** David Shearing **Prog Ed:** Dee Dutton
Ground: The Shooting Field, Steyning, West Sussex BN44 3RQ **(T)** 01903 814 601 **Capacity:**
Colours(change): All red (Yellow/black/yellow)

ADDITIONAL INFORMATION:
Honours: Sussex County League Division 2 1977-78, Division 1 1984-85, 85-86, League Cup 1978-79, 83-84, 85-86.

STORRINGTON

Founded: 1920

Secretary: Keith Dalmon **(T)** 07889 367 956 **(E)** keithdalmon@btinternet.com
Chairman: Malcolm McMichael **Manager:** Rick Hamilton **Prog Ed:**
Ground: Recreation Ground, Pulborough Road, Storrington RH20 4HJ **(T)** 01903 745 860 **Capacity:**
Colours(change): All blue (White/black/white)

ADDITIONAL INFORMATION:
Honours: Sussex County League Division 2 Cup 1979, Division 3 Cup 1998, Division 3 2005.
Vernon Wentworth Cup 1998, 2003.

WESTFIELD

Founded: 1927

Secretary: Gill Attewell **(T)** 07928 176 658 **(E)** gilljordan@rocketmail.com
Chairman: Graham Drinkwater **Manager:** Duncan Jones **Prog Ed:** Gill Attewell
Ground: The Parish Field, Main Road, Westfield TN35 4SB **(T)** 01424 751 011 **Capacity:**
Colours(change): Yellow & green/green/green (All blue)

ADDITIONAL INFORMATION:
Previous League: East Sussex 1971-97.
Honours: East Sussex 1977-78, League Cup 77-78. Hastings Senior Cup 2007-08.

WORTHING UNITED

Founded: 1952

Secretary: Malcolm Gamlen **(T)** 07743 322 571 **(E)** helsnmark@aol.com
Chairman: Glen Houchen **Manager:** Dom Di Paola **Prog Ed:** Malcolm Gamlen
Ground: The Robert Albon Memorial Ground, Lyons Way BN14 9JF **(T)** 01903 234 466 **Capacity:**
Colours(change): Sky blue & whites stripes/navy blue/navy blue (Red & white/red/red)

ADDITIONAL INFORMATION:
Previous Names: Wigmore Athletic 1952-88. Amalgamated with Southdown to form Worthing United in 1988.
Honours: Sussex County Division 2 1973-74, Division 3 1989-90.

DIVISION THREE CONSTITUTION 2010-11

BARNHAM	Mill Road, Slindon, Nr Arundel, West Sussex BN18 0LZ	07738 625 795
BOSHAM	Recration Ground, Walton Lane, Bosham, West Sussex PO10 8QF	07542 283 247
BROADBRIDGE HEATH	Boradbridge Heath Leisure Centre, Wickhurst Lane, Broadbridge Heath RH12 3YS	01403 211 311
DORKING WANDERERS	West Humble Playing Fields, London Road, Dorking, Surrey	07841 671 825
FERRING	The Glebelands, Ferring, West Sussex BN12 5JL	01903 872 529
FOREST	Roffey Sports & Social Club, Spooners Road, Roffey RH12 4DY	01403 210 223
HAYWARDS HEATH TOWN	Hanbury Park Stadium, Allen Road, Haywards Heath RH16 3PX	01444 412 837
HURSTPIERPOINT	Fairfield Recreation Ground, Cuckfield Road, Hurstpierpoint BN6 9SD	01273 834 783
IFIELD EDWARDS	Edwards Sports & Social Club, Ifield Green, Ifield, Crawley	01293 536 569
NEWHAVEN	Fort Road, Newhaven, East Sussex BN9 9DA	01273 513 940
PEASE POTTAGE VILLAGE	Finches Field, Old Brighton Road South, Pease Pottage RH11 9AH	01293 538 651
ROTTINGDEAN VILLAGE	Rottingdean Sports Centre, Falmer Road, Rottingdean BN2 7DA	01273 306 436
SALTDEAN UNITED	Hill Park Coombe Vale, Saltdean, Brighton BN2 8HJ	07879 587 174
SIDLESHAM	Recreation Ground, Selsey Road, Sidlesham, Nr Chichester PO20 7RD	01243 641 538
TD SHIPLEY	The Pavilion, Dragons Green, Dragons Lane, Shipley RH13 8GB	07804 325 228
UCKFIELD TOWN	Victoria Pavilion, VictoriaPleasure Ground, New Town, Uckfield TN22 5DJ	*01825 769 000

*Messages only

IN: Barnham (P - West Sussex League Premier Division), Ferring (Worthing & District League Premier Division)

OUT: Bexhill United (P)

Crawley Down F.C.

Lingfield FC - Photo: Roger Turner.

GROUND DIRECTIONS

ARUNDEL - Mill Road, Arundel, West Sussex BN18 9QQ - 01903 882 548
A27 from Worthing to Arundel over Railway Bridge to roundabout . Second exit into Queen Street to town centre and turn right over bridge. Car park leading to ground 100 yards on right.

CHICHESTER CITY - Oaklands Park, Oaklands Way, Chichester PO19 6AR - 07845 105 822
Half a mile north of the city centre, adjacent to festival theatre. Turn into Northgate car park and entrance to the ground is next to the Chichester Rackets Club.

CRAWLEY DOWN - The Haven Sportsfield, Hophurst Lane, Crawley Down RH10 4LJ - 01342 717140
From B 2028 South right into Vicarage Road ground 200 yards on left.
From B 2038 North left into Sandy Lane to War Memorial Hophurst Lane on left
From A22 Felbridge turn onto A264, fork left into Crawley Down. Two miles on right up hill.

CROWBOROUGH ATHLETIC - Crowborough Community Stadium, Alderbrook Recreation Ground, Fermor Road, TN6 3DJ
Entering Crowborough from the south on the A26, about half a mile past the Crow and Gate Pub, take the next right into Sheep Plain - This is also signposted for the Railway Station, which meanders into Hurtis Hill. At the mini-roundabout go straight into Fermor Road, take the second turning on the right and turn right immediately into Alderbrook Recreation Ground. The Stadium and parking is ahead of you.

EAST GRINSTEAD TOWN - East Court, East Grinstead RH19 3LS - 01342 325885
A264 Tunbridge Wells road (Moat Road) until mini roundabout at bottom of Blackwell Hollow ,turn immediately right by club sign then 1st left, ground 200 yards down lane past rifle club on right.

EASTBOURNE UNITED AFC - The Oval, Channel View Ropad, Eastbourne, East Sussex BN22 7LN - 011323 726989
From A22 follow signs to Eastbourne East seafront. Turn left onto seafront and left again into Channel View Road at Princess Park & ground is first right.

HAILSHAM TOWN - The Beaconsfield, Western Road, Hailsham, East Sussex BN27 3DN - 01323 840446
A22 to Arlington Road, turn east, then left into South Road- left into Diplocks Way until Daltons. Four miles from Polegate BR (Brighton- Eastbourne line).

HASSOCKS - The Beacon, Brighton Rd., Hassocks BN6 9NA - 01273 846040
Off A273 Pyecombe Road to Burgess Hill. Ground is 300 yards south of Stonepound crossroads (B2116) to Hurstpeirpoint or Hassocks.

LINGFIELD - Sports Pavilion, Godstone Road, Lingfield, Surrey RH7 6BT - 01342 834269
A22, 4 miles north of East Grinstead, to Mormon Temple roundabout, take exit Lingfield (B2028) Newchapel Road for 1 1/2 miles. Left at T junction into Godstone Road (B2029) and ground is 1/2 mile on left.

PAGHAM - Nyetimber Lane, Pagham, West Sussex PO21 3JY - 01243 266 112
Turn off A27 Chichester by-pass (signposted A259 Pagham). Ground in village of Nyetimber. Three miles from Bognor (BR). Buses 260 & 240

PEACEHAVEN & TELSCOMBE - The Sports Park, Piddinghoe Avenue, Peacehaven, E. Sussex BN10 8RJ - 01273 582471
From Brighton on A259, over roundabout & Piddinghoe Ave. is next left after 2nd set of lights - ground at end. From Newhaven, Piddinghoe Ave. is 1st right after 1st set of lights. 3 miles from Newhaven(BR). Peacehaven is served by Brighton to Newhaven & Eastbourne buses

REDHILL - Kiln Brow, Three Arch Road, Redhill, Surrey - 01737 762 129
On left hand side of A23 two and a half miles south of Redhill.

RINGMER - Caburn Ground, Anchor Field, Ringmer - 01273 812 738
From Lewes road turn right into Springett Avenue, opposite Ringmer village

RYE UNITED - Sydney Allnut Pavilion, Rye Football & Cricket Salts, Fishmarket Road, Rye TN31 7NU - 01797 223 855
Outskirts of Rye on the A268 joins A259 opposite Skinners Rover garage.

SELSEY - High Street Ground, Selsey, Chichester, West Sussex - 01243 603420
Through Selsey High Street to fire station. Take turning into car park alongside the station. Entrance is in the far corner. Regular buses from Chichester.

SHOREHAM - Middle Road, Shoreham-by-Sea, West Sussex BN43 6LT - 01273 454 261
From Shoreham (BR) go east over level crossing, up Dolphin Road. Ground is 150 yards on right.

SIDLEY UNITED - Gullivers Sports Ground, Glovers Lane, Sidley, Bexhill on Sea TN39 5BL - 01424 217 078
From Brighton: On A259 turn left at Little Common roundabout into Pear Tree Lane. Turn right into Turkey Road. Turn right onto A269 from Ninfield. Turn left at Glovers Lane and first left into North Road.

ST FRANCIS RANGERS - The Princess Royal Hospital, Lewes Road, Haywards Heath, RH16 4EX Tel No: 01444 474 021 and social club 01444 441 881
Enter through the main hospital entrance on the Lewes Road and follow signs to Sports Complex.

THREE BRIDGES - Jubilee Field, Jubilee Walk, Three Bridges Road, Crawley, West Sussex RH10 1LQ - 01293 442 000
From Three Bridges station turn left towards Crawley. Turn right at second lights into Three Bridges road. Take first left (opposite Plough Inn) into Jubilee Walk.

WICK - Crabtree Park, Coomes Way, Wick, Littlehampton, West Sussex BN17 7LS Tel No: 01903 713 535
A27 to Crossbush.A284 towards Littlehampton. After one mile over level crossing left into Coomes Way next to Locomotive pub. Ground at end.

DIVISION TWO

AFC UCKFIELD - The Oaks, Old Eastbourne Road, Uckfield, East Sussex TN22 5QL - 07847 662 337
Next to Rajdutt Restaurant on Old Eastbourne Road, south of Uckfield town centre.

BEXHILL UNITED - The Polegrove, Brockley Road, Bexhill-on-Sea, East Sussex TN39 3EX - 07815 425 682.
A27 to Little Common then fourth exit off roundabout to Cooden Beach. Left and follow to end, turn right into Brockby Road. Ground at bottom of hill on the right.

CLYMPING - Clymping Village Hall, Clymping, Littelhampton BN17 5GW - 07951 196 784.
Follow A259 west of Littlehampton. Just over the Bridge, on the right hand side before the small roundabout.

EAST PRESTON - Roundstone Recreation Ground, Lashmar Road, East Preston, Sussex BN16 1ES - 01903 776 026
From Worthing proceed west for 6 miles on A259. At Roundstone Brewers Fayre pub turn south, over level crossing turn left for 50 yards then first right into Roundstone Drive.

LANCING - Culver Road, Lancing, West Sussex BN15 9AX. - 01903 767 285.
From A27 turn south at Lancing Manor roundabout into Grinstead Lane, 3rd turning on right North Farm Rd. Turn left then immedlately. right into Culver Rd. From railway station take 3rd turning on left heading north.

LITTLE COMMON - Little Common Sports Pavilion, Little Common Recreation Ground, Green Lane, Bexhill-on-Sea, TN39 4PH - 01424 845 861.
From the west take the A259, at Little Common roundabout take second exit into Peartree Lane and then left into Little Common Recreation Ground car park.

LITTLEHAMPTON TOWN - The Sportsfield, St Flora's Road, Littlehampton BN17 6BD - 01903 716 390
Leave A259 at Waterford Business Park and turn into Horsham Road. After Shell Garage turn left into St. Floras Road. Ground is at the end of road on the left.

LOXWOOD - Loxwood Sports Association, Plaistow Road, Loxwood RH14 0SX - 01404 753 185
Leave A272 between Billinghurst and Wisborough Green and join the B2133 for 3.4 miles. On entering Loxwood Village take 1st left into Plaistow Road, ground situated 100 yards on the left.

MIDHURST & EASEBOURNE - Rotherfield, Dodsley Lane, Easebourne, Midhurst, W. Sussex GU29 9BE - 01730 816 557.
Ground one mile out of Midhurst on London Road (A286) opposite Texaco Garage. Ample car parking.

MILE OAK - Mile Oak Recreation Ground, Chalky Road, Portslade - 01273 423 854.
From A27 (Brighton Bypass) leave at A293 exit. Right at first roundabout. Ground 1 mile on right. Parking in the Sports Centre opposite the ground (park) entrance.

OAKWOOD - Tinsley Lane, Three Bridges, Crawley RH10 8AJ - 01293 515 742.
From the South on M23, take junction 10 exit left onto A2011, next roundabout take fourth exit right, next roundabout second exit, take first right into Tinsley Lane. Ground entrance 100 metres on left.

RUSTINGTON - Recreation Ground, Jubilee Avenue, Rustington, West Sussex BN16 3NB - 01903 770 495.
From the East follow A259 past Sainsburys. Left at next roundabout on to B2187 over Windmill Bridge. Straight on at roundabout, first right, then first left into Woodlands Avenue. Car park is 80 yards on your right, next to the Village hall. From the West proceed to Watersmead roundabout with Bodyshop on your left. Take B2187 half a mile, past BP garage, take third right into Albert Road, then first right into Woodlands Avenue.

SEAFORD TOWN - The Crouch, Bramber Road, Seaford BN25 1AG - 01323 892 221.
A259 to Seaford. At mini roundabout by station, turn left (coming from Newhaven) or RIGHT (from Eastbourne). At end of Church Street, across junction, then left at end. After 500m turn left up Ashurst Road Bramber Road is at the top.

SOUTHWICK - Old Barn Way, off Manor Hall Way, Southwick, Brighton BN42 4NT - 01273 701 010
A27 from Brighton take first left after Southwick sign to Leisure Centre. Ground adjacent. Five minutes walk from Fishergate or Southwick stations.

STEYNING TOWN - The Shooting Field, Steyning, W. Sussex BN44 3RP. - 01903 812 228.
Entering Steyning from the west. Take 1st left in the High St (Tanyard Lane) Follow into Shooting Field estate, ground is 4th turn on the left. Entering Steyning from the east. From the High St., turn right into Church St.. Turn left by Church into Shooting Field estate. NB Coaches MUST park in Church Street Car Park.

STORRINGTON - Recreation Ground, Pulborough Road, Storrington RH20 4HJ - 01903 745 860.
A24 right at roundabout at Washington. Four miles to Storrington through village. Third exit at roundabout and second right into Spearbridge Road.

WESTFIELD - The Parish Field, Main Road, Westfield TN35 4SB - 01483 751 011.
From Hastings take the A21, turning right onto the A28 towards Ashford. Travel through Westfield, and the ground is located off Westfield Lane on the left.

WORTHING UNITED - The Robert Albion Memorial Ground, Lyons Way, Worthing BN14 9JF. 01903 234 466.
From the West past Hill Barn roundabout to second set of traffic lights, turn left into Lyons Way. From East first set of traffic lights at end of Sompting bypass, turn right into Lyons Way.

DIVISION THREE

BARNHAM - Mill Road, Slindon, Nr Arundel, West Sussex BN18 0LZ - 07738 625 795
On the A27 at Fontwell take the A29 to Slindon and at the Slindon crossroads the ground is on the right.

BOSHAM - Bosham Recreation Ground, Walton Lane, Bosham, Chichester PO18 8QF - 01243 574 011.
From Chichester take the A259 towards Portsmouth. On reaching Bosham turn left at the Swan P.H. roundabout. 1/2 mile to T junction, turn left & car park 50 yds on left.

BROADBRIDGE HEATH - Wickhurst Lane, Broadbridge Heath, Horsham RH12 3YS - 01403 211 311
Alongside A24, Horsham north/south bypass. From the A24 Horsham Bypass, at the large roundabout/underpass take the Broadbridge Heath Bypass towards Guildford and then at the first roundabout turn left into Wickhurst Lane.

DORKING WANDERERS - West Humble Playing Fields, London Road, Dorking.
Take A24 to Dorking at roundabout stay on A24 to Leatherhead. Go past Denbies Vineyard on left. At end of vineyard take 2nd turning on the left straight into the playing field.

FERRING - The Glebelands, Ferring, West Sussex BN12 5JL
To Ferring main shops, turn right into Greystoke Road.

FOREST - Roffey Sports & Social Club, Spooners Road, Roffey RH12 4DY - 01403 210 223.
Spooners Road. is off the main Crawley road, 100 yds from the `Star' PH, towards Crawley

HAYWARDS HEATH TOWN - Hanbury Park Stadium, Haywards Heath RH16 3PX - 01444 412 837.
A272 to Haywards Heath town centre. At Sussex roundabout, north on B2708 (Hazelgrove Road) take first right into New England Road, then the 4th right (Allen Road) leads to ground.

HURSTPIERPOINT - Fairfield Rec. Ground, Cuckfield Road, BN6 9SD - 01273 834 783.
Directions: At Hurstpierpoint crossroads, go north into Cuckfield Road (B2117) for 1km. Ground entrance between houses nos.158 & 160.
Colours: All blue. Change: Green & white/white/green.

IFIELD EDWARDS - Edwards Sports & Social Club, Ifield Green, Rusper Road, Crawley. - 01293 420 598.
From A23 Crawley by-pass going north, left at roundabout signed Charlwood. Third left into Ifield Green, first right past Royal Oak (PH) into Rusper Road.

NEWHAVEN - Fort Road Recreation Ground, Newhaven, East Sussex BN9 9EE. - 01273 513 940.
A259, follow one-way system around town, left at Police Station into South Road, which becomes Fort Road.

PEASE POTTAGE VILLAGE - Finches Field, Old Brighton Road, Pease Pottage RH11 9AH - 01293 538 651
Off M23/A23 towards Brighton turn off at Pease Pottage. Past service station to roundabout, take 3rd exit over bridge sharp left, follow signs to Finches Field. Approx. 300 yards past Grapes Public House on the right.

ROTTINGDEAN VILLAGE - Rottingdean Sports Centre, Falmer Road, Rottingdean BN2 7DA. - 01273 306 436
After leaving the Rottingdean Village one way system go past Bazehill Road and the entrance to the ground is next on the right.

SALTDEAN UNITED - Hill Park, Coombe Vale, Saltdean, Brighton BN2 8HJ - 01273 309 898.
A259 coast road east from Brighton to Saltdean Lido, left into Arundel Drive West, and Saltdean Vale to bridle path at beginning of Combe Vale. Club 200yds along track.

SIDLESHAM - Recreation Ground, Selsey Road, Sidlesham, Nr Chichester PO20 7RD - 01243 641 538.
From Chichester bypass take the B2145 (Hunston/Selsey). Head towards Selsey. Upon entering Sidlesham, ground on right hand side (between houses).

TD SHIPLEY - The Pavilion, Dragons Lane, Shipley RH13 8GB - 07804 325 228.
Exit the A24 onto the A272 at the Buckbarn crossroads signposted Billinghurst. The ground is 1.5 miles on the right.

UCKFIELD TOWN - Victoria Pleasure Ground, Uckfield TN22 5DJ - 01825 769 400.
Take Eastbourne road (old A22) south of Uckfield town centre. Entrance to ground is 1/2 mile on the right (just after the Police station).

UNITED COUNTIES LEAGUE

www.htucfl.com

Sponsored by:
Hereward Teamwear

Founded: 1895

Recent champions:

2005: Cogenhoe United
2006: Woodford United
2007: Deeping Rangers
2008: Stotfold
2009: Stewarts & Lloyds Corby

Reserve Division One		P	W	D	L	F	A	Pts
St Neots Town Res.		30	20	6	4	87	27	66
Blackstones Res.		30	18	3	9	62	34	57
Bourne Town Res.		30	17	4	9	64	46	55
N'pton Sileby Rangers Res.		30	16	4	10	67	38	52
Stotfold Res.		30	15	4	11	79	59	49
Stewarts & Lloyds Res.	*-1*	30	15	5	10	71	52	49
Woodford United Res.	*-3*	30	15	6	9	70	59	48
Cogenhoe United Res.		30	14	4	12	65	73	46
Deeping Rangers Res.		30	11	8	11	56	67	41
P'boro. N'thern Star Res.	*-1*	30	11	6	13	63	67	38
Wellingboro. Whitworth Res.		30	11	2	17	50	89	35
Huntingdon Town Res.		30	9	6	15	55	66	33
Desborough Town Res.		30	10	3	17	50	64	33
Northampton Spencer Res.		30	8	5	17	41	77	29
Wellingborough Town Res.		30	7	6	17	48	61	27
Raunds Town Res.	*-1*	30	6	2	22	26	75	19

Premier Division		P	W	D	L	F	A	Pts
Daventry Town		**40**	**33**	**3**	**4**	**120**	**28**	**102**
St Neots Town		**40**	**29**	**8**	**3**	**83**	**26**	**95**
Long Buckby		**40**	**25**	**4**	**11**	**86**	**50**	**79**
Deeping Rangers		**40**	**23**	**6**	**11**	**73**	**53**	**75**
Boston Town		**40**	**21**	**7**	**12**	**70**	**50**	**70**
Newport Pagnell Town		**40**	**19**	**9**	**12**	**79**	**48**	**66**
Stotfold	***-3***	**40**	**20**	**8**	**12**	**80**	**60**	**65**
Cogenhoe United		**40**	**16**	**13**	**11**	**62**	**42**	**61**
Sleaford Town		**40**	**17**	**9**	**14**	**78**	**70**	**60**
St Ives Town	***-3***	**40**	**18**	**7**	**15**	**53**	**47**	**58**
Wellingborough Town		**40**	**16**	**8**	**16**	**52**	**62**	**56**
Stewarts & Lloyds Corby		**40**	**14**	**12**	**14**	**64**	**65**	**54**
Blackstones		**40**	**14**	**6**	**20**	**64**	**75**	**48**
Northampton Spencer		**40**	**13**	**8**	**19**	**49**	**66**	**47**
Daventry United		**40**	**14**	**5**	**21**	**48**	**78**	**47**
Holbeach United		**40**	**12**	**8**	**20**	**56**	**74**	**44**
Bourne Town		**40**	**11**	**9**	**20**	**57**	**87**	**42**
Desborough Town		**40**	**8**	**7**	**25**	**53**	**89**	**31**
Yaxley		**40**	**8**	**6**	**26**	**37**	**76**	**30**
Raunds Town		**40**	**7**	**5**	**28**	**29**	**84**	**26**
Rothwell Corinthians		**40**	**6**	**4**	**30**	**39**	**102**	**22**

	Blackstones	Boston Town	Bourne Town	Cogenhoe United	Daventry Town	Daventry United	Deeping Rangers	Desborough Town	Holbeach United	Long Buckby	Newport Pagnell Town	Northampton Spencer	Raunds Town	Rothwell Corinthians	Sleaford Town	St Ives Town	St Neots Town	Stewarts & Lloyds Corby	Stotfold	Wellingborough Town	Yaxley
Blackstones		0-2	2-2	0-2	0-4	2-2	2-3	2-3	0-0	1-2	2-0	1-1	2-1	3-1	4-4	2-1	2-4	2-2	1-3	1-0	3-1
Boston Town	4-0		2-2	3-2	0-1	1-0	3-1	1-2	1-0	0-2	2-0	1-2	2-2	6-1	2-2	3-0	0-2	1-1	3-0	1-2	1-2
Bourne Town	1-5	2-3	***P***	0-2	0-5	0-3	0-1	3-2	0-1	1-5	2-7	2-0	3-2	2-1	1-1	2-2	1-2	1-1	0-0	1-2	2-0
Cogenhoe United	4-2	1-3	1-1	***R***	3-4	2-0	2-2	0-0	2-0	0-2	2-1	1-0	4-0	4-0	1-1	1-2	0-0	1-1	1-2	1-2	0-0
Daventry Town	2-0	2-1	4-2	4-1	***E***	6-2	4-0	4-0	6-1	2-0	1-0	3-1	4-1	7-0	2-3	3-0	0-2	6-0	2-4	5-0	4-0
Daventry United	5-4	0-2	0-0	2-2	0-1	***M***	0-4	2-1	1-0	4-2	1-3	0-2	0-1	2-1	0-3	2-1	0-2	4-1	0-1	0-0	2-1
Deeping Rangers	2-0	1-0	3-0	0-2	0-3	3-0	***I***	2-1	3-1	2-1	0-4	2-0	3-0	3-1	3-2	1-2	1-1	2-0	2-3	0-1	4-0
Desborough Town	1-5	1-3	1-3	1-4	0-0	5-0	0-3	***E***	2-2	0-2	1-1	1-4	0-2	1-2	3-6	0-3	1-4	2-0	2-2	2-0	0-0
Holbeach United	0-1	1-1	4-1	0-2	1-3	0-1	0-3	5-3	***R***	0-1	1-4	2-1	3-1	1-3	2-2	1-2	1-3	3-2	3-1	4-4	2-1
Long Buckby	4-3	5-0	4-2	2-0	0-2	5-0	1-3	5-3	2-1		2-1	1-0	1-0	3-1	5-1	2-0	1-5	1-1	4-0	3-3	2-0
Newport Pagnell Town	2-1	1-1	5-2	0-0	2-2	2-3	6-0	5-0	1-2	0-0		4-0	2-3	2-1	1-3	1-1	2-1	2-2	1-0	2-1	0-1
Northampton Spencer	0-1	1-4	0-2	1-0	1-4	1-1	2-2	1-0	2-1	1-2	0-1	***D***	3-0	5-1	2-0	2-3	3-2	1-1	3-1	1-1	1-1
Raunds Town	2-1	1-2	0-2	0-0	0-3	0-2	2-2	0-5	1-3	2-1	0-4	0-0	***I***	1-3	1-4	0-1	0-1	1-5	0-5	0-1	1-3
Rothwell Corinthians	0-2	0-1	0-3	0-4	1-3	2-1	2-2	0-1	2-1	1-2	0-1	2-1	0-2	***V***	2-3	0-2	0-2	1-1	2-5	0-0	0-2
Sleaford Town	3-0	1-3	4-2	1-3	0-2	0-2	2-0	1-1	1-0	2-2	1-2	0-1	0-0	3-0	***I***	2-1	0-4	1-3	4-1	4-1	6-1
St Ives Town	0-2	0-1	6-2	0-2	0-2	3-1	0-3	2-1	0-1	2-1	0-0	3-0	3-0	1-1	0-1	***S***	1-1	0-1	1-3	3-1	1-0
St Neots Town	4-0	2-2	4-2	2-0	1-0	3-0	0-0	2-1	5-0	1-0	0-2	3-0	2-0	3-1	2-0	0-0	***I***	1-0	2-1	3-1	0-0
Stewarts & Lloyds Corby	2-1	4-2	0-2	1-1	0-4	2-1	1-2	2-1	1-1	0-3	4-2	5-1	0-2	2-1	6-1	1-2	2-2	***O***	1-2	1-2	2-1
Stotfold	0-3	0-1	1-1	1-3	0-0	4-0	1-3	3-2	2-2	2-0	2-1	6-2	1-0	7-2	1-1	0-0	0-2	1-1	***N***	3-1	4-1
Wellingborough Town	1-0	3-0	1-0	1-1	0-4	4-1	2-0	0-1	2-2	0-3	1-1	0-1	2-0	4-2	1-0	0-2	0-1	0-2	1-4		2-0
Yaxley	0-1	0-1	0-2	0-0	1-2	1-3	1-2	3-1	0-3	3-2	2-3	1-1	1-0	3-1	2-4	0-2	1-2	0-2	1-3	2-4	

Division One		P	W	D	L	F	A	Pts
Irchester United		30	23	1	6	72	30	70
Peterboro. Northern Star		30	21	5	4	78	27	68
Eynesbury Rovers	*-1*	30	21	4	5	80	47	66
N'thampton ON Chenecks		30	19	3	8	66	40	60
AFC Kempston Rovers	*-1*	30	17	5	8	73	41	55
Thrapston Town		30	13	9	8	55	47	48
Bugbrooke St Michaels		30	14	5	11	71	64	47
Huntingdon Town		30	12	7	11	48	57	43
N'thampton Sileby Rgrs		30	11	8	11	79	64	41
Wootton Blue Cross		30	9	7	14	43	62	34
Potton United		30	8	8	14	50	61	32
Wellingborough Whitworth		30	6	10	14	59	67	28
Buckingham Town		30	5	6	19	36	73	21
Olney Town		30	6	3	21	38	81	21
Burton Park Wanderers		30	4	7	19	32	76	19
Rushden & Higham Utd		30	4	6	20	30	73	18

Reserve Division Two		P	W	D	L	F	A	Pts
N'pton ON Chenecks Res.		22	15	3	4	61	30	48
AFC Kempston R. Res.	*-3*	22	16	2	4	66	32	47
Bugbrooke St Mich. Res.		22	12	2	8	63	44	38
Rothwell Corinthians Res.		22	11	5	6	43	29	38
Irchester United Res.		22	10	6	6	56	37	36
Daventry United Res.		22	9	3	10	41	38	30
Eynesbury Rovers Res.		22	9	3	10	44	54	30
Thrapston Town Res.		22	9	2	11	46	50	29
Buckingham Town Res.		22	7	4	11	35	66	25
St Ives Town Res.		22	7	3	12	45	48	24
Rushden & Higham Res.		22	3	4	15	20	54	13
Olney Town Res.		22	2	7	13	23	61	13

RESERVES CUP

FINAL *(April 22nd at Eynesbury Rovers)*
Stotfold Res. 2 Peterborough Northern Star Res. 1

RESERVE DIVISION TWO SUPPLEMENTARY CUP

FINAL *(April 29th at Raunds Town)*
Rothwell Cor. Res. 3 Daventry Utd Res. 3 *aet* (3-0p)

LEAGUE CUP

PRELIMINARY ROUND

Blackstones 3 Burton Park Wanderers 2
Daventry United 5 Northampton Sileby Rangers 0
Long Buckby 3 Buckingham Town 0
Northampton Spencer 0 **Stotfold** 1
Raunds Town 6 Yaxley 0

FIRST ROUND

Bourne Town 3 St Neots Town 2 *aet*
Bugbrooke St Michaels 1 **Rushden & Higham Utd** 2 *aet*
Cogenhoe United 3 Holbeach United 0
Daventry Town 4 Rothwell Corinthians 1
Daventry United 3 Olney Town 1
Deeping Rangers 1 **Boston Town** 2
Desborough Town 0 **St Ives Town** 1
Eynesbury Rovers 0 **Stewarts & Lloyds Corby** 1
Huntingdon Town 1 **AFC Kempston Rovers** 3
Long Buckby 3 Raunds Town 2
Newport Pagnell Town 3 Wellingborough Town 1
Potton United 0 **Blackstones** 5
Sleaford Town 2 **Peterborough Northern Star** 3
Stotfold 3 Irchester United 0
Wellingborough Whitworth 3 Thrapston Town 1
Wootton Blue Cross 3 Northampton ON Chenecks 0

SECOND ROUND

Bourne Town 2 **AFC Kempston Rovers** 3
Cogenhoe United 0 **Blackstones** 3
Daventry Town 3 Stotfold 1
Daventry United 5 Rushden & Higham United 1
Long Buckby 3 Peterborough Northern Star 2
Stewarts & Lloyds Corby 1 **Newport Pagnell Town** 3
Wellingborough Whitworth 0 **Boston Town** 2
Wootton Blue Cross 1 **St Ives Town** 2

QUARTER-FINALS

AFC Kempston Rovers 1 **Daventry Town** 3
Daventry United 3 Boston Town 1
Long Buckby 1 **Newport Pagnell Town** 3 *aet*
St Ives Town 4 Blackstones 2

SEMI-FINALS

Daventry United 0 **St Ives Town** 4
Newport Pagnell Town 4 Daventry Town 3 *aet*

FINAL

(April 20th at Cogenhoe United)
Newport Pagnell Town 1 **St Ives Town** 2 *aet*

	AFC Kempston	Buckingham T.	Bugbrooke S M	Burton Park W.	Eynesbury R.	Huntingdon T.	Irchester Utd	N. ON C'necks	N. Sileby Rgrs	Olney Town	P'borough NS	Potton United	Rushden & HU	Thrapston T.	W. Whitworth	Wootton BC
AFC Kempston Rovers		3-1	2-1	4-0	1-2	2-3	1-2	4-2	1-1	2-2	2-0	0-3	4-0	2-2	3-0	3-0
Buckingham Town	3-2		1-2	1-1	3-1	1-2	0-3	1-3	0-2	2-2	1-4	0-1	2-1	2-2	0-7	0-1
Bugbrooke St Michaels	0-4	4-3	***D***	3-4	1-3	5-1	0-2	3-4	3-2	7-2	1-6	4-1	3-0	2-1	0-0	2-1
Burton Park Wanderers	0-1	0-0	1-5	***I***	2-3	4-3	2-1	1-1	1-5	2-3	0-7	1-2	2-2	2-2	1-3	0-2
Eynesbury Rovers	2-1	5-4	2-1	2-0	***V***	1-1	0-0	5-1	5-3	7-1	2-4	5-1	3-1	3-0	3-3	4-3
Huntingdon Town	0-1	3-2	1-0	2-2	0-1	***I***	0-2	1-0	4-1	3-0	0-0	1-1	0-0	4-1	3-2	2-1
Irchester United	3-2	4-0	1-4	1-0	3-1	5-1	***S***	0-1	7-3	4-1	2-1	3-0	2-0	1-0	6-0	2-0
Northampton ON Chenecks	1-3	4-0	3-0	4-0	0-2	2-0	4-1	***I***	4-3	2-0	1-3	3-2	4-0	3-0	1-0	3-0
Northampton Sileby Rangers	1-4	2-0	4-4	3-1	4-4	6-1	0-1	1-1	***O***	2-0	0-1	3-3	2-2	1-3	7-3	3-1
Olney Town	1-6	1-2	1-2	2-1	2-3	4-0	0-2	0-2	0-6	***N***	2-6	3-2	0-0	0-2	2-0	1-2
Peterborough Northern Star	5-0	1-2	3-1	3-2	1-0	3-1	3-0	1-0	2-0	4-2		1-0	5-1	1-1	1-1	0-0
Potton United	3-7	3-3	0-0	4-0	1-2	1-2	1-3	2-3	2-2	2-0	0-3	***O***	1-0	1-2	2-2	1-1
Rushden & Higham United	0-1	2-1	2-3	1-2	0-2	0-2	3-6	2-3	3-1	0-1	0-4	0-3	***N***	1-1	3-7	1-1
Thrapston Town	2-2	4-0	3-3	3-0	1-3	2-0	0-4	1-3	1-1	2-1	2-1	4-2	4-0	***E***	0-0	5-2
Wellingborough Whitworth	1-1	2-0	1-2	0-0	3-2	5-5	0-1	2-2	2-3	4-3	2-3	3-3	1-2	1-2		3-4
Wootton Blue Cross	0-4	1-1	5-5	3-0	1-2	2-2	2-0	2-1	0-7	2-1	1-1	0-2	2-3	1-2	2-1	

IN: Irchester United (P), King's Lynn Town (formerly King's Lynn) (WS – Northern Premier League Premier Division), Peterborough Northern Star (P)
OUT: Bourne Town (R), Daventry Town (P - Southern League Division One Central), Stotfold (S - Spartan South Midlands League Premier Division)

BLACKSTONES

Founded: 1920 Nickname: Stones

Secretary: Ian MacGillivray **(T)** 01780 762 263 **(E)**
Chairman: Kevan Doyle **Manager:** Michael Goode & Darren Jarvis **Prog Ed:** Kevin Boor
Ground: Lincoln Road, Stamford, Lincs PE9 1SH **(T)** 01780 757 835
Capacity: 1,000 **Seats:** 100 **Covered:** yes **Midweek Matchday:** Wednesday **Clubhouse:** Yes **Shop:** No

Colours(change): Green/black/green. (Orange/black/orange)
Previous Names: Rutland Ironworks & Blackstone (until 1975)
Previous Leagues: Peterborough Works, Peterborough, Stamford & District
Records: **Att:** 700 v Glinton
Senior Honours: Lincs Senior Cup A 1992-93, 2003-04

10 YEAR RECORD

00-01	01-02	02-03	03-04	04-05	05-06	06-07	07-08	08-09	09-10
UCL P 12	UCL P 12	UCL P 16	UCL P 11	UCL P 15	UCL P 10	UCL P 8	UCL P 4	UCL P 13	UCL P 13

BOSTON TOWN

Founded: 1964 Nickname: Poachers

Secretary: Ron Bennett **(T)** 01205 354 252 **(E)**
Chairman: Mick Vines **Manager:** Martyn Lakin **Prog Ed:** Pat Megginson
Ground: Tattershall Road, Boston, Lincs PE21 9LR **(T)** 01205 365 470
Capacity: 6,000 **Seats:** 450 **Covered:** 950 **Midweek Matchday:** Tuesday **Clubhouse:** Yes **Shop:**

Colours(change): All Blue (Yellow/black/black)
Previous Names: Boston > 1994
Previous Leagues: Lincs, Central Alliance, Eastern co, Midland N. Co. E, C. Mids
Records: **Att:** 2,700 v Boston United FA Cup 1970. **Goalscorer:** Gary Bull 57 during 2006-07 season.
Senior Honours: Midland League 1974-75, 78-79, 80-81. Central Midlands 88-89
United Counties League 1994-95, 2000-01.

10 YEAR RECORD

00-01	01-02	02-03	03-04	04-05	05-06	06-07	07-08	08-09	09-10
UCL P 1	UCL P 8	UCL P 8	UCL P 5	UCL P 11	UCL P 6	UCL P 2	UCL P 6	UCL P 5	UCL P 5

COGENHOE UNITED

Founded: 1958 Nickname: Cooks

Secretary: Lewis Sander **(T)** 01604 408 285 **(E)**
Chairman: Derek Wright **Manager:** Andy Marks **Prog Ed:** Phil Wright
Ground: Compton Park, Brafield Road, Cogenhoe NN7 1ND **(T)** 01604 890 521
Capacity: 5,000 **Seats:** 100 **Covered:** 200 **Midweek Matchday:** Tuesday **Clubhouse:** Yes **Shop:** No

Colours(change): All Blue (Red/black/black)
Previous Names:
Previous Leagues: Central Northants Comb, prem 67-84
Records: **Att:** 1,000 Charity game 90 **Goalscorer & Appearances:** Tony Smith
Senior Honours: United Counties League 2004-05.

10 YEAR RECORD

00-01	01-02	02-03	03-04	04-05	05-06	06-07	07-08	08-09	09-10
UCL P 2	UCL P 3	UCL P 9	UCL P 6	UCL P 1	UCL P 5	UCL P 5	UCL P 9	UCL P 9	UCL P 8

DAVENTRY UNITED

Founded: 1968 Nickname: Motormen

Secretary: Nigel Foster **(T)** 07876 133 308 **(E)**
Chairman: Dave Hirons **Manager:** Darren Foster **Prog Ed:** See secretary
Ground: Daventry Town FC, Communications Pk, Browns Rd, Daventry, NN11 4NS **(T)** 01327 311 239
Capacity: 2,000 **Seats:** 250 **Covered:** 250 **Midweek Matchday:** Wednesday **Clubhouse:** Yes **Shop:** No

Colours(change): Blue & Yellow/blue/blue. (All red)
Previous Names: Ford Sports Daventry > 2007
Previous Leagues: Central Northants Combination 1968 - 1977.
Records:
Senior Honours: UCL Div.1 Champions 1992-93, 95-96. Premier 1999-00, 01-02.

10 YEAR RECORD

00-01	01-02	02-03	03-04	04-05	05-06	06-07	07-08	08-09	09-10
UCL P 4	UCL P 1	UCL P 11	UCL P 9	UCL P 6	UCL P 19	UCL P 20	UCL 1 5	UCL 1 2	UCL P 15

DEEPING RANGERS

Founded: 1964 Nickname: Rangers

Secretary: Haydon Whitham **(T)** 01778 380 455 **(E)**

Chairman: Kevin Davenport **Manager:** Pat Rayment **Prog Ed:** Robin Crowson

Ground: Deeping Sports Club, Outgang Road, Market Deeping, PE6 8LQ **(T)** 01778 344 701

Capacity: 1,000 **Seats:** 180 **Covered:** 250 **Midweek Matchday:** Tuesday **Clubhouse:** Yes **Shop:**

Colours(change): All claret & blue. (White/sky blue/sky blue)
Previous Names: None
Previous Leagues: Peterborough & District 1966 - 1999.
Records:
Senior Honours: Lincs Sen Cup, B Cup, Peterborough FA Cup (3),
UCL Premier Champions 2006-07

10 YEAR RECORD

00-01	01-02	02-03	03-04	04-05	05-06	06-07	07-08	08-09	09-10
UCL 1 2	UCL P 10	UCL P 5	UCL P 17	UCL P 12	UCL P 20	UCL P 1	UCL P 7	UCL P 4	UCL P 4

DESBOROUGH TOWN

Founded: 1896 Nickname: Ar Tam

Secretary: John Lee **(T)** 01536 760 002 **(E)**

Chairman: Ernie Parsons **Manager:** Martin McLeod **Prog Ed:** John Lee

Ground: Waterworks Field, Braybrooke Rd, Desborough NN14 2LJ **(T)** 01536 761 350

Capacity: 8,000 **Seats:** 250 **Covered:** 500 **Midweek Matchday:** Tuesday **Clubhouse:** Yes **Shop:**

Colours(change): All Blue. (All yellow)
Previous Names: None
Previous Leagues: None
Records: **Att:** 8,000 v Kettering Town
Senior Honours: N'hants/Utd Co. Champs 1900-01, 01-02, 06-07, 20-21, 23-24, 24-25, 27-28, 48-49, 66-67. Lge C 77-78, 00-01, 07-08.
Northants Senior Cup 1910-11, 13-14, 28-29, 51-52.

10 YEAR RECORD

00-01	01-02	02-03	03-04	04-05	05-06	06-07	07-08	08-09	09-10
UCL P 7	UCL P 5	UCL P 18	UCL P 16	UCL P 10	UCL P 18	UCL P 14	UCL P 3	UCL P 11	UCL P 18

HOLBEACH UNITED

Founded: 1929 Nickname: Tigers

Secretary: Karl Fawcett **(T)** 07763 282913 **(E)** holbeachunitedfc@yahoo.co.uk

Chairman: Dave Dougill **Manager:** John Chand **Prog Ed:** Mike Palmer

Ground: Carters Park, Park Road, Holbeach, Lincs PE12 7EE **(T)** 01406 424 761

Capacity: 4,000 **Seats:** 200 **Covered:** 450 **Midweek Matchday:** Tuesday **Clubhouse:** Yes **Shop:** No

Colours(change): Gold & black/black/gold & black.(Blue & white/blue/blue & white)
Previous Names:
Previous Leagues: Peterborough U Co L 46-55, Eastern 55-62, Midland Co 62-63
Records: **Att:** 4,094 v Wisbech 1954
Senior Honours: United Counties League 1989-90, 02-03.
Lincs Sen A Cup (4), Senior Cup B 57-58

10 YEAR RECORD

00-01	01-02	02-03	03-04	04-05	05-06	06-07	07-08	08-09	09-10
UCL P 14	UCL P 2	UCL P 1	UCL P 7	UCL P 3	UCL P 17	UCL P 11	UCL P 11	UCL P 16	UCL P 16

IRCHESTER UNITED

Founded: 1883 Nickname:

Secretary: Glynn Cotter **(T)** 01933 402514 **(E)**

Chairman: Geoff Cotter **Manager:** Daren Young **Prog Ed:** Geoff Cotter

Ground: Alfred Street, Irchester NN29 7DR **(T)** 01933 312877

Capacity: 1,000 **Seats:** none **Covered:** yes **Midweek Matchday:** **Clubhouse:** Yes **Shop:**

Colours(change): White & Red (All Blue)
Previous Names: Irchester Eastfield 1980-90
Previous Leagues: Northamptonshire/United Counties 1896-97, 30-36, Rushden & District 1936-69
Records:
Senior Honours: Northants Lge Div 2 1930-31, 31-32, Rushden & District Lge (9), Northants Jnr Cup 1929-30, 33-34, 48-49, 75-76.
United Counties League Division 1 2009-10

10 YEAR RECORD

00-01	01-02	02-03	03-04	04-05	05-06	06-07	07-08	08-09	09-10
UCL 1 17	UCL 1 9	UCL 1 3	UCL 1 14	UCL 1 9	UCL 1 15	UCL 1 16	UCL 1 16	UCL 1 16	UCL 1 1

KING'S LYNN TOWN

Founded: 1879 Nickname: Linnets

Secretary: Martin Davis **(T)** 07885 144 039 **(E)** office@kltown.co.uk
Chairman: Keith Chapman **Manager:** Kevin Boon & Gary Setchell **Prog Ed:** Martin Davis
Ground: The Walks Stadium, Tennyson Road, King's Lynn PE30 5PB **(T)** 01553 760 060
Capacity: 8,200 **Seats:** 1,200 **Covered:** 5,000 **Midweek Matchday:** Tuesday **Clubhouse:** Yes **Shop:** Yes

Colours(change): Yellow/blue (White/black)
Previous Names: King's Lynn > 2010
Previous Leagues: N'folk & Suffolk, Eastern Co. 1935-39, 48-54, UCL 1946-48, Midland Co. 1954-58, NPL 1980-81, Southern, Conf
Records: **Att:** 12,937 v Exeter City FAC 1st Rnd 1950-51. **Goalscorer:** Malcolm Lindsey 321. **Apps:** Mick Wright 1,152 (British Record)
Senior Honours: Southern League Division 1 East 2003-04, Premier Division 2007-08, League Cup 2004-05,

10 YEAR RECORD

00-01	01-02	02-03	03-04	04-05	05-06	06-07	07-08	08-09	09-10
SthP 3	SthP 20	SthE 6	SthE 1	SthP 11	SthP 3	SthP 3	SthP 1	Conf N 17	NP P dnf

LONG BUCKBY

Founded: 1937 Nickname: Bucks

Secretary: Eric Turvey **(T)** 07816 276 535 **(E)**
Chairman: Guy Loveland **Manager:** Glenn Botterill **Prog Ed:** Eric Turvey
Ground: Station Road, Long Buckby NN6 7QA **(T)** 01327 842 682
Capacity: 1,000 **Seats:** 200 **Covered:** 200 **Midweek Matchday:** Tuesday **Clubhouse:** Yes **Shop:** No

Colours(change): Claret & blue/claret/sky blue. (All orange).
Previous Names: Long Buckby Nomads
Previous Leagues: Rugby & District Central, Northants Combination pre 68
Records: **Att:** 750 v Kettering Town
Senior Honours: United Counties League Div.2 1970-71, 71-72.
Northants Senior Cup 2008-09. Munsell Cup 2009.

10 YEAR RECORD

00-01	01-02	02-03	03-04	04-05	05-06	06-07	07-08	08-09	09-10
UCL P 19	UCL P 18	UCL P 20	UCL P 21	UCL P 8	UCL P 21	UCL P 12	UCL P 2	UCL P 8	UCL P 3

NEWPORT PAGNELL TOWN

Founded: 1963 Nickname: Swans

Secretary: Stephen Handley **(T)** 01908 614 745 **(E)**
Chairman: Geoff Cardno **Manager:** Terry Shrieves **Prog Ed:** Wayne Harmes
Ground: Willen Road, Newport Pagnell MK16 0DF **(T)** 01908 611 993
Capacity: 2,000 **Seats:** 100 **Covered:** 100 **Midweek Matchday:** Tuesday **Clubhouse:** Yes **Shop:** No

Colours(change): White & Green/black/green & black (All Navy Blue)
Previous Names: Newport Pagnell Wanderers > 1972.
Previous Leagues: North Bucks 1963-71. South Midlands 1971-73.
Records:
Senior Honours: United Counties League Div.1 1981-82, 2001-02.
Bucks & Berks Intermediate Cup 2001-02. Berks & Bucks Senior Trophy 2009-10.

10 YEAR RECORD

00-01	01-02	02-03	03-04	04-05	05-06	06-07	07-08	08-09	09-10
UCL 1 6	UCL 1 1	UCL P 2	UCL P 13	UCL P 18	UCL P 15	UCL P 7	UCL P 15	UCL P 3	UCL P 6

NORTHAMPTON SPENCER

Founded: 1936 Nickname: Millers

Secretary: Nick Hillery **(T)** 01604 756 580 **(E)**
Chairman: Graham Wrighting **Manager:** Andy Peaks **Prog Ed:** Andy Goldsmith
Ground: Kingsthorpe Mill, Studand Road, Northampton NN5 6NE **(T)** 01604 718 898
Capacity: 2,000 **Seats:** 100 **Covered:** 350 **Midweek Matchday:** Tuesday **Clubhouse:** Yes **Shop:** No

Colours(change): Green/green/white. (All royal blue).
Previous Names: Spencer School Old Boys
Previous Leagues:
Records: **Att:** 800 v Nttm Forest 1993 **App;** P. Jelley 622 1984-2002
Senior Honours: United Counties League Div.1 1984-85. Premier 1991-92.
Northants Senior Cup Winners 2005-06

10 YEAR RECORD

00-01	01-02	02-03	03-04	04-05	05-06	06-07	07-08	08-09	09-10
UCL P 8	UCL P 17	UCL P 12	UCL P 18	UCL P 16	UCL P 3	UCL P 6	UCL P 13	UCL P 12	UCL P 14

PETERBOROUGH NORTHERN STAR

Founded: 1900 Nickname:

Secretary: Glen Harper **(T)** 01733 718 163 **(E)**

Chairman: Rodney Payne **Manager:** Chris Plummer **Prog Ed:** Rodney Payne

Ground: Chestnut Ave, Dogsthorpe, Eye, Peterborough, Cambs PE1 4PE **(T)** 01733 564 894

Capacity: 1,500 **Seats:** none **Covered:** yes **Midweek Matchday:** Wednesday **Clubhouse:** **Shop:**

Colours(change): Red/white/black (Black & white)
Previous Names: Eye Utd >2005
Previous Leagues: Peterborough Lge >2003
Records:
Senior Honours: Peterborough League 2002-03. Hinchingbrooke Cup 2009-10. United Counties League Division 1 2008-09.

10 YEAR RECORD

00-01	01-02	02-03	03-04	04-05	05-06	06-07	07-08	08-09	09-10
			UCL 1 3	UCL 1 4	UCL 1 9	UCL 1 5	UCL 1 2	UCL 1 1	UCL 1 2

RAUNDS TOWN

Founded: 1946 Nickname: Shopmates

Secretary: Dave Jones **(T)** 01933 651 874 **(E)**

Chairman: Pete Scanlon **Manager:** Ian Jackson **Prog Ed:** Dave Jones

Ground: Kiln Park, London Rd, Raunds, Northants NN9 6EQ **(T)** 01933 623 351

Capacity: 3,000 **Seats:** 250 **Covered:** 600 **Midweek Matchday:** Tuesday **Clubhouse:** Yes **Shop:** Yes

Colours(change): Red & black/black/black. (White/red/red).
Previous Names:
Previous Leagues: Rushden & Dist, Cent. Northants Comb, U.C.L. , Southern 1996-2000
Records: **Att:** 1500 v Crystal Palace 1991 **Goalscorer:** Shaun Keeble. **App:** Martin Lewis - 355
Senior Honours: United Counties League Div.1 1982-83. Premier 95-96.
Northants Senior Cup 90-91

10 YEAR RECORD

00-01	01-02	02-03	03-04	04-05	05-06	06-07	07-08	08-09	09-10
UCL P 3	UCL P 4	UCL P 15	UCL P 20	UCL P 20	UCL P 8	UCL P 13	UCL P 17	UCL P 10	UCL P 20

ROTHWELL CORINTHIANS

Founded: 1934 Nickname: Corinthians

Secretary: Mark Budworth **(T)** 01536 521 973 **(E)**

Chairman: Mark Budworth **Manager:** Jason Thurland **Prog Ed:** Mark Budworth

Ground: Sergeants Lawn, Desborough Road, Rothwell, NN14 6JQ **(T)** 01536 418 688

Capacity: **Seats:** 50 **Covered:** 200 **Midweek Matchday:** **Clubhouse:** Yes **Shop:** No

Colours(change): Red/black/red. (All blue).
Previous Names: None
Previous Leagues: Kettering & District Amateur/East Midlands Alliance 1934 - 1995.
Records:
Senior Honours: East Midlands Alliance Champions 1989-90, 94-95.

10 YEAR RECORD

00-01	01-02	02-03	03-04	04-05	05-06	06-07	07-08	08-09	09-10
UCL 1 7	UCL 1 14	UCL 1 8	UCL 1 12	UCL 1 8	UCL 1 10	UCL 1 7	UCL 1 3	UCL P 21	UCL P 21

SLEAFORD TOWN

Founded: 1968 Nickname: Town

Secretary: Steve Thomas **(T)** 07929 008 856 **(E)**

Chairman: Tony Farrow **Manager:** Brian Rowland **Prog Ed:** Paul Stafford

Ground: Estaforde Park, Boston Road, Sleaford, Lincs NG34 7GH **(T)** 01529 415 951

Capacity: **Seats:** 88 **Covered:** 88 **Midweek Matchday:** **Clubhouse:** Yes **Shop:**

Colours(change): Green/black/green. (All red).
Previous Names:
Previous Leagues: Lincolnshire
Records:
Senior Honours: United Counties League Div.1 2005-06.

10 YEAR RECORD

00-01	01-02	02-03	03-04	04-05	05-06	06-07	07-08	08-09	09-10
Lincs 6	Lincs 5	Lincs 2	Lincs 1	UCL 1 6	UCL 1 1	UCL 1 2	UCL P 14	UCL P 15	UCL P 9

ST. IVES TOWN

Founded: 1887 Nickname: Saints

Secretary: Greig Sarath **(T)** 07786 913 738 **(E)**

Chairman: Ashley Griffiths **Manager:** Warren Everdell & Jez Hall **Prog Ed:** Simon Clark

Ground: Westwood Road, St. Ives PE27 6WU **(T)** 01480 463 207

Capacity: **Seats:** Yes **Covered:** Yes **Midweek Matchday:** Tuesday **Clubhouse:** Yes **Shop:** No

Colours(change): White & black/black/black & white. (All white)
Previous Names: None
Previous Leagues: Cambs, Central Amateur, Hunts, Peterborough & District
Records:
Senior Honours: Hunts Senior Cup, Hunts Premier Cup, Hinchingbrooke Cup 2006-07. UCL Knockout Cup 2009-10.

10 YEAR RECORD

00-01	01-02	02-03	03-04	04-05	05-06	06-07	07-08	08-09	09-10
UCL 1 13	UCL 1 16	UCL 1 9	UCL 1 10	UCL 1 3	UCL P 9	UCL P 10	UCL P 5	UCL P 6	UCL P 10

ST. NEOTS TOWN

Founded: 1879 Nickname: Saints

Secretary: Peter Naylor **(T)** 07894 133 200 **(E)**

Chairman: John Delaney **Manager:** Dennis Greene **Prog Ed:** John Delaney

Ground: Rowley Park, Cambridge Road, St Neots, Cambs PE19 6SN **(T)** 01480 470 012

Capacity: 3,000 **Seats:** 250 **Covered:** 850 **Midweek Matchday:** Tuesday **Clubhouse:** Yes **Shop:** No

Colours(change): Sky & navy blue quarters/navy/navy. (Gold/black/black)
Previous Names: St. Neots & District > 1951.
Previous Leagues: S Midlands, Cent. Alliance, UCL, Eastern Co., Hunts
Records: **Att:** 2,000 v Wisbech 1966
Senior Honours: United Counties League 1967-68. Div.1 94-95.
Huntingdonshire Senior Cup x35 2009-10 the most recent. Huntingdonshire Premier Cup 2001-02.

10 YEAR RECORD

00-01	01-02	02-03	03-04	04-05	05-06	06-07	07-08	08-09	09-10
UCL P 5	UCL P 6	UCL P 13	UCL P 4	UCL P 14	UCL P 4	UCL P 17	UCL P 8	UCL P 17	UCL P 2

STEWARTS & LLOYDS CORBY

Founded: 1935 Nickname: The Foundrymen

Secretary: John Davies **(T)** 07588 018 397 **(E)**

Chairman: John Davies **Manager:** Steve Noble **Prog Ed:** Mandy Winch

Ground: Recreation Ground, Occupation Road, Corby NN17 1EH **(T)** 01536 401 497

Capacity: 1,500 **Seats:** 100 **Covered:** 200 **Midweek Matchday:** Tuesday **Clubhouse:** Yes **Shop:** No

Colours(change): Maroon & amber/maroon/maroon. (All navy blue).
Previous Names: Hamlet S & L 1989-92.
Previous Leagues: Kettering Amateur
Records: **Goalscorer:** Joey Martin 46
Senior Honours: United Counties League Div.1 1973-74, 74-75. Premier 85-86, 08-09.

10 YEAR RECORD

00-01	01-02	02-03	03-04	04-05	05-06	06-07	07-08	08-09	09-10
UCL P 11	UCL P 14	UCL P 6	UCL P 19	UCL P 21	UCL P 16	UCL P 16	UCL P 12	UCL P 1	UCL P 12

WELLINGBOROUGH TOWN

Founded: 2004 Nickname: Doughboys

Secretary: Mick Walden **(T)** 01933 400 063 **(E)**

Chairman: Martin Potton **Manager:** Rob Gould **Prog Ed:** Mick Walden

Ground: The Dog & Duck, London Road, Wellingborough NN8 2DP **(T)** 01933 441 388

Capacity: **Seats:** Yes **Covered:** Yes **Midweek Matchday:** Tuesday **Clubhouse:** Yes **Shop:**

Colours(change): Yellow/royal blue/yellow. (All white)
Previous Names: Original team (Formed 1867) folded in 2002 reforming in 2004
Previous Leagues: Metropolitan. Southern.
Records:
Senior Honours: United Counties League 1964-65.

10 YEAR RECORD

00-01	01-02	02-03	03-04	04-05	05-06	06-07	07-08	08-09	09-10
UCL P 18	UCL P 21				UCL 1 2	UCL P 3	UCL P 10	UCL P 18	UCL P 11

YAXLEY
Founded: 1900 Nickname: The Cuckoos

Secretary: Mrs Sandra Cole **(T)** 07982 924 123 **(E)**
Chairman: Jeff Lenton **Manager:** Gary Clipston **Prog Ed:** Jeff Lenton
Ground: Leading Drove, Holme Road, Yaxley, Peterborough PE7 3NA **(T)** 01733 244 928
Capacity: 1,000 **Seats:** 150 **Covered:** yes **Midweek Matchday:** Tuesday **Clubhouse:** Yes **Shop:** Yes

Colours(change): All blue. (All red).
Previous Names: Yaxley Rovers.
Previous Leagues: Peterborough & Dist., Hunts & West Anglia
Records: Goalscorer: Ricky Hailstone 16
Senior Honours: United Counties League Div.1 1996-97.
Hunts Senior Cup (7), UCL Cup 2005-2006

10 YEAR RECORD

00-01	01-02	02-03	03-04	04-05	05-06	06-07	07-08	08-09	09-10
UCL P 10	UCL P 11	UCL P 7	UCL P 8	UCL P 4	UCL P 7	UCL P 15	UCL P 16	UCL P 14	UCL P 19

DIVISION ONE INS & OUTS
IN: Bourne Town (R), Harborough Town (P – Northants Combination Premier Division), Rothwell Town (R - Southern League Division One Midlands)
OUT: Irchester United (P), Peterborough Northern Star (P)

A.F.C. KEMPSTON ROVERS

Secretary: Kevin Howlett **(T)** 01234 852 056 **(E)**
Chairman: Russell Shreeves **Manager:** **Prog Ed:** Mark Kennett
Ground: Hillgrounds Leisure, Hillgrounds Road, Kempston, Bedford MK42 8SZ **(T)** 01234 852 346 **Capacity:** 2,000
Colours(change): Red & white stripes/black/black (Blue & black stripes/blue/blue)

ADDITIONAL INFORMATION: Previous League: South Midlands 1927-53
Honours: U.C.L. Prem. 1973-74, Div 1 1957-58, 85-86, Div 2 1955-56, KO Cup 1955-56, 57-58, 59-60, 74-75, 76-77.
Beds Senior Cup 1908-09, 37-38, 76-77, 91-92.

BOURNE TOWN
Founded: 1883 Nickname: Wakes

Secretary: Andy Stubley **(T)** 07973 272 423 **(E)** btfc@btconnect.com
Chairman: Andy Stubley **Manager:** Darren Munton **Prog Ed:** Andy Stubley
Ground: Abbey Lawn, Abbey Road, Bourne, Lincs PE10 9EN **(T)** 01778 422 292 **Capacity:** 3,000
Colours(change): Claret & sky blue stripes/navy/navy. (Yellow/blue/blue).

ADDITIONAL INFORMATION: Previous League: Midland Combination 1961-63
Record Att: FA Trophy 1970 **Goalscorer:** David Scotney.
U.C.L. Champions 1968-69, 69-70, 71-72, 90-91. Lincolnshire Senior A Cup 1971-72, 2005-06.

BUCKINGHAM TOWN
Founded: 1883 Nickname: Robins

Secretary: Graham Rigby **(T)** 01280 816 815 **(E)**
Chairman: Tony Rosenberg **Manager:** Phil Simons **Prog Ed:** Carl Waine
Ground: Ford Meadow, Ford Street, Buckingham MK18 1AG **(T)** 01280 816 257 **Capacity:** 2,500
Colours(change): All red (All white)

ADDITIONAL INFORMATION: Previous League: Southern 1986-97. **Record Att:** 2,451 v Orient F.A.Cup 1984-85.
Paid: £7,000 to Wealdstone for Steve Jenkins 1992 Received: £1,000 from Kettering Town for Terry Shrieves.
Honours: Southern League Southern Division 1990-91. U.C.L. 1983-84, 85-86. Berks & Bucks Senior Cup 1983-84.

BUGBROOKE ST MICHAELS
Founded: 1929 Nickname: Badgers

Secretary: Debbie Preston **(T)** 07940 453 838 **(E)**
Chairman: William Marriott **Manager:** Lee Herbert **Prog Ed:** Debbie Preston
Ground: Birds Close, Gayton Road, Bugbrooke NN7 3PH **(T)** 01604 830 707 **Capacity:** 2,500
Colours(change): Yellow & blue/royal blue/blue (Black & white stripes/black/black)

ADDITIONAL INFORMATION: Previous League: Central Northants Combination 1952-87. **Previous Ground:** School Close.
Record Att: 1,156. **Golascorer:** Vince Thomas. **Apps:** Jimmy Nord.
Honours: Northants Junior Cup 1989-90, Central Northants Comb. x6. U.C.L. Division 1 Champions 1998-99.

BURTON PARK WANDERERS
Founded: 1961 Nickname: The Wanderers

Secretary: Sam Gordon **(T)** 07980 013 506 **(E)**
Chairman: Sue Neill **Manager:** Kevin Fox **Prog Ed:** Sue Neill
Ground: Latimer Park, Polwell Lane, Burton Latimer, Northants NN15 5PS **(T)** 07980 013506 **Capacity:**
Colours(change): Azure/black/black (Red/white/red)

ADDITIONAL INFORMATION: Previous League: Kettering Amateur.
Record Att: 253 v Rothwell, May 1989.

EYNESBURY ROVERS

Founded: 1897 Rovers

Secretary: Deryck Irons **(T)** 01234 268111 **(E)**
Chairman: Brian Abraham **Manager:** Matt Plumb **Prog Ed:** Graham Mills
Ground: Alfred Hall Memorial Ground, Hall Road, Eynesbury, St Neots PE19 2SF **(T)** 01480 477 449 **Capacity:** 2,000
Colours(change): Royal & white stripes/royal/royal (Red/white/red)

ADDITIONAL INFORMATION: Previous League: Eastern Counties 1952-63.
Record Att: 5,000 v Fulham 1953 (Stanley Matthews guested for Eynesbury). **Honours:** U.C.L. Division 1 1976-77. Huntingdonshire Senior Cup x11. Huntingdonshire Premier Cup 1950-51, 90-91, 95-96.

HARBOROUGH TOWN

Formed: 1976

Secretary: Pauline Winston **(T)** 01858 465 934 **(E)**
Chairman: Andy Winston **Manager:** Andrew Wilson **Prog Ed:** Tony Sansome
Ground: Bowden's Park, Northampton Road, Market Harborough, Leics. **(T)** 01858 467 339 **Capacity:**
Colours(change): Yellow and black (All red)

ADDITIONAL INFORMATION:
Previous League: Northants Combination.
Honours: Northants Combination 2009-10.

HUNTINGDON TOWN

Founded: 1995

Secretary: Russell Yezek **(T)** 07974 664818 **(E)**
Chairman: Hans Reif **Manager:** Al Lenihan **Prog Ed:** Russell Yezek
Ground: Jubilee Park, Kings Ripton Road,, Huntingdon, Cambridgeshire PE28 2NT **(T)** 07929 651 226 **Capacity:** 1,000
Colours(change): Red & black/red/red (Sky & navy/navy/navy)

ADDITIONAL INFORMATION:
Previous League: Cambridgeshire.
Honours: Cambridgeshire Div.1B 1999-2000. Hunts. Junior Cup 1999-00, 2000-01, 01-02. Hunts Scott Gatty Cup 2001-02.

NORTHAMPTON O.N. CHENECKS

Founded: 1946

Secretary: Trevor Cadden **(T)** 07894 425 823 **(E)**
Chairman: Eddie Slinn **Manager:** Graham Cottle **Prog Ed:** Simon Abbott
Ground: Old Northamptonians Sports Ground,Billing Road,Northampton NN1 5RX **(T)** 01604 634 045 **Capacity:** 1,350
Colours(change): White/navy/white (All red)

ADDITIONAL INFORMATION: Previous League: Northampton Town > 1969.
Honours: U.C.L. Div 1 1977-78, 79-80. Northants Junior Cup 2009-10.

NORTHAMPTON SILEBY RANGERS

Founded: 1968 Nickname: Sileby

Secretary: Dave Battams **(T)** 01604 590 085 **(E)**
Chairman: Robert Clarke **Manager:** Gary Petts **Prog Ed:**
Ground: Fernie Fields Sports Ground, Moulton, Northampton NN3 7BD **(T)** 01604 670366 **Capacity:** 700
Colours(change): All red (White/royal/white)

ADDITIONAL INFORMATION: Previous Name: Northampton Vanaid >2000 **Previous League:** Northampton Town > 1993.
Record Att: 78.
Honours: Northampton Town Lg 1988-89 89-90. UCL Div 1 1993-94, 2002-03. Northants Jnr Cup 93-94, 96-97, 97-98, 2002-03

OLNEY TOWN

Founded: 1903

Secretary: Mrs Karen Keeping **(T)** 07808 776 715 **(E)**
Chairman: Paul Tough **Manager:** Neil Griffiths **Prog Ed:** Paul Tough
Ground: Recreation Ground, East Street, Olney, Bucks MK46 4DW **(T)** 01234 712 227 **Capacity:** 2,000
Colours(change): Green & white stripes/green/green (Yellow & green/yellow/yellow)

ADDITIONAL INFORMATION:
Previous League: Rushden & District.
Honours: U.C.L. Div 1 1972-73. Berks & Bucks Intermediate Cup 1992-93.

POTTON UNITED

Founded: 1943 Nickname: Royals

Secretary: Mrs Bev Strong **(T)** 07703 442 565 **(E)**
Chairman: Alan Riley **Manager:** Tom Galvin & Declan Shilton **Prog Ed:** Mrs Bev Strong
Ground: The Hollow, Bigglewade Road, Potton, Beds SG19 2LU **(T)** 01767 261 100 **Capacity:** 2,000
Colours(change): All blue (Red/black/black)

ADDITIONAL INFORMATION: Previous League: Central Alliance 1956-61. **Previous Ground:** Recreation Ground > 1947.
Record Att: 470 v Hastings Town, FA Vase 1989.
Honours: U.C.L. 1986-87, 88-89, Div.1 2003-04. Beds Senior Cup x5. Huntingdonshire Premier Cup x4. E.Anglian Cup 1996-97

ROTHWELL TOWN

Founded: 1895 The Bones

Secretary: Roger Barratt **(T)** 01536 507 744 **(E)**
Chairman: Alan Trusler **Manager:** Dave Williams **Prog Ed:** Clair Martin
Ground: Home Close, Cecil Street, Rothwell, Northants NN14 2EZ **(T)** 01536 710 694 **Capacity:** 3,500
Colours(change): All white with blue trim (Yellow/black/black)

ADDITIONAL INFORMATION: Previous Name: Rothwell Town Swifts. **Previous League:** Southern.
Previous Grounds: Harrington Rd, Castle Hill. **Record Att:** 2,508 v Irthlingborough Diamonds, U.C.L. 1971.
Honours: U.C.L. 1992-93, 94-95. Northants Senior Cup 1899-1900, 1923-24, 59-60, 88-89, 96-96, 2001-02.

RUSHDEN & HIGHAM UNITED

Formed: 2007

Secretary: Chris Ruff **(T)** 01933 358 862 **(E)**
Chairman: Steve Whitney **Manager:** Aidy Mann **Prog Ed:** Chris Ruff
Ground: Hayden Road, Rushden, Northants NN10 0HX **(T)** 01933 410 036 **Capacity:**
Colours(change): Orange/orange/black (All blue)

ADDITIONAL INFORMATION:
Club was formed after the merger of Rushden Rangers and Higham Town.

THRAPSTON TOWN

Founded: 1960 Nickname: Venturas

Secretary: Mark Brown **(T)** 07885 640 947 **(E)** mark@datsprint.co.uk
Chairman: Mark Brown **Manager:** Joe Smyth **Prog Ed:** Mrs Cathy Stevens
Ground: Chancery Lane, Thrapston, Northants NN14 4JL **(T)** 01832 732 470 **Capacity:** 1,000
Colours(change): All royal blue (Purple/black/black)

ADDITIONAL INFORMATION:
Previous League: Kettering Amateur > 1978.
Honours: Kettering Amateur League 1970-71, 72-73, 73-74, 77-78. Northants Junior Cup 1987-88, 98-99, 03-04.

WELLINGBOROUGH WHITWORTH

Formed: 1973 Nickname: Flourmen

Secretary: Julian Souster **(T)** 01933 381 302 **(E)**
Chairman: Brian Higgins **Manager:** Steve Bicknell **Prog Ed:** Julian Souster
Ground: London Road, Wellingborough, Northants NN8 2DP **(T)** 01933 227 324 **Capacity:** 1,000
Colours(change): Red/black/red (All blue)

ADDITIONAL INFORMATION:
Previous Name: Whitworths. **Previous League:** East Midlands Alliance > 1985.
Honours: Rushden & District League 1976-77. Northants Junior Cup 1996. U.C.L. Division One 2006-07.

WOOTTON BLUE CROSS

Secretary: Bryan Keens **(T)** 01234 768 214 **(E)** brianbtg@aol.com
Chairman: Bryan Keens **Manager:** Andy Arnold **Prog Ed:**
Ground: Weston Park, Bedford Rd., Wootton MK43 9JT **(T)** 01234 767 662 **Capacity:** 2,000
Colours(change): Blue & white/blue/blue (Red & black stripes/black/red & black)

ADDITIONAL INFORMATION: Previous League: South Midlands 1946-55.
Previous Grounds: Recreation Ground, Fishers Field, Rose & Crown, Cockfield.
Record Att: 838 v Luton Beds Prem.Cup 1988. **Honours:** Beds Senior Cup 1970-71, 2001-02.

GROUND DIRECTIONS

AFC KEMPSTON ROVERS

Take A421 Bedford by pass turning as indicated to Kempston onto A5140 Woburn Road. At roundabout turn left into St John's Street then right into Bedford Road. After the shops and park on the left turn immediately left into Hillgrounds Road. Ground is past the swimming pool on right hand side.

BLACKSTONES FC

From Stamford Centre take A6121 towards Bourne. Turn left into Lincoln Road. Ground on the right hand side.

Go into town on A16 from Spalding. Turn left at roundabout into Liquor Pond Street becoming Queen Street over railway crossing along Sleaford Road. Turn right into Carlton Road then right at crossroads into Fydell Street. Over railway crossing and river take 2nd left (sharp turn) into Tattershall Road. Continue over railway crossing, ground on left.

BOURNE TOWN

From Town Centre turn east on A151 towards Spalding into Abbey Road. Ground approximately half a mile on right.

BUCKINGHAM TOWN

A421 ring road to Tesco roundabout. Turn right down hill towards town centre. Take slip road between Ford Garage and the Pub New Inn.

BUGBROOKE ST MICHAELS

At M1 Junction 16 take A45 to Northampton. At first roundabout follow signs to Bugbrooke. Go straight through village, ground entrance immediately past last house on the left.

BURTON PARK WANDERERS

From A14 take J10 towards Burton Latimer, at Alpro roundabout turn right, then straight over roundabout next to Versalift then right at Morrisions. Follow the round around the top of Morrisions continue until you are past the small Alumasc building on the left. Entrance to ground is next left.

COGENHOE UNITED

From A45 Northampton Ring Road turn as indicated to Billing/Cogenhoe. Go over River Nene and up hill ignoring first turning on left to Cogenhoe. Take next left and ground is on right hand side.

DAVENTRY UNITED

From Northampton or junction 16 of the M1 follow A45 westbound into Daventry, crossing the A5 on the way. At first roundabout bear left along A45 Daventry bypass. At next roundabout go straight over into Browns Road. The Club is at the top of this road

DEEPING RANGERS

From Town Centre head north on B1524 towards Bourne. Turn right onto Towngate East at Towngate Tavern Pub. Go straight over mini roundabout onto Outgang Road. Ground 1/4 mile on left. From A16 by pass at roundabout with the A15 Bourne Road turn towards Deeping then left into Northfields Road, then left into Towngate/Outgang Road. Ground 1/4 mile on left.

DESBOROUGH TOWN

Take exit 3 marked Desborough off the A14 and follow bypass for 2 miles. At roundabout turn right and ground is 200 yards on the left hand side.

EYNESBURY ROVERS

From the A1 take the A428 towards Cambridge. Turn left at the Tesco roundabout and continue on Barford Road for half a mile going straight on at 4 roundabouts. Turn left into Hardwick Road and left into Hall Road. Ground at end of road

HARBOROUGH TOWN

Half a mile south of Market Harborough on the A508. 4 miles north of the A14 junction 2 towards Market Harborough turn left towards Leisure Centre, but keep left passed inflatable dome on the right, then through large car park, club house straight in front, with parking area.

HOLBEACH UNITED

Approaching Town Centre traffic lights from Spalding Direction take Second Left, or from Kings Lynn direction take sharp right, into Park Road. Ground is 300 yards on the left.

HUNTINGDON TOWN

At the A1 Brampton Hut roundabout, follow signs for A14 East until reaching the Spittals Interchange roundabout, Follow the A141 towards St Ives/March and go over 3 roundabouts. Take next left turn at traffic lights towards Kings Ripton and the ground is on the left.

IRCHESTER UNITED

From A509 Wellingborough/Newport Pagnell Road turn into Gidsy Lane to Irchester. Turn left into Wollaston Road B659. Alfred Street is on left hand side with the ground at the end.

KINGS LYNN TOWN

At A17/A47 roundabout, over River Ouse bridge to Hardwick roundabout, follow Town Centre sign over two sets of traffic lights. At Southgate roundabout take 4th exit, Vancouver Avenue. Continue over mini roundabout to Tennyson Road. Ground is on left

LONG BUCKBY AFC

From the Town Centre turn into Station Road. Ground on left hand side. Parking is available in South Close adjacent to the Rugby Club (do NOT park "half on half off" the pavement outside the ground)

NEWPORT PAGNELL TOWN

From the A422 Newport Pagnell by pass turn into Marsh End Road, then first right into Willen Road.

NORTHAMPTON ON CHENECKS

Leave A45 at exit marked Bedford A428 and Town Centre. Take exit into Rushmere Road marked Abington, Kingsthorpe and County Cricket. At first set of lights turn left into Billing Road, sports ground 250 yards on the right.

NORTHAMPTON SILEBY RANGERS

Approach from A43 (Kettering): From large roundabout with traffic lights, take the A5076 Talavera Way exit, signpostedto Market Harborough, Moulton Park and Kingsthorpe. The entrance to the ground is about a quarter of a mile on the left. Approach from A45: Take exit to A43 Ring Road / Kettering / Corby. Go straight over 1 roundabout to large roundabout with traffic lights. Then follow directions above.

NORTHAMPTON SPENCER

The ground is in Kingsthorpe area of Northampton on A508, Market Harborough road out of Town. Look for W Grose's garage (Vauxhall) and turn left at traffic lights into Thornton Rd, then first right into Studlands Rd. Follow to bottom of hill and onto track between allotments. Ground is after a right turn at end of track.

OLNEY TOWN

From the North enter via A509 Warrington Road then turn left into Midland Road and immediately right into East Street. Ground on left hand side after Fire Station.

PETERBOROUGH NORTHERN STAR

From A1 turn on to A1139 Fletton Parkway. Follow signs for A47 Wisbech. Exit at Junction 7 (near Perkins Engines Site). At top of slip road turn left into Eastfield Road. At Traffic lights turn right into Newark Avenue and then first right in to Eastern Avenue. Take 2nd left in to Chestnut Avenue and the club is on the right behind steel Palisade Fencing

POTTON UNITED

From Sandy, take B1042 into Potton. Head towards Potton Town Centre and take right turn towards Biggleswade (B1040). The ground is on left hand side at foot of hill

RAUNDS TOWN

From North, East or West, take A14 J13 and follow A45 signs to Raunds. Turn left at roundabout by BP garage. From South follow A45 towards Thrapston. Turn right at roundabout by BP garage. Ground on left.

ROTHWELL CORINTHIANS

A14 to Rothwell. Take B669 towards Desborough. Ground on right at rear of cricket field opposite last houses on the left. Parking on verge or in adjacent field if gate open. Access to ground via footpath.

ROTHWELL TOWN

Leave the A14 at Junction 4. At the roundabout, take the 2nd exit onto B576/Kettering Road. Go through 1 roundabout. At next roundabout turn right in to Bridge Street. Take third left in to Tresham Street. At top of road turn left in to ground.

RUSHDEN AND HIGHAM UNITED

From A6/A45 Junction take Higham/Rushden bypass. At third roundabout turn right, then turn right immediately after the school. From Bedford (A6) take bypass and turn left at first roundabout then turn right immediately after the school

SLEAFORD TOWN

A15 Sleaford By-pass, roundabout to A17 Holdingham Roundabout third exit towards Boston on A17 Take second exit of A17 towards Sleaford ground is 1 mile on right hand side before you enter Sleaford

ST IVES TOWN

From A1123 Houghton Road rurn right at traffic lights into Ramsey Road. After Fire Station turn right into Westwood Road. Ground at end of road on right hand side immediately before St Ivo Recreation Centre Car Park

ST NEOTS TOWN

From town centre take B1428 Cambridge Road. Go under railway bridge and turn left at first roundabout. Follow road up the hill to the ground.

STEWARTS & LLOYDS CORBY

From the Oundle/Weldon Road turn at roundabout into A6086 Lloyds Road and continue to roundabout. Take second exit going over railway line along Rockingham Road. Continue over speed bumps then turn left into Occupation Road and first right into Cannock Road. Ground is beyond the British Steel Club and Rugby pitch.

THRAPSTON TOWN

Exit A14 at A605 roundabout, travel towards Peterborough till 1st roundabout (approx 700 metres).Take first exit into Thrapston. AT traffic lights turn into Oundle Road adjacent to Masons Arms Pub. Turn left into Devere Road and ground at bottom of hill

WELLINGBOROUGH TOWN 2004

Leave A.45 at Wellingborough turn-off, pass Tesco's Store on left-hand side, up to roundabout. Take first exit to town centre. Ground is 300 yards on right-hand side. Entry just past the Dog & Duck public house adjacent to entry to Whitworths ground

WELLINGBOROUGH WHITWORTH

Leave A45 by pass and go past Tescos etc. Turn left at roundabout then turn right immediately after Dog and Duck pub and go through 2nd gate down to the ground .

WOODFORD UNITED

A361 Daventry to Banbury Road. Turn left in Byfield. Follow road to Woodford Halse. Ground on left just past industrial estate.

WOOTTON BLUE CROSS

From A421 turn into Wootton as sign posted. Passing a garage on left hand side, turn right. Ground set back on right hand side behind post office and fish and chip shop.

YAXLEY

Leave A1 at Norman Cross and travel towards Peterborough. Turn off A15 at traffic lights. Bear immediately right and go past cemetery. At bottom of hill turn right into Main Street then left into Holme Road. After short distance go over small bridge and turn left between a bungalow and house into Leading Drove. Ground on left hand side.

WESSEX LEAGUE

www.wessexleague.co.uk

Sponsored by: Sydenhams

Founded: 1986

Recent champions:

2005: Lymington & New Milton

2006: Winchester City

2007: Gosport Borough

2008: AFC Totton

2009: Poole Town

Premier Division	P	W	D	L	F	A	Pts
Poole Town	42	35	4	3	128	40	109
Wimborne Town	42	29	4	9	113	43	91
Bemerton Heath H.	42	28	7	7	84	48	91
Bournemouth	42	27	7	8	87	49	88
Christchurch	42	22	12	8	91	66	78
Fareham Town	42	23	7	12	72	53	76
Totton & Eling	42	22	8	12	69	52	74
Blackfield & Langley	42	20	6	16	74	68	66
Newport IOW	42	15	14	13	61	55	59
Romsey Town	42	15	13	14	64	57	58
Winchester City	42	13	18	11	66	59	57
Moneyfields	42	15	8	19	60	72	53
Brockenhurst	42	13	12	17	62	77	51
Brading Town	42	14	7	21	54	68	49
Hayling United	42	11	11	20	51	84	44
Hamworthy United	42	11	9	22	49	62	42
Alresford Town	42	9	11	22	56	81	38
Alton Town	42	10	8	24	50	91	38
New Milton Town	42	9	9	24	45	70	36
Lymington Town	42	9	7	26	52	81	34
Laverstock & Ford	42	7	7	28	53	111	28
Cowes Sports	42	6	9	27	54	108	27

LEAGUE CUP

FIRST ROUND

Alresford Town 2 **Fawley** 3, **Alton Town** 3 Tadley Calleva 1
Downton 1 **Christchurch** 1 *aet* (5-6p)
East Cowes Victoria Athletic 3 Hythe & Dibden 2
Fareham Town 2 Winchester City 1
Hamble ASSC 1 AFC Portchester 0
Moneyfields 2 Stockbridge 1
Petersfield United 2 United Services Portsmouth 1
Totton & Eling 2 Blackfield & Langley 1 *aet*
Verwood 3 Romsey 2, **Whitchurch United** 3 Hayling United 1

SECOND ROUND

AFC Aldermaston 0 **Farnborough North End** 1
Alton Town 2 Andover NS 1, **Amesbury T.** 4 Bournemouth 2
Brading Town 1 **Fareham Town** 2
Brockenhurst 4 Verwood Town 2
East Cowes Victoria Athletic 0 **Lymington Town** 2
Fawley 0 **Whitchurch United** 2
Fleet Spurs 1 **Petersfield Town** 2
Hamble ASSC 5 **Ringwood Town** 5 *aet* (2-4p)
Horndean 0 **Cowes Sports** 1, Moneyfields 0 **Newport IOW** 1
New Milton 1 **Christchurch** 1 *aet* (4-5p), **Poole** 3 Warminster 1
Shaftesbury 1 **Hamworthy United** 3
Totton & Eling 0 **Bemerton Heath Harlequins** 1
Wimborne Town 1 **Laverstock & Ford** 2

THIRD ROUND

Amesbury 4 Brockenhurst 2, **Fareham T.** 3 Lymington Town 1
Farnborough North End 1 Alton Town 0
Hamworthy United 1 **Laverstock & Ford** 3
Newport IOW 2 Cowes 0, Petersfield 1 **Poole Town** 3 *aet*
Ringwood 1 **Bemerton** 3, Whitchurch United 1 **Christchurch** 6

QUARTER-FINALS

Amesbury Town 0 **Farnborough North End** 1
Bemerton Heath Harlequins 4 Laverstock & Ford 2
Christchurch 0 **Poole Town** 8, Fareham 1 **Newport IOW** 2

SEMI-FINALS

(played over two legs)

Farnborough NE 0 Poole Town 4, **Poole** 6 Farnborough NE 0
Newport IOW 1 Bemerton Hth Harlequins 2, **Bemerton Heath Harlequins** 0 Newport IOW 1 *(Bemerton win on away goals)*

FINAL

(May 3rd at Christchurch)

Poole Town 0 **Bemerton Heath Harlequins** 2

	Alres	Alton	Bem	Blac	Bou	Brad	Broc	Chri	Cow	Fare	Ham	Hay	Lav	Lym	Mon	NM	Nwp	Pool	Rom	Tott	Wim	Win
Alresford Town		2-1	0-1	0-1	1-2	1-0	1-1	2-1	2-0	2-3	3-0	2-3	3-0	4-2	0-2	0-2	1-1	1-2	0-1	0-2	1-3	2-2
Alton Town	3-1		1-2	2-0	0-2	1-4	0-2	2-2	2-2	1-2	2-1	0-1	1-1	1-0	3-6	2-2	1-0	1-6	0-3	1-4	2-1	2-2
Bemerton Hth Harlequins	0-2	5-0		2-1	3-2	2-0	4-0	3-1	2-1	1-1	1-1	2-1	4-2	4-1	2-1	2-0	1-0	1-2	3-3	1-2	2-2	0-3
Blackfield & Langley	2-1	2-1	0-2	***P***	0-1	2-2	3-1	2-3	3-0	2-2	3-0	4-1	5-2	3-2	1-4	1-0	2-1	1-3	2-5	1-0	2-1	1-1
Bournemouth	0-0	7-1	3-1	3-0	***R***	1-0	2-1	7-0	1-2	0-1	1-0	1-2	5-0	2-2	2-1	3-2	2-0	2-7	1-1	1-0	1-0	1-1
Brading Town	5-3	3-1	0-1	4-3	0-1	***E***	1-4	1-2	1-2	2-1	1-1	4-1	1-2	2-1	0-1	2-1	0-2	1-0	0-3	3-1	0-2	1-2
Brockenhurst	3-2	1-1	0-1	2-0	1-1	3-1	***M***	2-1	0-0	0-6	1-3	2-2	1-1	2-0	1-4	1-1	0-2	2-4	3-1	2-3	1-6	1-2
Christchurch	6-0	2-1	3-3	1-1	1-2	2-2	1-1	***I***	5-2	2-1	4-0	3-0	2-1	5-2	5-1	2-3	2-2	4-4	0-0	3-1	2-1	4-1
Cowes Sports	2-3	1-0	2-4	2-4	4-5	1-2	1-1	3-4	***E***	1-2	0-4	0-4	2-3	1-1	1-2	0-3	2-2	1-1	0-4	2-6	0-4	3-4
Fareham Town	3-1	3-1	0-3	2-1	3-2	2-0	3-1	1-2	2-0	***R***	1-1	1-0	2-0	1-0	0-3	1-2	2-1	2-3	1-1	2-3	1-4	1-1
Hamworthy United	1-1	3-1	1-3	3-2	1-2	4-0	0-1	1-1	0-1	0-2		3-0	1-3	1-0	2-3	0-2	1-2	1-3	0-0	0-1	0-1	4-2
Hayling United	3-2	1-3	0-1	0-1	0-3	2-2	2-2	1-1	2-1	1-1	2-1	***D***	1-2	0-1	2-2	0-1	0-0	2-5	1-2	0-2	2-3	1-0
Laverstock & Ford	1-1	1-2	0-3	1-3	2-4	1-0	1-1	1-2	0-1	3-1	1-1	2-3	***I***	2-6	2-4	0-1	1-4	0-1	3-3	1-1	1-5	1-6
Lymington Town	1-1	1-1	1-2	3-1	2-2	2-3	0-4	1-1	0-3	1-2	0-3	1-2	3-2	***V***	0-1	1-3	3-0	0-3	0-2	1-0	0-1	1-2
Moneyfields	3-3	1-2	1-2	1-2	0-2	2-1	0-0	0-1	3-3	0-2	0-0	0-1	1-0	1-2	***I***	0-0	0-3	1-6	2-1	2-3	0-3	0-0
New Milton Town	1-1	1-2	1-2	0-1	0-2	0-1	1-3	1-3	1-1	0-3	0-3	1-1	1-2	0-4	2-2	***S***	0-2	2-4	2-3	1-1	2-5	0-1
Newport IOW	0-0	4-2	0-0	1-1	0-0	0-0	3-1	2-0	5-2	1-2	1-0	3-0	3-1	1-3	0-2	1-5	***I***	2-2	3-2	3-1	0-0	0-0
Poole Town	6-0	4-0	2-1	1-2	5-0	2-0	3-0	3-0	2-1	3-2	3-0	7-1	6-1	1-0	2-0	1-0	3-0	***O***	3-0	4-0	0-3	3-1
Romsey Town	2-2	1-0	1-1	0-3	0-1	1-1	1-4	1-2	4-1	0-1	1-1	1-1	5-2	1-1	0-1	1-0	3-1	0-2	***N***	0-2	2-0	0-0
Totton & Eling	2-1	2-1	2-3	4-3	1-0	1-1	3-0	0-1	2-0	0-0	1-0	1-1	3-1	3-1	2-1	1-0	2-2	1-2	2-1		1-2	0-0
Wimborne Town	5-2	1-1	2-0	2-1	2-4	2-0	2-0	0-1	7-1	3-2	5-1	8-1	5-0	3-0	5-0	4-0	3-1	2-3	1-3	2-1		1-0
Winchester City	2-1	1-0	2-3	1-1	1-3	1-2	3-5	3-3	1-1	0-1	0-1	2-2	3-2	4-1	3-1	0-0	2-2	1-1	3-0	1-1	1-1	

Division One		P	W	D	L	F	A	Pts
Hamble ASSC		40	26	7	7	102	43	85
Fawley		40	25	7	8	125	63	82
Fleet Spurs		40	24	4	12	102	63	76
Downton		40	22	10	8	96	57	76
Ringwood Town		40	22	8	10	79	55	74
AFC Portchester		40	22	7	11	85	60	73
Verwood Town		40	21	5	14	72	57	68
Petersfield Town		40	20	6	14	88	74	66
Utd Services Portsmouth		40	19	8	13	96	73	65
Whitchurch United		40	16	13	11	85	50	61
Amesbury Town		40	17	10	13	92	84	61
Horndean		40	18	6	16	92	74	60
Stockbridge		40	16	10	14	81	75	58
Warminster Town		40	15	4	21	66	85	49
Tadley Calleva		40	12	11	17	68	75	47
Hythe & Dibden		40	14	5	21	72	84	47
East Cowes Vics Ath.		40	11	9	20	70	88	42
Farnborough North End		40	9	12	19	63	76	39
Andover New Street		40	7	8	25	75	141	29
Shaftesbury	*-1*	40	5	5	30	53	151	19
AFC Aldermaston		40	1	1	38	29	163	4

Combination One		P	W	D	L	F	A	Pts
Gosport Borough Res.		26	19	5	2	74	25	62
Christchurch Res.	*-1*	26	17	7	2	71	30	57
VTFC Res.		26	17	4	5	109	28	55
Moneyfields Res.		26	14	7	5	55	37	49
Bemerton Heath Res.		26	11	7	8	64	54	40
Alton Town Res.		26	11	6	9	49	50	39
Laverstock & Ford Res.		26	11	4	11	64	55	37
Petersfield Town Res.		26	9	5	12	50	61	32
AFC Totton Res.		26	9	4	13	53	50	31
Ringwood Town Res.		26	8	4	14	48	66	28
Brockenhurst Res.		26	7	4	15	35	75	25
Hamble ASSC Res.		26	5	8	13	31	63	23
Hayling United Res.		26	4	5	17	19	59	17
Lymington Town Res.		26	3	4	19	28	97	13

Combination Two		P	W	D	L	F	A	Pts
Fareham Town Res.		22	17	4	1	67	25	55
Poole Town Res		22	16	4	2	76	26	52
Totton & Eling Res.		22	12	3	7	68	38	39
Fawley Res.		22	11	4	7	62	44	37
Whitchurch United Res.		22	9	5	8	46	46	32
AFC Aldermaston Res		22	8	5	9	44	41	29
Romsey Town Res.		22	7	5	10	38	35	26
Blackfield/Langley Res.		22	8	2	12	31	66	26
AFC Portchester Res.	*-1*	22	6	7	9	31	39	24
Alresford Town Res.		22	6	6	10	36	45	24
Horndean Res.		22	3	5	14	32	77	14
Downton Res.		22	2	4	16	30	79	10

COMBINATION CUP

FINAL *(April 30th at Blackfield & Langley)*
Gosport B. Res. 3 Christchurch Res. 3 *aet* (4-1p)

	AFC Aldermaston	AFC Portchester	Amesbury Town	Andover New Street	Downton	East Cowes Victoria Athletic	Farnborough North End	Fawley	Fleet Spurs	Hamble ASSC	Horndean	Hythe & Dibden	Petersfield Town	Ringwood Town	Shaftesbury	Stockbridge	Tadley Calleva	United Services Portsmouth	Verwood Town	Warminster Town	Whitchurch United
AFC Aldermaston		0-8	1-2	1-4	0-2	1-3	0-4	0-8	0-4	2-3	2-5	1-6	2-1	0-5	0-1	1-6	0-6	1-3	0-2	1-1	1-2
AFC Portchester	2-1		3-4	2-1	2-2	5-2	3-0	1-1	1-3	3-2	3-2	4-0	1-1	1-2	1-1	2-1	1-1	1-0	0-1	3-0	2-1
Amesbury Town	6-0	1-3		9-3	1-3	5-1	3-2	1-1	0-1	3-3	4-3	3-1	0-2	3-1	3-1	2-2	1-5	1-1	3-2	3-2	2-1
Andover New Street	5-1	2-3	1-2		2-1	4-1	2-2	3-4	3-5	2-9	2-3	0-6	0-3	0-5	1-0	2-2	1-1	3-1	1-5	2-3	0-1
Downton	2-1	1-0	1-1	3-3	***D***	1-1	2-1	1-0	3-1	4-1	3-1	2-1	0-2	0-0	3-0	5-0	4-1	5-1	4-0	5-1	1-4
East Cowes Victoria Ath.	3-1	2-2	2-0	8-0	1-3	***I***	0-2	3-1	0-2	0-3	1-3	1-3	1-1	2-1	8-3	2-2	2-1	1-3	2-0	1-2	0-1
Farnborough North End	4-1	4-1	0-0	4-4	3-1	0-0	***V***	2-4	0-1	0-3	1-3	2-3	4-0	0-3	7-2	3-2	0-0	1-1	0-0	0-1	3-3
Fawley	9-1	1-0	3-1	10-1	1-1	2-1	6-1	***I***	3-4	3-2	5-3	4-2	2-5	2-0	7-0	2-1	2-0	6-1	0-0	0-3	1-1
Fleet Spurs	3-0	5-1	4-2	0-2	4-1	6-1	2-0	2-4	***S***	1-3	2-0	4-0	1-1	5-3	5-1	0-1	0-3	2-4	3-4	2-1	2-1
Hamble ASSC	3-0	4-0	1-1	4-3	2-0	1-1	3-1	2-0	3-1	***I***	3-1	3-0	1-0	2-2	6-0	1-3	2-0	1-0	5-1	4-1	0-0
Horndean	7-1	1-2	3-1	5-2	2-3	3-1	3-0	1-3	1-1	3-2	***O***	0-0	2-0	1-2	0-0	2-2	3-1	3-0	0-0	7-0	2-0
Hythe & Dibden	3-0	1-0	2-3	2-0	0-4	3-5	1-1	2-5	0-3	0-2	3-1	***N***	0-2	1-3	6-1	3-1	1-3	5-3	0-1	3-1	1-2
Petersfield Town	9-1	1-5	4-4	3-2	1-1	4-3	2-1	1-2	2-1	0-1	4-2	4-1		2-4	4-0	4-2	1-2	1-1	3-1	1-3	1-0
Ringwood Town	3-2	0-0	3-2	2-2	2-2	2-1	5-0	3-3	2-1	1-0	3-2	0-2	1-3		2-0	0-1	3-1	2-1	1-0	2-1	0-0
Shaftesbury	5-2	0-1	4-1	4-4	3-7	3-2	1-5	2-9	0-7	1-2	1-2	0-0	1-2	3-3	***O***	0-1	4-2	4-7	0-5	0-1	2-6
Stockbridge	2-1	1-2	4-4	2-0	2-1	2-2	1-1	6-2	3-4	2-2	1-4	3-3	3-2	2-1	6-1	***N***	2-1	3-0	0-2	2-0	2-0
Tadley Calleva	6-1	3-4	1-0	5-1	1-0	1-1	1-1	1-1	2-2	0-8	3-3	1-1	1-5	0-1	2-1	3-2	***E***	2-3	1-4	2-2	0-0
Utd Services Portsmouth	4-0	4-1	6-2	7-1	2-2	4-1	3-1	1-2	3-3	0-0	2-3	2-0	1-3	3-1	3-1	3-0	3-0		3-2	3-0	2-2
Verwood Town	5-0	1-5	1-2	3-2	2-5	0-1	2-1	1-0	3-2	2-0	2-1	5-3	5-2	2-3	1-0	3-0	1-0	1-3		0-0	0-0
Warminster Town	3-1	1-4	1-5	6-1	4-5	2-2	2-0	0-3	0-1	1-2	5-0	1-2	3-1	1-2	3-1	2-1	1-3	4-3	1-0		1-2
Whitchurch United	3-0	1-2	1-1	3-3	2-2	5-0	1-1	2-3	1-2	0-3	3-1	3-1	8-0	1-0	14-1	2-2	2-1	1-1	0-2	5-1	

ALRESFORD TOWN

Founded: 1898 Nickname:

Secretary: Keith Curtis **(T)** 07703 346672 **(E)** secretary.alresfordtownfc@gmail.com
Chairman: Trevor Ingram **Manager:** Tim Cole **Prog Ed:** Gregory Boughton
Ground: Alresbury Park, The Avenue, Alresford, Hants SO24 9EP **(T)** 01962 735 100
Capacity: **Seats:** Yes **Covered:** Yes **Midweek Matchday:** Tuesday **Clubhouse:** Yes **Shop:**

Colours(change): Black & white stripes/black/black & white. (All yellow)
Previous Names:
Previous Leagues: Winchester League, North Hants league, Hampshire League
Records:
Senior Honours: Winchester Lge Div 2 & Div 1

10 YEAR RECORD

00-01	01-02	02-03	03-04	04-05	05-06	06-07	07-08	08-09	09-10
Hant2 3	Hant2 2	Hant1 11	Hant1 8	Wex2 10	Wex2 20	Wex1 2	WexP 21	WexP 18	WexP 17

ALTON TOWN

Founded: 1919 Nickname:

Secretary: Jim McKell **(T)** 07740 099 374 **(E)** secretary@altontownfc.com
Chairman: Jim McKell **Manager:** John Robson **Prog Ed:** Imageprint
Ground: Alton (Bass) Sports Ground, Anstey Road, Alton, Hants GU34 2RL **(T)**
Capacity: 2,000 **Seats:** 200 **Covered:** 250 **Midweek Matchday:** Tuesday **Clubhouse:** Yes **Shop:** No

Colours(change): White/black/black (Yellow/green/yellow)
Previous Names: Present club formed in 1990 when Alton Town and Bass Alton merged.
Previous Leagues: Hampshire League >2002
Records:
Senior Honours: Hants Senior Cup 1958, 1969, 1972 & 1978.
Hampshire Champions 2001-02.

10 YEAR RECORD

00-01	01-02	02-03	03-04	04-05	05-06	06-07	07-08	08-09	09-10
HantP 7	HantP 1	Wex1 17	Wex1 18	Wex1 19	Wex1 20	WexP 17	WexP 14	WexP 19	WexP 18

BEMERTON HEATH HARLEQUINS

Founded: 1989 Nickname: Quins

Secretary: Andy Hardwick **(T)** 07905 568007 **(E)** secretarybhhfc@hotmail.com
Chairman: Steve Slade **Manager:** **Prog Ed:** Steve Brooks
Ground: The Clubhouse, Western Way, Bemerton Heath Salisbury SP2 9DT **(T)** 01722 331925 (Club) 331218 (Office)
Capacity: 2,100 **Seats:** 250 **Covered:** 350 **Midweek Matchday:** Tuesday **Clubhouse:** Yes **Shop:** No

Colours(change): Black & white quarters/black/black & white (Amber/white/white)
Previous Names: Bemerton Athletic, Moon FC & Bemerton Boys merged in 1989
Previous Leagues: Salisbury & Wilts Comb, Salisbury & Andover Sunday
Records: **Att:** 1,118 v Aldershot Town **App:** Keith Richardson
Senior Honours: Wiltshire Senior Cup 1992-93. Wessex League Cup 2009-10.

10 YEAR RECORD

00-01	01-02	02-03	03-04	04-05	05-06	06-07	07-08	08-09	09-10
Wex 11	Wex 11	Wex 18	Wex 12	Wex1 14	Wex1 14	WexP 11	WexP 13	WexP 12	WexP 3

BLACKFIELD & LANGLEY

Founded: 1935 Nickname:

Secretary: Doug Sangster **(T)** 07899 927 165 **(E)** doug-sangster@sky.com
Chairman: Andrew Hartman **Manager:** Jon Gittens **Prog Ed:** Andrew Hartman
Ground: Gang Warily Rec., Newlands Rd, Southampton, SO45 1GA **(T)** 02380 893 603
Capacity: 2,500 **Seats:** 180 **Covered:** nil **Midweek Matchday:** Tuesday **Clubhouse:** Yes **Shop:**

Colours(change): White/green/white. (All yellow).
Previous Names:
Previous Leagues: Southampton Senior. Hampshire.
Records: **Att:** 240
Senior Honours: Hants Div 97-88, Div 2 84-85, Southampton Senior Cup (4)

10 YEAR RECORD

00-01	01-02	02-03	03-04	04-05	05-06	06-07	07-08	08-09	09-10
Wex 21	Wex 17	Wex 21	Wex 21	Wex2 7	Wex2 14	Wex1 16	Wex1 10	Wex1 2	WexP 8

PREMIER INS & OUTS

IN: Fawley (P), Hamble ASSC (P)
OUT: Cowes Sports (R), Wimborne Town (P - Southern League Division One South & West)

BOURNEMOUTH
Founded: 1875 Nickname: Poppies

Secretary: Mike Robins **(T)** 07947 687 808 **(E)** poppies1875@hotmail.co.uk
Chairman: Bob Corbin **Manager:** Ken Vaughan **Prog Ed:** Mike Robins
Ground: Victoria Park, Namu Road, Winton, Bournemouth, BH9 2RA **(T)** 01202 515 123
Capacity: 3,000 **Seats:** 205 **Covered:** 205 **Midweek Matchday:** Tuesday **Clubhouse:** Yes **Shop:** Yes

Colours(change): All Red (all blue)
Previous Names: Bournemouth Rovers, Bournemouth Dean Park
Previous Leagues: Hampshire
Records: **Goalscorer:** Brian Chike
Senior Honours: Hampshire League

10 YEAR RECORD

00-01	01-02	02-03	03-04	04-05	05-06	06-07	07-08	08-09	09-10
Wex 14	Wex 18	Wex 14	Wex 20	Wex1 11	Wex1 7	WexP 5	WexP 5	WexP 15	WexP 4

BRADING TOWN
Founded: 1871 Nickname:

Secretary: Laurie Wallis **(T)** 07702 715 400 **(E)** bradingtown@hotmail.com
Chairman: Michelle Egleton **Manager:** Steve Brougham **Prog Ed:** Geoff Ruck
Ground: The Peter Henry Ground, Vicarage Lane, I.o.W. PO36 0AR **(T)** 01983 405 217
Capacity: **Seats:** **Covered:** **Midweek Matchday:** Wednesday **Clubhouse:** **Shop:**

Colours(change): White with red trim/red/red. (Blue/white/blue)
Previous Names:
Previous Leagues: Isle of Wight. Hampshire.
Records:
Senior Honours:

10 YEAR RECORD

00-01	01-02	02-03	03-04	04-05	05-06	06-07	07-08	08-09	09-10
HantP 6	HantP 8	HantP 17	HantP 18	Wex2 16	Wex2 3	WexP 10	WexP 15	WexP 14	WexP 14

BROCKENHURST
Founded: 1898 Nickname: The Badgers

Secretary: Paul Christopher **(T)** 07837 587 657 **(E)** pc500@btinternet.com
Chairman: Dave Stansbridge **Manager:** John Pyatt **Prog Ed:** Paul Christopher
Ground: Grigg Lane, Brockenhurst, Hants SO42 7RE **(T)** 01590 623 544
Capacity: 2,000 **Seats:** 200 **Covered:** 300 **Midweek Matchday:** Tuesday **Clubhouse:** Yes **Shop:**

Colours(change): Blue & white/blue/blue. (All green).
Previous Names:
Previous Leagues: Hampshire
Records: **Att:** 1,104 v St Albans City
Senior Honours: Hants Int Cup 61-62, Bournemouth Sen Cup 60-61,
Hampshire Lg 75-76

10 YEAR RECORD

00-01	01-02	02-03	03-04	04-05	05-06	06-07	07-08	08-09	09-10
Wex 9	Wex 6	Wex 20	Wex 9	Wex1 18	Wex1 21	WexP 13	WexP 6	WexP 5	WexP 13

CHRISTCHURCH
Founded: 1885 Nickname: Priory

Secretary: Ian Harley **(T)** 07900 133 954 **(E)** secretary@christchurchfc.co.uk
Chairman: Mick Ryan **Manager:** Graham Kemp **Prog Ed:** Dennis Miller
Ground: Hurn Bridge S.C, Avon Causeway, Christchurch BH23 6DY **(T)** 01202 473 792
Capacity: 1,200 **Seats:** 215 **Covered:** 265 **Midweek Matchday:** Tuesday **Clubhouse:** Yes **Shop:**

Colours(change): All Blue (All Red)
Previous Names:
Previous Leagues: Hampshire
Records: **App:** John Haynes
Senior Honours: Hants Jnr Cup (3), Hants Intermediate Cup 86-87,
Bournemouth Senior Cup (5)

10 YEAR RECORD

00-01	01-02	02-03	03-04	04-05	05-06	06-07	07-08	08-09	09-10
Wex 17	Wex 15	Wex 13	Wex 11	Wex1 17	Wex1 10	WexP 14	WexP 16	WexP 7	WexP 5

FAREHAM TOWN

Founded: 1946 Nickname: The Robins

Secretary: Ian Tewson **(T)** 07930 853 235 **(E)** iantewson@aol.com

Chairman: Nick Ralls **Manager:** Matt Parr **Prog Ed:** Ian Tewson

Ground: Cams Alders, Palmerston Drive, Fareham, Hants PO14 1BJ **(T)** 07810 844 466

Capacity: 2,000 **Seats:** 450 **Covered:** 500 **Midweek Matchday:** Wednesday **Clubhouse:** Yes **Shop:** Yes

Colours(change): Red/black/red. (White/black/black or All blue)

Previous Names:

Previous Leagues: Portsmouth, Hampshire & Southern

Records: Att: 2,015 v Spurs (friendly 1985)

Senior Honours: Hampshire Senior Cup 1957, 1963, 1968, 1993,
Hampshire League Champions.

10 YEAR RECORD

00-01	01-02	02-03	03-04	04-05	05-06	06-07	07-08	08-09	09-10
Wex 15	Wex 10	Wex 5	Wex 7	Wex1 16	Wex1 9	WexP 8	WexP 8	WexP 10	WexP 6

FAWLEY

Founded: 1923 Nickname:

Secretary: Sandie Earl **(T)** 07759 956257 **(E)** fawleysecretary@hotmail.co.uk

Chairman: Colin Stewart **Manager:** **Prog Ed:** Tim Hardiman

Ground: Waterside Spts & Soc. club, 179 Long Lane, Holbury, Soto, SO45 2QD **(T)** 02380 893750 (Club) 896621 (Office)

Capacity: **Seats:** **Covered:** **Midweek Matchday:** Wednesday **Clubhouse:** **Shop:**

Colours(change): All Blue (All yellow)

Previous Names:

Previous Leagues: Hants Premier

Records:

Senior Honours:

10 YEAR RECORD

00-01	01-02	02-03	03-04	04-05	05-06	06-07	07-08	08-09	09-10
									Wex1 2

HAMBLE ASSC

Founded: 1938 Nickname:

Secretary: Ward Puddle **(T)** 07801 305392 **(E)** hamble.assc@hotmail.co.uk

Chairman: Jennifer Headington **Manager:** Paul Masters **Prog Ed:** Ward Puddle

Ground: Folland Park, Kings Ave, Hamble, Southampton SO31 4NF **(T)** 02380 452 173

Capacity: 1,000 **Seats:** 150 **Covered:** 150 **Midweek Matchday:** Tuesday **Clubhouse:** Yes **Shop:** No

Colours(change): Sky blue/sky blue/maroon/ (White/red/red)

Previous Names: Folland Sports (pre 1990) Aerostructures SSC 90-97

Previous Leagues:

Records:

Senior Honours: Southampton Senior Cup 1984-85, 86-87, 91-92. Wessex League Division 1 2009-10.

10 YEAR RECORD

00-01	01-02	02-03	03-04	04-05	05-06	06-07	07-08	08-09	09-10
Wex 18	Wex 22	Wex 16	Wex 13	Wex1 21	Wex1 15	WexP 20	WexP 17	WexP 21	Wex1 1

HAMWORTHY UNITED

Founded: 1926 Nickname:

Secretary: Peter Gallop **(T)** 07897 959270 **(E)** sec-ham-utd-secretary@hotmail.co.uk

Chairman: Bruce Scammell **Manager:** Simon Browne **Prog Ed:** Jay Keating

Ground: The County Ground, Blandford Close, Hamworthy, Poole, BH15 4PR **(T)** 01202 674 974

Capacity: 2,000 **Seats:** **Covered:** **Midweek Matchday:** Wednesday **Clubhouse:** Yes **Shop:** No

Colours(change): Maroon & sky blue/sky blue/sky blue (Orange/black/black)

Previous Names: Hamworthy St. Michael merged with Trinidad Old Boys 1926

Previous Leagues: Dorset Premier

Records:

Senior Honours: Dorset Premier League 2002-03, 03-04.

10 YEAR RECORD

00-01	01-02	02-03	03-04	04-05	05-06	06-07	07-08	08-09	09-10
Dor P 5	Dor P 5	Dor P 1	Dor P 1	Wex1 15	Wex1 6	WexP 15	WexP 10	WexP 8	WexP 16

HAYLING UNITED

Founded: 1884 Nickname:

Secretary: Shirley Westfield **(T)** 07724 540 916 **(E)** shirley.westfield@ntlworld.com

Chairman: Argyll McLetchie **Manager:** Mark Poulton **Prog Ed:** Steve Hayward

Ground: Hayling College, Church Road, Hayling Island, Hampshire PO11 0NU **(T)**

Capacity: **Seats:** **Covered:** **Midweek Matchday:** Tuesday **Clubhouse:** Yes **Shop:** No

Colours(change): Black & white/black/black. (Yellow/white/white).
Previous Names:
Previous Leagues: Waterlooville & District > 1952 , Portsmouth 1952-91, Hampshire 1991-2004
Records:
Senior Honours: Hampshire Lge Div 1 Champions 2002-03, Wessex Div 1 2006-07

10 YEAR RECORD

00-01	01-02	02-03	03-04	04-05	05-06	06-07	07-08	08-09	09-10
Hant1 4	Hant1 3	Hant1 1	Hant1 5	Wex3 2	Wex2 2	Wex1 1	WexP 12	WexP 16	WexP 15

LAVERSTOCK & FORD

Founded: 1956 Nickname:

Secretary: Brian Ford **(T)** 07743 538 984 **(E)** sec.laverstockandfordfc@gmail.com

Chairman: Gino Nardiello **Manager:** Gino Nardiello **Prog Ed:** Michael Eyers

Ground: The Dell, Church Road, Laverstock, Salisbury, Wilts SP1 1QX **(T)** 01722 327 401

Capacity: **Seats:** **Covered:** **Midweek Matchday:** Tuesday **Clubhouse:** **Shop:**

Colours(change): Green & white hoops/green/green (Yellow/blue/white)
Previous Names:
Previous Leagues: Salisbury & District. Hampshire.
Records:
Senior Honours:

10 YEAR RECORD

00-01	01-02	02-03	03-04	04-05	05-06	06-07	07-08	08-09	09-10
Hant2 4	Hant2 3	Hant2 1	Hant1 11	Wex3 11	Wex3 2	Wex1 12	Wex1 2	WexP 20	WexP 21

LYMINGTON TOWN

Founded: 1876 Nickname:

Secretary: Russell Young **(T)** 07922 065 803 **(E)** russellyoung626@hotmail.com

Chairman: George Shaw **Manager:** Stuart Hussey **Prog Ed:** Derek Webb

Ground: The Sports Ground, Southampton Road, Lymington SO41 9ZG **(T)** 01590 671 305

Capacity: 3,000 **Seats:** 200 **Covered:** 300 **Midweek Matchday:** Tuesday **Clubhouse:** **Shop:**

Colours(change): Red/white/black. (Yellow/blue/yellow)
Previous Names:
Previous Leagues: Hampshire.
Records:
Senior Honours: Wessex Lge Cup 2006-07

10 YEAR RECORD

00-01	01-02	02-03	03-04	04-05	05-06	06-07	07-08	08-09	09-10
HantP 17	HantP 14	HantP 15	HantP 7	Wex2 1	Wex1 17	WexP 12	WexP 20	WexP 18	WexP 20

MONEYFIELDS

Founded: 1987 Nickname: Moneys

Secretary: Wayne Dalton **(T)** 07766 250812 **(E)** secretary@moneyfieldsfc.co.uk

Chairman: Paul Lipscombe **Manager:** Miles Rutherford **Prog Ed:** David Hayter

Ground: Moneyfields Sports Ground, Moneyfield Ave, Copnor, P'mouth PO3 6LA **(T)** 02392 665260 (Club) 07766 250812 (M)

Capacity: 1,500 **Seats:** 150 **Covered:** 150 **Midweek Matchday:** Tuesday **Clubhouse:** Yes **Shop:** Yes

Colours(change): Yellowy/navy/yellow. (White with blue/white/white).
Previous Names: Portsmouth Civil Service
Previous Leagues: Portsmouth. Hampshire.
Records: **Att:** 250 v Fareham, WexD1 05-06 **Goalscorer:** Lee Mould 86 **App:** Matt Lafferty - 229 **Win:** 9-0v Blackfield & Langley 01-02.
Senior Honours: Portsmouth Premier Champions 1990-91, 91-92. Senior Cup 1990-91.
Hampshire Champions 1996-97.

10 YEAR RECORD

00-01	01-02	02-03	03-04	04-05	05-06	06-07	07-08	08-09	09-10
Wex 16	Wex 9	Wex 10	Wex 17	Wex1 10	Wex1 11	WexP 7	WexP 7	WexP 3	WexP 12

NEW MILTON TOWN

Founded: 2007 Nickname: The Linnets

Secretary: Richard Phippard **(T)** 07515 775 442 **(E)** secretary.newmilton@yahoo.co.uk
Chairman: John Breaker **Manager:** Paul Hardyman **Prog Ed:** Richard Phippard
Ground: Fawcett Fields, Christchurch Road, New Milton, BH25 6QB **(T)** 01425 628 191
Capacity: 3,000 **Seats:** 262 **Covered:** 262 **Midweek Matchday:** Tuesday **Clubhouse:** **Shop:**

Colours(change): All maroon & sky blue/white/sky blue (Yellow & green/green/green)
Previous Names: Lymington Town > 1988, AFC Lymington 1988-98, Lymington & New Milton 1998-07
Previous Leagues: Isthmian. Southern.
Records:
Senior Honours: Wessex League 1998-99, 04-05.

10 YEAR RECORD

00-01	01-02	02-03	03-04	04-05	05-06	06-07	07-08	08-09	09-10
Wex 2	Wex 5	Wex 6	Wex 4	Wex1 1	Isth1 16	SthS 17	WexP 19	WexP 9	WexP 19

NEWPORT I.O.W.

Founded: 1888 Nickname: The Port

Secretary: John Simpkins **(T)** 07771 964 704 **(E)** simmo123@my-inbox.net
Chairman: Paul Phelps **Manager:** Derek Ohren **Prog Ed:** Peter Westhorpe
Ground: St George's Park, St George's Way, Newport PO30 2QH **(T)** 01983 525 027
Capacity: 5,000 **Seats:** 300 **Covered:** 1,000 **Midweek Matchday:** Wednesday **Clubhouse:** Yes **Shop:** Yes

Colours(change): Yellow/blue/yellow. (All green)
Previous Names:
Previous Leagues: I.O.W. 1896-28. Hants 28-86. Wessex 86-90.
Records: **Att:** 2,270 v Portsmouth (friendly) 07.07.2001. **Goalscorer:** Roy Grilfillan - 220 1951-57. **Apps:** Jeff Austin - 540 1969-87.
Senior Honours: Southern League Eastern Division 2000-01. Hants Senior Cup (x8).
I.O.W. Cup (34)

10 YEAR RECORD

00-01	01-02	02-03	03-04	04-05	05-06	06-07	07-08	08-09	09-10
SthE 1	SthP 19	SthE 16	SthE 19	Isth1 18	Isth1 22	SthS 20	SthS 22	WexP 6	WexP 9

POOLE TOWN

Founded: 1890 Nickname: The Dolphins

Secretary: Bill Reid **(T)** 01794 517 991 **(E)** secretary@pooletownfc.co.uk
Chairman: Clive Robbins **Manager:** Tommy Killick **Prog Ed:** Ian Claxton
Ground: Tatnam Ground, Oakdale School, School Lane, Poole BH15 3JR **(T)** 07771 604 289 (Match days)
Capacity: 2,000 **Seats:** 154 **Covered:** 120 **Midweek Matchday:** Tuesday **Clubhouse:** Yes **Shop:**

Colours(change): Red & white halves/red/red & white. (All sky blue).
Previous Names: Poole Rovers 1884, Poole Hornets 1886 - amalgamated on 20.09.1890 to form Town.
Previous Leagues: Western 1922-26, Southern 1926-30, Western 1930-57, Southern 5197-96, Hampshire 1996-2004
Records: **Att:** 10,224 v Queens Park Rangers, FA Cup 1st Rnd Replay, 1946 (at Poole Stadium).
Senior Honours: Western League 1956-57. Dorset Senior Cup (12),
Wessex League Champions 2008-09, 09-10.

10 YEAR RECORD

00-01	01-02	02-03	03-04	04-05	05-06	06-07	07-08	08-09	09-10
HantP 2	HantP 5	HantP 4	HantP 3	Wex2 2	Wex1 8	WexP 4	WexP 4	WexP 1	WexP 1

ROMSEY TOWN

Founded: 1886 Nickname:

Secretary: Penny Walters **(T)** 07876 467 452 **(E)** pwalters23@yahoo.co.uk
Chairman: Ken Jacobs **Manager:** Glenn Burnett **Prog Ed:** Cameron Melling
Ground: The Bypass Ground, South Front, Romsey, SO51 8GJ **(T)** 01794 513 685
Capacity: **Seats:** **Covered:** **Midweek Matchday:** Tuesday **Clubhouse:** Yes **Shop:**

Colours(change): White/black/black. (All blue).
Previous Names: None
Previous Leagues: Hampshire.
Records:
Senior Honours: Wessex League Champions 1989-90.

10 YEAR RECORD

00-01	01-02	02-03	03-04	04-05	05-06	06-07	07-08	08-09	09-10
Hant1 16	Hant1 15	Hant2 13	Hant2 2	Wex2 4	Wex2 13	Wex1 3	WexP 18	WexP 11	WexP 10

TOTTON & ELING

Founded: 1925 Nickname:

Secretary: Mike Clarke **(T)** 02380 862 143 **(E)** secretary@tottonandelingfc.co.uk
Chairman: Andy Tipp **Manager:** Andy Tipp **Prog Ed:** Margaret Fiander
Ground: Totton & Eling Sports Club, Southern Gardens, Totton SO40 8RW **(T)** 02380 862 143
Capacity: **Seats:** Yes **Covered:** Yes **Midweek Matchday:** Tuesday **Clubhouse:** **Shop:**

Colours(change): Red/black/red (All yellow)
Previous Names: BAT Sports > 2007
Previous Leagues: Hampshire.
Records: 2,763 v AFC Wimbledon, FA Vase (game switched to AFC Wimbedon).
Senior Honours: Hampshire Champions 1987-88, 88-89. Wessex Division 1 2008-09.

10 YEAR RECORD

00-01	01-02	02-03	03-04	04-05	05-06	06-07	07-08	08-09	09-10
Wex 13	Wex 19	Wex 11	Wex 15	Wex1 9	Wex1 18	Wex2 5	Wex1 5	Wex1 1	WexP 7

WINCHESTER CITY

Founded: Nickname:

Secretary: Bernadette McCarthy **(T)** 07884 225 611 **(E)** bernie.21@hotmail.com
Chairman: Tony Rees **Manager:** Paul McCarthy **Prog Ed:** Grant Payne
Ground: The City Ground, Hillier Way, Winchester SO23 7SR **(T)** 01962 810 200
Capacity: 2,500 **Seats:** 200 **Covered:** 275 **Midweek Matchday:** Tuesday **Clubhouse:** Yes **Shop:** Yes

Colours(change): Red with white trim/black/black (All white)
Previous Names: None
Previous Leagues: Hampshire 1898-71, 73-03. Southern 71-73, 06-09. Wessex 03-06.
Records: **Att:** 1,818 v Bideford, FA Vase Semi-final. **Goalscorer:** Andy Forbes. **Apps:** Ian Mancey.
Senior Honours: Hants Senior Cup 1932, 2005. Southampton Senior Cup 2000-01.
Hants Lge Champions 02-03. Wessex Lge 03-04, 05-06. F.A. Vase 2004.

10 YEAR RECORD

00-01	01-02	02-03	03-04	04-05	05-06	06-07	07-08	08-09	09-10
Hant1 1	HantP 3	HantP 1	Wex 1	Wex1 2	Wex1 1	SthW 13	SthW 17	SthW 22	WexP 11

DIVISION ONE INS & OUTS
IN: Cowes Sports (R), Pewsey Vale (P - Wiltshire League Premier Division)
OUT: AFC Aldermaston (R - Hampshire Premier League), Farnborough North End (S - Combined Counties League Division One), Fawley (P), Hamble ASSC (P)

AFC PORTCHESTER

Secretary: Colin Brans **(T)** 01329 311560 **(E)** colinbrans@yahoo.co.uk
Chairman: Mark Greenham **Manager:** Glen Bridgman **Prog Ed:** Peter Stiles
Ground: Wicor Recreation Ground Cranleigh Road Portchester Hampshire PO16 9DP **(T)** 07798 734678 **Capacity:**
Colours(change): Tangerine/tangerine & black/tangerine & black (Black & white/white/white)

ADDITIONAL INFORMATION:

AMESBURY TOWN

Founded: 1904

Secretary: Arthur Mundy **(T)** 07528 438103 **(E)** a.mundy094@virginmedia.com
Chairman: Jason Cameron **Manager:** Nick Homer **Prog Ed:** Mark Hilton
Ground: Bonnymead Park Recreation Road Amesbury SP4 7BB **(T)** 01980 623489 **Capacity:** 2,000
Colours(change): All blue (All yellow)

ADDITIONAL INFORMATION:
Previous Name: Amesbury FC. **Previous League:** Hampshire.
Record Att: 625 - 1997.

ANDOVER NEW STREET

Founded: 1895

Secretary: Mick Bugg **(T)** 07917 854794 **(E)** andovernewstreetfc@hotmail.co.uk
Chairman: Graham Waters **Manager:** Vince Rusher **Prog Ed:**
Ground: Foxcotte Park Charlton Andover Hampshire SP11 0HS **(T)** 01264 358358 **Capacity:**
Colours(change): Green & black/black/black (White/blue/white)

ADDITIONAL INFORMATION: Previous League: Hampshire Premier.
Record Att: 240.
Honours: Trophyman Cup 2003-04.

COWES SPORTS
Founded: 1881 Nickname: Yachtsmen

Secretary: Glynn M Skinner **(T)** 07854 889446 **(E)** csfcsecretary@yahoo.com
Chairman: Ian Lee **Manager:** Steve Taylor **Prog Ed:** Peter Jeffery
Ground: Westwood Park Reynolds Close off Park Rd Cowes Isle of Wight PO31 7NT **(T)** 01983 293793 **Capacity:** 1,850
Colours(change): Blue & White stripes/black/blue (Red/white/white)

ADDITIONAL INFORMATION: Club formed after the merger of Cowes and White Sports during 1980s.
Previous League: Hampshire > 1994.
Honours: Hampshire League 1993-94.

DOWNTON
Founded: 1905 Nickname: The Robins

Secretary: Jim Blake **(T)** 07712 180548 **(E)** therobins1@btinternet.com
Chairman: Mark Smith **Manager:** Jeff Softley **Prog Ed:** Pat Drinkwater
Ground: Brian Whitehead Sports Ground Wick Lane Downton Wiltshire SP5 3NF **(T)** 01725 512162 **Capacity:** 1,600
Colours(change): Red/white/red (Yellow/blue/yellow)

ADDITIONAL INFORMATION: Previous League: Hampshire > 1993.
Record Att: 55 v AFC Bournemouth - Friendly.
Honours: Wiltshire Senior Cup 1979-80, 80-81. Wiltshire Junior Cup 1949-50. Wessex League Cup 1995-96.

EAST COWES VICTORIA ATHLETIC

Secretary: Darren Dyer **(T)** 07725 128701 **(E)** ecvics@live.co.uk
Chairman: Jackie Milroy **Manager:** Kenny Adams **Prog Ed:** Darren Dyer
Ground: Beatrice Avenue Whippingham East Cowes Isle of Wight PO32 6PA **(T)** 01983 297165 **Capacity:**
Colours(change): Red & white stripes/black/black (All green)

ADDITIONAL INFORMATION:

FLEET SPURS

Secretary: Paul Hampshire **(T)** 07850 810133 **(E)** secretary@fleetspursfc.co.uk
Chairman: Bryan Sheppard **Manager:** Neil Baker **Prog Ed:** Paul Hampshire
Ground: Kennels Lane Southwood Farnborough Hampshire, GU14 0ST **(T)** **Capacity:**
Colours(change): Blue with red trim/blue/blue (Yellow/black/yellow)

ADDITIONAL INFORMATION:

HORNDEAN
Founded: 1887

Secretary: Michael Austin **(T)** 07983 969644 **(E)** horndeanfc1887@yahoo.co.uk
Chairman: David Sagar **Manager:** Alan Knight **Prog Ed:** Ian Sheppard
Ground: Five Heads Park Five Heads Road Horndean Hampshire PO8 9NZ **(T)** 02392 591 363 **Capacity:** 3,500
Colours(change): All red (All blue)

ADDITIONAL INFORMATION: Previous League: Hampshire 1972-2004.
Record Att: 1,560 v Waterlooville, Victory Cup, April 1971.
Goalscorer: Frank Bryson 348 (including 83 during the 1931-32 season)

HYTHE & DIBDEN

Secretary: Nikki Oakley **(T)** 07769 951982 **(E)** hythedibdenfc@aol.com
Chairman: Robert J Parsons **Manager:** **Prog Ed:** Vannessa Cox
Ground: Ewart Recreation Ground Jones Lane Hythe Southampton SO45 6AA **(T)** 02380 845264 (MD) **Capacity:**
Colours(change): Green/white/green (All blue)

ADDITIONAL INFORMATION:

PETERSFIELD TOWN

Secretary: Mark Nicoll **(T)** 07949 328240 **(E)** m.nicoll1@ntlworld.com
Chairman: Ian Essai **Manager:** Matt Short **Prog Ed:** Dave Bowers
Ground: Love Lane Petersfield Hampshire GU31 4BW **(T)** 01730 233416 **Capacity:**
Colours(change): Red & black stripes/black/black (All blue)

ADDITIONAL INFORMATION:
Previous Name: Petersfield United.
Previous League: Isthmian.

PEWSEY VALE

Secretary: Julie Wootton **(T)** 07789 168303 **(E)** secretary.pewseyvaleafc@hotmail.co.uk
Chairman: Alan Ritchie **Manager:** Adi Holcombe **Prog Ed:** Steve Wootton
Ground: Recreation Ground Kings Corner Ball Road Pewsey **(T)** 01672 562900 **Capacity:**
Colours(change): White/navy/navy (All yellow)

ADDITIONAL INFORMATION:
Previous League: Wiltshire.

RINGWOOD TOWN

Founded: 1879

Secretary: Aubrey Hodder **(T)** 07754 460501 **(E)** ringwoodtownfc@live.co.uk
Chairman: Steve Simpson **Manager:** Wayne Lockie **Prog Ed:** Ian Claxton
Ground: The Canotec Stadium Long Lane Ringwood Hampshire BH24 3BX **(T)** 01425 473448 **Capacity:**
Colours(change): All red (All blue)

ADDITIONAL INFORMATION:

SHAFTESBURY

Secretary: Chris Woods **(T)** 01747 853602 **(E)** jeanette.head1@virgin.net
Chairman: Steve & Pete Bevan **Manager:** Nick Bevan **Prog Ed:** Chris Woods
Ground: Cockrams Coppice Street Shaftesbury Dorset SP7 8PF **(T)** 01747 853990 **Capacity:**
Colours(change): All red (Green & white/green/green)

ADDITIONAL INFORMATION:
Previous League: Dorset Combination

STOCKBRIDGE

Secretary: Robin Smith **(T)** 01980 629781 **(E)** stockbridgefc@hotmail.co.uk
Chairman: Paul Barker **Manager:** Stuart Thompson **Prog Ed:** Mavis Savage
Ground: Stockbridge Recreation Ground High Street Stockbridge SP20 6EU **(T)** 07963 453162 **Capacity:**
Colours(change): All red (Blue & yellow/blue/blue & yellow)

ADDITIONAL INFORMATION:
Previous League: Hampshire.

TADLEY CALLEVA

Secretary: Carli Doyle **(T)** 07789 387166 **(E)** doyle319@btinternet.com
Chairman: G White **Manager:** Craig Effen **Prog Ed:** Steve Blackburn
Ground: Barlows Park Silchester Road Tadley Hampshire RG26 3PX **(T)** **Capacity:**
Colours(change): Yellow & black/black/yellow (Burgundy & blue/burgundy/blue)

ADDITIONAL INFORMATION:

UNITED SERVICES PORTSMOUTH

Secretary: Bob Brady **(T)** 07887 541782 **(E)** bob.brady@ukgateway.net
Chairman: Richard Stephenson Lt. RN **Manager:** Bob Brady **Prog Ed:** Bob Brady
Ground: Victory Stadium HMS Temeraire Burnaby Road Portsmouth PO1 2HB **(T)** 02392 724235 (Club) **Capacity:**
Colours(change): All royal blue (Red & white/red/red)

ADDITIONAL INFORMATION:
Previous Name: Portsmouth Royal Navy.

VERWOOD TOWN

Secretary: Roy Mortimer **(T)** 07801 713462 **(E)** vtfc@roymortimer.plus.com
Chairman: Michael Fry **Manager:** Adie Arnold **Prog Ed:** Dan Eldridge
Ground: Potterne Park Potterne Way Verwood Dorset BH21 6RS **(T)** 01202 814007 **Capacity:**
Colours(change): Red/black/black (Blue & white stripes/blue/yellow)

ADDITIONAL INFORMATION:
Previous League: Hampshire.

WARMINSTER TOWN

Secretary: Ashley Wain **(T)** 07734 959648 **(E)** warminstertownfc@hotmail.com
Chairman: Peter Russell **Manager:** Tom O'Brien **Prog Ed:** Jan Loftus
Ground: 73 Weymouth Street Warminster Wiltshire BA12 9NS **(T)** 01985 217828 **Capacity:**
Colours(change): Red & black stripes/black/red (Blue/dark blue/dark blue)

ADDITIONAL INFORMATION:
Previous League: Western

WHITCHURCH UNITED

Secretary: Paul Driver **(T)** 07921 548222 **(E)** driver999@btinternet.com
Chairman: Gary Shaughnessy **Manager:** Jim Macey **Prog Ed:** John Rutledge
Ground: Longmeadow Winchester Road Whitchurch Hampshire RG28 7RB **(T)** 01256 892493 **Capacity:**
Colours(change): Red & white stripes/black/red (All blue)

ADDITIONAL INFORMATION:

GROUND DIRECTIONS

AFC PORTCHESTER - Wicor Recreation Ground Cranleigh Road Portchester Hampshire PO16 9DP 07798 734678 (M)
Leave the M27 at Junction 11 and follow the signs to Portchester into Portchester Road. Carry on for approx 1 mile at the large roundabout, take the 3rd exit into Cornaway Lane and at the 'T' junction turn right in Cranleigh Road and follow the road to the end. Postcode for Satellite Navigation systems PO16 9DP

AFC TOTTON - Testwood Park Testwood Place Totton Southampton Hampshire SO40 3BE 02380 868981 (Club) 02380 263555 (Office)
Leave the M27 at Junction 3 and join the M271. At the roundabout take the second exit on to the slip road and join the A35 dual carriageway. Shortly after joining the carriageway take the next slip road on to the A36, which takes you under the bypass. Continue until you reach a roundabout; take the 3rd exit into Library Road. Follow this for approx 100 yards then turn left into Testwood Road, just after the Police Station. Testwood Place is the 2nd turning on the right with the ground entrance being 50 yards on the left. Postcode for Satellite Navigation systems SO40 3BE

ALRESFORD TOWN FC - Arlebury Park The Avenue Alresford Hampshire SO24 9EP 01962 735 100
Alresford is situated on the A31 between Winchester and Alton. Arlebury Park is on the main avenue into Alresford opposite Perins School.
Postcode for Satellite Navigation systems SO24 9EP

ALTON TOWN FC - Alton (Bass) Sports Ground Anstey Road Alton Hampshire GU34 2RL
Leave the A31 at the B3004 signposted to Alton. Follow the road round to the left passing Anstey Park on the right, the ground is then immediately on the left – opposite the turning into Anstey Lane. Postcode for Satellite Navigation systems GU34 2RL

AMESBURY TOWN FC - Bonnymead Park Recreation Road Amesbury SP4 7BB 01980 623489
From Salisbury take A345 to Amesbury, turn left just past the bus station and proceed through the one way system, when road splits with Friar Tuck Café and Lloyds Bank on left turn left and follow road over the river bridge and when road bears sharp right turn left into Recreation Road.
From A303 at Countess Roundabout go into Amesbury, straight over traffic lights, at mini-roundabout turn right into one way system and follow directions as above.
Postcode for Satellite Navigation systems SP4 7BB

ANDOVER NEW STREET FC - Foxcotte Park Charlton Andover Hampshire SP11 0HS 01264 358358 Weekends from Midday, Evenings from 1900 hrs
From Basingstoke follow the A303 to Weyhill roundabout. At roundabout turn right and 2nd roundabout turn left on to A342. Approx 1/2 mile turn right into Short Lane, continue into Harroway Lane to the 'T' junction at the top. Turn right into Foxcotte Lane and continue for about 3/4 mile then turn left, this still Foxcotte Lane, to the top some 3/4 mile to the roundabout straight across into Foxcotte Park. Postcode for Satellite Navigation systems SP11 0TA.

BEMERTON HEATH HARLEQUINS FC - The Clubhouse Western Way Bemerton Heath Salisbury Wiltshire SP2 9DT 01722 331925 (Club) 331218 (Office)
Turn off the A36 Salisbury to Bristol road at Skew Bridge (right turn if coming out of Salisbury), 1st left into Pembroke Road for 1/2 mile, 2nd left along Western Way – Ground is 1/4 mile at the end of the road. 40 minutes walk fro Salisbury railway station. Bus service 51 or 52 from the city centre.
Postcode for Satellite Navigation systems SP2 9DP

BLACKFIELD & LANGLEY FC - Gang Warily Community and Recreation Centre Newlands Road Fawley Southampton SO45 1GA 02380 893 603
Leave M27 at Junction 2 signposted A326 to Fawley. Head South along A326 through several roundabouts. Pass the Holbury P/H on your right at roundabout take the right fork signposted Lepe and Fawley.At the 1st set of traffic lights turn left then turn left into the ground, approx 200 yards. There is a sign at the traffic lights indicating Blackfield & Langley FC. Postcode for Satellite Navigation systems SO45 1GA

BOURNEMOUTH FC - Victoria Park Namu Road Winton Bournemouth Dorset BH9 2RA 01202 515 123
From the North and East – A338 from Ringwood. Take the 3rd exit signed A3060 Wimborne, going under the road you've just left. Stay on this road passing Castlepoint Shopping Centre (on your right), then the Broadway Hotel on your right, keep straight ahead passing the Horse & Jockey on your left, keep to the near-side lane. At roundabout take the 1st exit marked A347, pass Redhill Common on your right and the fire station on your left: continue on the A347 turning left at the filter with the pub – The Ensbury Park Hotel – immediately in front of you. 1st left into Victoria Avenue, and then third right into Namu Road, turning right at the end into the lane for the ground entrance.
From the West – A35 from Poole. Take the A3049 Dorset Way passing Tower Park (which is hidden from view) on your right, at the next roundabout take the second exit, and then the first exit at the next roundabout, taking up a position in the outside lane. At the next roundabout (with a pub called the Miller and Carter Steakhouse on your right) take the third exit, Wallisdown Road A3049. Go through the shopping area of Wallisdown across two roundabouts and at the third one take the first exit, you will see the ground on your right as you approach the pelican crossing. Turn right into Victoria Avenue, then third right into Namu Road, turning right at the end into the lane for the ground entrance. Postcode for Satellite Navigation systems BH9 2RA

BRADING TOWN FC - The Peter Henry Ground Vicarage Lane Brading Isle of Wight PO36 0AR 01983 405 217
Off the A3055 Ryde to Sandown Road. On entering Brading from Ryde take the first left off the mini roundabout – Vicarage Lane is adjacent to the main Brading car park. Postcode for Satellite Navigation systems PO36 0AR

BROCKENHURST FC - Grigg Lane Brockenhurst Hampshire SO42 7RE 01590 623544
Leave the M27 at Junction 1 and take the A337 to Lyndhurst. From Lyndhurst take the A337 signposted Brockenhurst, turn right at Careys Manor Hotel into Grigg Lane. Ground situated 200 yards on the right. Postcode for Satellite Navigation systems SO42 7RE

CHRISTCHURCH FC - Hurn Bridge Sports Club Avon Causeway Hurn Christchurc Dorset BH23 6DY 01202 473 792
A338 from Ringwood turn off at sign for Bournemouth International Airport (Hurn) on left. At T junction turn right, continue through traffic lights, at the small roundabout in Hurn turn right away from the Airport, exit signed Sopley and 100 yards on the right is Hurn Bridge Sports Ground. Postcode for Sat. Nav. systems BH23 6DY
COWES SPORTS FC - Westwood Park Reynolds Close off Park Road Cowes Isle of Wight PO31 7NT 01983 293 793
Turn left out of the Cowes pontoon, 1st right up Park Road approx 1/2 mile take the 4th right into Reynolds Close. Postcode for Sat. Nav. systems PO31 7NT
DOWNTON FC - Brian Whitehead Sports Ground Wick Lane Downton Wiltshire SP5 3NF 01725 512 162
The ground is situated 6 miles south of Salisbury on the A338 to Bournemouth. In the village – sign to the Leisure Centre (to west) – this is Wick Lane – football pitch and Club approx 1/4 mile on the left. Postcode for Satellite Navigation systems SP5 3NF
EAST COWES VICTORIA FC - Beatrice Avenue Whippingham East Cowes Isle of Wight PO32 6PA 01983 297 165
From East Cowes ferry terminal follow Well Road into York Avenue until reaching Prince of Wells PH, turn at the next right into Crossways Road then turn left into Beatrice Avenue, from Fishbourne follow signs to East Cowes and Whippingham Church, ground is 200 yards from the church on Beatrice Avenue.
Postcode for Satellite Navigation systems PO32 6PA
FAREHAM TOWN FC - Cams Alders Football Stadium Cams Alders Palmerston Drive Fareham Hampshire PO14 1BJ 07930 853 235 (Club)
Leave the M27 at Junction 11. Follow signs A32 Fareham – Gosport. Pass under the viaduct with Fareham Creek on your left, straight over at the roundabout then fork right – B3385 sign posted Lee-on-Solent. Over the railway bridge, Newgate Lane and turn immediately first right into Palmerston Business Park, follow the road to the ground. Postcode for Satellite Navigation systems PO14 1BJ
FAWLEY AFC - Waterside Sports and Social Club 179-182 Long Lane Holbury Southampton Hampshire SO45 2PA 02380 893750 (Club) 896621 (Office)
Leave the M27 at Junction 2 and follow the A326 to Fawley/Beaulieu. Head south for approx 7 miles. The Club is situated on the right hand side 2/3 mile after crossing the Hardley roundabout. The Club is positioned directly behind the service road on the right hand side. Postcode for Satellite Navigation systems SO45 2PA
FLEET SPURS FC - Kennels Lane Southwood Farnborough Hampshire, GU14 0ST
From the M3 Junction 4A take the A327 towards Farnborough/Cove. Left at the roundabout, over the railway line, left at the next roundabout Kennels Lane is on the right opposite the Nokia building, entrance is 100 yards on the left. Postcode for Satellite Navigation systems GU14 0ST
GOSPORT BOROUGH FC - Privett Park Privett Road Gosport Hampshire PO12 3SX 02392 583 986 (Club) 02392 501 042 (Office)
Leave the M27 at Junction 11, take the A32 Fareham to Gosport Road, at the Brockhurst roundabout (after 3 miles) take the 3rd exit into Military Road past HMS Sultan, left into Privett Road at the next roundabout. Ground is 300 yards on the left. Postcode for Satellite Navigation systems PO12 3SX
HAMBLE ASSC FC - Folland Park Kings Avenue Hamble-Le-Rice Southampton Hampshire SO31 4NF 02380 452 173
Leave the M27 at Junction 8 and take the turning for Southampton East At the Windhover roundabout take the exit for Hamble (B3397) Hamble Lane, proceed for 3 miles. Upon entering Hamble the ground is on the right via Kings Avenue, opposite the Harrier P/H. Postcode for Satellite Navigation systems SO31 4NF
HAMWORTHY UNITED FC - The County Ground Blandford Close Hamworthy Poole Dorset BH15 4BF 01202 674 974
From M27 to Cadnam – follow A31 to Ringwood – A347/A348 Ferndown - Bearcross – follow on this road until you pass the Mountbatten Arms on your left – turn right at next roundabout onto the A3049 and follow the signs to Dorchester and Poole. Continue on this dual carriageway over the flyover to the next roundabout – straight across and take the 2nd exit left off the dual carriageway to Upton / Hamworthy – go straight across 2 mini roundabouts and continue to Hamworthy passing the Co-op store on your left – then turn left at the 2nd set of traffic lights into Blandford Close. Postcode for Satellite Navigation systems BH15 4BF
HAYLING UNITED FC - College Ground The Hayling College Church Road Hayling Island,Hampshire PO11 0NU
From A27 take the Hayling Island exit, after crossing the Langstone Bridge continue past the Yew Tree P/H. After a mile turn left at the small roundabout into Church Road and after 1/2 mile turn left into Hayling College grounds.
NB All parking must be in front car park. Coaches to be parked in the lay-by outside the college. Postcode for Satellite Navigation systems PO11 0NU
HORNDEAN FC - Five Heads Park Five Heads Road Horndean Hampshire PO8 9NZ 02392 591 363
Leave A3(M) at Junction 2 and follow signs to Cowplain. Take the slip road passing Morrisons store on the right crossing over the mini roundabout then continue to the set of traffic lights ensuring you are in the right hand lane signed Horndean. Turn right at these traffic lights and continue on for approximately 400 yards until you reach the Colonial Bar on your left, next junction on your left after the Colonial Bar is Five Heads Road, turn left into Five Heads Road and the ground is approx 1/4 mile along this road. Postcode for Satellite Navigation systems PO8 9NZ
HYTHE & DIBDEN FC - Ewart Recreation Ground Jones Lane Hythe Southampton SO45 6AA 02380 845264 (Match days only) 07769 951982 (B)
Travel along the A326 then at the Dibden roundabout take the first left into Southampton Road. Continue for approx. 1 mile and then turn left into Jones Lane just before the Shell Filling Station and the ground is 200 yards on your left. Car parking is available in the Dibden Parish Hall car park at the bottom end of the ground.
Postcode for Satellite Navigation systems SO45 6AA
LAVERSTOCK & FORD FC - The Dell Church Road Laverstock Salisbury Wiltshire SP1 1QX 01722 327 401
From Southampton – At the end of the carriageway from Southampton (A36) turn right at traffic lights for the Park & Ride by the Tesco store. Turn left at the traffic lights over the narrow bridge then take the next turning into Manor Farm Road. Take the next turning right into Laverstock Road, (do not turn left under the railway bridge). Keep left into Laverstock village, past the Church and the Club is situated on the left hand side directly opposite the Chinese takeaway and shop.
From Bournemouth – Follow the A36 to Southampton past Salisbury College and straight across the Tesco roundabout take left at traffic lights into the Park & Ride (take the corner slowly, the road goes back on itself) then follow directions as above. Postcode for Satellite Navigation systems SP1 1QX
LYMINGTON TOWN FC - The Sports Ground Southampton Road Lymington Hampshire SO41 9ZG 01590 671 305 (Club)
From the North & East – Leave the M27 at Junction 1 (Cadnam/New Forest) and proceed via Lyndhurst then Brockenhurst on the A337. On the outskirts of Lymington proceed through main set of traffic lights with Royal Quarter Housing Development and the Police Station on your right hand side. Continue for just another 250 metres and turn left immediately into St Thomas's Park with he ground in front of you.
Alternatively, turn left at the traffic lights into Avenue Road then first right, Oberland Court, with the Lymington Bowling Club facing you.
If travelling from the direction of Christchurch & New Milton using the A337 pass the White Hart P/H on the outskirts of Pennington and proceed down and up Stanford Hill. Passing the Waitrose Supermarket on your left hand side, the ground is situated immediately on your right hand side sign posted St Thomas Park.
Postcode for Satellite Navigation systems SO41 9ZG
MONEYFIELDS FC - Moneyfields Sports Ground Moneyfield Avenue Copnor Portsmouth Hampshire PO3 6LA 02392 665 260 (Club) 07766 250 812 (M)
Leave the A27 from the West and East at the Southsea turn off (A2030). Head down the Eastern Road and turn right into Tangiers Road at the fourth set of traffic lights – continue along this road until you pass the school and shops on your left and take the next right into Folkestone Road carrying on through to Martins Road and the Moneyfields Sports & Social Club is directly in front of you. Postcode for Satellite Navigation systems PO3 6LA
NEW MILTON TOWN FC - Fawcett Fields Christchurch Road New Milton Hampshire BH25 6QB 01425 628 191
Leave the M27 at Junction 2 and follow the signs to Lyndhurst. Carry on this road over four roundabouts and take the next slip road.At the traffic lights turn right to Lyndhurst. Go around the one way system and follow the signs to Christchurch (A35). After 10 miles at the Cat and Fiddle Public House turn left and continue towards the Chewton Glen Hotel. First exit at roundabout A337 to New Milton.The ground is one mile on the left. Postcode for Sat. Nav. systems BH25 6QB
NEWPORT (IOW) FC LTD. - St Georges Park St Georges Way Newport Isle of Wight PO30 2QH 01983 525 027 (Club)
From the Fishbourne Car Ferry Terminal take the A3054 towards Newport. At the large roundabout in the town centre take the A3020 towards Sandown, under the footbridge then 1st exit off the next roundabout. The ground is 200 yards on the left. Postcode for Satellite Navigation systems PO30 2QH

PETERSFIELD TOWN FC - Love Lane Petersfield Hampshire GU31 4BW 01730 233 416

Off circulatory one-way system in the town centre. Approx 10 minutes walk from Petersfield train station. Postcode for Satellite Navigation systems GU31 4BW

PEWSEY VALE FC - Recreation Ground Kings Corner Ball Road Pewsey 01672 562 900

From Pewsey's King Alfred statue, take the B3087 Burbage Road for 100 yards and then turn right into the Co-op car park, park in top right hand corner next to the bowls and tennis club and then walk through to the ground. Postcode for Satellite Navigation systems SN9 5BS

POOLE TOWN FC LTD - Tatnam Ground Oakdale School School Lane off Palmer Road/Fleets Lane Poole Dorset BH15 3JR 07771 604289 (Match days only) Office 01202 674425 (Chris Reeves)

M27 from Southampton follow the A31 through Ringwood, continue on the A31 towards Poole/Dorchester/Weymouth. At the Merley roundabout turn left towards Poole – A349 then right at the next roundabout and follow the A349 to Poole. At the Fleetsbridge flyover/roundabout (Tesco on the right) go straight over into Fleet Lane (B&Q/Staples either side of Fleet Lane). Eventually on the right hand side you will see Poole motorcycles, turn left into the road opposite – Palmer Road then take the first right – School Lane and this will take you into the car park. Ground is on the right. *DO NOT park in Well Lane which is off Tatnam Road*
Postcode for Satellite Navigation systems BH15 3JR

RINGWOOD TOWN FC - The Canotec Stadium Long Lane Ringwood Hampshire BH24 3BX 01425 473 448

Travel to Ringwood via the A31 (M27). From Ringwood town centre travel 1 mile on the B3347 towards Christchurch. At the Texaco petrol station turn into Moortown Lane and after 200 yards turn right into Long Lane. The ground is situated 250 yards on your left. Postcode for Satellite Navigation systems BH24 3BX

ROMSEY TOWN FC - The Bypass Ground South Front Romsey Hampshire SO51 8GJ

The ground is situated on the south of the town on the A27/A3090 roundabout (Romsey by pass), adjacent to the Romsey Rapids and Broadlands Estate.
Postcode for Satellite Navigation systems SO51 8GJ

SHAFTESBURY FC - Cockrams Coppice Street Shaftesbury Dorset SP7 8PF - 01747 853 990

From the North (A350) at the Ivy Cross roundabout take 2nd exit (Salisbury/Blandford) after 300 yards turn right into Coppice Street and after 200 yards turn right into car park and ground is on the right. From East (A30) at Royal Chase roundabout take 3rd exit (Sherborne/Yeovil) and take 3rd left into Coppice Street and follow as above. Parking is not permitted in the Tesco Car Park. Postcode for Satellite Navigation systems SP7 8PF

SHOLING FC - VTFC Sports Ground Portsmouth Road Southampton SO19 9PW 02380 403 829

Leave the M27 at junction 8 and follow the signs to Hamble. As you drive up the dual carriageway, remain in the left hand lane. You come to the Windhover roundabout, take the 2nd exit getting into the lane marked "Hamble", take the right hand lane and go straight over at the small roundabout. After 200 yards bear right across the 2nd small roundabout (2nd exit). After 150 yards take the right hand lane and turn right into Portsmouth Road, sign posted Woolston. Continue for approx 1/2 mile until you see a large lay by on the left. The entrance to the VT Sports Ground is signposted opposite on your right next to the bus stop.
Postcode for Satellite Navigation systems SO19 9PW

STOCKBRIDGE FC - Stockbridge Recreation Ground High Street Stockbridge SP20 6EU 07963 453 162 (M)

From Stockbridge High Street turn right at BT Substation into ground. Postcode for Satellite Navigation systems SP20 6EU

TADLEY CALLEVA FC - Barlows Park Silchester Road Tadley Hampshire RG26 3PX

From M3 Basingstoke Junction 6 take the A340 to Tadley, travel through Tadley and at the main traffic lights turn right into Silchester Road, proceed for 0.5 mile then turn left into the car park. Postcode for Satellite Navigation systems RG26 3PX

TOTTON & ELING FC - Totton & Eling Sports Club Southern Gardens Southampton SO40 8RW 02380 862 143

Enter Totton Central via the M271 and follow the signs for Ringwood & Cadnam. At the 1st roundabout take the 1st exit – Ringwood Road, 2nd roundabout, adjacent to Asda take the 2nd exit. Continue for approx 1/4 mile and enter Southern Gardens opposite Abbotswood School. Postcode for Sat. Nav. systems SO40 8RW

UNITED SERVICES PORTSMOUTH FC - Victory Stadium HMS Temeraire Burnaby Road Portsmouth Hampshire PO1 2HB 02392 724235 (Clubhouse) 02392 725315 (Office)

Leave the M27 at Junction 12 and join the M275 to Portsmouth. Follow the signs to Gunwharf, turn right at the traffic lights into Park Road then left at the next set of lights into Burnaby Road and the entrance is at the end of this road on the right.via HMS Temeraire.

NB Car parking in HMS Temeraire is for Senior Club and Match Officials only on the production of a current Sydenhams League (Wessex) pass. Free car parking for players and supporters is at the Portsmouth University Nuffield car park opposite the Registry Public House – follow Anglesea Road and signs for Southsea/Ferry Terminals, go under railway bridge past lights, keeping US Rogby Stadium on your right into Hampshire Terrace and keeping right, LOOP back into Anglesey Road, go through pedestrian lights and then immediately left into the car park. From car park turn right past pedestrian lights into Cambridge Road, then right into Burnaby Road. Postcode for Satellite Navigation systems PO1 2HB

VERWOOD TOWN FC - POTTERNE PARK POTTERNE WAY VERWOOD DORSET BH21 6RS 01202 814 007

Turn off the A31 at Verwood/Matchams junctions just West of Ringwood Town centre exit (immediately after garage if coming from the East) to join the B3081. Follow the B3081 through the forest for approximately 4 miles coming into Verwood itself. At the second set of traffic lights turn left into Black Hill. At the roundabout take the 1st exit left into Newtown Road. At the end of Newtown Road turn left and then 1st left into Potterne Way. Note: Along Black Hill on the left you will pass Bradfords Building Merchants and the entrance to the Verwood Sports & Social Club where post match refreshments are made available.
Postcode for Satellite Navigation systems BH21 6RS

WARMINSTER TOWN FC - 73 Weymouth Street Warminster Wiltshire BA12 9NS 01985 217 828

A36 from Salisbury, head for town centre, turn left at traffic lights in the town centre signposted A350 Shaftesbury. Club is situated approx.
400 yards on left hand side at top of Weymouth Street. Postcode for Satellite Navigation systems BA12 9HS

WHITCHURCH UNITED FC - Longmeadow Winchester Road Whitchurch Hampshire RG28 7RB 01256 892 493

From the South – take the A34 (North), 2 miles north of Bullington Cross take the Whitchurch exit. Head for Whitchurch Town Centre. The ground is 500 yards on your right. Postcode for Satellite Navigation systems RG28 7RB

WINCHESTER CITY FC - The City Ground Hillier Way Abbotts Barton Winchester Hampshire SO23 7SR 01962 810 200

From Junction 9 on the M3 take the A33/A34 for one mile then follow the A33 for a further mile. Take the first left into Kings Worthy and follow the road for about three miles. When you enter the 30 mph zone take the second left first right then left into Hillier Way. Ground is on the right.
Postcode for Satellite Navigation systems SO23 7SR

WEST MIDLANDS (REGIONAL) LEAGUE

full-time.thefa.com/gen/Index.do?league=3244788

Sponsored by:

No sponsor

Founded: 1889

Recent champions:

2005: Tipton Town

2006: Market Drayton Town

2007: Shifnal Town

2008: Bridgnorth Town

2009: AFC Wulfrunians

Premier Division		P	W	D	L	F	A	Pts
Ellesmere Rangers		40	30	5	5	98	29	95
Bloxwich United		40	30	4	6	128	46	94
AFC Wulfrunians		40	28	4	8	83	31	88
Bustleholme		40	26	7	7	93	42	85
Dudley Town		40	24	6	10	86	52	78
Wellington		40	21	8	11	104	73	71
Tividale		40	22	5	13	76	61	71
Oldbury Athletic		40	23	1	16	89	67	70
Ledbury Town		40	18	8	14	78	77	62
Ludlow Town		40	19	4	17	92	74	61
Wednesfield		40	16	7	17	85	77	55
Bewdley Town		40	16	5	19	78	82	53
Darlaston Town		40	13	3	24	57	82	42
Bromyard Town		40	11	5	24	54	108	38
Dudley Sports		40	10	7	23	38	87	37
Wolverhampton Cas.	*-1*	40	9	10	21	66	98	36
Gornal Athletic		40	9	8	23	47	81	35
Goodrich		40	9	8	23	50	89	35
Lye Town		40	9	5	26	49	106	32
Heath Town Rangers	*-3*	40	10	4	26	53	98	31
Shawbury United		40	8	4	28	47	91	28

PREMIER DIVISION CUP

FIRST ROUND

AFC Wulfrunians 3 Ludlow Town 1 *aet*
Bloxwich United 0 **Dudley Town** 1
Bromyard Town 2 Goodrich 1 *aet*
Dudley Sports 1 **Wolverhampton Casuals** 3
Gornal Athletic 3 Lye Town 1

SECOND ROUND

AFC Wulfrunians 1 Darlaston Town 0
Bewdley Town 6 Oldbury Athletic 0
Bustleholme 3 Bromyard Town 1
Ellesmere Rangers 2 Tividale 2 *aet* (8-7p)
Gornal Athletic 3 Wolverhampton Casuals 2
Ledbury Town 7 Heath Town Rangers 0
Shawbury United 2 Wellington 1
Wednesfield 3 **Dudley Town** 4

QUARTER-FINALS

Bustleholme 2 Ellesmere Rangers 2 *aet* (4-3p)
Dudley Town 0 **AFC Wulfrunians** 2
Ledbury Town 6 Bewdley Town 1
Shawbury Utd 3 **Gornal Athletic** 1 *(Shawbury expelled)*

SEMI-FINALS

(played over two legs)
AFC Wulfs 3 Ledbury 1, Ledbury 1 **AFC Wulfrunians** 7
Gornal 2 Bustleholme 0, **Bustleholme** 5 Gornal Athletic 2

FINAL *(May 13th at Wolverhampton Casuals)*
AFC Wulfrunians 0 **Bustleholme** 1

	AFC Wulfs	Bewdley	Bloxwich	Bromyard	Bus'holme	Darlaston	Dudley S.	Dudley T.	Ellesmere	Goodrich	Gornal A.	Heath Town	Ledbury T.	Ludlow T.	Lye Town	Oldbury A.	Shawbury	Tividale	Wednesf'd	Wellington	W'ton Cas.
AFC Wulfrunians		4-0	1-0	3-0	4-1	2-1	2-0	1-2	0-0	2-0	3-0	2-1	2-0	3-0	4-0	4-0	1-0	1-3	5-1	1-0	1-1
Bewdley Town	0-1		1-1	5-0	1-4	3-0	5-0	3-3	2-3	2-1	1-2	1-0	1-2	1-0	4-2	3-4	3-1	3-3	1-3	6-3	2-3
Bloxwich United	2-1	5-0	**P**	3-2	1-0	3-1	1-0	2-0	3-0	2-0	2-1	4-1	1-3	7-2	7-1	2-4	3-0	4-3	7-1	3-2	6-1
Bromyard Town	1-4	2-1	0-7	**R**	1-4	3-2	1-1	0-4	0-4	3-1	1-0	5-2	3-0	2-5	1-2	1-2	2-1	0-0	2-3	0-6	2-2
Bustleholme	1-1	3-0	0-3	2-0	**E**	4-0	1-0	2-2	1-0	2-1	1-0	2-1	2-1	1-1	1-1	4-0	3-1	3-0	4-3	6-1	4-1
Darlaston Town	0-2	4-2	0-4	4-0	0-2	**M**	0-0	2-4	0-3	1-0	1-1	2-3	3-2	1-2	3-0	0-4	3-1	2-1	2-1	3-1	2-2
Dudley Sports	0-1	0-1	2-1	2-1	1-3	1-0	**I**	2-0	0-0	0-7	1-1	1-0	1-1	0-4	0-4	0-3	2-0	0-4	2-4	0-2	2-0
Dudley Town	2-1	1-0	4-1	3-1	1-1	3-2	4-1	**E**	2-2	5-0	1-1	2-1	3-0	2-0	3-0	1-3	3-2	2-4	2-1	2-5	2-0
Ellesmere Rangers	2-1	4-1	3-2	1-0	0-1	1-0	8-0	1-3	**R**	0-1	4-1	6-0	8-1	1-0	4-1	1-0	3-0	2-0	1-0	4-0	3-1
Goodrich	0-2	3-3	0-2	0-1	0-9	3-1	5-0	0-2	0-3		0-2	3-3	0-1	2-4	2-0	0-4	2-2	3-2	3-0	1-1	0-4
Gornal Athletic	1-2	1-2	1-5	2-2	2-1	2-4	2-1	0-2	1-1	3-0		1-3	3-4	0-5	2-4	1-6	3-0	0-3	1-2	0-3	0-0
Heath Town Rangers	0-2	2-2	1-4	0-3	0-2	0-3	2-4	1-0	0-2	3-3	1-5	**D**	3-5	3-4	5-0	1-4	3-1	1-0	1-2	0-5	2-2
Ledbury Town	2-1	1-2	0-0	3-3	2-6	3-1	4-2	3-1	1-1	2-2	3-0	1-2	**I**	3-1	2-0	3-4	4-0	2-2	2-5	1-2	4-1
Ludlow Town	0-2	1-2	3-3	6-2	0-2	7-2	0-3	2-1	1-2	0-1	1-0	1-2	3-1	**V**	3-0	1-2	0-1	5-1	4-3	5-2	2-2
Lye Town	2-3	2-0	0-5	3-2	1-3	2-1	1-1	1-3	1-3	1-1	3-1	1-3	1-2	1-2	**I**	3-2	1-1	0-4	1-6	0-4	0-2
Oldbury Athletic	2-4	2-1	0-3	3-1	2-0	3-1	3-2	0-1	2-3	2-3	3-1	0-1	1-2	2-1	3-1	**S**	0-2	1-3	1-2	1-2	6-0
Shawbury United	0-4	2-4	0-5	2-3	1-1	2-0	2-1	0-2	0-1	1-0	0-1	4-0	2-3	2-6	3-0	0-2	**I**	1-3	0-2	3-4	2-1
Tividale	3-1	0-2	2-3	3-0	2-1	2-1	2-0	3-1	0-4	1-1	0-1	1-0	2-0	0-2	1-0	1-3	3-2	**O**	3-2	1-0	2-1
Wednesfield	1-1	3-1	2-2	1-2	1-2	0-1	1-2	1-1	0-1	3-0	1-1	3-0	0-0	5-5	5-3	4-0	3-2	2-3	**N**	3-5	3-0
Wellington	1-0	2-3	2-4	5-0	3-1	3-1	4-1	2-0	2-3	5-0	2-2	1-0	1-1	4-2	3-3	2-2	1-1	2-2	3-2		2-2
Wolverhampton Casuals	1-3	4-3	1-5	6-1	2-2	0-2	2-2	0-6	0-5	5-1	2-0	4-1	1-3	0-1	1-2	1-3	5-2	2-3	0-0	3-6	

Division One	P	W	D	L	F	A	Pts
Wellington Amateurs	32	25	4	3	110	22	79
Stafford Town	32	25	4	3	121	43	79
Hanwood United	32	19	6	7	85	46	63
Bilbrook	32	19	4	9	70	47	61
Warley Development	32	17	3	12	62	52	54
Blackheath Town	32	15	6	11	75	60	51
Warstones Wdrs	32	15	3	14	70	79	48
Trysull	32	12	6	14	59	60	42
AFC Wombourne Utd	32	12	6	14	53	55	42
Bridgnorth Town Res.	32	13	3	16	64	76	42
Wolverhampton Utd	32	13	3	16	58	79	42
Bilston Town	32	10	8	14	55	65	38
Penn Croft	32	10	6	16	71	83	36
Shenstone Pathfinder	32	11	3	18	44	80	36
Riverway	32	7	3	22	53	93	24
Dudley United	32	7	3	22	41	94	24
Sporting Khalsa	32	4	5	23	43	100	17

Malvern Town Res. - record expunged

DIVISION ONE CUP

FIRST ROUND

Hanwood United 3 Bridgnorth Res. 2 *(at Bridgnorth)*
Malvern Town Res. v **Bilston Town** (w/o)

SECOND ROUND

AFC Wombourne United 2 Shenstone Pathfinder 0
Bilbrook 3 Hanwood 2, Dudley Utd 1 **Stafford Town** 6
Riverway 3 Penn Croft 2
Sporting Khalsa 3 Warley Development 2
Trysull 0 **Bilston Town** 3
Warstones Wanderers 1 **Wellington Amateurs** 2
Wolverhampton United 3 **Blackheath Town** 3 *aet* (1-3p)

QUARTER-FINALS

Bilbrook 1 **Stafford Town** 5, Bilston 0 **Blackheath T.** 1
Riverway 2 **AFC Wombourne United** 3
Sporting Khalsa 0 **Wellington Amateurs** 2

SEMI-FINALS

(played over two legs)
Blackheath Town 2 AFC Wombourne United 0,
AFC Wombourne United 1 **Blackheath Town** 3
Wellington Amateurs 2 Stafford Town 2, Stafford Town 3
Wellington Amateurs 3 *aet* (1-4p)

FINAL *(May 12th at AFC Wulfrunians)*

Wellington Amateurs 1 **Blackheath Town** 2

	AFC Womb'ne	Bilbrook	Bilston Town	Blackheath T.	Bridgn'th Res.	Dudley United	Hanwood Utd	Malvern T. Res.	Penn Croft	Riverway	Shenstone P.	Sporting Khalsa	Stafford Town	Trysull	Warley Devel.	Warstones W.	Wellington Ams	W'pton United
AFC Wombourne United		2-1	0-1	1-1	1-3	2-1	0-4	n/a	3-1	3-0	3-1	3-1	0-2	0-2	2-3	2-0	0-4	1-0
Bilbrook	0-0		3-1	2-2	5-0	2-2	1-0	n/a	2-1	3-2	4-0	4-0	0-4	3-0	2-0	2-4	1-0	6-2
Bilston Town	2-2	3-1		1-2	3-3	3-1	2-1	n/a	1-4	1-2	6-2	1-1	1-2	1-1	1-4	3-0	2-2	1-2
Blackheath Town	1-2	3-4	1-1	***D***	5-3	3-2	2-2	n/a	3-1	7-2	3-2	2-1	2-2	0-3	1-2	2-3	0-3	1-2
Bridgnorth Town Res.	1-3	0-3	1-2	2-0	***I***	1-0	2-5	n/a	2-2	3-2	6-0	2-1	1-4	3-1	1-3	6-3	1-3	5-1
Dudley United	0-6	1-2	0-1	0-5	1-2	***V***	1-0	n/a	4-1	1-1	1-3	3-2	1-6	3-1	0-3	1-1	0-10	2-0
Hanwood United	2-0	1-4	4-0	1-1	1-2	3-1	***I***	n/a	2-1	4-2	3-1	3-3	2-1	3-1	4-1	3-0	1-1	4-2
Malvern Town Res.	n/a	1-5	n/a	1-2	n/a	4-6	n/a	***S***	n/a	n/a	2-3	n/a	n/a	n/a	1-3	n/a	n/a	n/a
Penn Croft	4-2	0-2	2-2	1-4	1-1	5-1	2-2	n/a	***I***	4-1	3-1	1-2	2-2	4-3	2-3	3-3	0-5	2-4
Riverway	3-6	3-1	2-3	0-2	2-3	8-0	1-3	3-0	1-2	***O***	3-1	6-1	0-4	1-1	0-1	1-3	0-5	2-2
Shenstone Pathfinder	2-1	2-0	2-2	2-5	3-1	3-1	3-0	0-0	3-2	1-0	***N***	4-1	0-6	1-3	0-0	2-1	0-4	0-1
Sporting Khalsa	3-3	1-4	0-2	0-5	2-0	4-1	1-6	n/a	2-4	1-3	1-2		2-6	1-3	1-2	0-4	0-6	1-3
Stafford Town	2-1	6-1	4-1	2-3	5-0	4-0	4-2	n/a	0-6	7-0	7-0	6-3	***O***	1-0	3-0	5-4	3-1	7-1
Trysull	2-1	0-1	3-2	3-1	4-0	2-3	3-3	6-0	6-2	3-1	1-1	1-1	2-2	***N***	0-2	2-4	1-2	3-2
Warley Development	3-0	2-2	4-1	1-3	0-5	3-2	1-2	n/a	3-4	2-0	2-0	1-1	2-4	4-1	***E***	6-1	0-1	1-4
Warstones Wanderers	3-1	1-2	3-1	2-0	5-3	1-5	2-8	2-1	4-2	3-0	3-0	1-4	1-4	2-0	1-0		0-3	1-1
Wellington Amateurs	0-0	2-1	3-2	6-1	2-0	3-1	0-3	7-0	6-1	10-0	3-0	6-0	2-2	4-1	2-0	4-1		4-0
Wolverhampton United	2-2	2-1	3-1	1-4	3-1	3-1	0-3	n/a	3-1	2-4	3-2	2-1	2-4	1-2	1-3	3-5	0-3	

WEST MIDLANDS (REGIONAL) LEAGUE DIVISION ONE CONSTITUTION 2010-11

AFC WOMBOURNE UNITED . . . . . Castlecroft Stadium, Castlecroft Lane, Wolverhampton WV3 8NA. . . . . None
BILSTON TOWN . . . . Queen Street, Bilston, Wolverhampton WV14 7EX 01902 491498
BLACK COUNTRY RANGERS . . Tividale FC, The Beeches, Packwood Road, Tividale, Oldbury B69 1UL 01384 211743
BLACKHEATH TOWN . . . . York Road Sports & Social, York Road, Oldbury, Rowley Regis B65 0RR 0121 559 5564
BRIDGNORTH TOWN RES. . . . . Crown Meadow, Innage Lane, Bridgnorth WV16 4HS 01746 762747
HANWOOD UNITED . . . . Hanwood Recreation Ground, Hanwood, Shrewsbury SY5 8JN . . . . None
PENN CROFT . . . . Aldersley Leisure Village, Aldersley Road, Wolverhampton WV6 9NW. 01902 556200
SHENSTONE PATHFINDER . . Shenstone PF (Pavilion Club), Birmingham Road, Shenstone WS14 0LR 01543 481658
SPORTING KHALSA . . . . Willenhall Town FC, Gipsy Lane, Willenhall, Wolverhampton WS13 2HA. 01922 636586
STONE OLD ALLEYNIANS. . . . . Motiva Park, Yarnfield Road, Yarnfield, Stone ST15 0NF 01785 761891
TRYSULL . . . . Wolverhampton Casuals FC, Brinsford Lane, Coven Heath, Wolverhampton WV10 7PR 01902 783214
WARSTONES WANDERERS . . Bloxwich United FC, Grosvenor Park, Somerfield Rd, Bloxwich WS3 2EJ. None
WELLINGTON AMATEURS. . . . . School Grove, Oakengates, Telford TF2 6BQ. . . . . None
WEM TOWN. . . . . Butler Sports Centre, Bowens Field, Wem SY4 5AW. 01939 233287
WOLVERHAMPTON UNITED . Prestwood Road Sports Stadium, Wednesfield, Wolverhampton WV11 1HL. 01902 730881
WYRLEY . . . . Brereton Social FC, Red Lion Ground, Armitage Lane, Brereton, Rugeley WS15 1ED. 01889 585526

IN: Black Country Rangers (P), Stone Old Alleynians (P), Wem Town (P), Wyrley (formerly Wyrley Juniors) (P)
OUT: Bilbrook (W), Dudley United (W), Malvern Town Res. (WS - Worcester & District League), Riverway (R), Stafford Town (P), Warley Development (W)

Division Two	P	W	D	L	F	A	Pts
Black Country Rangers	22	18	2	2	89	28	56
Wem Town	22	17	1	4	95	27	52
Wyrley Juniors	22	15	3	4	58	35	48
Stone Old Alleynians	22	11	5	6	57	38	38
Penkridge Town	22	10	4	8	48	34	34
Malvern Rangers	22	10	2	10	55	47	32
Tenbury United	22	10	1	11	44	72	31
Bentley	22	7	2	13	53	70	23
Heath Town Rangers Res.	22	7	1	14	43	83	22
Wrens Nest	22	6	1	15	38	76	19
Mahal	22	4	4	14	34	68	16
Ettingshall Park Farm	22	3	2	17	25	61	11

Darlaston Town Reserves, Pensnett Panthers - records expunged

DIVISION TWO CUP

FIRST ROUND

Darlaston Town Res. 3 Ettingshall Park Farm 2 *aet*
Heath Town Rangers Res. 0 **Bentley** 4
Penkridge 5 Malvern Rangers 3, Tenbury 0 **Wem** 1
Wrens Nest 0 **Stone OA** 5, **Wyrley** (w/o) v Pensnett

QUARTER-FINALS

Mahal 3 **Black Co. Rgrs** 4, **Penkridge** 4 Bentley 2
Wem 4 Stone OA 1, **Wyrley** (w/o) v Darlaston Res.

SEMI-FINALS

(played over two legs)
Wem Town 2 Black Country Rangers 1,
Black Country Rangers 3 Wem Town 1 *aet*
Wyrley Juniors 2 Penkridge Town 2,
Penkridge Town 0 **Wyrley Juniors** 1

FINAL *(May 11th at Gornal Athletic)*
Black Country Rangers 3 Wyrley Juniors 0

	Ben	Bla	Dar	Ett	Hea	Mah	Mal	Pnk	PP	Sto	Ten	WT	WN	WJ
Bentley		3-4	5-2	1-4	6-4	3-0	1-0	4-0	n/a	3-7	1-4	0-9	6-3	2-3
Black Country Rangers	3-1	***D***	6-3	5-0	6-1	1-1	5-0	4-1	n/a	3-2	3-1	5-3	6-1	1-2
Darlaston Town Res.	n/a	n/a	***I***	n/a	n/a	1-5	n/a	1-2	1-5	2-9	6-4	2-3	0-8	1-5
Ettingshall Park Farm	3-3	1-7	1-2	***V***	2-1	4-3	1-2	0-0	1-0	2-3	0-3	1-4	1-2	1-4
Heath Town Rangers Res.	3-1	0-3	3-1	2-0	***I***	3-1	1-5	3-3	n/a	0-6	2-3	1-6	5-2	2-6
Mahal	0-4	0-9	5-0	4-2	3-4	***S***	3-6	1-0	n/a	2-0	2-4	2-4	1-6	1-1
Malvern Rangers	4-2	1-2	6-1	5-2	1-2	2-2	***I***	4-2	1-5	1-3	3-0	2-4	4-2	2-4
Penkridge Town	5-1	1-2	n/a	1-0	6-1	3-0	2-1	***O***	4-3	2-0	5-2	1-3	2-1	1-1
Pensnett Panthers	1-6	n/a	2-1	1-0	1-1	3-2	n/a	n/a	***N***	3-0	n/a	4-3	3-3	2-3
Stone Old Alleynians	4-2	4-4	8-3	1-0	8-1	2-2	2-0	0-0	6-3		1-0	1-5	4-1	0-0
Tenbury United	2-1	1-9	n/a	4-0	3-1	3-1	3-3	1-6	2-3	3-2	***T***	1-6	1-5	1-6
Wem Town	2-2	1-3	8-2	3-0	10-0	0-1	2-1	2-1	2-1	2-3	11-0	***W***	3-0	4-1
Wrens Nest	1-2	1-3	n/a	1-0	0-5	3-2	1-6	0-6	2-3	3-3	2-3	0-7	***O***	3-2
Wyrley Juniors	5-4	2-1	2-1	2-1	2-1	4-2	1-2	3-0	n/a	2-1	2-1	1-4	4-0	

WEST MIDLANDS (REGIONAL) LEAGUE DIVISION TWO CONSTITUTION 2010-11

AFC SMETHWICK. . . . . Holly Lane Sports & Social Club, Holly Lane, Erdington, Birmingham B24 9LH 0121 373 0979
BILSTON TOWN RES. . . . . Queen Street, Bilston, Wolverhampton WV14 7EX 01902 491498
ETTINGSHALL PARK FARM. . . . . Stafford Road, Fordhouses, Wolverhampton WV10 7EJ . . . . None
HEATH TOWN RANGERS RES. . . . Pendeford Lane, off Wobaston Road, Wolverhampton WV9 5HQ. . . . . None
LEOMINSTER TOWN . . . . Bridge Street Park, Bridge Street, Leominster HR6 8EA. 01568 611172
MAHAL. . . . . Hadley Stadium, Wilson Road, Smethwick, Warley B68 9JW 0121 434 4848
MALVERN RANGERS. . . . . Victoria Playing Fields, Pickersleigh Road, Malvern WR14 2QN . . . . None
PENKRIDGE TOWN . . . . Monkton Recreation Centre, Pinfold Lane, Penkridge, Stafford ST19 5QP . . . . None
PENN COLTS. . . . . Pendeford Lane, off Wobaston Road, Wolverhampton WV9 5HQ. . . . . None
RIVERWAY . . . . Beaconside Sports Centre, Staffs University, Weston Road, Stafford ST18 0AD 01785 353286
ST MARTINS. . . . . St Martins Playing Fields, Overton Road, St Martins, Oswestry SY11 3DG . . . . None
TEAM DUDLEY . . . . The Dell Stadium, Bryce Road, Brierley Hill DY5 4NE 01384 812943
TENBURY UNITED. . . . . Palmers Meadow, Burford, Tenbury Wells WR15 8AP . . . . None
WARSTONES WANDERERS RES. Wolverhampton Utd FC, Prestwood Rd Sports Stadium, Wednesfield WV11 1HL 01902 730881
WRENS NEST . . . . Gornal Athletic FC, Garden Walk, Lower Gornal, Dudley DY3 2NH 01384 358398

IN: AFC Smethwick (S - Midland Combination Division Two), Bilston Town Res. (N), Leominster Town (P - Hereford League Premier Division), Riverway (R), Penn Colts (P - youth football), St Martins (P - Shropshire County League Premier Division), Team Dudley (N), Warstone Wanderers Res. (N)

OUT: Bentley (W), Black Country Rangers (P), Darlaston Town Res. (WS), Pennsnett Panthers (WS), Stone Old Alleynians (P), Wem Town (P), Wyrley (formerly Wyrley Juniors) (P)

PRESIDENT'S CUP

(all teams in league)

FIRST ROUND

Bilbrook 1 Ettingshall Park Farm 0
Bilston Town 1 **Blackheath Town** 2
Black Country Rangers 3 Heath Town Rangers Res. 1
Bridgnorth Town Res. 1 Sporting Khalsa 0
Dudley United (w/o) v Malvern Town Res.
Penkridge Town 0 **Stafford Town** 1
Riverway 1 **Warley Development** 2
Shenstone Pathfinder 2 **AFC Wombourne United** 4
Stone Old Alleynians 3 Warstones Wanderers 2
Tenbury United 2 **Malvern Rangers** 4
Trysull 3 Pensnett Panthers 0
Wellington Amateurs 5 Bentley 1
Wem Town 7 Darlaston Town Res. 1
Wolverhampton United 1 Mahal 0
Wrens Nest 0 **Hanwood United** 1
Wyrley Juniors 3 Penn Croft 2

SECOND ROUND

Bustleholme 3 Ludlow Town 0

Competition suspended to 2010-11 due to inclement weather

A.F.C. WULFRUNIANS
Founded: 2005

Secretary: Ian Davies **(T)** 07989 953 738 **(E)** ian.davies3@jobcentreplus.gsi.gov.uk
Chairman: Jason Scott **Manager:** **Prog Ed:**
Ground: Castlecroft Stadium, Castlecroft Road, Wolverhampton WV3 8NA **(T)** 01902 761410 **Capacity:**
Colours(change): Red & white/black/red

ADDITIONAL INFORMATION:
Honours: West Midlands (Regional) League Premier Division 2008-09.

BEWDLEY TOWN
Founded: 1978

Secretary: Steve Godfrey **(T)** 07739 626 169 **(E)** steve_g09@fsmail.net
Chairman: Geoff Edwards **Manager:** Craig Payton **Prog Ed:**
Ground: Ribbesford Meadows, Ribbesford, Bewdley, Worcs DY12 2TJ **(T)** **Capacity:**
Colours(change): Blue with yellow trim/blue/blue

ADDITIONAL INFORMATION:

BLOXWICH UNITED
Founded: 2006

Secretary: Ian Mason **(T)** 07771 717 349 **(E)** i.mason@blueyonder.co.uk
Chairman: Rod Jones **Manager:** **Prog Ed:**
Ground: Red Lion Ground, Somerfield Road, Bloxwich, Walsall WS3 2EJ **(T)** 01922 405 835 **Capacity:**
Colours(change): All red

ADDITIONAL INFORMATION:

BROMYARD TOWN
Founded: 1893

Secretary: Richard Haverfield **(T)** 07885 849 948 **(E)** tony.haverfield@virgin.net
Chairman: Anthony Watkins **Manager:** Wayne Oliver **Prog Ed:**
Ground: Delahay Meadow, Stourport Road, Bromyard HR7 4NT **(T)** 01885 483 974 **Capacity:**
Colours(change): All blue

ADDITIONAL INFORMATION:

BUSTLEHOLME
Founded: 1975

Secretary: Angela Bowden **(T)** 07921 167 173 **(E)** bowdenfoster@aol.com
Chairman: Geoff Benbow **Manager:** Dean Webb **Prog Ed:**
Ground: Tipton Town F C, Wednesbury Oak Road, Tipton, West Mid. DY4 0BS **(T)** 0121 502 5534 **Capacity:**
Colours(change): Yellow/green/green

ADDITIONAL INFORMATION:

CRADLEY TOWN
Founded: 1948

Secretary: David Attwood **(T)** 07708 659 636 **(E)** d.attwood@sky.com
Chairman: Trevor Thomas **Manager:** Bob Green **Prog Ed:**
Ground: The Beeches, Beeches View Avenue, Cradley, Halesowen B63 2HB **(T)** 07799 363 467 **Capacity:**
Colours(change): Red & white/red/red

ADDITIONAL INFORMATION:

DARLASTON TOWN
Founded: 1874

Secretary: Paul Tonks **(T)** 07506 160 234 **(E)** samtonks50@hotmail.co.uk
Chairman: Paul Tonks **Manager:** Paul Tonks, Raj Singh&Craig Love **Prog Ed:**
Ground: City Ground, Waverley Road, Darlaston, West Mids WS10 8ED **(T)** **Capacity:**
Colours(change): Blue & white/blue/blue

ADDITIONAL INFORMATION:

PREMIER INS & OUTS

IN: Cradley Town (R - Midland Alliance), Shifnal Town (R - Midland Alliance), Stafford Town (P) OUT: Ellesmere Rangers (P - Midland Alliance), Ledbury Town (W - Herefordshire League Premier Division), Ludlow Town (W - Shropshire League Premier Division), Oldbury Athletic (W)

DUDLEY SPORTS
Founded: 1978

Secretary: John Lewis **(T)** 07737 099 385 **(E)** kath-john.lewis@blueyonder.co.uk
Chairman: Ashley Forrest **Manager:** **Prog Ed:**
Ground: Hillcrest Avenue, Brierley Hill, West Mids DY5 3QH **(T)** 01384 826 420 **Capacity:**
Colours(change): Green & white/green/green & white

ADDITIONAL INFORMATION:

DUDLEY TOWN
Founded: 1893

Secretary: David Ferrier **(T)** 07803 509 995 **(E)** stangriffin59@hotmail.co.uk
Chairman: Stephen Austin **Manager:** Steve Hinks **Prog Ed:**
Ground: The Dell Stadium, Bryce Road, Brierley Hill, West Mids DY5 4NE **(T)** 01384 812 943 **Capacity:**
Colours(change): Red/black/black

ADDITIONAL INFORMATION:

GOODRICH
Founded: 1995

Secretary: Graham Turvey **(T)** 07813 467 220 **(E)** graham.turvey@goodrich.com
Chairman: Graham Turvey **Manager:** **Prog Ed:**
Ground: Stafford Road, Fordhouses, Wolverhampton WV10 7EH **(T)** **Capacity:**
Colours(change): All red

ADDITIONAL INFORMATION:

GORNAL ATHLETIC
Founded: 1945

Secretary: Kevin Williams **(T)** 07762 585 149 **(E)** k.williams880@btinternet.com
Chairman: Nick Sanders **Manager:** Ian Rowe **Prog Ed:**
Ground: Garden Walk Stadium, Garden Walk, Lower Gornal, Dudley DY3 2NR **(T)** 01384 358 398 **Capacity:**
Colours(change): All royal blue

ADDITIONAL INFORMATION:

HEATH TOWN RANGERS
Founded: 2001

Secretary: Mark Hopson **(T)** 07966 505 425 **(E)** htr_fc@yahoo.co.uk
Chairman: Mark Hopson **Manager:** **Prog Ed:**
Ground: Wednesfield F C, Cottage Ground, Amos Lane, Wednesfield WV11 1ND **(T)** 01902 735 506 **Capacity:**
Colours(change): Blue & white/blue/blue & white

ADDITIONAL INFORMATION:

LYE TOWN
Founded: 1930

Secretary: Yvonne Bignell **(T)** 07921 662 837 **(E)**
Chairman: Anthony Archer **Manager:** **Prog Ed:**
Ground: Sports Ground, Stourbridge Road, Lye, Stourbridge, West Mids DY9 7DH **(T)** 01384 422 672 **Capacity:**
Colours(change): All blue

ADDITIONAL INFORMATION:

SHAWBURY UNITED
Founded: 1992

Secretary: Tracie Howells **(T)** 07950 740 089 **(E)** traciehowells72@yahoo.co.uk
Chairman: Wayne Price **Manager:** **Prog Ed:**
Ground: Wem Sports & Social Club, Bowensfield, Wem, Shrewsbury SY4 5AP **(T)** 01939 233 287 **Capacity:**
Colours(change): All royal blue

ADDITIONAL INFORMATION:

SHIFNAL TOWN

Founded: 1964

Secretary: Derek Groucott **(T)** 07910 120 512 **(E)** carolderek2@blueyonder.co.uk
Chairman: Dave Saffhill **Manager:** **Prog Ed:**
Ground: Phoenix Park, Coppice Green Lane, Shifnal, Shrops TF11 8PB **(T)** 01952 463 257 **Capacity:**
Colours(change): Red & white stripes/black/red

ADDITIONAL INFORMATION:
Honours: West Midlands (Regional) League Premier Division 2006-07.

STAFFORD TOWN

Founded: 1976

Secretary: David Howard **(T)** 07765 296 379 **(E)** staffordtown@hotmail.co.uk
Chairman: Gordon Evans **Manager:** **Prog Ed:**
Ground: Evans Park, Riverway, Stafford ST16 3TH **(T)** **Capacity:**
Colours(change): All red

ADDITIONAL INFORMATION:

TIVIDALE

Founded: 1954

Secretary: Ruth Archer **(T)** 07876 197 758 **(E)** ruth-tivi@sky.com
Chairman: Chris Dudley **Manager:** Leon Murray **Prog Ed:**
Ground: The Beeches, Packwood Road, Tividale, West Mids B69 1UL **(T)** 01384 211 743 **Capacity:**
Colours(change): All yellow

ADDITIONAL INFORMATION:

WEDNESFIELD

Founded: 1961

Secretary: David Saville **(T)** 07939 279 996 **(E)** wednesfield.fc@hotmail.com
Chairman: TBA **Manager:** **Prog Ed:**
Ground: Cottage Ground, Amos Lane, Wednesfield WV11 1ND **(T)** 01902 735 506 **Capacity:**
Colours(change): Red/black/black

ADDITIONAL INFORMATION:

WELLINGTON

Founded: 1968

Secretary: Michael Perkins **(T)** 01432 830 523 **(E)** perkins@haworth13.freeserve.co.uk
Chairman: Phillip Smith **Manager:** Colin Bowcott & Anthony Stokes **Prog Ed:**
Ground: Wellington Playing Field, Wellington, Hereford HR4 8AZ **(T)** **Capacity:**
Colours(change): Tangerine/royal blue/tangerine & white

ADDITIONAL INFORMATION:

WOLVERHAMPTON CASUALS

Founded: 1899

Secretary: Michael Green **(T)** 07870 737 299 **(E)** wtoncasualsfc@aol.com
Chairman: Barry Austin **Manager:** **Prog Ed:**
Ground: Brinsford Stadium, Brinsford Lane, Wolverhampton WS10 7PR **(T)** 01902 783 214 **Capacity:**
Colours(change): All green

ADDITIONAL INFORMATION:

WESTERN LEAGUE

www.toolstationleague.com

Sponsored by:

Toolstation

Founded: 1892

Recent champions:

2005: Bideford

2006: Bideford

2007: Corsham Town

2008: Truro City

2009: Bitton

Premier Division	P	W	D	L	F	A	Pts
Bideford	38	27	6	5	93	37	87
Willand Rovers	38	24	11	3	79	30	83
Ilfracombe Town	38	21	10	7	64	45	73
Bishop Sutton	38	19	6	13	69	55	63
Welton Rovers	38	16	13	9	66	52	61
Street	38	19	4	15	65	62	61
Bristol Manor Farm	38	16	11	11	70	55	59
Bitton	38	16	8	14	58	55	56
Brislington	38	14	9	15	44	48	51
Dawlish Town	38	14	9	15	57	63	51
Longwell Green Sports	38	13	10	15	50	63	49
Hallen	38	13	8	17	52	55	47
Wellington Town	38	13	7	18	63	72	46
Larkhall Athletic	38	12	10	16	61	72	46
Barnstaple Town	38	13	6	19	67	76	45
Radstock Town	38	12	5	21	44	63	41
Corsham Town	38	11	5	22	51	64	38
Sherborne Town	38	9	9	20	63	80	36
Melksham Town	38	10	5	23	41	84	35
Calne Town	38	8	8	22	51	77	32

	Barnstaple Town	Bideford	Bishop Sutton	Bitton	Brislington	Bristol Manor Farm	Calne Town	Corsham Town	Dawlish Town	Hallen	Ilfracombe Town	Larkhall Athletic	Longwell Green Sports	Melksham Town	Radstock Town	Sherborne Town	Street	Wellington Town	Welton Rovers	Willand Rovers
Barnstaple Town		3-2	1-2	3-0	3-1	3-1	3-4	1-1	1-0	1-0	0-2	0-2	0-3	4-0	3-5	4-2	2-2	2-2	2-3	0-1
Bideford	4-3		4-0	0-1	3-0	2-1	5-2	2-0	2-0	3-2	2-2	4-0	1-1	3-2	3-1	2-1	2-0	5-0	3-1	1-1
Bishop Sutton	5-1	0-1	***P***	2-0	1-0	1-2	3-1	4-3	0-0	2-1	3-1	4-1	1-1	5-0	2-1	1-1	0-1	3-1	3-6	1-2
Bitton	2-2	0-2	2-1	***R***	0-0	1-0	2-1	2-3	4-0	2-0	0-1	1-3	3-2	3-0	0-4	4-1	3-3	1-0	0-2	3-3
Brislington	1-1	2-0	1-1	2-0	***E***	0-0	2-0	0-1	0-1	0-1	1-2	3-1	1-0	4-1	0-0	1-6	2-0	2-3	0-2	1-3
Bristol Manor Farm	1-0	2-2	2-3	1-1	1-2	***M***	1-1	2-1	3-2	0-3	1-3	1-1	1-2	4-0	3-0	6-0	2-1	2-2	3-2	2-2
Calne Town	1-3	0-3	4-0	2-1	1-2	0-1	***I***	2-0	0-2	1-0	0-0	3-3	0-2	1-0	1-2	1-2	3-4	1-1	1-2	0-2
Corsham Town	4-0	0-2	0-1	3-1	0-1	2-3	4-0	***E***	0-1	2-1	1-1	0-1	4-0	1-2	1-2	2-0	2-4	2-1	1-1	0-4
Dawlish Town	3-1	3-2	0-1	0-3	2-1	2-0	3-3	1-1	***R***	0-3	3-3	1-0	3-1	0-1	3-2	0-2	0-4	5-2	2-2	0-2
Hallen	1-4	2-2	1-3	1-1	1-3	1-1	2-2	1-0	3-2		2-1	2-1	1-1	0-1	0-1	2-1	4-1	1-1	2-2	1-3
Ilfracombe Town	3-1	0-1	2-1	1-0	2-0	1-1	5-2	1-0	0-0	1-0	***D***	2-1	1-2	3-3	3-1	2-1	3-2	1-3	2-3	0-3
Larkhall Athletic	4-3	1-3	3-3	1-2	0-0	1-1	1-2	1-4	2-2	0-2	0-2	***I***	2-1	3-1	2-1	3-0	0-0	3-1	3-3	2-2
Longwell Green Sports	1-0	2-1	0-3	1-0	0-1	2-2	2-0	0-0	5-5	1-0	1-1	3-4	***V***	4-0	1-1	0-3	0-1	3-1	0-3	0-0
Melksham Town	1-1	0-3	2-1	2-4	1-1	1-3	2-1	2-1	0-4	1-3	1-3	3-2	5-0	***I***	3-0	0-0	3-0	0-1	1-2	0-5
Radstock Town	0-1	0-2	1-0	0-1	2-0	2-4	3-2	2-1	0-1	2-1	2-3	0-2	0-1	3-0	***S***	1-3	1-1	4-0	0-0	0-4
Sherborne Town	3-2	2-7	1-3	1-3	1-2	0-3	1-1	1-2	2-2	0-2	2-2	2-2	1-2	4-2	6-0	***I***	0-1	2-4	2-2	2-2
Street	4-2	0-5	0-1	2-3	1-3	2-1	1-3	5-4	2-0	1-0	0-1	3-2	4-1	2-0	3-0	1-4	***O***	3-0	2-0	1-0
Wellington Town	2-4	2-3	4-2	2-2	2-2	2-5	1-0	7-0	2-1	1-1	0-1	0-1	5-1	3-0	1-0	2-0	0-2	***N***	0-1	0-2
Welton Rovers	2-0	0-1	1-0	1-1	2-2	2-3	3-3	1-0	1-2	1-3	1-1	4-2	1-1	2-0	0-0	2-1	3-0	1-3		1-1
Willand Rovers	1-2	0-0	2-2	2-1	2-0	2-0	3-1	3-0	2-1	5-1	0-1	3-0	3-2	0-0	1-0	2-2	2-1	3-1	1-0	

Division One		P	W	D	L	F	A	Pts
Wells City		38	29	4	5	76	33	91
Odd Down		38	25	6	7	75	43	81
Gillingham Town		38	23	8	7	95	51	77
Bradford Town		38	21	10	7	82	50	73
Westbury United		38	22	5	11	81	49	71
Oldland Abbotonians		38	20	10	8	82	42	70
Hengrove Athletic		38	20	8	10	75	43	68
Keynsham Town	*-3*	38	22	5	11	68	45	68
Shrewton United		38	18	5	15	76	67	59
Bridport		38	16	6	16	65	66	54
Cadbury Heath		38	15	8	15	62	64	53
Portishead Town		38	14	6	18	53	59	48
Almondsbury UWE		38	13	4	21	79	84	43
Elmore		38	13	4	21	66	93	43
Clevedon United 2006		38	12	6	20	58	72	42
Chard Town		38	7	11	20	40	74	32
Shepton Mallet		38	8	6	24	33	78	30
Roman Glass St George		38	5	11	22	38	72	26
Devizes Town		38	8	2	28	40	104	26
Minehead Town		38	3	7	28	39	94	16

LES PHILLIPS CUP

PRELIMINARY ROUND

Bradford Town 0 **Keynsham Town** 1
Cadbury Heath 0 **Bishop Sutton** 1
Chard Town 2 Roman Glass St George 0 *aet*
Hengrove Athletic 2 **Shrewton United** 3 *aet*
Ilfracombe Town 6 Street 1
Minehead Town 2 Gillingham Town 2 *aet* (3-2p)
Radstock Town 3 Westbury United 1
Wellington Town 3 Melksham Town 1

FIRST ROUND

Bideford 5 Chard Town 0
Bishop Sutton 4 Sherborne Town 3
Bitton 0 **Hallen** 2
Brislington 0 **Bridport** 2
Calne Town 2 Barnstaple Town 1
Corsham Town 2 Almondsbury UWE 0
Elmore 1 **Shrewton United** 2
Ilfracombe Town 3 Longwell Green Sports 1
Keynsham Town 3 Devizes Town 1
Larkhall Athletic 3 Dawlish Town 1
Odd Down 3 Bristol Manor Farm 0
Oldland Abbs 3 **Clevedon Utd** 2 *aet (at Clevedon Town)*
(Oldland Abbotonians expelled)
Portishead Town 0 **Willand Rovers** 1
Radstock Town 3 Minehead Town 2
Shepton Mallet 0 **Welton Rovers** 4
Wellington Town 2 **Wells City** 1 *(Wellington expelled)*

SECOND ROUND

Bishop Sutton 3 Corsham Town 1
Bridport 2 Keynsham Town 1
Calne Town 1 Wells City 0
Clevedon United 2006 2 **Shrewton United** 3
Hallen 2 Willand Rovers 0
Larkhall Athletic 1 Ilfracombe Town 0
Odd Down 1 Bideford 0
Radstock Town 2 **Welton Rovers** 2 *aet* (3-4)

QUARTER-FINALS

Bishop Sutton 3 Odd Down 1 *aet*
Bridport 0 Larkhall Athletic 0 *aet* (5-4p)
Calne Town 0 **Hallen** 1
Welton Rovers 5 Shrewton United 0

SEMI-FINALS

Bridport 1 **Bishop Sutton** 1 *aet* (3-5p)
Welton Rovers 0 **Hallen** 1

FINAL *(May 1st at Bristol Manor Farm)*
Hallen 1 Bishop Sutton 0

	Alm	Bra	Bri	Cad	Cha	Cle	Dev	Elm	Gil	Hen	Key	Min	Odd	Old	Por	RG	She	Shr	Wel	Wb
Almondsbury UWE		1-1	2-4	0-1	4-0	2-0	9-2	5-1	2-7	2-3	1-2	3-1	1-3	0-3	1-2	1-4	3-2	1-2	0-2	1-4
Bradford Town	3-1		3-2	1-0	2-3	1-0	3-1	2-0	1-1	1-2	2-1	4-1	2-2	2-2	2-0	3-0	1-3	2-2	3-1	4-3
Bridport	2-2	1-5		3-2	1-0	3-1	4-0	1-4	1-1	0-1	4-4	2-2	3-0	1-2	2-1	0-0	4-0	1-4	0-1	4-2
Cadbury Heath	1-6	2-2	2-1		2-1	3-0	1-3	4-1	1-4	3-2	0-1	3-0	1-2	0-0	1-1	2-1	0-0	2-1	0-2	1-1
Chard Town	0-0	2-4	1-2	1-1	***D***	2-2	2-0	1-1	0-5	3-3	0-3	1-3	1-3	1-1	2-0	0-0	1-0	5-2	0-2	3-2
Clevedon United 2006	3-1	2-3	5-0	1-2	1-1	***I***	1-2	3-2	1-1	0-2	0-1	1-0	1-1	1-3	1-1	1-0	3-2	0-5	1-4	4-0
Devizes Town	2-4	0-2	1-3	4-0	0-0	2-4	***V***	2-3	3-4	0-3	0-3	4-1	0-2	1-2	2-3	2-1	1-0	0-6	0-2	0-2
Elmore	5-2	1-4	2-3	1-4	2-0	1-4	1-1	***I***	0-3	2-5	2-5	3-1	0-1	3-1	0-2	4-1	4-1	0-3	3-0	0-2
Gillingham Town	2-1	1-1	2-1	2-4	4-3	2-2	4-1	4-1	***S***	1-0	2-3	1-1	4-1	1-0	4-0	6-2	3-2	2-1	2-3	0-2
Hengrove Athletic	3-0	1-0	0-0	2-0	1-0	4-0	5-1	5-0	1-3	***I***	2-2	2-0	1-2	2-1	1-3	4-1	1-1	4-2	1-1	1-1
Keynsham Town	3-2	1-2	4-0	1-0	1-0	4-2	5-1	2-1	1-1	0-2	***O***	2-2	0-2	2-1	3-1	0-0	1-0	0-2	0-1	1-2
Minehead Town	2-3	0-6	1-2	2-3	2-0	4-1	0-1	2-3	0-3	1-3	0-1	***N***	0-3	1-4	2-4	1-2	0-4	1-2	1-1	1-4
Odd Down	1-3	0-0	4-1	3-1	3-1	0-1	3-1	1-1	2-1	2-1	1-0	2-0		2-1	3-2	5-1	0-1	4-1	2-0	1-1
Oldland Abbotonians	4-1	2-2	2-0	2-1	3-1	0-1	7-0	5-0	1-1	2-2	2-0	5-1	3-1	***O***	1-1	2-1	5-1	1-0	0-3	4-0
Portishead Town	1-2	4-1	0-1	0-1	2-1	2-1	0-1	1-4	1-2	1-0	1-4	1-1	1-2	3-3	***N***	0-2	0-1	3-2	2-0	1-1
Roman Glass St George	1-3	1-2	0-1	1-1	0-0	1-5	3-0	2-2	1-2	1-1	1-2	1-1	2-2	0-1	0-3	***E***	3-1	0-2	0-2	0-2
Shepton Mallet	1-0	1-0	0-5	1-6	0-0	2-1	3-1	1-2	0-1	0-2	0-1	0-0	1-3	1-1	0-1	1-1		1-3	0-4	0-4
Shrewton United	0-4	1-1	2-1	3-3	2-3	3-1	4-0	2-6	3-2	1-0	1-0	3-2	1-3	2-2	1-3	1-1	4-1		0-2	1-0
Wells City	2-2	3-2	1-0	3-1	2-0	3-1	2-0	4-0	1-5	2-1	3-2	2-1	2-1	1-0	1-0	4-1	3-0	4-1		0-0
Westbury United	4-3	1-2	2-1	4-2	8-0	2-1	2-0	3-0	2-1	3-1	1-2	4-0	1-2	1-3	2-1	2-1	5-0	1-0	0-2	

IN: Odd Down (P), Wells City (P)
OUT: Bideford (P - Southern League Division One South & West), Calne Town (R), Melksham Town (R)
PREMIER INS & OUTS

BARNSTAPLE TOWN

Founded: 1906 Nickname: Barum

Secretary: David Cooke **(T)** 07939 217 084 **(E)** dcooke81@yahoo.com
Chairman: Steve James **Manager:** Owen Pickard **Prog Ed:**
Ground: Mill Road, Barnstaple, North Devon EX31 1JQ **(T)** 01271 343 469
Capacity: 5,000 **Seats:** 250 **Covered:** 1,000 **Midweek Matchday:** Tuesday **Clubhouse:** Yes **Shop:** Yes

Colours(change): All red. (All blue)
Previous Names: Pilton Yeo Vale
Previous Leagues: North Devon, Devon & Exeter, South Western
Records: **Att:** 6,200 v Bournemouth FA Cup 1st Round 51-52 **App:** Ian Pope
Senior Honours: Western Champions 1952-53, 79-80, Devon Pro Cup (12), Devon Sen Cup 92-93. Western League Div.1 93-94.

10 YEAR RECORD

00-01	01-02	02-03	03-04	04-05	05-06	06-07	07-08	08-09	09-10
WestP 4	WestP 12	WestP 15	WestP 10	WestP 12	WestP 13	WestP 7	WestP 12	WestP 18	WestP 15

BISHOP SUTTON

Founded: 1977 Nickname: Bishops

Secretary: Steve Hillier **(T)** 07713 681 235 **(E)** steve45hillier@btinternet.com
Chairman: George Williams **Manager:** Lee Lashenko **Prog Ed:**
Ground: Lakeview, Wick Road, Bishops Sutton, Bristol BS39 5XN. **(T)** 01275 333 097
Capacity: 1,500 **Seats:** 100 **Covered:** 200 **Midweek Matchday:** Wednesday **Clubhouse:** Yes **Shop:** No

Colours(change): All Blue (all yellow)
Previous Names:
Previous Leagues: Weston & District (youth), Bristol & Avon, Somerset Senior >1991
Records: **Att:** 400 v Bristol City
Senior Honours: Somerset Junior Cup 1980-81. Western League Div.1 97-98.

10 YEAR RECORD

00-01	01-02	02-03	03-04	04-05	05-06	06-07	07-08	08-09	09-10
WestP 16	WestP 15	WestP 12	WestP 16	WestP 18	WestP 16	WestP 21	WestP 19	WestP 15	WestP 4

BITTON

Founded: 1922 Nickname: The Ton

Secretary: Mrs Becky Jones **(T)** 07590 123 982 **(E)** rebeccalangdon@btconnect.com
Chairman: John Langdon **Manager:** Rich Fey **Prog Ed:**
Ground: Recreation Ground, Bath Road, Bitton, Bristol BS30 6HX. **(T)** 0117 932 3222
Capacity: 1,000 **Seats:** 48 **Covered:** 200 **Midweek Matchday:** Wednesday **Clubhouse:** Yes **Shop:** No

Colours(change): Red & white/black/black (Yellow/green/yellow)
Previous Names:
Previous Leagues: Avon Premier Combination, Gloucestershire County
Records: **Goalscorer:** A. Cole
Senior Honours: Somerset Senior Cup 92-93. Les Phillips Cup 07-08. Western League Champions 2008-09.

10 YEAR RECORD

00-01	01-02	02-03	03-04	04-05	05-06	06-07	07-08	08-09	09-10
West1 5	West1 6	West1 8	West1 2	WestP 8	WestP 8	WestP 8	WestP 7	WestP 1	WestP 8

BRISLINGTON

Founded: 1956 Nickname: Bris

Secretary: Kevin Jacobs **(T)** 07976 724 202 **(E)** kevinjacobs919@btinternet.com
Chairman: Fred Hardwell **Manager:** Jeff Meacham **Prog Ed:**
Ground: Ironmould Lane, Brislington, Bristol BS4 4TZ **(T)** 0117 977 4030
Capacity: 2,000 **Seats:** 144 **Covered:** 1,500 **Midweek Matchday:** Tuesday **Clubhouse:** Yes **Shop:** No

Colours(change): Red & black/black/red. (Yellow & black/yellow/yellow)
Previous Names:
Previous Leagues: Somerset Senior until 1991
Records:
Senior Honours: Somerset Senior League 1988-89. Somerset Premier Cup 1992-93. Western Lge Div.1 1994-95.

10 YEAR RECORD

00-01	01-02	02-03	03-04	04-05	05-06	06-07	07-08	08-09	09-10
WestP 8	WestP 3	WestP 2	WestP 7	WestP 10	WestP 10	WestP 17	WestP 13	WestP 10	WestP 9

BRISTOL MANOR FARM
Founded: 1964 Nickname: The Farm

Secretary: Andy Radford **(T)** 07747 038 423 **(E)** andy@bristolmanorfarm.com
Chairman: Geoff Sellek **Manager:** John Black **Prog Ed:**
Ground: The Creek, Portway, Sea Mills, Bristol BS9 2HS **(T)** 0117 968 3571
Capacity: 2,000 **Seats:** 98 **Covered:** 350 **Midweek Matchday:** Tuesday **Clubhouse:** Yes **Shop:** No

Colours(change): Red/black/black (All yellow)
Previous Names:
Previous Leagues: Bristol Suburban 64-69, Somerset Senior 69-77
Records: **Att;** 500 v Portway **App:** M. Baird
Senior Honours: Glos Trophy 1987-88, Glos Am. Cup 1989-90.
Western Lge Div.1 82-83.

10 YEAR RECORD

00-01	01-02	02-03	03-04	04-05	05-06	06-07	07-08	08-09	09-10
WestP 18	WestP 19	WestP 11	WestP 3	WestP 7	WestP 3	WestP 12	WestP 16	WestP 5	WestP 7

CORSHAM TOWN
Founded: 1884 Nickname:

Secretary: Richard Taylor **(T)** 07944 183 973 **(E)** richtaylor_ctfc@hotmail.com
Chairman: Ken Baldwin **Manager:** Mel Gingell **Prog Ed:**
Ground: Southbank Ground, Lacock Road, Corsham SN13 9HS **(T)** 01249 715 609
Capacity: 1,500 **Seats:** no **Covered:** yes **Midweek Matchday:** Wednesday **Clubhouse:** Yes **Shop:** Yes

Colours(change): Red & white/red/red. (Yellow & blue/blue/blue)
Previous Names: None.
Previous Leagues: Wiltshire County
Records: **Att:** 550 v Newport Co. FA Cup **App:** Craig Chaplin
Senior Honours: Wiltshire Senior Cup 1975-76, 96-97, 04-05.
Western League 2006-07.

10 YEAR RECORD

00-01	01-02	02-03	03-04	04-05	05-06	06-07	07-08	08-09	09-10
West1 9	West1 9	West1 6	West1 5	WestP 2	WestP 2	WestP 1	WestP 5	WestP 19	WestP 17

DAWLISH TOWN
Founded: 1889 Nickname: Seasiders

Secretary: Sandra Walmsley **(T)** 07966 585 213 **(E)** san.bluenose@googlemail.com
Chairman: Dave Fenner **Manager:** Adam Kerswell **Prog Ed:**
Ground: Playing Fields, Sandy Lane, Exeter Rd, Dawlish EX7 0AF **(T)** 01626 863 110
Capacity: 2,000 **Seats:** 200 **Covered:** 200 **Midweek Matchday:** Tuesday **Clubhouse:** Yes **Shop:**

Colours(change): Green & white/green/green (All blue)
Previous Names: Dawlish > 1983
Previous Leagues: Devon & Exeter
Records: **Att:** 1,500 v Heavitee Utd
Senior Honours: Western Lge Div 1 Champions 05-06, Lg Cup 80-81, 83-84, 2007-08
Devon Premier Cup 69-70, 72-73, 80-81, Devon Snr Cup 57-58, 67-68, Devon St Lukes Cup 82-83, 2007-08

10 YEAR RECORD

00-01	01-02	02-03	03-04	04-05	05-06	06-07	07-08	08-09	09-10
WestP 11	WestP 6	WestP 13	WestP 17	West1 4	West1 1	WestP 10	WestP 2	WestP 4	WestP 10

HALLEN
Founded: 1949 Nickname:

Secretary: Richard Stokes **(T)** **(E)** sinbad88@hotmail.co.uk
Chairman: Barrie Phillips **Manager:** Gary Domone **Prog Ed:**
Ground: Hallen Centre, Moorhouse Lane, Hallen Bristol BS10 7RU **(T)** 0117 950 5559
Capacity: 2,000 **Seats:** 200 **Covered:** 200 **Midweek Matchday:** Monday **Clubhouse:** Yes **Shop:**

Colours(change): Royal blue & black/black/royal blue. (All yellow)
Previous Names: Lawrence Weston Ath, Lawrence Weston Hallen
Previous Leagues: Glous Co lg, Hellenic
Records: **Att:** 803 v Bristol Rovers 1997
Senior Honours: Gloucestershire Co. Lge 1988-89, 92-93. Western Lge Div.1 03-04.

10 YEAR RECORD

00-01	01-02	02-03	03-04	04-05	05-06	06-07	07-08	08-09	09-10
West1 4	West1 10	West1 4	West1 1	WestP 4	WestP 9	WestP 9	WestP 15	WestP 9	WestP 12

ILFRACOMBE TOWN
Founded: 1902 Nickname: Bluebirds

Secretary: Tony Alcock **(T)** 07973 469 673 **(E)** afalcock@aol.com
Chairman: Allan Day **Manager:** Barry Yeo **Prog Ed:**
Ground: Marlborough Park, Ilfracombe, Devon EX34 8PD **(T)** 01271 865 939
Capacity: 2,000 **Seats:** 60 **Covered:** 450 **Midweek Matchday:** Tuesday **Clubhouse:** Yes **Shop:**

Colours(change): Blue & white/blue/blue. (Yellow/red/red)
Previous Names:
Previous Leagues: North Devon, E Devon Premier, Exeter & Dist., Western,
Records: Att: 3,000 v Bristol City **Goalscorer:** Kevin Squire **App;** Bob Hancock 459
Senior Honours: E Devon Premier Lge, N. Devon Sen Lge, N. Devon Prem Lge.

10 YEAR RECORD

00-01	01-02	02-03	03-04	04-05	05-06	06-07	07-08	08-09	09-10
West1 16	West1 14	West1 18	West1 16	West1 8	West1 4	West1 3	WestP 8	WestP 14	WestP 3

LARKHALL ATHLETIC
Founded: 1914 Nickname: Larks

Secretary: Garry Davy **(T)** 01225 852 729 **(E)** garrydvy@aol.com
Chairman: Jim McClay **Manager:** Neil Kirkpatrick **Prog Ed:**
Ground: Plain Ham, Charlcombe Lane, Larkhall, Bath BA1 8DJ **(T)** 01225 334 952
Capacity: 1,000 **Seats:** Yes **Covered:** 50 **Midweek Matchday:** Wednesday **Clubhouse:** Yes **Shop:**

Colours(change): Blue/white/white (All red)
Previous Names: None
Previous Leagues: Somerset Senior
Records:
Senior Honours: Somerset Senior Cup 1975-76, Somerset Senior Champions.
Western Div 1 Champions 1988-89, 93-94, 94-95, 08-09.

10 YEAR RECORD

00-01	01-02	02-03	03-04	04-05	05-06	06-07	07-08	08-09	09-10
West1 15	West1 12	West1 13	West1 8	West1 5	West1 7	West1 5	West1 3	West1 1	WestP 14

LONGWELL GREEN SPORTS
Founded: 1966 Nickname: The Green

Secretary: David Heal **(T)** 07771 900 413 **(E)** dave@monaghannorthern.co.uk
Chairman: Chris Wyrill **Manager:** Julian Harmer **Prog Ed:**
Ground: Longwell Green Com. Centre, Shellards Road BS30 9DW **(T)** 0117 932 3722
Capacity: 1,000 **Seats:** Yes **Covered:** 100 **Midweek Matchday:** Tuesday **Clubhouse:** Yes **Shop:** Yes

Colours(change): Blue & white/black/black (All green)
Previous Names: None
Previous Leagues: Gloucestershire County.
Records: Att: 500 v Mangotsfield 2005
Senior Honours:

10 YEAR RECORD

00-01	01-02	02-03	03-04	04-05	05-06	06-07	07-08	08-09	09-10
				GlCo 2	West1 12	West1 8	West1 8	West1 2	WestP 11

ODD DOWN (BATH)
Founded: 1901 . Nickname: The Down

Secretary: Lorraine Brown **(T)** **(E)** lorainebrown@btinternet.com
Chairman: Eric Clarke **Manager:** Lee Burns **Prog Ed:**
Ground: Lew Hill Memorial Ground, Combe Hay Lane, Odd Down BA2 8AP **(T)** 01225 832 491
Capacity: 1,000 **Seats:** 160 **Covered:** 250 **Midweek Matchday:** Tuesday **Clubhouse:** Yes **Shop:** No

Colours(change): Blue & black/black/black (All red)
Previous Names:
Previous Leagues: Wilts Premier, Bath & District & Somerset Senior
Records: App: Steve Fuller 475 **Goalscorer:** Joe Matano 104
Senior Honours:

10 YEAR RECORD

00-01	01-02	02-03	03-04	04-05	05-06	06-07	07-08	08-09	09-10
WestP 17	WestP 11	WestP 9	WestP 9	WestP 13	WestP 15	WestP 11	WestP 21	West1 19	West1 2

RADSTOCK TOWN

Founded: 1895 Nickname:

Secretary: Simon Wilkinson **(T)** 07917 001 499 **(E)** rtfc@hotmail.co.uk
Chairman: TBA **Manager:** Terry Moore **Prog Ed:**
Ground: Southfields Recreation Ground, Southfields, Radstock BA3 2NZ **(T)** 01761 435 004
Capacity: 1,500 **Seats:** 80 **Covered:** yes **Midweek Matchday:** Tuesday **Clubhouse:** Yes **Shop:** No

Colours(change): Red/black/black. (All Yellow)
Previous Names: Radstock.
Previous Leagues: Somerset Senior League.
Records:
Senior Honours:

10 YEAR RECORD

00-01	01-02	02-03	03-04	04-05	05-06	06-07	07-08	08-09	09-10
SomP 5	SomP 7	SomP 10	SomP 3	West1 3	WestP 12	WestP 16	WestP 17	WestP 17	WestP 16

SHERBORNE TOWN

Founded: 1894 Nickname:

Secretary: Colin Goodland **(T)** 07929 090 612 **(E)** goody@cgoodland.freeserve.co.uk
Chairman: Steve Paradise **Manager:** Mickey Spencer **Prog Ed:**
Ground: Raleigh Grove, Terrace Playing Field, Sherborne DT9 5NS **(T)** 01935 816 110
Capacity: **Seats:** Yes **Covered:** Yes **Midweek Matchday:** Wednesday **Clubhouse:** Yes **Shop:**

Colours(change): Black & white/black/black. (Yellow/white/white).
Previous Names:
Previous Leagues: Dorset Prem Lge
Records: **Att:** 1,000 v Eastleigh, Andy Shephard Memorial match 27.07.03.
Senior Honours: Dorset Prem Lge 81-82, Dorset Senior Cup 2003-04

10 YEAR RECORD

00-01	01-02	02-03	03-04	04-05	05-06	06-07	07-08	08-09	09-10
Dor P 12	Dor P 2	Dor P 6	Dor P 5	Dor P 6	Dor P 2	West1 4	West1 2	WestP 12	WestP 18

STREET

Founded: 1880 Nickname: The Cobblers

Secretary: Ms Melanie Dowden **(T)** 07743 080 192 **(E)** melanie.dowden@clarks.com
Chairman: TBC **Manager:** Dave Pople **Prog Ed:** Phil Norton -Ashley
Ground: The Tannery Ground, Middlebrooks, Street BA16 0TA **(T)** 01458 445 987
Capacity: 2,000 **Seats:** 120 **Covered:** 25 **Midweek Matchday:** Tuesday **Clubhouse:** Yes **Shop:**

Colours(change): Green/green/white. (All red)
Previous Names: None
Previous Leagues: Somerset Senior.
Records: **Att;** 4,300 v Yeovil Town FA Cup 47
Senior Honours: Somerset Senior League 1996-97.

10 YEAR RECORD

00-01	01-02	02-03	03-04	04-05	05-06	06-07	07-08	08-09	09-10
West1 13	West1 8	West1 15	West1 12	West1 7	West1 3	WLaP 19	WestP 18	WestP 13	WestP 6

WELLINGTON TOWN

Founded: 1892 Nickname: Wellie

Secretary: Ken Pearson **(T)** 07789 055 942 **(E)** ken_pearson@btinternet.com
Chairman: Ken Bird **Manager:** Leigh Robinson **Prog Ed:**
Ground: Wellington Playing Field, North St, Wellington TA21 8NA **(T)** 01749 679 971
Capacity: 3,000 **Seats:** none **Covered:** 200 **Midweek Matchday:** Wednesday **Clubhouse:** Yes **Shop:** No

Colours(change): Tangerine/black/tangerine (Blue/white/blue)
Previous Names: None
Previous Leagues: Taunton Saturday, Somerset Senior.
Records: **Goalscorer:** Ken Jones
Senior Honours: Western League Div.1 Champions 2007-08.

10 YEAR RECORD

00-01	01-02	02-03	03-04	04-05	05-06	06-07	07-08	08-09	09-10
West1 14	West1 17	West1 12	West1 10	West1 14	West1 17	West1 7	West1 1	WestP 7	WestP 13

WELLS CITY

Founded: 1890 Nickname:

Secretary: Stephen Vowles **(T)** **(E)** stevievowles@aol.com
Chairman: Steve Loxton **Manager:** Tim Moxey **Prog Ed:** Michelle Payne
Ground: Athletic Ground, Rowdens Road, Wells, Somerset BA5 1TU **(T)** 01749 679 971
Capacity: **Seats:** **Covered:** **Midweek Matchday:** Tuesday **Clubhouse:** **Shop:**

Colours(change): Blue/blue/white (All yellow)
Previous Names:
Previous Leagues: Somerset County.
Records:
Senior Honours: Western League Division 1 2009-10

10 YEAR RECORD

00-01	01-02	02-03	03-04	04-05	05-06	06-07	07-08	08-09	09-10
SomP 10	SomP 3	SomP 15	SomP 14	SomP 9	SomP 5	SomP 5	SomP 2	West1 10	West1 1

WELTON ROVERS

Founded: 1887 Nickname: Rovers

Secretary: Malcolm Price **(T)** 07970 791 644 **(E)** malcolm@weltonr.plus.com
Chairman: Maurice Down **Manager:** Mark Leaney **Prog Ed:**
Ground: West Clewes, North Road, Midsomer Norton BA3 2QD **(T)** 01761 412 097
Capacity: 2,400 **Seats:** 300 **Covered:** 300 **Midweek Matchday:** Tuesday **Clubhouse:** Yes **Shop:** No

Colours(change): Green & white (Yellow/blue/yellow).
Previous Names: None
Previous Leagues: None
Records: **Att:** 2,000 v Bromley FA Am Cup 1963 **Goalscorer:** Ian Henderson 51
Senior Honours: Western Lge 1911-12, 64-65, 65-66, 66-67, 73-74. Div.1 59-60, 87-88.
Somerset Senior Cup (10). Somerset Premier Cup 2009-10.

10 YEAR RECORD

00-01	01-02	02-03	03-04	04-05	05-06	06-07	07-08	08-09	09-10
WestP 10	WestP 18	WestP 16	WestP 8	WestP 17	WestP 4	WestP 15	WestP 9	WestP 8	WestP 5

WILLAND ROVERS

Founded: 1946 Nickname: Rovers

Secretary: Tony Baker **(T)** 07788 758 711 **(E)** tonybaker@burnrew.gotadsl.co.uk
Chairman: Mike Mitchell **Manager:** Clive Jones **Prog Ed:** Steve Birley
Ground: Silver Street, Willand, Collumpton, Devon EX15 2RG **(T)** 01884 33885
Capacity: 2,000 **Seats:** 75 **Covered:** 150 **Midweek Matchday:** Wednesday **Clubhouse:** Yes **Shop:**

Colours(change): All White (Yellow/blue/yellow)
Previous Names: None.
Previous Leagues: Devon County.
Records: **Att:** 650 v Newton Abbot 1992-3 **Goalscorer:** Paul Foreman
Senior Honours: Devon Co Lge 1998-99,00-01, Western Lge Div 1 2004-05,
Les Phillips Cup 2006-07

10 YEAR RECORD

00-01	01-02	02-03	03-04	04-05	05-06	06-07	07-08	08-09	09-10
Devon 1	West1 15	West1 7	West1 6	West1 1	WestP 6	WestP 6	WestP 3	WestP 3	WestP 2

DIVISION ONE INS & OUTS
IN: Calne Town (R), Melksham Town (R), Merthyr Town (formerly Merthyr Tydfil) (R – Southern Prem)
OUT: Clevedon Utd 2006 (F), Minehead (R – Somerset Senior Prem), Odd Down (P), Wells City (P)

ALMONDSBURY U.W.E.

Secretary: Douglas Coles **(T)** **(E)** doug2004.coles@blueyonder.co.uk
Chairman: Mike Blessing **Manager:** **Prog Ed:**
Ground: The Field, Almondsbury, Bristol BS34 4AA **(T)** 01454 612 240 **Capacity:**
Colours(change): White & green/green/green (Yellow & blue/yellow/yellow)

ADDITIONAL INFORMATION:

BRADFORD TOWN

Founded: 1992

Secretary: Nikki Akers **(T)** 07866 693 167 **(E)** nikki.akers@3disp.co.uk
Chairman: Les Stevens **Manager:** Paul Shanley **Prog Ed:**
Ground: Bradford Sports & Social Club, Trowbridge Rd, Bradford on Avon BA15 1EW **(T)** 01225 866 649 **Capacity:**
Colours(change): Navy & white/navy/navy (Yellow/black/yellow)

ADDITIONAL INFORMATION:
Previous League: Wiltshire Senior.

BRIDPORT

Founded: 1885 Nickname: Bees

Secretary: Heather Scadding **(T)** 07957 526 268 **(E)** bridportfc@btconnect.com
Chairman: Adrian Scadding **Manager:** Trevor Senior **Prog Ed:**
Ground: St Mary's Field, Bridport, Dorset DT6 5LN **(T)** 01308 423 834 **Capacity:** 2,000
Colours(change): Red & black/black/red (All blue)

ADDITIONAL INFORMATION: **Previous League:** Dorset Combination 1984-89.
Record Att: 1,150 v Exeter City 1981.
Honours: Dorset Senior Cup x8. Dorset Senior Amateur Cup x6.

CADBURY HEATH

Secretary: Martin Painter **(T)** 0117 949 2844 **(E)** martinbristol1955@hotmail.com
Chairman: Steve Plenty **Manager:** **Prog Ed:**
Ground: Springfield, Cadbury Heath Road, Bristol BS30 8BX **(T)** 117 967 5731 (social cl) **Capacity:**
Colours(change): Red & white/red/red (Yellow/blue/blue)

ADDITIONAL INFORMATION:
Previous League: Gloucestershire County.
Honours: Gloucestershire County League 1998-99.

CALNE TOWN

Founded: 1886 Nickname: Lilywhites

Secretary: Shaun Smith **(T)** **(E)** s_k_smith@hotmail.com
Chairman: Mark Barnett **Manager:** Nick Vitale **Prog Ed:**
Ground: Bremhill View, Calne, Wiltshire SN11 9EE **(T)** **Capacity:**
Colours(change): White/black/black (All blue)

ADDITIONAL INFORMATION: **Previous League:** Wiltshire.
Record Att: 1,100 v Swindon, friendly 1987. **Goalscorer:** Robbie Lardner. **Apps:** Gary Swallow - 259.
Honours: Wiltshire Senior Cup x3.

CHARD TOWN

Nickname: The Robins

Secretary: Michael Hawes **(T)** 07906 904 138 **(E)** michael.hawes2@virgin.net
Chairman: (Acting) Mike Hone **Manager:** Glyn Shaw **Prog Ed:**
Ground: Denning Sports Field, Zembard Lane, Chard, Somerset TA20 1JL **(T)** 01460 61402 **Capacity:** 1,500
Colours(change): All red (White/blue/blue)

ADDITIONAL INFORMATION: **Previous League:** Somerset Senior 1948-75.
Honours: Somerset Senior League 1949-50, 53-54, 59-60, 67-68, 69-70. Somerset Senior Cup 1952-53, 66-67.
South West Counties Cup 1988-89.

DEVIZES TOWN

Founded: 1885

Secretary: John Dalley **(T)** **(E)** rowdesports@hotmail.co.uk
Chairman: Shaun Moffat **Manager:** **Prog Ed:**
Ground: Nursteed Road, Devizes, Wiltshire SN10 3DX **(T)** 01380 722 817 **Capacity:** 2,500
Colours(change): Red & white/black/red (All blue)

ADDITIONAL INFORMATION: **Previous Name:** Southbroom until early 1900s). **Previous League:** Wiltshire Premier.
Honours: Western League Division 1 1999-2000. Wiltshire Senior Cup x14.

ELMORE

Founded: 1947 Nickname: Eagles

Secretary: Neville Crocker **(T)** **(E)** neville.crocker@googlemail.com
Chairman: **Manager:** **Prog Ed:**
Ground: Horsdon Park, Heathcoat Way, Tiverton, Devon EX16 4DB **(T)** 01884 252 341 **Capacity:** 2,000
Colours(change): All green (Red & white/red/red)

ADDITIONAL INFORMATION: Previous League: South Western 1974-78.
Record Att: 1,713 v Tiverton Town Friday April 14th 1995. **Apps:** P Webber. **Win:** 17-0. **Defeat:** 2-7.
Honours: East Devon Senior Cup 1972-73, 75-76. Devon Senior Cup 1987-88.

GILLINGHAM TOWN

Secretary: Terry Lucas **(T)** 07873 587 455 **(E)** terrylucas@sky.com
Chairman: Dave Graham **Manager:** Adrian Foster **Prog Ed:**
Ground: Hardings Lane, Gillingham, Dorset SP8 4HX **(T)** 01747 823 673 **Capacity:**
Colours(change): All tangerine (Navy & sky/navy/sky)

ADDITIONAL INFORMATION:
Previous League: Dorset Premier.

HENGROVE ATHLETIC

Founded: 1948

Secretary: Graham Whittaker **(T)** 07970 848 285 **(E)** graham.whitaker1@tesco.net
Chairman: **Manager:** **Prog Ed:**
Ground: Norton Lane, Whitchurch, Bristol BS14 0BT **(T)** 01275 832 894 **Capacity:**
Colours(change): Green & white/black/black (All red)

ADDITIONAL INFORMATION:
Previous League: Somerset County 1974-2006.
Honours: Somerset County League Premier Division 2005-06. Somerset Senior Cup 1979-80.

KEYNSHAM TOWN

Founded: 1895 Nickname: K's

Secretary: John Peake **(T)** 07704 340 170 **(E)** helejohn@btinternet.com
Chairman: **Manager:** **Prog Ed:**
Ground: Crown Field, Bristol Road, Keynsham BS31 2DZ **(T)** 0117 986 5876 **Capacity:** 2,000
Colours(change): Gold/black/gold (White/blue/white)

ADDITIONAL INFORMATION:
Previous League: Somerset Senior.
Honours: Somerset Senior Cup 1951-52, 57-58, 2002-03.

MELKSHAM TOWN

Founded: 1876

Secretary: Mark Jeffery **(T)** **(E)** markmtfc@virginmedia.com
Chairman: Dave Wiltshire **Manager:** Adam Young **Prog Ed:**
Ground: The Conigre, Market Place, Melksham, Wiltshire SN12 6ES **(T)** 01225 702 843 **Capacity:** 1,500
Colours(change): Yellow/black/yellow (White/navy/navy)

ADDITIONAL INFORMATION: Previous League: Wiltshire
Record Att: 2,821 v Trowbridge Town, FA Cup 1957-58.
Honours: Western League Division 1 1979-80, 96-97. Wiltshire Shield x6. Wiltshire Senior Cup x4.

MERTHYR TOWN

Founded: 2010

Secretary: Jamie Mack **(T)** 07823 776 422 **(E)** james.mack2009@yahoo.co.uk
Chairman: TBC **Manager:** Garry Shephard **Prog Ed:**
Ground: Taffes Well FC, Rhiw Dda'r, Parish Road, Taffs Well, Cardiff CF15 7SA **(T)** 07980 363 675 **Capacity:**
Colours(change): Red/red/green (White/black/black)

ADDITIONAL INFORMATION:

OLDLAND ABBOTONIANS

Founded: 1910 Nickname: The O's

Secretary: Derek Jones **(T)** **(E)** avontruckandvan@btconnect.com
Chairman: Robert Boyd **Manager:** Spencer Thomas **Prog Ed:**
Ground: Aitchison Playing Field, Castle Road, Oldland Common, Bristol BS30 9PP **(T)** 0117 932 8263 **Capacity:**
Colours(change): Blue & white/blue/blue (All yellow)

ADDITIONAL INFORMATION:
Previous League: Somerset County.
Honours: Les Phillips Cup 2008-09.

PORTISHEAD TOWN

Founded: 1910 Nickname: Posset

Secretary: Brian Hobbs **(T)** 07791 412 724 **(E)** hobbs.posset@hotmail.co.uk
Chairman: **Manager:** **Prog Ed:**
Ground: Bristol Road, Portishead, Bristol BS20 6QG **(T)** 01275 817 600 **Capacity:** 1,000
Colours(change): White/black/black (All blue)

ADDITIONAL INFORMATION:
Previous League: Somerset County.
Honours: Somerset County League 2004-05.

ROMAN GLASS ST GEORGE

Secretary: Emily Baldwin **(T)** 07708 277 592 **(E)** emilyjaynebaldwin@blueyonder.co.uk
Chairman: **Manager:** **Prog Ed:**
Ground: Whiteway Road, St George, Bristol BS5 7RP **(T)** 0117 983 7707 **Capacity:**
Colours(change): White/black/black (All red)

ADDITIONAL INFORMATION:
Previous League: Gloucestershire County.
Honours: Gloucestershire County League 2006-07.

SHEPTON MALLET

Founded: 1986

Secretary: Gary Banfield **(T)** 07762 880 705 **(E)** gkrkb@tiscali.co.uk
Chairman: **Manager:** **Prog Ed:**
Ground: Playing Fields, Old Wells Road, West Shepton, Shepton Mallet BA4 5XN **(T)** 01749 344 609 **Capacity:** 2,500
Colours(change): Black & white/black/black (Claret/blue/blue)

ADDITIONAL INFORMATION: **Previous League:** Somerset Senior.
Record Att: 274 v Chippenham Town FA Cup 2000-01.
Honours: Somerset Senior League 2000-01.

SHREWTON UNITED

Secretary: Paul Robinson **(T)** 07786 802 688 **(E)** paul@shrewtonunitedfc.net
Chairman: G Foot **Manager:** Stuart Withers **Prog Ed:** Paul Robinson
Ground: Recreation Ground, Mill Lane, Shrewton, Wilts SP3 4JY **(T)** 07786 802 688 **Capacity:**
Colours(change): Marron & sky blue/sky blue/sky blue (Yellow/royal/royal)

ADDITIONAL INFORMATION:
Previous League: Wiltshire > 2003.
Honours: Wiltshire League Premier Division 2001-02, 02-03, Senior Cup 2001-02, 02-03.

WESTBURY UNITED

Founded: 1921 Nickname: White Horsemen

Secretary: Roger Arnold **(T)** 07919 380 911 **(E)** rogerarnold33@hotmail.com
Chairman: **Manager:** **Prog Ed:**
Ground: Meadow Lane, Westbury, Wiltshire BA13 3AF **(T)** 01373 823 409 **Capacity:** 3,500
Colours(change): Green & white/green/green (Gold & navy/navy/navy)

ADDITIONAL INFORMATION: **Previous League:** Wiltshire County. **Previous Ground:** Redland Lane (pre 1935).
Record Att: 4,000 v Llanelli FA Cup 1st Round 1937 & v Walthamstow Avenue FA Cup 1937.
Honours: Wiltshire League 1934-35, 37-38, 38-39, 49-50, 50-51, 55-56. Western League Div.1 1991-92. Wilts Senior Cup x4.

GROUND DIRECTIONS

BARNSTAPLE TOWN - Mill Road, Barnstaple, North Devon EX31 1JQ 01271 343469

From M5 South, exit junction 27, take A361 to Barnstaple, in town take A361 for Ilfracombe, then first left over bridge is Mill Road.

BISHOP SUTTON - Lakeview, Wick Road, Bishop Sutton BS39 5XN 01275 333097

On main A368 Bath to Weston-Super-Mare road at rear of Butchers Arms Public House.

BITTON - Recreation Ground, Bath Road, Bitton, Bristol BS30 6HX 0117 932 3222

From M4 leave at Junction 18. Take A46 towards Bath, at first roundabout take A420 for Wick / Bridgeyate. On approach to Bridgeyate turn left at mini-roundabout onto A4175 and follow for 2.2 miles, then turn left for Bath on A431. The ground is 100 yards on the right.

From Bath take A431, go through Kelston and Bitton village. Ground is on the left.

From Chippenham take A420 to Bristol and turn left at mini-roundabout onto A4175 and follow as above.

BRISLINGTON - Ironmould Lane, Brislington, Bristol BS4 4TZ 0117 977 4030

On A4 Bristol to Bath road, about 500 yards on Bath side of Park & Ride. Opposite the Wyevale Garden Centre.

BRISTOL MANOR FARM - The Creek, Portway, Sea Mills, Bristol BS9 2HS 0117 968 3571

Leaving M5 at Junction 18, take A4 marked Bristol. U-turn on dual carriageway by Bristol and West Sports Ground and then ground is half-mile on left hand side

CORSHAM TOWN - Southbank, Lacock Road, Corsham, Wiltshire SN13 9HS 01249 715609

A4 into Corsham, at Hare and Hounds Roundabout take the Melksham Road B3353 until the War Memorial, then Lacock Road. Ground a half a mile on the right side.

DAWLISH TOWN - The Playing Fields, Sandy Lane, Dawlish, Devon EX7 0AF 01626 863110

Exit Junction 30 M5, follow A379. On entering Dawlish from Exeter turn right into Sandy Lane signposted Leisure Centre and Sports Ground. Car park and clubhouse on the left.

HALLEN - Hallen Centre, Moorhouse Lane, Hallen, Bristol BS10 7RU 0117 950 5559

From Junction 17 M5 follow A4018 towards Bristol. At third roundabout turn right into Crow Lane. Proceed to T junction - turn right and right again at mini roundabout by Henbury Lodge Hotel. At next mini roundabout turn left into Avonmouth Way. Continue for 1.5 miles into Hallen village. At crossroads turn left into Moorhouse Lane

ILFRACOMBE TOWN - Marlborough Park, Ilfracombe, Devon EX34 8PD 01271 865 939

Take A361 for Ilfracombe and in town take first right after traffic lights. Follow Marlborough Road to top and ground is on the left.

LARKHALL ATHLETIC - Plain Ham, Charlcombe Lane, Larkhall, Bath BA1 8DJ 01225 334 952

Take A4 east from Bath city centre. After approximately 1 mile fork left into St Saviours Road. In Larkhall Square take left exit and turn right at T Junction. Road bears left into Charlcombe Lane where ground is on right as road narrows.

LONGWELL GREEN SPORTS - Longwell Green Community Centre, Shellards Road, Longwell Green BS30 9DW 0117 932 3722

Leave Junction 1 M32 follow signs for Ring Road (A4174). At Kingsfield roundabout turn into Marsham Way. At first set of traffic lights turn left into Woodward Drive. Continue to min roundabout and turn right into Parkway Road and continue to Shellards Road. Ground is situated to the rear of the Community Centre.

ODD DOWN - Lew Hill, Memorial Ground, Combe Hay Lane, Odd Down, Bath BA2 8AP 01225 832 491

Situated behind Odd Down Park & Ride on main A367 Bath to Exeter road.

RADSTOCK TOWN - Southfields Recreation Ground, Southfields, Radstock BA3 2NZ 01761 435 004

The town of Radstock is situated 15 miles south east of Bristol and 8 miles southwest of Bath on the A367. At the double roundabout in Radstock town centre take the A362 towards Frome. The ground is on the right hand bend, third turning. Turn right into Southfield, ground is 200 yards ahead.

SHERBORNE TOWN - Raleigh Grove, The Terrace Playing Field, Sherborne, Dorset DT9 5NS 01935 816 110

From Yeovil take A30 - marked Sherborne. On entering town turn right at traffic lights, over next traffic lights and at the next junction turn right. Go over bridge, take second left marked 'Terrace Pling Fields'. Turn into car park, football club car park is situated in the far right-hand corner.

STREET - The Tannery Field, Middlebrooks, Street, Somerset BA16 0TA 01458 445 987

Ground is signposted from both ends of A39 and B3151.

WELLINGTON - The Playing Field, North Street, Wellington, Somerset TA21 8NA 01749 679 971

Leave the M5 motorway at Junction 26 and follow directions to Wellington. At town centre traffic lights take turning into North Street. Take the next left adjacent to the Fire Station and signposted 'Car Park'. The ground is in the corner of the car park.

WELLS CITY - Athletic Ground, Rowdens Road, Wells, Somerset BA5 1TU 01749 679 971
From North & Southwest - Follow A39 to Strawberry Way to roundabout, follow A371 East Somerset Way and take right turn into Rowdens Road. Ground is on left. From East - Follow A371 from Shepton Mallet. After approximately 5 miles on East Somerset Way take left turn into Rowdens Road. Ground is on left.

WELTON ROVERS - West Clewes, North Road, Midsomer Norton BA3 2QD 01761 412 097
The ground is on the main A362 in Midsomer Norton

WILLAND ROVERS - Silver Street, Willand, Cullompton, Devon EX15 2RG 01884 33885
Leave M5 Junction 27 and take first left at roundabout. Follow signs to Willand. After passing Halfway House pub on right, go straight over mini-roundabout (signposted to Cullompton) ground is 400 metres on left hand side.

DIVISION ONE

ALMONDSBURY UWE - The Field, Almondsbury, Bristol BS34 4AA 01454 612 240
Exit M5 at Junction 16. Arriving from the south take the left exit lane. Turn left at lights and ground is 150m on right hand side. Arriving from east take right hand lane on slip road. Take 3rd exit and ground is 150m on right hand side.

BRADFORD TOWN - Bradford Sports & Social Club, Trowbridge Road, Bradford on Avon, Wiltshire BA15 1EW 01225 866 649
From Bath or Melksham on entering Bradford on Avon follow the signs for A363 to Trowbridge. The ground is after a mini roundabout and behind a stone wall on the right hand side. From Trowbridge, follow A363 to Bradford-on-Avon. The ground is just past shop on right, behind stone wall on left.

BRIDPORT - St Marys Field, Bridport, Dorset DT6 5LN 01308 423 834
Follow Bridport by-pass in any direction to the Crown Inn roundabout. Take exit to town centre, at first set of traffic lights (Morrisons) turn left. Ground is 200 yards on the right.

CADBURY HEATH - Springfield, Cadbury Heath Road, Bristol BS30 8BX 0117 967 5731 (social club)
M5-M4-M32 Exit 1 follow signs for ring road, exit roundabout for Cadbury Heath left, 100m mini roundabout straight across, 400m mini roundabout turn right into Tower Road North, 150m turn right into Cadbury Heath Road, ground 50m on right via Cadbury Heath Social Club car park.

CALNE TOWN - Bremhill View, Calne, Wiltshire SN11 9EE
Take A4 to Calne from Chippenham, on approaching Calne turn left at the first roundabout on to A3102 Calne bypass. At the next roundabout turn right, next left and then right and right again.

CHARD TOWN - Dening Sports Field, Zembard Lane, Chard, Somerset TA20 1JL 01460 61402
From A30 High Street, follow Swimming Pool/Sports Centre signs via Helliers road. Turn right into Crimchard, turn left into Zembard Lane. Ground is on right hand side.

DEVIZES TOWN - Nursteed Road, Devizes, Wiltshire SN10 3DX 01380 722 817
Leave Devizes on A342 for Andover. Ground is on the right hand side opposite Eastleigh Road.

ELMORE - Horsdon Park, Heathcoat Way, Tiverton, Devon EX16 4DB 01884 252 341
Leave M5 at Junction 27. Follow A373 towards Tiverton, dual-carriageway, for approximately 7 miles. Follow sign-post Tiverton and Industrial Estate, ground is 320 metres on right.

GILLINGHAM TOWN - Hardings Lane, Gillingham, Dorset SP8 4HX 01747 823 673
Proceed to middle of town to the High Street. Hardings Lane is a turning off of the High Street, at the Shaftesbury or Southern end of the High Street.

HENGROVE ATHLETIC - Norton Lane, Whitchurch, Bristol BS14 0BT 01275 832 894
Take A37 from Bristol through Whitchurch village past Maes Knoll pub, over hump bridge taking next turning on right, which is Norton Lane. Ground is immediately after Garden Centre.

KEYNSHAM TOWN - Crown Field, Bristol Road, Keynsham BS31 2DZ 0117 986 5876
On A4175 off the Bristol to Bath A4. On left immediately after 30mph sign.

MELKSHAM TOWN - The Conigre, Market Place, Melksham, Wiltshire SN12 6ES 01225 702 843
Turn into Market Place car park and then left into grounds of Cooper Avon Tyres Sports & Social Club (Melksham House) Ground situated at end of drive.

MERTHYR TOWN - Rhiw Dda'r, Parish Road, Taffs Well, Cardiff CF15 7SA 07980363675
Leave M4 at Junction 32, and at the roundabout ensure you are in the right hand lane signposted A470 Merthyr Tydfil. Take the exit for A470 Merthyr Tydfil. When you have joined A470 stay in the left hand lane and leave A470 after 800 yards signposted Taffs Well and Radyr. At the roundabout take the second exit signposted Taffs Well (A4054) and after 800 yards turn right at the traffic lights, signposted Park and Ride and Garth Estate. Drive through the industrial estate and take first exit at first roundabout (City Link is on your right hand side) and go straight on at next roundabout past Rhys Davies. At the end of the road turn right at T-junction, and Rhiw Dda'r ground is on your right hand side.

OLDLAND ABBOTONIANS - Aitchison Playing Field, Castle Road, Oldland Common, Bristol BS30 9PP 0117 932 8263

Exit M4 at Jct19 to M32. Exit M32 at Jct 1after 400 yds and take 1st exit from roundabout for A4174. Straight over traffic lights to next roundabout continuing on A4174. Go over five roundabouts for approximately 4.8 miles. At next roundabout take 1st exit to Deanery Road (A420) and continue for 0.9 miles to Griffin Public house and turn right into Bath Road (A4175) . Continue for 1.3 miles to Oldland Common High Street and look for Dolphin Public House. Turning for Castle Street is next left between Chinese Chip Shop and Post Office. Ground is at the end of Castle Road.

PORTISHEAD - Bristol Road, Portishead, Bristol BS20 6QG 01275 817 600

Leave M5 at Junction 19 and take road to Portishead. At outskirts of town take 1st exit from small roundabout sign-posted Clevedon and Police H.Q. Ground is 150 yds along road on left by bus stop.

ROMAN GLASS ST GEORGE - Whiteway Road, St George, Bristol BS5 7RP 0117 983 7707

Leave M32 at Jct 2, turn left to mini-roundabout, left into Fishponds Road. At traffic lights turn right into Royate Hill, under viaduct and rail bridge to end of road, turn left at lights into Whitehall Road, straight on at mini-roundabout and take next right into Plummers Hill. At end of road turn left into Clouds Hill Road, take third turning left approximately 1/4 mile (Worlds End pub on corner), up hill until road levels out, turn right into lane between houses No 168 - 170. Ground at end of lane.

SHEPTON MALLET - Playing Fields, Old Wells Road, West Shepton, Shepton Mallet BA4 5XN 01749 344 609

From the town take B3136 (Glastonbury Road) for approximately 1/2 mile. Turn right at junction of Old Wells Road near King William Public House. Approximately 300 yards up the Old Wells Road turn left into the playing fields.

SHREWTON UNITED - Recreation Ground, Mill Lane, Shrewton, Wilts SP3 4JY 07786 802 688

At the mini roundabout in the village turn into High Street and then turn left at the George Inn. Follow signs to the football club, approximately 200 metres on right hand side.

WESTBURY UNITED - Meadow Lane, Westbury, Wiltshire BA13 3AF 01373 823 409

From town centre proceed along Station Road towards rail station. At double mini roundabout turn right. Ground is 300 metres on left hand side opposite Fire Station.

Wells City 2010-11. Photo: Eric Marsh.

ANGLIAN COMBINATION LEAGUE

www.angliancombination.org.uk

Sponsored by:

Gleave & Associates

Founded: 1964

Recent champions:

2005: Blofield United

2006: Cromer Town

2007: Blofield United

2008: Wroxham Res.

2009: Sheringham

Premier Division	**P**	**W**	**D**	**L**	**F**	**A**	**Pts**
Blofield United	**30**	**20**	**5**	**5**	**87**	**34**	**65**
Cromer Town	**30**	**18**	**8**	**4**	**68**	**30**	**62**
Hempnall	**30**	**19**	**4**	**7**	**72**	**42**	**61**
North Walsham Town	**30**	**17**	**6**	**7**	**64**	**44**	**57**
Beccles Town	**30**	**18**	**2**	**10**	**63**	**41**	**56**
Acle United	**30**	**13**	**6**	**11**	**59**	**43**	**45**
Wroxham Res.	**30**	**13**	**6**	**11**	**68**	**68**	**45**
Mattishall	**30**	**12**	**7**	**11**	**57**	**44**	**43**
St Andrews	**30**	**11**	**5**	**14**	**47**	**50**	**38**
Brandon Town	**30**	**11**	**4**	**15**	**52**	**65**	**37**
Loddon United	**30**	**11**	**4**	**15**	**36**	**54**	**37**
Spixworth United	**30**	**10**	**5**	**15**	**41**	**44**	**35**
Sheringham	**30**	**10**	**3**	**17**	**44**	**65**	**33**
Dersingham Rovers	**30**	**9**	**3**	**18**	**38**	**68**	**30**
Watton United	**30**	**6**	**2**	**22**	**38**	**100**	**20**
Sprowston Athletic	**30**	**4**	**6**	**20**	**31**	**73**	**18**

	Acle United	Beccles Town	Blofield United	Brandon Town	Cromer Town	Dersingham R.	Hempnall	Loddon United	Mattishall	North Walsham	Sheringham	Spixworth Utd	Sprowston Ath.	St Andrews	Watton United	Wroxham Res.
Acle United	***P***	0-2	1-2	6-0	0-0	1-2	0-1	2-0	4-3	1-2	3-0	1-1	5-0	3-3	3-1	2-2
Beccles Town	1-1	***R***	2-4	0-2	2-1	4-1	2-1	4-1	2-0	4-2	2-1	2-1	4-0	3-1	3-2	3-0
Blofield United	2-2	2-1	***E***	3-1	1-3	1-0	2-1	6-1	1-1	4-0	5-0	1-0	6-0	2-0	8-1	1-3
Brandon Town	1-2	0-2	3-2	***M***	0-3	4-3	1-1	1-1	2-1	1-2	3-1	2-3	1-0	1-0	8-0	0-1
Cromer Town	1-3	3-1	2-1	1-0	***I***	4-0	1-2	3-0	0-0	4-1	3-0	1-0	5-0	2-2	4-1	2-2
Dersingham Rovers	1-4	0-5	1-6	3-1	1-4	***E***	1-5	1-3	1-3	1-1	1-1	0-2	3-0	3-1	4-1	2-1
Hempnall	2-1	4-2	0-4	8-2	3-4	1-0	***R***	2-2	2-1	4-0	5-0	4-0	3-1	4-2	1-3	1-1
Loddon United	0-2	1-2	0-1	0-3	1-4	2-0	0-1		0-1	2-3	1-2	1-0	1-0	1-0	1-1	1-7
Mattishall	4-1	2-1	1-1	4-2	0-1	1-2	0-1	1-2	***D***	2-2	3-0	2-3	3-1	1-1	8-2	3-1
North Walsham Town	3-0	1-0	3-0	4-1	3-0	1-0	2-2	1-2	1-2	***I***	4-1	2-1	0-0	3-0	3-1	5-0
Sheringham	2-0	4-1	0-2	1-1	2-2	2-0	1-3	1-3	1-3	1-2	***V***	0-2	5-0	4-3	2-1	6-1
Spixworth United	2-1	1-0	1-1	2-2	1-1	0-1	1-2	2-3	1-2	1-1	4-0	***I***	3-0	0-1	1-3	2-4
Sprowston Athletic	1-2	0-0	2-6	1-3	1-1	1-3	1-2	0-0	2-2	2-2	4-2	0-1	***S***	0-1	6-2	3-1
St Andrews	2-1	2-3	1-3	4-1	2-2	2-0	3-1	0-1	2-0	2-4	2-0	2-0	2-0	***I***	4-1	1-1
Watton United	0-4	0-3	1-1	2-4	0-2	3-0	3-1	1-4	2-1	1-5	0-2	1-4	1-3	2-0	***O***	0-6
Wroxham Res.	2-3	3-2	2-8	4-1	0-4	3-3	1-4	2-1	2-2	4-1	1-2	3-1	3-2	3-1	4-1	***N***

ANGLIAN COMBINATION PREMIER DIVISION CONSTITUTION 2010-11

ACLE UNITED .... Bridewell Lane, Acle, Norwich NR13 3RA 01493 752989
BECCLES TOWN .... College Meadow, Common Lane, Beccles NR34 7FA 07729 782817
BLOFIELD UNITED .... Old Yarmouth Road, Blofield, Norwich NR13 4LE 07748 863203
BRANDON TOWN .... Remembrance Playing Field, Church Road, Brandon IP27 0JB 01842 813177
CROMER TOWN .... Cabbell Park, Mill Road, Cromer NR27 0AD 07940 092131
DERSINGHAM ROVERS ..... Behind Feathers Hotel, Manor Road, Dersingham, King's Lynn PE31 6LN 01485 542707
HEMPNALL .... Bungay Road, Hempnall, Norwich NR15 2NG 01508 498086
KIRKLEY & PAKEFIELD RES.. . Kirkley & Pakefield Community Centre, Walmer Rd, Lowestoft NR33 7LE 01502 513549
LODDON UNITED .... George Lane Playing Field, Loddon, Norwich NR14 6NB 01508 528497
MATTISHALL .... Mattishall Playing Fields, South Green, Mattishall, Norwich NR20 3JY 01362 850246
NORTH WALSHAM TOWN .... Sports Centre, Greens Road, North Walsham NR28 0HW 01692 406888
NORWICH ST JOHNS .... Cringleford Recreation Ground, Oakfields Road, Cringleford NR4 6XE .... None
SHERINGHAM .... Recreation Ground, Weybourne Road, Sheringham NR26 8WD 01263 824804
SPIXWORTH .... Spixworth Village Hall, Crostick Lane, Spixworth, Norwich NR10 3NQ 01603 898092
ST ANDREWS........... Thorpe Recreation Ground, Laundry Lane, Thorpe St Andrew, Norwich NR7 0XQ 01603 300316
WROXHAM RES. .... Trafford Park, Skinners Lane, Wroxham NR12 8SJ 01603 783538

IN: Kirkley & Pakefield Res. (P), Norwich St Johns (P)
OUT: Sprowston Athletic (R), Watton United (R)
Spixworth United become Spixworth

DON FROST MEMORIAL CUP

(Premier Division champions v Mummery Cup holders)

(August 14th at Wroxham)

Sheringham 1 **Blofield United** 2

Division One		P	W	D	L	F	A	Pts
Kirkley & Pakefield Res.		30	20	5	5	82	33	65
Norwich St Johns		30	21	2	7	92	53	65
Long Stratton		30	21	2	7	70	43	65
Poringland Wanderers		30	17	3	10	76	55	54
Corton		30	15	6	9	68	48	51
Wymondham Town		30	13	9	8	58	49	48
Horsford United		30	12	9	9	60	50	45
Hindringham		30	13	6	11	52	57	45
Reepham Town		30	12	5	13	44	46	41
Wells Town		30	10	7	13	37	51	37
Caister		30	12	1	17	55	76	37
Bungay Town		30	9	8	13	45	55	35
Stalham Town		30	9	5	16	36	47	32
Holt United		30	6	12	12	43	55	30
Scole United		30	5	4	21	36	73	19
Sole Bay United	*-1*	30	2	2	26	19	82	7

MUMMERY CUP

(Premier Division and Division One teams)

FIRST ROUND

Acle Utd 7 Hindringham 1
Blofield United 4 Wymondham Town 1
Brandon Town 5 Sole Bay United 2
Corton 4 Bungay Town 1
Hempnall 4 Caister 0
Holt Utd 1 **Horsford Utd** 3
Loddon United 2 Kirkley & Pakefield Res. 1
Long Stratton 2 **Beccles Town** 2 *aet* (7-8p)
Mattishall 4 Sprowston Athletic 1
North Walsham Town 4 **Poringland W.** 4 *aet* (2-3p)
Reepham Town 1 **Sheringham** 2
Spixworth Utd 3 Scole 0
St Andrews 1 **Cromer** 3
Stalham Town 2 Norwich St Johns 0
Watton United 1 Dersingham Rovers 0
Wells Town 1 **Wroxham Res.** 5

SECOND ROUND

Blofield 4 Sheringham 1
Brandon Town 2 **Beccles Town** 7
Corton 0 **Hempnall** 1
Cromer Town 3 Poringland Wanderers 2
Spixworth 0 **Mattishall** 1
Stalham Town 0 **Horsford United** 3
Watton United 1 Loddon United 1 *aet* (3-2p)
Wroxham Res. 2 Acle 0

QUARTER-FINALS

Blofield Utd 2 Cromer 1
Hempnall 1 **Mattishall** 2
Horsford Utd 5 Watton 3
Wroxham Res. 4 **Beccles** 1
(Wroxham Res. expelled)

SEMI-FINALS

Blofield 4 Beccles Town 0
Horsford Utd 3 **Mattishall** 3 *aet* (1-3p)

FINAL

(May 3rd at Wroxham)
Mattishall 2 **Blofield Utd** 2 *aet* (7-8p)

	Bungay Town	Caister	Corton	Hindringham	Holt United	Horsford United	Kirkley/Pake. Res.	Long Stratton	Norwich St Johns	Poringland Wdrs	Reepham Town	Scole United	Sole Bay United	Stalham Town	Wells Town	Wymondham T.
Bungay Town		2-0	2-0	1-2	2-1	4-3	2-2	2-3	0-4	1-3	1-0	3-0	0-0	3-0	0-2	0-2
Caister	3-0		0-4	4-2	2-0	2-3	2-0	2-3	3-5	2-1	1-4	2-3	3-0	1-0	1-0	4-1
Corton	2-2	5-0	***D***	3-4	3-3	2-2	0-5	0-2	2-1	2-3	3-0	2-1	2-0	1-1	2-1	4-1
Hindringham	1-2	2-3	2-2	***I***	2-3	1-1	1-2	1-2	1-6	5-3	1-0	6-2	1-0	3-2	1-0	3-2
Holt United	2-2	4-1	0-0	1-1	***V***	0-0	0-5	0-1	0-5	1-1	0-1	3-1	2-0	1-0	1-1	1-2
Horsford United	2-2	1-1	0-1	4-0	5-3	***I***	4-1	3-2	0-2	1-2	1-4	4-1	1-0	3-0	4-1	2-2
Kirkley & Pakefield Res.	3-1	4-2	3-1	0-0	2-2	2-3	***S***	2-0	4-6	3-0	1-0	2-0	3-0	3-0	3-0	2-2
Long Stratton	2-0	4-0	2-7	2-2	2-0	3-0	0-4	***I***	4-1	1-1	3-2	5-2	5-0	1-0	5-1	2-1
Norwich St Johns	3-0	7-0	4-3	2-1	4-2	3-1	1-4	5-4	***O***	1-5	0-3	3-1	5-0	3-2	3-0	3-3
Poringland Wanderers	4-2	5-2	0-3	2-3	3-1	3-2	1-4	2-0	3-5	***N***	3-1	4-2	5-1	2-1	3-4	1-2
Reepham Town	2-1	3-1	1-0	2-1	3-3	1-3	0-5	0-1	0-2	1-4		0-0	6-1	0-1	1-0	1-1
Scole United	3-1	5-2	1-3	0-1	1-1	2-2	3-1	0-1	1-3	1-3	1-3	***O***	0-2	0-1	1-4	0-4
Sole Bay United	1-1	1-5	1-4	2-3	1-5	0-1	0-2	1-2	1-2	1-3	0-1	1-3	***N***	0-4	2-1	1-3
Stalham Town	2-5	3-4	2-4	0-0	2-1	2-1	1-5	1-0	0-0	2-1	3-0	1-1	5-0	***E***	0-1	0-2
Wells Town	1-1	1-0	2-3	4-0	1-1	2-2	0-4	1-5	2-1	0-0	2-2	1-0	1-0	0-0		1-4
Wymondham Town	2-2	3-2	2-0	0-1	1-1	1-1	1-1	2-3	3-2	0-5	2-2	4-0	3-2	1-0	1-2	

ANGLIAN COMBINATION DIVISION ONE CONSTITUTION 2010-11

BRADENHAM WANDERERS . . . . Hale Road, Bradenham, Thetford IP25 7RA . . . . Nor
BUNGAY TOWN . . . . Maltings Meadow, Ditchingham, Bungay NR35 2RU 01986 89402
CAISTER . . . . Caister Playing Fields, off Allendale Road, Caister-on-Sea NR30 5ES . . . . Nor
CORTON . . . . The Street, Corton, Lowestoft NR32 5HE . . . . Nor
HINDRINGHAM . . . . Sports & Social Club, Wells Road, Hindringham, Fakenham NR21 0PN 01328 87860
HOLT UNITED . . . . Sports Centre, Kelling Road, Holt NR25 7DU 01263 7112
HORSFORD UNITED . . . . Village Hall, Holt Road, Horsford NR10 3DN 01603 8933
LONG STRATTON . . . . Manor Road Playing Fields, Long Stratton, Norwich NR15 2XR . . . . Nor
PORINGLAND WANDERERS . Poringland Memorial Field, The Footpath, Poringland, Norwich NR14 7RF 01508 49519
REEPHAM TOWN . . . . Stimpson's Piece Recreation Ground, Bartle Court, Reepham, Norwich NR10 4LL . . . . Nor
SPROWSTON ATHLETIC . . Sprowston Sports & Social Club, Blue Boar Lane, Sprowston, Norwich NR7 8RJ. 01603 42768
STALHAM TOWN . . . . Rivers Park, Stepping Stone Lane, Stalham, Norwich NR12 9EP . . . . Nor
WATTON UNITED . . . . Watton Playing Field, Dereham Road, Watton, Thetford IP25 6EZ 01953 88128
WELLS TOWN . . . . Beach Road, Wells-next-the-Sea NR23 1DR. 01328 71090
WYMONDHAM TOWN . . . . Kings Head Meadow, Back Lane, Wymondham NR18 0LB 01953 60732

IN: Bradenham Wanderers (P), Sprowston Athletic (R), Watton United (R)

OUT: Kirkley & Pakefield Res. (P), Norwich St Johns (P), Scole United (R), Sole Bay United (now Southwold Town) (R)

Division Two		P	W	D	L	F	A	Pts
West Lynn SSC		28	23	2	3	108	39	71
Bradenham Wanderers		28	21	3	4	96	38	66
Mundford		28	19	7	2	73	43	64
Norwich CEYMS		28	17	6	5	80	45	57
Hellesdon		28	16	3	9	91	60	51
Thetford Rovers		28	14	5	9	78	50	47
Sprowston Athletic Res.		28	13	4	11	64	60	43
Downham Town Res.	-1	28	10	6	12	66	57	35
Wortwell	-1	28	10	4	14	55	62	33
Beccles Caxton	-1	28	8	3	17	35	56	26
Thorpe Village		28	7	4	17	48	71	25
Acle United Res.		28	6	6	16	36	67	24
Attleborough Town		28	6	5	17	32	72	23
Sprowston Wanderers	-1	28	5	5	18	44	113	19
Anglian Windows	-1	28	2	3	23	30	103	8

Gayton United - record expunged

C S MORLEY CUP

(Anglian Combination club reserve teams)

FINAL

(April 26th at Fakenham Town)

Cromer Town Res. 3

North Walsham Town Res. 0

	Acle United Res.	Anglian Windows	Attleborough Town	Beccles Caxton	Bradenham Wanderers	Downham Town Res.	Gayton United	Hellesdon	Mundford	Norwich CEYMS	Sprowston Athletic Res.	Sprowston Wanderers	Thetford Rovers	Thorpe Village	West Lynn SSC	Wortwell
Acle United Res.		3-0	1-1	2-0	1-2	0-3	n/a	4-1	0-2	0-7	1-2	1-3	1-3	3-2	0-2	2-5
Anglian Windows	1-2		4-2	3-4	0-5	1-1	n/a	2-12	0-1	0-1	0-4	3-5	0-8	0-4	0-2	1-7
Attleborough Town	1-0	0-1	***D***	0-0	1-3	1-4	n/a	0-3	1-5	3-2	1-2	2-1	0-1	2-0	1-1	3-2
Beccles Caxton	0-1	1-0	3-0	***I***	1-5	1-2	n/a	0-4	2-4	0-2	0-0	6-0	3-1	2-0	2-8	0-1
Bradenham Wanderers	1-0	4-0	4-1	3-1	***V***	3-1	n/a	4-0	2-3	4-4	9-0	3-3	3-2	4-2	3-0	3-0
Downham Town Res.	2-2	5-0	5-1	3-2	1-2	***I***	n/a	2-3	3-4	0-2	1-1	5-3	3-3	2-1	1-2	2-3
Gayton United	n/a	n/a	0-5	n/a	n/a	0-3	***S***	n/a	0-7	n/a	n/a	n/a	n/a	n/a	n/a	n/a
Hellesdon	1-0	6-0	6-1	2-1	4-2	5-1	n/a	***I***	3-0	2-4	2-1	6-0	1-1	2-1	2-5	2-2
Mundford	2-1	5-3	4-1	2-0	2-2	2-2	n/a	8-3	***O***	3-3	1-1	W-L	2-0	1-0	2-2	4-2
Norwich CEYMS	4-4	5-3	5-0	4-1	1-3	2-1	n/a	2-6	0-0	***N***	3-0	3-2	2-2	5-0	3-4	4-0
Sprowston Athletic Res.	3-2	4-3	1-1	3-0	1-5	W-L	n/a	3-1	3-4	1-2		10-0	3-2	1-5	2-3	4-0
Sprowston Wanderers	1-1	2-0	2-2	0-1	0-6	4-2	n/a	1-6	1-4	1-1	2-8	***T***	1-3	4-4	2-14	2-1
Thetford Rovers	8-0	W-L	1-4	W-L	4-3	2-2	n/a	6-3	1-1	1-2	6-2	7-0	***W***	2-3	0-1	4-3
Thorpe Village	2-2	1-1	4-1	2-2	3-5	1-4	n/a	3-2	1-4	1-3	1-0	4-0	0-4	***O***	2-5	0-2
West Lynn SSC	6-0	6-1	5-0	4-0	1-0	3-6	n/a	4-1	5-1	3-2	4-0	6-2	5-2	5-1		W-L
Wortwell	2-2	3-3	2-1	0-2	1-3	3-2	n/a	2-2	1-2	0-2	1-4	4-2	2-4	3-0	3-2	

ANGLIAN COMBINATION DIVISION TWO CONSTITUTION 2010-11

ACLE UNITED RES. . . . . Bridewell Lane, Acle, Norwich NR13 3RA 01493 752989
ATTLEBOROUGH TOWN. . . . . Recreation Ground, Station Road, Attleborough NR17 2AS 01953 455365
BECCLES CAXTON . . . . Caxton Meadow, adjacent. Beccles Station, Beccles NR34 9QH 01502 712829
DOWNHAM TOWN RES. . . . . Memorial Playing Field, Lynn Road, Downham Market PE38 9QE 01366 388424
FOULSHAM . . . . Playing Field, Guist Road, Foulsham, Dereham NR20 5RZ . . . . None
HELLESDON . . . . Hellesdon Community Centre, Wood View Road, Hellesdon, Norwich NR6 5QB. 01603 427675
HEMPNALL RES. . . . . Bungay Road, Hempnall, Norwich NR15 2NG 01508 498086
MUNDFORD . . . . The Glebe, Mundford, Thetford IP26 5EJ . . . . None
NORWICH CEYMS . . . . Hilltops Sports Centre, Main Road, Swardeston, Norwich NR14 8DU 01508 578826
SCOLE UNITED. Ransome Avenue Playing Field, Scole, Diss IP21 4EA. 01379 741204
SOUTHWOLD TOWN. . . . . Reydon High School, Wangford Road, Reydon, Southwold IP18 6QA . . . . None
SPROWSTON ATHLETIC RES. . Sprowston Spts/Social, Blue Boar Lane, Sprowston, Norwich NR7 8RJ 01603 427688
SPROWSTON WANDERERS . . . Sprowston Cricket Club, Barkers Lane, Sprowston, Norwich NR7 8QZ. 01603 404042
THETFORD ROVERS. Euston Park, Euston, Thetford IP24 2QP . . . . None
THORPE VILLAGE . . . . Thorpe Recreation Ground, Laundry Lane, Thorpe St Andrew, Norwich NR7 0XQ 01603 300316
WORTWELL . . . . Wortwell Playing Field, opposite Bell PH, High Road, Wortwell, Harleston IP20 0HH . . . . None

IN: Foulsham (P), Hempnall Res. (P), Scole United (R), Southwold Town (formerly Sole Bay United) (R)

OUT: Anglian Windows (R), Bradenham Wanderers (P), Gayton United (WS), West Lynn SSC (W)

Division Three		P	W	D	L	F	A	Pts
Hempnall Res.		30	25	1	4	95	40	76
Foulsham		30	24	1	5	104	44	73
Cromer Town Res.		30	19	2	9	78	48	59
Harleston Town	*-1*	30	16	6	8	92	43	53
Newton Flotman		30	16	5	9	54	37	53
Aylsham		30	13	8	9	50	34	47
North Walsham Res.	*-1*	30	14	3	13	56	60	44
Martham		30	12	6	12	77	63	42
Beccles Town Res.		30	12	6	12	55	62	42
East Harling		30	13	1	16	67	74	40
Marlingford	*-1*	30	13	2	15	38	54	40
Loddon United Res.		30	8	8	14	51	59	32
Easton	*-1*	30	9	4	17	46	77	30
Freethorpe		30	5	10	15	36	60	25
Caister Res.		30	4	4	22	47	129	16
Fakenham Town Res.	*-1*	30	1	5	24	27	89	7

CYRIL BALLYN CUP

(Division Two, Three, Four, Five and Six first teams and external league reserve sides)

FIRST ROUND
Anglian Windows 1 **Acle** 2
Bradenham Wanderers 4 Beccles Caxton 0
Buxton (w/o) v Necton SSC
East Harling 3 Swaffham Town Res. 2
Martham 0 **Mundford** 7
Newton Flotman 3 **Freethorpe** 3 *aet* (2-4p)
South Walsham 4 Fakenham Town Res. 0
Thetford Ath. 2 **Hemsby** 7

SECOND ROUND
Bradenham Wanderers 2 Sprowston Wanderers 1
Buxton 3 Sprowston Athletic Res. 3 *aet* (4-1p)
CNSOBU 0 **Waveney** 6
Easton 1 **Aylsham** 4
Freethorpe 0 **Thorpe V.** 2
Harleston 5 UEA 2 *aet*
Hellesdon 9 South Walsham 2
Hemsby 2 Marlingford 1
Hoveton Wherrymen 4 **Foulsham** 5
Mulbarton 0 **Mundford** 2
Redgrave 2 East Harling 1
Saham Toney 1 **Attleborough Town** 2
Thetford Rovers 2 Norwich CEYMS 1
Thorpe Rovers (w/o) v Gayton United
West Lynn 5 Acle Res. 1
Wortwell 2 Downham Town Res. 0

THIRD ROUND
Foulsham 6 Thorpe V. 0
Harleston 5 Mundford 1
Hemsby 4 Waveney 2
Redgrave Rangers 1 **Hellesdon** 2
Thetford Rov. 7 Buxton 1
Thorpe Rovers 2 Aylsham 2 *aet* (3-2p)
West Lynn SSC 3 Attleborough Town 1
Wortwell 2 **Bradenham Wanderers** 3

QUARTER-FINALS
Foulsham 2 **Harleston** 3
Hellesdon 0 **Bradenham** 1
Thetford Rovers 3 Thorpe Rovers 0
West Lynn 4 Hemsby 1

SEMI-FINALS
Bradenham Wanderers 1 **West Lynn SSC** 3
Harleston Town 3 Thetford Rovers 3 *aet* (5-4p)

FINAL
(May 5th at Watton United)
Harleston Town 3 **West Lynn SSC** 3 *aet* (7-8p)

	Aylshm	Becc.	Caister	Cromer	E. Harl.	Easton	Fak'nh.	F'sham	F'thrpe	Harl.	Hemp.	Loddon	Marl.	Mar.	N Flot.	N Wals.
Aylsham	***D***	1-2	6-1	0-1	1-0	6-0	4-0	5-3	1-2	0-0	1-2	0-0	4-5	3-1	1-0	1-1
Beccles Town Res.	5-0	***I***	1-2	4-1	3-2	2-1	2-1	1-1	4-2	0-5	0-1	4-1	0-4	2-2	0-1	4-2
Caister Res.	0-2	2-7	***V***	0-4	3-5	1-2	4-3	0-7	0-5	5-5	1-5	2-2	1-2	2-5	2-5	3-5
Cromer Town Res.	0-0	2-0	6-0	***I***	3-1	1-0	7-0	4-2	5-1	3-0	2-5	0-2	7-0	2-1	2-2	0-4
East Harling	0-1	2-4	6-2	4-1	***S***	3-1	W-L	1-3	2-1	3-1	2-5	1-2	2-1	2-5	5-0	1-3
Easton	2-1	2-2	3-2	2-9	3-2	***I***	7-0	1-2	0-0	1-9	2-3	0-5	0-1	2-0	1-1	1-3
Fakenham Town Res.	0-1	0-1	1-1	1-3	2-3	0-5	***O***	0-3	3-3	3-5	2-4	0-5	0-1	1-4	0-2	1-3
Foulsham	3-2	3-0	8-0	5-1	4-3	6-3	5-1	***N***	5-0	0-4	2-3	6-1	2-0	4-1	2-1	4-2
Freethorpe	1-1	2-1	2-3	1-2	2-2	1-1	4-1	0-2		W-L	1-2	1-2	0-3	1-3	1-1	1-2
Harleston Town	2-0	7-1	1-1	3-2	3-1	3-0	1-1	0-3	7-0		1-3	4-1	4-2	2-3	0-1	7-0
Hempnall Res.	1-3	4-0	4-2	0-1	7-1	7-1	2-2	3-4	3-2	4-1		4-0	4-0	2-1	4-1	2-1
Loddon United Res.	0-0	1-1	2-3	1-3	4-2	1-2	0-2	2-4	0-0	1-1	3-0	***T***	2-4	2-3	2-3	3-1
Marlingford	0-1	3-0	3-2	L-W	1-2	0-1	0-0	0-4	0-0	0-5	0-2	2-1	***H***	1-3	0-1	2-1
Martham	2-2	2-2	12-0	3-4	1-3	3-1	2-1	2-3	2-2	3-3	1-3	2-2	4-0	***R***	0-2	2-4
Newton Flotman	0-0	2-2	6-1	4-1	3-4	3-1	3-0	3-0	2-0	1-3	1-2	2-1	0-1	3-0	***E***	W-L
North Walsham Town Res.	0-2	3-0	4-1	2-1	4-2	W-L	4-1	0-4	0-0	0-5	1-4	2-2	1-2	2-4	1-0	***E***

ANGLIAN COMBINATION DIVISION THREE CONSTITUTION 2010-11

ANGLIAN WINDOWS . . . . Horsford Manor, Cromer Road, Norwich NR5 8AP 01603 40472
AYLSHAM . . . . Sir Williams Lane, Aylsham, Norwich NR11 6AN . . . . Nor
BECCLES TOWN RES.. . . . . College Meadow, Common Lane, Beccles NR34 7FA 07729 78281
BLOFIELD UNITED RES.. . . . . Old Yarmouth Road, Blofield, Norwich NR13 4LE. 07748 86320
CROMER TOWN RES.. . . . . Cabbell Park, Mill Road, Cromer NR27 0AD. 07940 09213
EAST HARLING . . . . Memorial Fields, Church Street, East Harling NR16 2NA 01953 71825
EASTON. . . . . Easton College, Bawburgh Road, Norwich NR9 5DX 01603 73120
FREETHORPE . . . . School Road, Freethorpe, Norwich NR13 3NZ 01493 70153
HARLESTON TOWN . . . . Recreation & Memorial Leisure Centre, Wilderness Lane, Harleston IP20 9DD 01379 85451
LODDON UNITED RES.. . . . . George Lane Playing Field, Loddon, Norwich NR14 6NB. 01508 52849
MARLINGFORD . . . . Bayer Social Club, Marlpit Lane, Norwich NR5 8YT 01603 78766
MARTHAM. . . . . Coronation Recreation Ground, Rollesby Road, Martham, Great Yarmouth NR29 4SP 01493 74025
NEWTON FLOTMAN . . . . . Newton Flotman Village Centre, Grove Way, Newton Flotman, Norwich NR15 1PU. . . . . Nor
NORTH WALSHAM TOWN RES. . . . . . Sports Centre, Greens Road, North Walsham NR28 0HW 01692 40688
SWAFFHAM TOWN RES.. . . . . Shoemakers Lane, off Cley Road, Swaffham PE37 7NT 01760 7227C
WYMONDHAM TOWN RES.. . . . . Kings Head Meadow, Back Lane, Wymondham NR18 0LB 01953 60732

IN: Anglian Windows (R), Blofield United Res. (P), Swaffham Town Res. (P), Wymondham Town (P)
OUT: Caister Res. (R), Fakenham Town (R), Foulsham (P), Hempnall Res. (P)

Division Four		P	W	D	L	F	A	Pts
Blofield United Res.		28	18	5	5	80	42	59
Wymondham Town Res.		28	19	0	9	66	44	57
Swaffham Town Res.		28	18	2	8	73	47	56
Sheringham Res.		28	18	1	9	66	51	55
UEA	*-1*	28	16	2	10	85	43	49
St Andrews Res.		28	15	4	9	71	47	49
Mattishall Res.		28	13	6	9	57	45	45
Thorpe Rovers		28	13	3	12	53	55	42
Hoveton Wherrymen		28	11	5	12	60	49	38
Spixworth United Res.		28	8	7	13	41	60	31
Bungay Town Res.		28	10	1	17	57	82	31
Long Stratton Res.		28	7	5	16	45	76	26
South Walsham		28	7	5	16	38	74	26
Watton United Res.	*-3*	28	6	6	16	39	68	21
Wells Town Res.	*-5*	28	4	2	22	35	93	9

Necton SSC - record expunged

Division Five		P	W	D	L	F	A	Pt
Hemsby		26	22	2	2	115	19	68
Waveney		26	20	3	3	91	25	63
Redgrave Rangers		26	19	2	5	99	33	59
Buxton FC		26	18	3	5	109	43	57
Stalham Town Res.	*-1*	26	16	2	8	58	37	49
Corton Res.		26	13	5	8	57	49	44
Norwich CEYMS Res.		26	10	6	10	48	50	36
Mundford Res.	*-3*	26	11	2	13	51	63	32
Brandon Town Res.		26	9	4	13	42	78	31
Poringland Wanderers Res.		26	6	4	16	41	79	22
Hindringham Res.	*-1*	26	7	2	17	42	82	22
Attleborough Town Res.		26	5	0	21	53	98	15
Sprowston Wanderers Res.	*-2*	26	5	0	21	30	104	13
Hellesdon Res.	*-1*	26	2	3	21	45	121	8

Division Six		P	W	D	L	F	A	Pt
Thetford Athletic		28	25	1	2	102	16	76
Mulbarton Wanderers		28	21	4	3	96	27	67
Saham Toney		28	21	0	7	123	32	63
Reepham Town Res.		28	19	1	8	70	43	58
Horsford United Res.	*-1*	28	16	1	11	75	54	48
Foulsham Res.	*-1*	28	15	1	12	85	69	45
Aylsham Res.		28	14	3	11	82	69	45
Holt United Res.		28	13	6	9	64	61	45
Scole United Res.	*-1*	28	11	2	15	56	60	34
Martham Res.		28	11	0	17	50	80	33
Easton Res.		28	7	2	19	44	111	23
Thorpe Village Res.		28	4	8	16	43	72	20
City of Norwich SOBU		28	6	1	21	35	94	19
East Harling Res.		28	4	5	19	50	105	17
Freethorpe Res.		28	5	1	22	31	113	16

	Blofield Res.	Bungay Res.	Hoveton W.	L Stratt'n Res.	Mat'shall Res.	Necton SSC	Sher'hm Res.	S. Walsham	Spixw'th Res.	St Andrews	Swaffham T.	Thorpe Rov.	UEA	Watton Res.	Wells T. Res.	Wymondham
Blofield United Res.		4-1	4-3	4-2	1-4	n/a	5-0	6-1	8-0	3-5	1-2	2-2	3-2	W-L	W-L	4-0
Bungay Town Res.	3-3	***D***	1-3	5-2	1-3	n/a	3-1	3-0	3-2	3-1	0-1	2-3	1-3	3-2	5-1	0-5
Hoveton Wherrymen	1-3	4-1	***I***	2-1	1-1	n/a	1-3	8-1	3-3	1-3	3-1	2-0	1-1	7-0	2-1	2-4
Long Stratton Res.	2-5	5-4	2-2	***V***	2-2	n/a	2-3	1-1	1-2	1-1	1-2	1-4	2-6	1-0	W-L	4-2
Mattishall Res.	3-1	4-0	1-0	2-1	***I***	n/a	0-1	6-0	1-1	1-5	0-2	3-0	4-1	3-3	5-4	0-2
Necton SSC	n/a	n/a	n/a	n/a	2-6	***S***	n/a	n/a	n/a	n/a	0-4	n/a	n/a	n/a	n/a	n/a
Sheringham Res.	3-1	4-2	1-0	3-0	3-2	n/a	***I***	1-0	4-3	1-3	1-0	4-2	5-0	4-2	W-L	0-1
South Walsham	3-3	2-6	3-1	4-0	1-1	n/a	3-1	***O***	0-2	3-4	0-3	1-2	0-5	2-2	2-1	1-2
Spixworth United Res.	1-1	3-1	1-0	1-4	3-1	n/a	3-1	1-4	***N***	1-1	2-2	0-1	W-L	1-4	1-2	1-2
St Andrews Res.	1-1	4-1	2-1	4-0	0-1	n/a	5-3	0-1	3-0		1-1	3-4	0-2	3-1	8-0	2-1
Swaffham Town Res.	1-3	7-0	0-2	3-2	3-2	n/a	5-3	1-0	1-6	5-3		2-1	2-1	1-3	7-2	5-1
Thorpe Rovers	0-3	6-0	3-0	5-1	0-1	n/a	0-3	0-2	1-1	2-0	2-4	***F***	0-6	W-L	5-0	3-1
UEA	1-2	3-0	2-3	L-W	6-2	5-0	4-4	8-0	5-0	4-0	3-2	6-2	***O***	4-2	W-L	6-1
Watton United Res.	0-2	0-2	2-2	3-3	2-2	n/a	2-1	2-0	3-0	1-3	2-7	1-1	0-3	***U***	W-L	0-7
Wells Town Res.	0-4	1-5	1-3	1-4	1-0	n/a	0-5	2-2	2-2	0-5	0-3	3-4	4-3	6-2	***R***	3-4
Wymondham Town Res.	1-3	5-1	3-2	5-0	0-2	n/a	2-3	2-1	1-0	4-1	2-0	3-0	3-0	W-L	2-0	

ANGLIAN COMBINATION DIVISION FOUR CONSTITUTION 2010-11

BUNGAY TOWN RES. . . . . Maltings Meadow, Ditchingham, Bungay NR35 2RU. 01986 894028
CAISTER RES. . . . . Caister Playing Fields, off Allendale Road, Caister-on-Sea NR30 5ES . . . . None
FAKENHAM TOWN RES. . . . . Clipbush Park, Clipbush Lane, Fakenham NR21 8SW 01328 855445
HEMSBY. . . . . Walters Lane, Hemsby NR29 4LE. 01493 733543
HOVETON WHERRYMEN . . . . Playing Field, Stalham Road, Hoveton, Wroxham NR12 8DG . . . . None
LONG STRATTON RES. . . . . Manor Road Playing Fields, Long Stratton, Norwich NR15 2XR . . . . None
MATTISHALL RES. . . . . Mattishall Playing Fields, South Green, Mattishall, Norwich NR20 3JY. 01362 850246
SHERINGHAM RES.. . . . . Recreation Ground, Weybourne Road, Sheringham NR26 8WD 01263 824804
SOUTH WALSHAM . . . . The Playing Field, South Walsham. . . . . None
SPIXWORTH RES.. . . . . Spixworth Village Hall, Crostick Lane, Spixworth, Norwich NR10 3NQ. 01603 898092
ST ANDREWS RES. . . . . . . Thorpe Recreation Ground, Laundry Lane, Thorpe St Andrew, Norwich NR7 0XQ 01603 300316
THORPE ROVERS . . . . Dussindale Park, Pound Lane, Thorpe, Norwich NR7 0SR . . . . None
UEA. . . . . UEA Sports Ground, Colney Lane, Norwich NR4 7RG . . . . None
WATTON UNITED RES. . . . . Watton Playing Field, Dereham Road, Watton, Thetford IP25 6EZ 01953 881281
WAVENEY . . . . Denes Community Centre, Yarmouth Road, Lowestoft NR32 4AH . . . . None

IN: Caister Res. (R), Fakenham Town (R), Hemsby (P), Waveney (P)

OUT: Blofield United Res. (P), Necton SSC (WS), Swaffham Town Res. (P), Wells Town Res. (R), Wymondham Town (P)

Spixworth United Res. become Spixworth Res.

BEDFORDSHIRE COUNTY LEAGUE

www.bedfordshirefootballleague.co.uk

Sponsored by:
No Sponsor

Founded: 1904

Recent champions:
2005: Caldecote
2006: Caldecote
2007: Westoning Recreation Club
2008: Campton
2009: Caldecote

	AFC	Bigg	Blun	Cald	Cam	Dunt	Ick	Melt	Oak	Ren	Rise	Shar	Sout	Wes	Wils	Wob
AFC Kempston Town	***P***	2-2	0-3	1-0	1-2	6-1	2-5	n/a	0-1	0-0	4-2	2-4	3-5	10-2	0-3	1-0
Biggleswade Utd Res.	0-1	***R***	1-6	1-4	2-3	2-1	0-5	n/a	1-3	2-0	n/a	4-1	2-0	6-0	2-1	1-4
Blunham	2-0	5-1	***E***	2-6	5-2	4-1	4-3	3-0	4-3	3-1	n/a	1-1	3-3	8-2	2-3	4-1
Caldecote	2-3	6-3	1-2	***M***	2-0	4-3	0-1	n/a	0-2	1-1	n/a	4-2	4-0	2-1	4-3	1-1
Campton	2-1	4-2	0-1	0-3	***I***	1-2	2-4	n/a	3-2	2-0	n/a	1-1	1-3	9-3	1-3	8-1
Dunton	2-0	0-2	1-4	1-2	2-2	***E***	1-4	n/a	0-0	1-2	10-0	1-2	2-0	0-0	2-2	1-0
Ickwell & Old Warden	4-1	5-1	0-5	2-1	2-3	4-1	***R***	n/a	2-1	1-1	n/a	3-1	6-2	6-3	0-3	2-1
Meltis Corinthians	n/a	n/a	n/a	n/a	n/a	n/a	n/a		n/a	n/a	n/a	2-1	n/a	n/a	n/a	n/a
Oakley Sports	6-1	W-L	4-0	0-4	2-2	4-1	2-4	n/a	***D***	5-2	n/a	0-3	2-1	3-2	3-3	3-4
Renhold United	3-3	2-4	1-6	1-4	1-0	4-2	1-1	n/a	0-0	***I***	n/a	3-1	2-2	4-1	2-2	2-4
Riseley Sports	n/a	1-5	n/a	n/a	0-9	n/a	n/a	n/a	n/a	1-2	***V***	0-3	0-3	1-4	n/a	n/a
Sharnbrook	0-2	1-1	1-2	1-4	3-0	2-0	0-4	n/a	2-3	1-1	n/a	***I***	2-4	2-1	0-1	3-1
Southill Alexander	1-2	2-0	6-1	2-2	2-1	2-3	5-0	3-4	0-1	5-2	n/a	3-0	***S***	6-0	7-3	1-2
Westoning Rec. Club	1-3	2-5	0-7	1-6	2-3	0-4	0-1	n/a	0-3	2-6	n/a	5-6	5-4	***I***	0-3	4-1
Wilshamstead	3-3	0-2	2-2	3-3	1-3	4-2	1-5	n/a	1-2	3-0	n/a	6-2	2-2	4-2	***O***	3-3
Woburn	1-1	5-3	1-2	2-3	4-2	2-2	1-2	n/a	3-4	1-2	n/a	2-4	3-2	7-1	0-3	***N***

Premier Division	**P**	**W**	**D**	**L**	**F**	**A**	**Pts**
Blunham	26	19	3	4	88	45	60
Ickwell & Old Warden	26	19	2	5	76	43	59
Caldecote	26	16	4	6	73	39	52
Oakley Sports	26	15	4	7	59	43	49
Wilshamstead	26	11	8	7	66	54	41
Southill Alexander	26	11	4	11	70	54	37
Campton	26	11	3	12	57	55	36
AFC Kempston Town	26	9	5	12	49	55	32
Biggleswade Utd Res.	26	10	2	14	50	63	32
Sharnbrook	26	9	4	13	46	59	31
Renhold United	26	7	9	10	44	57	30
Woburn	26	8	4	14	55	65	28
Dunton	26	6	5	15	37	59	23
Westoning Recreation	26	2	1	23	40	119	7

Meltis Cor. and Riseley - records expunged

BRITANNIA CUP

FIRST ROUND

Caldecote 4 Oakley Sports 1
Campton 1 Renhold United 0
Dunton 3 **Woburn** 6
Ickwell & OW 4 **Biggleswade United Res.** 4 *aet* (3-4p)
Meltis Cor. v **Westoning** (w/o)
Riseley Sports v **Southill** (w/o)
Sharnbrook 2 **Blunham** 3
Wilshamstead 6 AFC Kempston Town 2 *aet*

QUARTER-FINALS

B'wade U. Res. 3 Westoning 0
Blunham 3 **Woburn** 4 *aet*
Campton 0 **Caldecote** 3
Southill 4 Wilshamstead 2

SEMI-FINALS

B'wade U. Res. 1 **Caldecote** 5
Woburn 2 Southill Alexander 0

FINAL *(May 8th at Biggleswade United)*

Woburn 1 **Caldecote** 4

BEDFORDSHIRE LEAGUE PREMIER DIVISION CONSTITUTION 2010-11

AFC KEMPSTON TOWN . . . . Hillgrounds Road, Kempston, Bedford MK42 8SZ. 01234 852346
ARLESEY TOWN RES. . . . . Hitchin Road, Arlesey SG15 6RS. 01462 734504/734512
BIGGLESWADE UNITED RES. . . . . Second Meadow, Fairfield Road, Biggleswade SG18 0AA 01767 600408
BLUNHAM . . . . The Playing Fields, Blunham Road, Moggerhanger, Sandy MK44 3RG. . . . . None
CALDECOTE . . . . Harvey Close, Upper Caldecote, Biggleswade SG18 9BQ 01767 600236
DUNTON . . . . Horseshoe Close, Dunton SG18 8RY. . . . . None
FLITWICK TOWN. . . . . Flitwick Leisure Centre, Flitwick, Bedford MK45 1TH. 01462 611575
ICKWELL & OLD WARDEN . . . . Ickwell Green, Ickwell, Biggleswade SG18 9EF. 01767 627493
LEIGHTON UNITED . . . . Stanbridge Road, Tilsworth LU7 9PL 01525 211792
OAKLEY SPORTS. . . . . Oakley Village Sports Centre, Oakley, Bedford MK43 7RG . . . . None
RENHOLD UNITED. . . . . Renhold Playing Fields, Renhold, Bedford MK41 0LR . . . . None
SHARNBROOK . . . . Playing Fields, Lodge Road, Sharnbrook MK44 1JP . . . . None
SHEFFORD TOWN & CAMPTON. . . . . STMA Digswell, Hitchin Road, Shefford SG17 5JA 01462 813377
SOUTHILL ALEXANDER . . Biggleswade Town FC, Carlsberg Stadium, Langford Rd, Biggleswade SG18 9JT 07879 802105
WILSHAMSTEAD . . . . Jubilee Playing Fields, Bedford Road, Wilshamstead MK45 3HN . . . . None
WOBURN. . . . . Crawley Road, Woburn MK17 9QD . . . . None

IN: Arlesey Town Res. (S - Capital League West Division), Flitwick Town (P), Leighton United (P)
OUT: Meltis Corinthians (WS), Riseley Sports (WS), Westoning Recreation Club (R - Division Two)
Campton have merged with Shefford Town to become Shefford Town & Campton

Division One	P	W	D	L	F	A	Pt
Flitwick Town	30	23	1	6	74	39	70
Leighton United	30	20	4	6	83	42	64
Caldecote Res.	30	18	5	7	83	52	59
Marston Social	30	17	6	7	69	40	57
Bedford Sports Ath.	30	15	4	11	73	65	49
Meltis Albion	30	14	7	9	60	55	49
Ickwell/Old Wdn Res.	30	14	3	13	67	68	45
Henlow	30	14	3	13	58	61	45
Kempston	30	14	1	15	69	70	43
Sandy	30	12	2	16	77	59	38
FC Meppershall	30	11	5	14	77	79	38
AFC K'pston T. Res.	30	10	2	18	51	74	32
Blunham Res.	30	9	4	17	42	70	31
Campton Res.	30	9	3	18	49	77	30
Stevington	30	8	5	17	54	85	29
Kempston Hamm. S.	30	4	1	25	51	101	13

CENTENARY CUP

Final *(May 7th at Biggleswade United)*
Leighton United 1 Blunham Res. 0

Division Two	P	W	D	L	F	A	Pt
Potton Wanderers	26	22	2	2	120	25	68
Bedford Hatters	26	22	2	2	116	35	68
Marston Shelton Rov.	26	18	4	4	94	38	58
Brache Sparta Res.	26	16	6	4	87	39	54
Arlesey S. Galacticos	26	13	5	8	60	51	44
Shefford Town	26	10	5	11	65	58	35
Harpur	26	10	3	13	57	83	33
Kings	26	9	5	12	72	73	32
Marabese Ceramics	26	8	4	14	27	41	28
Great Barford	26	7	5	14	46	74	26
Clifton	26	5	10	11	48	74	25
Kempston Royals	26	6	5	15	41	75	23
Elstow Abbey	26	5	2	19	37	104	17
Shillington	26	1	2	23	32	132	5

JUBILEE CUP Final *(May 5th at B'wade U.)*
Bedford Hatters 4 Brache Sparta Res. 1

WATSON SHIELD

Final *(May 1st at Caldecote)*
M & DH Oakley 4 Renhold Village 1

Division Three	P	W	D	L	F	A	Pt
Queens Pk C'scents	18	13	3	2	63	24	42
Lidlington Utd Spts	18	10	4	4	43	31	34
Stopsley Park	18	9	4	5	65	39	31
Dunton Res.	18	9	4	5	48	36	31
Renhold Village	18	9	3	6	51	40	30
Caldecote A	18	7	2	9	40	73	23
Wilshamstead Res.	18	6	1	11	44	46	19
Riseley Sports Res.	18	6	0	12	46	66	18
Westoning Rec Res.	18	4	5	9	30	39	17
Sandy Res.	18	3	2	13	26	62	11

Division Four	P	W	D	L	F	A	Pt
Sharnbrook Res.	20	17	1	2	66	18	52
Sundon Park Rgrs	20	14	3	3	92	27	45
M & DH Oakley	20	13	0	7	61	39	39
Flitwick Town Res.	20	10	2	8	51	53	32
Thurleigh	20	8	4	8	45	45	28
Dinamo Flitwick	20	8	3	9	50	45	27
Eastcotts	20	7	4	9	40	44	25
Clifton Res.	20	7	4	9	50	55	25
Stewartby Village	20	7	0	13	45	61	21
Kempston Athletic	20	4	1	15	41	84	13
Bedford Park Rgrs	20	4	0	16	22	92	12

CAMBRIDGESHIRE COUNTY LEAGUE

Sponsored by: Kershaw and BIS

Founded: 1891

Recent champions:
2005: Fulbourn Institute
2006: Sawston United
2007: Great Shelford
2008: Waterbeach
2009: Fulbourn Institute

	Camb	Cott	Eaton	Ely C.	Ford	Fox	Fulb	Grea	Hist	Hund	Lake	Little	Need	New	Over	Water	West	Whitt
Cambridge Univ. Press	***P***	2-1	8-3	4-2	5-1	1-1	3-2	2-1	2-1	7-0	0-2	2-0	6-2	6-0	2-1	2-1	3-2	4-1
Cottenham United	0-5	***R***	3-1	4-0	2-1	3-0	0-3	0-4	1-0	2-0	2-4	3-3	5-0	3-0	1-1	0-1	0-3	2-3
Eaton Socon	2-1	2-2	***E***	1-0	4-2	2-1	2-4	1-1	1-1	3-1	0-3	0-3	3-1	0-4	1-1	1-0	2-1	2-1
Ely City Res.	0-3	2-1	1-1	***M***	0-0	2-2	1-5	2-1	1-4	3-3	4-3	1-4	2-0	3-1	1-4	1-0	2-1	4-1
Fordham	0-6	1-4	2-5	0-3	***I***	0-1	1-3	1-3	1-5	1-1	1-5	0-4	6-0	1-3	2-4	3-1	1-2	1-2
Foxton	1-1	0-3	3-1	2-3	8-2	***E***	0-2	1-3	2-2	3-1	2-6	0-3	3-0	1-2	1-3	4-3	3-3	2-1
Fulbourn Institute	1-0	5-2	5-1	3-0	15-0	3-0	***R***	1-0	2-1	4-0	1-0	4-1	9-0	2-0	5-1	5-1	2-1	1-0
Great Shelford	0-1	2-2	6-0	1-0	6-2	2-3	2-1		2-1	4-2	0-1	3-1	4-1	3-0	1-0	3-0	1-1	5-2
Histon A	0-2	2-4	1-1	1-2	5-0	6-0	2-1	0-3		0-1	1-1	3-3	2-1	3-1	0-4	2-2	3-1	3-3
Hundon	2-3	0-3	3-1	1-3	1-0	6-0	1-4	1-4	1-1		1-0	3-0	10-1	5-1	1-2	0-0	1-1	2-4
Lakenheath	1-2	7-2	3-2	9-3	6-1	7-0	1-2	0-3	2-0	0-3	***D***	4-2	9-1	4-1	4-0	3-2	5-4	2-1
Littleport Town	1-2	1-2	1-1	0-0	3-3	3-2	0-1	1-0	0-6	1-2	1-1	***I***	9-2	4-0	1-1	1-2	3-1	2-1
Needingworth United	0-4	0-2	0-2	2-1	1-3	4-5	2-4	1-3	3-5	0-2	0-5	0-6	***V***	0-3	0-4	2-2	0-7	0-4
Newmarket Town Res.	2-4	0-1	0-2	0-3	2-1	0-5	1-6	0-2	1-2	1-2	0-8	1-5	1-1	***I***	1-1	1-3	4-1	2-2
Over Sports	1-1	2-3	3-1	2-0	2-1	3-0	0-0	1-1	2-0	2-2	1-5	1-0	4-0	2-0	***S***	2-1	4-2	2-2
Waterbeach	1-3	2-1	3-1	4-0	2-0	1-1	0-1	0-1	2-2	2-3	0-1	1-0	4-0	3-2	1-1	***I***	1-4	0-2
West Wratting	0-1	3-3	1-0	1-3	4-1	3-2	1-3	1-2	5-1	2-0	0-3	5-1	7-0	2-1	5-2	1-1	***O***	0-3
Whittlesford United	2-3	1-3	2-1	2-1	2-1	3-0	0-0	4-1	2-3	1-0	4-2	1-0	6-4	8-2	1-2	2-1	4-1	***N***

Premier Division		P	W	D	L	F	A	Pts
Fulbourn Institute		34	29	2	3	110	25	89
Cambridge Univ. Press		34	28	3	3	101	35	87
Lakenheath		34	24	2	8	117	47	74
Great Shelford		34	22	4	8	78	35	70
Over Sports		34	17	10	7	66	47	61
Whittlesford United		34	18	4	12	78	59	58
Cottenham United		34	17	5	12	70	61	56
Histon A		34	12	9	13	69	60	45
Hundon		34	13	6	15	62	64	45
Littleport Town		34	12	7	15	68	59	43
Eaton Socon		34	12	7	15	51	72	43
West Wratting	*-3*	34	13	5	16	77	66	41
Ely City Res.	*-6*	34	14	5	15	54	71	41
Waterbeach		34	10	7	17	48	56	37
Foxton		34	10	6	18	59	88	36
Newmarket Town Res.		34	6	3	25	38	99	21
Fordham		34	3	3	28	41	120	12
Needingworth United		34	1	2	31	29	152	5

PREMIER DIVISION CUP

FIRST ROUND

Cambridge University Press 1 Hundon 0
Great Shelford (w/o) v Fordham

SECOND ROUND

Cambridge University Press 5 **Over Sports** 6 *aet*
Cottenham United 1 **West Wratting** 2
Ely City Res. 1 **Great Shelford** 2
Foxton 5 Needingworth United 0
Fulbourn Institute 3 Waterbeach 0
Lakenheath 6 Histon A 1
Littleport Town 5 Newmarket Town Res. 1
Whittlesford United 4 Eaton Socon 2

QUARTER-FINALS

Foxton 0 **Over Sports** 3
Fulbourn Institute 2 **West Wratting** 4
Lakenheath 2 Great Shelford 1
Whittlesford United 1 **Littleport Town** 4

SEMI-FINALS

Over Sports 2 **Lakenheath** 2 *aet* (3-5p)
West Wratting 2 Littleport Town 0

FINAL

(May 3rd at Histon)
Lakenheath 1 West Wratting 0

CAMBRIDGESHIRE COUNTY LEAGUE PREMIER DIVISION CONSTITUTION 2010-11

CHATTERIS TOWN .... West Street, Chatteris PE16 6HW 01354 692139
COTTENHAM UNITED ...... King George V Playing Field, Lamb Lane, Cottenham, Cambridge CB4 8TB 01954 250873
EATON SOCON .... River Road, Eaton Ford, St Neots PE19 3AU .... None
ELY CITY RES. .... The Unwin Ground, Downham Road, Ely CB6 2SH 01353 662035
FOXTON .... Hardman Road, off High Street, Foxton CB22 6RP .... None
FULBOURN INSTITUTE .... Fulbourn Recreation, Home End, Fulbourn CB1 5BS. .... None
GREAT SHELFORD .... Recreation Ground, Woollards Lane, Great Shelford CB2 5LZ. 01223 842590
HARDWICK. .... Egremont Road, Hardwick, Cambridge CB3 7XR .... None
HISTON A .... The Glass World Stadium, Bridge Road, Impington, Cambridge CB4 9PH 01223 237373
HUNDON .... Upper North Street, Hundon CO10 8EE. .... None
LAKENHEATH .... The Nest, Wings Road, Lakenheath IP27 9HW .... None
LITTLEPORT TOWN .... Sports Centre, Camel Road, Littleport, Ely CB6 1PU. 01353 860600
NEWMARKET TOWN RES. Sherbourn Stadium, Cricket Field Rd, off New Cheveley Rd, Newmarket CB8 8BT. 01638 663637
OVER SPORTS .... Over Recreation Ground, The Dole, Over, Cambridge CB4 5NW .... None
SOMERSHAM TOWN .... West End Ground, St Ives Road, Somersham, Huntingdon PE27 3EN. 01487 843384
WATERBEACH. .... Waterbeach Reacreation Ground, Cambridge Road, Waterbeach CB5 9NJ .... None
WEST WRATTING. .... Recreation Ground, Bull Lane, West Wratting CB1 5NJ. .... None
WHITTLESFORD UNITED .... The Lawn, Whittlesford CB2 4NG .... None

IN: Chatteris Town (P), Hardwick (P), Somersham Town (P)
OUT: Cambridge University Press (P - Eastern Counties League Division One), Fordham (R), Needingworth United (R)

Senior Division A		P	W	D	L	F	A	Pts
Chatteris Town		30	25	2	3	97	27	77
Hardwick		30	20	5	5	75	27	65
Somersham Town		30	19	5	6	75	35	62
Sawston United		30	14	10	6	72	55	52
Girton United		30	13	9	8	64	42	48
Brampton		30	13	5	12	67	57	44
Milton		30	14	2	14	76	69	44
RHS United		30	13	5	12	78	82	44
Cherry Hinton		30	12	5	13	54	61	41
Wisbech Town Res.		30	10	7	13	56	74	37
Hemingfords United		30	9	8	13	59	71	35
Soham Town Rgrs Res.		30	8	7	15	56	69	31
Castle Camps		30	8	4	18	45	83	28
Mildenhall Town Res.	*-3*	30	8	5	17	47	72	26
Debden		30	6	7	17	45	66	25
Great Paxton	*-3*	30	4	2	24	30	106	11

WILLIAM COCKELL CUP

FIRST ROUND

Cherry Hinton 4 Debden 1
Girton United 4 Chatteris Town 3
Great Paxton 3 Castle Camps 1
Hardwick 11 Wisbech Town Res. 1
Hemingfords United 2 **Brampton** 6
Mildenhall Town Res. 4 Soham Town Rgrs Res. 2
Milton 4 Sawston United 3
RHS United 2 Somersham Town 1

QUARTER-FINALS

Brampton 4 Great Paxton 0
Cherry Hinton 4 Girton United 1
Hardwick 6 Mildenhall Town Res. 1
RHS United 3 **Milton** 4

SEMI-FINALS

Cherry Hinton 0 **Brampton** 1
Milton 3 Hardwick 1

FINAL

(May 3rd at Histon)
Milton 5 Brampton 3

	Brampton	Castle Camps	Chatteris Town	Cherry Hinton	Debden	Girton United	Great Paxton	Hardwick	Hemingfords United	Mildenhall T. Res.	Milton	RHS United	Sawston United	Soham T. R. Res.	Somersham Town	Wisbech Town Res.
Brampton		1-0	1-3	4-2	4-0	2-1	4-1	0-2	2-2	2-2	3-2	3-4	1-1	0-2	2-3	2-1
Castle Camps	6-4		3-5	0-2	2-2	0-1	3-0	1-2	1-0	1-0	3-0	2-5	3-3	1-6	0-4	1-3
Chatteris Town	3-0	6-0	***S***	5-0	4-0	3-1	3-1	1-1	4-1	2-1	3-1	5-1	5-0	4-1	1-2	3-0
Cherry Hinton	1-1	3-1	1-5	***E***	2-1	0-0	7-0	0-4	1-3	0-1	1-1	5-0	1-3	1-3	4-3	1-4
Debden	3-6	4-2	0-5	0-1	***N***	0-2	5-1	4-1	1-4	6-0	0-4	2-2	2-3	0-0	0-1	0-1
Girton United	2-2	5-0	1-2	1-1	3-1	***I***	4-0	1-1	3-1	0-1	2-0	1-2	1-1	3-2	1-1	8-2
Great Paxton	0-4	3-1	0-4	2-2	0-2	0-4	***O***	1-2	0-4	2-0	0-6	2-3	3-3	3-1	1-6	1-3
Hardwick	2-1	0-1	3-1	1-2	2-1	3-0	4-0	***R***	4-1	2-1	4-0	7-0	2-0	4-0	1-1	4-0
Hemingfords United	1-2	2-3	0-2	2-0	2-2	2-2	7-0	2-5		2-2	3-2	0-9	4-2	1-4	1-1	2-2
Mildenhall Town Res.	3-0	2-2	1-2	3-4	1-0	2-2	4-1	2-4	1-1	***D***	3-5	5-4	1-2	3-2	1-2	4-2
Milton	1-3	5-0	0-2	1-0	5-1	0-4	5-1	1-0	3-1	4-3	***I***	4-3	3-4	5-1	1-4	1-3
RHS United	2-1	4-3	0-4	2-4	1-1	0-1	4-0	4-3	2-2	4-0	7-3	***V***	1-4	3-4	0-4	2-1
Sawston United	5-3	1-1	2-2	1-2	3-0	3-3	4-2	1-1	3-1	4-0	3-5	4-1		3-1	3-0	1-2
Soham Town Rgrs Res.	0-4	0-2	0-4	5-0	3-3	3-5	3-2	0-0	2-3	4-0	1-4	2-3	1-1	***A***	1-3	1-1
Somersham Town	1-0	4-2	1-2	4-1	0-3	4-0	3-1	0-1	4-0	3-0	3-1	2-2	1-2	2-2		5-0
Wisbech Town Res.	1-5	6-0	4-2	0-5	1-1	3-2	1-2	0-5	2-4	3-0	3-3	3-3	2-2	1-1	1-3	

CAMBRIDGESHIRE COUNTY LEAGUE SENIOR DIVISION A CONSTITUTION 2010-11

BRAMPTON .... Thrapston Road Playing Fields, Brampton, Huntingdon PE28 4TB .... None
CASTLE CAMPS........... Recreation Ground, Bumpstead Road, Castle Camps, Cambridge CB1 6SN .... None
CHERRY HINTON .... Recreation Ground, High Street, Cherry Hinton, Cambridge CB1 9HX........................ None
FORDHAM .... Recreational Ground, Carter Street, Fordham, Ely CB7 5NJ.................................. None
GIRTON UNITED .... Girton Recreation Ground, Cambridge Road, Girton CB3 0FH................................ None
HEMINGFORDS UNITED .... Peace Memorial PF, Manor Road, Hemingford Grey, Huntingdon PE28 9BX .... None
LINTON GRANTA .... Recreation Ground, Meadow Lane, Linton, Cambridge CB21 6HX .... None
MILDENHALL TOWN RES. .... Recreation Way, Mildenhall, Bury St Edmunds IP28 7HG..................... 01638 713449
MILTON .... Milton Recreation Ground, The Sycamores, Milton, Cambridge CB4 6ZN........................ None
NEEDINGWORTH UNITED .... Mill Field, Holywell Road, Needingworth PE27 8TE .... None
RHS UNITED .... Eternit Sports Ground, Whaddon Road, Meldreth SG8 5RL.......................... 01763 260250
SAWSTON UNITED................ Spicers Sports Ground, New Road, Sawston CB2 4BW.................................... None
SOHAM TOWN RANGERS RES.............. Julius Martin Lane, Soham, Ely CB7 5EQ 01353 720732/722139
SOHAM UNITED .... Qua Fen Common, Soham, Ely CB7 5DQ.. None
WIMBLINGTON .... Parkfield Sports & Social Club, Chapel Lane, Wimblington, March PE15 0QX............. 01354 741555
WISBECH TOWN RES......... Tom Wood's Beer Fenland Stadium, Lynn Road, Wisbech PE14 7AL .... None

IN: Fordham (R), Linton Granta (P), Needingworth United (R), Soham United (P), Wimblington (S - Peterborough & District League Premier Division)
OUT: Chatteris Town (P), Debden (R), Great Paxton (R), Hardwick (P), Somersham Town (P)

Senior Division B	P	W	D	L	F	A	Pts
Linton Granta	30	24	2	4	127	38	74
Soham United	30	22	5	3	92	40	71
Wisbech St Mary	30	22	1	7	93	39	67
West Row Gunners	30	19	3	8	93	49	60
West Wratting Res.	30	18	5	7	93	49	59
Outwell Swifts	30	14	4	12	75	63	46
Great Chesterford	30	13	7	10	66	64	46
Swavesey Institute	30	11	6	13	54	64	39
Ely City A	30	10	4	16	50	77	34
Fowlmere	30	8	8	14	47	73	32
Comberton United	30	9	5	16	46	80	32
Saffron Crocus	30	8	7	15	49	68	31
Haddenham Rovers	30	7	7	16	63	96	28
March T. Utd Res. *-3*	30	8	5	17	47	83	26
Cottenham Utd Res.	30	6	4	20	37	76	22
Bluntisham Rangers	30	1	7	22	21	94	10

PERCY OLDHAM CUP

FIRST ROUND

Bluntisham Rangers 4 Great Chesterford 0
Ely City A 2 **Cottenham United Res.** 3
Fowlmere 6 Saffron Crocus 2
Linton Granta 5 West Row Gunners 1
March Town United Res. 2 **Comberton United** 3
Soham United 5 Outwell Swifts 2
West Wratting Res. 1 **Haddenham Rovers** 2
Wisbech St Mary 5 Swavesey Institute 0

QUARTER-FINALS

Fowlmere 5 Comberton United 2
Haddenham Rovers 3 Cottenham United Res. 1 *aet*
Linton Granta 4 Bluntisham Rangers 0
Soham United 6 Wisbech St Mary 3 *aet*

SEMI-FINALS

Fowlmere 2 **Linton Granta** 5
Haddenham Rovers 2 **Soham United** 3

FINAL

(May 5th at Histon)
Linton Granta 3 Soham United 1

	Blun	Com	Cott	Ely	Fow	Gre	Had	Lin	Mar	Out	Saff	Soh	Swa	WR	WW	Wis
Bluntisham Rangers		0-1	2-5	1-2	2-2	0-2	0-2	0-6	0-0	0-6	0-4	1-2	0-1	0-3	0-3	0-3
Comberton United	4-1		2-0	0-2	0-5	5-5	1-2	0-3	1-1	2-1	2-1	1-4	1-7	3-3	1-2	0-4
Cottenham United Res.	4-1	0-4	***S***	2-1	1-0	0-2	2-2	1-5	3-0	3-1	0-4	0-2	2-3	3-3	0-3	0-3
Ely City A	1-1	1-3	2-2	***E***	1-4	0-3	3-2	1-8	4-2	1-3	2-2	0-2	3-1	2-3	1-3	0-6
Fowlmere	0-0	1-1	2-1	5-0	***N***	1-4	2-2	2-3	1-4	2-7	3-2	1-1	2-0	1-5	0-3	1-0
Great Chesterford	2-2	1-1	2-0	0-3	3-3	***I***	4-2	1-4	4-1	3-5	1-1	0-4	3-1	2-2	2-4	0-4
Haddenham Rovers	8-2	2-5	3-2	4-5	2-2	1-3	***O***	1-5	4-3	0-4	5-2	1-2	1-1	2-3	2-2	2-7
Linton Granta	5-1	3-2	3-0	4-0	5-0	4-1	10-2	***R***	6-1	5-1	3-2	1-4	5-2	5-4	1-3	6-0
March Town United Res.	0-3	1-0	4-2	2-2	1-2	0-2	1-1	0-7		5-0	3-1	2-4	2-3	1-2	0-7	2-1
Outwell Swifts	4-1	0-1	2-0	2-4	3-0	2-0	3-0	3-1	3-4	***D***	1-1	3-2	6-0	0-4	1-1	1-2
Saffron Crocus	4-0	2-0	2-1	2-0	2-1	0-6	2-2	0-9	2-3	3-3	***I***	1-4	2-3	0-3	0-2	0-2
Soham United	2-2	8-2	2-2	1-0	2-0	2-4	7-0	1-1	5-1	5-3	1-0	***V***	5-2	1-2	3-1	4-2
Swavesey Institute	0-0	6-2	1-0	1-3	1-1	3-0	2-3	0-0	1-1	6-1	0-3	1-1		3-1	3-2	0-1
West Row Gunners	5-0	4-0	4-1	3-0	8-0	7-2	2-0	1-2	4-1	2-3	5-1	3-4	2-1	***B***	0-2	0-3
West Wratting Res.	7-1	4-0	8-0	2-4	4-2	1-1	5-3	0-7	6-1	2-2	2-2	1-2	6-0	2-4		4-2
Wisbech St Mary	6-0	6-1	3-0	3-2	5-1	1-3	4-2	4-0	2-0	3-1	1-1	2-5	5-1	4-1	4-1	

CAMBRIDGESHIRE COUNTY LEAGUE SENIOR DIVISION B CONSTITUTION 2010-11

CAMBRIDGE CITY RES. . . . . The City Ground, Milton Road, Cambridge CB4 1UY 01223 357973
COMBERTON UNITED . . . . Recreation Ground, Hines Lane, Comberton CB3 7BZ . . . . None
DEBDEN . . . . Recreation Ground, High Street, Debden, Saffron Walden CB11 3LB . . . . None
ELY CITY A . . . . The Unwin Ground, Downham Road, Ely CB6 2SH 01353 662035
FOWLMERE . . . . Chrishall Road, Fowlmere, Royston SG8 7RE . . . . None
FULBOURN INSTITUTE RES. . . . . Fulbourn Recreation, Home End, Fulbourn CB1 5BS. . . . . None
GREAT CHESTERFORD. . . Great Chesterford Rec Ground, Newmarket Road, Great Chesterford CB10 1NS. . . . . None
GREAT PAXTON . . . . Recreation Ground, High Street, Great Paxton, St Neots PE19 6RG. . . . . None
LAKENHEATH RES.. The Nest, Wings Road, Lakenheath IP27 9HW . . . . None
LONGSTANTON . . . . Longstanton Recreation Ground, Over Road, Longstanton CB24 5DW. . . . . None
MELBOURN. . . . . The Recreation Ground, The Moor, Melbourn, Royston SG8 6EF . . . . None
OUTWELL SWIFTS . . . . The Nest, Wisbech Road, Outwell, Wisbech PE14 8PA. . . . . None
SAFFRON CROCUS . . . . Ickleton Recreation Ground, Frogge Street, Ickleton CB10 1NS . . . . None
SWAVESEY INSTITUTE. . . . . The Green, High Street, Swavesey CB24 4QU . . . . None
WEST ROW GUNNERS . . . . Beeches Road, West Row, Bury St Edmunds IP28 8NY . . . . None
WEST WRATTING RES. . . . . Recreation Ground, Bull Lane, West Wratting CB1 5NJ. . . . . None
WISBECH ST MARY . . . . Station Road, Wisbech St Mary, Wisbech PE13 4RT . . . . None

IN: Cambridge City Res. (N), Debden (R), Fulbourn Institute Res. (P - Division One A), Great Paxton (R), Lakenheath Res. (P - Division One B), Longstanton (P - Division One B), Melbourn (Division One A)

OUT: Bluntisham Rangers (R), Cottenham United Res. (R), Haddenham Rovers (R), Linton Granta (P), March Town United Res. (R), Soham United (P)

BIS LEAGUE FINALS

DIVISION ONE PLAY-OFF *(May 11th at Melbourn)* Melbourn 0 **Longstanton** 3
DIVISION TWO PLAY-OFF *(April 28th at Cambridge UP)* **Cambridge Univ. Press A** 0 Tuddenham Rov. 0 *aet* (4-2p)
DIVISION THREE PLAY-OFF *(May 13th at Chatteris Town)* Chatteris Town Res. 0 **City Life** 3
DIVISION FOUR PLAY-OFF *(May 11th at Figleaves)* Figleaves 1 **Fenstanton Res.** 3
DIVISION FIVE PLAY-OFF FINAL *(May 18th at West Wratting)* **West Wratting A** 1 Bar Hill Spts & Social 1 *aet* (5-4p)
CREAKE CHARITY SHIELD FINAL *(May 4th at Camb. City)* **Saffron Walden Town Res.** 5 Dullingham 1
JOHN ABLETT CUP FINAL *(May 6th at Cambridge City)* **Chatteris Town Res.** 2 Fenstanton Res. 0
HAIGH/PECK CUP FINAL *(May 7th at Histon)* **Bar Hill Sports & Social** 3 Melbourn Res. 2

Division One A	P	W	D	L	F	A	Pts
Melbourn	24	18	2	4	69	21	56
Fulbourn Institute Res.	24	16	4	4	49	23	52
Duxford United	24	16	4	4	50	26	52
Cambdge Univ. Press Res.	24	16	3	5	74	23	51
Gamlingay United	24	14	2	8	60	38	44
Girton United Res.	24	10	5	9	40	42	35
Saffron Walden Town Res.	24	10	1	13	26	41	31
Hardwick Res.	24	6	7	11	30	38	25
Steeple Bumpstead	24	6	5	13	47	68	23
Sawston Rovers	24	6	3	15	31	60	21
Barrington	24	5	4	15	38	53	19
Camden United	24	5	4	15	31	81	19
Cambourne Rovers	24	4	4	16	26	57	16

Division One B	P	W	D	L	F	A	Pts
Longstanton	24	21	1	2	110	39	64
Lakenheath Res.	24	18	0	6	91	41	54
Buckden	24	15	5	4	65	36	50
Eaton Socon Res.	24	15	4	5	58	37	49
Elsworth Sports	24	10	8	6	66	47	38
Waterbeach Res.	24	10	4	10	42	41	34
Hemingfords Utd Res.	24	9	3	12	43	53	30
Littleport Town Res.	24	8	4	12	43	66	28
Somersham Town Res.	24	6	7	11	25	48	25
St Ives Rangers	24	7	3	14	38	54	24
Fenstanton	24	6	3	15	43	62	21
Bottisham Sports	24	3	5	16	29	80	14
Sutton United FC	24	2	5	17	29	78	11

Division Two A	P	W	D	L	F	A	Pts
Cambridge Univ. Press A	26	21	2	3	77	32	65
Dullingham	26	16	3	7	88	47	51
Whittlesford United Res.	26	13	6	7	62	39	45
Ashdon Villa	26	15	0	11	60	40	45
Fulbourn Spts & Soc. Club	26	12	6	8	70	59	42
Newmarket Town A	26	11	7	8	57	62	40
Great Chishill	26	11	6	9	68	52	39
Papworth	26	9	8	9	57	46	35
Wilbraham	26	10	5	11	56	53	35
Thaxted Rangers	26	10	4	12	69	73	34
Bassingbourn	26	9	3	14	40	52	30
Great Shelford Res.	26	6	6	14	52	83	24
Balsham -9	26	6	4	16	49	63	13
Comberton United Res.	26	2	2	22	23	127	8

Division Two B	P	W	D	L	F	A	Pts
Tuddenham Rovers	26	22	1	3	85	28	67
Huntingdon Utd RGE	26	17	4	5	74	41	55
Doddington United	26	15	6	5	68	36	51
The Vine	26	14	3	9	59	49	45
Witchford	26	11	5	10	62	53	38
Over Sports Res.	26	9	9	8	47	38	36
March Rangers	26	11	2	13	50	57	35
Burwell Swifts	26	9	6	11	38	47	33
Wisbech St Mary Res.	26	9	5	12	51	62	32
Milton Res.	26	8	5	13	36	56	29
Barton Mills	26	8	4	14	35	63	28
Godmanchester Res. -9	26	10	6	10	46	42	27
Pymoor	26	7	6	13	59	70	27
Needingworth Res. -3	26	0	2	24	15	83	-1

Division Three A	P	W	D	L	F	A	Pts
City Life	24	17	4	3	76	32	55
RHS United Res.	24	14	4	6	69	45	46
Great Shelford A	24	14	3	7	81	49	45
Eaton Socon A	24	12	3	9	50	50	39
Steeple Morden	24	10	8	6	72	59	38
Sawston United Res.	24	11	4	9	71	38	37
Fulbourn Institute A	24	10	5	9	64	58	35
Great Chesterford Res.	24	10	5	9	52	55	35
Abington United	24	10	3	11	56	59	33
Lode	24	8	4	12	47	66	28
Hundon Res.	24	7	4	13	59	65	25
Linton Granta Res.	24	4	4	16	38	75	16
Foxton Res.	24	3	1	20	31	115	10

Division Three B	P	W	D	L	F	A	Pts
Chatteris Town Res.	28	20	3	5	97	39	63
Earith United	28	17	6	5	89	43	57
Bluntisham Rgrs Res.	28	16	6	6	74	41	54
Ely Crusaders	28	15	7	6	80	56	52
Isleham United	28	12	7	9	56	47	43
Hemingfords United A	28	11	7	10	66	66	40
Little Downham Swifts	28	10	9	9	57	47	39
Stretham Hotspurs	28	12	3	13	65	75	39
Mepal Sports	28	9	7	12	52	51	34
Brampton Res.	28	10	4	14	39	60	34
Fordham Res.	28	9	5	14	46	96	32
Exning Athletic	28	9	3	16	54	76	30
Estover Park	28	6	10	12	54	65	28
Wisbech St Mary A	28	7	5	16	52	76	26
Cottenham United A	28	4	4	20	38	81	16

Division Four A	P	W	D	L	F	A	Pt
Figleaves	26	20	5	1	89	41	65
Glemsford	26	17	3	6	87	31	54
Hardwick A	26	15	4	7	69	44	49
Duxford Utd Res.	26	15	4	7	57	36	49
Orwell	26	14	5	7	71	42	47
Fowlmere Res.	26	13	2	11	42	50	41
Debden Res.	26	12	4	10	52	52	40
Sawston R. Res.	26	12	2	12	66	83	38
Cherry H'ton Res.	26	10	5	11	46	65	35
Saffron Rangers	26	9	2	15	44	64	29
Litlington Athletic	26	8	4	14	75	62	28
Hempstead Utd	26	6	3	17	47	79	21
Mott MacDonald	26	4	2	20	38	85	14
Steeple B'std Res.	26	4	1	21	40	89	13

Division Four B	P	W	D	L	F	A	Pt
Fenstanton Res.	26	24	2	0	115	20	74
Tydd United	26	19	3	4	104	43	60
Emneth Spartans	26	16	1	9	81	55	49
W. Row Gun. Res.	26	15	3	8	60	30	48
Soham Utd Res.	26	13	4	9	46	37	43
Chatteris Town A	26	13	3	10	67	51	42
G'den Chequers	26	13	2	11	64	45	41
Cbdg Com Church	26	11	3	12	48	56	36
Milton A	26	11	2	13	43	72	35
Haddenham Res.	26	9	1	16	63	84	28
Wicken Amateurs	26	9	0	17	47	83	27
Burwell Swifts Res.	26	7	0	19	43	77	21
Outwell S. Res. -3	26	5	2	19	41	84	14
Barton Mills Res.	26	3	2	21	24	109	11

Division Five A	P	W	D	L	F	A	Pt
West Wratting A	22	19	2	1	77	23	59
Saffron Walden A	22	17	3	2	73	18	54
Dalehead United	22	14	3	5	58	42	45
Haverhill Athletic	22	13	2	7	90	50	41
Cas. Camps Res.	22	11	2	9	58	38	35
Saffron Dynamos	22	8	4	10	39	45	28
Hundon A	22	8	3	11	54	58	27
Cambridge Ath.	22	8	2	12	38	81	26
Sawston United A	22	8	0	14	54	63	24
Lode Res.	22	5	5	12	52	72	20
Dull'gham Res. -3	22	5	2	15	43	66	14
Newport Veterans	22	2	0	20	16	96	6

Division Five B	P	W	D	L	F	A	Pt
Meldreth	22	17	1	4	77	29	52
Gt Paxton Res. -3	22	16	2	4	78	26	47
Haslingfield	22	12	2	8	55	50	38
Melbourn Res.	22	11	5	6	46	42	38
City Life Res.	22	10	6	6	46	45	36
Therfield/Kelshall	22	10	5	7	48	38	35
Camb'rne Res. -3	22	10	3	9	45	53	30
Barrington Res.	22	8	3	11	40	44	27
Cbdge Ambas'drs	22	6	7	9	49	59	25
Papworth Res.	22	5	3	14	30	55	18
Gt Chishill Res.	22	5	0	17	44	62	15
Stple Morden Res.	22	2	3	17	36	91	9

Division Five C	P	W	D	L	F	A	Pt
Bar Hill Spts & S.	24	19	3	2	81	31	60
Longstanton Res.	24	18	1	5	101	36	55
Girton United A	24	17	2	5	75	35	53
Will'gham Wolves	24	15	3	6	64	48	48
Mepal Sports Res.	24	14	4	6	49	41	46
Elsworth S. Res.	24	10	4	10	43	42	34
Waterbeach A	24	10	2	12	56	50	32
Isleham Utd Res.	24	9	2	13	45	54	29
Witchford Res.	24	8	4	12	57	74	28
L. Downham Res.	24	6	2	16	62	93	20
Burwell Swifts A	24	4	2	18	40	107	14
Sutton Utd Res.	24	4	1	19	32	82	13
Swavesey Res. -9	24	6	2	16	35	47	11

Division Five D	P	W	D	L	F	A	Pt
Murrow Bell	20	16	0	4	72	31	48
W'bech Fen Stars	20	13	3	4	50	32	42
Chatt. Fen Tigers	20	13	2	5	69	36	41
Doddington Res.	20	13	2	5	59	33	41
Gorefield	20	9	3	8	65	80	30
March Rgrs Res.	20	6	6	8	34	44	24
Wisbech St M. B	20	6	2	12	41	63	20
Walsoken United	20	5	4	11	31	59	19
Coldham United	20	5	2	13	44	48	17
Upwell Town	20	5	2	13	44	56	17
Estover Park Res.	20	4	4	12	42	69	16

CENTRAL MIDLANDS LEAGUE

Sponsored by: Abacus Lighting

Founded:
1971

Recent champions:
2005: Dunkirk
2006: Barton Town Old Boys
2007: Bottesford Town
2008: Askern Welfare
2009: Radcliffe Olympic

	Blid	Cal	Cli	For	Gra	Har	Hat	Kim	Kin	Kirk	Lou	Net	New	Oll	Par	Pin	Sou	Sut	Wes
Blidworth Welfare		0-1	0-4	1-4	3-3	2-0	n/a	6-2	3-4	0-3	0-6	2-3	1-2	0-3	1-7	0-0	1-3	1-1	0-8
Calverton Miners Welf.	2-0	***S***	1-1	0-0	3-1	0-2	n/a	2-3	2-0	1-5	0-4	3-2	0-1	0-4	1-6	2-3	0-2	0-3	1-2
Clipstone Welfare	1-0	2-0	***U***	0-1	6-1	1-1	n/a	2-1	0-2	0-2	0-2	3-0	0-0	1-5	1-2	1-1	3-0	4-1	1-2
Forest Town	2-0	1-1	0-3	***P***	5-0	1-2	n/a	2-1	2-0	2-3	1-1	2-1	2-1	0-2	1-2	3-1	5-1	0-1	0-0
Grantham Rangers	0-1	1-1	2-2	0-6	***R***	4-2	1-3	1-0	1-2	0-7	1-4	0-0	1-3	1-1	1-6	1-4	2-2	1-5	0-5
Harworth Colliery Inst.	0-1	2-2	3-3	1-1	4-0	***E***	5-3	3-3	2-2	0-1	2-2	1-4	1-0	0-3	1-6	4-2	4-1	2-1	2-2
Hatfield Main	1-2	n/a	3-3	2-4	5-1	n/a	***M***	3-0	n/a	n/a	n/a	n/a	n/a	n/a	n/a	n/a	n/a	n/a	1-3
Kimberley Town	2-3	3-0	4-1	2-5	3-0	0-2	n/a	***E***	3-3	2-4	1-7	3-1	0-2	0-2	1-3	0-2	4-4	2-1	1-2
Kinsley Boys	1-1	4-0	4-2	6-1	4-1	2-2	n/a	2-1		3-1	0-0	4-1	0-3	1-1	1-0	2-3	3-2	1-3	0-2
Kirkby Town	2-2	2-1	7-2	0-2	2-1	3-2	n/a	2-0	1-2		3-2	6-0	1-1	0-2	5-2	0-0	2-3	0-6	2-5
Louth Town	3-0	3-1	3-1	1-5	5-0	4-1	n/a	5-1	3-0	1-0	***D***	3-1	2-1	2-2	2-1	4-0	4-0	2-1	1-0
Nettleham	2-1	0-3	2-2	0-1	2-3	1-1	n/a	1-0	1-5	0-7	1-7	***I***	0-4	0-3	0-5	0-0	0-3	0-4	1-2
Newark Town	0-1	1-0	3-1	0-3	1-1	3-0	6-0	2-2	2-0	2-2	1-2	4-0	***V***	2-0	3-0	4-1	4-2	0-3	2-2
Ollerton Town	4-2	2-0	1-1	2-1	4-0	5-0	n/a	2-1	3-2	3-1	0-1	0-1	2-2	***I***	4-1	3-0	1-0	1-1	0-0
Parramore Sports	3-1	2-0	0-2	3-3	10-1	1-2	n/a	3-2	1-5	5-3	3-4	0-3	6-1	2-1	***S***	1-2	2-1	1-2	2-3
Pinxton	1-1	3-3	0-2	1-3	4-1	2-0	4-3	3-1	2-2	1-0	0-0	3-1	0-1	3-2	3-3	***I***	1-2	0-2	2-2
Southwell City	0-1	0-0	0-6	0-2	4-1	2-5	n/a	2-0	4-0	6-2	0-3	2-1	0-3	0-2	5-4	2-2	***O***	0-2	4-3
Sutton Town	4-0	2-1	2-1	1-0	6-1	3-1	n/a	3-1	1-0	1-2	1-0	5-0	2-2	2-3	4-3	5-1	4-0	***N***	4-2
Westella & Willerby	5-1	3-0	2-0	1-1	3-0	4-1	n/a	2-0	1-1	1-0	1-2	2-0	1-4	3-2	0-1	1-0	5-0	1-1	

Supreme Division		P	W	D	L	F	A	Pts
Louth Town		**34**	**26**	**5**	**3**	**95**	**30**	**83**
Sutton Town	*-1*	**34**	**24**	**4**	**6**	**88**	**34**	**75**
Ollerton Town		**34**	**21**	**7**	**6**	**75**	**31**	**70**
Westella & Willerby		**34**	**20**	**8**	**6**	**78**	**37**	**68**
Newark Town		**34**	**18**	**8**	**8**	**65**	**39**	**62**
Forest Town		**34**	**18**	**7**	**9**	**68**	**39**	**61**
Kirkby Town		**34**	**17**	**4**	**13**	**81**	**61**	**55**
Parramore Sports		**34**	**17**	**2**	**15**	**97**	**70**	**53**
Kinsley Boys	*-1*	**34**	**15**	**8**	**11**	**68**	**56**	**52**
Clipstone Welfare		**34**	**12**	**8**	**14**	**60**	**55**	**44**
Pinxton		**34**	**11**	**11**	**12**	**51**	**59**	**44**
Harworth Coll. Inst.		**34**	**10**	**10**	**14**	**56**	**72**	**40**
Southwell City	*-3*	**34**	**12**	**4**	**18**	**57**	**82**	**37**
Blidworth Welfare		**34**	**7**	**6**	**21**	**37**	**86**	**27**
Calverton Miners W.		**34**	**6**	**7**	**21**	**32**	**70**	**25**
Kimberley Town		**34**	**6**	**4**	**24**	**50**	**85**	**22**
Nettleham		**34**	**6**	**4**	**24**	**30**	**94**	**22**
Grantham Rangers		**34**	**3**	**7**	**24**	**32**	**120**	**16**

Hatfield Main - record expunged

Premier Division		P	W	D	L	F	A	Pts
Church Warsop Welf.		**30**	**23**	**2**	**5**	**97**	**38**	**71**
Dronfield Town		**30**	**19**	**4**	**7**	**82**	**46**	**61**
Parkhouse		**30**	**19**	**2**	**9**	**80**	**53**	**59**
Yorkshire Main		**30**	**17**	**5**	**8**	**69**	**35**	**56**
Easington United		**30**	**16**	**8**	**6**	**56**	**39**	**56**
FC Brimington		**30**	**15**	**2**	**13**	**83**	**59**	**47**
Phoenix Spts & S.	*-1*	**30**	**13**	**8**	**9**	**52**	**43**	**46**
Bentley Colliery	*-3*	**30**	**14**	**3**	**13**	**62**	**56**	**42**
Thoresby Colliery W.		**30**	**12**	**2**	**16**	**40**	**52**	**38**
Bulwell Town		**30**	**11**	**3**	**16**	**47**	**58**	**36**
South Normanton		**30**	**11**	**3**	**16**	**44**	**65**	**36**
Thorne Colliery		**30**	**9**	**8**	**13**	**45**	**74**	**35**
Hutton Cranswick U.		**30**	**8**	**5**	**17**	**40**	**55**	**29**
Kiveton Park		**30**	**6**	**8**	**16**	**40**	**67**	**26**
FC05		**30**	**7**	**5**	**18**	**31**	**70**	**26**
Welbeck Welfare		**30**	**4**	**4**	**22**	**26**	**84**	**16**

CENTRAL MIDLANDS LEAGUE SUPREME DIVISION CONSTITUTION 2010-11

BLIDWORTH WELFARE. . . . Blidworth Welfare Miners SC, Mansfield Road, Blidworth, Mansfield NG21 0LR 01623 793361
CALVERTON MINERS WELFARE . Calverton Miners Welfare, Hollinwood Lane, Calverton NG14 6NR. 0115 965 4390
CHURCH WARSOP SPORTS & SOCIAL. . The Alley, Wood Lane, Church Warsop NG20 0SR 01623 842020
CLIPSTONE WELFARE. . . . . Lido Ground, Clipstone Road East, Clipstone, Mansfield NG21 5AZ. 01623 477978
DRONFIELD TOWN . . . . Stonelow Playing Fields, Stonelow Road, Dronfield S18 2DA . . . . None
HARWORTH COLLIERY INSTITUTE . Rec Ground, Scrooby Road, Bircotes, Doncaster DN11 8JT. 01302 750614
KIMBERLEY TOWN . . . . The Stag Ground, Nottingham Road, Kimberley NG16 2ND 0115 938 2788
KINSLEY BOYS. . . . . Kinsley Playing Fields, Wakefield Road, Kinsley WF9 5EH 07883 373232
KIRKBY TOWN. . . . . Summit Centre, Lowmoor Road, Kirkby-in-Ashfield NG17 7LL. 01623 751822
NETTLEHAM. . . . . Mulsanne Park, Field Close, off Greenfields, Nettleham, Lincoln LN2 2RX 01522 750007
NEWARK TOWN. Collingham FC, Station Road, Collingham NG23 7RA 01636 892303
OLLERTON TOWN . . . . The Lane, Walesby Lane, New Ollerton, Newark NG22 9UX. . . . . None
PARKHOUSE. . . . . Mill Lane Ground, Mill Lane, Clay Cross, Chesterfield S42 6AE 07816 758778
PARRAMORE SPORTS . . . . Don Valley Stadium, Worksop Road, Sheffield S9 3TL. 0114 223 3600
PINXTON . . . . Welfare Ground, Wharf Road, Pinxton NG16 6LG. 07989 324249
SOUTHWELL CITY. . . . . War Memorial Recreation Ground, Bishop's Drive, Southwell NG25 0JP 01636 814386
SUTTON TOWN . . . . The Fieldings, Huthwaite Road, Sutton-in-Ashfield NG17 2HB. 01623 552376
WESTELLA & WILLERBY . . . . Blackburn Leisure Social Club, Prescott Avenue, Brough HU15 1BB 01482 667353

IN: Church Warsop Sports & Social (formerly Church Warsop Welfare) (P), Dronfield Town (P), Parkhouse (P)

OUT: Forest Town (W - Notts Senior League Senior Division), Grantham Rangers (F), Hatfield Main (WS), Louth Town (P - Northern Counties East League Division One)

QUARTET CATERING LEAGUE CUP

FIRST ROUND
Easington United 6 Kinsley Boys 2
FC 05 0 **Louth Town** 3
Ollerton Town 2 Newark Town 2
Replay: **Newark Town** 1 Ollerton 0
SECOND ROUND
Blidworth Welfare 1 **Thoresby CW** 2
Calverton MW 3 Bulwell Town 1
Church Warsop 3 Sutton Town 1
Clipstone (w/o) v Hatfield Main
Easington United 1 **Yorkshire Main** 5
FC Brimington 4 **Westella/Willerby** 5
Grantham Rgrs 4 **Bentley Colliery** 5
Harworth Coll. Inst. 2 **Kirkby Town** 4
Kiveton Park 2 Kimberley Town 1
Louth Town 2 Dronfield Town 1
Nettleham 3 Hutton Cranswick Utd 0
Parkhouse 4 Parramore Sports 3
Phoenix Spts & S. 0 **Newark Town** 5
South Normanton 3 **Southwell City** 5
Thorne Colliery 2 Pinxton 1
Welbeck Welfare 1 Forest Town 1
Replay: **Forest Town** 5 Welbeck 2
THIRD ROUND
Church Warsop 0 **Kirkby Town** 1
Kiveton Park 0 **Bentley Colliery** 1
Louth Town 1 Yorkshire Main 0
Parkhouse 3 **Forest Town** 7
Southwell City 2 **Calverton MW** 3
Thoresby CW 3 Clipstone Welfare 2
Thorne Colliery 0 Newark Town 0
Replay: **Newark Town** 2 Thorne 1 *aet*
Westella & Willerby 5 Nettleham 0
QUARTER-FINALS
Bentley Colliery 1 **Newark Town** 3
Calverton MW 1 Kirkby Town 1
Replay: Kirkby Town 1 **Calverton** 4
Forest Town 0 Westella & Willerby 0
Replay: **Westella & W.** 1 Forest T. 0
Louth Town 3 Thoresby CW 0
SEMI-FINALS
Calverton MW 0 **Newark Town** 3
Louth T. 1 Westella & W. 1 aet (4-1p)
FINAL *(May 3rd at Alfreton Town)*
Louth T. 4 **Newark Town** 4 *aet* (1-3p)

	Ben	Bul	Chu	Dro	Eas	FCB	FC5	Hutt	Kive	Park	Pho	SN	Thor	Thn	Wel	Yor
Bentley Colliery		3-2	4-1	0-1	3-0	1-5	2-3	2-1	5-4	1-0	2-1	1-2	2-1	4-1	2-1	1-1
Bulwell Town	1-0		1-3	0-3	1-2	3-2	3-0	0-3	3-3	0-1	2-1	1-3	2-0	2-1	2-3	1-2
Church Warsop	3-1	3-0	***P***	1-1	2-3	3-5	3-1	4-1	2-2	2-1	3-2	3-1	3-1	3-1	9-0	0-1
Dronfield Town	5-2	2-2	1-3	***R***	1-0	4-2	3-2	4-1	0-1	2-4	2-3	2-0	5-1	4-1	4-0	4-3
Easington United	4-2	2-1	2-4	3-0	***E***	3-1	0-0	3-0	1-1	2-0	4-0	2-1	0-0	2-0	5-1	1-2
FC Brimington	3-1	4-0	1-2	1-2	1-2	***M***	3-1	3-2	7-1	4-2	1-1	6-0	1-4	3-0	0-1	2-3
FC05	2-4	1-1	1-5	2-6	1-0	1-7	***I***	2-2	3-0	1-4	0-2	0-3	1-0	1-0	2-2	0-1
Hutton Cranswick	1-0	2-0	0-2	2-0	1-1	4-1	1-4	***E***	2-2	2-3	0-0	0-1	2-0	1-2	3-0	1-2
Kiveton Park	1-1	1-3	0-2	0-3	1-3	2-4	2-0	4-0	***R***	2-2	0-2	3-1	0-1	0-2	1-1	0-4
Parkhouse	4-3	1-2	1-2	1-6	7-0	2-3	5-1	1-0	4-0		3-1	3-3	2-1	4-6	W-L	3-2
Phoenix S & S	2-1	6-1	0-4	1-3	2-2	2-2	2-0	4-1	2-1	0-1		2-2	0-2	1-1	3-2	0-0
South Normanton	3-4	2-7	1-4	2-4	1-3	1-5	2-0	2-0	0-3	0-3	1-2	***D***	0-1	3-0	3-0	1-0
Thoresby CW	1-0	0-3	0-4	3-2	1-2	3-1	1-0	2-1	1-1	1-4	0-3	2-3	***I***	5-1	2-3	3-2
Thorne Colliery	1-8	1-0	3-9	2-2	2-2	1-0	1-1	1-1	3-1	2-4	2-2	1-1	2-0	***V***	5-1	1-0
Welbeck Welfare	0-1	0-3	0-7	1-4	1-1	3-4	L-W	0-5	0-3	1-5	0-3	L-W	1-3	1-1		2-1
Yorkshire Main	1-1	3-0	2-1	2-2	1-1	4-1	5-0	5-0	5-0	3-5	0-2	3-1	1-0	8-0	2-1	

PHOENIX TROPHIES FLOODLIGHT CUP

FIRST ROUND
Ollerton 5 Harworth CI 1
Southwell 2 **Pinxton** 3
Sutton Town 4 Blidworth 1
SECOND ROUND
FC Brimington 5 Nettleham 1
Grantham Rgrs 2 **Clipstone** 5
Hatfield Main v **Kinsley** (w/o)
Louth Town 4 Ollerton Town 0
Parramore 4 Newark Town 3
Pinxton 5 Forest Town 2
S. Normanton 1 **Kimberley** 3
Sutton Town 4 Calverton 2
QUARTER-FINALS
Clipstone 1 Sutton Town 0
Kimberley Town 1 **Pinxton** 6
Kinsley 2 **Parramore Sports** 8
Louth T. 4 FC Brimington 0
SEMI-FINALS
Clipstone Welfare 2 Pinxton 1
Louth Town 5 Parramore 2
FINAL
(April 7th at Newark Town)
Louth Town 2 Clipstone 1

Reserve Supreme		P	W	D	L	F	A	Pt
Belper Town Res.		28	21	4	3	98	26	67
Mickleover S. Res.		28	20	3	5	106	33	63
Carlton T. Res.	*-6*	28	21	2	5	96	29	59
Staveley MW Res.		28	16	7	5	90	37	55
Holbrook MW Res.		28	14	4	10	68	52	46
Rainworth MW Res.		28	13	3	12	69	63	42
Shirebrook T. Res.		28	12	6	10	60	57	42
Teversal Res.		28	11	5	12	52	62	38
Sutton Town Res.		28	12	1	15	54	80	37
Graham St P. Res.		28	10	5	13	37	55	35
Dunkirk Res.		28	9	7	12	55	52	34
Radford Res.		28	7	4	17	45	71	25
Forest Town Res.		28	7	3	18	35	92	24
Heanor Town Res.		28	5	0	23	35	131	15
Blidworth W. Res.		28	2	6	20	27	87	12

Reserve Premier		P	W	D	L	F	A	Pt
Dronfield T. Res.	*+3*	22	19	1	2	65	22	61
Clipstone Welf. Res.		22	12	3	7	47	28	39
Newark Town Res.		22	12	2	8	64	42	38
Calverton MW Res.		22	12	2	8	51	43	38
Harworth CI Res.		22	10	6	6	55	41	36
Ollerton Town Res.		22	11	2	9	64	34	35
Kiveton Park Res.		22	10	1	11	44	40	31
Thoresby CW Res.		22	8	6	8	41	30	30
Sth Normanton Res.		22	9	2	11	46	45	29
Pinxton Res.		22	8	2	12	37	56	26
Church Warsop Res.		22	4	2	16	27	79	14
Nettleham Res.		22	2	1	19	28	109	7

PHOENIX TROPHIES RESERVES CUP
FINAL *(April 19th at Sutton Town)*
Belper Res. 2 Staveley MW Res. 0

PRESIDENT'S CUP FINAL
(May 5th at Clipstone Welfare)
South Normanton Res. 2 Calverton Miners Welfare Res. 1

CENTRAL MIDLANDS LEAGUE PREMIER DIVISION CONSTITUTION 2010-11

AFC HUCKNALL TOWN .... Watnall Road, Hucknall NG15 6EY 0115 963 0206/956 1253
BENTLEY COLLIERY .... Bentley Miners Welfare, The Avenue, Bentley, Doncaster DN5 0PN................. 01302 874420
BULWELL TOWN ...... Goosedale Sports Ground, Goosedale Lane, Moor Road, Bestwood Village NG15 8FG 0115 963 0180
EASINGTON UNITED .... Low Farm, Beak Street, Easington, Hull HU12 0TT .... None
FC BRIMINGTON................... Sandy Lane, Babbage Way, Worksop S80 1TN.. None
FC05 BILSTHORPE .... Bilsthorpe Sports Field, Eakring Road, Bilsthorpe, Newark NG22 8SX .... None
HUTTON CRANSWICK UNITED........ Rotsea Lane, Hutton Cranswick, Driffield YO25 9QG.................................. None
KIVETON PARK................. Kiveton Park MW, Hard Lane, Kiveton Park, Sheffield S26 6NB 07763 467979
MOORLANDS RAILWAY............ Moorlands Sports Ground, Newark Road, Lincoln LN6 8RT.............. 01522 520184/874111
NOTTINGHAM UNITED ...... Gresham Park Road, Wilford Lane, West Bridgford, Nottingham NG2 7YE .... None
PHOENIX SPORTS & SOCIAL . Phoenix Sports Complex, Bawtry Road, Brinsworth, Rotherham S60 5PA 01709 363864
SOUTH NORMANTON ATHLETIC ... ExChem, Lees Lane, South Normanton, Alfreton DE55 2AD 01773 581491
THORESBY COLLIERY WELFARE. . Thoresby Colliery SG, Fourth Avenue, Edwinstowe NG21 9NS................. 07802 417987
THORNE COLLIERY .... Moorends Welfare, Grange Road, Moorends, Thorne, Doncaster DN8 4LU.............. 07855 545221
WELBECK WELFARE....... Colliery Ground, Elkesley Road, Meden Vale, Warsop, Mansfield NG20 9PS 01623 842267
WHATTON UNITED .... Spa Lane, Orston NG13 9NX .... None
YORKSHIRE MAIN................. Edlington Lane, Edlington, Doncaster DN12 2DA........................... 07775 714558

IN: AFC Hucknall Town (N), Moorlands Railway (formerly Lincoln Moorlands Railway Res. (S - Lincolnshire League), Nottingham United (formerly AFC Nottingham United) (P - Midland Amateur Alliance Division Two), Whatton United (P - Grantham League Premier Division)
OUT: Church Warsop Welfare (now Church Warsop Sports & Social) (P), Dronfield Town (P), Parkhouse (P)
FC05 become FC05 Bilsthorpe

CHESHIRE LEAGUE

www.mcfl.co.uk

Sponsored by: Cheshire Building Society

Founded: 1919

Recent champions:
2005: Barnton
2006: Middlewich Town
2007: Middlewich Town
2008: Styal
2009: Woodley

	Bill	Clu	Cro	Eag	Gam	Gar	Gol	Gre	Knu	Lino	Mid	Pilk	Stal	Sty	Traf	Woo
Billinge		0-2	0-2	1-2	1-2	1-2	2-0	0-3	1-2	1-2	3-2	2-0	2-0	2-2	1-1	0-3
Club AZ	2-2		3-0	2-1	3-2	1-1	3-1	2-2	3-2	2-0	0-2	1-4	n/a	2-1	2-0	5-2
Crosfields-Rylands	2-2	0-3	***D***	1-1	2-3	2-0	5-0	1-1	3-0	1-2	1-2	3-0	n/a	3-4	2-0	0-2
Eagle Sports	2-0	2-5	0-2	***I***	0-0	5-0	2-3	0-2	3-1	3-0	1-1	2-0	n/a	3-5	1-0	2-3
Gamesley	1-2	0-1	2-1	3-1	***V***	2-0	0-0	3-1	1-3	1-1	2-2	3-1	2-1	4-1	4-2	1-4
Garswood United	0-2	1-2	0-1	2-2	2-4	***I***	2-0	0-1	1-1	0-2	0-4	2-1	2-0	2-0	0-2	0-0
Golborne Sports	1-1	0-3	1-0	1-2	0-2	1-2	***S***	2-1	4-1	1-0	0-0	1-3	n/a	2-4	2-4	0-1
Greenalls Padgate St Os.	0-1	1-2	2-0	1-1	2-1	2-1	3-2	***I***	0-1	3-0	0-3	0-2	n/a	7-1	3-2	3-3
Knutsford	0-0	3-0	0-2	4-0	3-0	4-1	3-3	1-0	***O***	5-0	2-2	1-4	1-1	7-2	4-4	3-0
Linotype & Cheadle HN	2-0	1-2	3-1	0-2	3-3	0-0	3-1	3-0	3-2	***N***	0-3	0-1	1-1	2-1	2-1	0-3
Middlewich Town	0-1	1-3	3-1	3-1	1-0	3-0	0-4	3-2	3-0	1-4		2-0	1-4	0-1	2-1	0-2
Pilkington	2-1	0-0	0-2	0-5	2-3	2-3	4-0	2-4	0-3	1-1	1-2	***O***	3-0	2-1	0-0	1-2
Stalybridge Celtic Res.	n/a	n/a	n/a	n/a	2-0	n/a	0-0	3-2	n/a	n/a	n/a	1-1	***N***	n/a	n/a	n/a
Styal	1-0	1-2	2-5	2-4	0-3	7-3	1-3	2-2	2-3	4-2	0-4	3-1	n/a	***E***	0-2	1-3
Trafford Res.	0-3	7-2	2-1	1-6	1-3	3-0	2-0	3-1	0-2	1-2	0-0	6-1	n/a	5-2		3-2
Woodley	2-1	0-1	2-2	1-2	6-4	3-3	3-2	3-1	4-0	2-2	5-0	2-1	n/a	3-3	1-1	

Division One	P	W	D	L	F	A	Pts
Club AZ	**28**	**20**	**4**	**4**	**59**	**37**	**64**
Woodley	**28**	**16**	**7**	**5**	**67**	**42**	**55**
Middlewich Town	**28**	**15**	**5**	**8**	**49**	**35**	**50**
Knutsford	**28**	**14**	**5**	**9**	**61**	**46**	**47**
Gamesley	**28**	**14**	**5**	**9**	**57**	**46**	**47**
Eagle Sports	**28**	**13**	**5**	**10**	**56**	**44**	**44**
Linotype & Cheadle HN	**28**	**12**	**5**	**11**	**40**	**46**	**41**
Trafford Res.	**28**	**11**	**5**	**12**	**54**	**49**	**38**
Greenalls Padgate St Os.	**28**	**11**	**5**	**12**	**48**	**45**	**38**
Crosfields-Rylands	**28**	**11**	**4**	**13**	**46**	**40**	**37**
Billinge	**28**	**8**	**6**	**14**	**31**	**40**	**30**
Pilkington	**28**	**8**	**3**	**17**	**36**	**55**	**27**
Styal	**28**	**8**	**3**	**17**	**54**	**81**	**27**
Golborne Sports	**28**	**7**	**4**	**17**	**35**	**57**	**25**
Garswood United	**28**	**6**	**6**	**16**	**28**	**58**	**24**

Stalybridge Celtic Res. - record expunged

Reserve Division	P	W	D	L	F	A	Pt
Golborne Sports Res.	30	20	5	5	66	32	65
Garswood United Res.	30	19	7	4	72	33	64
Middlewich Town Res.	30	17	4	9	69	48	55
Pilkington Res.	30	16	6	8	90	57	54
Linotype & Cheadle HN Res.	30	13	8	9	63	47	47
Greenalls Padgate SO Res.	30	14	5	11	67	53	47
Poynton Res.	30	13	6	11	53	44	45
Crosfields & Rylands Res.	30	10	10	10	50	49	40
Eagle Sports Res.	30	12	4	14	67	67	40
Gamesley Res.	30	10	9	11	49	61	39
Billinge Res.	30	9	9	12	53	55	36
Grappenhall Sports Res.	30	11	3	16	48	71	36
Styal Res.	30	9	6	15	61	72	33
Denton Town Res.	30	8	6	16	52	97	30
Daten Res.	30	5	7	18	34	60	22
Crewe Res.	30	5	3	22	57	105	18

RESERVES CUP

FINAL *(May 5th at Trafford)*

Linotype & CHN Res. 3 Garswood United Res. 2

PRESIDENT'S CUP

(First Round losers from divisional cups)

Not contested due to the inclement weather

CHESHIRE LEAGUE DIVISION ONE CONSTITUTION 2010-11

BILLINGE . . . . Billinge Community Sports & Soccer Centre, Carrmill Road, Billinge WN5 7TX 01744 893533
CLUB AZ . . . . Mulberries Sports Centre, Monk Heath, Alderley Edge, Macclesfield SK10 4TF 01625 514040
EAGLE SPORTS . . . . Eagle Sports Club, Thornton Road, Great Sankey, Warrington WA5 2SZ. 01925 632926
GAMESLEY . . . . Melandra Park, Melandra Castle Road, Gamesley, Glossop SK13 0JR. . . . . None
GARSWOOD UNITED . . . . The Wooders, Simms Lane End, Garswood Road, Garswood WN4 0XH. 01744 893968
GOLBORNE SPORTS . . . . Simpson Playing Fields, Stone Cross Road, Lowton WA3 2SL. 01942 510161
GREENALLS PADGATE ST OSWALDS . Carlsberg Tetley SC, Long Lane, Warrington WA2 8PU 01925 634904
KNUTSFORD . . . . Manchester Road, Knutsford WA16 0GU . . . . None
LINOTYPE & CHEADLE HN . . . . The Heath, Norbreck Avenue, Cheadle, Stockport SK8 2ET 0161 282 6574
LOSTOCK GRALAM . . . . The Park Stadium, Manchester Road, Lostock Gralam CW9 7PJ. 01606 42148
MIDDLEWICH TOWN. . . . . Seddon Street, Middlewich CW10 9DT 01606 835842
NORTHWICH VILLA . . . . 86 Witton Street, Northwich CW9 5AE . . . . None
PILKINGTON . . . . Ruskin Drive, Dentons Green, St Helens WA10 6RP. 01744 22893
RYLANDS. . . . . Rylands Recreation Club, Gorsey Lane, Warrington WA2 7RZ. 01925 625700
STYAL . . . . Altrincham Road, Styal, Wilmslow SK9 4JE 01625 529303
TARPORLEY VICTORIA . . . . Tattenhall Recreation Club, Field Lane, Tattenhall CH3 9QF. 01829 770710

IN: Lostock Gralam (P), Tarporley Victoria (P)
OUT: Stalybridge Celtic Res. (WS), Trafford Res. (W)
Crosfields-Rylands become Rylands, Woodley become Northwich Villa

J B PARKER DIVISION ONE CUP

FIRST ROUND

Billinge 1 **Garswood United** 2
Eagle Sports 1 **Pilkington** 2
Golborne Sports 2 **Woodley** 3
Greenalls Padgate St Oswalds 0 **Crosfields-Rylands** 1
Knutsford 4 Club AZ 0
Stalybridge Celtic Res. 1 **Linotype & Cheadle HN** 3
Styal 1 **Middlewich Town** 3
Trafford Res. 3 **Gamesley** 6

QUARTER-FINALS

Crosfields-Rylands 3 Knutsford 0
Gamesley 3 Pilkington 2
Garswood United 2 **Middlewich Town** 3
Woodley 3 Linotype & Cheadle HN 0

SEMI-FINALS

Crosfields-Ry. 2 Middlewich 0, Gamesley 1 **Woodley** 3

FINAL *(March 10th at Trafford)*

Woodley 3 Crosfields-Rylands 2

Division Two	P	W	D	L	F	A	Pts
Lostock Gralam	30	21	3	6	76	45	66
Tarporley Victoria	30	17	6	7	61	40	57
Denton Town	30	16	5	9	63	38	53
Crewe	30	16	5	9	62	43	53
Moore United	30	15	5	10	55	45	50
Maine Road Res.	30	15	3	12	53	49	48
Grappenhall Sports	30	14	5	11	62	56	47
Monk Sports	30	13	5	12	64	54	44
Whitchurch Alport	30	11	6	13	36	48	39
Barnton	30	11	5	14	60	68	38
Warrington Town Res.	30	10	7	13	53	55	37
Daten	30	9	8	13	43	58	35
Congleton Town Res.	30	10	3	17	53	60	33
Poynton	30	9	6	15	55	64	33
New Mills Res.	30	8	8	14	44	60	32
Malpas	30	1	8	21	32	89	11

DIVISION TWO CUP

FIRST ROUND

Congleton Town Res. 2 Denton Town 1
Crewe (w/o) v Whitchurch Alport
Daten 4 Moore United 0
Lostock Gralam 4 Grappenhall Sports 1
Maine Rd Res. 2 Barnton 1
Malpas 0 **Warrington Town Res.** 4
Monk Sports 3 Poynton 1
Tarporley Victoria 6 New Mills Res. 0

QUARTER-FINALS

Congleton Town Res. 2 Maine Road Res. 1
Crewe 4 Lostock Gralam 3
Daten 0 **Tarporley Vics** 4
Monk Sports 5 Warrington Town Res. 2

SEMI-FINALS

Congleton Res. 0 **Crewe** 1
Tarporley 0 **Monk Sports** 1

FINAL

(April 28th at Congleton Town)

Monk Sports 2 Crewe 1

	Barnton	Congleton	Crewe	Daten	Denton T.	Grap'hall	Lostock G.	Maine Rd	Malpas	Monk Spts	Moore Utd	New Mills	Poynton	Tarporley	Warr'gton	W'tchurch
Barnton		4-3	2-3	3-1	1-4	1-3	3-3	1-5	3-0	3-2	1-1	0-1	2-0	1-4	2-2	1-2
Congleton Town Res.	2-1		0-1	1-1	0-1	1-3	2-3	2-3	4-1	1-3	2-3	1-2	1-0	1-3	2-3	1-2
Crewe	4-0	2-1	***D***	1-2	3-3	3-1	1-4	0-1	5-1	4-0	2-1	1-2	4-1	1-2	4-1	2-1
Daten	1-1	1-1	2-0	***I***	1-0	1-2	1-2	1-2	4-1	3-0	4-1	3-3	0-3	1-3	1-2	1-1
Denton Town	1-0	2-3	1-1	9-0	***V***	3-1	0-1	1-4	1-0	1-1	3-0	1-2	3-2	1-3	3-1	0-1
Grappenhall Sports	5-3	3-0	1-2	1-2	0-1	***I***	1-3	2-1	3-0	1-5	5-1	2-0	3-2	2-3	1-1	2-0
Lostock Gralam	1-6	2-3	3-1	3-0	1-4	1-1	***S***	1-1	3-0	0-1	3-1	5-0	3-1	3-0	4-2	2-1
Maine Road Res.	2-3	3-2	1-2	1-0	0-2	2-5	2-5	***I***	2-2	4-1	0-1	1-3	4-0	2-1	0-1	0-0
Malpas	4-4	0-4	1-3	1-2	3-3	1-1	1-6	2-3	***O***	2-3	1-6	2-2	2-2	1-3	1-3	0-2
Monk Sports	0-1	1-2	1-2	5-1	1-1	1-1	1-2	5-1	4-1	***N***	1-2	2-1	5-3	2-2	4-0	4-5
Moore United	5-0	2-0	1-1	1-1	1-0	3-0	0-2	0-2	3-3	4-1		2-1	0-1	1-0	2-0	0-2
New Mills Res.	0-5	2-3	1-0	3-3	1-2	3-5	0-1	1-2	2-0	0-4	5-2	***T***	1-1	2-3	2-2	1-1
Poynton	2-3	3-3	2-4	1-1	2-4	4-1	3-1	2-1	6-0	1-2	2-4	2-0	***W***	0-4	2-2	1-0
Tarporley Victoria	2-3	3-0	1-1	2-0	3-2	3-3	1-3	0-1	2-0	3-1	2-2	1-0	2-2	***O***	1-0	2-0
Warrington Town Res.	4-2	1-4	3-2	1-2	1-4	5-0	7-0	3-0	0-0	1-1	0-3	2-2	1-2	2-0		1-2
Whitchurch Alport	1-0	1-3	2-2	3-2	0-2	0-3	0-5	0-2	0-1	1-2	0-2	1-1	3-2	2-2	2-1	

CHESHIRE LEAGUE DIVISION TWO CONSTITUTION 2010-11

BARNTON . . . . Townfield, Townfield Lane, Barnton, Northwich CW8 4LH . . . . None
CONGLETON TOWN RES. . . . . Booth Street Ground, off Crescent Road, Congleton CW12 4DG 01260 274460
CREWE . . . . Cumberland Arena, Thomas Street, Crewe CW1 2BD 01270 537150
DATEN . . . . Culcheth Sports Club, Charnock Road, Culcheth, Warrington WA3 5SH 01925 763096
DENTON TOWN . . . . Whittles Park, Heather Lea, Denton M34 6EJ . . . . None
GRAPPENHALL SPORTS . . . Grappenhall Sports Club, Stockton Lane, Grappenhall, Warrington WA4 3HQ 01925 600899
MAINE ROAD RES. . . . . . Manchester County FA Ground, Branthingham Road, Chorlton-cum-Hardy M21 0TT 0161 604 7620
MALPAS . . . . Malpas & District Sports Club, Oxheys, Wrexham Road, Malpas SY14 7EJ 01948 860662
MONK SPORTS . . . . Monk Sports & Social Club, Hillock Lane, Woolston, Warrington WA1 4NF 01925 812320
MOORE UNITED . . . . Carlsberg Tetley Club, Long Lane, Warrington WA2 8PU 01925 634904
POYNTON . . . . London Road North (A523), Poynton, Stockport SK12 1AG 01625 875765
RUDHEATH SOCIAL . . . . Moss Farm Leisure Complex, Winnington, Northwich CW8 4BG 01606 783835
RUNCORN TOWN RES. . . . . Pavilions Club, Sandy Lane, Weston Point, Runcorn WA7 4EX 01928 590508
WHITCHURCH ALPORT . . . . Yockings Park, Blackpark Road, Whitchurch SY13 1PG 01948 667415

IN: Rudheath Social (P - Sunday football), Runcorn Town Res. (S - West Cheshire League Division Three)

OUT: Lostock Gralam (P), New Mills Res. (S - North West Counties League Reserve Division), Tarporley Victoria (P), Warrington Town Res. (W)

DORSET PREMIER LEAGUE

full-time.thefa.com/Index.do?league=6392495

Sponsored by: Magna

Founded: 1957

Recent champions:
2005: Hamworthy Recreation
2006: Holt Utd
2007: Westland Sports
2008: Portland United
2009: Portland United

		P	W	D	L	F	A	Pts
Hamworthy Rec		**34**	**25**	**8**	**1**	**99**	**28**	**83**
Chickerell United	*-3*	**34**	**27**	**3**	**4**	**95**	**32**	**81**
Westland Sports		**34**	**21**	**8**	**5**	**87**	**30**	**71**
Swanage Town & H.		**34**	**20**	**7**	**7**	**84**	**55**	**67**
Holt United		**34**	**20**	**4**	**10**	**93**	**43**	**64**
Poole Borough		**34**	**18**	**8**	**8**	**79**	**52**	**62**
Weymouth Res.		**34**	**18**	**8**	**8**	**69**	**45**	**62**
Portland United		**34**	**18**	**5**	**11**	**72**	**49**	**59**
Wincanton Town	*-3*	**33**	**16**	**6**	**11**	**63**	**42**	**51**
Parley Sports		**33**	**13**	**4**	**16**	**55**	**67**	**43**
S'rminster Marsh.	*-3*	**34**	**12**	**8**	**14**	**62**	**70**	**41**
Blandford United		**34**	**10**	**5**	**19**	**54**	**64**	**35**
Sherborne Town Res.		**34**	**9**	**4**	**21**	**57**	**91**	**31**
Cobham Sports		**34**	**8**	**3**	**23**	**40**	**72**	**27**
Bridport Res.	*-3*	**34**	**8**	**4**	**22**	**58**	**107**	**25**
Hamworthy Utd Res.		**34**	**5**	**6**	**23**	**38**	**92**	**21**
Cranborne		**34**	**5**	**3**	**26**	**37**	**109**	**18**
Sturm. Newton U.	*-3*	**34**	**3**	**4**	**27**	**33**	**127**	**10**

Wincanton Town v Parley Sports not played

LEAGUE CUP

PRELIMINARY ROUND
Hamworthy Utd 1 **Chickerell Utd** 8
Poole Borough 1 **Wincanton** 3 *aet*

FIRST ROUND
Cobham Sports 2 Bridport Res. 1
Cranborne 4 Sturminster Newton 2
Hamworthy Rec 3 Portland Utd 2 *aet*
Holt United 0 **Westland Sports** 2
Parley Spts 2 Chickerell 2 (4-3p) *aet*
Sherborne Res. 2 **Blandford Utd** 5
Swanage Town & Herston 3 Weymouth Res. 0
Wincanton 7 Sturminster Marshall 1

QUARTER-FINALS
Blandford Utd 1 Wincanton Town 0
Hamworthy Rec 0 **Westland Sports** 1
Parley Sports 2 Cranborne 0
Swanage T&H 4 Cobham Sports 0

SEMI-FINALS
Parley Sports 0 **Westland Sports** 3
Swanage T&H 2 Blandford United 1

FINAL
(April 29th at Dorchester Town)
Swanage 3 Westland Sports 0

	Blan	Brid	Chic	Cob	Cra	HR	HU	Hol	Par	Poo	Por	She	SM	SN	Swa	Wes	Wey	Win
Blandford United		0-0	1-3	1-3	6-1	2-4	3-2	0-1	2-0	2-2	1-2	2-0	0-3	4-0	1-2	1-3	1-2	2-1
Bridport Res.	3-2		0-3	1-0	1-0	0-7	5-3	2-7	0-3	1-5	0-2	9-4	0-3	6-1	3-3	0-4	0-4	0-2
Chickerell United	2-1	2-0		2-0	5-0	1-3	4-1	3-2	2-1	3-1	2-0	8-1	1-1	3-0	4-3	1-2	1-2	5-0
Cobham Sports	0-1	1-3	1-6		0-1	0-1	0-2	0-1	0-2	0-3	0-2	4-1	1-2	3-1	5-5	0-2	2-4	0-2
Cranborne	1-6	3-1	0-1	0-3		1-3	6-1	0-3	1-1	1-8	2-4	1-2	3-2	3-2	0-4	1-5	1-1	0-3
Hamworthy Recreation	5-0	4-1	3-0	1-1	8-0		4-1	2-2	2-0	3-2	3-0	3-1	5-0	6-1	1-1	1-0	5-0	1-0
Hamworthy United Res.	0-2	3-1	1-5	1-2	4-3	3-3		0-6	0-2	1-1	0-2	3-1	0-6	1-1	3-0	0-2	0-3	0-1
Holt United	2-1	5-2	1-4	5-0	1-0	2-0	3-1		7-1	1-4	2-4	7-2	3-0	7-0	0-1	2-0	3-2	1-1
Parley Sports	1-1	4-3	0-3	1-2	2-0	0-4	4-0	2-1		0-2	5-2	0-3	1-4	4-1	2-7	0-1	3-0	1-3
Poole Borough	3-2	4-2	1-2	5-1	5-3	1-3	1-1	2-1	2-2		1-4	3-1	2-2	3-0	2-1	1-0	0-0	0-3
Portland United	2-3	2-0	0-1	2-1	8-0	0-1	1-1	1-4	1-1	1-0		2-1	2-2	7-0	6-1	1-1	0-1	1-3
Sherborne Town Res.	3-1	4-4	0-1	0-1	2-2	0-2	3-1	1-1	2-5	4-1	2-3		3-2	4-2	0-4	0-2	2-3	1-5
Sturminster Marshall	1-1	1-1	1-4	1-0	4-0	1-1	2-0	0-3	1-2	1-2	2-3	1-1		3-1	1-2	0-2	1-4	4-3
Sturminster Newton Utd	2-1	4-6	0-6	1-4	2-1	1-3	2-1	0-7	1-2	3-5	0-0	1-3	1-3		2-2	1-1	0-2	2-3
Swanage Town & Herston	3-1	5-2	2-3	2-1	2-1	2-2	3-0	1-0	2-1	1-1	1-0	1-4	4-0	8-0		1-1	3-1	3-1
Westland Sports	1-1	3-1	1-1	6-1	3-0	3-3	5-0	2-1	3-2	1-3	5-1	4-1	9-0	5-0	1-2		5-1	1-1
Weymouth Res.	3-1	5-0	1-1	1-0	3-1	1-2	2-2	1-1	4-0	1-1	1-3	1-0	3-3	6-0	4-0	0-2		1-1
Wincanton Town	3-0	4-0	1-2	3-3	3-0	0-0	3-1	3-0	n/a	0-2	1-3	1-0	2-4	4-0	1-2	1-1	0-1	

DORSET PREMIER LEAGUE CONSTITUTION 2010-11

BLANDFORD UNITED. . . . . Recreation Ground, Park Road, Blandford Forum DT11 7BX. . . . . None
BRIDPORT RES. St Marys Field, Skilling Hill Road, Bridport DT6 5LN 01308 423834
CHICKERELL UNITED. . . . . Weymouth College, Cranford Avenue, Weymouth DT4 7LQ. 01305 208892
CRANBORNE . . . . Recreation Ground, Penny's Lane, Cranborne, Wimborne BH21 5QE. 01725 517440
HAMWORTHY RECREATION. . Hamworthy Rec Club, Magna Rd, Canford Magna, Wimborne BH21 3AP 01202 881922
HAMWORTHY UNITED RES. . . . . The County Ground, Blandford Close, Hamworthy, Poole BH15 4BF 01202 674974
HOLT UNITED . . . . Gaunts Common, Holt, Wimborne BH21 4JR 01258 840379
MERLEY COBHAM SPORTS . . Cobham Sports & Social Club, Merley House Lane, Wimborne BH21 3AA 01202 885773
PARLEY SPORTS. . . . . Parley Sports Club, Christchurch Road, West Parley BH22 8SQ 01202 573345
POOLE BOROUGH. . . . . Turlin Moor Recreation Ground, Blandford Moor, Hamworthy, Poole BH21 5XX . . Club Office: 01202 674973
PORTLAND UNITED . . . . New Grove Corner, Grove Road, Portland DT5 1DP. 01305 861489
SHERBORNE TOWN RES. . . . . Raleigh Grove, The Terrace Playing Fields, Sherborne DT9 5NS. 01935 816110
STURMINSTER MARSHALL . . . . Churchill Close, Sturminster Marshall BH21 4BQ . . . . None
STURMINSTER NEWTON UTD . . . Barnetts Field, Honeymead Lane, Sturminster Newton DT10 7EW 01258 471406
SWANAGE TOWN & HERSTON . . . . . . Day's Park, off De Moulham Road, Swanage BH19 2JW 01929 424673
WESTLAND SPORTS. . . . . Alvington Lane, Yeovil BA22 8UX . . . . None
WEYMOUTH RES. . . . . Wessex Stadium, Radipole Lane, Weymouth DT4 9XJ. 01305 785558
WINCANTON TOWN . . . . Wincanton Sports Ground, Moor Lane, Wincanton BA9 9EJ. 01963 31815

Cobham Sports become Merley Cobham Sports

EDGAR MAIDMENT CHARITY SHIELD

(League Champions v League Cup holders)

(August 8th at Portland United)
Portland United 1 **Poole Borough** 4

ESSEX & SUFFOLK BORDER LEAGUE

www.essexsuffolkborderleague.freeserve.co.uk

Sponsored by:

Kent Blaxill

Founded: 1911

Recent champions:

2005: Gas Recreation

2006: Gas Recreation

2007: Gas Recreation

2008: Gas Recreation

2009: West Bergholt

	Alr	Brig	Ded	Earl	Gas	Gre	Hat	Hed	Holl	Litt	Mer	Tip	Univ	Wee	Wes	Whi
Alresford Colne Rgrs	***P***	5-1	2-2	3-0	2-4	0-1	2-1	2-1	5-2	1-2	3-1	4-0	1-0	4-1	0-1	2-1
Brightlingsea Regent	2-1	***R***	6-0	5-3	0-1	2-1	2-0	5-0	1-0	2-2	2-1	6-1	2-5	2-0	1-6	2-1
Dedham Old Boys	1-2	0-8	***E***	3-3	1-4	1-4	3-1	2-4	0-1	0-3	0-2	5-0	1-1	5-1	0-2	1-2
Earls Colne	0-2	1-0	4-0	***M***	1-2	1-3	6-0	2-1	2-1	1-3	2-0	9-3	0-1	5-0	1-2	2-6
Gas Recreation	3-1	6-1	7-0	5-0	***I***	2-1	2-2	7-0	6-0	3-0	5-1	7-0	6-2	11-1	4-0	W-L
Great Bentley	1-4	1-2	1-4	3-3	0-5	***E***	1-1	4-3	1-1	1-3	4-0	1-4	2-2	2-2	1-4	2-2
Hatfield Peverel	0-2	2-2	1-3	3-0	2-4	0-1	***R***	2-1	0-0	2-0	4-1	1-1	1-3	6-1	1-0	2-3
Hedinghams United	1-1	3-5	0-4	0-0	1-6	3-2	0-1		1-5	2-3	5-0	0-1	0-4	7-3	0-2	3-4
Holland	3-1	2-1	9-1	0-1	2-3	3-3	1-2	3-2	***D***	1-1	4-2	3-1	1-3	3-0	1-1	1-1
Little Oakley	1-3	3-1	3-2	0-1	2-3	3-1	1-0	4-1	1-2	***I***	3-0	3-0	2-3	6-0	4-1	0-0
Mersea Island	0-2	0-2	0-2	2-2	0-4	3-3	2-1	0-2	1-5	0-4	***V***	3-4	3-3	1-0	0-6	2-3
Tiptree Jobserve	0-2	0-3	1-1	5-6	3-8	3-0	1-2	5-4	2-0	1-6	4-3	***I***	2-1	5-0	0-2	2-2
University of Essex	1-0	0-2	2-4	3-1	0-2	3-1	2-0	4-3	2-1	3-0	3-1	5-5	***S***	5-0	3-3	1-1
Weeley Athletic	2-1	1-4	2-2	0-3	1-12	1-7	0-3	0-1	1-1	1-4	1-0	0-6	1-6	***I***	1-7	0-3
West Bergholt	2-1	2-0	7-2	3-2	3-1	5-1	2-0	4-0	3-0	3-0	5-1	2-1	3-2	2-1	***O***	2-1
White Notley	2-4	2-2	3-4	3-1	1-4	1-1	0-1	5-0	2-3	0-0	7-0	4-2	0-1	7-0	0-2	***N***

Premier Division		**P**	**W**	**D**	**L**	**F**	**A**	**Pts**
Gas Recreation		**30**	**28**	**1**	**1**	**137**	**28**	**85**
West Bergholt		**30**	**25**	**2**	**3**	**87**	**30**	**77**
University of Essex	*+2*	**30**	**17**	**6**	**7**	**74**	**49**	**59**
Brightlingsea Regent		**30**	**18**	**3**	**9**	**74**	**50**	**57**
Alresford Colne Rangers		**30**	**18**	**2**	**10**	**63**	**37**	**56**
Little Oakley		**30**	**17**	**4**	**9**	**67**	**39**	**55**
Holland		**30**	**12**	**7**	**11**	**59**	**51**	**43**
White Notley		**30**	**11**	**8**	**11**	**67**	**47**	**41**
Earls Colne		**30**	**12**	**4**	**14**	**63**	**62**	**40**
Hatfield Peverel		**30**	**11**	**5**	**14**	**42**	**47**	**38**
Tiptree Jobserve	*-1*	**30**	**10**	**4**	**16**	**63**	**93**	**33**
Dedham Old Boys		**30**	**9**	**5**	**16**	**54**	**86**	**32**
Great Bentley		**30**	**7**	**9**	**14**	**55**	**71**	**30**
Hedinghams United		**30**	**6**	**2**	**22**	**49**	**90**	**20**
Mersea Island		**30**	**3**	**3**	**24**	**30**	**95**	**12**
Weeley Athletic		**30**	**2**	**3**	**25**	**22**	**131**	**9**

A V LEE MEMORIAL TROPHY

(Premier Division champions v League Cup holders)

(August 5th at West Bergholt)

West Bergholt 0 **Team Bury** 0 (3-5p)

Reserve Premier Division		P	W	D	L	F	A	Pt
Gas Recreation Res.		24	16	3	5	72	26	51
West Bergholt Res.	*+3*	24	15	3	6	73	39	51
Holland FC Res.		24	16	2	6	73	30	50
University of Essex Res.		24	15	2	7	61	23	47
Alresford Colne Rgrs Res.		24	13	4	7	64	32	43
Little Oakley Res.	*-2*	23	14	0	9	60	33	39
Earls Colne Res.	*-3*	22	11	3	8	73	45	33
White Notley Res.		24	10	3	11	75	65	33
Great Bentley Res.		24	10	2	12	49	45	32
Dedham Old Boys Res.		23	8	2	13	64	49	26
Brightlingsea Regent Res.	*-1*	24	8	3	13	52	58	26
Clare Town Res.	*+6*	24	1	0	23	14	237	9
Coggeshall Town Res.	*-1*	24	2	3	19	33	81	8

Bures United - record expunged

Earls Colne Res. v Dedham Res., Earls Colne Res. v Little Oakley Res. not played

Reserve Division One		P	W	D	L	F	A	Pt
Foxash Social Res.		23	18	2	3	74	26	56
Hatfield Peverel Res.	*-3*	24	16	3	5	73	38	48
Mersea Island Res.	*-3*	23	13	3	7	58	38	39
Wormingford Wdrs Res.		24	12	3	9	59	47	39
Glemsford/Cavendish Res.		24	11	4	9	57	41	37
Hedinghams United Res.	*+3*	23	11	1	11	54	60	37
Boxted Lodgers Res.		24	9	5	10	40	48	32
Lawford Lads Res.		24	9	3	12	50	57	30
Gosfield United Res.	*+3*	24	7	5	12	43	56	29
Sudbury Athletic Res.		24	8	4	12	45	47	28
Tiptree Jobserve Res.		24	7	5	12	49	77	26
Bradfield Rovers Res.		24	6	3	15	33	64	21
Kirby Athletic Res.		23	5	3	15	36	72	18

Great Bradfords, Weeley Ath. Res. - records expunged

Hedinghams United Res. v Foxash Social Res., Kirby Athletic Res. v Mersea Island Res. not played

ESSEX & SUFFOLK BORDER LEAGUE PREMIER DIVISION CONSTITUTION 2010-11

ALRESFORD COLNE RANGERS........... Ford Lane, Alresford, Colchester CO7 8AU 07796 036467
BRIGHTLINGSEA REGENT .... North Road, Brightlingsea, Colchester CO7 0PL 01206 304199
DEDHAM OLD BOYS.......... Old Grammar School Ground, The Drift, Dedham, Colchester CO7 6AH .... None
EARLS COLNE .... Green Farm Meadow, Halstead Road, Earls Colne, Colchester CO6 2NG 01787 223584
GAS RECREATION .... Bromley Road, Colchester CO4 3JE 01206 860383
GREAT BENTLEY .... The Green, Heckfords Road, Great Bentley, Colchester CO7 8LY 01206 251532
HARWICH & PARKESTON .... The Royal Oak, Main Road, Dovercourt, Harwich CO12 4AA 01255 503643
HATFIELD PEVEREL .... Strutt Memorial Field, Maldon Road, Hatfield Peverel CM3 2HT .... None
HEDINGHAMS UNITED......... Lawn Meadow, Yeldham Road, Sible Hedingham, Halstead CO9 3QH.......................... None
HOLLAND.................... Eastcliff Sports Ground, Dulwich Road, Holland-on-Sea CO15 5HP................. 01255 814874
LITTLE OAKLEY .... War Memorial Club Ground, Harwich Road, Little Oakley, Harwich CO12 5ED 01255 880370
ROWHEDGE.......................... Rectory Road, Rowhedge CO5 7HR.......................... 01206 728022
SUDBURY ATHLETIC .... Delphi Sports Club, Alexandra Road, Sudbury CO10 2XH 01787 372331
TIPTREE JOBSERVE .... Warriors Rest, Maypole Road, Tiptree CO5 0EN .... None
UNIVERSITY OF ESSEX....... University Essex Sports Centre, Wivenhoe Park, Colchester CO4 3SQ 01206 873250
WEST BERGHOLT........... Lorkin Daniel Field, Lexden Road, West Bergholt, Colchester CO6 3BW.............. 01206 241525
WHITE NOTLEY .... Oak Farm, Faulkbourne, Witham CM8 1SF 01376 519864
WORMINGFORD WANDERERS... Wormingford PF, Main Road, Wormingford, Colchester CO6 3AF.......................... None

IN: Harwich & Parkeston (WS - Eastern Counties League Premier Division), Rowhedge (P), Sudbury Athletic (P), Wormingford Wanderers (P)

OUT: Mersea Island (R), Weeley Athletic (R)

Division One		P	W	D	L	F	A	Pts
Wormingford Wanderers		30	23	4	3	100	31	73
Rowhedge		30	22	4	4	96	31	70
Sudbury Athletic	*-3*	30	21	5	4	102	41	65
Coggeshall Town		30	20	5	5	102	43	65
Clare Town		30	17	4	9	76	74	55
Foxash Social		30	16	3	11	55	55	51
Kirby Athletic		30	16	3	11	54	55	51
Clacton United		30	13	2	15	81	59	41
Lawford Lads		30	12	5	13	67	58	41
Gosfield United	*+3*	30	12	2	16	44	57	41
Bradfield Rovers		30	11	1	18	48	62	34
West Clacton Alliance	*-3*	30	9	6	15	53	59	30
Boxted Lodgers	*-3*	30	10	2	18	50	68	29
Glemsford & Cavendish		30	6	4	20	42	78	22
Bures United	*+6*	30	3	3	24	35	121	18
Great Bradfords		30	2	1	27	30	143	7

LEAGUE CUP

FIRST ROUND

Bures United 0 **Bradfield Rovers** 0 *aet* (4-5p)

Coggeshall 1 **Clare Town** 2

Dedham 4 West Clacton 0

Earls Colne 3 Sudbury Athletic 1

Foxash 3 Mersea Island 1

Glemsford 4 Boxted 2 *aet*

Gt Bentley 1 **Clacton Utd** 2

Great Bradfords 0 **West Bergholt** 8

Hatfield Peverel 0 **Brightlingsea Regent** 1

Hedinghams United 1 **University of Essex** 2

Lawford Lads 2 **Gas Rec** 5

Rowhedge 0 **Alresford** 2

Tiptree J. 2 L. Oakley 1 *aet*

Weeley 2 Gosfield United 0

White Notley 3 Holland 2.

Wormingford 2 Kirby 1

SECOND ROUND

Alresford Colne Rangers 0 **West Bergholt** 1 *aet*

Clare 0 **Brightlingsea** 2

Foxash 2 Bradfield Rov. 1

Gas Rec 1 **Univ. Essex** 6

Glemsford 0 **Clacton Utd** 2

Weeley 0 **Earls Colne** 8

White Notley 3 Dedham 1

Wormingford Wanderers 0 **Tiptree Jobserve** 1

QUARTER-FINALS

Tiptree Jobserve 2 Clacton United 1

University of Essex 4 Earls Colne 0

West Bergholt 1 Brightlingsea Regent 0

White Notley 4 Foxash 2

SEMI-FINALS

University of Essex 0 **White Notley** 2

West Bergholt 2 Tiptree Jobserve 0

FINAL

(April 21st at AFC Sudbury)

West Bergholt 3 White Notley 2 *aet*

	Box	Bra	Bur	Clac	Clar	Cog	Fox	Gle	Gos	Gre	Kirb	Law	Row	Sud	Wes	Wor
Boxted Lodgers		1-4	6-2	2-2	1-4	2-4	1-2	3-2	1-0	7-0	0-4	2-0	0-2	1-2	2-1	0-2
Bradfield Rovers	1-0	***D***	2-0	3-0	2-3	1-3	2-0	3-1	0-3	5-2	0-1	1-1	2-4	2-4	0-3	2-4
Bures United	0-2	1-0	***I***	3-2	1-2	1-5	0-3	0-4	0-2	1-3	2-7	2-6	1-1	2-6	1-5	0-5
Clacton United	5-2	2-0	7-0	***V***	6-0	3-1	7-1	1-1	1-3	7-2	1-3	1-2	1-4	1-2	0-1	1-3
Clare Town	2-0	4-1	4-4	1-7	***I***	6-4	0-1	2-1	2-1	8-1	3-0	2-0	2-1	3-3	2-2	1-7
Coggeshall Town	2-0	3-1	10-0	3-0	4-1	***S***	2-2	4-1	1-0	7-1	5-0	1-1	2-2	2-1	4-3	2-2
Foxash Social	1-1	5-2	4-2	2-1	W-L	0-3	***I***	2-1	3-0	4-0	1-1	3-2	0-1	1-5	0-1	3-1
Glemsford & Cavendish	1-3	1-3	2-2	1-2	3-3	1-4	1-2	***O***	1-2	3-0	1-3	2-1	1-3	1-5	3-3	0-4
Gosfield United	2-0	1-0	6-0	1-5	4-3	0-4	2-1	0-1	***N***	7-0	1-0	1-3	0-2	1-4	2-5	1-4
Great Bradfords	3-4	0-5	0-1	2-3	2-4	0-5	1-3	4-2	0-1		0-3	0-7	0-9	1-7	0-4	1-6
Kirby Athletic	2-0	3-1	5-2	0-6	2-4	2-7	2-0	1-0	3-1	4-1		2-1	3-2	1-1	1-0	0-3
Lawford Lads	5-2	0-2	4-2	6-4	2-3	2-4	2-4	6-0	0-0	7-1	1-0		1-4	2-2	W-L	0-4
Rowhedge	5-2	6-0	4-0	4-1	6-1	3-2	1-0	7-0	6-0	4-1	2-0	2-3	***O***	1-1	2-0	1-1
Sudbury Athletic	4-2	3-0	4-1	3-1	2-4	2-0	7-3	1-2	1-0	7-1	4-1	4-0	1-2	***N***	7-1	3-1
West Clacton Alliance	0-1	1-2	5-2	1-2	0-1	4-3	1-4	2-1	2-2	3-3	0-0	1-1	2-4	1-4	***E***	1-4
Wormingford Wdrs	4-2	2-1	5-2	2-1	6-1	1-1	5-0	2-3	4-0	5-0	5-0	2-1	3-1	2-2	1-0	

ESSEX & SUFFOLK BORDER LEAGUE DIVISION ONE CONSTITUTION 2010-11

BARNSTON. . . . . High Easter Road, Barnston, Dunmow CM6 1LZ 07712 129459
BELL UNITED. . . . . Kynaston Road, Panfield, Braintree CM7 1WX . . . . None
BOXTED LODGERS . . . . The Playing Field, Cage Lane, Boxted, Colchester CO4 5RE 01206 271969
BRADFIELD ROVERS. . . . . The Playing Field, The Street, Bradfield, Manningtree CO11 2UU. . . . . None
BURES UNITED. Recreation Ground, Nayland Road, Bures CO8 5BX. . . . . None
CLACTON UNITED. . . . . Vista Road Recreation Ground, Vista Road, Clacton-on-Sea CO15 6DB. 01255 429647
CLARE TOWN. . . . . Playing Field, Harp Lane, Clare CO10 8PH . . . . None
COGGESHALL TOWN . . . . The Crops, West Street, Coggeshall CO6 1NS. 01376 562843
FOXASH SOCIAL . . . . Foxash Playing Field, Harwich Road, Lawford, Manningtree CO11 2LP 01206 231309
GOSFIELD UNITED . . . . The Playing Field, Church Lane, Gosfield, Halstead CO9 1UB . . . . None
KIRBY ATHLETIC. . . . . Kirby Playing Field, Halstead Road, Kirby Cross CO13 0LS . . . . None
LAWFORD LADS . . . . School Lane, Lawford, Manningtree CO11 2JA. 01206 397211
MERSEA ISLAND . . . . The Glebe, Colchester Road, West Mersea CO5 8RS 01206 385216
NEWBURY FOREST . . . . London Marathon Sports Ground, Forest Road, Hainault, Ilford IG6 3HJ 020 8500 3486
RAYNE. . . . . Rayne Village Hall, Oak Meadow, Gore Road, Rayne, Braintree CM77 6TX 01376 349408
ST OSYTH . . . . Cowley Park, Mill Street, St Osyth, Clacton-on-Sea CO16 8EJ . . . . None
WEELEY ATHLETIC. . . . . Vista Road Recreation Ground, Vista Road, Clacton-on-Sea CO15 6DB. 01255 429647
WEST CLACTON . . . . FC Clacton, Rush Green Bowl, Rush Green Road, Clacton-on-Sea CO16 7BQ 01255 432590

IN: Barnston (S - Essex Olympian League Division Three), Mersea Island (R), Newbury Forest (P - Romford & District League Senior Division), Rayne (P - Halstead & District League), St Osyth (N), Weeley Athletic (R)

OUT: Glemsford & Cavendish United (W), Rowhedge (P), Sudbury Athletic (P), Wormingford Wanderers (P)

Great Bradfords become Bell United

TOMMY THOMPSON CUP

FINAL *(May 3rd at Little Oakley)*

Holland Res. 2 Earls Colne Res. 0

RESERVES CUP

FINAL *(April 15th at Stanway Rovers)*

Earls Colne Res. 1 Wormingford Res. 1 *aet* (3-1p)

ESSEX OLYMPIAN LEAGUE

www.eofl.co.uk

Sponsored by:
ProKit UK

Founded: 1966

Recent champions:
2005: White Ensign
2006: Harold Wood Athletic
2007: White Ensign
2008: White Ensign
2009: Harold Wood Athletic

	Benfleet	Canning T.	Epping	Faces	Frenford Snr	Galleywood	Harold Wood	Kelvedon H.	Manford Way	Mountnessing	Ongar Town	Rayleigh T.	Westhamians	White Ensign
Benfleet		0-1	1-4	4-1	0-3	3-1	0-2	1-3	0-4	2-0	3-1	0-6	3-5	0-2
Canning Town	4-1	***P***	0-1	3-4	0-1	4-1	1-2	1-3	0-1	0-1	1-3	3-2	2-2	1-1
Epping	6-0	1-1	***R***	4-1	3-1	0-1	1-3	1-2	0-2	1-0	0-0	2-1	1-0	3-1
Faces	W-L	1-4	1-5	***E***	0-3	2-1	0-3	0-5	2-3	1-3	2-4	1-4	1-5	0-1
Frenford Senior	W-L	1-1	3-2	6-4	***M***	3-0	2-0	1-2	2-0	2-1	1-3	3-0	0-1	5-1
Galleywood	2-2	4-1	0-1	3-0	3-0	***I***	1-1	0-4	3-1	1-1	2-2	1-3	2-5	4-2
Harold Wood Athletic	7-0	1-0	1-2	1-1	2-1	3-2	***E***	0-4	1-0	3-1	4-2	0-0	4-2	3-1
Kelvedon Hatch	1-0	2-1	0-1	5-2	0-0	9-0	1-1	***R***	5-3	1-1	2-0	3-2	1-2	5-0
Manford Way	4-2	2-1	1-0	3-2	1-1	3-2	0-1	0-0		2-2	3-4	2-1	0-4	0-1
Mountnessing Boca	5-0	2-1	3-1	0-0	0-1	5-2	0-2	0-0	2-0		1-1	0-1	1-0	0-3
Ongar Town	2-1	1-3	2-0	5-1	1-2	1-3	1-2	0-6	2-1	2-2	***D***	2-1	2-6	1-1
Rayleigh Town	2-0	3-3	2-1	5-0	1-1	2-2	1-2	1-0	3-1	8-0	0-2	***I***	2-5	5-1
Westhamians	1-1	2-0	3-2	2-1	1-1	3-1	2-4	1-4	3-0	1-3	0-4	2-1	***V***	1-0
White Ensign	1-3	1-3	1-1	2-1	2-0	3-1	0-3	2-6	1-6	2-1	2-1	1-1	1-2	

Premier Division		P	W	D	L	F	A	Pts
Harold Wood Athletic		26	19	4	3	56	26	61
Kelvedon Hatch		26	18	5	3	74	21	59
Westhamians		26	16	3	7	61	42	51
Frenford Senior		26	14	5	7	44	29	47
Epping		26	13	3	10	44	31	42
Rayleigh Town		26	11	5	10	58	38	38
Ongar Town		26	11	5	10	49	50	38
Mountnessing Boca		26	9	7	10	35	38	34
Manford Way	*-3*	26	11	3	12	43	45	33
White Ensign		26	9	4	13	34	57	31
Galleywood		26	7	5	14	43	64	26
Canning Town	*-3*	26	7	5	14	40	44	23
Benfleet	*+3*	26	5	2	19	27	68	20
Faces	*+3*	26	3	2	21	29	84	14

Reserve Division One		P	W	D	L	F	A	Pt
Kelvedon Hatch Res.		22	16	1	5	66	30	49
Harold Wood Athletic Res.		22	14	4	4	49	19	46
Frenford Senior Res.		22	14	4	4	59	30	46
Rayleigh Town Res.		22	13	2	7	44	31	41
M & B Club Res.		22	10	2	10	33	40	32
Manford Way Res.		22	8	4	10	35	38	28
White Ensign Res.		22	7	5	10	35	44	26
Epping Res.	*-3*	22	7	7	8	38	36	25
Canning Town Res.		22	5	8	9	44	46	23
B. Stortford Swifts Res.	*+3*	22	5	4	13	33	45	22
Mountnessing Boca Res.		22	5	4	13	23	49	19
Faces Res.		22	4	3	15	19	70	15

Reserve Division Two		P	W	D	L	F	A	Pt
Westhamians Res.		22	18	2	2	74	19	56
Buckhurst Hill Res.		22	14	4	4	74	38	46
Ramsden Res.		22	13	3	6	62	38	42
Hutton Res.		22	10	3	9	48	40	33
Runwell Hospital Res.		22	10	3	9	51	54	33
Herongate Athletic Res.		22	10	2	10	42	38	32
Old Chelmsfordians Res.		22	9	2	11	47	48	29
Hannakins Farm Res.		22	8	3	11	41	47	27
Galleywood Res.		22	7	6	9	25	37	27
Benfleet Res.	*+2*	22	7	4	11	34	51	27
Leigh Ramblers Res.	*-1*	22	8	3	11	34	52	26
Barnston Res.		22	0	1	21	18	88	1

ESSEX OLYMPIAN LEAGUE PREMIER DIVISION CONSTITUTION 2010-11

BUCKHURST HILL........................ Roding Lane, Buckhurst Hill IG9 6BJ 020 8504 1189
CANNING TOWN .. Terence McMillan Stadium, Newham Leisure Centre, 281 Prince Regents Lane,London E13 8SD 020 7511 4477
EPPING .... Stonards Hill Recreation Ground, Tidy's Lane, Epping CM16 6SP 07932 532694
FRENFORD SENIOR.............. Oakfields Sports Ground, Forest Road, Barkingside IG6 2JL.................. 020 8500 1998
GALLEYWOOD................. Clarkes Field, Slades Lane, Galleywood, Chelmsford CM2 8RW.................. 01245 352975
HAROLD WOOD ATHLETIC ..... Harold Wood Recreation Park, Harold View, Harold Wood RM3 0LX 01708 348827
KELVEDON HATCH .... New Hall, School Road, Kelvedon Hatch, Brentwood CM15 0DH.................. 07768 274539
M & B CLUB .... Sanofi-Aventis Sports & Social Club, Dagenham Road, Dagenham RM7 0QX 020 8919 2156
MANFORD WAY .... London Marathon Sports Ground, Forest Road, Hainault IG6 3HJ................ 020 8500 3486
MOUNTNESSING... Brentwood Town FC, The Arena, Brentwood Centre, Doddinghurst Rd, Brentwood CM15 9NN 07776 232 071
ONGAR TOWN.................... Sports Ground, Love Lane, High Street, Ongar CM5 9BL.................... 01277 363838
RAYLEIGH TOWN............ Rayleigh Town Sports & Social Club, London Road, Rayleigh SS6 9DT 01268 784001
WESTHAMIANS .... London Playing Fields, Forest Road, Fairlop IG6 3AS.......................... 0208 500 3777
WHITE ENSIGN........ Borough Football Combination HQ, Eastwoodbury Lane, Southend-on-Sea SS2 6XG 01702 520482

IN: Buckhurst Hill (P), M & B Club (P)
OUT: Benfleet (R), Faces (now Aldborough Athletic) (R)
Mountnessing Boca become Mountnessing

Reserve Division Three	P	W	D	L	F	A	Pt
Lakeside Res.	20	15	4	1	95	27	49
Springfield Res.	20	15	2	3	73	30	47
Upminster Res.	20	13	3	4	49	20	42
Sandon Royals Res.	20	11	1	8	37	40	34
Southminster St Leo. Res.	20	10	2	8	47	37	32
Basildon Town Res.	20	9	2	9	37	36	29
Sungate Res.	20	8	3	9	60	50	27
Shenfield Association Res.	20	5	5	10	35	66	20
Writtle Res.	20	5	4	11	34	58	19
Maldon St Marys Res.	20	3	3	14	37	77	12
Leytonstone United Res.	20	1	1	18	23	86	4

Ryan Res. - record expunged

Division One	P	W	D	L	F	A	Pts
M & B Club	22	15	2	5	50	28	47
Buckhurst Hill	22	13	5	4	84	38	44
Southminster St Leo.	22	12	3	7	45	36	39
Hutton	22	11	1	10	56	49	34
Sungate	22	10	4	8	53	49	34
Hannakins Farm	22	9	3	10	35	43	30
Sandon Royals	22	9	3	10	37	56	30
Ryan	22	7	8	7	49	46	29
B. Stortford Swifts	22	7	4	11	32	49	25
Lakeside	22	7	2	13	28	45	23
Leigh Ramblers	22	6	4	12	40	53	22
Shell Club Corr'gham	22	4	5	13	35	52	17

SENIOR CUP

FIRST ROUND

BS Swifts 5 Herongate 0
Broomfield 2 Debden S. 1
Buckhurst Hill 4 Burnham Ramblers Res. 1
Galleyw'd 3 Leytonstone 2
Hutton 5 Sawbridgeworth Town Res. 0
Kelvedon H. 0 **Rayleigh** 1
Lakeside 1 **Benfleet** 5
M & B 1 **Manford Way** 2
Maldon SM 0 **Cranes Utd** 2
Newham United 3 Faces 1
Old Chelmsfordians 6 Sandon Royals 4
Ryan 1 **Canning Town** 2
Shell Club 5 **Springfield** 0
(Shell Club expelled)
Southminster 4 Shenfield 1
Wadham Ldge 6 Roydon 0
Westhamians 4 Basildon 2
White Ensign 0 **Romford Res.** 1
Writtle 3 Ramsden 1

SECOND ROUND

Barnston 3 Stansted Res. 1
Bishop's Stortford Swifts 0 **Harold Wood Athletic** 2
Broomfield 0 **Catholic United** 0 *aet* (2-3p)
Buckhurst Hill 2 **Cranes** 3
Epping 0 **Westhamians** 2
Galleywood 0 **Runwell Hospital** 0 *aet* (2-3p)
Manford W. 3 Canning T. 2
Newham United 5 Benfleet 5 *aet* (5-4p)
Old Chelmsfordians 4 Wadham Lodge 2
Rayleigh T. 5 Hutton 2 *aet*
Romford Res. 1 **Mountnessing** 1 *aet* (3-4p)
Springfield 4 Ongar Town 3
Sungate 1 **Leigh R.** 2
Takeley Res. 0 **Hannakins** 1
Upminster 1 **Frenford** 2
Writtle 3 **Southminster** 4

THIRD ROUND

Catholic United 3 Newham United 3 *aet* (8-7p)
Hannakins F. 2 Frenford 1
Harold Wood Athletic 1 **Old Chelmsfordians** 2
Manford Way 8 Leigh R. 2
Mountnessing 5 Springf'ld 0
Rayleigh 3 **Cranes** 6 *aet*
Southminster 2 Barnston 1
Westhamians 3 Runwell Hospital 2 *aet*

QUARTER-FINALS

Cranes United 3 Old Chelmsfordians 0
Hannakins Farm 3 Southminster St Leonards 1
Manford Way 4 Catholic 1
Westhamians 3 Mountnessing Boca 0

SEMI-FINALS

Manford W. 0 **H'kins Farm** 1
Westhamians 2 Cranes 1

FINAL

(May 11th at Billericay)
Westhamians 2 Hannakins Farm 1

	Bish	Buck	Han	Hutt	Lake	Leigh	M&B	Ryan	San	Shel	Sou	Sun
Bishop's Stortford Swifts	***D***	1-7	2-4	2-1	2-1	1-3	3-1	0-0	2-2	0-0	1-3	5-2
Buckhurst Hill	6-0	***I***	2-2	2-1	7-0	3-1	1-2	1-1	1-2	2-2	4-4	6-5
Hannakins Farm	W-L	0-5	***V***	1-3	3-1	2-0	2-3	0-3	2-2	1-1	0-2	1-4
Hutton	3-0	3-7	0-3	***I***	1-0	3-2	3-2	2-2	7-0	6-2	3-4	3-4
Lakeside	2-0	2-4	1-3	3-1	***S***	0-2	0-3	3-3	2-0	4-2	0-2	2-1
Leigh Ramblers	1-1	1-6	1-2	1-5	3-0	***I***	2-3	3-4	2-4	2-2	3-2	1-1
M & B Club	4-2	0-2	2-1	3-0	0-2	2-1	***O***	1-1	6-2	2-1	3-0	1-2
Ryan	2-3	1-1	6-2	5-1	2-4	0-1	1-1	***N***	5-3	4-3	3-5	2-1
Sandon Royals	3-2	0-4	0-4	0-1	2-0	4-1	0-3	3-0		3-2	0-4	3-2
Shell Club Corringham	0-1	1-8	2-0	2-3	2-0	2-4	1-2	4-2	0-1	***O***	3-1	1-3
Southminster St Leonards	0-2	6-3	1-2	2-1	1-0	2-1	0-3	3-1	1-1	0-0	***N***	0-1
Sungate	4-2	3-2	2-0	2-5	1-1	4-4	1-3	1-1	5-2	3-2	1-2	***E***

ESSEX OLYMPIAN LEAGUE DIVISION ONE CONSTITUTION 2010-11

ALDBOROUGH ATHLETIC . . Ford Spts & Social Club, Aldbrough Rd South, Newbury Park, Ilford IG3 8HG 020 8590 3797
BENFLEET . . . . The Club House, Woodside Extension, Manor Road, Benfleet, Rayleigh SS7 4BG 01268 743957
BISHOP'S STORTFORD SWIFTS . Silver Leys, Hadham Road (A1250), Bishop's Stortford CM23 2QE 01279 658941
HANNAKINS FARM . . . . Hannakins Farm Community Centre, Rosebay Avenue, Billericay CM12 0SY 01277 630851
HUTTON . . . . Fords Sports & Social Club, Gardiners Close, Basildon SS14 3AN 01268 281080
LAKESIDE . . . . Lakeside Pitches, Lakeside Retail Park, Thurrock RM20 2ZL 01375 379352
OLD CHELMSFORDIANS . . . . Lawford Lane, Roxwell Road, Chelmsford CM1 2NS 01245 420442
RUNWELL HOSPITAL . . . . Runwell Hospital, Runwell Chase, Wickford SS11 7QE. 07966 718801
RYAN . . . . Town Mead Leisure Park, Brooker Road, Waltham Abbey EN9 1JH. 01992 714949
SANDON ROYALS . . . . Sandon Sports Club, Woodhill Road, Sandon, Chelmsford CM2 7AQ 01245 476626
SOUTHMINSTER ST LEONARDS . . . . King George V PF, Station Road, Southminster CM0 7EW 07718 869883
SUNGATE . . . . Ford Sports & Social Club, Aldborough Road South, Newbury Park, Ilford IG3 8HG 020 8590 3797
THURROCK RES. . . . . Ship Lane, Grays RM19 1YN. 01708 865492

IN: Aldborough Athletic (formerly Faces) (R), Benfleet (R), Old Chelmsfordians (P), Runwell Hospital (P), Thurrock Res. (S - Essex & Herts Border Combination)

OUT: Buckhurst Hill (P), Leigh Ramblers (R), M & B Club (P), Shell Club Corringham (now Forest Glade) (R)

Division Two	P	W	D	L	F	A	Pts
Romford Res.	22	16	2	4	54	17	50
Runwell Hospital	22	16	2	4	57	21	50
Old Chelmsfordians	22	14	3	5	69	38	45
Broomfield	22	11	4	7	47	39	37
Maldon St Marys	22	10	2	10	41	44	32
Leytonstone United	22	8	6	8	36	39	30
Takeley Res.	22	9	2	11	38	38	29
Roydon	22	8	4	10	37	47	28
Burnham Ramb. Res.	22	8	3	11	39	56	27
Herongate Athletic	22	6	4	12	25	45	22
Stansted Res.	22	5	1	16	25	55	16
Sawbridgeworth Res.	22	3	3	16	24	53	12

DENNY KING MEMORIAL CUP

(Senior Cup First and Second Round losers)

FIRST ROUND

Sungate 4 Faces 2
White Ensign (w/o) v Kelvedon Hatch

SECOND ROUND

Benfleet 3 Sawbridgeworth Town Res. 1
Bishop's Stortford Swifts 6 Stansted Res. 1
Broomfield 2 Writtle 1
Burnham Ramblers Res. 0 **Epping** 2 *aet*
Debden Sports 1 Takeley Res. 0
Galleywood 2 Leytonstone United 0
Herongate Athletic 1 **Buckhurst Hill** 2
Hutton 2 Ongar Town 0
Lakeside 1 Basildon Town 1 *aet* (6-5p)
Ramsden 2 **Roydon** 5
Romford Res. 0 **Wadham Lodge** 1
Ryan 2 **Upminster** 6
Sandon Royals 1 **Shenfield Association** 2
Shell Club Corringham 1 **Canning Town** 2
Sungate 6 Maldon St Marys 2 *aet*
White Ensign 2 M & B 0

THIRD ROUND

Bish. Stortford Swifts 1 Debden Sports 1 *aet* (3-1p)
Broomfield 0 **Galleywood** 1
Buckhurst Hill 3 Benfleet 0
Epping 3 Canning Town 1
Hutton 4 White Ensign 1
Shenfield Association 0 **Roydon** 1
Sungate 1 Upminster 0
Wadham Lodge 1 Lakeside 0

QUARTER-FINALS

Bishop's Stortford Swifts 0 **Wadham Lodge** 1
Buckhurst Hill 5 Sungate 2
Epping 1 Roydon 0
Galleywood 2 **Hutton** 3

SEMI-FINALS

Buckhurst Hill 2 **Epping** 3
Wadham Lodge 2 Hutton 1 *aet*

FINAL

(May 13th at Billericay Town)

Wadham Lodge 1 Epping 1 *aet* (4-3p)

	Broomfield	Burnham Res.	Herongate Ath.	Leytonstone U.	Maldon St M.	O Chelmsford	Romford Res.	Roydon	Runwell Hosp.	Sawbdgeworth	Stansted Res.	Takeley Res.
Broomfield	***D***	2-3	2-2	2-1	1-3	2-2	1-3	1-2	1-4	3-0	4-1	1-1
Burnham Ramblers Res.	2-3	***I***	4-1	2-1	4-3	2-2	0-0	1-2	0-2	2-1	3-5	1-2
Herongate Athletic	1-2	0-0	***V***	0-0	2-0	1-3	0-2	1-1	0-5	2-1	6-2	0-1
Leytonstone United	1-1	2-3	4-2	***I***	1-2	2-2	0-3	4-3	4-2	W-L	0-3	0-1
Maldon St Marys	2-3	4-1	2-1	2-3	***S***	1-4	2-1	2-3	1-1	1-4	W-L	0-0
Old Chelmsfordians	2-5	7-1	W-L	3-4	2-3	***I***	2-0	3-0	0-2	3-1	5-0	6-3
Romford Res.	3-1	2-0	7-0	3-0	4-1	1-2	***O***	3-1	2-1	4-0	4-0	2-1
Roydon	2-0	3-4	0-2	1-1	4-2	3-5	1-3	***N***	0-3	3-1	0-0	2-1
Runwell Hospital	1-2	7-0	7-1	0-0	1-0	2-7	1-0	4-0		4-1	2-0	4-2
Sawbridgeworth Town Res.	1-6	4-1	1-2	2-2	1-2	1-5	1-1	1-1	0-3	***T***	2-1	0-1
Stansted Res.	0-1	2-1	0-1	0-1	1-4	2-3	2-5	4-3	L-W	2-0	***W***	0-6
Takeley Res.	2-3	1-4	1-0	2-5	2-4	2-1	0-1	1-2	0-1	4-1	4-0	***O***

ESSEX OLYMPIAN LEAGUE DIVISION TWO CONSTITUTION 2010-11

BROOMFIELD . . . . The Angel Meadow, Main Road, Broomfield, Chelmsford CM1 7AH. 01245 443819
BURNHAM RAMBLERS RES. . . . . Leslie Field, Springfield Road, Burnham-on-Crouch CM0 8TE 01621 784383
FOREST GLADE . . . . The Springhouse, Springhouse Road, Corringham SS17 7QT 01375 673100
HERONGATE ATHLETIC . . . . Adjacent to 77 Billericay Road, Herongate, Brentwood CM13 3PU 01277 810717
LEIGH RAMBLERS . . . . Belfairs Park, Eastwood Road North, Leigh-on-Sea SS9 4LR 01702 421077
LEYTONSTONE UNITED. . . . . Ilford Wanderers RFC, Forest Road, Hainault IG6 3HJ 020 8500 4622
MALDON ST MARYS . . . . Tiptree Sports Centre, Maypole Road, Tiptree CO5 0EJ 01621 817499
ROYDON. . . . . Roydon Playing Fields, Harlow Road, Roydon, Harlow CM19 5HE 07967 022714
STANSTED RES. Hargrave Park, Cambridge Road, Stansted CM24 8DL. 01279 812897
TAKELEY RES. . . . . Station Road (adjacent to rail bridge), Takeley, Bishop's Stortford CM22 6SG 01279 870404
UPMINSTER . . . . Hall Lane Playing Fields, Hall Lane, Upminster, Romford RM14 1AU 01708 220320
WADHAM LODGE . . . . Wadham Lodge Sports Ground, Kitchener Road, Walthamstow E17 4JP 020 8527 2444
WALTHAM ABBEY RES. . . . . Capershotts, Sewardstone Road, Waltham Abbey EN9 1LU. 01992 711287

IN: Leigh Ramblers (R), Forest Glade (formerly Shell Club Corringham) (R), Upminster (P), Wadham Lodge (P), Waltham Abbey Res. (S - Essex & Herts Border Combination)

OUT: Old Chelmsfordians (P), Romford Res. (W), Runwell Hospital (P), Sawbridgeworth Town Res. (R)

Division Three		P	W	D	L	F	A	Pts
Wadham Lodge		22	17	3	2	69	18	54
Upminster	*-3*	22	15	4	3	51	21	46
Cranes United	*+2*	22	13	4	5	47	24	45
Newham United		22	13	6	3	47	29	45
Catholic United		22	9	4	9	58	45	31
Shenfield Association		22	8	6	8	45	41	30
Basildon Town		22	9	3	10	38	37	30
Debden Sports Res.		22	6	6	10	53	55	24
Springfield		22	5	5	12	30	42	20
Ramsden	*-1*	22	6	3	13	24	65	20
Writtle	*+5*	22	3	2	17	22	59	16
Barnston	*-1*	22	4	2	16	22	70	13

RESERVES CUP

FINAL

(May 4th at Billericay Town)

Westhamians Res. 2 Frenford Senior Res. 0

	Barnston	Basildon Town	Catholic United	Cranes United	Debden Sports Res.	Newham United	Ramsden	Shenfield Association	Springfield	Upminster	Wadham Lodge	Writtle
Barnston	***D***	1-0	3-1	1-3	2-2	0-7	1-0	1-0	2-4	1-3	1-2	2-2
Basildon Town	3-0	***I***	2-2	0-1	2-0	2-2	1-2	2-4	0-2	2-0	1-0	6-0
Catholic United	7-1	5-3	***V***	4-2	0-3	0-2	7-0	1-1	3-2	0-4	2-3	3-1
Cranes United	6-1	6-2	0-0		4-3	1-2	5-0	2-5	1-0	1-0	0-1	1-0
Debden Sports Res.	3-2	3-4	4-1	0-1		2-3	4-4	2-2	4-4	3-5	4-4	5-3
Newham United	3-1	2-0	2-0	0-3	2-2		2-1	3-2	3-2	2-2	0-1	3-0
Ramsden	2-1	0-3	0-6	2-2	W-L	1-2		0-4	1-0	1-5	1-7	2-3
Shenfield Association	6-1	0-2	1-6	0-0	3-1	1-3	1-1	***T***	1-0	1-3	0-3	2-0
Springfield	2-0	0-0	5-3	0-3	2-4	1-1	1-3	3-3	***H***	0-0	0-3	1-0
Upminster	4-0	4-1	1-0	1-1	2-0	1-1	4-1	3-1	3-1	***R***	0-1	2-1
Wadham Lodge	9-0	3-0	4-4	1-0	3-1	4-0	6-0	3-3	2-0	0-1	***E***	5-0
Writtle	1-0	0-2	1-3	1-4	2-3	2-2	0-2	1-4	2-0	2-3	0-4	***E***

ESSEX OLYMPIAN LEAGUE DIVISION THREE CONSTITUTION 2010-11

BASILDON TOWN . . . . Selex Sports Ground, Gardiners Lane South, Gardiners Way, Basildon SS14 3AP 01268 883128
BOWERS & PITSEA RES. . Len Salmon Stadium, Crown Avenue, off Kenneth Rd, Pitsea, Basildon SS14 2BE 01268 452068
CASTLE UNITED. . . . . The Score, 100 Oliver Road, Leyton E10 5JY 020 8539 8474
CATHOLIC UNITED . . . . SE Essex College Spts Ground, Wellstead Gardens, Westcliff-on-Sea SS0 0AY. 01702 348786
DEBDEN SPORTS . . . . Chigwell Lane, Loughton, Ilford IG10 3TP 020 8508 9392
NEWHAM UNITED . . . . Cave Road, Plaistow E13 9DX 07939 788048
OLD SOUTHENDIAN . . . . Warner's Bridge Park, Chandlers Way, Southend-on-Sea SS2 5RE . . . . None
RAMSDEN . . . . Nursery Sports Ground, Downham Road, Ramsden Heath, Billericay CM11 1PU. 01268 711502
SAWBRIDGEWORTH TOWN RES. . . . . . Crofters End, West Road, Sawbridgeworth CM21 0DE. 01279 722039
SHENFIELD ASSOCIATION . . . . The Drive, Warley, Brentwood CM13 3BH. 01277 226816
SPRINGFIELD. . . . . Springfield Hall Park, Arun Close, Springfield, Chelmsford CM1 7QE 01245 492441
WRITTLE. . . . . Paradise Road Playing Fields, Writtle, Chelmsford CM1 3HW 01245 420332

IN: Bowers & Pitsea Res. (S - Essex & Herts Border Combination), Castle United (P - Ilford & District League Premier Division), Old Southendian (Southend Borough Combination Premier Division), Sawbridgeworth Town Res. (R)

OUT: Barnston (S - Essex & Suffolk Border League Division One), Cranes United (E), Upminster (P), Wadham Lodge (P)

SENIOR CHALLENGE CUP
(Prem Div champions v Senior Cup holders)

(August 29th at Harold Wood Athletic)

Harold Wood Athletic 3 Manford Way 0

RESERVE CHALLENGE CUP
(Res Div One champions v Reserves Cup holders)

(September 5th at Harold Wood Athletic)

Harold Wood Athletic Res. 3 M & B Club Res. 0

GLOUCESTERSHIRE COUNTY LEAGUE

www.countyleague.co.uk

Sponsored by: Surridge

Founded: 1968

Recent champions:
2005: Highridge Utd
2006: Lydney Town
2007: Roman Glass St George
2008: Hardwicke
2009: Slimbridge

	AXA	Berk	Bish	Brim	Chipp	DRG	Ellw'd	Han	Heny	High	K Stan	Kings	Patch	Rock	Tav	Thorn	Tuff	Yate
AXA		2-1	3-2	4-1	1-4	2-0	4-3	3-2	0-5	1-4	2-3	2-3	1-0	2-4	2-1	1-4	1-3	1-0
Berkeley Town	4-2		1-0	1-1	3-4	3-0	3-0	0-0	2-1	0-5	0-2	0-0	2-4	2-5	3-2	0-5	0-2	2-1
Bishops Cleeve Res.	1-3	1-1		1-2	2-1	1-1	3-1	1-1	1-1	1-0	1-1	4-2	6-2	1-0	1-1	1-6	3-3	1-0
Brimscombe & Thrupp	5-1	1-1	2-1		1-0	1-4	0-1	3-1	3-1	3-0	2-0	0-5	2-0	1-1	2-0	0-2	1-2	2-0
Chipping Sodbury Town	3-0	1-1	6-1	2-0		2-0	2-2	4-0	1-3	1-3	3-3	3-1	1-2	1-1	4-2	1-1	1-1	0-2
DRG Stapleton	3-1	2-2	2-2	0-3	3-0		5-2	0-1	1-0	2-2	0-2	1-1	4-2	0-0	0-0	0-0	1-1	0-3
Ellwood	3-3	2-1	0-0	1-1	0-3	0-1		0-4	1-2	2-3	0-6	1-1	2-2	0-2	1-1	2-6	0-1	1-5
Hanham Athletic	1-0	1-0	2-2	0-1	2-0	2-0	3-1		3-0	0-2	2-1	0-0	0-2	1-1	1-1	0-3	0-3	0-1
Henbury	1-2	6-2	2-1	0-1	1-2	0-1	2-0	1-1		1-4	2-6	2-2	2-1	2-1	0-2	0-3	1-2	1-2
Highridge United	1-1	5-1	2-1	2-0	3-1	3-1	2-1	1-2	1-1		1-1	1-1	3-2	2-1	0-0	1-1	5-1	2-1
Kings Stanley	5-1	2-2	1-1	1-2	2-2	2-0	4-0	1-4	0-1	1-3		3-0	1-0	1-0	7-3	2-0	1-2	1-0
Kingswood	1-2	4-1	0-0	1-3	0-0	3-1	0-0	2-0	2-2	4-1	2-0		1-1	0-4	1-2	2-3	0-2	1-4
Patchway Town	1-4	0-2	3-0	2-4	2-1	1-0	4-2	0-3	1-0	1-7	0-1	0-1		0-3	2-1	0-3	1-1	0-2
Rockleaze Avonside	5-2	3-1	0-2	3-1	3-6	1-0	1-1	0-1	2-0	1-3	3-2	0-1	3-1		1-2	1-1	1-0	2-2
Taverners	2-1	1-1	0-0	3-0	1-0	0-2	2-1	0-2	0-1	2-2	0-1	0-1	1-1	1-2		0-1	0-0	2-2
Thornbury Town	5-0	6-0	3-2	5-1	1-1	1-4	9-0	3-1	2-2	0-3	3-1	1-2	2-0	1-0	2-0		3-2	3-2
Tuffley Rovers	2-1	4-1	2-0	1-2	2-3	3-0	2-0	3-0	1-1	0-4	3-1	2-1	7-0	0-0	4-0	2-0		0-1
Yate Town Res.	5-0	2-1	2-0	4-5	1-0	1-2	2-2	4-2	2-2	3-2	2-4	3-2	2-0	4-0	3-2	2-1	5-2	

		P	W	D	L	F	A	Pts
Thornbury Town		34	22	6	6	90	36	72
Highridge United		34	21	8	5	83	40	71
Tuffley Rovers		34	19	7	8	66	39	64
Yate Town Res.	*-3*	34	20	4	10	75	46	61
Brimscombe/Thrupp		34	19	4	11	57	51	61
Kings Stanley		34	17	6	11	70	47	57
Hanham Athletic		34	14	7	13	43	44	49
Chipping Sodbury T.		34	13	9	12	64	51	48
Rockleaze A'side	*-5*	34	14	8	12	55	45	45
Kingswood		34	11	11	12	48	49	44
AXA		34	13	2	19	56	88	41
DRG Stapleton	*-3*	34	11	9	14	41	48	39
Henbury		34	10	8	16	47	56	38
Bishops Cleeve Res.		34	8	13	13	45	57	37
Berkeley Town		34	8	9	17	45	77	33
Taverners		34	7	11	16	35	52	32
Patchway Town		34	9	4	21	38	75	31
Ellwood		34	2	10	22	33	90	16

LES JAMES LEAGUE CUP

PRELIMINARY ROUND
Ellwood 0 **Taverners** 0 (1-4p)
Tuffley Rovers 1 Rockleaze Avonside 0

FIRST ROUND
Bishops Cleeve Res. 3 Berkeley Town 0
Chipping Sodbury Town 3 Brimscombe & Thrupp 1
DRG Stapleton 2 Henbury 1
Hanham Athletic 0 **Taverners** 1
Highridge United 2 **Kings Stanley** 2 (7-8p)
Kingswood 3 Patchway Town 0
Tuffley Rovers 2 AXA 1
Yate Town Res. 5 Thornbury Town 1

QUARTER-FINALS
DRG Stapleton 3 Bishops Cleeve Res. 0
Kings Stanley 2 Kingswood 0
Taverners 3 Chipping Sodbury Town 3 (3-2p)
Tuffley Rovers 1 **Yate Town Res.** 2

SEMI-FINALS
Kings Stanley 4 Yate Town Res. 0 *(at Slimbridge)*
Taverners 0 DRG Stapleton 0 (5-3p) *(at Yate Town)*

FINAL *(May 23rd at Brimscombe & Thrupp)*
Taverners 2 Kings Stanley 0

GLOUCESTERSHIRE COUNTY LEAGUE CONSTITUTION 2010-11

AXA . . . . AXA Sports Ground, Station Road, Henbury, Bristol BS10 7TB 0117 950 2303
BERKELEY TOWN . . . . Station Road, Berkeley, Gloucestershire GL13 9AJ 07831 232100
BISHOPS CLEEVE RES. . . . . Kayte Lane, Southam, Cheltenham GL52 3PD 01242 676166
BRIMSCOMBE & THRUPP . . . . The Meadow, London Road, Brimscombe, Stroud GL5 2SH 07828 427113
CHIPPING SODBURY TOWN . . . . . The Ridings, Wickwar Road, Chipping Sodbury, Bristol BS37 6BQ 07787 522100
DRG STAPLETON . . . . Frenchay Park Road, Frenchay, Bristol BS16 1LG 07954 132819
ELLWOOD . . . . Bromley Road, Ellwood, Coleford, Gloucestershire GL16 7LY 01594 832967
HANHAM ATHLETIC . . . . The Playing Fields Pavilion, 16 Vicarage Road, Hanham, Bristol BS15 3AH 07840 660527
HENBURY . . . . Arnell Drive Playing Field, Lorain Walk, Henbury, Bristol BS10 7AS 0117 959 0475
KINGS STANLEY . . . . Marling Close, Broad Street, Kings Stanley, Stonehouse, Gloucestershire GL10 3PN 01453 828975
KINGSWOOD . . . . Kingswood PF, Wickwar Road, Kingswood, Wotton-under-Edge, Gloucestershire GL12 8RF 07971 682091
PATCHWAY TOWN . . . . Scott Park, Coniston Road, Patchway, Bristol BS34 5JR 0117 949 3952
ROCKLEAZE RANGERS . . . . Coombe Dingle Sport Complex, Coombe Dingle, Bristol BS9 2BJ 0117 962 6718
TAVERNERS . . . . Nailsworth Primary School, Forest Green, Nailsworth, Stroud, Gloucestershire GL6 0ET 07826 841970
THORNBURY TOWN . . . . Mundy Playing Fields, Kington Lane, Thornbury, Bristol BS35 1NA 01454 413645
TUFFLEY ROVERS . . . . Glevum Park, Lower Tuffley Lane, Gloucester GL2 6DT 01452 423402
YATE TOWN RES. . . . . Lodge Road, Yate, Bristol BS37 7LE 01454 228103

OUT: Highridge United (W)

Rockleaze Avonside become Rockleaze Rangers

Thornbury Town - Back Row L.R: Mike Grove, Steve Alexander, Steve Thompson, Christian Irwin, Ashley Lloyd, Pete Fowler, Robert Malcolm, Alex Lippiatt, Tom Webb, Sammy Lippiatt.
Front Row L.R: Danny Thompson, Artem Azytski, James DeRosa, Dan Wood, Chris Parry, Ricki Lippiatt (captain), Adam Harley, Matt Morrison. Photo courtesy of the Gloucestershire Gazette.

Taveners - Back Row (L-R): Chris Preece, Duane Portlock, Josh Blunt, Craig Hughes, Mike Thornton, Russell Chamberlain (only just see the top of his head), Jay Redbond, Ian Preece, Paul Jennings.
Front Row: Tom Burridge, Craig Mills, Grant Henderson, Rich Davies, Rich Kerry
Right at the front: Tom Hanley

HAMPSHIRE PREMIER LEAGUE

www.hpfl.co.uk

Sponsored by: Puma Engineering

Founded: 2007

Recent champions:
2008: AFC Stoneham
2009: Colden Common

	Ston	Bou	Cla	Col	Fle	HC	Hea	Lip	Lis	Loc	Lyn	Ott	Ov	Pau	QK	SB	TS	Win
AFC Stoneham		n/a	3-0	1-3	1-2	4-2	2-1	5-1	2-1	2-0	5-1	0-0	5-3	2-1	1-4	5-1	1-1	3-1
Bournemouth University	0-4	***S***	0-2	1-1	n/a	5-3	1-3	3-8	n/a	0-2	n/a	1-3	3-1	4-3	1-3	6-3	2-1	1-2
Clanfield	0-1	2-1	***E***	0-3	0-3	1-1	5-5	3-0	3-2	2-1	3-0	3-1	8-1	1-2	1-4	1-2	1-3	0-1
Colden Common	2-1	6-0	2-1	***N***	4-1	8-2	W-L	1-0	4-2	2-1	2-0	2-0	3-2	1-3	1-0	4-1	3-3	4-0
Fleetlands	3-2	7-1	3-0	3-2	***I***	6-1	3-1	1-1	4-0	1-1	0-2	2-0	3-0	2-1	2-1	2-1	0-2	1-0
Hamble Club	2-2	n/a	3-2	1-2	1-0	***O***	2-1	0-1	1-6	0-2	2-3	0-4	3-1	1-2	2-5	1-0	2-0	2-1
Headley United	0-4	3-1	0-1	0-2	0-1	4-3	***R***	3-4	1-3	0-2	1-2	2-2	0-2	3-0	0-5	3-1	0-2	1-1
Liphook United	0-1	1-0	3-0	2-1	0-0	4-1	6-1		2-2	2-3	3-2	2-2	4-0	3-0	3-0	3-2	2-0	5-2
Liss Athletic	0-2	n/a	3-1	1-3	0-2	1-4	3-3	0-6		3-4	1-3	2-1	3-0	9-4	2-4	5-2	1-3	3-2
Locks Heath	4-1	1-0	1-1	0-6	0-2	3-0	4-1	1-1	2-0	***D***	2-1	0-2	2-3	4-0	1-4	2-2	0-3	0-1
Lyndhurst	3-0	2-3	2-2	1-4	1-2	2-1	2-1	0-5	1-3	3-1	***I***	1-4	1-1	3-2	1-4	4-1	0-4	1-2
Otterbourne	0-0	n/a	3-4	0-1	1-2	8-1	W-L	0-6	1-2	0-4	0-1	***V***	4-1	2-1	5-1	2-1	1-2	4-3
Overton United	0-3	2-2	1-2	1-2	0-2	2-1	1-0	0-1	2-3	0-2	5-1	1-2	***I***	1-1	1-4	0-1	2-2	1-1
Paulsgrove	2-4	n/a	5-1	1-3	5-0	2-2	5-1	0-4	4-1	2-3	3-2	2-4	4-0	***S***	1-1	1-1	3-2	5-4
QK Southampton	5-0	4-3	4-1	1-0	2-0	10-0	W-L	0-0	3-2	5-0	4-1	3-1	1-2	7-3	***I***	2-0	1-2	3-1
Sporting Bishops Waltham	1-2	3-5	4-3	0-9	1-6	2-1	1-1	1-1	2-3	1-1	0-1	3-4	6-1	2-5	1-3	***O***	1-4	0-1
Team Solent	2-1	3-1	6-0	2-2	2-1	8-1	2-1	2-1	6-0	4-0	8-0	1-0	4-0	3-2	1-1	1-1	***N***	4-1
Winchester Castle	0-0	n/a	2-2	1-0	0-1	1-2	1-3	0-3	2-1	1-2	4-1	2-3	1-1	1-3	0-1	2-1	0-1	

LEAGUE CUP

FIRST ROUND
Clanfield 5 Hamble Club 0
Winchester Castle 1 **Locks Heath** 5

SECOND ROUND
Clanfield 0 **Team Solent** 3
Colden Cmn 1 Fleetlands 1 *aet* (4-2p)
Liphook United 1 Headley United 0
Otterbourne 4 Liss Athletic 4 *aet* (3-1p)
Overton 3 Bournemouth University 2
Paulsgrove 3 Lyndhurst 1
QK Southampton 5 Locks Heath 3
Sporting Bishops Waltham 1 **AFC Stoneham** 6 *(at AFC Stoneham)*

QUARTER-FINALS
Otterbourne 1 **AFC Stoneham** 3
Overton United 2 **Paulsgrove** 3
QK S'thampton 2 Colden Common 1
Team Solent 1 Liphook United 0

SEMI-FINALS *(both at Locks Heath)*
AFC Stoneham 2 Team Solent 1
Paulsgrove 3 QK Southampton 1

FINAL
(May 8th at Winchester City)
AFC Stoneham 5 Paulsgrove 1

Senior Division		P	W	D	L	F	A	Pts
Colden Common		**32**	**25**	**2**	**5**	**86**	**32**	**77**
Team Solent		**32**	**23**	**6**	**3**	**90**	**30**	**75**
QK Southampton		**32**	**23**	**3**	**6**	**93**	**36**	**72**
Fleetlands		**32**	**22**	**3**	**7**	**61**	**33**	**69**
Liphook United		**32**	**19**	**7**	**6**	**79**	**34**	**64**
AFC Stoneham		**32**	**18**	**5**	**9**	**66**	**46**	**59**
Locks Heath		**32**	**14**	**5**	**13**	**53**	**56**	**47**
Otterbourne		**32**	**14**	**4**	**14**	**61**	**56**	**46**
Paulsgrove		**32**	**13**	**4**	**15**	**75**	**78**	**43**
Liss Athletic		**32**	**12**	**2**	**18**	**68**	**84**	**38**
Lyndhurst		**32**	**12**	**2**	**18**	**47**	**80**	**38**
Hamble Club		**32**	**9**	**3**	**20**	**46**	**98**	**30**
Clanfield	***-3***	**32**	**9**	**5**	**18**	**53**	**75**	**29**
Winchester Castle		**32**	**8**	**5**	**19**	**40**	**62**	**29**
Overton United		**32**	**6**	**5**	**21**	**36**	**80**	**23**
Sporting Bishops Waltham		**32**	**5**	**6**	**21**	**44**	**84**	**21**
Headley United	***-1***	**32**	**4**	**5**	**23**	**38**	**72**	**16**

Bournemouth University - record expunged

Combination	P	W	D	L	F	A	Pt
Winchester Castle Res.	26	19	6	1	75	17	63
Locks Heath Res.	26	16	5	5	67	29	53
Otterbourne Res.	26	13	6	7	66	46	45
Fleetlands Res.	26	13	6	7	53	36	45
Paulsgrove Res.	26	12	7	7	56	42	43
Clanfield Res.	26	11	8	7	67	51	41
Liphook United Res.	26	10	8	8	54	41	38
Colden Common Res.	26	9	6	11	44	51	33
QK Southampton Res.	26	9	5	12	45	54	32
AFC Stoneham Res.	26	8	6	12	35	42	30
Sporting Bishops Waltham Res.	26	6	7	13	32	65	25
Overton Utd Res	26	5	7	14	44	72	22
Hamble Club Res.	26	5	5	16	41	89	20
Liss Athletic Res.	26	3	4	19	30	74	13

Lyndhurst Res. - record expunged

COMBINATION CUP

FINAL *(May 8th at Winchester City)*
Otterbourne Res. 2 Paulsgrove Res. 1

HAMPSHIRE PREMIER LEAGUE SENIOR DIVISION CONSTITUTION 2010-11

AFC ALDERMASTON . . . . AWE Recreational Society, Aldermaston, Reading RG7 4PR 0118 982 7614/4544
AFC STONEHAM . . . . Pirelli Sports Ground, Chestnut Avenue, Eastleigh, Southampton SO50 9PF 07765 046429
CLANFIELD . . . . Peel Park, Chalton Lane, Clanfield, Waterlooville PO8 0PR 07765 238231
COLDEN COMMON . . . . Colden Common Rec., Main Road, Colden Common, Winchester SO21 1RP 01962 712365
FLEETLANDS . . . . DARA Fleetlands, Lederle Lane, Gosport PO13 0AA 023 9223 9723
HAMBLE CLUB . . . . Shell Mex Ground, Hamble Lane, Hamble-le-Rice, Southampton SO31 4TS 07818 204400
LIPHOOK UNITED . . . . Recreation Ground, London Road, Liphook GU30 7AN 07974 983114
LISS ATHLETIC . . . . Newman Collard Ground, Hill Brow Road, Liss GU33 7LH 07980 424834
LOCKS HEATH . . . . Locksheath Rec, 419 Warsash Road, Titchfield Common, Fareham PO14 4JX 01489 600932
LYNDHURST . . . . Wellands Road, Lyndhurst SO43 7AD 07772 030430
OTTERBOURNE . . . . Oakwood Park, Oakwood Avenue, Otterbourne SO21 2ED 01962 714681
OVERTON UNITED . . . . Overton Recreation Centre, Bridge Street, Overton RG25 3LZ 01256 770561
PAULSGROVE . . . . Paulsgrove Social Club, Marsden Road, Paulsgrove, Portsmouth PO6 4JB 02392 324102
QK SOUTHAMPTON . . . . . . Lordshill Recreation Centre, Redbridge Lane, Lordshill, Southampton SO16 0XN 07801 550337
SPORTING BISHOPS WALTHAM . . . . . Priory Park, Elizabeth Way, Bishop Waltham SO32 1SQ 07740 506777
TEAM SOLENT . . . . Hardmoor Sports Ground, Stoneham Lane, Eastleigh, Southampton SO50 9HT 023 8061 7574
UNIVERSITY OF PORTSMOUTH . . . Langston Campus, Furze Lane, Milton, Portsmouth PO4 8LW 023 9284 4526
WINCHESTER CASTLE . . . Hants Co. Council Sports, Petersfield Rd (A31),Chilcombe, Winchester SO23 8ZB 01962 866989

IN: AFC Aldermaston (R), University of Portsmouth (P - Portsmouth & District League Premier Division)
OUT: Bournemouth University (WS), Headley United (R - Aldershot & District League Premier Division)

HERTS SENIOR COUNTY LEAGUE

www.hsc.leaguemanager.biz

Sponsored by:
No sponsor

Founded: 1898

Recent champions:

2005: Hadley
2006: Whitewebbs
2007: Whitewebbs
2008: Hatfield Town
2009: Metropolitan Police Bushey

	Baldock	Bov'don	Chipp.	Codicote	Croxley	Cuffley	Ev'green	Hertfd H.	Lemsf'd	L. Lions	MP Bush	Mill End	Park St	S'dridge	Standon	Wormley
Baldock Town Letchworth	***P***	3-3	5-1	3-2	2-1	1-1	9-0	2-0	1-0	0-0	3-2	W-L	1-0	4-0	2-2	3-0
Bovingdon	0-0	***R***	2-2	1-1	2-0	5-3	5-1	2-3	1-0	0-2	2-2	4-1	0-4	4-3	1-2	2-3
Chipperfield Corinthians	0-3	0-1	***E***	3-2	2-2	2-1	7-0	1-3	5-1	1-2	1-2	2-0	2-0	0-1	6-2	1-2
Codicote	0-5	3-1	4-7	***M***	1-2	1-1	4-1	2-0	2-3	3-1	3-3	1-1	2-0	4-1	1-1	0-2
Croxley Guild	0-8	3-0	2-3	2-2	***I***	2-3	2-0	1-3	2-3	1-3	2-1	1-0	2-2	2-1	3-3	1-3
Cuffley	2-1	2-3	0-3	1-3	2-5	***E***	3-1	2-1	2-5	0-1	2-4	0-1	1-3	6-2	2-0	1-3
Evergreen	1-3	1-4	0-0	0-5	1-0	3-3	***R***	3-0	0-1	1-5	0-3	5-3	3-3	4-2	2-4	3-4
Hertford Heath	2-4	2-2	1-4	3-4	2-2	1-5	2-2		1-1	1-4	0-4	6-0	2-4	1-1	1-3	1-6
Lemsford	3-6	0-1	1-4	0-3	3-1	0-1	2-2	2-2	***D***	1-4	1-2	2-2	0-5	2-1	0-3	2-4
London Lions	1-3	5-0	1-0	4-0	4-1	3-3	1-1	3-1	2-0	***I***	3-2	3-0	2-0	3-1	2-1	2-1
Met. Police Bushey	0-7	3-2	6-1	3-1	3-0	5-2	2-0	3-0	3-0	2-2	***V***	3-1	3-2	2-3	3-1	2-4
Mill End Sports	1-5	0-1	2-2	1-2	0-1	1-1	3-0	5-0	0-3	1-2	2-5	***I***	1-3	1-1	5-0	0-6
Park Street Village	0-3	2-1	2-3	3-3	2-0	2-3	2-0	W-L	3-1	0-1	2-3	3-0	***S***	4-0	2-0	1-5
Sandridge Rovers	2-2	1-1	0-0	1-1	1-2	4-3	1-2	4-2	1-0	1-1	2-3	2-2	1-0	***I***	2-0	0-1
Standon & Puckeridge	2-0	1-2	2-0	2-2	3-3	3-2	1-1	4-1	3-1	0-5	2-2	2-0	3-1	3-1	***O***	1-2
Wormley Rovers	1-0	6-0	1-2	2-1	3-2	3-0	4-0	2-1	3-2	0-2	0-1	5-1	0-1	3-1	2-0	***N***

Premier Division		P	W	D	L	F	A	Pts
London Lions		**30**	**23**	**5**	**2**	**74**	**26**	**74**
Wormley Rovers		**30**	**24**	**0**	**6**	**81**	**34**	**72**
Baldock Letchworth	*-3*	**30**	**21**	**6**	**3**	**89**	**27**	**66**
Met. Police Bushey		**30**	**20**	**4**	**6**	**82**	**51**	**64**
Chipperfield Corinthians		**30**	**14**	**5**	**11**	**65**	**51**	**47**
Park Street Village		**30**	**14**	**3**	**13**	**56**	**46**	**45**
Codicote	+3	**30**	**11**	**9**	**10**	**63**	**58**	**45**
Standon & Puckeridge		**30**	**12**	**7**	**11**	**54**	**57**	**43**
Bovingdon		**30**	**12**	**7**	**11**	**53**	**59**	**43**
Croxley Guild		**30**	**9**	**6**	**15**	**48**	**66**	**33**
Cuffley		**30**	**9**	**5**	**16**	**58**	**72**	**32**
Sandridge Rovers		**30**	**7**	**8**	**15**	**42**	**63**	**29**
Lemsford		**30**	**7**	**4**	**19**	**40**	**70**	**25**
Evergreen		**30**	**5**	**7**	**18**	**38**	**88**	**22**
Mill End Sports		**30**	**4**	**6**	**20**	**35**	**71**	**18**
Hertford Heath		**30**	**4**	**6**	**20**	**43**	**82**	**18**

RESERVES CUP

FINAL

(May 1st at Oxhey Jets)

London Lions Res. 3 Standon & Puckeridge Res. 2

Reserve Division One	P	W	D	L	F	A	Pt
Hinton Res.	24	19	2	3	84	25	59
Baldock Town Letch. Res.	24	15	3	6	65	31	48
London Lions Res.	24	14	1	9	56	39	43
Codicote Res.	24	13	3	8	58	38	42
Park Street Village Res.	24	13	2	9	49	33	41
Met. Police Bushey Res.	24	12	3	9	48	43	39
Wormley Rovers Res.	24	12	2	10	44	44	38
Evergreen Res.	24	8	3	13	49	59	27
Cuffley Res.	24	7	5	12	41	52	26
Sarratt Res.	24	7	5	12	41	65	26
Bovingdon Res.	24	7	4	13	38	69	25
Sandridge Rovers Res.	24	6	3	15	38	83	21
Hertford Heath Res.	24	4	2	18	25	55	14

Reserve Division Two	P	W	D	L	F	A	Pt
Standon & Puckeridge Res.	22	18	2	2	79	30	56
Chipperfield Corinthians Res.	22	13	5	4	59	32	44
Croxley Guild Res.	22	13	4	5	71	52	43
Harpenden Rovers Res.	22	11	3	8	58	47	36
Letchworth GC Eagles Res.	22	10	5	7	44	35	35
Old Parmiterians Res.	22	10	3	9	56	42	33
Buntingford Town Res.	22	10	2	10	52	61	32
Knebworth Res.	22	7	4	11	37	56	25
Mill End Sports Res.	22	6	3	13	53	64	21
Lemsford Res.	22	5	4	13	39	58	19
Bedmond S & S Club Res.	22	4	4	14	32	59	16
Bushey Rangers Res.	22	5	1	16	39	83	16

HERTS SENIOR COUNTY LEAGUE PREMIER DIVISION CONSTITUTION 2010-11

BALDOCK TOWN LETCHWORTH ..... Herts County FA, Baldock Road, Letchworth SG6 2EN 01462 677622
BOVINGDON .... Green Lane, Bovingdon, Hemel Hempstead HP3 0LA 01442 832628
CHIPPERFIELD CORINTHIANS .... Queens Street, Chipperfield, Kings Langley WD4 9BT 07958 744441
CODICOTE .... Gosling Sports Park, Stanborough Road, Welwyn Garden City AL8 6XE 01707 331056
CROXLEY GUILD .... Croxley Guild of Sport, The Green, Croxley Green, Watford WD3 3JX 01923 770534
CUFFLEY .... King George's Playing Fields, Northaw Road East, Cuffley EN6 4LU 07815 174434
HARPENDEN ROVERS .... Acres Corner, Cravells Road, Harpenden Common AL5 1BQ .... None
HINTON .... Holtwhites Sports & Social, Kirkland Drive, Enfield EN2 0RU 020 8363 4449
LEMSFORD .... Welwyn Playing Fields, Ottway Walk, Welwyn AL6 9AT .... None
LETCHWORTH GARDEN CITY EAGLES Pixmore PF, Ledgers Lane, Baldock Road, Letchworth SG6 2EN .... None
METROPOLITAN POLICE BUSHEY .... Aldenham Road, Bushey, Watford WD2 3TR 01923 243947
SANDRIDGE ROVERS .... Spencer Recreation Ground, Sandridge, St Albans AL4 9DD 01727 835506
SARRATT .... King George V Playing Fields, George V Way, Sarratt WD3 6AU .... None
STANDON & PUCKERIDGE .... Station Road, Standon, Ware SG11 1QT 01920 823460
WORMLEY ROVERS .... Wormley Sports Club, Church Lane, Wormley EN10 7QF 01992 460650

IN: Harpenden Rovers (P), Hinton (P), Letchworth Garden City Eagles (P), Sarratt (P)

OUT: Evergreen (W), Hertford Heath (R), London Lions (P - Spartan South Midlands League Division One), Mill End Sports (R), Park Street Village (R - West Herts League Premier Division)

	AFC Hatf'd	Allenburys	Bedmond	Belstone	Bunt'gford	Bushey R.	Debden S.	Harpenden	Hinton	Kimpton R.	Knebworth	Letchworth	O. P'terians	Sarratt	St Peters	Walkern R.	Whitwell V.
AFC Hatfield Town		0-2	1-4	8-0	1-1	1-1	n/a	3-4	2-3	2-2	1-3	2-3	0-3	2-3	1-3	7-1	0-3
Allenburys Sports	0-1		1-5	3-2	3-1	0-3	3-3	1-5	0-2	4-1	1-3	L-W	2-3	3-1	2-3	2-2	0-3
Bedmond Sports & Social	6-2	6-0	***D***	1-2	3-0	2-4	n/a	2-3	3-6	7-0	6-1	1-3	0-0	2-1	2-1	4-0	2-3
Belstone	3-0	2-1	2-0	***I***	2-2	0-3	n/a	0-4	1-1	9-0	2-1	2-3	1-1	0-5	2-1	4-0	5-1
Buntingford Town	2-2	8-1	2-6	5-2	***V***	0-1	n/a	3-4	0-4	3-4	0-3	2-3	1-4	5-5	2-3	4-1	2-3
Bushey Rangers	3-2	2-1	2-1	0-2	4-1	***I***	n/a	0-1	0-2	3-0	2-1	1-4	5-1	2-3	1-2	5-0	2-2
Debden Sports	1-3	n/a	2-6	n/a	n/a	n/a	***S***	0-3	1-2	n/a	n/a	n/a	n/a	2-3	1-4	n/a	n/a
Harpenden Rovers	3-1	5-0	3-4	0-1	4-2	0-3	n/a	***I***	2-1	3-1	1-0	1-3	1-0	4-1	1-0	8-1	1-1
Hinton	7-3	1-2	6-1	1-2	5-4	1-0	n/a	0-1	***O***	6-1	2-0	5-1	3-0	2-3	4-1	4-0	6-1
Kimpton Rovers	3-2	3-0	2-3	1-3	3-5	3-4	2-2	3-2	1-3	***N***	3-3	2-10	0-2	2-0	1-1	2-2	0-3
Knebworth	1-1	2-1	0-3	0-1	3-4	0-3	n/a	1-1	0-3	1-2		2-2	5-0	1-0	2-3	4-2	3-0
Letchworth GC Eagles	5-1	5-1	5-1	4-2	1-0	2-0	n/a	2-2	3-2	5-0	2-1		2-2	0-1	1-0	3-3	5-2
Old Parmiterians	3-1	5-0	2-3	1-3	4-2	1-1	n/a	0-1	1-3	3-3	1-2	3-0	***O***	2-2	3-1	0-3	3-2
Sarratt	0-2	9-0	3-2	3-1	1-0	1-2	8-1	3-1	4-1	5-1	3-2	0-4	2-1	***N***	1-1	7-2	3-2
St Peters	1-0	6-0	2-1	0-2	5-1	0-2	n/a	2-3	2-5	2-2	4-3	0-6	1-0	1-1	***E***	7-0	0-2
Walkern Rangers	0-3	3-4	0-2	2-4	0-4	0-4	1-5	0-2	1-4	1-5	0-1	2-4	0-7	0-5	0-9		0-9
Whitwell Village	3-0	2-0	0-2	1-7	4-1	0-2	n/a	1-1	3-1	3-0	4-1	1-4	2-1	0-1	2-2	2-1	

Division One	**P**	**W**	**D**	**L**	**F**	**A**	**Pts**
Letchworth GCE	**30**	**23**	**4**	**3**	**95**	**42**	**73**
Hinton	**30**	**21**	**1**	**8**	**94**	**43**	**64**
Harpenden Rovers	**30**	**20**	**4**	**6**	**72**	**40**	**64**
Bushey Rangers	**30**	**19**	**3**	**8**	**65**	**34**	**60**
Sarratt	**30**	**18**	**4**	**8**	**77**	**48**	**58**
Belstone	**30**	**18**	**3**	**9**	**69**	**53**	**57**
Bedmond Spts/S.	**30**	**17**	**1**	**12**	**85**	**57**	**52**
Whitwell Village	**30**	**15**	**4**	**11**	**65**	**56**	**49**
St Peters	**30**	**13**	**5**	**12**	**64**	**53**	**44**
Old Parmiterians	**30**	**11**	**6**	**13**	**57**	**52**	**39**
Knebworth	**30**	**10**	**4**	**16**	**50**	**58**	**34**
Kimpton Rovers	**30**	**7**	**6**	**17**	**51**	**100**	**27**
Buntingford Town	**30**	**6**	**4**	**20**	**67**	**89**	**22**
Allenburys Sports	**30**	**7**	**1**	**22**	**35**	**94**	**22**
AFC Hatfield Town	**30**	**5**	**5**	**20**	**52**	**76**	**20**
Walkern Rangers	**30**	**1**	**3**	**26**	**27**	**130**	**6**

Debden Sports - record expunged

AUBREY CUP

FIRST ROUND

Cuffley 2 St Peters 1

SECOND ROUND

AFC Hatfield Town 0 **Park Street Village** 4

Bedmond 1 **Cuffley** 3

Buntingford Town 0 **London Lions** 7

Bushey Rgrs 2 Belstone 0

Chipperfield Corinthians 9 Whitwell Village 0

Codicote 2 **Wormley Rov.** 5

Debden Sports 1 **Letchworth Garden City Eagles** 5

Evergreen 4 Hinton 3

Harpenden Town 0 **Croxley Guild** 1

Hertford Heath 2 **Baldock Town Letchworth** 3

Kimpton Rovers 0 **Met. Police Bushey** 3

Knebworth 3 Allenburys Sports 2

Mill End Spts 1 **Lemsford** 2

Old Parmiterians 3 Bovingdon 0

Sandridge 5 Walkern Rgrs 0

Standon & P. 5 Sarratt 2

THIRD ROUND

Baldock 3 Croxley Guild 2

Cuffley 3 Chipperfield 2

Letchworth GC Eagles 1 Park Street Village 0 *aet*

Met. Police Bushey 10 Bushey Rangers 1

Old Parmiterians 0 **London Lions** 5

Sandridge 6 Evergreen 1

Standon 3 Lemsford 2

Wormley 5 Knebworth 0

QUARTER-FINALS

Letchworth GC Eagles 2 Baldock Town Letchworth 1

London Lions 3 Standon 2

M Police Bushey 2 Cuffley 0

Wormley Rovers 1 Sandridge Rovers 0

SEMI-FINALS

Letchworth 3 Wormley 0

L. Lions 0 **Metpol Bushey** 1

FINAL

(May 3rd at HCFA, Letchworth)

Metropolitan Police Bushey 0 **Letchworth Garden City Eagles** 2

HERTS SENIOR COUNTY LEAGUE DIVISION ONE CONSTITUTION 2010-11

AFC HATFIELD TOWN .... Birchwood Leisure Centre, Birchwood, Longmead, Hatfield AL10 0AN................ 01707 270772
AFC HERTFORD............ Hertford Town FC, Hertingfordbury Park, West Street, Hertford SG13 8EZ 01992 583716
ALLENBURYS SPORTS .... Glaxo Smith Kline, Westfield Park Road, Ware SG12 0DP .... None
BEDMOND SPORTS & SOCIAL .. Toms Lane Rec, Toms Lane, Bedmond, Abbots Langley WD5 0RB................. 01923 267991
BELSTONE .... The Medburn Ground, Watling Street, Radlett WD6 3AB.................... 020 8207 2395
BUNTINGFORD TOWN......... Sainsburys Distribution Centre, London Road, Buntingford SG9 9JR 01763 271522
BUSHEY RANGERS .... Moatfield, Bournehall Lane, Bushey WD23 3JU 020 8386 1875
EIGHT BELLS OLD HATFIELD........ Lemsford Vilage Hall, Brocket Road, Lemsford AL8 7TT 01707 333548
GOFFS OAK.......................... Goffs Oak Pavilion, Goffs Lane, EN7 5ET .... None
HERTFORD HEATH .... The Playing Field, Trinity Road, Hertford Heath SG13 7QS .... None
KIMPTON ROVERS .... Kimpton Recreation Ground, High Street, Kimpton, Hitchin SG4 8RA .... None
KNEBWORTH .... The Recreation Ground, Watton Road, Knebworth, Stevenage SG3 6AH...................... None
LONDON COLNEY BLUES .... Morris Playing Field, White Horse Lane, London Colney AL2 1JP............................ None
MILL END SPORTS .... King George V Playing Fields, Penn Road, Mill End, Rickmansworth WD3 8QX............ 01923 776392
OLD PARMITERIANS............. Thomas Parmiter Sports Centre, Garston, Watford WD25 0JU................ 01923 682805
ST PETERS .... Colney Heath FC, Recreation Ground, High Street, Colney Heath AL4 0NS 01727 826188
WHITWELL VILLAGE............ King George V Recreation Ground, Bradway, Whitwell SG4 8BE .... None

IN: AFC Hertford (N), Eight Bells (P - Sunday football), Goffs Oak (P - Hertford & District League Premier Division), Hertford Heath (R), London Colney Blues (N), Mill End Sports (R)

OUT: Debden Sports (WS), Harpenden Rovers (P), Hinton (P), Letchworth Garden City Eagles (P), Sarratt (P), Walkern Rangers (R)

KENT COUNTY LEAGUE

www.kentcountyfootballleague.co.uk

Sponsored by:

Vandanel

Founded: 1922

Recent champions:

2005: Cray Valley Paper Mills

2006: Lewisham Borough (Community)

2007: Holmesdale

2008: Norton Sports

2009: Hollands & Blair

Premier Division		P	W	D	L	F	A	PTS
Stansfeld O & B Club		30	22	3	5	72	34	69
Hollands & Blair		30	20	8	2	74	29	68
Sutton Athletic		30	19	6	5	67	31	63
Phoenix Sports		30	17	8	5	59	34	59
Canterbury City		30	17	4	9	67	41	55
Cray Valley Paper Mills		30	13	4	13	56	41	43
Rusthall		30	13	4	13	38	36	43
Bearsted		30	11	9	10	45	42	42
Fleet Leisure		30	12	6	12	44	48	42
Lewisham Borough (Com.)		30	11	5	14	45	51	38
Snodland		30	9	5	16	54	66	32
Bly Spartans		30	9	5	16	29	55	32
Tonbridge Invicta		30	8	5	17	35	60	29
Orpington		30	7	5	18	45	65	26
Milton & Fulston United		30	6	2	22	30	84	20
Coney Hall	-1	30	5	3	22	30	73	17

	Bearsted	Bly Spart.	Canterbury	Coney Hall	Cray Valley	Fleet Leis.	Hollands/B.	Lewisham	Milton & F.	Orpington	Phoenix S.	Rusthall	Snodland	Stansfeld	Sutton A.	Tonbdg I.
Bearsted		2-3	1-6	1-0	1-1	0-1	1-2	2-1	3-1	2-0	2-2	1-2	1-0	2-2	0-0	2-0
Bly Spartans	1-1		3-2	1-1	0-2	0-2	0-4	0-0	4-2	0-1	2-0	1-0	3-2	2-3	1-2	2-0
Canterbury City	1-3	4-0	***P***	4-0	4-0	1-1	2-2	0-0	4-1	4-2	1-2	1-3	4-1	2-1	1-0	2-0
Coney Hall	0-1	0-1	1-2	***R***	1-5	0-1	1-2	2-1	2-2	3-1	0-5	1-0	0-4	1-5	2-6	0-0
Cray Valley Paper Mills	0-1	4-1	4-1	1-0	***E***	5-0	1-3	1-2	3-0	1-1	2-2	2-1	1-2	1-2	0-1	0-1
Fleet Leisure	2-2	0-0	0-1	2-1	0-3	***M***	1-3	4-1	2-0	2-2	1-0	1-0	5-1	2-2	1-3	1-2
Hollands & Blair	3-3	2-1	1-0	4-0	6-3	2-0	***I***	1-2	2-1	1-1	1-1	3-1	1-1	0-1	6-2	2-2
Lewisham Boro. (Comm.)	3-0	1-2	3-4	3-0	1-3	4-2	0-4	***E***	3-0	0-4	0-0	0-0	1-1	1-3	3-2	1-2
Milton & Fulston United	0-4	2-0	1-3	2-4	2-1	1-0	0-4	0-1	***R***	0-3	0-4	1-1	1-2	0-3	1-3	1-0
Orpington	3-0	5-0	1-2	1-4	0-5	0-3	0-2	0-2	4-1		2-2	0-3	2-5	3-4	0-3	4-1
Phoenix Sports	3-2	5-0	1-0	4-1	1-1	2-1	2-3	3-2	2-0	1-0		0-0	2-6	1-4	1-0	2-1
Rusthall	1-0	1-0	2-0	2-1	1-0	1-2	1-1	2-1	1-4	2-0	2-3	***D***	2-0	0-3	0-2	0-1
Snodland	0-0	0-0	5-3	3-1	1-3	2-2	0-5	2-3	8-0	3-1	0-2	1-4	***I***	0-1	1-5	0-1
Stansfeld O & B Club	2-1	2-1	0-3	2-1	2-1	4-0	0-1	3-2	6-1	4-1	0-4	2-1	5-0	***V***	1-1	3-0
Sutton Athletic	2-2	3-0	1-1	3-1	2-0	3-1	1-3	2-0	4-1	3-1	0-0	3-0	3-1	1-0		1-1
Tonbridge Invicta	0-4	2-0	1-4	4-1	1-2	2-4	0-0	2-3	3-4	2-2	0-2	1-4	4-2	0-2	1-5	

KENT COUNTY LEAGUE PREMIER DIVISION CONSTITUTION 2010-11

BEARSTED .... Otham Sports Ground, Honey Lane, Otham, Maidstone ME15 8RG.................. 07860 360280
BLY SPARTANS................ Bly Spartans Sports Ground, Rede Court Road, Strood ME2 3TU.................. 01634 710577
BRIDON ROPES .... Meridian Sports Club, Charlton Park Road, Charlton SE7 8QS 020 8856 1923
CANTERBURY CITY .... Hersden Recreation Ground, The Sycamores, Hersden, Canterbury CT3 4HY 07847 578544
CHARLTON ATHLETIC COMMUNITY . Samuel Montagu YC, 122 Broadwalk, Kidbrooke SE3 8ND 020 8856 1126/9680
CRAY VALLEY PAPER MILLS ..... Badgers Sports Ground, Middle Park Avenue, Eltham SE9 5HT 07878 079566
FLEET LEISURE .... Fleet Leisure Sports Club, Nelson Road, Northfleet DA11 7EE.................. 01474 359222
HOLLANDS & BLAIR............. Star Meadow Sports Club, Darland Road, Gillingham ME7 3AN 01634 573839
LEWISHAM BOROUGH (COMMUNITY) . . . Ladywell Arena, Doggett Road, Catford SE6 4QX 020 8314 1986
PHOENIX SPORTS .... Phoenix Sports Club, Mayplace Road East, Barnehurst DA7 6JT.................. 01322 526159
RUSTHALL................... Jockey Farm, Nellington Lane, Rusthall, Tunbridge Wells TN4 8SH.................. 07865 396299
SNODLAND .... Potyn's Field, Paddlesworth Road, Snodland ME6 5DL 01634 241946
STANSFELD O & B CLUB .. Metrogas, Marathon PF, Forty Foot Way, Avery Hill Rd, New Eltham SE9 2EX............ 020 8859 1579
SUTTON ATHLETIC .... The Roaches, Parsonage Lane, Sutton-at-Hone, Dartford DA4 9HD 07788 446495
TONBRIDGE INVICTA.... Swanmead Sports Ground, Swanwead Way, off Cannon Lane, Tonbridge TN9 1PP 01732 350473
WOODSTOCK PARK......... Woodstock Park Sport & Social, Broadoak Road, Sittingbourne ME9 8HL 01795 410777

IN: Bridon Ropes (P - Division One West), Charlton Athletic Community (P - Division One West), Woodstock Park (P - Division One East)
OUT: Coney Hall (R - Division One West), Milton & Fulston United (R - Division One East), Orpington (R - Division One West)

GR ROOFING CHAMPIONS TROPHY

(Premier Division champions v Inter-Regional Challenge Cup holders)

Not contested in 2009-10

Division One East		P	W	D	L	F	A	Pts
Woodstock Park		24	17	3	4	77	36	54
Bromley Green		24	16	3	5	55	33	51
Premier		24	14	6	4	54	33	48
Staplehurst & MU		24	14	2	8	54	50	44
APM Mears		24	13	4	7	52	40	43
University of Kent		24	9	7	8	50	42	34
Sheerness East		24	10	4	10	43	50	34
Otford United		24	9	4	11	43	51	31
New Romney		24	9	3	12	49	46	30
Larkfield & NHW		24	6	8	10	50	52	26
AFC Sheppey	*-1*	24	6	4	14	33	54	21
Kennington		24	4	2	18	32	71	14
Oakwood		24	2	4	18	19	53	10

BILL MANKELOW INTER REGIONAL CHALLENGE CUP

(Premier and Division One teams)

FIRST ROUND
APM Mears 0 **Larkfield & New Hythe Wdrs** 1
Belvedere 5 Wickham Pk 2
Chipstead 0 **Bridon R.** 4
Farnborough Old Boys Guild 3 Rusthall 1
Greenways 2 Tudor Spts 1
Guru Nanak 0 **Charlton Athletic Community** 1
Oakwood 0 **Sheerness East** 3
Old Bexleians 0 **Metrogas** 4
Staplehurst & Monarchs United 1 **Kennington** 5

SECOND ROUND
Belvedere 1 Tonbridge I. 0
Bromley Green 0 **Hollands & Blair** 2
Canterbury City 8 New Romney 0
Charlton Athletic Community 0 **Fleet Leisure** 4
Cray Valley Paper Mills 3 Stansfeld O & B Club 1
Greenways 0 **Crockenhill** 3
Metrogas 5 Bridon Ropes 0
Milton & Fulston United 0 **Bly Spartans** 4
Orpington 1 **Farnborough Old Boys Guild** 1 *aet* (3-4p)
Otford United 1 **Bearsted** 2
Phoenix S. 3 Coney Hall 1
Sheerness E. 3 **Premier** 4
Snodland 2 **Kennington** 3
Sutton Athletic 1 **Lewisham Borough (Community)** 2
University of Kent 6 AFC Sheppey 2
Woodstock Park 0 **Larkfield & New Hythe Wdrs** 2

THIRD ROUND
Belvedere 0 **Phoenix** 2
Crockenhill 3 Metrogas 1 *aet*
Farnborough OB Guild 0 **Lewisham Borough (Community)** 1
Fleet Leisure 0 Cray Valley Paper Mills 0 *aet* (5-3p)
Kennington 3 Bly 2
Larkfield 2 **Bearsted** 4
Premier 1 **Canterbury** 2
University of Kent 0 **Hollands & Blair** 1

QUARTER-FINALS
Fleet Leisure 2 Bearsted 0
Hollands & Blair 2 Crockenhill 1
Kennington 0 **Phoenix** 4
Lewisham Borough (Community) 1 Canterbury City 1 *aet* (3-2p)

SEMI-FINALS
Lewisham 0 **Hollands/B.** 2
Phoenix 0 **Fleet Leisure** 3

FINAL
(May 6th at Chatham Town)
Hollands & Blair 2 Fleet Leisure 0

	She	Mea	Bro	Ken	Lar	New	Oak	Off	Pre	She	Sta	Uni	Woo
AFC Sheppey	***D***	1-2	0-4	3-0	0-1	4-0	2-0	0-3	2-3	0-0	2-4	3-4	2-4
APM Mears	3-1	***I***	6-3	1-0	5-2	0-1	0-0	2-3	1-1	1-2	3-1	1-1	1-0
Bromley Green	4-2	4-2	***V***	2-0	6-2	2-1	2-1	2-1	0-0	1-2	4-1	0-3	3-1
Kennington	1-2	3-7	0-2		1-4	2-1	0-4	2-4	0-4	2-3	2-4	2-0	1-2
Larkfield & New Hythe Wdrs	0-0	1-2	1-2	3-3	***O***	5-2	2-2	1-1	0-0	2-3	1-3	1-1	2-3
New Romney	2-2	2-3	0-3	5-0	6-2	***N***	3-0	4-0	2-1	2-0	7-2	3-1	1-1
Oakwood	1-3	0-1	0-3	2-3	0-6	2-1	***E***	0-2	1-2	0-0	0-2	0-1	1-4
Otford United	0-0	1-3	2-2	1-3	2-4	2-1	4-0		3-0	2-3	0-3	4-1	0-6
Premier	6-1	2-1	0-1	2-0	3-1	1-0	3-3	3-1	***E***	4-1	3-0	2-1	4-3
Sheerness East	0-3	0-1	1-2	3-1	2-1	3-3	3-0	4-4	5-2	***A***	1-4	4-1	1-4
Staplehurst & Monarchs United	3-0	4-2	3-0	3-2	1-1	3-1	2-1	1-3	1-1	4-1	***S***	2-1	1-5
University of Kent	6-0	1-1	2-2	3-3	3-3	3-1	2-1	3-0	0-2	3-1	5-1	***T***	1-2
Woodstock Park	3-0	6-3	2-1	6-1	1-4	4-0	2-0	3-0	5-5	3-0	4-1	3-3	

KENT COUNTY DIVISION ONE EAST CONSTITUTION 2010-11

APM. . . . . Cobdown Sports & Social Club Ditton Corner, Station Road, Aylesford ME20 6AU 01622 71777
BREDHURST JUNIORS. . . . . . Co-op Sports & Social Ground, St Georges Avenue, Sheerness ME12 1EJ. 01795 66388
BROMLEY GREEN . . . . The Swan Ground, Turner Close, Newton Rd, South Willesborough, Ashford TN24 0BB. 01233 64598
KENNINGTON . . . . Kennington Cricket Club, Ulley Road, Kennington, Ashford TN24 9HY. 07887 99521
LARKFIELD & NEW HYTHE WANDERERS New Hythe Lane, Larkfield, Maidstone ME20 6PU 07724 05097
MILTON & FULSTON UNITED . . . . Sittingbourne FC, Central Park, Eurolink, Sittingbourne ME10 3SB 01795 43507
NEW ROMNEY. . . . . The Maud Pavilion, Station Road, New Romney TN28 8LQ. 07710 07770
OTFORD UNITED . . . . Otford Recreation Ground, High Street, Otford, Sevenoaks TN14 5PG. 07802 73627
PREMIER. . . . . Hersden Recreation Ground, The Sycamores, Hersden, Canterbury CT3 4HY 07825 70450
SHEERNESS EAST . . . . . . Sheerness East WMC, 47 Queensborough Road, Halfway, Sheerness ME12 3BZ. 01795 66204
SHEPPEY UNITED . . . . Co-Steel Sheerness S&SC, Holm Place, Queensborough Road, Sheerness ME12 3DD. 07968 60046
STAPLEHURST & MONARCHS UNITED . . Jubilee SG, Headcorn Rd, Staplehurst TN12 0DS. 07703 28862
UNIVERSITY OF KENT. . The Oast House, Park Wood Rd, Giles Lane, University of Kent, Canterbury CT2 7SY 01227 82743

IN: Bredhurst Juniors (P - Division Two East), Milton & Fulston United (R)
OUT: Oakwood (F), Woodstock Park (P)
AFC Sheppey become Sheppey United

Division One West		P	W	D	L	F	A	Pts
Bridon Ropes		22	15	2	5	53	32	47
Charlton Ath. Community		22	14	3	5	69	31	45
Metrogas		22	12	4	6	63	32	40
Tudor Sports		22	12	4	6	49	36	40
Farnborough OB Guild		22	10	7	5	40	27	37
Crockenhill		22	11	2	9	46	38	35
Belvedere		22	9	5	8	49	42	32
Greenways		22	8	7	7	42	37	31
Wickham Park		22	6	5	11	26	52	23
Chipstead	*-1*	22	6	3	13	31	53	20
Guru Nanak		22	4	2	16	22	66	14
Old Bexleians		22	1	4	17	20	64	7

BARRY BUNDOCK WEST KENT CHALLENGE SHIELD

(Western region clubs from outside the Premier Division)

FIRST ROUND

Bexleians 2 Forest Hill Park 1
Bexley Borough 1 **Fleetdown United** 6
Charlton Athletic Community 3 Belvedere 2 *aet*
Chipstead 1 Blackheath United 0
Crofton Albion 2 **Tudor Sports** 2 *aet* (4-5p)
Farnborough Old Boys Guild 3 Old Bexleians 1
Halls 0 **Bridon Ropes** 3, Meridian 1 **Erith '147 Sports** 5
Metrogas 1 **Seven Acre Sports** 2 *aet*
Westerham 0 **Eltham Palace** 3

SECOND ROUND

Borough United 2 **Seven Acre Sports** 7 *aet*
Bridon Ropes 2 Wickham Park 0
Charlton Athletic Community 5 Crockenhill 3
Erith '147 Sports 0 **Bexleians** 3
Farnborough Old Boys Guild 0 Fleetdown 0 *aet* (5-4p)
Greenways 1 **Chipstead** 3
Guru Nanak (w/o) Chislehurst, **Tudor** 1 Eltham Palace 0

QUARTER-FINALS

Bridon Ropes 2 Bexleians 2 *aet* (2-1p)
Chipstead 1 Farnborough Old Boys Guild 0
Seven Acre Sports 2 **Charlton Athletic Community** 3
Tudor Sports 5 Guru Nanak 1

SEMI-FINALS

Charlton AC 2 **Tudor Sports** 5, Chipstead 0 **Bridon R.** 4

FINAL *(May 11th at Sevenoaks Town)*

Tudor Sports 2 Bridon Ropes 2 *aet* (6-5p)

	Belvedere	Bridon Ropes	Charlton Athletic Comm.	Chipstead	Crockenhill	Farnborough OB Guild	Greenways	Guru Nanak	Metrogas	Old Bexleians	Tudor Sports	Wickham Park
Belvedere	***D***	0-2	2-3	2-2	3-4	2-2	3-2	7-0	0-0	3-2	4-2	1-2
Bridon Ropes	5-2	***I***	4-2	3-1	1-1	3-0	3-0	0-1	0-5	5-3	2-1	3-1
Charlton Athletic Community	2-2	1-1	***V***	6-0	4-1	3-2	1-1	3-0	2-3	5-1	1-2	4-0
Chipstead	0-1	0-3	1-6		3-2	1-3	2-1	3-3	0-4	5-0	0-6	2-0
Crockenhill	3-2	2-3	1-4	1-0	***O***	0-1	0-0	6-1	4-2	3-0	1-0	3-1
Farnborough Old Boys Guild	1-1	1-2	2-0	1-0	2-4	***N***	2-2	3-1	3-1	4-0	1-1	0-0
Greenways	3-1	3-1	1-3	1-1	2-0	1-1	***E***	4-3	3-3	3-1	2-3	1-1
Guru Nanak	2-3	0-2	0-5	1-5	3-1	0-2	0-2		2-1	1-5	0-4	2-1
Metrogas	2-4	3-1	4-0	4-0	3-2	2-0	4-0	6-1	***W***	2-0	2-2	6-0
Old Bexleians	0-2	1-6	0-3	0-2	0-4	0-5	1-3	0-0	2-2	***E***	1-2	0-1
Tudor Sports	2-1	4-0	1-5	3-2	1-2	1-2	3-2	1-0	3-2	2-2	***S***	1-0
Wickham Park	1-3	0-3	2-6	2-1	2-1	2-2	0-5	2-1	3-2	1-1	4-4	***T***

KENT COUNTY LEAGUE DIVISION ONE WEST CONSTITUTION 2010-11

AFC SEVENOAKS .... Waller Park, Wood Lane, Darenth, Dartford DA2 7LR 01322 221006
BELVEDERE .... War Memorial Sports Ground, 101a Woolwich Road, Abbey Wood SE2 0DY 01322 436724
CHIPSTEAD .... Chipstead Recreation Ground, Chevening Road, Chipstead, Sevenoaks TN13 2SA 07753 603944
CONEY HALL .... Tiepigs Lane, Coney Hall, Bromley BR4 9BT 020 8462 9103
CROCKENHILL .... The Wested Meadow Ground, Eynsford Road, Crockenhill, Swanley BR8 8EJ 01322 662067
ELTHAM PALACE .... Beaverwood Lodge, Beaverwood Road, Chislehurst BR7 6HF 020 8300 1385
FARNBOROUGH OLD BOYS GUILD . Farnborough Spts Club, High Street, Farnborough BR6 7BA 01689 862949
FOREST HILL PARK .... Ladywell Arena, Doggett Road, Catford SE6 4QX 020 8314 1986
GREENWAYS .... Fleet Leisure Sports Club, Nelson Road, Northfleet DA11 7EE 01474 359222
METROGAS .... Marathon Playing Fields, Forty Foot Way, Avery Hill Road, New Eltham SE9 2EX 020 8859 1579
ORPINGTON .... Green Court Sports Club, Green Court Road, Crockenhill, Swanley BR8 8HJ 01322 666442
TUDOR SPORTS .... STC Sports Ground, Ivor Grove, New Eltham SE9 2AJ 020 8850 2057
WICKHAM PARK ...... Wickham Park Sports Club, 228-230 Pickhurst Rise, West Wickham, Bromley BR4 0AU 020 8777 2550

IN: AFC Sevenoaks (P - Division Two East), Coney Hall (R), Eltham Palace (P - Division Two West), Forest Hill Park (P - Division Two West), Orpington (R)

OUT: Bridon Ropes (P), Charlton Athletic Community (P), Guru Nanak (R - Division Two East), Old Bexleians (W)

PROMOTION PLAY-OFF

(Division One East v Division One West runners-up)

(May 15th at Bromley Green)

Bromley Green 0 **Charlton Athletic Community** 1

Division Two East		P	W	D	L	F	A	Pts
Bredhurst Juniors	*-3*	24	20	1	3	74	37	58
AFC Sevenoaks		24	17	2	5	49	31	53
Saga Sports & Social		24	15	4	5	57	36	49
Swale United		24	14	3	7	69	44	45
Malgo		24	13	4	7	71	40	43
Lanes End		24	11	6	7	46	36	39
Chartham Sports Club	*-1*	24	9	4	11	58	50	30
Borden Village		24	8	6	10	42	48	30
Platt United		24	7	6	11	35	46	27
Hawkenbury		24	7	4	13	50	67	25
Lydd Town		24	5	7	12	38	56	22
Pembury	*-1*	24	1	5	18	20	56	7
Tenterden Town		24	0	6	18	17	79	6

Hamstreet - record expunged

LES LECKIE CUP

(Eastern region clubs from outside the Premier Division)

FIRST ROUND

AFC Sevenoaks 7 Tenterden Town 0

APM Mears 3 Malgo 0

Bredhurst 5 Pembury 1

Hawkenbury 5 Hamstreet 1

Kennington 2 **Sheerness East** 3

Larkfield & New Hythe Wdrs 3 Lydd Town 2

N. Romney 2 **Lanes End** 6

Oakwood 3 Saga Spts/S. 1

Otford Utd 3 Platt United 0

Staplehurst & Monarchs United 1 **Bromley Green** 3

Swale 4 University of Kent 1

SECOND ROUND

AFC Sheppey v **AFC Sevenoaks** (w/o)

Borden Vill. 1 **Chartham** 2

Bredhurst 1 APM Mears 0

Hawkenbury 3 **Otford** 4

Lanes End 1 **Bromley Green** 2

Premier 2 **Larkfield** 3

Swale 1 **Sheerness East** 3

Woodstock Park 6 Oakwood 5 *aet*

QUARTER-FINALS

AFC Sevenoaks 0 **Larkfield & New Hythe Wdrs** 2

Bromley G. 4 Chartham 2

Otford 1 **Sheerness East** 4

Woodstock Park 2 Bredhurst Juniors 1

SEMI-FINALS

Sheerness East 0 **Bromley Green** 3

Woodstock Park 3 Larkfield & New HW 1 *aet*

FINAL

(May 5th at Faversham)

Bromley Green 0 **Woodstock Park** 1

	AFC S'noaks	Borden Village	Bredhurst J.	Chartham SC	Hamstreet	Hawkenbury	Lanes End	Lydd Town	Malgo	Pembury	Platt United	Saga Spts & S.	Swale United	Tenterden T.
AFC Sevenoaks		2-1	1-2	0-3	n/a	3-1	1-1	2-1	3-2	4-2	3-1	1-1	3-1	3-1
Borden Village	L-W	***D***	2-5	3-2	n/a	3-1	1-1	1-1	0-3	5-1	2-1	0-2	2-4	3-2
Bredhurst Juniors	2-0	4-2	***I***	1-2	n/a	5-2	4-1	4-0	3-2	4-1	1-3	3-2	1-0	1-0
Chartham Sports Club	1-4	2-2	2-2	***V***	n/a	2-0	0-2	2-2	1-4	2-0	2-0	2-0	3-4	7-2
Hamstreet	1-1	1-1	0-3	n/a		n/a	n/a	n/a	2-4	3-1	n/a	n/a	n/a	n/a
Hawkenbury	1-6	2-1	3-4	5-4	3-4	***T***	2-1	4-5	4-1	1-1	2-4	4-2	2-4	1-0
Lanes End	1-2	3-0	1-4	2-0	n/a	1-0	***W***	2-1	2-2	3-0	1-1	1-2	4-3	5-0
Lydd Town	0-2	2-2	1-4	1-1	n/a	2-2	2-3	***O***	4-1	1-0	3-0	1-2	2-5	2-2
Malgo	5-1	1-1	5-3	5-3	4-1	7-0	1-3	2-1		2-0	3-0	2-3	4-0	3-1
Pembury	0-1	2-3	1-3	1-5	2-4	1-1	1-1	5-1	0-3	***E***	1-2	0-3	1-4	0-0
Platt United	0-2	2-3	3-4	3-2	1-1	3-2	2-2	2-0	1-1	1-0	***A***	2-2	1-3	1-1
Saga Sports & Social	3-1	4-2	1-2	4-0	5-1	2-2	4-3	1-1	4-2	3-1	2-1	***S***	0-2	3-0
Swale United	0-2	1-1	0-4	3-1	2-1	3-1	3-1	7-2	2-2	2-0	4-1	3-4	***T***	10-1
Tenterden Town	1-2	0-2	2-4	0-9	1-3	2-7	0-1	0-2	0-8	1-1	0-0	0-3	1-1	

KENT COUNTY DIVISION TWO EAST CONSTITUTION 2010-11

BORDEN VILLAGE . . . . Borden Playstool, Wises Lane, Borden, Sittingbourne ME9 8LP 07921 912209
BROADSTAIRS . . . . Jackey Bakers Sports Groud, Highfield Road, Ramsgate CT12 6QX. . . . . None
CHARTHAM SPORTS CLUB . . Memorial Recreation Ground, Station Rd, Chartham, Canterbury CT4 7JA 07840 658936
GURU NANAK . . . . Guru Nanak Sports Ground, Khalsa Avenue, Gravesend DA12 1LV. 07956 514264
HAWKENBURY. . . . . Hawkenbury Recreation Ground, Hawkenbury Road, Tunbridge Wells TN2 5BJ 07899 806170
LYDD TOWN. . . . . The Lindsey Field, Dengemarsh Road, Lydd, Romney Marsh TN29 9JH 01797 321904
MALGO . . . . The Old County Ground, Norman Road, West Malling ME19 6RL 07850 751795
NK ACES. . . . . Kent Sports Club, Dunkirk Close, Gravesend DA12 5NN 01474 533272
PLATT UNITED. . . . . Stonehouse Field, Longmill Lane, St Marys Platt, Sevenoaks TN15 8ND. 07702 634344
SAGA SPORTS & SOCIAL . . . . South Road, Hythe CT21 6AR 07772 108324
ST NICHOLAS . . . . Bell Meadow, Bridges Close, St Nicholas-at-Wade, Birchington CT7 0PX 07866 265449
SWALE UNITED. . . . . UK Paper Sports Ground, Gore Court Road, Sittingbourne ME10 1QN 01795 564213
TENTERDEN TOWN . . . . Recreation Ground Road, High Street, Tenterden TN30 6RB 07720 785001

IN: Broadstairs (formerly Lesters Elite) (P - Canterbury & District League Premier Division), Guru Nanak (R - Division One West), NK Aces (formerly North Kent) (P - Bromley & District League Premier Division), St Nicholas (formerly AFC Aussie) (P - Thanet & District League Division One)

OUT: AFC Sevenoaks (P - Division One West), Bredhurst Juniors (P - Division One East), Hamstreet (WS), Lanes End (S - Division Two West), Pembury (W - Tonbridge & District League Division One)

FLOODLIGHT CUP

(All Eastern teams from Premier Division and selected teams from Division One East)

(Not contested in 2009-10)

Division Two West		P	W	D	L	F	A	Pts
Forest Hill Park		22	15	4	3	61	28	49
Eltham Palace		22	15	4	3	54	23	49
Seven Acre Sports		22	13	5	4	68	24	44
Bexleians		22	13	2	7	41	19	41
Fleetdown United		22	10	5	7	41	31	35
Erith '147 Sports		22	6	10	6	44	37	28
Crofton Albion		22	7	6	9	27	46	27
Bexley Borough	*-1*	22	6	8	8	41	42	25
Halls		22	7	4	11	41	47	25
Blackheath United		22	4	5	13	30	62	17
Meridian Sports	*-1*	22	3	5	14	31	56	13
Westerham		22	2	4	16	30	94	10

Borough United - record expunged

RESERVES CUP

FINAL

(April 27th at Sevenoaks Town)

Westerham Res. 1 New Romney Res, 0

Reserve Division East		P	W	D	L	F	A	Pt
Bearsted Res.		24	18	3	3	76	22	57
Canterbury City Res.	*-1*	24	16	2	6	71	32	49
Otford United Res.		24	12	10	2	47	19	46
Staplehurst/Monarchs Res.		24	12	5	7	62	44	41
University of Kent Res.	*-4*	24	11	4	9	66	41	33
Bromley Green Res.		24	9	5	10	58	61	32
Kennington Res.	*-4*	24	9	5	10	49	53	28
New Romney Res.		24	7	7	10	37	41	28
Larkfield & New HW Res.		24	8	2	14	48	73	26
APM Mears Res.	*-1*	24	7	5	12	46	52	25
Platt United Res.		24	6	4	14	37	77	22
Borden Village Res.	*-3*	24	6	4	14	53	84	19
Oakwood Res.		24	5	4	15	37	88	19

Reserve Division West		P	W	D	L	F	A	Pt
Fleetdown United Res.		22	16	3	3	56	28	51
Belvedere Res.		22	14	4	4	53	28	46
Westerham Res.		22	11	5	6	60	37	38
Stansfeld O & B Club Res.	*-3*	22	12	3	7	52	44	36
Greenways Res.		22	11	2	9	49	39	35
Orpington Res.		22	10	5	7	60	52	35
Bly Spartans Res.	*-1*	22	9	5	8	34	38	31
Fleet Leisure Res.		22	8	4	10	56	47	28
Coney Hall Res.		22	7	5	10	39	49	26
Chipstead Res.	*-1*	22	6	1	15	50	65	18
Rusthall Res.	*-1*	22	3	4	15	32	72	12
Crockenhill Res.		22	3	3	16	38	80	12

	Bexleians	Bexley Borough	Blackheath Utd	Borough United	Crofton Albion	Eltham Palace	Erith '147 Sports	Fleetdown Utd	Forest Hill Park	Halls	Meridian Sports	Seven Acre Spts	Westerham
Bexleians	***D***	0-1	2-0	7-3	0-1	1-2	1-1	3-0	2-0	3-2	6-2	0-1	5-0
Bexley Borough	0-1	***I***	3-1	2-1	3-4	1-2	1-1	3-3	1-1	3-1	1-1	1-1	5-4
Blackheath United	0-1	4-0	***V***	2-1	1-4	1-3	3-2	2-0	1-4	2-2	2-2	1-7	0-4
Borough United	n/a	0-2	n/a		1-1	2-3	n/a	n/a	n/a	0-5	0-1	1-3	4-1
Crofton Albion	0-3	1-0	3-3	3-3	***T***	0-4	1-1	1-1	1-1	1-0	2-2	0-6	2-2
Eltham Palace	0-2	4-0	3-0	8-0	2-0	***W***	1-1	0-3	2-5	5-1	3-3	3-1	8-0
Erith '147 Sports	5-0	0-0	1-1	4-0	3-0	1-2	***O***	0-1	2-4	1-1	4-0	1-1	6-2
Fleetdown United	1-0	2-2	3-0	n/a	2-0	0-2	2-3		0-4	2-1	2-1	2-2	4-1
Forest Hill Park	0-0	4-2	5-1	3-1	3-0	0-2	3-1	2-1	***W***	4-2	5-2	0-4	4-0
Halls	3-1	0-0	3-1	n/a	2-1	2-3	3-3	1-6	1-4	***E***	2-3	0-3	6-0
Meridian Sports	0-1	1-3	2-3	0-0	1-2	0-0	2-4	0-4	1-2	0-2	***S***	1-3	4-1
Seven Acre Sports	0-1	5-3	5-0	4-1	6-1	1-1	5-0	2-1	1-1	0-1	3-1	***T***	3-4
Westerham	0-8	1-8	3-3	n/a	0-2	0-2	3-3	1-1	1-5	1-5	1-2	1-8	

KENT COUNTY LEAGUE DIVISION TWO WEST CONSTITUTION 2010-11

BEXLEIANS .... Footscray Sports Club, 239 Footscray Road, London SE9 2EL 020 8850 4698
BEXLEY .... St Marys Recreation Ground, Lesley Close, Bourne Road, Bexley DA5 1LX 07944 552763
BEXLEY BOROUGH .... Apex Arena, Danson Youth Centre, Brampton Road, Bexleyheath DA7 4EZ............ 020 8303 6052
BLACKHEATH UNITED . . Bellingham Leisure & Lifestyle Centre, 14a Randlesdown Road, Bellingham SE6 3BT 020 8697 0043
CROFTON ALBION............... Crofton Albion Sports & Social, Weigall Road, Lee SE12 8HF 020 8856 8385
ERITH '147 SPORTS .... STC Sports Ground, Ivor Grove, New Eltham SE9 2AJ 020 8858 2057
FLEETDOWN UNITED .... Heath Lane Open Space, Heath Lane (Lower), Dartford DA1 2QE 01322 273848
HALLS .... Stone Recreation Ground, London Road, Greenhithe DA9 9DQ 01322 224246
HILDENBOROUGH ATHLETIC........ Tonbridge Farm, Darenth Avenue, Tonbridge TN10 3EH .... None
LANES END......................... Waller Park, Wood Lane, Darenth, Dartford DA2 7LR 01322 221006
MERIDIAN SPORTS .... Meridian Sports & Social, 110 Charlton Park Lane, Charlton SE7 8QS 020 8856 1923
SEVEN ACRE SPORTS....... Seven Acre Sports Club, Church Manor Avenue, Abbey Wood SE2 9HP 020 8310 4170
WESTERHAM ...... Westerham Sports Association, King George V PF, Costells Meadow, Westerham TN16 1BL....... 01959 561106

IN: Bexley (P - South London Alliance Division One), Hildenborough Athletic (P - Sevenoaks & District League Premier Division), Lanes End (S - Division Two East),

OUT: Borough United (WS), Eltham Palace (P - Division One West), Forest Hill Park (P - Division One West),

TOM STABLER TROPHY

(Annual Inter-League challenge)

(October 28th at Three Bridges)

Sussex County League Division Three 0 **Kent County League** 2

Stansfeld Oxford
& Bermondsey Club FC
Premier Division Champions

Hollands & Blair FC
Bill Manklow Inter Regional
Challenge Cup Winners

(Right) Paul Piggott - Hollands & Blair FC
AFORD Awards Manager of the Year
with John Mugridge - Life Vice President

(Left) Woodstock Park FC
Division One (East) Winners

Forest Hill Park FC
Division Two (West) Winners

Tudor Sports FC
Barry Bundock West Kent Challenge Shield Winners

Bob Taylor - Fleet Leisure FC
Kent County Football League Personality of the Year
with Geoff Jenkins - General Secretary
& Cyril Windiate - Chairman

Josh Rudd - Most Promising Referee of the Year & Assistant Referee of the Year Martin Staveley - Referee of the Year with Barry Bright - Football Association Vice Chairman

Woodstock Park FC
Les Leckie Cup Winners

Hollands & Blair FC
Bill Manklow Inter Regional Challenge Cup Winners

LEICESTERSHIRE SENIOR LEAGUE

full-time.thefa.com/gen/Index.do?league=651281

Sponsored by: Everards Brewery

Founded: 1896

Recent champions:
2005: Thurnby Rangers
2006: Friar Lane & Epworth
2007: Stapenhill
2008: Kirby Muxloe SC
2009: Anstey Nomads

	Asf	Ash	Ayl	Bir	Bla	Cot	Hig	Lei	Lut	Rat	Rot	Saf	Sil	Sta	TT	TN
Asfordby Amateurs	***P***	1-7	0-4	1-5	1-8	3-4	0-2	0-8	0-7	1-3	2-3	1-4	0-6	0-5	0-4	1-9
Ashby Ivanhoe	9-0	***R***	2-0	3-0	1-0	3-0	2-0	2-0	4-2	4-3	6-3	3-3	5-2	2-7	2-6	4-1
Aylestone Park	2-1	1-5	***E***	2-4	0-6	3-1	2-5	1-6	0-2	1-2	1-5	0-1	1-5	1-0	0-9	2-4
Birstall United	4-1	1-6	3-0	***M***	0-3	3-2	3-2	1-1	2-3	3-4	2-1	3-2	3-0	3-1	0-2	0-3
Blaby/Whetstone Athletic	7-1	4-1	1-0	4-2	***I***	5-2	1-0	2-3	2-2	4-0	3-1	0-0	4-1	6-0	0-1	2-2
Cottesmore Amateurs	0-5	2-6	1-1	2-5	1-2	***E***	2-4	0-4	1-6	3-1	2-2	1-7	1-5	3-4	3-7	0-6
Highfield Rangers	2-1	3-0	12-0	1-5	1-4	4-2	***R***	1-3	1-3	1-2	0-0	2-0	0-1	1-3	0-3	0-1
Leics Constabulary	4-0	3-0	5-2	1-0	2-0	5-1	3-1		2-1	1-2	2-6	3-2	2-1	2-2	1-1	1-0
Lutterworth Athletic	10-0	2-1	6-0	1-0	0-0	2-1	2-0	0-2	***D***	2-1	4-2	1-3	4-1	1-0	1-2	1-2
Ratby Sports	1-1	4-4	7-2	2-2	0-1	13-0	3-1	2-3	2-1	***I***	2-4	4-1	4-4	3-2	1-4	2-2
Rothley Imperial	2-2	1-2	2-1	2-6	0-1	5-3	1-4	0-3	1-1	2-5	***V***	1-3	2-2	2-1	0-2	4-2
Saffron Dynamo	5-1	4-1	5-3	1-6	1-3	4-2	6-1	2-1	0-1	0-1	3-2	***I***	5-1	2-3	0-6	0-3
Sileby Town	6-0	2-1	1-2	1-1	1-1	4-4	4-0	0-2	3-1	0-1	2-2	1-3	***S***	4-1	3-2	1-2
Stapenhill	3-0	1-2	5-0	2-2	4-3	2-3	0-0	1-2	1-3	1-0	0-2	1-3	2-2	***I***	1-4	2-0
Thurmaston Town	2-1	4-2	6-0	4-1	3-0	6-1	3-1	3-0	5-0	8-0	1-1	3-1	1-1	4-0	***O***	1-1
Thurnby Nirvana	6-0	8-0	3-0	4-0	2-2	5-2	2-4	1-0	3-2	4-1	2-2	4-2	1-1	0-0	3-2	***N***

Premier Division		P	W	D	L	F	A	Pts
Thurmaston Town	*-3*	**30**	**24**	**4**	**2**	**109**	**25**	**73**
Leics Constabulary		**30**	**21**	**3**	**6**	**75**	**35**	**66**
Thurnby Nirvana		**30**	**18**	**7**	**5**	**86**	**39**	**61**
Blaby & Whetstone Athletic		**30**	**18**	**6**	**6**	**79**	**33**	**60**
Ashby Ivanhoe		**30**	**18**	**2**	**10**	**90**	**68**	**56**
Lutterworth Athletic		**30**	**17**	**3**	**10**	**72**	**42**	**54**
Saffron Dynamo		**30**	**15**	**2**	**13**	**73**	**63**	**47**
Ratby Sports		**30**	**14**	**5**	**11**	**76**	**67**	**47**
Birstall United		**30**	**14**	**4**	**12**	**70**	**62**	**46**
Sileby Town		**30**	**10**	**9**	**11**	**66**	**58**	**39**
Rothley Imperial		**30**	**9**	**8**	**13**	**61**	**70**	**35**
Stapenhill	*-3*	**30**	**10**	**5**	**15**	**55**	**60**	**32**
Highfield Rangers		**30**	**10**	**2**	**18**	**54**	**62**	**32**
Aylestone Park		**30**	**5**	**1**	**24**	**32**	**115**	**16**
Cottesmore Amateurs		**30**	**3**	**3**	**24**	**50**	**132**	**12**
Asfordby Amateurs		**30**	**1**	**2**	**27**	**25**	**142**	**5**

PRESIDENT'S CUP

FINAL *(May 13th at Aylestone Park)*
Thurmaston Town Res. 2 Leics Constabulary Res. 1

Combination Division One	P	W	D	L	F	A	Pt
Thurmaston Town Res.	26	22	0	4	104	30	66
Birstall United Res.	26	17	5	4	73	23	56
Ibstock United Res.	26	15	6	5	83	48	51
Ratby Sports Res.	26	16	2	8	63	45	50
Leics Constabulary Res.	26	14	3	9	57	49	45
Sileby Town Res.	26	12	7	7	69	49	43
Holwell Sports Res.	26	12	4	10	61	44	40
Barrow Town Res.	26	12	3	11	55	63	39
Lutterworth Athletic Res.	25	9	4	12	47	63	31
Saffron Dynamo Res.	24	8	2	14	36	53	26
Blaby & Whetstone Ath. Res.	26	4	10	12	41	63	22
Rothley Imperial Res.	25	5	4	16	31	65	19
Earl Shilton Albion Res.	26	3	4	19	30	85	13
Anstey Nomads Res.	26	3	2	21	30	100	11

Ellistown Res., St Andrews Res. - records expunged
Saffron Dynamo Res. v Lutterworth Athletic Res., Saffron Dyn. Res. v Rothley Imperial Res. - not played

Combination Division Two	P	W	D	L	F	A	Pt
Ashby Ivanhoe Res.	26	23	2	1	82	23	71
Thurnby Nirvana Res.	26	23	0	3	98	33	69
Desford Res.	25	17	1	7	65	40	52
Bardon Hill Sports Res.	26	15	3	8	108	58	48
Lutterworth Town Res.	26	12	4	10	54	42	40
Barlestone St Giles Res.	26	10	6	10	56	44	36
Hathern Res.	26	11	3	12	42	48	36
Asfordby Amateurs Res.	26	8	6	12	69	68	30
Melton Mowbray Res.	25	9	2	14	47	56	29
Narboro. & Littlethorpe Res.	26	8	2	16	45	88	26
Highfield Rangers Res.	26	7	4	15	50	72	25
FC Khalsa Res.	26	7	2	17	31	80	23
Dunton & Broughton R. Res.	26	5	5	16	40	85	20
Cottesmore Amateurs Res.	26	5	2	19	32	82	17

Desford Res. v Melton Mowbray Res. - not played

LEICESTERSHIRE SENIOR LEAGUE PREMIER DIVISION CONSTITUTION 2010-11

ASFORDBY AMATEURS.... Hoby Road Sports Ground, Hoby Road, Asfordby, Melton Mowbray LE14 3TL 01664 434545
ASHBY IVANHOE .... Hood Park, North Street, Ashby-de-la-Zouch LE65 1HU 01530 412181
AYLESTONE PARK .... Dorset Avenue, Wigston, Leicester LE18 4WB 0116 277 5307
BIRSTALL UNITED.......................... Meadow Lane, Birstall LE4 4FN 0116 267 1230
BLABY & WHETSTONE ATHLETIC .. Blaby & Whetstone BC, Warwick Road, Whetstone LE8 6LW.............. 0116 286 4852
COTTESMORE AMATEURS .... Rogues Park, Main Street, Cottesmore, Oakham LE15 4DH.................. 01572 813486
FC DYNAMO................ Nanpantan Sports Ground, Nanpantan Road, Loughborough LE11 3YD 01509 237148
HIGHFIELD RANGERS .... 443 Gleneagles Avenue, Rushey Mead, Leicester LE4 7YJ 0116 266 0009
KIRBY MUXLOE SC RES. .... Ratby Lane, Kirby Muxloe, Leicester LE9 9AQ.......................... 0116 239 3201
LUTTERWORTH ATHLETIC................. Dunley Way, Lutterworth LE17 4NP 07837 668392
RATBY SPORTS .... Desford Lane, Ratby, Leicester LE6 0LE.............................. 0116 239 2474
ROTHLEY IMPERIAL................ Loughborough Road, Mountsorrell, Leicester LE7 7NH 0116 292 0538
SAFFRON DYNAMO .... Cambridge Road, Whetstone LE8 3LG.............................. 07957 151630
SILEBY TOWN................ Memorial Park, Seagrave Road, Sileby, Loughborough LE12 7TP 07708 231563/07860 842046
STAPENHILL........................ Maple Grove, Stapenhill, Burton-on-Trent DE15 1RW 01283 533133
THURMASTON TOWN .... Elizabeth Park, Checkland Road, Thurmaston, Leicester LE4 8FN................ 0116 260 2519

IN: FC Dynamo (P), Kirby Muxloe SC Res. (P)
OUT: Leics Constabulary (F), Thurnby Nirvana (P - East Midlands Counties League)

Division One		P	W	D	L	F	A	Pts
FC Dynamo		28	24	4	0	124	23	76
Kirby Muxloe SC Res.		28	21	3	4	73	25	66
Barlestone St Giles		28	18	6	4	72	37	60
Desford		28	19	2	7	85	32	59
Narborough/Littlethorpe		28	16	5	7	58	32	53
Hathern		28	12	3	13	42	43	39
Friar Lane & Epworth Res.		28	11	3	14	53	56	36
Lutterworth Town		28	10	5	13	29	62	35
Melton Mowbray	*-3*	28	10	5	13	49	45	32
Coalville Town Res.		28	10	2	16	42	58	32
Dunton & Broughton Rgrs		28	8	3	17	46	69	27
Evington		28	6	7	15	40	93	25
Earl Shilton Albion		28	6	5	17	35	83	23
FC Khalsa		28	5	5	18	42	68	20
Ravenstone	*-3*	28	4	2	22	36	100	11

BEACON BITTER CUP

FIRST ROUND

Ashby Ivanhoe 3 Asfordby Amateurs 2
Blaby & Whetstone Athletic 4 Saffron Dynamo 1
Cottesmore Amateurs 2 Birstall United 2 (5-4p)
Desford 3 Kirby Muxloe SC Res. 0
Dunton & Broughton Rangers 4 Coalville Town Res. 2
Earl Shilton Albion 1 **Friar Lane & Epworth Res.** 2
Evington 4 Ravenstone 0
Highfield Rangers 0 **Lutterworth Athletic** 2
Lutterworth Town 3 FC Khalsa 3 (7-6p)
Melton Mowbray 0 **Barlestone St Giles** 1
Narborough & Littlethorpe 1 **FC Dynamo** 3
Ratby Sports 6 Aylestone Park 1
Sileby Town 2 **Stapenhill** 3
Thurmaston Town 4 Rothley Imps 1
Thurnby Nirvana 1 **Leics Constabulary** 3

SECOND ROUND

Ashby Ivanhoe 3 Lutterworth Athletic 3 (2-1p)
Blaby & Whetstone Athletic 1 **Leics Constabulary** 3
Dunton & Broughton 2 **Friar Lane/Epworth Res.** 2 (4-5p)
FC Dynamo 6 Barlestone St Giles 1
Hathern 2 **Evington** 2 (1-4p)
Lutterworth Town 0 **Desford** 1
Stapenhill 0 **Ratby Sports** 3
Thurmaston Town 6 Cottesmore Amateurs 0

QUARTER-FINALS

Desford 0 **Thurmaston Town** 2
Evington 0 **Ashby Ivanhoe** 7
Leics Constabulary 1 Friar Lane & Epworth Res. 0
Ratby Sports 1 **FC Dynamo** 2 *(at FC Dynamo)*

SEMI-FINALS

Ashby Ivanhoe 0 **Thurmaston Town** 3
Leics Constabulary 3 FC Dynamo 1

FINAL *(May 11th at Barrow Town)*

Thurmaston Town 3 Leics Constabulary 1

	Bar	Coa	Des	Dun	Ear	Evi	Dyn	Kha	Fri	Hat	Kir	Lut	Mel	Nar	Rav
Barlestone St Giles		5-1	0-3	4-0	4-0	4-0	2-2	5-1	2-1	1-0	1-1	2-1	4-1	3-2	3-1
Coalville Town Res.	1-2	***D***	0-5	2-0	4-0	5-0	0-3	1-1	4-0	1-2	0-3	2-1	2-2	3-1	1-0
Desford	2-3	8-1	***I***	1-0	1-0	4-0	0-1	4-1	2-0	2-1	1-4	2-2	4-1	5-0	6-0
Dunton & Broughton Rgrs	1-3	4-1	1-5	***V***	0-0	5-1	2-7	2-1	3-1	2-1	0-1	4-0	1-3	2-1	1-3
Earl Shilton Albion	2-2	1-5	2-6	3-1	***I***	2-3	1-11	3-0	0-2	1-4	0-2	4-1	1-6	0-2	3-0
Evington	1-1	1-3	1-5	4-4	3-3	***S***	2-9	2-1	2-3	1-1	0-2	2-2	2-1	0-10	2-3
FC Dynamo	6-0	4-0	2-1	5-2	8-0	9-0	***I***	4-1	3-0	3-1	3-1	7-0	7-0	0-0	11-2
FC Khalsa	2-4	2-0	0-6	3-0	1-1	0-2	2-3	***O***	1-3	1-2	1-4	2-2	1-1	0-3	6-2
Friar Lane & Epworth Res.	1-1	3-1	0-1	5-3	3-2	4-4	1-2	1-2	***N***	1-2	2-1	1-2	0-0	4-2	7-1
Hathern	0-2	1-0	2-4	3-1	2-0	1-2	0-3	3-2	0-1		1-2	0-1	0-0	0-1	3-0
Kirby Muxloe SC Res.	1-2	4-2	3-1	5-2	9-0	5-0	1-1	3-2	2-1	4-0		4-1	2-1	1-0	1-0
Lutterworth Town	2-1	1-0	1-4	2-1	1-1	1-0	0-2	1-0	1-3	1-3	1-1	***O***	0-5	0-3	2-0
Melton Mowbray	3-0	2-0	4-1	2-3	1-3	2-2	0-2	2-0	4-0	1-2	0-3	0-1	***N***	0-1	4-1
Narborough & Littlethorpe	1-1	2-0	1-0	1-0	1-0	3-0	2-2	2-2	4-3	3-3	2-0	0-1	1-0	***E***	6-0
Ravenstone	0-10	0-2	1-1	1-1	0-2	0-3	2-4	2-6	4-2	2-4	0-3	8-0	1-3	2-3	

LEICESTERSHIRE SENIOR LEAGUE DIVISION ONE CONSTITUTION 2010-11

BARLESTONE ST GILES . . . . Barton Road, Barlestone CV13 0EP 01455 291392
BELGRAVE . . . . Co-Op Sports & Social Club, Birstall Road, Birstall, Leicester LE4 4DE 0116 267 4059
CATERPILLAR SPORTS . . . . Peckleton Lane, Desford, Leicester LE9 9JT 07856 179485
COALVILLE TOWN RES. . . . . Owen Street Sports Ground, Owen Street, Coalville LE67 3DA 01530 833365
DESFORD . . . . Sport in Desford, Peckleton Lane, Desford, Leicester LE9 9JU 01455 828786
DUNTON & BROUGHTON RANGERS . . . . Station Road, Dunton Bassett LE17 5LF 07780 957479
EARL SHILTON ALBION . . . . Stoneycroft Park, New Street, Earl Shilton LE9 7FR 01455 844277
FC KHALSA & EVINGTON Judge Meadow Community College, Marydene Drive, Evington, Leicester LE5 6HP 0116 2417580
FRIAR LANE & EPWORTH RES. . . . . . . Knighton Lane East, Aylestone Park, Leicester LE2 6FT 0116 283 3629
HATHERN . . . . Pasture Lane, Hathern, Loughborough LE12 5LJ 07952 113090
LUTTERWORTH TOWN . . . . Hall Lane, Bitteswell, Lutterworth LE17 4LN 01455 554046
MELTON MOWBRAY . . . . All England Sports Ground, Saxby Road, Melton Mowbray LE13 1BP 07977 266729
NARBOROUGH & LITTLETHORPE . . . . Leicester Road, Narborough LE19 2DG 0116 275 1855
NEWHALL UNITED. . . . . The Hadfields, St Johns Drive, Newhall, Swadlincote DE11 0SU 01283 551029
SHEPSHED DYNAMO RES.. . . . . The Dovecote, Butt Hole Lane, Shepshed, Loughborough LE12 9BN 01509 650992

IIN: Belgrave (P - Leicester & District League Division), Caterpillar (P - North Leicestershire League Premie Division), Newhall United (R - Midland Combination Division One), Shepshed Dynamo Res. (N)
OUT: FC Dynamo (P), Kirby Muxloe SC Res. (P), Ravenstone (W)
Evington have merged with FC Khalsa to form FC Khalsa & Evington

LIVERPOOL COUNTY PREMIER LEAGUE

www.liverpoolcountypremierleague.com

Sponsored by:

Frank Armitt

Founded: 2006

Recent champions:

2007: Waterloo Dock

2008: Waterloo Dock

2009: Waterloo Dock

	Aigburth PH	Albany Athletic	Birchfield	Cheshire Lines	East Villa	Ford Motors	Kingsley United	Lucas Sports	Old Xaverians	Page Celtic	Red Rum	Sacre Coeur FP	South Liverpool	South Sefton B.	St Aloysius	Waterloo Dock
Aigburth People's Hall	***P***	2-0	n/a	4-2	1-0	2-1	4-1	3-0	1-2	1-1	2-1	2-2	1-0	1-2	1-5	0-1
Albany Athletic	0-1	***R***	n/a	n/a	0-5	1-6	n/a	1-3	1-3	1-2	1-3	0-3	2-1	1-3	n/a	n/a
Birchfield	n/a	n/a	***E***	n/a	2-1	0-6	0-1	0-1	2-4	3-2	0-2	n/a	1-3	1-1	4-3	n/a
Cheshire Lines	2-2	1-2	1-2	***M***	0-1	1-4	2-2	1-2	2-2	0-3	2-2	2-0	1-0	0-1	0-2	1-2
East Villa	0-0	1-2	1-1	1-3	***I***	2-0	0-0	0-0	1-4	4-1	1-1	1-1	1-0	0-1	1-1	3-3
Ford Motors	2-3	n/a	2-0	4-2	1-3	***E***	9-2	2-1	1-1	0-1	1-1	1-1	2-0	0-0	0-0	3-5
Kingsley United	0-1	n/a	n/a	5-1	0-3	0-3	***R***	W-L	2-5	4-1	3-2	1-2	1-2	2-2	1-5	0-9
Lucas Sports	1-1	4-3	n/a	5-1	2-1	1-8	1-0		1-2	1-5	1-5	2-1	1-2	1-2	2-2	0-4
Old Xaverians	1-0	3-0	2-0	1-2	2-2	1-0	L-W	1-2	***D***	2-0	5-3	1-0	0-2	2-3	0-4	2-3
Page Celtic	1-2	1-0	4-2	0-2	1-2	1-0	4-0	4-1	2-5	***I***	1-2	2-3	2-3	1-0	0-4	2-0
Red Rum	1-5	n/a	n/a	3-1	1-2	2-2	4-2	3-5	2-1	3-1	***V***	1-3	2-3	3-3	3-4	0-1
Sacre Coeur Former Pup.	4-2	n/a	0-2	1-0	3-0	5-1	3-2	2-1	1-4	2-0	1-1	***I***	1-1	0-1	5-2	1-0
South Liverpool	2-1	n/a	5-1	3-4	3-1	1-1	3-0	4-2	0-5	0-3	3-1	2-2	***S***	0-0	0-1	2-2
South Sefton Borough	1-3	3-2	n/a	2-2	2-1	1-2	4-1	5-0	2-1	0-1	1-5	2-2	1-2	***I***	1-2	3-4
St Aloysius	1-1	n/a	n/a	1-1	3-3	3-2	3-1	3-3	2-2	1-0	1-0	4-2	2-0	1-2	***O***	2-2
Waterloo Dock	2-5	n/a	n/a	3-1	4-3	3-3	4-0	6-1	5-1	2-0	2-1	2-3	4-1	3-2	2-0	***N***

Premier Division		P	W	D	L	F	A	Pts
Waterloo Dock		26	18	4	4	78	40	58
St Aloysius	*-3*	26	14	9	3	59	35	48
Sacre Coeur Former Pupils		26	13	7	6	51	38	46
Aigburth People's Hall		26	13	6	7	49	36	45
South Liverpool	*+3*	26	11	5	10	39	42	41
Old Xaverians		26	12	4	10	53	43	40
South Sefton Borough		26	11	6	9	44	40	39
East Villa		26	8	9	9	37	38	33
Ford Motors		26	8	8	10	53	43	32
Page Celtic		26	10	1	15	38	44	31
Red Rum		26	7	6	13	53	57	27
Lucas Sports		26	7	4	15	37	68	25
Cheshire Lines		26	6	6	14	36	56	24
Kingsley United		26	5	3	18	30	77	18

Albany Athletic, Birchfield - records expunged

R A BRICKWORK PREMIER DIVISION CUP

FIRST ROUND

Albany Athletic v Aigburth People's Hall

Birchfield v Sacre Coeur Former Pupils

Cheshire Lines v East Villa

Kingsley United v Red Rum

Lucas Sports v Ford Motors

Old Xaverians v Waterloo Dock

South Sefton Borough v South Liverpool

St Aloysius v Page Celtic

Competition abandoned due to inclement weather

LIVERPOOL COUNTY PREMIER LEAGUE PREMIER DIVISION CONSTITUTION 2010-11

AIGBURTH PEOPLE'S HALL . . . . . Cheshire Lines FC, Southmead Road, Allerton, Liverpool L19 5NB 0151 427 7176
CHESHIRE LINES . . . . Southmead Road, Allerton, Liverpool L19 5NB 0151 427 7176
EAST VILLA . . . . Litherland Sports Park, Boundary Road, Litherland, Liverpool L21 7NW. 0151 288 6338
ESSEMMAY OLD BOYS . . . . Heron Eccles Playing Field, Abbottshey Avenue, Liverpool L18 7JT 0151 724 4796
FORD MOTORS. . . . . Ford Sports & Social Club, Cronton Lane, Widnes WA8 5AJ 0151 424 7078
LUCAS SPORTS. . . . . William Collins Memorial Ground, Commercial Road, Liverpool L5 7QY . . . . None
OLD XAVERIANS . . . . St Francis Xaviers College, Beconsfield Road, Liverpool L25 6EG. 0151 288 1000
PAGE CELTIC . . . . Huyton Arts & Sports Centre, Seel Road, Huyton, Liverpool L36 6DG 0151 477 8860
REMYCA UNITED . . . . Playfootball.com, Drummond Road, Thornton L20 6DX. . . . . None
RED RUM. . . . . Croxteth Community Comprehensive School, Parkstile Lane, Liverpool L11 0PB 0151 546 4168
SACRE COEUR FORMER PUPILS . Scargreen PF, Scargreen Ave, Norris Green, Liverpool L11 3BE . . . . None
SOUTH LIVERPOOL . . . . Jericho Lane, Aigburth, Liverpool L17 5AR. . . . . None
SOUTH SEFTON BOROUGH. . . . . Mill Dam Park, Bridges Lane, Sefton Village L29 7WA . . . . None
ST ALOYSIUS . . . . King George V Sports Complex, Long View Lane, Huyton, Liverpool L36 7UN 0151 443 5712
STONEYCROFT. . . . . Maiden Lane Playing Fields, Maiden Lane, Liverpool L13 9AN. . . . . None
WATERLOO DOCK. . . . . Edinburgh Park, Townsend Lane, Liverpool L6 0BB 0151 263 5267

IN: Essemmay Old Boys (P), Stoneycroft (P), REMYCA United (P)
OUT: Albany Athletic (WS), Birchfield (WS), Kingsley United (R)

LORD MAYOR'S CHARITY SHIELD

(Prem champs v Peter Coyne/George Mahon Cup holders)

(Not contested in 2009-10

Division One		P	W	D	L	F	A	Pts
Essemmay Old Boys	*-1*	28	18	3	7	73	46	56
Stoneycroft	*+2*	28	15	5	8	70	55	52
REMYCA United		28	15	4	9	59	46	49
Halewood Town		28	12	10	6	76	55	46
Leyfield	*-3*	28	14	7	7	51	36	46
Roma		28	14	4	10	61	61	46
Edge Hill BCOB	*+2*	28	12	5	11	65	68	43
Angus Village		28	12	6	10	70	61	42
Mackets Village	*+3*	28	9	5	14	56	63	35
BRNESC	*-3*	28	12	2	14	73	81	35
NELTC		28	8	8	12	55	61	32
Old Holts		28	8	6	14	51	74	30
Warbreck		28	7	6	15	72	87	27
Copperas Hill		28	6	7	15	48	63	25
Collegiate Old Boys	*+2*	28	5	8	15	56	79	25

East Villa Res. - record expunged

ROY WADE MEMORIAL CUP

FIRST ROUND

Angus Village v Halewood Town

Collegiate Old Boys v Roma

Copperas Hill v REMYCA United

East Villa Res. v Leyfield

Essemmay Old Boys v BRNESC

NELTC v Stoneycroft

Old Holts v Edge Hill BCOB

Warbreck v Mackets

Competition abandoned due

to inclement weather

	Angus Village	BRNESC	Collegiate Old B.	Copperas Hill	East Villa Res.	Edge Hill BCOB	Essemay Old B.	Halewood Town	Leyfield	Mackets Village	NELTC	Old Holts	REMYCA Utd	Roma	Stoneycroft	Warbreck
Angus Village		3-1	W-L	3-4	4-1	3-7	1-3	2-2	2-2	6-2	5-0	0-3	2-2	6-4	2-3	3-2
BRNESC	1-5		4-2	3-0	n/a	2-5	2-4	1-4	0-4	3-2	4-3	3-0	0-1	6-1	3-2	3-6
Collegiate Old Boys	3-1	4-6	***D***	3-0	2-2	4-0	0-3	3-3	1-2	0-3	0-2	3-3	1-1	7-4	3-3	2-2
Copperas Hill	2-3	1-2	6-2	***I***	1-2	1-3	1-2	3-2	2-1	2-2	1-2	2-2	1-1	2-0	3-4	1-0
East Villa Res.	0-1	n/a	n/a	n/a	***V***	1-6	1-3	5-2	1-3	n/a	1-2	4-3	n/a	n/a	n/a	n/a
Edge Hill BCOB	0-4	3-2	2-2	2-1	0-2	***I***	0-0	2-3	3-3	3-2	4-4	5-2	1-3	1-2	3-2	1-3
Essemmay Old Boys	1-5	7-1	2-1	6-4	n/a	3-3	***S***	4-0	2-0	1-3	1-4	6-2	3-1	3-1	2-6	2-1
Halewood Town	4-2	4-4	0-0	3-3	4-1	1-2	1-1	***I***	0-1	4-3	2-1	5-0	2-1	1-2	7-1	3-1
Leyfield	1-1	2-1	2-1	1-1	n/a	3-0	3-2	0-0	***O***	3-2	3-1	2-0	3-1	0-1	0-1	4-1
Mackets Village	3-2	1-0	0-2	1-0	n/a	3-2	1-3	2-2	3-1	***N***	3-3	1-1	0-2	1-1	3-2	1-2
NELTC	1-1	2-2	4-1	0-0	n/a	3-5	3-2	1-4	2-2	3-2		1-2	0-3	0-2	1-1	6-2
Old Holts	3-1	1-6	3-1	1-1	3-2	3-4	1-2	1-1	1-2	2-1	1-0	***O***	5-1	0-6	1-2	2-6
REMYCA United	2-0	3-0	4-2	3-0	n/a	5-0	0-2	2-7	2-1	2-3	2-2	2-0	***N***	4-2	3-1	4-1
Roma	0-1	2-3	4-4	2-1	n/a	1-0	W-L	6-3	2-0	3-2	4-2	3-6	1-0	***E***	1-1	3-3
Stoneycroft	3-3	4-3	7-0	4-2	n/a	2-1	0-3	2-4	0-2	4-3	1-0	3-1	4-0	3-0		3-0
Warbreck	2-3	5-7	8-4	5-3	3-0	1-3	1-3	4-4	3-3	4-3	1-4	4-4	2-4	1-3	1-1	

LIVERPOOL COUNTY PREMIER LEAGUE DIVISION ONE CONSTITUTION 2010-11

ALUMNI . . . . Jericho Lane, Aigburh, Liverpool L17 5AR . . . . None
ANGUS VILLAGE . . . . Joe Stone Memorial Ground, Lower Lane, Fazakerley, Liverpool L9 7AD . . . . None
BRNESC . . . . Melling Road, Aintree, Liverpool L9 0LQ. . . . . None
COLLEGIATE OLD BOYS. . . . . . . Alder Road Sports Club, Alder Road, West Derby, Liverpool L12 2BA . . . . None
COPPERAS HILL . . . . Breckside Park, Liverpool L6 4DJ . . . . None
CROXTETH. . . . . MYA, Long Lane, Aintree, Liverpool L9 7AA . . . . None
EDGE HILL BCOB. . . . . William Collins Memorial Ground, Commercial Road, Liverpool L5 7QY . . . . None
HALEWOOD TOWN . . . . Hollies Road Playing Fields, Hollies Road, Halewood, Liverpool L26 0TH. . . . . None
KINGSLEY UNITED. . . . . . . Quarry Bank School Playing Fields, Greenhill Road, Allerton, Liverpool L18 6HF. . . . . None
LEYFIELD . . . . Thomas Lane Playing Fields, Thomas Lane, Liverpool L14 5NR . . . . None
NELTC. . . . . Edinburgh Park, Townsend Lane, Liverpool L6 0BB . . . . None
OLD HOLTS . . . . Simpson Ground, Hillfoot Road, Liverpool L25 0ND 0151 486 3166
PINEWOODS . . . . Carr Lane Playing Fields, Carr Lane, Ainsdale, Southport PR8 3EE . . . . None
ROMA . . . . Kirkby Sports Centre, Valley Road, Kirkby L20 9PQ 0151 443 4404
SOUTH LIVERPOOL RES. . . . . Jericho Lane, Aigburth, Liverpool L17 5AR. . . . . None
WARBRECK. . . . . Playfootball.com, Drummond Road, Thornton L20 6DX. . . . . None

IN: Alumni (P - Division Two South), Croxteth (P - Division Two North), Kingsley United (R), Pinewoods (P - Division One North), South Liverpool Res. (P - Division Two South)

OUT: East Villa Res. (WS), Essemmay Old Boys (P), Mackets Village (R - I-Zingari Combination Division One), Stoneycrofts (P), REMYCA United (P)

Division Two North		P	W	D	L	F	A	Pts
Pinewoods		16	12	1	3	74	24	37
Croxteth		16	11	3	2	48	27	36
Walton Players		16	10	4	2	53	29	34
St Helens Town Res.		16	6	2	8	34	50	20
Bootle A		16	5	3	8	26	29	18
Warbreck Res.		16	6	0	10	29	48	18
Clubmoor Farmers		16	5	2	9	31	39	17
Redgate Rovers		16	5	0	11	24	50	15
Blueline		16	3	3	10	30	53	12

Division Two South		P	W	D	L	F	A	Pts
Alumni		14	12	0	2	49	25	36
South Liverpool Res.		14	10	0	4	35	22	30
Alder		14	6	2	6	28	22	20
Liobians	*+3*	14	4	5	5	21	24	20
Eli Lilly		14	6	2	6	27	32	20
Halebank		14	4	4	6	30	35	16
Old Xaverians Res.	*-3*	14	3	3	8	31	35	9
NELTC Res.		14	1	4	9	14	40	7

Unity - record expunged

LORD WAVERTREE CUP

(Division Two teams)

PRELIMINARY ROUND

Alumni 3 NELTC Res. 1
St Helens Town Res. v Old Xaverians Res.

SECOND ROUND

Alumni v Blueline
Croxteth v St Helens/Old Xaverians Res.
Eli Lilly v Clubmoor Farmers
Halebank v Liobians
Redgate Rovers v Warbreck Res.
South Liverpool Res. v Pinewoods
Unity v Bootle A
Walton Players v Alder

Competition abandoned due to inclement weather

JOHN GREGSON CUP

(Division Two teams)

SEMI-FINALS

Clubmoor Farmers 2 **Pinewoods** 3
Croxteth 4 St Helens Town 3

FINAL *(May 10th at Aintree Villa)*

Pinewoods 1 **Croxteth** 2

PETER COYNE / GEORGE MAHON CUP

(All first teams in league)

FIRST ROUND

Alder 0 **Pinewoods** 2, **Bootle A** 4 Halebank 0
BRNESC 2 Halewood 1, Clubmoor Farmers 3 **Blueline** 6
Croxteth 5 Collegiate OB 1, **Eli Lilly** 2 Redgate Rovers 1
Mackets 1 **Liobians** 2, Old Holts 3 **REMYCA United** 4 *aet*
St Helens Res. 3 **Edge Hill BCOB** 4, Stoneycroft 1 **Alumni** 4
Unity 0 **Leyfield** 5 *(at Leyfield)*
Walton Players 1 **Copperas Hill** 4, **Warbreck** 4 Angus V. 2

SECOND ROUND

Birchfield 1 **Alumni** 2
Blueline 2 **Aigburth People's Hall** 2 *aet* (2-4p)
Bootle A 1 **Page Celtic** 4
Cheshire Lines 3 Old Xaverians 1
Croxteth 3 Leyfield 1
Eli Lilly 3 Liobians 3 *aet* (4-3p)
Essemmay Old Boys 6 Edge Hill BCOB 2
Ford Motors 2 **NELTC** 3 *aet*
Kingsley United 1 **Copperas Hill** 3
Pinewoods 2 **East Villa** 3
Red Rum 0 **St Aloysius** 2
REMYCA United 2 **BRNESC** 3
Sacre Coeur Former Pupils 5 Lucas Sports 3
South Sefton Borough 4 Albany Athletic 2
Warbreck 2 **South Liverpool** 3
Waterloo Dock 2 Roma 1

THIRD ROUND

Aigburth People's Hall 1 Sacre Coeur FP 1 *aet* (4-3p)
Alumni 1 **Essemay Old Boys** 5
BRNESC 1 **NELTC** 2 *aet*
Cheshire Lines 0 **Croxteth** 1 *(at Croxteth)*
Eli Lilly 2 **Page Celtic** 3
Sth Sefton Boro. 2 **Copperas Hill** 1 *(Sth Sefton expelled)*
St Aloysius 1 **East Villa** 2
Waterloo Dock 5 South Liverpool 2

QUARTER-FINALS

Aigburth People's Hall 3 East Villa 2
Copperas Hill 0 **Page Celic** 6
Essemmay Old Boys 3 NELTC 2
Waterloo Dock 5 Croxteth 0

SEMI-FINALS

Aigburth People's Hall 1 **Waterloo Dock** 2
Page Celtic 1 Essemmay Old Boys 0 *(at Ford Motors)*

FINAL

(May 23th at Everton)

Waterloo Dock 4 Page Celtic 0

LIVERPOOL COUNTY PREMIER LEAGUE DIVISION TWO CONSTITUTION 2010-11

ALDER . . . . . Alder Road Sports Club, Alder Road, West Derby, Liverpool L12 2BA . . . . . Nor
BLUELINE . . . . . Buckley Hill Playing Fields, Buckley Hill Lane, Netherton, Bootle L29 1YB . . . . . Nor
CLUBMOOR FARMERS . . . . . Walton Sports Centre, Walton Hall Avenue L4 9XP. . . . . . Nor
COLLEGIATE OLD BOYS RES. . . Alder Road Sports Club, Alder Road, West Derby, Liverpool L12 2BA . . . . . Nor
ELI LILLY . . . . . Thomas Lane Playing Fields, Thomas Lane, Liverpool L14 5NR . . . . . Nor
LIOBIANS . . . . . Mersey Road, Aigburth, Liverpool L17 6AG . . . . . Nor
LIVERPOOL HOPE UNIVERSITY . . Hope Park Sports, Taggart Avenue, Childwall, Liverpool L16 9JD 0151 291 29
LIVERPOOL NORTH . . . . . Playfootball.com, Drummond Road, Thornton L20 6DX. . . . . . Nor
REDGATE ROVERS . . . . . Clarence House School, West Lane, Freshfield, Formby, Liverpool L37 7AZ 01704 821
WALTON PLAYERS. . . . . . Lower Breck Road, Anfield, Liverpool L6 0AG . . . . . Nor
WARBRECK RES. . . . . . Playfootball.com, Drummond Road, Thornton L20 6DX. . . . . . Nor
WATERLOO GSOB . . . . . Moss Lane, Litherland, Liverpool L21 7NW . . . . . Nor
WEST EVERTON XAVERIANS. . . . St Francis Xaviers College, Beconsfield Road, Liverpool L25 6EG. 0151 288 10

IN: Alder (S - Division Two South), Blueline (S - Division Two North), Clubmoor Farmers (S - Division Two North), Collegiate Old Boys Re (P - I-Zingari Combination Division One), Eli Lilly (S - Division Two South), Liobians (S - Division Two South), Liverpool Hope Univers (N), Liverpool North (N), Redgate Rovers (S - Division Two North), Walton Players (S - Division Two North), Warbreck Res. (S - Divisi Two North), Waterloo GSOB (P - Liverpool Old Boys League Division One) West Everton Xaviers (formerly Old Xaverians Res. (S Division Two South)

MANCHESTER LEAGUE

Sponsored by: Bridgewater Office Supplies

Founded: 1893

Recent champions:
2005: Prestwich Heys
2006: Prestwich Heys
2007: Prestwich Heys
2008: Wigan Robin Park
2009: Gregorians

	AVRO	Ath. T.	Chap	Dukin	E. M	Elton	Hind.	Hollin.	Leigh	MGre	O Alts	Prest	Roch	Roytn	Sprin	Stock	Walsh	Wyth
AVRO		2-2	4-1	4-3	3-1	2-1	3-3	5-1	5-0	2-4	1-1	1-1	2-3	3-2	2-2	2-1	3-2	4-2
Atherton Town	2-1	***P***	0-1	2-3	2-1	3-1	0-1	3-0	2-3	1-1	0-0	0-4	1-2	3-1	0-1	2-2	0-4	1-1
Chapel Town	1-3	4-1	***R***	3-2	1-2	3-2	2-2	1-4	1-3	1-1	1-3	0-0	2-0	3-0	2-2	1-3	1-2	1-3
Dukinfield Town	2-4	4-0	5-0	***E***	5-3	7-4	2-0	2-1	2-3	2-4	1-3	4-1	2-1	1-1	0-1	1-2	3-0	1-2
East Manchester	2-1	1-1	4-1	2-1	***M***	4-3	2-0	3-1	6-0	1-0	0-1	3-1	6-2	1-1	0-3	0-2	0-2	2-0
Elton Vale	2-3	0-3	8-2	0-2	1-1	***I***	2-2	2-7	2-2	1-4	1-4	1-5	1-1	3-1	2-1	1-6	0-1	1-2
Hindsford	1-4	2-2	1-1	1-0	2-3	4-4	***E***	3-0	3-3	2-0	0-7	2-0	1-2	2-2	2-2	1-1	1-2	0-4
Hollinwood	3-1	4-0	10-1	1-4	4-2	0-1	2-0	***R***	3-2	3-6	3-0	0-3	3-1	3-4	4-2	3-3	4-2	1-6
Leigh Athletic	0-3	1-1	1-1	5-3	1-1	4-1	1-2	3-0		3-1	3-4	2-2	3-3	0-4	3-1	2-3	0-6	1-4
Manchester Gregorians	1-4	5-2	4-0	2-3	1-0	4-1	4-0	1-1	0-1	***D***	1-3	4-1	3-1	2-2	0-1	2-0	0-1	1-0
Old Altrinchamians	0-4	4-0	2-0	1-0	1-2	2-0	5-0	3-4	5-1	1-1	***I***	2-1	4-0	4-2	1-1	6-0	3-4	0-1
Prestwich Heys	3-3	1-1	2-0	2-1	4-3	1-0	1-2	0-0	1-0	0-0	1-0	***V***	1-4	2-2	2-3	0-2	2-1	0-6
Rochdale Sacred Heart	0-4	2-1	2-3	0-4	0-4	1-2	2-7	1-4	5-4	1-1	1-2	0-3	***I***	1-1	1-2	0-2	3-3	1-1
Royton Town	0-2	1-2	3-1	1-1	4-1	1-1	0-1	1-1	5-3	0-3	1-0	2-0	1-0	***S***	0-0	2-3	0-2	0-2
Springhead	3-3	5-1	0-1	3-6	0-0	1-2	2-0	4-3	4-2	2-0	1-1	1-3	2-1	1-4	***I***	1-1	2-1	1-1
Stockport Georgians	2-2	2-1	2-1	1-2	1-1	0-1	1-2	1-1	1-0	3-1	0-1	2-0	0-1	1-1	1-3	***O***	2-1	3-0
Walshaw Sports Club	0-2	1-1	2-2	1-2	0-1	2-1	4-2	2-2	4-0	0-2	2-3	5-0	8-1	3-0	2-0	4-1	***N***	1-1
Wythenshawe Amateur	2-1	1-3	5-0	1-0	5-0	0-0	1-1	4-0	1-2	3-2	4-1	1-0	2-1	0-1	2-2	3-0	2-0	

Premier Division		P	W	D	L	F	A	Pts
AVRO		34	20	8	6	93	54	68
Wythenshawe Amateur		34	20	7	7	73	33	67
Old Altrinchamians		34	20	5	9	78	42	65
Walshaw Sports Club		34	17	5	12	75	47	56
Springhead		34	14	11	9	60	54	53
Stockport Georgians		34	15	8	11	55	50	53
Manchester Gregorians		34	15	7	12	66	47	52
Dukinfield Town	*-3*	34	17	2	15	81	60	50
East Manchester	*-4*	34	16	6	12	63	55	50
Hollinwood		34	14	6	14	81	77	48
Prestwich Heys		34	12	8	14	48	58	44
Royton Town		34	10	11	13	51	56	41
Hindsford		34	10	11	13	53	71	41
Leigh Athletic		34	10	7	17	62	90	37
Atherton Town		34	8	10	16	44	67	34
Chapel Town		34	8	7	19	44	88	31
Elton Vale		34	7	7	20	53	86	28
Rochdale Sacred Heart	*-6*	34	7	6	21	45	90	21

GILGRYST CUP

FIRST ROUND

(Dukinfield Town suspended from cup competition)

Stockport Georgians 1 Atherton Town 0

SECOND ROUND

AVRO 2 East Manchester 1
Chapel Town 1 Old Altrinchamians 1 *aet* (6-5p)
Elton Vale 2 **Hindsford** 3
Manchester Gregorians 3 **Hollinwood** 4
Prestwich Heys 2 **Royton Town** 3
Rochdale Sacred Heart 5 Leigh Athletic 3
Stockport Georgians 1 Wythenshawe Amateur 0
Walshaw Sports Club 4 Springhead 2

QUARTER-FINALS

Hindsford 1 **Chapel Town** 3
Rochdale Sacred Heart 1 **Hollinwood** 3
Royton Town 1 **AVRO** 1 *aet* (3-4p)
Walshaw Sports Club 2 Stockport Georgians 1

SEMI-FINALS

AVRO 2 **Walshaw Sports Club** 3
Chapel Town 2 **Hollinwood** 4

FINAL *(May 5th at Hyde United)*

Hollinwood 2 **Walshaw Sports Club** 2 *aet* (1-3p)

MANCHESTER LEAGUE PREMIER DIVISION CONSTITUTION 2010-11

AVRO . . . . Lancaster Club, Broadway, Failsworth, Oldham M35 0DX 0161 681 3083
ATHERTON TOWN . . . . Eckersley Fold Lane, Leigh Road, Atherton M46 0QQ 01942 884882
BURY AMATEURS . . . . Cams Lane, Radcliffe M26 3SW . . . .
DUKINFIELD TOWN . . . . Woodhams Park, Birch Lane, Dukinfield SK16 5AP 0161 343 4529
EAST MANCHESTER . . . . Wright Robinson Sports College, Abbey Hey Lane, Gorton M18 8RL 0161 370 5121
HINDSFORD . . . . Squires Lane, Tyldesley M29 8JF . . . . None
HOLLINWOOD . . . . Chapel Road Playing Fields, Grammar School Road, Hollinwood, Oldham OL8 4QY 0161 911 5017
LEIGH ATHLETIC . . . . Leigh Sports Village, Madley Park, Charles Street, Leigh WN7 4GX 01942 673500
MANCHESTER GREGORIANS . . . MCFC, Platt Lane Complex, Yew Tree Road, Fallowfield M14 7UU . . . . None
OLD ALTRINCHAMIANS . . . . Crossford Bridge Sports Ground, Danefield Road, Sale M33 7WR 0161 767 9233
PRESTWICH HEYS . . . . Sandgate Road, Whitefield M45 6WG 0161 773 8888
ROYTON TOWN . . . . Crompton Cricket Club Complex, Christine Street, Shaw, Oldham OL2 7SF 01706 847421
SPRINGHEAD . . . . Ashfield Crescent PF, St John Street, Lees, Oldham OL4 4DG 0161 627 0260
STOCKPORT GEORGIANS . . . . Cromley Road, Woodsmoor, Stockport SK2 7DT 0161 483 6581
WALSHAW SPORTS CLUB . . . . . . Walshaw Sports Club, Sycamore Road, Tottington, Bury BL8 3EG 01204 882448
WYTHENSHAWE AMATEUR . . . . Longley Lane, Northenden, Wythenshawe M22 4LA 0161 998 7268

IN: Bury Amateurs (P)

OUT: Chapel Town (R), Elton Vale (R), Rochdale Sacred Heart (R)

	Beechfield	Breightmet	Bury Amats	Fives Athletic	Heywood SJ	Monton Ams	Pennington	Salford Vics	West Didsbury	Wilmslow Alb.	Wyth'shawe T.
Beechfield United	***D***	1-2	2-3	5-1	2-1	1-1	2-2	3-1	1-1	5-1	0-1
Breightmet United	0-1	***I***	1-3	3-2	4-3	4-3	3-1	6-0	0-4	3-1	3-2
Bury Amateurs	0-1	1-1	***V***	1-1	3-0	1-2	2-0	1-1	3-2	1-0	2-1
Fives Athletic	4-1	1-1	2-3		2-1	1-5	2-1	3-1	1-1	2-2	2-1
Heywood St James	2-2	0-2	2-3	1-2		1-2	3-0	1-1	0-3	1-3	3-8
Monton Amateurs	1-3	1-1	0-3	5-0	2-2		3-2	6-0	3-1	6-1	3-2
Pennington	0-3	1-2	1-3	2-1	1-2	1-6		1-1	1-3	5-1	3-0
Salford Victoria	3-4	0-2	2-3	0-0	5-3	0-3	1-5		1-3	2-1	0-4
West Didsbury & Chorlton	5-2	5-1	1-3	4-0	5-0	5-0	5-0	5-2	***O***	4-0	0-0
Wilmslow Albion	1-0	1-1	0-1	1-1	6-2	1-1	3-2	5-2	0-1	***N***	0-5
Wythenshawe Town	5-1	0-1	1-6	5-3	5-0	1-3	3-4	1-4	0-1	2-0	***E***

Division One		**P**	**W**	**D**	**L**	**F**	**A**	**Pts**
Bury Amateurs		**20**	**15**	**3**	**2**	**46**	**21**	**48**
West Didsbury & Chorlton		**20**	**14**	**3**	**3**	**59**	**18**	**45**
Monton Amateurs		**20**	**12**	**4**	**4**	**56**	**31**	**40**
Breightmet United		**20**	**12**	**4**	**4**	**41**	**31**	**40**
Beechfield United		**20**	**9**	**4**	**7**	**40**	**35**	**31**
Wythenshawe Town		**20**	**8**	**1**	**11**	**47**	**39**	**25**
Fives Athletic		**20**	**6**	**6**	**8**	**31**	**44**	**24**
Wilmslow Albion		**20**	**5**	**4**	**11**	**28**	**47**	**19**
Pennington		**20**	**5**	**2**	**13**	**33**	**49**	**17**
Salford Victoria	***-3***	**20**	**3**	**4**	**13**	**27**	**60**	**10**
Heywood St James		**20**	**2**	**3**	**15**	**28**	**61**	**9**

MURRAY SHIELD

FIRST ROUND

Heywood St J. 4 Wilmslow Alb. 2

Manch. Jnrs v **Salford V.** (w/o)

Monton Amateurs 3 Fives 2

West Didsbury 4 Breightmet 1

Wythenshawe T. 2 **Bury Ams** 3

QUARTER-FINALS

Bury Amateurs (w/o) v Standians

Monton Amats 1 Beechfield 0

Pennington 3 Salford Victoria 0

West Didsbury 2 Heywood SJ 0

SEMI-FINALS

Monton Ams 2 Bury Amateurs 0

Pennington 1 **West Didsbury** 4

FINAL

(April 29th at Hyde United)

West Didsbury & Chorlton 3

Monton Amateurs 1 *aet*

DIV ONE SUPPLEMENTARY CUP

SEMI-FINALS

Pennington 6 Heywood St James 1

Wythenshawe Town 3 Breightmet United 2 *aet*

FINAL

(May 11th at AVRO)

Wythenshawe Town 2 Pennington 1

MANCHESTER LEAGUE DIVISION ONE CONSTITUTION 2010-11

BEECHFIELD UNITED	Salford Sports Village, Littleton Road, Salford M7 3NQ	0161 604 7600
BREIGHTMET UNITED	Moss Park, Bury Road, Breightmet, Bolton BL2 6NY	01204 533930
CHAPEL TOWN	Rowton Park, Willow Drive, Chapel-en-le-Frith, High Peak SK23 0ND	None
ELTON VALE	Elton Sports Club, Elton Vale Road, Bury BL8 2RZ	0161 762 0666
FIVES ATHLETIC	Harriet Street, Walkden, Worsley M28 3QA	None
HEYWOOD ST JAMES	Phoenix Ground, Shepherd Street, Heywood OL10 1JW	None
MONTON AMATEURS	Granary Lane, Worsley M28 4PH	None
PENNINGTON	Jubilee Park, Leigh Road, Atherton M46 0PJ	None
ROCHDALE SACRED HEART	Fox Park, Belfield Mill Lane, Rochdale OL16 2UB	None
SALFORD VICTORIA	Salford Sports Village, Lower Kersal, Littleton Road, Salford M7 3NQ	0161 604 7600
WEST DIDSBURY & CHORLTON	Brookburn Road, Chorlton-cum-Hardy M21 8EH	None
WILMSLOW ALBION	Oakwood Farm, Styal Road, Wilmslow SK9 4HP	01625 535823
WYTHENSHAWE TOWN	Ericstan Park, Timpson Road, Baguley M23 9RT	0161 998 5076

IN: Chapel Town (R), Elton Vale (R), Rochdale Sacred Heart (R)

OUT: Bury Amateurs (P), Manchester Juniors (WN)

Division Two	P	W	D	L	F	A	Pt
Dukinfied Res.	30	20	6	4	83	46	66
Walshaw SC Res.	30	19	4	7	92	62	61
Springhead Res.	30	13	9	8	76	52	48
East Manch. Res.	30	13	6	11	62	59	45
P'wich Heys Res.	30	14	2	14	57	54	44
AVRO Res.	30	13	4	13	72	68	43
Monton Ams Res.	30	12	6	12	56	63	42
Leigh Ath. Res.	30	12	5	13	68	83	41
Hindsford Res.	30	13	2	15	56	79	41
M Gregorians Res.	30	11	6	13	54	56	39
Stockport G. Res.	30	11	5	14	70	63	38
Old Alts Res.	30	11	5	14	60	65	38
Elton Vale Res.	30	10	5	15	45	58	35
Rochdale SH Res.	30	10	5	15	81	96	35
Wyth'shawe A.Res.	30	9	7	14	50	60	34
Beechfield Res.	30	8	5	17	73	91	29

Division Three		P	W	D	L	F	A	Pt
Fives Ath. Res.		24	20	1	3	104	38	61
Hollinwood Res.		24	18	3	3	92	48	57
W. Didsbury Res.		24	13	5	6	56	36	44
Dukinfield T. A	*-6*	24	14	2	8	60	39	38
Bury Amateurs A		24	12	2	10	46	55	38
W'shawe T. Res.		24	9	4	11	65	69	31
Chapel Town Res.		24	8	7	9	53	57	31
M Gregorians A		24	8	5	11	55	55	29
Royton Town Res.		24	8	3	13	43	53	27
Stockport Geo. A		24	7	2	15	52	80	23
Breightmet Res.		24	6	5	13	38	74	23
Atherton T. Res.		24	5	6	13	58	80	21
Bury Amats Res.		24	4	3	17	38	76	15

Division Four	P	W	D	L	F	A	Pt
Hollinwood A	18	12	1	5	61	35	37
Prestwich Heys A	18	11	2	5	56	35	35
Manc. Gregs B	18	10	1	7	41	29	31
Leigh Athletic A	18	9	2	7	34	45	29
Wilmslow A. Res.	18	9	0	9	39	35	27
Pennington Res.	18	7	2	9	49	55	23
Salford V. Res.	18	7	1	10	48	60	22
Walshaw SC A	18	5	5	8	37	51	20
Bury Amateurs B	18	5	4	9	42	53	19
West Didsbury A	18	6	0	12	45	54	18

DIV FOUR SUPPLEMENTARY CUP FINAL

(May 11th at AVRO)

Pretwich Heys A 2 Wilmslow Albion A 2 *aet* (4-3p)

OPEN TROPHY

FINAL *(May 12th at Trafford)*

Stockp't G. Res. 2 **Prestwich H. Res. 2** *aet* (5-4p) *(Stockport expelled)*

LEAGUE CUP

FINAL *(May 3rd at Salford City)*

West Didbury Res. 2 Fives A. Res. 0

MIDDLESEX COUNTY LEAGUE

www.mcfl.org.uk

Sponsored by: Cherry Red

Founded: 1984

Recent champions:

2005: Hanworth Villa

2006: Battersea Ironsides

2007: Sport London E Benfica

2008: Indian Gymkhana

2009: Bethnal Green United

	Bet	Bro	Cop	Dep	Hay	Hou	Ind	Int	Kod	Mar	Nor	Sin	Slo	Sou	Sto	Val	Will
Bethnal Green United Res.	***P***	W-L	2-2	4-1	1-3	L-W	1-0	1-2	1-0	3-2	n/a	0-3	3-1	0-2	3-0	3-0	0-3
Broadfields United	1-0	***R***	3-2	2-2	2-2	0-0	2-3	0-2	1-0	3-0	n/a	0-1	3-1	3-3	n/a	1-1	n/a
Copland	2-0	2-2	***E***	0-2	0-0	1-0	1-5	0-2	1-1	3-2	n/a	4-0	2-1	2-1	2-0	6-3	3-1
FC Deportivo Galicia	3-1	n/a	0-4	***M***	0-7	0-2	1-4	3-4	1-2	1-7	1-2	1-2	1-3	1-2	2-3	4-2	0-5
Hayes Gate	4-2	3-2	4-1	7-0	***I***	4-1	3-0	3-1	5-2	4-3	n/a	3-2	3-2	2-5	3-2	5-0	3-4
Hounslow Wanderers	2-0	2-3	2-3	5-1	4-2	***E***	3-1	2-4	1-1	1-1	4-5	1-1	0-3	2-1	4-2	3-1	2-4
Indian Gymkhana	5-1	n/a	3-1	10-1	2-1	2-2	***R***	0-2	1-1	0-0	3-2	1-1	2-1	4-2	0-1	2-1	1-1
Interwood	0-0	3-1	9-2	5-1	0-0	6-0	4-3		2-0	2-3	n/a	3-1	5-2	4-0	9-3	6-1	3-0
Kodak (Harrow)	1-3	2-3	4-4	6-1	2-2	0-3	0-2	3-7		2-1	n/a	5-4	1-1	3-1	2-2	3-1	0-1
Marsh Rangers	2-0	1-1	1-1	5-1	4-1	5-3	1-0	1-3	5-0	***D***	2-2	5-0	1-4	3-3	3-1	3-1	0-3
North Kensington	n/a	n/a	n/a	n/a	1-2	n/a	n/a	0-2	n/a	n/a	***I***	n/a	n/a	3-0	n/a	n/a	n/a
Singh Sabha Slough	4-3	n/a	2-2	2-1	L-W	2-1	2-2	0-7	5-3	0-1	2-2	***V***	0-1	5-1	8-1	2-1	L-W
Sloane	2-0	0-2	1-0	2-1	2-3	2-2	2-3	0-3	4-1	2-2	1-0	7-0	***I***	1-0	6-1	2-1	W-L
Southall	2-2	n/a	1-2	2-1	0-3	2-1	1-3	2-5	2-0	2-3	n/a	1-0	2-2	***S***	4-1	4-1	0-5
Stonewall	0-4	n/a	1-0	2-1	2-7	0-1	1-1	1-4	2-1	4-1	0-2	1-1	1-1	1-0	***I***	1-1	1-1
Vallance	0-1	n/a	1-5	2-4	1-6	0-2	1-3	0-8	0-2	1-3	2-3	3-3	1-0	0-2	1-2	***O***	0-3
Willesden Constantine	2-1	1-1	1-1	2-1	4-3	0-2	1-2	1-2	1-2	3-4	n/a	3-1	3-1	4-1	4-2	1-1	***N***

Premier Division		P	W	D	L	F	A	Pts
Interwood		28	24	2	2	112	33	74
Hayes Gate		28	19	3	6	91	47	60
Willesden Constantine		28	16	4	8	61	37	52
Marsh Rangers		28	15	5	8	72	49	50
Indian Gymkhana		28	14	7	7	62	38	49
Copland		28	13	7	8	55	50	46
Sloane		28	13	5	10	56	42	44
Hounslow Wanderers		28	13	5	10	52	49	44
Bethnal Green Utd Res.		28	10	3	15	40	48	33
Southall		28	10	3	15	46	61	33
Kodak (Harrow)		28	8	7	13	48	64	31
Singh Sabha Slough	*-3*	28	9	6	13	51	62	30
Stonewall		28	8	6	14	39	75	30
FC Deportivo Galicia		28	4	0	24	35	102	12
Vallance		28	1	3	24	26	89	6

Broadfields United, North Kensington - records expunged

ALEC SMITH CUP

FIRST ROUND

North Kensington 4 Copland 1

SECOND ROUND

Bethnal Green United Res. 3 Stonewall 0

Broadfields United 7 Southall 1

Hayes Gate 6 FC Deportivo Galicia 1

Hounslow Wanderers 3 Singh Sabha Slough 2

Indian Gymkhana 1 Willesden Const. 1 *aet* (4-2p)

Kodak (Harrow) 1 **Marsh Rangers** 2

North Kensington v **Interwood** (w/o)

Sloane 4 Vallance 0

QUARTER-FINALS

Bethnal G. Res. 1 Indian G. 0, **Hayes G.** 5 Sloane 1

Interwood 3 Broadfields United 0

Marsh Rangers 2 Hounslow Wanderers 1

SEMI-FINALS

Hayes Gate 3 Marsh Rangers 1

Interwood 4 Bethnal Green Res. 1

FINAL *(April 24th at Yeading)*

Hayes Gate 3 **Interwood** 4

MIDDLESEX COUNTY LEAGUE PREMIER DIVISION CONSTITUTION 2010-11

BROADFIELDS UNITED . . . Broadfields Country Club, Broadfields, Headstone Lane, North Harrow HA2 6NN 020 8421 4739/5260

FC DEPORTIVO GALICIA. . . . . Osterley Sports Club, Tentelow Lane, Osterley, Southall UB2 4LW. 020 8574 3774

HOUNSLOW WANDERERS. . . . Rosedale College, Wood End Green Road, Hayes, Middlesex UB3 2SE 020 8573 2097

INDIAN GYMKHANA. . . . . Indian Gymkhana Club, Thornbury Avenue, Osterley TW7 4NQ. 020 8568 4009

INTERWOOD. . . . . Peter May Sports Centre, Wadham Road, Walthamstow E17 4HR. 020 8531 9358

KODAK (HARROW) . . . . Zoom Leisure Centre, Kodak Sports Ground, Harrow View, Harrow HA2 6QQ 020 8427 1957

SINGH SABHA SLOUGH . . . . Burnham Grammar School, Hogfair Lane, Burnham, Bucks SL1 7HG 01628 604812

SLOANE . . . . Burton Court, St Leonards Terrace, London SW3 4QG . . . . None

SOUTHALL . . . . Northolt Rugby Club, Cayton Road, Greenford 020 8813 1701

SPORTING HACKNEY . . . . Haggerston Park, Hackney E2 8NP . . . . None

SPRINGFIELD . . . . Frederick Knights Sports Ground, 80 Willoughby Lane, Tottenham N17 0RT . . . . None

STEDFAST UNITED . . . . Stockley Park, Chestnut Avenue, Yiewsley UB7 8BU. . . . . None

STONEWALL . . . . Barn Elms Playing Fields, Queen Elizabeth Walk, Barnes SW13 0DG . . . . None

TOKYNGTON MANOR. . . . . Viking FC, Western Avenue, Greenford UB6 8GA 020 8578 2706

WILLESDEN CONSTANTINE. . . . . Alperton Sports Ground, Alperton Lane, Wembley HA0 1JH 020 8997 9909

IN: Sporting Hackney (P - Divsion One Central & East), Springfield (P - Divsion One Central & East), Stedfast United (P - Divsion One West), Tokyngton Manor (R - Spartan South Midlands League Division One)

OUT: Bethnal Green United Res. (R - Division One Central & East), Copland (W), Hayes Gate (P - Combined Counties League Division One), Marsh Rangers (F), North Kensington (WS - Division One West), Vallance (R - Division One Central & East)

SENIOR OPEN CUP

FIRST ROUND

Indian Gymkhana 1 Bethnal Green United Res. 0
Kentish Town 3 Harrow St Mary's 1
Kodak (Harrow) (w/o) v My Generation Sports
LPOSSA 1 **Marsh Rangers** 4
Stonewall 1 **Sloane** 2

SECOND ROUND

Copland 1 FC Team 0
Greens United 4 **Willesden Constantine** 4 *aet* (0-3p)
Grosvenor House 1 **Interwood** 2
Hayes Gate 4 The Wilberforce Wanderers 2
Hendon A 1 London United Football Academy 0
Hillingdon (w/o) v London City
Hounslow Wanderers 3 Singh Sabha Slough 2
Kentish Town 1 **Marsh Rangers** 4
Kodak (Harrow) 6 **Indian Gymkhana** 6 *aet* (1-4p)
North Greenford United Social 3 Vallance 1
Regents Park 0 **Broadfields United** 5
Sandgate 1 North Kensington 0
Sloane 0 **Sporting Hackney** 1
Springfield 2 Brentham 1
St Johns Arsenal Deaf 3 FC Assyria 2
Stedfast United 3 Southall 2

THIRD ROUND

Broadfields United 4 Hendon A 1
Hayes Gate 3 St Johns Arsenal Deaf 2
Hounslow Wanderers 1 **Stedfast United** 2
Interwood 4 **Sandgate** 5
Marsh Rangers 3 Hillingdon 1
North Greenford Utd Social 1 **Willesden Constantine** 10
Sporting Hackney 1 Indian Gymkhana 1 *aet* (2-1p)
Springfield 2 Copland 0

QUARTER-FINALS

Broadfields United 0 **Springfield** 1
Hayes Gate 4 Marsh Rangers 2
Sandgate 0 **Stedfast United** 1
Sporting Hackney 4 Willesden Constantine 2

SEMI-FINALS

Sporting Hackney 0 **Stedfast United** 1
Springfield 0 **Hayes Gate** 1

FINAL

(May 8th at Yeading)
Hayes Gate 3 Stedfast United 2

Division One Central & East		P	W	D	L	F	A	Pt
Sporting Hackney		18	13	3	2	64	24	42
Springfield		18	13	2	3	30	16	41
Hendon A		18	10	3	5	51	22	33
FC Team		18	8	4	6	40	27	28
The Wilberforce Wdrs		18	8	2	8	41	41	26
FC Baresi		18	7	4	7	37	49	25
Regents Park		18	5	1	12	28	60	16
Kentish Town		18	4	1	13	20	58	13
St Johns Arsenal Deaf	*-3*	18	3	6	9	39	47	12
London Utd F'ball Acad.	*-9*	18	5	2	11	28	34	8

London Irish - record expunged

Division Two		P	W	D	L	F	A	Pt
Imperial College Old Boys		22	17	1	4	72	30	52
Kensington Dragons		22	15	4	3	78	32	49
Hanworth Villa A		22	16	1	5	80	43	49
Junior All Stars	*-3*	22	13	2	7	63	44	38
Hilltop	*-3*	22	12	1	9	45	58	34
Barn Elms		22	10	1	11	43	47	31
Grange Park	*-6*	22	11	2	9	66	52	29
CB Hounslow Utd Social		22	7	4	11	38	54	25
Uxbridge Town	*-3*	22	7	2	13	46	57	20
Warren		22	6	2	14	40	64	20
Maiwand		22	2	1	19	31	96	7
Harrow Club	*-9*	22	4	3	15	41	66	6

Senior Reserve Division		P	W	D	L	F	A	Pt
Brentham Res.		24	19	4	1	61	22	61
Broadfields United Res.		24	17	2	5	61	26	53
Hillingdon Res.	*-6*	24	16	3	5	57	29	45
Indian Gymkhana Res.		24	13	3	8	67	40	42
North Kensington Res.		24	11	6	7	63	49	39
Hayes Gate Res.		24	10	5	9	53	39	35
Sporting Hackney Res.		24	10	2	12	69	66	32
Feltham Res.		24	8	7	9	62	69	31
Sloane Res.		24	9	3	12	40	60	30
Kodak (Harrow) Res.	*-3*	24	7	3	14	28	55	21
Imperial College OB Res.		24	4	6	14	37	68	18
Kensington Dragons Res.		24	3	8	13	33	57	17
CB Hounslow Utd S. Res.		24	0	6	18	20	71	6

Division One West	P	W	D	L	F	A	Pt
Stedfast United	20	16	1	3	93	36	49
Sandgate	20	12	5	3	63	32	41
Grosvenor House	20	11	7	2	60	28	40
Chiswick Homefields	20	10	4	6	65	44	34
LPOSSA	20	10	4	6	56	35	34
Hillingdon	20	9	6	5	44	34	33
FC Assyria	20	9	2	9	42	64	29
North Greenford Utd Soc.	20	6	4	10	45	51	22
Brentham	20	4	3	13	36	50	15
Greens United	20	3	2	15	37	75	11
Harrow St Mary's	20	1	0	19	13	105	3

My Generation Sports - record expunged

Division Three Hounslow & District		P	W	D	L	F	A	Pt
Eutectic		18	14	2	2	62	29	44
West London Saracens		18	12	2	3	44	14	38
Hanworth Sports		18	11	4	3	59	30	37
Apna Southall		18	11	3	4	45	37	36
AFC Heathrow		18	11	2	4	47	33	35
Dynamo	*-6*	18	7	3	8	62	32	18
Barnhill Explorers		18	4	1	12	36	69	13
AFC London (AMU)		18	2	4	12	34	65	10
Discover	*-6*	18	2	0	15	16	54	0
West Side Rangers	*-6*	18	2	3	13	30	72	0

JIM ROGERS DIVISION ONE PRESIDENT'S CUP

FINAL *(April 10th at Yeading)*
Stedfast United 3 Sporting Hackney 2 *aet*

SIR JOHN SALMOND DIVISION TWO CUP FINAL

(May 3rd at Yeading)
Barn Elms 3 Grange Park 2 *aet*

JEFF NARDIN SENIOR RESERVE DIVISION TROPHY

FINAL *(April 17th at Yeading)*
Feltham Res. 3 Hillingdon Res. 1

P D MARDON DIVISION THREE CUP FINAL

(April 27th at Yeading)
West London Saracens 2 Eutectic 1

JUNIOR OPEN CUP FINAL

(May 1st at Yeading)
Kensington Dragons 2 Hillingdon Res. 1

NORTH BERKS LEAGUE

www.nbfl.co.uk

Sponsored by:
No sponsor

Founded: 1909

Recent champions:

2005: Drayton
2006: Lambourn Sports
2007: Ardington & Lockinge
2008: Lambourn Sports
2009: Saxton Rovers

	AFC Wallingford	Crowmarsh Gifford	Didcot Casuals	Drayton	Faringdon Town	Harwell Village	Lambourn Sports	Saxton Rovers	Warborough & Shillingford	Wootton & Dry Sandford
AFC Wallingford		3-0	2-4	3-4	2-2	7-0	5-0	0-2	4-1	2-2
Crowmarsh Gifford	2-2	***D***	0-2	3-1	4-2	0-3	1-0	1-4	6-1	2-4
Didcot Casuals	2-1	0-1	***I***	1-0	2-2	1-1	6-2	0-2	6-1	4-1
Drayton	3-1	3-2	1-3	***V***	1-4	1-1	2-2	1-4	5-1	1-1
Faringdon Town	3-0	0-1	1-0	4-1		5-1	0-1	1-2	6-1	3-2
Harwell Village	1-2	2-4	1-0	4-2	0-3		1-2	0-2	3-1	0-0
Lambourn Sports	2-4	3-1	2-2	1-2	5-3	1-6	***O***	3-5	5-1	3-3
Saxton Rovers	4-2	6-0	4-1	2-0	2-2	3-1	2-1	***N***	4-0	5-0
Warborough & Shillingford	1-4	1-6	3-6	0-8	2-10	1-2	1-1	L-W	***E***	1-3
Wootton & Dry Sandford	2-2	4-4	2-3	1-0	2-2	6-1	2-2	0-6	3-1	

Division One	**P**	**W**	**D**	**L**	**F**	**A**	**Pts**
Saxton Rovers	**18**	**17**	**1**	**0**	**59**	**13**	**52**
Didcot Casuals	**18**	**10**	**3**	**5**	**43**	**27**	**33**
Faringdon Town	**18**	**9**	**4**	**5**	**53**	**29**	**31**
Crowmarsh Gifford	**18**	**8**	**2**	**8**	**38**	**41**	**26**
AFC Wallingford	**18**	**7**	**4**	**7**	**46**	**35**	**25**
Wootton & Dry Sandford	**18**	**5**	**8**	**5**	**38**	**42**	**23**
Drayton	**18**	**6**	**3**	**9**	**36**	**38**	**21**
Harwell Village	**18**	**6**	**3**	**9**	**28**	**41**	**21**
Lambourn Sports	**18**	**5**	**5**	**8**	**36**	**47**	**20**
Warborough & Shillingford	**18**	**0**	**1**	**17**	**18**	**82**	**1**

Division Two	P	W	D	L	F	A	Pt
Harwell International	22	19	1	2	77	18	58
Childrey United	21	16	1	4	71	31	49
Long Wittenham Athletic	22	14	3	5	77	37	45
Botley United	22	11	2	9	56	58	35
Benson	22	10	4	8	45	38	34
Grove Rangers	22	10	3	9	53	47	33
East Hendred	21	9	3	9	44	37	30
Steventon	22	6	4	12	47	53	22
Marcham	22	6	4	12	39	53	22
Saxton Rovers Res.	22	7	1	14	49	74	22
Lambourn Sports Res.	22	7	1	14	41	69	22
Coleshill United	22	1	3	18	21	105	6

Childrey United v East Hendred not played

Division Three	P	W	D	L	F	A	Pt
Hanney United	22	17	1	4	59	24	52
Bampton Town	22	15	2	5	77	33	46
Benson Lions	22	13	4	5	49	33	43
Faringdon Town Res.	22	13	2	7	58	35	41
Kintbury Rangers Res.	22	10	5	7	55	55	37
Wootton & Dry Sandford Res.	22	10	3	9	52	52	33
Benson Res.	22	9	4	9	49	49	30
Sutton Courtenay	22	8	3	11	50	70	27
Drayton Res.	22	7	3	12	29	52	26
Shrivenham A	22	6	1	15	36	55	19
Harwell Village Res.	22	4	8	10	33	48	18
Harwell International Res..	22	1	2	19	28	69	5

NORTH BERKS LEAGUE DIVISION ONE CONSTITUTION 2010-11

AFC WALLINGFORD............ Wallingford Sports Park, Hithercroft Road, Wallingford OX10 9RB 01491 835044
CHILDREY UNITED........... Childrey Playing Field, Sparsholt Road, Childrey, Wantage OX12 9PN............... None
CROWMARSH GIFFORD .... Crowmarsh Recreation Ground, Crowmarsh Gifford, Wallingford OX10 8EB 07951 959090
DIDCOT CASUALS .... Didcot Town Training Pitch, Ladygrove, Didcot OX11 7GA.............................. None
DRAYTON .... Recreation Ground, Lockway, Drayton, Abingdon OX14 4LF............................. None
FARINGDON TOWN .... Tucker Park, Park Road, Faringdon SN7 7DP 01367 241759
HARWELL INTERNATIONAL .... Main Gate, Harwell International Business Centre, Didcot OX11 0RA 01235 820220
HARWELL VILLAGE .... Westfields Recreation Ground, Harwell, Didcot OX11 0LG............................ None
KINTBURY RANGERS .... Inkpen Road, Kintbury, Hungerford RG17 9TY 01488 657001
LAMBOURN SPORTS.............. Bockhampton Road, Lambourn, Hungerford RG17 7PS 01488 72214
SAXTON ROVERS .... Recreation Ground, Caldecott Road, Abingdon OX14 5HR .... None
WOOTTON & DRY SANDFORD...... Community Centre, Besseleigh Road, Wootton OX13 6DN .... None

IN: Childrey United (P), Harwell International (P), Kintbury Rangers (W - Hellenic League Division One East)
OUT: Warborough & Shillingford (R)

Division Four	P	W	D	L	F	A	Pt
Stanford-in-the-Vale	20	16	3	1	112	24	53
Uffington United	20	11	4	5	72	45	37
Grove Rangers Res.	20	11	2	7	55	43	35
Challow United	20	10	4	6	69	47	34
Faringdon Town A	20	8	5	7	50	42	33
Didcot Casuals Res.	20	9	4	7	97	66	31
Hagbourne United	20	8	3	9	58	55	27
Coleshill United Res.	20	7	5	8	45	41	24
East Hendred Res.	20	7	2	11	47	48	23
Marcham Res.	20	6	2	12	49	52	19
Appleton Stars	20	0	0	20	13	204	0

Division Five	P	W	D	L	F	A	Pt
Long Wittenham Ath. Res.	20	12	4	4	68	37	41
Steventon Res.	20	11	4	5	56	36	37
Didcot Casuals A	20	13	1	6	55	39	37
Bampton Town Res.	20	11	3	6	75	37	36
Sutton Courtenay Res.	20	11	2	7	57	41	35
Stanford-in-the-Vale Res.	20	10	2	8	57	43	35
Benson Lions Res.	20	8	3	9	43	54	27
Uffington United Res.	20	7	5	8	57	41	26
Hanney United Res.	20	4	5	11	32	68	18
Hagbourne United Res.	20	4	3	13	44	83	15
Challow United Res.	20	2	2	16	43	108	8

CHARITY SHIELD

FIRST ROUND
Benson 3 **Marcham** 4
Benson Lions 2 **AFC Wallingford** 4
Botley United 4 East Hendred 3
Childrey United 5 Grove Rangers 1
Coleshill United 5 **Steventon** 6
Crowmarsh Gifford 0 **Faringdon** 1
Didcot Casuals 5 Harwell Village 3 *aet*
Drayton 5 Uffington United 0
Hanney Utd v **Saxton Rovers** (w/o)
Lambourn Sports 12 Appleton 0
Stanford-in-the-Vale 0 **Harwell International** 5
Sutton Courtenay 0 **Wootton & DS** 3

SECOND ROUND
AFC Wallingford 0 **Didcot Casuals** 3
Bampton Town 3 **Wootton & Dry Sandford** 4
Botley United 7 Warborough & Shillingford 6
Childrey United 3 Marcham 0
Drayton 5 Harwell International 5 *aet* (3-1p)
Faringdon Town 6 Challow United 0
Long Wittenham Athletic 2 Steventon 1
Saxton Rovers 4 Lambourn Sports 1

QUARTER-FINALS
Childrey United 1 **Drayton** 5
Didcot Casuals 3 **Wootton & Dry Sandford** 4
Faringdon Town 3 Saxton Rovers 2
Long Wittenham Athletic 5 Botley United 1

SEMI-FINALS
Faringdon Town 2 Long Wittenham Athletic 0
(at Ardington & Lockinge)
Wootton & Dry Sandford 0 **Drayton** 3
(at Harwell Village)

FINAL
(May 1st at Abingdon United)
Drayton 3 **Faringdon Town** 4 *aet*

NORTH BERKS CUP

FIRST ROUND
AFC Wallingford 11 Stanford-in-the-Vale 2
Benson Lions 14 Appleton Stars 0
Challow United 2 **Childrey United** 7
Crowmarsh Gifford 5 Lambourn 1
Drayton 3 **Benson** 4
Faringdon Town 3 Sutton Courtenay 0
Grove Rangers 3 Steventon 1
Harwell International 6 Uffington 3
Harwell Village 2 **Didcot Casuals** 2 *aet* (5-6p)
Long Wittenham Athletic 6 Marcham 1
Warborough & Shillingford 0 **East Hendred** 3
Wootton & Dry Sandford 2 **Saxton Rovers** 3

SECOND ROUND
AFC Wallingford 2 Faringdon Town 1
Bampton Town 3 Botley United 2
Benson 3 Coleshill United 1
Crowmarsh Gifford 6 Childrey United 2
Didcot Casuals 1 Hanney United 0
Grove Rangers 1 **East Hendred** 2
Long Wittenham Athletic 2 Harwell International 0
Saxton Rovers 6 Benson Lions 0

QUARTER-FINALS
Benson 3 Bampton Town 2
Didcot Casuals 2 **AFC Wallingford** 3
East Hendred 1 **Saxton Rovers** 6
Long Wittenham Athletic 3 Crowmarsh Gifford 1

SEMI-FINALS
Benson 0 **Saxton Rovers** 7
(at Lambourn Sports)
Long Wittenham Athletic 0 **AFC Wallingford** 6
(at Kintbury Rangers)

FINAL
(May 8th at Abingdon United)
Saxton Rovers 1 AFC Wallingford 0

CENTENARY CUP

SEMI-FINALS
Faringdon Town 1 Long Wittenham Ath. 0 *(at Wantage)*
Saxton Rovers 3 Didcot Casuals 0 *(at Abingdon Town)*

FINAL
(October 28th at Abingdon Town)
Saxton Rovers 1 **Faringdon Town** 2

WAR MEMORIAL CUP

FINAL *(April 23rd at Wantage Town)*
Harwell International 4 Bampton Town 1

LEAGUE CUP

FINAL *(April 24th at AFC Wallingford)*
Bampton Town Res. 1 East Hendred Res. 0

A G KINGHAM CUP

FINAL *(May 8th at Abingdon United)*
Benson Res. 5 Kintbury Rangers Res. 4 *aet*

NAIRNE PAUL CUP

FINAL *(May 1st at Abingdon United)*
Didcot Casuals Res. 2 Shrivenham A 0

NORTHANTS COMBINATION LEAGUE

www.northantscombination.co.uk

Sponsored by: MDH Teamwear

Founded: N/K

Recent champions:
2005: Caledonian Strip Mills
2006: Corby Hellenic Fisher
2007: Harpole
2008: Harpole
2009: Harpole

	Brixworth AS	Corby Khalsa	Corby Peg.	Harborough	Harpole	Heyford Ath.	Kislingbury	Medbourne	Milton	Moulton	Q. Eleanor	Roade	Weldon Utd	Whitefield N.
Brixworth All Saints		5-0	3-0	3-3	1-1	4-0	2-3	3-2	4-1	1-1	3-2	3-0	0-2	3-3
Corby Khalsa	1-3	***P***	0-3	1-5	2-4	1-1	2-0	1-1	1-2	4-1	1-1	1-6	1-2	2-2
Corby Pegasus	0-2	0-4	***R***	0-4	2-5	2-3	2-4	3-2	2-2	0-4	5-5	2-5	0-5	2-0
Harborough Town	2-1	2-0	7-2	***E***	2-1	2-0	2-2	3-1	2-1	4-2	3-2	2-5	1-2	4-0
Harpole	0-3	2-2	2-0	4-2	***M***	0-1	3-1	3-1	4-0	1-2	3-4	5-2	2-1	4-3
Heyford Athletic	0-3	2-1	1-3	1-2	2-3	***I***	1-2	3-6	3-2	0-1	1-1	4-5	0-3	1-2
Kislingbury	3-2	1-2	5-3	3-2	1-1	3-1	***E***	2-0	2-1	3-2	3-0	4-3	2-3	2-2
Medbourne	1-2	2-0	8-3	1-1	2-2	1-1	1-2	***R***	3-2	6-2	2-1	2-2	0-2	6-2
Milton	0-4	1-1	2-2	1-8	0-1	2-0	1-3	2-1		0-2	1-1	0-1	1-1	2-4
Moulton	2-1	8-1	3-2	0-1	1-0	1-2	0-1	1-3	0-1		1-0	2-3	1-1	1-3
Queen Eleanor Gt Houghton	1-3	1-4	6-2	0-0	1-4	2-1	0-2	0-3	5-2	2-2	***D***	0-3	0-3	3-1
Roade	2-2	3-0	3-1	1-3	1-1	2-0	3-5	0-5	3-0	2-2	1-0	***I***	2-1	5-1
Weldon United	1-1	1-0	3-0	1-3	3-1	2-3	5-1	1-4	5-0	4-4	4-2	5-1	***V***	5-1
Whitefield Norpol	1-5	3-1	5-3	0-2	0-1	2-0	2-5	2-3	3-0	3-2	0-1	1-3	2-1	

Premier Division		P	W	D	L	F	A	Pts
Harborough Town		26	18	4	4	72	35	58
Kislingbury		26	18	3	5	65	46	57
Weldon United		26	16	4	6	67	33	52
Brixworth All Saints		26	15	6	5	67	32	51
Roade		26	15	4	7	67	52	49
Harpole		26	14	5	7	58	40	47
Medbourne		26	12	5	9	67	46	41
Moulton		26	9	5	12	48	49	32
Q. Eleanor Gt Houghton		26	6	6	14	41	58	24
Heyford Athletic		26	6	3	17	32	58	21
Corby Khalsa		26	5	6	15	34	62	21
Milton		26	4	5	17	27	66	17
Corby Pegasus		26	4	3	19	44	93	15
Whitefield Norpol	*-33*	26	9	3	14	48	67	-3

NORTHANTS COMB./ NORTHAMPTON TOWN LEAGUE CHAMPIONS CUP

Not contested in 2009-10

PREMIER DIVISION CUP

FIRST ROUND

Corby Pegasus 3 **Kislingbury** 1
(Corby Pegasus expelled)
Harborough Town 2 **Milton** 2 *aet* (4-5p)
Harpole 2 **Weldon United** 4
Medbourne 4 Whitefield Norpol 2
Moulton 2 Corby Khalsa 1
Roade 2 Heyford Athletic 1

QUARTER-FINALS

Medbourne 1 **Queen Eleanor Great Houghton** 3
Milton 4 Kislingbury 2
Moulton 2 Brixworth All Saints 2 *aet* (3-1p)
Roade 2 **Weldon United** 5

SEMI-FINALS

Moulton 0 **Queen Eleanor Great Houghton** 1
Weldon United 4 Milton 1

FINAL

(May 11th at Northampton Town)
Queen Eleanor Great Houghton 2 Weldon United 1

NORTHANTS COMBINATION PREMIER DIVISION CONSTITUTION 2010-11

BRIXWORTH ALL SAINTS .... St Davids Close, off Froxhill Crescent, Brixworth NN6 9EA 01604 880073
CORBY KHALSA .... Corby Rugby Club, Rockingham Road, Corby NN17 1AE.................... 01536 204466
CORBY PEGASUS.............. West Glebe South Pavilion, Cottingham Road, Corby NN17 1EL.................. 01536 402041
HARPOLE .... Playing Field, Larkhall Lane, Harpole NN7 4DP.. None
HEYFORD ATHLETIC .... Nether Heyford Playing Field, Nether Heyford NN7 3LL.. None
KISLINGBURY .... Playing Fields, Beech Lane, Kislingbury, Northampton NN7 4AL.................. 01604 831225
MEDBOURNE .... Medbourne Sports & Social Club, Hallaton Road, Medbourne LE16 8DR.................. None
MILTON .... Collingtree Road, Milton Malsor, Northampton NN7 3AU .... None
MOULTON......................... Brunting Road, Moulton, Northampton NN3 7QF 01604 492675
QUEEN ELEANOR GREAT HOUGHTON . Leys Lane, Great Houghton, Northampton NN4 7AL.................... 01908 542675
ROADE.............................. Connolly Way, Hyde Road, Roade NN7 2LU............................ 01604 862814
WELDON UNITED .... Corby Business Academy, Priors Hall Estate, Gretton Road, Corb. NN17 5EB.................. None
WELFORD VICTORIA .... Welford Sports Field, Newlands Road, Welford NN6 6HR.......................... None
WHITEFIELD NORPOL ...... Sports Ground, Wootton Hall Police HQ, Mereway, Northampton NN4 0JF .... None

IN: Welford Victoria (P)
OUT: Harborough Town (P - United Counties League Division One)

Division One		P	W	D	L	F	A	Pts
Welford Victoria		24	17	4	3	61	29	55
Corby Kingfisher Athletic	*+2*	24	15	3	6	55	24	50
James King Blisworth	*-1*	24	16	2	6	81	31	49
Ringstead Rangers		24	15	3	6	58	30	48
Kettering Nomads	*+2*	24	13	5	6	52	31	46
Wootton St George		24	11	3	10	49	41	36
Daventry Drayton Grange		24	10	3	11	50	59	33
Earls Barton United		24	8	7	9	38	36	31
Stanwick Rovers		24	8	2	14	36	59	26
Stanion United		24	7	3	14	40	67	24
Finedon Volta		24	6	4	14	40	59	22
Spratton	*+2*	24	5	3	16	33	66	20
Cold Ashby Rovers	*-14*	24	2	4	18	31	92	-4

DIVISION ONE CUP FINAL *(May 6th at N'ton Sileby Rgrs)*
James King Blisworth 2 Weldon Victoria 2 *aet* (5-4p)

Division Two		P	W	D	L	F	A	Pts
Corby Danesholme Vikings		26	20	3	3	96	42	63
Gretton	*-3*	26	19	3	4	103	39	57
W'boro. Old Grammarians		26	16	5	5	64	32	53
Wellingborough Ranelagh		26	15	5	6	74	37	50
Kettering Orchard Park		26	15	3	8	53	43	48
Clipston		26	13	6	7	60	50	45
Great Doddington		26	10	6	10	64	63	36
Burton United		26	10	4	12	63	77	34
Islip United	*+2*	26	7	7	12	62	81	30
Wollaston Victoria		26	8	4	14	55	67	28
Corby Strip Mills		26	8	4	14	42	74	28
Bective Wanderers	*-4*	26	5	5	16	27	68	16
Weedon		26	2	5	19	48	99	11
Ristee Towers		26	2	4	20	40	79	10

DIV. TWO CUP FINAL *(April 22nd at Harborough Town)*
Gretton 1 Burton United 0

Division Three		P	W	D	L	F	A	Pts
Corby Everards		22	17	3	2	97	32	54
Wellingborough Rising Sun		22	14	5	3	58	30	47
Corby Eagles	*+2*	22	13	5	4	84	44	46
Corby Locomotives		22	10	3	9	84	54	33
Kettering Ise Lodge	*-14*	22	12	9	1	46	21	31
Wilby	*+2*	22	9	2	11	67	78	31
Wellingborough WMC	*+2*	22	8	4	10	38	57	30
Wellingborough Saxons		22	8	2	12	53	56	26
Hillmorton		22	7	4	11	41	60	25
Wilbarston	*+4*	22	3	5	14	33	85	18
Dainite Sports	*+4*	22	3	4	15	33	80	17
Crick Athletic	*+2*	22	2	6	14	48	85	14

DIVISION THREE CUP FINAL
(April 20th at Wellingborough Town)
Wellingborough Saxons 2 Wilby 1

Division Four		P	W	D	L	F	A	Pts
Long Buckby Ravens	*+2*	24	19	2	3	99	34	61
Corby Talisman		24	15	3	6	88	61	48
West Haddon		24	15	2	7	71	47	47
Corby Kingswood	*+2*	24	14	2	8	63	43	46
AFC Wymington	*-8*	24	15	3	6	92	46	40
Kettering Park Rovers		24	12	1	11	77	62	37
CSV United		24	12	0	12	73	75	36
Walgrave Amber		24	10	2	12	68	64	32
Finedon Kennedys		24	9	2	13	42	68	29
Yardley United		24	8	2	14	57	73	26
FC Higham		24	8	2	14	36	59	26
Higham Dragons		24	7	3	14	48	81	24
Corby Hearth		24	0	0	24	24	125	0

DIV. FOUR CUP FINAL *(April 8th at Wellingborough T.)*
FC Higham 1 Walgrave 0

Reserve Premier Division		P	W	D	L	F	A	Pts
Weldon United Res.	*+2*	26	19	5	2	89	24	64
Harborough Town Res.		26	19	3	4	77	28	60
Whitefield Norpol Res.	*-4*	26	14	8	4	69	24	46
Roade Res.	*-4*	26	14	7	5	53	44	45
Harpole Res.		26	12	4	10	51	49	40
Kislingbury Res.		26	10	4	12	54	50	34
Moulton Res.		26	9	6	11	52	46	33
Corby Khalsa Res.		26	9	3	14	53	53	30
Kettering Nomads Res.		26	7	8	11	42	57	29
Northampton ON Chenecks A		26	8	4	14	34	58	28
Milton Res.		26	7	5	14	38	64	26
Gretton Res.		26	8	2	16	45	81	26
Bugbrooke St Michaels A	*-6*	26	9	1	16	53	84	22
Corby Pegasus Res.	*+2*	26	5	4	17	42	90	21

Reserve Division One		P	W	D	L	F	A	Pts
James King Blisworth Res.		26	21	2	3	134	23	65
Brixworth All Saints Res.		26	20	2	4	96	38	62
Kettering Orchard Pk Res.	*+2*	26	19	2	5	102	40	61
Medbourne Res.		26	19	1	6	82	40	58
Heyford Athletic Res.		26	14	4	8	68	49	46
Stanion United Res.		26	12	6	8	68	57	42
Wollaston Victoria Res.		26	12	4	10	69	68	40
Corby Locomotives Res.	*+8*	26	5	8	13	39	63	31
Weldon United A	*-2*	26	8	3	15	52	68	25
Wootton St George Res.	*-2*	26	7	4	15	39	57	23
Ringstead Rangers Res.		26	5	5	16	32	126	17
Queen Eleanor GH Res.		26	6	4	16	47	65	16
Finedon Volta Res.	*-5*	26	5	4	17	35	84	14
Bugbrooke St Michaels B	*-4*	26	3	3	20	34	119	8

Reserve Division Two		P	W	D	L	F	A	Pts
Earls Barton United Res.		20	18	0	2	75	21	54
Harpole A		20	13	1	6	70	35	40
Weedon Res.		20	11	5	4	76	42	38
Wellingborough OG Res.		20	10	4	6	55	35	34
Islip United Res.	*-3*	20	10	2	8	62	43	29
Dav. Drayton Grange Res.	*-4*	20	9	3	8	44	48	26
Spratton Res.		20	7	4	9	52	45	25
Crick Athletic Res.		20	8	1	11	51	62	25
Stanwick Rovers Res.	*+2*	20	6	5	9	37	48	25
Dainite Sports Res.		20	2	2	16	26	93	8
Wilby Res.		20	2	1	17	34	110	7

RESERVE PREMIER DIVISION CUP FINAL
(April 29th at Northampton Sileby Rangers)
Harborough Town Res. 1 Bugbrooke St Michaels A 0

RESERVE DIVISION ONE CUP FINAL
(April 13th at Wellingborough Town)
Brixworth All Saints Res. 1
James King Blisworth Res. 0

RESERVE DIVISION TWO CUP FINAL
(April 27th at Wellingborough Town)
Weedon Res. 3
Wellingborough Old Grammarians Res. 0

NORTHERN ALLIANCE

northernfootballalliance.org.uk

Sponsored: Pin Point Recruitment

Founded: 1890

Recent champions:
2005: Shankhouse
2006: Team Northumbria
2007: Harraby Catholic Club
2008: Walker Central
2009: Walker Central

	Alnwick T.	Ashington C.	Blyth Town	Carlisle City	Cramlington	Harraby CC	Heaton Stan.	Heddon	Killingworth	Murton	Newc. Univ.	Ponteland	Seaton Del.	Shankhouse	Stocksfield	Walker Cent.	Wark
Alnwick Town	***P***	0-1	3-1	2-0	4-1	0-2	1-3	3-1	2-2	10-1	4-1	0-3	2-2	2-2	1-1	0-1	2-0
Ashington Colliers	3-1	***R***	1-0	1-1	1-2	2-0	1-1	0-2	4-1	1-1	3-2	2-1	0-2	0-0	1-1	0-0	0-4
Blyth Town	2-1	0-2	***E***	2-2	1-0	4-2	2-4	2-1	3-1	4-2	1-1	1-0	1-2	2-1	1-2	3-1	0-3
Carlisle City	3-1	3-2	0-3	***M***	4-2	1-3	1-1	0-2	1-1	0-4	2-2	2-1	2-0	1-1	4-3	1-2	3-2
Cramlington Town	2-1	2-1	0-0	0-0	***I***	2-2	2-2	3-2	0-1	0-4	1-0	3-4	3-4	1-1	3-3	0-3	0-5
Harraby Catholic Club	2-1	1-1	2-1	0-1	9-0	***E***	5-0	3-2	2-1	4-1	3-0	0-1	3-0	1-0	4-1	4-0	1-3
Heaton Stannington	3-2	6-0	0-3	4-0	1-3	2-2	***R***	4-1	3-3	7-2	1-0	2-2	2-1	3-3	4-0	1-2	3-2
Heddon	1-2	1-3	0-2	0-1	2-2	2-3	3-0		1-2	4-1	3-3	0-1	4-4	1-2	2-3	1-5	2-1
Killingworth Sporting	0-2	2-0	2-1	1-1	0-0	1-4	2-1	2-4		3-2	4-1	1-0	1-0	1-1	2-0	2-2	0-2
Murton	2-1	1-3	0-2	0-3	0-2	1-0	1-1	2-0	1-1	***D***	2-0	4-0	4-1	2-0	1-0	0-0	1-3
Newcastle University	4-3	2-0	1-4	1-1	1-2	0-6	1-3	0-0	0-2	0-0	***I***	4-2	3-6	2-5	0-1	1-3	0-5
Ponteland United	3-3	0-2	3-2	4-2	1-0	1-2	0-2	3-2	2-0	1-0	0-0	***V***	1-0	1-3	0-2	1-6	1-1
Seaton Delaval Amateurs	2-3	0-1	2-2	2-0	4-0	1-0	5-4	1-1	2-3	1-3	5-0	2-2	***I***	5-0	1-2	3-2	1-2
Shankhouse	3-5	1-2	3-1	1-1	3-1	1-2	2-1	3-2	2-3	2-6	3-1	1-4	3-1	***S***	0-1	2-4	3-3
Stocksfield	0-3	0-4	1-4	1-3	1-1	0-3	2-3	4-3	0-4	1-1	3-2	0-4	5-4	1-4	***I***	0-4	0-5
Walker Central	2-2	2-4	1-2	3-1	3-0	1-1	1-0	1-1	3-0	5-0	1-2	0-3	3-0	4-1	1-1	***O***	1-1
Wark	3-1	2-2	5-5	1-1	2-5	4-1	1-2	6-2	3-2	1-3	4-4	1-1	6-2	5-2	2-0	2-1	***N***

Premier Division		P	W	D	L	F	A	Pts
Harraby Catholic Club		32	20	4	8	77	36	64
Wark		32	17	8	7	90	52	59
Walker Central		32	16	8	8	68	40	56
Blyth Town		32	16	5	11	62	49	53
Ashington Colliers		32	15	8	9	48	42	53
Killingworth Sporting		32	14	8	10	51	50	50
Heaton Stannington	*-4*	32	15	8	9	74	56	49
Ponteland United		32	14	6	12	51	50	48
Murton		32	13	6	13	53	61	45
Carlisle City		32	11	11	10	46	53	44
Alnwick Town		32	12	6	14	68	57	42
Seaton Delaval Amateurs		32	11	5	16	66	68	38
Shankhouse		32	10	8	14	59	70	38
Stocksfield		32	9	6	17	40	79	33
Cramlington Town	*-4*	32	9	9	14	43	70	32
Heddon		32	6	6	20	53	72	24
Newcastle University		32	4	8	20	39	83	20

KICKS LEISURE CHALLENGE CUP

PRELIMINARY ROUND

Alnwick Town 7 Newcastle University 0

FIRST ROUND

Ashington Colliers 5 Stocksfield 1
Carlisle City 2 Alnwick Town 1 *aet (at Alnwick T.)*
Heaton Stannington 1 **Blyth Town** 2
Killingworth Sporting 0 **Seaton Delaval Amateurs** 2
Murton 0 **Harraby Catholic Club** 5
Shankhouse 3 Cramlington Town 1 *aet*
Walker Central 2 **Heddon** 3
Wark 2 **Ponteland United** 3

QUARTER-FINALS

Blyth Town 2 Ashington Colliers 1
Carlisle City 1 Harraby Catholic Club 0
Ponteland United 4 Seaton Delaval Amateurs 1 *aet*
Shankhouse 1 Heddon 0

SEMI-FINALS

Blyth Town 0 **Ponteland United** 2
Shankhouse 3 Carlisle City 1

FINAL

(May 17th at Killingworth Sporting)
Ponteland United 3 Shankhouse 1 *aet*

NORTHERN ALLIANCE PREMIER DIVISION CONSTITUTION 2010-11

ALNWICK TOWN .... St James's Park, Weavers Way, Alnwick NE66 1BG........................ 01665 603162
ASHINGTON COLLIERS.............. Hirst Welfare, Alexandra Road, Ashington NE63 9HF 07517 764653
BLYTH TOWN........................ South Newsham Playing Fields, Blyth NE24 3PP .... None
CARLISLE CITY................. Sheepmount Sports Complex, Sheepmount, Carlisle CA3 8XL.................... 01228 625599
CRAMLINGTON TOWN .... Sporting Club of Cramlington, Highburn, Cramlington NE23 6YB................. 01670 591970
GATESHEAD RUTHERFORD Farnacres, Beggarswood Pk, Coach Lane, Lobley Hill, Gateshead NE11 8HJ................ None
HARRABY CATHOLIC CLUB .... Harraby Community Centre, Edgehill Road, Carlisle CA1 3SL .... None
HEATON STANNINGTON ... Grounsell Park, Newton Road, High Heaton, Newcastle-upon-Tyne NE7 7HP .... None
KILLINGWORTH SPORTING... Amberley Park, Garth 21, Killingworth. Newcastle upon Tyne NE12 6SE .... None
MURTON........................ Recreation Park, Church Lane, Murton, Seaham SR7 9RD .... None
PERCY MAIN AMATEURS ...... Purvis Park, St John's Green, Percy Main, North Shields NE29 6HE................ 0191 257 4831
PONTELAND UNITED . The Leisure Centre Ground, Callerton Lane, Ponteland, Newcastle-upon-Tyne NE20 9EG........ 01661 825441
SEATON DELAVAL AMATEURS...... Wheatridge Park, Seaton Delaval, Whitley Bay NE25 0QH .... None
SHANKHOUSE................ Northburn Sports Complex, Crawhall Lane, Cramlington NE23 3YP.............. 01670 714154
STOCKSFIELD.................. Stocksfield Sports Ground, Main Road, Stocksfield NE43 7NN None0
WALKER CENTRAL .... Monkchester Green, Walker, Newcastle-upon-Tyne NE6 5LJ..................... 0191 265 7270
WARK.............................. Wark Sports Club, Wark, Hexham NE48 3NP 01434 230259

IN: Gateshead Rutherford (P), Percy Main Amateurs (P)
OUT: Heddon (R), Newcastle University (R)

KICKS LEISURE STAN SEYMOUR LEAGUE CUP

FIRST ROUND

Carlisle City 6 Alnwick Town 1
Chopwell OC 2 Northbank Carlisle 0
Cramlington Blue Star 1 **Peterlee T.** 7
G'hd Rutherford 1 **Hebburn Reyrolle** 4
Gosf'th Bohemians 4 Cramlington T. 2
Harraby CC 12 Willington Quay Saints 0
Heaton Stannington 2 Killingworth 0
Hexham 0 **Forest Hall** 2
Newcastle BT 3 Ashington Colliers 1
Newcastle Chemfica 6 Amble 2
Newcastle EE 1 **Seaton Delaval** 5
Newcastle University 3 Seaton Burn 1
Percy Main Amateurs 1 Amble United 0
South Shields Utd 2 **Wallsend Town** 3
Stobswood Welfare 2 Stocksfield 1
Whitley Bay A 2 Cullercoats 1
Whitley Bay Town 0 **Wallsend BC** 3

SECOND ROUND

Cullercoats CP 6 Newcastle BT 1
Forest Hall 0 **Chopwell Officials Club** 2
Gosforth Bohemians 2 Wideopen 0
Harraby CC 6 Berwick United 0
Murton 0 **Blyth Town** 4
Newcastle Chemfica 2 Wallsend T. 1
Newcastle Univ. 5 Morpeth SC 2
North Shields Athletic 1 **Ponteland** 3
Percy Main Amateurs 1 **Heddon** 2
Peterlee Town 1 **Hebburn Reyrolle** 4
Swalwell 0 **Stobswood Welfare** 6
Walker Central 0 **Heaton Stannington** 3
Wallington 3 Tynemouth United 0
Wallsend Boys Club 2 Seaton Delaval Amateurs 1
Wark 4 Carlisle City 1
Whitley Bay A 0 **Shankhouse** 1

THIRD ROUND

Chopwell OC 1 **Blyth T.** 3 *(at Blyth T.)*
Cullercoats Custom Planet 1 **Heddon** 2
Hebburn Reyrolle 5 Wallsend BC1
Newcastle Chemfica 1 **Ponteland** 3
Newcastle University 2 Wallington 1
Shankhouse 3 **Gosforth Bohemians** 4
Stobswood 0 **Heaton Stannington** 3
Wark 1 **Harraby Catholic Club** 2

QUARTER-FINALS

Blyth Town 3 **Harraby Catholic Club** 4
Gosforth Bohemians 1 **Ponteland** 3
Heaton Stan'gton 2 **Hebburn Reyrolle** 3
Newcastle University 0 **Heddon** 3

SEMI-FINALS

Heddon 1 Harraby Catholic Club 0
Ponteland United 1 **Hebburn Reyrolle** 3

FINAL *(May 3rd at Heaton Stann.)*
Heddon 1 **Hebburn Reyrolle** 3

Division One		P	W	D	L	F	A	Pts
Gateshead Rutherford		30	22	3	5	76	43	69
Percy Main Amateurs		30	21	5	4	69	35	68
Amble United		30	20	5	5	73	30	65
Whitley Bay A		30	19	4	7	100	50	61
Morpeth Sporting Club		30	18	1	11	71	64	55
Hebburn Reyrolle		30	15	6	9	68	54	51
South Shields United		30	15	3	12	63	49	48
Cullercoats		30	14	3	13	75	55	45
Gosforth Bohemians		30	13	4	13	56	48	43
Peterlee Town		30	13	4	13	66	65	43
Chopwell Officials C.		30	10	3	17	51	71	33
Berwick United		30	8	3	19	45	96	27
Wallington	*-6*	30	7	7	16	44	63	22
Newcastle East End	*-3*	30	7	3	20	50	88	21
Northbank Carlisle		30	6	1	23	35	74	19
Seaton Burn	*-3*	30	2	5	23	31	88	8

PIN POINT PERSONNEL COMBINATION CUP

FIRST ROUND

Cullercoats 3 Chopwell 1
Gatesh'd R'fd 2 **Percy Main** 3
Hebburn Reyrolle 2 Peterlee Town 1
Morpeth SC 2 **Wallington** 5
Newcastle East End 2 **Berwick United** 3 *aet*
Northbank Carlisle 0 **Whitley Bay A** 4
Seaton Burn 0 **Amble Utd** 2
South Shields United 2 Gosforth Bohemians 0

QUARTER-FINALS

Berwick United 2 South Shields United 1
Cullercoats 1 **Whitley Bay A** 3
Hebburn R. 1 Amble Utd 0 *aet*
Percy Main 4 Wallington 1 aet

SEMI-FINALS

Hebburn Reyrolle 3 Whitley Bay A 1 *aet*
Percy Main 3 Berwick United 1

FINAL *(May 29th at Ponteland)*
Percy Main Amateurs 1 Hebburn Reyrolle 0

	Amb	Ber	Cho	Cull	Gate	Gos	Heb	Mor	New	Nort	Perc	Pete	Seat	Sou	Wall	Whit
Amble United		6-0	5-1	1-5	2-0	2-2	1-0	0-3	4-0	6-0	5-0	2-0	4-0	2-0	1-1	1-0
Berwick United	0-4		2-1	0-4	1-4	1-2	3-3	0-5	4-2	3-1	1-3	2-5	2-1	4-3	1-1	0-4
Chopwell Officials Club	1-3	3-4	***D***	4-0	0-1	2-0	1-2	2-0	1-0	2-1	2-2	1-3	3-0	1-3	1-2	2-1
Cullercoats	0-2	2-0	5-1	***I***	0-3	1-0	3-3	3-4	3-1	3-1	1-1	1-2	6-0	2-3	5-3	2-3
Gateshead Rutherford	4-1	7-0	3-2	3-2	***V***	2-1	2-4	2-1	1-0	1-0	0-1	3-2	1-1	1-1	4-3	5-1
Gosforth Bohemians	0-0	1-2	3-1	2-1	1-2	***I***	4-1	6-0	2-1	2-1	0-1	1-3	6-0	3-1	3-2	1-4
Hebburn Reyrolle	2-2	5-1	4-0	5-2	2-2	2-0	***S***	1-2	2-5	3-0	2-3	3-0	4-0	0-6	1-1	0-2
Morpeth Sporting Club	0-1	2-1	6-2	3-3	2-3	3-2	1-3	***I***	4-3	2-1	2-3	1-6	4-1	2-0	0-2	2-4
Newcastle East End	1-5	3-1	2-1	0-3	1-4	2-2	1-2	4-0	***O***	0-4	0-2	0-2	4-2	2-6	2-1	2-4
Northbank Carlisle	1-2	3-2	2-5	3-2	2-3	0-1	3-4	0-2	0-3	***N***	1-5	3-3	2-0	1-2	1-3	0-4
Percy Main Amateurs	3-0	4-1	2-1	2-0	2-1	1-1	2-0	2-3	5-1	2-0		4-4	1-2	2-0	2-0	4-2
Peterlee Town	2-0	1-3	1-2	0-4	2-4	3-4	1-2	0-3	4-1	5-1	2-4	***O***	5-2	1-3	4-1	2-2
Seaton Burn	0-3	3-3	3-3	1-4	1-2	5-1	0-2	2-3	3-3	0-1	1-3	0-1	***N***	1-2	1-1	0-3
South Shields United	1-3	4-2	2-2	0-2	2-3	1-0	1-3	3-4	3-1	2-0	0-2	0-0	5-1	***E***	3-0	1-0
Wallington	0-2	2-1	1-2	0-5	1-3	3-2	2-0	1-2	2-2	0-1	1-1	1-2	4-0	1-3		2-6
Whitley Bay A	3-3	7-0	8-1	4-1	4-2	0-3	3-3	3-5	11-3	2-1	1-0	7-0	2-0	3-2	2-2	

NORTHERN ALLIANCE DIVISION ONE CONSTITUTION 2010-11

AMBLE UNITED . . . . Running Track Pitch, Coquet High School, Acklington Road , Amble NE65 0NG 01665 710636
BERWICK UNITED ULTRAS . Swan Centre for Leisure, Northumberland Rd, Berwick-on-Tweed TD15 2AS 01289 330603
CHOPWELL OFFICIALS CLUB. . . . . . . Welfare Park, Chopwell, Newcastle-upon-Tyne NE17 7BZ . . . . None
CULLERCOATS. . . . . Links Avenue, Farringdon Road, Cullercoats NE30 3EY . . . . None
FOREST HALL . . . . Palmersville Community Centre, Great Lime Road, Forest Hall NE12 9HW . . . . None
GOSFORTH BOHEMIANS . . . . Benson Park, Gosforth, Newcastle-upon-Tyne . . . . None
HEBBURN REYROLLE . . . . Hebburn Sports Ground, 16 South Drive, Hebburn NE31 1UN 0191 483 5101
HEDDON . . . . Bullockstead Sports Complex, Ponteland Road, Kenton Bank Foot, Newcastle-upon-Tyne NE13 8AH . . . 0191 271 1153
MORPETH SPORTING CLUB . . . Morpeth Town FC, Craik Park, Morpeth Common, Morpeth NE61 2YX. 01670 513785
NEWCASTLE EAST END . . . . . . Millers Dene Sports Ground, Fossway, Newcastle-upon-Tyne NE6 4YA . . . . None
NEWCASTLE UNIVERSITY . . . . . Cochrane Park, Etherstone Avenue, Newcastle-upon-Tyne NE7 7JX . . . . None
NORTH SHIELDS ATHLETIC . . . . . Collingwood View PF, West Percy Road, North Shields NE29 7RQ . . . . None
PETERLEE TOWN . . . . Eden Lane Playing Fields, Peterlee SR8 5DS. 0191 586 3004
SOUTH SHIELDS UNITED. . . . . The Dell, Quarry Lane, South Shields NE34 7NL . . . . None
STOBSWOOD WELFARE. . . . . Stobswood Welfare Ground, Stobswood, Morpeth NE61 3AZ . . . . None
WALLINGTON . . . . Oakford Park, Scots Gap, Morpeth NE61 4EJ . . . . None
WHITLEY BAY A . . . . Hillheads Park, Rink Way, off Hillheads Road, Whitley Bay NE25 8HR 0191 291 3637

IN: Forest Hall (P), Heddon (R), Newcastle University (R), North Shields Athletic (P), Stobswood Welfare (P)
OUT: Gateshead Rutherford (P), Northbank Carlisle (R), Percy Main Amateurs (P), Seaton Burn (R)
Berwick United become Berwick United Ultras

Division Two		P	W	D	L	F	A	Pts
North Shields Athletic		30	21	6	3	81	33	69
Stobswood Welfare		30	20	4	6	84	51	64
Forest Hall		30	15	10	5	70	38	55
Amble		30	16	7	7	69	38	55
Wallsend Town		30	16	4	10	72	42	52
Wideopen & District		30	15	4	11	64	59	49
Newcastle Chemfica	*-3*	30	16	0	14	66	57	45
Hexham		30	10	10	10	51	43	40
Swalwell		30	11	7	12	63	61	40
Wallsend Boys Club	*-6*	30	13	5	12	54	51	38
Tynemouth United		30	12	2	16	67	86	38
Newcastle British Telecom		30	9	6	15	52	74	33
Willington Quay Saints		30	6	6	18	39	87	24
Cullercoats C. Planet	*-3*	30	7	3	20	54	76	21
Cramlington Blue Star		30	6	3	21	42	92	21
Whitley Bay Town	*-6*	30	6	5	19	48	88	17

PIN POINT PERSONNEL AMATEUR CUP

FIRST ROUND

Amble 6 Hexham 1
Cullercoats Custom Planet 2 Cramlington BS 1 *aet*
Forest Hall 3 Whitley Bay Town 1
Newcastle British Telecom 2 Swalwell 0
Wallsend Boys Club 1 **North Shields Athletic** 2
Wallsend Town 0 **Stobswood Welfare** 2
Wideopen & District 4 Tynemouth United 0
Willington Quay Saints 1 **Newcastle Chemfica** 3 *aet*

QUARTER-FINALS

Amble 3 Cullercoats Custom Planet 0
Forest Hall 2 **Stobswood Welfare** 3
Newcastle Chemfica 4 Newcastle British Telecom 0
North Shields Athletic 3 Wideopen & District 1

SEMI-FINALS

Newcastle Chemfica 1 **North Shields Athletic** 4
Stobswood Welfare 3 Amble 2

FINAL *(May 6th at Swalwell)*

North Shields Athletic 0 **Stobswood Welfare** 2

	Ambl	Cram	Cull	For	Hexh	NBT	NC	North	Stob	Swal	Tyne	WBC	WallT	Whit	Wide	Will
Amble		7-0	4-1	1-0	2-1	1-5	4-2	3-0	1-2	3-3	2-2	1-0	0-1	1-2	2-2	4-0
Cramlington Blue Star	1-4		1-3	1-2	1-1	1-1	0-2	0-3	2-7	1-5	2-8	0-4	1-2	3-1	1-2	3-2
Cullercoats Custom P.	1-2	8-2	***D***	0-3	1-3	1-1	0-3	0-1	2-3	4-2	2-3	2-3	2-1	3-3	2-3	2-1
Forest Hall	2-2	0-1	5-1	***I***	2-1	4-1	6-4	0-0	2-1	3-3	5-0	2-2	3-1	3-2	2-1	1-1
Hexham	0-0	2-1	4-0	1-1	***V***	3-1	1-0	1-1	1-1	1-1	2-0	0-4	2-1	6-1	0-0	4-1
Newcastle British Tel.	4-0	2-2	2-6	0-4	2-2	***I***	3-1	2-2	1-3	1-1	3-1	3-2	0-10	3-1	2-4	3-2
Newcastle Chemfica	1-0	3-1	4-0	2-0	2-1	3-0	***S***	1-0	3-1	2-5	3-2	1-5	0-4	5-1	1-2	4-1
North Shields Athletic	2-1	4-2	3-2	1-1	3-1	3-2	2-1	***I***	3-1	2-1	1-1	1-0	4-1	6-1	3-0	10-0
Stobswood Welfare	1-3	3-1	5-4	2-0	4-2	1-0	0-6	5-2	***O***	6-3	0-5	2-1	1-1	2-2	8-0	4-0
Swalwell	1-4	1-0	3-1	3-3	2-2	1-0	3-2	0-1	1-3	***N***	4-1	1-3	0-2	0-3	0-1	1-1
Tynemouth United	1-2	2-5	0-1	2-1	5-3	3-1	1-3	1-9	0-7	4-2		0-4	5-1	3-2	4-1	3-2
Wallsend Boys Club	2-2	2-3	2-1	0-3	0-0	1-3	1-0	2-3	1-3	0-5	4-3	***T***	0-3	1-1	3-1	2-0
Wallsend Town	0-1	4-1	4-1	0-0	1-0	1-2	2-4	1-1	1-2	4-1	2-1	4-0	***W***	2-3	2-1	5-1
Whitley Bay Town	1-7	0-4	2-2	1-6	2-0	3-0	4-2	0-2	1-2	1-4	2-4	1-2	2-6	***O***	1-2	2-2
Wideopen & District	0-0	4-0	2-1	3-3	3-2	4-3	3-1	2-3	0-2	1-2	6-1	1-2	2-4	3-1		4-3
Willington Quay Saints	0-5	3-1	1-0	0-3	0-4	3-1	4-0	0-5	2-2	1-4	4-1	1-1	1-1	2-1	0-6	

NORTHERN ALLIANCE DIVISION TWO CONSTITUTION 2010-11

AMBLE . . . . Amble Welfare Ground, Acklington Road, Amble NE65 0NG. . . . . None
CRAMLINGTON UNITED Shankhouse FC, Northburn Sports Complex, Crawhall Lane, Cramlington NE23 3YP 01670 714154
CULLERCOATS CUSTOM PLANET. . Burradon Welfare Ground, Front Street, Burradon NE23 7NG . . . . None
HEXHAM . . . . Wentworth Leisure Centre, Wentworth Park, Hexham NE46 3PD. 01434 607080
NEWCASTLE BRITISH TELECOM . . . . Dudley Recreation Ground, Dudley NE23 7HS . . . . None
NEWCASTLE CHEMFICA . . . . Heaton Sports Ground, Heaton, Newcastle-upon-Tyne NE6 5NY . . . . None
NORTHBANK CARLISLE. . . . . Sheepmount Sports Complex, Sheepmount, Carlisle CA3 8XL. 01228 625599
RED HOUSE FARM . . . . Kingston Park Road, Newcastle-upon-Tyne NE3 2HY. 0191 285 2181
SEATON BURN . . . . Seaton Burn Welfare, Seaton Burn, Newcastle-upon-Tyne . . . . None
SIMONSIDE SOCIAL CLUB . . . . Boldon Community Association, New Road, Boldon Colliery NE35 9DS. . . . 0191 536 4180(Cricket Club)
SWALWELL . . . . Spa-Well Road, Derwenthaugh, Blaydon-on-Tyne NE21 6JA. . . . . None
TYNEMOUTH UNITED. . Bullockstead Sports Complex, Ponteland Rd, Kenton Bank Foot, Newcastle NE13 8AH 0191 271 1153
WALLSEND BOYS CLUB . . . . St Peter's Road, Wallsend NE28 7LQ. . . . . None
WALLSEND TOWN . . . . Langdale School Ground, Mitford Gardens, Wallsend NE28 0HG . . . . None
WHITLEY BAY TOWN. . . . . Burradon Welfare Ground, Front Street, Burradon NE23 7NG . . . . None
WIDEOPEN & DISTRICT . . . . Lockey Park, Great North Road, Wideopen, Newcastle-upon-Tyne NE13 6LN . . . . None
WILLINGTON QUAY SAINTS. . . . Wallsend Rising Sun Ground, King's North Road, Wallsend NE28 9JJ . . . . None

IN: Northbank Carlisle (R), Seaton Burn (R), Red House Farm (P - Youth football), Simonside Social Club (P - Durham Alliance)
OUT: Forest Hall (P), North Shields Athletic (P), Stobswood Welfare (P)
Cramlington Blue Star become Cramlington United

CHARITY CUP

(League Cup First Round losers)

PRELIMINARY ROUND

Amble United 4 Cramlington Blue Star 2 *aet*

FIRST ROUND

Amble United v Ashington Colliers
Cramlington Town 0 **Cullercoats** 7
Gateshead Rutherford 1 **Northbank Carlisle** 3 *aet*
Killingworth Sporting v Amble
Newcastle East End v Alnwick Town
Seaton Burn v Stockfield
South Shields United 0 **Hexham** 1
Whitley Bay Town 8 Willington Quay Saints 4

Competition abandoned due to inclement weather

OXFORDSHIRE SENIOR LEAGUE

www.football.mitoo.co.uk/News.cfm?LeagueCode=OSL2010

Sponsored by:
No sponsor

Founded: N/K

Recent champions:
2005: Berinsfield CA
2006: Oxford University Press
2007: Garsington
2008: Rover Cowley
2009: Garsington

	Adder	BCS	Blet	Chad	Enst	Eynsh	Frit	Gars	Hors	Kenn	Marst	OUP	Rover	Stone
Adderbury Park		5-1	1-0	4-0	3-0	2-1	n/a	2-2	1-0	1-1	1-0	3-2	4-3	0-0
BCS Bardwell	n/a	***P***	0-3	0-0	n/a	0-3	n/a	0-5	n/a	n/a	2-1	2-3	0-9	n/a
Bletchington	3-2	1-0	***R***	W-L	3-0	2-0	0-1	1-5	3-2	4-1	0-4	4-1	1-1	2-1
Chadlington	3-4	5-1	2-7	***E***	1-3	0-2	1-2	0-11	2-2	2-0	3-5	0-1	1-2	0-3
Enstone Sports	2-5	3-2	1-2	1-1	***M***	0-2	4-1	0-6	0-0	2-2	0-1	0-0	2-2	0-1
Eynsham Association	0-8	n/a	2-5	1-0	5-0	***I***	n/a	0-5	1-5	1-3	2-1	0-2	0-4	0-3
Fritwell	n/a	1-0	1-1	n/a	3-3	n/a	***E***	n/a	1-4	2-1	0-2	4-1	2-0	3-1
Garsington	1-3	W-L	4-0	6-0	5-0	8-2	n/a	***R***	1-1	3-0	4-1	2-0	1-2	5-0
Horspath	1-0	n/a	3-3	7-1	3-1	1-2	1-1	0-2		1-3	1-1	7-0	2-3	2-1
Kennington United	0-1	4-0	2-1	5-0	1-1	1-2	3-2	2-2	0-4		2-0	0-1	1-7	2-0
Marston Saints	0-1	6-1	1-4	3-2	1-2	3-3	3-1	1-3	1-2	1-0	***D***	3-2	4-4	1-0
Oxford University Press	0-3	3-4	1-2	3-5	1-2	1-2	n/a	1-3	2-2	0-2	1-2	***I***	1-5	0-2
Rover Cowley	1-2	4-0	2-0	W-L	3-0	5-0	n/a	2-2	6-1	1-1	3-1	4-0	***V***	5-0
Stonesfield Sports	1-2	n/a	1-4	7-1	0-2	0-2	1-1	1-4	2-1	2-2	3-3	3-2	2-6	

Premier Division	P	W	D	L	F	A	Pts
Adderbury Park	22	17	3	2	53	21	54
Garsington	22	16	4	2	85	19	52
Rover Cowley	22	15	5	2	71	26	50
Bletchington	22	14	2	6	51	37	44
Horspath	22	8	6	8	48	36	30
Marston Saints	22	8	4	10	38	43	28
Eynsham Association	22	9	1	12	30	59	28
Kennington United	22	7	6	9	31	37	27
Stonesfield Sports	22	7	3	12	33	46	24
Enstone Sports	22	4	6	12	19	48	18
Oxford University Press	22	3	2	17	22	56	11
Chadlington	22	2	2	18	24	77	8

BCS Bardwell, Fritwell - records expunged

PRESIDENT'S CUP

FIRST ROUND
Adderbury Park 1 **Kennington United** 2
Broughton & N. Newington 5 Middleton Cheney 3
Chadlington 3 Oakley 1
Enstone Sports 5 Mansfield Road 4
Freeland 1 **Bletchington** 2
Hinksey 4 Stonesfield Sports 1
Marston Saints 0 **Garsington** 2
North Oxford 0 **Rover Cowley** 10
Oxford University Press 1 **Horspath** 3
Slade Farm United 5 Kidlington Old Boys 2
Yarnton 1 Charlton United 0

SECOND ROUND
Enstone Sports 0 **Bletchington** 2
Eynsham Association 7 Long Crendon 0
Fritwell 5 Watlington Town 0
Garsington 3 Slade Farm United 1
Hinksey 6 Chadlington 1
Horspath 1 BCS Bardwell 0
Rover Cowley 5 Broughton & North Newington 1
Yarnton 2 **Kennington United** 5

QUARTER-FINALS
Garsington 1 Bletchington 0
Hinksey 2 Fritwell 1
Horspath 2 Kennington United 1 *aet*
Rover Cowley 1 Eynsham Association 0

SEMI-FINALS
Hinksey 5 Rover Cowley 2 *aet*
Horspath 0 **Garsington** 1

FINAL
(May 3rd at Kidlington)
Garsington 4 Hinksey 3 *aet*

BEN TURNER CUP

(President's Cup First Round losers)

FIRST ROUND
Adderbury Pk 3 Freeland 1
Marston Sts 4 Watlington 1
Nth Oxford 0 **Mansfield Rd** 1
Oakley Utd 2 **Stonesfield** 3
Oxford U. Press 1 Charlton Utd 4 *(Charlton Utd expelled)*

QUARTER-FINALS
Kidlington OB 0 **Marston** 2
L. Crendon 0 **Mansfield Rd** 6
M. Cheney 1 **Stonesfield** 2
OUP 0 **Adderbury Park** 1

SEMI-FINALS
Mansfield Rd 1 **Stonesfield Spts** 2 *(at Iffley Rd Spts Cte)*
Marston 0 **Adderbury Park** 2

FINAL
(April 5th at Oxford UP)
Adderbury Park 2
Stonesfield Sports 1

OXFORDSHIRE SENIOR LEAGUE PREMIER DIVISION CONSTITUTION 2010-11

ADDERBURY PARK ...... Lucy Plackett Playing Field, Round Close Road, Adderbury, Banbury OX17 3EE .... None
BLETCHINGTON .... Rover Cowley Sports Ground, Romanway, Cowley, Oxford OX4 6NL .... None
ENSTONE SPORTS .... Charlbury Road, Enstone OX2 6UT 01608 677823
EYNSHAM ASSOCIATION .... Oxford Road, Eynsham, Witney OX29 4DA .... None
FREELAND .... The Simon Hole Memorial Ground, Wroslyn Road, Freeland, Witney OX29 8HL .... None
GARSINGTON .... Garsington Sports Club, Denton Lane, Garsington, Oxford OX44 9EL 01865 361720
HINKSEY .... Brasenose College Spts Ground, Abingdon Road, Oxford OX1 4PN 01865 243478
HORSPATH .... Brookes University, Wheatley, Oxford OX4 6LB .... None
KENNINGTON UNITED .... Playfield Road, Kennington, Oxford OX1 5RS .... None
MANSFIELD ROAD .... The University Club, Mansfield Road, Oxford OX1 3SZ 01865 271044
MARSTON SAINTS .... Boults Lane, Old Marston, Oxford OX3 0PW 01865 203970
OXFORD UNIVERSITY PRESS .... Jordan Hill, Banbury Road, Oxford OX2 8EF .... None
ROVER COWLEY .... Rover Cowley Football Ground, Romanway, Cowley, Oxford OX4 6NL .... None
STONESFIELD SPORTS ...... Stonesfield Playing Field, Field Close, Longmore, Stonesfield OX29 8HA .... None

N: Freeland (P), Hinksey (P), Mansfield Road (P)
OUT: BCS Bardwell (WS), Chadlington (R), Fritwell (WS)

CLARENDON CUP FINAL

FINAL

(May 3rd at Kidlington)

Bletchington Res. 1 Garsington Res. 0

IVOR GUBBINS CUP FINAL

FINAL

(April 5th at Oxford University Press)

Fritwell Res. 2 Eynsham Association Res. 1

Division One	P	W	D	L	F	A	Pts
Hinksey	**26**	**23**	**1**	**2**	**103**	**30**	**70**
Freeland	**26**	**19**	**5**	**2**	**86**	**31**	**62**
Mansfield Road	**26**	**18**	**2**	**6**	**82**	**35**	**56**
Broughton & North N'ton	**26**	**16**	**3**	**7**	**77**	**37**	**51**
Slade Farm United	**26**	**12**	**7**	**7**	**49**	**39**	**43**
Kidlington Old Boys	**26**	**12**	**6**	**8**	**59**	**49**	**42**
Charlton United	**26**	**11**	**5**	**10**	**48**	**52**	**38**
Yarnton	**26**	**10**	**4**	**12**	**55**	**53**	**34**
Oakley United	**26**	**8**	**5**	**13**	**47**	**48**	**29**
Middleton Cheney	**26**	**7**	**2**	**17**	**41**	**79**	**23**
Watlington Town	**26**	**5**	**4**	**17**	**37**	**79**	**19**
Eynsham Association Res.	**26**	**5**	**3**	**18**	**41**	**92**	**18**
North Oxford	**26**	**5**	**3**	**18**	**35**	**86**	**18**
Garsington Res.	**26**	**4**	**4**	**18**	**28**	**78**	**16**

Division Two	P	W	D	L	F	A	Pt
Bletchingdon Res.	16	12	2	2	47	18	38
Adderbury Park Res.	16	12	1	3	58	26	37
Horspath Res.	16	10	1	5	42	21	31
Freeland Res.	16	9	2	5	42	24	29
Marston Saints Res.	16	9	1	6	41	33	28
Broughton & North New. Res.	16	5	3	8	36	44	18
Yarnton Res.	16	2	4	10	21	61	10
Long Crendon	16	2	3	11	18	45	9
Oxford University Press Res.	16	2	1	13	21	54	7

Fritwell Res. - record expunged

Division Three	P	W	D	L	F	A	Pt
Oakley Res.	12	10	2	0	49	17	32
Slade Farm United Res.	12	10	1	1	40	10	31
Charlton Res.	12	6	0	6	34	35	18
Watlington Res.	12	5	1	6	21	32	16
Stonesfield Res.	12	4	1	7	29	32	13
Chadlington Res.	12	4	0	8	17	30	12
Enstone Res.	12	0	1	11	15	49	1

	Broughton/N. Newington	Charlton United	Eynsham Assoc. Res.	Freeland	Garsington Res.	Hinksey	Kidlington Old Boys	Mansfield Road	Middleton Cheney	North Oxford	Oakley United	Slade Farm United	Watlington Town	Yarnton
Broughton & Nth New'gton		0-2	5-0	1-3	7-1	0-1	1-0	3-4	5-1	3-1	1-1	2-1	3-1	5-0
Charlton United	0-1	***D***	3-0	0-3	2-1	1-5	1-1	0-1	4-4	4-0	2-1	2-0	2-1	1-1
Eynsham Association Res.	0-5	1-3	***I***	0-9	3-0	2-3	0-2	1-7	2-1	2-3	2-6	2-2	6-0	4-1
Freeland	4-2	4-2	2-0	***V***	7-0	1-2	6-1	4-1	2-2	1-1	W-L	4-0	6-3	2-0
Garsington Res.	1-6	2-0	2-3	3-3	***I***	L-W	2-2	2-0	0-3	0-3	1-6	0-2	2-2	0-1
Hinksey	4-1	4-0	10-1	4-2	12-1	***S***	8-2	4-0	8-1	W-L	4-1	3-0	W-L	8-5
Kidlington Old Boys	3-3	7-2	2-1	1-4	2-0	3-1	***I***	0-2	2-4	5-1	3-0	1-1	4-2	4-2
Mansfield Road	3-2	1-3	6-0	0-0	6-1	1-0	2-1	***O***	7-0	6-2	4-1	2-0	5-0	3-1
Middleton Cheney	1-4	3-2	4-1	1-4	0-3	L-W	1-4	1-5	***N***	3-0	0-3	0-2	0-2	2-1
North Oxford	1-5	1-5	3-1	2-4	3-3	2-8	2-0	2-5	2-3		0-5	0-4	1-4	0-6
Oakley United	1-3	0-1	3-3	2-4	1-0	1-2	1-4	1-1	4-1	1-1	***O***	1-1	2-1	3-2
Slade Farm United	1-1	6-2	5-2	1-1	W-L	1-6	1-1	3-1	4-1	5-1	2-1	***N***	1-3	1-1
Watlington Town	2-4	3-3	3-3	0-3	0-3	2-2	0-3	0-8	5-2	0-2	2-0	1-4	***E***	0-3
Yarnton	0-4	1-1	2-1	2-3	4-0	2-4	1-1	3-1	3-2	3-1	3-1	0-1	7-0	

OXFORDSHIRE SENIOR LEAGUE DIVISION ONE CONSTITUTION 2010-11

BROUGHTON & NORTH NEWINGTON. . Shutford Road, North Newington Banbury OX16 9AT . . . . None
CHADLINGTON . . . . Chadlington Sports & Social, Chapel Road, Chadlington, Chipping Norton OX7 3NX 01608 676723
CHARLTON UNITED . . . . Charlton PF, Oddington Road, Charlton-on-Otmoor, Kidlington OX5 2TJ . . . . None
KIDLINGTON OLD BOYS . . . . Exeter Close, Crown Road, Kidlington OX5 1AP . . . . None
LONG CRENDON . . . . Rec Ground, Chearsley Road, Long Crendon, Aylesbury HP18 9AP. . . . . None
MIDDLETON CHENEY . . . . Astrip Road, Middleton Cheney, Banbury OX17 2PG. . . . . None
NORTH OXFORD . . . . Rover Cowley Cricket Ground, Romanway, Cowley, Oxford OX4 6NL . . . . None
NORTHWAY. . . . . Northway Sports Centre, Maltfield Road, New Marston, Oxford OX3 9RG 01865 742048
OAKLEY UNITED. . . . . Playfield Fields, Oxford Road, Oakley, Aylesbury HP18 9RE. . . . . None
OXFORD IRISH . . . . Cowley Marsh, Cowley Road, Oxford OX4 2HH. . . . . None
QUARRY . . . . Quarry Recreation Ground, Margret Road, Headington OX3 8NQ. . . . . None
SLADE FARM UNITED. . . . . Bicester Community College, Queens Avenue, Bicester OX26 2NS. 01869 243331
WATLINGTON TOWN . . . . Shirburn Road, Watlington OX49 5BZ . . . . None
YARNTON. . . . . Green Lane, Yarnton OX5 1TE 01865 842037

IN: Chadlington (R), Long Crendon (P), Northway (P - Oxford City FA Division One), Oxford Irish (P - Oxford City FA Premier Division), Quarry (P - Oxford City FA Premier Division)

OUT: Eynsham Association Res. (R), Garsington Res. (R), Freeland (P), Hinksey (P), Mansfield Road (P)

PETERBOROUGH & DISTRICT LEAGUE

www.pdfl.org

Sponsored by:

ChromaSport

Founded: 1902

Recent champions:

2005: Whittlesey United

2006: Ortonians

2007: Peterborough Sports

2008: Perkins Sports

2009: Ramsey Town

	AFC Fletton	Alconbury	Crowland Town	Deeping Sports	Leverington Spts	Moulton Harrox	Oundle Town	Parson Drove	Peterborough Spts	Pinchbeck United	Ramsey Town	Rutland Rangers	Stamford B'dere	Uppingham Town	Whittlesey United	Wimblington
AFC Fletton	***P***	3-0	3-6	6-1	1-2	1-2	0-3	5-2	2-0	0-3	1-2	0-3	6-2	1-3	4-6	7-3
Alconbury	3-2	***R***	0-2	1-0	1-5	4-0	0-1	3-2	2-2	0-4	1-3	2-0	6-0	1-5	1-4	2-2
Crowland Town	1-1	3-2	***E***	2-3	3-1	2-1	1-1	3-0	6-1	1-1	2-2	3-2	4-5	7-2	0-0	1-5
Deeping Sports	0-7	1-3	0-5	***M***	0-4	0-2	0-3	1-2	2-2	2-2	0-2	0-7	2-2	2-3	0-5	3-1
Leverington Sports	1-2	1-2	2-3	6-0	***I***	2-1	3-1	6-0	3-2	1-1	1-3	1-2	7-1	6-1	1-1	2-1
Moulton Harrox	3-2	1-1	3-2	3-1	0-2	***E***	0-5	1-2	0-2	0-2	1-1	0-1	4-0	3-0	0-2	2-0
Oundle Town	2-4	1-1	3-1	11-0	1-4	3-0	***R***	1-2	2-0	1-2	3-2	2-2	2-1	5-0	2-1	3-1
Parson Drove	1-6	2-6	0-2	3-1	1-4	3-4	0-5		2-1	4-7	2-3	0-6	4-1	2-3	0-7	0-5
Peterborough Sports	4-1	2-2	0-2	1-2	1-2	1-3	1-3	5-1	***D***	0-3	0-5	1-6	4-2	2-2	0-4	3-3
Pinchbeck United	0-2	2-0	1-3	1-0	3-2	5-0	2-1	3-1	3-1	***I***	2-1	4-4	3-0	1-1	0-0	1-1
Ramsey Town	5-0	1-1	3-1	5-2	4-3	3-0	1-1	2-2	2-3	4-3	***V***	1-3	4-3	0-2	2-0	4-0
Rutland Rangers	0-0	2-0	4-0	2-0	2-2	2-2	1-2	5-0	1-0	1-1	2-1	***I***	4-0	3-0	4-1	1-0
Stamford Belvedere	0-3	0-8	1-2	4-4	0-3	4-2	0-3	6-0	0-2	0-4	2-5	1-4	***S***	2-4	2-4	2-2
Uppingham Town	1-1	1-3	0-0	4-0	1-1	2-0	3-3	3-2	1-0	1-1	1-1	1-4	2-0	***I***	2-3	3-1
Whittlesey United	3-0	1-0	2-0	4-1	0-0	4-3	4-1	10-2	5-0	0-3	4-3	1-2	4-1	2-2	***O***	4-1
Wimblington	0-3	4-6	0-2	2-1	4-5	5-0	1-5	2-1	5-3	1-6	0-3	1-3	1-2	2-3	2-4	***N***

Premier Division		P	W	D	L	F	A	Pts
Rutland Rangers		30	21	6	3	83	27	69
Whittlesey United		30	20	5	5	90	39	65
Pinchbeck United		30	18	9	3	74	33	63
Moulton Harrox		30	18	5	7	80	38	59
Ramsey Town		30	17	6	7	78	46	57
Deeping Sports		30	17	5	8	83	43	56
Coates Athletic	*-1*	30	16	6	8	70	49	53
Uppingham Town		30	13	9	8	57	59	48
AFC Fletton		30	13	3	14	74	62	42
Alconbury		30	12	6	12	62	57	42
Leverington Sports		30	10	3	17	41	64	33
Parson Drove		30	6	5	19	44	77	23
Wimblington		30	6	4	20	56	85	22
Oundle Town		30	6	1	23	43	117	19
Stamford Belvedere		30	4	3	23	44	107	15
Crowland Town		30	3	4	23	29	105	13

JACK HOGG CHARITY SHIELD

(League champions v Peterborough Senior Cup holders)

(August 8th at Peterborough Northern Star)

Ramsey Town 3

Rutland Rangers 2

PETERBOROUGH & DISTRICT LEAGUE PREMIER DIVISION CONSTITUTION 2010-11

ALCONBURY...................... Great North Road, Alconbury, Huntingdon PE28 4EX 01480 891313
COATES ATHLETIC .... Manor Leisure Centre, Station Road, Whittesey, Peterborough PE17 1UA 01733 202298
CROWLAND TOWN .... Snowden Field, Thorney Road, Crowland PE6 0AL 01733 211548
DEEPING SPORTS................ Outgang Road, Towngate East, Market Deeping PE6 8LQ 01778 344701
EYE SPORTS & SOCIAL............... Lindisfarne Road, Eye, Peterborough PE6 7ED.............................. None
LEVERINGTON SPORTS .... Church Road, Leverington, Wisbech PE12 5ED 01945 465082
MOULTON HARROX .... Broad Lane, Moulton, Spalding PE12 6PN.......................... 01406 371991
NETHERTON UNITED .... The Grange, Mayors Walk, Peterborough PE3 6EU .... None
OUNDLE TOWN .... Station Road, Oundle, Peterborough PE8 4BZ...................... 07950 964205
PARSON DROVE.......................... Main Road, Parson Drove, Wisbech PE13 4LA................................ None
PINCHBECK UNITED .... Glebe Playing Fields, Knight Street, Pinchbeck, Spalding PE11 3RB 07966 303275
RAMSEY TOWN .... Cricketfield Lane, Ramsey, Huntingdon PE26 1BG 01487 814218
RUTLAND RANGERS .... Greetham Community Centre, Great Lane, Greetham, Oakham LE15 7NG............. 01572 813117
STAMFORD BELVEDERE .... Queen Eleanor School, Green Lane, Stamford PE9 1HE 01780 751011
UPPINGHAM TOWN...................... North Street East, Uppingham LE15 9QL 01572 821446
WHITTLESEY UNITED .... Manor Leisure Centre, Station Road, Whittlesey, Peterborough PE7 1UA 01733 202298

IN: Eye Sports & Social (P), Netherton United (P)

OUT: AFC Fletton (F), Wimblington (S - Cambridgeshire County League Senior A)

PETERBOROUGH SENIOR CUP

(Premier Division teams and top eight Division One first teams)

FIRST ROUND

AFC Fletton 3 **Eye Sports & Social** 3 *aet* (1-3p)
Deeping Sports 1 **Alconbury** 5
Kings Cliffe United 0 **Uppingham Town** 0 *aet* (4-5p)
Leverington Sports 2 Moulton Harrox 1
Parson Drove 3 Pinchbeck United 1
Ramsey Town 2 Stilton United 0
Rutland Rangers 5 Ketton 1

SECOND ROUND

Crowland Town 1 **Whittlesey United** 6
Eye Sports & Social 2 **Ramsey Town** 5
Leverington Sports 5 Peterborough Sports 0
Parson Drove 1 **Netherton United** 2
Rutland Rangers 1 Oundle Town 0
Uppingham Town 2 Coates Athletic 2 *aet* (5-4p)
Warboys Town 3 Stamford Belvedere 2
Wimblington 1 **Alconbury** 8

QUARTER FINALS

Alconbury 0 **Rutland Rangers** 3
Netherton United 3 Leverington Sports 0
Uppingham Town 2 Whittlesey United 1
Warboys Town 0 **Ramsey Town** 2

SEMI-FINALS

Rutland Rangers 1 Netherton United 0
Uppingham Town 0 **Ramsey Town** 1

FINAL

(April 21st at Peterborough United)
Rutland Rangers 3 Ramsey Town 2

Division One		P	W	D	L	F	A	Pt
Eye Sports & Social		22	16	4	2	83	28	52
Netherton United		22	14	3	5	67	42	45
Kings Cliffe United		22	14	3	5	65	43	45
Long Sutton Athletic		22	11	5	6	60	41	38
Thorney		22	11	4	7	49	50	37
Powerleague		22	11	3	8	55	57	36
Stilton United	*-1*	22	8	4	10	50	55	27
Ketton		22	7	4	11	47	45	25
Warboys Town		22	7	3	12	50	68	24
Peterborough Sports		22	5	2	15	48	77	17
Manea United	*-5*	22	6	2	14	56	59	15
Werrington Town		22	3	1	18	39	104	10

Division Two		P	W	D	L	F	A	Pt
Langtoft United		18	16	2	0	97	15	50
Sawtry		18	12	4	2	47	20	40
SSPIO		18	11	4	3	60	21	37
Castor & Ailsworth		18	11	0	7	44	40	33
Hampton Sports		18	8	4	6	39	42	28
Peterborough Rovers		18	7	4	7	43	32	25
Gedney Hill		18	6	1	11	39	52	19
Parkside	*-1*	18	2	5	11	23	51	10
Guyhirn		18	2	1	15	18	53	7
Benwick Athletic	*-1*	18	1	3	14	31	85	5

Combination One		P	W	D	L	F	A	Pt
Holbeach United Res.	*-3*	21	17	2	2	67	22	50
Ramsey Town Res.	*-1*	22	14	1	7	59	43	42
Pinchbeck United Res.	*-2*	22	12	6	4	54	34	40
Moulton Harrox Res.		22	11	6	5	68	34	39
Netherton United Res.		22	11	5	6	59	44	38
Whittlesey United Res.		22	10	1	11	46	42	31
Wimblington Res.		22	9	4	9	48	44	31
Deeping Sports Res.		22	7	7	8	34	37	28
Long Sutton Athletic Res.		22	4	7	11	23	48	19
Langtoft United Res.		22	5	3	14	31	72	18
AFC Fletton Res.	*-1*	22	3	3	16	32	70	11
Parson Drove Res.	*-4*	21	3	5	13	21	52	10

Holbeach United Res. v Parson Drove Res. not played

PETERBOROUGH CHALLENGE CUP

FINAL *(April 30th at Peterborough Northern Star)*
Long Sutton Athletic 2 Langtoft United 0

PETERBOROUGH JUNIOR CUP

FINAL *(April 23rd at Peterborough Northern Star)*
Moulton Harrox Res. 3 Pinchbeck United Res. 1

PETERBOROUGH MINOR CUP

FINAL *(April 9th at Peterborough Northern Star)*
Powerleague Res. 2 Hampton Sports Res. 0

Combination Two		P	W	D	L	F	A	Pt
Alconbury Res.	*-1*	24	18	4	2	69	36	57
Eye Sports & Social Res.		24	14	5	5	62	42	47
Werrington Town Res.		24	12	5	7	66	48	41
Peterborough Rovers Res.	*-1*	24	12	5	7	73	56	40
Ketton Res.		24	10	5	9	51	43	35
Leverington Sports Res.		24	8	7	9	47	59	31
Rutland Rangers Res.	*-2*	24	10	2	12	55	52	30
Coates Athletic Res.		24	8	6	10	50	50	30
Crowland Town Res.		24	8	6	10	40	50	30
Kings Cliffe United Res.	*-1*	24	9	3	12	42	59	29
Stamford Belvedere Res.		24	7	7	10	44	49	28
Netherton United A		24	8	2	14	54	59	26
Ramsey Town A		24	2	3	19	29	79	9

Combination Three		P	W	D	L	F	A	Pt
Peterborough Sports Res.	*-1*	22	13	4	5	77	42	42
Hampton Sports Res.	*-3*	22	13	4	5	93	48	40
Uppingham Town Res.	*-2*	22	13	2	7	68	51	39
Sawtry Res.	*-1*	22	11	4	7	60	41	36
Thorney Res.	*-1*	22	12	1	9	60	47	36
Powerleague Res.	*-2*	22	11	5	6	61	40	35
FC Inter Res.		22	10	3	9	56	44	33
Warboys Town Res.	*-1*	22	9	1	12	55	67	27
Stilton United Res.	*-1*	22	7	3	12	62	91	23
Leverington Sports A		22	7	2	13	37	77	23
Manea United Res.		22	5	2	15	34	82	17
Wimblington A		22	5	1	16	29	62	16

READING LEAGUE

full-time.thefa.com/Index.do?league=6151604

Sponsored by:

No sponsor

Founded: 1989

Recent champions:

2005: Marlow United

2006: Cookham Dean

2007: Ascot United

2008: Westwood United

2009: Woodley Town

	Berks County Sports	Cookham Dean	Frilsham & Yattendon	Highmoor/IBIS	Mortimer	Rabson Rovers	Reading YMCA	Sandhurst Devels	Taplow United	Theale Royal Mail	Westwood United	Woodcote & Stoke Row
Berks County Sports	***S***	1-1	1-1	2-2	1-2	n/a	1-4	0-1	1-2	4-5	1-2	0-4
Cookham Dean	2-1	***E***	W-L	0-0	1-3	n/a	2-0	2-3	4-0	1-2	3-1	0-1
Frilsham & Yattendon	0-4	2-3	***N***	2-4	0-5	W-L	2-0	3-2	2-2	2-0	4-2	0-2
Highmoor/IBIS	5-1	1-2	6-3	***I***	5-1	n/a	1-1	1-3	4-1	4-3	4-1	4-2
Mortimer	2-1	1-3	2-2	n/p	***O***	6-1	1-2	0-5	0-5	2-2	2-3	1-2
Rabson Rovers	n/a	2-6	n/a	n/a	L-W	***R***	n/a	n/a	2-4	n/a	n/a	n/a
Reading YMCA	5-0	1-1	1-1	1-0	5-2	W-L		4-3	7-0	1-3	1-1	2-0
Sandhurst Devels	3-1	2-1	2-2	1-3	0-2	n/a	2-0		3-0	4-1	1-2	3-0
Taplow United	2-1	1-4	2-1	2-3	0-0	n/a	0-1	0-3		1-3	2-0	0-4
Theale Royal Mail	2-3	1-1	1-4	7-3	4-3	3-1	2-3	0-2	3-3	***D***	1-2	2-5
Westwood United	3-2	0-1	2-1	2-1	1-2	n/a	2-6	3-1	4-0	0-5	***I***	2-2
Woodcote & Stoke Row	2-2	3-2	4-0	1-1	2-1	n/a	2-3	2-1	2-2	2-2	3-2	***V***

Senior Division	P	W	D	L	F	A	Pts
Reading YMCA	20	12	4	4	48	26	40
Woodcote & Stoke Row	20	11	5	4	45	30	38
Sandhurst Devels	20	12	1	7	45	27	37
Highmoor/IBIS	19	10	4	5	52	36	34
Cookham Dean	20	10	4	6	34	24	34
Westwood United	20	9	2	9	35	43	29
Theale Royal Mail	20	7	4	9	49	50	25
Mortimer	19	6	3	10	32	44	21
Frilsham & Yattendon	20	5	5	10	32	45	20
Taplow United	20	5	4	11	25	50	19
Berks County Sports	20	2	4	14	28	50	10

Rabson Rovers - record expunged

Mortimer v Highmoor/IBIS not played

Premier Division		P	W	D	L	F	A	Pts
Highmoor/IBIS Res.		19	16	0	3	47	24	48
Unity		19	14	1	4	46	18	43
Wokingham/E. A	*+3*	20	12	1	7	54	31	40
Marlow United Res.		20	12	2	6	49	30	38
Park United		20	10	5	5	46	32	35
West Reading	*-3*	20	10	3	7	45	37	30
Cookham Dean Res.		20	8	1	11	37	45	25
REME Arborfield		20	5	1	14	37	68	16
Westwood Utd Res.		20	4	2	14	21	41	14
Ashridge Park		20	4	2	14	35	61	14
AFC Corinthians		20	4	2	14	32	62	14

Spencers Wood - record expunged

Unity v Highmoor/IBIS Res. not played

READING LEAGUE SENIOR DIVISION CONSTITUTION 2010-11

COOKHAM DEAN..... Alfred Major Recreation Ground, Hillcrest Avenue, Cookham Rise, Maidenhead SL6 9NB........ 01628 819423
FRILSHAM & YATTENDON ..... Frilsham Playing Field, Frilsham Common, Frilsham, near Hermitage................ 01635 201847
HIGHMOOR/IBIS .... Prudential IBIS Sports Club, Scours Lane, Reading RG3 6AY.................. 0118 942 4130
MORTIMER........... Alfred Palmer Memorial Playing Fields, West End Road, Mortimer, Reading RG7 3TW .... None
READING YMCA................ Reading Town FC, Scours Lane, Tilehurst, Reading RG30 6AY.................. 0118 945 3555
SANDHURST DEVELS......... Sandhurst Memorial Ground, York Town Road, Sandhurst GU47 9BJ .... None
TAPLOW UNITED..................... Stanley Jones Field, Berry Hill, Taplow SL6 0DA 01628 621745
THEALE .... Theale Recreation Ground, Englefield Road, Theale, Reading RG7 5AS...................... None
UNITY............................ Cintra Park, Cintra Avenue, Reading RG2 7AU 0118 954 7275
WESTWOOD UNITED.......... Cotswold Sports Centre, Downs Way, Tilehurst, Reading RG31 6LS 0118 941 4690
WOKINGHAM & EMMBROOK RES. .. Emmbrook S&S Club, Lowther Rd, Wokingham RG41 1JB 0118 978 0209
WOODCOTE & STOKE ROW ...... Woodcote Recreation Ground, Woodcote, Reading RG8 0QY .... None

IN: Unity (P), Wokingham & Emmbrook Res. (formerly Wokingham & Emmbrook A) (P)
OUT: Berks County Sports (R), Rabson Rovers (WS)
Theale Royal Mail become Theale

BERKS TROPHY CENTRE INTERMEDIATE CUP

FINAL *(May 22nd at Reading Town)*
Highmoor/IBIS Res. 3 Reading YMCA Rapids 1

BERKS TROPHY CENTRE JUNIOR CUP

FINAL *(May 21st at Reading Town)*
Winnershe Rangers 2 Newtown Henley Res. 0

	AFC Corinthians	Ashridge Park	Cookham Dean Res.	Highmoor/IBIS Res.	Marlow United Res.	Park United	REME Arborfield	Spencers Wood	Unity	West Reading	Westwood Utd Res.	Wokingham & Ebk A
AFC Corinthians	***P***	2-5	1-1	0-1	4-4	2-4	3-4	0-3	0-4	1-3	3-1	0-2
Ashridge Park	6-1	***R***	2-4	3-6	1-3	2-4	1-3	1-1	0-0	1-1	1-0	1-6
Cookham Dean Res.	1-2	2-1	***E***	0-5	1-2	1-3	3-0	1-2	2-4	0-2	2-0	1-2
Highmoor/IBIS Res.	6-4	W-L	3-1	***M***	0-3	1-3	4-3	n/a	0-1	3-0	5-2	3-1
Marlow United Res.	3-0	3-0	1-2	0-2	***I***	3-3	5-0	W-L	3-2	1-3	6-1	3-2
Park United	2-0	2-4	4-1	0-1	0-1	***E***	6-0	3-1	1-2	1-1	1-1	0-5
REME Arborfield	1-4	8-2	2-7	L-W	1-2	1-3	***R***	3-1	2-7	4-2	3-1	1-5
Spencers Wood	1-4	n/a	2-1	n/a	n/a	0-0	3-2		2-1	0-1	3-1	0-2
Unity	3-2	4-0	2-0	n/p	1-0	2-3	3-0	2-1		3-2	0-1	1-2
West Reading	3-0	4-3	4-1	3-4	2-5	0-0	5-3	n/a	0-3	***D***	5-1	1-0
Westwood United Res.	1-2	5-2	1-2	0-1	1-0	1-3	0-0	n/a	0-3	0-2	***I***	4-0
Wokingham & Emmbrook A	7-1	3-0	4-5	0-2	4-1	3-3	5-1	5-0	0-1	3-2	W-L	***V***

BERKS TROPHY CENTRE SENIOR CUP

(Senior and Premier Division teams)

FIRST ROUND
Highmoor/Ibis 0 **Berks Co. Spts** 4
Marlow U. Res 0 **Reading YMCA** 2
REME Arborfield 0 **Wok'gham A** 2
Unity 1 Cookham Dean 0
West Reading 2 Ashridge Park 0

SECOND ROUND
AFC Corinthians 2 **Frilsham & Y.** 3
Berks Co. Spts 1 West Reading 0
Mortimer 2 Westwood United 1
Park United 0 **Reading YMCA** 2
Rabson Rovers v **Unity** (w/o)
Theale RM 3 Sandhurst Devels 2
Wok'gham A (w/o) v Spencers W.
Woodcote & SR 6 Taplow United 1

QUARTER-FINALS
Berks CS 1 **Woodcote & SR** 2
Theale RM 1 **Reading YMCA** 4
Unity 1 **Frilsham & Yattendon** 5
Wokingham A 5 Mortimer 1

SEMI-FINALS
Frilsham 1 **Wokingham A** 4
Woodcote 6 Reading YMCA 4 *aet*

FINAL
(May 14th at Reading FC)
Woodcote & Stoke Row 1
Wokingham & Emmbrook A 0

READING LEAGUE PREMIER DIVISION CONSTITUTION 2010-11

ASHRIDGE PARK .... Cantley Park, Twyford Road, Wokingham RG40 5QT .... None
BERKS COUNTY SPORTS. . . Berks Co. Sports & Social Club, Sonning Lane, Sonning, Reading RG4 6ST .... None
COOKHAM DEAN RES..... Alfred Major Rec Ground, Hillcrest Ave., Cookham Rise, Maidenhead SL6 9NB 01628 819423
HIGHMOOR/IBIS RES............. Prudential IBIS Sports Club, Scours Lane, Reading RG3 6AY.................. 0118 942 4130
MARLOW UNITED .... Gossmore Park, Gossmore Lane, Marlow SL7 1QF .... None
NEWTOWN HENLEY .... Harpsden Village, Henley-on-Thames RG9 4HH .... None
PARK UNITED......... Bishopswood Sports Ground, Horsepond Road, Sonning Common, Reading RG4 9BT .... None
REME ARBORFIELD...... Sports Pavilion, Biggs Lane, Hazelbrook Barracks,Arborfield, Reading RG2 9NH.................. None
SOUTH READING........... Lower Whitley Recreation Ground, Basingstoke Road, Reading RG2 0JA .... None
WEST READING............ Victoria Recreation Ground, Kentwood Hill, Tilehurst, Reading RG31 6HH .... None
WESTWOOD UNITED RES...... Cotswold Sports Centre, Downs Way, Tilehurst, Reading RG31 6LX......................... None
WOODLEY TOWN RES. ..... Woodford Park Leisure Centre, Haddon Drive, Woodley Reading RG5 4LY 0118 921 6969
IN: Berks County Sports (R), Newtown Henley (P), South Reading (P), Woodley Town Res. (P)
OUT: AFC Corinthians (R), Unity (P), Spencers Wood (WS), Wokingham & Emmbrook A (now Wokingham & Emmbrook Res.) (P)
Marlow United Res. become Marlow United

Division One		P	W	D	L	F	A	Pt
South Reading		22	22	0	0	104	23	66
Newtown Henley		22	12	3	7	58	37	39
Woodley Town Res.	*+3*	22	10	4	8	42	39	37
SRCC	*+3*	22	10	3	9	47	59	36
Hurst		22	10	4	8	49	57	34
Sandhurst Devels Res.	*-3*	22	11	2	9	61	38	32
Sonning		22	10	2	10	50	51	32
Barton Rovers FC		22	8	3	11	65	59	27
Goring United	*-3*	22	8	5	9	36	43	26
Theale Royal Mail Res.		22	5	6	11	39	54	21
Berks County Sports Res.		22	6	2	14	38	77	20
Mortimer Res.		22	2	2	18	27	79	8

Division Three	P	W	D	L	F	A	Pt
Wargrave	22	18	2	2	94	27	56
Winnershe Rangers	22	18	1	3	78	20	55
Wrightchoice CSA	22	13	3	6	47	31	42
Radstock	22	13	2	7	68	37	41
AFC Corinthians Res.	22	11	4	7	77	47	37
Goring United Res.	22	9	2	11	43	52	29
Sandhurst Devels A	22	9	1	12	51	47	28
Taplow United A	22	7	5	10	41	46	26
Compton	22	8	1	13	34	56	25
Sonning A	22	6	0	16	32	86	18
The Hop Leaf	22	4	2	16	18	94	14
Sonning Sports	22	3	3	16	36	76	12

Division Two	P	W	D	L	F	A	Pt
Reading YMCA Rapids	20	14	5	1	60	22	47
Wrightchoice CSA Youth	20	12	6	2	57	20	42
Wokingham & E'brook B	20	12	3	5	48	33	39
Highmoor/IBIS A	20	10	5	5	46	36	35
Twyford & Ruscombe	20	10	2	8	55	37	32
Turnpike Sports	20	9	4	7	47	43	31
Woodley Town A	20	7	3	10	30	49	24
Hurst Res.	20	6	5	9	53	57	23
Woodcote/Stoke Row Res.	20	6	0	14	29	57	18
Taplow United Res.	20	3	2	15	30	63	11
Linear United	20	3	1	16	28	66	10

Division Four		P	W	D	L	F	A	Pt
Frilsham/Yatt'don Res.	*-3*	16	15	0	1	66	16	42
Park United Res.		16	13	0	3	51	20	39
Woodley Saints		16	10	1	5	47	30	31
Newtown Henley Res.		16	7	2	7	33	28	23
Kickz		16	6	1	9	42	58	19
Shinfield Royal Oak		16	4	5	7	32	54	17
SRCC Res.		16	4	2	10	19	41	14
Woodley Town B	*+3*	16	3	1	12	21	52	13
Unity Res.		16	2	4	10	25	37	10

SOMERSET COUNTY LEAGUE

www.thefa.com/full-time/SCFL

Sponsored by:

Errea

Founded: 1890

Recent champions:

2005: Mangotsfield United Res.

2006: Hengrove Athletic

2007: Burnham United

2008: Nailsea United

2009: Bridgwater Town Res.

Premier Division		P	W	D	L	F	A	Pts
Bridgwater Town Res.		34	22	10	2	79	31	76
Bishops Lydeard		34	22	6	6	72	43	72
Watchet Town		34	20	9	5	77	37	69
Shirehampton		34	17	8	9	79	59	59
Backwell United		34	16	6	12	63	48	54
Castle Cary		34	17	2	15	61	54	53
Cheddar	*-13*	34	19	8	7	103	51	52
Nailsea United	*-1*	34	15	7	12	80	57	51
Brislington Res.		34	14	5	15	67	64	47
St George Easton-in-G.		34	14	4	16	64	72	46
Winscombe	*-1*	34	12	6	16	65	73	41
Mangotsfield Utd Res.	*-4*	34	12	5	17	50	53	37
Cutters Friday		34	11	3	20	62	87	36
Paulton Rovers Res.		34	10	5	19	44	62	35
Glastonbury Town		34	8	10	16	45	79	34
Taunton Blackbrook		34	10	4	20	53	89	34
Frome Town Res.		34	9	6	19	51	103	33
Timsbury Athletic		34	5	2	27	41	94	17

	Bac	Bis	Bdg	Bris	Cas	Che	Cut	Fro	Gla	Man	Nai	Pau	Shi	StG	Tau	Tim	Wat	Win
Backwell United		3-2	0-2	2-0	3-1	0-2	1-0	2-0	6-0	1-0	2-2	3-0	1-1	2-1	8-2	5-0	1-1	2-0
Bishops Lydeard	1-3	***P***	2-1	3-0	1-2	5-4	2-0	1-0	2-1	3-0	4-1	2-1	3-1	1-1	2-1	1-1	0-2	3-1
Bridgwater Town Res.	0-0	0-0	***R***	4-0	1-1	2-2	4-1	3-2	4-0	2-0	2-1	2-1	4-2	0-0	6-1	3-0	2-2	2-1
Brislington Res.	1-1	0-2	3-3	***E***	0-1	2-3	5-3	1-3	1-2	4-1	1-1	3-1	1-0	4-2	4-2	4-1	0-3	6-2
Castle Cary	1-3	3-2	0-3	1-2	***M***	0-2	1-2	6-0	2-0	2-0	2-3	3-0	0-1	1-0	2-4	2-1	3-2	4-2
Cheddar	4-1	2-4	0-0	2-1	3-2	***I***	7-1	4-1	4-1	1-0	1-1	3-1	5-1	4-0	8-2	6-0	0-2	3-3
Cutters Friday	0-2	1-1	1-4	2-1	1-2	3-1	***E***	2-0	3-1	1-4	3-1	6-3	2-6	2-4	2-2	3-2	2-2	2-3
Frome Town Res.	4-2	1-3	2-2	2-0	2-0	0-9	3-2	***R***	2-2	2-1	2-3	0-2	1-7	2-4	1-3	3-2	2-10	3-3
Glastonbury Town	2-2	2-6	1-3	1-3	1-1	0-0	2-3	2-2		3-2	0-3	1-1	1-5	1-2	2-2	2-0	1-1	3-1
Mangotsfield United Res.	2-1	1-2	0-1	2-1	0-1	3-2	2-0	1-1	0-0	***D***	2-2	3-1	4-2	6-1	6-0	1-0	2-2	1-0
Nailsea United	3-1	4-0	1-2	2-3	1-2	2-4	6-2	8-0	1-2	6-1	***I***	1-0	3-3	4-0	1-3	4-1	2-1	2-2
Paulton Rovers Res.	1-2	1-3	1-1	1-3	1-0	3-3	3-1	0-1	3-0	0-0	1-0	***V***	0-1	2-1	3-2	0-2	2-3	1-1
Shirehampton	2-1	1-1	3-2	2-1	4-1	0-5	1-0	3-1	2-2	2-1	2-2	2-0	***I***	1-2	2-2	5-0	2-2	4-3
St George Easton-in-Gordano	3-1	1-2	1-3	3-3	2-4	3-3	4-7	2-0	1-2	3-0	2-0	1-0	2-4	***S***	0-1	4-3	1-3	2-3
Taunton Blackbrook	2-0	1-3	0-4	0-3	2-4	2-1	0-2	3-3	2-3	1-0	2-3	1-2	3-0	0-2	***I***	0-2	0-1	1-4
Timsbury Athletic	5-1	0-2	1-2	3-4	4-2	1-2	2-1	1-2	1-3	0-4	1-3	2-3	0-5	2-4	0-2	***O***	1-1	1-4
Watchet Town	1-0	1-1	0-1	3-2	1-0	2-1	2-1	4-0	4-1	4-0	2-1	2-1	1-1	1-2	2-0	5-1	***N***	4-1
Winscombe	2-0	1-2	1-4	0-0	0-4	2-2	3-0	5-3	4-0	1-0	1-2	3-4	2-1	0-3	3-4	1-0	2-0	

SOMERSET COUNTY LEAGUE PREMIER DIVISION CONSTITUTION 2010-11

ASHTON & BACKWELL UNITED . . The Playing Fields, West Town Road, Backwell, Bristol BS48 3HG 01275 462612
BISHOPS LYDEARD. . . . . Darby Way, Bishops Lydeard TA4 3BE . . . . None
BRIDGWATER TOWN RES.. . . . . Fairfax Park, College Way, Bath Road, Bridgwater TA6 4TZ. 01278 446899
BRISLINGTON RES. . . . . Ironmould Lane, Brislington, Bristol BS4 5SA 0117 977 4030
CASTLE CARY . . . . Donald Pither Memorial PF, Catherines Close, Castle Cary BA7 7HP 01963 351538
CHEDDAR. . . . . Bowdens Park, Draycott Road, Cheddar BS27 3RL 01934 743736
CLEVEDON UNITED . . . . Coleridge Vale Playing Fields, Southley Road, Clevedon BS21 6PF. 01275 871878
CUTTERS FRIDAY . . . . The Cutters Club, Stockwood Lane, Stockwood, Bristol BS14 8SJ 01275 839830
GLASTONBURY TOWN. . . . . Abbey Moor Stadium, Godney Road, Glastonbury BA6 9AF. 01458 831460
LANGFORD ROVERS . . . . Westland United FC, Winterstoke Road, Weston-super-Mare BS24 9AA. 01934 632037
MANGOTSFIELD UNITED RES. . . . . Cossham Street, Mangotsfield, Bristol BS17 3EN. 0117 956 0119
MINEHEAD . . . . Recreation Ground, Irnham Road, Minehead TA24 5DP 01643 704989
NAILSEA UNITED . . . . Grove Sports Ground, Old Church, Nailsea BS48 4ND. 01275 856892
SHIREHAMPTON . . . . Recreation Ground, Penpole Lane, Shirehampton, Bristol BS11 0EA. 0117 923 5461
ST GEORGE EASTON-IN-GORDANO . . . . Court Hay, Easton-in-Gordano, Bristol BS20 0PY. 01275 374235
STOCKWOOD GREEN . . . . Hursley Lane, Woolard Lane, Whitchurch, Bristol BS14 0QY 01275 891300
TAUNTON BLACKBROOK . . . . Taunton Town FC, Wordsworth Drive, Taunton TA1 2HG 01823 278191
WATCHET TOWN. . . . . Memorial Ground, Doniford Road, Watchet TA23 0TG 01984 631041
WINSCOMBE. . . . . Recreation Ground, The Lynch, Winscombe BS25 1AP . . . . 01934 842720(cricket club)

IN: Clevedon United (P), Langford Rovers (P), Minehead (R - Western League Division One), Stockwood Green (P)
OUT: Frome Town Res. (W), Paulton Rovers Res. (W), Timsbury Athletic (R)
Backwell United have merged with Ashton Boys (youth football) to form Ashton & Backwell United

Division One	P	W	D	L	F	A	Pts
Clevedon United	34	23	7	4	75	23	76
Stockwood Green	34	22	5	7	85	32	71
Langford Rovers	34	21	6	7	100	54	69
Ilminster Town	34	19	6	9	75	44	63
Odd Down Res.	34	18	9	7	67	47	63
Fry Club	34	14	11	9	52	28	53
Nailsea Town	34	16	5	13	63	51	53
Cleeve West Town	34	14	10	10	54	51	52
Portishead T. Res.	34	15	6	13	57	62	51
Bishop Sutton Res.	34	14	6	14	63	62	48
Saltford	34	12	7	15	54	54	43
Street Res.	34	11	7	16	52	58	40
Burnham United	34	11	7	16	68	79	40
Larkhall Ath. Res. *-1*	34	12	0	22	66	88	35
Keynsham T. Res.	34	8	9	17	42	70	33
Nailsea United Res.	34	8	5	21	49	91	29
Radstock Town Res.	34	6	4	24	40	102	22
Worle *-1*	34	5	4	25	44	110	18

PREMIER / DIVISION ONE CUP

FIRST ROUND
Clevedon United 0 **St George Easton-in-Gord.** 2
Glastonbury Town 3 **Paulton Rovers Res.** 4
Nailsea Utd 4 Castle Cary 3

SECOND ROUND
Backwell Utd 3 Fry Club 1
B. Lydeard (w/o) v Radstock
Bridgwater Town Res. 3 St George Easton-in-Gordano 1
Burnham Utd 1 **Watchet** 5
Cleeve West 1 Nailsea T. 0
Cutters 5 Langford Rovers 3
Frome Town Res. 3 Worle 1
Ilminster 4 Paulton Res. 0
Keynsham Town Res. 1 **Cheddar** 3
Larkhall Athletic Res. 2 **Brislington Res.** 3
Nailsea Utd 1 Timsbury 0
Portishead Res. 0 **Saltford** 1
Stockwood Green Robs 0 **Odd Down Res.** 4
Street Res. 1 **Shirehampton** 2
Taunton Blackbrook 1 **Mangotsfield United Res.** 7
Winscombe 3 Bishop Sutton Res. 3 *aet* (4-1p)

THIRD ROUND
Backwell 1 **Nailsea United** 2
Bridgwater Town Res. 2 Cutters Friday 0
Brislington Res. 1 **Bishops Lydeard** 4
Cheddar 0 **Ilminster Town** 1
Frome T. Res. 2 **Saltford** 3
Mangotsfield United Res. 3 Cleeve West Town 0
Odd Down Res. 4 Shirehampton 0
Winscombe 4 Watchet 3 *aet*

QUARTER-FINALS
Bridgwater Town Res. 3 Mangotsfield United Res. 1
Ilminster 0 **Bish. Lydeard** 4
Saltford 0 **Nailsea United** 3
Winscombe 2 **Odd Down Res.** 4

SEMI-FINALS
Bridgwater Town Res. 1 Bishops Lydeard 0
Odd Down Res. 0 **Nailsea United** 2

FINAL
(*May 13th at Street*)
Bridgwater Town Res. 2 Nailsea United 0

	Bis	Bur	Cle	Clv	Fry	Ilm	Key	Lan	Lark	NT	NU	Odd	Por	Rad	Salt	Stoc	Stre	Wor
Bishop Sutton Res.		1-1	2-2	1-3	1-1	4-2	3-0	3-1	1-4	2-0	3-2	2-3	1-4	10-2	0-3	0-1	4-1	5-1
Burnham United	2-4		1-1	0-2	0-2	7-5	1-1	0-1	1-4	5-0	6-0	4-4	2-3	2-1	3-2	3-1	3-2	6-1
Cleeve West Town	1-2	1-0		1-4	0-1	2-1	5-3	0-4	3-1	0-1	5-2	1-0	1-0	3-0	0-2	0-3	2-2	3-0
Clevedon United	4-0	3-0	1-1	***D***	1-0	1-1	1-0	1-2	4-1	0-0	3-0	2-2	4-0	2-0	2-0	0-0	3-0	4-1
Fry Club	2-0	4-1	3-1	1-2	***I***	1-1	1-1	2-1	3-0	1-2	0-0	0-1	1-1	1-1	2-0	1-0	1-1	5-0
Ilminster Town	3-1	2-1	2-0	2-0	2-1	***V***	2-0	2-2	2-0	0-0	3-1	2-1	3-0	3-2	1-2	6-0	1-3	6-0
Keynsham Town Res.	0-0	1-1	1-1	1-1	1-1	0-1	***I***	0-6	4-2	0-3	1-2	0-3	2-3	2-1	2-0	0-5	2-1	2-1
Langford Rovers	3-1	9-2	6-1	3-3	2-0	1-0	3-2	***S***	6-4	4-1	1-1	0-1	2-5	5-1	3-1	1-1	2-4	3-1
Larkhall Athletic Res.	8-1	0-4	0-3	0-2	1-2	1-0	2-3	5-2	***I***	2-3	4-2	1-3	1-2	2-0	2-3	0-7	3-1	1-3
Nailsea Town	2-2	1-2	1-2	1-3	1-0	1-0	0-3	0-1	2-3	***O***	4-3	3-0	3-0	3-3	1-1	4-1	1-0	8-1
Nailsea United Res.	2-1	1-1	1-3	0-3	2-7	0-3	2-3	3-6	3-1	2-1	***N***	0-3	5-2	1-2	1-1	1-1	1-3	5-1
Odd Down Res.	3-2	1-1	1-1	2-1	0-2	0-1	2-2	2-2	5-2	3-1	4-2		1-4	2-1	1-1	1-0	1-0	2-0
Portishead Town Res.	0-0	3-0	1-1	1-2	0-0	2-3	1-0	0-3	2-1	0-5	5-0	0-3	***O***	5-1	1-1	1-1	2-1	2-1
Radstock Town Res.	0-3	1-3	2-4	0-3	0-4	1-7	2-1	0-1	2-3	2-5	1-2	0-0	4-2	***N***	3-1	2-1	0-5	0-5
Saltford	0-1	5-0	2-2	0-1	2-2	0-1	3-1	2-7	2-3	1-2	2-0	2-1	2-1	4-2	***E***	0-1	2-1	1-1
Stockwood Green	1-0	3-2	0-0	2-0	1-0	4-2	6-1	2-1	4-0	3-0	6-0	2-3	5-0	5-0	3-1		3-0	4-0
Street Res.	0-1	2-1	0-0	0-4	1-0	1-1	2-2	1-1	0-2	1-0	1-0	2-5	1-2	1-1	2-1	0-5		6-0
Worle	0-1	7-2	1-3	0-5	0-0	4-4	2-0	2-5	3-2	0-3	0-2	3-3	1-2	1-2	0-4	2-3	1-6	

SOMERSET COUNTY LEAGUE DIVISION ONE CONSTITUTION 2010-11

BERROW . . . . Red Road Playing Fields, Berrow, Burnham-on-Sea TA8 2LY . . . . None
BISHOP SUTTON RES. . . . . Lake View, Wick Road, Bishop Sutton, Bristol BS39 5XP 01275 333097
BURNHAM UNITED. . . . . Burnham Road Playing Fields, Cassis Close, Burnham-on-Sea TA8 1NN 01278 794615
CLEEVE WEST TOWN. . . . . King George V Playing Fields, Meeting House Lane, Cleeve BS49 4PD 01934 832173
FROME COLLEGIANS. . . . . Selwood School, Berkley Road, Frome BA11 2EF . . . . None
FRY CLUB . . . . Fry Club, Somerdale, Keynsham, Bristol BS31 2AU 0117 937 6500/6501
ILMINSTER TOWN . . . . Recreation Ground, Ilminster TA19 0EF . . . . None
KEYNSHAM TOWN . . . . Crown Field, Bristol Road, Keynsham, Bristol BS31 2BE. 0117 986 5876
LARKHALL ATHLETIC RES. . . . . Plain Ham, Charlcombe Lane, Larkhall, Bath BA1 8DJ. 01225 334952
NAILSEA TOWN . . . . Fryth Way, Pound Lane, Nailsea BS48 2AS . . . . None
NAILSEA UNITED RES. . . . . Grove Sports Ground, Old Church, Nailsea BS48 4ND. 01275 856892
ODD DOWN RES. . . . . Lew Hill Memorial Ground, Combe Hay Lane, Odd Down, Bath BA2 8PH 01225 832491
PORTISHEAD TOWN RES. . . . . Bristol Road Playing Fields, Portishead, Bristol BS20 6QB 01275 847136
PURNELL SPORTS . . . . Paulton Rovers FC, Winterstoke Road, Paulton BS39 7RF 01761 412907
SALTFORD. . . . . Playing Fields, Norman Road, Saltford BS31 0BQ 01225 873725
STREET RES. . . . . The Tannery Ground, Middlebrooks, Street BA16 0TA 01458 445987
TIMSBURY ATHLETIC . . . . Recreation Ground, North Road, Timsbury, Bath BA2 0JH 01761 472523
WESTON ST JOHNS . . . . Coleridge Road, Bournville Estate, Weston-super-Mare BS23 3UP 01934 612862

IN: Berrow (P - Division Two West), Frome Collegians (P - Division Two East), Purnells Sports (P - Division Two East), Timsbury Athletic (R), Weston St Johns (P - Division Two West)

OUT: Clevedon United (P), Langford Rovers (P), Radstock Town Res. (R - Division Two East), Stockwood Green (P), Worle (R - Division Two West)

	Clutton	Cutters Friday Res.	Dundry Athletic	Frome Collegians	Fry Club Res.	Hengrove Athletic Res.	Imperial	Peasedown Athletic	Purnells Sports	Shepton Mallet Res.	Stockwood Green Robs Res.	Timsbury Athletic Res.	Tunley Athletic	Welton Rovers Res.	Westfield
Clutton		4-2	3-3	1-3	1-1	1-1	1-1	1-3	0-1	2-2	0-1	5-1	1-6	2-1	2-2
Cutters Friday Res.	2-1	***D***	5-2	0-0	1-0	2-1	4-2	1-1	0-2	8-2	3-2	5-0	1-2	3-2	3-2
Dundry Athletic	6-0	2-1	***I***	2-3	4-2	0-1	2-4	4-5	0-2	6-0	3-4	8-2	3-1	0-3	1-0
Frome Collegians	6-1	3-1	2-0	***V***	2-1	2-2	2-1	4-0	2-1	8-0	3-0	7-1	6-0	1-1	2-1
Fry Club Res.	2-1	0-0	0-2	1-2		0-4	2-2	0-2	1-2	1-1	4-2	5-0	0-0	0-0	3-0
Hengrove Athletic Res.	6-1	1-0	3-1	3-3	6-0	***T***	0-1	1-0	1-2	11-0	4-0	2-1	3-3	4-1	3-0
Imperial	3-0	0-1	1-3	0-2	0-0	1-5	***W***	2-0	3-1	4-2	1-0	2-3	3-1	0-0	1-4
Peasedown Athletic	0-1	5-2	4-1	2-3	0-0	2-4	3-2	***O***	2-0	3-0	0-0	2-0	5-1	4-1	4-5
Purnell Sports	3-1	4-1	1-0	3-4	5-2	3-1	1-0	2-1		10-0	3-1	4-0	4-0	1-1	3-3
Shepton Mallet Res.	1-2	1-5	0-3	0-3	0-1	0-6	0-4	1-3	0-6	***E***	2-1	2-0	1-2	3-1	0-8
Stockwood GR Res.	0-0	1-2	2-1	0-2	0-1	1-1	3-0	0-1	4-5	3-1	***A***	0-0	0-2	2-0	2-0
Timsbury Athletic Res.	0-4	1-0	2-2	1-3	2-3	0-2	2-0	0-2	0-2	2-1	0-1	***S***	2-5	0-4	0-4
Tunley Athletic	3-4	3-2	3-0	1-4	1-0	3-2	4-2	1-2	0-2	6-0	4-3	6-0	***T***	1-1	2-2
Welton Rovers Res.	4-1	3-0	2-0	0-2	7-0	3-2	2-2	2-1	0-1	4-4	0-1	2-0	1-2		0-0
Westfield	6-2	4-1	3-1	1-3	2-1	1-4	1-2	1-2	1-1	7-2	5-0	2-1	3-1	5-0	

Division Two East		P	W	D	L	F	A	Pts
Frome Collegians		28	24	4	0	87	25	76
Purnell Sports		28	21	3	4	75	29	66
Hengrove Athletic Res.		28	17	5	6	84	32	56
Peasedown Athletic		28	16	3	9	59	40	51
Tunley Athletic		28	14	4	10	64	57	46
Westfield		28	13	5	10	73	47	44
Cutters Friday Res.		28	13	3	12	56	51	42
Welton Rovers Res.		28	9	8	11	46	42	35
Imperial	*-2*	28	10	5	13	44	49	33
Dundry Athletic		28	10	2	16	60	59	32
Stockwood GR Res.		28	9	4	15	34	48	31
Fry Club Res.		28	7	8	13	31	49	29
Clutton		28	7	7	14	43	70	28
Timsbury Athletic Res.		28	4	2	22	21	85	14
Shepton Mallet Res.		28	3	3	22	26	120	12

SOMERSET COUNTY LEAGUE DIVISION TWO EAST CONSTITUTION 2010-11

CLUTTON. . . . . Warwick Fields, Upper Bristol Road, Clutton, Bristol BS39 5TA. . . . . Non

CUTTERS FRIDAY RES.. . . . . The Cutters Club, Stockwood Lane, Stockwood, Bristol BS14 8SJ 01275 83983

DUNDRY ATHLETIC. . . . . Dundry Playing Field, Crabtree Lane, Dundry, Bristol BS41 8LN. 0117 964 553

FRY CLUB RES. . . . . Fry Club, Somerdale, Keynsham, Bristol BS31 2AU 0117 937 6500/650

HENGROVE ATHLETIC RES. . . . . Norton Lane, Whitchurch, Bristol BS14 0BT 01275 83289

IMPERIAL. . . . . Bristol Imperial Sports Club, West Town Lane, Whitchurch, Brislington BS4 5DT. 01275 54600

PEASEDOWN ATHLETIC . . . . . Miners Welfare Park, Church Road, Peasedown St John, Bath BA2 8AF. 01761 43731

PURNELL SPORTS RES. . . . . Greyfield Sports & Social Club, Bristol Road, Paulton BS39 7NX 01761 41280

RADSTOCK TOWN RES.. . . . . Southfield Recreation Ground, Frome Hill, Radstock BA3 3NZ. 01761 43500

SHEPTON MALLET RES. . . . . . West Shepton Playing Fields, Old Wells Road, Shepton Mallet BA4 5XN. 01749 34460

STOCKWOOD GREEN RES. . . . . Hursley Lane, Woolard Lane, Whitchurch, Bristol BS14 0QY 01275 89130

TIMSBURY ATHLETIC RES. . . . . Recreation Ground, North Road, Timsbury, Bath BA2 0JH 01761 47252

TUNLEY ATHLETIC. . . . . The Recreation Centre, Bath Road, Tunley BA2 0EB. . . . . Non

WELTON ROVERS RES.. . . . . West Clewes, North Road, Midsomer Norton BA3 2QD 01761 41209

WESTFIELD . . . . Fosseway Playing Fields, Charlton Lane, Midsomer Norton BA3 4BD . . . . Non

IN: Radstock Town Res. (R), Purnells Sports Res. (P - Mid-Somerset League Premier Division)

OUT: Frome Collegians (P), Purnells Sports (P)

Division Two West		P	W	D	L	F	A	Pts
Berrow		28	20	4	4	86	44	64
Weston St Johns		28	18	5	5	94	38	59
Westland United		28	17	4	7	71	41	55
Banwell		28	16	4	8	61	35	52
Combe St Nich.	*-2*	28	16	4	8	58	32	50
Yatton Athletic		28	14	1	13	83	61	43
Congresbury		28	13	4	11	63	50	43
Wells City Res.		28	12	6	10	51	50	42
Creech St Michael		28	11	4	13	62	60	37
Backwell Utd Res.		28	8	7	13	47	63	31
Churchill Club	*-9*	28	10	6	12	52	62	27
Long Ashton		28	5	9	14	44	66	24
Cheddar Res.	*-3*	28	7	6	15	39	62	24
Wrington-Redhill		28	5	5	18	30	59	20
Burnham U. Res.	*-3*	28	3	1	24	19	137	7

DIVISION TWO CUP

FIRST ROUND

Berrow 2 Creech 1, **Cheddar Res.** 4 Cutters Friday Res. 2
Churchill Club 8 Timsbury Athletic Res. 0
Combe St Nicholas 6 Banwell 0
Dundry Athletic 2 **Backwell United Res.** 5
Frome Collegians 11 Shepton Mallet Res. 0
Hengrove Athletic Res. 0 **Clutton** 2
Imperial 2 Burnham United Res. 1
Long Ashton 3 Congresbury 1
Peasedown Athletic 2 Fry Club Res. 1
Tunley Athletic 0 **Purnell Sports** 2
Westfield 4 Wells City Res. 0
Wrington-Redhill 1 **Westland United** 1 *aet* (2-3p)
Yatton Athletic 5 Weston St Johns 4

SECOND ROUND

Berrow 3 Long Ashton 4 *(Long Ashton expelled)*
Churchill Club 3 Peasedown Athletic 2
Clutton 6 Yatton Athletic 5 *aet*
Combe St Nicholas 0 **Westland United** 4
Imperial 3 Backwell United Res. 1
Stockwood GR Res. 1 **Cheddar Res.** 3
Welton Rovers Res. 1 **Frome Collegians** 3
Westfield 1 **Purnell Sports** 3 *aet*

QUARTER-FINALS

Berrow 2 Frome Collegians 1
Cheddar Res. 4 **Purnells Sports** 4 *aet* (4-5p)
Imperial 2 Churchill 1, **Westland United** 3 Clutton 0

SEMI-FINALS

Berrow 3 Imperial 0, **Purnell Spts** 2 Westland United 1

FINAL *(May 11th at Street)*

Berrow 1 Purnell Sports 1 *aet* (7-6p)

	Bac	Ban	Ber	Bur	Che	Chu	Com	Con	Cre	Lon	Well	Wstl	WSJ	Wri	Yatt
Backwell United Res.		2-2	2-4	9-0	3-3	5-2	1-5	1-1	2-1	1-2	0-1	0-2	0-6	0-0	3-2
Banwell	2-0	***D***	3-1	9-1	3-0	4-0	0-2	1-0	3-2	0-1	2-0	1-2	1-2	2-0	3-2
Berrow	6-0	1-1	***I***	4-1	4-2	2-2	4-0	4-1	1-0	4-2	3-0	2-1	5-1	1-0	3-5
Burnham United Res.	1-1	1-3	0-4	***V***	1-5	1-0	0-5	1-0	1-8	1-2	1-5	0-2	0-6	1-3	2-4
Cheddar Res.	1-1	0-2	1-5	5-0		3-3	3-0	0-4	0-2	0-0	1-0	2-2	0-1	1-1	2-4
Churchill Club	5-1	3-1	1-1	5-1	4-1	***T***	1-0	3-0	3-1	3-3	1-1	2-1	0-6	1-0	1-2
Combe St Nicholas	2-0	1-1	4-0	7-0	0-1	4-2	***W***	0-1	2-0	2-0	0-0	2-0	4-2	2-0	0-4
Congresbury	1-1	3-2	3-4	8-0	4-0	3-1	2-4	***O***	1-3	3-2	4-1	2-3	1-1	3-1	5-4
Creech St Michael	2-3	2-2	1-9	4-0	2-0	4-2	0-1	3-2		1-1	3-2	0-1	2-1	7-0	2-4
Long Ashton	0-1	0-3	2-3	8-0	1-2	2-2	1-4	2-2	3-3	***W***	3-7	0-1	0-4	2-2	3-2
Wells City Res.	3-2	3-2	2-2	3-1	2-0	2-0	1-1	2-3	1-2	3-1	***E***	0-2	2-8	3-1	2-0
Westland United	6-3	0-1	2-3	6-1	4-1	4-1	3-0	3-1	4-0	1-1	2-2	***S***	0-4	4-3	3-0
Weston St Johns	2-1	2-3	1-2	12-0	3-0	5-2	3-3	2-1	5-2	5-2	0-0	3-3	***T***	2-2	3-0
Wrington-Redhill	0-1	4-1	0-2	1-3	1-2	1-2	1-0	1-2	4-3	0-0	0-2	0-6	0-1		3-2
Yatton Athletic	1-3	0-3	6-2	8-0	5-3	3-0	1-3	0-2	2-2	6-0	5-1	6-3	2-3	3-1	

SOMERSET COUNTY LEAGUE DIVISION TWO WEST CONSTITUTION 2010-11

ASHTON & BACKWELL UNITED RES. . The Playing Fields, West Town Rd, Backwell BS48 3HG 01275 462612
BANWELL . . . . Riverside Ground, Riverside, Banwell BS29 6EE 01934 820773
BURNHAM UNITED RES. . . . . . Burnham Road Playing Fields, Cassis Close, Burnham-on-Sea TA8 1NN 01278 794615
CHEDDAR RES. . . . . Bowdens Park, Draycott Road, Cheddar BS27 3RL 01934 743736
CHURCHILL CLUB . . . . Ladymead Lane, Churchill, Winscombe BS25 5NH 01934 852739
COMBE ST NICHOLAS . . . . Slades Cross, Combe St Nicholas TA20 3HQ 01460 234743
CONGRESBURY . . . . Broadstones Playing Fields, Stonewell Lane, Congresbury BS49 5DL 01934 832150
CREECH ST MICHAEL . . . . Creech St Michael Rec, Hyde Lane, Creech St Michael, Taunton TA3 5QJ . . . . None
LONG ASHTON . . . . Long Ashton Rec., Keedwell Hill, Long Ashton BS41 9DP . . . . None
WELLS CITY RES. . . . . The Athletic Ground, Rowdens Road, Wells BA5 1TU 01749 679971
WESTLAND UNITED . . . . Westland Sports Club, Winterstoke Road, Weston-super-Mare BS24 9AA 01934 632037
WORLE . . . . Worle Recreation Ground, Station Road, Worle, Weston-super-Mare BS22 6AU . . . . None
WRINGTON-REDHILL . . . . Recreation Ground, Silver Street, Wrington BS40 5QE . . . . None
YATTON ATHLETIC . . . . Hangstones Playing Fields, Stowey Road, Yatton BS49 4HY . . . . None

IN: Worle (R)

OUT: Berrow (P), Weston St Johns (P)

Backwell United Res. have merged with Ashton Boys (youth football) to form Ashton & Backwell United Res.

STAFFORDSHIRE COUNTY SENIOR LEAGUE

www.staffordshirecsl.co.uk

Sponsored by:

No sponsor

Founded: 1957

Recent champions:

2005: Fegg Hayes

2006: Hanley Town

2007: Wolstanton United

2008: Wolstanton United

2009: Foley

Premier Division		P	W	D	L	F	A	Pts
Stretton Eagles		34	27	2	5	111	36	83
Kidsgrove Athletic Res.		34	22	6	6	73	40	72
Wolstanton United		34	22	3	9	69	40	69
Hanley Town		34	21	3	10	78	47	66
Redgate Clayton		34	20	4	10	91	64	64
Newcastle Town Res.		34	18	8	8	72	44	62
Ball Haye Green		34	17	6	11	72	43	57
Foley	*-3*	34	15	7	12	46	45	49
Manor Inne		34	13	6	15	49	68	45
Abbey Hulton United		34	13	5	16	65	67	44
Norton		34	11	8	15	59	58	41
Congleton Vale		34	11	8	15	44	61	41
Florence		34	10	9	15	37	45	39
Sandbach United		34	9	7	18	56	75	34
Barlaston		34	9	3	22	43	75	30
Goldenhill Wanderers		34	6	10	18	58	85	28
Holt JCB		34	5	5	24	38	84	20
Eccleshall AFC		34	5	4	25	29	113	19

	Abb	Ball	Barl	Cong	Ecc	Flor	Foley	Gold	Han	Holt	Kids	Man	New	Nort	Red	Sand	Stret	Wols
Abbey Hulton United		0-2	1-0	2-0	3-0	3-3	2-1	4-4	2-1	1-3	0-3	0-0	2-1	4-0	3-1	4-0	0-4	2-3
Ball Haye Green	4-1	***P***	4-1	2-2	4-1	4-1	0-1	1-1	4-0	4-1	0-2	4-1	2-3	1-0	1-3	3-0	2-2	0-1
Barlaston	2-4	0-2	***R***	3-0	3-1	0-0	1-2	0-3	1-2	2-1	0-2	1-2	1-3	4-0	1-3	3-0	0-6	1-2
Congleton Vale	1-4	0-3	2-0	***E***	1-2	1-0	1-2	0-2	1-1	3-1	4-2	1-0	0-1	1-1	2-3	0-1	2-1	0-2
Eccleshall AFC	0-4	0-3	1-0	3-6	***M***	0-1	0-3	3-3	3-2	1-4	0-1	1-3	0-0	0-3	0-3	1-1	1-8	0-5
Florence	3-2	2-2	1-1	0-1	0-1	***I***	0-1	1-0	0-1	1-0	2-1	1-2	1-1	0-3	1-1	2-0	1-2	1-2
Foley	4-3	0-3	2-3	1-1	0-1	1-0	***E***	0-0	1-3	3-0	0-2	3-1	0-0	2-2	0-3	5-5	2-1	1-0
Goldenhill Wanderers	1-1	1-1	2-5	1-1	4-2	1-3	1-4	***R***	0-5	4-1	1-2	1-2	2-5	3-1	4-4	0-3	2-6	1-3
Hanley Town	3-1	1-0	4-0	3-1	7-0	4-2	2-0	4-1		2-0	0-1	1-0	1-1	1-3	3-5	2-0	1-3	1-4
Holt JCB	2-4	0-5	0-1	1-3	2-2	2-2	0-2	6-3	0-2	***D***	2-5	0-0	0-3	1-4	1-2	2-4	0-4	2-0
Kidsgrove Athletic Res.	3-1	2-1	3-2	7-0	4-1	1-0	3-0	3-2	1-1	0-1	***I***	3-0	1-0	1-1	1-1	1-2	1-5	1-1
Manor Inne	3-2	2-0	0-0	1-3	3-0	1-0	0-0	2-2	1-2	2-0	4-4	***V***	3-2	2-1	3-1	0-3	1-5	0-1
Newcastle Town Res.	2-1	2-2	2-3	0-0	3-1	0-0	3-1	2-1	1-3	1-1	4-2	4-1	***I***	3-1	4-1	3-1	1-2	0-1
Norton	3-1	5-1	4-2	0-0	9-1	0-1	0-1	0-1	2-5	1-1	1-2	2-1	1-4	***S***	2-3	1-1	0-3	1-1
Redgate Clayton	1-0	2-1	6-1	4-1	8-1	2-3	2-0	2-1	3-1	5-2	2-2	8-2	2-4	2-5	***I***	2-0	1-4	1-2
Sandbach United	5-0	1-2	3-1	1-3	2-1	1-1	2-2	2-2	2-4	2-0	0-2	4-5	1-4	1-1	1-3	***O***	3-6	0-1
Stretton Eagles	1-0	2-1	6-0	2-2	3-0	2-3	W-L	3-1	0-5	2-0	0-1	4-0	5-1	3-0	4-1	5-2	***N***	5-0
Wolstanton United	3-3	2-3	1-0	4-0	7-0	1-0	0-1	3-2	3-0	4-1	1-3	4-1	0-4	0-1	3-0	3-2	1-2	

STAFFORDSHIRE COUNTY SENIOR LEAGUE PREMIER DIVISION CONSTITUTION 2010-11

ABBEY HULTON UNITED . . . . Birches Head Road, Abbey Hulton, Stoke-on-Trent ST2 8DD 01782 54423

BALL HAYE GREEN . . . . Ball Haye Green WMC, Ball Haye Green, Leek ST13 6BH 01538 37192

CONGLETON VALE . . Biddulph Victoria FC, Knypersley S&S, Tunstall Road, Knypersley, Stoke-on-Trent ST8 7AQ. 01782 52273

ECCLESHALL AFC. . . . . Pershall Park, Chester Road, Eccleshall ST21 6NE 01785 85135

FLORENCE . . . . Florence Sports & Social, Lightwood Road, Longton, Stoke-on-Trent ST3 4JS. 01782 31288

FOLEY . . . . Whitcombe Road, Meir, Stoke-on-Trent ST3 6NU 01782 59527

GOLDENHILL WANDERERS . . Sandyford Cricket Club, Shelford Rd, Sandyford, Stoke-on-Trent ST6 5LA 01782 83900

HANLEY TOWN. . . . . Abbey Lane, Abbey Hulton, Bucknall, Stoke-on-Trent ST2 8AU 01782 26723

KIDSGROVE ATHLETIC RES.. The Seddon Stadium, Hollinwood Rd, Kidsgrove, Stoke-on-Trent ST7 1DH. 01782 78241

MANOR INNE . . . . Alsager Town FC, Town Ground, Woodland Court, Alsager ST7 2DP 01270 88233

NEWCASTLE TOWN RES. Lyme Valley Parkway Stadium, Buckmaster Ave, Clayton, Newc.-u-Lyme ST5 3BF. . . . 01782 662351/ 62235

NORTON. . . . . Norton CC & MW Institute, Community Drive, Smallthorne, Stoke-on-Trent ST6 1QF 01782 83829

REDGATE CLAYTON. . . . . Northwood Lane, Clayton, Newcastle-under-Lyme ST5 4BN 01782 71740

SANDBACH UNITED. . . . . . . Winsford United FC, The Barton Stadium, Wharton Road, Winsford CW7 3AE 01606 55844

STONE DOMINOES RES. . . . . Motiva Park, Yarnfield Lane, Yarnfield, Stone ST15 0NF 01782 76189

WOLSTANTON UNITED . . Bradwell Comm. Centre, Riceyman Rd, Bradwell, Newcastle-under-Lyme ST5 8LF 01782 66081

IN: Stone Dominoes Res. (P)

OUT: Barlaston (W - Sunday football), Holt JCB (R), Stretton Eagles (S - Midland Combination Division One)

Division One	P	W	D	L	F	A	Pts
Barton United	28	21	2	5	72	27	65
Stone Dominoes Res.	28	19	5	4	86	43	62
Cheadle Town OB	28	19	4	5	67	30	61
Keele University	28	18	4	6	86	35	58
Chesterton	28	13	7	8	77	48	46
Congleton Athletic	28	12	8	8	53	52	44
Wolstanton Utd Res.	28	13	3	12	70	43	42
Alsager Town Res.	28	11	7	10	48	51	40
Longton Harriers	28	10	6	12	64	62	36
Ashbourne	28	10	4	14	46	66	34
Hanley Town Res.	28	8	7	13	47	62	31
Northwood Town	28	8	4	16	58	89	28
Talbot Athletic	28	5	8	15	31	70	23
Redgate Clayton Res.	28	5	4	19	38	76	19
Hawkins Sports	28	1	1	26	21	110	4

LEAGUE CUP

(Premier and Division One teams)

FIRST ROUND

Abbey Hulton United 3 **Hanley Town** 7
Alsager Town Res. 2 Sandbach United 1
Ashbourne 0 **Congleton Athletic** 6
Ball Haye Green 6 Norton 3 *aet*
Cheadle Town Old Boys 2 Eccleshall AFC 0 *(at Eccleshall)*
Chesterton 0 **Wolstanton United Res.** 1
Florence 4 Goldenhill Wanderers 0
Hanley Town Res. 0 **Barton United** 2
Hawkins Sports 4 Northwood Town 2
Kidsgrove Athletic Res. 1 Congleton Vale 0
Longton Harriers 7 Stone Dominoes Res. 0
Newcastle Town Res. 5 Manor Inne 1
Redgate Clayton Res. 0 **Barlaston** 1
Stretton Eagles 3 Foley 0, Talbot Athletic 1 **Holt JCB** 2
Wolstanton United 1 **Redgate Clayton** 3

SECOND ROUND

Alsager Town Res. 0 **Cheadle Town Old Boys** 1
Ball Haye Green 1 Newcastle Town Res. 0
Barlaston 2 Wolstanton United Res. 0
Florence 2 Kidsgrove Athletic Res. 1 *aet*
Hanley Town 2 **Redgate Clayton** 3
Hawkins Sports 1 **Congleton Athletic** 2
Holt JCB 1 **Stretton Eagles** 2
Longton Harriers 0 **Barton United** 3

QUARTER-FINALS

Barton United 4 **Ball Haye Green** 7 *aet*
Cheadle Town Old Boys 4 Congleton Athletic 1
Florence 0 **Stretton Eagles** 1
Redgate Clayton 2 Barlaston 0

SEMI-FINALS

Cheadle 2 **Ball Haye Green** 3, **Stretton** 3 Redgate Clayton 1

FINAL *(April 7th at Kidsgrove Athletic)*

Ball Haye Green 2 Stretton Eagles 1 *aet*

	Alsager	A'bourne	Barton U	Cheadle	Ch'ton	Cong. A.	Hanley	Hawkins	Keele	Longton	Northw'd	Redgate	Stone	Talbot	Wol'ton
Alsager Town Res.		3-4	3-0	1-1	1-3	1-1	0-2	2-1	1-4	3-3	2-2	1-0	2-1	3-1	2-1
Ashbourne	2-2	***D***	0-1	1-2	2-3	2-3	1-2	4-0	1-4	0-6	4-1	2-1	1-4	3-1	0-0
Barton United	3-1	4-0	***I***	2-0	2-0	5-0	4-2	8-0	0-0	2-0	9-2	3-0	2-3	3-2	2-5
Cheadle Town Old Boys	0-1	3-2	0-1	***V***	2-1	4-0	1-1	5-1	4-1	1-0	1-0	3-0	2-2	3-1	2-0
Chesterton	2-2	3-0	2-2	2-3	***I***	2-2	3-0	13-0	0-3	2-2	3-0	6-0	2-3	2-2	2-1
Congleton Athletic	1-1	0-0	0-3	2-3	3-2	***S***	3-3	3-2	1-0	2-0	4-1	4-2	0-0	3-2	1-3
Hanley Town Res.	1-2	1-1	0-2	1-2	2-4	3-2	***I***	2-1	3-2	2-3	3-3	2-2	2-5	3-0	2-1
Hawkins Sports	1-0	0-1	0-4	0-3	0-2	0-2	2-2	***O***	4-5	1-4	0-2	0-5	3-6	2-3	0-10
Keele University	3-0	7-1	0-2	2-1	1-3	5-1	1-0	9-0	***N***	2-1	4-0	5-0	8-2	0-0	3-1
Longton Harriers	1-3	1-4	2-3	2-2	2-2	1-2	7-2	3-0	3-2		6-4	3-2	0-5	2-2	1-0
Northwood Town	2-3	2-3	1-2	1-6	4-1	0-1	3-1	4-2	3-7	1-1		5-3	1-6	5-1	4-1
Redgate Clayton Res.	2-5	1-3	1-2	0-3	2-2	2-8	2-0	1-0	0-4	6-2	1-2	***O***	2-2	0-0	0-3
Stone Dominoes Res.	3-0	5-0	2-0	4-2	2-5	2-2	2-2	3-1	0-1	4-2	5-1	4-0	***N***	4-1	1-0
Talbot Athletic	3-2	0-3	1-0	0-5	3-4	0-0	1-2	1-0	1-1	0-4	1-1	2-1	0-4	***E***	1-9
Wolstanton United Res.	3-1	6-1	0-1	1-3	2-1	3-2	2-1	3-0	2-2	3-2	8-3	0-2	1-2	1-1	

STAFFORDSHIRE COUNTY SENIOR LEAGUE DIVISION ONE CONSTITUTION 2010-11

ALSAGER TOWN RES. . . . . The Town Ground, Woodland Court, Alsager ST7 2DP 01270 882336
ASHBOURNE . . . . Cockayne Avenue, Ashbourne, Derbyshire DE6 1EJ . . . . None
AUDLEY . . . . Town Fields, Old Road, Bignall, Stoke-on-Trent ST7 8QH 01782 723482
BARTON UNITED . . . . Holland SC, Efflinch Lane, Barton-under-Needwood, Burton-upon-Trent DE13 8ET 01283 713972
CHEADLE TOWN OLD BOYS . . . . South Moorlands Leisure Centre, Allen Street, Cheadle ST10 1HJ 01538 753883
CHESTERTON . . . . Red Street Community Centre, Talke Road, Chesterton, Newcastle-under-Lyme ST5 7AH . . . . None
CONGLETON ATHLETIC . . . . Back Lane Playing Fields, Back Lane, Congleton CW12 4RB . . . . None
HANLEY TOWN RES. . . . . Abbey Lane, Abbey Hulton, Bucknall, Stoke-on-Trent ST2 8AU 01782 267234
HOLT JCB . . . . JCB Lakeside Club, Hollington Road, Rocester, Uttoxeter ST14 5HY 01889 591057
KEELE UNIVERSITY . . . . Sports Centre, Keele University, Keele ST5 5BG 01782 733368
LONGTON HARRIERS . . . . Malthouse, Leek Road, Cellarhead ST3 5DF . . . . None
NORTHWOOD TOWN . . . . Northwood Stadium, Keeling Road, Hanley, Stoke-on-Trent ST1 6PA 01782 234400
REDGATE CLAYTON RES. . . . . Northwood Lane, Clayton, Newcastle-under-Lyme ST5 4BN 01782 717409
STRETTON EAGLES RES. . . . Shobnall Sports & Social Club, Shobnall Road, Burton-on-Trent DE14 2BB 01283 567991
TALBOT ATHLETIC . . . . Bradeley Sports Centre, Chell Heath Road, Bradeley ST6 7LH . . . . None
WOLSTANTON UNITED RES. . Bradwell Com. Cte, Riceyman Rd, Bradwell, Newcastle-u-Lyme ST5 8LF 01782 660818

IN: Audley (P), Holt JCB (R), Stretton Eagles Res. (P)
OUT: Hawkins Sports (R), Stone Dominoes Res. (P)

PRESIDENT'S TROPHY

(Division One and Division Two teams)

FIRST ROUND

AFC Waterhayes 1 **Kidsgrove Athletic Youth** 5
Audley 1 Stone Doms Res. 0
Barton Utd 10 Cheadle SMU 0
Congleton Athletic 1 **Florence Res.** 1 *aet* (5-6p)
Hawkins Sports 7 Tunstall 1
Longton 6 Abbey Hulton Res. 1
Northwood T. 7 Chesterton 5
Norton Y & A 1 **Wolstanton United Res.** 7
Sandbach Res. 2 **Redgate Res.** 4
Stone OA Res. 3 Foley Res. 0
Stretton Res. 0 **Alsager Res.** 1

SECOND ROUND

Audley 2 Kidsgrove Youth 1
Cheadle TOB 3 Hawkins Spts 1
Longton Harr. 4 **Ashbourne** 6
Northwood Town 3 Barton U. 0
Redgate Res. 6 Florence Res. 2
Rugeley 0 Stone Old Alleynians Res. 1 *(Stone OA expelled)*
Talbot Athletic 1 **Alsager Res.** 5
Wolstanton Res. 1 **Hanley Res.** 2

QUARTER-FINALS

Audley 1 Alsager Town Res. 0
Cheadle Town Old Boys 3 Redgate Clayton Res. 2
Hanley Res. 3 Rugeley Rgrs 0
Northwood T. 4 Ashbourne 6

SEMI-FINALS

Hanley Res. 0 **Cheadle TOB** 1
Northwood Town 0 **Audley** 2

FINAL

(April 14th at Norton United)
Audley 0 **Cheadle Town OB** 1

Division Two	P	W	D	L	F	A	Pts
Stretton Eagles Res.	26	23	2	1	115	23	71
Audley	26	19	5	2	86	23	62
Florence Res.	26	19	3	4	74	29	60
Abbey Hulton Utd Res.	26	19	3	4	69	41	60
Stone Old A'nians Res.	26	13	2	11	67	53	41
Keele University Res.	26	12	2	12	64	57	38
Foley Res.	26	10	4	12	68	61	34
Norton Y & A	26	10	3	13	55	60	33
Cheadle SMU	26	9	5	12	51	56	32
Kidsgrove Athletic Yth	26	8	5	13	49	49	29
Sandbach United Res.	26	8	3	15	74	67	27
Rugeley Rangers	26	6	3	17	37	78	21
AFC Waterhayes	26	5	2	19	47	67	17
Tunstall Town	26	0	0	26	16	208	0

	AFC	Abb	Aud	Che	Flor	Fol	Kee	Kids	Nort	Rug	San	Ston	Stre	Tun
AFC Waterhayes		1-2	1-8	4-3	0-4	3-4	3-4	1-3	2-2	4-1	1-5	1-2	1-3	9-0
Abbey Hulton United Res.	2-1	***D***	1-0	1-1	3-1	4-2	0-5	1-0	2-2	1-0	3-3	2-1	4-2	8-2
Audley	3-0	3-0	***I***	4-1	0-0	3-2	2-0	3-2	3-1	5-0	3-2	5-1	0-0	7-0
Cheadle SMU	3-2	1-5	1-2	***V***	1-1	2-1	1-0	0-0	0-1	0-1	2-1	4-2	2-5	8-0
Florence Res.	2-0	3-2	0-2	1-0	***I***	3-1	2-1	5-0	4-2	0-0	3-0	3-2	1-5	8-0
Foley Res.	1-2	1-5	5-5	4-2	2-3	***S***	1-2	1-1	2-0	9-0	2-2	1-0	0-5	8-0
Keele University Res.	2-1	0-2	0-8	4-4	1-4	3-2	***I***	1-2	3-4	5-1	4-4	1-3	2-4	9-0
Kidsgrove Athletic Youth	1-0	1-2	2-2	0-0	0-4	2-3	0-1	***O***	1-2	4-1	1-2	2-2	1-3	11-1
Norton Y & A	3-3	1-2	0-2	4-2	0-4	3-2	0-3	2-0	***N***	2-1	3-4	2-3	2-5	11-0
Rugeley Rangers	3-2	0-1	1-4	1-3	1-3	2-2	2-5	3-4	0-2		2-1	3-2	1-4	7-1
Sandbach United Res.	2-1	2-3	1-4	3-5	1-2	1-3	1-4	1-2	3-1	6-2	***T***	2-3	2-5	9-0
Stone Old Alleynians Res.	1-0	1-3	2-1	6-2	1-4	1-2	2-1	2-0	3-1	1-1	3-2	***W***	1-3	15-1
Stretton Eagles Res.	1-0	7-0	0-0	2-0	3-0	5-0	4-1	6-2	5-0	7-0	4-2	3-1	***O***	12-0
Tunstall Town	2-4	0-10	0-7	1-3	1-9	2-7	0-2	0-7	1-4	0-3	1-12	3-6	0-12	

DIVISION TWO CUP

FIRST ROUND

AFC Waterhayes 4 Sandbach United Res. 2
Audley 2 Stretton Eagles Res. 1
Cheadle SMU 6 Tunstall Town 0
Kidsgrove AY 2 Florence Res. 1
Rugeley 1 **Abbey Hulton Res.** 6

QUARTER-FINALS

AFC Waterhayes 0 **Kidsgrove AY** 5
Audley 4 Cheadle SMU 0
Foley Res. 1 **Stone OA Res.** 3
Norton Y&A 1 Abb. Hulton Res. 0

SEMI-FINALS

Audley 5 Kidsgrove Athletic Yth 0
Norton Y & A 2 Stone OA Res. 1

FINAL

(March 29th at Newcastle Town)
Audley 4 Norton Y & A 0

STAFFORDSHIRE COUNTY SENIOR LEAGUE DIVISION TWO CONSTITUTION 2010-11

ABBEY HULTON UNITED RES. . . . . . Birches Head Road, Abbey Hulton, Stoke-on-Trent ST2 8DD 01782 544232
AUDLEY RES. . . . . Town Fields, Old Road, Bignall, Stoke-on-Trent ST7 8QH. 01782 723482
BRADWELL. . . . . Tricketts Lane, Willaston, Nantwich CW5 6PZ . . . . None
CHEADLE SOUTH MOORLANDS UNITED South Moorlands Leisure Centre, Thorley Drive, Cheadle ST10 1HJ 01538 753883
CHEADLE TOWN OLD BOYS RES. . . . . Malthouse, Leek Road, Cellarhead ST3 5DF . . . . None
FLORENCE RES.. . . . . Florence Sports & Social, Lightwood Road, Longton, Stoke-on-Trent ST3 4JS. 01782 312881
HAWKINS SPORTS . . . . Hawkins Sports Club, Coppice Lane, Cheslyn Hay, Walsall WS6 7EY 01922 417286
KIDSGROVE ATHLETIC YOUTH. . . Birchenwood Sports Centre, Kidsgrove, Stoke-on-Trent ST7 4AY . . . . None
LEA HALL . . . . Lea Hall WMC, Sandy Lane, Rugeley WS15 2LE
MMU CHESHIRE . . . . Alsager Campus, Hassall Road, Alsager ST7 2HL 0161 247 5311
RUGELEY RANGERS. . . . . Green Lane Playing Fields, Rugeley WS15 2GS . . . . None
SANDBACH UNITED RES. . . . . . . Legends Club, Bentley Works, Sunnybank Road, Crewe CW2 6WD 01270 656868
STONE OLD ALLEYNIANS RES. . . . . Springbank Park, Yarnfield Road, Yarnfield, Stone ST15 0NF 01785 761891
TALBOT ATHLETIC RES. . . . . Bradeley Sports Centre, Chell Heath Road, Bradeley ST6 7LH. . . . . None
TUNSTALL TOWN . . . . Alsager Leisure Club, Hassal Road, Alsager ST7 2HP. 01270 529501

IN: Audley Res. (N), Bradwell (N), Cheadle Town Old Boys Res. (N), Hawkins Sports (R), Lea Hall (N - youth football), MMU Cheshire (P Crewe & District League), Talbot Athletic Res. (N)
OUT: AFC Waterhayes (W), Audley (P), Foley Res. (W), Keele University Res. (W), Norton Y & A (W), Stretton Eagles Res. (P)

LEEK & MOORLAND CUP

(Staffordshire County Senior League sides affiliated to Leek & District FA)

FIRST ROUND

Ball Haye Green 2 Manor Inne 0
Barlaston 0 **Hanley Town** 3
Foley 0 **Congleton Vale** 2 *aet*
Newcastle T. Res. 4 Redgate Clay. 1
Stretton E. 2 Kidsgrove Res. 1 *aet*

SECOND ROUND

Chesterton 3 **Congleton Vale** 3 *aet* (4-5p)
Eccleshall AFC 2 **Cheadle T. OB** 3
Hanley Town 2 Florence 0
Northwood T. 0 **Newcastle T. Res.** 10
Norton 0 **Ball Haye Green** 2
Stone Dominoes Res. 1 Goldenhill 0
Stretton Eagles 7 Abbey Hulton 2
Wolstanton Utd 5 Talbot Athletic 2

QUARTER-FINALS

Cheadle TOB 1 **Newcastle T. Res.** 2
Congleton Vale 3 Ball Haye Green 1
Hanley Town 2 **Stretton Eagles** 5
Wolstanton 5 Stone Doms Res. 1

SEMI-FINALS

Newcastle Res. 1 **Congleton V.** 2 *aet*
Stretton Eagles 2 Wolstanton Utd 1

FINAL

(March 26th at Ball Haye Green)
Stretton Eagles 2 Congleton Vale 1

SUFFOLK & IPSWICH LEAGUE

www.suffolkandipswichleague.co.uk

Sponsored by: Kingsley Healthcare

Founded: 1896

Recent champions:

2005: East Bergholt United

2006: East Bergholt United

2007: Grundisburgh

2008: Brantham Athletic

2009: Grundisburgh

	Achilles	Capel Plough	Coplestonians	Crane Sports	East Bergholt	Felixstowe U.	Framlingham	Grundisburgh	Ipswich Ath.	Leiston St M.	Melton St A.	Old Newton U.	Ransomes S.	Stowupland	Westerfield U.	Woodbdge A.
Achilles	***S***	0-2	7-1	1-0	1-2	2-1	3-3	6-4	4-1	1-1	1-2	3-1	3-1	2-1	2-3	3-2
Capel Plough	0-2	***E***	5-0	0-2	2-1	1-1	1-1	1-4	0-1	2-1	1-0	1-1	4-0	5-1	1-1	0-3
Coplestonians	0-2	0-3	***N***	0-1	2-0	1-4	1-1	4-1	1-1	0-0	1-0	2-1	1-3	5-0	4-1	3-1
Crane Sports	2-1	2-0	2-1	***I***	0-0	1-2	1-0	1-0	2-2	2-1	3-1	1-2	0-0	1-0	1-1	2-3
East Bergholt Utd	2-2	4-0	0-0	3-2	***O***	0-0	1-1	2-0	2-4	1-1	2-1	1-2	3-2	4-2	2-1	2-4
Felixstowe United	1-0	3-0	3-0	3-0	1-3	***R***	2-3	0-1	1-1	1-0	3-2	1-1	0-0	8-1	1-0	1-1
Framlingham Town	1-2	1-3	5-3	2-3	4-4	1-5		0-3	0-3	1-2	1-2	6-2	1-0	2-0	3-0	2-2
Grundisburgh	1-2	3-0	1-2	0-2	2-0	2-2	2-1		3-3	4-1	4-1	1-3	1-1	9-1	2-1	1-3
Ipswich Athletic	0-0	0-2	4-1	6-4	1-1	1-2	2-2	5-2	***D***	4-0	3-0	1-1	1-1	1-2	3-2	2-3
Leiston St Marg.	1-4	0-1	3-1	2-1	1-3	0-5	1-3	1-0	0-1	***I***	2-0	2-5	2-2	6-0	3-2	3-4
Melton St Audrys	0-1	1-3	3-2	2-0	0-3	2-2	1-1	1-0	0-4	2-0	***V***	2-3	1-0	4-1	1-2	4-2
Old Newton United	4-2	0-6	4-2	2-3	2-0	2-1	5-4	1-2	1-0	1-0	2-2	***I***	3-0	3-3	2-0	3-1
Ransomes Sports	4-1	2-1	0-1	2-1	0-0	0-2	0-0	0-0	1-0	1-1	1-0	3-1	***S***	2-0	1-1	1-0
Stowupland Falcons	1-10	0-5	1-2	1-2	0-2	1-2	2-5	0-6	2-9	1-4	0-6	1-7	0-5	***I***	1-4	0-3
Westerfield United	1-1	4-2	6-1	0-1	0-2	0-6	2-1	0-0	1-2	3-2	5-2	2-4	0-4	2-0	***O***	1-3
Woodbridge Athletic	2-2	3-3	5-0	3-1	1-0	0-2	1-1	0-1	3-1	5-0	2-2	3-2	1-0	3-4	4-1	***N***

Senior Division		P	W	D	L	F	A	Pts
Old Newton United		30	17	5	8	71	56	56
Felixstowe United	*-4*	30	17	8	5	66	27	55
Achilles		30	16	6	8	71	45	54
Woodbridge Athletic		30	16	6	8	71	48	54
Crane Sports		30	15	4	11	44	41	49
East Bergholt United		30	13	9	8	50	39	48
Capel Plough		30	14	5	11	55	42	47
Grundisburgh		30	13	5	12	60	45	44
Ransomes Sports		30	11	10	9	37	30	43
Ipswich Athletic	*-6*	30	13	9	8	67	44	42
Framlingham Town		30	8	10	12	57	59	34
Melton St Audrys		30	10	4	16	45	55	34
Coplestonians		30	10	4	16	42	68	34
Westerfield United		30	9	5	16	47	62	32
Leiston St Marg.	*-3*	30	8	5	17	41	61	26
Stowupland Falcons		30	2	1	27	27	129	7

Division One		P	W	D	L	F	A	Pts
Haughley United		26	15	4	7	52	41	49
Stanton		26	13	8	5	55	31	47
Thurston		26	15	2	9	61	40	47
Wenhaston United		26	15	1	10	60	31	46
Stonham Aspal		26	14	3	9	63	44	45
Saxmundham Sports		26	13	3	10	49	37	42
St Johns		26	11	6	9	54	42	39
Wickham Market		26	10	9	7	46	45	39
BT Trimley		26	10	7	9	39	44	37
Halesworth Town		26	10	4	12	45	56	34
Mendlesham		26	9	6	11	45	51	33
Cockfield United		26	9	4	13	38	55	31
Bramford Road OB		26	3	4	19	34	77	13
St Edmunds	*-1*	26	3	3	20	39	86	10

SUFFOLK & IPSWICH LEAGUE SENIOR DIVISION CONSTITUTION 2010-11

ACHILLES .... Pauls Social Club, Selmet Close, Ipswich IP2 9BA 01473 604874
CAPEL PLOUGH .... Friars, Capel St Mary, Ipswich IP9 2XS .... None
COPLESTONIANS .... Copleston High School, Copleston Road, Ipswich IP4 5HD 01473 244178
CRANE SPORTS.............. Gresham Sports & Social Club, Tuddenham Road, Ipswich IP4 3QJ 01473 250816
EAST BERGHOLT UNITED .... Gandish Road, East Bergholt, Colchester CO7 6TP........................ 01473 728581
FELIXSTOWE UNITED .... Trimley Sports & Social Club, High Road, Trimley St Martin, Felixstowe IP11 0RJ 01394 275240
FRAMLINGHAM TOWN .... Sports Field, Badlingham Road, Framlingham, Woodbridge IP13 9HS.................. 01728 724038
GRUNDISBURGH .... The Playing Field, Ipswich Road, Grundisburgh, Woodbridge IP13 6TJ 07974 047221
HAUGHLEY UNITED............. King George V Playing Field, Green Road, Haughley IP14 3RA 01449 673460
IPSWICH ATHLETIC .... Bourne Vale Social Ground, Halifax Road, Ipswich IP2 8RE........................ 01473 687685
MELTON ST AUDRYS .... St Audrys Sports & Social Club, Lodge Farm Lane, Melton, Woodbridge IP12 1LX .... None
OLD NEWTON UNITED............... Church Road, Old Newton, Stowmarket IP14 4ED 01449 770035
RANSOMES SPORTS.......... Ransomes Sports & Social Club, Sidegate Avenue, Ipswich IP4 4JJ 01473 726134
STANTON................ Stanton Recreation Ground, Bury Road, Stanton, Bury St Edmunds IP31 2BX........................ None
WESTERFIELD UNITED ..... Rushmere Sports Club, The Street, Rushmere St Andrew, Ipswich IP5 1DE.............. 01473 272525
WOODBRIDGE ATHLETIC RAF Woodbridge, Rock Barracks, Otley Road, Sutton Heath Estate, Woodbridge IP2 3LU............ None

IN: Haughley United (P), Stanton (P)

OUT: Leiston St Margarets (R), Stowupland Falcons (R)

CLUB COLOURS JUNIOR CUP

FINAL *(April 23rd at Framlingham Town)*

Claydon Res. 1 Trimley Red Devils Res. 0

J R TRAVEL RESERVES CUP

FINAL *(April 30th at Needham Market)*

Achilles Res. 3 Woodbridge Athletic Res. 1

OMNICO CUP

FIRST ROUND

AFC Brickmakers 0 **Halesworth** 3
Albion Mills 1 **AFC Crowley** 2
Bramford United 1 BT Trimley 0
Claydon 2 Bramford Road OB 1 *aet*
Cockfield United 1 **Haughley Utd** 2
Dennington United 0 **Waterside** 3
Elmswell 2 AFC Titans 1
Felixstowe Harpers 1 **Sizewell** 3 *aet*
Henley Athletic 4 Mendlesham 3
Parkside United 5 Tacket St BBOB 1
Salvation Army 4 St Clements Hospital 2
Shotley (w/o) v Wickham Market
Sporting 87 2 **St Johns** 3
Sproughton Spts 2 **Somersham** 4 *aet*
St Edmunds 1 **Stonham Aspal** 2
Stradbroke 0 **Saxmundham Sports** 3
Tattingstone Utd 2 Benhall St Mary 1
Trimley Red Devils 3 **Stanton** 4
Ufford Sports 1 **Bildeston Rangers** 5
Walsham-le-Willows A 6 Needham Market Vets 0
Wenhaston United 1 Ipswich Exiles 0

SECOND ROUND

Bramford United 3 Coddenham 2
Cedars Park 1 **Bacton United** 7
Claydon 14 Bildeston Rangers 0
Elmswell 1 **Halesworth Town** 2
Haughley Utd 8 Great Blakenham 0
Salvation Army 0 **AFC Crowley** 3
Saxmundham Sports 12 Woolverstone United 2
Shotley 2 **Parkside United** 4
Sizewell 2 Tattingstone United 1
Somersham 3 Willis 0
St Johns 3 Walsham-le-Willows A 2
Stonham Aspal 0 **Henley Athletic** 2
Thurston 3 **Stanton** 3 *aet* (2-4p)
Waterside 3 AFC Hoxne 1
Wenhaston 20 Ipswich Rovers 0

THIRD ROUND

Achilles 7 Westerfield United 1
AFC Crowley 1 Saxmundham Spts 1 *aet* (5-4p)
Aldeburgh Town 1 **Ransomes Spts** 6
Bacton United 2 Parkside Utd 1 *aet*
Claydon 2 Melton St Audrys 0
Crane Sports 2 Coplestonians 0
Felixstowe United 6 **Leiston St M.** 3 *aet (Felixstowe United expelled)*
Framlingham Town 5 Sizewell 0
Grundisburgh 1 East Bergholt Utd 3 *(East Bergholt United expelled)*
Halesworth Town 1 **Capel Plough** 2
Henley Athletic 4 Waterside 2
Old Newton United 3 Somersham 1
St Johns 6 **Wenhaston** 6 *aet* (2-4p)
Stanton 2 Haughley United 1
Stowupland Falcons 1 **Bramford United** 2 *(at Bramford United)*
Woodbridge Ath. 3 Ipswich Athletic 0

FOURTH ROUND

AFC Crowley 3 Henley Athletic 1
Bramford Utd 1 **Framlingham Town** 6
Claydon 0 **Achilles** 1
Leiston St M. 5 Bacton 5 *aet* (8-7p)
Old Newton United 1 **Stanton** 3
Ransomes Sports 5 Grundisburgh 0
Wenhaston United 1 **Capel Plough** 4
Woodbridge Athletic 0 **Crane Spts** 2

QUARTER-FINALS

AFC Crowley 0 **Ransomes Sports** 5
Capel Plough 1 Crane Sports 0
Leiston St M. 1 **Framlingham Town** 3
Stanton 1 Achilles 1 *aet* (5-4p)

SEMI-FINALS

Framlingham Town 0 **Capel Plough** 1
Stanton 1 **Ransomes Sports** 2

FINAL

(May 4th at Woodbridge Town)
Ransomes Sports 2 Capel Plough 1

Intermediate Division A		P	W	D	L	F	A	Pt
Woodbridge Athletic Res.		26	19	3	4	91	26	60
Crane Sports Res.		26	19	3	4	85	31	60
Grundisburgh Res.		26	15	4	7	75	48	49
Melton St Audrys Res.	*-1*	26	13	7	6	60	35	45
Achilles Res.	*-1*	26	14	3	9	55	48	44
Westerfield United Res.		26	11	6	9	51	34	39
Ransomes Sports Res.		26	9	7	10	39	39	34
Ipswich Athletic Res.	*-1*	26	9	6	11	60	55	32
Old Newton United Res.		26	7	7	12	52	75	28
Coplestonians Res.		26	7	6	13	55	70	27
St Johns Res.		26	7	5	14	42	87	26
East Bergholt United Res.		26	5	10	11	37	47	25
Stanton Res.	*-1*	26	5	4	17	29	84	18
Capel Plough Res.	*-3*	26	4	5	17	27	79	14

Intermediate Division B		P	W	D	L	F	A	Pt
Saxmundham Sports Res.		24	19	2	3	80	22	59
Framlingham Town Res.		24	18	2	4	93	30	56
Felixstowe United Res.		24	16	3	5	59	31	51
Mendlesham Res.	*-1*	24	11	4	9	48	45	36
Stowupland Falcons Res.		24	11	3	10	51	51	36
Wickham Market Res.		24	11	2	11	41	44	35
Leiston St Margarets Res.	*-3*	24	10	2	12	43	48	29
Wenhaston United Res.		24	7	5	12	44	57	26
Stonham Aspal Res.		24	7	5	12	36	50	26
BT Trimley Res.		24	6	8	10	34	48	26
Bramford Road OB Res.	*-5*	24	8	4	12	39	62	23
Thurston Res.	*-1*	24	7	3	14	42	78	23
Cockfield United Res.	*-5*	24	2	3	19	32	76	4

Division Two	P	W	D	L	F	A	Pt
Trimley Red Devils	26	20	3	3	80	34	63
Ipswich Exiles	26	18	5	3	61	27	59
Claydon	26	15	3	8	52	44	48
Bacton United	26	15	1	10	81	51	46
Henley Athletic	26	14	4	8	62	37	46
Sporting 87	26	12	4	10	59	43	40
Somersham	26	12	4	10	50	40	40
Bramford United	26	12	2	12	57	54	38
Parkside United	26	11	3	12	74	56	36
Elmswell	26	9	5	12	51	53	32
Salvation Army	26	8	5	13	52	55	29
AFC Hoxne	26	8	3	15	47	75	27
Stradbroke United	26	5	1	20	45	74	16
Willis	26	1	1	24	18	146	4

Division Three		P	W	D	L	F	A	Pt
Gt Blakenham	*-1*	26	20	2	4	76	38	61
AFC Crowley		26	19	3	4	83	35	60
Coplestonians A		26	17	3	6	92	52	54
Benhall St Mary		26	14	4	8	53	40	46
Albion Mills	*-1*	25	13	3	9	64	41	41
Bildeston Rgrs	*-3*	26	14	1	11	81	72	40
Waterside	*-4*	26	13	3	10	63	54	38
Tacket St BBOB		26	11	2	13	67	56	35
Ufford Sports		26	8	3	15	45	62	27
Sproughton Sports		26	8	3	15	52	76	27
Woolverstone	*-4*	26	8	5	13	67	83	25
Ips. Exiles Res.	*-1*	26	6	2	18	47	86	19
AFC Brickmkrs	*-2*	26	4	7	15	45	89	17
Sizewell Assocs		25	4	3	18	41	92	15

Sizewell Assocs v Albion Mills not played

Division Four		P	W	D	L	F	A	Pt
Walsham-le-W. A		24	19	4	1	79	26	61
Bacton Utd Res.		24	17	3	4	65	27	54
St Clements Hosp.		24	15	1	8	53	36	46
Tattingstone Utd		24	13	4	7	71	34	43
Henley Ath. Res.		24	12	5	7	55	39	41
Aldeburgh Town		24	11	4	9	69	41	37
Coddenham		24	10	6	8	51	42	36
Sporting 87 Res.		24	10	4	10	55	52	34
Claydon Res.		24	9	2	13	48	49	29
Salvation A. Res.		24	6	3	15	37	55	21
Stonham Aspal A		24	6	2	16	37	67	20
Wlv'stone Res.	*-1*	24	3	1	20	41	93	9
Stowupland A	*-6*	24	4	3	17	18	118	9

Division Five		P	W	D	L	F	A	Pt
Albion Mills Res.		24	17	4	3	81	39	55
Bramf'd U. Res.	*-3*	24	17	1	6	67	41	49
AFC Hoxne Res.		24	13	3	8	79	58	42
Benhall SM Res.		24	13	3	8	63	48	42
Old Newton A	*-1*	24	13	4	7	62	54	42
East Bergholt A	*-1*	24	11	4	9	55	42	36
Coddenham Res.		24	11	2	11	59	60	35
Elmswell Res.	-4	24	10	6	8	57	54	32
St Clements Res.		24	8	5	11	51	56	29
Dennington Utd		24	8	5	11	54	70	29
AFC Titans		24	7	4	13	53	61	25
Somersham Res.		24	5	3	16	30	57	18
Sizewell A. Res.		24	1	0	23	22	93	3

Division Six		P	W	D	L	F	A	Pt
Cedars Park		22	17	4	1	118	25	55
Trimley Res.	*+2*	22	14	4	4	85	26	48
Westerfield A	*-2*	22	14	5	3	90	27	45
Crowley Res.	*+1*	22	10	4	8	60	58	35
F'stowe Harpers		22	9	6	7	53	50	33
Needham M. Vets		22	9	5	8	44	41	32
Shotley		22	9	3	10	59	80	30
Sproughton Res.		22	9	1	12	57	55	28
Aldeburgh Res.		22	7	6	9	30	51	27
Stradbroke Res.	*-1*	22	8	1	13	42	74	24
Halesworth Res.		22	4	1	17	40	93	13
Ipswich Rovers	*-6*	22	0	4	18	18	116	-2

SURREY ELITE INTERMEDIATE LEAGUE

Sponsored by:
No sponsor

Founded: 2008

Recent champions:
2009: Eversley

	Batt	Blet	Croy	Elm	EpA	EpE	Esh	Hor	Old	Oxt	Reig	Ripl	Spel	Tong	Wan	Woo
Battersea Ironsides		3-0	8-0	3-2	1-1	2-2	n/a	5-0	0-1	2-0	7-0	5-0	4-2	1-0	1-4	7-2
Bletchingley	2-2		4-2	7-1	2-2	1-6	n/a	6-0	5-0	4-2	1-1	3-1	5-2	4-5	2-4	6-2
Croydon Greenside	3-1	1-1		3-0	0-2	1-2	n/a	2-0	0-5	0-2	4-0	2-3	3-0	0-3	1-1	5-2
Elm Grove	3-8	3-0	0-0		2-1	3-1	9-0	1-1	5-0	2-1	2-0	2-3	0-4	1-2	2-2	4-0
Epsom Athletic	1-2	3-0	W-L	3-0		0-3	n/a	3-1	3-2	1-2	3-3	2-0	4-5	3-0	2-2	7-0
Epsom Eagles	1-1	4-2	4-0	4-1	5-1		n/a	2-1	6-1	2-1	5-0	0-0	4-1	5-2	W-L	11-1
Esher	n/a	0-14	n/a	n/a	n/a	L-W		n/a	n/a	n/a	n/a	n/a	n/a	0-2	n/a	3-2
Horsley	0-3	2-3	0-3	3-2	4-3	1-4	2-2		4-2	2-0	1-1	3-2	1-5	1-2	4-3	4-1
Old Rutlishians	2-5	2-0	2-2	0-1	1-2	1-1	n/a	2-0		5-0	3-4	4-1	1-3	3-2	W-L	1-0
Oxted & District	1-4	1-0	1-0	2-3	1-2	1-0	n/a	2-3	0-1		1-2	1-0	5-1	1-1	1-1	1-2
Reigate Priory	1-2	1-6	2-1	2-1	0-5	0-4	7-1	1-3	0-1	1-1		0-0	1-4	0-6	0-8	2-3
Ripley Village	1-1	2-4	0-0	3-4	1-1	2-3	n/a	4-2	1-1	4-3	4-1		1-2	1-3	2-1	7-0
Spelthorne Sports	0-4	4-1	2-0	4-0	1-2	5-4	n/a	1-4	2-2	2-1	0-2	0-1		2-0	W-L	7-0
Tongham	0-3	3-3	2-2	3-3	0-2	3-3	n/a	1-1	5-1	1-1	3-2	5-1	0-4		1-3	2-0
Wandgas Sports	1-6	1-3	3-3	1-0	1-1	0-5	n/a	0-0	3-0	3-0	4-2	4-1	2-3	2-6		6-2
Woodmansterne Hyde	0-4	1-0	W-L	1-5	1-6	1-3	n/a	0-5	2-3	0-1	0-5	0-6	0-4	0-4	L-W	

LEAGUE CUP

FIRST ROUND

Bletchingley 2 Oxted & District 2 *aet* (4-3p)
Croydon Greenside 4 Horsley 0
Elm Grove 1 **Epsom Athletic** 5
Epsom Eagles 1 **Battersea Ironsides** 2
Esher 1 **Reigate Priory** 6
Old Rutlishians 1 Tongham 0
Wandgas Sports 3 Ripley Village 1
Woodmansterne Hyde 1 **Spelthorne Sports** 3

QUARTER-FINALS

Battersea Ironsides 1 Old Rutlishians 0
Croydon Greenside 1 **Bletchingley** 3
Spelthorne 3 Epsom Ath. 0, **Wandgas** 4 Reigate Priory 0

SEMI-FINALS

Bletchingley 1 Battersea Iron. 1 *aet* (4-3p) *(at Redhill)*
Wandgas 1 Spelthorne 1 *aet* (4-2p) *(at Raynes Pk Vale)*

FINAL *(May 8th at Ashford Town (Middx))*
Bletchingley 0 **Wandgas Sports** 4

Intermediate Division		P	W	D	L	F	A	Pts
Epsom Eagles	*+3*	28	20	5	3	94	33	68
Battersea Ironsides		28	20	5	3	95	30	65
Epsom Athletic		28	15	6	7	66	40	51
Bletchingley	*+3*	28	12	5	11	75	61	44
Spelthorne Sports	*-9*	28	17	1	10	70	52	43
Tongham		28	12	7	9	65	53	43
Old Rutlishians		28	12	4	12	47	57	40
Wandgas Sports	*-3*	28	11	7	10	60	48	37
Elm Grove		28	11	4	13	53	62	37
Horsley		28	11	4	13	51	64	37
Ripley Village		28	9	6	13	52	57	33
Croydon Greenside		28	7	7	14	38	50	28
Oxted & District		28	8	4	16	34	49	28
Reigate Priory	*+3*	28	6	5	17	34	83	26
Woodmansterne Hyde		28	4	0	24	21	116	12

Esher - record expunged

Reserve Division		P	W	D	L	F	A	Pt
Spelthorne Sports Res.		27	19	4	4	74	32	61
Elm Grove Res.		27	18	5	4	88	33	59
Battersea Ironsides Res.		27	17	6	4	78	34	57
Ripley Village Res.	*+3*	27	13	6	8	63	40	48
Epsom Athletic Res.		27	13	3	11	66	53	42
Epsom Eagles Res.	*-1*	27	11	3	13	49	67	35
Croydon Greenside Res.	*-3*	27	8	6	13	51	57	27
Reigate Priory Res.	*+3*	27	5	6	16	45	82	24
Oxted & District Res.		27	6	3	18	38	69	21
W'mansterne Hyde Res.	*-1*	27	3	2	22	28	113	10

RESERVES CUP FINAL
(May 3rd at Carshalton Athletic)
Battersea Ironside Res. 2 Epsom Eagles Res. 1 *aet*

SURREY ELITE INTERMEDIATE LEAGUE INTERMEDIATE DIVISION CONSTITUTION 2010-11

BATTERSEA IRONSIDES...... Battersea Ironsides S&S Club, Burntwood Lane, Earlsfield SW17 0AW............... 020 8874 9913
BLETCHINGLEY.................... Grange Meadow, High Street, Bletchingley RH1 4PE...................... 01883 742844
BURPHAM.................... Sutherland Memorial Park, Clay Lane, Burpham, Guildford GU4 7JU...................... None
COULSDON UNITED........................ Woodplace Lane, Coulsdon CR5 1NE.................................. 01737 557509
CRESCENT ROVERS......... Wallington Sports & Social Club, Mollison Drive, Wallington SM6 9BY.............. 020 8647 2558
CROYDON GREENSIDE...... Croydon Postal Sports Ground, Trenham Drive, Warlingham CR6 9RU..................... None
EPSOM ATHLETIC................ Goals Deckers Tolworth, Kingston Road, Tolworth KT5 9NT..................... 020 8337 2425
HERSHAM ELM GROVE.......... Desborough Island, Walton Lane, Walton-on-Thames KT12 1QP.......................... None
HORSLEY............................ Toms Field, Long Reach, West Horsley KT24 6NE........................ 01483 282516
OXTED & DISTRICT......................... Master Park, Church Lane, Oxted RH8 9LD.............................. 01883 716001
REIGATE PRIORY................ Reigate Priory Cricket Club, off Park Lane, Reigate RH2 8JX...................... 01737 240872
RIPLEY VILLAGE............................ The Green, Ripley, Woking GU23 6AN................................. 01483 225484
SPELTHORNE SPORTS......... Spelthorne Sports Club, 296 Staines Road West, Ashford TW15 1RY................... 01932 783625
TONGHAM.............................. Recreation Ground, Poyle Road, Tongham GU10 1DU........................... 01252 782893
TOOTING BEC..... Raynes Park Vale FC, Prince George's Playing Fields, Grand Drive, Raynes Park SW20 9LN...... 020 8540 8843
VIRGINIA WATER................... The Timbers, Crown Road, Virginia Water GU25 4HS............................ 01344 843811

IN: Burpham (P - Surrey Intermediate League (West) Premier Division), Coulsdon United (R - Combined Counties League Division One), Crescent Rovers (W - Combined Counties League), Tooting Bec (P - Surrey South Eastern Combination Intermediate Division One), Virginia Water (P - Surrey Intermediate League (West) Premier Division)

OUT: Esher (WS - Kingston & District League Premier Division), Old Rutlishians (R - Surrey South Eastern Combination Intermediate League Division One), Wandgas Sports (R - Surrey South Eastern Combination Intermediate League Division One), Woodmansterne Hyde (R - Redhill & District League Premier Division)

Epsom Eagles have merged with Combined Counties League Premier Division side Banstead Athletic

Elm Grove have merged with Hersham (Guildford & Woking Alliance Premier Division) to become Hersham Elm Grove

WEARSIDE LEAGUE

www.wearside-football-league.org.uk

Sponsored by: No sponsor

Founded: 1892

Recent champions:

2005: Darlington Railway Athletic

2006: Whitehaven Amateurs

2007: Birtley Town

2008: New Marske Sports Club

2009: Newton Aycliffe

		P	W	D	L	F	A	Pts
Scarborough Town		36	29	5	2	140	31	92
Ryhope Colliery Welfare		36	27	5	4	97	29	86
Teesside Athletic		36	23	6	7	83	40	75
New Marske Sports Club		36	21	8	7	108	64	71
Cleator Moor Celtic		36	22	3	11	101	65	69
Annfield Plain		36	20	8	8	65	48	68
Easington Colliery		36	18	7	11	84	52	61
Ashbrooke Belford House		36	17	5	14	78	74	56
Kirkbymoorside		36	13	12	11	73	59	51
Jarrow		36	15	5	16	79	64	50
Windscale	*-3*	36	14	9	13	71	59	48
Boldon Community Assoc.		36	14	4	18	77	82	46
Wolviston		36	12	8	16	55	65	44
Houghton Town		36	11	5	20	54	95	38
Silksworth CC		36	11	5	20	45	90	38
Hartlepool		36	6	5	25	50	98	23
Guisborough Town HC		36	6	3	27	46	133	21
Coxhoe Athletic		36	4	6	26	42	112	18
Willington	*-3*	36	4	1	31	33	121	10

WEARSIDE LEAGUE CONSTITUTION 2010-11

ANNFIELD PLAIN .... Derwent Park, West Road, Annfield Plain DH9 8PZ .... None
ASHBROOKE BELFORD HOUSE ... Silksworth Park, Blind Lane, Silksworth, Sunderland SR3 1AX .... None
BOLDON COMMUNITY ASSOCIATION . Boldon Welfare, New Road, Boldon Colliery NE35 9DS .... 0191 536 4180 (Cricket Club)
CLEATOR MOOR CELTIC .... Celtic Club, Birks Road, Cleator Moor CA25 5HR 01946 812476
COXHOE ATHLETIC .... Beechfield Park, Coxhoe DH6 4SD. .... None
DARLINGTON CLEVELAND BRIDGE Eastbourne Sports Complex, Bourne Avenue, Darlington DL1 1LJ 01325 243177/243188
EASINGTON COLLIERY .... Welfare Park Ground, Easington Colliery, Peterlee SR8 3JZ 0191 489 6930
HARTLEPOOL .... Grayfields Enclose, Jesmond Gardens, Hartlepool TS24 8QS .... None
HOUGHTON TOWN .... Houghton Sports Complex, Leyburn Drive, Houghton-le-Spring DH4 5AH 01915 536466
JARROW .... Perth Green Community Association, Inverness Road, Jarrow NE32 4AQ.............. 0191 489 3743
KIRKBYMOORSIDE .... Kirkby Mills, Kirkbymoorside, York YO62 6NS .... None
NEW MARSKE........................ Gurney Street, New Marske, Redcar TS11 8EG 01642 479808
PRUDHOE TOWN .... Kimberley Park, Broomhouse Road, Prudhoe NE42 5EH.................... 01661 835900
REDCAR ATHLETIC .... Green Lane, Redcar TS10 3RW.. None
RYHOPE COLLIERY WELFARE ... Ryhope Rec Park, Ryhope Street, Ryhope, Sunderland SR2 0AB................. 0191 521 2843
SILKSWORTH .... Silksworth Park, Blind Lane, Silksworth, Sunderland SR3 1AX............................ None
STOCKTON TOWN .... Bishopton Road West, Stockton-on-Tees TS19 0QD.............................. None
WILLINGTON.................... Hall Lane Ground, Hall Lane Estate, Willington DL15 0QF 01388 746221
WINDSCALE........................ Falcon Field, Smithfield, Egremont CA22 2QN 01946 820421
WOLVISTON.................. Metcalfe Park, Wynyard Road, Wolviston, Billingham TS22 5NE 07768 321651

IN: Darlington Cleveland Bridge (P - Teesside League Division One), Prudhoe Town (N), Stockton Town (P - Teesside League Division Two)
OUT: Guisborough Town HC (now Guisborough Town Res.) (R - Teesside League Division Two), Scarborough Town (W)
Teesside Athletic become Redcar Athletic

MONKWEARMOUTH CHARITY CUP

PRELIMINARY ROUND

Cleator Moor Celtic 4 Kirkbymoorside 2
Guisborough Town HC 2 Ashbrooke Belford House 1
Silksworth CC 2 Hartlepool 1

FIRST ROUND

Annfield Plain 3 Boldon Community Association 1
Cleator Moor Celtic 5 Willington 0
Easington Colliery 3 **Guisborough Town HC** 3 *aet* (3-5p)
Jarrow (w/o) v Silksworth CC
Ryhope Colliery Welfare 3 New Marske Sports Club 2
Scarborough Town 2 Houghton Town 0
Teesside Athletic 4 Coxhoe Athletic 1
Wolviston 4 Windscale 2

QUARTER-FINALS

Annfield Plain 2 Jarrow 1
Cleator Moor Celtic 2 Teesside Athletic 2 *aet* (4-2p)
Scarborough Town 3 **Ryhope Colliery Welfare** 4
Wolviston 1 Guisborough Town HC 0

SEMI-FINALS

Cleator Moor Celtic 3 Wolviston 1
Ryhope Colliery Welfare 1 Annfield Plain 0

FINAL

(April 5th at Ryhope Colliery Welfare)
Ryhope Colliery Welfare 1 Cleator Moor Celtic 0

	Annfield Plain	Ashbrooke Belford House	Boldon Comm. Association	Cleator Moor Celtic	Coxhoe Athletic	Easington Colliery	Guisborough Town HC	Hartlepool	Houghton Town	Jarrow	Kirkbymoorside	New Marske Sports Club	Ryhope Colliery Welfare	Scarborough Town	Silksworth CC	Teesside Athletic	Willington	Windscale	Wolviston
Annfield Plain		2-0	3-2	2-1	4-0	3-2	2-0	6-3	1-2	1-0	2-2	2-2	1-0	0-1	4-0	1-2	1-0	1-4	4-1
Ashbrooke Belford H.	3-3		2-3	3-1	3-1	3-3	3-0	3-0	1-0	1-0	1-3	3-6	0-4	1-1	6-0	0-6	6-1	1-1	1-4
Boldon Community A.	1-3	0-5		1-1	2-1	1-4	6-0	2-1	3-4	4-1	2-1	2-3	1-4	0-4	3-2	1-1	4-1	1-2	3-2
Cleator Moor Celtic	2-0	5-1	2-1		3-4	1-0	8-0	3-1	4-3	0-5	3-2	5-4	1-3	3-3	3-0	3-4	5-0	4-1	3-1
Coxhoe Athletic	0-0	2-3	3-3	2-5		1-4	5-2	3-3	3-1	1-4	1-5	2-3	0-6	2-6	2-2	0-4	1-2	2-2	0-2
Easington Colliery	2-3	3-1	2-1	3-2	3-0		3-1	3-1	8-1	1-3	2-2	6-1	1-2	1-0	1-1	1-2	2-1	0-0	2-2
Guisboro. Town HC	0-1	0-5	1-0	2-4	3-0	0-7		2-4	2-5	1-7	1-4	1-2	0-1	0-5	1-2	4-6	3-0	3-9	2-2
Hartlepool	1-2	2-3	1-3	2-3	1-0	2-1	1-1		1-8	2-3	2-2	1-1	1-1	1-4	1-2	0-2	2-1	0-2	1-2
Houghton Town	2-2	1-4	0-8	0-5	2-0	0-0	0-3	3-1		2-0	2-2	1-3	1-2	0-2	0-0	0-2	3-2	2-3	1-2
Jarrow	4-1	1-2	2-3	4-0	3-0	3-3	5-2	3-0	2-3		2-1	1-2	0-2	1-6	7-1	1-2	3-0	2-2	3-3
Kirkbymoorside	2-2	1-2	2-1	0-1	0-0	5-1	2-2	4-2	4-0	0-0		3-3	0-4	1-3	1-0	1-2	1-0	1-0	2-2
New Marske SC	0-2	0-2	4-3	2-1	3-2	3-2	14-1	6-0	3-0	5-1	3-3		1-3	2-2	1-2	2-0	3-2	3-2	1-1
Ryhope Colliery Welf	3-0	3-2	5-2	1-0	7-0	0-1	3-1	3-1	5-0	0-0	2-2	3-3		1-2	5-1	3-0	3-0	5-1	1-0
Scarborough Town	4-0	4-0	4-0	5-1	4-1	2-0	6-0	5-0	9-1	5-0	3-5	3-1	1-0		7-2	7-1	8-1	2-0	8-0
Silksworth CC	1-3	3-0	2-1	1-3	2-0	0-5	6-3	0-5	4-1	1-0	0-5	0-4	1-2	0-2		1-4	2-2	2-1	2-2
Teesside Athletic	0-0	5-0	3-0	0-0	5-0	0-1	3-1	3-0	1-1	3-0	1-0	1-2	1-2	1-1	3-0		5-0	4-2	1-1
Willington	0-1	1-5	3-4	0-7	2-3	1-4	0-2	2-5	1-0	1-2	1-2	0-10	1-5	1-7	1-0	1-3		2-0	0-1
Windscale	0-0	2-0	2-2	3-5	5-0	2-0	0-1	4-0	2-3	0-5	3-0	0-0	1-1	3-3	1-0	3-0	5-1		0-1
Wolviston	1-2	2-2	1-3	1-3	3-0	1-2	2-0	2-1	0-1	3-1	3-2	1-2	1-2	0-1	0-2	0-2	3-1	2-3	

SUNDERLAND SHIPOWNERS CUP

PRELIMINARY ROUND

Hartlepool 0 Silksworth CC 0 *aet* (5-3p)
Scarborough Town 2 Annfield Plain 2 *aet* (4-3p)
Willington 1 **Guisborough Town HC** 1 *aet* (3-4p)

FIRST ROUND

Boldon Community Association 4 Easington Colliery 1
Cleator Moor Celtic 2 **Scarborough Town** 8
Guisborough Town HC 2 **Jarrow** 4
Houghton Town 1 **Ryhope Colliery Welfare** 4
Kirkbymoorside 1 **Coxhoe Athletic** 2
New Marske Sports Club 1 Hartlepool 0
Teesside Athletic 2 Windscale 1
Wolviston 2 **Ashbrooke Belford House** 3

QUARTER-FINALS

New Marske Sports Club 3 Boldon Community Association 1
Ryhope Colliery Welfare 2 Ashbrooke Belford House 1
Scarborough Town 3 Jarrow 0 *(at Jarrow)*
Teesside Athletic 3 Coxhoe Athletic 1

SEMI-FINALS

New Marske Sports Club 1 **Scarborough Town** 6
Teesside Athletic 2 Ryhope Colliery Welfare 1

FINAL

(May 3rd at Teesside Athletic)
Teesside Athletic 2 **Scarborough Town** 3

LEAGUE CUP

PRELIMINARY ROUND

Ashbrooke Belford House 0 **New Marske Sports Club** 2
Houghton Town 1 **Jarrow** 3
Willington 1 **Scarborough Town** 2

FIRST ROUND

Boldon Community Association 6 Coxhoe Athletic 1
Easington Colliery 6 Silksworth CC 2
Guisborough Town HC 0 **New Marske Sports Club** 7
Kirkbymoorside 3 Cleator Moor Celtic 1
Hartlepool 1 **Jarrow** 2
Scarborough Town 2 Teesside Athletic 1
Windscale 1 **Annfield Plain** 2
Wolviston 1 **Ryhope Colliery Welfare** 3

QUARTER-FINALS

Easington Colliery 3 Annfield Plain 2
Jarrow 0 **New Marske Sports Club** 2
Kirkbymoorside 0 **Ryhope Colliery Welfare** 3
Scarborough Town 8 Boldon Community Association 1

SEMI-FINALS

New Marske Sports Club 2 Scarborough Town 1
Ryhope Colliery Welfare 1 **Easington Colliery** 2

FINAL

(May 21st at Easington Colliery)
Easington Colliery 3 New Marske Sports Club 2

WEST CHESHIRE LEAGUE

www.west-cheshire.org.uk

Sponsored by: Carlsberg

Founded: 1892

Recent champions:

2005: Heswall
2006: Poulton Victoria
2007: West Kirby
2008: West Kirby
2009: West Kirby

	Blacon YC	C. Ld Res.	Castrol S.	Christleton	E'mere Pt	Halton	Helsby	Heswall	Maghull	Marine R.	Newton	Runcorn T.	Upton AA	V'hall Res.	West Kirby	Willaston
Blacon Youth Club		0-5	0-0	0-2	1-2	0-2	1-2	0-1	0-2	1-1	0-3	1-6	1-5	2-2	1-4	0-1
Cammell Laird Res.	4-0		3-0	1-0	1-3	1-1	1-0	2-0	1-3	5-1	4-0	3-2	4-0	2-0	3-0	3-1
Castrol Social	3-0	0-1	***D***	3-0	0-1	2-1	3-2	0-1	2-2	0-0	4-1	1-1	0-1	2-1	1-1	1-2
Christleton	2-1	1-4	2-0	***I***	0-1	3-2	0-5	3-5	1-4	2-3	2-1	2-4	3-1	1-2	1-7	1-2
Ellesmere Port	1-1	0-2	1-1	0-2	***V***	0-1	0-2	1-2	2-1	0-0	0-4	0-2	1-2	4-3	1-2	4-1
Halton	2-0	0-2	0-1	3-1	0-0	***I***	2-1	1-1	2-2	1-2	0-2	1-2	1-2	2-1	1-5	1-3
Helsby	9-0	0-4	4-1	3-0	1-2	2-0	***S***	1-3	4-2	3-1	2-1	2-3	7-2	4-2	0-2	1-3
Heswall	3-0	2-1	1-1	4-1	4-0	3-0	2-1	***I***	2-1	2-0	3-1	0-4	3-1	3-1	1-2	0-0
Maghull	2-1	0-1	3-1	1-2	4-0	0-0	0-3	2-1	***O***	1-5	1-3	1-2	1-1	4-2	2-3	4-3
Marine Res.	0-0	0-4	3-1	5-2	1-2	0-0	3-1	2-5	0-5	***N***	1-2	0-1	4-1	2-1	0-2	2-2
Newton	3-1	0-2	2-2	3-4	4-0	2-2	3-0	1-2	1-2	2-1		1-0	2-1	1-3	0-0	1-0
Runcorn Town	6-1	0-0	3-0	6-1	2-1	1-2	2-0	1-1	5-1	2-1	2-2	***O***	4-1	5-1	0-0	3-1
Upton Athletic Association	2-1	1-5	2-0	1-1	3-1	1-2	1-4	2-1	3-5	2-0	1-6	0-7	***N***	3-3	0-2	1-4
Vauxhall Motors Res.	2-1	1-6	0-1	0-3	2-0	2-1	2-4	2-4	2-3	2-3	0-2	0-6	2-0	***E***	1-4	1-2
West Kirby	3-0	2-2	1-0	0-1	3-1	2-0	2-1	1-2	0-0	4-0	4-0	4-2	2-0	9-1		2-1
Willaston	2-0	3-4	0-1	2-1	3-1	2-2	4-3	1-2	0-3	3-1	5-1	1-3	3-2	1-4	2-3	

Division One		P	W	D	L	F	A	Pts
Cammell Laird Res.	*-3*	30	24	3	3	81	21	72
West Kirby		30	22	5	3	76	25	71
Runcorn Town		30	21	5	4	87	30	68
Heswall		30	21	4	5	64	34	67
Maghull		30	14	5	11	62	53	47
Newton		30	14	4	12	55	49	46
Helsby	*-3*	30	15	0	15	72	52	42
Willaston	*-3*	30	14	3	13	58	56	42
Castrol Social		30	9	8	13	32	40	35
Marine Res.		30	9	6	15	42	59	33
Ellesmere Port		30	9	4	17	30	55	31
Christleton	*-3*	30	11	1	18	45	74	31
Upton Athletic Assn		30	9	3	18	43	80	30
Halton	*-3*	30	8	8	14	33	46	29
Vauxhall Motors Res.		30	7	2	21	46	85	23
Blacon Youth Club		30	0	5	25	15	82	5

PYKE CUP

FIRST ROUND

Blacon Youth Club 0 **West Kirby** 4
Cammell Laird Res. 1 **Newton** 3 *(at Newton)*
Castrol Social 1 Vauxhall Motors Res. 1 *aet* (4-2p)
Ellesmere Port 0 **Helsby** 2
Maghull 3 Heswall 0 *aet*
Marine Res. 1 **Christleton** 5
Runcorn Town 1 Halton 0
Willaston 3 **Upton Athletic Association** 4

QUARTER-FINALS

Christleton 0 **Castrol Social** 5
Helsby 3 **Upton Athletic Association** 4
Maghull 5 **Newton** 6 *aet*
Runcorn Town 2 **West Kirby** 3

SEMI-FINALS

Castrol Social 3 Newton 1
West Kirby 4 Upton Athletic Association 2

FINAL

(May 6th at Vauxhall Motors)
West Kirby 2 **Castrol Social** 2 *aet* (2-3p)

WEST CHESHIRE LEAGUE DIVISION ONE CONSTITUTION 2010-11

BLACON YOUTH CLUB .... Cairns Crescent Playing Fields, Blacon, Chester CH1 5JF .... None
CAMMELL LAIRD RES............ Kirklands, St Peters Road, Rock Ferry, Birkenhead CH42 1PY 0151 645 3121
CHRISTLETON...................... Little Heath Road, Christleton, Chester CH3 7AH...................... 01244 336589
ELLESMERE PORT .... Whitby Sports & Social Club, Chester Road, Whitby, Ellesmere Port CH66 2NX....... 0151 200 7080/7050
GROVES .... Groves & Social Club, Chester Road, Whitby, Ellesmere Port CH65 4ER 0151 357 3712
HELSBY...................... Helsby Community Sports Club, Chester Road, Helsby WA6 0DL 01928 722267
HESWALL .... Gayton Park, Brimstage Road, Heswall CH60 1XG....................... 0151 342 8172
MAGHULL .... Old Hall Field, Hall Lane, Maghull L31 7BB.......................... 0151 526 7320
MARINE RES.................... Arriva Stadium, College Road, Crosby, Liverpool L23 3AS 0151 924 1743/4046
MARSHALLS.................. IM Marsh Campus, Barkhill Road, Aigburth, Liverpool L17 6BD................ 0151 231 5233
NEWTON .... Millcroft, Frankby Road, Greasby CH47 0NB 0151 677 8282
SOUTHPORT TRINITY.............. Rookery Sports Ground, Roe Lane, Southport PR9 7HR 01704 225841
UPTON ATHLETIC ASSOCIATION... Cheshire County S&S, Plas Newton Lane, Chester CH2 1PR 01244 318167
VAUXHALL MOTORS RES.... Vauxhall Sports Ground, Rivacre Road, Hooton, Ellesmere Port CH66 1NJ 0151 328 1114/327 2294
WEST KIRBY .... Marine Park, Greenbank Road, West Kirby CH48 5HL.......................... None
WILLASTON................. Johnston Recreation Ground, Neston Road, Willaston CH64 2TL........................ None

IN: Marshalls (P), Southport Trinity (P)
OUT: Halton (F), Runcorn Town (P - North West Counties League Division One)
Castrol Social become Groves

COOPER SMITH TROPHY

Not contested in 2009-10

Division Two	P	W	D	L	F	A	Pts
Southport Trinity	28	18	5	5	70	31	59
Marshalls	28	18	4	6	73	40	58
Chester Nomads	28	17	7	4	54	30	58
Mossley Hill Athletic	28	17	6	5	56	32	57
New Brighton	28	14	10	4	55	28	52
Maghull	28	11	7	10	48	35	40
Ashville	28	10	6	12	49	39	36
AFC Bebington Athletic	28	10	5	13	46	54	35
Mallaby	28	11	2	15	38	53	35
Heswall Res.	28	9	6	13	44	52	33
FC Pensby	28	10	3	15	45	63	33
West Kirby Res.	28	8	6	14	54	58	30
Bronze Social	28	7	4	17	41	74	25
Grange Athletic	28	7	1	20	37	80	22
Capenhurst Villa	28	6	2	20	30	71	20

WEST CHESHIRE BOWL

FIRST ROUND

Capenhurst Villa 3 Bronze Social 0
FC Pensby 0 **Ashville** 1
Grange Athletic 0 **Heswall Res.** 3
Maghull Res. 3 Mallaby 0
Marshalls 2 Southport Trinity 1
Mossley Hill Athletic 2 New Brighton 0
West Kirby Res. 3 AFC Bebington Athletic 1

QUARTER-FINALS

Ashville 2 Maghull Res. 1 *aet*
Marshalls 5 Capenhurst Villa 0
Mossley Hill Athletic 4 Heswall Res. 0
West Kirby Res. 4 **Chester Nomads** 5 *aet*
(at Chester Nomads)

SEMI-FINALS

Ashville 1 **Chester Nomads** 4
Marshalls 0 **Mossley Hill Athletic** 1

FINAL

(April 27th at Runcorn Town)
Chester Nomads 1 **Mossley Hill Athletic** 3

	AFC Bebington	Ashville	Bronze Social	Capenhurst Villa	Chester Nomads	FC Pensby	Grange Athletic	Heswall Res.	Maghull	Mallaby	Marshalls	Mossley Hill Ath.	New Brighton	Southport Trinity	West Kirby Res.
AFC Bebington Athletic		0-0	3-0	2-1	0-2	3-3	2-1	2-4	3-2	4-1	0-2	4-5	3-3	0-1	1-1
Ashville	1-2	***D***	1-2	5-0	3-0	3-3	4-0	3-0	1-0	0-1	3-1	1-2	0-0	1-4	3-1
Bronze Social	1-3	2-1	***I***	5-1	1-5	0-3	0-1	0-0	1-1	1-2	1-5	2-3	2-3	1-2	3-3
Capenhurst Villa	2-1	2-1	3-5	***V***	0-1	3-2	1-0	0-3	1-0	1-2	1-2	0-3	1-4	1-5	1-4
Chester Nomads	2-0	3-1	2-2	3-2	***I***	2-0	3-0	4-2	1-1	1-0	0-1	1-1	2-2	1-1	2-0
FC Pensby	3-2	2-0	2-1	1-1	1-2	***S***	1-2	2-1	0-2	1-0	1-3	1-0	1-3	2-3	0-2
Grange Athletic	2-1	1-1	5-2	2-3	0-1	3-4	***I***	2-3	1-4	4-1	0-3	3-6	0-3	0-7	3-2
Heswall Res.	0-1	2-0	1-3	2-1	2-2	4-1	2-3	***O***	5-2	1-1	1-3	0-0	1-1	1-1	4-2
Maghull	5-1	0-3	4-1	2-0	1-1	4-1	2-0	3-0	***N***	5-0	1-2	0-0	0-1	0-0	1-4
Mallaby	2-0	0-2	4-1	3-1	1-2	1-2	4-1	3-1	3-1		1-5	0-4	1-4	2-3	2-1
Marshalls	0-2	0-5	6-0	5-1	5-3	5-3	4-2	1-2	1-2	1-1		2-2	1-1	4-1	2-0
Mossley Hill Athletic	4-1	3-2	1-2	1-0	0-2	5-1	2-1	2-0	0-0	1-0	1-3	***T***	2-1	2-1	3-0
New Brighton	3-0	5-1	0-1	0-0	1-3	3-0	3-0	3-1	1-1	2-0	0-0	2-3	***W***	1-0	0-0
Southport Trinity	1-3	1-1	3-0	5-1	1-0	3-0	3-0	3-1	2-1	1-2	3-1	2-0	3-3	***O***	5-0
West Kirby Res.	2-2	2-2	6-1	2-1	1-3	2-4	8-0	3-0	1-3	2-0	2-5	0-0	1-2	2-5	

WEST CHESHIRE LEAGUE DIVISION TWO CONSTITUTION 2010-11

AFC BEBINGTON ATHLETIC . . . . Unilever Sports Ground, Bromborough CH62 3PU. . . . . None
ASHVILLE. . . . . Villa Park, Cross Lane, Wallasey Village, Wallasey CH45 8RH 0151 638 2127
BRONZE SOCIAL . . . . Unilever Sports Ground, Bromborough CH62 3PU. . . . . None
CAPENHURST VILLA. . . . . Capenhurst Sports Ground, Capenhurst Lane, Capenhurst CH1 6ER . . . . None
CHESTER NOMADS . . . . Garrison Ground, Eaton Road, Chester CH4 7ER. . . . . None
HALE . . . . Hale Park, The High Street, Hale Village, Liverpool L24 4AF. . . . . None
HESWALL RES. . . . . Gayton Park, Brimstage Road, Heswall CH60 1XG. 0151 342 8172
MAGHULL RES. . . . . Old Hall Field, Hall Lane, Maghull L31 7BB. 0151 526 7320
MALLABY. . . . . Unilever Sports Ground, Bromborough CH62 3PU. . . . . None
MOSSLEY HILL ATHLETIC . . . . Mossley Hill Athletic Club, Mossley Hill Road, Liverpool L18 8DX 0151 724 4377
NEW BRIGHTON . . . . Harrison Drive, Wallasey Village, Wallasey CH45 3HL . . . . None
PRESCOT CABLES RES. . . . St Helens Sports College, Elton Head Road, Lea Green, St Helens WA9 5AU. 01744 678859
RICHMOND RAITH ROVERS . . . . Childwall Sports College, Queens Drive, Fiveways L15 6XZ 0151 722 1561
WEST KIRBY RES. . . . . Marine Park, Greenbank Road, West Kirby CH48 5HL . . . . None

IN: Hale (P), Prescot Cables Res. (P), Richmond Raith Rovers (P)

OUT: FC Pensby (W), Grange Athletic (F), Marshalls (P), Southport Trinity (P)

Division Three		P	W	D	L	F	A	Pts
Hale		24	19	1	4	85	42	58
Prescot Cables Res.		24	17	4	3	72	18	55
Richmond Raith Rovers		24	17	4	3	70	30	55
Runcorn Town Res.		24	17	3	4	76	29	54
Ashville Res.		24	13	4	7	61	39	43
Christleton Res.		24	13	2	9	51	32	41
Manor Athletic		24	10	3	11	45	55	33
Ellesmere Port Res.		24	8	3	13	39	58	27
Upton AA Res.	*-3*	24	7	2	15	41	56	20
Blacon Youth Club Res.		24	5	2	17	19	81	17
Capenhurst Villa Res.		24	3	4	17	20	70	13
Mossley Hill Ath. Res.	*-3*	24	4	3	17	32	58	12
Mersey Royal	*-6*	24	4	3	17	30	73	9

Southport Trinity Res., St Werburghs - records expunged

WEST CHESHIRE SHIELD

FIRST ROUND

Ashville Res. 4 Southport Trinity Res. 0
Blacon Youth Club Res. 0 **Christleton Res.** 6
Capenhurst Villa Res. 3 **Prescot Cable Res.** 5
Ellesmere Port Res. 3 Hale 1
Mersey Royal (w/o) v St Werburghs
Richmond Raith Rovers 4 Mossley Hill Athletic Res. 0
Runcorn Town Res. 5 Upton AA Res. 3

QUARTER-FINALS

Ashville Res. 2 Ellesmere Port Res. 2 *aet* (4-2p)
Christleton Res. 1 **Richmond Raith Rovers** 3
Mersey Royal 1 Manor 1 *aet* (4-5p) *(Manor expelled)*
Runcorn Town Res. 2 **Prescot Cables Res.** 4 *aet*

SEMI-FINALS

Ashville Res. 1 Richmond Raith Rovers 0 *aet*
Prescot Cables Res. 4 Mersey Royal 1

FINAL *(April 29th at Vauxhall Motors)*
Ashville Res. 1 Prescot Cables Res. 0 *aet*

	Ashville Res.	Blacon Res.	C'hurst Res.	Christ'ton Res.	E'mere Pt Res.	Hale	Manor Athletic	Mersey Royal	Moss. HA Res.	Prescot Res.	Richmond RR	Runc. T. Res.	S'port T. Res.	St Werburghs	Upton AA Res.
Ashville Res.	***D***	2-0	6-0	1-0	1-1	2-4	5-1	1-0	4-0	2-4	5-0	1-2	n/a	3-0	5-3
Blacon Youth Club Res.	1-6	***I***	1-2	2-2	2-1	1-1	1-3	0-4	2-3	0-14	0-5	0-4	3-3	6-1	1-4
Capenhurst Villa Res.	0-3	0-1	***V***	1-6	0-1	1-4	1-1	2-2	1-1	0-2	1-4	0-6	1-4	2-0	2-2
Christleton Res.	1-0	2-0	3-0	***I***	7-2	2-1	4-0	6-0	2-0	0-2	1-4	0-2	3-2	7-3	1-0
Ellesmere Port Res.	1-1	6-0	4-1	1-2	***S***	1-3	2-5	1-0	2-1	1-2	0-2	2-1	n/a	3-3	1-1
Hale	5-3	8-1	4-2	4-1	8-2	***I***	2-1	6-1	6-1	2-1	4-1	4-3	W-L	16-0	4-3
Manor Athletic	3-4	1-2	3-2	0-1	3-2	2-4	***O***	3-1	2-1	1-1	1-3	1-2	1-3	5-4	2-1
Mersey Royal	2-2	3-0	1-2	2-2	2-1	1-3	1-3	***N***	2-3	1-4	0-5	2-4	n/a	n/a	0-3
Mossley Hill Athletic Res.	0-3	0-1	2-0	0-2	1-3	1-3	1-3	6-0		0-1	2-2	4-7	4-1	n/a	1-5
Prescot Cables Res.	4-0	1-2	6-0	2-1	6-0	3-1	4-2	5-0	1-0		1-2	0-0	8-1	4-0	4-0
Richmond Raith Rovers	1-1	4-1	4-1	2-1	5-2	4-2	8-0	3-0	1-1	0-0	***T***	1-2	2-1	10-0	1-0
Runcorn Town Res.	6-0	4-0	3-0	3-2	3-0	1-2	2-2	4-0	3-2	2-2	1-3	***H***	14-0	n/a	5-1
Southport Trinity Res.	1-2	4-0	3-0	0-2	1-5	0-4	1-1	3-3	0-3	n/a	L-W	3-3	***R***	2-2	2-1
St Werburghs	0-5	5-0	3-5	n/a	1-2	2-5	n/a	1-4	2-3	n/a	n/a	3-2	3-1	***E***	n/a
Upton AA Res.	0-3	1-0	0-1	3-2	1-2	3-0	0-2	4-5	2-1	1-2	3-5	0-6	6-3	4-2	***E***

WEST CHESHIRE LEAGUE DIVISION THREE CONSTITUTION 2010-11

AFC BEBINGTON ATHLETIC RES. . . . . . . Unilever Sports Ground, Bromborough CH62 3PU . . . . None
ASHVILLE RES. . . . . Villa Park, Cross Lane, Wallasey Village, Wallasey CH45 8RH 0151 638 2127
BLACON YOUTH CLUB RES. . . . . Cairns Crescent Playing Fields, Blacon, Chester CH1 5JF . . . . None
CAPENHURST VILLA RES. . . . . . Capenhurst Sports Ground, Capenhurst Lane, Capenhurst CH1 6ER . . . . None
CHRISTLETON RES. . . . . Little Heath Road, Christleton, Chester CH3 7AH 01244 336589
ELLESMERE PORT RES. . . Whitby Sports & Social Club, Chester Road, Whitby, Ellesmere Port CH66 2NX 0151 200 7080/7050
HALE RES. . . . . Hale Park, The High Street, Hale Village, Liverpool L24 4AF . . . . None
HELSBY RES. . . . . Helsby Community Sports Club, Chester Road, Helsby WA6 0DL 01928 722267
MANOR ATHLETIC . . . . OC Sports & Leisure Club, 28 Bridle Road, Bromborough CH62 6AR 0151 356 6159
MARSHALLS RES. . . . . IM Marsh Campus, Barkhill Road, Aigburth, Liverpool L17 6BD 0151 231 5233
MERSEY ROYAL . . . . Unilever Sports Ground, Bromborough CH62 3PU . . . . None
MERSEYSIDE POLICE . . . . Riversdale Road, Aigburth, Liverpool L19 3QN 0151 724 5214
MOSSLEY HILL ATHLETIC RES. . . Mossley Hill Athletic Club, Mossley Hill Road, Liverpool L18 8DX 0151 724 4377
NEW BRIGHTON RES. . . . . Harrison Drive, Wallasey Village, Wallasey CH45 3HL . . . . None
RUNCORN LINNETS RES. . . . . Millbank Linnets Stadium, Murdishaw Avenue, Runcorn WA7 6HP 07050 801733
UPTON ATHLETIC ASSOCIATION RES. . . . . Plas Newton Lane, Chester CH2 1PR 01244 318167

IN: AFC Bebington Athletic Res. (formerly AFC Bebington Athletic Youth) (P - West Cheshire League Youth Division), Hale Res. (formerly Hale Youth) (P - West Cheshire League Youth Division), Helsby Res. (P - Chester & District League Premier Division), Marshalls Res. (P - I Zingari Combination Division One), Merseyside Police (N), New Brighton Res. (P - Birkenhead & Wirral League Division One), Runcorn Linnets Res. (N)
OUT: Southport Trinity Res. (WS), St Werburghs (WS), Runcorn Town Res. (S - Cheshire League Division Two)

BILL WEIGHT MEMORIAL CUP

(Divisional champions and Pyke Cup holders)

SEMI-FINALS

Helsby 0 **Newton** 1
West Kirby 3 FC Pensby 1

FINAL

(September 8th at Ashville)
Newton 1 **West Kirby** 3

WEST LANCASHIRE LEAGUE

westlancashireleague.pitchero.com

Sponsored by: Sports 360

Founded: 1904

Recent champions:
2005: Kirkham & Wesham
2006: Kirkham & Wesham
2007: Kirkham & Wesham
2008: Garstang
2009: Charnock Richard

	Darwen	B'pool R.	Charn R.	Coppull	Dalton	Eagley	Euxton	Freckl't'n	Fulwood	Garstang	Has. SM	Lostock	Poulton	S'clough	Tempest	Turton	Vic'town
AFC Darwen	***P***	0-3	2-0	3-1	2-3	0-2	0-2	1-1	0-1	3-2	1-0	0-1	0-0	1-0	1-2	1-0	0-6
Blackpool Wren Rovers	1-2	***R***	5-1	4-0	5-0	1-0	3-0	3-1	1-0	1-2	7-0	3-1	6-0	1-0	3-2	4-0	2-1
Charnock Richard	4-1	2-2	***E***	3-1	6-4	1-2	3-1	2-1	1-2	1-5	2-3	5-2	0-4	2-0	7-0	3-2	1-2
Coppull United	0-3	1-4	3-2	***M***	1-0	0-3	0-3	0-0	0-2	2-1	3-1	1-1	3-1	2-1	4-1	1-0	0-1
Dalton United	1-0	5-2	0-6	3-1	***I***	2-1	2-1	4-0	1-2	3-4	0-2	0-2	4-2	2-1	2-5	3-2	1-2
Eagley	1-2	2-2	2-2	2-0	0-3	***E***	3-0	4-2	1-3	1-1	4-1	3-5	0-2	1-1	1-2	3-3	1-1
Euxton Villa	1-3	1-1	2-2	1-2	1-0	1-1	***R***	3-1	0-0	0-2	1-1	2-2	1-4	1-0	2-1	2-2	1-2
Freckleton	1-2	2-4	1-2	1-0	4-1	0-0	1-0		2-1	0-2	2-0	0-3	0-2	0-0	5-1	0-2	3-2
Fulwood Amateurs	4-1	1-0	0-1	1-0	2-0	2-1	1-1	2-1		4-1	2-0	0-2	2-1	5-4	2-3	2-0	1-5
Garstang	1-1	2-1	0-2	0-1	3-1	2-1	1-2	1-2	1-1	***D***	1-0	0-1	2-2	1-0	3-2	2-0	0-0
Haslingden St Mary's	0-3	1-4	1-3	1-3	2-3	3-0	0-2	2-0	3-2	1-1	***I***	0-0	1-0	2-2	1-1	0-3	1-0
Lostock St Gerards	0-2	1-1	0-2	4-1	1-1	1-1	0-0	0-0	2-1	2-2	5-2	***V***	3-1	4-1	2-1	2-3	7-0
Poulton Town	4-1	2-1	1-1	1-0	4-0	4-0	4-0	5-1	2-1	3-0	3-1	1-1	***I***	2-3	4-0	3-2	2-1
Stoneclough	2-0	3-5	1-3	3-3	2-1	2-1	2-1	2-2	2-2	0-5	1-4	0-3	2-1	***S***	3-2	2-0	4-1
Tempest United	5-4	0-2	1-6	2-3	2-0	2-2	1-1	1-2	1-4	1-4	0-0	7-4	2-2	6-0	***I***	0-7	1-2
Turton	4-1	5-1	4-4	3-1	1-2	1-2	0-6	1-1	0-4	2-1	2-1	0-3	3-0	1-3	5-0	***O***	1-2
Vickerstown CC	3-1	1-3	1-6	0-3	0-0	1-1	3-4	2-1	0-1	0-3	2-1	1-1	3-3	4-1	2-3	1-2	***N***

Premier Division		P	W	D	L	F	A	Pts
Blackpool Wren Rovers		32	21	4	7	86	39	67
Fulwood Amateurs		32	19	4	9	58	38	61
Poulton Town		32	17	6	9	70	45	57
Charnock Richard	*-3*	32	18	5	9	86	56	56
Lostock St Gerards		32	15	11	6	66	42	56
Garstang		32	15	7	10	56	41	52
Vickerstown CC		32	12	6	14	52	60	42
AFC Darwen		32	13	3	16	42	56	42
Coppull United		32	13	3	16	41	56	42
Dalton United		32	13	2	17	52	69	41
Euxton Villa		32	10	10	12	44	48	40
Stoneclough		32	10	6	16	48	69	36
Eagley		32	8	11	13	47	53	35
Freckleton		32	9	7	16	38	55	34
Tempest United		32	9	5	18	58	90	32
Turton	*-9*	32	12	4	16	61	61	31
Haslingden St Mary's		32	8	6	18	36	63	30

RICHARDSON CUP

PRELIMINARY ROUND
Charnock Richard 3 Haslingden St Mary's 2

FIRST ROUND
AFC Darwen 2 **Euxton Villa** 3 *aet*
Blackpool Wren Rovers 2 Charnock Richard 1
Coppull United 0 **Lostock St Gerards** 0 *aet* (5-6p)
Freckleton 3 Eagley 2
Poulton Town 3 **Garstang** 5
Stoneclough 1 **Vickerstown CC** 2
Tempest United 2 **Dalton United** 3
Turton 0 **Fulwood Amateurs** 2

QUARTER-FINALS
Blackpool Wren Rovers 0 **Fulwood Amateurs** 2
Dalton United 1 Garstang 0
Euxton Villa 3 Lostock St Gerards 1
Vickerstown CC 0 **Freckleton** 1

SEMI-FINALS
Freckleton 2 Dalton United 0 *(at Milnthorpe)*
Fulwood Amateurs 2 Euxton Villa 1 *aet (at Croston)*

FINAL
(May 5th at LCFA, Leyland)
Freckleton 1 **Fulwood Amateurs** 2 *aet*

WEST LANCASHIRE LEAGUE PREMIER DIVISION CONSTITUTION 2010-11

3LACKPOOL WREN ROVERS .... Bruce Park, School Road , Marton, Blackpool FY4 5EL 01253 760570
:HARNOCK RICHARD .... Mossie Park, Charter Lane, Charnock Richard, Chorley PR7 5LZY................. 01257 794288
:OPPULL UNITED .... Springfield Road, Coppull PR7 5FJ 01257 795190
)ALTON UNITED .... Railway Meadow, Beckside Road, Dalton-in-Furness LA15 8DP 07743 271736
:AGLEY......................... Eagley Sports Complex, Dunscar Bridge, Bolton BL7 9PQ 01204 306830
:UXTON VILLA .... Jim Fowler Memorial Ground, Runshaw Hall Lane, Euxton, Chorley PR7 6HH.................... None
'LEETWOOD HESKETH .... Fylde Road, Southport PR9 9XH 01704 227968
'RECKLETON............... Hodgson Memorial Ground, Bush Lane, Freckleton, Preston PR1 1SB 01772 679174
'ULWOOD AMATEURS .... Lightfoot Lane, Fulwood, Preston PR2 3LP 01772 861827
3ARSTANG .... Riverside Community Centre, High Street, Garstang PR3 1AF................... 01995 601586
.OSTOCK ST GERARDS .... Wateringpool Lane, Lostock Hall PR5 5UA.............................. None
'OULTON TOWN .... Cottam Hall Playing Fields, Blackpool Old Road, Poulton-le-Fylde FY6 7RH 01253 896150
3TONECLOUGH....... Brook Street, opposite Europa Business Park, Stoneclough, Kearsley, Bolton BL4 7RX .... None
'EMPEST UNITED............... Tempest Road, Chew Moor Village, Lostock, Bolton BL6 4HP 01942 811938
'HORNTON CLEVELEYS............ Bourne Road, Cleveleys, Thornton Cleveleys FY5 4QA 01253 869666
/ICKERSTOWN CC............... Park Vale, Mill Lane, Walney, Barrow-in-Furness LA14 3ND .... None

V: Fleetwood Hesketh (P), Thornton Cleveleys (P)

)UT: AFC Darwen (P - North West Counties League Division One), Haslingden St Mary's (R), Turton (R)

WILF CARR MEMORIAL TROPHY

(Premier Division champions v Richardson Cup holders)

(August 1st at Charnock Richard)

Charnock Richard 2
Dalton United 1

Division One		P	W	D	L	F	A	Pts
Thornton Cleveleys		26	22	2	2	92	20	68
Fleetwood Hesketh		26	18	5	3	65	28	59
Slyne-with-Hest		26	14	7	5	65	36	49
Norcross & Warbreck		26	13	7	6	57	37	46
Hawcoat Park		26	12	6	8	53	43	42
Burnley United	*-6*	26	12	7	7	60	43	37
Crooklands Casuals		26	10	5	11	67	54	35
Hesketh Bank		26	10	5	11	55	54	35
Wyre Villa		26	9	4	13	44	55	31
Millom		26	8	5	13	50	59	29
Mill Hill St Peters		26	8	3	15	49	56	27
Croston Sports		26	7	5	14	38	47	26
Milnthorpe Corinthians		26	6	5	15	41	60	23
Crosshills	*-3*	26	0	0	26	19	163	-3

PRESIDENT'S CUP

FIRST ROUND

Crosshills 0 **Millom** 9
Croston Sports 2 Milnthorpe Corinthians 1
Mill Hill St Peters 1 Hawcoat Park 0
Norcross & Warbreck 1 **Hesketh Bank** 2
Thornton Cleveleys 1 **Burnley United** 4
Wyre Villa 1 **Slyne-with-Hest** 6

QUARTER-FINALS

Crooklands Casuals 1 **Fleetwood Hesketh** 3
Mill Hill St Peters 2 Burnley United 2 *aet* (7-6p)
Millom 3 **Hesketh Bank** 0 *(Millom expelled)*
Slyne-with-Hest 6 Croston Sports 0

SEMI-FINALS

Fleetwood Hesketh 1 Mill Hill St P. 0 *(at Croston)*
Slyne-with-Hest 0 **Hesketh Bank** 3
(at Blackpool Wren Rovers)

FINAL

(May 6th at AFC Fylde)

Fleetwood Hesketh 1 **Hesketh Bank** 3

	Burnley United	Crooklands Casuals	Crosshills	Croston Sports	Fleetwood Hesketh	Hawcoat Park	Hesketh Bank	Mill Hill St Peters	Millom	Milnthorpe Corries	Norcross & W'breck	Slyne-with-Hest	Thornton Cleveleys	Wyre Villa
Burnley United		2-1	11-3	1-0	1-2	3-5	3-2	3-0	3-2	3-3	2-3	1-1	0-1	3-1
Crooklands Casuals	1-4	***D***	17-0	1-4	2-2	1-4	1-0	3-1	2-2	2-0	3-2	1-1	0-2	4-0
Crosshills	0-1	4-5	***I***	0-6	0-6	1-3	1-3	0-6	1-2	0-2	1-6	0-6	0-11	2-3
Croston Sports	0-1	3-2	4-1	***V***	0-2	1-2	2-5	5-1	2-2	1-2	1-1	0-4	0-2	3-2
Fleetwood Hesketh	3-1	2-1	7-1	1-0	***I***	2-0	6-2	2-1	3-3	2-0	6-0	1-1	1-1	2-0
Hawcoat Park	2-1	3-2	8-1	3-1	3-0	***S***	1-1	2-0	1-1	3-2	1-1	2-3	0-1	1-2
Hesketh Bank	2-2	1-2	5-0	0-0	1-4	4-1	***I***	2-1	3-0	3-1	1-5	4-0	2-2	2-3
Mill Hill St Peters	1-1	3-4	8-1	2-0	0-1	3-2	1-1	***O***	5-4	5-2	1-2	2-2	0-2	2-4
Millom	2-6	2-1	6-0	0-1	0-3	1-2	5-2	5-1	***N***	3-1	0-6	3-1	2-3	2-2
Milnthorpe Corinthians	0-1	2-2	8-0	2-2	4-2	0-0	0-3	1-2	4-0		2-2	3-2	0-3	1-4
Norcross & Warbreck	1-1	1-1	8-0	2-0	1-2	1-1	3-2	1-0	1-0	4-1	***O***	1-0	1-3	0-0
Slyne-with-Hest	1-1	4-2	5-0	0-0	3-0	2-2	6-1	3-1	3-2	4-0	5-1	***N***	2-1	3-2
Thornton Cleveleys	4-2	3-2	13-0	5-0	1-2	3-1	3-1	3-1	2-0	5-0	3-1	4-1	***E***	8-0
Wyre Villa	2-2	2-4	3-2	3-2	1-1	5-0	1-2	0-1	0-1	2-0	0-2	1-2	1-3	

WEST LANCASHIRE LEAGUE DIVISION ONE CONSTITUTION 2010-11

BAC/EE SPRINGFIELD. . . . . BAC Sports Ground, South Meadow Lane, Preston PR1 8JP 01772 4643
BURNLEY UNITED. . . . . Barden Sports Ground, Barden Lane, Burnley BB10 1JQ . . . . No
CROOKLANDS CASUALS . . . . Longlands Park, Greystone Lane, Dalton-in-Furness LA15 8PX 01229 4650
CROSTON SPORTS . . . . Old Emmanuel School, Westhead Road, Croston, Leyland PR26 9RR. 01772 6002
HASLINGDEN ST MARY'S . . . . South Shore Street, Haslingden, Rossendale BB4 5DX 01706 2218
HAWCOAT PARK . . . . Hawcoat Park Sports Ground, Hawcoat Lane, Barrow-in-Furness LA14 4HF 01229 8252
HESKETH BANK . . . . Centenary Sports Ground, Station Road, Hesketh Bank PR4 6SR. . . . . No
LONGRIDGE TOWN . . . . Inglewhite Road, Longridge, Preston PR3 2DB . . . . No
MILL HILL ST PETERS . . . . Opposite Mill Hill Hotel, Bridge Street, Buncer Lane, Blackburn BB2 2QY 01254 6755
MILLOM. . . . . Millom RL Club, Devonshire Road, Millom LA18 4PG 01229 7720
NORCROSS & WARBRECK . . . . Anchorsholme Lane, Thornton Cleveleys, Blackpool FY5 1LX. 01253 8598
SLYNE-WITH-HEST . . . . Bottomdale Road, Slyne, Lancaster LA2 6BG . . . . No
TURTON . . . . Thomasson Fold, Turton, Edgworth, Bolton BL7 0PD 07929 9651
WYRE VILLA. Hallgate Park, Stalmine Village, Poulton-le-Fylde FY6 0LB 01253 7014

IN: BAC/EE Springfield (P), Haslingden St Mary's (R), Longridge Town (P), Turton (R)

OUT: Crosshills (R - Craven & District League Premier Division), Fleetwood Hesketh (P), Milnthorpe Corinthians (R), Thornton Clevele (P)

Division Two		P	W	D	L	F	A	Pts
BAC/EE Springfield		22	19	2	1	89	21	59
Longridge Town	*-3*	22	18	1	3	80	24	52
Lytham Town		22	13	4	5	67	39	43
Furness Cavaliers		22	12	2	8	59	47	38
Furness Rovers		22	10	4	8	38	33	34
Lancashire Constabulary		22	10	2	10	52	60	32
Todmorden Borough		22	8	4	10	38	45	28
Askam United		22	9	1	12	51	67	28
Whinney Hill	*-3*	22	8	4	10	50	58	25
Walney Island		22	4	3	15	21	53	15
Bolton County		22	3	2	17	30	77	11
GSK Ulverston Rangers		22	3	1	18	22	73	10

CHALLENGE CUP

FIRST ROUND

Furness Cavaliers 1 Bolton County 0
Furness Rovers 4 Askam United 1
Lancashire Constabulary 1 **BAC/EE Springfields** 4
Todmorden Borough 4 GSK Ulverston Rangers 0

QUARTER-FINALS

BAC/EE Springfields 2 Furness Rovers 1
Lytham Town 5 Whinney Hill 1
Todmorden Borough 1 **Longridge Town** 4
Walney Island 1 Furness Cavaliers 4
(Furness Cavaliers expelled)

SEMI-FINALS

BAC/EE Springfields 2 Longridge Town 1
(at AFC Darwen)
Lytham Town 3 Walney Island 0
(at Milnthorpe Corinthians)

FINAL

(April 28th at AFC Blackpool)
Lytham Town 1 **BAC/EE Springfields** 3

	Askam Utd	BAC/EE	Bolton Co.	Furness Cav.	Furness Rov.	GSK Ulv'ton	Lancs Const.	Longridge	Lytham Town	Todmorden	Walney Is.	Whinney H.
Askam United	***D***	1-9	2-3	0-4	1-2	5-1	6-2	3-1	1-5	5-0	2-1	1-4
BAC/EE Springfield	8-0	***I***	7-1	2-2	2-0	5-0	2-0	5-3	4-3	4-0	6-0	6-1
Bolton County	2-5	0-4	***V***	0-3	0-4	2-2	2-5	0-5	2-4	2-3	1-4	2-0
Furness Cavaliers	1-4	4-0	5-1	***I***	3-1	6-2	2-1	1-8	1-2	2-1	3-0	1-5
Furness Rovers	2-1	2-3	2-1	3-1	***S***	4-1	1-2	1-5	1-3	2-0	1-1	1-1
GSK Ulverston Rangers	2-1	0-1	1-2	2-6	0-2	***I***	2-3	0-2	0-5	2-1	0-1	1-2
Lancashire Constabulary	0-2	1-2	4-2	4-2	2-1	10-1	***O***	1-8	0-6	2-2	2-1	3-3
Longridge Town	8-0	0-0	2-0	2-1	3-2	5-0	4-2	***N***	4-1	3-0	2-0	3-1
Lytham Town	4-0	0-6	6-2	2-2	2-2	1-2	5-1	0-3		5-2	2-1	3-3
Todmorden Borough	2-0	1-4	2-0	3-5	0-0	3-2	1-2	5-0	2-2	***T***	2-0	3-1
Walney Island	2-7	0-1	1-1	0-2	0-2	2-1	2-5	1-6	0-2	1-1	***W***	3-1
Whinney Hill	4-4	2-8	6-4	4-2	1-2	4-0	3-0	0-3	0-4	1-4	3-0	***O***

WEST LANCASHIRE LEAGUE DIVISION TWO CONSTITUTION 2010-11

AMBLESIDE UNITED	Hillard Park, Vicarage Road, Ambleside LA22 9DH	None
ASKAM UNITED	Duddon Road, James Street, Askam-in-Furness LA16 7AH	01229 464576
BOLTON COUNTY	Radcliffe Road, Darcy Lever, Bolton BL3 1AN	07745 456378
FURNESS CAVALIERS	Rampside Road, Barrow-in-Furness LA13 0HN	None
FURNESS ROVERS	Wilkie Road, Barrow-in-Furness LA14 5UQ	None
GSK ULVERSTON RANGERS	off North Lonsdale Road, Ulverston LA12 9DZ	01229 582261
KENDAL COUNTY	Netherfield Cricket Club, Parkside Road, Kendal LA9 7BL	01539 724051
LADYBRIDGE	Tempest Road, Lostock, Bolton BL6 4EL	None
LANCASHIRE CONSTABULARY	Police HQ, Saunders Lane, Hutton, Preston PR4 5SG	01772 412970
LYTHAM TOWN	Lytham Academy, Ballam Road, Lytham St Annes FY8 4LE	01253 733873
MILNTHORPE CORINTHIANS	Strands Lane, Milnthorpe LA7 7AE	01539 562135
TODMORDEN BOROUGH	Bellholme, Warland, Rochdale Road, Todmorden OL14 6UH	None
WALNEY ISLAND	Tummerhill Play Flos, Ocean Road, Walney, Barrow-in-Furness LA14 3HN	None
WHINNEY HILL	Burnley Road, Clayton-le-Moors, Accrington BB5 5NF	None

IN: Ambleside United (P - Westmorland League Division One), Kendal County (P - Westmorland League Division One), Ladybridge (P - Lancashire Amateur League Division Three), Milnthorpe Corinthians (R)
OUT: BAC/EE Springfield (P), Longridge Town (P)

Reserve Div. One		P	W	D	L	F	A	Pt
Euxton Villa Res.		26	17	4	5	63	33	55
Charnock R. Res.		26	13	7	6	51	37	46
Garstang Res.		26	13	6	7	48	33	45
Fleetwood H. Res.		26	14	3	9	59	47	45
Eagley Res.		26	12	4	10	63	65	40
Haslingden SM Res.		26	10	6	10	43	44	36
Thornton C. Res.		26	10	5	11	48	42	35
Norcross & W. Res.		26	10	5	11	53	54	35
Poulton Town Res.		26	10	4	12	63	61	34
Fulwood Ams Res.		26	9	7	10	45	45	34
Tempest United Res.		26	8	8	10	51	58	32
Turton Res.		26	9	4	13	36	57	31
Freckleton Res.		26	6	5	15	38	62	23
Bpl Wren R. Res.	*-3*	26	3	8	15	31	54	14

Reserve Div. Two		P	W	D	L	F	A	Pt
Stoneclough Res.		22	15	5	2	54	24	50
BAC/EE S'fields Res.		22	14	4	4	66	35	46
Hesketh Bank Res.		22	12	5	5	58	28	41
Lytham Town Res.		22	11	4	7	51	52	37
Wyre Villa Res.		22	10	6	6	37	48	36
Coppull United Res.		22	10	4	8	49	33	34
Milnthorpe Cor. Res.		22	7	4	11	44	56	25
Burnley U. Res.	*-6*	22	9	3	10	53	46	24
Mill Hill St Ptrs Res.		22	6	6	10	37	49	24
Todmorden B. Res.		22	6	4	12	44	61	22
Bolton County Res.		22	2	7	13	26	50	13
Whinney Hill Res.		22	2	4	16	35	72	10

HOUSTON CUP

FINAL

(May 10th at Blackpool Wren Rovers)

Burnley United Res. 4
Thornton Cleveleys Res. 1

WILTSHIRE LEAGUE

http://full-time.thefa.com/Index.do?league=8864128

Sponsored by: Plaister Autos

Founded: 1976

Recent champions:
2005: Corsham Town Res.
2006: Corsham Town Res.
2007: Corsham Town Res.
2008: Wroughton
2009: New College Swindon

	Bra	Cal	Cor	Dev	CY	KC	Mar	Mel	New	Pew	Pur	Shr	Tro	War	WU	Wes	Wro
Bradford Town Res.	***P***	0-5	5-0	7-0	3-3	7-1	6-1	2-1	0-2	1-8	2-4	2-1	3-0	2-2	2-2	4-4	1-3
Calne Town Res.	1-1	***R***	1-1	3-0	1-4	0-5	3-3	4-1	2-6	1-2	2-0	1-2	2-0	n/a	1-3	2-1	1-1
Corsham Town Res.	2-4	5-4	***E***	4-6	0-1	1-2	6-2	1-2	1-6	0-2	2-0	4-3	1-4	n/a	3-6	3-2	3-3
Devizes Town Res.	1-0	4-5	3-0	***M***	1-2	0-2	0-1	1-1	1-9	1-3	5-1	3-1	1-5	n/a	0-5	0-5	0-3
FC Chippenham Youth	5-0	1-0	1-1	3-1	***I***	1-5	4-3	1-4	3-7	3-4	0-4	0-2	5-0	6-0	2-1	5-0	1-2
KC	5-0	0-0	2-0	5-1	1-1	***E***	4-0	5-3	0-3	3-1	5-2	2-3	6-2	n/a	0-1	2-0	3-0
Marlborough Town	1-1	1-4	1-6	3-3	0-0	0-3	***R***	1-1	0-2	2-7	1-2	0-4	2-0	2-3	1-3	1-2	1-3
Melksham Town Res.	0-1	2-1	3-0	4-0	1-3	4-2	2-1		0-4	0-3	5-0	1-1	1-3	6-1	1-1	0-3	0-3
New College Swindon	11-0	3-0	7-1	5-1	5-3	1-1	3-0	3-0		4-2	3-1	3-5	2-0	n/a	4-3	4-0	3-0
Pewsey Vale	2-3	7-4	2-1	0-0	4-1	1-0	3-0	8-0	2-2	***D***	2-0	3-4	5-0	6-0	2-0	3-0	4-0
Purton Res.	1-3	1-1	1-2	4-4	2-0	2-1	0-0	3-2	1-2	2-1	***I***	6-1	3-1	n/a	0-1	2-0	0-1
Shrewton United Res.	3-0	3-1	4-1	3-0	1-4	3-3	2-0	1-0	2-2	2-1	1-1	***V***	2-1	5-1	1-2	2-1	4-1
Trowbridge Town Res.	2-2	2-0	5-1	2-4	0-5	1-4	2-1	2-6	1-2	1-7	6-2	1-4	***I***	n/a	0-1	1-1	1-5
Warminster Town Res.	n/a	0-0	n/a	1-1	n/a	1-5	2-3	n/a	n/a	n/a	0-3	n/a	5-0	***S***	n/a	n/a	1-0
Westbury United Res.	2-0	2-1	4-0	8-0	2-1	1-5	2-0	2-1	0-0	1-1	1-0	5-0	3-1	3-0	***I***	6-0	1-0
Westside	1-5	1-1	1-2	1-0	0-1	0-4	1-3	1-2	0-2	0-3	1-3	1-3	3-0	4-0	0-2	***O***	4-3
Wroughton	4-1	4-1	1-1	3-1	4-4	1-2	2-2	1-4	0-2	0-1	0-5	2-1	0-1	n/a	0-2	1-2	***N***

Premier Division		P	W	D	L	F	A	Pts
New College Swindon		30	25	4	1	112	30	79
Westbury United Res.		30	22	4	4	73	27	70
Pewsey Vale		30	21	3	6	94	36	66
KC	*-1*	30	19	4	7	83	40	60
Shrewton United Res.		30	18	4	8	69	52	58
FC Chippenham Youth		30	14	5	11	68	59	47
Bradford Town Res.		30	12	6	12	66	76	42
Purton Res.	*-1*	30	12	4	14	53	56	39
Wroughton		30	11	5	14	51	57	38
Melksham T. Res.	*-1*	30	11	4	15	52	62	36
Calne Town Res.	*-1*	30	8	7	15	53	66	30
Corsham T. Res.	*-1*	30	8	4	18	53	88	27
Trowbridge T. Res.		30	8	2	20	45	84	26
Westside		30	7	3	20	36	70	24
Devizes Town Res.		30	6	4	20	42	98	22
Marlborough Town		30	3	7	20	32	81	16

Warminster Town Res. - record expunged

CORSHAM PRINT SENIOR CUP

FIRST ROUND
Calne Res. 1 Bradford Town Res. 4 *(Bradford Res. expelled)*

SECOND ROUND
Calne Town Res. 0 **FC Chippenham Youth** 1
Devizes Town Res. 1 **Wroughton** 3
KC 7 Warminster Town Res. 2
New College Swindon 2 Marlborough Town 0
Pewsey V. 6 Corsham Res. 1
Purton Res. 0 **Melksham Town Res.** 2
Shrewton United Res. 4 Trowbridge Town Res. 0
Westside 0 **Westbury United Res.** 3

QUARTER-FINALS
KC 2 **Pewsey Vale** 3
Melksham Town Res. 1 **Shrewton United Res.** 2
New College 0 **Wroughton** 1
Westbury United Res. 3 FC Chippenham Youth 1

SEMI-FINALS
Westbury United Res. 1 Shrewton United Res. 0
Wroughton 0 **Pewsey Vale** 1

FINAL
(May 1st at Corsham Town)
Pewsey 1 Westbury Res. 0

Division One		P	W	D	L	F	A	Pt
Minety		18	14	2	2	59	19	44
SKS Blyskawica		18	13	4	1	51	25	43
Chalke Valley		18	11	3	4	71	31	36
Swindon NALGO		18	9	1	8	50	46	28
Byrons Wanderers		18	6	4	8	36	40	22
Intel		18	6	4	8	31	38	22
Pewsey Vale Res.		18	4	6	8	28	43	18
AFC NPower	*-1*	18	5	4	9	29	48	18
Swindon Irons		18	5	1	12	30	56	16
Malmesbury V. Res.		18	1	3	14	16	55	6

Division Two		P	W	D	L	F	A	Pt
Wilton Town		18	14	0	4	48	22	42
Moredon Cheney		18	12	4	2	52	31	40
Pembroke		18	10	2	6	45	34	32
Lower Stratton		18	9	2	7	38	36	29
Wroughton Res.	-3	18	8	6	4	41	28	27
KMLC	-1	18	7	3	8	46	45	23
Marlborough Res.		18	4	4	10	26	44	16
FC Chip'ham Y. Res.		18	5	1	12	36	61	16
Ramsbury		18	4	2	12	26	42	14
Chiseldon	-3	18	5	0	13	36	51	12

FOUNTAIN TROPHIES JUNIOR CUP

FINAL
(May 1st at Corsham Town)
Wroughton Res. 3 Byrons Wdrs 0

WILTSHIRE LEAGUE PREMIER DIVISION CONSTITUTION 2010-11

AFC AMESBURY TOWN . . . . Bonnymead Park, Recreation Road, Amesbury SP4 7BB. 01980 62348
AFC BRADFORD TOWN . . . . Avon Sports Ground, Trowbridge Road, Bradford-on-Avon BA15 1EE. 01225 8666
AFC NPOWER . . . . Hooper's Field, Rotten Row, Wanborough, Swindon SN4 0AN . . . . No
CHALKE VALLEY. . . . . Recreation Ground, Chalke Valley Sports Centre, Broadchalke SP5 5HC. . . . . No
CORSHAM TOWN RES. . . . . Southbank Ground, Lacock Road, Corsham SN13 9HS 01249 7156
DEVIZES TOWN RES. . . . . Nursteed Road, Devizes SN10 3EJ 01380 7228
FC CHIPPENHAM YOUTH . Stanley Park Spts Ground, Stanley Lane, London Road, Chippenham SN15 3RR 01249 4639
MARLBOROUGH TOWN. . . . . Elcot Lane, Marlborough SN8 2BG 01672 5133
MOREDON CHENEY . . . . Farm Lane, Aldbourne, Marlborough SN8 2DS . . . . No
NEW COLLEGE SWINDON Swindon Supermarine FC, Highworth Road, South Marston, Swindon SN3 4SF. 01793 8287
PURTON REDHOUSE . . . . The Red House, Church Street, Purton SN5 4DY 01793 7702
RGV SHREWTON . . . . Shrewton United FC, Recreation Ground, Mill Lane, Shrewton, Salisbury SP3 4JU. 07796 0981
VALE.OF PEWSEY. . . . . Recreation Ground, Kings Corner, Ball Road, Pewsey SN9 5BS 01672 5629
SKS BLYSKAWICA. . . . . . Greendown Community School, Grange Park Way, Grange Park, Swindon SN5 6HN. 01793 8742
SOUTHBROOK . . . . Southbrook Recreation Ground, Pinehurst Road, Swindon SN2 1RJ. . . . . No
WILTON TOWN . . . . Castle Meadow, Castle Lane, North Street, Wilton SP2 0HG. . . . . No
WILTS CALNE . . . . Calne Town FC, Lickhill Road, Bremhill View, Calne SN11 8AE 01249 8191
WROUGHTON . . . . The Weir Field, Wroughton WMC, Devizes Road, Wroughton SN4 0SA 01793 8123

IN: AFC Amesbury Town (N), AFC NPower (P), Chalke Valley (P), Moredon Cheney (P - Division Two), Vale of Pewsey (formerly Pews Vale Res.) (P), SKS Blyskawica (P), Wilton Town (P - Division Two)

OUT: KC (W), Melksham Town Res. (W), Pewsey Vale (P - Wessex League Division One), Trowbridge Town Res. (W), Warminster To Res. (WS), Westbury United Res. (W)

Bradford Town Res. become AFC Bradford Town, Calne Town Res. become Wilts Calne, Purton Res. become Purton Redhous Shrewton United Res. become RGV Shrewton, Westside become Southbrook

CORNWALL COMBINATION

www.comboleaguearchive.atbhost.net

Sponsored by: Jollys

Founded: 1959

Recent champions:
2005: Goonhavern
2006: Truro City Res.
2007: Illogan RBL
2008: Truro City Res.
2009: Perranporth

		P	W	D	L	F	A	Pts
Illogan RBL		38	32	3	3	140	23	99
Penryn Athletic Res.		38	28	10	0	128	25	94
Perranwell		38	25	8	5	90	32	83
Falmouth Town Res.		38	21	7	10	95	62	70
Helston Athletic		38	22	3	13	126	59	69
St Just		38	21	5	12	112	58	68
St Day		38	22	2	14	117	72	68
St Agnes		38	20	6	12	111	61	66
Troon		38	19	8	11	96	55	65
Newquay Res.		38	19	4	15	91	66	61
Penzance Res.		38	18	3	17	87	89	57
RNAS Culdrose		38	17	3	18	90	81	54
Mullion		38	15	5	18	65	81	50
St Ives Town		38	14	3	21	70	85	45
Porthleven Res.	*-3*	38	13	5	20	62	105	41
Hayle Res.	*-3*	38	12	5	21	74	78	38
Holmans Sports Club		38	8	2	28	53	117	26
Wendron United Res.		38	6	5	27	62	135	23
Ludgvan		38	3	3	32	38	168	12
Portreath		38	0	0	38	26	281	0

SUPPLEMENTARY CUP

(Combination Cup Preliminary and First Round losers)

PRELIMINARY ROUND
Mullion 1 **Helston Athletic** 3
St Ives Town 0 **Hayle Res.** 1
St Just 6 Porthleven Res. 2
Wendron United Res. 3 Portreath 1

QUARTER-FINALS
Helston Athletic 1 **St Just** 4
Ludgvan 1 **Holmans Sports Club** 4
Perranwell 1 **Hayle Res.** 2
Wendron United Res. 2 **Falmouth Town Res.** 3

SEMI-FINALS
Falmouth Town Res. 2 St Just 2 *aet* (4-3p) *(at Penzance)*
Hayle Res. 0 **Holmans** 4 *(at Helston Athletic)*

FINAL
(May 23rd at Wendron United)
Falmouth Town Res. 4 Holmans Sports Club 2

GEORGE EVELY CUP

(Cornwall Combination Cup winners v East Cornwall League Cup winners)

(May 16th at Nanpean Rovers)
Illogan RBL 2
Plymouth Parkway Res. 0

	Falmouth T. Res.	Hayle Res.	Helston Athletic	Holmans SC	Illogan RBL	Ludgvan	Mullion	Newquay Res.	Penryn Ath. Res.	Penzance Res.	Perranwell	Porthleven Res.	Portreath	RNAS Culdrose	St Agnes	St Day	St Ives Town	St Just	Troon	Wendron U. Res.
Falmouth Town Res.		3-1	3-1	2-2	1-0	4-0	1-1	2-1	0-3	0-3	0-2	2-0	11-1	4-3	2-2	4-2	3-1	1-4	1-0	0-0
Hayle Res.	0-1		3-3	3-0	0-5	4-0	5-1	0-2	0-0	2-3	1-3	2-2	5-0	2-3	1-5	0-2	2-0	1-1	4-2	5-2
Helston Athletic	5-1	3-2		5-1	0-1	5-0	5-1	1-2	0-2	2-3	1-2	7-1	13-0	2-1	1-3	3-1	1-3	2-0	3-1	6-1
Holmans Spts Club	1-5	0-4	0-2		1-7	3-0	1-0	2-0	1-1	0-1	0-2	1-2	12-0	0-5	0-2	0-2	1-2	0-6	0-1	4-0
Illogan RBL	1-0	3-1	1-1	1-0		4-0	5-1	1-0	1-1	1-0	2-0	3-0	7-0	3-2	6-2	4-2	5-0	3-1	3-0	7-0
Ludgvan	3-7	1-6	0-8	2-4	2-7		1-7	1-6	1-4	2-3	0-4	1-0	5-1	1-3	0-7	1-6	1-1	0-5	0-5	3-3
Mullion	2-2	1-0	1-1	6-1	1-4	6-2		1-4	0-3	2-1	0-0	3-2	1-0	1-2	1-3	1-6	1-0	0-3	3-1	2-1
Newquay Res.	1-4	1-2	2-1	3-0	0-3	4-0	5-2		2-2	3-1	0-1	7-1	4-0	1-5	2-1	2-2	6-3	3-2	2-2	4-3
Penryn Athletic Res.	5-1	4-0	3-0	3-0	1-1	6-0	4-0	1-0		4-2	1-1	8-1	11-1	3-0	4-1	3-2	4-0	3-1	1-0	2-0
Penzance Res.	2-5	3-2	1-3	12-2	1-6	6-3	4-3	1-0	0-3		4-2	0-0	5-2	0-2	3-3	1-4	0-3	2-1	0-5	3-3
Perranwell	0-0	4-1	4-2	6-0	0-4	3-0	1-0	3-0	1-1	9-1		4-1	2-0	2-1	0-2	1-4	1-0	3-0	1-1	2-0
Porthleven Res.	0-2	2-1	2-4	2-0	0-3	2-0	0-2	4-2	3-3	1-0	1-7		7-2	1-5	2-4	3-2	2-1	0-4	1-5	5-2
Portreath	1-2	1-7	1-9	0-2	0-17	1-2	2-9	0-8	0-14	0-10	0-6	3-5		0-7	3-6	2-4	0-10	0-12	1-6	1-3
RNAS Culdrose	2-2	3-1	2-1	5-2	0-2	3-1	0-1	6-3	1-5	0-2	0-2	3-1	10-1		2-5	3-0	2-1	2-5	0-2	0-1
St Agnes	2-3	2-0	0-4	3-0	0-3	5-1	0-1	0-3	0-2	0-1	1-1	5-1	12-0	6-0		0-1	3-1	1-1	5-0	4-2
St Day	4-2	2-1	2-5	4-3	0-3	7-0	2-0	1-1	1-2	4-1	1-2	1-3	14-1	4-1	3-2		2-0	0-3	2-3	7-3
St Ives Town	1-0	3-1	1-4	5-0	0-7	3-3	4-1	1-0	0-4	1-2	0-3	1-1	6-0	6-1	2-7	0-1		2-1	0-5	1-2
St Just	3-2	5-0	3-1	6-3	2-1	5-0	0-1	5-3	3-3	2-0	1-1	4-1	7-0	2-0	2-2	3-6	2-3		1-0	4-3
Troon	2-6	1-1	2-4	4-2	1-0	5-0	4-0	0-1	0-0	3-1	1-1	1-1	6-0	2-2	1-1	2-0	5-1	4-2		7-2
Wendron Utd Res.	0-6	1-3	2-7	3-4	2-5	5-1	1-1	1-3	0-4	1-4	0-3	0-1	4-1	3-3	1-4	3-9	1-3	1-0	2-6	

CORNWALL COMBINATION CUP

PRELIMINARY ROUND
Helston Athletic 3 Ludgvan 0
Perranwell 5 Porthleven Res. 0
RNAS Culdrose 2 Mullion 1
Troon 2 St Just 1

FIRST ROUND
Hayle Res. 1 **St Agnes** 3
Illogan RBL 3 Falmouth Town Res. 0
Penryn Athletic Res. 7 Wendron United Res. 1
Penzance Res. 4 St Ives Town 2
Portreath 0 **Newquay Res.** 10
RNAS Culdrose 2 Holmans Sports Club 1
St Day 3 Perranwell 0
Troon 3 Helston Athletic 1

QUARTER-FINALS
Illogan RBL 2 Penryn Athletic Res. 0
Penzance Res. 1 **RNAS Culdrose** 2
St Agnes 1 Newquay Res 0
St Day 4 Troon 1

SEMI-FINALS
Illogan RBL 6 RNAS Culdrose 1
(at Mullion)
St Agnes 3 St Day 1
(at Illogan RBL)

FINAL
(April 4th at Penryn Athletic)
St Agnes 0 **Illogan RBL** 3

CORNWALL COMBINATION CONSTITUTION 2010-11

FALMOUTH TOWN RES.	Bickland Park, Bickland Water Road, Falmouth TR11 4PB	01326 375156
HAYLE RES.	Trevassack Park, Viaduct Hill, Hayle TR27 5HT	01736 757157
HELSTON ATHLETIC	Kellaway Parc, Clodgy Lane, Helston TR13 8BN	01326 573742
HOLMANS SPORTS CLUB	Blaythorne Memorial Sports Ground, Pendarves, Camborne TR14 7QG	01209 713631
ILLOGAN RBL	Oxland Park, Richards Lane, Illogan, Redruth TR16 4HA	01209 216488
LUDGVAN	Ludgvan Community Centre, Fairfield, Ludgvan TR20 8ES	01736 740774
MULLION	Clifden Parc, Clifden Close, Mullion, Helston TR12 7EQ	01326 240676
NEWQUAY RES.	Mount Wise, Clevedon Road, Newquay TR7 2BU	01637 872935
PENDEEN ROVERS	Borlase Park, Pendeen, Penzance TR19 7DZ	01736 787867
PENRYN ATHLETIC RES.	Kernick, Kernick Road, Penryn TR10 8QF	01326 375182
PENZANCE RES.	Penlee Park, Alexandra Place, Penzance TR18 4NE	01736 361964
PERRANWELL	King George V Playing Field, School Hill, Perranwell Station TR3 7LA	01872 870202
PORTHLEVEN RES.	Gala Parc, Mill Lane, Porthleven TR13 9LQ	01326 574754
RNAS CULDROSE	Sports Field, RNAS Culdrose, Helston TR12 7RH	01326 574121x7167
ST AGNES	Enys Park, West Polperro, St Agnes TR5 0SS	01872 553673
ST DAY	Vogue, St Day, Redruth TR16 5NP	None
ST IVES TOWN	The Saltings, Lelant TR6 3DL	None
ST JUST	Lafrowda Park, St Just, Penzance TR19 7RY	01736 788503
TROON	Grouter Park, Croft Common, Troon, Camborne TR14 9HT	None
WENDRON UNITED	Underlane, Carnkie, Wendron, Helston TR13 0EH	01209 860946

IN: Pendeen Rovers (P - Falmouth-Helston League Division One)
OUT: Portreath (P - Falmouth-Helston League Division One)
Wendon United Res. become Wendron United

DEVON & EXETER LEAGUE

www.defleague.co.uk

Sponsored by:
No sponsor

Founded: 1900

Recent champions:
2005: Exmouth Town Res.
2006: Heavitree Social United
2007: Axminster Town
2008: University of Exeter Res.
2009: St Martins

	Alphington Res.	Budleigh S. Res.	Clyst Valley	Exeter Uni. Res.	Exmouth Amtrs	Feniton	Hatherleigh Town	Heavitree S. Utd	Newtown	Otterton	Sidmouth Town	St Martins	Thorverton	Topsham Town	Wellington T. Res.	Willand Ro. Res.
Alphington Res.	***P***	0-2	2-2	1-4	2-1	4-1	1-1	1-2	4-3	5-0	0-3	1-3	3-3	0-0	4-3	2-3
Budleigh Salterton Res.	3-0	***R***	1-3	1-2	1-0	5-2	1-0	1-2	0-5	1-2	0-3	2-3	0-3	2-0	3-0	3-3
Clyst Valley	0-1	1-4	***E***	2-2	0-2	2-0	3-4	2-4	0-0	2-0	0-4	1-2	2-3	0-1	2-2	1-1
Exeter University Res.	2-2	4-3	2-6	***M***	0-1	6-0	1-3	7-0	1-3	12-0	3-1	4-1	2-2	0-0	3-1	2-3
Exmouth Amateurs	2-0	0-3	1-2	0-3	***I***	2-0	3-0	1-2	3-1	4-1	1-4	3-5	1-2	0-2	4-1	2-1
Feniton	3-2	1-0	1-4	3-2	2-0	***E***	6-6	1-0	3-3	2-1	0-1	2-2	4-9	0-3	1-1	1-3
Hatherleigh Town	2-2	1-1	0-1	2-1	1-0	1-2	***R***	1-1	1-3	4-0	1-3	1-1	1-1	2-2	2-0	2-2
Heavitree Social United	2-2	3-1	2-1	1-3	4-1	4-1	2-1		3-1	3-0	1-0	3-4	2-2	1-3	9-3	1-4
Newtown	6-0	2-3	1-0	5-3	6-1	2-1	7-1	3-1	***D***	2-1	3-1	3-1	1-4	1-1	2-6	1-3
Otterton	1-2	2-2	1-6	1-5	0-4	2-1	2-5	0-3	4-6	***I***	0-5	1-4	2-5	0-8	4-2	2-2
Sidmouth Town	2-2	10-1	2-1	3-2	3-0	3-3	5-1	1-1	3-1	8-1	***V***	1-1	3-4	6-0	4-2	1-3
St Martins	0-5	5-1	2-1	1-1	2-0	1-0	4-0	1-1	3-0	11-0	5-2	***I***	1-4	4-2	2-7	0-0
Thorverton	4-3	7-0	4-0	3-1	4-6	5-2	2-1	2-0	3-0	8-1	0-2	5-2	***S***	2-3	2-0	0-0
Topsham Town	1-0	7-2	1-3	1-0	1-0	7-2	1-2	7-2	1-2	9-2	0-2	1-5	2-0	***I***	2-0	1-0
Wellington Town Res.	1-0	1-3	2-0	1-1	2-1	5-4	2-2	0-3	1-3	9-0	0-4	1-0	0-7	1-5	***O***	5-0
Willand Rovers Res.	4-0	2-0	2-1	3-0	5-0	3-0	1-2	1-2	2-0	0-5	0-1	5-0	0-1	2-4	0-0	***N***

Premier Division		P	W	D	L	F	A	Pts
Thorverton		30	21	5	4	101	45	68
Sidmouth Town		30	20	4	6	91	37	64
Topsham Town		30	18	4	8	76	43	58
St Martins		30	16	6	8	76	58	54
Heavitree Social United		30	16	5	9	65	56	53
Newtown		30	16	3	11	76	59	51
Willand Rovers Res.		30	14	7	9	58	40	49
Exeter University Res.		30	12	6	12	79	54	42
Hatherleigh Town		30	9	10	11	51	61	37
Budleigh Salterton Res.		30	11	3	16	50	74	36
Exmouth Amateurs		30	11	0	19	44	60	33
Clyst Valley		30	9	5	16	49	54	32
Alphington Res.		30	8	8	14	51	64	32
Wellington Town Res.		30	9	5	16	59	77	32
Feniton		30	7	5	18	49	89	26
Otterton	*-1*	30	4	2	24	36	140	13

Division One		P	W	D	L	F	A	Pts
Seaton Town		26	22	1	3	75	34	67
Beer Albion		26	12	7	7	50	32	43
Bow AAC		26	11	8	7	45	35	41
East Budleigh		26	12	4	10	39	37	40
Sidbury United		26	12	4	10	37	36	40
Cullompton Rangers Res.		26	11	5	10	44	47	38
Exeter University A		26	9	7	10	45	42	34
Heavitree Social Utd Res.		26	9	7	10	55	54	34
Halwill		26	9	6	11	52	49	33
Morchard Bishop		26	8	7	11	40	43	31
Elmore Res.	-1	26	10	2	14	53	59	31
Culm United		26	7	7	12	41	58	28
Broadclyst		26	7	7	12	34	56	28
Beacon Knights		26	4	6	16	38	66	18

DEVON & EXETER LEAGUE PREMIER DIVISION CONSTITUTION 2010-11

ALPHINGTON RES. . . . . The Chronicles, Church Road, Alphington, Exeter EX2 8SW 01392 279556
BEER ALBION . . . . Furzebrake, Stovar Long Lane, Beer EX12 3DY 01297 625863
BUDLEIGH SALTERTON RES. . . . . Greenway Lane, Budleigh Salterton EX9 6SG 01395 443850
CLYST VALLEY . . . . Winslade Park, Exmouth Road, Clyst St Mary EX5 1DA . . . . None
EXMOUTH AMATEURS . . . . Warren View, Halsdon Avenue, Exmouth EX8 3DH 01395 222619
HATHERLEIGH TOWN . . . . The Sportsfield, Okehampton Road, Hatherleigh, Okehampton EX20 3LH 01837 810346
HEAVITREE SOCIAL UNITED . . . . Wingfield Park, East Wonford Hill, Exeter EX1 3BS 01392 273020
NEWTOWN . . . . Newton St Cyres FC, Recreation Ground, Station Road, Newton St Cyres EX5 5AT 01392 851546
SEATON TOWN. . . . . Hillymead, Colyford Road, Seaton EX12 2DF 01297 24141
SIDMOUTH TOWN . . . . Manstone Recreation Ground, Manstone Lane, Sidmouth EX10 9TF 01395 577087
ST MARTINS . . . . Minster Park, Reddaway Drive, Exminster EX6 8SL. 01392 823909
THORVERTON. . . . . Recreation Playing Field, Raddon Road, Thorverton, Exeter EX5 5PJ . . . . None
TOPSHAM TOWN . . . . Coronation Field, Exeter Road, Topsham EX3 0LT 01392 873678
UNIVERSITY OF EXETER RES. . . . . University Sports Ground, Topsham Road, Topsham EX3 0LY 01392 879542
WELLINGTON TOWN RES. . . . . Wellington Playing Field, North Street, Wellington TA21 8NA 01823 664810
WILLAND ROVERS RES. . . . . Silver Street, Willand, Cullompton EX15 2SL. 01884 33885

IN: Beer Albion (P), Seaton Town (P)
OUT: Feniton (R), Otterton (R - Division Eight)

EAST DEVON SENIOR CUP

FIRST ROUND
Beer Albion 2 **Alphington Res.** 3
Bow AAC 0 **Budleigh Salt. Res.** 1
Broadclyst 1 **St Martins** 4
Culm United 0 **Exmouth Amateurs** 2
Hatherleigh T. 0 **Beacon Knights** 1
Morchard Bishop 3 Heavitree 2 *aet*
Newtown 4 Elmore Res. 1
Otterton 0 **Willand Rovers Res.** 2
Seaton Town 5 Feniton 0
Sidmouth 2 Cullompton Res. 1
Topsham Town 4 Wellington Res. 2

SECOND ROUND
Beacon Knights 3 **Newtown** 4
Budleigh S. Res. 4 Topsham 3 *aet*
Clyst Valley 3 Thorverton 0
East Budleigh 0 **Sidmouth Town** 1
Halwill 2 Sidbury United 0
Seaton T. 4 Morchard Bishop 3 *aet*
St Martins 5 Alphington Res. 0
Willand Res. 1 Exmouth Amateurs 2
(Exmouth Amateurs expelled)

QUARTER-FINALS
Clyst Valley 4 **Halwill** 5 *aet*
Newtown 2 Budleigh Salterton Res. 0
Sidmouth Town 2 Seaton Town 2 *aet*
(4-5p) *(Seaton Town expelled)*
St Martins 4 Willand Rovers Res. 2

SEMI-FINALS
Newtown 2 Sidmouth Town 0
St Martins 1 Halwill 0

FINAL *(May 22nd at Topsham Town)*
Newtown 2 St Martins 0

BILL SLEE CUP

(May 16th at Crediton United)
Topsham Town Res. 1 Witheridge Res. 1 *aet* (3-1p)

FOOTBALL EXPRESS CUP

FINAL *(May 9th at Crediton United)*
Thorverton Res. 3 Lords XI 0

GEARY CUP

FINAL *(May 18th at Cullompton Rovers)*
Topsham Town A 2 Rockbeare Rangers 1 *aet*

Division Two		P	W	D	L	F	A	Pts
Tipton St John		26	17	7	2	80	31	58
Barnstaple Town Res.		26	17	7	2	67	26	58
Honiton Town		26	15	6	5	60	37	51
Witheridge Res.		26	12	9	5	55	39	45
Westexe Rovers		26	11	5	10	54	41	38
Exeter University B		26	11	5	10	56	49	38
Newtown Res.		26	10	4	12	62	49	34
Uplowman Athletic		26	9	7	10	45	53	34
North Tawton		26	9	4	13	63	59	31
Axminster Town Res.	*-4*	26	10	5	11	52	63	31
Exeter Civil Serv. Res.	*-3*	26	8	7	11	47	64	28
Exmouth Ams Res.	*-6*	26	8	5	13	38	79	23
Upottery		26	2	9	15	32	61	15
Dawlish Town Res.	*-1*	26	1	4	21	39	99	-6

Division Three		P	W	D	L	F	A	Pts
Sidmouth Town Res.		26	24	0	2	81	30	72
Phoenix Club		26	20	1	5	81	32	61
Colyton		26	19	2	5	82	41	59
Royal Marines Res.	*-1*	26	16	1	9	84	39	48
Clyst Valley Res.		26	15	2	9	62	42	47
Topsham Town Res.		26	13	4	9	70	58	43
Chard Town Res.		26	12	1	13	57	50	37
Pinhoe	*-1*	26	12	1	13	52	56	36
South Zeal United		26	11	0	15	57	75	33
Winkleigh		26	6	7	13	43	65	25
Crescent	*-1*	26	7	2	17	46	70	22
Lympstone		26	5	2	19	34	99	17
Lapford		26	4	3	19	30	72	15
Kentisbeare	*-1*	26	3	4	19	27	77	12

Division Four		P	W	D	L	F	A	Pt
Dawlish United		24	19	2	3	77	33	59
Offwell Rangers		24	15	4	5	64	38	49
Sandford		24	15	3	6	72	52	48
Bampton		24	13	5	6	56	44	44
Countess Wear Dyn		24	14	1	9	67	43	43
St Martins Res.	*-1*	24	12	2	10	63	54	37
Okehampton Res.		24	10	3	11	57	52	33
Seaton Town Res.		24	10	3	11	50	45	33
Newton St Cyres		24	7	4	13	43	76	25
Tedburn St Mary		24	7	2	15	58	83	23
Sidbury U. Res.	*-1*	24	5	4	15	44	65	18
Newtown A		24	5	3	16	44	75	18
Crediton Res.	*-2*	24	5	2	17	34	69	15

Division Five		P	W	D	L	F	A	Pt
Wellington Town A		26	22	2	2	87	21	68
Hemyock		26	21	1	4	93	32	64
Bickleigh Res.		26	19	4	3	91	33	61
Thorverton Res.	*-4*	26	19	2	5	63	32	55
Colaton Raleigh		26	15	3	8	101	52	48
Lords XI		26	10	5	11	69	60	35
Cullompton Rgrs A		26	10	3	13	51	67	33
Westexe R. Res.		26	9	3	14	40	63	30
Sampford Peverell		26	7	4	15	37	66	25
Dunkeswell Rov.		26	7	3	16	41	82	24
Woodbury		26	7	2	17	41	84	23
Exm'th Ams A	*-1*	26	5	8	13	35	59	22
Feniton Res.		26	6	4	16	43	68	22
Broadclyst Res.		26	1	4	21	15	88	7

Division Six		P	W	D	L	F	A	Pt
Exeter Univ. C		24	16	3	5	81	45	51
Heavitree SU A		24	15	4	5	67	44	49
Beer Albion Res.		24	14	4	6	68	41	46
AFC Sidford		24	12	7	5	61	45	43
Cheriton Fitzpaine		24	13	2	9	70	49	41
Alphington A	*-1*	24	12	4	8	77	64	39
Awliscombe Utd		24	11	3	10	46	47	36
Exmouth T. 2006		24	10	4	10	59	51	34
Uplowman Res.		24	8	4	12	60	75	28
Silverton	*-1*	24	7	5	12	40	65	25
Axmouth United		24	6	2	16	44	75	20
UAU Exeter		24	5	4	15	54	74	19
Ottery SM Res.	*-2*	24	2	4	18	37	89	8

Division Seven		P	W	D	L	F	A	Pt
Dawlish Town A		24	16	5	3	77	33	53
Beacon K. Res.	*-2*	24	16	3	5	86	39	49
Hatherleigh Res.		24	13	4	7	68	44	43
Culm United Res.		24	11	7	6	59	41	40
Clyst Valley A		24	11	7	6	62	48	40
Rockbeare Rgrs		24	12	3	9	62	39	39
E. Budleigh Res.		24	9	7	8	45	52	34
Bampton Res.		24	7	7	10	44	52	28
Priory		24	9	1	14	58	79	28
Honiton T. Res.		24	8	3	13	58	61	27
Amory Argyle		24	8	2	14	48	66	26
Langdon	*-2*	24	6	1	17	38	105	17
Okehampton A. A		24	3	4	17	41	87	13

Division Eight		P	W	D	L	F	A	Pt
Bradninch		26	18	3	5	98	45	57
Five Star Security		26	16	4	6	65	40	52
Halwill Res.		26	16	4	6	71	48	52
Bow AAC Res.		26	15	6	5	73	40	51
Buckland & Milber		26	14	5	7	89	43	47
Amory Pk Rgrs	*-3*	26	14	6	6	97	52	45
Dawlish U. Res.	*-1*	26	13	7	6	77	43	45
Follygate		26	13	4	9	69	68	43
Sandford Res.	*-1*	26	11	1	14	53	76	33
Newton SC Res.	*-1*	26	6	4	16	46	68	21
North Tawton Res.		26	5	3	18	49	92	18
Lympstone Res.		26	4	5	17	39	99	17
Met Office		26	4	4	18	43	91	16
Langdon Res.	*-1*	26	4	2	20	45	109	13

Division Nine		P	W	D	L	F	A	Pt
Topsham Town A		26	20	3	3	94	34	63
Hemyock Res.		26	19	2	5	114	43	59
Countess WD Res.		26	18	1	7	74	44	55
Morch. Bish. Res.		26	15	6	5	74	45	51
Colyton Res.		26	12	5	9	65	49	41
Lapford Res.		26	11	6	9	68	59	39
Tipton St J. Res.		26	11	4	11	72	53	37
Seaton Town A	*-1*	26	10	5	11	62	63	34
Feniton A		26	9	6	11	72	86	33
Offwell Rgrs Res.		26	7	8	11	74	76	29
Winkleigh Res.		26	8	3	15	51	92	27
Tedburn Res.	*-3*	26	6	3	17	51	101	18
Otterton Res.	*-5*	26	6	3	17	45	107	16
Cheriton F. Res.	*-1*	26	1	3	22	35	99	5

DORSET COUNTY LEAGUE

full-time.thefa.com/Index.do?league=3520598

Sponsored by: No sponsor

Founded: N/K

Recent champions:
2005: Chickerell United.
2006: Sturminster Marshall
2007: Wincanton Town
2008: Chickerell United
2009: Parley Sports

	Mat	WM	Bis	Eas	Kan	Mor	Oke	Sto	Tin	Upw	War	Wey	Wit	Woo
AC Matravers		7-1	1-0	1-3	1-1	n/a	2-2	3-4	0-1	2-6	0-2	1-1	1-4	3-1
AFC West Moors	n/a	***S***	4-1	0-1	1-2	n/a	1-3	n/a	1-3	1-2	n/a	2-5	n/a	1-1
Bishop's Caundle	0-5	1-0	***E***	1-6	3-3	3-1	1-1	4-0	1-0	1-3	2-0	2-2	0-3	2-1
Easton United	4-0	n/a	8-0	***N***	4-2	n/a	2-3	7-4	8-1	4-4	5-2	1-2	7-1	5-1
Kangaroos	0-7	8-1	1-4	2-3	***I***	4-0	3-3	2-3	0-1	1-8	0-1	0-3	1-1	2-3
Moreton	n/a	n/a	n/a	n/a	n/a	***O***	n/a	n/a	n/a	n/a	n/a	0-2	n/a	n/a
Okeford United	5-3	n/a	0-1	0-3	0-2	n/a	***R***	3-1	0-0	1-2	1-0	1-0	0-0	0-2
Stourpaine	5-2	3-1	1-4	2-10	3-0	n/a	1-2		1-1	1-3	0-7	2-4	5-3	5-1
Tintinhull	8-0	4-0	2-2	1-5	3-3	n/a	2-1	6-2		3-1	2-0	2-2	0-1	1-0
Upwey & Broadwey	4-1	4-0	2-0	1-3	5-1	n/a	3-1	4-2	2-0		0-0	1-1	4-0	1-2
Wareham Rangers	1-0	3-0	1-1	4-2	3-1	7-0	2-0	3-1	1-0	0-2	***D***	3-1	0-4	5-0
Weymouth Sports	4-1	n/a	0-1	1-2	5-0	n/a	6-1	5-3	2-0	1-3	1-1	***I***	0-2	2-3
Witchampton United	2-4	2-0	2-1	2-0	1-0	n/a	1-0	1-5	2-1	3-1	4-1	3-0	***V***	2-1
Wool RBL	2-3	n/a	0-2	0-2	4-4	n/a	3-2	2-1	1-4	1-4	1-1	1-3	2-4	

Senior Division	P	W	D	L	F	A	Pts
Easton United	22	17	1	4	94	35	52
Upwey & Broadway	22	15	3	4	64	29	48
Witchampton United	22	15	2	5	46	34	47
Wareham Rangers	22	11	4	7	38	28	37
Weymouth Sports	22	9	5	8	46	34	32
Tintinhull	22	9	5	8	39	35	32
Bishops Caundle	22	9	5	8	33	42	32
Okeford United	22	6	5	11	27	40	23
Stourpaine	22	7	1	14	52	77	22
AC Matravers	22	6	3	13	41	60	21
Wool RBL	22	6	2	14	32	58	20
Kangaroos	22	1	6	15	29	69	9

AFC West Moors, Moreton - records expunged

Reserve Division	P	W	D	L	F	A	Pt
Portland Utd Res.	18	14	2	2	55	20	44
Gillingham T. Res	18	13	1	4	52	24	40
Swanage Res.	18	11	4	3	43	15	37
Chickerell Res.	18	10	2	6	49	22	32
Wincanton T. Res.	18	8	4	6	36	32	28
Shaftesbury Res.	18	7	1	10	25	39	22
Wareham R. Res.	18	6	3	9	21	48	21
Holt United Res.	18	3	5	10	23	34	14
Blandford U. Res.	18	2	4	12	13	33	10
Stur. Newton Res.	18	3	0	15	16	66	9

Division One	P	W	D	L	F	A	Pt
Kingston Lacy	26	19	5	2	86	40	62
Crossways	26	17	4	5	98	49	55
Bere Regis	26	16	5	5	84	55	53
FC Windowman	26	17	1	8	84	54	52
Piddletrenthide U.	26	14	4	8	73	40	46
Chickerell Utd A	26	14	2	10	65	49	44
Poundbury Rov.	26	14	1	11	72	51	43
Child Okeford	26	12	5	9	72	54	41
The Balti House	26	10	4	12	61	63	34
Stalbridge	26	7	4	15	57	75	25
Mere Town	26	6	4	16	41	72	22
Lytchett Red Tri.	26	6	1	19	29	92	19
Corfe Castle	26	3	5	18	44	108	14
Cranborne Res.	26	3	3	20	45	109	12

DORSET COUNTY LEAGUE SENIOR DIVISION CONSTITUTION 2010-11

BISHOP'S CAUNDLE . . . . Bishop's Caundle Recreation Ground, Bishop's Caundle DT9 5NQ . . . . None
CHICKERELL UNITED RES. . . . . Weymouth College, Cranford Avenue, Weymouth DT4 7LQ. 01305 208892
GILLINGHAM TOWN RES. . . . . Hardings Lane, Gillingham SP8 4HX. 01747 823673
KINGSTON LACY . . . . Pamphill Village Green, Wimborne BH21 4ED 01202 888260
OKEFORD UNITED. . . . . . . Recreation Ground, Castle Lane, Okeford Fitzpaine, Blandford Forum DT11 0RL . . . . None
POOLE BOROUGH RES. . . . Turlin Moor Recreation Ground, Blandford Moor, Hamworthy, Poole BH21 5XX . . Club Office: 01202 674973
PORTLAND UNITED RES. . . . . New Grove Corner, Grove Road, Portland DT5 1DP. 01305 861489
STOURPAINE. . . . . Dick Draper Memorial Fields, Stourpaine, Blandford Forum DT11 8TJ . . . . None
SWANAGE TOWN & HERSTON RES. . . Day's Park, off De Moulham Road, Swanage BH19 2JW 01929 424673
TINTINHULL . . . . Montacute Road, Tintinhull, Yeovil BA22 8QD . . . . None
UPWEY & BROADWEY. . . . . Dorchester Road, Upwey, Weymouth DT3 5AW. . . . . None
WAREHAM RANGERS . . . . Purbeck Sports Centre, Worgret Road, Wareham BH20 4PH 01929 556454
WEYMOUTH SPORTS. . . . . Weymouth College, Cranford Avenue, Weymouth DT4 7LQ. 01305 208892
WITCHAMPTON UNITED . . . . Crichel Park, Witchampton BH21 5AU 01258 840986

IN: Chickerell United Res. (P - Reserve Division), Gillingham Town Res. (P - Reserve Division), Kingston Lacy (P), Poole Borough Res. (P - Reserve Division), Portland United Res. (P - Reserve Division), Swanage Town & Herston Res. (P - Reserve Division)
OUT: AC Matravers (R), AFC West Moors (WS), Kangaroos (R), Moreton (WS), Easton United (F), Wool RBL (R)

Division Two	P	W	D	L	F	A	Pt
Stur. Marshall Res.	24	19	1	4	106	33	58
Blandford Sports	24	19	1	4	112	50	58
Milborne Sports	24	17	6	1	97	28	57
Granby Rovers	24	12	4	8	65	61	40
The Antelope Inn	24	11	4	9	92	66	37
Dorchester Sports	24	10	6	8	62	40	36
Wyke Regis SC	24	8	6	10	41	59	30
Stickland United	24	8	6	10	38	57	30
Upwey/B'wey Res.	24	7	6	11	49	61	27
Mdn Newton/Catt.	24	6	4	14	54	92	22
AC Matravers Res.	24	6	2	16	43	81	20
Puddletown	24	3	5	16	32	102	14
Witchampton Res.	24	2	5	17	36	97	11

Division Three		P	W	D	L	F	A	Pt
Bridport A		22	17	3	2	113	32	54
Gillingham T. A		22	14	2	6	65	32	44
Piddlehinton Utd		22	14	2	6	69	47	44
Swanage A	*+3*	21	11	2	8	48	42	38
FC Windowman		20	11	2	7	60	51	35
Donhead Utd	*+3*	21	9	4	8	52	51	34
Okeford United		22	9	2	11	39	63	29
Athletico Dorch.		22	8	2	12	53	61	26
Shaftesbury A		22	8	2	12	51	74	26
Stourpaine Res.	*-6*	20	8	3	9	48	47	21
Wool RBL		22	5	1	16	36	70	16
Handley Sports		22	2	1	19	36	100	7

FC Windowman v Donhead United, FC Windowman v Stourpaine Res., Swanage T&H A v Stourpaine Res. not played

Division Four	P	W	D	L	F	A	Pt
Corfe Mullen United	24	17	5	2	88	25	56
Soccer	24	18	2	4	80	33	56
Poole Link	24	16	5	3	98	33	53
Galaxy Windows	24	14	3	7	69	31	45
Flight Refuelling	24	13	5	6	76	36	44
Owermoigne	24	11	3	10	76	60	36
Poundbury R. Res.	24	8	5	11	60	57	29
Besh. Caundle Res.	24	7	7	10	62	56	28
Pimperne Sports	24	8	3	13	64	72	27
Wyke Victoria	24	8	2	14	56	124	26
Littlemoor	24	6	0	18	50	81	18
Milborne Spts Res.	24	5	1	18	33	117	16
Stalbridge Res.	24	3	3	18	28	115	12

EAST CORNWALL LEAGUE

www.football.mitoo.co.uk/News.cfm?LeagueCode=ECRNW2010

Sponsored by: Cornish Guardian

Founded: 1960

Recent champions:

2005: Foxhole Stars

2006: Saltash United Res.

2007: Foxhole Stars

2008: Torpoint Athletic Res.

2009: Torpoint Athletic Res.

	Bere Alston United	Biscovey	Bodmin Town Res.	Bude Town	Lanreath	Launceston Res.	Liskeard At. Res.	Morwenstow	Plym. Parkway Res.	Probus	Saltash United Res.	St Stephen	Sticker	Tavistock Res.	Torpoint Athletic Res.	Wadebridge T. Res.
Bere Alston United	***P***	3-0	0-3	2-2	1-1	1-1	4-1	2-1	0-4	1-3	6-3	2-2	1-2	1-1	0-2	3-0
Biscovey	3-3	***R***	3-1	2-3	4-5	1-3	1-0	1-4	0-4	3-1	2-2	3-4	3-1	4-3	2-5	4-2
Bodmin Town Res.	1-1	2-0	***E***	0-3	3-2	1-5	7-3	3-1	3-2	0-1	1-2	4-2	4-0	1-3	0-6	2-0
Bude Town	7-0	2-1	0-3	***M***	2-1	3-1	1-2	3-1	3-1	4-1	2-2	3-1	0-2	2-1	0-2	1-3
Lanreath	0-3	2-3	1-4	2-1	***I***	0-1	4-2	0-5	0-3	4-6	1-2	2-2	4-3	1-1	0-2	2-4
Launceston Res.	0-2	2-3	0-1	1-1	0-3	***E***	2-1	1-3	2-1	0-1	4-0	4-0	3-1	1-2	1-3	1-1
Liskeard Athletic Res.	0-5	2-0	0-4	3-4	0-4	4-1	***R***	0-10	2-3	3-2	2-5	5-2	6-0	3-2	4-4	1-3
Morwenstow	2-2	2-0	0-0	1-1	8-3	2-0	3-4		2-3	3-3	1-1	3-1	4-4	1-4	1-3	1-1
Plymouth Parkway Res.	2-1	1-0	4-2	3-4	7-4	3-0	5-0	4-1	***D***	2-2	1-1	1-0	1-1	5-0	3-5	2-1
Probus	1-2	1-1	3-0	7-1	3-2	2-2	3-1	2-1	1-3	***I***	1-3	1-1	2-2	2-2	4-2	1-2
Saltash United Res.	3-1	4-1	4-2	3-1	2-0	6-4	5-0	2-1	2-1	4-1	***V***	2-1	0-0	3-4	3-4	4-1
St Stephen	1-0	1-1	2-3	1-5	2-5	2-2	4-2	2-2	1-2	1-3	3-1	***I***	2-3	1-4	0-6	0-1
Sticker	1-2	3-1	3-1	1-1	2-1	0-3	6-0	3-2	1-3	2-2	0-5	3-2	***S***	2-1	1-5	1-1
Tavistock Res.	1-3	1-0	1-1	2-1	2-3	0-2	1-1	3-2	1-4	0-4	6-2	3-2	0-1	***I***	2-5	4-1
Torpoint Athletic Res.	4-0	3-3	0-2	2-0	6-0	2-0	2-1	4-1	1-1	4-1	1-1	8-1	3-1	4-1	***O***	4-0
Wadebridge Town Res.	0-3	3-1	2-1	0-3	0-0	3-0	2-1	2-2	1-2	1-2	1-4	2-0	0-0	8-1	1-3	***N***

Premier Division	**P**	**W**	**D**	**L**	**F**	**A**	**Pts**
Torpoint Athletic Res.	30	24	4	2	105	35	76
Plymouth Parkway Res.	30	20	4	6	81	42	64
Saltash United Res.	30	18	6	6	81	54	60
Bude Town	30	15	5	10	64	52	50
Bodmin Town Res.	30	15	3	12	60	54	48
Probus	30	13	8	9	67	57	47
Bere Alston United	30	12	8	10	55	52	44
Sticker	30	11	8	11	50	63	41
Wadebridge Town Res.	30	11	6	13	47	54	39
Tavistock Res.	30	11	5	14	57	71	38
Launceston Res.	30	10	5	15	47	53	35
Morwenstow	30	8	9	13	71	62	33
Biscovey	30	8	5	17	51	73	29
Lanreath	30	8	4	18	57	84	28
Liskeard Athletic Res.	30	8	2	20	54	99	26
St Stephen	30	4	6	20	44	86	18

SUPPLEMENTARY CUP

(League Cup First Round losers)

FIRST ROUND

Biscovey 2 **Plymstock United Res.** 4 *aet*
Callington Town Res. 3 **Lanreath** 4
Holsworthy Res. 0 **Camelford Res.** 1
Nanpean Rovers 0 **Launceston Res.** 6
Saltash United Res. 0 St Stephens Borough 1
(St Stephens Borough expelled)
St Columb Major 2 St Blazey Res. 3
(St Blazey Res. expelled)
St Stephen 2 **Edgcumbe** 2 *aet* (2-4p)

QUARTER-FINALS

Camelford Res. 3 St Columb Major 0
Edgcumbe 7 Millbrook Res. 3
Lanreath 2 **Plymstock United Res.** 3 *aet*
Saltash United Res. 5 Launceston Res. 0

SEMI-FINALS

Plymstock United Res. 3 Edgcumbe 1
Saltash United Res. 3 Camelford Res. 2

FINAL *(May 23rd at Torpoint Athletic)*

Plymstock United Res. 1 **Saltash United Res.** 6

EAST CORNWALL LEAGUE PREMIER DIVISION CONSTITUTION 2010-11

BERE ALSTON UNITED .... Recreation Field, The Down, Bere Alston PL20 7HG .... None
BISCOVEY .... Par Athletics Track, Moorland Road, Par, St Austell PL24 2PB .... None
BODMIN TOWN RES.. .... Priory Park, Bodmin PL31 2AE 01208 78165
BUDE TOWN .... Broadclose, Bude EX23 8DR .... None
LANREATH .... Rally Park, Lanreath Village Hall, Lanreath PL13 2NX .... None
LAUNCESTON RES. .... Pennygillam, Pennygillam Industrial Estate, Launceston PL15 7ED 01566 773279
MORWENSTOW .... Playing Field, Shop, Morwenstow, Bude EX23 9SL .... None
PLYMOUTH PARKWAY RES. .... Bolitho Park, St Peters Road, Manadon, Plymouth PL5 3QZ .... None
PROBUS .... Recreation Ground, Probus TR2 4JS .... None
SALTASH UNITED RES.. .... Kimberley Stadium, Callington Road, Saltash PL12 6DX 01752 845746
ST DENNIS .... Boscawen Park, St Dennis PL26 8AP 01726 822635
ST STEPHENS BOROUGH .... Saltmill Park, Saltmill Lane, Saltash PL12 6LG .... None
STICKER .... Burngallow Park, Burngallow Lane, Sticker, St Austell PL26 7EN 01726 71003
TAVISTOCK RES. .... Langsford Park, Crowndale Road, Tavistock PL19 8DD 01822 614447
TORPOINT ATHLETIC RES. .... The Mill, Mill Lane, Torpoint PL11 2NA 01752 812889
WADEBRIDGE TOWN RES. .... Bodieve Park, Bodieve Road, Wadebridge PL27 7AJ 01208 812537

IN: St Dennis (P), St Stephens Borough (P)
OUT: Liskeard Athletic Res. (R), St Stephen (R)

Division One	P	W	D	L	F	A	Pts
St Dennis	28	25	1	2	113	23	76
St Stephens Borough	28	19	3	6	86	49	60
Edgcumbe	28	18	3	7	88	42	57
St Blazey Res.	28	17	5	6	66	36	56
Polperro	28	15	7	6	73	33	52
Plymstock United Res.	28	14	5	9	72	51	47
Millbrook Res.	28	12	5	11	73	63	41
St Dominick	28	13	2	13	53	63	41
Roche	28	12	4	12	39	38	40
Camelford Res.	28	10	3	15	46	64	33
Elburton Villa Res.	28	8	5	15	40	51	29
Callington Town Res.	28	8	5	15	48	77	29
Holsworthy Res.	28	7	2	19	56	76	23
Nanpean Rovers	28	4	4	20	53	85	16
St Columb Major	28	0	2	26	17	172	2

LEAGUE CUP

FIRST ROUND

Bere Alston United (w/o) v Lifton
Bodmin Town Res. 2 Edgcumbe 1
Bude Town 4 Camelford Res. 1
Elburton Villa Res. 2 Lanreath 2 *aet* (4-1p)
Liskeard Athletic Res. 1 Launceston Res. 0
Morwenstow 3 Biscovey 2, Nanpean Rovers 0 **Probus** 1
Plymstock United Res. 1 **Plymouth Parkway Res.** 2 *aet*
Polperro 4 St Stephen 2, **Roche** 3 Holsworthy Res. 2
St Columb Major 3 **Torpoint Athletic Res.** 10
St Dominick 6 Callington Town Res. 1
St Stephens Borough 2 **St Dennis** 5
Sticker 4 St Blazey Res. 0
Tavistock Res. 4 Saltash United Res. 0
Wadebridge Town Res. 1 Millbrook Res. 1 *aet* (3-2p)

SECOND ROUND

Elburton Res. 3 Bude Town 0, Morwenstow 2 **Probus** 3
Polperro 2 **Plymouth Parkway Res.** 4
Roche 0 **Bodmin Town Res.** 1
St Dominick 4 Bere Alston United 3
Tavistock Res. 2 Sticker 1
Torpoint Athletic Res. 2 St Dennis 0
Wadebridge Town Res. 5 Liskeard Athletic Res. 1

QUARTER-FINALS

Bodmin Town Res. 1 Wadebridge T. Res. 1 *aet* (8-7p)
Elburton Villa Res. 0 **Tavistock Res.** 2
Plymouth Parkway Res. 8 St Dominick 0
Torpoint Athletic Res. 2 Probus 1

SEMI-FINALS *(played over two legs)*

Bodmin Town Res. 3 Plymouth Parkway Res. 3,
Plymouth Parkway Res. 4 Bodmin Town Res. 0
Torpoint Athletic Res. 3 Tavistock Res. 0, Tavistock Res. 0
Torpoint Athletic Res. 3

FINAL

(May 2nd at Saltash United)
Torpoint Athletic Res. 2 **Plymouth Parkway Res.** 4

	Call	Cam	Edg	Elb	Hol	Mill	Nan	Plym	Polp	Roc	StBla	StC.	StDe	StDo	StSte
Callington Town Res.		2-1	0-2	2-2	4-0	1-5	2-2	4-4	2-0	2-1	1-0	1-0	0-6	1-3	1-2
Camelford Res.	5-1	***D***	1-5	1-4	1-1	1-4	5-0	0-0	1-0	0-1	3-4	4-0	0-5	2-2	1-3
Edgcumbe	5-0	2-3	***I***	3-0	1-0	3-1	7-1	3-1	2-2	0-1	6-1	12-0	1-4	5-2	4-2
Elburton Villa Res.	2-0	0-1	1-3	***V***	0-1	1-3	3-2	2-2	0-1	0-1	0-0	1-0	1-3	0-3	0-1
Holsworthy Res.	8-4	3-2	1-2	2-5	***I***	6-3	2-1	0-1	0-1	0-0	1-4	10-0	1-4	0-1	1-3
Millbrook Res.	3-3	1-2	3-1	3-2	3-2	***S***	5-5	3-3	4-0	2-3	3-2	10-1	0-3	3-0	1-2
Nanpean Rovers	2-2	1-3	2-3	1-3	3-2	2-3	***I***	0-2	1-3	0-3	1-2	7-2	0-2	6-1	1-3
Plymstock United Res.	3-2	1-2	1-2	2-1	6-1	1-0	4-2	***O***	1-3	3-2	3-3	8-0	1-5	6-1	4-0
Polperro	6-1	7-0	2-2	2-2	1-0	1-1	0-0	3-2	***N***	5-0	0-1	13-0	0-0	7-2	4-4
Roche	1-2	2-0	1-0	1-1	6-2	2-1	3-0	1-2	0-1		0-0	0-0	0-3	1-0	1-3
St Blazey Res.	4-1	3-1	1-1	6-0	4-2	5-0	2-0	2-1	0-2	2-0		4-0	2-1	3-1	1-1
St Columb Major	1-5	0-5	1-8	4-7	3-7	0-3	2-8	0-4	0-4	0-5	0-6	***O***	0-9	0-2	1-1
St Dennis	3-2	3-0	6-1	0-1	6-0	7-2	6-4	5-2	3-0	1-0	2-1	12-0	***N***	4-1	3-1
St Dominick	2-0	3-0	2-1	1-0	4-2	1-1	4-0	2-3	1-4	2-1	1-2	5-1	1-3	***E***	4-2
St Stephens Borough	4-2	6-1	2-3	2-1	3-1	3-2	6-1	2-1	3-1	6-2	4-1	11-1	1-4	5-1	

EAST CORNWALL LEAGUE DIVISION ONE CONSTITUTION 2010-11

CALLINGTON TOWN RES. Ginsters Marshfield Parc, Callington College, Launceston Road, Callington PL17 7DR 01579 382647
CAMELFORD RES. . . . . Trefew Park, Trefew, Camelford PL32 9TS . . . . None
EDGCUMBE . . . . Millbrook FC, Mill Park, off Southdown Road, Millbrook, Torpoint PL11 1EN 01752 822113
ELBURTON VILLA RES. Haye Road, Elburton, Plymouth PL9 8HS 01752 480025
HOLSWORTHY RES. Upcott Field, North Road, Holsworthy EX22 6HF 01409 254295
KILKHAMPTON . . . . Lamb Park, Kilkhampton, Bude EX23 9TH . . . . None
LISKEARD ATHLETIC RES. . . . . Lux Park, Coldstyle Lane, Liskeard PL14 3HY 01579 342665
MILLBROOK . . . . Mill Park, off Southdown Road, Millbrook, Torpoint PL11 1EN 01752 822113
NANPEAN ROVERS . . . . Victoria Park, Victoria Bottoms, Nanpean PL26 7YE 01726 823435
PLYMSTOCK UNITED RES. . . . . Dean Cross, Dean Cross Road, Plymstock PL9 7AZ 01752 406776
POLPERRO . . . . Killigarth, Polperro, Looe PL13 2JG . . . . None
ROCHE . . . . Trezaise Road, Roche, St Austell PL26 8HD 01726 890718
ST BLAZEY RES. . . . . Blaise Park, Station Road, St Blazey PL24 2ND 01726 814110
ST DOMINICK . . . . Lovells Park, St Dominick PL12 6SU . . . . None
ST STEPHEN . . . . Trethosa Road, St Stephen, St Austell PL26 7PZ . . . . None
ST TEATH . . . . Playing Fields, North Road, St Teath, Bodmin PL30 3JX . . . . None

IN: Kilkhampton (S - North Devon League Senior Division), Liskeard Athletic Res. (R), Millbrook (R - South West Peninsula League Division One West), St Stephen (R), St Teath (P - Duchy League Premier Division)
OUT: Lifton (WN), St Dennis (P), St Columb Major (R - Duchy League Premier Division), St Stephens Borough (P)

GLOUCESTERSHIRE NORTHERN SENIOR LEAGUE

www.glosnsl.co.uk

Sponsored by: Errea

Founded: 1922

Recent champions:

2005: Lydney Town
2006: Berkeley Town
2007: Tuffley Rovers
2008: Slimbridge
2009: Longlevens

	Barnwood United	Bredon	Broadwell Amats	Brockworth Albion	Cheltenham C S	Dursley Town	Gala Wilton	Longlevens	Lydbrook Athletic	Ramblers	Sharpness	Shortwood Res.	Star	Stonehouse Town	Tetbury Town	Wotton Rovers
Barnwood United		2-4	0-1	1-4	2-0	2-1	4-2	1-8	1-1	3-2	2-2	3-2	1-2	1-1	0-5	5-1
Bredon	0-0		3-4	1-1	1-3	2-2	1-1	0-2	1-2	0-2	0-2	2-2	3-2	0-3	1-2	2-0
Broadwell Amateurs	1-2	0-0	***D***	1-1	3-1	5-1	2-2	1-1	5-1	2-2	0-0	2-0	2-1	2-2	5-3	2-1
Brockworth Albion	2-0	6-2	2-3	***I***	6-0	3-1	3-1	1-3	0-3	2-2	0-3	2-1	1-3	1-3	1-1	1-0
Cheltenham Civil Service	2-6	1-1	0-6	0-5	***V***	1-5	0-1	0-2	1-4	0-0	0-2	2-4	1-2	0-2	1-4	3-1
Dursley Town	4-3	2-0	2-1	3-1	4-0	***I***	2-2	1-2	1-1	1-7	0-2	5-1	0-0	1-1	3-2	3-0
Gala Wilton	1-1	5-1	1-1	0-1	4-0	1-1	***S***	1-1	4-1	1-2	0-1	1-1	1-3	2-3	0-5	5-0
Longlevens	3-5	3-1	1-1	0-2	7-0	3-1	9-0	***I***	5-0	4-3	3-2	5-1	3-1	4-2	2-4	2-3
Lydbrook Athletic	3-0	3-1	2-2	2-0	3-2	5-4	1-0	5-3	***O***	0-0	1-1	3-0	2-2	3-2	1-1	3-1
Ramblers	0-4	2-1	0-1	3-0	7-0	1-0	2-0	1-2	3-4	***N***	1-2	9-0	0-1	1-5	0-0	1-2
Sharpness	3-2	4-1	0-2	4-0	4-2	0-0	1-1	3-2	0-1	1-1		2-0	3-0	1-0	3-1	2-0
Shortwood United Res.	3-0	0-3	0-3	3-0	4-1	2-0	0-0	1-0	3-2	1-1	1-0	***O***	3-1	1-1	4-2	3-0
Star	2-4	0-2	1-2	1-2	5-0	3-3	1-3	1-0	0-4	1-2	0-3	3-0	***N***	2-1	3-1	3-1
Stonehouse Town	2-1	4-1	2-2	8-0	7-1	0-3	2-0	0-3	1-0	1-2	1-4	0-1	3-4	***E***	3-3	4-0
Tetbury Town	3-1	1-1	3-0	2-2	4-0	1-1	4-1	1-1	1-0	3-1	0-0	1-0	3-2	2-1		4-1
Wotton Rovers	3-3	6-2	1-4	1-2	2-1	4-4	0-3	3-2	0-0	4-1	0-3	1-0	0-2	0-3	0-2	

Division One		**P**	**W**	**D**	**L**	**F**	**A**	**Pts**
Sharpness		**30**	**19**	**7**	**4**	**58**	**22**	**64**
Tetbury Town		**30**	**16**	**9**	**5**	**69**	**39**	**57**
Broadwell Amateurs	*-3*	**30**	**16**	**11**	**3**	**66**	**36**	**56**
Lydbrook Athletic		**30**	**16**	**8**	**6**	**61**	**45**	**56**
Longlevens		**30**	**17**	**4**	**9**	**86**	**46**	**55**
Stonehouse Town		**30**	**13**	**6**	**11**	**68**	**46**	**45**
Star		**30**	**13**	**3**	**14**	**52**	**54**	**42**
Brockworth Albion	*-3*	**30**	**13**	**5**	**12**	**52**	**56**	**41**
Shortwood United Res.		**30**	**12**	**5**	**13**	**42**	**55**	**41**
Ramblers		**30**	**11**	**7**	**12**	**59**	**46**	**40**
Dursley Town		**30**	**10**	**10**	**10**	**59**	**56**	**40**
Barnwood United		**30**	**11**	**6**	**13**	**60**	**68**	**39**
Gala Wilton		**30**	**7**	**10**	**13**	**44**	**54**	**31**
Wotton Rovers		**30**	**7**	**3**	**20**	**36**	**75**	**24**
Bredon		**30**	**5**	**8**	**17**	**38**	**67**	**23**
Cheltenham Civil Service		**30**	**2**	**2**	**26**	**23**	**108**	**8**

GLOUCESTERSHIRE NORTHERN SENIOR LEAGUE DIVISION ONE CONSTITUTION 2010-11

BARNWOOD UNITED . . . . . . Walls Sports & Social Club, Hammond Way, Barnwood, Gloucester GL4 3HG. 01452 610277
BROADWELL AMATEURS . . . . The Hawthorns, Poolway Road, Broadwell, Coleford GL16 7BE 01594 837347
BROCKWORTH ALBION . . . . Parton Road, Churchdown, Gloucester GL3 2JH 01452 713528
DURSLEY TOWN . . . . War Recreation Memorial Ground, Kingshill Road, Dursley GL11 4BJ 01453 546122
GALA WILTON . . . . . . The Gala Wilton Club, Fairmile Gardens, Tewkesbury Road, Longford, Gloucester GL2 9EB 01452 524447
LEONARD STANLEY . . . . Stanley Park, Marsh Road, Leonard Stanley, Stonehouse GL10 3ND . . . . None
LONGLEVENS . . . . The Pavilion, Longlevens PF, Longford Lane, Longlevens, Gloucester GL2 9EU. 01452 530388
LYDBROOK ATHLETIC . . . . Reeds Sports Ground, Lower Lydbrook GL17 9PD 01594 860870
NEWTON HEATH & STROUD . . . . The Newlands, Southam Lane, Bishops Cleeve GL52 3PE . . . . None
RAMBLERS. . . . . Winget, Tuffley Park, Tuffley Avenue, Gloucester GL1 5NS 01452 524621
SHARPNESS . . . . Berkeley Power Station, Berkeley GL13 9PB. . . . . None
SHORTWOOD UNITED RES. . . . . Meadowbank, Shortwood, Nailsworth, Stroud GL6 0SJ. 01453 833936
SMITHS ATHLETIC . . . . Dowty Rotol Sports Ground, Hatherley Lane, Staverton, Cheltenham GL51 4NF 01242 525515
STAR . . . . Bishops Cleeve Playing Fields, Cheltenham Road, Bishops Cleeve GL52 8LZ. . . . . None
STONEHOUSE TOWN. Oldends Lane, Stonehouse GL10 2DG . . . . None
TETBURY TOWN . . . . Preston Park, Cirencester Road, Tetbury GL8 8EZ . . . . None

IN: Leonard Stanley (P), Newton Heath & Stroud (P), Smiths Athletic (P)
OUT: Bredon (R), Cheltenham Civil Service (R), Wotton Rovers (R)

FIRST ROUND
Aylburton Rovers 0 **Lydbrook** 4
Bourton Rovers 1 **Star** 5
Bredon 1 **Longlevens** 3
Dursley Town 1 Brockworth Albion 0
Gala Wilton 4 Soudley 0
Harrow Hill Res. 2 **Cheltenham CS** 3
Hatherley Rangers 1 **Shortwood United Res.** 1 *aet* (2-4p)
Leonard Stanley 3 **Sharpness** 4
Longford 1 **Broadwell Amateurs** 2
Newton Heath & Stroud 1 Cam 0
Smiths Athletic 6 FC Barometrics 2
Tetbury Town 5 Ramblers 3
Tidenham 1 **Barnwood United** 3
Viney St Swithins 3 Mitcheldean 0
Winchcombe Town 3 **Stonehouse Town** 3 *aet* (3-4p)
Wotton Rovers 0 **Chalford** 1

SECOND ROUND
Chalford 5 Cheltenham CS 1
Dursley Town 3 Stonehouse Town 1
Gala Wilton 1 **Barnwood United** 2
Longlevens 3 Tetbury Town 1
Lydbrook 5 Viney St Swithins 1
Sharpness 3 Shortwood Utd Res. 1
Smiths 1 **Broadwell Amateurs** 2
Star 0 **Newton Heath & Stroud** 1

QUARTER-FINALS
Chalford 2 **Longlevens** 7
(at Longlevens)
Dursley 0 **Broadwell** 0 *aet* (2-4p)
Lydbrook Ath 0 **Barnwood United** 2
Sharpness 3 Newton Hth & Stroud 0

SEMI-FINALS
Barnwood United 1 Longlevens 0
Sharpness 3 Broadwell Amats 2

FINAL *(October 7th at Tuffley Rovers)*
Barnwood United 1 **Sharpness** 2

REG DAVIS MEMORIAL CUP

Division Two	P	W	D	L	F	A	Pts
Leonard Stanley	30	19	8	3	67	23	65
Smiths Athletic	30	18	6	6	79	43	60
Newton Heath & Stroud	30	17	6	7	72	45	57
Winchcombe Town	30	16	7	7	68	39	55
Soudley	30	17	3	10	71	51	54
FC Barometrics	30	17	3	10	69	49	54
Aylburton Rovers	30	14	7	9	59	44	49
Hatherley Rangers	30	12	7	11	72	64	43
Longford	30	13	1	16	43	63	40
Cam Bulldogs	30	12	2	16	58	76	38
Harrow Hill Res.	30	7	14	9	52	57	35
Viney St Swithins	30	10	3	17	54	68	33
Bourton Rovers	30	10	3	17	51	86	33
Chalford	30	6	7	17	46	67	25
Tidenham	30	5	5	20	37	77	20
Mitcheldean	30	4	4	22	38	84	16

	Ayl	Bou	Cam	Cha	Bar	Har	Hat	Leo	Lon	Mit	New	Smi	Sou	Tid	Vin	Win
Aylburton Rovers		4-1	2-0	4-1	4-2	2-2	3-1	0-0	0-2	3-1	0-4	2-2	2-0	4-0	2-0	0-3
Bourton Rovers	3-2		1-4	4-1	4-1	3-3	2-4	1-2	0-3	2-1	8-1	2-8	3-1	3-1	2-1	2-2
Cam Bulldogs	0-1	3-1	***D***	4-3	3-6	5-5	2-3	0-3	1-4	0-3	1-5	3-2	6-2	2-0	2-1	2-3
Chalford	1-1	1-1	1-3	***I***	2-4	0-1	1-6	1-2	1-0	2-1	2-3	2-1	3-0	0-0	5-0	1-1
FC Barometrics	4-0	5-0	0-2	3-2	***V***	0-0	1-4	0-1	0-1	4-0	2-0	1-4	1-0	2-1	2-1	2-1
Harrow Hill Res.	2-2	0-1	2-3	3-2	2-2	***I***	1-2	2-2	3-1	4-2	1-4	0-0	1-0	1-1	2-2	2-2
Hatherley Rangers	1-4	5-0	3-3	1-1	2-3	4-3	***S***	0-3	3-1	7-0	1-1	2-2	1-3	3-2	3-4	0-4
Leonard Stanley	3-1	3-0	1-0	1-0	3-0	0-0	1-3	***I***	4-3	0-0	1-1	7-0	2-2	5-0	3-1	1-1
Longford	0-4	0-2	3-0	2-2	1-0	3-1	0-4	1-4	***O***	4-2	3-2	1-2	0-3	3-2	0-3	0-5
Mitcheldean	1-0	3-1	2-5	2-2	3-8	3-4	2-2	0-4	0-3	***N***	1-2	1-2	2-5	3-2	1-2	0-3
Newton Heath & Stroud	0-2	2-1	2-1	3-2	1-2	2-0	2-1	1-1	3-0	1-1		1-4	1-2	2-1	2-0	2-1
Smiths Athletic	3-2	7-2	4-0	2-1	1-3	3-1	0-0	3-2	7-0	2-0	2-2	***T***	2-0	1-1	2-1	0-1
Soudley	2-2	6-0	5-0	5-2	2-1	1-2	5-1	2-0	2-0	2-1	0-8	5-2	***W***	3-1	2-1	2-3
Tidenham	1-1	3-1	4-1	2-3	1-5	1-1	3-2	0-2	0-1	4-0	0-5	0-5	0-4	***O***	0-3	2-4
Viney St Swithins	1-4	6-0	4-1	4-1	2-2	2-2	4-0	0-5	2-3	2-1	1-6	0-4	1-3	1-3		1-3
Winchcombe Town	3-1	3-0	0-1	3-0	1-3	2-1	3-3	0-1	1-0	2-1	3-3	0-2	2-2	6-1	2-3	

GLOUCESTERSHIRE NORTHERN SENIOR LEAGUE DIVISION TWO CONSTITUTION 2010-11

BOURTON ROVERS . . . . Rissington Road, Bourton-on-the-Water, Cheltenham GL54 2AY 01451 821977
BREDON . . . . Bredon Playing Fields, Main Road, Bredon, Tewkesbury GL20 7EG 01684 773152
CAM BULLDOGS . . . . Cam Sports Club, Everlands, Cam, Dursley GL11 5NL 01453 546736
CHALFORD . . . . Chalford Sports Club, Highfield Way, Chalford Hill, Stroud GL6 8BD 01453 884214
CHELTENHAM CIVIL SERVICE . . . . Tewkesbury Road, Uckington, Cheltenham GL51 9SL 01242 680424
FC BAROMETRICS . . . . The Newlands, Southam Lane, Bishops Cleeve GL52 3PE . . . . None
FRAMPTON UNITED . . . . Bell Field, Bridge Road, Frampton-on-Severn GL2 7EY . . . . None
HARROW HILL . . . . Larksfield Road, Harrow Hill, Drybrook GL17 9JP 01594 543873
HATHERLEY RANGERS . . . . . St Marks Sports Ground, Brooklyn Road, St Marks, Cheltenham GL51 8DT . . . . None
LONGFORD . . . . Playing Field, Longford Lane, Gloucester GL2 9EU . . . . None
MORETON RANGERS . . . . London Road (A44), Moreton-in-Marsh GL56 0HN . . . . None
SOUDLEY . . . . Soudley Playing Field, Upper Soudley, Cinderford GL14 2TZ . . . . None
VINEY ST SWITHINS. . . . . Viney Sports & Social Club, Viney Hill, Lydney GL15 4NF 01594 510658
WINCHCOMBE TOWN . . . . Winchcombe School, Greet Road, Winchcombe, Cheltenham GL54 5LB 01242 602233
WOTTON ROVERS . . . . Synwell Playing Fields, Synwell Lane, Wotton-under-Edge GL12 7HQ 01453 842929

IN: Bredon (R), Cheltenham Civil Service (R), Frampton United (P - Stroud & District League Division One), Moreton Rangers (P - Cheltenham Association League Division One), Wotton Rovers (R)
OUT: Aylburton Rovers (R - North Gloucestershire League Division One), Leonard Stanley (P), Mitcheldean (R - North Gloucestershire League Premier Division), Newton Heath & Stroud (P), Smiths Athletic (P), Tidenham (R - North Gloucestershire League Premier Division)
Harrow Hill Res. become Harrow Hill

HAMPSHIRE LEAGUE 2004

www.hampshireleague2004.com

Sponsored by:
Magnata Care

Founded: 2004

Recent champions:

2005: Sporting BTC

2006: Mottisfont.

2007: Mottisfont

2008: Mottisfont

2009: Netley Central Sports

	Andover Res.	Broughton	Crusaders	Durley	Fair Oak	Four Marks	Hedge End Rangers	Horndean United	Infinity	Michelmersh & Tim.	Mottisfont	Netley Centra Spts	Portsmouth R. Navy	Twyford
Andover Res.		2-1	0-10	3-1	4-3	1-1	1-2	1-3	7-6	1-3	0-5	1-2	1-2	5-0
Broughton	0-5		3-1	4-3	0-2	2-5	1-4	1-0	8-1	5-1	1-2	3-2	2-4	5-2
Crusaders	3-5	0-4		0-2	1-4	2-1	0-3	1-2	1-0	0-2	1-2	1-5	1-1	1-2
Durley	3-0	2-1	0-0		2-2	4-0	0-0	5-0	5-1	2-1	4-1	1-4	0-0	n/a
Fair Oak	4-1	5-1	7-2	L-W		4-1	2-1	6-2	2-1	2-2	4-2	1-2	2-1	n/a
Four Marks	1-1	1-4	2-3	4-1	0-1		1-2	0-2	3-2	2-1	1-3	1-1	4-1	0-3
Hedge End Rangers	4-1	1-2	5-0	0-0	0-2	4-1		2-1	3-2	2-1	1-3	1-4	4-2	2-0
Horndean United	1-1	3-2	2-2	6-0	0-1	2-2	0-2		5-2	1-1	0-3	0-5	1-2	n/a
Infinity	2-3	3-2	4-0	2-4	2-2	1-2	2-5	2-3		3-7	2-3	1-3	3-2	n/a
Michelmersh & Timsbury	3-0	4-0	6-2	1-6	1-5	1-2	2-2	1-1	2-0		0-4	0-3	2-3	n/a
Mottisfont	4-1	3-1	8-5	0-4	2-1	1-3	3-1	3-1	6-1	3-3		0-3	3-3	3-3
Netley Central Sports	9-1	1-0	3-1	3-0	3-3	1-0	1-0	1-0	4-1	10-0	2-0		3-0	4-0
Portsmouth Royal Navy	2-0	1-6	4-1	3-2	0-1	4-1	1-2	0-0	2-2	3-1	2-0	0-3		3-0
Twyford	n/a	n/a	n/a	n/a	n/a	0-3	2-2	n/a	n/a	2-1	n/a	n/a	n/a	

	P	W	D	L	F	A	Pts
Netley Central Sports	24	21	2	1	78	16	65
Fair Oak	24	16	4	4	66	31	52
Mottisfont	24	15	2	7	64	45	47
Hedge End Rangers	24	14	3	7	51	33	45
Durley	24	12	5	7	51	36	41
Portsmouth Royal Navy	24	10	5	9	43	45	35
Broughton	24	10	0	14	54	56	30
Four Marks	24	8	4	12	39	49	28
Horndean United	24	7	6	11	36	46	27
Michelmersh & Timsbury	24	7	5	12	46	62	26
Andover Res.	24	7	3	14	41	75	24
Crusaders	24	4	3	17	38	75	15
Infinity	24	3	2	19	46	84	11

Twyford - record expunged

TROPHYMAN LEAGUE CUP

Competition abandoned due to inclement weather

HAMPSHIRE LEAGUE 2004 CONSTITUTION 2010-11

ANDOVER RES. . . . . The Portway Stadium, West Portway Industrial Estate, Andover SP10 3LF 01264 351302
BOTLEY VILLAGE . . . . Botley Recreation Ground, High Street, Botley, Southampton SO30 2EA. 01489 780440
BROUGHTON . . . . The Sportsfield, Buckholt Road, Broughton, Stockbridge SO20 8DA. 01794 301150
CRUSADERS . . . . Worthies Sports & Social Club, Eversley Park, Kings Worthy, Winchester SO23 7NJ 01962 880457
DURLEY. . . . . Kytes Lane, Durley, Southampton SO32 2AE. . . . . None
FAIR OAK . . . . Lapstone Park, Pavilion Close, Botley Road, Fair Oak, Eastleigh SO50 7AN . . . . None
FOUR MARKS. . . . . The Recreation Ground, Upland Lane, Four Marks, Alton GU34 5AF . . . . None
HEDGE END RANGERS . . . . . . Norman Rodaway Rec Ground, Heathouse Lane, Hedge End SO30 0LE. . . . . None
HORNDEAN UNITED . . . . . King George V Playing Field, Southwick Road, Denmead, Waterlooville PO7 6XT . . . . None
HYTHE & DIBDEN RES. . . . . . . Ewart Recreation Ground, Jones Lane, Hythe, Southampton SO45 6FD 023 8084 5264
INFINITY . . . . Taunton's College, Hill Lane, Southampton SO15 5RL 023 8051 1811
LYMINGTON TOWN RES.. . . . . The Sports Ground, Southampton Road, Lymington SO41 9ZG 01590 671305
MICHELMERSH & TIMSBURY . . Timsbury Rec Trust, Mannyngham Way, Timsbury, Romsey SO51 0NJ 01794 368955
MOTTISFONT . . . . Bengers Lane, Mottisfont, Romsey SO51 0LR . . . . None
NETLEY CENTRAL SPORTS. . . . . Netley Recreation Ground, Station Road, Netley Abbey SO21 5AF 023 8045 2267
PORTSMOUTH ROYAL NAVY . . Victory Stadium, HMS Temeraire, Burnaby Road, Portsmouth PO1 2EJ 023 9272 5315/4235
UPHAM. . . . . Ray's Farm Recreation Ground, Shoe Lane, Upham, Southampton SO32 1JJ. . . . . None
WARSASH WASPS . . . . Meadowside Leisure Centre, Whiteley Way, Whiteley, Fareham PO15 7LJ 01489 577464

IN: Botley Village (N), Hythe & Dibden Res. (P - Southampton Senior League Senior One), Lymington Town Res. (Wessex League Combination One), Upham (P - Winchester & District League Division One), Warsash Wasps (P - Southampton Senior League Senior One)

OUT: Twyford (WS)

HEREFORDSHIRE LEAGUE

full-time.thefa.com/ListPublicResult.do?league=9582209

Sponsored by: Hereford Times

Founded: N/k

Recent champions:
2005: Ewyas Harold
2006: Ewyas Harold
2007: Wellington Rangers
2008: Wooferton
2009: Westfields Res.

	Bro	Ewy	Fow	Her	Hin	Hol	Kin	Led	Leo	Peg	Ros	Wel	Wes
Bromyard Town Res.		1-6	0-1	1-5	2-5	2-0	2-1	0-4	0-4	2-2	n/a	0-1	2-4
Ewyas Harold	4-0	***P***	3-1	3-2	2-2	3-1	2-1	5-1	1-1	2-0	1-6	1-0	3-2
Fownhope	1-2	0-1	***R***	1-1	2-3	2-2	3-1	0-1	0-5	1-4	n/a	1-2	1-2
Hereford Lads Club	4-0	1-0	2-1	***E***	0-1	2-2	1-1	2-3	1-4	1-0	11-5	0-2	0-4
Hinton	3-1	0-2	2-1	1-1	***M***	6-1	1-2	0-3	1-3	3-6	n/a	1-3	1-4
Holme Lacy	2-3	2-4	3-1	2-3	2-1	***I***	2-2	5-9	0-7	0-4	n/a	0-5	0-6
Kington Town	4-1	2-0	2-2	2-0	3-0	4-0	***E***	2-4	1-4	0-3	n/a	2-3	3-3
Ledbury Town Res.	12-1	7-2	7-1	4-2	1-2	10-2	1-2	***R***	1-6	7-1	n/a	2-3	3-1
Leominster Town	6-1	0-1	4-2	5-0	3-1	6-2	6-1	3-1		3-0	n/a	3-4	4-3
Pegasus Juniors Res.	4-5	3-1	4-0	2-2	0-2	5-3	3-3	4-2	1-1	***D***	n/a	3-1	2-6
Ross Town	n/a	n/a	n/a	n/a	n/a	n/a	1-3	2-3	n/a	0-9	***I***	n/a	n/a
Wellington Res.	2-0	1-1	4-0	2-0	3-1	3-1	1-0	1-1	1-3	2-3	n/a	***V***	1-3
Westfields Res.	2-2	2-5	3-0	1-2	1-2	4-3	3-1	3-4	1-1	1-3	n/a	3-2	

Premier Division	P	W	D	L	F	A	Pts
Leominster Town	22	17	3	2	82	24	54
Ewyas Harold	22	15	3	4	52	30	48
Wellington Res.	22	14	2	6	47	29	44
Ledbury Town Res.	22	14	1	7	88	48	43
Pegasus Juniors Res.	22	11	4	7	57	48	37
Westfields Res.	22	11	3	8	62	45	36
Hinton	22	9	2	11	39	46	29
Kington Town	22	7	5	10	40	45	26
Hereford Lads Club	22	7	5	10	32	42	26
Bromyard Town Res.	22	5	2	15	28	77	17
Fownhope	22	2	3	17	22	58	9
Holme Lacy	22	2	3	17	35	92	9

Ross Town - record expunged

STRONGBOW SENIOR CUP

FIRST ROUND

Fownhope 5 Bromyard Town Res. 1
Hereford Lads Club 2 Leominster Town 2 *aet* (4-2p)
Hinton 2 Ross Town 1
Holme Lacy 4 Wellington Res. 3
Kington Town 5 Pegasus Juniors Res. 3

QUARTER-FINALS

Fownhope 1 **Holme L.** 4, Lads Club 1 **Ewyas H.** 3
Kington Town 2 **Hinton** 4
Ledbury Town Res. 2 Westfields Res. 1

SEMI-FINALS

Ewyas Harold 3 **Ledbury Town Res.** 3 *aet* (3-5p)
Holme Lacy 4 Hinton 2

FINAL *(May 3rd at Westfields)*

Holme Lacy 1 **Ledbury Town Res.** 6

JOURNAL TROPHY

FIRST ROUND

Holme Lacy 1 **Lads Club** 3, **Kington Town** 4 Hinton 3
Leominster 6 Fownhope 0, **Pegasus Res.** 2 Wellington Res. 1
Ross Town v **Westfields Res.** (w/o)

QUARTER-FINALS

Bromyard Town Res. 0 **Ledbury Town Res.** 8
Lads Club 1 **Ewyas Harold** 2, **Leominster** 4 Kington 2
Westfields Res. 2 **Pegasus Juniors Res.** 3

SEMI-FINALS

Leominster Town (w/o) v Ewyas Harold
Pegasus Juniors Res. 4 Ledbury Town Res. 0

FINAL *(April 28th at Hinton)*

Leominster Town 2 Pegasus Juniors Res. 0

HEREFORDSHIRE LEAGUE PREMIER DIVISION CONSTITUTION 2010-11

BARTESTREE . . . . New Street, Ledbury HR8 2EL . . . . None
BROMYARD TOWN RES. . . . . Delahay Meadow, Stourport Road, Bromyard HR7 4NT 01885 483974
EWYAS HAROLD . . . . Ewyas Harold Recreation Ground, Ewyas Harold HR2 0TX . . . . None
FOWNHOPE . . . . Malt House Field, Capler Lane, Fownhope HR1 4PJ . . . . None
HAY ST MARYS A . . . . Forest Road, Hay-on-Wye HR3 5DY . . . .
HEREFORD LADS CLUB . . . . County Ground, Widemarsh Common, Hereford HR4 9NA . . . . None
HINTON . . . . Broomy Hill, Hereford HR4 0LH . . . . None
HOLME LACY . . . . Holme Lacy Playing Fields, Holme Lacy HR2 6PL . . . . None
KINGTON TOWN . . . . Park Road Ground, Kington HR5 3AW 01544 231007
LEDBURY TOWN . . . . New Street Ground, New Street, Ledbury HR8 2EL 07879 268205
LEOMINSTER TOWN RES. . . . . Bridge Street Park, Bridge Street, Leominster HR6 8EA 01568 611172
PEGASUS JUNIORS RES. . . . . Old School Lane, Hereford HR1 1EX 07980 456995/07931 971765
WELLINGTON RES. . . . . Wellington Playing Fields, Wellington, Hereford HR4 8AZ . . . . None
WESTFIELDS RES. . . . . Allpay Park, Widemarsh Common, Hereford HR4 9NA 07860 410548

IN: Bartestree (P), Hay St Marys A (P), Leominster Town Res. (P - Division Three)
OUT: Leominster Town (P - West Midlands League Division Two), Ross Town (WS)
Ledbury Town Res. become Ledbury Town

Division One	P	W	D	L	F	A	Pt
Leintwardine	18	15	2	1	107	29	47
Bartestree	18	12	2	4	61	30	38
Ewyas Harold Res.	18	10	4	4	46	32	34
Stoke Prior	18	9	2	7	51	50	29
Wellington Colts	18	9	0	9	68	38	27
Hinton Res.	18	6	6	6	45	46	24
Woofferton Res.	18	7	3	8	42	53	24
Hay St Marys A	18	5	3	10	28	57	18
Shobdon	18	3	3	12	28	49	12
Fownhope Res.	18	1	1	16	19	111	4

Division Two	P	W	D	L	F	A	Pt
Kingstone Rovers	24	15	5	4	79	47	50
Weobley	24	15	3	6	73	51	48
Bucknell United	24	13	5	6	62	40	44
Orcop Juniors	24	12	4	8	83	70	40
Pegasus J. Colts	24	9	9	6	78	69	36
Burghill	24	10	4	10	56	63	34
Dore Valley	24	9	6	9	64	60	33
Hereford LC Colts	24	9	4	11	62	78	31
Kington T. Res.	24	7	7	10	48	60	28
Holme Lacy Res.	24	8	3	13	57	54	27
Ledbury Colts *-3*	24	6	7	11	44	66	22
Toros	24	6	3	15	45	76	21
Pencombe	24	6	2	16	49	66	20

Division Three	P	W	D	L	F	A	Pt
Ledbury Town A	24	22	2	0	123	24	68
Leominster Res.	24	19	3	2	94	30	60
Holmer	24	15	2	7	85	37	47
Weston	24	11	6	7	60	45	39
Heref'd Civil Serv.	24	12	2	10	73	63	38
Orleton Colts	24	11	3	10	73	72	36
Bartestree Res.	24	11	2	11	76	67	35
Wye Valley Rov.	24	11	1	12	54	77	34
Tenbury Town	24	8	5	11	54	78	29
Kingstone Harriers	24	6	2	16	46	73	20
Relentless	24	6	0	18	46	115	18
Wolseley	24	5	2	17	53	88	17
Toros Colts	24	3	2	19	39	107	11

HUMBER PREMIER LEAGUE

www.humberprem.com

Sponsored by:

No sponsor

Founded: 2000

Recent champions:

2005: Reckitts

2006: Reckitts

2007: Sculcoates Amateurs

2008: Sculcoates Amateurs

2009: Chalk Lane

Premier Division	P	W	D	L	F	A	Pts
Reckitts	26	18	4	4	75	29	58
Hornsea Town	26	15	4	7	57	40	49
Sculcoates Amateurs	26	14	6	6	64	38	48
Hessle Rangers	26	13	5	8	52	41	44
Beverley Town	26	12	6	8	48	37	42
Hall Road Rangers Res. *-3*	26	14	1	11	71	63	40
Chalk Lane	26	10	9	7	49	33	39
Hedon Rangers	26	12	3	11	65	51	39
Hessle Sporting Club	26	10	5	11	57	53	35
North Ferriby United Res.	26	10	3	13	54	58	33
Malet Lambert YC	26	6	7	13	44	74	25
St Andrews	26	7	3	16	46	78	24
Pocklington Town	26	6	4	16	32	50	22
Westella & Willerby Res.	26	3	4	19	25	94	13

Cleethorpes Town - record expunged

	Beverley Town	Chalk Lane	Cleethorpes Town	Hall Road Rangers Res.	Hedon Rangers	Hessle Rangers	Hessle Sporting Club	Hornsea Town	Malet Lambert YC	North Ferriby United Res.	Pocklington Town	Reckitts	Sculcoates Amateurs	St Andrews	Westella & Willerby Res.
Beverley Town		1-0	n/a	3-1	3-3	2-0	2-1	0-3	0-2	4-0	1-1	1-1	1-0	4-1	5-2
Chalk Lane	1-1		n/a	4-3	2-2	0-0	4-1	1-1	1-3	2-2	2-1	1-1	2-1	1-2	8-1
Cleethorpes Town	n/a	n/a	***P***	n/a	n/a	n/a	n/a	n/a	n/a	n/a	n/a	n/a	n/a	n/a	n/a
Hall Road Rangers Res.	3-0	0-3	2-2	***R***	1-5	3-3	6-3	0-3	3-6	6-1	5-3	0-2	2-1	2-0	7-0
Hedon Rangers	3-1	1-1	n/a	4-5	***E***	3-0	0-4	1-2	3-1	1-2	3-1	0-5	5-1	5-1	3-2
Hessle Rangers	2-1	2-0	n/a	1-3	1-0	***M***	3-0	2-3	4-0	3-2	2-3	0-4	2-0	4-1	2-1
Hessle Sporting Club	7-5	1-1	n/a	1-4	0-3	2-0	***I***	4-1	9-0	2-2	2-0	1-3	1-1	3-0	5-1
Hornsea Town	0-0	4-0	2-3	2-1	2-1	3-3	4-1	***E***	5-1	1-3	2-1	0-2	1-3	5-1	4-0
Malet Lambert YC	1-3	0-5	n/a	1-4	1-6	3-3	1-2	4-1	***R***	2-4	0-3	2-5	2-2	3-2	4-0
North Ferriby United Res.	1-0	1-1	5-2	2-3	2-3	1-3	3-0	0-3	2-0		1-0	3-6	3-4	2-3	4-0
Pocklington Town	0-1	0-3	n/a	5-1	3-2	1-4	1-2	1-2	0-0	2-0	***D***	0-3	1-5	1-2	0-0
Reckitts	0-4	1-0	n/a	1-3	3-2	4-1	1-1	2-0	1-1	3-1	3-0	***I***	1-2	7-2	7-0
Sculcoates Amateurs	1-1	1-0	n/a	5-0	2-0	1-1	2-1	1-2	1-1	4-2	2-1	4-2	***V***	5-2	6-1
St Andrews	1-4	0-3	3-1	3-2	2-5	0-1	4-2	5-1	3-3	2-3	1-1	0-5	3-3		3-0
Westella & Willerby Res.	2-0	2-3	n/a	1-3	3-1	0-5	1-1	2-2	2-2	0-7	1-2	0-2	0-6	3-2	

HUMBER PREMIER LEAGUE PREMIER DIVISION CONSTITUTION 2010-11

BEVERLEY TOWN . . . . Recreation Ground, Norwood, Beverley HU17 9HW 01482 862520
BRIDLINGTON SPORTS CLUB . . . Bridlington SC, Dukes Park, Moorfield Road, Bridlington YO16 4LE 01262 606016
CHALK LANE . . . . Hull University, Inglemire Lane, Hull HU6 7TE 01482 466000
CROWN . . . . Fitling Road, Humbleton, Hull HU11 4NS . . . . None
HALL ROAD RANGERS RES. . . . . Dene Park, Dene Close, Beverley Road, Dunswell, Hull HU6 0AB 01482 850101
HEDON RANGERS . . . . Destiny Fitness, Staithes Road, Hedon, Hull HU12 8DX 01482 896113
HESSLE RANGERS . . . . Blackburn Leisure, Prescott Avenue, Brough HU15 1BB . . . . None
HESSLE SPORTING CLUB . . . . South Hunsley School, Melton, North Ferriby HU14 3HS 01482 631208
HORNSEA TOWN . . . . Hollis Recreation Ground, Atwick Road, Hornsea HU18 1EL . . . . None
MALET LAMBERT YC . . . . Malet Lambert School, James Reckitt Avenue, Hull HU8 0JD 01482 374211
NORTH FERRIBY UNITED RES. . . . . Grange Lane, Church Road, North Ferriby HU14 3AA 01482 634601
POCKLINGTON TOWN . . . . The Balk, Pocklington, York YO42 2NZ 01759 303638
RECKITTS . . . . Humberside Police Spts Ground, Inglemire Lane, Hull HU6 8JG 01482 856954
SCULCOATES AMATEURS . . . . . Hull & East Riding Spts Ground, Chanterlands Avenue, Hull HU5 4ED 01482 342156
ST ANDREWS . . . . East Mount Recreation Ground, Waveney Road, Hull HU8 9NB 01482 326111x2317
WESTELLA & WILLERBY RES. . . . . Hill Top Club, Willerby Low Road, Willerby HU16 5JD . . . . None

IN: Bridlington Sports Club (P), Crown (P)

OUT: Cleethorpes Town (WS)

ivision One	P	W	D	L	F	A	Pts
rown	22	15	4	3	69	35	49
ridlington Sports Club	22	15	2	5	91	41	47
orth Cave	22	14	4	4	76	25	46
orth Ferriby Athletic	22	13	3	6	69	42	42
ransholme Athletic	22	11	4	7	49	44	37
ingburn Athletic	22	8	5	9	36	35	29
carborough Athletic Res.	22	9	2	11	48	70	29
randesburton	22	7	3	12	32	52	24
ast Riding Rangers	22	6	3	13	34	58	21
ithernsea	22	5	6	11	33	61	21
ong Riston	22	5	2	15	39	69	17
ter Charter	22	4	2	16	31	75	14

GRAYS CUP

FIRST ROUND

Brandesburton 0 **Scarborough Athletic Res.** 6
Hall Road Rangers Res. 1 **Chalk Lane** 3
Hessle Sporting Club 3 Inter Charter 1
Kingburn Athletic 2 **Bridlington Sports Club** 4
Long Riston 2 **Westella & Willerby Res.** 4
Malet Lambert YC 3 Hornsea Town 0
North Cave 3 **Hessle Rangers** 4
North Ferriby Athletic v **Crown** (w/o)
Sculcoates Amateurs 2 North Ferriby United Res. 1
Withernsea 4 East Riding Rangers 3

SECOND ROUND

Bransholme Athletic 0 **Bridlington Sports Club** 5
Chalk Lane 2 Scarborough Athletic Res. 0
Hedon Rangers 3 Reckitts 2 *aet*
Hessle Rangers 0 **Crown** 2
Pocklington Town 0 **Beverley Town** 2
Sculcoates Amateurs 4 Malet Lambert YC 2
St Andrews 5 **Hessle Sporting Club** 6 *aet*
Westella & Willerby Res. 5 Withernsea 0

QUARTER-FINALS

Beverley Town 5 Hessle Sporting Club 0
Chalk Lane 2 Westella & Willerby Res. 0
Hedon Rangers 2 Bridlington Sports Club 0
Sculcoates Amateurs 3 Crown 0

SEMI-FINALS

Chalk Lane 0 **Sculcoates** 2 *(at Westella & Willerby)*
Hedon Rgrs 0 **Beverley** 0 *aet* (2-4p) *(at Westella & Will.)*

FINAL

(May 7th at North Ferriby United)
Sculcoates Amateurs 0 **Beverley Town** 1

	Brandesburton	Bransholme Athletic	Bridlington Sports Club	Crown	East Riding Rangers	Inter Charter	Kingburn Athletic	Long Riston	North Cave	North Ferriby Athletic	Scarborough Ath. Res.	Withernsea
Brandesburton	***D***	0-2	1-3	3-5	1-2	2-1	0-2	2-1	0-6	3-4	5-1	1-1
Bransholme Athletic	2-2	***I***	0-1	0-1	2-1	3-2	5-2	2-3	1-0	3-3	3-2	4-1
Bridlington Sports Club	6-1	3-1	***V***	4-5	6-1	9-2	2-1	5-0	0-3	2-3	9-0	13-1
Crown	1-1	2-1	4-4	***I***	2-0	4-1	3-1	6-4	2-2	3-1	4-0	1-1
East Riding Rangers	0-2	2-5	2-4	2-3	***S***	1-1	0-3	5-4	1-0	1-4	2-1	3-0
Inter Charter	2-0	5-0	1-5	0-4	0-5	***I***	1-3	0-4	0-3	2-4	1-3	3-1
Kingburn Athletic	0-1	1-1	2-3	2-1	2-2	1-2	***O***	1-0	2-2	2-3	4-2	1-2
Long Riston	1-4	3-4	2-3	1-10	4-3	2-2	1-3	***N***	0-1	1-1	1-3	3-1
North Cave	3-0	2-2	5-3	4-5	7-0	7-0	2-0	0-1		3-1	12-2	4-2
North Ferriby Athletic	8-1	4-2	2-2	0-2	5-0	3-1	0-1	5-0	1-3	***O***	4-3	5-1
Scarborough Athletic Res.	1-0	4-5	1-3	2-1	1-0	5-3	1-1	5-2	0-5	4-2	***N***	1-1
Withernsea	0-2	0-1	3-1	1-0	1-1	6-1	1-1	3-1	2-2	2-6	2-6	***E***

HUMBER PREMIER LEAGUE DIVISION ONE CONSTITUTION 2010-11

RANDESBURTON . . . . . . Brandesburton Playing Fields, Catwick Lane, Brandesburton, Driffield YO25 8SB . . . . None
RANSHOLME ATHLETIC . . . . Hull University, Inglemire Lane, Hull HU6 7TE 01482 466000
AST RIDING RANGERS . . . . Wyke VI Form College, Grammar School Road, Hull HU5 4NX 01482 346347
ODGSONS . . . . Longcroft School 3G, Burton Road, Molescroft Road, Beverley HU17 7EH 01482 862171
OWDEN AMATEURS . . . . The Ashes Playing Field, Treeton Road, Howden, Goole DN14 7DN . . . . None
TER CHARTER . . . . East Mount Recreation Ground, Waveney Road, Hull HU8 9NB 01482 326111x2317
NGBURN . . . . Springhead FC, Springfield Lane, Willerby Rd, Hull HU5 5YJ . . . . None
ONG RISTON . . . . Long Riston Playing Fields, Main Street, Long Riston, Hull HU11 5JF . . . . None
ORTH CAVE . . . . North Cave Playing Fields, Church Street, North Cave, Brough HU15 2LJ . . . . None
ORTH FERRIBY ATHLETIC . . . . South Hunsley School, Melton, North Ferriby HU14 3HS 01482 631208
CARBOROUGH ATHLETIC RES. George Pindar College, Moor Lane, Eastfield, Scarborough YO11 3LW 01723 582194
ITHERNSEA . . . . Hull Road, Withernsea HU19 2EG . . . . None

: Hodgsons (P - East Riding County League Premier Division), Howden Amateurs (P - East Riding County League Premier Division)
JT: Bridlington Sports Club (P), Crown (P)

LINCOLNSHIRE LEAGUE

full-time.thefa.com/Index.do?league=6657134

Sponsored by:
Sills & Betteridge

Founded: 1948

Recent champions:
2005: Wyberton
2006: Hykeham Town
2007: Skegness Town
2008: Skegness Town
2009: CGB Humbertherm

	Bos	CGB	Clee	Grim	Harv	Hec	Horn	Hyk	LM	Lin	LT	LU	Rus	Skg	Skel	
Boston Town Res.		0-1	2-1	4-4	0-4	0-6	0-1	1-1	1-2	2-3	3-3	3-0	0-0	0-2	2-2	0
CGB Humbertherm	3-0		3-2	5-0	1-2	3-2	0-2	0-2	2-3	4-1	1-2	2-2	0-0	2-2	1-2	2
Cleethorpes Town Res.	8-0	1-4		1-2	1-3	0-1	0-4	1-4	3-0	1-4	1-5	n/a	0-0	0-1	0-4	1
Grimsby Borough Res.	0-2	0-2	L-W		0-8	3-5	2-2	1-6	4-3	0-6	3-2	n/a	0-2	1-2	0-9	L
Harvest	2-0	1-2	10-0	5-1		2-0	2-0	1-3	8-2	3-0	5-3	6-2	4-1	3-1	7-1	5
Heckington United	4-2	2-3	1-1	2-0	1-10		3-1	1-7	3-1	1-1	3-4	n/a	0-6	0-2	5-2	0
Horncastle Town	2-2	0-3	2-1	1-1	0-3	1-1		2-2	0-3	0-2	6-2	3-2	1-3	0-2	3-2	3
Hykeham Town	10-1	6-0	3-0	10-0	1-0	2-0	6-0		6-2	1-0	2-3	3-0	0-2	2-3	2-0	0
Lincoln Moor. Rail Res.	1-3	0-6	W-L	3-4	1-5	3-4	1-3	2-3		0-4	4-2	2-0	0-4	0-2	2-3	3
Lincoln United Res.	W-L	1-0	2-1	7-1	0-1	2-2	1-0	0-3	4-0		3-0	n/a	1-3	1-1	3-1	5
Louth Town Res.	5-1	0-2	6-0	1-1	0-5	5-0	0-4	3-3	2-1	1-0		3-0	0-5	2-1	3-4	2
Louth United	n/a	n/a	2-0	2-0	1-5	2-2	0-1	4-2	1-0	1-7	1-2		n/a	2-2	2-0	1
Ruston Sports	2-0	1-1	6-1	2-1	0-1	3-1	4-2	0-2	1-0	5-2	1-2	6-0		3-1	3-0	1
Skegness Town	5-0	0-2	8-0	4-0	1-1	2-2	1-0	0-4	4-3	1-1	2-0	1-1	0-2		1-1	1
Skellingthorpe PFC	1-0	5-1	3-3	2-2	3-2	3-0	2-3	1-3	2-2	2-2	3-0	3-1	0-3	1-4		0
Sleaford Town Res.	2-1	3-1	4-0	8-0	0-2	0-0	1-0	3-1	3-2	5-0	3-0	4-0	4-0	2-2	3-1	

		P	W	D	L	F	A	Pts
Harvest		28	23	1	4	105	23	70
Hykeham Town		28	20	4	4	95	27	64
Sleaford Town Res.		28	18	7	3	68	33	61
Ruston Sports		28	18	5	5	63	25	59
Skegness Town		28	14	7	7	56	35	49
Lincoln United Res.		28	14	5	9	56	40	47
CGB Humbertherm		28	14	4	10	55	42	46
Louth Town Res.	*+2*	28	11	3	14	58	71	38
Skellingthorpe PFC		28	10	6	12	60	61	36
Heckington United		28	9	6	13	50	71	33
Horncastle Town		28	9	5	14	43	54	32
Lincoln Moor. Rail Res.		28	5	2	21	44	89	17
Grimsby Borough Res.	*-1*	28	4	5	19	31	104	16
Boston Town Res.		28	3	6	19	27	81	15
Cleethorpes Town Res.		28	3	4	21	28	83	13

Louth United - record expunged

LEAGUE CUP

FIRST ROUND

Cleethorpes Town Res. 6 Louth United 1
Harvest 4 Lincoln United Res. 0
Heckington United 3 Skellingthorpe PFC 1
Horncastle Town 1 **Lincoln Moorlands Rail Res.**
Hykeham Town (w/o) v CGB Humbertherm
Louth Town Res. 1 **Boston Town Res.** 6
Skegness Town 1 Ruston Sports 0
Sleaford Town Res. 5 Grimsby Borough Res. 1

QUARTER-FINALS

Cleethorpes Town Res. 0 **Hykeham Town** 4
Heckington United 4 **Harvest** 5 *aet*
Lincoln Moorlands Res. 0 **Boston Town Res.** 2
Skegness Town 2 **Sleaford Town Res.** 4

SEMI-FINALS

Boston Town Res. 1 **Harvest** 3
Sleaford Town Res. 3 Hykeham Town 1

FINAL

(April 24th at Lincoln United)
Sleaford Town Res. 2 Harvest 1

SUPPLEMENTARY CUP

(League Cup First Round losers)

FIRST ROUND

Grimsby Borough Res. 2 Louth United 0
Horncastle Town 1 CGB Humbertherm 1 *aet* (5-4p)
Ruston Sports 3 Louth Town Res. 1
Skellingthorpe PFC 2 **Lincoln United Res.** 6 *aet*

SEMI-FINALS

Grimsby Borough Res. 0 **Ruston Sports** 3
Lincoln United Res. 6 Horncastle Town 0

FINAL *(April 24th at Lincoln United)*
Lincoln United Res. 3 Ruston Sports 1 aet

LINCOLNSHIRE LEAGUE CONSTITUTION 2010-11

BOSTON UNITED RES. . . . . Jakemans Stadium, York Street, Boston PE21 6JN. 01205 364406/362
CGB HUMBERTHERM . . . . Fulstow Playing Fields, Thoresby Road, Fulstow, Louth LN11 0XS . . . . N
CLEETHORPES TOWN . . . . Lucarly's Wilton Road, Humberston, Grimsby DN36 4AW. 01472 812
GRIMSBY BOROUGH RES. . . . . . . Grimsby Community Stadium, Bradley Road, Grimsby, DN37 0AG . . . . N
HECKINGTON UNITED . . . . Heckington Sports Club, Howell Road, Heckington, Sleaford NG34 9RX. 01529 460
HORNCASTLE TOWN . . . . The Wong, Boston Road, Horncastle LN9 6EY . . . . N
HYKEHAM TOWN . . . . Memorial Hall Ground, Newark Road, North Hykeham, Lincoln LN6 9RY. 01522 88
LINCOLN UNITED RES. . . . . Sports Pavilion, Ashby Avenue, Hartsholme, Lincoln LN6 0DY 01522 696400/690
LOUTH TOWN RES. . . . . Park Avenue, Louth LN11 8BY 07712 653
RUSTON SPORTS . . . . RMSC, Newark Road, Lincoln LN6 8RB. 01522 882
SKEGNESS TOWN . . . . Burgh Road, Skegness PE25 2RJ. 01754 612
SKELLINGTHORPE PFC . . . . Monson Park Playing Field, Skellingthorpe, Lincoln LN6 5UE . . . . N
SLEAFORD TOWN RES. . . . . Eslaforde Park, Boston Road, Sleaford NG34 9GH 01529 415
SWINESHEAD INSTITUTE . . . . The Causeway, South Street, Swineshead, Boston PE20 3UA . . . . N

IN: Boston United Res. (P - youth football), Swineshead Institute (P - Boston League Premier Division)
OUT: Boston Town Res. (W), Harvest (F), Lincoln Moorlands Railway Res. (now Moorlands Railway) (S - Central Midlands Le Premier Division), Louth United (WS)
Cleethorpes Town Res. become Cleethorpes Town

NORTH DEVON LEAGUE

northdevonfootballleague.org.uk

Sponsored by:
No sponsor

Founded: 1904

Recent champions:

2005: Morwenstow
2006: Boca Seniors
2007: Boca Seniors
2008: Boca Seniors
2009: Boca Seniors

	App	Barn	Bide	Boc	Brad	Brau	Com	Geo	Hart	Ilf	Mor	Nor	Put	Sha	Tdg	Trng
Appledore Res.	**P**	0-4	3-1	4-3	2-0	1-2	6-0	7-0	7-0	6-0	5-1	2-0	2-4	0-2	2-2	0-4
Barnstaple AAC	4-0	**R**	3-0	2-3	1-3	1-1	3-2	1-2	6-0	8-1	7-1	1-2	2-0	3-2	3-1	3-1
Bideford Res.	1-2	0-4	**E**	2-1	5-0	1-2	0-2	2-0	5-0	6-1	1-0	0-1	0-2	1-1	0-0	2-1
Boca Seniors	3-2	2-1	3-2	**M**	2-0	2-1	5-2	0-1	13-0	6-3	W-L	2-1	8-0	0-0	12-3	2-0
Bradworthy United	3-0	3-2	1-2	4-3	**I**	2-1	3-3	3-2	5-0	1-1	9-1	2-1	4-0	1-4	2-0	1-1
Braunton	2-0	10-2	0-0	0-3	2-1	**E**	3-2	3-2	10-1	5-1	5-0	3-3	3-1	0-1	5-3	4-0
Combe Martin	2-0	1-1	W-L	3-0	1-2	1-4	**R**	6-1	16-0	6-0	16-1	3-0	2-1	1-4	3-2	5-1
Georgeham & Croyde	2-2	0-3	0-1	1-1	0-7	0-1	0-3		5-0	3-1	2-2	3-5	3-4	1-5	3-3	2-1
Hartland	0-7	1-6	0-6	1-5	0-2	0-7	1-5	3-2	**D**	0-6	0-5	1-6	1-5	1-9	0-4	1-7
Ilfracombe Town Res.	1-2	0-7	2-4	0-6	0-8	2-6	0-5	3-2	6-0	**I**	1-2	2-2	1-0	0-4	5-2	1-5
Morwenstow Res.	1-0	1-4	1-8	0-11	2-3	0-2	1-7	1-1	3-0	2-2	**V**	2-4	1-3	3-4	1-5	3-2
North Molton Spts Club	1-0	1-1	1-0	0-3	2-0	3-1	1-0	W-L	7-0	4-0	6-1	**I**	4-1	0-1	4-0	0-1
Putford	3-2	1-1	0-4	3-3	1-2	0-2	2-4	2-3	3-0	4-0	2-0	2-2	**S**	1-2	2-2	0-3
Shamwickshire Rovers	3-1	0-1	0-1	3-2	1-0	0-0	6-2	8-1	14-0	8-1	W-L	3-1	4-1	**I**	2-0	3-4
Torridgeside	2-0	2-5	1-4	L-W	2-2	0-4	2-1	1-3	11-1	3-6	16-0	1-2	2-1	2-5	**O**	0-1
Torrington	5-1	2-2	3-5	4-5	1-4	2-1	4-1	2-3	5-0	3-1	2-2	1-5	3-4	2-1	2-1	**N**

Premier Division		P	W	D	L	F	A	Pts
Shamwickshire Rov.		**30**	**22**	**3**	**5**	**100**	**31**	**69**
Boca Seniors		**30**	**21**	**3**	**6**	**109**	**43**	**66**
Braunton		**30**	**20**	**4**	**6**	**90**	**35**	**64**
Barnstaple AAC		**30**	**18**	**5**	**7**	**92**	**43**	**59**
Bradworthy United		**30**	**18**	**4**	**8**	**78**	**43**	**58**
North Molton SC		**30**	**18**	**4**	**8**	**69**	**37**	**58**
Combe Martin		**30**	**17**	**2**	**11**	**105**	**54**	**53**
Bideford Res.	***-3***	**30**	**16**	**3**	**11**	**64**	**35**	**48**
Torrington		**30**	**14**	**3**	**13**	**73**	**63**	**45**
Appledore Res.		**30**	**12**	**2**	**16**	**66**	**56**	**38**
Putford		**30**	**10**	**4**	**16**	**53**	**70**	**34**
Georgeham/Croyde	***-3***	**30**	**8**	**5**	**17**	**48**	**81**	**26**
Torridgeside	***-3***	**30**	**7**	**5**	**18**	**73**	**81**	**23**
Ilfracombe Town Res.		**30**	**6**	**3**	**21**	**48**	**120**	**21**
Morwenstow Res.	***-6***	**30**	**5**	**4**	**21**	**38**	**128**	**13**
Hartland		**30**	**1**	**0**	**29**	**12**	**198**	**3**

BRAYFORD CUP

FIRST ROUND

Appledore Res. 0 **Shamwickshire Rovers** 2
Barnstaple AAC 2 **North Molton Sports Club** 5
Boca Seniors 0 **Torrington** 2 *(at Torrington)*
Braunton 5 Morwenstow 1
Combe Mtn 3 **Torridgeside** 5
Georgeham 1 **Bradworthy** 3
Hartland 0 **Bideford Res.** 6
Ilfracombe Town Res. 1 Putford 1 *aet* (4-3p)

QUARTER-FINALS

Bideford Res. 3 Nth Molton 1
Bradworthy 0 **Torridgeside** 2
Braunton 3 Shamwickshire 1
Ilfracombe Town Res. 2 Torrington 0

SEMI-FINALS

Bideford Res. 2 **Torridgeside** 5 *aet*
Ilfracombe Town Res. 2 **Braunton** 3

FINAL *(May 8th at Torrington)*
Braunton 3 Torridgeside 0

NORTH DEVON LEAGUE PREMIER DIVISION CONSTITUTION 2010-11

APPLEDORE RES. .... Marshford, Churchill Way, Appledore EX39 1PA 01237 475015
BARNSTAPLE AAC .... Pottington Road, Barnstaple EX31 1JQ .... None
BIDEFORD RES. .... The Sports Ground, Kingsley Road, Bideford EX39 2NG 01237 474974
BOCA SENIORS .... Tarka Tennis Centre, Seven Brethren Bank, Barnstaple EX31 2AS 01271 377701
BRADWORTHY UNITED .... North Road, Bradworthy, Holsworthy EX22 7TJ .... None
BRAUNTON .... Lobb Sports Field, Saunton Road, Braunton EX33 1EB .... None
COMBE MARTIN .... Hollands Park, Chapel Lane, Combe Martin, Ilfracombe EX34 0EW .... None
DOLTON RANGERS .... The Playing Field, Cleave Hill, Dolton EX19 8QT .... None
GEORGEHAM & CROYDE .... The Recreation Ground, Newberry Road, Georgeham EX33 1QF .... None
ILFRACOMBE TOWN RES. .... Marlborough Park, Marlborough Road, Ilfracombe EX34 8PD 01271 865939
NORTH MOLTON SPORTS CLUB.......... Rocksfield, Old Road, North Molton EX36 3HG .... None
PUTFORD .... Allardice Hall, Parkham, Bideford EX39 5PL 01237 451242
SHAMWICKSHIRE ROVERS . . Pollyfield Comm. Centre, Avon Road, East-the-Water, Bideford EX39 4BL .... None
TORRIDGESIDE .... Donnacroft, Great Torrington EX38 7HT .... None
TORRINGTON .... Vicarage Field, School Lane, Great Torrington EX38 7AJ 01805 622853

IN: Dolton Rangers (P)
OUT: Hartland (R), Morwenstow Res. (W)

Senior Division		P	W	D	L	F	A	Pt
Braunton Res.		28	21	3	4	88	34	66
Dolton Rangers		28	20	4	4	86	42	64
Chittlehampton		28	18	6	4	92	34	60
Shebbear United		28	18	5	5	99	48	59
Bratton Fleming		28	16	4	8	98	45	52
Pilton Acads	*-3*	28	14	4	10	64	45	43
Northam Lions		28	11	3	14	69	72	36
South Molton		28	10	6	12	58	93	36
B'staple AAC Res.		28	10	3	15	52	72	33
Kilkhampton		28	7	7	14	51	77	28
Nth Molton SC Res.		28	6	7	15	56	74	25
Combe Martin Res.		28	7	3	18	38	90	24
Bude Town Res.	*-3*	28	7	5	16	54	75	23
S'shire Rov. Res.	*-6*	28	6	5	17	54	77	17
Landkey Town		28	3	7	18	44	125	16

Int. Division One		P	W	D	L	F	A	Pt
Woolsery		26	21	3	2	103	30	66
Park United		26	17	2	7	90	52	53
Torrington Res.		26	15	5	6	75	39	50
Clovelly		26	13	2	11	86	73	41
Equalizers		26	12	4	10	63	59	40
High Bickington		26	12	4	10	52	54	40
Ilfracombe Town A		26	11	6	9	72	66	39
Braunton A		26	11	5	10	82	71	38
Lynton & Lynmouth		26	9	5	12	59	63	32
Anchor		26	8	5	13	63	83	29
Northam Lions Res.		26	9	2	15	56	76	29
Merton		26	7	5	14	43	70	26
Sporting Barum		26	7	1	18	55	105	22
Buckland Brewer	*-3*	26	4	3	19	31	89	12

Int. Division Two		P	W	D	L	F	A	Pt
Wrey Arms		30	29	1	0	116	29	88
Woolacombe/M'hoe		30	25	1	4	148	43	76
Woolsery Res.		30	17	2	11	93	63	53
Putford Res.		30	16	4	10	55	53	52
Barnstaple		30	14	2	14	103	87	44
Bradworthy Res.		30	14	2	14	90	97	44
Northside Atlantic		30	13	4	13	95	84	43
Torrideside Res.		30	12	5	13	76	84	41
Pilton Acads Res.	*-3*	30	13	4	13	67	57	40
North Molton SC A		30	12	4	14	55	69	40
Bratton Fleming Res.		30	12	3	15	90	78	39
Northam Lions A		30	12	2	16	75	85	38
South Molton Res.		30	7	6	17	59	95	27
Chittlehampton Res.		30	7	3	20	47	96	24
Hartland Res.	*-3*	30	7	5	18	49	98	23
Landkey T. Res.	*-3*	30	5	2	23	23	51	14

COMBE MARTIN CUP
Final *(April 24th at Combe Martin)*
Braunton Res. 2 Chittlehampton 0

ARLINGTON CUP Final
(April 17th at Bideford)
Woolsery 2
Park United 1

NORTH DEVON JOURNAL CUP
Final *(April 10th at Ilfracombe Town)*
Wrey Arms 3 Pilton Academicals Res. 1

NOTTS SENIOR LEAGUE

Founded: 2004

Recent champions:
2005: Wollaton
2006: Wollaton
2007: Cotgrave
2008: Caribbean Cavaliers.
2009: Bilborough Pelican

www.nottsseniorleague.co.uk Sponsored by: Precision Training

	Att	Bas	Bil	Boo	Bul	Car	Cli	Cot	Ged	Huc	Key	Kim	Lin	Mag	New	Nott	Rud	Woll
Attenborough		2-2	1-3	2-4	0-3	4-2	3-1	0-1	1-0	2-1	4-3	1-5	1-4	1-2	2-0	0-2	1-4	3-2
Basford United	4-2	***S***	2-1	3-3	2-3	4-3	1-2	5-0	3-1	1-2	8-2	0-2	4-0	4-0	3-1	4-0	6-0	0-1
Bilborough Pelican	2-1	1-4	***E***	4-0	3-1	2-1	2-1	4-0	1-1	6-2	6-0	0-1	2-1	2-0	n/a	1-1	2-0	2-1
Boots Athletic	0-1	2-2	2-0	***N***	2-0	3-0	2-3	1-1	3-1	1-1	1-0	3-2	4-0	2-1	n/a	2-0	2-1	2-0
Bulwell	6-0	1-3	3-1	1-2	***I***	1-4	1-1	1-2	3-1	4-2	2-2	1-0	3-3	2-1	n/a	3-1	5-2	1-3
Caribbean Cavaliers	2-3	3-2	2-0	1-2	5-2	***O***	1-1	1-3	2-1	3-3	4-1	0-3	3-1	3-3	n/a	2-1	4-1	0-3
Clifton	2-2	0-0	3-0	3-0	2-0	5-3	***R***	6-0	2-1	1-1	6-0	2-2	7-0	4-2	n/a	3-2	3-1	3-0
Cotgrave Welfare	1-1	0-2	1-0	4-1	6-3	2-1	1-3		3-1	0-4	1-1	1-5	2-0	1-1	4-0	4-3	6-1	1-1
Gedling Southbank	1-2	2-3	2-9	0-3	6-2	3-3	3-2	0-2		3-2	3-1	0-1	5-2	4-3	n/a	3-0	2-3	3-1
Hucknall Rolls Leisure	4-0	1-2	3-2	3-0	1-2	2-1	5-4	1-1	4-0	***D***	5-2	0-1	3-0	2-2	n/a	2-0	2-1	1-1
Keyworth United	0-1	0-3	6-2	2-1	1-3	2-1	1-2	2-0	1-3	1-5	***I***	0-2	4-1	3-3	n/a	3-2	1-3	3-3
Kimberley Miners Welfare	4-2	2-3	2-0	4-0	1-6	1-2	0-2	2-1	2-4	2-2	4-2	***V***	4-0	3-3	n/a	0-2	5-0	1-0
Linby Colliery Welfare	3-2	3-4	0-4	0-3	0-0	0-1	1-3	0-0	3-2	1-0	1-3	2-0	***I***	2-1	n/a	3-2	0-3	1-2
Magdala Amateurs	0-4	0-1	0-4	0-4	0-0	0-2	1-3	3-1	3-0	0-1	1-3	1-2	0-5	***S***	5-0	2-1	3-1	2-4
Newark Flowserve	n/a	n/a	1-2	n/a	n/a	n/a	n/a	n/a	n/a	n/a	0-2	0-1	n/a	n/a	***I***	n/a	4-1	2-2
Notts Police	1-3	1-1	1-3	0-3	0-5	3-2	3-3	3-3	3-0	2-2	2-1	1-1	2-6	0-1	n/a	***O***	4-1	3-2
Ruddington Village	4-1	3-1	1-4	0-1	2-2	3-4	0-2	1-4	2-2	0-8	1-2	1-4	3-2	2-1	n/a	2-2	***N***	2-2
Wollaton	4-2	1-1	1-1	1-1	1-1	1-2	3-1	3-3	3-0	3-3	1-0	0-2	3-1	2-2	n/a	4-1	4-0	

SENIOR CUP

FIRST ROUND

Attenborough 5 Ruddington Village 1
Awsworth Villa 2 Beeston 1
Basford Utd 3 Linby Colliery Welfare 0
Bilborough Pelican 3 Notts Police 1
Bottesford 1 **Cotgrave Welfare** 2
Clifton 0 **Kimberley Miners Welfare** 2
Gedling Southbank 3 **Cavibbean Cav.** 4
Netherfield Albion 3 **Hucknall Rolls Leisure** 4
Sandhurst 3 Bilborough Town 1 *aet*
Vernon Villa 1 **Boots Athletic** 3
Wollaton 4 **Magdala Amateurs** 6

SECOND ROUND

Attenborough 4 Sandhurst 2
Bilborough Pelican 0 **Basford United** 2
Cotgrave 0 **Caribbean Cavaliers** 2
Keyworth United 1 **Awsworth Villa** 2
Kimberley MW 2 Boots Athletic 0
Magdala Amateurs 2 **Bulwell** 3
Nottinghamshire 1 **Matrixgrade** 2
Underwood 2 **Hucknall Rolls Leis.** 3 *aet*

QUARTER-FINALS

Attenborough 0 **Basford United** 1
Awsworth Villa 5 Matrixgrade 4
Hucknall Rolls Leisure 3 Bulwell 2
Kimberley MW 0 **Caribbean Cavaliers**

SEMI-FINALS

Awsworth Villa 1 **Caribbean Cavaliers**
Basford Utd 1 **Hucknall Rolls Leisure**

FINAL *(May 20th at Arnold Town)*

Hucknall Rolls Leisure 2
Caribbean Cavaliers 2 *aet* (3-4p)

Senior Division	P	W	D	L	F	A	Pt
Clifton	32	20	7	5	86	42	67
Basford United	32	19	6	7	85	44	63
Boots Athletic	32	19	5	8	60	41	62
Kimberley Miners W.	32	19	4	9	70	42	61
Bilborough Pelican	32	18	3	11	74	45	57
Hucknall Rolls Leis.	32	15	9	8	78	49	54
Bulwell	32	14	7	11	71	60	49
Cotgrave Welfare	32	13	9	10	56	61	48
Wollaton	32	12	11	9	61	49	47
Caribbean Cavaliers	32	14	4	14	68	66	46
Attenborough	32	12	3	17	53	77	39
Gedling Southbank	32	10	3	19	58	78	33
Keyworth United	32	9	4	19	53	85	31
Linby Colliery Welf.	32	9	3	20	46	80	30
Notts Police	32	7	7	18	49	75	28
Ruddington Village	32	8	4	20	49	92	28
Magdala Amateurs	32	6	7	19	42	73	25

Newark Flowserve - record expunged

Division One	P	W	D	L	F	A	Pt
Wollaton Res.	34	24	2	8	83	41	74
Awsworth Villa	34	19	6	9	100	51	63
Clifton Res.	34	17	10	7	82	61	61
Boots Athletic Res.	34	18	5	11	90	63	59
Arnold Town Res.	34	18	5	11	80	59	59
Cotgrave Welf. Res.	34	17	8	9	73	57	59
Basford United Res.	34	16	9	9	64	53	57
Greenwood M. Res.	34	14	8	12	66	53	50
Matrixgrade	34	15	5	14	55	63	50
Gedling S'bank Res.	34	13	5	16	67	72	44
Keyworth Utd Res.	34	13	5	16	59	90	44
Sandhurst	34	12	6	16	60	64	42
Bilborough Res. *-3*	34	13	5	16	69	80	41
Netherfield Albion *-3*	34	13	4	17	68	78	40
Southwell City Res.	34	10	5	19	66	72	35
Radcliffe Olym. Res.	34	7	6	21	56	92	27
Calverton MWe Ac.	34	6	9	19	45	97	27
Kimberley MW Res.	34	7	5	22	52	89	26

Division Two	P	W	D	L	F	A
Vernon Villa	30	26	2	2	133	44
Hucknall RL Res.	30	23	3	4	88	33
Nottinghamshire	30	23	3	4	94	40
Ruddington V. Res.	30	19	4	7	108	47
Bulwell Res.	30	18	1	11	90	74
Carlton Town Acad.	30	17	3	10	97	65
Underwood Villa	30	16	4	10	103	64
Beeston	30	16	3	11	94	57
Awsworth Villa Res.	30	14	4	12	75	54
Linby CW Res.	30	9	4	17	53	78
Magdala Ams Res.	30	9	1	20	57	82
Newark F. Acad. *-3*	30	7	7	16	65	84
Caribbean C. Res.	30	7	3	20	48	105
Bilborough Town	30	5	5	20	45	108
Bottesford *-3*	30	4	3	23	39	127
Sandhurst Res.	30	0	4	26	26	153

RESERVES CUP Final *(May 19th at Calvert*
Carlton T. Acad. 4 Newark F. Academy

NOTTS SENIOR LEAGUE SENIOR DIVISION CONSTITUTION 2010-11

ATTENBOROUGH . . . . Village Green, The Strand, Attenborough NG9 6AU 0115 925 74
AWSWORTH VILLA . . . . Shilo Park, Attewell Road, Awsworth NG16 2SY 0115 849 87
BASFORD UNITED . . . . Greenwich Avenue, Bagnall Road, Basford, Nottingham NG6 0LE 01949 8394
BILBOROUGH PELICAN . . . Brian Wakefield Sports, Trentside Lane, Old Lenton Lane, Nottingham NG7 2SA 0115 929 47
BOOTS ATHLETIC . . . . Rolls Royce Sports & Social, Watnall Road, Hucknall NG15 6EU 0115 964 23
BULWELL . . . . Greenwich Avenue, Bagnall Road, Basford, Nottingham NG6 0LE 01949 8394
CLIFTON . . . . Green Lane, Clifton, Nottingham NG11 9AY 0115 921 54
COTGRAVE WELFARE . . . . The Woodview Ground, Woodview, Cotgrave, Nottingham NG12 3PJ 0115 989 24
FC CAVALIERS . . . . Carrington Sports Ground, Mansfield Road, Nottingham NG5 2EJ . . . . Nc
FOREST TOWN . . . . Forest Town Academy, Clipstone Road West, Forest Town, Mansfield NG19 0EE 01623 6246
GEDLING SOUTHBANK . . . . Carlton Recreation Ground, Carlton Hill, Nottingham NG4 1BG 0115 926 63
HUCKNALL ROLLS LEISURE . . . . Rolls Royce Sports & Social, Watnall Road, Hucknall NG15 6EU 0115 964 23
KEYWORTH UNITED . . . . Platt Lane Sports Complex, Keyworth, Nottingham NG12 5GE 0115 974 55
KIMBERLEY MINERS WELFARE . . . . Digby Street, Kimberley, Nottingham NG16 2HP 0115 938 40
LINBY COLLIERY WELFARE . . . . Church Lane, Linby Village, Linby NG15 8AB 0115 953 84
NOTTINGHAMSHIRE POLICE . Bestwood Workshops, Park Rd, Bestwood Village, Nottingham NG6 8TQ 0115 967 09
WOLLATON . . . . Wollaton Cricket Club, Wollaton Road, Wollaton, Nottingham NG8 2AA 0115 928 38

IN: Awsworth Villa (P), Forest Town (W - Central Midlands League Supreme Division)
OUT: Magdala Amateurs (R), Ruddington Village (R), Newark Flowserve (WS)
Caribbean Cavaliers become FC Cavaliers

SHEFFIELD & HALLAMSHIRE SENIOR LEAGUE

Sponsored by: Windsor Food Services

Founded: N/A

Recent champions:

2005: Athersley Recreation

2006: Mexborough Main St.

2007: Athersley Recreation

2008:Wombwell Main

2009: Athersley Recreation

	Ath	Cari	Davy	Dea	Dinn	HS	Han	Mex	Mill	Oug	Pen	Shef	Stoc	Wom
Athersley Recreation		7-1	0-0	n/a	4-0	4-3	0-1	2-1	1-2	4-2	2-0	0-2	1-0	0-2
Caribbean Sports	2-4	***P***	2-1	3-3	2-1	0-7	1-2	3-2	1-3	3-2	2-1	2-3	0-3	3-1
Davy Parramores	1-2	1-2	***R***	4-1	1-0	3-2	0-3	n/a	1-3	4-4	1-3	0-9	3-2	1-5
Dearne Colliery MW	0-1	5-3	0-3	***E***	1-0	1-2	1-2	n/a	2-0	n/a	2-4	1-0	n/a	5-3
Dinnington Town Res.	0-1	5-0	2-0	0-0	***M***	2-2	1-4	3-1	1-1	2-0	0-2	2-2	3-0	1-3
HSBC	0-4	2-1	2-3	4-3	2-1	***I***	1-3	4-2	3-0	2-0	1-3	0-3	3-7	2-3
Handsworth	1-3	2-2	3-1	3-1	1-1	3-2	***E***	3-3	1-2	1-3	3-0	3-0	1-0	1-1
Mexborough Main Street	n/a	0-1	2-2	4-0	1-3	n/a	1-3	***R***	3-0	n/a	1-0	n/a	0-3	2-1
Millmoor Juniors	0-3	4-2	1-1	2-0	0-0	2-0	2-1	0-1		2-2	5-1	2-2	0-2	1-4
Oughtibridge War Memorial SC	2-4	0-1	4-3	3-4	5-3	1-0	2-2	3-2	3-0		2-2	2-2	2-0	2-1
Penistone Church	4-1	0-2	5-0	5-0	2-0	0-1	1-5	2-2	0-1	1-1	***D***	2-0	1-0	2-3
Sheffield Res.	0-0	2-2	1-1	4-0	2-1	8-1	3-2	3-0	1-1	2-0	3-0	***I***	1-0	5-1
Stocksbridge Park Steels Res.	0-0	4-0	0-0	1-2	0-2	2-1	0-3	2-0	4-1	3-1	2-0	2-1	***V***	2-1
Wombwell Main	1-3	2-2	4-0	5-1	1-1	1-4	2-0	n/a	2-2	2-1	0-1	2-3	2-2	

Premier Division		P	W	D	L	F	A	Pts
Sheffield Res.	***-1***	**22**	**12**	**7**	**3**	**55**	**26**	**42**
Athersley Recreation	***-3***	**22**	**14**	**3**	**5**	**48**	**24**	**42**
Handsworth		**22**	**12**	**4**	**6**	**46**	**28**	**40**
Millmoor Juniors		**22**	**9**	**7**	**6**	**35**	**36**	**34**
Stocksbridge PS Res.		**22**	**10**	**3**	**9**	**35**	**27**	**33**
Wombwell Main		**22**	**9**	**5**	**8**	**44**	**39**	**32**
Penistone Church		**22**	**9**	**2**	**11**	**31**	**35**	**29**
Oughtibridge WMSC		**22**	**7**	**6**	**9**	**41**	**44**	**27**
Caribbean Sports		**22**	**8**	**3**	**11**	**33**	**57**	**27**
HSBC	***-1***	**22**	**7**	**1**	**14**	**41**	**54**	**21**
Dinnington Town Res.	***-3***	**22**	**5**	**6**	**11**	**29**	**35**	**18**
Davy Parramores		**22**	**4**	**5**	**13**	**26**	**59**	**17**

Dearne Colliery MW, Mexborough Main Street - records expunged

Division One		P	W	D	L	F	A	Pt
Ecclesfield Red Rose		24	17	4	3	88	36	55
Aston		24	16	4	4	77	42	52
South Kirkby Colliery		24	16	3	5	64	35	51
High Green Villa		24	15	5	4	62	31	50
Hallam Res.		24	14	4	6	55	38	46
Everest		24	11	4	9	64	47	37
Wickersley		24	10	6	8	45	40	36
Worsbrough Common	*-7*	24	10	1	13	56	55	24
Worsbrough BMW Res.	*-3*	24	8	2	14	42	76	23
Sheffield Athletic		24	5	2	17	40	82	17
Thorpe Hesley		24	4	4	16	41	68	16
Brinsworth Whitehill	*-3*	24	5	4	15	42	76	16
Silkstone United		24	2	3	19	24	74	9

Division Two		P	W	D	L	F	A	Pt
Frecheville CA		22	15	3	4	61	32	48
South Elmsall Utd Services		22	14	4	4	65	30	46
Upton & Harewood Soc.	*-3*	22	16	0	6	64	25	45
Handsworth Res.		22	14	1	7	58	40	43
Penistone Church Res.		22	12	3	7	37	25	39
Bramley Sunnyside Juniors		22	8	4	10	44	53	28
Thorncliffe		22	8	4	10	45	64	28
Athersley Recreation Res.		22	6	6	10	39	46	24
Sheffield City	*-1*	22	7	3	12	39	53	23
Sheffield Bankers		22	6	5	11	34	50	23
De La Salle Old Boys		22	3	5	14	28	60	14
Sheffield Lane Top		22	3	2	17	32	68	11

Phoenix Sports & Social Res. - record exunged

LEAGUE CUP

FIRST ROUND

Athersley Res. 1 **Mexborough Main St** 2
Bramley Sunnyside 9 Sheffield Bankers 1
Dinnington T. Res. 1 S Kirkby 1 *aet* (5-4p)
Handsworth 5 Silkstone United 1
HSBC 6 Brinsworth Whitehill 0
Sheffield City 0 **Hallam Res.** 4
Sheffield Res. 4 Millmoor Juniors 1
Wickersley 5 Phoenix Res. 0

SECOND ROUND

Aston 0 Davy Parramores 1 *(Davy expelled)*
Bramley SJ 2 **Penistone Church Res.** 3
Caribbean Sports v **Athersley Rec** (w/o)
De La Salle 2 Dearne 4 *(Dearne expelled)*
Ecclesfield Red Rose 1 Wickersley 0
Frecheville CA 5 Worsbrough BMW Res. 0
Hallam Res. 2 **Dinnington Res.** 2 *aet* (0-3p)
Handsworth Res. 2 **Handsworth** 3
High Green Villa 6 South Elmsall US 2
Oughtibridge 3 Mexborough Main Street 1
Penistone Church 5 Wombwell Main 1
Sheffield Athletic 1 HSBC 0
Sheffield Res. 7 Sheffield Lane Top 0
Stockbridge Park Steels Res. 2 Everest 1
Upton & Harewood S. 8 Thorpe Hesley 2
Worsbrough Common 3 Thorncliffe 2

THIRD ROUND

Athersley Recreation 3 Aston 2
Ecclesfield Red Rose 1 **High Green Villa** 2
Frecheville CA 1 **Penistone Church** 2
Handsworth 4 Oughtibridge WMSC 1
Penistone Church Res. 3 De La Salle OB 2
Sheffield Athletic 1 **Sheffield Res.** 3
Stocksbridge Res. 4 Upton & Harewood 2
Worsbrough Common 0 **Dinnington Res.** 5

QUARTER-FINALS

Handsworth 2 **Sheffield Res.** 4
High Green Villa 1 Athersley 1 *aet* (4-2p)
Penistone Ch. Res. 2 **Dinnington Res.** 3
Stocksbridge Res. 1 Penistone Church 0

SEMI-FINALS

High Green Villa 1 **Dinnington Town Res.** 4
Sheffield Res. 1 **Stocksbdge Res.** 1 *aet* (4-5p)

FINAL *(April 8th at Stocksbridge PS)*

Stocksbridge Res. 1 Dinnington Res. 0

SHEFFIED & HALLAMSHIRE COUNTY SENIOR LEAGUE PREMIER DIVISION CONSTITUTION 2010-11

ATHERSLEY RECREATION . . . . . Sheerien Park, rear of 125 Ollerton Road, Athersley North S71 3DP. . . . . None
CARIBBEAN SPORTS . . . . Caribbean Sports Centre, The Common, Ecclesfield, Sheffield S35 3WL . . . . None
DAVY. . . . . Davy Sports & Social Club, Prince of Wales Road, Darnall, Sheffield S9 4ER . . . . None
DINNINGTON TOWN RES. . Phoenix Park, Res. Centre, 131 Laughton Rd (The Stute), Dinnington S25 2PP 01909 518555
ECCLESFIELD RED ROSE . . . Civil Service Sports Ground, Green Lane, Ecclesfield, Sheffield S35 9WY. 0114 246 5009
HIGH GREEN VILLA . . . . High Green Playing Fields, Mortomley Close, High Green, Sheffield S35 3HZ . . . . None
MILLMOOR JUNIORS. . . Grange Park Football Ground, Droppingwell Road, Kimberworth, Rotherham S61 2RB . . . . None
OUGHTIBRIDGE WAR MEMORIAL SC . . . . . Station Lane, Oughtibridge, Sheffield S35 0JS . . . . None
PENISTONE CHURCH . . . . Memorial Ground, Church View Road, Penistone S36 6AT 01226 370095
SHEFFIELD RES. . . . . The Bright Finance Stadium, Stubley Hollow, Sheffield Road, Dronfield S18 2GD 01246 29262
SOUTH KIRKBY COLLIERY. . . . . Millar's Walk, Stockingate, South Kirkby, Pontefract WF9 3UZ 01977 643438
STOCKSBRIDGE PARK STEELS RES. . . Bracken Moor Lane,Stocksbridge, Sheffield S36 5AN 0114 288 8305/2045
SWALLOWNEST MINERS WELFARE. . Swallownest MW, Rotherham Rd, Swallownest S26 4UR 0114 287 2510
WOMBWELL MAIN . . . . Wombwell Main Cricket Club, Windmill Lane, Wombwell, Barnsley S73 0LP. 01226 211123

IN: Ecclesfield Red Rose (P), High Green Villa (P), South Kirkby Colliery (P), Swallownest Miners Welfare (formerly Aston) (P)

OUT: Dearne Colliery MW (WS), Handsworth (P - Northern Counties East League Division One), HSBC (W - Veterans football), Mexborough Main Street (WS)

Davy Parramores become Davy

SHROPSHIRE COUNTY LEAGUE

www.scpfl.co.uk

Sponsored by:

Sportsjamkits.com

Founded: 1950

Recent champions:

2005: Broseley Juniors

2006: Hanwood United

2007: Hanwood United

2008: Hanwood United

2009: Wem Town

	Broseley Juniors	Clee Hill United	Ellesmere Rangers Res.	Haughmond	Impact United	Ludlow Town Res.	Morda United	Newport County Borough	Shifnal Town Res.	Shifnal United	St Martins	Telford Juniors
Broseley Juniors	**P**	4-0	1-4	0-1	2-3	5-2	2-0	1-3	1-2	1-0	0-4	2-2
Clee Hill United	0-2	**R**	3-4	0-2	1-5	2-3	1-1	3-6	1-1	1-1	1-2	1-1
Ellesmere Rangers Res.	3-2	4-1	**E**	1-3	2-3	3-1	1-3	5-1	n/a	2-1	0-2	3-1
Haughmond	1-2	3-0	2-1	**M**	3-1	5-3	3-2	1-0	n/a	1-2	1-4	0-5
Impact United	5-0	7-2	4-0	0-4	**I**	3-1	2-5	2-1	4-0	0-3	3-2	1-2
Ludlow Town Res.	6-1	5-2	2-3	2-2	2-5	**E**	7-2	8-3	n/a	2-0	2-4	2-3
Morda United	1-5	4-1	0-5	0-3	0-2	3-1	**R**	7-1	n/a	0-1	0-3	0-0
Newport County Borough	1-0	2-3	0-0	1-3	0-2	1-3	2-0		1-6	3-4	1-2	3-3
Shifnal Town Res.	5-3	n/a	n/a	n/a	0-3	0-4	n/a	n/a		2-2	n/a	n/a
Shifnal United	4-2	3-0	1-3	0-2	1-1	1-0	2-1	2-0	7-0	**D**	0-4	1-0
St Martins	2-1	8-0	4-2	1-0	0-1	4-0	3-4	3-0	5-0	3-3	**I**	2-0
Telford Juniors	4-0	4-1	1-1	0-2	3-1	0-4	4-0	1-0	n/a	1-1	1-1	**V**

Premier Division	P	W	D	L	F	A	Pts
St Martins	20	15	2	3	58	20	47
Haughmond	20	14	1	5	42	25	43
Impact United	20	13	1	6	51	34	40
Ellesmere Rangers Res.	20	11	2	7	47	36	35
Shifnal United	20	10	4	6	31	27	34
Telford Juniors	20	8	7	5	36	26	31
Ludlow Town Res.	20	8	1	11	56	52	25
Broseley Juniors	20	7	1	12	33	46	22
Morda United	20	6	2	12	33	49	20
Newport County Borough	20	4	2	14	29	53	14
Clee Hill United	20	1	3	16	23	71	6

Shifnal Town Reserves - record expunged

PREMIER DIVISION CUP

FIRST ROUND

Broseley Juniors 2 Shifnal United 0

Clee Hill United 2 **Telford Juniors** 2 *aet* (3-4p)

Shifnal Town Res. 0 **Impact United** 5

St Martins 2 Newport County Borough 1

QUARTER-FINALS

Broseley Juniors 5 Ludlow Town Res. 3

Haughmond 2 **Ellesmere Rangers Res.** 4

St Martins 4 Impact United 1

Telford Juniors 3 Morda United 0

SEMI-FINALS

Ellesmere Rangers Res. 4 Broseley Juniors 3

St Martins 3 Telford Juniors 0

FINAL

(May 6th at Ellesmere Rangers)

Ellesmere Rangers Res. 2 St Martins 1

SHROPSHIRE COUNTY LEAGUE PREMIER DIVISION CONSTITUTION 2010-11

BROSELEY JUNIORS . . . . Birchmeadow, Broseley TF12 5LP . . . . None
DAWLEY VILLA . . . . Shukers Field, Avenue Road, Newport TF10 7EA 01952 825801
ELLESMERE RANGERS RES. . . . . Beech Grove Playing Fields, Ellesmere SY12 0BT . . . . None
FC HODNET . . . . Hodnet Sports Centre, Shrewsbury Street, Hodnet, Market Drayton TF9 6DB . . . . None
HAUGHMOND . . . . Mereside Recreation Centre, Springfield, Shrewsbury SY2 6LH 01743 357793
IMPACT UNITED . . . . Grainger Road, Leegomery, Telford TF1 6UJ . . . . None
KETLEY BANK UNITED . . . . . . Ketley Bank Recreation Ground, Dukes Hill, Ketley Bank, Telford TF2 6DB . . . . None
LUDLOW TOWN . . . . SBS Stadium, Bromfield Road, Ludlow SY8 2BY 01584 876000
MORDA UNITED . . . . Weston Road, Morda, Oswestry SY10 9NS 01691 659621
NEWPORT TOWN . . . . Shukers Field, Avenue Road, Newport TF10 7EA 01952 825801
SHIFNAL UNITED . . . . Idsall Sports Centre, Coppice Green Lane, Shifnal TF11 8PD 01952 460499
TELFORD JUNIORS . . . . Ironbridge Power Station, Buildwas Road, Ironbridge TF8 7BL . . . . None

IN: FC Hodnet (P), Ketley Bank United (P), Ludlow Town (W - Midland Alliance), Newport Town (P)
OUT: Clee Hill United (R), Ludlow Town Res. (W), Shifnal Town Res. (WS), St Martins (P - West Midlands League Division Two)
Newport County Borough become Dawley Villa

Division One		P	W	D	L	F	A	Pts
Newport Town		22	19	2	1	82	19	59
Ketley Bank United		22	16	3	3	60	27	51
FC Hodnet		22	13	4	5	43	22	43
Oakengates Athletic		22	12	3	7	42	40	39
Wroxeter Rovers		22	11	1	10	40	46	34
Church Stretton	*-3*	22	9	4	9	33	33	28
Wrockwardine Wood		22	7	5	10	33	45	26
Whitchurch A'pt Res.		22	6	6	10	39	46	24
Brown Clee		22	6	3	13	41	41	21
Wellington Ams Res.		22	5	5	12	42	60	20
Morda United Res.		22	4	4	14	20	48	16
Meole Brace		22	2	4	16	30	78	10

INSIGHT RON JONES CUP

(all teams in league)

FIRST ROUND

Brown Clee 5 Wrockwardine Wood 3
Ellesmere Rangers Res. 3 Haughmond 2
Ludlow Town Res. 6 Whitchurch Alport Res. 0
Meole Brace 0 **Shifnal United** 5
Oakengates Athletic 2 **Wroxeter Rovers** 4
Shifnal Town Res. v **St Martins** (w/o)
Telford Juniors 1 **FC Hodnet** 2
Wellington Amateurs Res. 2 Impact United 1

SECOND ROUND

Broseley Juniors 1 **St Martins** 3
Brown Clee 5 Clee Hill United 4 *aet*
Church Stretton Town 1 **Ketley Bank United** 5
FC Hodnet 7 Morda United 1
Morda Utd Res. 4 Wellington Amateurs Res. 4 *aet* (4-2p)
Newport County Borough 2 **Ludlow Town Res.** 3
Newport Town 3 Ellesmere Rangers Res. 2
Shifnal United 5 Wroxeter Rovers 1

QUARTER-FINALS

Brown Clee 1 **Ludlow Town Res.** 2
FC Hodnet 1 **Newport Town** 2 *aet*
Ketley Bank United 4 Morda United Res. 1
Shifnal United 1 **St Martins** 2

SEMI-FINALS

Ketley Bank United 5 **Ludlow Town Res.** 5 *aet* (1-3p)
Newport Town 2 St Martins 2 *aet* (6-5p)

FINAL

(May 12th at Ellesmere Rangers)
Newport Town 2 Ludlow Town Res. 0

SENTINEL NEWS DIVISION ONE CUP

	Bro	Chur	Hod	Ket	Meo	Morda	Newpt	Oak	Well	Whit	Wroc	Wrox
Brown Clee	***D***	0-0	1-3	1-3	3-3	1-0	0-1	0-1	1-1	7-3	5-2	4-2
Church Stretton Town	2-1	***I***	1-0	2-3	5-1	1-1	0-3	0-3	3-1	2-1	1-1	0-2
FC Hodnet	3-2	3-1	***V***	0-0	2-1	2-0	1-1	3-1	2-0	2-2	1-2	3-0
Ketley Bank United	3-2	3-0	1-0	***I***	4-5	6-3	1-1	3-2	4-0	2-1	2-1	3-2
Meole Brace	3-6	1-1	0-3	0-5	***S***	2-3	0-5	1-2	4-4	1-1	0-4	0-2
Morda United Res.	1-0	0-2	0-2	0-4	0-4	***I***	1-2	0-2	2-3	2-2	2-0	2-5
Newport Town	3-1	3-0	3-2	2-0	7-1	4-1	***O***	8-2	2-1	6-1	1-2	3-0
Oakengates Athletic	3-2	0-4	3-5	1-1	6-1	2-0	0-6	***N***	3-2	3-1	3-0	2-1
Wellington Amateurs Res.	0-4	0-4	1-4	2-0	6-1	1-1	1-7	0-0		2-2	2-4	5-2
Whitchurch Alport Res.	1-0	2-0	2-0	1-6	3-0	0-1	1-3	0-0	6-1	***O***	1-1	7-2
Wrockwardine Wood	2-0	2-3	0-0	0-4	3-0	0-0	2-6	0-2	1-7	3-1	***N***	2-2
Wroxeter Rovers	1-0	2-1	0-2	1-2	3-1	3-0	1-5	2-1	3-2	2-0	2-1	***E***

FIRST ROUND

Brown Clee 4 Ketley Bank Utd 1
Hodnet 5 Newport T. 5 *aet* (13-12p)
Whitchurch Alport Res. 2 Meole Brace 0
Wrockwardine W. 4 Oakengates 2

QUARTER-FINALS

Brown Clee 3 Whitchurch Res. 1
Church Stretton 3 Morda Res. 1
Hodnet 1 **Wellington Ams Res.** 2
Wrockwardine Wood 3 Wroxeter 0

SEMI-FINALS

Wellington Amateurs Res. 2 **Brown Clee** 4 *aet (at Brown Clee)*
Wrockwardine Wood 2 **Church Stretton Town** 4

FINAL

(May 22nd at Ellesmere Rangers)
Brown Clee 1 **Church Stretton Town** 5

SHROPSHIRE COUNTY LEAGUE DIVISION ONE CONSTITUTION 2010-11

ATLAS . . . . Grainger Road, Leegomery, Telford TF1 6UJ . . . . None
BISHOPS CASTLE TOWN . . . . The Community College, Bishops Castle SY9 5AY 01588 638257
BROWN CLEE . . . . Hall Meadow, Cleobury North, Bridgnorth WV16 6RP . . . . None
CHURCH STRETTON TOWN . . . . Russell's Meadow, Church Stretton SY6 6AT . . . . None
CLEE HILL UNITED . . . . Knowle Sports Ground, Tenbury Road, Clee Hill, Ludlow SY8 3NE . . . . None
HANWOOD UNITED RES. . . . . Hanwood Recreation Ground, Hanwood, Shrewsbury SY5 8JN . . . . None
MEOLE BRACE . . . . Church Road, Meole Brace, Shrewsbury SY3 9HF . . . . None
OAKENGATES ATHLETIC . . . . . Hadley Learning Community, Waterloo Road, Hadley, Telford TF1 5NU . . . . None
WELLINGTON AMATEURS RES. . . . . School Grove, Oakengates, Telford TF2 6BQ . . . . None
WHITCHURCH ALPORT RES. . . . . Yockings Park, Blackpark Road, Whitchurch SY13 1PG 01948 667415
WROXETER ROVERS . . . . Unison Sports Club, Abbey Foregate, Shrewsbury SY2 6AL . . . . None

IN: Atlas (P - Telford Combination), Bishops Castle Town (P - Montgomeryshire Amateur League Division One), Clee Hill United (R), Hanwood United Res. (P - Shropshire Alliance)

OUT: FC Hodnet (P), Ketley Bank United (P), Morda United Res. (R - Montgomeryshire Amateur League Division Two), Newport Town (P), Woofferton (WN), Wrockwardine Wood (W)

SURREY INTERMEDIATE LEAGUE (WESTERN)

Sponsored by:
No sponsor

Founded: 1891

Recent champions:
2005: Tongham
2006: Old Rutlishians
2007: Knaphill
2008: Horsley
2009: Ripley Village

	Abb	Bur	Chi	Mer	Mil	OS	Sho	Vir	Wok	Wor	Wre	Yat	YG
Abbey Rangers		1-2	3-0	2-2	2-3	2-0	1-1	1-4	6-0	3-4	1-1	4-0	1-
Burpham	1-1	***P***	5-3	3-0	3-1	3-0	2-1	3-3	5-0	3-1	3-3	3-1	2-
Chiddingfold	3-1	0-3	***R***	0-3	0-2	2-1	1-0	1-5	7-1	2-3	2-3	2-3	2-
Merrow	1-1	2-3	1-1	***E***	2-0	2-3	2-5	2-3	1-2	4-4	0-5	2-3	2-
Milford & Witley	1-0	1-2	1-2	2-3	***M***	5-0	1-1	0-1	4-0	1-3	1-2	3-2	1-
Old Salesians	3-5	1-7	4-3	0-2	3-1	***I***	3-2	1-2	1-1	0-1	3-2	1-1	3-
Shottermill & Haslemere	1-3	1-1	1-2	2-2	2-1	2-1	***E***	1-3	1-1	3-3	3-3	0-2	1-
Virginia Water	1-1	1-3	2-1	3-1	2-0	4-1	2-1	***R***	4-0	3-0	1-2	1-0	5-
Woking & Horsell	1-6	1-11	1-5	0-6	0-4	4-5	1-3	2-7		1-3	0-5	1-4	1-
Worplesdon Phoenix	1-3	0-2	2-2	7-0	2-0	8-0	2-0	2-0	6-0	***D***	1-3	3-1	2-
Wrecclesham	1-2	3-3	2-0	3-3	7-2	1-0	2-0	1-1	8-2	0-1	***I***	6-2	4-
Yateley	2-4	1-1	1-0	0-3	2-1	3-1	0-2	0-1	9-0	4-4	0-2	***V***	1-
Yateley Green	2-1	2-1	5-0	6-0	2-0	1-0	2-0	2-2	4-0	1-2	1-4	4-2	

Premier Division	P	W	D	L	F	A	Pts
Burpham	**24**	**17**	**6**	**1**	**75**	**29**	**57**
Virginia Water	**24**	**17**	**4**	**3**	**61**	**26**	**55**
Wrecclesham	**24**	**15**	**6**	**3**	**73**	**32**	**51**
Worplesdon Phoenix	**24**	**14**	**4**	**6**	**65**	**39**	**46**
Abbey Rangers	**24**	**11**	**6**	**7**	**55**	**35**	**39**
Yateley Green	**24**	**12**	**1**	**11**	**51**	**37**	**37**
Yateley	**24**	**8**	**3**	**13**	**44**	**51**	**27**
Merrow	**24**	**7**	**6**	**11**	**46**	**59**	**27**
Chiddingfold	**24**	**8**	**2**	**14**	**41**	**54**	**26**
Milford & Witley	**24**	**8**	**1**	**15**	**36**	**43**	**25**
Shottermill & Haslemere	**24**	**6**	**7**	**11**	**34**	**41**	**25**
Old Salesians	**24**	**7**	**2**	**15**	**35**	**66**	**23**
Woking & Horsell	**24**	**1**	**2**	**21**	**20**	**124**	**5**

RESERVES CUP

FINAL *(April 14th at Godalming Town)*
Yateley Green Res. 3 Pyrford Res. 0

LEAGUE CUP

FIRST ROUND
AFC Bedfont Green 8 Hammer United 3
Burpham 1 **Virginia Water** 3
Godalming & Farncombe Ath 1 **Abbey Rangers** 8
Shalford 3 Ewhurst 0 *aet*
Shottermill & Haselmere 1 **AFC Bourne** 2
Unis Old Boys 1 **Cranleigh** 2
University of Surrey 2 **Merrow** 2 *aet* (2-4p)
Wrecclesham 10 Burymead 0
Yateley 3 Milford & Witley 1
Yateley Green 2 Woking & Horsell 0

SECOND ROUND
Abbey Rangers 3 Old Salesians 0
AFC Bourne 1 **Wrecclesham** 3
Chiddingfold 1 AFC Bedfont Green 0
Cranleigh 4 Guildford City Weysiders 2
Merrow 2 **Pyrford** 6
Royal Holloway Old Boys 1 **Yateley** 2
Shalford 1 **Yateley Green** 4
Worplesdon Phoenix 1 Virginia Water 0

QUARTER-FINALS
Cranleigh 1 **Chiddingfold** 2
Worplesdon Phoenix 0 **Pyrford** 4
Yateley 2 Abbey Rangers 2 *aet* (4-1p)
Yateley Green 2 Wrecclesham 2 *aet* (13-12p)

SEMI-FINALS
Pyrford 3 Yateley 2
Yateley Green 3 Chiddingfold 1

FINAL *(May 6th at Godalming Town)*
Yateley Green 1 Pyrford 1 *aet* (6-5p)

SURREY INTERMEDIATE LEAGUE (WESTERN) PREMIER DIVISION CONSTITUTION 2010-11

AFC BOURNE . . . . Heath End Recreation Ground, Upper Weybourne Way, Farnham GU9 9DD . . . . N
ABBEY RANGERS . . . . Addlestone Moor, Addlestone Moor Road, Addlestone KT15 2QH 01932 442
CHIDDINGFOLD. . . . . Chiddingfold Recreation Ground, Coxcombe Lane, Chiddingfold GU8 4QA . . . . N
GUILDFORD CITY WEYSIDERS . . . . Shalford Park, Shalford Road, Guildford GU4 8HB 01483 573
MERROW . . . . The Urnfield, Downside Road, Guildford GU4 8PH 01483 567
MILFORD & WITLEY . . . . Burton Pavilion, Milford Heath Road, Milford GU8 5BX. 01483 860
PYRFORD. . . . . Pyrford Cricket Ground, Coldharbour Road, Pyrford, Woking GU22 8ST. 01932 342
ROYAL HOLLOWAY OLD BOYS . . . . . Royal Holloway College PF, Prune Hill, Egham TW20 9TR 01784 438
SHOTTERMILL & HASLEMERE . . . . Woolmer Hill Sports Ground, Haslemere GU27 1QA. 01428 643
UNIVERSITY OF SURREY . . . . Surrey Sports Park, Richard Meyjes Road. Guildford GU2 7XH. 01483 689
WORPLESDON PHOENIX. . . . . Worplesdon Memorial Ground, Perry Hill, Worplesdon GU3 3RF . . . . N
WRECCLESHAM. . . . . Wrecclesham Recreation Ground, Riverdale, Wrecclesham, Farnham GU10 4PJ . . . . N
YATELEY . . . . The Green, Reading Road, Yateley GU46 7RP . . . . N
YATELEY GREEN . . . . Sean Devereux Park, Chandlers Lane, Yateley GU46 7SZ . . . . N

IN: AFC Bourne (P), Guildford Gity Weysiders (P), Pyrford (P), Royal Holloway Old Boys (P), University of Surrey (P)
OUT: Burpham (P - Surrey Elite Intermediate League), Old Salesians (R), Virginia Water (P - Surrey Elite Intermediate League), Wokin Horsell (R), Wrecclesham (P - Surrey Elite Intermediate League)

Division One	P	W	D	L	F	A	Pts
University Surrey	24	18	3	3	74	18	57
Ryl Holloway OB	24	18	0	6	78	31	54
Pyrford	24	17	2	5	67	28	53
AFC Bourne	24	17	1	6	86	34	52
Guildf. City Wey.	24	17	1	6	74	28	52
Cranleigh	24	14	2	8	66	35	44
AFC B'font Green	24	10	5	9	55	60	35
Shalford	24	8	2	14	42	51	26
Unis Old Boys	24	6	4	14	44	57	22
Godalming & FA	24	4	6	14	37	68	18
Ewhurst	24	6	0	18	23	85	18
Burymead	24	2	5	17	24	98	11
Hammer United	24	3	1	20	26	103	10

Reserve Prem Div	P	W	D	L	F	A	Pts
Wrecclesham Res.	24	20	1	3	85	29	61
Burpham Res.	24	16	5	3	64	22	53
Virginia Wtr Res.	24	15	2	7	46	28	47
Milford & W. Res.	24	13	5	6	53	32	44
Merrow Res.	24	12	5	7	44	40	41
Worplesdon Res.	24	12	1	11	56	49	37
Yateley G. Res.	24	11	2	11	54	41	35
Yateley Res.	24	10	3	11	51	57	33
Abbey Rgrs Res.	24	10	3	11	41	47	33
O Salesians Res. *-1*	24	9	3	12	34	56	29
Chiddingfold Res.	24	6	1	17	45	74	19
Shottermill Res.	24	5	2	17	38	68	17
Woking & H. Res.	24	0	1	23	24	92	1

Reserve Div One	P	W	D	L	F	A	Pts
Cranleigh Res.	24	22	2	0	105	14	
Univ. Surrey Res.	24	17	4	3	85	30	
Pyrford Res.	24	15	5	4	74	36	
AFC Bed. G. Res.	24	14	5	5	84	30	
Burymead Res.	24	10	3	11	47	67	
Shalford Res.	24	8	8	8	59	47	
Guild. CW Res. *-3*	24	10	3	11	51	54	
Unis Old B. Res.	24	9	3	12	41	59	
R. Holloway Res.	24	8	5	11	36	44	
AFC Bourne Res.	24	8	5	11	46	62	
God./Farn. A. Res.	24	3	5	16	40	76	
Ewhurst Res.	24	3	3	18	24	97	
Hammer Utd Res.	24	2	3	19	25	101	

TEESSIDE LEAGUE

full-time.thefa.com/Index.do?leagueid=2880396

Sponsored by: Jack Hatfields Sports

Founded: 1891

Recent champions:
2005: Carlin How WMC
2006: Carlin How WMC
2007: Carlin How WMC
2008: BEADS
2009: BEADS

	BEA	DCB	DC	DG	Fish	Gra	Nort	Nun	RM	RT	Sou	Stok	Tho
BEADS	***D***	6-0	3-0	8-1	6-0	5-2	4-3	1-2	3-0	3-0	0-1	3-1	0-1
Darlington Cleveland Bridge	1-3	***I***	3-1	3-1	1-0	5-1	1-2	1-0	4-3	3-3	1-7	2-1	3-0
Darlington Croft	1-3	1-1	***V***	3-1	0-1	3-1	0-0	1-1	1-2	2-0	0-5	1-1	2-0
Darlington Grammar Sch. RA	1-4	5-1	3-2	***I***	1-3	3-6	4-3	2-5	2-6	1-2	3-3	3-5	4-5
Fishburn Park	0-3	1-2	1-1	5-2	***S***	2-5	3-1	1-2	2-2	2-0	1-0	0-3	1-1
Grangetown Boys Club	1-3	1-0	5-1	8-2	5-0	***I***	2-2	5-1	6-1	1-5	1-2	3-1	3-0
North Ormesby Sports	2-1	3-1	4-4	7-3	5-2	4-4	***O***	2-1	3-1	3-2	1-0	2-0	4-3
Nunthorpe Athletic	2-3	1-3	1-3	2-0	4-2	0-7	3-1	***N***	3-1	2-4	1-4	1-4	0-1
Richmond Mavericks	1-2	1-3	2-2	1-2	1-0	2-1	4-0	1-3		0-2	1-2	2-2	3-0
Richmond Town	1-1	0-1	0-2	6-1	6-0	0-1	7-0	4-0	2-0		0-1	3-3	3-2
South Bank St Peters	2-3	3-1	2-3	4-3	4-0	3-6	5-3	5-1	4-3	3-3	***O***	2-1	5-0
Stokesley Res.	2-3	0-2	2-3	4-3	3-0	1-1	0-0	0-0	1-7	2-2	1-1	***N***	1-2
Thornaby Dubliners	0-2	4-1	1-1	7-0	4-1	2-4	2-1	8-1	1-0	8-0	1-3	0-2	***E***

J V MADDEN TROPHY

(League champions v McMillan Bowl holders)

(Aug 5th at BEADS) **BEADS** 4 Nunthorpe Athletic 1

Division One	P	W	D	L	F	A	Pts
BEADS	24	19	1	4	73	25	58
South Bank St Peters	24	16	3	5	71	38	51
Grangetown Boys Club	24	14	3	7	80	48	45
Darlington Cleveland Bdge	24	13	2	9	44	48	41
North Ormesby Sports	24	11	5	8	56	57	38
Richmond Town	24	10	5	9	55	42	35
Thornaby Dubliners	24	11	2	11	53	45	35
Darlington Croft	24	8	8	8	38	43	32
Stokesley Res.	24	6	8	10	41	46	26
Nunthorpe Athletic	24	8	2	14	37	64	26
Richmond Mavericks	24	7	3	14	45	51	24
Fishburn Park	24	6	3	15	28	62	21
Darlington Gram. Sch. RA	24	4	1	19	51	103	13

LOU MOORE TROPHY

(Division One teams)

FIRST ROUND

Darlington Cleveland Bdge 4 Stokesley Res. 3 *aet*
Darlington Croft 5 Darlington Grammar SRA 2
Grangetown Boys Club 4 Fishburn Park 0
North Ormesby Sports 4 Richmond Mavericks 2
Thornaby Dubliners 5 Nunthorpe Athletic 1

QUARTER-FINALS

Darlington Croft 2 **Darlington Cleveland Bridge** 3
North Ormesby Sports 0 **BEADS** 3
Richmond Town 2 South Bank St Peters 1
Thornaby Dubliners 0 **Grangetown Boys Club** 1

SEMI-FINALS

Darlington Cleveland Bridge 4 **Grangetown BC** 11
Richmond Town 2 **BEADS** 5

FINAL

(May 5th at Guisborough Town)
BEADS 1 **Grangetown Boys Club** 3

R T RAINE TROPHY

(McMillan Bowl First Round losers)

FIRST ROUND

Richmond Mavericks (w/o) v Guisborough Town BS
South Bank St Peters 6 Teesside Athletic Res. 0
South Park Rgrs 1 **Darlington Grammar School SRA** 2

QUARTER-FINALS

Darlington Croft 3 **South Bank St Peters** 4
Grangetown YCC 0 **St Mary's College** 2
Great Ayton 2 Norton & Stockton Anc. Res. 2 *aet* (5-4p)
Richmond Mavericks 4 Darlington Grammar SRA 1

SEMI-FINALS

South Bank St Peters 5 Richmond Mavericks 2
St Mary's College 2 Great Ayton United 1

FINAL

(April 5th at Teesside Athletic)
St Mary's College 1 South Bank St Peters 0

TEESSIDE LEAGUE DIVISION ONE CONSTITUTION 2010-11

ACKLAM STEELWORKS . . . . Acklam Steelworks Sports Club , Park Road South , Middlesbrough TS4 2RD 01642 818717
BEADS . . . . Beechwood & Easterside SC, Marton Road, Middlesbrough TS4 3PP 01642 311304
DARLINGTON GRAMMAR SCHOOL RA . . . Darl'gton RA, Brinkburn Rd, Darlington DL3 9LF 01325 468125
FISHBURN PARK . . . . Eskvale School, Broomfield Park, Whitby YO22 4HS. . . . . None
GRANGETOWN BOYS CLUB . . . Grangetown YCC, Trunk Road, Grangetown, Middlesbrough TS6 7HP 01642 455435
NORTH ORMESBY SPORTS . . . . . . Unity City Academy, Ormesby Road, North Ormesby TS3 8RE 01642 326262
NORTON WMC . . . . Grangefield YCC, Oxbridge Road, Stockton-on-Tees TS18 4DA . . . . None
NUNTHORPE ATHLETIC . . . . Recreation Club, Guisborough Road, Nunthorpe TS7 0LD 01642 313251
RICHMOND MAVERICKS. . . Brompton-on-Swale Sports Ground, Brompton-on-Swale, Richmond DL10 7HT . . . . None
RICHMOND TOWN . . . . Earls Orchard Playing Fields, Sleegill, Richmond DL10 4RH. . . . . None
STOKESLEY RES. . . . . Stokesley Sports Club, Broughton Road, Stokesley, Middlesbrough TS9 5JQ 01642 710051
THORNABY DUBLINERS . . . . . . Harold Wilson Sports Complex, Badger Avenue, Thornaby TS17 0EX . . . . None

IN: Acklam Steelworks (P), Norton WMC (formerly Coulby Newham) (P)
OUT: Darlington Cleveland Bridge (P - Wearside League), Darlington Croft (F), South Bank St Peters (F)

McMILLAN BOWL

FIRST ROUND
Coulby Newham 3 Darlington Croft 1
Darlington Cleveland Bridge 5 Teesside Athletic Res. 2
Fishburn Park 4 Grangetown YCC 2 *aet*
Grangetown Boys Club 6 Darlington Grammar SRA 2
Norton & Stockton Ancients Res. 0 **BEADS** 6
Redcar Newmarket 4 Richmond Mavericks 3 *aet*
Redcar Rugby Club 5 Guisborough Town Black Swan 1
Richmond Town 2 South Bank St Peters 1
South Park Rangers 3 **Thornaby Dubliners** 6
St Mary's College 0 **Acklam Steelworks** 5
Stokesley Res. 2 Great Ayton United 2 *aet* (5-3p)

SECOND ROUND
Acklam Steelworks 1 **Coulby Newham** 1 *aet* (4-5p)
Cargo Fleet 4 **North Ormesby Sports** 4 *aet* (4-5p)
Fishburn Park 1 **Whinney Banks YCC** 6
Nunthope Athletic 1 **Grangetown Boys Club** 3
Redcar Newmarket 2 **Darlington Cleveland Bridge** 4
Redcar Rugby Club 2 **Stokesley Res.** 3
Richmond Town 1 **Thornaby Dubliners** 2
Stockton Town 0 **BEADS** 2

QUARTER-FINALS
Coulby Newham 2 **Whinney Banks YCC** 3 *aet*
Darlington Cleveland Bridge 0 **Stokesley Res.** 2
Grangetown Boys Club 2 **BEADS** 3
Thornaby Dubliners 3 **North Ormesby Sports** 4

SEMI-FINALS
North Ormesby Sports 4 Stokesley Res. 4 *aet* (7-6p)
Whinney Banks YCC 2 **BEADS** 2 *aet* (2-3p)

FINAL *(May 10th at Guisborough Town)*
BEADS 2 North Ormesby Sports 1

Division Two		P	W	D	L	F	A	Pts
Coulby Newham		26	20	1	5	97	36	61
Acklam Steelworks		26	18	3	5	92	46	57
Whinney Banks YCC		26	17	2	7	104	43	53
Stockton Town		26	16	5	5	78	37	53
Cargo Fleet	*-3*	26	17	4	5	74	40	52
Norton & Stockton Res		26	12	6	8	62	46	42
Great Ayton United		26	11	5	10	51	51	38
Redcar Rugby Club	*-3*	26	12	3	11	61	66	36
St Mary's College		26	9	3	14	52	66	30
Redcar Newmarket		26	7	5	14	46	83	26
South Park Rangers		26	5	5	16	29	71	20
Teesside Athletic Res.		26	4	5	17	33	78	17
Grangetown YCC		26	5	1	20	39	72	16
G'boro. T. Black Swan	*-3*	26	4	2	20	37	120	11

ALEX BURNESS PLATE

(Division Two teams)

FIRST ROUND
Acklam Steelworks 2 **Redcar Rugby Club** 4
Cargo Fleet 4 Guisborough Town Black Swan 0
Norton & Stockton Ancients Res. 0 **Grangetown YCC** 1
Stockton Town 3 St Mary's College 2
Teesside Athletic Res. 2 South Park Rangers 1
Whinney Banks YCC 3 Great Ayton United 1

QUARTER-FINALS
Coulby Newham 4 Grangetown YCC 2
Redcar Rugby Club 2 Stockton Town 1
Redcar Newmarket 0 **Whinney Banks YCC** 6
Teesside Athletic Res. 2 **Cargo Fleet** 6

SEMI-FINALS
Coulby Newham 2 Cargo Fleet 0
Redcar Rugby Club 1 **Whinney Banks YCC** 3

FINAL *(May 3rd at Stokesley)*
Whinney Banks YCC 1 **Coulby Newham** 2

	Ack	Car	Coul	Gra	GtAy	Guis	Nort	RN	RRC	SPk	SM	Stoc	Tees	Whin
Acklam Steelworks		0-4	2-1	4-2	5-0	6-0	5-1	4-0	2-1	7-2	3-3	3-3	3-1	3-1
Cargo Fleet	5-3	***D***	1-2	2-3	3-2	5-0	1-2	3-0	5-1	3-0	4-1	1-1	2-2	1-0
Coulby Newham	3-0	9-0	***I***	3-0	2-5	10-1	4-1	4-0	4-1	2-0	5-4	6-2	4-0	4-3
Grangetown YCC	1-2	1-3	1-4	***V***	3-2	5-4	0-2	1-0	2-4	1-1	2-3	0-2	7-1	0-3
Great Ayton United	0-2	2-4	1-2	4-2	***I***	2-0	1-1	3-2	2-2	1-0	2-0	1-1	3-0	3-3
Guisboro. T. Black Swan	3-5	0-1	1-11	2-1	0-3	***S***	1-3	0-2	1-2	3-3	1-5	4-3	0-6	3-10
Norton/Stockton A. Res	1-1	2-2	2-2	3-0	1-2	4-3	***I***	4-3	2-1	1-2	6-0	0-0	2-0	0-3
Redcar Newmarket	0-4	4-2	0-5	5-4	2-2	6-1	2-1	***O***	1-4	2-2	2-0	1-4	2-2	1-7
Redcar Rugby Club	1-6	2-2	1-0	1-0	2-1	10-0	5-5	0-4	***N***	7-1	4-1	1-3	2-0	1-9
South Park Rangers	0-3	0-6	0-3	1-0	4-0	1-1	0-8	7-1	1-0		0-1	0-5	1-2	1-1
St Mary's College	2-3	1-3	1-3	3-1	3-2	1-3	1-2	3-3	2-3	7-1	***T***	2-1	2-2	2-3
Stockton Town	6-4	1-4	5-1	3-0	5-1	3-0	3-1	5-0	8-1	2-0	0-1	***W***	2-2	2-1
Teesside Athletic Res.	0-9	0-2	0-2	3-2	2-4	0-3	0-6	3-3	0-2	2-1	2-3	1-4	***O***	1-3
Whinney Banks YCC	5-3	1-5	4-1	7-0	0-2	12-2	4-1	8-0	4-2	2-0	5-0	1-4	4-1	

TEESSIDE LEAGUE DIVISION TWO CONSTITUTION 2010-11

BILLINGHAM TOWN INTERMEDIATES. . . . . Bedford Terrace, Billingham TS23 4AF 01642 560043
CARGO FLEET . . . . Pallister Park, Ormesby Road, Middlesbrough TS3 7AP 01642 251454
DARLINGTON RUGBY CLUB . . . . Darlington Rugby Club, Grange Road, Darlington DL1 5NR . . . . None
GRANGETOWN YCC . . . . Grangetown YCC, Trunk Road, Grangetown, Middlesbrough TS6 7HP 01642 455435
GREAT AYTON UNITED . . . . Leven Park, Easby Lane, Great Ayton, Middlesbrough TS9 6JJ 01642 723723
GUISBOROUGH TOWN RES. . . . . . King George Ground, Howlbeck Road, Guisborough TS14 6LA 01287 636925
NORTON & STOCKTON ANCIENTS RES. Station Road, Norton, Stockton-on-Tees TS20 1PE 01642 530203
REDCAR ATHLETIC RES.. . . . . Green Lane, Redcar TS10 3RW. . . . . None
REDCAR NEWMARKET . . . . Rye Hills School, Redcar Lane, Redcar TS10 1PE 01642 484269
REDCAR RUGBY CLUB . . . . Redcar Rugby Club, Mackinlay Park, Green Lane, Redcar TS10 3RW. 01642 482733
ST MARY'S COLLEGE. . . . . St Mary's College, Saltersgill Lane, Middlesbrough TS4 3JP. 01642 814680
STOCKTON TOWN RES.. . . . . Bishopton Road West, Stockton-on-Tees TS19 0QD . . . . None
STOCKTON WEST END. . Tilery Rec Field, Stockton Sports Centre, Talbot Street, Stockton-on-Tees TS20 2AY 01642 528282
WHINNEY BANKS YCC . . . . Hall Garth School, Hall Drive, Acklam, Middlesbrough TS5 7JX 01642 813776

IN: Billingham Town Intermediates (N), Darlington Rugby Club (N), Guisborough Town Res. (formerly Guisborough Town HC) (S - Wearside League), Stockton Town Res. (N), Stockton West End (N)
OUT: Acklam Steelworks (P), Coulby Newham (now Norton WMC) (P), Guisborough Town Black Swan (W), South Park Rangers (W), Stockton Town (P - Wearside League)
Teesside Athletic Res. become Redcar Athletic Res.

WEST RIDING COUNTY AMATEUR LEAGUE

www.wrc.leaguemanager.biz

Sponsored by:

No sponsor

Founded: 1922

Recent champions:

2005: Golcar United

2006: Bay Athletic

2007: Wibsey

2008: Bay Athletic

2009: Bay Athletic

	Albion Sports	Ardsley Celtic	Bay Athletic	Brigh'se Res.	Campion	Golcar United	Halifax Irish	Hall Green U.	Kirkburton	Lower Hopton	Marsden	Meltham Ath.	Ovenden WR	Storthes Hall	Tyersal	Wibsey
Albion Sports	***P***	4-1	1-5	W-L	2-1	5-1	3-1	5-1	5-0	3-1	4-1	6-3	2-0	1-0	2-3	5-1
Ardsley Celtic	3-4	***R***	1-5	1-0	1-3	1-4	1-1	3-2	2-3	1-3	0-3	3-2	0-2	0-3	0-1	0-3
Bay Athletic	1-1	4-0	***E***	2-0	2-1	1-0	4-1	2-1	4-1	3-2	5-1	3-1	2-0	1-2	4-1	2-0
Brighouse Town Res.	2-6	1-0	0-1	***M***	1-6	2-1	2-0	1-1	1-2	1-0	2-3	1-2	0-3	2-4	1-3	1-1
Campion	3-3	2-1	0-0	3-2	***I***	4-0	2-2	4-2	1-0	2-0	4-1	2-0	2-0	1-0	3-1	5-2
Golcar United	1-1	2-0	4-2	5-0	3-3	***E***	8-0	1-3	1-2	2-3	1-1	2-2	0-1	2-1	3-0	3-2
Halifax Irish Club	1-3	1-4	1-7	4-2	0-5	2-3	***R***	2-2	1-7	0-5	0-6	2-1	1-2	0-5	0-6	0-4
Hall Green United	6-4	1-1	0-8	2-0	1-2	3-2	2-1		5-1	0-2	0-3	1-4	2-2	5-2	3-2	1-1
Kirkburton	0-2	2-3	L-W	2-3	0-1	2-3	5-0	3-2	***D***	2-4	1-3	7-1	0-4	4-1	2-3	3-4
Lower Hopton	1-5	1-0	2-1	4-1	4-1	4-1	4-1	4-0	0-2	***I***	2-3	5-0	1-3	1-5	1-0	0-2
Marsden	3-1	5-1	2-2	2-1	1-1	1-0	2-1	2-1	2-1	3-2	***V***	0-4	3-3	1-3	1-3	2-1
Meltham Athletic	1-2	2-4	1-3	1-1	6-2	3-2	1-3	5-2	4-1	2-0	9-1	***I***	4-2	1-0	1-2	1-1
Ovenden West Riding	1-2	3-1	1-0	1-4	1-1	3-1	7-1	3-0	6-1	1-2	3-4	3-1	***S***	0-2	1-4	1-0
Storthes Hall	1-2	3-1	0-3	2-0	2-2	1-4	7-1	2-0	0-0	3-3	1-3	1-0	0-0	***I***	1-1	1-1
Tyersal	1-1	4-3	2-3	1-7	1-1	1-1	2-2	2-3	2-1	0-2	3-3	0-0	3-3	0-0	***O***	3-2
Wibsey	3-2	1-1	1-4	3-0	1-2	2-2	1-0	3-2	2-0	1-0	2-2	1-2	6-1	0-3	2-1	***N***

Premier Division	P	W	D	L	F	A	Pts
Bay Athletic	30	23	3	4	84	28	72
Albion Sports	30	21	4	5	87	47	67
Campion	30	18	8	4	70	40	62
Marsden	30	17	6	7	68	62	57
Lower Hopton	30	16	1	13	63	49	49
Ovenden West Riding	30	14	5	11	61	50	47
Storthes Hall	30	13	7	10	56	40	46
Wibsey	30	12	7	11	54	50	43
Tyersal	30	11	9	10	56	57	42
Meltham Athletic	30	12	4	14	65	63	40
Golcar United	30	11	6	13	63	56	39
Hall Green United	30	9	5	16	54	77	32
Kirkburton	30	9	1	20	55	70	28
Brighouse Town Res.	30	7	3	20	39	66	24
Ardsley Celtic	30	6	3	21	38	75	21
Halifax Irish Club	30	3	4	23	30	113	13

PREMIER DIVISION CUP

FIRST ROUND

Bay Athletic 2 **Albion Sports** 5

Brighouse Town 1 **Hall Green United** 3 *aet*

Campion 1 Golcar United 0

Halifax Irish Club 2 **Marsden** 7

Meltham Athletic 6 Lower Hopton 4 *aet*

Ovenden West Riding 2 Kirkburton 0

Storthes Hall 5 Ardsley Celtic 1

Tyersal 3 **Wibsey** 4

QUARTER-FINAL

Albion Sports 3 Ovenden West Riding 2

Marsden 1 **Storthes Hall** 2

Meltham Athletic 1 **Hall Green United** 2

Wibsey 0 **Campion** 4

SEMI-FINAL

Campion 0 **Albion Sports** 3 *(at Brighouse Town)*

Hall Green 2 **Storthes Hall** 3 *aet (at AFC Emley)*

FINAL

(May 17th at Bay Athletic)

Storthes Hall 2 **Albion Sports** 4

WEST RIDING COUNTY AMATEUR LEAGUE PREMIER DIVISION CONSTITUTION 2010-11

ALBION SPORTS . . . . Myra Shay, Barkerend Road, Bradford BD3 0AB 07771 685001
BAY ATHLETIC . . . . Syngenta Sports, 509 Leeds Road, Huddersfield HD2 1YJ 01484 514367
BRIGHOUSE TOWN RES. . . . . St Giles Road, Hove Edge, Brighouse HD6 2PL 01484 380088
CAMPION . . . . Manningham Mills Sports Ground, Scotchman Road, Manningham, Bradford BD9 4SH 01274 546726
GOLCAR UNITED . . . . Longfield Recreation Ground, Golcar, Huddersfield HD7 4AZ 07779 700098
HALL GREEN UNITED . . . . . Crigglestone Sports Club, Painthorpe Lane, Crigglestone, Wakefield WF4 3JU 01924 254544
HUNSWORTH. . . . . Birkenshaw Middle School, Bradford Road, Gomersal, Cleckheaton BD19 4BE 07711 197741
KIRKBURTON. Gregory Playing Fields, Kirkburton, Huddersfield HD8 0XH 07738 987582
LOWER HOPTON. Woodend Road, Lower Hopton, Mirfield WF14 8PP 01924 492048
MARSDEN. . . . . Fall Lane, Marsden, Huddersfield HD7 6LX 01484 844191
OVENDEN WEST RIDING . . . . Natty Lane, Illingworth, Halifax HX2 9DS 01422 244350
STEETON . . . . Summer Hill Lane, Steeton BD20 6RX 01585 683387
STORTHES HALL. . . . . Police Sports Ground, Woodfield Park, Lockwood Scar, Huddersfield HD4 6BW 07957 691189
TINGLEY ATHLETIC . . . . The Crescent, East Ardsley, Wakefield WF3 2EG 07950 131889
TYERSAL . . . . Arkwright Street, off Dick Lane, Tyersal, Bradford BD4 8JL 07710 006241
WIBSEY . . . . Westwood Park, Cooper Lane, Bradford BD6 3NN 07739 521551

IN: Hunsworth (P), Steeton (P)
OUT: Halifax Irish Club (R), Meltham Athletic (R - Huddersfield & District League Division One)
Ardsley Celtic become Tingley Athletic

Division One		P	W	D	L	F	A	Pts
Steeton		24	17	1	6	77	42	52
Hunsworth		24	15	6	3	58	39	51
Littletown		24	15	2	7	87	47	47
Ventus & Yeadon Celtic		24	14	1	9	84	50	43
Bronte Wanderers		24	12	5	7	61	49	41
Salts		24	11	6	7	65	45	39
Heckmondwike Town		24	11	3	10	69	58	36
Dudley Hill Rangers		24	6	9	9	51	60	27
Overthorpe Sports	*+3*	24	7	2	15	37	64	26
Tyersal Res.	*-3*	24	8	4	12	58	84	25
Wakefield City		24	6	5	13	45	62	23
Eastmoor		24	6	4	14	49	76	22
Hemsworth Miners W. Res.		24	3	2	19	47	112	11

Keighley Shamrocks - record expunged

DIVISION ONE CUP

FIRST ROUND

Hemsworth Miners Welfare Res. 4 Keighley Shamrocks 0

Hunsworth 8 Eastmoor 2

Littletown 2 Bronte Wanderers 0

Salts 2 **Steeton** 4

Tyersal Res. 3 Dudley Hill Rangers 2

Wakefield City 4 **Ventus & Yeadon Celtic** 6

QUARTER-FINALS

Hemsworth Miners Welfare Res. 1 **Littletown** 2

Steeton 2 Hunsworth 0

Tyersal Res. 3 **Heckmondwike Town** 6

Ventus & Yeadon Celtic 7 Overthorpe Sports 1

SEMI-FINALS

Littletown 2 Heckmondwike Town 1

(at Lower Hopton)

Ventus & Yeadon Celtic 2 Steeton 2 *aet* (5-4p)

(at Campion)

FINAL *(May 11th at Campion)*

Ventus & Yeadon Celtic 1 Littletown 0

	Bronte Wanderers	Dudley Hill Rangers	Eastmoor	Heckmondwike Town	Hemsworth Miners W. Res.	Hunsworth	Keighley Shamrocks	Littletown	Overthorpe Sports	Salts	Steeton	Tyersal Res.	Ventus & Yeadon Celtic	Wakefield City
Bronte Wanderers		2-1	1-1	3-1	7-2	1-3	n/a	1-1	2-1	3-3	2-5	3-1	1-0	2-0
Dudley Hill Rangers	3-1	***D***	3-3	3-4	6-1	4-1	n/a	1-2	0-0	1-1	0-5	2-2	3-3	1-0
Eastmoor	5-1	1-1	***I***	3-2	4-2	1-3	n/a	0-3	1-2	1-5	2-2	1-3	1-6	2-1
Heckmondwike Town	2-2	2-2	7-1	***V***	8-2	2-2	n/a	4-0	4-2	3-5	1-2	1-2	3-2	5-3
Hemsworth MW Res.	2-7	3-4	0-6	L-W	***I***	1-2	n/a	0-5	3-2	2-5	4-3	2-7	2-9	3-3
Hunsworth	0-3	2-2	3-2	5-3	5-3	***S***	4-0	1-0	1-1	2-2	1-4	3-1	3-0	3-1
Keighley Shamrocks	0-1	n/a	n/a	0-6	n/a	n/a	***I***	1-5	n/a	0-4	n/a	2-5	n/a	n/a
Littletown	3-3	8-0	7-2	3-0	7-1	1-3	2-0	***O***	6-4	1-10	0-3	7-0	4-2	7-0
Overthorpe Sports	1-3	2-0	2-3	1-6	0-3	0-4	n/a	1-3	***N***	2-1	2-4	2-0	3-2	1-0
Salts	6-3	3-2	3-0	1-3	5-1	1-1	4-0	0-2	0-2		0-2	4-2	3-1	1-0
Steeton	2-0	5-3	8-4	2-4	5-2	0-1	n/a	5-2	3-0	4-2	***O***	1-2	3-2	2-0
Tyersal Res.	2-5	2-2	5-2	5-3	5-4	4-5	n/a	0-9	3-2	1-1	3-4	***N***	1-9	4-4
Ventus & Yeadon Celtic	4-3	3-2	3-1	5-1	3-0	0-2	5-0	5-3	8-1	5-2	2-1	4-2	***E***	3-1
Wakefield City	0-2	4-5	3-2	2-0	4-4	2-2	n/a	1-3	4-3	1-1	3-2	4-1	4-3	

WEST RIDING COUNTY AMATEUR LEAGUE DIVISION ONE CONSTITUTION 2010-11

AFC EMLEY RES. . . . . The Welfare Ground, off Upper Lane, Emley, Huddersfield HD8 9RE 01924 849329
BAY ATHLETIC RES. . . . . Syngenta Sports, 509 Leeds Road, Huddersfield HD2 1YJ 01484 514367
BRONTE WANDERERS . . . . Marley Stadium, Aireworth Road, Keighley BD21 4DB 01535 609910
DUDLEY HILL RANGERS . . . . Newhall Park School, Newhall Road, Bierley, Bradford BD4 6AF 07967 359883
EASTMOOR . . . . King George V Playing Fields, Woodhouse Road, Eastmoor, Wakefield WF1 4RD 01924 375367
HALIFAX IRISH CLUB . . . . Natty Lane, Illingworth, Halifax HX2 9DS 01422 360134
HECKMONDWIKE TOWN . . . . Cemetery Road, Heckmondwike WF16 9ED 01924 442907
LITTLETOWN . . . . Beck Lane, Heckmondwike WF16 0JZ 07930 852796
OVERTHORPE SPORTS . . . . Overthorpe Park, Edge Top Road, Dewsbury WF12 0BG 01924 464164
SALTS . . . . Salts Playing Fields, Hirst Lane, Saltaire, Shipley BD18 4DD 01274 583427
TYERSAL RES. . . . . Arkwright Street, off Dick Lane, Tyersal, Bradford BD4 8JL 07710 006241
VENTUS & YEADON CELTIC . . . . Dam Lane, Yeadon, Leeds LS19 7US 07721 468967
WAKEFIELD CITY . . . . West Yorks Sports & Social, Walton Lane, Sandal, Wakefield WF2 6NG 01924 258760
WESTBROOK YMCA . . . . Lawnswood YMCA, Otley Road, Leeds LS16 6HQ 0113 261 2484

IN: AFC Emley Res. (P), Bay Athletic Res.(P), Halifax Irish Club (R), Westbrook YMCA (P)

OUT: Hemsworth Miners Welfare Res. (R - Doncaster Senior League Division One), Hunsworth (P), Keighley Shamrocks (WS), Steeton (P)

Division Two	P	W	D	L	F	A	Pts
Bay Athletic Res.	26	23	2	1	133	31	71
Westbrook YMCA	26	19	3	4	59	32	60
AFC Emley Res.	26	17	4	5	61	28	55
Campion Res.	26	16	4	6	74	37	52
West Horton	26	15	4	7	68	54	49
Storthes Hall Res.	26	12	3	11	68	49	39
Steeton Res.	26	10	5	11	47	63	35
Golcar United Res.	26	10	3	13	46	60	33
Kirkburton Res.	26	9	2	15	63	90	29
Ardsley Celtic Res.	26	8	3	15	48	69	27
Crag Road United	26	7	3	16	42	63	24
Rawdon Old Boys	26	5	4	17	31	68	19
Morley Town	26	4	4	18	33	85	16
Dudley Hill Athletic	26	3	4	19	49	93	13

DIVISION TWO CUP

FIRST ROUND

AFC Emley Res. 4 Dudley Hill Athletic 2

Bay Athletic Res. 2 Campion Res. 2 *aet* (8-7p)

Crag Road 1 **Storthes Hall Res.** 4 *(at Storthes Hall)*

Golcar United Res. 1 **Westbrook YMCA** 3

Kirkburton Res. 4 Morley Town 1

Rawdon Old Boys 4 Steeton Res. 3

QUARTER-FINALS

AFC Emley Res. 2 Ardsley Celtic Res. 1

Kirkburton Res. 1 **Rawdon Old Boys** 4

Storthes Hall Res. 4 Bay Athletic Res. 3

Westbrook YMCA 4 West Horton 3

SEMI-FINALS

Storthes Hall Res. 0 **AFC Emley Res.** 1 *aet*

Westbrook YMCA 1 **Rawdon Old Boys** 2

FINAL

(May 18th at Littletown)

AFC Emley Res. 2 Rawdon Old Boys 0

	AFC Emley	Ardsley C.	Bay A. Res.	Campion	Crag Road	Dudley Hill	Golcar Res.	Kirkburton	Morley Town	Rawdon OB	Steeton Res.	Storthes Hall	West Horton	Westbrook
AFC Emley Res.		2-1	1-1	4-2	2-0	4-1	2-1	1-0	5-2	1-0	4-0	3-2	1-1	L-W
Ardsley Celtic Res.	2-4	***D***	0-4	2-2	3-1	2-6	2-3	2-4	2-0	1-0	0-2	0-1	1-5	0-1
Bay Athletic Res.	4-0	4-3	***I***	0-3	5-1	4-4	10-1	10-3	7-0	12-0	4-2	2-0	7-0	6-2
Campion Res.	3-0	3-0	1-4	***V***	3-0	1-1	2-0	7-1	3-0	9-0	3-2	3-0	1-3	1-2
Crag Road United	0-2	2-2	1-3	1-4	***I***	3-2	1-3	7-2	4-2	3-4	1-3	1-2	1-1	0-2
Dudley Hill Athletic	0-4	1-3	0-8	1-3	0-2	***S***	3-3	2-2	3-1	1-2	2-6	3-5	2-3	2-3
Golcar United Res.	0-1	0-1	0-4	2-3	1-2	4-2	***I***	3-1	2-0	4-2	0-2	1-0	2-0	2-2
Kirkburton Res.	0-6	1-7	2-8	4-4	5-1	5-1	1-4	***O***	2-4	2-1	3-0	4-2	8-1	1-2
Morley Town	1-5	1-4	0-6	0-3	3-7	3-1	4-3	0-3	***N***	0-3	4-3	1-2	1-4	0-2
Rawdon Old Boys	0-0	0-4	2-3	2-4	0-0	1-2	2-1	5-2	1-1		0-1	1-1	2-4	1-2
Steeton Res.	0-5	1-1	0-6	2-4	1-0	7-5	2-2	1-0	2-2	2-0	***T***	4-3	1-1	1-2
Storthes Hall Res.	2-2	10-2	3-4	2-0	5-0	6-1	2-3	1-4	2-2	4-1	6-1	***W***	4-2	1-0
West Horton	2-0	7-2	2-3	1-1	3-1	4-2	4-1	5-3	5-0	2-0	4-0	2-1	***O***	1-5
Westbrook YMCA	3-2	4-1	0-4	3-1	0-2	4-1	5-0	5-0	1-1	2-1	1-1	2-1	4-1	

WEST RIDING COUNTY AMATEUR LEAGUE DIVISION TWO CONSTITUTION 2010-11

CAMPION RES. . . . . Manningham Mills Sports Ground, Scotchman Road, Manningham, Bradford BD9 4SH 01274 546726
CRAG ROAD UNITED . . . . Apperley Road, Greengates, Bradford BD10 0PX 07781 808212
GOLCAR UNITED RES. . . . . Longfield Recreation Ground, Golcar, Huddersfield HD7 4AZ 07779 700098
HUDDERSFIELD YMCA. . . . . New Hey Road, Huddersfield HD3 3XF 01484 654052
KIRKBURTON RES. . . . . Gregory Playing Fields, Kirkburton, Huddersfield HD8 0XH 07738 987582
LEPTON HIGHLANDERS. . . Lepton Highlanders S&S Club, Wakefield Road, Lepton, Huddersfield HD8 0LX 01484 608552
LONG LEE JUNIORS . . . . Marley Activities & Coaching Centre, Aireworth Road, Keighley BD21 4DB 01535 609910
MORLEY TOWN . . . . Glen Road, Morley, Leeds LS27 9HG 07709 727085
OVENDEN WEST RIDING RES.. . . . . Natty Lane, Illingworth, Halifax HX2 9DS 01422 244350
RAWDON OLD BOYS . . . . Hanson Field, Billing View, Rawdon, Leeds LS19 6PR 07748 828237
STEETON RES. . . . . Summer Hill Lane, Steeton BD20 6RX 01585 683387
STORTHES HALL RES. . . . . Police Sports Ground, Woodfield Park, Lockwood Scar, Huddersfield HD4 6BW 07957 691189
TINGLEY ATHLETIC RES. . . . . The Crescent, East Ardsley, Wakefield WF3 2EG 07950 131889
WEST HORTON . . . . Myra Shay, Bakerend Road, Bradford BD3 0AB 07974 176987
IN: Huddersfield YMCA (P), Lepton Highlanders (P - Huddersfield & District League Division One), Long Lee Juniors (P - Craven & District League Premier Division), Ovenden West Riding Res. (P)
OUT: AFC Emley Res. (P), Bay Athletic Res.(P), Dudley Hill Athletic (R - Sunday football), Westbrook YMCA (P)

Division Three	P	W	D	L	F	A	Pt
Huddersfield YMCA	20	16	2	2	85	19	50
Ovenden West Riding Res.	20	14	2	4	71	32	44
Albion Sports Res.	20	12	3	5	57	32	39
Ventus & Yeadon Celtic Res.	20	11	3	6	75	47	36
Lower Hopton Res.	20	9	4	7	42	36	31
Hall Green United Res.	20	9	3	8	52	54	30
Marsden Res.	20	5	6	9	47	53	21
Salts Res.	20	5	2	13	44	57	17
Bronte Wanderers Res.	20	5	2	13	35	79	17
Littletown Res.	20	4	3	13	28	68	15
Wakefield City Res.	20	3	4	13	28	87	13

DIVISION THREE CUP

FINAL

(May 7th at Ardsley Celtic)

Huddersfield YMCA 3 Ovenden West Riding Res, 0

WEST YORKSHIRE LEAGUE

full-time.thefa.com/ListPublicResult.do?league=7516712

Sponsored by:

No sponsor

Founded: 1928

Recent champions:

2005: Nostell Miners Welfare

2006: Leeds Met Carnegie

2007: Bardsey

2008:Carlton Athletic

2009: Knaresborough Town

Premier Division		P	W	D	L	F	A	Pts
Bardsey		30	21	6	3	90	47	69
Sherburn White Rose		30	18	4	8	58	41	58
Leeds City		30	16	8	6	70	51	56
Knaresborough Town		30	15	9	6	72	48	54
Beeston St Anthony's		30	15	5	10	65	53	50
Boroughbridge		30	14	6	10	57	43	48
Altofts		30	12	7	11	64	56	43
Field Sports & Social		30	12	5	13	53	53	41
Rothwell Athletic		30	11	6	13	41	55	39
Otley Town	*+3*	30	10	3	17	50	76	36
Pool		30	10	5	15	51	71	35
Whitkirk Wanderers		30	9	7	14	60	64	34
Ripon City	*-6*	30	9	10	11	52	53	31
Carlton Athletic		30	8	7	15	63	76	31
Aberford Albion		30	6	7	17	33	53	25
Ossett Common Rovers		30	4	5	21	36	75	17

	Aberford Albion	Altofts	Bardsey	Beeston St Anthony's	Boroughbridge	Carlton Athletic	Field Sports & Social	Knaresborough Town	Leeds City	Ossett Common Rovers	Otley Town	Pool	Ripon City	Rothwell Athletic	Sherburn White Rose	Whitkirk Wanderers
Aberford Albion	**P**	1-1	0-6	1-3	1-2	0-2	0-3	1-1	0-2	2-0	3-1	0-2	1-1	3-0	2-0	3-1
Altofts	1-1	**R**	2-5	1-2	1-0	2-3	6-0	3-1	1-5	3-0	4-1	1-1	2-2	1-1	2-2	3-3
Bardsey	3-2	3-1	**E**	2-2	3-2	3-1	4-1	3-3	2-2	8-1	4-1	4-3	3-2	1-1	0-0	5-1
Beeston St Anthony's	2-0	0-5	2-3	**M**	2-2	1-2	1-5	2-4	3-2	3-0	4-0	2-0	0-1	2-2	2-4	4-3
Boroughbridge	1-0	1-3	2-1	1-2	**I**	6-2	1-1	0-2	1-1	4-0	2-4	4-1	2-0	6-0	0-2	2-1
Carlton Athletic	0-0	2-1	1-3	2-5	1-2	**E**	4-1	3-3	2-3	3-0	1-2	0-2	3-3	6-1	3-3	2-2
Field Sports & Social	1-0	1-3	1-4	2-1	2-3	2-1	**R**	3-1	0-2	3-1	1-4	4-0	1-1	0-1	3-1	0-1
Knaresborough Town	6-1	6-3	1-3	3-4	2-0	3-2	0-2		1-3	1-1	2-0	2-2	4-1	2-1	1-0	3-2
Leeds City	2-0	0-3	2-2	1-0	2-2	1-5	3-3	1-1	**D**	4-0	3-0	5-4	2-1	2-1	1-4	2-3
Ossett Common Rovers	1-1	0-2	1-3	0-4	0-1	5-2	0-5	1-1	2-3	**I**	1-2	9-2	2-3	2-3	0-1	0-0
Otley Town	0-4	1-5	1-2	0-2	3-1	8-3	1-1	1-5	0-3	1-1	**V**	3-2	2-4	0-4	2-1	2-1
Pool	2-1	6-2	3-2	0-0	2-1	3-0	2-3	0-0	4-4	1-0	2-4	**I**	0-4	2-1	1-3	2-0
Ripon City	2-1	1-0	5-0	2-4	1-1	3-3	1-1	1-1	2-3	2-3	1-1	1-0	**S**	2-0	1-4	2-5
Rothwell Athletic	2-0	1-2	0-3	3-3	0-1	2-2	3-1	2-4	2-1	0-3	3-2	2-0	1-0	**I**	1-1	1-0
Sherburn White Rose	2-1	3-0	1-2	2-1	0-3	3-1	W-L	0-3	1-4	2-0	2-1	4-2	2-1	3-1	**O**	3-1
Whitkirk Wanderers	3-3	3-0	2-3	0-2	3-3	3-1	3-2	2-5	1-1	5-2	4-2	5-0	1-1	0-1	1-4	**N**

WEST YORKSHIRE LEAGUE PREMIER DIVISION CONSTITUTION 2010-11

ALTOFTS . . . . Altofts Sports Club, Lock Lane, Altofts, Normanton WF6 2QJ 01924 8927

BARDSEY . . . . The Sportsfield, Keswick Lane, Bardsey LS17 9AQ 01937 5742

BEESTON ST ANTHONY'S . . Beggars Hill, Sunnyview Gardens, Beeston Road, Beeston, Leeds LS11 8QU 0113 270 72

BOROUGHBRIDGE . . . . Aldborough Road, Boroughbridge, York YO51 9EA 01423 3242

CARLTON ATHLETIC . . . . Carlton Cricket Club, Town Street, Carlton, Wakefield WF3 3QU 0113 282 1

EAST END PARK WMC . . . . Skelton Road, Leeds LS9 9EP . . . . Nc

FIELD SPORTS & SOCIAL. . . . Field Sports Ground, Hollingwood Lane, Lidget Green, Bradford BD7 2RQ 01274 5467

KELLINGLEY WELFARE. . . Kellingley (Knottingley) SC, Marine Villa Road, Knottingley, Wakefield WF11 8ER 01977 6731

KNARESBOROUGH TOWN. . . . . Manse Lane, Knaresborough HG5 8LF 07773 6799

LEEDS CITY . . . . Adel WMA, Church Lane, Adel, Leeds LS16 8DE 0113 293 05

OTLEY TOWN . . . . Old Show Ground, Pool Road, Otley LS20 1DY 01943 451

POOL. . . . . Pool Sports & Social Club, Arthington Lane, Pool-in-Wharfedale, Otley LS21 1LG. 0113 284 39

RIPON CITY . . . . Mallorie Park Drive, Ripon HG4 2QD. 01765 6005

ROTHWELL ATHLETIC. . . . . Royds Lane, Rothwell, Leeds LS26 0BE . . . . Club HQ: 0113 282 07

SHERBURN WHITE ROSE. . . . . . Recreation Ground, Finkle Hill, Sherburn-in-Elmet, Leeds LS25 6EB . . . . Nc

WHITKIRK WANDERERS . . . . . . Whitkirk Sports & Social Club, Selby Road, Whitkirk, Leeds LS15 0AA 0113 264 66

IN: East End Park WMC (P), Kellingley Welfare (P)

OUT: Aberford Albion (R), Ossett Common Rovers (R)

Division One	P	W	D	L	F	A	Pts
Kellingley Welfare	28	20	5	3	70	28	65
East End Park WMC	28	20	2	6	84	37	62
Wetherby Athletic	28	17	3	8	77	48	54
Robin Hood Athletic	28	15	3	10	61	40	48
Horbury Town	28	13	4	11	57	56	43
Oxenhope Recreation	28	13	3	12	51	38	42
Baildon Trinity Ath.	28	13	2	13	44	41	41
Wyke Wanderers	28	12	2	14	46	72	38
Old Centralians	28	10	6	12	43	51	36
Hartshead	28	9	7	12	32	50	34
Kippax	28	10	3	15	47	57	33
Nostell MW Res.	28	10	3	15	44	54	33
Ilkley Town	28	9	5	14	48	49	32
Old Headingley	28	8	7	13	50	61	31
Howden Clough	28	2	3	23	34	106	9

LEAGUE CUP

FIRST ROUND
Bardsey 1 **Knaresborough Town** 3
Boston Spartans 2 South Milford 1
Great Preston 2 **Old Centralians** 7
Hunslet 2 **Wetherby** 5
Kellingley 5 Aberford 2
Leeds Gryphons 5 Carlton Athletic 1
Mount 1 **Sherburn WR** 3
Nostell Res. 0 **Field** 2
Ossett Common Rovers 3 East End Park 3 *aet* (4-2p)
Otley 1 **Horbury Town** 3
Pool 3 Swillington Saints 0
Rothwell Ath. 0 **Leeds C.** 1
Rothwell Town 2 **Howden Clough** 3
Whitkirk 7 Stanley United 1

SECOND ROUND
Altofts 8 Boston Spartans 2
Barwick 3 O. Headlingley 1
Boroughbridge 1 **Glasshoughton Res.** 3
Featherstone 2 **Ripon** 3
Hartshead 0 **Pool** 3
Horbury Town 0 **Beeston** 7
Howden Clough (w/o) v Tadcaster Magnet Sports
Ilkley 2 **Sherburn WR** 6
Knaresborough Town 1 **Kellingley Welfare** 2
Leeds City 2 Field 1
Leeds Gryphons 3 Robin Hood Athletic 2
Ossett Common Rovers 1 **Brighouse OB** 1 *aet* (3-4p)
Oxenhope Recreation 3 Baildon Trinity Athletic 2
Whitkirk 0 **Wetherby** 1
Woodhouse Hill WMC 4 Kippax 1 *aet*
Wyke Wanderers 2 Old Centralians 1

THIRD ROUND
Beeston St A. 4 Leeds Gryphons 4 *aet* (3-2p)
Brighouse OB 0 **Ripon** 3
Howden Clough 2 **Altofts** 6
Kellingley 6 Barwick 1
Oxenhope Recreation 1 **Wetherby Athletic** 3
Pool 3 Leeds City 1
Woodhouse Hill WMC 0 **Sherburn White Rose** 5
Wyke Wanderers 2 **Glasshoughton W. Res.** 5

QUARTER-FINALS
Altofts 1 **Sherburn WR** 2
Glasshoughton Welfare Res. 3 **Pool** 3 *aet* (4-5p)
Kellingley 1 **Ripon City** 2
Wetherby 2 **Beeston** 3

SEMI-FINALS
Beeston St Anthony's 3 Ripon City 1 *(at Nostell)*
Pool 1 **Sherburn White Rose** 4 *aet* (at Nostell)

FINAL
(May 6th at Wakefield)
Sherburn White Rose 1 Beeston St Anthony's 0

	Bai	Eas	Har	Hor	How	Ilk	Kell	Kip	Nos	OC	OH	Oxe	Rob	Wth	Wyk
Baildon Trinity Athletic		0-2	0-1	2-2	5-0	1-0	0-1	0-1	0-1	3-2	2-1	0-1	1-1	3-1	2-1
East End Park WMC	2-0	***D***	2-3	6-0	4-0	5-0	2-2	5-2	1-0	1-2	3-5	2-0	4-2	3-0	7-2
Hartshead	1-2	1-2	***I***	2-1	1-1	1-0	2-2	0-2	W-L	0-1	1-1	2-1	0-5	0-5	3-1
Horbury Town	3-1	4-2	3-0	***V***	5-0	2-1	2-3	0-6	3-2	2-2	1-1	3-2	4-0	0-2	3-1
Howden Clough	1-3	1-3	0-2	3-4	***I***	0-2	0-4	3-3	0-1	2-2	4-6	L-W	1-6	2-4	1-2
Ilkley Town	0-2	1-1	3-1	5-2	7-4	***S***	0-2	4-1	5-0	0-0	1-2	2-2	1-2	3-4	2-0
Kellingley Welfare	2-0	0-2	2-1	1-2	7-0	3-1	***I***	3-1	3-3	1-0	4-1	2-1	1-1	3-3	4-0
Kippax	1-3	1-2	1-1	2-1	2-0	2-0	1-3	***O***	1-2	1-4	1-0	2-0	0-5	1-4	7-1
Nostell Miners Welf. Res.	2-3	2-5	1-1	3-2	4-0	2-3	0-2	3-0	***N***	2-4	1-2	0-3	1-2	1-4	3-1
Old Centralians	2-1	0-6	3-2	1-1	1-3	2-0	0-2	3-0	2-3		2-2	2-1	1-4	0-2	1-2
Old Headingley	2-4	1-4	1-1	0-3	7-1	0-2	1-6	0-0	1-1	2-1		0-1	2-3	1-5	2-3
Oxenhope Recreation	3-0	3-2	2-0	2-0	9-1	2-1	2-3	2-1	0-1	1-1	2-2	***O***	1-0	0-2	8-1
Robin Hood Athletic	2-0	3-1	8-2	3-2	3-2	0-0	0-2	2-1	0-1	0-1	0-1	2-1	***N***	0-2	0-1
Wetherby Athletic	3-5	1-2	0-3	2-0	9-1	2-2	1-2	3-2	3-2	3-1	3-2	4-1	2-4	***E***	1-1
Wyke Wanderers	2-1	1-3	0-0	1-2	0-3	4-2	1-0	3-4	3-2	4-2	1-4	2-0	4-3	3-2	

WEST YORKSHIRE LEAGUE DIVISION ONE CONSTITUTION 2010-11

ABERFORD ALBION . . . . Bunkers Hill, Main Street (South), Aberford LS25 3DE . . . . None
BAILDON TRINITY ATHLETIC. . . . . The Dell, Cliffe Lane, West Baildon, Shipley BD17 5LB . . . . None
BRIGHOUSE OLD BOYS . . . . Lightcliffe & Hipperholme School, Stoney Lane, Lightcliffe, Halifax HX3 8TL 01422 201028
HARTSHEAD . . . . Littletown Recreation Ground, Hartshead 01274 873365
HORBURY TOWN . . . . Slazengers Sports Complex, Engine Lane, Horbury, Wakefield WF4 5NH 01924 274228
ILKLEY TOWN. . . . . Denton Road, Ilkley LS29 0AA . . . . None
KIPPAX . . . . Rear of Swillington MW, Wakefield Road, Swillington LS26 8DT . . . . None
MOUNT ST MARY'S . . . . David Young Academy, off North Parkway, Seacroft, Leeds LS14 6NU. . . . . None
NOSTELL MINERS WELFARE . Miners Welfare Ground, Middle Lane, New Crofton, Wakefield WF4 1LB. 01924 866010
OLD CENTRALIANS . . . . West Park Playing Fields, North Parade, West Park, Leeds LS16 5AY . . . . None
OSSETT COMMON ROVERS . . . . Illingworth Park, Manor Road, Ossett WF5 0LH. . . . . None
OXENHOPE RECREATION. . . . . Marley Playing Fields, Aireworth Road, Keighley BD21 4DB. 01535 609910
ROBIN HOOD ATHLETIC. . . . . Behind Coach & Horses, Rothwell Haigh, Leeds LS26 0SF. 0113 282 1021
SWILLINGTON SAINTS . . . . Welfare Sports Ground, Wakefield Road, Swillington, Leeds LS26 8DT . . . . None
WETHERBY ATHLETIC. . . . . . Wetherby Sports Association, The Ings, Boston Road, Wetherby LS22 5HA 01937 585699
WYKE WANDERERS . . The Albert Morton Memorial PF, New Popplewell Lane, Scholes, Cleckheaton BD19 6NN . . . . None
IN: Aberford Albion (R), Brighouse Old Boys (P), Mount St Mary's (P), Ossett Common Rovers (R), Swillington Saints (P)
OUT: East End Park WMC (P), Howden Clough (R), Kellingley Welfare (P), Old Headingley (R)

Division Two		P	W	D	L	F	A	Pts
Brighouse Old Boys		26	22	1	3	95	29	67
Leeds Gryphons		26	20	2	4	102	34	62
Mount St Mary's		26	19	4	3	69	32	61
Swillington Saints	*+3*	26	18	3	5	82	55	60
Glasshoughton Welf. Res.		26	14	3	9	58	40	45
Featherstone Colliery		26	14	2	10	62	52	44
Hunslet	*-6*	26	12	5	9	72	52	35
Stanley United		26	10	5	11	65	60	35
Barwick		26	9	1	16	50	76	28
Great Preston		26	7	0	19	36	82	21
Rothwell Town		26	5	5	16	48	68	20
Boston Spartans		26	6	2	18	46	77	20
Woodhouse Hill WMC		26	5	2	19	46	94	17
South Milford		26	2	3	21	45	125	9

LEAGUE TROPHY

FINAL *(May 4th at Nostell Miners Welfare)*

Knaresborough Town Res. 4 Wetherby Athletic Res. 1

Alliance One		P	W	D	L	F	A	Pt
Beeston St Anthony's Res.		30	25	1	4	101	29	76
Wetherby Athletic Res.		30	20	2	8	84	43	62
Robin Hood Athletic Res.		30	17	5	8	73	43	56
Bardsey Res.		30	16	4	10	64	57	52
Leeds City Res.		30	13	9	8	74	47	48
Whitkirk Wanderers Res.		30	13	4	13	60	60	43
Aberford Albion Res.		30	12	5	13	50	64	41
Knaresborough Town Res.		30	11	6	13	57	62	39
Sherburn White Rose Res.		30	10	8	12	61	66	38
Horbury Town Res.		30	11	4	15	53	73	37
Ripon City Res.		30	9	9	12	50	54	36
Boroughbridge Res.		30	10	6	14	46	56	36
Carlton Athletic Res.		30	11	3	16	53	76	36
Ossett Common Rovers Res.		30	9	4	17	47	69	31
Field Sports & Social Res.		30	7	4	19	35	57	25
Rothwell Athletic Res.		30	7	4	19	33	85	25

Alliance Two		P	W	D	L	F	A	Pt
Old Headingley Res.		26	22	1	3	94	27	67
Brighouse Old Boys Res.		26	18	5	3	80	41	59
East End Park WMC Res.		26	16	4	6	86	46	52
Kippax Res.		26	13	9	4	63	46	48
Stanley United Res.		26	12	4	10	54	57	40
Baildon Trinity Athletic Res.		26	11	6	9	62	49	39
Altofts Res.	*-4*	26	13	2	11	67	45	37
Rothwell Town Res.		26	11	4	11	60	54	37
Ilkley Town Res.		26	10	3	13	63	61	33
Howden Clough Res.		26	9	1	16	60	90	28
Hartshead Res.		26	6	5	15	50	82	23
Boston Spartans Res.		26	6	4	16	57	88	22
Otley Town Res.		26	6	4	16	37	74	22
Woodhouse Hill WMC Res.		26	2	2	22	32	105	8

	Barwick	Boston Spa.	Brigh'se OB	Featherstone	G'houghton	Gt Preston	Hunslet	Leeds Gryph.	Mount SM	Rothwell T.	South Milford	Stanley Utd	Swillington	Woodhse Hill
Barwick		1-4	0-2	5-3	0-1	3-1	3-1	2-5	0-3	5-1	1-2	2-0	3-5	5-4
Boston Spartans	3-1	**D**	0-3	0-2	0-3	2-4	2-6	3-9	4-0	0-3	3-3	2-5	0-2	6-0
Brighouse Old Boys	7-0	5-2	**I**	2-1	5-2	7-1	4-1	2-1	2-3	2-1	6-0	3-2	5-1	10-0
Featherstone Colliery	2-1	6-0	1-2	**V**	1-1	5-1	2-6	1-1	3-2	4-3	2-0	3-0	0-2	3-2
Glasshoughton Welf. Res.	4-0	4-0	0-3	2-0	**I**	1-0	4-0	1-4	1-2	1-0	6-1	3-1	0-3	4-1
Great Preston	0-2	1-4	2-4	1-4	1-5	**S**	1-3	0-7	1-3	3-2	4-2	4-9	1-2	2-1
Hunslet	7-0	2-1	0-3	2-1	4-2	0-1	**I**	1-1	0-2	2-2	7-2	2-2	3-1	3-0
Leeds Gryphons	6-0	4-1	2-1	8-1	3-0	2-1	4-3	**O**	1-2	6-1	5-0	6-1	1-3	3-2
Mount St Mary's	3-2	2-0	2-1	4-0	2-2	1-0	3-3	2-4	**N**	3-1	4-1	1-0	2-0	3-1
Rothwell Town	1-1	1-0	1-1	1-2	1-3	2-0	1-8	0-4	3-3		2-3	1-1	1-3	1-2
South Milford	1-6	1-5	1-3	1-7	1-5	2-3	2-3	0-4	0-8	3-11	**T**	4-7	3-6	5-5
Stanley United	3-1	4-0	2-4	2-5	1-0	4-0	2-2	0-1	0-2	3-1	4-4	**W**	4-1	3-1
Swillington Saints	6-4	3-3	3-6	3-2	2-2	5-1	4-3	4-2	1-1	1-0	5-1	4-2	**O**	5-3
Woodhouse Hill WMC	1-2	2-1	0-2	0-1	4-1	0-2	2-0	2-8	1-6	4-6	3-2	3-3	2-7	

WEST YORKSHIRE LEAGUE DIVISION TWO CONSTITUTION 2010-11

BARWICK . . . . Back of Village Hall, Chapel Lane, Barwick-in-Elmet, Leeds LS15 4HL . . . . Club HQ: 0113 281 3065

FEATHERSTONE COLLIERY . Featherstone MW, Cresseys Corner, Green Lane, Featherstone WF7 6EH . . . . None

GARFORTH RANGERS . . . . Great North Road, Micklefield, Leeds LS25 4AF . . . . None

GLASSHOUGHTON WELFARE RES. . . . . Leeds Road, Glasshoughton, Castleford WF10 4PF 01977 511234

GREAT PRESTON . . . . Berry Lane, Great Preston LS25 8AX . . . . None

HOWDEN CLOUGH . . . . Batley Sports Centre, Windmill Lane, Batley WF17 0QD 01924 326181

HUNSLET . . . . Community Sports Club, Anchor Street, Hunslet Green, Leeds LS10 2AT 0113 270 6851

OLD HEADINGLEY . . . . Collingham & Linton SA, Harewood Road, Collingham, Wetherby LS22 5BL . . . . None

ROTHWELL JUNIORS . . . . Fleet Lane, Rothwell, Leeds LS26 8NX . . . . None

ROTHWELL TOWN . . . . off Fifth Avenue, Leeds Road, Rothwell, Leeds LS26 0HG . . . . None

SOUTH MILFORD . . . . The Maltings, Common Lane, South Milford, Leeds LS25 5BU . . . . None

STANLEY UNITED . . . . Welfare Sports Ground, Saville Road, Methley, Leeds LS26 0DT . . . . None

UK RICHMOND . . . . South Leeds Stadium, Middleton Grove, Leeds LS11 5DJ 0113 271 1675

WOODHOUSE HILL WMC. . . . . Woodlands School Playing Field, Wakefield Road, Normanton WF6 1BB 01924 893462

IN: Garforth Rangers (P - Wakefield & District League Division Two), Howden Clough (R), Old Headingley (R), Rothwell Juniors (youth football), UK Richmond (N)

OUT: Brighouse Old Boys (P), Mount St Mary's (P), Swillington Saints (P), Tadcaster Magnet Sports (WN)

WESTMORLAND LEAGUE

www.westmorlandfootball.co.uk

Sponsored by: Bluefin

Founded: 1919

Recent champions:
2005: Wetheriggs United
2006: Wetheriggs United
2007: Kendal County
2008: Ambleside United
2009: Ambleside United

	Amb	App	Burn	Carv	Con	KCel	KCo	Kes	Kirk	Lune	Pen	Sed	Shap	Weth
Ambleside United		4-1	7-0	6-1	6-1	5-2	0-3	2-3	3-2	6-3	2-0	1-0	2-1	2-0
Appleby	0-2	***D***	0-1	4-1	3-0	2-1	1-2	0-1	1-1	3-2	1-2	2-5	1-6	3-2
Burneside	0-0	3-1	***I***	0-1	2-0	3-2	0-3	2-2	1-2	2-0	2-1	2-1	2-3	1-1
Carvetii United	1-2	1-0	4-0	***V***	6-0	4-1	4-2	3-3	4-3	6-0	4-1	3-3	6-1	1-2
Coniston	3-3	1-9	0-3	4-6	***I***	3-3	0-4	0-6	0-3	3-0	0-2	0-8	2-3	0-6
Kendal Celtic	1-2	4-0	1-2	1-6	1-0	***S***	0-4	0-7	1-4	3-2	1-2	2-3	3-7	3-2
Kendal County	2-3	6-1	1-1	1-2	3-0	5-1	***I***	3-5	1-0	3-0	2-1	2-3	1-1	4-0
Keswick	3-1	3-2	4-0	5-1	2-1	2-1	0-2	***O***	1-2	4-2	4-0	2-0	2-1	3-0
Kirkoswald	3-4	5-0	1-2	4-2	8-2	1-0	3-2	2-2	***N***	7-0	2-3	2-4	4-2	3-3
Lunesdale United	0-1	2-5	1-4	0-5	3-3	1-1	0-4	1-3	1-4		3-2	0-4	1-8	0-4
Penrith Rangers	0-4	0-2	3-3	2-2	9-0	1-1	2-0	3-2	1-0	2-1	***O***	1-2	1-3	0-1
Sedbergh Wanderers	2-3	8-2	3-0	4-1	4-3	6-1	0-2	2-3	0-1	7-1	7-1	***N***	0-1	1-2
Shap	2-3	0-0	3-1	3-1	5-2	4-3	1-2	3-2	0-4	2-1	0-1	3-4	***E***	5-4
Wetheriggs United	2-2	3-0	2-3	1-2	6-1	3-3	2-1	2-3	0-3	2-0	0-1	1-3	2-3	

Division One	P	W	D	L	F	A	Pts
Ambleside United	26	20	3	3	76	36	63
Keswick	26	19	3	4	77	36	60
Kendal County	26	16	2	8	65	31	50
Sedbergh Wanderers	26	16	1	9	84	42	49
Kirkoswald	26	15	3	8	74	40	48
Carvetii United	26	15	3	8	78	53	48
Shap	26	15	2	9	71	55	47
Burneside	26	12	5	9	40	47	41
Penrith Rangers	26	11	3	12	42	49	36
Wetheriggs United	26	9	4	13	53	51	31
Appleby	26	8	2	16	44	66	26
Kendal Celtic	26	4	4	18	41	81	16
Coniston	26	1	3	22	29	114	6
Lunesdale United	26	1	2	23	25	98	5

HIGH SHERIFF'S CUP

FIRST ROUND
Ambleside United 4 Appleby 1
Carvetii United 6 Sedbergh Wanderers 0
Kendal Celtic 1 **Keswick** 6
Kendal County 7 Coniston 1
Penrith Rangers 1 Lunesdale United 0
Wetheriggs United 4 Shap 1

QUARTER-FINALS
Burneside 2 Kirkoswald 1
Kendal County 4 Keswick 0
Penrith Rangers 3 Carvetii United 0
Wetheriggs United 3 **Ambleside United** 3 *aet* (8-9p)

SEMI-FINALS
Ambleside United 3 Burneside 2 *(at Kendal Town)*
Penrith Rangers 2 Kendal County 0 *(at Shap)*

FINAL
(April 27th at Kendal Town)
Penrith Rangers 1 Ambleside United 0

WESTMORLAND LEAGUE DIVISION ONE CONSTITUTION 2010-11

APPLEBY . . . . The Board Close, Chapel Street, Bolton, Appleby-in-Westmorland CA16 6QR . . . . None
BURNESIDE . . . . Cricket Pavilion, Hollins Lane, Burneside, Kendal LA9 6QL . . . . None
CARVETII UNITED . . . . Coltsford Common, Brough, Kirkby Stephen CA17 4EW . . . . None
ENDMOOR KGR . . . . Woodside Road, Endmoor, Kendal LA8 0HE . . . . None
KENDAL CELTIC . . . . Jubilee Playing Fields, Mintsfeet Road, Kendal LA9 6LU . . . . None
KESWICK . . . . Fitz Park, Keswick CA12 4NF. . . . . None
KIRKOSWALD . . . . The Old Show Field, Kirkoswald CA10 1DL . . . . None
PENRITH RANGERS . . . . Frenchfield, Brougham, Penrith CA10 2AA . . . . None
SEDBERGH WANDERERS . . . . Hogwill Lanr Playing Field, Sedbergh LA10 5HD . . . . None
SHAP . . . . Memorial Playing Field, Shap CA10 3PW . . . . None
STAVELEY UNITED . . . . Ayland Recreation Ground, Staveley LA8 9LN . . . . None
WETHERIGGS UNITED . . . . Gilwilly Recreation Ground, Castletown, Penrith CA11 9BL . . . . None

IN: Endmoor KGR (P), Staveley United (P)
OUT: Ambleside United (P - West Lancs League Division Two), Coniston (R), Kendal County (P - West Lancs League Division Two), Lunesdale United (R)

Division Two	P	W	D	L	F	A	Pts
Staveley United	22	16	3	3	62	17	51
Endmoor KGR	22	15	4	3	67	19	49
Ibis	22	15	3	4	72	30	48
Kendal Co. Res.	22	14	2	6	52	40	44
Kendal United	22	11	5	6	59	29	38
Shap Res.	22	10	3	9	49	54	33
Wetheriggs Res.	22	9	4	9	41	44	31
Keswick Res.	22	9	2	11	47	43	29
Windermere SC	22	7	4	11	47	61	25
Appleby Res.	22	4	2	16	31	67	14
Greystoke	22	4	1	17	44	79	13
Dent *-3*	22	1	1	20	17	105	1

MASON & FREEMAN CUP
Final *(May 12th at Burneside)*
Endmoor KGR 2 Kendal County Res. 0

Division Three	P	W	D	L	F	A	Pts
Alston Moor SC	22	18	1	3	58	19	55
Penrith Rgrs Res.	22	17	1	4	56	30	52
Langwathby Utd	22	15	3	4	83	31	48
Ambleside Res.	22	13	1	8	63	54	40
Kirkby Thore Rgrs	22	12	2	8	57	43	38
Wetheriggs Utd A	22	11	2	9	57	47	35
Burneside Res.	22	7	5	10	49	51	26
Ullswater United	22	6	4	12	39	59	22
Milnthorpe C. A	22	6	2	14	47	82	20
Sedbergh Res.	22	5	4	13	49	59	19
Carvetii Utd Res.	22	5	1	16	49	77	16
Windermere Res.	22	3	2	17	25	80	11

PETER DAWSON MEMORIAL SHIELD
Final *(May 5th at Shap)*
Alston Moor 2 Burneside Res. 2 *aet* (5-4p)

Division Four	P	W	D	L	F	A	Pts
Kendal Celtic Res.	20	16	3	1	82	27	51
Langwathby Res.	20	16	1	3	84	21	49
Staveley Utd Res.	20	11	5	4	70	35	38
Burneside A	20	10	4	6	54	36	34
Esthwaite Vale	20	9	5	6	45	43	32
Ibis Res.	20	9	2	9	47	47	29
E'moor KGR Res.	20	6	5	9	39	62	23
Braithwaite	20	6	2	12	39	41	20
Lunesdale Res.	20	5	1	14	26	67	16
Penrith Saints	20	3	4	13	26	54	13
Coniston Res.	20	2	2	16	14	93	8

Windermere SC A - record expunged

AUSTIN WREN CUP
Final *(May 6th at Carvetii United)*
Langwathby Res. 3 Kendal Celtic Res. 2 *aet*

OTHER LEAGUES 2009-10

ACCRINGTON COMBINATION
(Bracewells Transport /Ashton Hoy)

Premier Division	P	W	D	L	F	A	Pt
Edenfield	18	16	2	0	73	16	50
Bridge Inn	18	16	0	2	78	26	48
Church Town -3	18	11	3	4	46	21	33
Crown Rovers -3	18	9	1	8	36	36	25
Park -6	18	9	3	6	40	22	24
Ramsbottom T.	18	6	3	9	23	31	21
Oswaldtwistle A -3	18	7	2	9	36	37	20
Wellington FC -3	18	3	5	10	23	49	11
Whinney Hill A	18	1	1	16	18	66	4
Acc'ton Abbey -3	18	1	2	15	25	94	2

Division One	P	W	D	L	F	A	Pts
Church Kirk	18	15	2	1	69	21	47
Hapton	18	14	3	1	96	29	45
Rose & Crown FC	18	10	4	4	66	43	34
St Mary's Coll. OB	18	9	4	5	39	37	31
Accrington Town	18	10	0	8	55	42	30
Black Horse FC	18	7	3	8	46	48	24
Church T. Res. -3	18	7	3	8	60	49	21
Burn. Rd Bowling	18	5	1	12	37	61	16
Globe Bullough Pk	18	1	1	16	34	84	4
Sydney St WMC -3	18	1	1	16	18	106	1

ALDERSHOT & DISTRICT LEAGUE

Premier Division	P	W	D	L	F	A	Pts
Fleet Spurs Res.	16	11	1	4	33	21	34
Bagshot	16	9	3	4	45	21	30
Hale Rovers	16	9	1	6	49	37	28
Frimley	16	8	0	8	37	35	24
Farnboro. NE Res.	16	7	0	9	42	49	21
Frimley Select	16	6	2	8	25	30	20
Sth Farnborough	16	6	1	9	37	42	19
Sandhurst Sports	16	6	1	9	29	47	19
Hindhead Ath. -3	16	5	1	10	22	37	13

Division One	P	W	D	L	F	A	Pts
W. Meon/Warnfd	18	13	1	4	50	19	40
Aldershot Spartans	18	12	0	6	69	44	36
Watchetts	18	11	3	4	42	26	36
Eversley A	18	10	2	6	46	38	32
Wey Valley	18	7	4	7	42	48	25
Letef Select	18	7	2	9	33	38	23
Fleet Spurs A	18	5	4	9	30	40	19
Hartley Wintney A	18	6	0	12	29	49	18
AFC Froyle	18	4	4	10	31	50	16
Headley Utd Res.	18	4	2	12	19	39	14

Division Two	P	W	D	L	F	A	Pts
Old Farnboronians	20	19	0	1	85	12	57
Gentleman Jim	20	13	3	4	56	24	42
Shalford B	20	11	2	7	45	48	35
Bagshot Res.	20	11	1	8	45	31	34
Alton United	20	9	3	8	44	49	30
Courtmoor	20	7	4	9	37	50	25
Four Marks Res.	20	5	6	9	41	63	21
Hindhead Res. -3	20	7	2	11	34	54	20
Lindford -3	20	6	4	10	51	52	19
Farnham Utd -3	20	5	5	10	44	63	17
Real Tek	20	1	2	17	17	53	5

Division Three	P	W	D	L	F	A	Pts
Frogmore Rgrs	20	15	2	3	66	37	47
West End Village	20	14	3	3	59	36	45
Yateley A	20	11	3	6	56	41	36
Normandy	20	10	5	5	55	38	35
Fleet Spurs Vets	20	10	4	6	58	39	34
Duke of York	20	10	2	8	45	29	32
BOSC United	20	7	3	10	52	50	24
Wrecclesham A	20	7	2	11	56	61	23
Inter Mytchett Crus	20	6	2	12	43	33	20
Lindford Res.	20	5	0	15	26	84	15
Shalford C	20	2	0	18	29	97	6

ALTRINCHAM & DISTRICT LEAGUE

Division One	P	W	D	L	F	A	Pts
AFC Quarry	22	18	2	2	80	29	56
O. Alt'chamians A	22	16	2	4	58	32	50
Atlantic	22	12	3	7	59	42	39
Knutsford Res.	22	11	2	9	64	39	35
Cringlewood	22	10	5	7	58	41	35
Sale Amatuers	22	9	7	6	56	32	34
Salford	22	11	1	10	59	44	34
Sale Rovers	22	9	7	6	34	26	34
Kartel Sports	22	5	4	13	37	57	19
Old York	22	4	6	12	31	65	18
Heaton Moor Pho.	22	5	3	14	39	74	18
Styal A	22	1	0	21	23	117	3

Division Two	P	W	D	L	F	A	Pts
Wilmslow Sports	20	17	2	1	94	23	53
Irlam A	20	16	1	3	105	30	49
Trafford United	20	12	2	6	70	38	38
AFC Partington	20	12	0	8	84	41	36
Egerton	20	11	1	8	78	54	34
Lounge About	20	9	2	9	73	52	29
Wythenshaw T. A	20	9	2	9	52	57	29
Northenden Vics	20	9	1	10	52	65	28
Unicorn Athletic	20	4	2	14	39	95	14
Timperley Wdrs	20	3	3	14	40	69	12
Conway Rangers	20	0	0	20	26	189	0

Brooklands - record expunged

ANDOVER & DISTRICT LEAGUE

	P	W	D	L	F	A	Pts
Ludgershall Spts	24	20	1	3	137	22	61
AFC Andover	24	18	5	1	112	33	59
Danebury Sports	24	18	1	5	124	40	55
Vernham Labels	24	17	1	6	120	52	52
Downton Sports	24	15	2	7	91	48	47
ABC United	24	12	3	9	102	47	39
Inkpen Sports	24	12	2	10	101	66	38
Whitchurch Utd A	24	12	1	11	73	61	37
King's Somborne	24	8	0	16	43	69	24
Test Valley Lions	24	6	1	17	61	91	19
AFC Star	24	5	1	18	75	119	16
AFC Danebury	24	4	0	20	39	148	12
TVL Geriatrics	24	0	0	24	21	303	0

ASHFORD & DISTRICT LEAGUE

Premier Division	P	W	D	L	F	A	Pts
AFC Ocean	12	10	0	2	47	9	30
Rolvenden	12	10	0	2	45	20	30
New Romsey A	12	8	0	4	30	20	24
Bethersden	12	5	0	7	31	33	15
Willesborough CC	12	4	0	8	26	32	12
Wittersham	11	3	0	8	20	45	9
Lydd Town A	11	1	0	10	16	56	3

Division One	P	W	D	L	F	A	Pts
Ashford Inter	14	13	0	1	47	14	39
Riverside Inn	14	10	0	4	52	21	30
Woodchurch	14	9	1	4	39	22	28
AFC Ocean Res.	14	8	1	5	34	20	25
Lydd United	14	6	2	6	25	28	20
Ruckinge United	14	4	1	9	22	41	13
Tenterden T. Res.	14	3	1	10	33	50	10
Ship Inn	14	0	0	14	15	71	0

AYLESBURY & DISTRICT LEAGUE

Premier Division	P	W	D	L	F	A	Pts
Bucks CC	22	19	1	2	98	31	58
Bierton	22	14	2	6	81	48	44
Aston Park	22	14	2	6	71	39	44
Elmhurst	22	13	4	5	86	53	43
Aylesb'y Dynamos	22	11	4	7	55	34	37
Walton Ct Wdrs	22	10	3	9	69	64	33
Hale Leys United	22	8	4	10	49	58	28
Downley Albion	22	8	4	10	45	58	28
Berkhamsted Spts	22	7	4	11	54	60	25
St Johns	22	7	2	13	56	66	23
Aston Clinton Res.	22	2	6	14	25	66	12
Wingrave	22	0	2	20	21	133	2

Division One	P	W	D	L	F	A	Pts
P & IC United	24	23	1	0	105	17	70
Bucks CC Res.	24	15	4	5	70	44	49
Thame Town	24	15	2	7	63	40	47
Wendover	24	13	2	9	61	38	41
Bedgrove Dyns	24	12	2	10	61	45	38
Quarrendon Ryls	24	9	6	9	49	51	33
Britannia	24	10	2	12	71	69	32
Bedgrove United	24	10	2	12	46	44	32
Bierton Res.	24	7	5	12	46	47	26
Lane End	24	8	2	14	47	59	26
Long Marston	24	8	1	15	40	73	25
Haydon United	24	7	3	14	42	61	24
Mandeville	24	3	0	21	26	139	9

Division Two	P	W	D	L	F	A	Pts
P & IC Utd Res.	28	20	6	2	93	35	66
Haddenham Utd	28	18	5	5	64	47	59
Fairford Leys	28	15	9	4	75	36	54
FC Spandits	28	17	2	9	108	80	53
Long Marston Res.	28	16	4	8	66	45	52
Great Milton	28	14	4	10	92	66	46
Quainton	28	11	11	6	64	45	44
St Johns Res.	28	11	6	11	62	63	39
Rose & Crown	28	9	7	12	53	57	34
Lane End Res.	28	8	7	13	56	80	31
Wendover Res.	28	9	2	17	47	73	29
Aston Clinton A	28	6	6	16	35	65	24
Brill United	28	6	4	18	40	90	22
Bedgrove Utd Res.	28	4	7	17	30	57	19
Wingrave Res.	28	4	4	20	50	96	16

Division Three	P	W	D	L	F	A	Pts
Keltic Colts	28	23	0	5	124	34	69
Bedgrove D. Res.	28	22	2	4	132	41	68
Ludgershall	28	20	3	5	102	47	63
Downley Alb. Res.	28	17	4	7	86	67	55
Oving	28	15	4	9	66	59	49
Stone Magnets	28	15	3	10	80	64	48
Great Milton Res.	27	13	1	13	79	69	40
Aylesbury Wolves	27	12	1	14	86	88	37
Quarrendon Res.	28	10	5	13	72	85	35
Aylesbury Pk Rgrs	28	10	4	14	61	96	34
Haddenham Res.	28	8	4	16	80	100	28
Sparta Royals	28	7	3	18	47	110	24
Excel Dents	28	7	2	19	40	51	23
Fairford Leys Res.	28	5	2	21	38	113	17
AC Meadowcroft	28	4	4	20	43	112	16

BANBURY & LORD JERSEY FA

Premier Division	P	W	D	L	F	A	Pts
Bishops Itchington	18	14	4	0	63	27	46
ABK Sports	18	11	2	5	48	34	35
Wroxton Sports	18	10	2	6	67	44	32
Bodicote Sports	18	9	4	5	60	30	31
Cropredy	18	7	4	7	41	48	25
KEA -3	18	9	1	8	43	55	25
Fenny Compton	18	5	3	10	38	49	18
Hornton	18	5	1	12	36	64	16
Steeple Aston	18	4	2	12	33	44	14
The Bell Sports	18	4	1	13	45	79	13

Arncott - record expunged

Division One	P	W	D	L	F	A	Pts
Highfield Old Boys	18	15	1	2	101	26	46
Deddington Town	18	15	1	2	77	32	46
Woodford United A	18	10	4	4	51	26	34
Bardwell	18	10	0	8	43	43	30
Kings Sutton	18	8	1	9	42	65	25
B. Itchington Res.	18	7	2	9	31	62	23
Drayton Village	18	4	4	10	39	57	16
Glory Farm	18	5	1	12	43	62	16
Heyford United	18	3	4	11	39	48	13
Heyford Athletic A	18	2	4	12	26	71	10

Beckley Sports - record expunged

Division Two	P	W	D	L	F	A	Pts
FC Naranja	20	18	1	1	79	17	55
The Swan FC	20	15	2	3	89	30	47
Bloxham	20	14	2	4	54	31	44
Abba Athletic	20	9	1	10	53	55	28
Mid. Cheney Res.	20	9	0	11	56	51	27
Deddington Res.	20	7	6	7	36	44	27
Cropredy Res.	20	8	2	10	41	41	26
Priors United	20	6	2	12	43	64	20
Heyford Utd Res.	20	5	3	12	41	74	18
Croughton OB	20	4	4	12	29	45	16
Souldern	20	3	1	16	24	93	10

Division Three	P	W	D	L	F	A	Pts
ABK Sports Res.	20	13	4	3	69	23	43
Heyford Ath. B +3	20	10	5	5	66	35	38
Kings Sutton Res.	20	12	2	6	52	52	38
Bodicote S. Res.	20	11	3	6	37	35	36
Stple Aston Res.	20	9	4	7	44	29	31
Wroxton Spts Res.	20	7	4	9	50	56	25
Finmere	20	7	4	9	52	59	25
F. Compton Res.	20	6	6	8	45	61	24
The Bell Spts Res.	20	8	0	12	42	65	24
KEA Res. -4	20	7	3	10	46	51	20
Banbury Galaxy	20	1	3	16	25	62	6

Glory Farm Res. - record expunged

BATH & DISTRICT LEAGUE
(Roper Rhodes Bathrooms)

Division One	P	W	D	L	F	A	Pts
University of Bath	16	11	2	3	60	34	35
Chew Valley Snrs	16	11	1	4	48	18	34
Trowbridge House	16	10	2	4	50	33	32
Saltford Res.	16	8	1	7	40	31	25
Odd Down A	16	8	1	7	41	38	25
Great Western	16	6	5	5	47	39	23
Frys Club Old B.	16	5	2	9	23	41	17
Civil Serv. Larkhall	16	3	1	12	28	68	10
Weston Rovers	16	1	3	12	19	54	6

Oldfield Sports - record expunged

BECKETT LEAGUE
(RJF Homes)

Premier Division	P	W	D	L	F	A	Pt
Union Rovers	22	14	3	5	51	22	45
Gillamoor	22	13	4	5	68	37	43
K'moorside Res. -6	22	15	2	5	48	27	41
Aislaby United	22	11	4	7	34	35	37
Kirkdale United	22	9	5	8	47	35	32
Thornton Dale	22	9	3	10	42	40	30
Sinnington	22	9	3	10	47	46	30
Slingsby	22	9	2	11	54	59	29
Bagby & Balk	22	8	3	11	49	70	27
Old Malton A	22	8	2	12	42	60	26
Rosedale	22	5	3	14	25	46	18
Heslerton Res.	22	4	2	16	25	55	14

Division One	P	W	D	L	F	A	Pts
Pro Pak	22	17	3	23	71	25	54
Bay Horse	22	17	0	5	66	36	51
Norton United FC	22	13	3	6	56	30	42
Duncombe Park	22	12	4	6	68	43	40
Thornt'n-le-D. Res.	22	9	3	10	42	39	30
Ryedale SC Res.	22	9	3	10	42	49	30
Huntington -3	22	10	2	10	60	66	29
Gillamoor Res.	22	8	3	11	45	49	27
Amotherby/S. Res.	22	8	3	11	47	61	27
Union Rov. Res.	22	4	6	12	26	60	18
Rillington A. Res.	22	3	5	14	23	60	14
Ampleforth	22	3	3	16	36	67	12

BIRMINGHAM AFA

Premier Division	P	W	D	L	F	A	Pts
Sutton United	24	18	3	3	51	16	57
Village	24	15	4	5	56	24	49
Shirley Athletic	24	14	4	6	64	41	46
Wake Green Ams	24	13	3	8	47	37	42
Aston	24	12	5	7	56	38	41
Boldmere Spts/S.	24	13	2	9	61	54	41
Old Wulfrunians	24	9	6	9	46	42	33
Handsworth GSOB	24	10	1	13	51	44	31
Walsall Phoenix	24	7	5	12	41	61	26
AFC Somers	24	6	6	12	40	61	24
Silhill	24	7	2	15	41	60	23
Flamengo	24	1	12	11	30	49	15
Cresconians	24	4	1	19	28	85	13

Division One	P	W	D	L	F	A	Pts
Inter Vaughans	20	17	1	2	69	16	52
St Francis	20	16	1	3	62	21	49
Harborne Town	20	9	3	8	40	37	30
Athletic Sparkhill	20	8	3	9	41	38	27
Village Res.	20	7	6	7	37	38	27
Sutton Utd Res.	20	7	5	8	47	57	26
H'wth GSOB Res.	20	5	7	8	32	44	22
CPA Holy Name	20	6	3	11	36	71	21
Ajax CV JKS	20	6	4	10	47	40	19
Wake Green Res.	20	5	4	11	28	45	19
Resolution	20	3	5	12	29	61	14

Kynoch - record expunged

Division Two	P	W	D	L	F	A	Pts
St Georges Warriors	22	18	1	3	69	21	55
Crusaders	22	14	2	6	82	41	44
Balsalorna	22	14	1	7	66	35	43
O. W'frunians Res.	22	13	4	5	62	31	43
Parkfield Amateurs	22	12	1	9	53	39	37
Bustleholme Ath.	22	11	1	10	53	50	34
West Hagley	22	9	5	8	49	49	32
Desi -3	22	6	7	9	38	51	22
Silhill Res.	22	7	1	14	38	68	22
Sutton United A	22	5	3	14	40	65	18
Great Barr	22	5	3	14	28	59	18
Village A	22	2	3	17	26	95	9

Old Nortonians, Resolution Res. - records expunged

Division Three	P	W	D	L	F	A	Pts
St Pauls	24	17	6	1	81	34	57
Shere Punjab	24	16	5	3	65	28	53
Shirley Ath. Res.	24	13	5	6	86	47	44
Billesley United	24	12	3	9	64	59	39
Erdington Albion	24	11	5	8	59	45	38
AFC Hayes Harr.	24	10	7	7	56	43	37
Britannia Old Boys	24	11	2	11	52	56	35
CPA H. Name Res.	24	9	7	8	43	54	34
Malremo Rangers	24	8	5	11	44	45	29
Walsall Pho. Res.	24	6	7	11	46	58	25
Wake Green A. A	24	6	2	16	41	81	20
Silhill A	24	5	1	18	52	89	16
Cresconians Res.	24	2	5	17	38	88	11

Acocks Green - record expunged

BISHOP'S STORTFORD, STANSTED & DISTRICT LEAGUE

Premier Division	P	W	D	L	F	A	Pts
North Weald	16	11	3	2	39	22	25
Heath Rovers	16	10	3	3	29	22	23
Alemite Athletic	16	9	2	5	44	42	20
Loughton	16	7	3	6	38	36	17
Sheering	16	7	1	8	40	34	15
Potter Street	16	6	2	8	36	26	14
Hatfield Heath	16	4	3	9	34	53	11
Old Street	16	4	2	10	35	45	10
Salv. Army Harlow	16	4	1	11	32	47	9

Division One	P	W	D	L	F	A	Pts
Birchanger	18	12	3	3	31	16	27
Alemite Ath. Res.	18	12	1	5	56	24	25
Avondale Rangers	18	8	3	7	33	21	19
Sheering Res.	18	7	3	8	21	32	17
North Weald Res.	18	6	4	8	23	30	16
Thorley Park	18	6	3	9	21	29	15
Hatfield Hth Res.	18	2	3	13	17	50	7

Pelly Green - record expunged

Division Two	P	W	D	L	F	A	Pts
Albury	21	15	3	3	66	27	33
Hertfordshire Rgrs	21	13	2	6	69	27	28
Heath Rov. Res.	21	12	4	5	45	29	28
Dunmow Rhodes	21	12	3	6	64	37	27
Frontiers	21	9	5	7	63	40	23
Potter Street Res.	21	5	2	14	35	100	12
Thaxted Rgrs Res.	21	4	3	14	31	73	11
Lower Street	21	1	4	16	24	64	6

BLACKBURN & DISTRICT COMBINATION

Premier Division	P	W	D	L	F	A	Pts
The Ivy Hotel	18	13	1	4	71	22	40
Blackburn United	18	13	1	4	48	18	40
Prince of Wales	18	13	3	2	61	32	39
Bank Top Rovers	18	12	2	4	62	32	38
Knuzden	18	9	3	6	36	26	30
Witton Albion FC	18	9	2	7	48	46	29
Rishton United	18	5	4	9	29	45	19
Alexandra Hotel	18	3	0	15	28	90	12
Feildens Arms	18	3	1	14	23	56	10
Islington	18	1	1	16	33	72	4

Division Two	P	W	D	L	F	A	Pts
Blue Star	18	11	3	4	59	36	36
Blackburn Olympic	18	10	4	4	71	33	34
Belthorn Dog Inn	18	10	3	5	56	44	33
Mill Hill Res.	18	9	4	5	51	34	31
George Hotel	18	7	7	4	42	39	27
Blackburn Utd Res.	18	7	5	6	31	38	26
Max Local	18	7	3	8	46	57	24
Rishton Utd Res.	18	6	4	8	37	46	22
Feniscowles/P. Res.	18	2	4	12	35	62	12
Worth Avenue	18	1	3	14	19	58	6

Division Three	P	W	D	L	F	A	Pts
Aqueduct +2	24	17	4	3	76	30	57
Fallons Ales	24	14	6	4	66	41	48
Rishton United A	24	13	3	8	71	49	42
Navigation	24	9	5	10	48	45	32
Knowles Arms -3	24	10	5	9	51	52	32
Whalley Range C	24	6	8	10	57	63	26
Witton Inn -1	24	7	6	11	57	66	26
Hole I'Th Wall	24	5	3	16	38	91	18
Pendle Youth -8	24	5	4	15	38	65	11

BOSTON & DISTRICT LEAGUE
(Cropley's Suzuki)

Premier Division	P	W	D	L	F	A	Pts
Wyberton	18	14	3	1	77	18	45
Billinghay Athletic	18	13	3	2	85	29	42
Swineshead Inst.	18	12	1	5	69	14	37
Spilsby Town	18	9	3	6	34	24	30
Coningsby	18	9	2	7	44	42	29
Freiston	18	9	1	8	53	51	28
Woodhall Spa Utd	18	7	2	9	38	53	23
Kirton Town	18	4	2	12	36	73	14
Skegness T. Res.	18	4	0	14	32	57	12
Westside Rangers	18	0	1	17	14	121	1

Division One	P	W	D	L	F	A	Pts
Old Doningtonians	22	17	2	3	72	31	53
Old Leake	22	15	2	5	68	36	47
Pointon	22	14	4	4	66	29	46
Fishtoft	22	14	4	4	49	39	46
Spalding Town	22	11	3	8	52	41	36
Spalding Harriers	22	10	2	10	56	40	32
Wyberton Res.	22	10	2	10	44	47	32
Sutterton	22	9	4	9	55	63	31
Swineshead Res.	22	7	2	13	41	56	23
Holbeach Bank	22	4	2	16	32	65	14
Coningsby Res.	22	3	3	16	32	62	12
Wainfleet United	22	2	2	18	19	77	8

Nortoft United - record expunged

Division Two	P	W	D	L	F	A	Pts
Castle Colts	20	18	1	1	89	25	55
Billinghay A. Res.	20	16	1	3	77	27	49
Boston Town OB	20	15	2	3	60	22	47
Fishtoft Res.	20	12	2	6	69	42	38
Mareham United	20	11	1	8	65	55	34
Kirton Leisure	20	9	1	10	60	61	28
Westside R. Res.	20	7	1	12	35	76	22
Spalding T. Res.	20	5	2	13	38	69	17
Fosdyke -1	20	5	1	14	35	76	15
Tydd St Mary	20	2	3	15	29	59	9
Old Donns Res.	20	2	1	17	37	82	7

Skegness WMC, Sportsman - records expunged

Division Three	P	W	D	L	F	A	Pts
Benington	26	19	4	3	123	58	61
Friskney	26	17	2	7	84	49	53
Skegness Town A	26	15	4	7	79	40	49
Boston Utd Com.	26	13	7	6	57	49	46
Freiston Res.	26	13	3	10	65	68	42
FC Kirton	26	12	3	11	57	64	39
Woodhall Spa Res.	26	11	5	10	74	61	38
Kirton Town Res	26	10	5	11	64	73	35
Park United	26	9	5	12	60	67	32
Mareham U. Res.	26	8	2	16	70	83	26
Holbeach Bk Res.	26	7	5	14	53	74	26
Pointon Res.	26	7	4	15	57	98	25
Eastville, Midville	26	5	7	14	51	79	22
Spalding H. Res.	26	5	6	15	43	74	21

BOURNEMOUTH LEAGUE
(Hayward)

Premier Division	P	W	D	L	F	A	Pts
B'mouth Electric	22	15	3	4	85	28	48
Westover B'mouth	22	15	2	5	61	25	47
H'wthy Rec. Res.	22	14	3	5	58	30	45
Old Oakmeadians	22	10	6	6	52	37	36
Parley Spts Res.	22	9	4	9	52	52	31
Dorset Knob	22	8	3	11	41	73	27
Pennington St Mks	22	6	8	8	38	42	26
Sway	22	6	7	9	28	31	25
Suttoners Civil	22	7	4	11	48	63	25
Redlynch & WU	22	6	6	10	41	48	24
Mudeford Mens C.	22	6	6	10	25	46	24
Verwood T. Res.	22	2	4	16	33	87	10

Division One	P	W	D	L	F	A	Pts
Portcastrian	22	17	4	1	73	24	55
Trinidad	22	13	7	2	55	26	46
Alderholt	22	11	7	4	54	28	40
B'mth El'ctric Res.	22	13	1	8	48	35	40
Allendale	22	12	2	8	67	44	38
Ferndown Town	22	10	6	6	55	38	36
Harrington United	22	10	3	9	67	51	33
Poole Boro. Res.	22	7	6	9	42	36	27
Redhill Rangers	22	6	4	12	38	75	22
St Mary's	22	5	2	15	32	63	17
AFC Highcliffe	22	2	4	16	36	92	10
Fordingbridge Tks	22	2	2	18	26	81	8

Division Two	P	W	D	L	F	A	Pts
Tuakana	22	17	3	2	91	34	54
Twynham Rgrs	22	16	1	5	60	35	49
Bisterne United	22	14	5	3	45	25	47
N. Milton Linnets	22	14	4	4	43	22	46
Ferndown Sports	22	10	4	8	43	41	34
Suttoners Civ. Res.	22	9	5	8	48	48	32
MPloy	22	7	5	10	31	50	26
Sway Res.	22	6	5	11	36	58	23
Westover Res.	22	5	5	12	47	52	20
Cobham Sp. Res.	22	5	3	14	34	60	18
Walkford	22	3	6	13	37	49	15
JP Morgan -8	22	2	2	18	38	79	0

Division Three	P	W	D	L	F	A	Pts
Fencing Centre	24	17	2	5	71	34	53
Cherry Bees	24	16	4	4	71	34	52
Suttoners Civil A	24	16	2	6	64	42	50
Queens Park Ath.	24	15	4	5	81	38	49
AFC Burton	24	15	3	6	51	35	48
Parkside Wdrs	24	12	7	5	65	49	43
Wallisdown Con	24	11	5	8	57	48	38
Stourvale	24	11	2	11	67	52	35
Seabournes	24	5	6	13	37	61	21
Redlynch/W. Res.	24	7	0	17	41	70	21
O O'meadians Res.	24	5	4	15	42	59	19
Ringwood United	24	3	4	17	21	80	13
AFC Parkstone	24	1	1	22	14	80	4

Division Four	P	W	D	L	F	A	Pts
Parley Sports A *-1*	22	16	2	4	71	28	49
S Coast Dem'tion	22	14	3	5	82	35	45
Bournem'th UST	22	13	4	5	58	31	43
N. Milton Eagles	22	14	1	7	53	39	43
Burley	22	11	4	7	50	38	37
FC Athletico	22	12	0	10	86	56	36
Albany Athletic	22	11	3	8	59	45	36
Magpies *-3*	22	10	3	9	70	47	30
Henleys Electric	22	8	5	9	60	51	29
Fifa Standards *-2*	22	4	2	16	34	68	12
W. Moors Res. *-5*	22	4	1	17	22	110	8
Shamrock	22	1	0	21	20	117	3

Division Five	P	W	D	L	F	A	Pts
AFC Pennington	24	21	0	3	113	28	63
Bisterne Rangers	24	20	1	3	86	23	61
Branksome Celtic	24	19	1	4	102	29	58
Mudeford MC Res.	24	15	3	6	69	33	48
Screw-It Carpentry	24	13	3	8	109	45	42
Bournemth Res. *-1*	24	12	4	8	88	48	39
Walker Scott	24	7	3	14	61	68	24
Little Brit Inn	24	7	3	14	44	86	24
Rockbourne	24	6	4	14	47	77	22
Twynham R. Res.	24	7	0	17	42	129	21
Griffin	24	6	2	16	27	88	20
Bransgore United	24	5	2	17	34	85	17
Chaplins	24	5	0	19	34	117	15

Division Six	P	W	D	L	F	A	Pts
Vienna Windows	22	21	1	0	109	18	64
Claymoor Const.	22	19	0	3	82	25	57
Townsend Spartans	22	17	1	4	111	37	52
AFC Bransgore	22	14	2	6	75	41	44
Queens Pk A. Res.	22	11	4	7	75	50	37
Portcastrian Res.	22	9	3	10	49	63	30
Ringwood Athletic	22	9	1	12	52	69	28
F'bridge T. Res. *-2*	22	4	5	13	37	69	15
Bransgore U. Res.	22	4	2	16	40	98	14
AFC Burton Res	22	4	2	16	40	100	14
B'mouth Hospital	22	4	2	16	36	111	14
Alderholt Res. *-2*	22	4	1	17	36	61	11

BRADFORD TELEGRAPH & ARGUS LEAGUE

	P	W	D	L	F	A	Pts
TVR United	18	13	2	3	67	40	41
Thornbury YCC	18	12	4	2	49	30	40
Bradford Arms	18	11	3	4	59	40	33
Lidget Green	18	8	6	4	46	36	30
White Abbey	18	8	4	6	41	38	28
Bradford All Stars	18	8	0	10	40	47	24
West Bowling Utd	18	5	2	11	31	47	17
Sporting Athletic	18	3	2	13	42	60	11
Abun. Life Church	18	3	2	13	42	60	11
W. Brad. Spartans	18	2	2	14	28	50	8

All Nations, Ventnor Youth - records expunged

BRIGHTON, HOVE & DISTRICT LEAGUE

Premier Division	P	W	D	L	F	A	Pts
Montpelier Villa	20	14	4	2	53	22	46
O & G United	20	14	1	5	47	31	43
Hikers BHA	20	11	4	5	52	27	37
B'ton Electricity	20	10	5	5	32	23	35
AFC Stanley	20	9	2	9	31	33	29
Brighton Nth End	20	7	4	9	36	44	25
Portslade Athletic	20	7	2	11	29	45	23
Ovingdean	20	6	3	11	33	46	21
CCK	20	5	4	11	35	35	19
Southern Rgrs OB	20	5	4	11	29	42	19
American Express	20	4	3	13	25	54	15

Crew Club Sports - record expunged

Division One	P	W	D	L	F	A	Pts
AFC Falmer Fal. *-3*	20	16	1	3	50	16	46
Ampito	20	12	1	7	55	39	37
Coversure Athletic	20	11	2	7	34	31	35
Hair Razors	20	10	3	7	35	36	33
Montpelier View	20	9	4	7	40	29	31
Rott'gdean V. Res.	20	8	4	8	36	37	28
BSM08	20	8	4	8	35	37	28
Teamstats.net *+3*	20	5	5	10	32	43	23
M'pelier Villa Res.	20	6	1	13	35	47	19
Ricardo	20	5	4	11	27	45	19
Constant Service	20	5	1	14	34	53	16

Midway - record expunged

Division Two	P	W	D	L	F	A	Pts
ORB 360 *+6*	18	14	0	4	62	24	48
Newhvn W. Hart	18	12	5	1	53	23	41
American E. Res.	18	10	3	5	67	20	33
PHS United *+3*	18	9	2	7	34	42	32
Chailey *-15*	18	15	0	3	59	20	30
B. Brigade OB *+3*	18	5	2	11	37	61	20
Rott'gdean Vill. A	18	6	0	12	29	55	18
AFC B'ton/Hove *-3*	18	6	1	11	49	51	16
Rott'dean Dyn. *+3*	18	4	0	14	29	75	15
Portslade Res. *-3*	18	1	3	14	22	70	9

Division Three	P	W	D	L	F	A	Pts
M'pelier View Res.	18	16	0	2	66	14	48
Vista	18	14	1	3	59	20	43
S'thern ROB Res.	18	12	2	4	57	34	38
Saltdean Sharks	18	10	3	5	44	18	33
Dyke Road Tavern	18	8	4	6	40	29	28
Midway Res.	18	9	1	8	49	43	28
Montpelier Villa A	18	5	3	10	32	52	18
Boys Brigade Res.	18	3	3	12	18	61	12
Hove Park Tavern	18	2	1	15	20	59	7
Southwick Rgrs	18	1	2	15	14	69	5

BRISTOL DOWNS LEAGUE

Division One	P	W	D	L	F	A	Pts
Sneyd Park	26	18	5	3	74	25	59
Torpedo	26	17	5	4	64	28	56
Ashley	26	18	2	6	54	31	56
Bristol Barcelona	26	16	4	6	67	33	52
Saints Old Boys	26	15	1	10	55	55	46
Lawes Juniors	26	11	7	8	54	37	40
Sporting Greyh'nd	26	9	5	12	43	43	32
Cotswool Old B.	26	10	1	15	46	57	31
AFC Bohemia	26	9	3	14	47	59	30
Clifton St Vincents	26	7	7	12	44	55	28
Jamaica Bell	26	8	3	15	41	62	27
Portland Old Boys	26	8	2	16	39	59	26
Cabot Asset Fin.	26	5	4	17	34	70	19
Easton Cowboys	26	5	3	18	32	80	18

Division Two	P	W	D	L	F	A	Pts
Retainers	26	20	5	1	92	19	65
Sneyd Park Res.	26	21	1	4	77	31	64
Lion	26	15	5	6	57	41	50
Tebby	26	15	2	9	67	44	47
Clifton Rockets *-3*	26	13	3	10	70	59	39
Hydez	26	12	3	11	51	44	39
Clifton St V. Res.	26	12	2	12	47	39	38
Hare-on-the-Hill	26	12	2	12	35	44	38
St Andrew's	26	11	0	15	55	92	33
Torpedo Res.	26	10	0	16	42	49	30
Ashley Res.	26	8	2	16	41	68	26
Cotswool Res.	26	7	2	17	43	79	23
B. Barcelona Res.	26	6	3	17	36	54	21
E. Cowboys Res.	26	5	0	21	27	77	15

Division Three	P	W	D	L	F	A	Pts
Evergreen FC	26	20	4	2	79	28	64
Stoke Bishop	26	19	5	2	73	33	62
Sp'ting G'hnd Res.	26	14	5	7	64	41	47
Retainers Res.	26	14	2	10	49	39	44
Sneyd Park A	26	11	5	10	64	59	38
Clifton Rkts Res.	26	11	3	12	67	65	36
Durdham Down AS	26	10	3	13	43	59	33
LA Cricketers	26	10	2	14	46	59	32
Clifton St Vinc. A	26	8	7	11	48	50	31
Portland OB Res.	26	9	4	13	46	67	31
Severnside	26	11	2	13	64	63	29
Torpedo A	26	8	4	14	51	77	28
Luccombe Garage	26	6	3	17	42	67	21
Beachcroft LLP	26	5	3	18	60	89	18

Division Four	P	W	D	L	F	A	Pts
Jersey Rangers	26	18	5	3	93	45	59
Wellington Wdrs	26	18	3	5	97	39	57
Sneyd Park B	26	18	3	5	69	41	57
Bengal Tigers	26	13	4	9	53	61	43
Cotham Old Boys	26	12	4	10	72	69	40
Saints Old B. Res.	26	12	3	11	69	60	39
Hydez Res.	26	9	4	13	72	72	31
West Town Utd	26	10	1	15	65	65	31
NCSF United	26	8	7	11	52	54	31
Clifton St Vinc. B	26	10	1	15	44	71	31
Retainers A	26	8	3	15	51	84	27
Conham Rangers	26	7	5	14	44	61	26
Lion Res.	26	6	8	12	49	73	26
Tebby Res.	26	6	3	17	37	72	21

BRISTOL PREMIER COMBINATION

Premier Division	P	W	D	L	F	A	Pts
Longwell GS Res.	26	20	4	2	74	20	64
AEK Boco	26	18	3	5	80	38	57
Mendip United	26	15	6	5	61	29	51
Wick FC	26	14	6	6	64	47	48
Talbot Knowle U.	26	12	6	8	62	50	42
Bitton Res.	26	10	8	8	60	47	38
Hallen Res.	26	10	4	12	54	58	34
Pucklechurch Spts	26	8	6	12	45	52	30
Hartcliffe	26	8	4	14	50	64	28
Nicholas Wdrs	26	8	4	14	37	67	28
St Philips MAS	26	7	6	13	63	70	27
RG St George Res.	26	8	3	15	43	61	27
Winterbourne Res.	26	6	6	14	49	70	24
S. Bristol Central	26	3	4	19	18	87	13

Division One	P	W	D	L	F	A	Pts
Seymour United	24	18	3	3	68	18	57
Lawrence Rovers	24	15	4	5	63	30	49
Patchway T. Res.	24	14	5	5	53	35	47
Oldland Abs Res.	24	13	6	5	61	33	45
Fishponds Athletic	24	12	2	10	46	49	38
Highridge Utd Res.	24	11	4	9	42	36	37
Olveston United	24	10	6	8	37	28	36
Shaftesbury Crus.	24	10	5	9	49	48	35
Totterdown United	24	9	7	8	35	43	34
Frampton Athletic	24	5	5	14	22	48	20
Greyfriars Athletic	24	4	4	16	33	79	16
Henbury Res.	24	4	3	17	21	49	15
Brimsham Green	24	2	4	18	30	64	10

BRISTOL & AVON LEAGUE

	P	W	D	L	F	A	Pts
De-Veys	24	21	3	0	122	23	66
British Royal SC	24	19	5	0	105	21	62
Carmel United	24	17	1	6	105	34	52
FC Bristol	24	15	4	5	79	40	49
Lawrence R. Res.	24	13	6	5	66	32	45
Lg Ashton Res. *-3*	24	13	1	10	75	64	37
Imperial Res.	24	11	2	11	62	45	35
Bideford Old Boys	24	9	4	11	53	46	31
Iron Acton Res.	24	6	1	17	29	94	19
Golden Hill S Res.	24	5	2	17	28	88	17
Greyfriars B *-3*	24	5	2	17	24	106	14
Bradley Stoke A	24	3	2	19	20	69	11
Wessex Wdrs A	24	1	3	20	24	130	6

Knowle Reds - record expunged

BRISTOL & DISTRICT LEAGUE

Senior Division	P	W	D	L	F	A	Pts
Made-for-Ever	24	20	1	3	98	30	61
Shirehampton Res.	24	17	4	3	72	33	55
Old Sodbury	24	16	5	3	55	24	53
Hanham Ath. Res.	24	12	4	8	73	44	40
AXA Res.	24	9	5	10	43	46	32
Nicholas W. Res.	24	9	3	12	41	60	30
Coalpit Heath	24	9	2	13	60	59	29
Hallen A	24	9	1	14	42	67	28
Wick Res.	24	7	5	12	48	62	26
St Pancras	24	7	5	12	49	68	26
RG St George A	24	6	6	12	49	70	24
Crosscourt United	24	7	3	14	46	78	24
Miners Rangers	24	3	6	15	32	67	15

Division One	P	W	D	L	F	A	Pts
Brislington Crick.	24	19	4	1	112	24	61
Longwell GS A	24	16	5	3	86	36	53
Seymour Utd Res.	24	13	7	4	57	39	46
Chip. Sodbury Res.	24	12	6	6	66	38	42
Rangeworthy	24	10	7	7	51	39	37
Hambrook	24	10	4	10	48	51	34
Bendix	24	9	4	11	41	53	31
Bitton A	24	7	7	10	49	60	28
Sea Mills Park	24	7	7	10	46	60	28
Talbot Knowle Res.	24	7	6	11	46	73	27
Pucklechurch Res.	24	6	3	15	32	68	21
Hartcliffe Res.	24	3	5	16	41	79	14
S Bris. Cent. Res.	24	3	3	18	35	90	12

Division Two	P	W	D	L	F	A	Pts
Eden Grove	24	21	2	1	103	19	65
Warmley Saints	24	16	6	2	93	31	54
Patchway Town A	24	16	3	5	67	35	51
AEK Boco Res.	24	15	1	8	84	45	46
Iron Acton	24	11	3	10	54	60	36
Hanham Ath. A	24	10	5	9	41	38	35
Stockwood Wdrs	24	8	8	8	49	57	32
Broadwalk	24	10	2	12	64	73	32
Fry Club A	24	8	5	11	52	70	29
Nicholas Wdrs A	24	6	3	15	30	65	21
Winterbourne A	24	5	5	14	40	68	20
Greyfriars A. Res.	24	2	6	16	25	85	12
Shaft'bury C. Res.	24	2	3	19	30	86	9

Division Three	P	W	D	L	F	A	Pts
DRG S'ton Res.	22	18	3	1	75	24	57
Shireway Sports	22	13	6	3	57	26	45
Bradley Stoke T.	22	10	7	5	52	36	37
Chipping S'bury A	22	11	4	7	47	35	37
Mendip Utd Res.	22	10	5	7	64	52	35
Tilly Rangers	22	9	4	9	52	43	31
Oakland	22	8	5	9	47	58	29
St Philips M. Res.	22	8	2	12	60	67	26
Totterdown U. Res	22	7	0	15	46	65	21
Olveston U. Res.	22	6	3	13	28	50	21
Highridge Utd A	22	5	3	14	34	65	18
Shirehampton A	22	6	0	16	28	69	18

Division Four	P	W	D	L	F	A	Pts
St George Rgrs	26	20	1	5	92	42	61
JDH Builders	26	19	3	4	78	49	60
Southmead Com.	26	18	3	5	98	60	57
Portville Warriors	26	16	2	8	95	63	50
Henbury A	26	14	3	9	69	49	45
Horfield United	26	13	2	11	85	78	41
Made-for-Ever Res.	26	11	1	14	67	74	34
Longwell GS B	26	10	2	14	60	59	32
Hillfields Old Boys	26	10	2	14	54	74	32
Frampton A. Res.	26	10	0	16	47	81	30
Talbot Knowle A	26	8	2	16	57	85	26
AXA A	26	6	4	16	58	73	22
Oldland Abbs A	26	7	0	19	67	78	21
Fry Club B	26	6	3	17	46	108	21

Division Five	P	W	D	L	F	A	Pts
Soundwell Victoria	26	23	1	2	109	33	70
Roman Glass B	26	21	3	2	101	30	66
Wick A	26	16	5	5	69	47	53
Hambrook Res.	26	16	2	8	96	56	50
Coalpit Heath Res.	26	12	6	8	78	41	42
Hartcliffe A	26	10	4	12	53	73	34
Brimsham G. Res.	26	9	3	14	63	63	30
St Nicholas	26	9	3	14	45	88	30
Pucklechurch A	26	8	5	13	46	66	29
South Bristol C. A	26	8	3	15	56	79	27
Fishponds A. Res.	26	7	6	13	50	84	27
Bradley Stoke Res.	26	7	5	14	55	85	26
Bendix Res.	26	8	1	17	40	79	25
Greyfriars Ath. A	26	3	3	20	28	65	12

Division Six	P	W	D	L	F	A	Pts
Patchway Nth End	26	20	4	2	91	27	64
Real Thornbury	26	18	4	4	86	30	58
Hallen B	26	17	3	6	96	46	54
Brazil	26	17	2	7	84	52	53
AEK Boco A	26	15	2	9	74	54	47
Seymour United A	26	12	2	12	66	68	38
Bris. Cricktrs Res.	26	10	7	9	53	60	37
Longwell G. OB	26	11	4	11	57	74	37
Crosscourt U. Res.	26	7	6	13	52	59	27
Oldland Abbs B	26	8	2	16	44	81	26
Rangeworthy Res.	26	6	4	16	45	76	22
Stockw'd W. Res.	26	6	4	16	57	90	22
St Pancras Res.	26	6	2	18	40	81	20
AXA B	26	4	4	18	33	80	16

BRISTOL & SUBURBAN LEAGUE

Premier Div One	P	W	D	L	F	A	Pts
St Aldhelms	26	19	4	3	74	26	61
Southmead CSA	26	18	4	4	86	31	58
CTK Southside	25	16	5	4	71	43	53
S. Glos Hambrook	26	14	6	6	63	44	47
Avonmouth	25	12	5	8	66	59	41
Ashton United FC	26	11	6	9	63	55	39
Cadbury Hth Res.	26	11	5	10	67	60	38
Broad Plain House	26	10	5	11	48	54	35
Old Georgians	26	10	4	12	54	67	33
Winford PH	26	7	5	14	43	75	26
Alm'sbury T. Res.	26	6	4	16	32	59	22
Fishponds Old B.	26	6	3	17	48	68	20
Glenside 5 Old B.	26	5	4	17	47	79	19
Stoke Gifford Utd	26	4	4	18	36	78	16

Premier Div Two	P	W	D	L	F	A	Pts
Bristol Athletic	26	15	6	5	66	33	51
A'bury UWE Res.	26	16	3	7	78	46	51
Bristol Telephones	26	15	4	7	51	39	49
Ridings High	26	14	5	7	58	41	47
Lockleaze	26	13	5	8	53	41	44
St Aldhelms Res.	26	13	4	9	46	40	43
Severn Beach	26	13	3	10	58	53	41
Brislington A	26	11	5	10	58	58	38
Little Stoke	26	11	2	13	56	48	35
Whitchurch	26	9	4	13	53	67	31
Tytherington Res.	26	8	4	14	41	63	28
Bristol North West	26	5	9	12	45	74	24
Wessex Wdrs	26	5	6	15	51	65	21
Lawrence Weston	26	3	2	21	37	83	11

Division One	P	W	D	L	F	A	Pts
Imperial Saints	28	27	0	1	129	32	81
Avonmouth Res.	28	18	3	7	81	42	56
Easton Cow. Sub.	28	16	7	5	88	43	55
Ridings High Res.	28	16	6	6	75	41	54
Old Cothamians	28	15	4	9	61	51	49
Filton Athletic	28	14	5	9	71	66	47
Broad P. Hse Res.	28	13	4	11	72	80	43
Totterdown PoB	28	11	8	9	65	58	41
Rockleaze A. Res.	28	10	4	14	59	68	34
Keynsham T. A	28	8	6	14	67	74	30
Ashton Seniors	28	8	4	16	48	66	28
Ashton Rangers	28	6	6	16	44	84	24
Fishponds OB Res.	28	7	2	19	45	101	23
Hengrove Ath. A	28	5	5	18	40	76	20
B. T'phones Res.	28	2	4	22	28	91	10

Division Two	P	W	D	L	F	A	Pts
Cartwheel Sports	26	21	2	3	108	35	65
S'mead CSA Res.	26	18	4	4	87	48	58
Ingleside	26	17	5	4	70	33	56
Thrissell Nomads	26	18	2	6	62	39	56
CTK S'thside Res.	26	15	4	7	81	47	49
Downend Foresters	26	13	5	8	80	65	44
Mangotsfield U. A	26	12	4	10	73	55	40
Tyndalls Pk Rgrs	26	11	2	13	58	51	35
Corinthian Sports	26	10	2	14	62	69	32
Stoke Gifford Res.	26	8	4	14	50	63	28
Alm'bury UWE A	26	7	2	17	47	101	23
Little Stoke Res.	26	5	2	19	40	88	17
St Aldhelms A	26	3	2	21	28	93	11
Oldbury Crusaders	26	2	4	20	20	79	10

Cadbury Heath A - record expunged

Division Three	P	W	D	L	F	A	Pts
Lebeq United	28	23	0	5	122	56	69
Bristol County	28	22	2	4	122	39	68
Golden Hill Sports	28	19	2	7	83	41	59
Lockleaze Res.	28	15	5	8	55	42	50
Parson Street OB	28	14	1	13	83	72	43
Ashton Utd Res.	28	13	4	11	87	81	43
BW Athletic	28	13	3	12	109	85	42
Broad Plain Hse A	28	11	7	10	62	60	40
O. Georgians Res.	28	11	6	11	66	69	39
Hanham A. Colts	28	9	4	15	51	76	31
Severn Beach Res.	28	9	3	16	43	85	30
Fishponds OB A	28	8	3	17	48	92	27
Sefton Park	28	8	1	19	52	93	25
O Cothamians Res.	28	7	3	18	44	73	24
Glenside 5 Res.	28	5	2	21	40	103	17

Division Four	P	W	D	L	F	A	Pts
Wanderers	24	16	2	6	86	46	50
Law. Weston Res.	24	15	1	8	86	44	46
Avonmouth A	23	14	1	8	80	54	43
Filton Athletic Res.	24	13	4	7	70	63	43
Emersons Green	24	12	5	7	75	60	41
Brandon TT Sports	23	13	1	9	43	51	40
Oldbury Crus. Res.	24	12	3	9	54	52	39
S. Glos (Hmb) Res.	24	10	3	11	61	61	33
St Annes Town	24	7	8	9	50	52	29
AFC Spartans	24	8	2	14	50	68	26
Coupland Insulation	24	7	3	14	41	66	24
Wessex W. Res.	24	5	2	17	48	86	17
Winford PH Res.	24	3	5	16	31	72	14

Ridings High A - record expunged

Division Five	P	W	D	L	F	A	Pts
Mangotsfield U. B	26	22	0	4	133	31	66
Poker County UK	26	19	2	5	117	54	59
Stoke Rangers	26	18	2	6	133	57	56
Fishponds OB B	26	16	2	8	101	51	50
AEK Boco Colts	26	15	4	7	61	48	49
Rolls Royce	26	15	2	9	111	84	47
Rockleaze A'side A	26	13	4	9	82	66	43
Parson St OB Res.	26	10	4	12	77	66	34
Whitchurch Res.	26	9	4	13	56	90	31
T'down PoB Res.	26	9	2	15	61	99	29
Stoke Gifford U. A	26	8	3	15	46	95	27
L'rence Weston A	26	4	4	18	54	109	16
Whiteladies	26	4	2	20	45	114	14
Knowle Rangers	26	2	1	23	27	140	7

BROMLEY & DISTRICT LEAGUE

Premier Division	P	W	D	L	F	A	Pts
North Kent Aces	16	14	2	0	62	17	44
AFC Mottingham	16	12	3	1	58	17	39
South East Athletic	16	9	1	6	38	28	28
Phoenix Spts Res.	16	5	5	6	27	33	20
OPK	16	5	5	6	24	32	20
Heathfield FC	16	4	6	6	27	38	18
Holmesdale A	16	5	3	8	31	43	18
Rotherhithe	16	2	3	11	20	48	9
Highfield Rovers	16	0	4	12	15	46	4

Eden Park Rangers Res. - record expunged

Division One	P	W	D	L	F	A	Pts
Univ. of Greenwich	16	11	3	2	46	22	36
Welling Park	16	10	4	2	43	20	34
Barnet Wood	16	10	2	4	38	25	32
Running Horses	16	7	3	6	37	29	24
Iron Tugboat City	16	6	3	7	34	36	21
Old Addeyans	16	5	4	7	37	37	19
AFC Heathfield	16	5	1	10	26	42	16
Dulwich Town +3	16	3	3	10	37	45	15
O. Colf'ns Res. -3	16	3	1	12	19	61	7

Ilderton Athletic - record expunged

Division Two	P	W	D	L	F	A	Pts
Chislehurst Dyn.	18	13	2	3	66	26	41
Bexley Boro. Res.	18	12	1	5	43	24	37
Crockenhill Old B.	18	11	3	4	38	27	36
AFC Bromley	18	10	3	5	47	37	33
Old Colfeians A	18	9	4	5	52	40	31
Latter-Day Sts -3	18	9	2	7	46	52	26
Crofton Albion A	18	6	1	11	32	40	19
Charlton Ath. Deaf	18	5	2	11	35	54	17
Farnboro. OBG B	18	1	4	13	22	47	7
Royston FC	18	1	4	13	11	45	7

BURTON & DISTRICT LEAGUE

Pedigree Division	P	W	D	L	F	A	Pts
Real Medina	22	17	2	3	75	33	53
Horninglow	22	14	1	7	64	37	43
Stretton Spartans	22	13	2	7	57	33	41
Barton Utd Res.	22	11	5	6	56	32	38
Lichfield City Res.	22	11	3	8	41	40	36
The Seal Inn	22	11	2	9	55	38	35
The Dart	22	11	2	9	67	69	35
The Drum	22	10	0	12	56	55	30
Gresley A	22	8	2	12	44	47	26
Ashbourne Res.	22	4	4	14	42	69	16
The Sump	22	4	4	14	32	67	16
Overseal St Matt.	22	3	3	16	36	105	12

TAG Division	P	W	D	L	F	A	Pts
Horninglow Res.	16	12	1	3	85	49	37
Barton Royal Oak	16	11	1	4	69	35	34
FC Kaleef	16	11	1	4	59	25	34
Barton United Yth	16	10	1	5	56	27	31
Blacksmiths Arms	16	8	3	5	81	36	27
Grange Inn	16	7	1	8	60	51	22
Midway FC	16	4	3	9	62	73	15
Gresley B	16	2	1	13	21	52	7
Whittington Brenstar	16	1	0	15	23	168	3

CANTERBURY & DISTRICT LEAGUE
(Barton PO & Stores)

Premier Division	P	W	D	L	F	A	Pts
Lesters Elite	18	14	3	1	43	19	45
Ash	18	14	1	3	60	24	43
Chilham	18	11	3	4	61	26	36
Red Arrow	18	11	2	5	42	33	35
University Kent A	18	11	1	6	33	30	34
Charing	18	8	0	10	35	38	24
Monument Eagles	18	6	0	12	37	45	18
Premier Res.	18	4	0	14	32	48	12
Cramptons	18	3	0	15	17	36	9
Snowdown	18	3	0	15	24	85	9

Division One	P	W	D	L	F	A	Pts
Minster	14	11	1	2	41	22	34
Betteshanger	14	10	1	3	52	27	31
Blean	14	8	2	4	28	21	26
Burgess Hodgson	14	4	4	6	36	39	16
Europeans	14	4	3	7	32	30	15
St Stephens FC	14	4	2	8	44	44	14
Sturry	14	3	4	7	21	30	13
Chartham SC Res.	14	3	1	10	19	60	10

Division Two	P	W	D	L	F	A	Pts
St Margarets	14	12	0	2	46	17	36
Bekesbourne	14	10	2	2	52	28	32
Post Office	14	10	1	3	60	45	31
Gentil Knight	14	8	1	5	48	34	25
Sentinels	14	5	1	8	24	39	16
Chilham Res.	14	4	1	9	25	48	13
Woodnesborough	14	3	1	10	33	54	10
Sturry Res.	14	0	1	13	21	44	1

Ash Res. - record expunged

Division Three	P	W	D	L	F	A	Pts
Monument Res.	16	13	1	2	61	23	40
Wingham	16	12	2	2	66	23	38
Herne Bay Athletic	16	10	5	1	60	24	35
The Swan	16	10	1	5	91	43	31
Wall Tavern	16	6	2	8	46	34	20
USA Staff	16	6	1	9	55	51	19
The Two Sawyers	16	4	0	12	39	58	12
Canterbury City A	16	3	2	11	33	81	11
CC Hornets	16	1	0	15	15	129	3

Ashford Borough Res. - record expunged

CAPITAL LEAGUE

Central Division	P	W	D	L	F	A	Pts
Aveley Res.	16	12	1	3	45	13	37
Hornchurch Res.	16	9	1	6	35	18	28
Cheshunt Res.	16	8	3	5	25	19	27
Redbridge Res.	16	8	1	7	30	27	25
St Albans City Res.	16	7	2	7	28	30	23
Enfield Town Res.	16	7	1	8	21	33	22
Potters Bar T. Res.	16	5	2	9	20	36	17
Hertford Town Res.	16	5	1	10	18	30	16
Harlow Town Res.	16	5	0	11	25	41	15

Eastern Division	P	W	D	L	F	A	Pts
Bromley Res.	18	11	2	5	46	28	35
Braintree Town A	18	10	3	5	40	18	33
B. Stortford Res.	18	9	3	6	36	26	30
Chelmsford Res.	18	9	1	8	36	30	28
Concord Rgrs Res.	18	8	4	6	32	28	28
Billericay T. Res.	18	10	1	9	33	35	25
Canvey Is. Res.	18	7	3	8	27	38	24
Witham Town A	18	6	2	10	33	43	20
Bigg'wade T. Res.	18	5	2	11	21	39	17
Brentwood T. Res.	18	4	5	9	18	37	17

Western Division	P	W	D	L	F	A	Pts
Harrow Boro. Res.	16	11	4	1	29	14	37
Hayes & YU Res.	16	12	0	4	56	20	36
Staines Town Res.	16	8	4	4	43	25	28
Hitchin Town Res.	16	8	2	6	34	32	26
Hemel H'stead A	16	7	2	7	30	24	23
Arlesey Town Res.	16	6	4	6	33	40	22
Wingate & F. Res.	16	4	4	8	36	42	16
Windsor & E. Res.	16	3	3	10	17	48	12
Burnham Res.	16	1	1	14	13	46	4

CENTRAL & SOUTH NORFOLK LEAGUE
(Crown Fire)

Division One	P	W	D	L	F	A	Pts
Dickleburgh	22	14	5	3	79	37	46
Bridgham United	22	14	3	5	58	26	45
Dereham Town A	22	13	5	4	66	37	44
Swaffham Town A	22	12	4	6	65	37	40
Gressenhall	22	13	2	7	41	30	40
Cockers	22	11	3	8	55	42	36
Hingham Athletic	22	10	4	8	56	46	34
Cranworth	22	8	1	13	47	55	25
Shipdham	22	7	3	12	36	49	24
Narborough	22	6	3	13	40	55	21
Rockland United	22	4	3	15	32	62	15
Yaxham	22	1	2	19	20	119	5

Division Two	P	W	D	L	F	A	Pts
Thetford Rov. Res.	20	15	2	3	60	36	47
Tacolneston	20	11	8	1	57	21	41
Bunwell	20	11	4	5	58	43	37
Morley Village	20	10	6	4	52	30	36
West End FC	20	7	5	8	47	39	26
Wymondham T. A	20	7	5	8	40	36	26
Necton SSC Res.	20	7	4	9	40	48	25
Nostro	20	7	3	10	38	47	24
Shropham United	20	6	5	9	42	43	23
Hingham Ath. Res.	20	3	3	14	21	56	12
Saham Toney Res.	20	3	1	16	26	82	10

Division Three	P	W	D	L	F	A	Pts
Bradenham Res.	20	16	2	2	59	21	50
Hethersett Athletic	20	15	2	3	69	19	47
Castle Acre Swifts	20	15	2	3	60	22	47
Northwold S&SC	20	14	0	6	63	32	42
Sporle	20	8	4	8	61	40	28
Bawdeswell	20	8	2	10	48	55	26
Gressenhall Res.	20	7	1	12	36	60	22
Gt Cressingham	20	5	3	12	34	57	18
Wendling *-3*	20	6	2	12	39	57	17
Hindolveston	20	3	1	16	30	83	10
Shipdham Res.	20	3	1	16	20	73	10

Division Four	P	W	D	L	F	A	Pts
Splitz United	20	18	1	1	82	17	55
Thurton & Ashby	20	16	1	3	91	27	49
Stoke Ferry	20	10	4	6	59	50	34
Breckland Wdrs	20	10	2	8	67	39	32
Methwold Rovers	20	8	6	6	56	39	30
Narborough Res.	20	7	5	8	35	48	26
Shropham U. Res.	20	8	1	11	47	80	25
Rampant Horse	20	7	3	10	58	53	24
Colkirk	20	6	2	12	37	59	20
Scarning United	20	6	0	14	45	71	18
Beetley United	20	1	1	18	24	118	4

CHELTENHAM ASSOCIATION LEAGUE

Division One	P	W	D	L	F	A	Pts
Moreton Rangers	26	23	2	1	83	15	71
Endsleigh	26	15	6	5	66	32	51
Whaddon United	26	16	3	7	66	36	51
Newton	26	15	5	6	85	38	50
Finlay Rovers	26	15	3	8	56	44	48
Siddington	26	12	4	10	54	50	40
Bishops Cleeve A	26	11	5	10	47	50	38
Star Res.	26	11	4	11	69	51	37
Woodmancote	26	9	5	12	52	54	32
Kings	26	7	9	10	38	46	30
Apperley/Tewk. D.	26	7	5	14	43	63	26
Winchcombe Res.	26	5	3	18	30	77	18
Andoversford	26	3	4	19	43	103	13
Prestbury Rov. *-3*	26	2	4	20	30	103	7

Division Two	P	W	D	L	F	A	Pts
Real Whaddon *-3*	22	19	2	1	116	33	56
AC Olympia	22	14	4	4	64	33	46
Broadway United	22	12	4	6	70	40	40
Dowty Dynamos	22	11	6	5	69	53	39
Bredon Res.	22	12	1	9	53	43	37
Falcons	22	11	1	10	60	49	34
Cinderford Res. *-1*	22	7	5	10	63	73	25
Northway	22	7	4	11	50	66	25
Northleach Town	22	7	4	11	44	60	25
Gala Wilton Res.	22	6	5	11	35	56	23
Charlton Rovers	22	5	1	16	44	71	16
Chelt'hm CS Res.	22	2	1	19	28	119	7

Shipton Oliffe - record expunged

Division Three	P	W	D	L	F	A	Pts
Glouc. Elmleaze	26	20	3	3	99	24	63
FC Electrics	26	19	3	4	86	37	60
Barometrics Res. *-1*	26	19	2	5	91	42	58
Brockworth Res.	26	18	3	5	94	49	57
St Marks CA	26	14	1	11	54	41	43
Belmore *-4*	26	13	5	8	65	41	40
Tewkesbury Town	26	12	2	12	63	60	38
Smiths Ath. Res.	26	10	4	12	48	57	34
Chelt. Saras A *-3*	26	11	1	14	74	99	31
Bourton Rov. Res.	26	8	3	15	47	77	27
C'down Panthers	26	6	5	15	57	61	23
Elmbridge Old B.	26	5	5	16	52	95	20
Phoenix United	26	4	5	17	35	75	17
Cheltenham CS A	26	1	2	23	23	130	5

Division Four	P	W	D	L	F	A	Pts
C & G	26	20	3	3	103	29	63
Hanley Swan	26	19	5	2	108	29	62
Upton Town	26	19	3	4	85	35	60
Charlton Rov. Res.	26	14	2	10	64	52	44
Southside	26	14	1	11	77	48	43
Falcons Res.	26	13	4	9	56	52	43
Star A	26	11	6	9	59	55	39
Smiths Athletic A	26	10	2	14	58	80	32
Tivoli Rovers	26	9	3	14	64	63	30
Finlay	26	8	6	12	65	92	30
Bredon A	26	8	1	17	56	87	25
Kings Res.	26	6	4	16	38	77	22
Andoversford Res.	26	6	3	17	50	123	21
Ap./Tewk Dyn Res.	26	2	3	21	40	101	9

Division Five	P	W	D	L	F	A	Pts
Chelt. Saracens B	24	18	3	3	101	39	57
RSG	24	18	2	4	95	42	56
66 Star United *-8*	24	16	4	4	89	39	44
Gala Wilton A	24	13	5	6	65	37	44
Fintan	24	13	5	6	58	41	44
Ap./Tewk. Dyn. A	24	11	3	10	57	53	36
Leckhampton Rov.	24	10	3	11	37	48	33
Tewkesb'y T. Res.	24	6	6	12	38	80	24
Cleevonians	24	5	8	11	51	53	23
Cheltenham CS B	24	5	4	15	33	65	19
Sherborne Harriers	24	5	3	16	50	77	18
Barometrics A *-1*	24	5	4	15	46	100	18
Charlton Kings *-4*	24	4	4	16	50	96	12

Division Six	P	W	D	L	F	A	Pts
FC Lakeside	20	17	1	2	96	30	52
WMK	20	14	2	4	111	27	44
Montpellier	20	14	2	4	84	33	44
AC Olympia Res.	20	13	0	7	55	37	39
Dowty Dyn. Res.	20	13	0	7	63	52	39
Priors	20	10	4	6	80	49	34
Winchcombe T. A	20	8	4	8	52	52	28
Chelt. Saras C	20	5	1	14	58	94	16
Charlton Rov. A *-3*	20	5	0	15	39	87	12
Northleach Res.	20	2	1	17	30	100	4
Belmore Res. -7	20	1	1	18	32	139	-4

St Pauls - record expunged

CHESTER & DISTRICT LEAGUE

Premier Division	P	W	D	L	F	A	Pts
Helsby Res.	24	20	2	2	104	28	62
Highfield Athletic	24	20	2	2	100	31	62
Waggon & Horses	24	19	2	3	98	46	59
Chester Nm. Res.	24	11	6	7	68	50	39
Sutton Way Villa	24	12	2	10	67	57	38
City Bar	24	12	2	10	75	70	38
Newton Bears	24	10	4	10	73	82	34
Kelsall	24	10	3	11	79	74	33
Crossway	24	9	1	14	52	82	28
Hoole Rangers	24	7	2	15	59	75	23
Parkgate	24	7	1	16	48	82	22
AFC Beb'gton Res.	24	5	0	19	34	97	15
Tarvin Athletic	24	0	1	23	41	112	1

Division One	P	W	D	L	F	A	Pts
FC Pensby Res.	22	21	0	1	85	25	63
Castrol Woodlands	22	15	3	4	60	25	48
Railway Athletic	22	14	4	4	65	45	46
Saughall Thursday	22	12	2	8	54	40	38
Barrow Athletic	22	9	5	8	60	50	32
Netherton SC	22	9	4	9	51	53	31
Duddon United	22	6	5	11	40	50	23
Chester Nmds A	22	6	5	11	43	58	23
Rangers Breaks	22	6	4	12	45	55	22
Ashton	22	6	3	14	47	68	21
Highfield Ath. Res.	22	6	2	14	51	79	14
Cestrian Alex	22	3	1	18	51	104	10

Division Two	P	W	D	L	F	A	Pts
Manor Ath. Res.	20	18	1	1	112	11	55
Neston Nomads	20	17	0	3	89	34	51
Kelma	20	16	2	2	102	28	50
Halfway Hse Celtic	20	10	2	8	49	41	32
Westmeter	20	8	3	9	50	49	27
Frodsham Vets	20	8	1	11	55	73	25
Hoole Rgrs Res.	20	8	1	11	51	73	25
Lodge Bar	20	5	4	11	35	74	19
Vicars X Doves	20	5	3	12	47	84	18
Boughton Athletic	20	4	2	14	34	69	14
Saughall Th. Res.	20	1	1	18	30	109	4

Division Three	P	W	D	L	F	A	Pts
Shaftsbury Youth	18	15	2	1	83	22	47
Peacock 09	18	15	2	1	73	18	47
Raby Villa	18	13	2	3	83	29	41
Newton Bears Res.	18	12	1	5	64	35	37
Uberlube *-3*	18	8	2	8	48	48	23
Blacon United	18	6	4	8	43	47	22
Chester Celtic	18	6	3	9	49	49	21
Crossway Res.	18	5	2	11	42	57	17
Barrow Ath. Res.	18	2	0	16	24	79	6
Vicars Cross Vets	18	0	0	18	9	134	0

Union Vaults - record expunged

CHESTERFIELD & DISTRICT AMATEUR LEAGUE

	P	W	D	L	F	A	Pts
Th. Horse Shoes	26	23	2	1	131	27	71
Nags Head	26	21	2	3	109	36	65
Hopflower	26	18	4	4	91	33	58
Clowne MWRJC	26	16	4	6	75	43	52
Tibshelf	26	16	2	8	61	46	50
Chesterfield Town	26	12	6	8	70	41	42
Shirebrook Rgrs	26	11	0	15	57	75	33
Holmewood	26	10	2	14	44	81	32
Duckmanton Com.	26	10	1	15	58	72	31
Renishaw Social	26	8	4	14	64	66	28
Clowne Wdrs	26	6	5	15	39	99	23
Holmefield Arms	26	5	3	18	40	72	18
Clowne MWTRB	26	4	6	16	41	74	18
Tansley	26	0	3	23	24	139	3

North Wingfield United - record expunged

CIRENCESTER & DISTRICT LEAGUE
(Combat Splatt Paintball)

Division One	P	W	D	L	F	A	Pts
Bibury	24	20	2	2	91	29	62
Avonvale United	24	18	2	4	70	23	56
The Beeches	24	13	3	8	66	50	42
Ashton Keynes	24	12	4	8	57	40	40
Real Fairford	24	12	3	9	64	40	39
South Cerney	24	9	10	5	49	44	37
Stratton United	24	9	5	10	57	61	32
Oaksey	24	7	9	8	43	46	30
Kingshill Sports	24	8	3	13	51	63	27
Oakridge	24	8	2	14	58	86	26
CHQ United *-6*	24	9	0	15	51	91	21
Tetbury Town A	24	3	4	17	40	70	13
Poulton	24	3	3	18	34	88	12

Down Amney - record expunged

Division Two	P	W	D	L	F	A	Pts
Bibury Res. *-3*	30	24	4	2	132	42	73
Minety Res.	30	21	1	8	87	44	64
Real Fairford Res.	30	20	1	9	82	56	61
Avonvale Res. *-3*	30	20	2	8	122	51	59
Lechlade	30	18	5	7	97	69	59
Corinium Sports	30	14	5	11	67	53	47
The Beeches Res.	30	13	7	10	84	76	46
Chalford A	30	11	3	16	58	71	36
A. Keynes Res. *-9*	30	14	3	13	61	76	36
Down Ampney	30	9	7	14	61	79	34
Oaksey Res.	30	9	1	20	58	96	28
CHQ Utd Res. -5	30	8	7	15	86	97	26
S Cerney Res. *-12*	30	11	5	14	65	76	26
Stratton Utd Res.	30	8	2	20	68	109	26
Kingshill S Res. *-3*	30	8	3	19	46	74	24
Poulton Res.	30	3	2	25	43	148	11

COLCHESTER & EAST ESSEX LEAGUE

Premier Division	P	W	D	L	F	A	Pts
Colne Engaine	18	14	1	3	62	18	43
Harwich & Park. A	18	12	2	4	46	23	38
Univ. of Essex A	18	12	2	4	38	25	38
Priory Ravens	18	9	3	6	41	33	30
Wimpole	18	9	2	7	37	41	29
Castle	18	8	1	9	44	45	25
Tollesbury	18	6	2	10	46	45	20
Cinque Port	18	5	4	9	28	39	19
Colch. Hotspurs	18	5	3	10	35	47	18
Harwich Rangers	18	0	0	18	22	83	0

Division One	P	W	D	L	F	A	Pts
Oyster	20	15	2	3	70	27	47
Eastcliff	20	14	1	5	45	19	43
Univ. of Essex B	20	13	1	6	67	34	40
Colchester Athletic	20	10	4	6	43	33	34
Brightlingsea A	20	9	4	7	45	41	31
Stoke-by-Nayland	20	7	5	8	34	50	26
AXA FC	20	7	3	10	41	47	24
Wimpole Res.	20	6	3	11	45	57	21
AFC Informa	20	5	5	10	31	54	20
FC Clacton Res.	20	4	3	13	35	68	15
Feering United	20	3	3	14	39	65	12

Division Two	P	W	D	L	F	A	Pts
Boxford Rovers	16	16	0	0	89	12	48
Brantham Ath. A	16	10	3	3	54	27	33
Clacton Utd Res.	16	9	4	3	60	28	31
New Field	16	8	2	6	36	36	26
Univ. of Essex C	16	3	6	7	36	49	15
Lexden Rovers	16	4	2	10	24	48	14
Abbey Fields	16	3	4	9	37	73	13
Great Bentley A	16	4	1	11	23	62	13
Nayland Rangers	16	3	2	11	41	65	11

Division Three	P	W	D	L	F	A	Pts
Belle Vue Social	20	14	3	3	59	22	45
Witchfinders	20	14	0	6	66	38	42
Kelvedon Social	20	12	4	4	58	31	40
Dellows	20	10	4	6	48	42	34
Lexden Allstars	20	9	3	8	39	36	30
Tey	20	8	4	8	38	34	28
Sporting Rebels	20	7	2	11	34	42	23
Marks Tey	20	6	2	12	45	54	20
Univ. of Essex D	20	6	1	13	27	50	19
Stoke-N'land Res.	20	6	1	13	27	55	19
Langham Lodgers	20	4	4	12	31	68	16

COVENTRY ALLIANCE

Premier Division	P	W	D	L	F	A	Pts
Alvis	30	23	4	3	84	32	73
Christ The King	30	15	10	5	60	33	55
Stockton	30	17	4	9	77	52	55
Woodlands WMC	30	16	4	10	60	45	52
Mount Nod H'way	30	15	3	12	75	63	48
Witherley United	30	12	5	13	52	60	41
Folly Lane BCOB	30	12	5	13	53	64	41
Dunlop Sports	30	11	7	12	59	60	40
Bedworth Ex-Serv.	30	10	9	11	60	55	39
Triumph Athletic	30	10	7	13	44	48	37
The Bell AEI Rug.	30	11	3	16	56	53	36
Hawkes Mill Spts	30	10	6	14	51	61	36
Ambleside Sports	30	10	6	14	46	63	36
Bulkington S & S	30	9	6	15	56	63	33
Bourton/Frankton	30	10	3	17	36	62	33
Potters Green	30	7	2	21	33	88	20

Division One	P	W	D	L	F	A	Pts
Christ King Res.	22	17	2	3	79	27	53
Peugeot Sports	22	15	4	3	59	24	49
Collycroft Sports	22	15	0	7	59	31	45
Alvis Res.	22	12	3	7	54	33	39
Copsewood Cov.	22	10	2	10	42	51	32
Coundon Court OB	22	8	6	8	53	43	30
Coventry Univ.	22	10	0	12	57	49	30
Coventry Colliery	22	7	3	12	40	63	24
Stockton Res.	22	7	3	12	46	75	24
Stock'ford AA Pav.	22	6	4	12	36	58	22
Nun. Griff & Coton	22	5	2	15	32	68	17
Kenilw'th Wardens	22	4	3	15	35	70	15

Division Two	P	W	D	L	F	A	Pts
Fillongley	18	14	1	3	70	31	43
Brooklands/Jaguar	18	13	3	2	60	18	42
Hartshill	18	11	4	3	72	28	37
Brinklow	18	8	3	7	32	27	27
Peugeot Spts Res.	18	6	2	10	34	52	20
Dunlop Spts Res.	18	5	4	9	37	55	19
Shilton	18	5	3	10	31	56	18
Folly Lane Res.	18	4	5	9	31	46	17
Coundon Ct Res.	18	4	4	10	32	65	16
Balsall & Berkswell	18	3	5	10	38	59	14

Division Three	P	W	D	L	F	A	Pts
Church Lawford	22	17	3	2	75	33	54
Whitnash	22	16	2	4	85	27	50
Mount Nod Res.	22	16	2	4	90	48	50
Brooklands/J. Res.	22	11	7	4	51	32	40
Jaguar-Daimler	22	10	2	10	45	38	32
Coventry Uni. Res.	22	9	3	10	47	44	30
Christ The King A	22	7	4	11	43	58	25
Copsew'd C. Res.	22	7	2	13	44	60	23
Bedworth ES Res.	22	7	3	12	29	60	21
Folly Lane A	22	5	4	13	34	64	18
Bulkington Res.	22	5	2	15	36	64	17
Sporting Club GNP	22	3	4	15	32	83	13

CRAVEN & DISTRICT FA
(Devonshire Carpets)

Premier Division	P	W	D	L	F	A	Pts
Long Lee Juniors	20	15	3	2	69	20	48
Cowling *-1*	20	12	4	4	62	30	39
Skipton LMS	20	13	3	4	63	40	39
Rolls	20	11	4	5	53	46	37
Grassington Utd	20	10	4	6	53	38	34
Gargrave	20	8	2	10	53	58	26
WFC Clitheroe	20	7	4	9	44	45	25
Grindleton	20	6	5	9	47	54	23
Pendle Athletic	20	5	4	11	33	44	19
Waddington	20	3	1	16	39	84	10
Cononley Sports	20	2	2	16	41	98	8

Hellifield Sports - record expunged

Division One	P	W	D	L	F	A	Pts
Embsay	26	18	2	6	64	30	56
Ighton Leigh	26	17	2	7	89	57	53
Bingley Town	26	16	3	7	70	43	51
Settle United	26	16	2	8	87	51	50
Trawden Celtic	26	14	5	7	76	56	47
Chatburn *-3*	26	16	1	9	68	50	46
Oxenhope R. Res.	26	14	2	10	87	52	44
Silsden White Star	26	13	5	8	69	47	44
AFC Padiham	26	10	4	12	50	61	34
Skipton LMS Res.	26	7	5	14	58	56	26
Oakworth	26	7	3	16	43	62	24
Bradley	26	5	7	14	39	69	22
Skipton Town	26	3	4	19	32	116	13
Gargrave Res.	26	3	1	22	22	104	10

Division Two	P	W	D	L	F	A	Pts
Carleton	26	22	0	4	114	21	66
Wilsden Juniors	26	21	1	4	139	29	64
Earby Town	26	19	2	5	88	35	59
Rolls Res.	26	18	4	4	93	36	58
Long Lee J. Res.	26	16	2	8	92	45	50
Pendle Ren'gades	26	14	2	10	73	50	44
Embsay Res.	26	14	2	10	55	57	44
Ingrow & Worh V.	26	13	1	12	92	69	40
Grindleton Res.	26	11	4	11	63	70	37
Grass'gton Res. *-3*	26	9	1	16	55	76	25
Barn'wick Barons	26	6	1	19	65	102	19
Oakworth Res.	26	3	0	23	52	96	9
Cononley S. Res.	26	3	0	23	47	164	9
Skipton Town Res.	26	3	0	23	12	190	9

CRAWLEY & DISTRICT LEAGUE

Premier Division	P	W	D	L	F	A	Pts
Merstham Newton	16	13	3	0	52	15	42
Faygate United A	16	11	2	3	61	28	35
Furnace G. Galaxy	16	10	3	3	46	17	33
Phoenix United	16	10	2	4	40	22	32
Chagos Island	16	6	2	8	30	36	20
Broadfield	16	6	1	9	43	52	19
Ifield Edwards Res.	16	4	1	11	35	61	13
Real Hydraquip	16	2	4	10	27	54	10
Maidenbower Vill.	16	0	2	14	14	63	2

Division One	P	W	D	L	F	A	Pts
Sporting Crawley	14	13	1	0	61	19	40
Wingspan	14	9	2	3	50	27	29
Border Wanderers	14	9	1	4	63	35	28
Phoenix Utd Res.	14	6	3	5	36	30	21
Horley Wanderers	14	6	1	7	34	38	19
Rowfant Village	14	3	3	8	34	53	12
R. Hydraquip Res.	14	2	2	10	26	49	8
Worth Park Rgrs	14	1	1	12	29	82	4

Bewbush United, Ifields Edwards A - records expunged

Division Two	P	W	D	L	F	A	Pts
Ifield Edwards B	18	15	1	2	67	28	46
FG Galaxy Res.	18	14	1	3	75	20	43
Sptg Crawley Res.	18	11	2	5	69	50	35
Cherry Lane	18	6	4	8	30	40	22
Stones	18	4	2	12	38	79	14
Sporting Devils	18	3	2	13	42	73	11
Wingspan Res.	18	2	4	12	41	72	10

Broadfields Res. - record expunged

CREWE & DISTRICT LEAGUE

	P	W	D	L	F	A	Pts
MMU Cheshire	22	18	2	2	80	28	56
Barnton Res.	22	14	2	6	68	41	44
Sandbach Utd A	22	12	2	8	82	50	38
Curshaws	22	11	5	6	48	39	38
Tarporley V. Res.	22	10	4	8	53	34	34
Lostock G. Res.	22	10	1	11	48	65	31
Bentley FC	22	9	3	10	75	68	30
Sandbach Town	22	9	2	11	56	63	29
Malpas Res.	22	7	6	9	38	47	27
Winnington A. Res.	22	8	3	11	46	81	27
Cuddington	22	4	3	15	48	70	15
Winnington Ave.	22	3	1	18	39	95	10

CROOK & DISTRICT LEAGUE
(Frank Hudson Transport)

Division One	P	W	D	L	F	A	Pts
Coundon/Leeholme	12	10	1	1	52	10	31
Shildon ERWMC	12	10	0	2	38	18	30
Middlestone MMA	12	6	1	5	29	35	19
Roddymoor -6	12	7	1	4	47	24	16
Barnard Castle	12	3	1	8	25	47	10
H-le-W. Australian	12	2	0	10	22	57	6
Willington WMC -3	12	1	2	9	22	44	2

Bishop Auckland Cumberland Arms - record expunged

Division Two	P	W	D	L	F	A	Pts
Evenw'd White S.	16	11	2	3	39	24	35
Framwellgate MS	16	10	3	3	64	22	33
Stanhope T. S&S	16	10	2	4	44	35	32
BA Masons Arms	16	6	3	7	42	38	21
Wearhead United	16	7	0	9	30	34	21
Heighington	16	5	4	7	37	51	19
N Ayc. Cumby Rov.	16	5	3	8	36	48	18
Crook Town Wdrs	16	4	4	8	27	34	16
Etherley Welf. -3	16	2	3	11	26	59	6

CUMBERLAND COUNTY LEAGUE
(Tesco)

Premier Division	P	W	D	L	F	A	Pts
Netherhall	18	15	2	1	62	16	47
Longtown	18	14	1	3	56	16	43
Aspatria	18	10	4	4	60	26	34
Cockermouth	18	10	4	4	47	19	34
Wigton Harriers	18	9	3	6	33	28	30
Mirehouse	18	7	2	9	37	39	23
Bransty Rangers	18	7	0	11	45	59	21
Friz'gton Whitestar	18	4	4	10	23	48	16
Whitehaven Amtr	18	4	0	14	27	49	12
Whitehvn Mnrs -3	18	0	0	18	17	107	-3

Division One	P	W	D	L	F	A	Pts
Carlisle Amateurs	22	17	3	2	87	23	54
FC32	22	15	4	3	94	29	49
Carlisle C. Res.	22	13	5	4	68	25	44
Cleator M. Res. -3	22	11	3	8	56	52	33
Sth Workington -3	22	10	5	7	51	42	32
Wigton Athletic -3	22	10	4	8	62	59	31
Hts of Liddesdale	22	8	5	9	64	57	29
Silloth	22	7	5	10	44	47	26
Windscale Res.	22	6	4	12	39	58	22
Parton United	22	5	3	14	40	70	18
St Bees -3	22	6	2	14	53	79	17
Parton Utd Res.	22	2	1	19	16	133	7

DONCASTER SENIOR LEAGUE

Premier Division	P	W	D	L	F	A	Pts
Edlington Town	30	22	4	4	90	38	70
Swinton Station A.	30	16	8	6	65	37	56
Mexboro. Pocket	30	17	3	10	64	43	54
Kinsley Boys Res.	30	16	5	9	80	48	53
Retford Town	30	16	3	11	84	64	51
Ross'ton M. Res.	30	14	7	9	78	64	49
Hemsworth Alpha	30	13	8	9	71	59	47
FC Thorne Town	30	12	8	10	71	58	44
Sutton Rovers	30	12	5	13	65	58	41
Askern Villa Res.	30	12	3	15	65	77	39
South Kirkby Res.	30	11	5	14	62	90	38
Doncaster Deaf	30	9	4	17	60	79	31
Yorks Main Res.	30	9	4	17	60	84	31
South Elmsall Res.	30	8	6	16	57	99	30
Edlington Rangers	30	6	6	18	53	94	24
Bawtry Town	30	6	3	21	49	82	21

Division One	P	W	D	L	F	A	Pts
Maltby MW JFC	26	21	4	1	94	27	67
Swinton Station	26	16	3	7	84	45	51
Ackworth United	26	14	4	8	69	43	46
Bramley SJ Res.	26	14	1	11	66	65	43
ISG Doncaster	26	12	5	9	60	57	41
Adwick Park Rgrs	26	12	4	10	83	52	40
Woodlands Rhinos	26	10	7	9	64	76	37
Carcroft Village	26	10	4	12	84	65	34
FC Tavern	26	11	1	14	65	80	34
Bawtry Town Res.	26	11	0	15	66	92	33
Upton Brookside	26	9	2	15	44	80	29
S. Kirkby Travel.	26	8	4	14	56	61	28
H'wth Alpha Res.	26	7	5	14	47	64	26
South Kirkby	26	5	0	21	35	110	15

DUCHY LEAGUE
(Bodmin Sports Trophies)

Premier Division	P	W	D	L	F	A	Pts
St Teath	22	19	1	2	107	16	58
Gunnislake +2	22	17	4	1	71	20	57
Torpoint Ath. A -3	22	16	1	5	70	25	46
Saltash Unted A	22	12	2	8	49	46	38
Fowey United	22	12	1	9	82	50	37
Lamerton	22	9	5	8	42	56	32
St Mawgan	22	6	4	12	41	61	22
St Cleer	22	6	4	12	54	76	22
Looe Town -1	22	5	7	10	46	65	21
Foxhole S. Res. +3	22	5	3	14	27	67	21
St Dominick Res.	22	6	2	14	35	66	20
Pensilva	22	0	4	18	25	101	4

Division One	P	W	D	L	F	A	Pts
Altarnun	22	16	2	4	51	26	50
Mevagissey	22	15	0	7	58	30	45
Probus Res. -3	22	14	3	5	49	24	42
Launceston Utd	22	13	2	7	54	46	41
Tywardreath RBL	22	11	2	9	56	44	35
Bodmin Saints -3	22	11	1	10	56	42	31
Grampound	22	6	8	8	36	46	26
Boscastle	22	8	2	12	47	58	26
Week St Mary	22	7	5	10	41	54	26
Godolphin A. Res.	22	5	5	12	42	39	20
St Stephen Res.	22	5	5	12	36	61	20
Maker-with-Rame	22	3	1	18	28	84	10

Division Two	P	W	D	L	F	A	Pts
St Newlyn East	24	19	2	3	102	49	59
Looe Town Res.	24	15	2	7	85	49	47
Bere Alston Res.	24	15	1	8	81	51	46
Pelynt	24	12	6	6	67	49	42
Lanreath Res.	24	13	2	9	64	50	41
Polperro Res.	24	12	5	7	63	54	41
Calstock	24	12	3	9	77	66	39
Lostwithiel	24	8	4	12	61	66	28
Holywell Bay/Cub.	24	6	7	11	46	61	25
St Breward	24	7	3	14	38	72	24
AFC Bodmin	24	6	5	13	58	65	23
Camelford A	24	4	4	16	40	90	16
Delabole Utd -6	24	4	2	18	36	96	8

Division Three	P	W	D	L	F	A	Pts
St Austell Res.	24	21	2	1	91	29	65
Premier Sixes	24	18	3	3	109	32	57
St Dennis Res.	24	14	5	5	60	34	47
Gunnislake Res.	24	15	2	7	71	51	47
Queens Rangers	24	12	4	8	52	41	40
Wadebridge T. A	24	10	6	8	52	41	36
Stratton United	24	11	1	12	71	53	34
Biscovey Res.	24	10	3	11	58	65	33
Roche Res.	24	10	3	11	51	67	33
St Minver	24	9	3	12	50	55	30
Nanpean R. Res.	24	3	3	18	33	86	12
Pensilva Res.	24	3	1	20	18	95	10
Gorran Res. -3	24	1	2	21	27	94	2

Division Four	P	W	D	L	F	A	Pts
Charle	24	16	6	2	66	23	54
Sticker Res.	24	15	3	6	57	22	48
Lewdown Rovers	24	13	6	5	52	44	45
Tingatel	24	13	2	9	58	56	41
Callington Town A	24	11	7	6	69	61	40
Mount Charles -3	24	11	3	10	56	52	33
Altarnun Res.	24	10	2	12	53	54	32
North Petherwin	24	9	4	11	71	69	31
St Teath Res.	24	8	6	10	54	59	30
Southgate Seniors	24	9	2	13	43	48	29
Newquay Minor -3	24	7	4	13	43	57	22
Stoke Climsland	24	7	0	17	31	70	21
Grampound Res.	24	2	5	17	34	72	11

Division Five	P	W	D	L	F	A	Pts
Charlest'n Sts +3	24	19	1	4	81	27	61
St Cleer Res.	24	19	1	4	134	42	58
Tregony	24	18	2	4	96	32	56
Padstow United	24	16	2	6	88	38	50
Bridgerule -3	24	15	0	9	73	58	42
Pelynt Res.	24	9	4	11	44	65	31
Mev'gissey Res. -3	24	9	4	11	67	62	28
North Hill	24	8	3	13	56	62	27
St N'lyn E. Res. -3	24	8	4	12	38	82	25
St Mawgan Res. -3	24	8	2	14	36	59	23
Duke of Cornwall	24	5	2	17	37	94	17
Boscastle Res.	24	3	6	15	34	75	15
Delabole Res. -3	24	2	3	19	24	112	6

DURHAM ALLIANCE
(Carcraft)

	P	W	D	L	F	A	Pts
Whitehill	28	24	2	2	147	26	74
Cornforth United	28	18	5	5	87	53	59
Hartlepool Town	28	17	5	6	75	48	56
Brandon BL	28	14	3	11	78	72	45
Birtley Town Res.	28	12	7	9	68	61	43
Shildon Railway -1	28	12	6	10	53	55	41
Brandon U. Res.	28	10	6	12	56	66	36
Simonside Social	28	9	9	10	67	78	36
Wheatley Hill SC	28	10	4	14	61	76	34
Hebburn T. Jnrs	28	10	4	14	67	83	34
Washington Town	28	9	6	13	58	75	33
Leam Rangers	28	7	8	13	61	65	29
H'pool St Francis	28	8	4	16	57	86	28
Ebchester	28	5	8	15	58	86	23
Durham Gdn Hse	28	5	3	20	35	98	18

EAST BERKSHIRE LEAGUE

Premier Division	P	W	D	L	F	A	Pts
Waltham	22	13	6	3	55	27	45
Slough Heating	22	12	5	5	45	28	41
Wraysbury	21	12	4	5	44	27	40
Slough Laurenc.	22	12	2	8	58	40	38
FC Beaconsf'd -3	22	12	2	8	50	34	35
Orchard Pk R. +3	22	9	5	8	47	34	35
Ad. Cunningham	21	8	3	10	46	61	27
Windsor Great Pk	22	7	3	12	38	46	24
Chalvey WMC Sp.	22	6	5	11	35	65	23
Iver Heath Rovers	22	7	1	14	37	59	22
Burnham Utd FC	22	4	9	9	28	37	21
Maidenhead Town	22	6	1	15	31	56	19

Division One	P	W	D	L	F	A	Pts
Stoke Green	20	13	3	4	52	24	42
Burnham Beeches	20	11	4	5	52	28	37
Britwell	20	11	4	5	64	45	37
Eton Wick S & S	20	12	1	7	52	42	37
Falcons	20	9	3	8	42	45	30
Iver	20	6	11	3	57	45	29
New Hanford	20	6	5	9	43	52	23
Datchet -1	20	5	7	8	41	41	21
Stoke Poges +2	20	5	3	12	30	42	20
Old Windsor	20	4	7	9	28	54	19

Foxes - record expunged

Division Two	P	W	D	L	F	A	Pts
Delaford	16	14	1	1	67	17	43
Alpha Arms Acads	16	12	1	3	74	30	37
New Windsor OB	16	9	3	4	43	30	30
Richings Park	16	8	2	6	66	49	26
Slough Htg Res.	16	8	2	6	47	41	26
Burnham Swan	16	7	2	7	29	35	23
S. Laur'cians Res.	16	4	2	10	26	53	14
Campion United	16	2	1	13	21	63	7
Boyne Hill	16	0	2	14	31	86	2

AFC Langley - record expunged

Division Three	P	W	D	L	F	A	Pts
Beaconsfield Town	18	17	0	1	81	25	51
Stoke Road Legion	18	13	1	4	71	37	40
AFC Ascot	18	10	1	7	49	43	31
Braybrooke	18	7	5	6	48	39	26
The Mitre	18	7	3	8	46	57	24
Frontline	18	5	6	7	45	40	21
Hurley	18	5	3	10	26	56	18
Orchard Pk R. Res.	18	5	2	11	35	58	17
Willow Wanderers	18	4	4	10	49	58	16
Old Windsor Res.	18	4	1	13	27	64	13

Iver Heath Rovers Res. - record expunged

Division Four	P	W	D	L	F	A	Pts
Alpha AA Res.	16	14	1	1	81	19	43
Windsor GP Res.	16	11	0	5	49	28	33
Stoke Green Res.	16	10	1	5	46	34	31
Stanwell	16	9	1	6	37	32	28
Swinley Forest	16	7	3	6	42	40	24
Datchet CC	16	3	4	9	29	54	13
SA Stainash	16	4	1	11	24	60	13
North Maidenhead	16	3	3	10	27	55	12
Chalvey Spts Res.	16	3	2	11	30	43	11

Division Five	P	W	D	L	F	A	Pts
B'field SYCOB OB	16	12	1	3	64	29	37
The Crown	16	11	1	4	50	30	34
Upton Park Rgrs	16	9	5	2	50	16	32
New Park United	16	9	2	5	43	36	29
Maid'hd Partizan	16	8	2	6	41	38	26
Ad. Cun'gham Res.	16	6	3	7	40	45	21
Mercian United	16	4	1	11	29	53	13
Beac'field T. Res.	16	3	2	11	32	51	11
Wexham Royals	16	1	1	14	28	79	4

EAST CHESHIRE LEAGUE
(Trade Mark Collections)

	P	W	D	L	F	A	Pts
Boarhound	22	21	1	0	105	28	64
Club AZ Res.	22	12	5	5	78	52	41
Poynton Nomads	22	12	3	7	52	42	39
Mary Dendy	22	12	2	8	56	52	38
Wilmslow Sp.Res.	22	11	3	8	65	43	36
Inter Macc	22	11	2	9	59	49	35
Poynton Kings	22	10	3	9	66	57	33
High Lane	22	9	5	8	59	53	32
Old Alts Youth	22	6	4	12	42	62	22
Juno United *-6*	22	6	4	12	35	58	16
Old Alts B	22	3	2	17	34	100	11
Poynton A *-3*	22	1	2	19	27	82	2

EAST LANCASHIRE LEAGUE
(Donald Race & Newton Solicitors)

Division One	P	W	D	L	F	A	Pts
Rimington	26	20	4	2	106	40	64
Hurst Green	26	17	3	6	89	43	54
Enfield FC	26	15	4	7	73	44	49
Canberra	26	15	4	7	64	42	49
Langho	26	14	6	6	61	33	48
Stacksteads St Jo.	26	13	3	10	70	64	42
Worsthorne	26	13	1	12	71	56	40
Read United	26	12	4	10	65	52	40
Mill Hill	26	11	6	9	78	57	39
Oswaldtwistle SM	26	12	2	12	61	57	38
Goodshaw United	26	6	4	16	40	92	22
Colne United	26	6	1	19	45	92	19
Borrowdale Utd	26	3	1	22	37	117	10
Bacup CC	26	2	3	21	50	121	9

Division Two	P	W	D	L	F	A	Pts
Pendle Forest Spts	18	15	2	1	69	21	47
Burnley GSOB	18	11	5	2	70	33	38
Barrowford Celtic	18	12	2	4	51	23	38
Burnley Belvedere	18	8	6	4	42	35	30
Padiham A	18	9	1	8	42	46	28
Rock Rovers	18	7	4	7	40	47	25
Feniscowles/Pleas.	18	6	3	9	46	41	21
Barnoldswick T. A	18	5	1	12	37	63	16
Clitheroe RBL	18	4	1	13	29	59	13
Peel Park	18	0	1	17	23	81	1

Sabden - record expunged

Reserve Division	P	W	D	L	F	A	Pts
Worsthorne Res.	26	21	1	4	109	40	64
Pendle Forest Res.	26	20	1	5	98	50	61
Langho Res.	26	16	4	6	99	46	52
Burnley GSOB Res.	26	15	5	6	85	58	50
Hurst Green Res.	26	14	3	9	79	45	45
Barrowford C. Res.	26	14	3	9	79	58	45
Rimington Res.	26	12	4	10	57	46	40
Oswaldtwistle Res.	26	11	6	9	54	54	39
Enfield FC Res.	26	10	6	10	53	61	36
Stacksteads Res.	26	8	5	13	51	71	29
Peel Park Res.	26	7	2	17	55	96	23
Rock Rovers Res.	26	4	3	19	40	85	15
Colne United Res.	26	4	2	20	36	100	14
Read United Res.	26	2	3	21	31	116	9

EAST LINCS COMBINATION

Division One	P	W	D	L	F	A	Pts
A&G Auto Repairs	22	17	5	0	87	20	56
Waltham Tea Gdns	22	17	2	3	75	24	53
North Somercotes	22	14	3	5	62	24	45
Saltfleet United	22	14	2	6	63	32	44
Louth United Res.	22	12	3	7	93	35	39
Sutton	22	11	3	8	67	35	36
Alford Town	22	10	2	10	50	42	32
Grainthorpe	22	10	1	11	65	53	31
Manby	22	4	2	16	29	90	14
AFC Louth	22	4	4	14	33	83	16
North Thoresby	22	4	0	18	32	86	11
Tetford	22	1	1	19	22	144	4

Division Two	P	W	D	L	F	A	Pts
Holton-le-Clay	22	17	1	4	70	23	52
Louth Old Boys	22	16	4	2	72	38	52
Keelby United	22	16	3	3	75	35	51
Barnoldby	22	12	3	7	67	42	39
Burgh	22	11	4	7	70	44	37
Scamblesby	22	9	4	9	51	47	31
Golden Fleece	22	10	0	12	59	69	30
Donington	22	9	1	12	57	63	28
Mablethorpe Ath.	22	8	3	11	61	78	27
Theddlethorpe	22	4	5	13	48	80	17
Nth S'cotes Res.	22	3	2	17	37	78	11
Sutton Res.	22	1	2	19	28	103	5

Division Three	P	W	D	L	F	A	Pts
Tetney Rovers	18	18	0	0	89	20	54
Chapel Swifts	18	13	1	4	73	24	40
Healing Hotspurs	18	12	2	4	74	37	38
PK Construction	18	10	0	8	61	52	30
Louth OB Res.	18	9	0	9	47	59	27
Mablethorpe Res.	18	7	1	9	47	66	22
AFC Goldn Fleece	18	7	0	11	37	53	21
Sutton Colts	18	4	3	11	43	83	15
M'bone & Cleaver	18	3	2	13	40	61	11
Ludford	18	2	1	15	38	95	7

Division Four	P	W	D	L	F	A	Pts
Waltham TG Res.	16	14	2	0	51	15	44
Holton-le-Clay Res.	16	13	0	3	55	19	40
Ingoldmells	16	13	0	3	70	24	39
Legbourne	16	5	5	6	39	33	20
Chapel Swifts Res.	16	4	3	9	39	49	15
Samuels	16	5	0	11	26	61	15
Sutton Veterans	16	3	4	9	24	32	13
Alford Town Res.	16	2	4	10	27	53	10
Theddlethorpe Res.	16	3	1	12	28	73	10

Alford United, Laceby Arms - records expunged

EAST MIDLANDS SENIOR LEAGUE

Premier Division	P	W	D	L	F	A	Pts
Derby Singh Bros	24	17	6	1	97	35	57
Heanor Colls Res.	24	18	1	5	74	42	55
Black Panthers	24	16	4	4	89	47	52
Allenton Sports	24	16	2	6	93	33	50
Sudbury Park	24	14	5	5	102	62	47
Loscoe Dynamo	24	10	1	13	69	53	31
Ambergate	24	8	4	12	47	66	28
GAD Singh Bros	24	8	2	14	59	96	26
Cotmanhay	24	7	3	14	38	60	24
Codnor Miners	24	7	3	14	51	87	24
Spondon Rovers	24	6	5	13	55	72	23
Derby Deaf	24	5	1	18	37	72	16
Stanley Common	24	4	3	17	37	123	15

County Sports - record expunged

EAST RIDING AMATEUR LEAGUE
(Admiral Signs)

Premier Division	P	W	D	L	F	A	Pts
Pinefleet Wolfreton	22	19	1	2	77	31	58
Eddie Beedle	22	13	7	2	62	27	46
The Lair	22	13	2	7	56	43	41
Sutton Fields Rgrs	22	10	6	6	53	47	36
AFC West Hull	22	9	5	8	60	42	32
Quaddy Rangers	22	9	4	9	52	42	31
AFC Preston	22	9	2	11	38	53	29
AFC Hull	22	8	1	13	50	67	25
Kingburn A. Res.	22	5	6	11	38	60	21
Swiss Cottage RBL	22	6	2	14	52	72	20
SC Electrical	22	6	1	15	42	64	19
Cavalier Wdrs	22	5	3	14	30	62	18

Division One	P	W	D	L	F	A	Pts
Bev. Road Rgrs	22	16	4	2	66	28	52
Goodwin	22	15	2	5	76	41	47
Willerby H. Homes	22	12	3	6	71	34	39
AFC Piper	22	10	5	7	56	49	35
West Hull United	22	8	7	7	55	62	31
Pinefleet W. Res.	22	9	3	10	73	60	30
Anlaby Park	22	9	2	11	53	62	29
Cross Keys Cott.	22	8	4	10	44	53	28
Paull Wanderers	22	6	5	11	45	51	23
Spring Bank Tigers	22	7	2	12	41	55	23
AFC Hull Res.	22	5	2	15	44	86	17
AFC W. Hull B *-1*	22	4	5	13	38	81	16

Division Two	P	W	D	L	F	A	Pts
Queens County	22	17	1	4	82	24	52
AFC Malt Shovel	22	15	3	4	58	28	48
Hull Corinthians	22	14	5	3	81	34	47
AFC Orchard	22	13	6	3	59	29	45
Banks Harbour	22	12	3	7	80	53	39
Grassroots (BHE)	22	11	5	6	71	54	38
Kingburn Ath. A	22	10	0	12	50	62	30
Duke of Wellington	22	8	1	13	36	61	25
Kingstown	22	6	6	10	55	65	24
Okapi	22	5	2	15	44	98	17
Orchard Park Utd	22	2	2	18	51	132	8
Kingston Tigers	22	2	0	20	26	53	6

EAST RIDING COUNTY LEAGUE

Premier Division	P	W	D	L	F	A	Pts
Hodgsons	22	17	2	3	75	29	53
Artfuldodgerny.com	22	16	3	3	74	32	51
Wawne Ferry	22	12	5	5	80	47	41
Beverley T. Res.	22	13	0	9	58	41	39
Viking Raiders	22	12	2	8	59	43	38
Goole Goods Office	22	9	2	11	52	48	29
North Cave Res.	22	7	4	11	38	59	25
Howden Amateurs	22	5	7	10	36	55	22
Holme Rovers	22	5	7	10	49	75	22
Easington U. Res.	22	6	4	12	32	74	22
Reckitts Res.	22	5	3	14	40	58	18
Sculcoates A. Res.	22	3	5	14	21	53	14

Division One	P	W	D	L	F	A	Pts
AFC Rovers	22	17	5	0	60	26	56
Driff. Evening Inst.	22	15	3	4	62	36	48
South Cave Utd	22	15	2	5	58	36	47
Park Athletic	22	14	4	4	59	26	46
Little Weighton	22	11	4	7	37	36	37
Gilberdyke	22	10	3	9	51	59	33
Beverley T. Jnrs	22	9	1	12	29	46	28
Mill Lane United	22	6	7	9	33	42	25
Haltemprice	22	6	1	15	28	60	19
Westella/W. Jnrs	22	4	4	14	29	41	16
Aldborough Utd	22	4	1	17	38	63	13
Trades/Lab. Club	22	2	3	17	22	35	9

Division Two	P	W	D	L	F	A	Pts
Hedon Rgrs Res.	22	18	3	1	76	24	57
Barrel Walkington	22	16	2	4	71	32	50
St George's	22	16	0	6	97	49	48
Withernsea Res.	22	10	4	8	55	65	34
Leven Members C.	22	9	3	10	63	66	30
Howden Ams Res.	22	8	5	9	44	49	29
Brandesburton Res.	22	8	3	11	36	50	27
FC Ridings	22	7	6	9	42	73	27
West Hull Amats	22	6	7	9	41	64	25
Skidby Millers	22	4	7	11	39	49	19
Long Riston Res.	22	3	5	14	45	79	14
Hedon United	22	3	3	16	25	34	12

Division Three	P	W	D	L	F	A	Pts
Wawne Ferry Res.	20	16	2	2	63	26	50
Waterloo	20	12	0	8	58	36	36
Hornsea Res. *-3*	20	13	0	7	63	45	36
Skirlaugh	20	9	3	8	54	47	30
Bishop Burton U.	20	9	3	8	45	58	30
Molescroft Rgrs	20	8	5	7	47	42	29
Mkt Weighton Utd	20	7	6	7	44	43	27
Patrington United	20	7	4	9	43	58	25
Roos	20	5	5	10	31	53	20
Highland Laddie	20	4	3	13	46	61	15
ER Rgrs Res. *-3*	20	4	1	15	31	56	10

Division Four	P	W	D	L	F	A	Pts
Haltemprice Rgrs	22	18	0	4	109	21	54
Sth Cave U. Res.	22	17	2	3	74	22	53
Shiptonthorpe Utd	22	17	1	4	61	28	52
Viking R'ders Res.	22	13	2	7	66	47	41
Eastrington Vill.	22	10	2	10	51	48	32
Leven MC Res.	22	10	1	11	58	50	31
Hedon Rgrs Jnrs	22	9	4	9	49	55	31
Holme Rov. Res.	22	9	2	11	44	68	29
Howden Town	22	7	2	13	43	71	23
Molescroft Res.	22	5	0	17	32	85	15
North Newbald	22	4	1	17	25	62	13
Brandesburton Ac.	22	4	1	17	27	82	13

Division Five	P	W	D	L	F	A	Pts
Goole Goods Res.	20	18	2	0	103	30	56
Eastern Raiders	20	13	3	4	68	33	42
Gilberdyke Res.	20	13	0	7	75	41	39
Hornsea Town A	20	9	3	8	57	48	30
Skirlaugh Res.	20	8	4	8	44	29	28
Mkt Weighton Res.	20	8	4	8	56	47	28
Haltemprice Res.	20	8	0	12	46	49	24
Withernsea A	20	8	0	12	35	77	24
Shiptonthorpe Res.	20	6	3	11	40	39	21
Easington U. Cas.	20	6	0	14	33	82	18
Eastrington V. Res.	20	3	1	16	18	100	10

EAST SUSSEX LEAGUE

(K & P Motoring World)

Premier Division	P	W	D	L	F	A	Pts
St Leonards S. *+3*	18	9	5	4	47	32	35
Rock-a-Nore *+3*	18	8	5	5	40	36	32
Sedlescombe	18	8	6	4	33	26	30
Hollington Utd *-6*	18	10	5	3	63	35	29
Peche Hill Select	18	8	3	7	49	33	27
Punnetts Town	18	8	3	7	34	36	27
Polegate Town	18	7	3	8	28	40	24
Peasmarsh & Iden	18	6	5	7	32	37	23
Jnr Club Tackleway	18	3	3	12	31	56	12
Hooe Sports	18	3	2	13	23	49	11

Division One	P	W	D	L	F	A	Pts
Wadhurst United *+3*	20	17	0	3	51	23	54
Robertsbridge Utd	20	14	4	2	50	20	46
White Knight	20	12	2	6	53	32	38
Mountfield United	20	11	3	6	43	27	36
Hollington Res. *-3*	20	11	2	7	45	43	32
Eastbourne Town A	20	7	3	10	37	35	24
Catsfield	20	7	3	10	35	48	24
W'sheaf Willingdon	20	5	4	11	25	44	19
Bexhill AAC	20	4	6	10	27	43	18
Crowhurst	20	4	3	13	30	47	15
Icklesham Casuals	20	1	4	15	43	77	7

Division Two	P	W	D	L	F	A	Pts
Peasmarsh Res. *+3*	20	14	1	5	55	44	46
Old Town Athletic	20	14	1	5	61	28	43
Ninfield United	20	12	2	6	51	37	38
Sandhurst	20	11	3	6	55	43	36
Hurst	20	10	4	6	56	43	34
Hastings Rangers	20	8	1	11	37	43	25
Cinque Ports	20	6	6	8	48	48	24
Northiam	20	7	3	10	45	61	24
Ticehurst	20	7	0	13	44	60	21
Herstmonceux *-3*	20	6	3	11	40	53	18
Battle Baptists	20	1	4	15	25	57	7

Division Three	P	W	D	L	F	A	Pts
E'bne Dynamos	18	16	1	1	58	21	49
Eastbourne Galaxy	18	14	3	1	61	18	45
Hawkhurst United	18	9	4	5	38	26	31
Battle Rangers	18	9	0	9	46	35	27
Demon Barbers	18	6	5	7	25	34	23
Beulah Baptists	18	6	4	8	30	48	22
Magham Down	18	5	1	12	27	40	16
Nelson Tigers	18	5	1	12	23	40	16
Hollington Utd A	18	4	4	10	37	55	16
Mayfield	18	3	3	12	27	55	12

Division Four	P	W	D	L	F	A	Pts
E'bne Fishermen	18	15	2	1	81	23	47
Cranbrook Town	18	13	1	4	67	25	40
St Helens	18	11	0	7	47	50	33
Travaux	18	10	1	7	51	44	31
Pebsham Sibex *+2*	18	7	5	6	32	30	28
Hast. Rgrs Res.	18	6	4	8	42	45	22
Punnetts Res. *-1*	18	5	4	9	38	48	18
Icklesham Res.	18	5	3	10	40	59	18
Ninfield Utd Res.	18	3	2	13	27	71	11
Burwash	18	2	4	12	26	56	10

Division Five	P	W	D	L	F	A	Pts
Orington	18	12	4	2	61	27	40
JC Tackleway Res.	18	9	4	5	27	30	31
Peche Hill S. Res.	18	9	3	6	39	26	30
Peasmarsh/Iden A	18	9	3	6	46	35	30
Victoria Baptists	18	8	3	7	43	29	27
Guestling Rgrs	18	8	3	7	32	32	27
Sedlescombe Res.	18	6	6	6	33	34	24
Bexhill AAC Res.	18	6	3	9	23	41	21
Eastbourne Ath.	18	6	2	10	34	46	20
Northiam Res.	18	1	1	16	16	54	4

Division Six	P	W	D	L	F	A	Pts
Wadhurst Utd Res.	16	14	2	0	50	10	44
Hastings Elite	16	13	0	3	64	24	39
HG Aerospace	16	10	2	4	53	25	32
Westfield A	16	6	2	8	32	43	20
Catsfield Res.	16	5	4	7	43	38	19
Parkfield	16	5	3	8	34	39	18
JC Tackleway A	16	5	3	8	24	46	18
Battle Baptists Res.	16	5	2	9	26	42	17
Heathf'ld Hotspurs	16	0	0	16	10	69	0

Division Seven	P	W	D	L	F	A	Pts
Magham D. Res.	20	17	0	3	70	26	51
AFC Sidley	20	13	3	4	67	20	42
Polegate T. Res.	20	13	2	5	61	25	41
Orington Res. *+3*	20	8	3	9	44	68	30
Sandhurst Res.	20	9	1	10	44	57	28
Eastbourne Rgrs	20	8	2	10	39	39	26
Hampden Pk Utd	20	8	2	10	47	55	26
Rob'sbdge Res. *-1*	20	6	5	9	29	42	22
Winkney Seniors	20	6	3	11	28	50	21
Ltle Common A *-1*	20	4	7	9	45	55	18
Herstm'ceux Res.	20	2	4	14	25	62	10

ENFIELD ALLIANCE

(GR Roberts)

Premier Division	P	W	D	L	F	A	Pts
Supreme Athletic	14	11	2	1	59	22	35
Haringey Union	14	10	2	2	50	17	32
Edmonton Golazo	14	8	1	5	11	31	25
Young Limers	14	6	2	6	20	27	20
Brimsdown R. Res.	14	6	4	4	27	18	19
Renegades	14	4	0	10	36	48	12
Larmans	14	2	3	9	11	40	9
Crescent Rangers	14	2	0	12	18	59	6

Holdbrook United - record expunged

Division One	P	W	D	L	F	A	Pts
Ed. Golazo Res.	12	11	1	0	45	10	34
PERME	12	6	1	5	38	34	19
Persian	12	5	2	5	29	32	17
Santos AFC	12	3	1	8	21	35	10
Wheatsheaf	12	2	1	9	22	44	7

Haringey Borough Res., Lea Valley Church & Community, The Lordship - records expunged

ESKVALE & CLEVELAND LEAGUE

(Wilf Noble)

	P	W	D	L	F	A	Pts
Boosbeck St Aid.	32	28	2	2	150	33	86
Dormanst'n Corus	32	25	2	5	135	47	74
Lingdale	32	22	6	4	121	45	72
Hollybush United	32	20	6	6	106	60	66
Lingdale United	32	19	3	10	104	70	60
Staithes Athletic	32	17	5	10	80	52	56
Great Ayton Res.	32	15	7	10	72	57	52
Goldsborough Utd	32	16	4	12	91	60	49
Lealholm	32	15	3	14	95	83	48
Stokesley A	32	13	6	13	92	91	39
Loftus Athletic	32	10	5	17	55	84	35
Boosbeck United	32	8	6	18	55	102	30
Carlin How WMC	32	6	8	18	47	94	26
Whitby Fishermans	32	6	3	23	53	142	21
Fox Inn	32	5	4	23	48	100	19
Brotton Rail Arms	32	5	4	23	45	127	19
North Skelton BH	32	4	2	26	37	139	11

ESSEX BUSINESS HOUSES LEAGUE

Premier Division	P	W	D	L	F	A	Pts
Flanders	18	15	1	2	62	18	46
Toby	18	11	2	5	46	27	35
Ultrachem TKO	18	10	1	7	44	35	31
AFC Kings	18	8	3	7	30	28	27
Brampton Park	17	8	2	7	44	38	26
Bancroft	18	7	3	8	28	33	24
Rainham WMC	18	7	3	8	36	45	24
West Essex	17	6	3	8	26	36	21
Loass	18	3	3	12	31	60	12
Melbourne Sports	18	3	1	14	18	45	10

Division One	P	W	D	L	F	A	Pts
West Green	18	16	0	2	90	27	48
Stags Head	18	13	1	4	50	33	40
Barking Boro. Sns	17	11	2	4	41	20	35
Juva	17	9	1	7	52	56	28
Blue Marlin	18	8	2	8	35	22	26
Platinum	18	8	1	9	41	39	25
Snaresbrook	14	5	1	8	27	35	16
Collier Row Snrs	17	5	0	12	28	55	15
Harold Park	18	4	2	12	30	47	14
Loass Res.	17	2	0	15	13	73	6

Division Two	P	W	D	L	F	A	Pts
Toby Res.	16	13	2	1	53	21	41
Barking Borough	16	11	2	3	46	26	35
S. Sabha Barking	16	10	1	5	49	32	31
FC Romania	15	7	2	6	53	35	23
West Essex Res.	16	7	1	8	36	42	22
Beckton CSI	16	6	1	9	37	42	19
Gem	16	4	2	10	19	24	14
Sth Woodf'd Wdrs	15	3	1	11	31	82	10
West Green Res.	14	2	2	10	27	47	8

ESSEX & HERTS BORDER COMBINATION

	P	W	D	L	F	A	Pts
Heybridge Res.	28	16	4	8	63	43	52
Thurrock Res.	28	14	7	7	62	47	49
Barking Res.	28	13	7	8	59	42	46
Canvey Island A	28	11	6	11	58	53	39
Waltham Ab. Res.	28	12	3	13	49	49	39
Tilbury Res.	28	10	7	11	50	46	37
Gt Wakering Res.	28	11	2	15	54	68	35
Bowers/P. Res. *+3*	28	5	4	19	36	83	22

FALMOUTH-HELSTON LEAGUE

Division One	P	W	D	L	F	A	Pts
Pendeen Rovers	28	24	1	3	98	28	73
Falmouth Albion	28	21	2	5	76	31	65
St Agnes Res. *-3*	28	21	1	6	91	37	61
Penryn Athletic A	28	18	1	9	82	43	55
Mawnan	28	14	8	6	70	46	50
Falmouth Town A	28	15	1	12	84	55	46
Constantine *-3*	28	14	5	9	65	63	44
Mousehole Res.	28	13	3	12	61	58	42
Chacewater *+2*	28	10	6	12	67	70	38
Perranwell Res. *+3*	28	8	6	14	60	61	33
St Keverne	28	7	4	17	44	69	25
Falmouth Athletic	28	7	3	18	63	67	24
Camborne Pk *+2*	28	6	4	18	38	94	24
Troon Res. *+3*	28	3	3	22	37	138	15
Holmans Res. *-2*	28	3	4	21	29	105	11

Division Two	P	W	D	L	F	A	Pts
Perranporth Res.	30	26	2	2	133	28	80
Mullion Res.	30	21	2	7	90	44	65
Carharrack	30	20	3	7	98	53	63
St Day Res.	30	17	5	8	87	48	56
Penryn Athletic B	30	16	3	11	61	61	51
Rosudgeon *-3*	30	16	4	10	89	54	49
Trispen *+3*	30	13	7	10	79	57	49
Culdrose Res. *-3*	30	14	3	13	61	76	42
Stithians	30	12	3	15	62	53	39
Frogpool & C. *+3*	30	11	2	17	42	96	38
Helston Ath. Res.	30	10	4	16	72	96	34
Wendron United A	30	10	4	16	48	78	34
Lizard Argyle	30	10	2	18	69	81	32
Mawnan Res.	30	8	3	19	56	101	27
Hayle A	30	5	4	21	44	82	19
Porthleven Rgrs	30	4	3	23	43	126	15

Division Three	P	W	D	L	F	A	Pts
Lanner	28	17	9	2	83	40	60
Stithians Res. *-3*	28	17	5	6	66	34	53
Cury *-3*	28	16	7	5	80	49	52
Con'tine Res. *+2*	28	15	3	10	102	64	50
St Day A	28	16	2	10	101	69	50
Pendeen Res. *-6*	28	16	4	8	67	55	46
Wendron B *+6*	28	10	5	13	59	74	41
Carharrack Res. *+6*	28	11	3	14	62	75	39
Frogpool Res. *+3*	28	10	6	12	60	89	39
Fal. Ath. Res. *+2*	28	11	3	14	64	79	38
Hayle B *+6*	28	9	4	15	73	88	37
Marazion Blues *-3*	28	12	2	14	76	59	35
Ruan Minor	28	11	2	15	60	61	35
Camb. Park Res.	28	4	5	19	39	95	17
Lizard Argyle Res.	28	4	2	22	36	97	14

Troon A - record expunged

FURNESS PREMIER LEAGUE

Premier Division	P	W	D	L	F	A	Pts
Vickerstown Res.	22	18	2	2	77	20	56
Kirkby United	22	16	4	2	77	37	52
Haverigg United	22	11	5	6	59	41	38
Barrow Celtic	22	11	5	6	54	40	38
Bootle FC	22	10	6	6	52	42	36
Dalton Utd Res.	22	8	8	6	32	23	32
Hawcoat Pk Res.	22	8	5	9	49	55	29
Barrow Wdrs	22	7	5	10	44	42	26
Holker Res. *-3*	22	8	4	10	38	59	25
Millom Res.	22	5	1	16	35	69	16
Furness Cav. Res.	22	2	4	16	30	67	10
Furness R Res. *-3*	22	1	5	16	27	79	5

Division One	P	W	D	L	F	A	Pts
SDO	16	11	3	2	57	19	36
Barrow Island	16	11	2	3	53	20	35
Crooklands Res.	16	10	2	4	56	27	32
Askam Utd Res.	16	10	2	4	49	22	32
Vickerstown CC A	16	7	2	7	35	34	23
Walney Is. Res.	16	6	1	9	39	40	19
Millom A	16	4	2	10	25	61	14
Dalton United A	16	2	3	11	17	51	9
Hawcoat Park A	16	2	1	13	16	73	7

Furness Rovers A - record expunged

Division Two	P	W	D	L	F	A	Pts
Barrow Wdrs Res.	18	16	0	2	110	17	48
Barrow Athletic	18	14	2	2	77	20	44
GSK Ulv'ston Res.	18	9	2	7	59	44	29
Swarthmoor Res.	18	8	3	7	44	42	27
Haverigg Utd Res.	18	7	4	7	27	36	25
Barrow Celtic Res.	18	7	4	7	39	54	25
Holker Old Boys A	18	6	5	7	47	45	17
Walney Island A	18	3	5	10	35	65	11
Askam United A	18	3	1	14	30	94	10
Furness Cav. A	18	2	4	12	24	75	7

Allithwaite Rangers Res. - record expunged

GAINSBOROUGH & DISTRICT LEAGUE

Division One	P	W	D	L	F	A	Pts
White Lion	18	14	2	2	60	29	44
AFC Friendship	18	13	3	2	65	25	42
G'boro. T. Canute	18	12	2	4	72	35	38
Harworth Colliery	18	6	1	11	22	57	19
Mattersey	18	6	0	12	33	41	18
Rampton Hospital	18	5	0	13	28	39	15
Retford Town Res.	18	3	0	15	22	76	9

Division Two	P	W	D	L	F	A	Pts
BFC Birches	14	12	2	0	71	13	38
Bridon	14	8	3	3	48	28	27
AFC Ropery	14	8	2	4	44	26	26
Wroot	14	5	2	7	46	35	17
East Drayton	14	4	5	5	28	35	17
Marshalls Sports	14	3	3	8	25	52	12
Fox/H. Will'gham	14	3	2	9	30	64	11
FC Blues	14	3	1	10	20	59	10

Blyton - record expunged

GRANTHAM & DISTRICT LEAGUE

Premier Division	P	W	D	L	F	A	Pts
Buckminster Utd	22	18	2	2	93	29	56
Whatton United	22	17	2	3	83	32	53
Ruskington Rov.	22	16	4	2	80	34	52
Greyhounders	22	14	4	4	65	26	46
RHP Newark	22	11	2	9	71	47	35
Barkston & Syston	22	11	2	9	52	51	35
Barrowby	22	7	3	12	46	51	24
Royal Queen	22	6	3	13	44	84	21
Ancaster Rovers	22	6	2	14	45	82	20
Bottesford Res.	22	5	3	14	44	72	18
Gran. Squash C.	22	3	5	14	37	82	14
Croxton	22	1	2	19	13	83	5

Red Lion Bourne - record expunged

Division One	P	W	D	L	F	A	Pts
Beehive United	26	25	0	1	115	23	75
Broadway Grange	26	23	1	2	121	28	70
Grantham United	25	15	3	7	80	38	48
Morton	26	13	5	8	76	67	44
Skillington	26	13	2	11	56	45	41
CK Dons	26	13	1	12	65	63	40
Baston	26	12	3	11	84	84	39
Lord Harrowby	26	12	1	13	78	85	37
Caythorpe	25	10	2	13	72	80	32
Heckington Millers	26	9	4	13	76	79	31
Harrowby Athletic	26	8	2	16	55	71	26
Pointon Colts	26	7	1	18	45	100	22
Ancaster R. Res.	26	4	1	21	46	121	13
Baston Res.	26	3	2	21	21	106	11

Three Gables - record expunged

GRAVESEND LEAGUE

Premier Division	P	W	D	L	F	A	Pts
Lullingstone Castle	21	16	2	3	77	16	50
Viewpoint	20	15	2	3	114	21	47
Craggs Farm	20	15	2	3	75	22	47
Millers Cottage	21	12	0	9	51	26	36
NK Aces	21	11	0	10	64	48	33
Stone Club & Inst.	21	7	2	12	45	41	23
Meopham	21	2	0	19	22	126	6
Woodlands Ath.	21	1	0	20	15	163	3

Division One	P	W	D	L	F	A	Pts
Earl Grey	18	11	1	6	57	33	34
Bean	18	9	2	7	41	34	29
Culverstone Utd	18	8	3	7	53	54	27
Viewpoint Res.	18	8	2	8	49	63	26
Fleetdown Utd B	18	7	3	8	45	38	24
NK Aces Res.	18	7	3	8	32	41	24
The Rising Eagles	18	5	2	11	52	66	17

Division Two	P	W	D	L	F	A	Pts
AZ 82	18	13	2	3	74	36	41
Ash Green	18	12	3	3	63	38	39
Kent Celts	18	11	2	5	47	27	35
Horton Kirby	18	11	2	5	48	29	35
Oakfield	18	10	3	5	50	39	33
Real Man of Kent	18	8	2	8	56	42	26
Joydens Wood	18	6	3	9	41	60	21
Fleetway Printers	18	4	3	11	32	61	15
Meopham Res.	18	3	1	14	34	62	10
YMCA Dartford	18	1	1	16	30	81	4

GREAT YARMOUTH & DISTRICT LEAGUE

Division One	P	W	D	L	F	A	Pts
Catfield *-6*	18	17	1	0	84	7	46
MK United	18	13	4	1	88	17	43
Albion *-3*	18	12	2	4	62	29	35
Lacon Arms	18	11	2	5	46	24	35
Shrublands	18	7	3	8	35	55	24
Gt Yarm'th Int. *-3*	18	6	2	10	37	53	17
Reedham *-6*	18	6	4	8	52	63	16
Hemsby Res.	18	4	2	12	24	79	14
Tramway	18	1	3	14	28	83	6
Gt Yarmth Peelers	18	1	1	16	27	73	4

Division Two	P	W	D	L	F	A	Pts
Bohemians	20	16	4	0	69	10	52
Norfolk & Chance	20	14	2	4	54	29	44
Caister United A *-3*	20	13	2	5	61	42	38
Gt Yarmouth Utd	20	10	2	8	44	32	32
Feathers	20	9	3	8	47	33	30
MK United Res.	20	8	4	8	43	48	28
Prostar Windows	20	6	3	11	33	53	21
Carpathians	20	6	2	12	38	57	20
Sth Yarmouth *-3*	20	4	6	10	32	49	15
Martham A	20	5	0	15	40	79	15
Gorleston Wdrs	20	3	4	13	36	65	13

Paperclip - record expunged

GRIMSBY & DISTRICT LEAGUE
(ABP Grimsby & Immingham)

Division One	P	W	D	L	F	A	Pts
Number One Pub	26	24	1	1	130	17	73
Imm. Bluestone	26	23	1	2	164	48	70
Caistor Tennyson	26	18	2	6	103	56	56
Nicol Construction	26	16	3	7	98	55	51
Imm. Blossom Way	26	13	4	9	78	84	43
Car Services	26	12	5	9	71	67	41
AS Motors Old B.	26	10	7	9	73	59	37
Mitchells	26	10	3	13	69	89	33
City Elect. Factors	26	8	4	14	50	83	28
FSRC	26	8	2	16	77	115	26
NELC	26	6	3	17	53	108	21
Fizz	26	6	2	18	54	103	20
Everyone Active	26	5	3	18	70	113	18
FB Old Boys	26	2	2	22	38	131	8

GUILDFORD & WOKING ALLIANCE

Premier Division	P	W	D	L	F	A	Pts
Pirbright Sports	22	18	2	2	70	25	56
Lightwater United	22	17	2	3	74	34	53
Holmbury St Mary	22	13	2	7	45	35	41
Millmead	22	12	4	6	60	43	40
Shepperton FB	22	11	4	7	54	41	37
Hambledon	22	10	4	8	53	30	34
Emmanuel	22	10	1	11	53	58	31
Windlesham	22	6	5	11	40	53	23
Surrey Athletic	22	7	1	14	33	60	22
Milford & Witley A	22	5	1	16	41	71	16
Ockham	22	5	1	16	25	57	16
Hersham	22	3	3	16	34	75	12

Division One	P	W	D	L	F	A	Pts
Abbey Rangers A	20	18	0	2	92	10	54
New Haw Wdrs	20	14	2	4	63	34	44
Spelthorne Spts A	20	9	4	7	48	45	31
Knaphill A	20	9	4	7	35	34	31
AFC Woburn Arms	20	8	3	9	45	37	27
Guildford CW A	20	8	3	9	40	55	27
W. Byfleet Albion	20	6	7	7	33	35	25
Puttenham United	20	7	3	10	32	54	24
Univ. of Surrey A	20	5	4	11	33	48	19
AFC Bedfont G. A	20	5	1	14	42	68	16
Weybrook Wdrs	20	4	3	13	35	78	15

Division Two	P	W	D	L	F	A	Pts
Tongham Res.	20	16	2	2	65	21	50
Cobham United	20	13	4	3	58	24	43
Weybridge Town	20	11	4	5	61	31	37
Oatlands	20	10	5	5	55	28	35
FC Shepperton	20	10	3	7	54	32	33
AFC Gomshall	20	9	2	9	47	50	29
Elstead	20	8	2	10	36	46	26
Lightwater U. Res.	20	7	0	13	34	49	21
Mytchett Rangers	20	6	0	14	28	61	18
Dunsfold	20	5	0	15	28	67	15
Windlesham Res.	20	4	0	16	32	89	12

HALIFAX & DISTRICT LEAGUE
(Ziggy's Spice House)

Premier Division	P	W	D	L	F	A	Pts
Elland United	20	14	1	5	65	31	43
Greetland	20	13	3	4	71	43	42
Ryburn United	20	9	9	2	53	35	36
Hebden Royd RS	20	11	2	7	52	44	35
Warley Rangers	20	9	5	6	43	41	32
Siddal Athletic	20	7	4	9	51	62	25
Holmfield	20	6	4	10	41	54	22
Halifax Irish Ctre	20	5	6	9	41	48	21
Midgley United	20	5	6	9	46	56	21
Shelf United	20	4	5	11	44	62	17
Calder	20	2	5	13	36	67	11

Luddenfoot - record expunged

Division One	P	W	D	L	F	A	Pts
Sowerby United	20	15	1	4	68	26	46
Stump Cross	20	13	3	4	61	26	42
Stainland United	20	12	3	5	49	46	39
Sowerby Bridge	20	11	2	7	55	46	35
Mixenden Utd *-3*	20	11	2	7	61	51	32
Northowram *+3*	20	8	2	10	45	55	29
Martin's Nest	20	8	2	10	50	57	26
Denholme United	20	8	1	11	62	65	25
Hebden Royd Res.	20	7	3	10	45	55	24
Brighouse OB A	20	5	1	14	29	48	16
Salem	20	1	2	17	27	77	5

Siddall Athletic Res. - record expunged

Division Two	P	W	D	L	F	A	Pts
AFC Crossleys	22	16	3	3	91	36	51
Volunteer Arms	22	15	5	2	68	32	50
Junction FC	22	16	1	5	65	42	49
Copley United *+3*	22	10	2	10	78	70	35
Kingston	22	9	5	8	58	60	32
FC Bull Head	22	10	2	10	57	68	32
Halifax Athletic	22	9	4	9	51	46	31
Shelf United Res.	22	7	4	11	46	58	25
Ryburn Utd Res.	22	6	3	13	43	62	21
Warley Rgrs Res.	22	6	2	14	49	69	20
Elland Allstars	22	6	2	14	47	77	20
Halifax IC Res. *-3*	22	4	3	15	44	77	12

Division Three	P	W	D	L	F	A	Pts
Greetland Res.	20	15	4	1	77	27	49
Sowerby B. Res.	20	13	1	6	80	36	40
Sowerby Utd Res.	20	12	2	6	50	31	38
Wadsworth United	20	11	2	7	58	41	35
Elland Utd Res.	20	9	6	5	56	45	33
Midgley Utd Res.	20	9	2	9	48	41	29
Denholme U. Res.	20	8	4	8	45	55	28
Crossleys Res.	20	9	1	10	65	81	28
Calder Res.	20	5	2	13	39	54	17
FC Bulls Hd Res.	20	4	1	15	51	72	10
Salem Res.	20	2	1	17	29	115	7

HALSTEAD & DISTRICT LEAGUE
(Treadfast)

	P	W	D	L	F	A	Pts
Rayne	18	17	0	1	87	22	51
Belchamps *+2*	18	9	5	4	70	34	34
Kedington *+3*	17	9	4	4	48	35	34
Acton Crown	18	10	3	5	45	33	33
Pebmarsh	18	9	2	7	62	45	29
Glem. Gladiators *-1*	18	8	1	9	52	49	24
Sporting 77	18	4	6	8	30	53	18
Essex Arms	18	2	5	10	33	45	14
Punch 68	17	3	2	11	25	71	11
Toppesfield	18	3	0	15	26	91	9

HARROGATE & DISTRICT LEAGUE

Premier Division	P	W	D	L	F	A	Pts
Kirkby Malzeard	24	18	4	2	85	30	58
Thirsk Falcons	24	18	2	4	76	23	56
Bedale Town	24	16	1	7	84	49	49
Kirk Deighton Rgrs	24	14	4	6	58	27	46
Bramham	24	14	3	7	56	56	45
Pateley Bridge	24	12	3	9	57	43	39
Harold Styans	24	11	1	12	60	57	34
Burley Trojans	24	10	1	13	52	68	31
Otley Rovers	24	9	2	13	55	57	29
Otley Town A	24	5	4	15	38	66	19
Killinghall Nomads	24	5	2	17	42	91	17
Sherwood	24	5	1	18	36	96	16
Harlow Hill	24	3	4	17	43	79	13

Division One	P	W	D	L	F	A	Pts
Harrogate RA A	22	17	3	2	93	39	54
Knaresboro. Celtic	22	17	2	3	84	49	53
Beckwithshaw Sts	22	13	2	7	50	32	41
Thirsk Falc. Res.	22	12	3	7	52	38	39
Bramhope	22	11	3	8	51	48	36
Pannal Sports	22	10	5	7	74	52	35
Harold Styans Res.	22	11	1	10	58	56	34
Masham	22	7	2	13	35	41	23
Pool Res.	22	6	4	12	33	50	22
Clifford	22	6	4	12	50	70	22
Kirk Deighton Res.	22	5	1	16	38	62	16
Addingham	22	2	0	20	32	113	6

Guiseley Red Lion - record expunged

Division Two	P	W	D	L	F	A	Pts
Wigton Moor	24	17	4	3	88	33	55
Westbrook Res.	24	14	6	4	85	41	48
Wetherby Ath. A	24	11	7	6	70	48	40
Harlow Hill Res.	24	11	6	7	52	43	39
Kirkby Malz. Res.	24	11	6	7	47	43	39
Pool A	24	10	2	12	51	48	32
Dalton Athletic	24	9	5	10	49	54	32
Burley Troj. Res.	24	9	3	12	50	50	30
Beckwithshaw Res.	24	9	2	13	45	66	29
Boroughbridge A	24	8	4	12	47	68	28
Pannal Spts Res.	24	7	6	11	50	72	27
Brafferton Rgrs	24	8	2	14	37	66	26
Bramham Res.	24	3	5	16	45	84	14

Division Three	P	W	D	L	F	A	Pts
Bedale Town Res.	24	20	4	0	94	15	64
Ripon Red Arrows	24	19	2	3	119	26	59
Wigton Moor Res.	24	15	3	6	77	46	48
Hampsthwaite U.	24	13	3	8	82	46	42
Catterick Village	24	13	3	8	67	46	42
Pannal Sports A	24	11	2	11	69	69	35
Otley Rovers Res.	24	10	2	12	72	74	32
Helperby United	24	9	3	12	61	81	30
Thirsk Falcons A	24	7	5	12	63	78	26
Ilkley Town A	24	8	2	14	51	68	26
Pateley Bdge Res.	24	8	2	14	53	103	26
Kirkby Malzeard A	24	3	3	18	28	83	12
Addingham Res.	24	2	2	20	34	135	8

HERTFORD & DISTRICT LEAGUE
(KB Tyres & Mercury)

Premier Division	P	W	D	L	F	A	Pts
Bengeo Trinity	20	15	2	3	68	17	32
Greenbury United	20	13	4	3	48	22	30
Cheshunt A	20	12	3	5	50	18	27
Broxb'ne Badgers	20	11	5	4	42	19	27
Westmill	20	11	4	5	56	31	26
Waltham Abbey A	20	10	5	5	40	37	25
Baldock Cannon	20	8	3	9	47	49	19
Goffs Oak	20	5	4	11	34	51	14
St Margaretsb'y A	20	5	4	11	35	62	14
Elizabeth Allen OB	20	2	0	18	26	69	4
Buntingford Wdrs	20	1	0	19	14	85	2

Division One	P	W	D	L	F	A	Pts
Saracens	22	16	2	4	67	22	34
Royston Town A	22	14	4	4	66	29	32
Harlow Link	22	14	2	6	77	38	30
Oracle C'ponents	22	14	0	8	60	45	28
Inter	22	12	0	10	66	56	24
Warewolves	22	10	2	10	49	37	22
Cottered	22	10	2	10	57	58	22
Bald. Cannon Res.	22	6	8	8	32	41	20
Waltham Abbey B	22	6	4	12	32	55	16
Wodson Park B	22	6	3	13	28	54	15
Watton-at-Stone	22	6	3	13	42	85	15
Much Hadham	22	2	2	18	32	88	6

Division Two	P	W	D	L	F	A	Pts
White Lion	22	17	1	4	104	29	35
Broxb'ne B. Res.	22	14	3	5	79	36	31
Roydon Spartans	22	11	5	6	56	41	27
Hertford Celtic	22	12	1	9	62	46	25
County Hall Rgrs	22	10	5	7	57	45	25
Braughing	22	11	3	8	46	38	25
Thundridge	22	11	3	8	42	37	25
Westmill Res.	22	10	3	9	58	70	23
Bengeo Trin. Res.	22	7	6	9	38	51	20
E'beth Allen Res.	22	5	4	13	43	60	14
Mangrove	22	4	2	16	35	113	10
Bunt'gford W. Res.	22	1	2	19	23	77	4

Division Three	P	W	D	L	F	A	Pts
Ware Lions Re-Utd	22	17	2	3	67	19	36
Nazeing	22	15	3	4	71	37	33
Broxbourne B. A	22	15	2	5	49	36	32
Ware Lions OB	22	13	3	6	77	34	29
Elizabeth Allen A	22	11	4	7	71	58	26
Mangrove Res.	22	9	3	10	44	50	21
Deaconsfield	22	7	5	10	42	53	19
Thundridge Res.	22	7	5	10	53	72	19
Cottered Res.	22	7	4	11	45	57	18
Westwell	22	6	2	14	38	49	14
Saracens Res.	22	4	1	17	44	71	9
Watton-at-S. Res.	22	3	2	17	52	117	8

HOPE VALLEY AMATEUR LEAGUE

Premier Division	P	W	D	L	F	A	Pts
Whaley Bridge	24	21	2	1	117	21	65
Dronfield W'dhse	24	19	2	3	71	29	59
Buxton Town *-6*	24	20	4	0	110	22	58
Dove Holes	24	16	1	7	75	42	49
Harpur Hill	24	12	3	9	58	40	39
Brampton FC	24	9	3	12	60	71	30
Tintwistle Villa	24	7	5	12	52	62	26
Grindleford	24	7	3	14	45	62	24
Dronfield Town A	24	7	3	14	34	73	24
Hayfield *-3*	24	8	2	14	59	86	23
Totley Sports	24	5	3	16	37	82	18
Hunters Bar	24	4	6	14	29	75	18
Buxton Christians	24	2	1	21	25	107	7

Division A	P	W	D	L	F	A	Pts
Bakewell Town	24	18	4	2	97	48	58
Furness Vale	24	16	5	3	89	38	53
Bradwell	24	16	3	5	70	41	51
Hathersage	24	15	2	7	77	42	47
Tideswell United	24	14	5	5	72	41	47
Whaley Bdge Res.	24	11	3	10	71	49	36
Blazing Rag	24	11	3	10	68	58	36
Dron. W'hse Res.	24	9	6	9	49	48	33
Dronfield T. B *-3*	24	7	5	12	46	72	23
Dove Holes Res.	24	6	4	14	43	69	22
Grindleford Res.	24	5	4	15	52	82	19
Buxworth	24	4	4	16	39	87	16
Queens	24	0	0	24	23	121	0

Division B	P	W	D	L	F	A	Pts
Peak Dale	26	19	4	3	87	36	61
Edale	26	19	3	4	108	45	51
Red Lion	26	16	3	7	88	52	51
Youlgrave United	26	14	7	5	77	40	49
Tideswell Utd BS	26	14	6	6	71	41	48
Eyam	26	15	2	9	88	39	47
Bamford	26	13	5	8	55	51	44
Calver	26	11	2	13	59	64	35
Stoney Middleton	26	9	6	11	36	42	33
FC Utd Tideswell	26	9	2	15	50	61	29
Baslow	26	6	7	13	48	67	25
Furness Vale Res.	26	6	2	18	49	80	20
Buxworth Res.	26	6	0	20	35	90	18
Queens Res.	26	0	1	25	21	164	1

HUDDERSFIELD & DISTRICT LEAGUE

Division One	P	W	D	L	F	A	Pts
Newsome WMC	22	18	4	0	93	23	58
Diggle	22	13	6	3	57	31	45
Lepton H'landers	22	14	3	5	57	37	45
Shepley	22	13	4	5	63	53	43
Uppermill	22	10	3	9	44	33	33
Britannia Sports	22	10	1	11	59	55	31
Moldgreen	22	9	2	11	51	58	29
Cumberworth	22	6	6	10	31	34	24
Hepworth United	22	6	4	12	52	70	22
Meltham A. Res.	22	5	6	11	35	53	21
Heywood Irish Cte	22	4	6	12	45	69	18
Wooldale Wdrs	22	0	3	19	21	92	3

Division Two	P	W	D	L	F	A	Pts
Netherton	22	19	3	0	75	34	60
Berry Brow Liberal	22	16	3	3	63	28	51
Skelmanthorpe	22	15	1	6	56	39	46
Lamb Inn	22	11	5	6	55	33	38
Scholes CC	22	9	3	10	40	41	30
Honley	22	7	6	9	53	55	27
Scissett	22	6	6	10	39	56	24
Westend	22	7	2	13	46	65	23
Kirkheaton Rovers	22	6	4	12	37	47	22
Slaithwaite United	22	6	3	13	40	52	21
KKS Ashbrow	22	5	3	14	49	75	18
New Mill	22	4	3	15	31	59	15

Division Three	P	W	D	L	F	A	Pts
Holmbridge	22	19	0	3	79	27	57
Royal Dolphins	22	16	2	4	65	33	50
Savile Town Res.	22	14	4	4	51	32	46
Brook Motors	22	12	1	9	60	46	37
Grange Moor	22	9	8	5	44	37	35
Upperthong	22	10	4	8	51	39	34
Dalton Crusaders	22	10	3	9	51	45	33
Hud. YMCA Res.	22	8	4	10	32	48	28
HV Academicals	22	7	1	14	29	57	22
Paddock Rangers	22	6	2	14	38	57	20
Mount	22	4	1	17	31	54	13
AFC Waterloo	22	1	2	19	26	82	5

Division Four	P	W	D	L	F	A	Pts
Shelley	20	19	1	0	129	21	58
Heyside	20	16	2	2	123	33	50
Linthwaite Athletic	20	12	1	7	79	64	37
Flockton	20	11	1	8	65	56	34
Fenay Bridge	20	8	2	10	45	59	26
Rastrick CC	20	7	4	9	35	52	25
FC Railway	20	6	4	10	47	100	22
Hade Edge	20	6	4	10	49	54	22
AFC Lindley	20	3	6	11	36	77	15
Sport Together	20	3	3	14	27	73	12
Cartworth Moor	20	3	2	15	27	73	11

Reserve Div One	P	W	D	L	F	A	Pts
Diggle Res.	22	17	2	3	90	29	53
Lepton H. Res.	22	13	4	5	53	32	43
Newsome Res.	22	12	5	5	57	28	41
Berry Brow Res.	22	10	7	5	51	41	37
Britannia S. Res.	22	10	4	8	43	42	34
Netherton Res.	22	11	1	10	64	50	34
Uppermill Res.	22	9	4	9	46	46	31
Cumberw'th Res.	22	7	4	11	39	58	25
Shepley Res.	22	6	6	10	30	43	24
Kirkheaton Res.	22	6	5	11	39	54	23
Meltham Ath. A	22	7	2	13	28	57	23
Heyw'd Irish Res.	22	1	2	19	26	86	5

Reserve Div. Two	P	W	D	L	F	A	Pts
Diggle A	22	17	5	0	84	25	56
Westend Res.	22	17	1	4	93	28	52
Honley Res.	22	13	4	5	49	33	43
Slaithwaite Res.	22	9	3	10	40	49	30
Uppermill A	22	8	6	8	43	41	30
Heyside Res.	22	8	4	10	47	45	28
Scholes Res.	22	8	2	12	49	74	26
New Mill Res.	22	7	4	11	42	65	25
Wooldale W. Res.	22	7	3	12	39	69	24
Upperthong Res.	22	6	3	13	36	45	21
Mount Res.	22	6	3	13	37	60	21
Meltham Ath. B	22	5	4	13	35	60	19

Reserve Div. Three	P	W	D	L	F	A	Pts
Shelley Res.	22	17	1	4	90	31	52
Netherton A	22	14	3	5	65	42	45
Honley A	22	13	2	7	75	37	41
KKS A'brow Res.	22	13	1	8	72	43	40
Kirkheaton Rov. A	22	11	2	9	54	48	35
Skelm'thorpe Res.	22	10	4	8	58	59	34
Cumberworth A	22	8	5	9	52	56	29
Holmbridge Res.	22	8	3	11	58	60	27
Brook Mtrs Res.	22	7	1	14	52	60	22
HV Acads Res.	22	7	1	14	42	81	22
Paddock R. Res.	22	5	5	12	50	63	20
Cartworth M. Res.	22	5	0	17	36	124	15

Reserve Div. Four	P	W	D	L	F	A	Pts
Britannia Sports A	24	18	4	2	86	33	58
Hade Edge Res.	24	17	4	3	90	35	55
Berry Brow Libs A	24	15	4	5	76	42	49
Westend A	24	12	5	7	66	45	41
AFC Lindley Res.	24	12	4	8	69	40	40
Meltham Ath. C	24	12	4	8	64	46	40
Scissett A	24	12	3	9	66	46	39
Flockton Res.	24	11	5	8	55	56	38
Netherton B	24	8	4	12	63	62	28
AFC Wat'loo Res.	24	6	4	14	49	79	22
Cumberworth B	24	4	1	19	34	108	13
Scholes CC A	24	3	3	18	37	92	12
Mount A	24	3	1	20	41	112	10

ILFORD & DISTRICT LEAGUE

Premier Division	P	W	D	L	F	A	Pts
Castle United	18	17	1	0	100	12	52
Redbridge Elite	18	13	0	5	70	28	39
Chingford Athletic	18	11	1	6	74	38	34
Forest United	18	9	2	7	62	49	29
East London Elite	18	9	1	8	48	39	28
FC Barolle	18	7	4	7	58	44	25
St Francis	18	7	2	9	33	41	23
London & Essex	18	5	2	11	33	51	17
Trelawny	18	3	1	14	29	115	10
Midland	18	2	0	16	33	123	6

Division One	P	W	D	L	F	A	Pts
Glendale	16	13	2	1	50	11	41
Chingford A. Res.	16	10	3	3	49	30	33
East Londoners	16	10	2	4	44	25	32
Esprit	16	6	4	6	35	29	22
St Francis Res.	16	7	1	8	33	39	22
Clockwork	16	5	2	9	36	45	17
Ryan A	16	4	4	8	42	48	16
Manor Park Utd	16	4	1	11	28	55	13
Newham Utd Res.	16	3	1	12	28	63	10

Division Two	P	W	D	L	F	A	Pts
Castle Utd Res.	18	13	1	4	68	25	40
Chingford Harriers	18	12	3	3	41	27	39
AAH Romford	18	12	2	4	64	33	38
RYPSA	18	11	3	4	34	25	36
Redbdge Elite Res.	18	10	2	6	44	34	32
Melbourne S. Res.	18	7	4	7	48	47	25
Ryan B	18	5	1	12	36	55	16
Val Park Athletic	18	2	6	10	24	31	12
Bethnal G. Celtic	18	2	4	12	25	85	10
Newham Royals	18	2	2	14	38	60	8

ISLE OF WIGHT LEAGUE

Division One	P	W	D	L	F	A	Pts
West Wight	26	22	4	0	90	13	70
Northwood St J.	26	22	1	3	90	29	67
GKN	26	16	4	6	75	43	52
Oakfield	26	13	6	7	73	50	45
Binstead/COB *+3*	26	11	6	9	77	50	42
Newport IOW Res.	26	11	6	9	73	49	39
Shanklin	26	8	7	11	47	59	31
Newchurch	26	8	7	11	53	69	31
Cowes Spts Res.	26	9	1	16	50	66	28
Carisbrooke Utd	26	8	4	14	51	69	28
St Helens BS *-3*	26	9	4	13	49	72	28
Brighstone	26	7	6	13	31	61	27
Sandown	26	6	5	15	38	61	23
Niton	26	1	1	24	18	124	4

Division Two	P	W	D	L	F	A	Pts
Brading Town Res.	22	18	2	2	75	22	56
Ventnor	22	16	3	3	80	21	51
E. Cowes VA Res.	22	14	0	8	63	36	42
Whitecroft/Barton	22	11	4	7	64	38	37
Rookley	22	12	1	9	61	42	37
Seaview	22	11	2	9	53	33	35
Ryde Saints	22	11	1	10	60	53	34
Shanklin VYCC	22	10	3	9	59	39	33
Arreton Athletic	22	6	4	12	45	75	22
Yarmouth & C'bne	22	4	4	14	41	68	16
Wroxall	22	4	1	17	40	115	13
Kyngs Towne	22	1	3	18	21	120	6

Division Three	P	W	D	L	F	A	Pts
Osborne Coburg	24	22	0	2	111	26	66
Pan Sports	24	20	1	3	113	41	61
Wakes	24	12	3	9	94	67	39
Bembridge	24	9	3	12	49	70	30
East Cowes YOB	24	6	2	16	58	114	20
Cowes Old Boys	24	5	0	19	52	98	15
Gurnard Sports	24	4	3	17	31	92	15

Combination One	P	W	D	L	F	A	Pts
West Wight Res.	26	20	2	4	96	30	62
Brading Town A	26	18	5	3	77	33	59
Oakfield Res.	26	15	3	8	65	43	48
Binstead Res.	26	15	2	9	62	57	47
Northwood Res.	26	14	4	8	63	53	46
Shanklin Res. *-3*	26	14	5	7	79	34	44
GKN Res.	26	14	1	11	59	46	43
Ryde Saints Res.	26	12	6	8	77	46	42
St Helens BS Res.	26	12	3	11	83	69	39
Whitecroft Res.	26	10	2	14	49	57	32
Carisbrooke Res.	26	8	0	18	71	139	24
Brighstone Res.	26	5	4	17	32	54	19
Sandown Res.	26	4	1	21	29	99	13
Newchurch Res.	26	2	0	24	21	103	6

Combination Two	P	W	D	L	F	A	Pts
East Cowes Vics A	18	17	1	0	69	10	52
Ventnor Res.	18	14	0	4	81	28	42
Shank. VYCC Res.	18	11	0	7	57	31	33
Osborne Co. Res.	18	10	2	6	56	38	32
Yarmouth/C. Res.	18	9	2	7	48	45	29
Seaview Res. *-1*	18	8	1	9	47	60	24
Niton Res.	18	5	3	10	20	38	18
Bembridge Res.	18	4	2	12	22	62	14
Wakes Res.	18	3	3	12	19	60	12
K. Towne Res. *+2*	18	1	2	15	19	66	7

KIDDERMINSTER & DISTRICT LEAGUE

Premier Division	P	W	D	L	F	A	Pts
Wyre Forest	26	21	1	4	94	40	64
Old Hill	26	17	2	7	71	35	53
Kings Heath OB	26	16	5	5	73	45	53
KS Athletic	26	14	7	5	50	31	49
Wollescote Villa	26	15	3	8	60	44	48
Birch Coppice	26	14	5	7	57	50	47
Cradley Lib. Club	26	11	3	12	57	55	36
Cookley	26	9	4	13	39	58	31
Oldswinford Harr.	26	8	4	14	48	54	28
Two Gates	26	8	4	14	57	70	28
Kinver	26	7	4	15	64	78	25
Burlish Olympic	26	6	5	15	37	64	23
Furnace Sports	26	4	5	17	45	85	17
Areley Kings	26	2	8	16	28	71	14

Division One	P	W	D	L	F	A	Pts
Lodge Farm	22	17	1	4	85	31	52
Dudley Wood Ath.	22	16	2	4	88	33	50
Dud. White Swan	22	14	1	7	63	43	43
Pensnett Roost	22	12	4	6	51	38	40
Orton Vale	22	8	8	6	47	34	32
Claverley	22	10	2	10	50	59	32
Old Hill Res.	22	7	5	10	44	48	26
Lodgefield Park	22	8	5	9	34	40	26
GDIS	22	6	6	10	30	50	24
Netherton Wdrs	22	4	9	9	43	53	21
Blackheath Libs	22	4	4	14	24	65	16
Three Crowns U.	22	1	3	18	20	85	6

KINGSLEY LEAGUE
(Hodgson Insurance)

	P	W	D	L	F	A	Pts
Phoenix Rising	22	22	0	0	134	19	66
Black Torrington	22	16	4	2	110	32	52
Lifton	22	14	2	6	65	30	44
Holsworthy A	22	11	3	8	62	47	36
Bradworthy Utd A	22	9	4	9	47	60	31
Week St M. Res.	22	8	3	11	50	97	27
Kilkhampton Res.	22	7	3	12	42	46	24
Tarka Athletic	22	7	3	12	36	54	24
Bridgerule Res.	22	7	2	13	68	56	23
Merton Res.	22	6	3	13	43	102	21
Hartland A	22	5	2	15	31	102	17
Morwenstow A	22	3	5	14	36	79	14

KINGSTON & DISTRICT LEAGUE

Premier Division	P	W	D	L	F	A	Pts
Claygate & Ditton	16	10	4	2	48	16	34
Summerstown	16	10	3	3	56	19	33
Chessington KC	15	8	3	4	36	25	27
AFC Molesey	15	7	4	4	36	15	25
Maori/Molesey V.	16	7	1	8	28	39	22
LM United	16	6	1	9	30	55	19
O Rutlishians Res.	16	4	3	9	22	45	15
SHFC London	16	4	2	10	23	41	14
Robin Hood	16	4	1	11	19	43	13

Division One	P	W	D	L	F	A	Pts
AFC Watermans	16	14	0	2	49	15	42
AC Malden	16	10	3	3	49	25	33
Kingston Albion	16	10	2	4	36	21	32
AFC Westend	16	7	2	7	26	30	23
Repton	16	7	1	8	32	26	22
Merton Rovers	16	5	4	7	30	28	19
Esher United	16	4	3	9	17	40	15
Thornton Heath	16	3	2	11	26	61	11
Wandsworth Cor.	16	3	1	12	12	31	10

Division Two	P	W	D	L	F	A	Pts
Maori & MV Res.	16	10	5	1	38	17	35
Darkside	16	11	2	3	45	30	35
Esher Res.	16	8	2	6	43	34	26
Oxshott Royals	16	7	3	6	29	24	24
NPL A	16	6	2	8	27	27	20
Epsom Casuals	16	6	1	9	23	38	19
Wandle	16	5	2	9	26	39	17
Surrey Fire	16	5	1	10	25	39	16
Lower Green	16	5	0	11	35	43	15

Division Three	P	W	D	L	F	A	Pts
Sunbury Galaxy	20	14	2	4	66	27	44
Old Rutlishians A	20	12	4	4	44	28	40
O. R'hamptonians	20	13	1	6	39	25	40
Red Star	20	11	2	7	60	35	35
St Martins	20	9	5	6	36	40	32
Surbiton Eagles	20	8	6	6	44	44	30
Double H	20	9	2	9	46	39	29
Chess'on KC Res.	20	6	3	11	42	52	21
AFC Hampton	20	5	5	10	37	40	20
Lower Green Res.	20	4	1	15	26	75	13
NPL B	20	2	3	15	27	62	9

Division Four	P	W	D	L	F	A	Pts
Rich. & King. OB	16	16	0	0	86	18	48
Summerst'wn Res.	16	12	0	4	57	25	36
Banstead Town	16	7	3	6	44	44	24
Twickenham Ath.	16	7	2	7	36	32	23
Westside A	16	6	4	6	22	30	22
Dynamo Kingston	16	6	3	7	29	35	21
Merton Social	16	4	3	9	25	41	15
Barnslake	16	4	1	11	24	53	13
Chessington KC A	16	1	2	13	14	59	5

Epsom Casuals Res. - record expunged

Division Five	P	W	D	L	F	A	Pts
Hook Venturers	18	13	1	4	66	28	40
Claygate & D. Res.	18	12	2	4	58	23	38
AFC Molesey Res.	17	11	4	2	51	18	37
Darkside Res.	18	12	0	6	38	33	36
AFC W'mans Res.	18	11	1	6	51	34	34
AFC Kingston	17	10	3	4	49	26	33
Stoke Rangers	18	4	1	13	22	47	13
Mtr Racing Ewell	18	3	1	14	29	68	10
Red Star Res.	18	1	5	12	16	59	8
St Martins FC Res.	18	2	2	14	15	59	8

LANCASHIRE AMATEUR LEAGUE

Premier Division	P	W	D	L	F	A	Pts
Little Lever SC	26	18	4	4	52	29	58
Chaddertonians	26	16	7	3	65	33	55
Howe Bridge Mills	26	15	5	6	56	33	50
Chew Moor Brook	26	15	4	7	64	44	49
Old Boltonians	26	15	1	10	62	48	46
Rossendale Ams	26	12	6	8	47	37	42
Old Mancunians	26	12	4	10	53	39	40
Bury GSOB	26	11	7	8	51	38	40
Failsw'h Dynamos	26	9	8	9	47	44	35
Roch. St Clements	26	9	8	9	42	46	35
Old Blackburnians	26	4	4	18	31	74	16
Radcliffe Town	26	4	3	19	38	75	15
Horwich RMI	26	3	6	17	27	68	15
Bolton Wyresdale	26	3	5	18	34	61	14

Division One	P	W	D	L	F	A	Pts
Horwich Victoria	26	20	2	4	103	43	62
Castle Hill	26	20	1	5	84	35	61
Ross'dale A. Res.	26	16	2	8	77	44	50
Prairie United	26	15	2	9	81	48	47
Hindley Juniors	26	12	6	8	67	53	42
Thornleigh	26	14	0	12	59	64	42
Mostonians	26	13	1	12	65	55	40
Broughton Amats	26	11	4	11	57	61	37
Ainsworth	26	11	2	13	52	85	35
O Blackburn. Res.	26	10	4	12	58	53	34
Little Lever Res.	26	9	5	12	55	53	32
Tyldesley United	26	9	2	15	46	65	29
Bolton Lads Club	26	3	1	22	40	113	10
Lymm	26	2	2	22	32	104	8

Division Two	P	W	D	L	F	A	Pts
Prestwich	24	19	3	2	71	24	60
Hesketh Casuals	24	18	2	4	92	44	56
Chad'tonians Res.	24	17	0	7	66	38	51
Bol. Ambassadors	24	14	1	9	67	46	43
Rochdale SC Res.	24	12	4	8	68	50	40
O.Boltonians Res.	24	12	4	8	53	45	40
Radcliffe Boys	24	12	1	11	70	51	37
Accrington Ams	24	11	2	11	62	60	35
O'ham Hulmeians	24	9	1	14	62	69	28
Old Mancs Res.	24	7	5	12	47	60	26
Bury GSOB Res.	24	5	6	13	42	57	21
Mostonians Res.	24	5	1	18	57	93	16
Astley Bridge	24	0	0	24	27	147	0

Division Three	P	W	D	L	F	A	Pts
Roach Dynamos	26	19	5	2	88	42	62
Chew Moor Res.	26	18	5	3	102	41	59
Ladybridge	26	15	4	7	89	54	49
Ros'dale Ams A	26	14	2	10	68	57	44
Bacup United	26	11	9	6	59	43	42
Castle Hill Res.	26	11	7	8	71	64	40
Ashtonians	26	10	7	9	47	43	37
Tottington United	26	9	5	12	44	58	32
Failsworth D. Res.	26	8	6	12	50	60	30
Bolt. W'dale Res.	26	8	6	12	59	73	30
Broughton A. Res.	26	5	10	11	61	71	25
Rochdale SC A	26	7	3	16	38	79	24
Little Lever SC A	26	5	5	16	46	75	20
Lymm Res.	26	3	4	19	37	99	13

Division Four	P	W	D	L	F	A	Pts
Chaddertonians A	20	15	1	4	55	27	46
Radcliffe T. Res.	20	14	3	3	76	36	45
Old Blackburn. A	20	10	3	7	48	43	33
Old Mancunians A	20	9	3	8	50	42	30
R'cliffe Boys Res.	20	9	3	8	43	40	30
Horwich Vics Res.	20	9	2	9	73	47	29
Horwich RMI Res.	20	7	8	5	46	42	29
Old Boltonians A	20	6	3	11	44	69	21
Acc'ton Ams Res.	20	6	1	13	49	72	19
Hesketh Cas. Res.	20	4	4	12	24	52	16
Prairie Utd Res.	20	4	3	13	40	78	15

Division Five	P	W	D	L	F	A	Pts
Hesketh Cas. A	26	16	2	8	79	59	50
Rossendale A. B	26	14	7	5	80	57	49
Old Boltonians B	26	15	3	8	94	60	48
B. Amb'dors Res.	26	13	3	10	69	57	42
Mostonians A	26	13	2	11	74	59	41
Thornleigh Res.	26	12	4	10	92	74	40
Oldham H. Res.	26	12	4	10	81	67	40
Roach Dyn. Res.	26	11	6	9	81	71	39
Rochdale SC B	26	10	6	10	63	61	36
Howe B Mills Res.	26	10	4	12	48	50	34
Ainsworth Res.	26	9	3	14	50	98	30
Bury GSOB A	26	7	6	13	54	77	27
Lymm A	26	7	4	15	72	88	25
Tottington U. Res.	26	5	2	19	65	124	17

Division Six	P	W	D	L	F	A	Pts
Prestwich Res.	18	13	1	4	63	27	40
Broughton Ams A	18	12	3	3	53	32	39
Radcliffe Town A	18	11	2	5	66	34	35
Ashtonians Res.	18	11	1	6	47	35	34
Chaddertonians B	18	9	4	5	50	40	31
Old Blackburn. B	18	6	5	7	39	43	23
Thornleigh B	18	5	2	11	49	66	17
Bolt. Wyresdale A	18	5	2	11	28	49	17
Old Mancunians B	18	5	1	12	38	54	16
Thornleigh A	18	1	3	14	25	78	6

Hesketh Casuals B - record expunged

Division Seven	P	W	D	L	F	A	Pts
Broughton Ams B	18	12	3	3	77	38	39
Rossendale A. C	18	11	5	2	61	37	38
Old. Hulmeians A	18	11	2	5	63	52	35
Bolt. Wyresdale B	18	9	4	5	37	32	31
Horwich RMI A	18	9	3	6	44	32	30
Rossendale A. D	18	6	5	7	57	60	23
Radcliffe Town B	18	5	2	11	48	60	17
Mostonians B	18	4	3	11	38	59	15
Old. Hulmeians B	18	4	2	12	33	59	14
Bury GSOB B	18	4	1	13	33	62	13

LANCASHIRE LEAGUE
(Galaxy Football.co.uk)

Division One	P	W	D	L	F	A	Pts
Harrogate T. Res.	24	17	1	5	66	30	52
Guiseley Res.	24	15	2	7	70	38	47
Ossett Alb. Res.	24	14	3	7	65	36	45
Farsley Celtic Res.	24	13	3	8	59	33	42
Wakefield Res.	24	12	1	10	55	39	40
Thackley Res.	24	12	1	11	45	38	37
Eccleshill Utd Res.	24	11	4	9	51	52	37
Bradford PA Res.	24	10	5	9	51	37	35
Ossett Town Res.	24	10	0	14	45	49	30
Silsden Res.	24	9	0	15	39	78	27
Harrogate RA Res.	24	8	2	14	40	52	26
Pontefract C. Res.	24	6	3	15	39	79	21
Yorks Ams Res.	24	5	1	18	25	91	16

Division Two	P	W	D	L	F	A	Pts
Southport Res.	20	14	4	2	64	21	46
Woodley Spts Res.	20	15	1	4	41	27	46
Lancaster C. Res.	20	13	0	7	36	26	39
Fleetwood T. Res.	20	10	3	7	54	49	33
Stalybridge A	20	7	7	6	37	33	28
Bamber Bdge Res.	20	8	3	9	34	34	27
AFC Fylde Res.	20	7	3	10	44	49	24
Formby Res.	20	5	4	11	29	46	19
Curzon Ash. Res.	20	5	3	12	38	39	18
Workington Res.	20	5	3	12	31	58	18
Barrow Res.	20	5	1	14	28	56	16

LANCASHIRE & CHESHIRE AMATEUR LEAGUE

Premier Division	P	W	D	L	F	A	Pts
Whalley Range	26	18	5	3	79	38	59
Spurley Hey	26	13	6	7	68	45	45
South Manchester	26	11	9	6	57	45	42
Rochdalians	26	12	5	9	52	51	41
Hazel Grove	26	12	4	10	51	55	40
Old Ashtonians	26	11	6	9	58	51	39
Mellor	26	12	2	12	56	55	38
Old Stretfordians	26	10	6	10	65	70	36
Govan Athletic	26	10	4	12	57	69	34
Hooley Bdg Celtic	26	9	4	13	62	64	31
Old Trafford	26	8	5	13	74	70	29
Bedians	26	7	7	12	40	60	28
Moston Brook	26	8	2	16	60	83	26
Abacus Media	26	6	5	15	50	73	23

Division One	P	W	D	L	F	A	Pts
Cheadle Hulme V.	26	18	5	3	81	33	59
Stoconians	26	17	7	2	73	33	58
AFC Oldham	26	14	4	8	75	39	46
Newton FC	26	13	4	9	50	49	43
Chorltonians -3	26	14	3	9	60	46	42
Burnage Metro	26	9	7	10	45	53	34
Parrswood Celtic	26	10	2	14	46	64	32
Eagle -3	26	10	4	12	57	58	31
Alkrington Dyn. -3	26	10	4	12	46	57	31
Newton Heath	26	8	4	14	54	65	28
Irlam Steel	26	6	9	11	42	57	27
Milton FC -3	26	9	2	15	60	78	26
Gatley	26	6	5	15	42	78	23
Hollingworth OB	26	5	6	15	47	68	21

Division Two	P	W	D	L	F	A	Pts
Deans	24	17	4	3	105	48	55
Heaton Mersey	24	16	4	4	69	36	52
North Reddish -6	24	15	2	7	67	35	41
Droylsden Ams -3	24	12	5	7	88	55	38
Tintwistle Athletic	24	12	2	10	65	52	38
Moorside Rangers	24	11	5	8	53	46	38
Aldermere	24	9	3	12	65	58	30
New East Manch.	24	9	2	13	62	71	29
Oldham Victoria	24	8	5	11	47	73	29
Santos	24	8	3	13	42	68	27
Norris Villa -3	24	8	5	11	46	84	26
VIP	24	5	3	16	38	73	18
Manchester Rov.	24	2	5	17	26	74	11

Standians - record expunged

Division A	P	W	D	L	F	A	Pts
Rochdalians Res.	26	22	4	0	88	24	70
Bedians Res.	26	22	3	1	78	9	69
Chorltonians Res.	26	16	4	6	84	47	52
Barr Hill -3	26	14	2	10	53	32	41
Mellor Res.	26	10	6	10	43	47	36
Whalley Rge Res.	26	10	4	12	65	70	34
Hazel Grove Res.	26	9	5	12	43	61	32
Urmston Town	26	9	4	13	49	68	31
Moston Bk Res.	26	7	10	9	49	69	31
O Ashton. Res. -3	26	8	5	13	40	59	26
Gatley Res. -3	26	8	2	16	46	67	23
Newton H. Res. -6	26	7	5	14	43	53	20
Sth Manch. Res.	26	6	1	19	45	88	19
Newton FC Res.	26	5	3	18	37	69	18

Division B	P	W	D	L	F	A	Pts
Alkrington D. Res.	26	19	3	4	87	41	60
Gorse Hill Athletic	26	18	3	5	106	49	57
Deans Res.	26	18	3	5	87	44	57
Old Trafford Res.	26	16	3	7	70	48	51
Burnage M.o Res.	26	15	4	7	56	46	49
Old Stretford. Res.	26	13	6	7	64	49	45
Spurley Hey Res.	26	13	4	9	73	51	43
Chorltonians A	26	13	3	10	71	64	42
Hooley Bdge Res.	26	8	4	14	58	71	28
Irlam Steel Res.	26	6	5	15	46	97	23
Stoconians Res.	26	5	4	17	42	71	19
Bridge Colts -3	26	5	4	17	49	92	16
Hollingwth Res. -6	26	5	5	16	41	66	14
Aldermere Res. -3	26	0	5	21	29	90	2

Division C	P	W	D	L	F	A	Pts
Cheadle H. Res.	26	18	5	3	88	44	59
Whalley Range A	26	18	4	4	110	60	58
Moorside R. Res.	26	17	2	7	87	57	53
Eagle Res.	26	15	4	7	77	50	49
Denton West End	26	11	5	10	78	83	38
Abacus M. Res.	26	12	1	13	73	83	37
Burnage Metro A	26	9	6	11	72	90	33
Milton FC Res.	26	9	4	13	70	83	31
Old Stretford. A	26	9	3	14	59	63	30
Droy. Ams Res. -3	26	9	4	13	77	77	28
Chorltonians B	26	8	4	14	62	82	28
Parrswood Res.	26	8	2	16	53	73	26
Oldham Vics Res.	26	7	2	17	59	96	23
Mellor A	26	9	0	17	62	86	21

Division D	P	W	D	L	F	A	Pts
Bedians A	22	20	1	1	87	27	61
Irlam Steel A	22	14	2	6	66	41	44
Staly	22	13	3	6	74	40	42
Chorltonians C	22	13	2	7	81	49	41
Stoconians A	22	11	6	5	59	36	39
Santos Res. -3	22	12	2	8	78	57	37
Govan Ath. Res.	22	10	4	8	43	37	34
AFC Oldham Res.	22	10	3	9	60	52	33
O. Stretfordians B	22	5	4	13	44	63	19
Denton WE Res.	22	5	1	16	37	97	16
Mellor B	22	3	2	17	37	82	11
Heaton M. Res.	22	1	0	21	22	107	3

Division E	P	W	D	L	F	A	Pts
Deans A	22	17	0	5	80	44	51
Hooley Bdge C. A	22	16	2	4	83	51	50
Old Ashtonians A	22	14	4	4	74	30	46
Chorltonians D	22	14	1	7	83	46	43
Burnage Metro B	22	10	4	8	56	54	34
Stoconians B	22	9	4	9	51	51	31
Moston Brook A	22	8	5	9	60	49	29
Newton FC A *-3*	22	8	1	13	50	68	22
Spurley Hey A	22	7	1	14	44	80	22
Aldermere A	22	6	3	13	36	61	21
AFC Oldham A	22	6	1	15	52	77	19
O. Stretfordians C	22	2	4	16	23	81	10

Division F	P	W	D	L	F	A	Pts
Moston Brook B	20	14	5	1	67	37	47
Stoconians C	20	14	2	4	71	38	44
Old Ashtonians B	20	11	5	4	63	41	38
Alkrington Dyn. A	20	11	4	5	56	40	37
Bedians B	20	10	3	7	53	39	33
Staly Res.	20	9	1	10	42	49	28
Whalley Range B	20	7	4	9	52	73	25
Chorltonians E	20	6	4	10	42	46	22
AFC Oldham B	20	4	3	13	51	76	15
Aldermere B *-3*	20	5	1	14	45	54	13
Burnage Metro C	20	2	2	16	19	68	8

LEEDS RED TRIANGLE LEAGUE

Premier Division	P	W	D	L	F	A	Pts
Halton Moor	20	14	3	3	95	37	45
Red Star Harehills	20	13	2	5	55	33	41
Halfway H. Morley	20	12	4	4	76	49	40
Woodman	20	12	2	6	90	48	38
Crossgates WMC	20	11	4	5	87	46	37
Churwell	20	9	4	7	81	53	31
New Farnley CC	20	8	5	7	60	49	29
Hunslet Res.	20	7	1	12	62	71	22
Seacroft WMC	20	5	4	11	46	75	19
Middleton Park	20	2	2	16	37	127	8
Ranch Legends	20	1	1	18	33	134	4

North East Leeds - record expunged

Division One	P	W	D	L	F	A	Pts
Beeston St Ant. A	30	23	3	4	137	47	72
Dudley Hill R. Res.	30	22	3	5	152	37	69
Leodis	30	20	4	6	146	57	64
Horsforth	30	20	3	7	118	47	63
P of Wales Brad.	30	18	2	10	116	74	56
Merlins	30	17	3	10	106	63	54
New Farnley Res.	30	16	5	9	97	55	53
S. Leeds Pythons	30	17	1	12	109	89	52
Drighlington Adw.	30	14	5	11	110	67	47
Churwell Res.	30	13	4	13	96	85	43
Drigh. Malt Shovel	30	11	4	15	76	76	37
S. Leeds Sts PA	30	9	2	19	66	113	29
Red Sea	30	8	2	20	72	111	26
Leeds Deaf	30	5	4	21	45	151	19
Ring of Bells	30	2	2	26	26	221	8
Middleton Pk Res.	30	1	1	28	41	220	4

LEICESTER CITY LEAGUE
(Liquid Envy)

Premier Division	P	W	D	L	F	A	Pts
Braders	12	9	1	2	69	30	28
S. Wigston Wdrs	12	8	2	2	48	19	26
Saff. Lounge Bar	12	8	0	4	44	33	24
Victoria	12	5	2	5	32	40	17
Swallow Rangers	12	3	2	7	32	61	11
Aylestone United	12	2	2	8	22	44	8
Wigston Athletic	12	2	1	9	27	47	7

Division A	P	W	D	L	F	A	Pts
FC Cricks	12	9	1	2	54	23	28
AFC Aylestone	12	9	0	3	53	27	27
Park End	12	7	3	2	58	27	24
FC Rowlatts	12	5	3	4	49	42	18
Cosby Victory	12	5	1	6	29	56	16
Shakha	12	2	0	10	27	61	6
Kirkland	12	1	0	11	17	51	3

LEICESTER & DISTRICT LEAGUE

Premier Division	P	W	D	L	F	A	Pts
Belgrave	24	17	5	2	87	29	56
Kingsway Rgrs	24	16	4	4	67	29	52
Magna	24	11	6	7	44	32	39
Mountsorrel Ams	24	12	3	9	76	65	39
Houghton Rangers	24	10	6	8	41	33	36
Blaby United	24	10	5	9	56	60	35
Cosby United	24	10	4	10	51	56	34
Birstall RBL	24	9	5	10	54	48	32
Oadby Boys Club	24	7	9	8	49	50	30
Mids Syston St P.	24	6	7	11	50	62	25
County Hall	24	7	4	13	33	49	25
Glenfield Town	24	6	4	14	38	67	22
Welby Lane U. *-3*	24	2	4	18	25	91	7

Division One	P	W	D	L	F	A	Pts
G. Nanak Gurdwar	22	18	1	3	91	37	55
Topps United	22	17	1	4	76	26	52
FC Kirkland	22	16	1	5	85	40	49
North Kilworth	22	10	4	8	41	42	34
Kibworth Town	22	10	4	8	54	64	34
Thurnby United	22	9	3	10	54	46	30
Glen Villa	22	9	2	11	43	53	29
Huncote	22	8	2	12	44	60	26
Hinckley Athletic	22	7	4	11	47	52	25
Queniborough	22	5	3	14	52	83	18
Burbage Old Boys	22	4	3	15	24	69	15
St Patricks	22	4	2	16	35	74	14

Division Two	P	W	D	L	F	A	Pts
Newbold Verdon	20	16	1	3	75	19	49
Leicester Tile	20	14	5	1	98	32	47
Birstall Social	20	14	3	3	58	18	45
Sporting Sapcote	20	12	0	8	54	36	36
Oakham Imperial	20	10	2	8	66	38	32
FC Barlestone SG	20	9	2	9	41	37	29
Fleckney Athletic	20	8	3	9	38	51	27
FC Desford	20	7	3	10	41	65	24
Thurlaston M'pies	20	4	1	15	31	67	13
Broughton Astley	20	3	0	17	11	77	9
FC Barwell	20	2	2	16	22	95	8

Reserve Prem Div	P	W	D	L	F	A	Pts
GN Gurdwar Res	22	16	4	2	66	33	52
Birstall RBL Res.	22	15	3	4	64	33	48
Cosby Utd Res.	22	12	4	6	50	39	40
FC Kirkland Res.	22	10	6	6	50	44	36
Magna Res.	22	8	9	5	46	40	33
Belgrave Res.	22	9	5	8	71	53	32
Houghton R. Res.	22	7	4	11	43	43	25
County Hall Res.	22	6	7	9	46	49	25
Glenfield T. Res.	22	6	6	10	43	50	24
St Patricks Res.	22	7	3	12	33	67	24
Glen Villa Res.	22	5	2	15	37	62	17
Welby Lane Res.	22	4	1	17	27	63	13

Reserve Div One	P	W	D	L	F	A	Pts
Kingsway R. Res.	22	20	2	0	117	17	62
Nth Kilworth Res.	22	16	3	3	85	40	51
Mountsorrel Res.	22	14	4	4	68	31	46
Oadby BC Res.	22	12	1	9	57	45	37
Thurnby Utd Res.	22	10	2	10	57	54	32
Topps United Res.	22	7	4	11	56	67	25
Queniboro. Res.	22	8	1	13	62	75	25
M. Syston SP Res.	22	7	3	12	43	57	24
Huncote Res.	22	7	3	12	36	55	24
Oakham I. Res.	22	6	4	12	48	82	22
Thurlaston M. Res.	22	7	0	15	42	91	21
Kibworth T. Res.	22	4	1	17	35	92	13

LINCOLN & DISTRICT LEAGUE
(W J Harrison Printers)

	P	W	D	L	F	A	Pts
Cherry Knights	20	18	1	1	95	23	55
FC Rustons Utd	20	13	1	6	98	43	40
Ivy Tavern CSA	20	12	3	5	86	37	39
Waddington Utd	20	12	0	8	76	46	36
Fulbeck United	20	11	2	7	59	39	32
Metheringham	20	9	3	8	73	47	30
Ruston Sprts Res.	20	6	5	9	52	46	23
Mkt Rasen Town	20	8	3	9	73	36	21
Horncastle Res.	20	6	2	12	44	58	20
Pride	20	4	2	14	45	53	14
Blacksmiths	20	0	0	20	8	281	0

LIVERPOOL CMS LEAGUE

Premier Division	P	W	D	L	F	A	Pts
Western Speke	20	18	2	0	115	26	56
King Charles	20	15	2	3	65	27	47
Carters Arms	20	14	2	4	87	38	44
Bennetts	20	11	2	7	73	52	35
Credit Union	20	11	1	8	62	49	34
Polonia Camps	20	7	5	8	40	50	26
Mersey Harps	20	5	3	12	29	66	18
Coyne	20	5	3	12	38	82	18
Vegas	20	5	1	14	29	77	16
Everton Deaf	20	4	1	15	22	82	13
Holy Name	20	4	0	16	16	27	12

Division One	P	W	D	L	F	A	Pts
FC Stadium	24	20	1	3	108	40	61
Phoenix United	24	19	1	4	114	40	58
Glasshouse	24	15	3	6	94	51	48
The Claremont	24	15	1	8	74	47	46
Elmoore	24	13	5	6	52	38	44
The Clock	24	12	1	11	64	60	37
Ev'ton Foundation	24	11	2	11	71	71	35
Ashgrove	24	7	4	13	49	85	25
Delagoa	24	7	3	14	56	78	24
Lowerhouse	24	6	4	14	37	71	22
Engineers	24	5	5	14	58	78	20
Mandela	24	6	1	17	60	126	19
Provey	24	4	1	19	56	108	13

LIVERPOOL OLD BOYS AMATEUR LEAGUE

Division One	P	W	D	L	F	A	Pts
Waterloo GSOB	18	12	5	1	39	19	41
Naylorsfield	18	11	2	4	48	28	38
Heygreen Old B.	18	10	3	4	47	26	33
Quarry Bank OB	18	10	2	6	45	41	32
Old Xaverians B	18	7	6	5	34	24	27
Oaks Institute OB	18	6	3	9	28	45	21
Wavertree WDOB	18	5	3	10	30	45	18
FC Salle	18	4	4	10	30	46	16
Bankfield OB *-3*	18	5	3	10	33	41	15
Cardinal Newman	18	2	3	13	31	50	9

Division Two	P	W	D	L	F	A	Pts
Old Cathinians	20	19	0	1	92	36	57
Quarry Bank Res.	20	14	4	2	54	40	46
Old Holts Res.	20	13	0	7	73	35	39
Roby College OB	20	12	3	5	57	47	39
Liverpool Medics	20	8	3	8	43	38	30
S. Coeur Res. *-3*	20	8	4	8	43	47	25
Ercanil Old Boys	20	6	4	10	40	52	22
Alsop Old Boys	20	6	2	12	49	61	20
Old Bootleians	20	6	1	13	42	52	19
W'loo GSOB Res.	20	4	3	12	40	67	15
Collegiate OB Res.	20	1	0	19	24	82	3

Division Three	P	W	D	L	F	A	Pts
South Mersey	20	13	4	3	66	33	43
De La Salle OB	20	13	4	3	48	21	43
Old Xaverians C	20	13	4	3	61	37	43
Waterloo GSOB A	20	11	2	7	46	35	35
Mossley Hill	20	8	5	7	51	48	29
Convocation	20	8	4	8	50	51	28
Blue Coat Old B.	20	7	5	8	39	48	26
O. Cathinians Res.	20	5	6	9	54	64	21
Alumni Res. *-3*	20	4	4	12	43	64	13
Corinthian FC	20	3	3	14	25	61	12
C. Newman Res.	20	2	5	13	22	43	11

Division Four	P	W	D	L	F	A	Pts
Quarry Bk OB A	22	20	1	1	104	19	61
O. Bootleians Res.	22	17	1	3	96	35	55
Alsop OB Res. *-3*	22	15	3	4	68	38	45
Card. Newman A	22	13	2	7	62	30	41
Old Cathinians A	22	13	2	7	68	46	41
Hope Park	22	10	3	9	60	57	33
Liobians A	22	7	3	12	57	80	24
Civserv	22	5	5	12	46	74	20
Kingsford	22	4	2	14	32	79	17
Rhein	22	5	2	15	26	74	17
Collegiate OB A	22	5	1	15	33	67	16
Richmond	22	2	3	17	30	83	9

Division Five	P	W	D	L	F	A	Pts
De La Sal. OB Res.	22	13	3	6	68	41	42
Quarry Bk OB B	22	13	3	6	71	45	42
Old Instonians	22	12	3	7	57	39	39
Old Bootleians A	22	10	8	4	74	40	38
Waterloo GSOB B	22	12	2	8	64	54	38
Essemmay A *-3*	22	11	3	8	65	56	35
St Mary's COB *-1*	22	10	6	6	49	43	35
Kingsford Res.	22	8	3	11	50	69	27
Business Sch. *-1*	22	6	6	10	52	52	23
Rockville W. Res.	22	6	3	13	34	69	21
W'tree WDOB Res.	22	5	4	13	34	61	19
Liobians B	22	3	2	17	38	87	11

LONDON COMMERCIAL LEAGUE

Division One	P	W	D	L	F	A	Pts
HFC	16	13	2	1	50	25	41
British Airways	16	13	0	3	70	26	39
Roxeth	16	12	1	3	53	26	37
Shebu Allstars	16	7	2	7	43	38	23
Charing Cross Ass.	16	6	1	9	30	46	19
Manor House	16	5	3	8	29	35	18
East Fulham	16	4	2	10	29	45	14
Harrow Weald M.	16	3	2	11	23	33	11
Hillingdon Irish	16	1	3	12	22	75	6

Division Two	P	W	D	L	F	A	Pts
Fulham Dyn. Spts	18	15	1	2	58	19	46
Sporting Duet	18	12	3	3	56	27	39
Brit. Airways Res.	18	9	3	6	45	35	30
West End Rgrs	18	9	1	8	36	31	28
Travaux FC	18	8	4	6	36	36	28
St Martins AFC	18	8	1	9	35	36	25
Sudbury Court	18	6	3	9	23	32	21
Old Alpertonians	18	5	4	9	34	64	19
Somerville Old B.	18	4	2	12	40	59	14
Rebal Alliance	18	2	2	14	37	61	8

Division Three	P	W	D	L	F	A	Pts
North Greenford B	22	16	5	1	64	15	53
Southall Rangers	22	15	3	4	85	29	48
Northwood A	22	13	5	4	64	34	44
New Hanford Res.	22	10	9	3	42	33	39
British Airways A	22	10	4	8	64	49	34
Sandgate Old B.	22	10	3	9	71	45	33
Abbey Nat. S&SC	22	9	4	9	48	47	31
Greenwood	21	8	6	7	46	43	30
Hillingdon A	22	7	4	11	39	56	25
Hadley B	22	6	3	13	40	46	21
Viking Sports	22	2	2	18	34	92	8
TWS	21	1	0	20	25	133	3

Division Four	P	W	D	L	F	A	Pts
British Airways B	22	20	1	1	102	28	61
Barnet Mun. Off.	22	15	2	5	66	37	47
Ruislip Villa	22	13	5	4	57	25	44
LPOSSA Res.	22	10	4	8	63	51	34
Ealing Old Boys	22	10	4	8	50	50	34
Chiswick H. Res.	22	10	3	9	69	59	33
Hounslow W. Res.	22	8	7	7	53	46	31
Lampton Park	22	6	4	12	51	67	22
Oriel Allstars	22	6	3	13	37	74	21
St Gabriels	22	5	5	12	51	70	20
Harrow Lyons	22	5	2	15	37	78	17
Old Alperton. Res.	22	3	2	17	31	82	11

LOWESTOFT & DISTRICT LEAGUE
(Notley's)

Division One	P	W	D	L	F	A	Pts
Norton Athletic FC	24	19	3	2	81	27	60
Oxford Arms *-3*	24	16	3	5	78	45	48
Spexhall	24	15	2	7	72	53	47
Waveney Res.	24	14	4	6	72	41	46
Barsham	24	13	4	7	61	33	43
Hearts of Oak	24	12	4	8	78	32	40
Blundeston M. *-3*	24	10	5	9	67	57	32
Pot Black	24	10	2	12	54	55	32
Ole Frank *-3*	24	10	3	11	66	60	30
Kirkley & Pake. A	24	8	3	13	45	62	27
Corton WH Seltic	24	4	2	18	38	77	14
Mutford/Wrentham	24	2	6	16	41	100	12
Bec. Caxton Res.	24	2	1	21	27	138	7

Division Two	P	W	D	L	F	A	Pts
AFC Star	26	21	2	3	113	28	65
Gt Yar. Town Hall	26	18	2	6	102	46	56
Pakefield Re-Utd	26	17	4	5	69	44	55
Suffolk Punch	26	14	5	7	86	50	47
Hopton	26	12	4	10	69	61	40
Corton A	26	12	2	12	59	77	38
Norton Ath. Res.	26	12	2	12	66	86	38
Low Int'national *-3*	26	11	6	9	63	51	36
Ellingham	26	11	2	13	65	75	35
Crusaders AFC	26	8	2	16	41	78	26
Tudor	26	7	3	16	54	98	24
Bungay Town A	26	6	5	15	47	71	23
Sole Bay Res. *-3*	26	6	5	15	37	65	20
Harleston Res. *-3*	26	2	6	18	36	77	9

Division Three	P	W	D	L	F	A	Pts
Waveney Gunners	26	19	3	4	93	32	60
Spexhall Res.	26	18	0	8	58	39	54
Waveney A	26	16	2	8	83	51	50
Earsham	26	13	8	5	57	36	47
Kirkley & Pake. B	26	14	4	8	49	50	46
Norman Warrior	26	13	4	9	81	53	43
Corton WHS Res.	26	13	3	10	57	43	42
Oxford Arms Res.	26	9	4	13	53	64	31
Blund'ton M. Res.	26	9	4	13	47	78	31
Mutford & W. Res.	26	8	5	13	43	51	29
Marquis of Lorne	26	7	6	13	40	56	27
Westhall *-3*	26	7	3	16	39	63	21
Factory Arms	26	5	3	18	30	69	18
Carlton Rgrs *-6*	26	5	3	18	33	78	12

LUTON DISTRICT & SOUTH BEDS LEAGUE

Premier Division	P	W	D	L	F	A	Pts
Stopsley Common	18	14	1	3	73	34	43
Christians in Sport	18	13	0	5	63	22	39
St Josephs	18	12	3	3	54	30	39
Ewe & Lamb	18	10	0	8	41	31	30
Offley Social	18	9	2	7	71	43	29
Lewsey Park	18	9	1	8	58	46	28
USL Galacticos	18	8	0	10	49	58	24
Luton Leagrave	18	6	2	10	46	55	20
Caddington Res.	18	2	1	15	28	73	7
Stopsley Pk Res.	18	2	0	16	22	113	6

Division One	P	W	D	L	F	A	Pts
Real F'n'E	16	14	0	2	93	26	42
Farley Boys	16	13	1	2	66	10	40
Christ.in Sport Res.	16	9	3	4	62	31	30
Co-Op Sports	16	8	2	6	61	43	26
The 61 FC A	16	7	2	7	42	50	23
LB Galaxy	16	6	3	7	39	82	21
Square	16	3	1	12	24	58	10
St Josephs Res.	16	3	1	12	25	66	10
L. Leagrave Res.	16	1	3	12	21	67	6

Stopsley Park Youth - record expunged

MAIDSTONE & DISTRICT LEAGUE
(Express Cabs)

Premier Division	P	W	D	L	F	A	Pts
Shepway United	20	19	0	1	87	18	57
Eccles	20	17	0	3	60	17	51
Leeds SV	20	12	1	7	37	37	37
Smarden	20	9	3	8	37	39	30
Addington	20	8	4	8	29	29	28
MPE	20	7	1	12	37	60	22
East Malling	20	6	3	11	22	41	21
AFC Biddenden	20	6	2	12	30	39	20
Headcorn	20	6	2	12	50	62	20
Hunton	20	5	5	10	38	51	20
Ditton United	20	3	3	14	13	47	12

Division One	P	W	D	L	F	A	Pts
Castle Colts	20	16	3	1	74	23	51
Downswood	20	14	3	3	93	29	45
Three Suttons	20	13	4	3	88	31	43
West Farleigh	20	10	6	4	45	31	36
Cobdown United	20	10	1	9	52	47	31
Lenham Wdrs	20	7	6	7	54	43	27
Aylesford	20	6	2	12	48	81	20
Yalding	20	5	4	11	38	66	19
Malgo Res.	20	6	1	13	35	75	19
Trisports	20	4	3	13	40	71	15
Eccles Res.	20	2	1	17	29	99	7

Division Two	P	W	D	L	F	A	Pts
Aylesford Res.	20	16	2	2	68	17	50
Regal United	20	13	3	4	76	56	42
Larkfield	20	12	4	4	62	36	40
RKP United	20	12	3	5	67	29	39
Saxon Chief	20	11	5	4	74	38	38
Malgo A	20	8	7	5	42	33	31
Parkwood Jupitors	20	7	1	12	43	52	22
Maidstone Athletic	20	6	3	11	38	59	21
Hunton Res.	20	5	5	10	41	49	20
Wheatsheaf Celtic	20	2	2	16	24	82	8
Headcorn Res.	20	0	1	19	24	108	1

Division Three	P	W	D	L	F	A	Pts
W'nut Tree Loose	18	14	1	3	73	34	43
Addington Res.	18	13	2	3	65	22	41
Hollingbourne	18	12	3	3	84	36	39
W. Farleigh Res.	18	9	5	4	67	37	32
Thurnham United	18	7	5	6	35	43	26
Kingshill Spitfires	18	7	1	10	31	47	22
Staplehurst/M. A	18	5	1	12	34	44	16
Lenham Wdrs Res.	18	5	1	12	33	77	16
Phoenix United	18	4	3	11	27	46	15
Sutton Saints Res.	18	2	2	14	35	98	8

Larkfield & New Hythe Wdrs A - record expunged

MATLOCK & DISTRICT LEAGUE

	P	W	D	L	F	A	Pts
Shirland Miners W.	22	19	2	1	85	29	59
Darley Dale Lions	22	17	3	2	94	31	54
Matlock Town Yth	22	13	2	7	83	45	41
Hilcote United	22	10	5	7	76	54	35
Kings Arms	22	10	4	8	51	45	34
Riddings Rovers	22	10	1	11	68	62	31
AFC Lea Holloway	22	10	4	8	44	64	31
Harveys Bar	22	8	5	9	46	59	29
Tibshelf Com. Res.	22	7	3	12	31	45	25
Laburnum Saints	22	7	2	13	46	52	23
Ashbourne A	22	5	3	14	47	76	18
Black Hippo	22	0	0	22	26	133	0

Bakewell Youth - record expunged

MID-ESSEX LEAGUE
(Broch Group)

Premier Division	P	W	D	L	F	A	Pts
Braintree/Bocking	22	17	1	4	52	21	52
Scotia Billericay	22	15	2	5	57	34	47
Byfleet Rangers	21	14	3	4	68	29	45
Focus Ferrers *+3*	22	9	4	9	46	47	34
Silver End United	22	10	2	10	39	42	32
Little Waltham *-4*	22	10	4	8	38	33	30
Harold Wood A. A	22	7	5	10	46	44	26
S'thminster SL A	22	7	4	11	50	48	25
U. Chelm. Ch. *-1*	22	6	5	11	35	52	22
Beacon Hill R. *-7*	22	8	2	12	32	46	19
Springfield Rouge	20	5	1	14	28	60	16
Manford Way A	21	5	1	15	29	64	16

Ravens - record expunged

Division One	P	W	D	L	F	A	Pts
St Clere's	22	18	2	2	85	24	56
Forest Glade	22	17	0	5	74	27	51
Great Baddow	21	17	0	4	66	33	51
Scotia B'cay Res.	22	14	2	6	58	27	44
Sparta Basildon	22	12	4	6	50	37	40
Rhodesia United	22	11	4	7	55	43	37
Manford Way B	22	10	1	11	43	42	31
Frenford Senior A	22	6	3	13	31	50	21
Bradwell Utd *-4*	22	4	4	14	39	61	12
Old C'fordians A	22	3	3	16	23	81	12
Mundon Victoria	22	3	3	16	18	76	12
Shelley Royals	21	3	0	18	39	80	9

Tillingham Hotspur - record expunged

Division Two	P	W	D	L	F	A	Pts
Ferrers Athletic	24	23	1	0	86	16	70
Writtle Manor *-1*	24	19	3	2	77	36	59
Swan Mead	24	16	3	5	62	33	51
Shenfield Holland	24	13	5	6	61	31	44
Boreham	24	12	1	11	55	57	37
Hutton A	24	9	6	9	49	50	33
Harold Wood B *-1*	24	9	2	13	46	63	28
Brendans	24	7	5	12	49	65	26
Battlesbridge	24	7	4	13	40	52	25
Sungate A *-1*	24	7	4	13	39	48	24
St Margarets FC	24	5	5	14	39	59	20
Stock United	24	5	1	18	33	59	16
City Colts	24	3	2	19	24	91	11

Division Three	P	W	D	L	F	A	Pts
Broomfield Res.	24	18	2	4	77	27	56
Ltle Waltham Res.	24	16	3	5	67	28	51
Sp. Brentwood *-3*	24	17	2	5	81	33	50
Scotia Billericay A	24	15	2	7	55	36	47
E2V Technologies	24	14	3	7	48	44	45
Brain/Bck Res. *+2*	24	12	2	10	40	45	40
Byfleet Rgrs Res.	24	12	2	10	72	65	38
Old Chelmfords B	24	11	3	10	41	41	36
Latchingdon	24	8	2	14	44	43	26
Wickham Ryls *+1*	24	6	5	13	32	51	24
Epping A	24	5	2	17	33	74	17
Frenford Senior B	24	3	2	19	24	73	11
Bradwell Utd Res.	24	2	4	18	32	86	10

Division Four	P	W	D	L	F	A	Pts
White Hart Utd FC	26	19	4	3	68	26	61
Felsted Rovers	26	14	5	6	67	39	47
Beacon H. Res. *+3*	26	13	4	9	67	52	46
Durning	25	14	2	9	58	64	44
G Baddow Res. *+2*	26	12	5	9	54	43	43
Springfield A *-1*	26	13	3	10	45	41	41
Burnham Ram. A	26	11	4	11	87	68	37
Focus Ferrers Res.	25	10	5	11	57	38	35
Batt'bdge Res. *-4*	26	11	4	11	61	64	33
Runwell Hosp. A	25	9	5	11	56	62	32
Mundon V. Res.	26	8	4	14	40	62	28
Tillingham Res. *-4*	26	9	4	13	54	78	27
Crays Hill United	25	6	3	16	40	62	14
Marconi Athletic	26	3	4	19	23	78	13

ivision Five	P	W	D	L	F	A	Pts
t Clere's Res.	26	22	2	2	79	24	68
ilver End Res.	26	14	5	7	75	35	47
attlesbridge A	26	15	3	8	61	43	47
eacon Hill Rov. A	26	13	5	8	54	49	47
helley Ryls Res.	26	13	6	7	69	52	41
laldon St Mary A	26	11	7	8	44	49	40
JC Churches Res.	26	9	8	9	63	53	35
oreham Res.	26	12	4	10	63	56	33
Vickham R. Res.	26	12	3	11	52	53	33
2V Techs Res.	26	8	2	16	49	66	29
urnham Ram. B	26	9	2	15	40	71	29
larks Farm	26	8	0	18	54	78	27
unmow	26	6	1	19	39	78	19
ld Chelmsford. C	26	3	6	17	45	80	15

MID-SOMERSET LEAGUE
(Trophies of Radstock)

remier Division	P	W	D	L	F	A	Pts
leadow Rangers	18	13	4	1	50	18	43
urnells Spts Res.	18	13	2	3	57	30	41
hilcompton Spts	18	7	5	6	36	34	26
oleford Athletic	18	7	4	7	45	37	25
Vestfield Res.	18	7	3	8	51	50	24
arrington Gurney	18	7	3	8	32	40	24
Vookey	18	6	3	9	27	39	21
elrose	18	5	4	9	33	43	19
lells & Vobster U.	18	6	0	12	29	40	18
hew Magna	18	3	4	11	24	53	13

ivision One	P	W	D	L	F	A	Pts
ilton United	18	14	1	3	73	25	43
vercreech Rov.	18	10	4	4	50	28	34
Vells City A	18	10	4	4	45	26	34
toke Rovers	18	8	5	5	46	40	29
unley Ath. Res.	18	8	2	8	43	46	26
akhill	18	7	3	8	29	42	24
emple Cloud	18	6	5	7	37	45	23
lastonbury Res.	18	6	1	11	46	62	19
rome Coll. Res.	18	5	3	10	39	48	18
rome T. Spts Res.	18	1	2	15	25	71	5

ivision Two	P	W	D	L	F	A	Pts
leadow Rgrs Res.	20	16	2	2	61	29	50
Velton Arsenal	20	16	1	3	74	23	49
hilcompton Res.	20	11	3	6	48	40	36
lutton Res.	20	10	2	8	46	41	32
lells/Vobster Res	20	9	2	9	45	41	29
. Gurney Res.	20	9	2	9	46	55	29
Vookey Res.	20	9	1	10	46	42	28
hilcompton Utd	20	7	3	10	37	42	24
nterhound	20	7	2	11	58	44	23
elrose Res.	20	3	1	16	17	68	10
oleford Ath. Res.	20	3	1	16	34	87	10

ivision Three	P	W	D	L	F	A	Pts
Vestfield A -3	20	18	0	2	86	33	51
C Sun Sports	20	13	4	3	84	44	43
urnells Sports A	20	14	0	6	58	27	42
hepton Mallet A	20	11	2	7	62	42	35
adstock Town A	20	10	3	7	66	63	33
amerton Athletic	20	10	2	8	56	62	32
emple C. Res. +3	20	6	2	12	42	51	23
heddar B -9	20	7	4	9	48	48	16
vercreech Res.	20	5	1	14	40	62	16
toke Rov. Res.	20	2	1	17	26	102	7
ilton Res. -13	20	4	1	15	38	72	0

MID-SUSSEX LEAGUE
(Gray Hooper Holt LLP)

remier Division	P	W	D	L	F	A	Pts
indfield	26	21	2	3	80	24	65
astbourne Bor. A	26	20	1	5	60	30	61
arvis Brook	26	17	1	8	61	40	52
Visdom Sports	26	14	3	9	63	49	45
Villingdon Athletic	26	15	0	11	44	35	45
alcombe	26	13	4	9	57	42	43
ld Varndeanians	26	12	2	12	53	46	38
otherfield	26	12	2	12	50	50	38
aresfield Village	26	11	2	13	37	50	35
rawley Down A	26	9	3	14	45	53	30
orest Row	26	6	4	16	31	60	22
assocks A	26	6	2	18	34	75	20
. Grinstead Utd	26	6	1	19	31	63	19
ckfield T. Res.	26	5	3	18	31	60	18

Division One	P	W	D	L	F	A	Pts
Roffey	22	15	1	6	77	31	46
Cuckfield Town	22	13	7	2	58	33	46
AFC Ringmer	22	14	1	7	68	35	43
Lewes Bridgeview	22	14	1	7	58	37	43
Village of Ditchling	22	11	6	5	56	44	39
O V'deanians Res.	22	9	3	10	56	52	30
Franklands Village	22	8	5	9	44	47	29
Buxted	22	7	5	10	37	41	26
Wisdom Spts Res.	22	7	5	10	49	57	26
Hartfield	22	5	7	10	33	50	22
Horsted Keynes	22	5	2	15	36	74	17
Heath Pilgrims	22	2	1	19	27	98	7

Division Two	P	W	D	L	F	A	Pts
Dormansland Rkts	20	16	2	2	76	20	50
Turners Hill	20	13	3	4	49	31	42
Cuckfield Rangers	20	12	3	5	46	29	39
AFC Grinstead	20	12	2	6	60	36	38
Ardingly	20	7	6	7	35	42	27
Lindfield Res.	20	7	5	8	37	40	26
Felbridge	20	7	2	11	41	59	23
Newick	20	6	3	11	37	54	21
Keymer/Hassocks	20	5	3	12	36	58	18
Ashurst Wood	20	5	3	12	33	57	18
Hurstpierp'nt Res.	20	2	4	14	25	49	10

Division Three	P	W	D	L	F	A	Pts
Framf'ld/Blackboys	20	15	4	1	58	15	49
Burgess Hill Alb.	20	14	5	1	61	20	47
E Grinst'd Town A	20	12	3	5	49	29	39
East Court	20	10	3	7	49	34	33
Peacehaven Utd	20	10	2	8	48	38	32
West Hoathly	20	8	2	10	29	35	26
Willingdon A. Res.	20	8	1	11	35	43	25
Fletching	20	5	3	12	33	56	18
Uckfield Town A	20	5	3	12	42	68	18
Sporting Lindfield	20	5	1	14	32	59	16
Maresfield V. Res.	20	4	1	15	28	67	13

Division Four	P	W	D	L	F	A	Pts
Barcombe	16	12	0	4	52	22	36
Furnace G. Rov.	16	11	2	3	54	24	35
Cuckfield T. Res.	16	9	0	7	36	34	27
Scaynes Hill	16	8	1	7	46	38	25
Plumpton Athletic	16	8	0	8	40	36	24
Roffey Res.	16	7	1	8	46	43	22
O' V'deanians A +3	16	4	0	12	23	47	15
E. Grin. U. Res. -3	16	5	2	9	22	46	14
Burg. Hill Alb. Res.	16	4	2	10	31	60	14

Division Five	P	W	D	L	F	A	Pts
Copthorne	20	14	3	3	55	29	45
V. of Ditchling Res.	20	13	3	4	57	33	42
Turners Hill Res.	20	13	2	5	57	32	41
Ansty Spts & Soc.	20	11	6	3	90	34	39
E. Grinstead Wdrs	20	12	1	7	61	45	37
Fairwarp	20	11	2	7	55	40	35
Wivelsfield Green	20	8	3	9	67	64	27
Handcross Village	20	7	2	11	43	61	23
Danehill	20	4	1	15	47	85	13
Newick Res.	20	3	2	15	28	84	11
Nutley	20	1	1	18	29	82	4

Division Six	P	W	D	L	F	A	Pts
Balcombe Res.	20	15	2	3	73	31	47
Dormansland Res.	20	15	2	3	65	31	47
Buxted Res.	20	11	5	4	49	24	38
Copthorne Rovers	20	10	3	7	42	31	33
Ardingly Res.	20	8	5	7	49	35	29
Jarvis Brook Res.	20	8	5	7	47	52	29
Lindfield A	20	7	6	7	49	38	27
Forest Row Res.	20	6	4	10	40	51	22
Bolney Rovers	20	6	3	11	52	60	21
Wisdom Sp. A +3	20	3	1	16	32	84	13
Heath Pil. Res. -3	20	2	2	16	26	87	5

Division Seven	P	W	D	L	F	A	Pts
Copthorne Res.	18	14	1	3	76	23	43
R'dean Village Vets	18	12	3	3	48	36	39
Franklands V. Res.	18	10	4	4	61	36	34
Ashurst W. Res. +3	18	9	2	7	46	43	32
Maresfield Vill. A	18	9	3	6	35	26	30
Hor. Keynes Res.	18	6	4	8	36	43	22
Felbridge Res. -6	18	8	1	9	38	56	19
Hartfield Res. +3	18	4	1	13	37	63	16
Fletching Res.	18	5	0	13	33	53	15
Fairfield	18	2	3	13	19	50	9

Division Eight	P	W	D	L	F	A	Pts
Halsford Lions	20	15	0	5	61	24	45
Rotherfield Res.	20	14	2	4	74	28	44
Ansty S&S Res. +3	20	13	2	5	50	35	44
Barcombe Res.	20	12	2	6	44	37	38
E. Grin. Town B	20	11	3	6	38	27	36
Willingdon A +3	20	8	4	8	33	34	31
Cuckfield T. A -3	20	9	3	8	43	34	27
West Hoathly Res.	20	7	1	12	35	52	22
Uckfield T. B -3	20	4	3	13	39	62	12
Danehill Res.	20	3	3	14	36	68	12
Burgess H. Alb. A	20	2	1	17	22	74	7

Division Nine	P	W	D	L	F	A	Pts
EG Mavericks	20	15	3	2	65	30	48
United Services	20	12	3	5	82	44	39
Cuckfield R. Res.	20	11	1	8	55	54	34
Copthorne A	20	10	2	8	67	63	32
Lindfield B	20	9	4	7	42	40	31
Plumpton A. Res.	20	9	3	8	43	33	30
Framfield Res.	20	8	4	8	69	65	28
Wivelsfield G. Res.	20	8	2	10	50	55	26
Handcross V. Res.	20	8	1	11	40	42	25
Scaynes Hill Res.	20	5	1	14	36	69	16
Maresfield Vill. B	20	2	2	16	25	79	8

Division Ten	P	W	D	L	F	A	Pts
Fairwarp Res.	18	15	2	1	88	18	46
Hassocks Hornets	18	15	0	3	70	28	45
Copthorne R. Res.	18	9	3	6	49	49	30
Buxted A	18	9	1	8	46	42	28
Ardingly A	18	7	3	8	49	48	24
Lindfield C	18	7	1	10	44	44	24
Heath Rangers	18	7	3	8	40	44	24
Rotherfield A	18	5	1	12	39	60	16
Maresfield Vill. C	18	4	4	10	46	94	16
Scaynes Hill A	18	2	2	14	29	73	8

MIDLAND AMATEUR ALLIANCE

Premier Division	P	W	D	L	F	A	Pts
Southwell Amats	26	25	1	0	111	23	76
Old Elizabethans	26	20	3	3	102	46	63
Acorn Athletic	26	18	3	5	98	55	57
Brunts Old Boys	26	14	2	10	75	70	44
Woodborough U.	26	13	3	10	61	60	42
Team DNF	26	13	2	11	59	54	41
Eastwood	26	10	5	11	59	64	35
Wollaton A	26	10	3	13	70	70	33
Pinxton North End	26	7	7	12	63	77	28
Steelers	26	8	2	16	53	79	26
TVFC	26	6	5	15	58	75	23
Beeston OB Assn	26	5	5	16	34	69	20
Nott'hamshire Res.	26	6	2	18	47	97	20
Monty Hind OB	26	5	1	20	41	92	16

Division One	P	W	D	L	F	A	Pts
Coronation	26	22	1	3	111	36	67
Southwell A. Res.	26	14	6	6	70	38	48
Beeston OBA Res.	26	14	6	6	68	44	48
Radcliffe Olym. A	26	14	5	7	62	52	47
Bassingfield	26	12	6	8	65	55	42
EMTEC	26	11	6	9	81	72	39
Sherwood Colliery	26	11	4	11	65	46	37
O. E'bethans Res.	26	8	5	13	50	70	29
Nott'ghamshire A	26	6	10	10	51	64	28
Lady Bay	26	7	7	12	60	92	28
Broadmeadows	26	7	3	16	39	64	24
Wollaton B	26	6	6	14	50	82	24
Eaton Hall Coll.	26	6	6	14	33	65	24
Derbys Ams Res.	26	5	7	14	41	66	22

Division Two	P	W	D	L	F	A	Pts
Nuthall Athletic	22	19	1	2	92	18	58
FC Interski	22	17	3	2	73	31	54
Tibshelf Comm.	22	13	2	7	64	37	41
Sherwood C. Res.	22	13	1	8	57	37	40
AFC Nottm United	22	11	3	8	61	49	36
Old Bemrosians	22	10	6	6	50	52	36
Selston Res.	22	9	1	12	59	50	28
Town Mill	22	8	1	13	56	63	25
Ravenshead	22	7	2	13	33	66	23
Chilwell Villa	22	5	2	15	48	86	17
Nott'ghamshire B	22	4	3	15	35	79	15
Cambdge Knights	22	3	1	18	29	89	10

MIDLANDS REGIONAL ALLIANCE

Premier Division	P	W	D	L	F	A	Pts
Allenton United	34	28	3	3	124	33	87
Melbourne Dyn.	34	27	3	4	104	41	84
Wirksworth Town	34	25	4	5	102	38	79
Long Eaton Res.	34	23	1	10	88	41	70
Rowsley	34	18	5	11	84	65	59
Cromford	34	15	7	12	69	60	52
Willington FC	34	16	4	14	80	80	52
Cas. Donington T.	34	16	4	14	63	63	52
Ashover	34	13	7	14	57	74	46
Newmount	34	12	8	14	60	72	44
Holbrook St Mich.	34	13	4	17	80	83	43
Derby Rolls RL	34	11	8	15	53	66	41
Belper United	34	9	8	17	40	59	35
Chellaston	34	10	4	20	44	95	34
Sandiacre Town	34	9	4	21	68	112	31
Matlock Town Res.	34	8	1	25	44	78	25
Borrowash V. Res.	34	7	4	23	49	90	25
Allestree -2	34	4	5	25	46	105	15

Division One	P	W	D	L	F	A	Pts
Swanwick Pent Rd	30	23	4	3	123	23	73
Heanor Colliers	30	23	3	4	111	42	72
Selston	30	20	2	8	106	51	62
Punjab United	30	20	1	9	72	46	61
Matlock Sports	30	16	5	9	84	45	53
Cotes Park	30	13	6	11	69	77	45
Shirland Athletic	30	13	2	15	83	76	41
Derby RRL Res.	30	12	4	14	61	70	40
Derbyshire Ams	30	11	5	14	61	71	38
Mickleover RBL	30	11	5	14	69	80	38
Holb'k SM Res. -6	30	11	6	13	51	77	33
Bargate Rovers	30	9	4	17	53	101	31
Findern	30	8	5	17	35	83	29
Little Eaton	30	7	3	20	48	105	24
Ripley -3	30	7	3	20	51	88	21
Pastures	30	6	2	22	55	97	20

Division Two	P	W	D	L	F	A	Pts
Derby Royals	28	24	3	1	112	22	75
Belper Utd Res.	28	20	2	6	74	39	62
Mick. RBL Res.	28	19	4	5	79	25	61
Rowsley Res.	28	19	3	6	86	35	60
Woolley Moor Utd	28	13	7	8	63	32	46
Wirksworth T. Res.	28	13	7	8	54	40	46
Swanwick PR Res.	28	14	1	13	80	59	43
Wirksworth Iv'hoe	28	12	4	12	46	42	40
Melbourne D. Res.	28	10	5	13	48	55	35
Castle Don. T. Res.	28	9	5	14	43	70	32
Pastures Res.	28	7	6	15	56	82	27
Sandiacre Res. -1	28	6	7	15	60	71	24
Findern Res.	28	5	4	19	26	100	19
Hilton Harriers	28	4	2	22	38	86	14
Bargate Rov. Res.	28	3	4	21	20	127	13

MINING LEAGUE
(One & All Sports)

Division One	P	W	D	L	F	A	Pts
Illogan RBL Res.	30	26	2	2	149	43	80
Robartes Arms	30	20	3	7	77	50	63
Four Lanes	30	20	1	9	102	57	61
St Buryan	30	19	1	10	89	74	58
Threemilestone	30	17	5	8	79	54	56
Goonhavern Ath.	30	17	4	9	81	60	55
Storm -2	30	16	4	10	88	72	50
Halsetown	30	14	4	12	105	66	46
Gwinear C'tn -1	30	13	6	11	79	68	44
Newlyn Non-Ath.	30	13	3	14	86	93	42
Redruth United	30	10	5	15	47	70	35
Gulval	30	8	4	18	46	85	28
Sennen	30	6	6	18	40	74	24
Trevenson Utd -1	30	5	4	21	49	112	18
Chacewater Res.	30	4	3	23	44	107	15
St Ives Town Res.	30	4	1	25	40	116	13

NORTH & MID-HERTS LEAGUE

Premier Division	P	W	D	L	F	A	Pts
Probuild	14	13	0	1	25	10	39
Welwyn GC Res.	14	11	0	3	50	24	33
Asia	14	8	1	5	45	44	25
Potters Bar Crus.	14	8	0	6	40	26	24
London Colney A	14	5	4	5	24	24	19
Colney Athletic	14	3	2	9	18	28	11
Fairlands	14	2	1	11	14	35	7
Baldock TL A	14	2	0	12	25	50	6

FC June 1984, London Road, Park Street Village A - records expunged

Division One	P	W	D	L	F	A	Pts
Welwyn Gdn C. A	22	19	0	3	114	31	57
City Hearts	22	15	3	4	104	52	48
Global	22	14	1	7	79	39	43
Inn on the Green	22	14	1	7	76	42	43
Warriors XI	22	11	4	7	75	39	37
Probuild Res.	22	11	2	9	67	60	35
Wodson Park A	22	10	2	10	52	46	32
St Albans Wdrs	22	10	0	12	47	60	30
Kings Sports Res.	22	6	5	11	45	41	23
St Ippolyts	22	6	2	14	49	51	20
Bedwell Rangers	22	4	2	16	39	78	14
St Albans C. Yth D	22	1	0	21	12	220	3

NORTH BUCKS & DISTRICT LEAGUE

Premier Division	P	W	D	L	F	A	Pts
Steeple Claydon	26	23	1	2	89	25	70
Grendon Rangers	26	17	4	5	76	33	55
Brackley Sports	26	16	1	9	70	46	49
Silverstone	26	15	4	7	57	37	49
Stewkley	26	13	1	12	63	54	40
Bletchley Manor	26	12	4	10	59	56	40
Deanshanger Ath.	26	11	3	12	43	61	36
Wolverton Town	26	10	1	15	60	70	31
MK Titans	26	9	4	13	55	79	31
Thornborough Ath.	26	9	2	15	60	60	29
Southcott Vill. RA	26	9	2	15	48	57	29
Castlethorpe	26	8	4	14	48	64	28
Sherington	26	6	5	15	47	94	23
Syresham	26	4	4	18	30	69	16

Intermediate Division	P	W	D	L	F	A	Pts
Potterspury	22	19	3	0	85	25	60
Yardley Gobion	22	14	4	4	70	37	46
AFC Santander	22	14	2	6	54	37	44
Stoke Hammond	22	11	4	7	71	38	37
Great Horwood	22	10	7	5	61	54	37
Great Linford	22	10	6	6	54	39	36
Twyford United	22	11	1	10	68	53	34
Brackley S. Res.	22	8	2	12	60	59	26
E & H	22	7	4	11	44	53	25
MK Titans Res.	22	6	3	13	41	55	21
Hanslope	22	2	4	16	31	88	10
Marsh Gibbon	22	0	0	22	7	108	0

Wing Village, Wolverton Town Res. - records expunged

Division One	P	W	D	L	F	A	Pts
Heath Panthers U.	26	21	3	2	86	23	66
Denbigh Spts & S.	26	21	2	3	97	33	65
Wicken Sports	26	20	2	4	97	32	62
S. Claydon Res.	26	20	2	4	77	25	62
MK Wdrs Res.	26	15	6	5	74	41	51
Woughton	26	13	2	11	77	67	41
Deanshanger Res.	26	9	3	14	62	62	30
Stoke Ham. Res.	26	8	6	12	63	69	30
Royal British Leg.	26	6	6	14	51	66	24
Grendon R. Res.	26	7	2	17	33	64	23
Sherington Res.	26	7	2	17	44	96	23
Charlton	26	5	6	15	55	94	21
Westbury	26	3	4	19	40	104	13
Yard. Gobion Res.	26	3	2	21	36	116	11

Division Two	P	W	D	L	F	A	Pts
Stewkley Res.	28	22	1	5	120	36	67
Potterspury Res.	28	21	2	5	97	42	65
Castlethorpe Res.	28	19	4	5	101	45	61
Old Stratford	28	19	2	7	101	42	59
Southcott V. Res.	28	18	4	6	99	53	58
Wicken Spts Res.	28	14	3	11	61	74	45
Olney Town Colts	28	13	4	11	65	75	43
Twyford Utd Res.	28	12	2	14	84	70	38
Great Linford Res.	28	12	2	14	58	70	38
H. Panthers Res.	28	11	3	14	47	74	36
Syresham Res.	28	8	2	18	60	81	26
Hanslope Res.	28	7	3	18	35	87	24
Gt Horwood Res.	28	6	4	18	51	88	22
Wing Village Res.	28	5	1	22	34	95	16
M. Gibbon Res.	28	4	1	23	28	109	13

NORTH EAST NORFOLK LEAGUE
(Optic Night Club)

Division One	P	W	D	L	F	A	Pts
Gimingham	22	15	4	3	78	37	49
Ludham	22	15	2	5	61	31	47
East Ruston	22	11	3	8	57	58	36
Coltishall	22	9	6	7	70	46	33
Nth Walsham OB	22	10	3	9	54	42	33
Runton	22	10	3	9	56	52	33
N. Walsham T. A	22	11	0	11	62	66	33
Horning	22	9	5	8	51	49	32
Corpusty/Saxthorpe	22	9	4	9	46	48	31
Hickling	22	9	3	10	43	50	30
Mundesley	22	4	5	13	30	47	17
Lyng	22	1	0	21	16	98	3

Division Two	P	W	D	L	F	A	Pts
Aldborough Lions	20	17	1	2	81	31	52
Briston	20	16	3	1	89	33	51
Aylsham A	20	12	2	6	65	35	38
Buxton Res.	20	8	2	10	42	52	26
Haisborough Ath.	20	7	3	10	49	51	24
Corpusty & S. Res.	20	7	3	10	36	41	24
Stalham Town A	20	6	5	9	46	57	23
Holt United A	20	6	4	10	52	59	22
Mundesley Res.	20	6	2	12	42	72	20
Erpingham	20	5	3	12	39	90	18
Felmingham	20	5	2	13	37	57	17

Division Three	P	W	D	L	F	A	Pts
Worstead	16	13	1	2	76	18	40
Cromer Youth OB	16	11	3	2	49	18	36
Blakeney	16	8	5	3	45	39	29
Briston Res. -3	16	9	3	4	56	41	27
Aldborough L. Res.	16	4	4	8	39	53	16
Gimingham Res.	16	4	4	8	32	47	16
East Ruston Res.	16	2	6	8	26	61	12
Holt United Colts	16	2	5	9	25	43	11
Cawston	16	2	3	11	19	47	9

NORTH GLOUCESTERSHIRE LEAGUE
(BL Boseley Construction)

Premier Division	P	W	D	L	F	A	Pts
Minsterworth	26	22	0	4	101	31	66
Woolaston	26	19	4	3	81	26	61
Newent Town	26	18	4	4	66	28	58
Ruardean Hill Rgrs	26	14	7	5	49	28	49
Westbury United	26	11	7	8	56	47	40
Staunton & Corse	26	12	3	11	50	51	39
Coleford United	26	11	3	12	65	63	36
Lydney Town Res.	26	9	5	12	49	72	32
Huntley	26	9	3	14	57	55	3[illegible]
Broadwell A. Res.	26	7	5	14	41	66	26
Mushet/Coalway U.	26	7	4	15	45	79	25
Milkwall	26	7	4	15	46	88	25
Whitecroft	26	5	4	17	31	65	19
Ellwood Res.	26	3	3	20	21	59	12

Baker Street - record expunged

Division One	P	W	D	L	F	A	Pts
Newnham United	24	17	4	3	82	39	55
English Bicknor	24	17	3	4	67	21	54
Lydbrook Ath. Res.	24	15	3	6	67	27	48
Bream Amateurs	24	11	5	8	74	54	38
Rank Outsiders	24	11	4	9	52	46	37
Redbrook Rovers	24	11	3	10	60	54	36
Mitcheldean Res.	24	10	5	9	43	54	35
Yorkley	24	10	4	10	56	41	34
Sedbury United	24	10	3	11	63	62	33
Blakeney	24	9	3	12	55	71	30
Aylburton R. Res.	24	6	3	15	40	59	21
Howle Hill	24	7	0	17	43	81	21
Harrow Hill A	24	2	0	22	21	114	6

Division Two	P	W	D	L	F	A	Pts
Ruardean Hill Res.	22	16	2	4	70	34	50
Newent T. Res.	22	14	4	4	60	36	46
St Briavels	22	11	1	10	64	39	34
Woolaston Res.	22	10	4	8	54	50	34
Staunton/C. Res.	22	10	2	10	39	45	32
Whitecroft Res.	22	9	4	9	49	41	3[illegible]
Westbury U. Res.	22	9	3	10	48	48	3[illegible]
Lydney Town A	22	8	4	10	45	59	2[illegible]
Puma	22	8	2	12	40	60	26
Lydbrook Ath. A	22	7	4	11	35	59	25
Longhope	22	7	3	12	41	50	24
Worrall Hill	22	4	5	13	25	49	17

Division Three	P	W	D	L	F	A	Pts
Ruspidge United	22	17	3	2	77	24	54
Soudley Res.	22	17	3	2	56	21	54
White Horse	22	13	3	6	57	37	4[illegible]
Minsterworth Res	22	12	5	5	71	50	4[illegible]
Puma Res.	22	10	5	7	48	40	35
Tidenham Res.	22	9	2	11	43	61	2[illegible]
Blakeney Res.	22	7	6	9	51	66	2[illegible]
Mushet & C. Res.	22	8	2	12	34	55	2[illegible]
Milkwall Res.	22	7	3	12	40	54	2[illegible]
Redbrook R. Res	22	6	4	12	49	52	2[illegible]
Mitcheldean A	22	4	0	18	31	59	1[illegible]
Coleford Utd Res.	22	3	2	17	28	66	1[illegible]

Division Four	P	W	D	L	F	A	Pts
3ling United	20	15	3	2	69	29	48
Redmarley	20	15	1	4	70	24	46
Rank Out. Res.	20	12	4	4	40	22	40
ʼuma A	20	10	2	8	50	47	32
:ng. Bicknor Res.	20	9	4	7	43	38	31
.onghope Res.	20	9	2	9	61	60	29
Yorkley Res.	20	8	4	8	46	45	28
3ream Ams Res.	20	8	2	10	45	47	26
St Briavels Res.	20	7	0	13	28	55	21
.ittledean	20	3	1	16	32	78	10
Whitecroft A	20	2	1	17	19	58	7

Tidenham A - record expunged

NORTH LANCASHIRE & DIST. LEAGUE
(Lancaster Honda)

Premier Division	P	W	D	L	F	A	Pts
Marsh United	26	16	6	4	56	27	54
Cartmel & District	26	14	7	5	50	29	49
Highgrove	26	13	7	6	64	37	46
Carnforth Rangers	26	14	4	8	65	41	46
Galgate	26	10	10	6	53	48	40
ngleton	26	12	4	10	52	53	40
TC Dynamos	26	12	3	11	61	43	39
Morecambe Ryls	26	11	6	9	50	39	39
Storeys *-3*	26	13	2	11	45	33	38
Slyne-w-H. Res.	26	11	4	11	47	62	37
Bentham	26	9	3	14	49	64	30
Bowerham	26	6	4	16	46	63	22
Kirkby Lonsdale	26	3	6	17	33	92	15
Halton Rangers	26	3	4	19	45	85	13

Division One	P	W	D	L	F	A	Pts
Swarthmoor SC	26	15	6	5	57	37	51
ngleton Res.	26	13	6	7	63	47	45
Freehold	26	13	5	8	62	45	44
Millhead	26	12	5	9	67	61	41
Storeys Res.	26	12	3	11	53	57	39
Bolton-le-Sands	26	11	5	10	47	40	38
Marsh Utd Res.	26	9	8	9	41	48	35
Boys Club	26	9	7	10	53	45	34
Cartmel/D. Res. *-3*	26	10	6	10	44	47	33
Mcbe Royals Res.	26	9	6	11	53	61	33
College	26	9	6	11	39	49	33
Caton United	26	9	5	12	57	63	32
Highgrove Res. *-3*	26	5	8	13	43	55	20
Overton/M'ton *-3*	26	5	6	15	40	64	18

Division Two	P	W	D	L	F	A	Pts
rimpell	24	19	2	3	93	24	59
.rnside	24	18	3	3	88	22	57
urness Rovers B	24	12	7	5	55	35	43
Westgate Wdrs	24	11	4	9	57	55	37
Carnforth Res. *-3*	24	12	3	9	80	66	36
orrisholme	24	10	6	8	57	49	36
.llithwaite Rgrs	24	9	8	7	43	40	35
Grange *-6*	24	10	2	12	55	57	26
Slyne-with-Hest A	24	7	5	12	39	59	26
Bentham Res.	24	5	6	13	52	75	21
Kirkby L. Res. *-4*	24	6	3	15	33	70	17
Halton R. Res. *-6*	24	6	2	16	49	87	14
Caton United Res.	24	3	5	16	39	101	14

Division Three	P	W	D	L	F	A	Pts
Galgate Res.	20	13	5	2	54	27	44
Heysham	20	11	5	4	45	28	38
Morecambe Gold	20	12	2	6	47	31	38
Hoghuls	20	9	7	4	36	27	34
Gregson	20	9	6	5	38	25	33
Boys Club Res. *-3*	20	9	6	5	46	29	30
Burton Thistle	20	7	5	8	39	33	26
Villa Royale	20	5	4	11	27	57	19
FC Moorlands	20	4	6	10	34	49	18
Highgrove Colts	20	5	3	12	39	55	18
Bolton-le-S. Res.	20	0	3	17	16	60	3

Division Four	P	W	D	L	F	A	Pts
illing	22	16	4	2	71	25	52
arnforth Rgrs A	22	12	5	5	56	38	41
verton/M'tn Res.	22	11	4	7	65	54	37
rimpell Res.	22	12	1	9	64	54	37
.rnside Res.	22	10	4	8	64	48	34
Millhead Res.	22	9	4	9	55	47	31
reehold Res.	22	9	4	9	48	58	31
College Res. *-3*	22	8	5	9	57	51	26
urton Th. Res. *-3*	22	8	5	9	34	51	26
ngleton A	22	7	2	13	39	62	23
eysham Res.	22	4	5	13	36	64	17
Gregson Res.	22	2	5	15	27	64	11

NORTH LEICESTERSHIRE LEAGUE

Premier Division	P	W	D	L	F	A	Pts
Caterpillar	26	20	2	4	86	32	62
Falcons	26	19	2	5	76	34	59
Markfield	26	18	2	6	82	47	56
Genesis	26	18	2	6	73	48	56
Anstey Town	26	16	3	7	74	46	51
Shepshed Amats	26	13	3	10	45	41	42
Whitwick Wdrs	26	10	5	11	52	44	35
Sileby Saints	26	11	2	13	50	49	35
Ingles	26	10	4	12	49	53	34
Loughborough	26	10	2	14	54	61	32
Loughboro. T. *-1*	26	8	2	16	45	77	25
Asfordby Vill. *-3*	26	6	3	17	41	70	18
Woodhse Imperial	26	5	1	20	37	88	16
Sutton Bonington	26	1	3	22	22	96	6

Division One	P	W	D	L	F	A	Pts
Birstall Old Boys	20	15	1	4	78	43	46
Anstey Crown	20	14	2	4	77	38	44
Sileby Victoria	20	14	1	4	66	28	43
Belton Villa	20	12	3	5	56	35	39
East Leake Ath.	20	11	4	5	80	38	37
Deportivo de la Z.	20	8	6	6	59	49	30
Loughborough Ath.	20	7	2	11	39	64	23
Kegworth Imperial	20	4	10	6	55	47	22
ATI Garryson	20	3	5	14	28	53	14
Sut. Bonington Ac	20	3	4	13	28	52	13
Loughborough Res.	20	0	0	20	17	136	0

Division Two	P	W	D	L	F	A	Pts
Bagworth Colliery	22	16	4	2	86	39	52
Ingles Res. *-8*	22	15	1	6	79	41	38
Thringstone Rgrs	22	13	5	4	68	44	44
Moira United	22	14	1	7	73	48	43
The Railway EWM	22	13	3	6	56	35	42
Markfield Res.	22	11	2	9	54	45	35
E. Leake A. Res.	22	9	1	12	50	56	28
Castle Donington	22	8	3	44	49	54	27
Loughborough A	22	7	4	11	46	57	25
Thurmaston Rgrs	22	5	0	17	36	71	15
Woodh'se I. Res.	22	3	4	15	37	94	13
Loughborough U.	22	3	2	17	37	87	11

Division Three	P	W	D	L	F	A	Pts
Greenhill YC	22	18	1	3	118	25	55
Thringstone MW	22	18	1	3	103	25	55
Caterpillar Res.	22	16	3	3	75	30	51
Whitwick W. Res.	22	13	3	6	68	34	42
L'boro. Emmanuel	22	10	4	8	63	62	33
Ferrari	22	10	2	10	59	69	32
Belgrave A	22	9	1	12	51	66	28
Long Clawson	22	8	2	12	47	67	26
Sileby Saints Res.	22	8	0	14	54	74	24
Measham Imperial	22	6	1	15	57	64	19
Mountsorrel	22	5	0	17	32	73	15
ATI G'son Res. *-1*	22	2	0	20	21	159	5

Division Four	P	W	D	L	F	A	Pts
Markfield A	22	20	1	1	97	22	61
Sileby Vics Res.	22	19	1	2	99	36	58
Coalville Lbr Club	22	12	3	7	62	55	39
Genesis Res.	22	10	6	6	82	48	36
Birstall OB Res.	22	10	3	9	55	47	33
Shepshed A. Res.	22	10	2	10	59	67	32
L'boro. U. Res. *-7*	22	9	5	8	74	58	25
S. Bonington Res.	22	5	6	11	49	70	21
Greenhill YC Res.	22	5	4	13	30	73	19
Loughboro. Galaxy	22	4	4	14	33	66	16
Anstey Crown Res.	22	4	6	12	41	62	18
C. Donington Res.	22	3	1	18	29	106	10

NORTH NORTHUMBERLAND LEAGUE

Division One	P	W	D	L	F	A	Pts
Rothbury	16	13	1	2	62	18	40
Lowick United	16	11	5	0	52	14	38
Alnwick Town Res.	16	9	3	4	48	23	30
Shilbottle CW *+3*	16	6	4	6	38	30	25
Acklington Athletic	16	6	1	9	34	57	19
Ash'ton Booze Bros	16	4	4	8	37	41	16
Bedlington Res. *-6*	16	7	1	8	47	56	16
Berwick Town	16	3	2	11	20	46	11
Berwick U. Res. *-3*	16	1	3	12	26	79	3

Division Two	P	W	D	L	F	A	Pts
Lynemouth Inst.	20	16	2	2	103	27	50
Springhill	20	14	3	3	85	31	45
Belford *+3*	19	12	3	4	49	33	42
Alnmouth United	20	9	3	8	44	43	30
Boulmer *-3*	20	8	5	7	59	50	26
Embleton WR *-6*	20	10	1	9	55	44	25
Craster Rovers	20	7	4	9	39	61	25
Bamburgh Castle	20	6	3	11	44	48	21
Wooler	20	4	3	13	43	71	15
Hedgeley Rov. *-3*	20	4	2	14	22	67	11
Rothbury Res. *-3*	19	4	1	14	32	100	10

NORTH WEST NORFOLK LEAGUE
(Build Centre)

Division One	P	W	D	L	F	A	Pts
Reffley Royals	22	16	5	1	87	28	53
Pott Row	22	16	2	4	73	25	50
Terrington	22	11	4	7	51	40	37
Wiggenhall	22	11	3	8	47	50	36
Docking	22	10	5	7	68	49	35
West Winch	22	10	5	7	50	41	35
Heacham	22	9	5	8	64	48	32
Sutton Bridge	22	6	6	10	52	60	24
Lynn Napier	22	5	5	12	34	62	20
Ingoldisthorpe	22	5	3	14	37	73	18
Sandringham *-3*	22	5	5	12	49	75	17
Lynn Docklands	22	3	2	17	26	87	11

Division Two	P	W	D	L	F	A	Pts
Lynn Discovery	20	15	1	4	118	34	46
Old Hunstanton	20	14	4	2	74	34	46
Terrington Res.	20	11	4	5	62	38	37
Gt Massingham *-3*	20	12	3	5	74	29	36
Flitcham *-3*	20	11	4	5	53	24	34
Gayton Utd Res.	20	10	3	7	61	48	33
Watlington	20	9	1	10	61	59	28
Ing'thorpe Res. *-6*	20	6	1	13	29	82	13
Gaywood *-3*	20	4	3	13	30	73	12
Castle Rising	20	1	2	17	20	114	5
Hunstanton *-12*	20	3	2	15	23	70	-1

Division Three	P	W	D	L	F	A	Pts
Dersingham Res.	26	19	3	4	111	47	60
South Creake	26	18	2	6	113	37	56
Discovery Royals	26	16	3	7	92	52	51
William Burt	26	15	5	6	72	45	50
Denver	26	13	6	7	48	41	45
W. Lynn Riverside	26	13	4	9	58	65	43
Walsingham	26	11	7	8	52	53	40
Wigg'hall Res. *-3*	26	10	9	7	59	42	36
C. Rising Res. *-3*	26	11	3	12	67	70	33
Snettisham	26	7	3	16	48	93	24
West Winch Res.	26	4	8	14	47	72	20
Burnham Mkt *-3*	26	6	5	15	62	96	20
Smithdon	26	3	5	18	36	93	14
Heacham Res. *-6*	26	4	1	21	36	95	7

Division Four	P	W	D	L	F	A	Pts
Sedgeford	20	19	1	0	126	32	58
Birchwood	20	13	3	4	73	47	42
The Woottons	20	11	1	8	40	40	34
Dersingham R. A	20	10	0	10	49	59	30
Sutton Bdge Res.	20	9	2	9	61	57	29
Snet'shm Res. *-3*	20	9	2	9	54	49	26
Lynn Napier Res.	20	7	2	11	30	43	23
Greyfriars *-6*	20	6	5	9	37	51	17
Springwood	20	5	2	13	43	69	17
Watlington Res. *-6*	20	6	3	11	54	68	15
Pentney *-3*	20	3	3	14	35	87	9

NORTHAMPTON TOWN LEAGUE
(Peter Smith Recruitment)

Premier Division	P	W	D	L	F	A	Pts
N'ton Harlequins	18	15	2	1	60	18	47
Delapre Old Boys	18	15	1	2	71	21	46
Hometech	18	10	3	5	47	35	33
Liberty Stars	18	8	4	6	27	29	28
Fox & Hounds	18	8	3	7	43	25	27
FC Crispin	18	7	2	9	33	53	23
Ket. Orchard Park	18	6	4	8	43	45	22
Univ. N'pton *-3*	18	5	2	11	40	48	14
Thorplands United	18	2	2	14	27	72	8
K'thorpe Cladding	18	2	1	15	21	66	7

Ashley Rovers, Hitec Roofing - records expunged

Division One	P	W	D	L	F	A	Pts
AFC Wombles	20	16	2	2	72	19	50
Denton	20	14	3	3	72	33	45
SPA	20	12	2	6	54	27	38
N'ton Quins Res.	20	12	1	7	61	54	37
Mereway United	20	11	1	8	59	44	34
EYS Hotspur	20	10	1	9	54	71	31
J. King Blisworth A	20	8	6	6	50	29	30
Northants Police	20	5	2	13	27	39	17
West Haddon Res.	20	5	2	13	35	64	17
Thorplands Res.	20	3	2	15	36	91	11
Corby SM Res.	20	3	0	17	40	89	9

Real Dragoon - record expunged

NORWICH & DISTRICT BUSINESS HOUSES LEAGUE

Division One	P	W	D	L	F	A	Pts
Yelverton	20	17	1	2	60	16	52
Marlborough OB	20	13	2	5	51	31	41
Drayton	20	10	4	6	51	38	34
Costessey Crown	20	10	1	9	51	48	31
UEA Res. *-8*	20	12	2	6	60	29	30
Loddon United A	20	7	5	8	40	49	26
Mousehold Ath.	20	7	4	9	42	44	25
Salhouse Rovers	20	6	4	10	39	48	22
Homecare Utd *-2*	20	7	3	10	32	61	22
Wensum Albion	20	4	0	16	23	54	12
Jarrolds	20	2	4	14	30	61	10

Division Two	P	W	D	L	F	A	Pts
Jubilee Rangers	22	17	4	1	65	24	55
Lingw'd Canvaners	22	13	5	4	48	30	44
Norwich Medics	22	12	5	5	61	35	41
Costessey Sports	22	12	2	8	78	43	38
Dyers Arms	22	10	2	10	55	41	32
Sprowston B'hive	22	10	1	11	67	61	31
Sth Walsham Res.	22	9	4	9	43	48	31
Horsford United A	22	9	3	10	57	53	30
UEA A *-8*	22	10	4	8	57	45	26
Mousehold Res.	22	5	2	15	24	95	17
Hempnall A	22	3	4	15	33	71	13
Taverham	22	2	4	16	29	71	10

Division Three	P	W	D	L	F	A	Pts
Cost. Crown Res.	20	12	6	2	55	33	42
Yelverton Res.	20	11	5	4	38	26	38
Blofield United A	20	10	4	6	52	35	34
Hockering	20	9	4	7	46	35	31
N. Flotman Res.	20	7	7	6	31	32	28
Reepham A *-5*	20	9	5	6	48	42	27
Drayton Res.	20	7	4	9	56	55	25
Ketts Tav Toucans	20	7	3	10	28	37	24
Horsford Utd B *-2*	20	7	4	9	47	55	23
Old Catton Rovers	20	6	2	12	43	41	20
Thorpe Village A	20	1	4	15	19	72	7

Hellesdon Wanderers - record expunged

NOTTS AMATEUR ALLIANCE

Premier Division	P	W	D	L	F	A	Pts
Burton Joyce	24	17	3	4	79	43	54
Santos FC	24	15	3	6	63	46	48
East Valley United	24	15	2	7	73	43	47
Aspley Beacons	24	13	3	8	72	51	42
Headstocks	24	13	3	8	60	54	42
FC Samba	24	12	5	7	62	45	41
Kashmir	24	12	0	12	51	47	36
Ashland Rovers	24	10	4	10	53	53	34
Trident	24	9	3	12	62	70	30
Coopers Arms	24	9	1	14	56	77	28
Gedling Sthbank A	24	5	4	15	34	71	19
Nuthall	24	5	3	16	36	57	18
Calverton MW A	24	3	2	19	32	76	11

Peacock United - record expunged

Division One	P	W	D	L	F	A	Pts
Real United *-3*	22	17	1	4	107	51	49
Kirton Brickworks	22	13	5	4	70	31	44
Nottm Sikh Lions	22	12	3	7	79	54	39
Vernon Villa Res.	22	11	3	8	69	48	36
Kimberley MW A	22	10	4	8	49	47	34
AFC Bridgford	22	10	3	9	59	46	33
Premium	22	9	2	11	46	56	29
Notts Metropolis	22	9	2	11	43	58	29
Clifton United	22	8	3	11	42	52	27
Grey Goose	22	7	2	13	42	83	23
Boots Athletic A	22	5	3	14	40	73	18
Bilborough T. Res.	22	4	3	15	36	83	15

Gedling Town Res. - record expunged

Division Two	P	W	D	L	F	A	Pts
Durham Ox	26	20	2	4	91	40	62
Clifton Wanderers	26	19	3	4	83	37	60
Arnold Town A	26	15	5	6	74	45	50
Bingham Town	26	15	2	9	84	66	47
AFC Bridgf'd Res.	26	13	2	11	61	57	41
FC Dynamo	26	12	4	10	70	61	40
Netherfield Sns	26	12	2	12	57	55	38
Burton Joyce Utd	26	12	2	12	84	88	38
Ali Islam	26	9	5	12	54	64	32
Premium Res.	26	9	3	14	62	82	30
Robin Hood Colts	26	8	5	13	52	69	29
Sherwood Social	26	7	4	15	53	66	25
Netherfield A. Res.	26	4	6	16	55	92	18
FC Samba Res.	26	3	3	20	40	98	12

Division Three	P	W	D	L	F	A	Pts
Notts Metro Res.	22	21	0	1	127	31	63
Kirk Hallam	22	17	1	4	92	47	52
FC Geordie	22	14	3	5	73	56	45
Beeston Rovers	22	11	7	4	68	48	40
Three Crowns	22	11	2	9	76	61	35
Kimberley MW Ac.	22	10	3	9	59	55	33
Clifton Tigers	22	9	2	11	59	66	29
Red Heart	22	7	3	12	39	54	24
Netherfield S. Res.	22	6	2	14	51	84	20
Bestwood	22	4	4	14	53	82	16
Globo Gym	22	3	4	15	35	91	13
Beeston Rylands	22	3	1	18	40	97	10

East Bridgford - record expunged

PERRY STREET & DISTRICT LEAGUE

Premier Division	P	W	D	L	F	A	Pts
Lyme Regis	22	19	1	2	62	18	58
South Petherton	22	16	4	2	88	21	52
Beaminster	22	17	1	4	82	28	52
Barrington	22	10	3	9	46	51	33
Misterton	22	9	5	8	41	42	32
Ilminster T. Res.	22	8	5	9	51	49	29
Combe St N. Res.	22	8	2	12	38	50	26
Merriott Rovers	22	8	2	12	40	61	26
Perry Street & YH	22	7	3	12	39	60	24
W. Horse Sym'by	22	6	4	12	43	51	22
Crewkerne	22	5	4	13	43	57	19
Charmouth	22	0	4	18	23	108	4

Division One	P	W	D	L	F	A	Pts
Farway United	20	12	6	2	65	29	42
W./Mid Chinnock	20	13	3	4	75	48	42
Winsham	20	12	3	5	49	33	39
Forton Rangers	20	12	2	6	45	32	38
Ilminster T. Colts	20	11	5	4	47	35	38
Netherbury	20	10	3	7	42	38	33
Lyme Regis Res.	20	6	3	11	45	52	21
Perry Street Res.	20	5	4	11	47	61	19
Thorncombe	20	4	4	12	32	41	16
Chard Rangers	20	4	2	14	34	70	14
Pymore	20	2	3	15	27	69	9

Merriott Rovers Res. - record expunged

Division Two	P	W	D	L	F	A	Pts
Millwey Rise	20	17	3	0	71	22	54
Norton Athletic	20	13	3	4	74	39	42
Shep. Beauchamp	20	12	3	5	66	29	39
Beaminster Res.	20	11	2	7	52	41	35
Forton Rgrs Res.	20	8	5	7	42	40	29
S. Petherton Res.	20	7	6	7	59	51	27
Dowlish & Donyatt	20	8	2	10	63	63	26
Hinton St George	20	7	3	10	47	54	24
Uplyme	20	6	2	12	41	61	20
Drimpton	20	4	1	15	41	89	13
Chard United	20	2	0	18	27	94	6

Division Three	P	W	D	L	F	A	Pts
Hawkchurch	20	13	3	4	65	40	42
Crewkerne Rgrs	20	12	2	6	66	41	38
Luso-Chard	20	12	1	7	71	45	37
Fivehead United	20	9	4	7	39	34	31
Crewkerne Res.	20	8	6	6	45	41	30
Millwey Rise Res.	20	10	0	10	42	45	30
Lyme Bantams *-3*	20	10	2	8	52	41	29
Misterton Res. *-1*	20	8	3	9	48	57	26
Combe St Nich. A	20	5	4	11	29	39	19
S. B'champ Res.	20	5	4	11	37	54	19
Chard Rgrs Res.	20	3	1	16	27	84	10

White Horse Symondsbury Res. - record expunged

Division Four	P	W	D	L	F	A	Pts
Chard United Res.	20	14	3	3	74	34	45
Farway Utd Res.	20	12	3	5	71	37	39
Winsham Res.	20	10	6	4	71	55	36
Ilminster T. A *-3*	20	11	2	7	54	51	31
Barrington Res.	20	9	3	8	60	52	30
Waytown Hounds	20	9	2	9	61	54	29
Hinton St G. Res.	20	8	4	8	45	55	28
Combe St Nich. B	20	8	2	10	66	55	26
T'combe Res. *-3*	20	5	4	11	38	58	16
Hawkchurch Res.	20	4	3	13	33	63	15
Charm'th Res. *-1*	20	3	2	15	22	81	10

PLYMOUTH & WEST DEVON COMBINATION

Division One	P	W	D	L	F	A	Pts
Tamarside	26	19	5	2	89	46	62
Mount Gould	26	18	4	4	104	34	58
Old Suttonians	26	20	3	3	98	32	57
Wessex Rangers	26	18	3	5	88	34	57
Univ. of Plymouth	26	18	3	5	90	43	57
Roborough	26	13	3	10	77	54	42
Western Mort. S.	26	11	2	13	56	59	35
Staddiscombe Colts	26	8	4	14	62	83	28
SWEB	26	8	4	14	55	85	28
Horrabdge Rg. SA	26	8	3	15	47	91	27
Ordulph Arms	26	7	4	15	42	64	25
Utd Serv Mermaid	26	7	4	15	40	63	22
Yelverton	26	2	1	23	33	112	10
Plym. Parkway A	26	3	1	22	41	122	10

Division Two	P	W	D	L	F	A	Pts
Roborough Res.	24	16	3	5	97	56	51
Ivybridge Res.	24	14	6	4	68	49	48
Univ. Plym'th Res.	24	15	3	6	84	49	45
Cafe Roma	24	12	3	9	63	59	39
Chard United FC	24	11	3	10	62	49	36
Lee Moor WMOV	24	12	0	12	75	75	36
Chaddlew'd MOB	24	10	5	9	65	57	35
Shakespeare	24	11	1	12	57	69	34
Staddiscombe Res.	24	10	3	11	56	58	33
Plymouth YMCA	24	9	4	11	72	62	31
Plym. Trophyman	24	9	3	12	68	63	30
Morley Rangers	24	6	1	17	45	87	19
Old Sutts Res.	24	3	1	20	34	113	7

Kings Arms Tamerton - record expunged

Division Three	P	W	D	L	F	A	Pts
Windsor Car Sales	21	16	1	4	79	40	49
Plymouth Marjon	21	14	0	7	89	42	42
Yealm Old Boys	21	12	3	6	66	51	39
Lee Moor	21	9	0	12	58	66	27
Univ. Plymouth A	21	9	2	10	54	59	26
Hooe St John	21	8	1	12	52	77	22
Cofely	21	7	3	11	49	66	21
Morley Rgrs Res.	21	3	2	16	37	83	8

PORTSMOUTH & DISTRICT LEAGUE

Premier Division	P	W	D	L	F	A	Pts
Univ Portsmouth	18	14	2	2	80	30	44
Portsea Comm.	18	14	0	4	56	28	42
Waterlooville SC	18	11	3	4	62	34	36
Wymering	18	10	4	4	52	35	34
Shearer United	18	7	2	9	62	57	23
Prospect	18	7	2	9	46	51	23
Old Portmuthians	18	7	2	9	28	39	23
St Helena Bobs	18	6	1	11	52	51	19
Horndean A	18	3	2	13	38	102	11
Farefield Sports	18	1	2	15	24	74	5

Division One	P	W	D	L	F	A	Pts
Fleur-de-Lys	18	14	3	1	55	28	45
Denmead/Purb'k	18	12	1	5	65	35	37
P'mth Kurdish Utd	18	13	0	5	55	33	36
AFC Ventora	18	10	4	4	54	34	34
Paulsgrove Social	18	9	3	6	43	42	30
Rovers Reunited	18	7	0	11	34	51	21
Newcome Arms	18	5	2	11	40	48	17
NAP Construct. *-3*	18	5	0	13	36	60	12
Segensworth *-3*	18	5	0	13	26	64	12
Cosham Blues	18	3	1	14	35	64	10

Division Two	P	W	D	L	F	A	Pts
Southside	16	12	2	2	62	20	38
Meon	16	12	2	2	64	31	38
Carberry	16	7	4	5	40	31	25
AFC Hereford *-3*	16	8	4	4	35	37	25
Cosham Res. *-3*	16	8	2	6	36	44	23
Inter Solent	16	7	1	8	34	30	22
AFC Hilsea	16	3	3	10	39	56	12
Farefield Sp.Res.	16	3	1	12	22	49	10
Portchester	16	2	1	13	16	60	7

Pelhams Arms - record expunged

Division Three	P	W	D	L	F	A	Pts
Mead End	14	12	1	1	65	23	37
FC Southsea	14	11	0	3	39	16	33
The Unit *-3*	14	9	1	4	42	22	25
Compass Rose	14	7	2	5	40	26	23
Cosham Pk Rgrs	14	4	4	6	38	38	16
Castle Rovers	14	3	3	8	22	54	12
Queens Pk Grovers	14	2	1	11	21	60	7
Westover	14	1	2	11	27	57	5

PRESTON & DISTRICT LEAGUE

Premier Division	P	W	D	L	F	A	Pts
Appley Bridge	26	19	5	2	88	29	62
Burscough Rich.	26	20	1	5	99	27	61
Leyland Red Rose	26	18	4	4	98	49	58
Ainsdale United	26	17	3	6	55	37	54
Southport Amats	26	13	5	8	59	44	44
Lostock St G. Res.	26	12	4	10	43	45	40
Preston Wdrs	26	12	5	9	52	37	38
Leyland	26	10	2	14	68	73	32
Southport Trinity A	26	9	3	14	42	49	27
Baxters	26	8	2	16	51	88	26
New Longton Rov.	26	7	4	15	53	60	25
Charnock Rich. A	26	5	3	18	40	85	18
Tarleton Corries	26	5	3	18	28	75	15
Croston Spts Club	26	4	2	20	34	112	14

Hoghton West End - record expunged

Division One	P	W	D	L	F	A	Pts
Eccleston/Heskin	22	15	3	4	84	45	48
CCA	22	15	2	5	82	52	47
Town Green	22	12	6	4	63	39	42
Hoole United	22	12	1	9	61	51	37
Mawdesley	22	11	1	10	43	45	34
Preston GSA	22	9	6	7	52	41	33
Sumners	22	8	4	10	50	54	28
Southport Trinity B	22	7	5	10	34	46	26
Highcross	22	7	4	11	42	60	25
Southport A. Res.	22	5	4	13	49	68	19
Walton-le-Dale	22	5	4	13	42	62	19
Walmer Bridge	22	5	2	15	34	73	17

Division Two	P	W	D	L	F	A	Pts
Penwortham Town	20	15	3	2	89	43	48
Birkdale United	20	12	5	3	60	39	44
Deepdale	20	12	5	3	72	44	41
Eccleston/H. Res.	20	10	6	4	59	39	36
Wyre	20	10	2	8	76	49	32
Newman College	20	8	4	8	48	53	28
Burscough Bridge	20	7	4	9	53	64	25
Preston United	20	7	2	11	51	64	23
Leyland RR Res.	20	6	1	13	53	74	16
Adlington	20	3	3	14	22	52	12
Farington Villa	20	2	1	17	24	86	7

Division Three	P	W	D	L	F	A	Pts
Blessed Sacrement	18	18	0	0	107	20	54
Adelphi	18	11	2	5	64	43	35
Hoghton WE Res.	18	10	3	5	59	42	33
Catforth	18	10	1	7	58	42	31
Longridge T. Res.	18	9	2	7	44	47	26
Chipping	18	7	3	8	46	47	24
New Longton Res.	18	7	0	11	48	62	21
Leyland Res.	18	6	2	10	38	53	20
Muldoons	18	4	2	12	45	76	11
Eccleston & H. A	18	0	1	17	19	96	1

Leyland Red Rose A, Tarleton Corinthians Res. - records expunged

Division Four	P	W	D	L	F	A	Pts
P'wortham St Ter.	22	19	1	2	141	32	58
Skelmersdale Ath.	22	17	1	4	127	46	52
Leyland Athletic	22	14	2	6	74	53	44
AFC Walton	22	13	4	5	97	39	43
Hoole United Res.	22	11	2	9	45	60	35
Ribbleton Rovers	22	12	1	9	72	51	34
Ribchester	22	11	2	9	57	47	32
New Longton A	22	8	3	11	56	58	27
Walmer Bdge Res.	22	5	2	15	23	74	17
Hesketh Bank A	22	5	1	16	48	84	16
Tarleton Cor. A	22	5	0	17	32	107	12
Chorley Athletic	22	2	1	19	32	153	7

REDHILL & DISTRICT LEAGUE

Premier Division	P	W	D	L	F	A	Pts
Brockham	20	18	0	2	66	25	54
Horley Town A	20	12	5	3	48	25	41
Real Holmesdale	20	11	7	2	50	25	40
Limpsfield Blues	20	11	3	6	47	29	36
AFC Woodhatch	20	8	4	8	64	53	28
Charlwood	20	6	4	10	32	46	22
Walton Heath	20	6	2	12	45	53	20
Frenches Athletic	20	6	2	12	34	50	20
Chipstead A	20	5	3	12	30	59	18
Tatsfield Rovers	20	5	2	13	30	47	17
Smallfield	20	5	2	13	26	60	17

Division One	P	W	D	L	F	A	Pts
Westcott	20	18	1	1	82	17	55
Holland Sports	20	16	2	2	87	20	50
Merstham A	20	13	3	4	55	34	42
Woodcote Old B.	20	9	6	5	41	23	33
Bookham A	20	8	3	9	47	42	27
Reigate Hill	20	7	3	10	51	58	24
Reigate Sala	20	7	1	12	38	62	22
Reed	20	6	3	11	31	57	21
Woodland Albion	20	6	0	14	38	71	18
Warlingham A	20	4	2	14	33	76	14
S. Godstone Res.	20	3	2	15	32	75	11

Division Two	P	W	D	L	F	A	Pts
Racing Epsom	16	11	4	1	72	24	37
Bletchingley Res.	16	10	3	3	52	28	33
South Park A	16	9	5	2	46	24	32
Monotype	16	6	5	5	37	28	23
RH123 Ath. Res.	16	6	3	7	43	49	21
Nutfield Res.	16	5	3	8	36	45	18
Merstham N. Res.	16	4	5	7	27	40	17
Horley Town B	16	2	5	9	31	59	11
Charlwood Res.	16	2	1	13	16	63	7

Division Three	P	W	D	L	F	A	Pts
Warlingham B	18	14	1	3	61	19	43
Reigate Hill Res.	18	12	2	4	82	45	38
Heath Old Boys	18	12	2	4	70	33	38
Alliance	18	11	1	6	75	47	34
Overton Athletic	18	9	2	7	29	27	29
Holland Spts Res.	18	8	2	8	38	44	26
Limpsfield B. Res.	18	7	1	10	42	46	22
Reigate Priory A	18	4	3	11	39	55	15
Oxted & District A	18	3	0	15	17	76	9
Brockham Res.	18	3	0	15	14	75	9

Division Four	P	W	D	L	F	A	Pts
Caterham OB Res.	20	18	1	1	80	12	55
Horley	20	12	4	4	58	30	40
Real H'sdale Res.	20	12	3	5	71	27	39
The Plough Ifield	20	10	1	9	53	47	31
Wal'gton New For.	20	10	1	9	44	48	31
Walton Hth Res.	20	8	5	7	40	42	29
Merstham B	20	6	3	11	33	52	21
RH123 Athletic A	20	6	2	12	35	60	20
Park Lane	20	5	4	11	29	49	19
AFC Redhill	20	4	4	12	27	50	16
Frenches A. Res.	20	3	4	13	30	83	13

Division Five	P	W	D	L	F	A	Pts
Godstone	18	18	0	0	119	13	54
Court Lodge	18	13	0	5	75	25	39
Westcott Res.	18	11	1	6	57	41	34
Nutfield A	18	8	0	10	49	47	24
Merstham C	18	4	2	12	33	87	14
Reigate Priory B	18	3	3	12	35	81	12
Horley Res.	18	2	2	14	29	103	8

ROCHDALE ALLIANCE
(Rochdale Online)

Premier Division	P	W	D	L	F	A	Pts
Weavers Arms *+2*	16	13	2	1	55	13	43
Wardle	16	13	2	1	58	21	41
Whitworth Vall. *-1*	16	9	1	6	42	28	27
Roca Juniors	16	7	1	8	35	38	22
Rochdale Asia *+2*	16	6	2	8	30	42	22
Fothergill/Whittles	16	5	3	8	44	39	18
Asia FC *-3*	16	4	6	6	30	26	15
Harlequin *-1*	16	2	3	11	23	63	8
Dusty Miller *-1*	16	2	2	12	14	62	7

Division One	P	W	D	L	F	A	Pts
Syke	18	16	1	1	126	20	49
Castleton	18	15	2	1	74	25	47
Weavers A. Res.	18	12	2	4	59	48	38
Hargreaves	18	11	2	5	56	36	35
Sudden Carling	18	7	0	11	37	45	21
Rochdale SH A *+1*	18	5	3	10	36	65	19
Jacks House *+2*	18	4	2	12	43	57	16
Waggon Athletic	18	5	1	12	54	74	16
Wardle Res. *-4*	18	4	3	11	20	48	11
Woodbank *-1*	18	2	2	14	14	107	9

Division Two	P	W	D	L	F	A	Pts
Whitworth V. Res.	18	15	1	2	76	18	46
Castleton Res. *+2*	18	13	3	2	82	31	44
Wardle A *+2*	18	13	2	3	64	33	43
AFC Royton *+2*	18	11	1	6	46	42	36
Sun Hotel	18	8	2	8	61	45	26
R'dale Asia Res.	18	6	3	9	47	54	21
Todmorden Vets	18	5	2	11	41	61	17
Donkey Dodgers	18	2	5	11	40	73	11
Fothergill/W. Res.	18	3	1	14	26	82	10
S. Carling Res. *-6*	18	2	4	12	25	57	4

ROCHESTER & DISTRICT LEAGUE

Premier Division	P	W	D	L	F	A	Pts
Hollands & B. Res.	20	14	4	2	54	15	46
FC Quayside	20	12	6	2	55	22	42
BAE Spts & Social	20	13	2	5	65	23	41
Park Regis	20	11	4	5	52	39	37
Gillingham Green	20	8	8	4	29	20	32
Medway Knights	20	8	3	9	38	49	27
Cannon 24	20	7	1	12	37	42	22
Medway City	20	6	3	11	34	44	21
Lordswood Ath.	20	6	3	11	42	53	21
Cliffe Woods	20	4	1	15	23	75	13
Evolution	20	3	1	16	33	80	10

Bredhurst, Greenwich Thistle - records expunged

Division One	P	W	D	L	F	A	Pts
Luton Athletic	20	14	4	2	67	23	46
Upchurch	20	12	4	4	47	25	40
Pegasus	20	12	2	6	57	32	38
Stockbury Athletic	20	10	7	3	52	30	37
Fitters United	20	10	5	5	63	37	35
Grain Athletic	20	9	1	10	48	71	28
Bredhurst J. Res.	20	7	4	9	43	48	25
Red Lion	20	7	2	11	46	53	23
Medway Queen	20	4	7	9	24	47	19
Riverside	20	4	5	11	38	38	17
Milton & FU Res.	20	0	1	19	16	97	1

Three Sisters - record expunged

Division Two	P	W	D	L	F	A	Pts
Pegasus Res.	20	14	4	2	78	34	46
Plough/Chequers	20	13	0	7	55	45	39
Minster WMC	20	12	2	6	56	43	38
Collyers	20	9	5	6	55	35	32
Insanity	20	9	4	7	53	43	31
Cliffe Woods Res.	20	9	3	8	52	34	30
JD Decking	20	10	0	10	53	48	30
Park Regis Res.	20	8	6	6	44	49	30
Cobras	20	7	2	11	42	60	23
Strood	20	1	6	13	20	74	9
Bredhurst Res.	20	1	2	17	26	69	5

Division Three	P	W	D	L	F	A	Pts
Medway Colts	24	22	2	0	92	12	68
Cliffe Woods A	24	21	2	1	101	27	65
Hoo Village	24	15	2	7	66	51	47
Cliffe Wds Lions	24	13	3	8	62	45	42
Medway Athletic	24	10	7	7	55	42	37
Emerald Star	24	11	4	9	56	49	37
Sharsted Sports	24	11	4	9	60	74	37
Outer Fenn	24	10	3	11	50	43	33
The Huntsman	24	9	1	14	60	62	28
Woodcoombe S&S	24	6	5	13	43	69	23
Southern Belle	24	6	1	17	63	88	19
Mossy's Tavern	24	4	0	20	40	103	12
Kings Head	24	0	2	22	25	108	2

Division Four	P	W	D	L	F	A	Pts
Snodland Nomads	24	19	1	4	90	36	58
Princes Pk Nemesis	24	16	4	4	66	39	52
Swale United Res.	24	15	3	6	72	30	48
Hoo Institute	24	14	4	6	72	29	46
Lepsons AWR	24	14	4	6	50	39	46
Upchurch Res.	24	12	0	12	54	79	36
The Rose Inn Gill.	24	11	2	11	59	44	35
W. Horse Borstal	24	10	4	10	45	49	34
Real Knights	24	11	1	12	60	73	34
Rainham 84	24	7	3	14	43	70	24
Walderslade	24	5	4	15	36	59	19
Em. Star Classics	24	3	1	20	22	53	10
Riverside Res.	24	3	1	20	25	94	10

Division Five	P	W	D	L	F	A	Pts
Young Planners	24	17	3	4	99	36	54
Sturdee	24	16	4	4	75	43	52
Windermere Wdrs	24	13	5	6	72	49	44
SCC Old Boys	24	13	2	9	63	58	41
Sirtcom	24	12	2	10	68	54	38
O'Connell's	24	11	4	9	55	56	37
White Stallions	24	10	5	9	65	69	35
Medway Rams	24	9	6	9	49	45	33
AFC Phoenix	24	10	3	11	58	60	33
Bleakwood Rgrs	24	7	8	9	66	61	29
Park FC	24	5	5	14	44	67	20
Bowaters	24	3	6	15	49	83	15
Slade 05	24	2	3	19	31	113	9

Division Six	P	W	D	L	F	A	Pts
Snodland Town	24	21	1	2	78	29	64
Rainham 84 Rgrs	24	19	2	3	100	45	59
Halfway United	24	16	4	4	76	43	52
Livingstone Arms	24	16	1	7	89	49	49
Invicta Colts	24	13	1	10	54	42	40
Beechwood 76	24	11	3	10	66	53	36
Rainh'm Cricketers	24	10	3	11	55	68	33
Outer Fenn Res.	24	8	4	12	60	45	28
S'thern Belle Res.	24	7	2	15	64	67	23
Medway Rovers	24	7	2	15	40	94	23
The Weston Arms	24	7	0	17	58	79	21
Woodcoombe Res.	24	4	3	17	39	100	15
Snod. Roosters	24	3	2	19	40	105	11

ROMFORD & DISTRICT LEAGUE

Senior Division	P	W	D	L	F	A	Pts
Newbury Forest	18	13	2	3	60	30	41
Duckwood	18	11	2	5	53	32	35
Newtown Wesley	18	9	4	5	39	35	31
Old Barkabbeyans	18	8	5	5	40	28	29
Debden Sports A	18	8	4	6	28	34	28
Stifford Clays Soc.	18	8	3	7	31	32	27
Heath Park	18	6	5	7	32	31	23
East Ham WMC	18	4	5	9	37	43	17
Brabazon Sports	18	5	2	11	23	50	17
Clack United	18	1	2	15	18	46	5

Premier Division	P	W	D	L	F	A	Pts
Millhouse	20	16	3	1	70	17	51
Upney Royal Oak	20	14	3	3	47	15	45
O. Bark'yans Res.	20	9	6	5	43	28	33
Allied Rec	20	7	7	6	30	35	28
Rush Green	20	7	5	8	52	64	26
Phoenix	20	7	4	9	33	31	25
OG United	20	7	4	9	33	43	25
Liberty	20	6	4	10	38	39	22
May & Baker	20	5	4	11	29	48	19
Mansard Rovers	20	4	5	11	26	53	17
Canning Town A	20	5	1	14	22	50	16

Division One	P	W	D	L	F	A	Pts
Aveley Northend	22	19	2	1	72	23	59
Euro Dagenham	22	15	4	3	49	26	49
Cromer Park	22	14	3	5	70	26	45
Harold W. Hospital	22	11	3	8	41	45	36
Haver Town	22	8	8	6	48	36	32
O Barkabbeyans A	22	9	5	8	50	44	32
Verona	22	7	4	11	48	51	25
Emeronians	22	7	4	11	43	46	25
Fulbrook Royals	22	6	5	11	41	54	23
Upminster A	22	6	2	14	38	71	20
Aveley WMC	22	5	2	15	26	51	17
Northend	22	2	4	16	27	81	10

Division Two	P	W	D	L	F	A	Pts
AFC Stanford	18	15	1	2	63	13	46
Spartan Athletic	18	14	1	3	72	24	43
Ferns Seniors	18	13	1	4	52	31	40
E. Ham WMC Res.	18	13	0	5	54	28	39
Oakwood Sports	18	10	0	8	46	32	30
Coryton Athletic	18	6	1	11	40	51	19
O Barkabbeyans B	18	4	4	10	24	61	16
Northend Res.	18	4	2	14	25	54	14
Real Dagenham	18	2	4	12	28	56	10
Haver Town Res.	18	0	4	14	21	75	4

Division Three	P	W	D	L	F	A	Pts
Iona	20	18	1	1	99	15	55
Merit	20	13	3	4	71	53	42
Eastside Rovers	20	12	5	3	74	24	41
Northend A	20	11	6	3	57	27	39
Markyate	20	11	3	6	69	53	36
Elmhurst	20	8	4	8	64	46	28
Aveley N'thd Res.	20	8	2	10	59	55	26
Lionside United	20	5	4	11	52	72	19
Upminster B	20	4	3	13	30	80	15
Co-Op United	20	1	4	15	18	85	7
Canning Town B	20	0	3	17	22	106	3

SALISBURY & DISTRICT LEAGUE

Premier Division	P	W	D	L	F	A	Pts
Alderbury	18	13	2	3	65	30	41
Friends Provident	18	11	2	5	49	27	35
Stockton/Codford	18	11	2	5	48	31	35
Chalke Valley Res.	18	9	2	7	41	33	29
Tisbury	18	7	8	3	35	27	29
S. Newton/Wishf'd	18	7	2	9	43	42	23
Nomansland	18	7	1	10	28	39	22
Porton Sports	18	4	6	8	28	34	18
Enford	18	3	3	12	19	66	12
West Harnham	18	3	2	13	32	59	11

RGV Netherton - record expunged

Division One	P	W	D	L	F	A	Pts
Boscombe Down	20	17	0	3	57	25	51
S'henge Snooker	20	14	2	4	66	34	44
Greyhound Ames.	20	13	3	4	68	38	42
Durrington WMC	20	11	2	7	61	48	35
Whiteparish	20	10	2	8	60	49	32
The Coach & H.	20	9	2	9	42	50	29
Alderbury Res.	20	8	2	10	42	52	26
Porton Sports Res.	20	4	5	11	40	65	17
Tisbury Res.	20	4	3	13	39	54	15
Stockton/C. Res.	20	3	4	13	38	67	13
Winterslow	20	4	1	15	32	63	13

Hopback United - record expunged

Division Two	P	W	D	L	F	A	Pts
Chalke Valley Rfg	22	18	1	3	80	34	52
Wilton Town Res.	22	16	2	4	97	40	50
Figheldean Rgrs	22	16	2	4	97	41	50
Alderholt A	22	13	6	3	74	40	45
George & Dragon	22	13	1	8	81	51	40
Boscombe D. Rec	22	10	4	8	58	60	34
Burgess Trees	22	10	1	11	54	62	31
SN/Wishford Res.	22	6	2	14	53	59	20
Devizes Inn	22	5	1	16	47	81	16
Langford FC	22	5	1	16	43	82	16
Value Cars	22	4	2	16	33	87	14
Victoria Hotel	22	3	3	16	33	113	12

Winterslow United - record expunged

SCARBOROUGH & DISTRICT LEAGUE
(Scarborough Evening News)

Division One	P	W	D	L	F	A	Pts
Eastfield	22	18	3	1	103	11	57
Filey Town	22	18	2	2	90	25	56
West Pier	22	14	5	3	64	29	47
Newlands Park *-1*	22	14	1	7	49	37	42
Edgehill	22	11	3	8	63	47	36
Cayton Corries	22	10	2	10	42	54	32
Hunmanby United	22	7	5	10	31	47	26
Ayton	22	8	2	12	46	69	26
Sherburn	22	6	2	14	34	85	20
Scalby	22	5	0	17	26	66	15
Fishburn Pk Res.	22	4	1	17	22	60	13
Seamer Sports	22	3	2	17	20	60	11

SCUNTHORPE & DISTRICT LEAGUE
(TSW Printers)

Division One	P	W	D	L	F	A	Pts
AFC Brumby	18	18	0	0	100	10	54
Epworth Town	18	11	1	6	44	32	34
Barton T. OB Res.	18	10	4	4	49	38	34
Limestone Rgrs	18	9	2	7	50	45	29
Scunthonians	18	8	2	8	57	41	26
Scotter United	18	7	4	7	42	53	25
BBM	18	7	3	8	37	50	24
Swinefleet Juniors	18	6	3	9	34	48	21
Haxey Town	18	2	2	14	26	63	8
Crosby Colts	18	1	1	16	27	86	4

Messingham Trinity Jnrs - record expunged

Division Two	P	W	D	L	F	A	Pts
College Wdrs	18	12	3	3	47	23	39
AFC Brumby Res.	18	12	3	3	56	42	39
Crosby Colts Res.	18	9	2	7	48	37	29
Crowle Town Colts	18	8	5	5	36	25	29
Barnetby United	18	8	3	7	51	42	27
Epworth T. Res.	18	7	4	7	32	34	25
New Holland Villa	18	6	6	6	47	41	24
Jailhouse	18	7	0	11	48	59	21
Sherpa	18	3	3	12	33	58	12
Scunthonians Res.	18	3	1	14	33	70	10

Division Three	P	W	D	L	F	A	Pts
Revision	24	23	0	1	104	26	69
Crosby Colts Jnr	24	16	3	5	109	56	51
Ashby Star	24	12	2	9	92	55	38
Scotter Utd Res.	24	12	2	10	54	56	38
Luddington	24	9	2	12	46	57	29
Barrow Wanderers	24	9	2	13	43	70	29
College Wds Res.	24	7	2	15	34	73	23
W Butterwick Wdrs	24	5	4	15	37	70	19
Briggensians	24	4	3	17	41	97	15

Division Four	P	W	D	L	F	A	Pts
Barton TOB Colts	24	20	1	3	102	36	61
AFC Blades	24	18	1	5	86	37	55
Auld South Yorks	24	16	1	7	91	45	49
Men's Health	24	12	3	9	71	59	39
Scunthorpe Rgrs	24	11	3	10	77	53	36
Epworth Town A	24	8	4	12	62	52	28
Santon	24	9	1	14	42	100	28
Limestone R. Res.	24	3	3	18	22	84	12
Parkwood Athletic	24	2	1	21	33	120	7

SELBY & DISTRICT LEAGUE

Division One	P	W	D	L	F	A	Pts
Moorends Coms	22	17	1	4	72	27	52
Pontefract Cobbler	22	16	2	4	83	33	50
Rock Inn	22	14	2	6	68	53	44
Ferrybridge Ams	22	11	3	8	60	36	36
Pontefract Town	22	10	6	6	76	61	36
Magnet Hotel	22	10	2	10	54	60	32
Knottingley Albion	22	8	3	11	46	47	27
Willow Park	22	6	6	10	51	64	24
Pollington	22	7	1	14	64	72	22
Garforth Rgrs A	22	5	7	10	44	72	22
Sherburn WR A	22	5	5	12	40	67	20
Old Castle	22	3	2	17	52	118	11

Division Two	P	W	D	L	F	A	Pts
Magnet Celtics	26	20	1	5	109	40	61
Micklefield Town	26	19	2	5	116	56	59
Wetherby Ath. B	26	16	4	6	72	50	52
Drax	26	12	6	8	69	58	42
Rileys Rangers	26	12	3	11	72	77	39
Monk Fryston	26	10	5	11	63	61	35
Rock Inn Res.	26	10	3	13	71	84	33
G'forth WMC Res.	26	9	5	12	57	70	32
Fairburn United	26	8	7	11	64	76	31
Kellington	26	8	6	12	81	80	30
Hensall Athletic	26	8	5	13	57	78	29
Garforth	26	8	4	14	62	95	28
Gt Preston Res. *-1*	26	7	4	15	63	80	24
Selby RSSC Res.	26	7	1	18	42	93	22

SEVENOAKS & DISTRICT LEAGUE
(Bat & Ball Sports)

Premier Division	P	W	D	L	F	A	Pts
Hildenborough Ath.	22	18	3	1	79	18	57
Halstead	22	15	2	5	80	35	47
Nomads	22	15	2	5	70	35	47
Kemsing	22	14	2	6	75	35	44
Eynsford	22	11	4	7	58	40	37
St Lawrence	22	11	2	9	68	47	35
Borough Green U.	22	10	4	8	51	42	34
Ide Hill	22	11	0	11	63	55	33
Ton. Bapt. Church	22	8	1	13	40	63	25
Ightham	22	3	3	16	29	90	12
AW London	22	2	4	16	31	89	10
Orpington A	22	0	1	21	23	118	1

ivision One	P	W	D	L	F	A	Pts
.ingsdown Racers	21	17	3	1	92	36	54
unton Green	22	14	1	7	49	40	43
:hipstead A	22	13	1	8	69	42	40
ildenboro. Res.	22	11	4	7	58	37	37
/esterham A	22	12	0	10	53	47	36
ynsford Res.	22	8	5	9	42	51	29
leetdown Utd A	22	7	5	10	36	59	26
alls Res.	22	7	4	11	36	38	25
eal	22	5	7	10	45	57	22
/ilderpark	22	6	3	13	29	55	21
t Lawrence Res.	21	3	6	12	38	71	15
'oaks Weald -12	22	7	3	12	36	50	12

ivision Two	P	W	D	L	F	A	Pts
ld Boars	17	13	2	2	62	23	41
otters	20	12	3	5	52	32	39
.ingsdown Res.	20	10	3	7	38	30	33
eal Res.	20	9	4	7	46	41	31
rpington B	20	9	3	8	54	44	30
alstead Res.	19	9	3	7	56	48	30
emsing Res.	19	8	1	10	61	58	25
/ilderpark Res.	20	7	3	10	44	58	24
tford United A	19	7	1	11	45	65	22
adlow Rovers	20	5	2	13	34	60	17
omads A	20	4	3	13	44	77	15

Tonbridge Saracens - record expunged

ivision Three	P	W	D	L	F	A	Pts
wanley Oaks	23	18	0	5	96	30	54
/esterham B	24	17	3	4	79	47	54
orough GU Res.	24	16	3	5	79	40	51
omads B	24	14	5	5	79	51	47
ildenborough A	24	13	3	8	78	49	42
e Hill Res.	24	12	4	8	47	51	40
W London Res.	24	9	4	11	43	58	31
on. Bapt. C. Res.	23	10	1	12	49	67	31
adius	24	8	3	13	48	64	27
hipstead B	23	7	4	12	50	74	25
ihtham Res.	24	7	2	15	38	55	23
eal A	24	4	3	17	28	81	15
orough Green	23	1	1	21	24	71	4

SHROPSHIRE ALLIANCE

	P	W	D	L	F	A	Pts
anwood Utd Res.	24	20	1	3	100	41	61
ock	24	16	1	7	67	45	49
rees United	24	15	3	6	79	36	48
swestry Boys C.	24	15	2	7	60	38	47
/eston Rhyn	24	12	5	7	61	37	41
opesgate United	24	13	1	10	66	46	40
ayston Hill	24	12	2	10	67	69	38
udlow T. Colts	24	10	3	11	50	50	33
swestry T. Lions	24	7	5	12	45	67	26
t Martins Res.	24	6	2	16	39	70	20
innerley	24	6	1	17	41	77	19
ockshutt	24	5	3	16	49	95	18
rown Colts	24	4	1	19	48	101	13

SOUTH DEVON LEAGUE
(Woolcombe Beer Watts Solicitors)

remier Division	P	W	D	L	F	A	Pts
/atts B. Bearne	26	21	2	3	95	45	65
oton Athletic	26	18	3	5	74	34	57
rixham Villa -3	26	17	3	6	87	37	51
rixham United	26	13	5	8	53	39	44
almpton Res. -3	26	14	4	8	67	54	43
'kerswell & Chel.	26	11	6	9	63	51	39
hagford	26	11	5	10	65	60	38
obotskerswell	26	11	3	12	61	70	36
'aldon Athletic	26	8	7	11	53	71	31
shburton -6	26	9	5	12	59	65	26
ast Allington U.	26	6	6	14	49	68	24
otnes/D. Res. -3	26	7	3	16	44	68	21
ele Rovers	26	4	2	20	36	93	14
ngsteignton A.	26	2	6	18	30	81	12

ivision One	P	W	D	L	F	A	Pts
uckland A. Res.	26	22	1	3	101	21	67
plepen Athletic	26	18	5	3	78	32	59
:averton/Land. -3	26	17	2	7	83	41	50
arbertonford	26	15	4	7	73	49	49
oddiswell Athletic	26	15	4	7	62	41	49
hudleigh Athletic	26	11	5	10	51	53	38
rixham Villa Res.	26	11	3	12	56	56	36
Ab. Spurs Res.	26	8	8	10	47	55	32
artmouth Res.	26	9	4	13	60	59	31
viera Spurs	26	9	4	13	49	75	31
Paignton Villa	26	7	2	17	41	81	23
Galmpton TG A -3	26	6	4	16	46	89	19
Upton Ath. Res. -6	26	5	6	15	36	53	15
Paignton Saints -3	26	3	0	23	27	105	6

Division Two	P	W	D	L	F	A	Pts
Stoke Gab. Res.	26	21	3	2	92	22	66
Buckfastleigh Rg.	26	19	2	5	94	40	59
Kingskerswell Res.	26	16	4	6	64	31	52
Teign Village	26	15	5	6	49	33	50
Langdon	26	13	6	7	57	40	45
Newton Abbot 66	26	13	3	10	62	46	42
Brixhm U. Res. -3	26	13	3	10	76	54	39
Beesands Rovers	26	10	6	10	59	66	36
Newton United	26	8	6	12	60	63	30
Kingsteignton Res.	26	7	5	14	53	79	26
East Allington Res.	26	8	1	17	36	75	25
Hele Rov. Res. -3	26	6	5	15	34	60	20
Meadowbrook -3	26	4	4	18	27	74	13
M'tonhampst'd -6	26	1	3	22	19	99	0

Division Three	P	W	D	L	F	A	Pts
Teignmouth Res.	26	21	1	4	108	41	61
Stoke Fleming	26	18	7	1	102	38	61
Hookhills United	26	19	4	3	95	33	61
Staverton/L. Res.	26	14	3	9	69	52	45
Bovey Tracey Res.	26	12	5	9	72	44	41
Watts BB Res.	26	12	3	11	38	47	39
Liverton Utd Res.	26	9	3	14	57	73	30
Dartmouth A	26	8	4	14	30	68	28
Totnes & DSC A	26	9	0	17	43	87	27
Broadhempston -6	26	9	5	12	36	42	26
South Brent	26	7	4	15	56	62	25
Waldon Ath. Res.	26	8	1	17	35	60	25
Foxhole United -6	26	7	6	13	43	65	21
NA Spurs A -12	26	5	2	19	37	109	5

Division Four	P	W	D	L	F	A	Pts
Buckland Ath. A	26	23	1	2	108	30	70
Denbury Athletic	26	19	3	4	93	34	60
Watcombe Wdrs	26	17	4	5	93	48	55
Babbacombe Cor.	26	14	3	9	83	61	45
Ilsington Villa	26	13	4	9	84	56	43
Torbay Christians	26	12	4	10	69	56	40
Loddiswell A. Res.	26	13	0	13	65	76	39
Stoke Gabriel A	26	11	5	10	69	66	38
A'kerswell Res. -9	26	13	1	12	78	77	31
Brixham Town	26	8	2	16	66	94	26
Kingskerswell A	26	6	5	15	42	68	23
Malborough Utd	26	6	3	17	62	81	21
Ashburton Res. -6	26	4	3	19	47	112	9
Newton U. Res. -3	26	4	0	22	35	135	9

Division Five	P	W	D	L	F	A	Pts
Ipplepen Ath. Res.	26	17	5	4	87	39	56
Brixham Villa A	26	15	4	7	75	45	49
Bab'cmbe C. Res.	26	14	6	6	72	57	48
Stoke Fleming Res.	26	14	4	8	72	63	46
Chagford Res.	26	13	3	10	77	60	42
Watts Blake B. A	26	12	5	9	52	44	41
Chudleigh A. Res.	26	11	4	11	64	56	37
Marldon	26	11	4	11	78	74	37
H'bertonf'd Res. -6	26	11	6	9	88	65	33
Sth Brent Res. -3	26	9	5	12	59	65	29
Paignton Sts Res.	26	6	6	14	51	87	24
Riviera Sp. Res.	26	6	5	15	56	71	23
B'hempstn Res. -3	26	7	5	14	46	68	23
Newton 66 Res. -3	26	4	2	20	40	123	11

Division Six	P	W	D	L	F	A	Pts
Bishopsteignton U.	16	15	1	0	55	14	46
Bovey Tracey A	16	11	0	5	59	27	33
Buckfastleigh Res.	16	9	2	5	34	30	29
Paignt'n V Res. -3	16	9	0	7	48	46	24
Kingsbdge/Kellaton	16	7	1	8	34	34	22
Teign Village Res.	16	5	2	9	23	50	17
Dittisham Utd -3	16	6	1	9	48	42	16
Denbury Res. -3	16	1	3	12	28	66	3
Jackz -15	16	4	0	12	28	48	-3

SOUTH LONDON ALLIANCE

Premier Division	P	W	D	L	F	A	Pts
Eden Park Rgrs	26	18	4	4	69	33	58
Tudor Sports Res.	26	17	3	6	70	45	54
New Park	26	14	5	7	57	41	47
Blackheath Wdrs	26	14	3	9	68	60	45
Parkhurst Rgrs	26	13	5	8	45	48	44
Sutton Ath. Res.	26	12	3	11	53	50	39
Wickham Wdrs	26	11	4	11	46	50	37
Knights Old Boys	26	10	5	11	53	53	35
Cray Valley Res.	26	10	4	12	60	55	34
Metrogas Res.	26	10	4	12	64	65	34
Johnson & Phillips	26	8	6	12	39	42	30
Drummond Ath.	26	6	8	12	34	48	26
Old Roan	26	6	4	16	49	76	22
F'boro. OBG Res.	26	3	2	21	28	69	11

Division One	P	W	D	L	F	A	Pts
Bridon Ropes Res.	20	13	4	3	51	22	43
Southwark Boro.	20	13	1	6	64	41	40
FC Hollington	20	12	1	7	57	38	37
Old Roan Res.	20	11	3	6	69	53	36
Lewisham Athletic	20	10	3	7	57	47	33
Eltham Town	20	9	1	10	38	40	28
Bexley	20	8	2	10	33	54	26
Thames Borough	20	7	4	9	39	49	25
Beaverwood	20	6	2	12	38	56	20
Old Colfeians	20	5	4	11	46	56	19
Long Lane	20	3	1	16	26	62	10

Elite, NASFAT, Old Town New Boys - records expunged

Division Two	P	W	D	L	F	A	Pts
Bridon Ropes A	20	13	6	1	50	19	45
Tudor Sports A	20	11	4	5	39	25	37
Seven Acre Res.	20	10	5	5	47	45	35
Crofton Alb. Res.	20	9	3	8	44	45	30
Avery Hill College	20	9	2	9	52	45	29
Shirley Seniors	20	8	4	8	48	33	28
Chislehurst Sports	20	8	4	8	35	39	28
Blackh'th W. Res.	20	7	2	11	36	46	23
West Bromley Alb.	20	6	4	10	39	53	22
Johnson & P. Res.	20	3	7	10	28	42	16
Beckenham Ryls	20	4	3	13	23	49	15

Holborough, Metrogas A - records expunged

Division Three	P	W	D	L	F	A	Pts
FC Elmstead	24	17	3	4	80	26	54
Wickham Pk Res.	24	16	3	5	70	39	51
Bexlians Res.	24	15	4	5	64	32	49
Red Velvet	24	14	3	7	60	44	45
Longlands Athletic	24	14	1	9	61	68	43
Old Roan A	24	11	5	8	53	45	38
West Hill	24	12	1	11	68	65	37
AFC Wickham	24	9	5	10	64	61	32
Eltham Town Res.	24	8	3	13	51	65	27
Elite Res.	24	8	3	13	49	82	27
Lions Athletic	24	7	1	16	38	36	22
Bexley Res.	24	3	5	16	31	67	14
Farnboro. OBG A	24	3	1	20	41	100	10

FC Acacia - record expunged

Division Four	P	W	D	L	F	A	Pts
Dartford Town	20	15	3	2	81	29	48
Eltham Town A	20	14	0	6	76	33	42
Seven Acre Sp. A	20	13	2	5	78	43	41
Sutton Dynamo	20	13	0	7	44	32	39
Long Lane Res.	20	12	2	6	68	44	38
Lewisham A. Res.	20	11	2	7	46	46	35
Oldsmiths	20	7	1	12	40	40	22
Crayford Arrows	20	6	1	13	29	57	19
Beaverwood Res.	20	5	1	14	34	67	16
FC Sporting	20	4	1	15	34	48	13
West Hill Res.	20	3	1	16	23	114	10

FC Kickz - record expunged

SOUTH YORKSHIRE AMATEUR LEAGUE

Premier Division	P	W	D	L	F	A	Pts
Jubilee Sports	16	13	2	1	68	29	41
Warncliffe	16	10	3	3	47	26	33
Gleadless	16	8	4	4	45	31	28
Millmoor Jnrs Res.	16	8	0	8	40	49	24
New Bohemians	16	7	2	7	35	40	23
Sheffield West End	16	6	4	6	37	38	22
Boynton Sports	16	4	3	9	31	37	15
Farm Road S & S	16	3	2	11	32	57	11
Oxspring United	16	2	2	12	33	61	8

Division One	P	W	D	L	F	A	Pts
Sheffield Medics	14	11	1	2	52	20	34
Aston Res.	14	7	3	4	33	24	24
Noah's Ark	14	6	4	4	38	27	22
Worsbro. Dale Dyn.	14	7	0	7	37	43	21
Half Moon	14	5	5	4	35	34	20
Shef. Bankers Res.	14	4	3	7	34	45	15
Yemeni Com. Assn	14	4	1	9	33	55	13
Hoyland Town	14	3	1	10	25	39	10

Phoenix Sports & Social A - record expunged

Division Two	P	W	D	L	F	A	Pts
Manor Castle	12	11	0	1	66	12	33
Royston	12	10	0	2	57	16	30
Winterhill	12	6	2	4	39	39	20
Aviva FC	12	5	1	6	30	45	16
De La Salle Res.	12	4	0	8	24	55	12
Thurgoland Welf.	12	2	1	9	19	46	7
Barnsley I'national	12	1	2	9	26	48	5

Horns Inn - record expunged

SOUTHAMPTON LEAGUE
(Drew Smith Homes)

Premier Division	P	W	D	L	F	A	Pts
Bush Hill	22	17	0	5	78	25	51
Spartans	22	16	2	4	76	36	50
Solent WTL	22	14	3	5	60	37	45
AFC Solent	22	13	4	5	64	41	43
Brendon	22	11	1	10	60	48	34
BTC Southampton	22	11	1	10	62	58	34
Nursling	22	9	3	10	46	48	30
Northend United	22	9	2	11	44	48	29
Bishopstoke WMC	22	8	3	11	43	56	27
Sporting Wessex	22	6	4	12	45	60	22
Freemantle	22	4	1	17	31	72	13
Capital	22	1	2	19	25	105	5

Senior Division	P	W	D	L	F	A	Pts
London Airways	24	19	1	4	76	28	58
AFC Redbridge	24	17	2	5	93	28	53
Hythe & Dib. Res.	24	14	4	6	76	26	46
Warsash Wasps	24	13	7	4	75	33	46
AFC Hiltingbury	24	13	5	6	56	42	44
Burridge	24	12	5	7	66	52	41
Netley CS Res.	24	10	5	9	50	50	35
Hythe Aztecs	24	9	5	10	43	41	32
Sholing Sports	24	7	6	11	45	52	27
BTC S'pton Res.	24	7	2	15	29	76	23
Durley Res.	24	5	5	14	43	75	20
Wellow	24	5	2	17	28	92	17
Michelmersh Res.	24	0	1	23	15	100	1

Jnr Division One	P	W	D	L	F	A	Pts
Forest Town NFC	18	15	2	1	52	18	47
Allbrook	18	13	2	3	61	27	41
Hare & Hounds	18	10	6	2	63	34	36
Veracity Vipers	18	8	6	4	42	34	30
Cadnam United	18	7	3	8	32	35	24
R. Sun Colden C.	18	6	2	10	33	32	20
Braishfield	18	6	2	10	33	51	20
Hedge End Town	18	4	4	10	42	55	16
Inmar	18	3	2	13	25	51	11
Otterbourne A	18	2	3	13	14	60	9

Booker Sports, WEB - records expunged

Jnr Division Two	P	W	D	L	F	A	Pts
Wheatshield Wdrs	14	9	3	2	48	27	30
BTC S'thampton A	14	9	1	4	39	22	28
S'pton Energy	14	8	2	4	30	28	26
Langley Manor	14	7	1	6	24	20	22
AFC Grains	14	6	3	5	28	18	21
Compton FC	14	5	3	6	39	25	18
Lowford	14	4	1	9	29	46	13
Priory Rovers	14	1	0	13	12	63	3

Rownhams - records expunged

Jnr Division Three	P	W	D	L	F	A	Pts
Warren Social *-6*	18	16	1	1	78	26	43
Chamberlayne	18	11	2	5	59	31	35
Yacht Sports	18	11	2	5	55	30	35
Wombles	18	10	3	5	42	32	33
Warsash W. Res.	18	8	1	9	44	46	25
Mark One	18	5	5	8	31	33	20
Priory Rov. Res.	18	5	3	10	43	49	18
AFC Redbdge Res.	18	5	3	10	36	66	18
Wildern United	18	4	3	11	36	68	15
Test Park	18	2	3	13	37	80	9

Jnr Division Four	P	W	D	L	F	A	Pts
Thornhill H. Kicks	18	13	2	3	66	41	41
East Boldre	18	13	1	4	67	33	40
Northend Utd Res.	18	12	3	3	47	28	39
QK S'thampton A	18	11	2	5	65	51	35
Compton FC Res.	18	8	4	6	46	38	28
AFC Stoneham A	18	8	3	7	38	36	27
Polygon	18	5	2	11	42	69	17
Sparky Albion	18	4	1	13	32	51	13
Eastleigh United	18	4	0	14	28	43	12
Saints	18	2	2	14	23	64	8

Capital Res. - record expunged

Jnr Division Five	P	W	D	L	F	A	Pts
Banjo's	16	14	0	2	71	16	42
FC Wellington	16	12	0	4	50	20	36
Athletico Romsey	16	11	1	4	44	25	34
Riverside Reds	16	10	0	6	50	27	30
Hamble Utd Res.	16	7	2	7	45	26	23
Manor Wasps	16	6	1	9	42	48	19
AFC Station	16	6	0	10	33	51	18
London Airw. Res.	16	3	2	11	28	56	11
Ampthill Athletic	16	0	0	16	12	106	0

SOUTHEND BOROUGH COMBINATION

Premier Division	P	W	D	L	F	A	Pts
Southchurch HOS	22	19	2	1	61	22	40
Old Southendian	22	17	1	4	62	22	35
Shoebury Town	22	16	2	4	65	29	34
Rochford Town	22	15	3	4	72	42	33
Weir Sports	22	11	5	6	52	41	27
All Claims	22	12	2	8	39	34	26
Blackgate Gunners	22	7	2	13	35	48	16
Leigh Town	22	5	6	11	28	59	16
Corinthians	22	6	3	13	38	54	15
Borough Rovers	22	6	2	14	43	54	14
Thundersley Utd	22	2	1	19	24	71	5
Emstar United	22	0	3	19	25	68	3

Division One	P	W	D	L	F	A	Pts
Stambridge United	22	20	1	1	98	22	41
Ensign	22	16	1	5	66	29	33
Catholic Utd Res.	22	16	1	5	60	26	33
Zebra Sports	22	13	4	5	74	37	30
Rayford Athletic	22	14	2	6	67	31	30
Cupids Co. Club	22	12	2	8	46	39	26
Hullbridge S. Res.	22	7	4	11	39	35	18
Westcliff Amateur	22	7	2	13	42	69	16
O. S'thendian Res.	22	6	3	13	37	57	15
BKS Sports	22	5	3	14	31	78	13
Southend Colls	22	3	3	16	21	68	9
Thames Park	22	0	0	22	19	109	0

Division Two	P	W	D	L	F	A	Pts
Castle Point Gas	20	19	1	0	91	27	39
Sceptre Elite	20	15	2	3	78	29	32
Weir Sports Res.	20	13	3	4	83	29	29
White Horse Rgrs	20	11	2	7	55	41	24
Ashingdon	20	9	5	6	49	45	23
Leigh Town Res.	20	10	2	8	57	65	22
Earls Hall United	20	9	1	10	44	47	19
Thorpe Athletic	20	6	3	11	42	61	15
Catholic United A	20	4	1	15	31	71	9
Trinity (S)	20	2	2	17	23	66	4
Cupids CC Res.	20	1	2	17	24	96	4

Division Three	P	W	D	L	F	A	Pts
FC Toro	22	17	2	3	73	24	36
Heathfield	22	16	2	4	72	23	34
Leigh Ramblers A	22	12	2	8	61	51	26
Ashingdon Res.	22	10	4	8	44	37	24
Southchurch Res.	22	11	1	10	37	45	23
Elmwood Old B.	22	9	4	9	48	42	22
Little Theatre Club	22	9	4	9	52	52	22
Corinthians Res.	22	9	3	10	43	48	21
Earls Hall Utd Res.	22	8	1	13	48	64	17
Old Southendian A	22	4	8	10	35	42	16
S'thend Colls Res.	22	4	4	14	37	85	12
Leigh Town A	22	3	5	14	27	64	11

Division Four	P	W	D	L	F	A	Pts
Barnf' Hurricanes	18	12	3	3	47	26	27
Southend Trojans	18	10	4	4	45	29	24
Rayford Ath. Res.	18	10	2	6	49	31	22
Westcliff United	18	10	1	7	54	42	21
Thundersley Res.	18	8	3	7	43	18	19
Little Theatre Res.	18	8	2	8	31	50	18
Southend Colls A	18	6	4	8	34	47	16
Southchurch H. A	18	6	2	10	38	51	14
Weir Sports A	18	6	1	11	45	60	13
Leigh Ramblers B	18	2	2	14	25	57	6

Division Five	P	W	D	L	F	A	Pts
Rochford T. Res.	18	14	3	1	98	16	31
Rawreth Sports	18	14	1	3	69	26	29
Sceptre Elite Res.	18	13	3	2	57	23	29
Sporting Hadleigh	18	8	3	7	56	36	19
Southend Rgrs	18	6	5	7	51	61	17
Rayford Athletic A	18	6	3	9	47	55	15
Old S'thendian B	18	4	6	8	48	51	14
Landwick	18	5	2	11	33	67	12
Southend Colls B	18	4	2	12	45	73	[illegible]
Stambridge Res.	18	2	0	16	21	117	[illegible]

SOUTHEND & DISTRICT LEAGUE

Premier Division	P	W	D	L	F	A	Pts
Club Sirrus	16	14	0	2	46	16	[illegible]
Signet United	16	9	2	5	56	45	[illegible]
Rayleigh Town A	16	5	5	6	31	41	[illegible]
AFC Horndon	16	5	3	8	47	51	[illegible]
White Hart United	16	1	2	13	24	51	[illegible]

Division One	P	W	D	L	F	A	Pts
Sparkbridge	18	14	2	2	58	17	[illegible]
Thundersley Rov.	18	10	4	4	44	29	[illegible]
Sparco	18	10	1	7	44	39	[illegible]
Kg John Barmy A.	18	9	2	7	45	27	[illegible]
Hockley Spartans	18	8	5	5	36	29	[illegible]
Wickford Rangers	18	2	1	15	19	52	[illegible]
Chalkwell Park	18	2	1	15	22	75	[illegible]

SOUTHPORT & DISTRICT LEAGUE

	P	W	D	L	F	A	Pts
Christ The King OB	26	20	3	3	125	37	[illegible]
Sandy Lane	26	16	4	6	104	59	[illegible]
St Pauls	26	16	4	6	91	64	[illegible]
Redgate Rov. Res.	26	16	3	7	79	49	[illegible]
Pinewoods Res.	26	16	2	8	89	53	[illegible]
Formby Dons	26	15	4	7	66	46	[illegible]
Leisure Sports	26	15	1	10	57	50	[illegible]
Trojan Security *-6*	26	15	1	10	82	50	[illegible]
Formby Athletic	26	11	6	9	72	67	[illegible]
Birkdale Crown	26	9	2	15	49	75	[illegible]
Poulton Wdrs	26	6	0	20	53	98	[illegible]
Banks	26	6	0	20	50	97	[illegible]
Rye Motors	26	3	0	23	27	129	[illegible]
Massams	26	2	2	22	36	106	[illegible]

SPEN VALLEY & DISTRICT LEAGUE

Premier Division	P	W	D	L	F	A	Pts
Ravensthorpe Rgrs	16	13	3	0	61	20	[illegible]
Jardy's	16	13	2	1	93	21	[illegible]
Savile Town	16	8	4	4	66	59	[illegible]
Black Horse	16	8	1	7	43	50	[illegible]
Bradford	16	6	5	5	50	32	[illegible]
FC Bosnia *-1*	16	5	2	9	41	72	[illegible]
Youth 2000	16	3	3	10	36	57	[illegible]
George Healey	16	3	1	12	39	66	[illegible]
Howden Clough A	16	2	1	13	30	82	[illegible]

Division One	P	W	D	L	F	A	Pts
Sporting Armley	16	13	3	0	59	22	[illegible]
Quarry	16	9	3	4	55	35	[illegible]
Norfolk	16	8	3	5	51	42	[illegible]
Fairbank	16	6	4	6	33	46	[illegible]
Marsh FC	16	5	5	6	38	44	[illegible]
White Rose	16	6	2	8	41	49	[illegible]
Inter Batley	16	6	0	10	38	44	[illegible]
Black Bull	16	3	3	10	41	54	[illegible]
Wellington (Yorks)	16	3	3	10	30	50	[illegible]

ST EDMUNDSBURY & DISTRICT LEAGUE
(Glasswells)

Division One	P	W	D	L	F	A	Pts
Ixworth Pykkerell	18	16	1	1	62	12	[illegible]
Priors FC	18	13	2	3	48	18	[illegible]
Bartons	18	11	2	5	52	31	[illegible]
Barrow FC	18	10	1	7	54	36	[illegible]
Barons	18	10	1	7	53	42	[illegible]
Westbury United	18	7	1	10	46	47	[illegible]
Lawshall Swan	18	6	4	8	30	38	[illegible]
Bushel	18	6	1	11	30	58	[illegible]
Haughley Utd Res.	18	2	2	14	18	66	[illegible]
CAS	18	0	3	15	15	60	[illegible]

Division Two	P	W	D	L	F	A	Pts
Elephant & Castle	22	16	2	4	84	40	[illegible]
RF Saints	22	15	4	3	76	35	[illegible]
Mildenhall United	22	12	4	6	61	32	[illegible]
Tollgate Inn	22	12	2	8	55	53	[illegible]
Beck Row	22	11	4	7	52	52	[illegible]
Bury Rovers	22	10	5	7	63	52	[illegible]
Black Boy	22	8	6	8	46	53	[illegible]
Garboldisham	22	7	4	11	56	59	[illegible]
Wickhambrook	22	6	3	13	33	66	[illegible]
Pakenham Fox	22	5	4	13	54	86	[illegible]
Bacton Utd Res.	22	4	5	13	39	58	[illegible]
Sporting 87 A	22	2	5	15	37	70	[illegible]

ST HELENS & DISTRICT LEAGUE

Premier Division	P	W	D	L	F	A	Pts
Prescot Leisure	22	17	3	2	73	24	54
York +5	22	14	4	4	56	26	51
Knowsley Sth -7	22	18	3	1	96	17	50
Rainford Nth End	22	9	7	6	52	48	34
New Street	22	9	3	10	49	51	30
Greenfield	22	8	4	10	53	53	28
Clock Face Miners	22	6	8	8	45	56	26
Boilermakers +3	22	6	4	12	51	65	25
Sony	22	7	4	11	43	59	25
Junction	22	6	3	13	44	62	21
Old Congs	22	5	4	13	43	88	19
Pilkington A	22	1	5	16	24	80	8

Division One	P	W	D	L	F	A	Pts
Bath Springs	20	17	3	0	76	16	54
Sidac Social Res.	20	13	7	0	69	26	46
Shoe	20	11	2	7	46	36	35
Prescot Leis. Res.	20	10	3	7	44	46	33
Penlake Res.	20	11	2	7	57	39	35
Bold Rangers	20	8	6	6	61	55	30
Sportsmans	20	7	4	9	35	41	25
Rainford NE Res.	20	5	3	12	37	53	18
Eccleston United	20	4	5	11	37	50	17
Waterside FC	20	5	1	14	35	78	16
Thatto Heath	20	1	0	19	19	76	3

Division Two	P	W	D	L	F	A	Pts
Sidac Social A	22	8	2	1	48	25	54
Sumner Street	22	8	3	0	45	18	53
Knowsley S. Res.	22	7	3	1	43	18	49
Mill House	22	6	0	5	28	15	43
Clock Face M. Res.	22	6	1	4	28	22	41
Brown Edge	22	8	0	3	47	22	37
Lingholme	22	3	2	6	34	38	28
Carborundum	22	3	2	6	22	31	24
Junction Res.	22	2	1	8	28	47	23
Boilermakers Res.	22	1	0	10	21	46	12
Waterside FC Res.	22	2	0	9	18	46	10
Ship	22	0	1	10	6	38	7

STRATFORD ALLIANCE

Division One	P	W	D	L	F	A	Pts
Bidford Boys Club	24	22	1	1	117	28	67
Halfords Athletic	24	16	2	6	112	46	50
Stoneleigh	24	16	2	6	79	43	50
Evesham U. Res.	24	14	3	7	66	50	45
Quinton	24	12	4	8	49	40	40
Seven Stars	24	10	4	10	65	69	34
Studley Swan	24	9	6	9	73	55	33
Hen. Forest Res.	24	10	2	12	70	56	32
Kenilworth Res.	24	9	4	11	64	59	31
FISSC	24	9	2	13	54	54	29
Stratford Town B	24	6	1	17	34	100	19
Bretforton OB -6	24	6	0	18	42	108	12
Shipston E. Res.	24	1	1	22	8	125	4

Division Two	P	W	D	L	F	A	Pts
Cubbington Albion	22	16	1	5	85	29	49
Alcester Town	22	16	1	5	72	29	49
Blockley Sports	22	13	6	3	72	49	45
Studley United	22	14	1	7	85	29	43
Ilmington Revol.	22	13	4	5	72	45	43
RS Sports	22	8	6	8	57	49	30
Badsey Rangers	22	9	3	10	47	61	30
Henley Forest A	22	8	4	10	44	47	28
Claverdon	22	6	2	14	39	63	20
Coventry Am Res.	22	6	2	14	43	95	20
Bidford BC Res.	22	4	3	15	30	70	15
Alveston Res.	22	2	1	19	34	114	7

Stratford Celtic - record expunged

Division Three	P	W	D	L	F	A	Pts
Golden Lion	24	21	2	1	117	29	65
Moreton Rgrs Res.	24	18	3	3	72	29	57
Snitterf'ld Snipers	24	17	4	3	100	31	55
Kenilworth W. Res.	24	16	2	6	100	33	50
Badsey United	24	14	2	8	65	52	44
Tysoe United	24	14	1	9	87	58	43
FISSC Res.	24	11	0	13	53	62	33
RS Sports Res.	24	7	4	13	41	79	25
Bishopton	24	7	3	14	57	102	24
Inkberrow Res.	24	7	2	15	40	77	23
Shipston Colts	24	6	4	14	48	83	22
Henley Forest B	24	2	2	20	39	120	8
Quinton Res.	24	1	1	22	22	86	4

STROUD & DISTRICT LEAGUE

Division One	P	W	D	L	F	A	Pts
Frampton United	26	23	2	1	96	14	71
Marshall Langston	26	18	5	3	77	27	59
Hardwicke Res.	26	19	2	5	73	33	59
Whitminster	26	14	6	6	77	47	48
Kings Stan. Res.	26	14	4	8	69	53	46
Tuffley Rov. Res.	26	13	4	9	63	48	43
Matson	26	11	6	9	56	61	39
Abbeymead Rov.	26	9	3	14	58	68	30
Randwick	26	8	5	13	42	55	29
Minchinhampton	26	9	2	15	48	68	29
Longlevens Res.	26	6	4	16	42	70	22
Charfield	26	2	8	16	34	89	14
Ebley Omega	26	2	7	17	31	83	13
Cashes Green	26	2	6	18	30	80	12

Division Two	P	W	D	L	F	A	Pts
Stonehouse Res.	26	19	2	5	78	32	59
Horsley United	26	18	4	4	69	24	58
Tetbury Town Res.	26	18	2	6	94	35	56
Quedgeley Wdrs	26	14	6	6	58	33	48
Thornbury T. Res.	26	15	3	8	62	38	48
Kingswood Res.	26	13	6	7	63	54	45
Gloucester CS	26	12	6	8	55	42	42
Uley	26	12	5	9	53	40	41
Dursley T. Res.	26	9	2	15	40	67	29
Shurdington Rov.	26	8	2	16	29	70	26
Whiteshill United	26	7	4	15	35	54	25
Tibberton United	26	6	3	17	37	67	21
Wotton Rov. Res.	26	6	3	17	34	65	21
Coaley Rovers	26	1	0	25	26	112	3

Division Three	P	W	D	L	F	A	Pts
Slimbridge Res.	26	22	3	1	122	34	69
Ramblers Res.	26	18	4	4	79	39	58
BA Rangers	26	14	7	5	67	38	49
AC Royals	26	12	6	8	56	41	42
Eastcombe	26	11	8	7	45	41	41
Cam B'dogs Res.	26	11	7	8	51	63	40
Frampton U. Res.	26	11	4	11	48	51	37
Upton St Leonards	26	10	6	10	63	52	36
Berkeley T. Res.	26	9	6	11	49	53	33
Trident	26	10	3	13	45	69	33
M'hampton Res.	26	7	3	16	53	84	24
Sharpness Res.	26	5	5	16	53	83	20
Wickwar Wdrs	26	5	3	18	49	77	18
Longford Res.	26	4	1	21	26	81	13

Division Four	P	W	D	L	F	A	Pts
Abbeymead Res.	24	18	1	5	89	43	55
Taverners Res. -3	24	18	2	4	72	26	53
Barnwood U. Res.	24	17	2	5	70	35	53
Matchplay	24	15	4	5	79	41	49
Whitminster Res.	24	12	2	10	69	68	38
Brimscombe Res.	24	10	5	9	37	36	35
Chalford Res.	24	10	2	12	43	52	32
Longlevens A	24	9	5	10	39	48	32
Gl'cester CS Res.	24	9	3	12	30	36	30
Stonehouse T. A	24	7	6	11	46	50	27
Quedgeley Res.	24	6	1	17	35	74	19
Uley Res.	24	5	2	17	45	92	17
Charfield Res.	24	2	1	21	25	78	7

Division Five	P	W	D	L	F	A	Pts
Didmarton	24	20	4	0	118	22	64
AFC Phoenix	24	19	4	1	106	23	61
Arlingham	24	14	1	9	72	63	43
Ramblers A	24	13	2	9	69	40	41
Ebley Omega Res.	24	12	4	8	82	60	40
Randwick Res.	24	12	4	8	61	51	40
Alkerton Rangers	24	12	2	10	65	65	38
Glevum United	24	10	3	11	67	79	33
Leonard S. Res.	24	9	2	13	61	66	29
Nympsfield	24	6	3	15	66	84	21
Dursley Town A	24	5	2	17	47	95	17
Wotton Rovers A	24	5	2	17	33	88	17
North Nibley	24	1	3	20	24	135	6

Division Six	P	W	D	L	F	A	Pts
Stroud Imperial	24	16	4	4	93	42	52
Tredworth Tigers	24	16	4	4	81	43	52
Whitminster A	24	17	0	7	85	42	51
Chip. Sodbury B	24	13	2	9	52	49	41
Upton St L. Res.	24	11	2	11	63	55	35
Brockworth A. A	24	11	2	11	42	43	35
Horsley Utd Res.	24	10	4	10	62	63	34
Stroud Harriers -3	24	10	5	9	61	54	32
Cashes G. Res.	24	9	2	13	55	71	29
Victoria Celtic -3	24	8	3	13	51	60	24
Eastcombe Res.	24	5	5	14	39	72	20
Trident Res. -6	24	6	3	15	51	94	15
Longlevens B -3	24	5	2	17	39	86	14

Division Seven	P	W	D	L	F	A	Pts
Hardwicke A	22	18	3	1	92	33	57
Bush	22	17	3	2	114	22	54
Sherston	22	15	4	3	94	31	49
BA Rangers Res.	22	13	1	8	86	43	40
Coaley Rov. Res.	22	9	4	9	46	62	31
Woodchester	22	9	2	11	52	81	29
Quedgeley W. A	22	6	5	11	45	65	23
Cam Bulldogs A	22	6	3	13	37	72	21
Randwick A	22	5	5	12	51	77	20
Uley A	22	6	2	14	47	87	20
Stonehouse T. B	22	5	3	14	55	97	18
Wickwar Res. -3	22	5	1	16	48	97	13

Division Eight	P	W	D	L	F	A	Pts
McCadam	22	14	5	3	74	31	47
Avonvale A	22	14	3	5	72	49	45
Matchplay Res.	22	13	3	6	66	47	42
Sharpness A	22	10	5	7	90	62	35
Berkeley T. A -3	22	11	5	6	63	45	35
Linden Snakes -3	22	11	4	7	74	56	34
Stroud Imp. Res.	22	7	5	10	47	68	26
Stratford Wdrs	22	7	4	11	65	62	25
GL United -3	22	8	3	11	71	59	24
Hawk. Stallions -3	22	5	6	11	47	80	18
Shurdington Res.	22	2	5	15	39	100	11
Alkerton Res. -9	22	4	4	14	37	86	7

SUBURBAN LEAGUE

Premier Division	P	W	D	L	F	A	Pts
Sutton United Res.	30	23	4	3	99	33	73
AFC Wimb'dn Res.	30	20	3	7	80	38	63
Leatherhead Res.	30	17	5	8	65	51	56
Tooting/M'ham Res.	30	15	4	11	49	54	49
Uxbridge Res.	30	14	6	10	62	54	48
Basingstoke Res.	30	14	5	11	67	68	47
Northwood Res.	30	13	6	11	50	46	45
Wealdstone Res.	30	13	5	12	59	55	44
Met Police Res.	30	10	9	11	57	62	39
Tonbridge A. Res.	30	12	1	17	70	61	37
Eastleigh Res.	30	10	4	16	62	70	34
Whyteleafe Res.	30	10	4	16	46	63	34
Beaconsfield Res.	30	8	7	15	45	70	31
Bedfont G. Res.	30	9	2	19	46	74	29
Ashford (Mx) Res.	30	8	4	18	43	58	28
Three Bridges Res.	30	8	3	19	44	87	27

Ash United Res. - record expunged

Northern Division	P	W	D	L	F	A	Pts
Hampton/RB Res	34	26	4	4	108	33	82
Hemel H. Res.	34	24	7	3	111	36	79
Leighton T. Res.	34	19	8	7	77	55	65
Bedfont Res.	34	17	11	6	80	54	62
Chalfont SP Res.	34	19	5	10	75	61	62
Camberley T. Res.	34	19	3	12	76	56	60
Sandhurst T. Res.	34	16	7	11	72	60	55
Boreham W. Res.	34	16	6	12	96	61	54
Harefield U. Res.	34	15	7	12	83	81	52
Tring Athletic Res.	34	13	5	16	51	69	44
Newport Pag. Res.	34	10	7	17	59	79	37
Chesham U. Res.	34	10	6	18	63	69	36
AFC Hayes Res.	34	9	9	16	48	61	36
N. Greenford Res.	34	10	5	19	67	92	35
Leverstock G. Res.	34	8	7	19	57	83	31
Hartley Wint. Res.	34	8	7	19	41	72	31
Cove Res.	34	6	7	21	40	82	25
Bracknell T. Res.	34	4	3	27	26	126	15

Southern Division	P	W	D	L	F	A	Pts
Woking Res.	32	27	1	4	132	30	82
Welling Utd Res.	32	23	4	5	113	42	73
Merstham Res.	32	23	4	5	91	56	73
Corinthian C. Res.	32	18	7	7	88	48	61
E. Grinstead Res.	32	19	4	9	73	48	61
Epsom/Ewell Res.	32	18	4	10	73	44	58
Chipstead Res.	32	19	0	13	88	67	57
Horley Town Res.	32	15	6	11	62	62	51
H'sham YMCA Res.	32	14	2	16	55	82	44
Oakwood Res.	32	10	5	17	60	93	35
Colliers W. Res.	32	10	3	19	55	79	33
Godalming T. Res.	32	9	2	21	52	91	29
Crowborough Res.	32	8	4	20	50	79	28
Cobham Res.	32	7	5	20	67	98	26
Molesey Res.	32	7	5	20	49	93	26
Raynes PV Res.	32	7	5	20	43	97	26
Chess'ton/H. Res.	32	4	7	21	41	83	19

SURREY SOUTH EASTERN COMBINATION

Int. Div One		P	W	D	L	F	A	Pts
Tooting Bec	*+3*	24	16	3	5	67	22	54
FC Triangle	*+2*	24	16	2	6	60	38	52
Puretown		24	15	5	4	59	31	50
Battersea	*-4*	24	13	3	8	60	43	38
Westminster Cas.		24	11	3	10	44	44	36
St Andrews		24	11	3	10	48	51	36
Sutton High		24	10	5	9	45	30	35
NPL		24	10	4	10	60	66	34
Sth Godstone	*+2*	24	8	3	13	42	57	29
Old Plymouthians		24	7	4	13	46	69	25
Thornton Hth Rov.		24	6	4	14	35	57	22
Croygas Pho.	*-1*	24	6	3	15	38	64	20
Sporting Bahia	*+1*	24	4	4	16	34	66	17

Tadworth - record expunged

Int. Div Two		P	W	D	L	F	A	Pts
RH123 Athletic		22	16	2	4	70	28	50
AFC Cubo		22	15	3	4	62	25	48
Weston Green	*-3*	22	15	3	4	61	30	45
Merton Abbey	*+2*	22	11	7	4	57	36	42
Fulham Deaf		22	12	4	6	69	45	40
Caterham Old B.		22	12	3	7	60	29	39
Cheam VW	*-3*	22	9	2	11	36	37	26
Westside FC	*+3*	22	6	3	13	48	51	24
Nutfield	*-4*	22	8	4	10	30	41	24
Ashtead	*+3*	22	4	0	18	20	84	15
Yourstory		22	4	2	16	42	88	14
AFC Ewell		22	2	3	17	16	77	9

Trinity - record expunged

Junior Division One	P	W	D	L	F	A	Pts
Tolworth Athletic	20	11	5	4	49	29	38
St Andrews Res.	20	11	3	6	55	36	36
Trinity Res.	20	10	3	7	55	43	33
Norton	20	9	3	8	55	50	30
Supercala	20	7	7	6	43	39	28
Shaftesbury Town	20	7	7	6	43	43	28
Worcester Park A	20	7	6	7	49	44	27
Batt. I'sides GSA	20	6	8	6	39	40	26
Wilf Kroucher	20	6	6	8	50	60	24
Cheam VW Res.	20	4	4	12	24	45	16
NPL Res.	20	3	6	11	33	66	15

Junior Division Two		P	W	D	L	F	A	Pts
Tadworth		22	17	4	1	55	20	55
Kerria Knights	*+3*	22	14	5	3	56	31	50
Wandgas S. Res.		22	15	4	3	59	30	49
Batt. Ironsides A		22	11	7	4	53	30	40
Street FC		22	11	3	8	65	57	36
Crescent Rov. A		22	10	2	10	62	52	32
Ashtead Res.		22	8	1	13	31	60	25
O. P'mthians Res.		22	6	6	10	34	39	24
Westside FC Res.		22	5	7	10	46	70	22
Battersea Res.		22	5	3	14	46	65	18
Destiny Academy		22	5	2	15	40	54	17
Mole Valley A	*-6*	22	2	2	18	28	67	2

Jnr Division Three		P	W	D	L	F	A	Pts
Pilgrims Well	*-3*	20	16	3	1	70	22	48
Park Boys	*+6*	20	12	1	7	56	41	43
Croy. G. u-23s	*+5*	20	11	3	6	77	36	41
Norton Res.		20	9	4	7	52	39	38
Ttng Bec Res.	*+6*	20	8	4	8	51	38	34
Sutton High Res.		20	10	3	7	49	38	33
Epsom Ath. A	*+2*	20	7	6	7	29	40	29
Trinity A	*+9*	20	3	2	15	34	69	20
Crescent R. B	*+3*	20	4	1	15	34	76	16
Rollers Athletic	*+3*	20	1	3	16	18	92	9
Oakhill United	*-39*	20	14	0	6	67	42	3

Jnr Division Four		P	W	D	L	F	A	Pts
Surbiton Town	*-1*	24	16	3	5	78	31	50
Shirley Town	*-1*	24	15	6	3	71	32	50
Epsom Eagles A		24	15	5	4	59	30	50
O. Plymouthians A		24	12	5	7	60	40	41
Cheam Vill. W. A		24	12	3	9	73	64	39
Thornton HR Res.		24	12	2	10	63	47	38
Addington Athletic		24	11	3	10	53	54	36
Old Town		24	10	3	11	41	43	33
St Andrews A		24	8	2	14	51	65	26
Epsom Athletic B		24	7	2	15	41	106	23
Croydon G. B	*+2*	24	5	5	14	32	67	22
Kerria Kn. Res.	*-1*	24	7	1	16	52	44	21
Fulham Deaf Res.		24	5	2	17	47	98	17

TAUNTON & DISTRICT LEAGUE
(Silver Street Volkswagen)

Division One	P	W	D	L	F	A	Pts
Highbridge Town	18	12	1	5	39	28	37
Bridgwater Sports	18	10	2	6	44	26	32
Middlezoy Rovers	18	8	7	3	43	26	31
Porlock	18	7	6	5	45	26	27
Staplegrove	18	8	3	7	45	39	27
Locomotives	18	8	2	8	39	35	26
Dulverton Town	18	8	2	8	31	37	26
Cannington Colts	18	7	2	9	51	49	23
Alcombe Rovers	18	3	4	11	29	49	13
Nether Stowey	18	4	1	13	24	75	13

Division Two	P	W	D	L	F	A	Pts
B. Lydeard Res.	24	19	5	0	82	19	62
Predators	24	18	2	4	98	39	56
B'water Spts Res.	24	14	2	8	70	43	44
White Hart Rgrs	24	11	1	12	48	51	34
Minehead T. Res.	24	10	3	11	55	57	33
Wembdon	24	9	6	9	65	68	33
Sampford Blues	24	9	5	10	50	58	32
Watchet T. Res.	24	8	4	12	52	54	28
Westonzoyland	24	5	13	6	40	51	28
Taun. Civil Service	24	8	4	12	36	60	28
Staplegrove Res.	24	8	2	14	43	75	26
Sydenham Rgrs	24	7	3	14	46	69	24
Hulan	24	3	4	17	44	85	13

Division Three	P	W	D	L	F	A	Pts
North Petherton	22	18	1	3	85	30	55
Appletree	22	15	1	6	76	38	46
Redgate	22	13	0	9	76	65	39
Williton	22	12	2	8	62	46	38
Old Inn All Stars	22	11	2	9	70	76	35
Middlezoy R. Res.	22	10	2	10	52	49	32
B'wtr Sports Colts	22	8	5	9	56	53	29
Wembdon Saints	22	8	5	9	50	56	29
Highbridge Res.	22	8	1	13	44	63	25
Norton Fitzwarren	22	6	3	13	58	75	21
Exmoor Rangers	22	5	3	14	48	82	18
Alcombe R. Res.	22	4	3	15	44	88	15

Spaxton - record expunged

Division Four	P	W	D	L	F	A	Pts
Porlock Res.	24	17	5	2	96	33	56
Stogursey G'hnds	24	15	5	4	83	38	50
B. Lydeard Colts	24	13	6	5	73	38	45
Hamilton Hawks	24	12	6	6	65	39	42
N. Fitzwarren Res.	24	12	5	7	94	55	41
Staplegrove Colts	24	11	5	8	92	67	38
Milverton Rangers	24	11	4	9	89	72	37
West'zoyland Res.	24	10	6	8	71	46	36
Rhode Lane Wdrs	24	11	1	12	68	75	34
Dulverton T. Res.	24	10	3	11	65	59	33
Neth. Stowey Res.	24	6	3	15	51	94	21
N. Petherton Res.	24	1	4	19	39	116	7
B'wtr G'hoppers	24	0	1	23	23	177	1

TELFORD COMBINATION

	P	W	D	L	F	A	Pts
The Warren	18	12	5	1	75	30	29
Atlas	18	11	3	4	70	27	25
Madeley Sports	18	11	3	4	56	30	25
Hadeley Park Alb.	18	10	5	3	49	29	25
AFC Wellington	18	8	3	7	40	43	19
HQ Sports/Social	18	8	2	8	37	38	18
Shifnal Utd Res.	18	6	5	7	42	35	17
Shifnal Wanderers	18	6	1	11	35	50	13
Much Wenlock	18	3	3	12	34	49	9
Denso	18	0	0	18	18	125	0

THANET & DISTRICT LEAGUE

Division One	P	W	D	L	F	A	Pts
AFC Aussie	12	10	1	1	41	18	31
Texcel Solutions	12	10	0	2	32	14	30
Hugin Viking Ath.	12	6	0	6	28	20	18
AFC Margate	12	5	2	5	34	33	17
Brenlam Flooring	12	5	0	7	34	27	15
Barnaby Rudge	12	3	0	9	20	57	9
Hazy Shade	12	1	1	10	15	35	4

Division Two	P	W	D	L	F	A	Pts
Pfizer	10	10	0	0	54	20	30
Westcliff United	10	6	1	3	50	26	19
Minster Res.	10	5	1	4	39	23	16
Everybody's Inn	9	3	1	5	21	33	10
The Oddfellows	9	2	1	6	27	44	7
Orb United	10	1	0	9	13	58	3

TONBRIDGE & DISTRICT LEAGUE

Premier Division	P	W	D	L	F	A	Pts
Hadlow Evolution	16	12	2	2	41	11	38
Insulators	16	12	1	3	33	16	37
Woodlands	16	7	1	8	35	49	22
Southborough	16	6	2	8	29	24	20
High Brooms Cas.	16	6	2	8	37	36	20
Blackham /Ashurst	16	5	4	7	29	32	19
Tonbridge I. Res.	16	6	1	9	20	30	19
East Peckham Jnrs	16	5	3	8	24	33	18
Hawkenbury Res.	16	4	2	10	24	41	14

Tunbridge Wells United - record expunged

Division One		P	W	D	L	F	A	Pts
AFC Valour		18	16	1	1	65	21	49
High Brooms Res.		18	12	2	4	73	26	38
Hadlow Harrow		18	12	2	4	52	31	38
Paddock Wood		18	11	0	7	38	34	33
Southboro. Res.	*-1*	18	9	5	4	48	30	31
Roselands		18	9	2	7	43	41	29
Pembury Res.	*-2*	18	5	2	11	26	47	19
Leigh		18	4	2	12	32	46	14
Hawkenbury A		18	3	1	14	29	80	10
Tonbridge Inv. A		18	0	1	17	22	72	1

Division Two		P	W	D	L	F	A	Pts
Penshurst Park		20	16	0	4	80	23	48
Dowgate	*+3*	20	13	4	3	60	16	46
Capel S&S	*-6*	20	16	2	2	72	18	44
W'lands Res.	*-3*	20	14	3	3	90	30	42
FC Revolution	*-3*	20	13	4	3	102	37	40
Ashton Prime		20	9	1	10	42	46	28
Roselands Res.	*+9*	20	5	1	14	29	98	25
AFC Valour Res.		20	7	0	13	34	55	21
Frant		20	5	0	15	40	71	12
Brenchley Res.	*+3*	20	2	0	18	32	110	9
Paddock W. Res.		20	2	1	17	23	100	7

TROWBRIDGE & DISTRICT LEAGUE

Division One		P	W	D	L	F	A	Pts
Seend United		22	18	3	1	79	22	57
The Deverills		22	18	2	2	55	21	56
Freshford United		22	11	6	5	51	40	39
Trowbridge Wdrs		22	11	5	6	69	48	38
Blue Circle		22	8	6	8	47	48	30
Frome Town Spts		22	9	3	10	39	53	30
Bradford United		22	8	5	9	56	57	29
Broughton FC		22	6	6	10	53	61	24
Sem'ton Magpies		22	6	5	11	55	75	23
Lavington	*-4*	22	7	1	14	34	46	18
Steeple Ashton		22	5	2	15	43	64	17
Bromham		22	3	0	19	26	72	9

Division Two		P	W	D	L	F	A	Pts
Foresters	*-1*	20	17	1	2	108	18	51
Westbury Utd A		20	14	5	1	68	19	47
Seend Utd Res.		20	12	2	6	58	52	38
FC Northbridge		20	11	3	6	60	48	36
Bratton		20	8	5	7	56	40	29
Westwood Social		20	8	4	8	40	58	28
FC Chip'hm Yth A		20	7	4	9	66	67	25
North Bradley		20	6	5	9	48	51	23
Heytesbury		20	5	4	11	43	52	19
Calne Eagles		20	3	3	14	41	58	12
The Stiffs	*-1*	20	1	0	19	11	136	2

Division Three		P	W	D	L	F	A	Pts
Castle Combe		22	19	2	1	85	23	59
Chippenham OB		22	18	2	2	92	25	56
Trowbdge W. Res.		22	14	2	6	84	45	44
Worton/Chev.	*+2*	22	12	3	7	71	56	41
Fever	*-2*	22	10	3	9	61	50	31
Bratton Res.		22	9	3	10	47	59	30
The Lamb		22	9	3	10	63	79	30
Frome Town S. A		22	9	2	11	55	69	29
The Angel		22	5	4	13	45	78	19
Bradf'd U. Res.	*-1*	22	5	4	13	33	57	18
United	*-1*	22	3	3	16	32	62	11
Mere Town YDT		22	3	1	18	34	99	10

TYNE & WEAR LEAGUE

	P	W	D	L	F	A	Pts
Gleneagles	18	16	1	1	101	25	49
Thorney Close Inn	18	16	1	1	101	26	49
Sandhills	18	11	0	7	65	38	33
FC Chesters	18	9	2	7	59	52	29
Chaplins	18	8	1	9	44	51	25
Newbottle WMC -3	18	7	3	8	47	55	21
Music Rooms	18	6	1	11	52	83	19
G'hd Snooker Cte	18	5	3	10	51	78	18
Rock Skool	18	3	4	11	39	77	13
SAFC Foundation	18	1	0	17	30	104	3

Newbiggin Hall - record expunged

TYNESIDE AMATEUR LEAGUE

Division One	P	W	D	L	F	A	Pts
Winlaton Vulcan	26	19	4	3	85	26	61
Blyth Town Res.	26	17	2	7	79	38	53
New York	26	13	6	7	62	49	45
Red Star Benwell	26	13	5	8	73	51	44
Walker Cent. Res.	26	13	2	11	63	49	41
Blyth Spartans A	26	11	5	10	46	47	38
Lindisfarne Ath.	26	11	3	12	46	70	36
Wallsend Roma	26	9	8	9	79	62	35
West Jesmond	26	9	6	11	52	59	33
Bellingham	26	9	5	12	54	61	32
Gosf'th Boh. Res.	26	8	7	11	48	49	31
Blyth Rangers	26	7	10	9	45	53	31
Cow. Pin Point -6	26	4	9	13	54	86	15
Wardley -3	26	2	2	22	31	117	5

Blakelaw - record expunged

Division Two	P	W	D	L	F	A	Pts
Whic. Lang Jacks	24	18	2	4	95	49	56
Grainger Park BC	24	14	4	6	80	49	46
G, Rutherf'd Res.	24	14	4	6	60	41	46
New. Diggers Utd	24	12	4	8	71	46	40
Stella Board Inn	24	12	4	8	85	73	40
Killingw'th Plough	24	13	1	10	57	59	40
New. RVI Lochside	24	9	4	11	59	63	31
N. Chemfica Res.	24	9	2	13	44	51	29
Newc. Medicals	24	8	3	13	48	69	27
Cramlington T. A	24	7	5	12	50	62	23
L'benton Charnw'd	24	6	5	13	60	85	23
Cullercoats A	24	6	4	14	55	79	22
Gos. Bohemians A	24	5	4	15	49	87	19

WAKEFIELD & DISTRICT LEAGUE

Premier Division	P	W	D	L	F	A	Pts
Thornhill	20	13	3	4	67	33	42
Gate	20	13	2	5	56	39	41
Horb. Cherry Tree	20	13	1	6	52	34	40
Battyeford Airedale	20	11	4	5	45	37	37
Rothwell	20	10	2	8	38	27	32
Rose & C. Darton	20	10	2	8	51	44	32
Ryecroft Sports	20	9	2	9	47	43	29
Dodworth MW	20	7	5	8	42	37	26
Crofton Sports	20	8	2	10	45	49	26
Snydale Athletic	20	1	3	16	22	69	6
Walton	20	1	2	17	27	80	5

Division One	P	W	D	L	F	A	Pts
Rose of York	24	20	2	2	74	29	62
Dewsbury Rgrs OB	24	19	3	2	101	29	60
Outwood Victoria	24	19	1	4	79	35	58
AFC Alverthorpe	24	13	5	6	66	43	44
FC Wasps -1	24	14	2	8	78	37	43
Kingstone UWMC	24	11	4	9	96	61	37
AFC Shepherds A.	24	10	7	7	55	31	37
Crofton Spts Res.	24	11	0	13	59	67	33
Eastmoor Res.	24	7	2	15	49	96	23
Oss. Two Brewers	24	5	3	16	48	79	18
Amaranth OB -3	24	6	2	16	47	62	17
Old Bank WMC	24	4	1	19	42	86	13
Fieldhead H. -3	24	1	0	23	20	159	0

Division Two	P	W	D	L	F	A	Pts
Garforth Rangers	20	16	1	3	84	18	49
Morley C & SC	20	15	2	3	82	37	47
AFC Two Brewers	20	12	5	3	72	34	41
Garforth WMC	20	13	2	5	65	35	41
Little Bull	20	11	4	5	48	36	37
Village FC	20	9	3	8	38	34	30
Wrenthorpe	20	7	2	11	36	51	23
Scissett Res.	20	4	5	11	41	62	17
Featherstone Res.	20	5	1	14	31	66	16
Dews. ROB Res.	20	3	0	17	28	99	9
Waterloo	20	1	3	16	19	72	6

Division Three	P	W	D	L	F	A	Pts
Hopetown	20	20	0	0	87	21	60
Inns of Court	20	12	5	3	57	28	41
Thornes	20	13	2	5	49	25	41
Horbury Town A	20	9	6	5	44	33	33
Garforth Rgrs Res.	20	7	4	9	45	43	25
Prostar	20	8	1	11	59	61	25
Crofton Sports A	20	6	3	11	34	45	21
Snydale Ath. Res.	20	5	5	10	38	54	20
Plough	20	6	1	13	37	62	19
Victoria Horbury	20	5	1	14	42	73	16
Blue Light S & S	20	5	0	15	40	87	15

WARRINGTON & DISTRICTLEAGUE

(Sindh & Luqmans Cuisine)

Premier Division	P	W	D	L	F	A	Pts
Blackbrook	22	17	1	4	74	34	52
Runcorn Albion	22	17	1	4	60	26	52
Whiston Cross	22	11	6	5	59	39	39
Ravenhead Knaugh	22	12	3	7	51	38	39
Sidac Social	22	10	5	7	45	44	35
St Michaels DH	22	8	5	9	48	49	29
Haydock	22	8	5	9	41	49	29
Beeches	22	6	6	10	37	46	24
Vulcan	22	7	3	12	27	39	24
Cronton Villa	22	5	8	9	28	37	23
Moorfield	22	4	3	15	29	63	15
Halton Borough	22	1	6	15	19	54	9

Division One	P	W	D	L	F	A	Pts
Windle Labour C.	22	14	5	3	59	29	47
Grange SC	22	14	2	6	49	31	44
Penlake	22	11	7	4	62	36	40
Fife Rangers	22	11	4	7	59	41	37
Whiston C. Res.	22	11	2	9	45	53	35
Rainhill Town	22	10	2	10	44	31	32
Orford Blackburne	22	9	2	11	52	49	29
Burtonwood Alb.	22	7	7	8	50	48	28
Ford Motors Res.	22	7	6	9	37	43	27
Legion	22	6	8	8	39	49	26
Widnes Bayer	22	5	4	13	29	62	19
Cronton Villa Res.	22	2	1	19	24	77	7

Division Two	P	W	D	L	F	A	Pts
Runcorn Alb. Res.	22	17	2	3	76	27	53
Avon Athletic	22	15	1	6	51	37	46
Rainhill Town Res.	22	14	3	5	53	31	45
Croft	22	11	3	8	50	35	36
St Mich. DH Res.	22	10	5	7	43	46	35
Village Social	22	10	2	10	59	42	32
Lomax	22	9	1	12	59	62	28
Winwick	22	7	2	13	48	60	23
Fife Rangers Res.	22	6	5	11	37	49	23
Spartak	22	6	5	11	49	62	23
Monk Res.	22	5	3	14	37	70	18
Halebank Res.	22	5	2	15	32	73	17

Division Three	P	W	D	L	F	A	Pts
Mosscroft	22	20	1	1	101	27	61
Avon Athletic Res.	22	19	2	1	87	31	59
St Michaels DH A	22	13	2	7	44	40	41
Villa Rainhill	22	12	1	9	70	18	37
Runcorn Albion A	22	9	1	12	39	59	28
Vulcan Res.	22	7	6	9	32	49	27
Burtonwood Res.	22	7	4	11	43	54	25
Moore Utd Res.	22	6	5	11	43	66	23
Widnes Parklands	22	6	5	11	35	59	23
Culcheth SC	22	6	3	13	53	86	21
Moorfield Res.	22	6	2	14	39	58	20
Rainhill Town A	22	3	4	15	19	58	13

Division Four	P	W	D	L	F	A	Pts
Smiths SD	22	20	1	1	90	15	61
Blackbrook Res.	22	15	2	5	56	35	47
Blue Lion	22	14	1	7	66	43	43
Halton Boro. Res.	22	11	2	9	48	38	35
Widnes Dragons	22	10	4	8	53	49	34
Orford BA Res.	22	10	4	8	50	50	34
Penketh United	22	10	3	9	48	43	33
Grappenhall S. A	22	9	2	11	46	69	29
Haydock Res.	22	8	1	13	34	54	25
Roundhouse Rov.	22	5	2	15	27	50	17
Grange SC Res.	22	5	2	15	25	59	17
Franworth Griffin	22	3	0	19	26	64	9

Division Five	P	W	D	L	F	A	Pts
Legion Res.	20	16	0	4	63	29	48
Crosfields	20	14	3	3	53	24	45
Windle LC Res.	20	13	2	5	65	39	41
St Michaels DH B	20	8	4	8	45	40	28
Beechw'd Howd.	20	8	3	9	34	50	27
Newton-le-Willows	20	7	4	9	48	47	25
Cronton Villa A	20	7	3	10	41	44	24
Culcheth SC Res.	20	7	3	10	33	44	24
Moorfield A	20	6	2	12	24	54	20
Halton Borough A	20	4	4	12	38	44	16
Kirkfield	20	4	4	12	19	48	16

WEARSIDE COMBINATION

(TWR Trade Frames)

Premier Division	P	W	D	L	F	A	Pts
Sund. Jolly Potter	20	16	1	3	109	35	49
Sund. Redhouse	20	13	3	4	85	47	42
Sund. Hendon	20	12	3	5	73	46	39
Sund. Blue House	20	11	3	6	72	51	36
Sund. Hylton CW	20	9	3	8	53	44	30
Sun. Chesters BB	20	9	3	8	60	56	30
Sund. Aquatic Sp.	20	8	4	8	68	72	28
Sun. Colonel Prior	20	8	3	9	58	57	27
Houghton T. Res.	20	6	4	10	59	69	22
Dawdon -6	20	3	2	15	37	105	5
Hendon Grange G	20	0	1	19	28	120	1

Division One	P	W	D	L	F	A	Pts
Washington CC	26	22	4	0	109	29	70
Colliery Tavern	26	21	3	2	142	28	66
Hylton Colliery J.	26	17	3	6	122	55	54
Arms C. Coachwks	26	16	2	8	92	62	50
Shiney Row TR	26	13	3	10	84	71	42
The Cambridge	26	11	6	9	76	70	39
Sund. Usworth	26	11	3	12	65	87	36
S. Sassco.co.uk	26	10	3	13	70	80	33
SR Country Pk Inn	26	8	4	14	70	58	28
S. The Saltgrass	26	7	6	13	62	75	27
E. Dur. Spartans	26	7	4	15	66	104	25
Sund. Times Inn	26	8	1	17	60	110	25
Sund. Park View	26	6	5	15	51	88	23
Sund. The Cove	26	1	1	24	24	176	4

WENSLEYDALE LEAGUE

(Wensleydale Creamery)

	P	W	D	L	F	A	Pts
Bowes	28	25	3	0	188	22	78
Colburn Town	28	22	2	4	143	32	68
R'mond Academy	28	18	7	3	113	45	61
Buck Inn Broncos	28	18	1	9	124	65	55
Buck Inn Old Boys	28	15	5	8	102	62	50
Hawes United	28	13	7	8	67	63	46
Leyburn United -3	28	14	3	11	114	72	42
Redmire United	28	12	3	13	72	70	39
Spennithorne & H.	28	11	3	14	74	80	36
R. Mavericks Res.	28	9	5	14	56	60	32
Unicorn	28	9	3	16	64	94	30
Reeth/Dist. AC	28	8	3	17	60	105	27
Carperby Rovers	28	8	2	18	54	121	26
Askrigg United	28	3	2	23	37	131	11
Hawes Utd Res.	28	0	1	27	13	259	1

WEST HERTS LEAGUE

(Arlon Printers)

Premier Division	P	W	D	L	F	A	Pts
Hemel H. Rovers	22	18	2	2	99	34	56
SWR Garage Doors	22	18	2	2	79	25	56
Martin Baker Rov.	22	13	4	5	72	28	43
Tring Athletic A	22	13	2	7	50	37	41
Kings Sports	22	13	1	8	78	53	40
Hadley A	22	12	3	7	62	50	39
Inter Hemel	22	8	3	11	59	83	27
Croxley Coach/H.	22	6	3	13	25	54	21
Oxhey Jets A	22	5	3	14	41	69	18
Oxhey	22	4	4	14	29	64	16
Metpol Bushey A	22	4	1	17	23	72	13
Sun Postal Rov.	22	2	4	16	29	77	10

Division One	P	W	D	L	F	A	Pts
SWR Gar. D. Res.	24	18	4	2	108	35	58
Hemel H. Rv. Res.	24	18	3	3	72	35	57
Aldenham	24	15	4	5	95	54	49
O. Parmiterians A	24	13	4	7	69	45	43
Martin Baker Res.	24	12	3	9	60	44	39
Harp'den Rovers A	24	11	2	11	53	57	35
Bovingdon A	24	10	4	10	48	51	34
St Albans Sports	24	10	2	12	52	56	32
Glenn Sports	24	10	2	12	51	60	32
Oxhey Wanderers	24	8	6	10	62	67	30
Hunton Bridge	24	5	2	17	32	80	17
Oxhey Jets B	24	4	2	18	42	103	14
Sun Postal Spts A	24	2	2	20	24	81	8

Division Two	P	W	D	L	F	A	Pts
Maple Cross	24	22	1	1	117	18	67
Philippine United	24	18	4	2	97	29	58
Rickmansw'th SG	24	17	3	4	67	34	54
Wheathampstead	24	12	5	7	67	44	41
Hemel H. Rov. A	24	10	3	11	53	66	33
Tring Athletic B	24	9	3	12	53	59	30
Portland Arms	24	8	4	12	48	60	28
Croxley C&H Res.	24	7	6	11	54	64	27
Mill End Sports A	24	8	3	13	51	68	27
Langleybury CC	24	7	4	13	48	68	25
Oxhey Res.	24	5	4	15	25	77	19
Harpenden Rov. B	24	5	3	16	27	82	18
Potten End	24	4	5	15	42	80	17

WEST LONDON AFA

Premier Division	P	W	D	L	F	A	Pts
Primrose Hill	16	11	1	4	50	29	34
Racing Chiswick	16	9	4	3	41	25	31
Bishops Park	16	7	5	4	36	26	26
Sevenths	16	7	4	5	41	29	25
Arian	16	6	6	4	44	28	24
AFC Angel	16	7	1	8	24	32	22
Mavericks	16	4	3	9	19	37	15
Clissold Park Rgrs	16	3	4	9	23	43	13
Panthers	16	3	2	11	23	52	11

Resolute - record expunged

Division One	P	W	D	L	F	A	Pts
Earlsberg Eagles	14	12	0	2	43	17	36
Inter Markfield	14	9	1	4	42	26	28
West End	14	7	2	5	41	21	23
Milton Rovers	14	6	1	7	28	33	19
Iranian Assoc.	14	5	2	7	19	30	17
Atholl	14	5	1	8	22	43	16
Northern Town	14	5	0	9	27	37	15
Olympic Waterloo	14	3	1	10	21	36	10

Division Two	P	W	D	L	F	A	Pts
Hub Athletic	16	13	2	1	55	27	41
North Acton	16	9	4	3	45	31	31
Tower Hamlets B.	16	7	3	6	34	34	24
Racing Chis. Leg.	16	7	1	8	36	27	22
Viva Capri	16	6	3	7	32	30	21
Sevenths Res.	16	5	3	8	21	35	18
Inter Markf'ld Res.	16	5	3	8	27	51	18
West End Res.	16	5	1	10	29	29	16
Primrose Hill Res.	16	4	2	10	33	48	14

WEST SUSSEX LEAGUE

Premier Division	P	W	D	L	F	A	Pts
Newtown Villa	22	17	3	2	77	27	54
Barnham	22	14	4	4	71	28	46
Cowfold	22	12	6	4	58	22	42
Billingshurst	22	13	2	7	50	36	41
Clymping Res.	22	11	3	8	46	56	36
Upper Beeding	22	9	5	8	47	43	32
Lancing United	22	10	2	10	43	40	32
Univ. Chichester	22	9	4	9	49	31	31
East Dean	22	4	6	12	35	50	18
Southwater	22	4	5	13	32	72	17
Stedham United	22	4	1	17	30	84	13
Petworth	22	3	3	16	20	69	12

Division One	P	W	D	L	F	A	Pts
Angmering	20	17	1	2	75	21	52
Fishbourne	20	14	3	3	52	27	45
West Chiltington	20	14	1	5	57	20	43
Ashington Rovers	20	11	3	6	55	41	36
Watersfield	20	9	3	8	43	37	30
Faygate United	20	8	3	9	46	47	27
Hunston CC	20	6	5	9	41	50	23
Lavant	20	6	4	10	35	57	22
Partridge Green	20	5	2	13	30	49	17
Henfield	20	4	0	16	30	61	12
Wittering United	20	3	1	16	26	80	10

Division Two North	P	W	D	L	F	A	Pts
Holbrook	22	19	1	2	89	24	58
Capel	22	16	1	5	81	37	49
AFC Roffey	22	13	3	6	63	46	42
Wisboro. Green	22	11	1	10	42	38	34
Pulborough	22	9	5	8	48	47	32
Horsham Trinity	22	9	2	11	48	49	29
Alfold	22	9	2	11	35	38	29
Billingshurst Res.	22	8	2	12	45	56	26
Barns Green	22	6	7	9	27	42	25
Newdigate	22	6	5	11	39	67	23
Fittleworth -1	22	6	3	13	52	84	20
Horsham Olympic	22	2	4	16	32	73	10

Division Two South	P	W	D	L	F	A	Pts
Barnham Res.	20	17	2	1	65	13	53
Newtown V. Res.	20	16	1	3	67	27	49
Fernhurst	20	10	2	8	34	34	32
Lodsworth	20	9	3	8	33	33	30
Worthing BCOB	20	8	6	6	31	32	30
Lancing Utd Res.	20	9	2	9	33	31	29
General Henry	20	8	2	10	39	46	26
Yapton	20	6	4	10	39	44	22
Predators	20	6	3	11	24	41	21
Hunston CC Res.	20	6	2	12	37	46	20
The Sportsman	20	0	3	17	17	72	3

Div Three North	P	W	D	L	F	A	Pts
Cowfold Res.	20	18	0	2	85	15	54
Rudgwick	20	17	0	3	71	19	51
Ash'ton Rov. Res.	20	13	1	6	80	55	40
TD Shipley Res.	20	12	1	7	36	34	37
Henfield Res.	20	9	2	9	57	41	29
Holbrook Res.	20	8	3	9	58	60	27
Southwater Res.	20	7	3	10	44	66	24
Pulborough Res.	20	7	2	11	54	48	23
Slinfold	20	3	5	12	29	75	14
Ockley	20	2	4	14	27	91	10
Horsham Baptists	20	2	3	15	39	76	9

Div Three South	P	W	D	L	F	A	Pts
Barnham A	18	14	2	2	82	26	44
Newtown Villa A	18	15	2	1	53	23	44
Boxgrove	18	12	1	5	72	38	34
Rustington Pk Snrs	18	9	2	7	47	37	29
The Ship	18	8	3	7	44	34	27
Angmering Res.	18	7	1	10	39	35	22
Harting	18	6	1	11	30	40	19
Square Deal	18	5	1	12	33	81	16
Stedham Utd Res.	18	3	3	12	17	44	12
Petworth Res.	18	3	0	15	26	85	9

Division Four North	P	W	D	L	F	A	Pts
Forest Res.	18	14	1	3	59	18	43
U. Beeding Res.	18	11	2	5	52	33	35
W. Chiltington Res.	18	10	3	5	47	31	33
Barns Green Res.	18	8	3	7	31	26	27
Rusper	18	7	5	6	39	33	26
Horsham Trin. Res.	18	6	5	7	32	37	23
Henfield A	18	6	4	8	30	36	22
Newdigate Res.	18	6	3	9	36	55	21
Wisboro. G. Res.	18	6	1	11	35	61	19
Plaistow	18	1	3	14	20	51	6

Division Four South	P	W	D	L	F	A	Pts
Fishbourne Res.	16	11	3	2	55	16	36
Tangmere	16	11	2	3	58	40	35
Lavant Res.	16	10	3	3	51	29	33
Selsey A	16	8	5	3	48	31	29
Yapton Res.	16	6	3	7	55	45	21
Coal Exchange -3	16	6	4	6	39	49	19
Lodsworth Res.	16	2	4	10	22	53	10
Ambassadors	16	1	6	9	28	49	9
Milland	16	0	4	12	25	69	4

Division Five Cent	P	W	D	L	F	A	Pts
Cowfold A	16	16	0	0	59	8	48
Horsham Crus.	16	13	1	2	65	16	40
Holbrook B	16	10	0	6	58	32	30
Slinfold Res.	16	7	2	7	48	39	23
Horsham Trinity A	16	7	1	8	35	33	22
Horsham O. Res.	16	4	3	9	20	58	15
Hor. Baptists Res.	16	4	2	10	24	50	14
Southwater A	16	3	1	12	26	44	10
Broadf'd Bdge Res.	16	3	0	13	13	68	9

Division Five North	P	W	D	L	F	A	Pts
Faygate U. Res.	14	12	1	1	52	16	37
Holbrook A	14	9	1	4	43	25	28
Billingshurst A	14	8	3	3	45	35	27
Rudgwick Res.	14	7	1	6	36	35	22
Ockley Res.	14	6	2	6	52	39	20
Capel Res.	14	4	1	9	29	41	13
Alfold Res.	14	4	0	10	30	44	12
Broadford Bridge	14	1	1	12	14	66	4

Partridge Green Res. - record expunged

Division Five South	P	W	D	L	F	A	Pts
Graffham	18	16	1	1	99	26	49
Whyke United	18	13	0	5	74	45	39
Chapel	18	11	3	4	54	38	36
Watersfield Res.	18	11	0	7	43	27	33
Rogate 08	18	9	0	9	40	43	27
Rust'gton PS Res.	18	6	2	10	36	55	20
Vapours	18	6	2	10	39	65	20
Fittleworth Res.	18	5	4	9	39	66	19
Regis Veterans	18	3	1	14	27	58	10
Fernhurst Res.	18	2	3	13	26	54	9

Petworth A - record expunged

WESTON & DISTRICT LEAGUE

Division One	P	W	D	L	F	A	Pts
Weston SJ Sp'bar	20	13	4	3	52	20	43
East Worle	20	12	6	2	58	28	42
Kewstoke Lions	20	10	6	4	51	24	36
Portish'd Town A	20	9	4	7	49	33	31
KVFC	20	9	2	9	44	48	29
Nailsea T. Res.	20	9	1	10	41	35	28
Hutton	20	9	1	10	40	42	28
Cleeve West Res.	20	8	4	8	40	43	28
Nailsea United A	20	8	3	9	39	28	27
Churchill Res. -1	20	5	3	12	38	56	17
Bournville Rovers	20	1	0	19	24	119	3

Division Two	P	W	D	L	F	A	Pts
Draycott	22	17	1	4	91	30	52
Clevedon Utd Res.	22	17	1	4	63	31	52
Selkirk United	22	13	2	7	59	35	41
Winscombe Res.	22	12	3	7	54	36	39
Clarence Park	22	12	2	8	72	56	38
Westland U. Res.	22	10	5	7	58	46	35
Portishead WMC	22	8	2	12	40	62	26
Locking Park	22	8	2	12	45	72	26
St George EG Res.	22	7	4	11	44	48	25
Yatton Ath. Res.	22	7	2	13	59	63	23
Portish'd Town B	22	3	4	15	45	79	13
Worle Res.	22	4	0	18	23	95	12

Division Three	P	W	D	L	F	A	Pts
Weston St J. Res.	18	13	4	1	66	20	43
Nailsea United B	18	12	1	5	60	37	37
Axbridge Town	18	11	3	4	68	36	36
Cleeve West T. A	18	10	3	5	47	25	33
Cong'sbury Res. -1	18	7	3	8	29	40	23
Wedmore	18	6	3	9	40	51	21
Kewstoke L. Res.	18	5	4	9	35	48	19
Burnham United A	18	5	2	11	29	57	17
Winscombe A	18	5	1	12	26	61	16
Wrington-R. Res.	18	3	2	13	29	54	11

Division Four	P	W	D	L	F	A	Pts
Blagdon -3	22	15	2	5	67	33	44
Clevedon Dons	22	13	3	6	81	43	42
Berrow Res.	22	13	2	7	71	47	41
Westend FC	22	11	5	6	46	50	38
Cheddar A	22	10	3	9	46	45	33
Clevedon Utd A	22	8	7	7	44	41	31
King Alfred SC	22	9	3	10	48	44	30
Nailsea U. Colts	22	7	5	10	43	59	26
Hutton Res.	22	6	6	10	37	54	24
Banwell Res.	22	6	6	10	44	62	24
East Worle Res. -1	22	6	3	13	41	60	20
South Park Rgrs	22	3	5	14	39	69	14

Division Five	P	W	D	L	F	A	Pts
Tickenham United	18	15	2	1	89	23	47
Dynamo Dury	18	15	0	3	83	34	45
Sparta Kewstoke	18	12	2	4	71	33	38
Weston SJS Res.	18	9	1	8	63	60	28
Draycott Res.	18	7	4	7	42	46	25
St George EG A	18	6	5	7	43	43	23
Portishead Colts	18	6	2	10	39	55	20
AFC Nailsea	18	4	4	10	43	61	16
KVFC Res. -1	18	3	4	11	33	53	12
Kewstoke L. A -1	18	0	2	16	22	120	1

Division Six	P	W	D	L	F	A	Pts
Sporting Weston	22	19	2	1	104	18	59
Dolphin Athletic	22	16	2	4	60	21	50
Wstn Super S'gulls	22	14	2	6	86	40	44
Selkirk Utd Res.	22	12	4	6	46	32	40
Dynamo Dury Res.	22	10	3	9	51	52	33
Weston Players	22	9	5	8	72	67	32
Worle Rangers -1	22	9	4	9	59	51	30
Yatton Athletic A	22	6	4	12	54	68	22
St George EG B -1	22	6	2	14	46	112	19
Wedmore Res.	22	4	6	12	38	69	18
AFC Nailsea Res.	22	3	4	15	31	82	13
Axbridge T. Res.	22	2	6	14	43	78	12

WIGAN & DISTRICT AMATEUR LEAGUE

'remier Division	P	W	D	L	F	A	Pts
Vinstanley St Aid.	24	17	1	6	62	31	52
ir Tree Rangers	24	16	3	5	70	33	51
ownall Green U.	24	14	2	8	59	40	44
ickerstaffe	24	12	5	7	59	54	41
tandish St Wilf.	24	13	1	10	47	46	40
indley Town	24	11	5	8	69	56	38
FC Scholes	24	10	5	9	61	46	35
lewburgh United	24	8	5	11	32	43	29
hevington -3	24	9	4	11	53	48	28
eigh Phoenix	24	6	5	13	38	61	23
ighfield	24	6	5	13	41	69	23
emberton	24	5	6	13	34	56	21
ice Central	24	3	5	16	34	76	14

)ivision One	P	W	D	L	F	A	Pts
idlow Athletic	22	16	5	1	61	25	53
igmoor	22	15	6	1	70	22	51
ice	22	15	4	3	62	41	49
t Judes	22	12	5	5	46	30	41
yldesley	22	7	5	10	46	42	26
oppull Celtic	22	8	2	12	40	51	26
Vinstanley Res.	22	5	7	10	31	43	22
therton Town A	22	5	7	10	36	52	22
ddleston	22	5	5	12	40	60	20
p Holland	22	5	5	12	39	64	20
Vorsley Mesnes	22	5	4	13	35	54	19
Vigan Rovers	22	4	5	13	35	57	17

Eagle & Hawk - record expunged

)ivision Two	P	W	D	L	F	A	Pts
arnworth Town	24	18	4	2	73	33	58
therton Royal	24	16	3	5	74	36	51
rmskirk	24	16	2	6	93	45	50
hevington Res.	24	15	2	7	58	39	47
oose Green Utd	24	13	6	5	81	46	45
eigh Legion	24	12	3	9	48	46	39
pringfield	24	9	6	9	52	48	33
ir Tree R. Res.	24	8	3	13	51	78	27
tandish SW Res.	24	7	4	13	38	58	25
ickerstaffe Res.	24	7	3	14	43	50	24
lindley Celtic -6	24	9	1	14	58	75	22
indley T. Res. -3	24	5	2	17	41	74	14
igan Rov. Res.	24	1	1	22	30	112	4

)ivision Three	P	W	D	L	F	A	Pts
lewburgh U. Res.	24	20	2	2	90	20	62
oundry	24	20	2	2	99	30	62
owton Toby	24	13	6	5	92	64	45
rrell	24	11	5	8	68	50	38
oars Head	24	9	7	8	58	49	34
arnworth Res.	24	10	4	10	56	62	34
spull	24	10	2	12	44	51	32
ulcheth Athletic	24	9	3	12	61	56	30
indley Town OB	24	7	9	8	66	62	30
shton Villa	24	8	5	11	69	85	29
lountain Dew	24	7	4	13	59	98	25
owton Rams	24	5	2	17	44	84	17
'instanley Warr.	24	1	1	22	31	126	4

WIMBLEDON & DISTRICT AMATEUR LEAGUE

'remier Division	P	W	D	L	F	A	Pts
FC Battersea	20	14	3	3	48	18	45
outh E. London	20	14	2	4	63	31	44
laremont	20	13	1	6	41	27	40
nion	20	11	2	7	49	35	35
rentnal	20	6	7	7	43	42	25
roydon Red Star	20	7	4	9	25	39	25
eal Phoenix	20	8	0	12	38	59	24
oldfingers	20	7	2	11	43	51	23
art. Wandsworth	18	7	1	10	27	34	22
WCA	19	6	2	11	35	39	20
olmw'd Co. Dazz.	19	2	2	15	17	54	8

Spartak Clapham - record expunged

ivision One	P	W	D	L	F	A	Pts
FC Cubo Res.	16	11	2	3	40	18	35
FC Northcote	16	11	1	4	40	23	34
rompton S. Cas.	16	7	3	6	37	30	24
ondon Lionhearts	16	7	3	6	36	39	24
Vadham Coll. OB	16	6	5	5	29	28	23
ancaster Youth	16	5	3	8	26	37	18
cean	16	5	2	9	33	38	17
GA Vets	16	4	3	9	34	38	15
yde Park Thurs.	16	5	0	11	18	42	15

South Wimbledon - record expunged

Division Two	P	W	D	L	F	A	Pts
Battersea Old Firm	18	16	2	0	64	15	50
Brentside	18	10	0	8	46	44	30
Peperami	18	8	5	5	41	31	29
Sth West Eleven	18	8	5	5	40	31	29
Sporting Brixton	18	8	4	6	33	28	28
Balham Rangers	18	7	2	9	37	35	23
Cosmos United	18	5	3	10	39	68	18
AFC Cubo A	18	5	2	11	28	44	17
Rivelino City	18	4	5	9	26	48	17
Kiwi	18	3	4	11	30	40	13

Division Three	P	W	D	L	F	A	Pts
Bar Sia	16	11	5	0	41	17	38
Battersea Lions	16	10	5	1	43	21	35
Merton Orient	16	8	3	5	37	27	27
Inter Old Boys	16	7	4	5	44	25	25
Nottingham Old B.	16	7	3	6	37	25	24
Foundation	16	4	5	7	30	45	17
SE London Res.	16	4	3	9	26	39	15
London Korean U.	16	4	0	12	29	58	12
Boca Seniors FC	16	1	4	11	24	54	7

WINCHESTER & DISTRICT LEAGUE

	P	W	D	L	F	A	Pts
Upham	12	12	0	0	57	10	36
Makiki Lounge	12	9	0	3	41	20	27
Sutton Scotney	12	5	2	5	21	22	17
Micheldever Pho.	12	5	1	6	16	34	16
Infinity Res.	12	5	0	7	40	26	15
Ropley	12	3	1	8	31	35	10
Eastleigh Town	12	1	0	11	3	62	3

Ronin - record expunged

WITNEY & DISTRICT FA

Premier Division	P	W	D	L	F	A	Pts
Hailey	20	18	1	1	81	28	55
Ducklington	20	15	1	4	51	26	46
Charlbury Town	20	13	2	5	51	25	41
Witney Royals	20	11	3	6	49	29	36
Hanborough	20	9	3	8	32	24	30
Spartan Rangers	20	9	2	9	41	37	29
Combe	20	7	0	13	38	55	21
Minster Lovell	20	7	0	13	33	59	21
Kingham All Blacks	20	5	3	12	31	57	18
Brize Norton	20	4	2	14	27	45	14
West Witney	20	2	3	15	20	69	9

Division One	P	W	D	L	F	A	Pts
Wychwood Forest	22	19	3	0	79	22	60
AC Finstock	22	15	4	3	72	40	49
FC Chequers	22	14	5	3	64	28	47
Chipping Norton T.	22	14	4	4	67	28	46
North Leigh A +3	22	7	4	11	39	38	28
Witney Wdrs +3	22	7	4	11	50	57	28
Duck'gton Res. +3	22	8	1	13	45	56	28
Aston	22	6	4	12	40	49	22
Hanborough Res.	22	4	6	12	28	52	18
Brize Norton Res.	22	5	2	15	34	81	17
Milton	22	3	3	16	27	85	12
FC Mills -18	22	9	2	11	53	62	11

Division Two	P	W	D	L	F	A	Pts
Chad Park	22	17	3	2	67	26	54
FC Nomads	22	16	2	4	57	25	50
Witney Ryls Res.	22	13	2	7	68	37	41
Southrop	22	13	2	7	65	43	41
Middle Barton	22	10	5	7	42	32	35
Charlbury T. Res.	22	9	3	10	37	49	30
Wootton Sports	22	9	1	12	31	46	28
Ducklington A	22	7	4	11	44	56	25
Spartan Rgrs Res.	22	6	4	12	49	50	22
Two Rivers	22	6	3	13	37	65	21
Tackley	22	5	3	14	31	61	18
West Witney Res.	22	3	4	15	28	66	13

Division Three	P	W	D	L	F	A	Pts
Stanton Harcourt	24	21	1	2	134	25	64
Carterton A	24	21	0	3	83	26	63
Hailey Res.	24	19	2	3	84	32	59
Eynsham Sports	24	15	3	6	95	69	48
FC Chequers Res.	24	13	2	9	53	39	41
Chip. Norton Res.	24	11	1	12	58	64	34
Minster Lovell Res.	24	7	6	11	50	48	27
Aston Res.	24	8	2	14	48	53	26
Kingham AB Res.	24	8	2	14	46	63	26
Freeland A	24	8	2	14	39	61	26
FC Mills Res.	24	6	2	16	46	104	20
Spartan Rgrs A	24	5	3	16	49	86	18
Milton Res.	24	1	0	23	25	140	3

Division Four	P	W	D	L	F	A	Pts
Witney Royals A	24	20	2	2	81	34	62
North Leigh B	24	20	0	4	78	40	60
FC Hollybush	24	18	4	2	92	26	58
Wychwood F. Res.	24	14	3	7	86	47	45
Ducklington B	24	13	4	7	56	52	43
Eynsham Ass. A	24	13	2	9	66	47	41
Freeland B	24	12	3	9	74	48	39
AFC Marlborough	24	10	5	9	78	49	35
Combe Res.	24	9	1	14	59	57	28
Corinthians	24	5	0	19	39	115	15
Fieldtown	24	4	2	18	25	60	14
Brize Norton A	24	3	0	21	36	93	9
Eynsham S. Res.	24	2	0	22	34	136	6

WORCESTER & DISTRICT LEAGUE

	P	W	D	L	F	A	Pts
Powick	16	14	1	1	69	17	43
VBL Sports	16	12	2	2	85	23	38
Hallow WMC	16	11	1	4	46	35	34
Martley Spurs	16	10	0	6	78	30	30
Univ. of Worcester	16	8	3	5	48	36	27
GDL Saturday	16	3	3	10	29	65	12
West Malvern TC	16	3	1	12	30	75	10
Northway FC	16	2	2	12	24	75	8
P'wood Res. -3,-1g	16	2	1	13	25	79	4

YORK LEAGUE
(Minster Engineering)

Premier Division	P	W	D	L	F	A	Pts
Haxby United	26	19	2	5	103	47	59
Old Malton St M.	26	17	3	6	69	40	54
Dunnington	26	16	4	6	65	46	52
Huntington Rovers	26	12	5	9	84	71	41
York St John Univ.	26	13	1	12	75	66	40
Hamilton Panthers	26	12	3	11	62	69	39
Poppleton United	26	11	4	11	55	59	37
Kartiers (Selby)	26	10	4	12	50	54	34
Copmanthorpe	26	9	5	12	52	71	32
Riccall United	26	10	0	16	59	60	30
Tadcaster Res. -3	26	10	1	15	50	65	28
Dringhouses	26	8	2	16	53	76	26
Wilberfoss	26	7	4	15	41	63	25
Wig'ton G'hoppers	26	6	6	14	50	81	24

Tate & Lyle Selby - record expunged

Division One	P	W	D	L	F	A	Pts
York Railway Inst.	24	17	4	3	86	33	55
Easingwold Town	24	16	4	4	52	32	52
Tockwith	24	15	4	5	66	39	49
Post Office	24	13	5	6	59	41	44
Malton & Norton	24	13	3	8	49	36	42
Nestle R'tree -3	24	12	5	7	68	57	38
Pocklington Res.	24	10	5	9	49	48	35
Hemingbrough U.	24	7	6	11	51	61	27
Thorpe United	24	6	7	11	48	56	25
Bishopthorpe Utd	24	7	4	13	44	56	25
Amotherby & Swin.	24	5	3	16	42	68	18
Ouseburn United	24	3	5	16	36	81	14
Stamford Bridge	24	2	5	17	35	77	11

Division Two	P	W	D	L	F	A	Pts
St Clements	24	17	4	3	75	28	55
Selby RSSC	24	16	3	5	64	31	51
Heworth	24	15	4	5	76	44	49
Terrington Glory	24	14	4	6	66	44	46
Heslington	24	12	4	8	59	37	40
Rawcliffe Rangers	24	10	5	9	61	52	35
Church Fenton WH	24	9	4	11	63	61	31
Huby United	24	10	1	13	42	66	31
Elvington Harriers	24	7	6	11	48	52	27
Fulford United	24	6	5	13	35	59	23
Aviva	24	6	2	16	43	76	20
Osbaldwick	24	6	2	16	38	82	20
Rufforth United	24	5	2	17	40	78	17

Division Three	P	W	D	L	F	A	Pts
Strensall	24	21	3	0	145	28	66
Crayke	24	17	3	4	64	25	54
Cliffe	24	14	5	5	76	37	47
Barmby Moor	24	13	4	7	66	46	43
Civil Service York	24	13	4	7	66	51	43
Wheldrake	24	11	3	10	69	45	36
Stillington	24	10	5	9	64	55	35
F1 Racing	24	9	4	11	45	63	31
LNER Builders	24	7	6	11	48	61	27
Bishop Wilton	24	8	1	15	44	78	25
Moor Lane	24	5	2	17	55	108	17
Selby Olympia	24	3	2	19	38	113	11
Melbourne	24	2	4	18	33	103	10

Reserve Division A	P	W	D	L	F	A	Pts
Old Malton Res.	22	18	0	4	77	37	54
York SJ Univ. Res.	22	13	1	8	85	50	40
Bishopthorpe Res.	22	12	4	6	59	42	40
Copm'thorpe Res.	22	10	5	7	57	43	35
Wigginton G. Res.	22	9	5	8	51	49	32
Huntington Res.	22	10	2	10	51	51	32
Haxby Utd Res.	22	9	5	8	56	57	32
Dunnington Res.	22	9	4	9	49	47	31
Kartiers Res.	22	9	3	10	47	50	30
Dringhouses Res.	22	6	1	15	36	66	19
Hamilton P. Res.	22	5	3	14	41	74	18
Wilberfoss Res.	22	4	3	15	35	78	15

Reserve Division B	P	W	D	L	F	A	Pts
Easingwold Res.	22	15	3	4	63	26	48
Aviva Res.	22	15	0	7	73	34	45
Riccall Utd Res.	22	12	5	5	56	40	41
Thorpe Utd Res.	22	12	2	8	58	45	38
Heslington Res.	22	10	6	6	59	45	36
Pocklington T. A	22	9	2	11	42	35	29
York Rail. I. Res.	22	9	1	12	55	60	28
Tockwith Res.	22	8	4	10	41	53	28
Heworth Res. -3	22	9	3	10	45	56	27
Stamford B. Res.	22	5	6	11	32	60	21
Poppleton U. Res.	22	5	3	14	38	64	18
Ouseburn Res. -3	22	4	3	15	28	72	12

YORKSHIRE OLD BOYS LEAGUE

Senior Division A	P	W	D	L	F	A	Pts
Alwoodley Old B.	18	12	2	4	48	18	38
Stanningley Old B.	18	12	2	4	57	38	38
Gildersome Spurs	18	10	3	5	43	31	33
Wortley	18	9	5	4	45	25	32
Leeds Medics/Dent	18	9	5	4	37	29	32
Hudd. Amateur	18	7	3	8	35	49	24
Leeds Univ. OB	18	4	5	9	31	40	17
Ealandians	18	5	1	12	35	47	16
St Nicholas FC	18	4	1	13	25	56	13
Trinity & ASCOB	18	3	3	12	27	50	12

Heckmondwike GSOB - record expunged

Senior Division B	P	W	D	L	F	A	Pts
Leeds M & D Res.	22	15	4	3	70	25	49
Old Modernians	22	15	3	4	49	26	48
FC Headingley	22	13	3	6	75	40	42
Shire Academics	22	13	3	6	72	37	42
Old Batelians	22	11	3	8	56	63	36
Wheelwright OB	22	10	4	8	56	52	34
Calverley	22	10	3	9	45	45	33
Bramley Jnrs OB	22	9	2	11	51	62	29
Gildersome Res.	22	9	1	12	47	48	28
St Bedes Old B.	22	7	3	12	47	58	24
Old Collegians	22	3	1	18	24	75	10
Sandal Athletic	22	1	2	19	31	92	5

Division One	P	W	D	L	F	A	Pts
Wortley Res.	21	16	2	3	71	33	50
Old Thornesians	22	13	4	5	55	36	43
Collingham JOB	22	12	2	8	49	38	38
Bainbridge	22	11	3	8	58	47	36
Moortown Old B.	22	10	4	8	52	37	34
Old Centralians	22	11	1	10	52	52	34
Leeds M. & D. A	22	8	5	9	46	49	29
East Ardsley Wdrs	22	9	1	12	46	60	28
Shadwell	21	8	0	13	47	56	24
Leeds I'dependent	22	7	2	13	30	61	23
Western Jnrs OB	22	5	5	12	42	56	20
East Leeds -14	22	5	3	14	34	57	4

Division Two	P	W	D	L	F	A	Pts
Grangefield OB	24	17	4	3	81	34	55
Bramley J. Res.	24	17	3	4	67	31	54
Beeston Old Boys	24	16	3	5	94	44	51
E. Leeds Trin. OB	24	14	3	7	66	42	45
Hudd.Amatr Res.	24	13	6	5	63	47	45
O Modernians Res.	24	11	5	8	60	48	38
Trin./ASCOB Res.	24	9	3	12	46	52	30
Alwoodley OB Res.	24	8	6	10	51	59	30
Farnley Sports	24	8	3	13	36	53	27
Gildersome S. A	24	6	4	14	47	85	22
Shire Acad. Res.	24	5	5	14	38	60	20
Ealandians Res.	24	4	3	17	40	84	15
Heck. GSOB Res.	24	2	4	18	34	84	10

Division Three	P	W	D	L	F	A	Pts
Wortley A	22	16	3	3	46	17	51
Colton Acad'cals	22	13	2	7	62	32	41
Wdhse Moor Meth.	22	11	7	4	43	29	40
Leeds M & D B	22	11	3	8	52	35	36
St Bedes OB Res.	22	11	2	9	46	41	35
Leeds Ind. Res.	22	9	3	10	50	45	30
O. Collegians Res.	22	7	6	9	44	48	27
Old Batelians Res.	22	8	1	13	44	57	25
Colton Acad. Res.	22	8	1	13	45	68	25
Grangefield Res.	22	6	5	11	37	54	23
Old Cents Res.	22	6	4	12	41	63	22
Wheelwright Res.	22	6	3	13	37	58	21

Division Four	P	W	D	L	F	A	Pts
Bramley JOB A -1	24	18	2	4	86	30	55
Sandal Wanderers	24	16	4	4	74	33	52
Old Modernians A	24	15	3	6	77	43	48
Leeds City Old B.	24	14	6	4	65	51	48
Colton Juniors	24	12	2	10	62	43	38
Old Thorn'ns Res.	24	11	3	10	58	48	36
E. Ardsley W. Res.	24	10	3	11	54	45	33
Old Modernians B	24	9	3	12	46	59	30
Colton Acad. A	24	7	5	12	62	91	26
Sandal Ath. Res.	24	6	6	12	47	52	24
Shadwell Res.	24	6	6	12	39	71	24
Hudd. Amateur A	24	4	6	14	47	82	18
Ealandians A	24	2	3	19	36	105	9

Division Five	P	W	D	L	F	A	Pts
Leeds C. OB Res.	22	16	4	2	64	32	52
Old Batelians A	22	15	2	5	106	59	47
Old Centralians A	22	14	5	3	49	29	47
Alwoodley OB A	22	12	2	8	66	51	38
Old Thornesians A	22	11	2	9	56	49	35
St Bedes Old B. A	22	10	3	9	53	48	33
Hudd. Amateur B	22	10	2	10	68	51	32
Shadwell A	22	10	1	11	66	62	31
Old Modernians C	22	8	1	13	59	85	25
Old Collegians A	22	7	3	12	43	48	24
Old Centralians B	22	3	3	16	35	71	12
Wheelwright A	22	2	0	20	30	110	6

ALL LEAGUE TABLES IN THIS SECTION ARE CONFIRMED AS FINAL EVEN IF SOME GAMES REMAINED UNPLAYED

WELSH PREMIER LEAGUE

www.low.org.uk

Sponsored by: Principality Building Society

Founded: 1992

Recent champions:
2005: Total Network Solutions
2006: Total Network Solutions
2007: The New Saints
2008: Llanelli
2009: Rhyl

	P	W	D	L	F	A	Pts
The New Saints	34	25	7	2	69	13	82
Llanelli	34	25	5	4	79	26	80
Port Talbot Town	34	19	8	7	55	23	65
Aberystwyth Town	34	19	7	8	54	41	64
Bangor City	34	19	6	9	75	45	63
Rhyl	34	18	8	8	74	43	62
Airbus UK Broughton	34	12	13	9	49	37	49
Prestatyn Town	34	12	12	10	53	53	48
Neath Athletic	34	12	11	11	41	37	47
Carmarthen Town	34	12	9	13	45	38	45
Bala Town	34	12	9	13	39	47	45
Haverfordwest County	34	11	11	12	43	47	44
Newtown	34	10	11	13	54	57	41
Gap Connah's Quay	34	11	8	15	31	42	41
Porthmadog	34	6	6	22	23	66	24
Welshpool Town	34	6	5	23	30	70	23
Caersws	34	3	4	27	26	94	13
Elements Cefn Druids	34	1	6	27	16	77	9

	Aberystwyth Town	Airbus UK B'ton	Bala Town	Bangor City	Caersws	Carmarthen Town	Elem. Cefn Druids	Gap Conn. Quay	Haverfordwest Co.	Llanelli	Neath Athletic	Newtown	Port Talbot Town	Porthmadog	Prestatyn Town	Rhyl	The New Saints	Welshpool Town
Aberystwyth Town		0-3	1-0	2-1	3-2	1-2	4-1	1-2	2-1	1-1	1-1	2-1	2-1	1-0	2-3	2-2	1-3	1-1
Airbus UK Broughton	2-0		0-1	1-5	3-0	2-2	1-1	4-0	3-1	0-1	1-1	2-0	0-0	1-2	2-0	2-2	0-0	1-2
Bala Town	1-1	1-2		2-1	2-0	1-3	1-0	2-2	1-1	0-1	1-0	1-1	1-1	0-0	2-4	0-4	0-1	2-1
Bangor City	0-1	3-0	6-3		7-1	3-2	3-1	0-0	3-2	2-3	3-1	0-0	1-1	2-0	4-0	3-1	0-1	3-2
Caersws	0-4	0-4	1-3	1-3		0-3	1-0	1-0	0-2	0-2	0-1	1-1	1-2	1-2	1-5	2-2	0-3	3-0
Carmarthen Town	0-0	0-1	2-1	2-2	1-0		4-0	1-0	2-2	1-2	0-1	1-2	3-1	1-3	1-2	0-1	1-2	1-1
Elements Cefn Druids	0-3	1-1	1-2	0-1	1-1	0-1		0-1	1-2	2-5	0-1	0-2	0-1	1-0	0-5	1-1	0-0	0-1
Gap Connah's Quay	0-3	0-1	0-1	0-1	5-0	0-0	3-1		1-1	1-0	2-0	3-1	0-3	3-0	1-1	0-2	1-0	0-0
Haverfordwest County	0-1	1-1	1-1	2-2	3-1	2-1	1-0	1-0		0-1	1-2	1-2	1-1	2-0	3-3	2-4	0-0	1-0
Llanelli	4-0	2-2	2-0	3-2	7-1	1-0	4-0	5-0	1-1		2-1	3-2	1-0	5-0	4-1	3-1	0-2	2-1
Neath Athletic	1-3	0-0	2-1	0-1	5-3	1-1	1-1	1-1	1-2	2-1		1-1	0-1	3-2	1-1	2-0	0-1	4-0
Newtown	1-2	3-3	0-1	2-5	4-1	0-0	4-2	0-0	2-1	0-2	1-0		2-2	1-3	3-2	2-4	0-2	4-1
Port Talbot Town	1-2	2-1	0-0	2-1	4-0	0-1	7-0	1-0	1-0	0-0	2-0	2-1		5-0	1-1	2-1	2-0	3-0
Porthmadog	0-1	0-1	0-2	0-2	1-1	1-4	1-0	0-1	0-0	0-4	1-4	1-1	0-1		2-0	0-2	1-1	2-3
Prestatyn Town	0-2	2-2	2-1	1-1	1-0	0-0	2-0	3-2	3-0	1-5	0-0	1-1	0-3	1-1		0-0	0-1	2-1
Rhyl	1-1	2-1	5-2	5-1	3-1	2-1	6-0	4-1	1-2	0-0	0-1	4-2	2-0	4-0	1-1		1-2	4-1
The New Saints	4-0	2-1	0-0	2-1	4-0	2-0	4-0	3-0	4-0	1-0	2-2	2-2	1-0	5-0	5-0	4-0		4-0
Welshpool Town	1-3	0-0	1-2	1-2	3-1	1-3	2-1	0-1	1-3	1-2	0-0	1-5	0-2	2-0	0-5	1-2	0-1	

LOOSEMORE'S SOLICITORS LEAGUE CUP KNOCK-OUT STAGE

(see next page for details of the group stage)

QUARTER-FINALS

Bala Town 2 **Gap Connah's Quay** 3, **Port Talbot Town** 3 Welshpool Town 1
Porthmadog 1 **Rhyl** 4, **The New Saints** 4 Llanelli 1

SEMI-FINALS

(played over two legs)

Gap Connah's Quay 2 Rhyl 1, **Rhyl** 4 Gap Connah's Quay 0
Port Talbot Town 0 The New Saints 0, **The New Saints** 2 Port Talbot Town 0

FINAL *(April 27th at Airbus UK Broughton)*

Rhyl 1 **The New Saints** 3

LOOSEMORE'S SOLICITORS LEAGUE CUP GROUP STAGE

GROUP ONE

	P	W	D	L	F	A	Pts
Port Talbot Town	**4**	**3**	**1**	**0**	**8**	**3**	**10**
Neath Athletic	4	1	1	2	5	8	4
Carmarthen Town	4	0	2	2	3	5	2

Carmarthen Town 0 Port Talbot Town 1
Carmarthen Town 2 Neath Athletic 3
Neath Athletic 0 Carmarthen Town 0
Neath Athletic 1 Port Talbot Town 4
Port Talbot Town 1 Carmarthen Town 1
Port Talbot Town 2 Neath Athletic 1

GROUP TWO

	P	W	D	L	F	A	Pts
Llanelli	4	2	2	0	13	4	8
Aberystwyth Town	4	1	2	1	5	11	5
Haverfordwest County	4	0	2	2	2	5	2

Aberystwyth Town 0 Haverfordwest County 0
Aberystwyth Town 2 Llanelli 2
Haverfordwest County 1 Aberystwyth Town 2
Haverfordwest County 1 Llanelli 1
Llanelli 2 Haverfordwest County 0
Llanelli 8 Aberystwyth Town 1

GROUP THREE

	P	W	D	L	F	A	Pts
Porthmadog	4	2	1	1	9	4	7
Gap Connah's Quay	4	2	1	1	6	7	7
Caersws	4	0	2	2	2	6	2

Caersws 0 Gap Connah's Quay 0
Caersws 1 Porthmadog 1
Gap Connah's Quay 3 Caersws 1
Gap Connah's Quay 3 Porthmadog 2
Porthmadog 2 Caersws 0
Porthmadog 4 Gap Connah's Quay 0

GROUP FOUR

	P	W	D	L	F	A	Pts
Rhyl	4	4	0	0	11	2	12
Prestatyn Town	4	1	1	2	5	7	4
Airbus UK Broughton	4	0	1	3	3	10	1

Airbus UK Broughton 0 Prestatyn Town 2
Airbus UK Broughton 1 Rhyl 2
Prestatyn Town 0 Rhyl 3
Prestatyn Town 2 Airbus UK Broughton 2
Rhyl 2 Prestatyn Town 1
Rhyl 4 Airbus UK Broughton 0

GROUP FIVE

	P	W	D	L	F	A	Pts
Welshpool Town	4	3	1	0	11	5	10
Bala Town	4	2	1	1	7	3	7
Elements Cefn Druids	4	0	0	4	5	15	0

Bala Town 1 Welshpool Town 2
Bala Town 2 Elements Cefn Druids 1
Elements Cefn Druids 0 Bala Town 4
Elements Cefn Druids 2 Welshpool Town 4
Welshpool Town 0 Bala Town 0
Welshpool Town 5 Elements Cefn Druids 2

GROUP SIX

	P	W	D	L	F	A	Pts
The New Saints	4	3	1	0	13	6	10
Bangor City	4	2	0	2	7	8	6
Newtown	4	0	1	3	5	11	1

Bangor City 0 The New Saints 2
Bangor City 3 Newtown 0
Newtown 1 Bangor City 2
Newtown 2 The New Saints 4
The New Saints 2 Newtown 2
The New Saints 5 Bangor City 2

WELSH PREMIER TEAMS IN EUROPE

UEFA CHAMPIONS LEAGUE

SECOND QUALIFYING ROUND

1st Leg: *(July 14th at Rhyl)*
RHYL 0 Partizan Belgrade 4 Att: 1,726
2nd Leg: *(July 21st at Partizan Belgrade)*
Partizan Belgrade 8 RHYL 0 Att: 9,368

EUROPA CUP

FIRST QUALIFYING ROUND

1st Leg: *(July 2nd at Fram Reykjavik)*
Fram Reykjavik 2 THE NEW SAINTS 1 Att: 592
2nd Leg: *(July 9th at The New Saints)*
THE NEW SAINTS 1 **Fram Reykjavik** 2 Att: 933

1st Leg: *(July 2nd at Airdrie)*
Motherwell 0 LLANELLI 1 Att: 4,307
2nd Leg: *(July 9th at Llanelli Scarlets)*
LLANELLI 0 **Motherwell** 3 Att: 3,025

SECOND QUALIFYING ROUND

1st Leg: *(July 16th at FC Honka)*
FC Honka 2 BANGOR CITY 0 Att: 1,668
2nd Leg: *(July 23rd at Wrexham)*
BANGOR CITY 0 **FC Honka** 1 Att: 602

WELSH PREMIER LEAGUE CONSTITUTION 2010-11

ABERYSTWYTH TOWN
Park Avenue Stadium, Maesgogerddan, Aberystwyth, Ceredigion SY23 1PG
Tel: 01970 630380
Manager: Alan Morgan
Colours: Green, black & white
www.atfc.org.uk

AIRBUS UK BROUGHTON
Broughton Wings Sports & Social Club, Broughton, Flintshire CH4 0DR
Tel: 01244 368390
Manager: Craig Harrison
Colours: Blue
www.airbusfc.com

BALA TOWN
Maes Tegid Stadium, Castle Street, Bala, Gwynedd LL23 7BF
Tel: 01678 521823
Manager: Colin Caton
Colours: Red & black
www.balatownfc.co.uk

BANGOR CITY
The Stadium, Farrar Road, Bangor, Gwynedd LL57 1LJ
Tel: 01248 355852
Manager: Neville Powell
Colours: Blue
www.bangorcityfc.com

CARMARTHEN TOWN
Richmond Park, Priory Street, Carmarthen, Carmarthenshire SA31 1LR
Tel: 01267 222851
Manager: Tomi Morgan
Colours: Old gold & black
www.carmarthentownafc.net

HAVERFORDWEST COUNTY
Bridge Meadow Stadium, Bridge Meadow Lane, Haverfordwest, Pembrokeshire SA61 2EX
Tel: 01437 769048
Manager: Derek Brazil
Colours: Royal blue
www.haverfordwestcounty.co.uk

LLANELLI
Stebonheath Park, Penallt Road, Stebonheath, Llanelli, Carmarthenshire SA15 1EY
Tel: 01554 772973
Manager: Andy Legg
Colours: Red
www.llanelliafc.org

NEATH ATHLETIC
The Gnoll, Gnoll Park Road, Neath, West Glamorgan SA11 3BU
Tel: 01639 620177
Manager: Andrew Dyer
Colours: White & black
www.neathfc.com

NEWTOWN
Latham Park, Park Lane, Newtown, Powys SY16 1EN
Tel: 01686 623120
Manager: Darren Ryan
Colours: Red & white
www.newtownafc.co.uk

PORT TALBOT TOWN
The GenQuip Stadium, Victoria Road, Aberavon, Port Talbot, West Glamorgan SA12 6AD
Tel: 01639 882465
Manager: Mark Jones
Colours: Blue & white
www.porttalbottown.co.uk

PRESTATYN TOWN
Bastion Gardens, Bastion Road, Prestatyn, Denbighshire LL19 7ES
Tel: 01745 856905
Manager: Neil Gibson
Colours: Blue
www.ptfconline.co.uk

THE NEW SAINTS
The Venue, Burma Road, Park Hall, Oswestry, Shropshire SY11 4AS
Tel: 01691 684840
Manager: Mike Davies
Colours: Green & white
www.tnsfc.co.uk

OUT: Caersws (R - Cymru Alliance), Elements Cefn Druids (now Cefn Druids) (R - Cymru Alliance), Gap Connah's Quay (R - Cymru Alliance), Porthmadog (R - Cymru Alliance), Rhyl (R - Cymru Alliance), Welshpool Town (now Technogroup Welshpool) (R - Cymru Alliance)

CYMRU ALLIANCE

www.cymru-alliance.co.uk

Sponsored by: Huws Gray
Founded: 1990
Recent champions:
2005: Buckley Town
2006: Glantraeth.
2007: Llangefni Town
2008: Prestatyn Town
2009: Bala Town

	Berr	Beth	Buck	Caer	Den	Flint	Gres	Guil	Holy	Lex	Lldu	Llfair	Llngf	Llgln	Mold	Pen	Ruth
Berriew		1-0	1-4	2-1	1-1	2-4	4-1	1-2	2-1	1-3	1-1	2-1	1-4	2-3	2-4	0-1	2-1
Bethesda Athletic	6-1		1-2	1-2	3-3	1-3	3-0	2-3	3-0	6-1	4-5	1-1	0-3	1-1	0-2	5-1	2-4
Buckley Town	3-0	4-4		2-2	0-1	1-0	6-0	2-1	0-0	0-1	1-1	1-1	1-2	4-1	5-1	2-1	3-0
Caernarfon Town	3-1	1-4	0-1		3-1	0-2	2-5	2-3	0-3	2-1	5-1	2-2	1-4	4-0	2-3	2-4	1-2
Denbigh Town	2-0	5-2	0-0	2-0		2-2	1-1	4-1	4-1	5-0	1-2	1-2	0-2	1-2	2-0	1-2	2-2
Flint Town United	3-0	1-1	0-0	2-1	2-2		2-1	2-0	5-1	1-0	0-0	3-0	5-1	3-1	3-1	0-1	1-0
Gresford Athletic	0-0	0-6	0-2	0-3	1-4	3-3		1-1	0-3	2-4	0-3	1-0	0-2	2-0	2-0	2-5	0-3
Guilsfield	1-1	1-1	1-1	3-1	4-4	2-7	6-1		2-0	0-1	0-1	2-0	0-2	3-2	4-0	0-0	2-3
Holyhead Hotspur	5-0	5-0	1-1	5-1	2-0	0-2	1-1	2-3		5-1	0-1	4-2	0-4	2-1	1-2	2-0	1-2
Lex XI	0-3	3-3	0-2	1-0	2-2	1-2	0-3	3-3	0-1		2-2	0-4	2-3	2-2	4-2	2-2	1-2
Llandudno Town	5-1	0-0	2-0	4-0	1-0	1-2	4-0	1-2	4-1	4-0		3-1	0-0	3-0	0-1	5-0	4-1
Llanfairpwll	1-5	1-0	1-2	1-1	4-1	1-3	2-0	0-1	1-1	0-3	2-1		0-4	1-2	2-1	0-1	1-2
Llangefni Town	5-1	0-1	2-1	1-1	2-1	4-2	3-0	1-1	1-2	3-0	1-1	3-0		8-0	5-1	2-0	5-1
Llangollen Town	2-2	1-4	4-0	4-3	6-1	1-4	4-0	2-0	1-2	1-3	2-3	4-1	0-4		6-4	0-2	1-2
Mold Alexandra	1-4	1-4	0-2	3-1	1-2	0-4	2-1	3-1	2-0	1-2	1-4	2-3	1-6	6-2		1-1	3-3
Penrhyncoch	4-3	0-0	1-3	1-1	4-0	0-8	3-0	2-0	4-0	2-1	0-0	2-0	1-3	1-0	1-3		4-0
Ruthin Town	1-2	3-1	0-1	0-2	1-0	0-3	5-0	1-1	2-1	1-1	2-6	1-2	2-5	0-3	1-0	0-0	

		P	W	D	L	F	A	Pts
Llangefni Town		32	25	4	3	95	27	79
Flint Town United		32	23	6	3	84	29	75
Llandudno Town		32	19	8	5	73	31	65
Buckley Town		32	17	9	6	57	30	60
Penrhyncoch		32	16	7	9	51	46	55
Guilsfield		32	12	9	11	54	54	45
Ruthin Town		32	13	5	14	48	61	44
Holyhead Hotspur	*-3*	32	13	4	15	53	52	40
Bethesda Athletic		32	10	9	13	70	59	39
Denbigh Town		32	10	9	13	56	56	39
Llangollen Town		32	11	3	18	59	78	36
Berriew		32	10	5	17	49	74	35
Mold Alexandra		32	11	2	19	53	80	35
Lex XI		32	9	7	16	45	70	34
Llanfairpwll		32	9	5	18	38	60	32
Caernarfon Town	*-3*	32	8	5	19	50	69	26
Gresford Athletic		32	5	5	22	28	87	20

LEAGUE CUP

PRELIMINARY ROUND
Lex XI 1 **Bethesda Athletic** 2
Mold Alexandra 7 Caernarfon Town 2

FIRST ROUND
Berriew 0 **Llanfairpwll** 2
Buckley Town 0 **Holyhead Hotspur** 1
Denbigh Town 0 **Llangollen Town** 1
Flint Town United 1 Llangefni Town 0
Glantraeth v **Penrhyncoch** (w/o)
Llandudno Town 3 Gresford Athletic 1
Mold Alexandra 0 **Bethesda Athletic** 3
Ruthin Town 2 **Guilsfield** 3

QUARTER-FINALS
Flint Town United 6 Penrhyncoch 1
Llanairpwll 1 Guilsfield 0
Llandudno Town 4 Holyhead Hotspur 2
Llangollen Town 3 **Bethesda Athletic** 4

SEMI-FINALS
Bethesda Athletic 0 **Flint Town Utd** 3 *(at Buckley)*
Llandudno Town 1 Llanfairpwll 0 *(at Llangefni)*

FINAL
(May 8th at Buckley Town)
Flint Town United 0 **Llandudno Town** 2

CYMRU ALLIANCE CONSTITUTION 2010-11

BUCKLEY TOWN .... Globe Way, Liverpool Way, Buckley CH7 3LL.................................. Non
CAERSWS .... Recreation Ground, Bridge Street, Caersws SY17 5DT............................ 01686 68875
CEFN DRUIDS .... Plas Kynaston Lane, Plas Kynaston, Cefn Mawr, Wrexham LL14 3AT............... 01978 82433
FLINT TOWN UNITED.................... Cae Y Castell, March Lane, Flint CH6 5PJ 01352 73098
GAP CONNAH'S QUAY .... Deeside Stadium, Kelsterton Road, Connah's Quay CH5 4BR.................. 01244 83121
GUILSFIELD .... Community Centre, Guilsfield, Welshpool SY21 9ND................................ Non
LLANDUDNO TOWN .... Maesdu Park, Builder Street, Llandudno LL30 1HH 01492 86094
LLANGEFNI TOWN .... Cae Bob Parry, Talwrn Road, Llangefni LL77 7LP.............................. 01248 72499
PENRHYNCOCH .... Cae Baker, Penrhynchoch, Aberystwyth SY23 3XH 01970 82899
PORTHMADOG............................ Y Traeth, Porthmadog LL49 9PP 01766 51468
RHAYADER TOWN .... Y Weirglodd, Water Lane, Bridge Street, Rhayader LD6 5AN 01597 81006
RHOS AELWYD .... Ponciau Park, Clarke Street, Ponciau, Wrexham LL14 1RT .... Non
RHYDYMWYN .... Vicarage Road, Rhydymwyn, Mold CH7 5HL.. Non
RHYL .... Belle Vue Stadium, Grange Road, Rhyl LL18 4BY.............................. 01745 33832
RUTHIN TOWN .... Memorial Playing Fields, Park Road, Ruthin LL15 1NB.. Non
TECHNOGROUP WELSHPOOL . Maesydre Recreation Grounds, Howells Drive, Welshpool SY21 7SU............... 01938 55556

IN: Caersws (R - Welsh Premier League), Elements Cefn Druids (now Cefn Druids) (R - Welsh Premier League), Gap Connah's Quay (R Welsh Premier League), Porthmadog (R - Welsh Premier League), Rhayader Town (P - Mid-Wales League), Rhos Aelwyd (P - Wels National League (Wrexham Area) Premier Division), Rhydymwyn (P - Welsh Alliance), Rhyl (R - Welsh Premier League), Welshpool Tow (now Technogroup Welshpool) (R - Welsh Premier League)

OUT: Berriew (R - Mid-Wales League), Bethesda Athletic (R - Welsh Alliance Division One), Caernarfon Town (R - Welsh Alliance Divisio One), Denbigh Town (R - Welsh Alliance Division One), Glantraeth (WN), Gresford Athletic (R - Welsh National League (Wrexham Area Premier Division), Holyhead Hotspur (R - Welsh Alliance Division One), Lex XI (R - Welsh National League (Wrexham Area) Premie Division), Llanfairpwll (R - Welsh Alliance Division One), Llangollen Town (R - Welsh National League (Wrexham Area) Premier Division Mold Alexandra (R - Welsh National League (Wrexham Area) Premier Division)

WELSH LEAGUE

www.welshleague.org.uk

Sponsored by: MacWhirter

Founded: 1904

Recent champions:

2005: Ton Pentre
2006: Goytre United
2007: Neath
2008: Goytre United
2009: ENTO Aberaman Athletic

Reserve Division Central	P	W	D	L	F	A	Pt
Bryntirion Athletic Res.	22	18	1	3	81	29	55
Cardiff Corinthians Res.	22	15	3	4	64	29	48
Cambrian & Clydach Res.	22	12	4	6	55	41	40
Porthcawl Town Res.	22	10	4	8	42	38	34
AFC Porth Res.	22	10	3	9	48	44	33
Troedyrhiw	22	8	6	8	39	37	30
Bettws Res.	22	9	3	10	30	31	30
AFC Llwydcoed Res.	22	7	8	7	45	48	29
Treharris Ath Western Res.	22	6	7	9	41	50	25
Llantwit Fardre Res.	22	4	4	14	33	60	16
Caerau Ely Res.	22	4	3	15	47	90	15
Pontyclun Res.	22	2	8	12	39	67	14

Division One	P	W	D	L	F	A	Pts
Goytre United	34	19	12	3	86	47	69
Cambrian/Clydach VBGC	34	19	11	4	73	42	68
Afan Lido	34	19	6	9	74	37	63
Caldicot Town	34	16	7	11	78	54	55
Bryntirion Athletic	34	15	9	10	67	60	54
Taffs Well	34	15	5	14	72	60	50
Barry Town	34	12	13	9	46	41	49
Pontardawe Town	34	13	8	13	59	56	47
Bridgend Town	34	12	9	13	57	55	45
Aberaman Athletic	34	12	8	14	56	68	44
West End	34	12	8	14	62	84	44
Cardiff Corinthians	34	12	7	15	63	69	43
Garden Village	34	12	6	16	46	52	42
Ton Pentre	34	11	8	15	56	65	41
Ely Rangers	34	10	6	18	46	67	36
Bettws	34	9	9	16	38	59	36
Dinas Powys	34	9	4	21	50	83	31
Caerleon	34	8	6	20	37	67	30

	Ab'man	Afan L.	Barry	Bettws	B'dgend	B'tirion	C'leon	Caldicot	Camb.	Cardiff	Dinas P.	Ely Rgrs	Garden	Goytre	P'rdawe	Taffs W.	Ton P.	W. End
Aberaman Athletic		0-0	0-2	1-1	4-0	2-2	1-0	1-0	2-6	2-4	1-2	5-3	2-4	2-2	3-1	3-2	1-1	1-1
Afan Lido	2-0		2-0	2-1	1-3	1-2	3-0	2-1	1-1	2-0	9-1	4-0	1-0	1-2	2-1	7-1	1-0	5-0
Barry Town	2-2	2-0		3-0	1-2	3-2	1-3	0-0	1-3	2-0	1-1	1-1	1-2	2-2	0-0	2-1	2-2	1-1
Bettws	1-1	1-1	1-0	***D***	2-0	2-2	2-0	2-3	0-2	1-3	2-0	2-3	3-1	2-2	0-3	1-0	0-0	1-5
Bridgend Town	3-2	2-2	0-1	1-2	***I***	1-1	0-0	2-0	0-2	4-1	2-0	0-1	2-2	1-1	1-2	2-4	2-0	4-0
Bryntirion Athletic	3-1	2-1	1-1	2-0	1-1	***V***	2-0	0-1	3-4	2-2	2-1	2-1	3-0	1-3	0-1	0-2	3-1	1-2
Caerleon	2-3	3-0	1-2	1-0	3-1	3-2	***I***	1-3	1-1	3-0	2-1	2-1	2-2	0-6	1-3	0-0	1-3	2-3
Caldicot Town	5-2	1-4	1-1	4-1	4-4	3-3	3-1	***S***	3-0	5-2	6-0	3-0	0-1	1-3	1-2	0-3	3-2	7-1
Cambrian/Clydach	2-0	1-1	0-0	2-2	1-1	1-2	3-1	3-3	***I***	3-1	1-0	1-1	2-0	1-2	3-1	3-1	1-2	1-1
Cardiff Corinthians	2-1	1-3	2-0	3-0	3-2	2-2	2-0	2-2	2-5	***O***	4-2	1-2	1-1	0-3	2-2	1-2	3-0	4-0
Dinas Powys	1-2	1-1	1-3	5-0	1-2	2-4	3-1	0-3	2-3	3-1	***N***	0-5	3-1	1-3	2-1	2-1	4-3	1-3
Ely Rangers	0-1	1-2	0-1	0-0	4-1	5-2	2-0	3-2	0-3	0-4	1-1		1-3	1-3	1-3	0-4	0-4	4-2
Garden Village	1-2	2-1	2-1	1-0	0-4	1-2	2-0	0-2	2-4	1-2	3-1	3-0	***O***	1-2	2-1	1-1	0-0	0-0
Goytre United	3-0	2-1	1-1	3-2	5-1	3-4	1-1	1-1	1-1	5-2	1-0	1-1	1-0	***N***	6-3	4-4	0-0	3-4
Pontardawe Town	4-0	1-3	2-3	3-3	2-0	2-0	1-1	0-1	0-2	2-2	3-1	3-1	3-1	1-1	***E***	0-4	3-2	2-2
Taffs Well	1-4	1-4	1-2	1-2	1-1	1-2	4-0	5-3	1-2	3-2	3-1	0-0	2-1	4-1	1-0		4-3	7-1
Ton Pentre	1-3	1-3	1-0	0-1	0-4	4-4	4-0	1-3	1-1	2-0	3-3	2-1	0-4	0-5	2-1	2-1		6-1
West End	4-1	2-1	3-3	1-0	1-3	2-3	2-1	1-0	3-4	2-2	2-3	1-2	2-1	2-4	2-2	3-1	2-3	

WELSH LEAGUE DIVISION ONE CONSTITUTION 2010-11

ABERAMAN ATHLETIC. . . . . Aberaman Park, Cardiff Road, Aberaman, Aberdare CF44 6AA 07506 680185
AFAN LIDO . . . . Marston's Stadium, Princess Margaret Way, Aberavon Beach, Port Talbot SA12 6PE. 01639 892960
BARRY TOWN . . . . Jenner Park Athletic Stadium, Barry Road, Barry CF62 9BG. 01446 735858
BRIDGEND TOWN . . . . The Brewery Field, Tondu Road, Bridgend CF35 6HD 01656 669478/662602
BRYNTIRION ATHLETIC . . . . Bryntirion Park, Llangewydd Rpad, Bryntirion, Bridgend CF31 4JU 01656 652702
CAERAU ELY. . . . . Cwrt-y-Ala, Ely, Cardiff CF5 5QT 07788 585726
CALDICOT TOWN. . . . . Jubilee Way, Caldicot NP26 4NA 07802 665937
CAMBRIAN & CLYDACH VALE BGC . . . . Highfield Road, Clydach Vale, Tonypandy CF40 2XX 07980 558495
CARDIFF CORINTHIANS . . . . Riverside Ground, Station Road, Radyr, Cardiff CF15 8AB 02920 843407
CWMBRAN CELTIC . . . . Celtic Park, Henllys Way, Cwmbran NP44 7LP. 07968 947897
GARDEN VILLAGE . . . . Stafford Common, Victoria Road, Kingsbridge, Gorseinon, Swansea SA4 3AB 01792 533188
GOYTRE UNITED . . . . Glenhafod Park, Goytre, Port Talbot SA13 2YP 01639 898983/895615
PENRHIWCEIBER RANGERS. . Glasbrook, Glasbrook Terrace, Penrhiwceiber, Mountain Ash CF45 3SY. 07774 743840
PONTARDAWE TOWN . . . . Recreation Ground, Alloy Industrial Estate, Pontardawe SA8 4HL 01792 862228
TAFFS WELL . . . . Rhiw Dda'r, Parish Road, Taffs Well, Cardiff CF15 7SA. 02920 811080
WEST END . . . . Pri Deri Park, Eigen Crescent, Mayhill, Swansea SA1 6LB 07754 537012

IN: Caerau Ely (P), Cwmbran Celtic (P), Penrhiwceiber Rangers (P)

*OUT: *Bettws (R), Caerleon (R), Dinas Powys (R), *Ely Rangers (R), Ton Pentre (R)*

** - SUBJECT TO APPEAL*

Division Two	P	W	D	L	F	A	Pts
Penrhiwceiber Rgrs	34	21	8	5	79	53	71
Cwmbran Celtic	34	21	6	7	75	33	69
Caerau Ely	34	18	7	9	82	53	61
AFC Llwydcoed	34	17	4	13	74	62	55
Ammanford	34	16	6	12	67	47	54
Croesyceiliog	34	13	13	8	58	42	52
Treharris A. Western	34	15	6	13	69	67	51
AFC Porth	34	14	7	13	47	49	49
Llangeinor	34	15	2	17	47	59	47
Newport YMCA	34	11	13	10	54	52	46
Newcastle Emlyn	34	13	6	15	54	57	45
UWIC	34	11	11	12	57	59	44
Cardiff Bay Quins	34	11	9	14	52	66	42
Cwmbran Town	34	10	7	17	47	62	37
Llanwern	34	10	7	17	52	77	37
Tredegar Town	34	6	14	14	35	46	32
Maesteg Park	34	7	11	16	51	72	32
Porthcawl Town	34	6	5	23	34	78	23

NATHANIAL CAR SALES LEAGUE CUP

(all teams in league)

FIRST ROUND
Aberbargoed Buds 3 **Croesyceiliog** 4
Afan Lido 3 Pentwyn 1
Barry Town 1 Risca United 0
Bettws 0 Corus 0 aet (6-5p)
Bridgend 1 Aberaman 0
Bryntirion 4 Maesteg Park 0
Caldicot 3 Penrhiwceiber 1
Cambrian/C. 4 Pontypridd 1
Cwmaman I. 2 Cwmbran C. 1
Cwmbran T. 0 **Ammanford** 2 *aet*
Ely R. 1 **Llwydcoed** 2 *aet*
Garden Village 0 **Porthcawl** 2
Garw 1 **Treharris Athletic** 5
Goytre 4 Cwmaman United 2
Llangeinor 1 Troedyrhiw 0
Llantwit Fardre 0 **Abertillery Bluebirds** 1 *aet*
Newcastle Emlyn 3 Newport YMCA 3 *aet* (4-3p)
Newport CS 1 **Pontardawe** 2
Seven Sisters 1 **AFC Porth** 2
Taffs Well 3 Caerau Ely 2
UWIC 0 **Llanwern** 1
West End 5 Tredegar Town 1

SECOND ROUND
Afan Lido 3 Cardiff Bay 1
Barry Town 3 Dinas Powys 0
Bryntirion Ath. 3 Goytre 2
Caerleon 1 **Cardiff Corithians** 1 *aet* (6-7p)
Caldicot Town 1 **Llangeinor** 2
Cambrian/C. 5 Briton Ferry 0
Croesyceiliog 1 Bettws 0
Cwmaman 2 **Bridgend** 3 *aet*
Goytre Utd 5 Llanwern 3 *aet*
Monmouth Town 2 **AFC Llwydcoed** 3 *aet*
Newcastle E. 3 **AFC Porth** 4 *aet*
Pontardawe 1 **Ammanford** 2
Pontyclun 1 **Abertillery** 5
South Gower 2 Taffs Well 1
Ton Pentre 1 **West End** 6
Treharris 3 **Porthcawl** 4 *aet*

THIRD ROUND
Afan Lido 2 Abertillery 1 *aet*
AFC Porth 5 Porthcawl 1
Ammanford 2 **Goytre Utd** 3 *(at Goytre United)*
Barry Town 4 Bryntirion 2
Bridgend Town 3 West End 0
Cambrian/C. 3 Sth Gower 1
Cardiff Cor. 3 **Llwydcoed** 4
Llangeinor 0 **Croesyceiliog** 2

QUARTER-FINALS
Afan Lido 5 Llwydcoed 3 *aet*
AFC Porth 1 **Croesyceiliog** 2
Bridgend 1 **Barry** 1 *aet* (2-4p)
Goytre Utd 4 Cambrian/C. 1

SEMI-FINALS
Barry T. 1 **Croesyceiliog** 2 *(at Taffs Well)*
Goytre United 1 Afan Lido 0 *(at Maesteg Park)*

FINAL
(May 25th at Bridgend Town)
Goytre Utd 1 **Croesyceiliog** 3

	Llwy	Porth	Amm	Caer	CBay	Croe	CC	CT	Lgr	Lwn	Mae	NE	Nwp	Pen	Por	Tdg	Treh	UWC
AFC Llwydcoed		3-1	4-3	0-2	1-3	3-4	0-1	3-0	4-2	3-2	2-1	3-3	3-2	2-2	4-1	4-1	4-5	2-1
AFC Porth	0-1		0-2	0-2	2-0	2-3	2-2	0-3	2-0	2-0	2-2	2-1	2-2	2-1	3-1	1-0	0-2	3-2
Ammanford	2-1	4-1		0-3	1-2	0-2	2-1	0-2	4-0	2-1	6-0	0-2	0-1	0-1	8-2	1-1	2-0	2-3
Caerau Ely	2-0	1-2	3-2	***D***	3-3	1-3	3-0	3-1	1-2	3-0	3-1	1-3	3-3	3-5	3-0	2-1	5-1	3-3
Cardiff Bay Quins	2-0	0-0	0-4	0-3	***I***	1-0	0-2	1-2	4-0	4-0	1-3	2-1	2-2	0-4	0-0	1-1	1-2	1-0
Croesyceiliog	0-1	0-0	1-2	1-1	4-1	***V***	1-0	3-1	1-0	1-1	1-2	2-2	1-1	1-3	4-0	1-0	5-0	0-0
Cwmbran Celtic	2-1	3-1	4-0	1-2	5-0	1-2	***I***	1-1	3-0	6-0	6-2	1-1	2-2	1-3	4-0	1-0	2-0	1-0
Cwmbran Town	0-2	0-2	0-1	3-3	2-1	1-1	2-3	***S***	1-2	0-2	3-3	4-1	1-1	0-2	2-1	0-1	0-3	0-2
Llangeinor	1-2	0-2	1-0	3-4	3-1	2-1	1-2	1-4	***I***	3-1	1-0	3-1	0-2	2-3	2-1	2-2	0-2	1-0
Llanwern	3-3	4-2	0-3	4-3	2-5	3-3	0-3	3-2	0-2	***O***	2-1	1-3	3-1	0-0	1-2	1-0	2-4	3-3
Maesteg Park	0-2	1-0	1-2	1-1	3-3	3-1	1-3	2-2	1-1	1-2	***N***	1-2	2-0	1-1	2-4	1-1	2-5	2-4
Newcastle Emlyn	3-1	1-2	1-1	2-0	2-2	2-1	1-3	1-2	0-1	2-1	0-1		1-3	2-3	1-0	2-0	1-2	3-2
Newport YMCA	3-2	1-3	1-1	3-2	4-1	2-2	1-1	3-1	0-3	3-0	0-0	0-1	***T***	4-2	2-3	1-0	1-0	1-3
Penrhiwceiber Rgrs	4-3	2-1	3-5	0-3	5-2	2-2	1-1	5-2	1-0	1-4	3-0	3-1	3-2	***W***	2-1	1-0	1-1	2-0
Porthcawl Town	1-5	0-3	1-3	0-4	0-2	1-3	0-2	0-1	2-3	0-1	0-0	0-3	0-0	1-1	***O***	0-2	2-1	2-0
Tredegar Town	1-2	0-0	0-0	1-1	2-2	1-1	0-3	1-1	4-2	1-1	3-1	1-1	1-1	2-3	1-5		1-0	4-1
Treharris Athletic W.	3-2	4-1	2-2	0-3	2-3	1-1	2-1	2-3	1-2	3-2	5-5	4-1	2-0	3-3	3-1	1-1		2-4
UWIC	1-1	1-1	2-2	4-2	1-1	1-1	1-3	2-0	2-1	2-2	0-4	4-2	1-1	1-3	2-2	1-0	3-1	

WELSH LEAGUE DIVISION TWO CONSTITUTION 2010-11

AFC LLWYDCOED . . . . Llwydcoed Football Ground, Merthyr Road, Llwydcoed, Aberdare CF44 0UT 01685 873924
AFC PORTH . . . . Dinas Park, Dinas, Porth, Rhondda CF40 1JG 07974 252940
ABERBARGOED BUDS . . . . Recreation Ground, Bedwellty Road, Aberbargoed CF81 9AY 07773 407902
ABERTILLERY BLUEBIRDS . . . . Cwmnantygroes Field, Six Bells, Abertillery NP13 2PW 01495 213999
AMMANFORD . . . . Ammanford Recreation Ground, Manor Road, Ammanford SA18 3AP 07749 261362
* BETTWS . . . . North Site, Bettws Road, Bettws, Bridgend CF32 8SG 07887 530804
CAERLEON . . . . Cold Bath Road, Caerleon, Newport NP18 1NF 01633 420074
CROESYCEILIOG . . . . Woodland Road, Croesyceiliog, Cwmbran NP11 2DZ 01633 485157
CWMAMAN INSTITUTE . . . . Canolfan Cwmaman, Glanaman Rd, Cwmaman, Aberdare CF44 6HY 07786 588890
DINAS POWYS . . . . The Murch, Sunnycroft Lane, Dinas Powys CF64 4QQ 07852 488552
* ELY RANGERS . . . . Station Road, Wenvoe, Cardiff CF5 6AG 02920 598725
LLANGEINOR . . . . Llangeinor Park, Bettws Road, Llangeinor, Bridgend CF32 8NU 01656 871676
NEWCASTLE EMLYN . . . . Parc Emlyn, Lower Car Park, New Road, Newcastle Emlyn SA38 9BG 01239 710994
NEWPORT YMCA . . . . Mendalgief Road, Newport NP20 2HF 01633 266872
TON PENTRE . . . . Ynys Park, Sawmill Villas, Llanfoist Street, Ton Pentre CF41 7AF 01443 442625/432813
TREHARRIS ATHLETIC WESTERN. . . Athletic Ground, Commercial Terrace, Treharris CF46 5PY 07960 079887

*IN: Aberbargoed Buds (P), Abertillery Bluebirds (P), *Bettws (R), Caerleon (R), Cwmaman Institute (P), Dinas Powys (R), *Ely Rangers (R), Ton Pentre (R)*

*OUT: Caerau Ely (P),*Cardiff Bay Harlequins (R), Cwmbran Celtic (P), *Cwmbran Town (R), *Llanwern (R), Maesteg Park (W), Penrhiwceiber Rangers (P), Porthcawl Town (R), *Tredegar Town (R), *UWIC (R)*

** - SUBJECT TO APPEAL*

Division Three	**P**	**W**	**D**	**L**	**F**	**A**	**Pts**
Aberbargoed Buds	**34**	**21**	**7**	**6**	**74**	**41**	**70**
Abertillery Bluebirds	**34**	**22**	**3**	**9**	**81**	**38**	**69**
Cwmaman Institute	**34**	**19**	**11**	**4**	**70**	**34**	**68**
Briton Ferry Llansawel	**34**	**19**	**7**	**8**	**65**	**48**	**64**
Pontypridd Town	**34**	**18**	**9**	**7**	**67**	**41**	**63**
Corus Steel	**34**	**16**	**8**	**10**	**53**	**42**	**56**
Cwmamman United	**34**	**16**	**8**	**10**	**61**	**55**	**56**
Monmouth Town	**34**	**15**	**6**	**13**	**82**	**71**	**51**
Goytre	**34**	**14**	**6**	**14**	**66**	**69**	**48**
South Gower	**34**	**13**	**8**	**13**	**61**	**63**	**47**
Newport Civil Service	**34**	**14**	**4**	**16**	**50**	**55**	**46**
Seven Sisters	**34**	**13**	**6**	**15**	**62**	**58**	**45**
Pontyclun	**34**	**12**	**5**	**17**	**58**	**62**	**41**
Troedyrhiw	**34**	**10**	**7**	**17**	**56**	**75**	**37**
Llantwit Fardre	**34**	**9**	**9**	**16**	**46**	**60**	**36**
Risca United	**34**	**8**	**7**	**19**	**47**	**65**	**31**
Pentwyn Dynamos	**34**	**5**	**3**	**26**	**56**	**109**	**18**
Garw SBGC	**34**	**3**	**4**	**27**	**50**	**119**	**13**

CLASSIC SPORTWEAR RESERVES CUP

FINAL *(May 21st at Afan Lido)*

West End Res. 2 Cardiff Corinthians Res. 1

Reserve Division East	P	W	D	L	F	A	Pt
Cwmbran Celtic Res.	24	19	1	4	72	30	58
Ely Rangers Res.	24	14	6	4	68	38	48
Croesyceiliog Res.	24	15	2	7	66	37	47
Caldicot Town Res.	24	13	5	6	73	33	44
Monmouth Town Res.	24	11	7	6	70	57	40
Abertillery Bluebirds Res.	24	11	7	6	54	50	40
Newport YMCA Res.	24	10	7	7	49	48	37
Caerleon Res.	24	9	4	11	46	48	31
Dinas Powys Res.	24	8	6	10	48	51	30
Newport Civil Service Res.	24	6	3	15	48	70	21
Cwmbran Town Res.	24	4	7	13	28	58	19
Risca United Res.	24	3	4	17	31	67	13
Aberbargoed Buds Res.	24	3	1	20	23	89	10

Reserve Division West	P	W	D	L	F	A	Pt
Pontardawe Town Res.	22	17	3	2	72	21	54
Neath Res.	22	14	3	5	75	31	45
Garden Village Res.	22	14	3	5	74	33	45
West End Res.	22	12	2	8	72	40	38
Afan Lido Res.	22	11	4	7	62	51	37
South Gower Res.	22	8	6	8	55	57	30
Briton Ferry Llansawel Res.	22	8	4	10	37	44	28
Corus Steel Res.	22	8	2	12	36	66	26
Goytre United Res.	22	6	4	12	41	70	22
Newcastle Emlyn Res.	22	5	4	13	35	65	19
Ammanford Res.	22	4	3	15	25	57	15
Cwmamman United Res.	22	3	6	13	32	81	15

	Ab'bg	A'till'y	B.Fer	Corus	Cwml.	CwmU	Garw	Goyt.	L Far.	Monm	Newp	Pent	P'clun	P'prid	Risca	Sev S.	SGwr	Troed.
Aberbargoed Buds		1-1	3-2	2-2	0-2	2-0	5-0	0-2	0-0	2-0	2-1	5-0	1-1	2-2	2-1	2-0	4-1	3-0
Abertillery Bluebirds	3-1		2-3	0-1	0-1	5-3	4-0	0-1	4-2	5-0	3-1	3-0	2-0	0-2	2-0	2-0	3-0	2-1
Briton F. Llansawel	1-3	2-1	***D***	4-0	1-1	0-0	5-0	1-1	2-1	3-5	2-1	3-2	1-0	3-1	1-1	3-2	2-1	3-0
Corus Steel	1-1	4-1	0-0	***I***	2-1	1-2	2-0	2-3	0-1	2-1	4-0	3-0	2-1	2-1	2-1	2-2	1-2	0-0
Cwmaman Institute	0-1	1-1	1-1	1-2	***V***	1-0	6-0	2-0	2-2	3-1	1-1	1-1	1-2	2-1	4-3	2-1	1-0	3-0
Cwmamman United	0-2	0-0	5-6	1-0	2-2	***I***	3-1	0-0	4-2	3-2	2-1	3-2	2-1	2-0	4-1	3-1	1-0	1-1
Garw SBGC	3-5	1-5	2-3	2-3	1-4	1-0	***S***	1-6	0-0	2-5	2-5	6-2	3-4	1-1	1-2	1-6	1-4	1-1
Goytre	1-2	0-4	1-0	2-1	2-3	1-3	7-4	***I***	4-2	1-2	2-2	2-1	2-2	1-2	4-4	2-1	2-3	2-1
Llantwit Fardre	2-4	0-2	1-0	2-1	1-2	1-1	3-0	0-1	***O***	2-2	1-2	2-2	1-1	2-0	0-2	2-1	1-3	1-2
Monmouth Town	1-2	1-5	3-0	2-3	1-1	5-2	5-4	5-2	4-0	***N***	4-0	4-0	2-1	3-3	2-2	2-3	1-1	3-4
Newport Civil Serv.	1-2	0-3	1-0	1-2	0-4	2-0	2-1	3-0	3-0	1-0		5-1	1-0	0-2	2-0	1-3	1-1	1-2
Pentwyn Dynamos	2-3	1-3	6-1	4-5	0-3	1-2	2-1	2-5	1-5	3-6	3-2	***T***	1-6	1-4	0-1	2-3	2-2	3-1
Pontyclun	2-2	0-1	2-4	1-0	1-3	3-4	3-0	4-1	5-1	1-2	0-3	3-2	***H***	0-1	3-1	1-4	2-1	2-0
Pontypridd Town	1-0	4-1	0-2	0-0	1-1	4-3	4-1	2-0	0-0	4-1	2-2	0-4	5-0	***R***	5-0	2-1	5-2	1-1
Risca United	0-3	0-1	0-2	0-1	2-3	0-1	2-3	2-0	2-2	1-2	0-1	3-2	1-1	1-1	***E***	6-1	0-3	2-1
Seven Sisters	2-1	4-1	0-2	1-1	1-1	2-2	2-1	3-0	0-3	2-1	3-0	4-0	1-2	1-2	1-1	***E***	3-0	0-3
South Gower	3-0	1-6	0-0	1-1	1-1	1-1	7-4	4-4	1-2	0-1	3-2	2-1	2-0	0-2	2-1	3-2		2-3
Troedyrhiw	3-6	2-5	1-2	1-0	1-5	3-1	1-1	1-4	2-1	3-3	0-1	7-2	4-3	1-2	2-4	1-1	2-4	

WELSH LEAGUE DIVISION THREE CONSTITUTION 2010-11

BRITON FERRY LLANSAWEL . . . . Old Road, Briton Ferry, Neath SA11 2HA 07952 777361
CAERAU UNITED. . . . . Athletic Ground, Humphries Terrace, Caerau, Bridgend CF34 0SG 01656 732471
* CARDIFF GRANGE HARLEQUINS Cardiff International Stadium, Leckwith Road, Cardiff CF11 8AZ 02920 788399
CORUS STEEL. . . . . Corus Sports Ground, Margam, Port Talbot SA13 2NF 01639 882066
CWMAMMAN UNITED. . . . . Grenig Park, Penpound Lane, Glanaman, Ammanford SA18 1EJ. 07977 925808
* CWMBRAN TOWN. . . . . Cwmbran Stadium, Henllys Way, Cwmbran NP44 3XL. 01633 627100
GOYTRE. . . . . Plough Road, Penperlleni, Pontypool NP4 0AL. 07790 419852
* LLANWERN . . . . Newport Stadium, Spytty Park, Langland Way, Newport NP19 0PT 07762 013310
MONMOUTH TOWN . . . . Monmouth Sports Ground, Chippenham, Monmouth NP25 5EY 07990 800939
NEWPORT CIVIL SERVICE . . . . Civil Service Sports Club, Shannon Close, Bettws NP20 6LX 08457 555555
PONTYCLUN . . . . The Ivor Park, Cowbridge Road, Pontyclun CF72 9BS. 07814 214383
PONTYPRIDD TOWN . . . . Ynysangharad Park, Pontypridd CF37 4PE 01443 486571
PORTHCAWL TOWN ATHLETIC. . . . . Locks Lane, Porthcawl CF36 3HY. 07866 545830
RISCA UNITED. . . . . Ty-Isaf Park, Isaf Road, Risca, Newport NP11 6EG 07950 753629
SOUTH GOWER. . . . . South Gower Sports Club, Scurlage, Gower, Swansea SA3 1BA 01792 390857
* TREDEGAR TOWN . . . . Tredegar Leisure Complex, Stable Lane, Tredegar NP22 4BH. 01495 723554
TREOWEN STARS. . . . . Bush Park, Newbridge NP11 3RH. 01495 248249
* UWIC. . . . . Cyncoed Campus, UWIC, Cyncoed Road, Cardiff CF23 6XD 02920 416777

IN: Caerau United (South Wales Amateur League Division One), Cardiff Bay Harlequins (R), Cwmbran Town (R), Llanwern (R), Porthcawl Town (R), Tredegar Town (R), Treowen Stars (P - Gwent County League Division One), UWIC (R)

*OUT: Aberbargoed Buds (P), Abertillery Bluebirds (P), Cwmaman Institute (P), Garw SBGC (R - Neath & District League Premier Division), *Llantwit Fardre (R - South Wales Amateur League Division One), *Pentwyn Dyamos (R - South Wales Senior League Division One), *Seven Sisters (R - South Wales Senior League Division One), Troedyrhiw (R - South Wales Amateur League Division One)*

Cardiff Bay Harlequins become Cardiff Grange Harlequins, Porthcawl Town become Porthcawl Town Athletic

** - SUBJECT TO APPEAL*

WELSH ALLIANCE

welshallianceleague.pitchero.com

Sponsored by: Lock Stock

Founded: 1935

Recent champions:
2005: Bodedern
2006: Prestatyn Town
2007: Denbigh Town
2008: Bethesda Athletic
2009: Bethesda Athletic

	Amlwch Town	Barmouth & D.	Blaenau Ffest.	Conwy United	Glan Conwy	Halkyn United	Holywell Town	Llanberis	Llandudno J.	Llandyrnog Utd	Llanrug United	Llanrwst United	Nantlle Vale	Nefyn United	Pwllheli	Rhydymwyn
Amlwch Town		0-4	0-3	1-5	0-2	5-1	2-5	3-2	0-5	1-7	1-2	0-5	4-1	0-1	0-5	0-3
Barmouth & Dyffryn Utd	2-0		1-2	4-2	2-4	4-0	1-1	5-0	1-2	5-0	2-1	3-0	2-1	0-0	1-1	1-3
Blaenau Ffestiniog Amats	5-1	0-2		0-3	3-3	3-1	1-3	4-0	0-1	2-4	3-4	2-0	8-2	1-1	1-5	3-6
Conwy United	5-0	0-0	4-0		0-1	5-2	4-1	2-2	0-1	3-2	2-2	2-1	0-0	0-1	2-1	1-1
Glan Conwy	3-1	3-4	5-3	2-3		9-1	3-2	2-2	2-1	6-0	3-4	3-1	6-2	4-2	3-2	0-2
Halkyn United	4-1	0-4	3-4	1-3	1-2		1-5	3-3	0-12	2-3	3-4	0-2	3-0	3-1	0-5	1-1
Holywell Town	3-2	3-1	5-0	0-0	1-2	10-0		0-1	4-1	1-1	1-1	4-3	4-1	5-0	2-2	0-1
Llanberis	3-0	3-2	4-1	3-3	1-3	8-1	3-2		0-6	3-2	4-2	1-2	3-1	1-3	4-1	2-6
Llandudno Junction	7-0	3-1	4-3	2-2	2-0	7-0	4-1	0-0		3-1	1-2	0-0	4-4	3-1	2-2	1-3
Llandyrnog United	1-2	0-1	1-1	0-5	0-2	2-1	1-1	1-1	1-0		0-2	1-1	0-3	3-4	2-2	2-1
Llanrug United	6-1	1-3	4-0	2-2	1-3	4-2	1-3	2-2	1-2	4-0		3-0	5-0	0-1	0-4	1-2
Llanrwst United	3-2	1-1	1-0	2-2	2-0	5-0	2-1	2-2	2-1	2-1	2-2		3-0	2-1	1-3	0-3
Nantlle Vale	3-3	0-1	0-5	1-5	0-4	3-1	0-2	1-8	1-3	2-1	0-2	1-1		1-2	0-5	0-7
Nefyn United	4-0	3-4	4-0	0-5	2-2	3-1	1-0	1-3	2-2	2-3	1-1	3-4	2-0		2-4	2-0
Pwllheli	5-0	1-3	2-0	0-0	3-5	4-0	2-1	3-0	0-2	0-0	0-1	1-3	3-0	4-0		3-2
Rhydymwyn	11-0	3-1	1-4	3-1	5-1	1-0	1-1	0-2	2-1	3-2	3-0	1-0	3-0	3-0	0-0	

		P	W	D	L	F	A	Pts
Rhydymwyn		30	21	4	5	81	30	67
Glan Conwy		30	20	3	7	88	53	63
Llandudno Junction		30	17	6	7	83	36	57
Barmouth & Dyffryn Utd		30	17	5	8	66	38	56
Conwy United		30	14	11	5	71	36	53
Pwllheli		30	15	7	8	73	37	52
Llanrwst United		30	14	7	9	53	44	49
Llanrug United		30	14	6	10	65	51	48
Llanberis		30	13	8	9	71	64	47
Holywell Town		30	13	7	10	72	43	46
Nefyn United		30	12	5	13	50	59	41
Blaenau Ffestiniog Ams		30	10	3	17	62	75	33
Llandyrnog United		30	7	7	16	42	66	28
Nantlle Vale		30	3	4	23	28	100	13
Amlwch Town		30	4	1	25	30	116	13
Halkyn United	*-3*	30	3	2	25	36	123	8

G A MORTIMERS NORMAC PRECISION COOKSON CUP

FIRST ROUND

Amlwch Town 0 **Blaenau Ffestioniog Amateurs** 5
Conwy United 4 Rhydymwyn 1
Halkyn United 1 **Barmouth & Dyffryn United** 2
Holywell United 2 Llanrwst United 1
Llanberis 0 **Glan Conwy** 4
Llanrug United 0 **Llandyrnog United** 1
Nantlle Vale 1 **Nefyn United** 2 *aet*
Pwllheli 3 **Llandudno Junction** 4

QUARTER-FINALS

Blaenau Ffestiniog Amateurs 1 **Holywell Town** 0
(Blaenau Ffestiniog Amateurs expelled)
Conwy United 2 Nefyn United 1
Glan Conwy 6 Barmouth & Dyffryn United 0
Llandudno Junction 3 Llandyrnog United 2

SEMI-FINALS

Glan Conwy 1 **Conwy United** 2
Holywell Town 0 **Llandudno Junction** 3

FINAL

(March 18th at Llandudno Town)
Conwy United 1 Llandudno Junction 0

WELSH ALLIANCE DIVISION ONE CONSTITUTION 2010-11

BARMOUTH & DYFFRYN UNITED . . . . Wern Mynach, Park Road, Barmouth LL42 1PL . . . . None
BETHESDA ATHLETIC . . . . Parc Meurig Park, Bethesda, Bangor LL57 3NT . . . . None
CAERNARFON TOWN . . . . The Oval, Marcus Street, Caernarfon LL55 2HT 01286 676885
CONWY UNITED . . . . The Morfa, Penmaen Road, Conwy LL32 8HA 01492 573080
DENBIGH TOWN . . . . Central Park, Park Street, Denbigh LL16 3DD 01745 812505
GLAN CONWY . . . . Cae Ffwt, Llanrwst Road, Glan Conwy, Colwyn Bay LL28 5SP . . . . None
GWALCHMAI . . . . Maes Meurig, Gwalchmai, Holyhead LL65 4SA . . . . None
HOLYHEAD HOTSPUR . . . . The New Stadium, Kingsland, Holyhead LL65 2YE 01407 764111
HOLYWELL TOWN . . . . Halkyn Road, Holywell CH8 7SJ . . . . None
LLANBERIS . . . . Ffordd Padarn, Llanberis, Caernarfon LL55 4SU . . . . None
LLANDUDNO JUNCTION . . . . The Flyover, Victoria Drive, Llandudno Junction LL31 9PG . . . . None
LLANFAIRPWLL . . . . Maes Eilian, Ffordd Caergybi, Llanfairpwllgwyngyll LL61 5YG . . . . None
LLANRUG UNITED . . . . Eithin Duon, Llanrug, Caernarfon LL55 4DA 01286 677543
LLANRWST UNITED . . . . Gwydyr Park, Llanrwst LL26 0PN . . . . None
NEFYN UNITED . . . . Caer Delyn, Nefyn, Pwllheli LL53 6HA . . . . None
PWLLHELI . . . . Dwyfor Leisure Centre, Recreation Road, Pwllheli LL53 5PF 01758 613437

IN: Bethesda Athletic (R - Cymru Alliance), Caernarfon Town (R - Cymru Alliance), Denbigh Town (R - Cymru Alliance), Gwalchmai (P - Gwynedd League), Holyhead Hotspur (R - Cymru Alliance), Llanfairpwll (R - Cymru Alliance)
OUT: Amlwch Town (R - Division Two), Blaenau Ffestiniog Amateurs (R - Division Two), Halkyn United (R - Division Two), Llandyrnog United (R - Division Two), Nantlle Vale (R - Division Two), Rhydymwyn (P - Cymru Alliance)

CLWYD LEAGUE

clwydfootballleague.co.uk

Sponsored by: MacKenzie Jones

Founded: 1973

Recent champions:
2005: ABS Sports
2006: Castle Rhuddlan
2007: Prestatyn Town Res.
2008: Prestatyn Town Res.
2009: Prestatyn Town Res.

	Abergele Rovers	Aston Park Rgrs	Brynford United	Connah's Quay T.	Greenfield	Llansannan	Mochdre Sports	Penmaenmawr P.	Rhuddlan Town	Shotton Steel	Sychdyn
Abergele Rovers	***P***	3-1	1-2	1-2	5-2	2-1	3-1	2-0	4-3	4-3	3-1
Aston Park Rangers	2-4	***R***	4-5	0-5	1-2	0-1	5-2	0-1	2-3	1-2	1-2
Brynford United	1-3	2-2	***E***	5-1	2-2	2-1	3-5	5-3	3-0	2-5	1-1
Connah's Quay Town	1-1	5-0	3-0	***M***	2-2	3-2	4-1	4-3	4-2	4-1	2-2
Greenfield	3-5	2-1	0-1	1-1	***I***	3-1	2-0	4-2	1-0	0-4	1-0
Llansannan	1-3	2-2	3-0	0-1	2-2	***E***	2-3	0-2	1-0	3-3	3-1
Mochdre Sports	1-3	6-0	2-0	1-2	4-1	4-2	***R***	5-2	4-2	1-1	4-0
Penmaenmawr Phoenix	2-0	2-0	5-0	3-7	3-7	2-2	3-1		1-3	3-2	2-0
Rhuddlan Town	3-4	2-5	2-1	1-4	1-0	1-2	2-1	5-4	***D***	7-1	3-4
Shotton Steel	0-0	2-5	2-0	3-2	1-1	2-0	2-2	6-4	2-4	***I***	1-1
Sychdyn	1-2	4-2	0-1	4-6	1-2	2-3	3-3	4-2	1-4	3-2	***V***

Premier Division	P	W	D	L	F	A	Pts
Abergele Rovers	20	15	2	3	53	31	47
Connah's Quay Town	20	14	4	2	63	33	46
Greenfield	20	9	5	6	38	37	32
Mochdre Sports	20	9	3	8	51	42	30
Rhuddlan Town	20	9	0	11	48	49	27
Shotton Steel	20	7	6	7	45	47	27
Brynford United	20	8	3	9	36	45	27
Penmaenmawr Phoenix	20	8	1	11	49	57	25
Llansannan	20	6	4	10	32	38	22
Sychdyn	20	5	4	11	35	48	19
Aston Park Rangers	20	3	2	15	34	57	11

PREMIER DIVISION CUP

FINAL *(April 30th at Prestatyn Town)*
Abergele Rovers 2 Connah's Quay Town 1

PRESIDENT'S CUP

FINAL *(May 14th at Flint Town United)*
Abergele Rovers 4 Shotton Steel 1

R.E.M. JONES CUP

FINAL *(April 23rd at Denbigh Town)*
St Asaph 3 Wepre Rangers 2

HALKYN CUP

FINAL *(April 16th at Halkyn United)*
FC Nomads 3 Rhuddlan Town Res. 1

CLWYD LEAGUE PREMIER CONSTITUTION 2010-11

ABERGELE ROVERS .... Parc Pentre Mawr, Abergele LL22 7RE .... None
ASTON PARK RANGERS.............. 33 Club, Shotton Lane, Shotton, Deeside CH5 1ST .... None
BRYNFORD UNITED .... Recreation Ground, Hafod-y-Bryn, Brynford, Holywell CH8 8AQ .... None
CAERWYS .... Lon Yr Ysgol, Caerwys, Mold CH7 5PZ .... None
LLANSANNAN.................. Cae Chwareuon, Maes Gogor, Llansannan, Conwy LL16 5LJ .... None
MELIDEN.................................. Dawson Drive, Prestatyn LL19 8SY .... None
MOCHDRE SPORTS........... Mochdre Sports Club, Swan Road, Mochdre, Colwyn Bay LL28 5HA 01492 546661
RHOS UNITED.................... Brookfield Drive, Rhos-on-Sea, Colwyn Bay LL28 4SB .... None
RHUDDLAN TOWN .... Pengwern College, Bodelwyddan Road, Rhuddlan, Rhyl LL18 5UH .... None
SHOTTON STEEL............. Deeside Leisure Centre, Chester Road West, Queensferry CH5 1SA 01244 845440
ST ASAPH.............................. Roe Plas Meadows, St Asaph LL17 0SU .... None
SYCHDYN .... Sychdyn Sports Association, Wat's Dyke Way, Sychdyn CH7 6DX .... None

IN: Caerwys (P), Meliden (P), Rhos United (P), St Asaph (P)

OUT: Connah's Quay Town (P - Welsh Alliance Division Two), Greenfield (P - Welsh Alliance Division Two), Penmaemawr Phoenix (P - Welsh Alliance Division Two)

Division One	P	W	D	L	F	A	Pt
St Asaph	22	19	2	1	96	18	59
Meliden	22	19	1	2	100	28	58
Caerwys	22	15	0	7	67	49	45
Rhos United	22	14	0	8	64	51	42
Point of Ayr	22	13	2	7	83	55	41
Mostyn Dragons	22	12	3	7	72	37	39
Wepre Rangers	22	10	0	12	52	57	30
Betws-yn-Rhos	22	8	0	14	50	78	24
Llannefydd	22	5	3	14	36	64	18
Y Glannau	22	5	1	16	34	72	16
Carrigydrudion	22	3	2	17	37	86	11
Bro Cernyw	22	1	2	19	25	121	5

Division Two	P	W	D	L	F	A	Pt
FC Nomads	20	20	0	0	100	15	60
Rhuddan T. Res.	20	15	1	4	85	38	46
Shotton S. Res.	20	11	3	6	63	45	36
Abergele Res. *-3*	20	11	1	8	42	40	31
Flint Town Utd A	20	9	3	8	43	42	30
Rhyl Athletic	20	8	4	8	57	54	28
Holywell T. Res.	20	8	2	10	39	66	26
Aston Park Res.	20	7	1	12	44	63	22
Con. Quay Tigers	20	6	3	11	34	52	21
Llanrwst Utd Res.	20	4	1	15	24	54	13
Flint Mountain	20	1	1	18	20	82	4

Reserve Division	P	W	D	L	F	A	Pt
Flint Town U. Res.	18	16	1	1	64	22	49
Prestatyn T. Res.	18	14	2	2	72	27	44
Denbigh T. Res.	18	12	1	5	60	34	37
Glan Conwy Res.	18	8	4	6	48	41	28
Llandudno J. Res.	18	7	3	8	46	32	24
Rhyl Res.	18	7	3	8	38	45	24
Gap Conn. Q. Res.	18	6	1	11	37	41	19
Llandudno T. Res.	18	5	3	10	42	40	18
Llandyrnog Res. *-3*	18	5	1	12	31	56	13
Halkyn Utd Res.	18	0	1	17	13	113	1

GWENT COUNTY LEAGUE

www.gwentfa.co.uk

Sponsored by: Welsh Autoparts

Founded: 1980

Recent champions:
2005: Clydach Wasps
2006: Aberbargoed Buds
2007: Newport Civil Service
2008: Newport Civil Service
2009: Abertillery Bluebirds

	Abercarn United	Abertillery Excelsior	Albion Rovers	Blaenavon Blues	Cefn Fforest	Chepstow Town	Clydach Wasps	Coed Eva Athletic	Cwmffrwdoer Sports	Govilon	Lliswerry	Mardy	Pentwynmawr Athletic	Spencer Youth & Boys	Treowen Stars	Undy Athletic
Abercarn United		4-1	0-0	2-0	1-2	2-2	1-2	5-2	3-0	7-2	3-2	1-0	1-1	2-1	0-2	2-4
Abertillery Excelsior	1-2		2-3	0-2	4-0	2-3	1-0	0-1	5-1	0-0	1-1	3-1	3-1	4-2	0-4	1-2
Albion Rovers	2-3	5-0	***D***	8-0	3-2	3-1	0-3	4-0	4-1	5-1	1-0	1-0	2-0	4-3	0-1	2-1
Blaenavon Blues	0-2	0-2	0-3	***I***	1-3	0-3	1-2	2-1	1-1	2-0	1-0	3-4	2-1	1-1	1-1	1-0
Cefn Fforest	0-4	1-1	0-8	0-2	***V***	2-4	1-4	2-4	3-5	1-6	2-7	2-3	3-0	2-2	0-1	1-1
Chepstow Town	1-2	2-1	1-2	3-0	3-1	***I***	3-1	6-4	2-0	3-0	3-2	8-0	4-3	6-1	1-3	3-3
Clydach Wasps	1-1	3-1	0-1	3-1	4-0	2-2	***S***	2-3	6-1	3-1	0-0	3-1	7-0	4-2	2-3	4-1
Coed Eva Athletic	0-1	5-2	1-1	1-1	2-1	3-4	6-3	***I***	5-1	1-3	2-2	3-5	1-3	4-2	2-2	2-1
Cwmffrwdoer Sports	4-2	1-2	3-4	2-4	2-1	2-4	0-3	3-4	***O***	1-4	1-1	4-1	3-1	3-1	0-0	3-5
Govilon	1-1	5-3	2-2	2-2	9-2	2-3	1-2	6-1	0-5	***N***	5-4	13-0	1-2	5-3	3-6	0-4
Lliswerry	2-2	1-2	2-4	2-1	6-0	1-1	1-2	4-2	3-0	2-0		5-2	1-1	8-0	1-2	1-1
Mardy	1-2	1-3	1-5	3-2	0-5	1-2	2-5	0-1	0-2	0-3	1-10	***O***	2-2	2-3	1-4	1-7
Pentwynmawr Athletic	2-3	1-1	1-4	4-2	3-5	1-2	2-2	2-1	6-2	1-3	1-6	4-3	***N***	7-1	1-5	3-1
Spencer Youth & Boys	1-2	1-4	1-3	4-2	1-1	1-2	1-3	4-4	5-2	1-1	3-2	4-2	2-2	***E***	2-5	0-3
Treowen Stars	1-5	5-1	2-1	3-2	2-0	0-2	1-3	4-1	8-2	3-2	3-0	4-0	3-0	8-1		3-2
Undy Athletic	4-4	1-0	0-3	4-1	3-2	3-5	1-1	2-0	4-0	2-2	1-2	1-3	3-1	5-0	1-2	

Division One	**P**	**W**	**D**	**L**	**F**	**A**	**Pts**
Treowen Stars	**30**	**24**	**3**	**3**	**91**	**37**	**75**
Albion Rovers	**30**	**23**	**3**	**4**	**88**	**32**	**72**
Chepstow Town	**30**	**22**	**4**	**4**	**89**	**48**	**70**
Clydach Wasps	**30**	**19**	**5**	**6**	**80**	**40**	**62**
Abercarn United	**30**	**18**	**7**	**5**	**70**	**42**	**61**
Undy Athletic	**30**	**13**	**6**	**11**	**71**	**53**	**45**
Lliswerry	**30**	**11**	**8**	**11**	**79**	**48**	**41**
Govilon	**30**	**11**	**6**	**13**	**83**	**72**	**39**
Coed Eva Athletic	**30**	**11**	**5**	**14**	**67**	**78**	**38**
Abertillery Excelsior	**30**	**11**	**4**	**15**	**51**	**59**	**37**
Pentwynmawr Athletic	**30**	**8**	**6**	**16**	**57**	**79**	**30**
Blaenavon Blues	**30**	**8**	**5**	**17**	**38**	**65**	**29**
Cwmffrwdoer Sports	**30**	**8**	**3**	**19**	**55**	**92**	**27**
Spencer Youth & Boys	**30**	**5**	**6**	**19**	**54**	**103**	**21**
Cefn Fforest	**30**	**5**	**4**	**21**	**45**	**96**	**19**
Mardy	**30**	**5**	**1**	**24**	**41**	**115**	**16**

GWENT COUNTY LEAGUE DIVISION ONE CONSTITUTION 2010-11

ABERCARN UNITED . . . . Welfare Ground, Abercarn, Blackwood NP12 3XX 01495 243047
ABERTILLERY EXCELSIOR . . . . Woodland Field, Cwmtillery, Abertillery NP13 1LA. 01495 215676
AC PONTYMISTER . . . . Pontymister Recreation Ground, Pontymister, Caerphilly NP11 6LT . . . . None
ALBION ROVERS. Kimberley Park, Malpas Road, Newport NP20 6WE . . . . None
BLAENAVON BLUES . . . . The Memorial Ground, Stable Road, Blaenavon, Pontypool NP4 9RQ . . . . None
CHEPSTOW TOWN. . . . . Larkfield Ground, Newport Road, Chepstow NP16 5PR 01291 629220
CLYDACH WASPS . . . . Recreation Ground, Park Crescent, Clydach, Abergavenny NP7 0LR . . . . None
COED EVA ATHLETIC. . . . . Cwmbran Park, Wesley Street, Cwmbran NP44 3LX. 01633 485491
CWMFFRWDOER SPORTS . Cwmffrwdoer Spts Grd, Gwenhallt Ind. Est., Cwmffrwdoer, Pontypool NP4 6TN . . . . None
GOVILON . . . . King George V Playing Fields, Govilon, Abergavenny NP7 9NU 01873 830516
LLISWERRY . . . . Spytty Park, Newport NP9 0RH 01633 281087
PILCS . . . . PILCS Sports & Social Club, New Road, Griffithstown, Pontypool NP4 0TL. 01495 762039
PENTWYNMAWR ATHLETIC . . Welfare Ground, High St, Pentwynmawr, Newbridge, Newport NP11 4HQ 01495 243403
SPENCER YOUTH & BOYS . . . . Ringland Park, Newport NP18 2TA. . . . . None
UNDY ATHLETIC . . . . Undy Playing Fields, The Causeway, Undy, Caldicot NP26 3EN 01633 881352

IN: AC Pontymister (P), PILCS (P)

OUT: Cefn Fforest (R), Mardy (R), Treowen Stars (P - Welsh League Division Three)

COUNTY MOTORS CUP

FIRST ROUND

Abergavenny 1 **Abertillery Excel.** 4
Crickhowell 0 **Undy Athletic** 3
Cromwell Youth 4 **Fairfield United** 6
Llanwern RTB 2 RTB Ebbw Vale 1
Malpas Gladiators 0 **Sudbrook CC** 1
Mardy 2 Clydach Wasps 1
Pentwynmawr 3 Albion Rovers 2
Pill 1 **Cwmffrwdoer Sports** 2
Rockfield Rovers 2 **Chepstow** 7
Rogerstone 0 **Spencer Yth & Boys** 1
Tranch 2 Villa Dino Christchurch 1
Trethomas Bluebirds 2 **PILCS** 4

SECOND ROUND

Abercarn United 5 New Inn 1
Abertillery Excelsior 6 Race 2
AC Pontymister 3 Govilon 1
Blaenavon Blues 2 Sebastopol 0
Chepstow Town 2 **Llanwern RTB** 3
Coed Eva Athletic 4 Fairfield Utd 2
Cwmffrwdoer 3 Underwood SC 2
Fleur-de-Lys Welfare 2 Pentwynmawr Athletic 0
Llanhilleth Ath. 6 Caldicot Castle 2
Newport Corinthians 2 Mardy 1
Panteg 1 **Undy Athletic** 4
PILCS 3 Trinant 0
Spencer Youth & Boys 0 **Lliswerry** 5
Sudbrook Cricket Club 6 Tranch 3
Treowen Stars 5 Lucas Cwmbran 0
Whiteheads 3 Cefn Fforest 1

THIRD ROUND

Abercarn United 2 **Lliswerry** 3
Abertillery Excelsior 2 Blaenavon 1
Llanwern RTB 0 **Fleur-de-Lys** 5
Newport Corinthians 3 Llanhilleth 2
PILCS 4 Cwmffrwdoer Sports 3
Treowen Stars 5 Sudbrook CC 3
Undy Athletic 4 **AC Pontymister** 6
Whiteheads 3 Coed Eva Athletic 2

QUARTER-FINALS

Fleur-de-Lys 1 Abertillery Excelsior 0
Lliswerry 2 **AC Pontymister** 3
PILCS 4 Newport Corinthians 3
Treowen Stars 3 Whiteheads 1

SEMI-FINALS

AC Pontymister 3 Fleur-de-Lys 2 *(at Llanhilleth Athletic)*
Treowen Stars 2 PILCS 1 *(at Abertillery Excelsior)*

FINAL *(May 21st at Abergavenny)*
Treowen Stars 2 AC Pontymister 0

Division Two	P	W	D	L	F	A	Pts
AC Pontymister	26	20	1	5	98	34	61
PILCS	26	18	5	3	84	34	59
Panteg	26	16	4	6	70	47	52
Sudbrook Cricket Club	26	15	1	10	87	64	46
Newport Corinthians	26	12	8	6	60	52	44
Tranch	26	13	4	9	78	58	43
Cromwell Youth	26	13	3	10	63	61	42
Fairfield United	26	11	4	11	60	62	37
RTB Ebbw Vale	26	9	4	13	62	66	31
Llanhilleth Athletic	26	7	8	11	57	67	29
Trethomas Bluebirds	26	6	4	16	39	79	22
Malpas Gladiators	26	6	2	18	43	97	20
Rogerstone Welfare	26	4	4	18	48	86	16
Trinant	26	4	4	18	60	102	16

Division Three		P	W	D	L	F	A	Pts
Fleur-de-Lys Welfare		26	20	2	4	84	38	62
Llanwern RTB	-3	26	20	3	3	97	29	60
Rockfield Rovers		26	18	3	5	94	44	57
Pill		26	16	6	4	89	30	54
Whiteheads		26	13	5	8	87	53	44
Abergavenny Thursdays		26	11	3	12	74	77	36
Lucas Cwmbran		26	10	5	11	68	75	35
Race		26	10	4	12	59	70	34
Villa Dino Christchurch		26	10	2	14	68	84	32
Underwood Social Club		26	8	7	11	64	87	31
Sebastopol		26	8	3	15	42	79	27
New Inn		26	6	2	18	36	93	20
Caldicot Castle		26	5	4	17	42	82	19
Crickhowell		26	0	5	21	35	98	5

	AC	Cro	Fai	Lla	Mal	New	PIL	Pan	RTB	Rog	Sud	Tra	Tre	Trin
AC Pontymister		3-0	8-0	4-2	6-0	2-1	1-2	3-5	5-2	7-1	2-1	3-2	8-0	2-3
Cromwell Youth	0-3	***D***	4-2	1-1	1-2	1-2	1-6	1-0	3-2	5-3	2-4	4-3	1-0	2-0
Fairfield United	1-0	2-4	***I***	2-2	4-3	1-1	3-2	2-4	4-0	0-2	2-3	1-2	8-0	6-4
Llanhilleth Athletic	2-7	0-3	1-1	***V***	3-1	4-4	2-2	1-2	1-2	5-2	1-5	1-1	5-1	5-4
Malpas Gladiators	1-7	5-8	1-5	1-2	***I***	3-4	1-1	2-4	1-5	3-1	3-8	1-9	1-0	4-3
Newport Corinthians	0-0	2-4	1-5	3-1	5-1	***S***	2-1	3-2	1-1	2-0	4-3	2-2	4-1	2-4
PILCS	1-2	2-1	4-1	1-1	0-0	5-1	***I***	4-2	5-0	4-3	6-2	5-0	6-2	2-2
Panteg	4-3	3-3	3-0	5-0	3-1	2-2	0-6	***O***	3-1	7-1	3-2	2-2	1-1	2-1
RTB Ebbw Vale	1-5	2-0	7-0	4-4	3-1	2-2	1-3	1-4	***N***	1-2	7-2	0-1	3-6	4-2
Rogerstone Welfare	1-2	3-3	3-3	1-6	2-3	0-1	2-4	3-1	1-4		3-4	2-3	4-3	3-5
Sudbrook Cricket Club	2-3	5-2	0-1	2-1	5-1	1-0	2-3	0-1	3-0	1-1	***T***	3-2	4-2	6-3
Tranch	1-2	3-1	1-2	3-1	6-0	1-5	1-2	1-3	4-3	5-2	7-5	***W***	4-4	4-1
Trethomas Bluebirds	0-3	0-3	1-0	2-1	1-0	1-2	0-3	0-3	1-1	3-1	2-3	1-6	***O***	3-0
Trinant	1-7	3-5	1-4	3-4	1-3	4-4	1-4	3-1	2-5	1-1	2-11	2-4	4-4	

GWENT COUNTY LEAGUE DIVISION TWO CONSTITUTION 2010-11

CEFN FFOREST . . . . Welfare Ground, Ty Isha Terrace, Cefn Fforest, Blackwood NP12 1ER. . . . . None
CROMWELL YOUTH . . . . Hartridge Comprehensive School, Ringland Way, Newport NP18 2TA . . . . None
FAIRFIELD UNITED . . . . Garndiffaith Ravine, Pontypool NP4 7RQ 01495 773745
FLEUR-DE-LYS WELFARE . . . . . Islwyn Park, Commercial Street, Pontllanfraith, Blackwood NP12 2BW. . . . . None
LLANHILLETH ATHLETIC . . . . . . Llanhilleth Park, Commercial Road, Llanhilleth, Abertillery NP13 2HT 01495 217840
MALPAS UNITED . . . . Westfield, Darwin Drive, Malpas, Newport NP20 6FR . . . . None
MARDY . . . . Mardy Playing Field, St Davids Road, Mardy, Abergavenny NP7 6PP . . . . None
NEWPORT CORINTHIANS . . . . Coronation Park, Stephenson Street, Newport NP19 0RB. 01633 274717
PANTEG. . . . . Panteg House Sports Ground, Greenhill Road, Griffithstown NP4 5BE. 01495 763605
RTB EBBW VALE . . . . Eugene Cross Park, Pontygof, Ebbw Vale NP23 5AZ 01495 302995
ROGERSTONE WELFARE. . Rogerstone Welfare Grounds, Tregwilym Rd, Rogerstone, Newport NP10 9EQ . . . . None
SUDBROOK CRICKET CLUB . . . . Sudbrook Cricket Club, Mill Lane, Caldicot NP26 4BN 01291 424801
TRANCH . . . . Tranch Recreation Ground, Wainfelin, Pontypool NP4 6AX . . . . None
TRETHOMAS BLUEBIRDS. . . . . Llanfabon Drive, Trethomas, Caerphilly CF83 8GJ. . . . . None

IN: Cefn Fforest (R), Fleur-de-Lys Welfare (P), Mardy (R)
OUT: AC Pontymister (P), PILCS (P), Trinant (R)
Malpas Gladiators become Malpas United

	Abergavenny	Caldicot Cas.	Crickhowell	Fleur-de0Lys	Llanwern RTB	Lucas C'bran	New In	Pill	Race	Rockfield R.	Sebastopol	Underwood	Villa Dino C.	Whiteheads
Abergavenny Thursdays		3-1	2-0	0-3	1-9	2-4	6-0	2-3	3-2	2-2	4-1	5-6	3-3	2-3
Caldicot Castle	1-2	***D***	2-2	0-1	0-4	3-2	1-2	0-2	3-1	0-3	3-0	1-2	1-3	3-6
Crickhowell	5-5	3-5	***I***	0-4	2-9	0-4	1-3	0-7	0-1	1-3	1-2	3-3	3-5	0-5
Fleur-de-Lys Welfare	3-0	5-0	2-1	***V***	2-1	9-1	3-0	1-0	5-2	0-1	3-0	9-2	4-0	0-0
Llanwern RTB	3-2	3-3	4-0	5-1		5-2	4-1	2-0	1-2	1-3	1-1	3-1	5-0	4-1
Lucas Cwmbran	3-2	1-3	2-1	2-4	0-3		8-4	4-5	5-3	4-4	2-1	2-2	3-2	1-1
New Inn	0-5	4-2	0-0	3-4	1-6	0-3		0-5	0-3	1-6	0-2	0-5	0-5	1-3
Pill	8-1	1-1	1-1	2-3	1-1	2-0	2-2		5-1	1-2	6-1	9-0	2-2	1-1
Race	3-5	3-3	5-2	1-3	0-5	2-1	5-2	1-4	***T***	1-2	1-2	2-2	0-4	2-1
Rockfield Rovers	3-5	12-1	8-4	5-3	1-3	5-2	3-2	0-2	4-4	***H***	0-1	5-1	7-0	4-0
Sebastopol	2-6	3-1	5-1	1-4	1-2	1-1	2-3	0-6	2-5	2-1	***R***	1-1	5-4	3-6
Underwood Social Club	4-2	3-1	2-0	3-3	1-3	3-3	1-3	1-6	3-4	1-2	3-2	***E***	7-3	2-2
Villa Dino Christchurch	3-1	6-3	4-2	3-4	0-6	2-4	3-4	2-4	1-3	0-4	6-0	4-3	***E***	3-1
Whiteheads	2-3	5-0	5-2	5-1	2-4	6-4	5-0	1-4	2-2	2-4	8-1	9-2	5-0	

GWENT COUNTY LEAGUE DIVISION THREE CONSTITUTION 2010-11

ABERGAVENNY THURSDAYS ...... Penypound Stadium, Pen-Y-Pound, Abergavenny NP7 7RN.................. 01873 856341
CALDICOT CASTLE .... Caldicot Castle Grounds, Caldicot NP26 4HU 01291 431584
LUCAS CWMBRAN .... Girlings Sports & Social, Edlogan Way, Cwmbran NP44 2JJ.................... 01633 861624
MARSHIELD .... Marshall Village Hall, Wellfield Road, Marshfield, Cardiff CF3 2UB .... None
NEW INN .... Woodfield Road Recreation Ground, New Inn, Pontypool NP4 0PS..................... 01495 755169
PILL .... Pill Sports Ground, Courtybella Terrace, Newport NP19 2LD 01633 662668
RACE....................... Coleg Gwent, Blaendare Road, Upper Race, Pontypool NP4 5YE 01495 333100
RHYMNEY........................ The Eisteddfod Field, Rhymney, Tredegar NP22 5HE .... None
ROCKFIELD ROVERS .... Rockfield Community Centre, Cornwallis Close, Monmouth NP25 5DN........................ None
SEBASTOPOL...................... Alexandra Road, Sebastopol, Pontypool NP4 4BJ.................................. None
TREVETHIN .... The Ruffets, Trevethin, Pontypool .... None
TRINANT .... Trinant Recreation, Trinant, Caerphilly NP11 3LG .... None
UNDERWOOD SOCIAL CLUB....... Larch Grove Playing Fields, Llanmartin, Newport NP20 6JB................... 01633 413506
WHITEHEADS .... Whiteheads Sports Ground, Park View, Bassaleg NP10 8LA 01633 893227

IN: Marshfield (P - Newport & District League Premier Division X), Rhymney (P - North Gwent League Premier Division), Trevethin (P - Gwent Central League Premier Division), Trinant (R)

OUT: Crickhowell (R - Gwent Central League Premier Division), Fleur-de-Lys Welfare (P), Llanwern RTB (R - Newport & District League Premier Division X), Villa Dino Christchurch (R - Newport & District League Premier Division X)

GWENT COUNTY FEEDER LEAGUES 2009-10

EAST GWENT LEAGUE
(Chepstow Racecourse)

Division One	P	W	D	L	F	A	Pt
Tippling	21	16	2	3	80	36	50
Thornwell R & W	21	14	1	6	75	38	43
Underwood Ath.	21	13	1	7	75	49	40
Portskewett/Sdbk	21	12	2	7	68	54	38
Chepstow Rovers	21	8	4	9	61	59	28
Bulwark	21	6	3	12	49	65	21
Mathern Wdrs	21	3	3	15	41	76	12
Severn Tunnel NPC	21	3	2	16	31	103	11

Division Two	P	W	D	L	F	A	Pt
Undy Athletic Res.	21	16	3	2	114	30	51
Tintern Abbey	21	14	4	3	123	24	46
Caldicot Town A	21	15	1	5	98	25	46
Chepstow T. Res.	21	15	0	6	82	35	45
Rockfield R. Res.	21	6	2	13	36	94	20
Sudbrook CC Res.	21	4	3	14	32	91	15
Cald. Castle Res.	21	3	3	15	31	96	12
Wyesham Wdrs	21	2	2	17	28	149	8

Division Three	P	W	D	L	F	A	Pt
Blackrock Rovers	21	18	0	3	102	20	54
Caldicot Town B	21	15	3	3	88	22	48
Chepstow Town A	21	13	4	4	102	35	43
S Tunnel NPC Res.	21	13	1	7	90	54	40
Undy Athletic A	21	11	2	8	78	59	35
Sudbrook CC A	21	5	0	16	40	101	15
Chepstow Athletic	21	4	0	17	49	112	12
Wyesham W. Res.	21	0	0	21	24	168	0

GWENT CENTRAL LEAGUE
(Knauf Insulation)

Premier Division		P	W	D	L	F	A	Pt
Trevethin		24	21	1	2	124	47	64
Pontypool Town		24	17	2	5	85	41	53
Pandy		24	14	3	7	64	45	45
Usk Town		24	10	3	11	79	68	33
Gilwern & District		24	8	4	12	55	79	28
Llanarth	*-12*	24	4	4	16	51	97	4
Llanfoist	*-3*	24	0	3	21	34	115	0

Division One		P	W	D	L	F	A	Pt
Clydach W. Res.		26	21	2	3	128	37	65
Goytre Res.		26	20	2	4	100	39	62
Tranch Res.		26	18	3	5	111	49	57
Panteg Res.	*-3*	26	19	1	6	126	43	55
PILCS Res.		26	15	6	5	89	41	51
Blaenavon Res.		26	14	5	7	77	49	47
Mardy Res.		26	14	2	11	76	69	44
Fairfield U. Res	*-3*	26	12	3	11	55	44	36
Govilon Res.		26	10	3	13	73	72	33
Sebastopol Res.		26	4	6	16	40	91	18
Race Res.		26	4	5	17	41	109	17
Cwm'doer Res.	*-6*	26	3	3	20	36	129	6
New Inn Res.	*-6*	26	3	2	21	37	123	5
A'gavenny Res.	*-12*	26	3	2	21	27	127	-1

Division Two		P	W	D	L	F	A	Pt
Prescoed		20	19	0	1	140	20	57
Clydach Wasps A		20	12	2	6	61	50	38
Pontypool Res.	*-3*	20	8	0	12	66	71	21
Trevethin Res.	*-9*	20	9	0	11	70	73	18
Usk Town Res.	*-6*	20	6	3	11	34	77	15
Llanarth Res.	*-3*	20	3	1	16	34	114	7

NORTH GWENT LEAGUE
(Ryan Transport)

Premier Division	P	W	D	L	F	A	Pt
Rhymney	18	17	1	0	102	11	52
Tredegar Athletic	18	15	2	1	76	18	47
Garnlydan Athletic	18	13	0	5	51	37	39
Nantyglo	18	9	1	8	52	45	28
Pantside	18	8	3	7	67	45	27
Cwm	18	7	2	9	45	51	23
Tredegar Arms	18	6	4	8	60	47	22
Castle Inn Briery Hill	18	4	2	12	34	67	14
Rassau Rangers	18	1	3	14	15	77	6
Dugout	18	1	0	17	13	117	3

Division One	P	W	D	L	F	A	Pt
Neaudd Wen	21	18	2	1	115	25	56
Brynmawr Town	21	16	1	4	106	51	49
Fleur-de-Lys Res.	21	14	2	5	60	40	44
The Oak	21	13	2	6	87	54	41
Pontllanfraith S'tns	21	8	1	12	55	65	25
PFS Athletic	21	7	0	14	58	61	21
Cuod Deon Drag.	21	3	0	18	22	112	9
King David	21	1	0	20	17	112	3

Reserve Division	P	W	D	L	F	A	Pt
A'tillery Excel. Res.	26	21	4	1	93	37	67
Trinant Ath. Res.	26	17	1	8	81	48	52
Abercarn Res.	26	16	2	8	86	50	50
Treowen S. Res.	26	14	6	6	75	41	48
Ynysddu C. Res.	26	15	3	8	88	57	48
Pentwynmawr Res.	26	15	3	8	64	47	48
Abertillery Excel. B	26	11	3	12	62	53	36
RTB E. Vale Res.	26	10	3	13	83	88	33
A'tillery B'bds Res.	26	9	4	13	62	75	31
Ynysddu Crus. A	26	9	3	14	57	97	30
Rhymney Res.	26	8	3	15	58	84	27
Llanhilleth A. Res.	26	9	0	17	60	91	27
Cefn Fforest Res.	26	5	3	18	43	92	18
Abertillery Excel. A	26	1	6	19	34	86	9

GWYNEDD LEAGUE

www.cynghrair-gwynedd-league.co.uk

Sponsored by:
Teejac Sports

Founded: 1983

Recent champions:
2005: Porthmadog Res.
2006: Pwllheli
2007: Barmouth & Dyffryn United
2008: Llanllyfni
2009: Blaenau Ffestiniog Amateurs

	Beaumaris	Bethel	Bodedern	B'newydd	Caer'fon	Gaerwen	G'chmai	Holyhead	L'fechan	L'stumdwy	Pentraeth	P'madog	U. Bangor
Beaumaris Town		2-2	2-2	8-0	3-2	0-4	2-5	3-1	4-0	5-2	n/a	5-2	4-2
Bethel	5-1		1-2	1-1	1-3	4-2	2-3	1-5	8-1	4-1	2-1	3-3	5-3
Bodedern Athletic	4-0	4-1		3-1	2-1	0-0	1-1	2-0	1-0	10-1	5-1	3-0	4-0
Bontnewydd	0-1	1-2	2-4		0-2	0-2	1-5	0-3	0-0	1-3	3-1	0-6	1-2
Caernarfon Wanderers	3-1	3-2	2-2	4-2		0-2	3-3	5-0	3-3	5-2	6-1	2-2	2-1
Gaerwen	2-1	0-3	0-6	3-3	2-2		0-0	2-3	1-0	2-2	n/a	3-3	3-0
Gwalchmai	1-1	2-2	3-1	6-2	1-0	6-1		1-0	5-0	2-1	3-0	7-2	3-0
Holyhead Hotspur Res.	4-1	0-5	0-2	2-1	0-1	1-2	3-1		3-0	4-1	4-0	2-0	2-1
Llanfairfechan Town	1-3	5-4	0-2	2-2	1-2	0-1	2-5	0-1		7-1	2-2	0-4	2-2
Llanystumdwy	3-5	0-0	1-2	2-1	3-3	1-4	0-1	2-2	1-4		1-0	1-2	1-1
Pentraeth Nurseries	1-5	0-0	0-0	n/a	0-4	n/a	0-7	3-2	3-3	3-8		2-3	4-3
Porthmadog Res.	1-8	0-4	2-1	4-0	4-0	1-1	1-2	0-2	3-0	2-2	n/a		2-4
University of Bangor	0-6	2-3	1-2	0-1	1-5	3-3	0-2	1-2	1-3	6-0	0-2	0-1	

	P	W	D	L	F	A	Pts
Gwalchmai	22	16	5	1	65	25	53
Bodedern Athletic	22	16	4	2	60	19	52
Holyhead Hotspur Res.	22	13	1	8	40	32	40
Beaumaris Town	22	12	3	7	66	46	39
Caernarfon Wanderers	22	11	6	5	53	38	39
Bethel	22	10	5	7	63	44	35
Gaerwen	22	9	8	5	40	39	35
Porthmadog Res.	22	8	5	9	45	50	29
Llanfairfechan Town	22	4	4	14	31	57	16
University of Bangor	22	3	3	16	31	57	12
Llanystumdwy	22	2	6	14	31	73	12
Bontnewydd	22	1	4	17	20	65	7

Pentraeth Nurseries - record expunged

BLACK DRAGON BADGES GWYNEDD PREMIER CUP

FIRST ROUND
Bethel 2 **Gaerwen** 2 *aet* (1-3p)
Gwalchmai 6 Porthmadog Res. 0
Holyhead Hotspur Res. 5 Bontnewydd 0
Llanystumdwy 1 **Bodedern Athletic** 1 *aet* (3-4p)
SEMI-FINALS *(played over two legs)*
Boderdern Athletic 0 Gwalchmai 3,
Gwalchmai 1 Bodedern Athletic 4 *aet* (4-2p)
Gaerwen 1 Holyhead Hotspur Res. 1,
Holyhead Hotspur Res. 0 Gaerwen 0 *aet* (5-4p)
FINAL *(April 21st at Llangefni Town)*
Holyhead Hotspur Res. 1 **Gwalchmai 1** *aet* (3-4p)

JOHN SMITHS GWYNEDD CUP

FIRST ROUND
Beaumaris Town 1 **Pentraeth Nurseries** 2
Bethel 1 **Gaerwen** 2
Bodedern Athletic 2 Llanystumdwy 2 *aet* (4-2p)
Gwalchmai 2 Caernarfon Wanderers 1
Holyhead Hotspur Res. 5 Llanfairfechan Town 1
QUARTER-FINALS
Bontnewydd 2 Porthmadog Res. 1
Gaerwen 1 Holyhead Hotspur Res. 2
(Holyhead Hotspur Res. expelled)
Pentraeth Nurseries 0 **Gwalchmai** 16
University of Bangor 2 Bodedern Athletic 1
SEMI-FINALS
Bontnewydd 1 **Gaerwen** 2
University of Bangor 1 **Gwalchmai** 2
FINAL *(May 11th at Llanfairpwll)*
Gwalchmai 1 Gaerwen 0

ERYRI SHIELD

FIRST ROUND
Caernarfon Wanderers 1 **Beaumaris Town** 5
SEMI-FINALS *(played over two legs)*
Llanfairfechan Town 2 University of Bangor 3,
University of Bangor 3 Llanfairfechan Town 2
Pentraeth Nurseries v Beaumaris Town (w/o)
FINAL *(April 28th at Bangor City)*
University of Bangor 1 **Beaumaris Town** 3

GWYNEDD LEAGUE CONSTITUTION 2010-11

BANGOR CITY RES. .... The Stadium, Farrar Road, Bangor LL57 1LJ. 01248 355852
BEAUMARIS TOWN .... Beach Road, Bangor LL57 1DG .... None
BETHEL .... Coed Boelyn, Bethel, Caernarfon LL55 1AX .... None
BONTNEWYDD .... Cae Stanley, Bontnewydd, Caernarfon LL55 2YA .... None
BRO GORONWY. .... Cae Nerys, Moelfre LL72 8NA .... None
GLANTRAETH. .... Trefdraeth, Bodorgan, Anglesey LL62 5EU 01407 840401
HOLYHEAD HOTSPUR RES. .... The New Stadium, Kingsland, Holyhead LL65 2YE 01407 764111
LLANFAIRFECHAN TOWN .... Recreation Ground, Station Road, Llanfairfechan LL33 0BD. .... None
LLANYSTUMDWY .... Parc Dwyfor, Llanystumdwy, Cricieth LL52 0SR .... None
PORTHMADOG RES. .... Y Traeth, Porthmadog LL49 9PP 01766 514687
UNIVERSITY OF BANGOR .... Maesglas Sports Field, Ffriddoedd Road, Bangor LL57 2EH. 01248 382571

IN: Bangor City Res. (P - Caernarfon & District League Division One), Bro Goronwy (P - Anglesey League), Glantraeth (N)
OUT: Bodedern Athletic (P - Welsh Alliance Division Two), Caernarfon Wanderers (P - Welsh Alliance Division Two), Gaerwen (P - Welsh Alliance Division Two), Gwalchmai (P - Welsh Alliance Division One), Pentraeth Nurseries (WS)

MID-WALES LEAGUE

Sponsored by: Spar

Founded: N/A

Recent champions:
2005: Aberystwyth Town Res.
2006: Llanrhaeadr
2007: Presteigne St Andrews
2008: Aberystwyth Town Res.
2009: Newtown Res.

	AbT	AbU	BS	Cae	Car	Dol	Dyf	Hay	Lfyl	Lrh	LV	Nbg	Nwt	Pen	Pre	Rha	TB	Wat
Aberystwyth Town Res.		0-2	1-0	1-0	3-1	3-1	0-4	2-1	2-1	4-1	4-1	3-3	1-1	4-3	4-4	5-0	1-1	3-0
Aberystwyth University	1-3		0-1	6-0	2-2	1-2	1-2	4-2	2-2	2-0	3-2	4-1	2-0	1-3	1-0	0-1	1-2	0-1
Bow Street	2-3	0-2		4-3	2-2	3-0	1-2	3-0	3-1	2-3	2-1	3-2	1-3	2-2	1-0	1-2	5-1	4-0
Caersws Res.	0-1	1-4	2-3		0-3	2-2	1-7	0-2	5-3	0-0	2-4	1-1	2-3	4-3	0-2	2-3	0-1	0-4
Carno	3-2	2-0	1-1	5-1		4-0	1-0	3-1	5-1	4-0	1-0	5-1	2-2	0-1	0-1	3-0	3-0	2-3
Dolgellau AA	4-3	1-2	1-3	2-1	2-3		2-1	1-3	3-1	2-4	1-6	1-2	2-3	1-3	1-3	2-3	2-2	2-4
Dyffryn Banw	1-3	3-0	3-3	8-0	2-1	3-3		4-1	9-1	2-1	1-2	1-4	4-1	3-4	0-2	3-3	3-2	0-2
Hay St Marys	3-1	3-0	3-1	3-2	0-1	5-3	1-3		4-0	0-0	2-4	6-0	3-1	5-6	0-1	1-2	2-3	2-1
Llanfyllin Town	4-4	0-3	0-8	6-1	1-6	1-1	3-3	0-3		0-2	1-4	1-0	2-4	2-2	2-4	0-5	1-3	0-4
Llanrhaeadr	4-0	3-0	2-3	4-0	2-0	1-0	1-2	2-1	1-0		4-4	6-1	2-1	2-2	3-1	1-2	2-2	3-1
Llansantffraid Village	3-3	4-2	1-2	4-1	2-0	8-0	1-3	4-0	5-1	2-0		6-2	3-0	3-3	1-7	2-1	5-1	2-4
Newbridge-on-Wye	1-4	1-2	3-4	3-6	0-2	4-1	0-0	4-2	2-0	1-2	2-1		1-5	0-2	1-1	2-3	2-2	0-1
Newtown Res.	1-2	2-0	0-1	3-0	1-2	5-0	0-1	2-2	3-2	0-1	0-1	2-3		0-4	6-2	4-4	0-0	1-0
Penparcau	0-0	3-1	3-2	3-1	4-3	4-1	3-0	3-2	14-0	0-1	3-1	7-0	2-1		0-3	3-2	1-2	3-0
Presteigne St Andrews	4-3	0-0	1-4	6-0	2-1	1-1	2-1	1-4	6-0	1-2	3-2	5-0	3-2	2-2		1-2	1-1	2-1
Rhayader Town	0-1	3-2	1-0	6-0	2-3	7-1	2-2	5-2	2-2	2-2	1-1	5-0	4-3	1-2	3-0		5-1	3-0
Tywyn & Bryncrug	1-1	3-0	1-3	5-1	0-0	2-1	5-1	1-5	7-1	2-1	3-3	10-0	2-1	2-3	3-1	1-2		3-0
Waterloo Rovers	2-2	1-3	1-4	4-0	1-2	3-1	1-1	5-2	1-1	3-3	1-1	2-1	0-0	3-0	0-0	0-2	1-2	

		P	W	D	L	F	A	Pts
Penparcau		34	22	6	6	101	55	72
Rhayader Town		34	21	6	7	89	53	69
Carno		34	20	5	9	76	40	65
Bow Street		34	20	4	10	82	51	64
Aberystwyth Town Res.		34	18	9	7	77	58	63
Llanrhaeadr		34	18	7	9	66	47	61
Presteigne St Andrews		34	17	7	10	73	52	58
Llansantffraid Village		34	17	6	11	94	64	57
Tywyn & Bryncrug		34	16	9	9	77	59	57
Dyffryn Banw		34	16	7	11	83	58	55
Waterloo Rovers		34	13	7	14	55	55	46
Aberystwyth University		34	14	3	17	54	54	45
Hay St Marys		34	14	2	18	76	73	44
Newtown Res.		34	11	6	17	61	61	39
Newbridge-on-Wye		34	7	5	22	48	106	26
Dolgellau AA		34	5	5	24	48	104	20
Caersws Res.		34	3	3	28	39	119	12
Llanfyllin Town	*-3*	34	2	7	25	41	131	10

LEAGUE CUP

PRELIMINARY ROUND

Newtown Res. 1 Waterloo Rovers 0 *aet*
Penparcau 5 Presteigne St Andrews 3

FIRST ROUND

Aberystwyth Town Res. 0 **Dyffryn Banw** 2
Aberystwyth University 5 **Rhayader** 5 *aet* (4-5p)
Bow Street (w/o) v Llanfyllin Town
Dolgellau AA 2 **Hay St Marys** 3
Llanrhaeadr 0 **Carno** 1
Llansantffraid Village 4 Caersws Res. 0
Penparcau 4 Newtown Res. 0
Tywyn & Bryncrug 4 Newbridge-on-Wye 1

QUARTER-FINALS

Bow Street 2 Tywyn & Bryncrug 1
Carno 1 **Llansantffraid Village** 1 *aet* (3-4p)
Penparcau 5 **Hay St Marys** 5 *aet* (4-5p)
Rhayader Town 1 **Dyffryn Banw** 2

SEMI-FINALS

Bow Street 2 Hay St Marys 1 *(at Newtown)*
Llansantffraid Village 2 Dyffryn Banw 1

FINAL *(May 3rd at Newtown)*

Llansantffraid Village 2 Bow Street 1

MID-WALES LEAGUE DIVISION ONE CONSTITUTION 2010-11

ABERYSTWYTH UNIVERSITY . . . . Vicarage Fields, Llanbadarn, Aberystwyth SY23 3AN 01970 623036
BERRIEW . . . . The Recreation Ground, Berriew, Welshpool SY21 8AL . . . . None
BOW STREET . . . . Cae Piod, Rhydypennau Playing Fields, Bow Street SY24 5AD . . . . None
BUILTH WELLS . . . . Lant Field, Pendre, Builth Wells LD2 3DG . . . . None
CARNO . . . . Ty Brith Field, Carno Community Centre, Carno SY17 5LH . . . . None
DOLGELLAU AA . . . . Cae Marian, Dolgellau LL40 1UU . . . . None
DYFFRYN BANW . . . . Cae Morfa, Banw Primary School, Llangadfan, Welshpool SY21 0NW 01938 820226
LLANIDLOES TOWN . . . . Victoria Park, Victoria Avenue, Llanidloes SY18 6AT 01686 412196
LLANRHAEADR . . . . The Recreation Field, Llanrhaeadr Ym Mochnant SY10 0DJ . . . . None
LLANSANTFFRAID VILLAGE . . . . Treflan, Llansantffraid SY22 6BJ . . . . None
NEWBRIDGE-ON-WYE . . . . Penbont Field, Newbridge-on-Wye LD1 6NB . . . . None
PENPARCAU . . . . Min-y-Ddol, Penparcau, Aberystwyth SY23 1RG . . . . None
PRESTEIGNE ST ANDREWS . . . . Llanandras Park, Clatterbrune Estate, Presteigne LD8 2LB 01544 267838
TYWYN & BRYNCRUG . . . . Cae Chwarae Bryncrug, Tywyn LL23 9PD . . . . None
WATERLOO ROVERS . . . . Maesydre Recreational Grounds, Welshpool SY21 7SU . . . . None

IN: Berriew (R - Cymru Alliance), Builth Wells (P - Mid-Wales League (South)), Llanidloes Town (P - Mid-Wales League (South))

OUT: Aberywyth Town Res. (W), Caersws Res. (R - Montgomeryshire Amateur League Division One), Hay St Marys (W), Llanfyllin Town (R - Division Two), Newtown Res. (R - Montgomeryshire Amateur League Division One), Rhayader Town (P - Cymru Alliance)

DIVISION TWO (New for 2010-11): Aberaeron (P - Cardiganshire League Division One), Abermule (P - Montgomeryshire Amateur League Division One), Bont (P - Aberystwyth & District League Division One), Four Crosses (P - Montgomeryshire Amateur League Division One), Kerry (P - Montgomeryshire Amateur League Division One), Llandrindod Wells (P - Mid-Wales League (South)), Llanfair United (P - Montgomeryshire Amateur League Division One), Llanfyllin Town (R), Meifod (P - Montgomeryshire Amateur League Division One), Montgomery Town (P - Montgomeryshire Amateur League Division One), Rhosgoch Rangers (P - Mid-Wales League (South)), Talgarth Town (P - Mid-Wales League (South)), Tregaron Turfs (P - Aberystwyth & District League Division One)

SOUTH WALES AMATEUR LEAGUE

www.southwalesamateurleague.co.uk

Sponsored by: Monnington Group

Founded: 1946

Recent champions:

2005: Cambrian & Clydach Vale B. & G.C.

2006: Llangeinor

2007: Cwmaman Institute

2008: AFC Porth

2009: Corus Steel

	AFC Bargoed Redz	Aber Valley YMCA	Baglan Dragons	Caerau United	Cardiff Draconians	Carnetown BGC	Kenfig Hill	Llantwit Major	Merthyr Saints	Rhoose	Rhydyfelin	Splott Albion	Trefelin BGC	Treforest	Turberville Arms	Ynysddu Crusaders
AFC Bargoed Redz		0-6	1-1	3-5	3-11	1-4	7-5	1-4	1-4	1-6	1-9	1-6	0-4	1-2	0-4	1-1
Aber Valley YMCA	8-0		2-3	1-4	2-2	1-1	1-2	0-2	6-2	0-0	1-2	3-3	3-0	1-1	6-2	5-0
Baglan Dragons	5-0	4-6	***D***	0-1	4-3	5-1	1-3	2-5	0-2	0-1	2-0	4-3	2-6	0-2	4-1	7-1
Caerau United	13-0	5-2	2-0	***I***	6-0	3-0	2-1	0-1	3-0	0-0	6-2	4-1	1-1	7-2	2-0	6-0
Cardiff Draconians	3-0	2-3	4-2	4-4	***V***	3-1	4-2	2-4	1-5	1-5	3-2	1-2	2-3	1-3	4-2	4-3
Carnetown BGC	3-2	1-2	1-2	2-2	4-2	***I***	2-3	2-5	8-4	1-1	3-3	1-0	0-5	3-2	3-3	3-3
Kenfig Hill	5-3	1-1	2-1	2-4	3-2	4-1	***S***	2-2	0-2	2-2	3-4	4-1	0-2	2-1	5-0	4-1
Llantwit Major	6-0	3-4	1-2	1-4	4-4	2-4	3-0	***I***	3-3	1-3	2-1	5-0	0-3	0-3	4-1	1-1
Merthyr Saints	6-3	2-3	1-1	2-11	2-3	2-2	1-1	2-1	***O***	0-6	2-2	7-6	2-6	0-4	4-1	6-3
Rhoose	10-0	3-2	3-1	2-2	0-1	7-0	2-3	1-0	7-3	***N***	3-0	2-1	0-0	1-1	1-2	8-3
Rhydyfelin	4-1	0-0	1-1	7-2	2-1	4-1	2-1	0-1	6-4	3-1		1-2	1-1	3-1	4-1	2-3
Splott Albion	7-0	2-1	0-2	5-4	1-3	0-2	2-1	2-2	5-1	0-6	6-2	***O***	4-5	1-2	4-1	5-2
Trefelin BGC	6-0	3-2	2-2	2-1	4-0	2-3	4-2	2-2	2-1	4-1	2-0	5-0	***N***	2-2	7-0	3-4
Treforest	8-0	2-1	2-4	0-3	1-3	3-3	0-1	2-2	6-0	1-3	1-0	4-1	3-3	***E***	4-0	2-1
Turberville Arms	2-2	3-4	1-0	1-6	1-3	3-1	0-4	0-5	4-1	1-0	2-1	1-2	2-7	0-1		2-3
Ynysddu Crusaders	4-0	1-3	3-0	1-4	1-1	0-3	1-0	2-5	3-6	1-4	2-1	0-5	2-2	3-3	0-2	

Division One	P	W	D	L	F	A	Pts
Caerau United	**30**	**21**	**5**	**4**	**117**	**43**	**68**
Trefelin BGC	**30**	**19**	**8**	**3**	**98**	**42**	**65**
Rhoose	**30**	**17**	**7**	**6**	**89**	**35**	**58**
Llantwit Major	**30**	**14**	**7**	**9**	**77**	**53**	**49**
Treforest	**30**	**14**	**7**	**9**	**69**	**50**	**49**
Aber Valley YMCA	**30**	**13**	**7**	**10**	**80**	**56**	**46**
Kenfig Hill	**30**	**14**	**4**	**12**	**68**	**59**	**46**
Cardiff Draconians	**30**	**13**	**4**	**13**	**78**	**79**	**43**
Rhydyfelin	**30**	**12**	**5**	**13**	**69**	**60**	**41**
Splott Albion	**30**	**13**	**2**	**15**	**77**	**77**	**41**
Baglan Dragons	**30**	**12**	**4**	**14**	**62**	**61**	**40**
Carnetown BGC	**30**	**10**	**8**	**12**	**64**	**79**	**38**
Merthyr Saints	**30**	**10**	**5**	**15**	**77**	**108**	**35**
Ynysddu Crusaders	**30**	**7**	**6**	**17**	**53**	**98**	**27**
Turberville Arms	**30**	**8**	**2**	**20**	**43**	**92**	**26**
AFC Bargoed Redz	**30**	**1**	**3**	**26**	**33**	**162**	**6**

SOUTH WALES AMATEUR LEAGUE DIVISION ONE CONSTITUTION 2010-11

ABER VALLEY YMCA . . . . Abertridwr Park, Tridwr Road, Abertridwr, Caerphilly CF83 4DN . . . . None
BAGLAN DRAGONS . . . . Evans Bevan Field, Baglan, Port Talbot SA12 8BH . . . . None
BLAENRHONDDA . . . . Blaenrhondda Park, Brook Street, Blaenrhondda CF42 5SF. 01443 774772
CARDIFF DRACONIANS . . . . Llanidloes Road, Gabalfa, Cardiff CF14 2ST . . . . None
CARNETOWN BGC . . . . . . Cae Carnetown, Grovers Field, Grovers Lane, Carnetown, Abercynon CF45 4PF . . . . None
KENFIG HILL . . . . Central Athletic Ground, Croft Goch, Kenfig Hill, Bridgend CF33 6HA . . . . None
LLANHARRY . . . . Recreation Ground, Llanharry CF72 9LJ . . . . None
* LLANTWIT FARDRE. . . . . Tonteg Park, Main Road, Tonteg, Pontypridd CF38 1ND 01443 207393
LLANTWIT MAJOR . . . . Windmill Lane, Llantwit Major CF61 2SU . . . . None
RHOOSE . . . . Ceri Road, Rhoose, Barry CF62 3HF. . . . . None
RHYDYFELIN. . . . . Upper Boat Playing Field, Hawthorn, Pontypridd CF37 5UP . . . . None
SPLOTT ALBION . . . . University Playing Field, Llanrumney, Cardiff CF3 4JN . . . . None
TON & GELLI BOYS CLUB . . . . Ton Pentre FC, Ynys Park, Sawmill Villas, Ton Pentre CF41 7AF. 01443 432813
TREFELIN BGC . . . . Ynys Park, Cwmavon Road, Port Talbot SA12 8RD 07811 054030
TREFOREST . . . . White Tips Stadium, Dan-Y-Bryn Road, Treforest, Pontypridd CF37 1RX. 01443 485532
* TROEDYRHIW. . . . . The Willows Community Centre, Bridge Street, Troedyrhiw, Merthyr Tydfil CF48 4DS. 01443 692198

*IN: Blaenrhondda (P), Llanharry (P), *Llantwit Fardre (R - Welsh League Division Three), Ton & Gelli Boys Club (P), *Troedyrhiw (R - Welsh League Division Three)*

*OUT: AFC Bargoed Redz (R), Caerau United (P - Welsh League Division Three), *Merthyr Saints (R), Turberville Arms (now Penygraig) (R), *Ynysddu Crusaders (R)*

** - SUBJECT TO APPEAL*

Division Two		P	W	D	L	F	A	Pts
Ton & Gelli Boys Club		26	19	4	3	73	30	61
Llanharry		26	18	2	6	65	47	56
Blaenrhondda		26	15	3	8	77	48	48
Llangynwyd Rangers		26	15	2	9	81	52	47
Ferndale Boys Club	*-3*	26	15	2	9	65	58	44
Hirwaun Welfare		26	12	4	10	64	55	40
Graig		26	10	6	10	52	55	36
Pencoed Athletic		26	9	9	8	54	62	36
Taffs Well Res.		26	9	5	12	52	55	32
Cwm Ni		26	8	8	10	47	57	32
Brynna		26	9	2	15	46	63	29
Trelewis Welfare		26	8	4	14	61	83	28
FC Abercwmboi		26	4	2	20	42	79	14
Penarth Town		26	3	3	20	40	75	12

AFC Talbot Green, Gilfach Goch Athletic - records expunged

W J OWEN CUP

FIRST ROUND

AFC Bargoed 0 **Ynysddu** 6
AFC Talbot 0 **Cwm Ni** 3
Baglan 3 Turberville 2
FC Abercwmboi 0 **Taffs Well Res.** 2
Gilfach Goch Athletic v **Carnetown BGC** (w/o)
Graig 2 **Treforest** 3 *(at Treforest)*
Hirwaun Welf. 4 Brynna 2
Llangynwyd 1 Llanharry 0
Llantwit Major 1 **Aber Valley YMCA** 3
Merthyr Sts 6 Kenfig Hill 5
Pencoed Ath. 1 **Caerau** 5
Rhoose 4 Ferndale BC 1
Rhydyfelin 1 Blaenrhondda 0
Splott 4 Cardiff Dracs 0
Ton & Gelli 6 Penarth 1
Trefelin 5 Trelewis Welf. 0

SECOND ROUND

Carnetown 3 **Aber Valley** 4
Cwm Ni 2 Llangynwyd 0
Merthyr Sts 5 Hirwaun 1
Rhydyfelin 0 **Caerau** 2
Taffs Well Res. 3 **Splott** 5
Ton & Gelli 3 Rhoose 2 *aet*
Trefelin 3 Baglan 2 *aet*
Ynysddu 0 **Treforest** 3

QUARTER-FINALS

Aber Valley YMCA 2 **Ton & Gelli BC** 2 *aet* (1-3p)
Cwm Ni 0 **Splott Albion** 4
Merthyr Sts 2 **Treforest** 5
Trefelin BGC 1 **Caerau** 5

SEMI-FINALS

Splott Albion 2 **Treforest** 3
Ton & Gelli 0 **Caerau** 3

FINAL

(May 7th at Taffs Well)
Caerau Utd 3 Treforest 0

	AFC Talbot	Blaenrhondda	Brynna	Cwm Ni	FC Ab'boi	Ferndale BC	Gilfach Goch	Graig	Hirwaun Wel.	Llangynwyd	Llanharry	Penarth T.	Pencoed A.	Taffs Well Res.	Ton & Gelli	Trelewis
AFC Talbot Green		1-0	n/a	1-1	2-2	n/a	1-1	n/a	0-10	1-3	2-6	n/a	1-3	0-4	1-4	n/a
Blaenrhondda	3-2		2-2	2-2	3-2	2-3	n/a	6-3	2-3	3-0	2-1	1-0	5-1	5-1	2-2	9-1
Brynna	n/a	1-2	***D***	0-1	4-3	3-4	n/a	1-3	1-4	3-2	0-1	5-2	1-3	0-5	0-1	4-2
Cwm Ni	n/a	0-3	0-3	***I***	1-1	2-0	n/a	2-4	2-1	1-5	4-2	5-2	0-2	1-2	2-1	1-3
FC Abercwmboi	3-0	2-4	2-3	2-5	***V***	2-4	5-1	2-6	4-1	1-3	2-4	3-1	1-2	2-1	1-4	1-1
Ferndale Boys Club	4-0	5-2	5-1	2-2	3-1	***I***	n/a	3-1	4-2	0-3	0-4	3-1	2-2	1-3	0-2	5-1
Gilfach Goch Athletic	n/a	3-5	0-4	5-3	n/a	1-7	***S***	2-3	0-7	2-2	n/a	n/a	n/a	1-2	0-5	1-5
Graig	n/a	2-1	3-1	1-1	0-1	3-1	5-1	***I***	4-1	3-2	0-2	0-0	2-2	3-3	0-2	0-2
Hirwaun Welfare	3-2	0-1	3-1	2-4	4-1	3-2	4-2	2-2	***O***	5-4	1-2	6-1	5-1	1-0	1-1	4-1
Llangynwyd Rangers	n/a	2-3	1-2	2-2	4-1	5-1	5-2	5-1	4-2	***N***	1-2	8-1	5-2	3-1	1-3	5-4
Llanharry	n/a	3-2	2-1	4-0	2-1	1-3	5-3	2-0	3-3	3-2		4-3	4-3	0-2	0-3	3-1
Penarth Town	n/a	3-2	2-3	2-2	3-2	2-3	2-1	1-3	0-2	2-3	2-3	***T***	0-0	6-1	1-4	1-2
Pencoed Athletic	5-1	0-6	2-2	2-2	1-0	2-3	n/a	3-0	4-2	2-2	2-2	2-1	***W***	4-2	3-3	2-2
Taffs Well Res.	0-0	1-0	1-2	5-2	6-0	3-4	1-0	0-0	1-1	1-2	1-5	2-0	4-3	***O***	1-2	1-1
Ton & Gelli Boys Club	n/a	5-0	2-1	1-1	4-0	3-0	n/a	7-1	3-1	2-3	3-5	2-1	4-1	4-1		3-2
Trelewis Welfare	n/a	3-7	5-1	3-2	5-4	2-4	n/a	2-7	2-4	1-4	5-1	4-2	2-3	3-3	1-2	

SOUTH WALES AMATEUR LEAGUE DIVISION TWO CONSTITUTION 2010-11

AFC BARGOED REDZ. . . . . Bargoed Park, Bargoed CF81 8UJ . . . . None
BRYNNA . . . . Brynna Welfare Ground, Heol Dewi, Brynna, Pontyclun CF72 9SP 01443 226646
CAERAU BOYS CLUB. . . . . Metcalfe Street, Caerau, Maesteg CF34 0TB . . . .
CWM NI . . . . Blaenrhondda FC, Blaenrhondda Park, Brook Str, Blaenrhondda CF42 5SF 01443 774772
FC ABERCWMBOI . . . . Recreation Ground, Abercwmboi, Rhondda CF44 6BL . . . . None
FERNDALE BOYS CLUB. . . . . Maerdy Park, Rowley Terrace, Maerdy, Ferndale CF43 4BH. . . . . None
GRAIG . . . . Pontypridd Town FC, Ynysangharad Park, Pontypridd CF37 4PE. 01443 486571
HIRWAUN WELFARE. . . . . Manchester Place, Hirwaun, Aberdare CF44 9RB. 01685 811900
LLANGYNWYD RANGERS. . . . . Llangynwyd Playing Fields, Llangynwyd, Maesteg CF34 9SN . . . . None
* MERTHYR SAINTS . . . . ICI Pavilion, Pant, Merthyr Tydfil CF48 2SR 07962 016872
PENCOED ATHLETIC . . . . Recreation Ground, Felindre Road, Pencoed, Bridgend CF35 5PB . . . . None
PENYGRAIG. . . . . Ely Field, Penygraig, Tonypandy CF40 1EZ . . . . None
STM SPORTS . . . . University Playing Fields, Llanrumney, Cardiff CF3 4JN. . . . . None
TAFFS WELL . . . . Rhiw Dda'r, Parish Road, Taffs Well, Cardiff CF15 7SA. 02920 811080
TRELEWIS WELFARE . . . . Parc Taff Bargoed, Trelewis CF46 6AB . . . . None
* YNYSDDU CRUSADERS . . . . Nine Mile Point Recreation Ground, Ynysddu, Newport NP11 7JG 01495 200377

*IN: AFC Bargoed Redz (R), Caerau Boys Club (P - Bridgend & District League Premier Division), *Merthyr Saints (R), Penygraig (formerly Turberville Arms) (R), STM Sports (P - Cardiff Combination Premier Division), *Ynysddu Crusaders (R)*

OUT: AFC Talbot Green (WS), Blaenrhondda (P), Gilfach Goch Athletic (WS), Llanharry (P), Penarth Town (R), Ton & Gelli Boys Club (P)

SOUTH WALES SENIOR LEAGUE

www.southwalesfaseniorleague.co.uk

Sponsored by: Thomas, Carroll

Founded: N/A

Recent champions:

2005: Bridgend Street

2006: Sully Sports

2007: Sully Sports

2008: Fairwater

2009: Fairwater

	Brecon Corinthians	Bridgend Street	Cogan Coronation	Cwm Welfare	Cwmbach Royal Stars	Fairwater	Fochriw	Grange Albion	Lewistown	Llanrumney United	Penydarren Boys Club	St Athan	St Josephs	Sully Sports	Tonypandy Albion	Tonyrefail BGC
Brecon Corinthians		1-8	0-0	3-3	1-4	3-5	5-4	0-1	0-0	1-6	0-3	1-4	0-5	0-3	2-6	5-2
Bridgend Street	3-0		1-1	2-0	5-0	5-2	7-1	1-1	1-1	3-0	1-0	7-3	7-4	2-1	6-5	1-0
Cogan Coronation	4-2	1-2	***D***	0-1	3-1	2-1	3-1	0-0	2-2	2-2	4-0	4-1	5-2	2-1	2-1	0-2
Cwm Welfare	10-3	0-0	1-0	***I***	6-0	3-1	4-0	3-0	4-1	1-3	2-1	2-1	4-0	0-2	3-2	2-3
Cwmbach Royal Stars	2-3	2-7	4-2	1-3	***V***	2-0	3-2	1-5	1-1	2-4	2-1	3-2	3-1	1-3	4-2	3-3
Fairwater	1-2	0-3	2-3	0-1	2-0	***I***	3-2	2-1	2-7	0-5	4-5	1-2	6-1	1-1	0-1	1-3
Fochriw	2-1	0-2	2-4	1-2	2-3	6-2	***S***	2-1	2-6	1-1	1-1	1-3	4-1	2-1	2-5	4-3
Grange Albion	2-0	1-2	3-2	1-3	4-0	2-0	1-0	***I***	2-0	2-1	5-3	2-3	3-1	3-3	3-2	1-2
Lewistown	4-2	0-4	2-0	2-1	2-4	2-1	3-2	0-1	***O***	4-6	3-3	2-2	6-1	4-1	2-3	1-0
Llanrumney United	4-0	0-0	0-6	2-1	1-3	2-0	7-1	0-4	3-2	***N***	0-2	2-0	12-0	2-3	4-1	2-1
Penydarren Boys Club	4-1	3-6	2-2	1-2	3-2	4-3	5-2	2-2	2-2	4-1		3-1	4-0	2-3	3-4	2-1
St Athan	6-3	2-2	2-1	1-2	2-0	7-0	3-1	1-4	0-1	2-4	0-0	***O***	1-2	2-1	3-0	3-1
St Josephs	3-3	0-6	1-2	1-5	4-3	1-2	4-0	0-3	0-4	3-5	1-1	2-2	***N***	3-2	1-3	3-4
Sully Sports	5-0	0-3	1-0	1-1	4-1	4-3	3-0	1-2	5-2	2-4	3-2	5-1	4-0	***E***	3-2	3-1
Tonypandy Albion	5-1	3-4	1-1	3-1	3-0	3-8	4-4	1-0	0-3	2-2	1-3	2-1	2-4	0-2		3-4
Tonyrefail BGC	3-0	2-2	2-3	2-3	3-2	2-3	2-0	0-0	3-1	2-3	2-2	2-1	2-1	0-3	2-1	

Division One	**P**	**W**	**D**	**L**	**F**	**A**	**Pts**
Bridgend Street	**30**	**23**	**7**	**0**	**103**	**34**	**76**
Cwm Welfare	**30**	**20**	**3**	**7**	**74**	**38**	**63**
Llanrumney United	**30**	**18**	**4**	**8**	**88**	**55**	**58**
Sully Sports	**30**	**18**	**3**	**9**	**74**	**46**	**57**
Grange Albion	**30**	**17**	**5**	**8**	**60**	**36**	**56**
Cogan Coronation	**30**	**14**	**7**	**9**	**61**	**43**	**49**
Lewistown	**30**	**13**	**7**	**10**	**70**	**58**	**46**
Penydarren Boys Club	**30**	**12**	**8**	**10**	**71**	**61**	**44**
Tonyrefail BGC	**30**	**13**	**4**	**13**	**59**	**59**	**43**
St Athan	**30**	**12**	**4**	**14**	**62**	**61**	**40**
Tonypandy Albion	**30**	**11**	**3**	**16**	**71**	**78**	**36**
Cwmbach Royal Stars	**30**	**11**	**2**	**17**	**57**	**84**	**35**
Fairwater	**30**	**8**	**1**	**21**	**56**	**85**	**25**
Fochriw	**30**	**6**	**3**	**21**	**52**	**93**	**21**
St Josephs	**30**	**6**	**3**	**21**	**50**	**108**	**21**
Brecon Corinthians	**30**	**4**	**4**	**22**	**43**	**112**	**16**

SOUTH WALES SENIOR LEAGUE DIVISION ONE CONSTITUTION 2010-11

AFC BUTETOWN . . . . Bute Park, Loudon Square, Bute Street, Butetown, Cardiff CF1 5JT . . . . None
BRIDGEND STREET . . . . Splott Park, Splott, Cardiff CF24 2YE . . . . None
CADOXTON BARRY . . . . Parc Bryn-Y-Don, Dinas Powys CF64 4TR . . . . None
COGAN CORONATION . . . . Cogan Recreation Field, Andrew Road, Penarth CF64 2NT . . . . None
CWM WELFARE . . . . Mount Pleasant Park, Castellau Road, Beddau, Pontypridd CF38 2AA 01443 202320
CWMBACH ROYAL STARS. . . . . . . Blaennant-Y-Groes Rec Ground, Cwmbach, Aberdare CF44 0PB. . . . . None
GRANGE ALBION . . . . Coronation Park, Sloper Road, Cardiff CF11 8TB . . . . None
LEWISTOWN. . . . . Lewistown, Blackmill Road, Ogmore Vale, Bridgend CF32 7NR . . . . None
LLANRUMNEY UNITED . . . . Riverside Park, Hartland Road, Llanrumney, Cardiff CF3 9JL . . . . None
* PENTWYN DYNAMOS . Pentwyn Leis. Centre, Parc Coed-y-Nant,Bryn Celyn Rd, Pentwyn, Cardiff CF23 7EZ. 02920 549211
PENYDARREN BOYS CLUB . . . . . . The Bont, Rockery Road, Penydarren, Merthyr Tydfil CF47 9HL 01685 375241
* SEVEN SISTERS . . . . Welfare Ground, Dulais Road, Seven Sisters, Neath SA10 9EY 01639 700354
ST ATHAN . . . . Community Centre Field, Glyndwr Avenue, St Athan, Barry CF62 4PP. . . . . None
SULLY SPORTS . . . . BP Sports & Social Club, South Road, Swanbridge, Sully CF64 5SP 02920 530629
TONYPANDY ALBION. . . . . King George's Running Track, Clydach Vale, Tonypandy CF40 2RQ. . . . . None
TONYREFAIL BGC. . . . . Tynybryn Park, Tonyrefail, Porth, Rhondda CF39 8EW . . . . None

*IN: AFC Butetown (P), Cadoxton Barry (P), *Pentwyn Dynamos (R - Welsh League Division Three), *Seven Sisters (R - Welsh League Division Three)*

*OUT: Brecon Corinthians (R), *Fairwater (R), *Fochriw (R), St Josephs (R)*

** - SUBJECT TO APPEAL*

C W BRUTY CUP

Division Two		P	W	D	L	F	A	Pts
Cadoxton Barry		30	19	7	4	86	43	64
AFC Butetown		30	19	2	9	84	47	59
AFC Caerphilly		30	17	6	7	80	55	57
Ynyshir/W'stn	*-1, -3 gls*	30	17	5	8	74	46	55
Ynyshir Albion	*-3*	30	15	9	6	68	46	51
AFC Whitchurch		30	14	6	10	74	46	48
St Albans		30	14	5	11	64	54	47
Lisvane/Llanishen	*+2*	30	13	3	14	75	67	44
Penrhiwceiber Cons		30	12	7	11	60	58	43
Tongwynlais		30	13	4	13	73	74	43
Penrhiwfer		30	12	2	16	64	75	38
Nelson Cavaliers		30	10	4	16	66	82	34
Stanleytown		30	9	4	17	57	72	31
AFC Llwynypia		30	9	1	20	47	111	28
Cascade		30	6	4	20	48	90	22
Hopkinstown		30	3	7	20	37	94	16

FIRST ROUND

AFC Caerphilly 1 **Penydarren Boys Club** 5

Brecon 0 **AFC Whitchurch** 4

Bridgend St 3 Stanleytown 0

Cwm 1 **Cadoxton** 4 *aet*

Fairwater 3 AFC Llwynypia 2

Fochriw 5 Ynyshir & Wattstown BYC 3

Hopkinstown 1 **Penrhiwfer** 1 *aet* (6-7p)

Lisvane/Llanishen 3 **Cogan Coronation** 7

Llanrumney United 3 Cwmbach Royal Stars 2

Nelson Cav. 2 **Grange A.** 8

St Albans 5 Penrhiwceiber Cons 1

St Athan 7 Tonyrefail BGC 1

Sully Sports 4 Lewistown 4 *aet* (4-1p)

Tongwynlais 2 AFC Butetown 1

Tonypandy 5 St Josephs 3

Ynyshir Alb. 6 Cascade 2

SECOND ROUND

Fairwater 1 **Cogan Coronation** 5 *(at Cogan)*

Grange Alb. 2 Bridgend St 1

Penrhiwfer 3 Fochriw 2 *aet*

St Albans 2 Llanrumney United 2 *aet* (5-3p) *(at Llanrumney United)*

St Athan 1 **Penydarren** 2

Tongwynlais 1 **Whitchurch** 6

Tonypandy 6 Cadoxton 2

Ynyshir Albion 3 **Sully** 5

QUARTER-FINALS

Cogan 0 **AFC Whitchurch** 1

Grange Albion 4 **Sully** 5

Penydarren 9 Penrhiwfer 0

St Albans 3 Tonypandy 1

SEMI-FINALS

Penydarren 3 Sully Spts 3 *aet* (3-1p)

St Albans 2 **Whitchurch** 3

FINAL

(May 15th at Grange Alb.)

Penydarren Boys Club 3 AFC Whitchurch 1

	Butetown	Caerphilly	Llwynypia	AFC Whit.	Cadoxton B.	Cascade	Hopkinstown	Lisvane/Llan.	Nelson Cav.	P'ceiber C.	Penrhiwfer	St Albans	Stanleytown	Tongwynlais	Ynyshir Alb.	Ynyshir & W.
AFC Butetown		1-0	10-0	1-0	1-2	6-1	6-1	1-4	5-1	1-2	3-1	1-2	5-0	4-1	1-0	3-1
AFC Caerphilly	6-0		4-3	2-1	3-3	2-1	0-0	3-1	5-2	2-1	2-0	5-0	2-6	0-1	1-3	0-1
AFC Llwynypia	2-7	5-6	***D***	2-7	2-4	2-3	1-0	0-5	4-2	4-2	0-1	2-1	0-5	5-4	1-4	0-3
AFC Whitchurch	1-2	1-1	6-0	***I***	4-1	2-1	7-0	0-0	4-0	0-1	4-1	3-2	3-1	2-6	3-3	2-1
Cadoxton Barry	1-1	4-4	1-3	3-1	***V***	2-2	2-1	3-0	5-2	4-0	0-0	0-1	5-0	3-0	2-0	2-1
Cascade	1-2	3-3	5-0	0-2	1-11	***I***	1-3	1-6	1-2	2-2	1-2	0-2	1-2	2-6	1-2	0-5
Hopkinstown	1-1	1-3	1-1	0-3	1-3	1-4	***S***	3-2	1-6	1-4	3-5	2-3	2-2	0-3	1-4	1-3
Lisvane/Llanishen	2-6	2-3	0-2	2-1	4-6	6-1	3-2	***I***	5-0	1-2	2-3	3-1	4-3	L-W	2-1	3-3
Nelson Cavaliers	2-3	1-2	2-0	4-2	1-3	3-4	2-2	4-3	***O***	3-3	3-4	1-4	3-0	4-2	3-3	2-1
Penrhiwceiber Cons	5-0	3-3	4-1	1-4	1-2	2-2	2-0	4-1	3-0	***N***	1-3	3-3	3-1	0-3	2-4	2-5
Penrhiwfer	2-7	1-3	3-4	2-1	2-2	2-0	6-0	3-5	1-3	1-2		5-1	3-2	2-5	1-3	2-1
St Albans	4-0	1-3	2-0	2-2	0-1	4-2	5-1	4-1	5-1	1-1	3-1	***T***	2-1	1-1	0-3	3-0
Stanleytown	0-3	1-4	0-1	1-1	1-2	1-2	8-1	0-3	3-2	2-0	4-2	3-2	***W***	0-4	2-2	1-4
Tongwynlais	1-2	2-5	5-0	2-6	3-7	2-1	1-4	2-4	0-5	2-2	4-2	3-2	2-2	***O***	5-2	2-4
Ynyshir Albion	1-0	3-2	7-1	1-1	2-1	1-2	1-1	1-1	3-1	1-2	3-2	1-1	2-0	1-1		3-3
Ynyshir & Wattstown BYC	2-1	3-1	7-1	3-0	1-1	4-2	2-2	4-0	1-1	1-0	3-1	4-2	2-5	2-0	2-3	

SOUTH WALES SENIOR LEAGUE DIVISION TWO CONSTITUTION 2010-11

AFC CAERPHILLY . . . . Morgan Jones Park, Nantgarw Road, Caerphilly CF83 1AP . . . . Non
AFC WHITCHURCH . . . . Whitchurch Hospital, Park Road, Whirchurch, Cardiff CF14 7XB . . . . Non
BRECON CORINTHIANS . . . . The Rich Field, The Watton, Brecon LD3 7HL 01874 62403
* FAIRWATER . . . . Poplar Park, Poplar Road, Fairwater, Cardiff CF5 3PU . . . . Non
* FOCHRIW . . . . Fochriw Welfare Ground, Fochriw, Bargoed CF81 9LL . . . . Non
LISVANE/LLANISHEN . . . . The Village Field, Heol Y Delyn, Lisvane, Cardiff CF14 0SR . . . . Non
LLWYNYPIA BGC . . . . Ynyscynon Park, Llwynypia, Tonypandy CF40 2LN . . . . Non
NELSON CAVALIERS . . . . Wern Field, Caerphilly Road, Nelson, Treharris CF46 6NL . . . . Non
PENRHIWCEIBER CONS . . . . Abercynon Road, Penrhiwceiber CF45 3TE . . . . Non
PENRHIWFER . . . . Tylorstown Recreation Ground, Tylorstown, Stanleytown CF43 3ES . . . . Non
PENYRHEOL . . . . Aneurin Park, Penyrheol, Caerphilly CF83 2RD . . . . Non
ST ALBANS . . . . Kenyon Road, Tremorfa Park, Tremorfa, Cardiff CF24 2RN . . . . Non
ST JOSEPHS . . . . Maes-Y-Coed Road, Heath, Cardiff CF14 4HH . . . . Non
STANLEYTOWN . . . . Tylorstown Recreation Field, Tylorstown, Stanleytown CF43 3ES . . . . Non
TONGWYNLAIS . . . . Ironbridge Road, Tongwynlais, Cardiff CF15 7NH . . . . Non
YNYSHIR ALBION . . . . Ynyshir Oval, Church Terrace, Ynyshir, Rhondda CF39 0NW . . . . Non
YNYSHIR & WATTSTOWN BYC . . . . Ynyshir Oval, Church Terrace, Ynyshir, CF39 0NW . . . . Non

*IN: Brecon Corinthians (R), *Fairwater (R), *Fochriw (R), Llwynypia BGC (P - Rhondda & District League Premier Division), Penyrheol (P Taff Ely Rhymney Valley Alliance Premier Division), St Josephs (R)*

OUT: AFC Butetown (P), AFC Llwynypia (R), Cadoxton Barry (P), Cascade (R), Hopkinstown (R)

** - SUBJECT TO APPEAL*

OTHER WELSH LEAGUES 2009-10

ABERYSTWYTH & DISTRICT LEAGUE
(Cambrian Tyres)

Division One	P	W	D	L	F	A	Pt
Bont	20	14	3	3	60	25	45
Tregaron Turfs	20	13	5	2	65	26	44
P'rhyncoch Res. *-4*	20	14	0	6	64	35	38
Aber. Univ. Res.	20	11	0	9	47	43	33
Bow Street Res.	20	9	3	8	39	53	30
Tywyn & B. Res.	20	8	5	7	39	35	29
Machynlleth	20	6	5	9	36	41	23
Aberdyfi	20	5	5	10	35	51	20
Padarn United *-3*	20	5	5	10	38	51	17
Llanilar	20	2	6	12	25	56	12
Llanrhystud	20	1	7	12	28	60	10

Division Two	P	W	D	L	F	A	Pt
Trawsgoed	20	16	1	3	60	22	49
Dolgellau AA Res.	20	14	3	3	43	19	45
Aber. Univ. A *-4*	20	14	2	4	47	25	40
Borth United	20	11	2	7	61	34	35
Corris United	20	10	1	9	63	53	31
Penparcau Res. *-4*	20	10	1	9	71	54	27
Talybont	20	8	3	9	45	45	27
FC Phoenix	20	7	1	12	39	48	22
Llanon	20	4	3	13	27	68	15
Penrhyncoch A	20	4	2	14	35	74	14
Aberdyfi Res.	20	1	3	16	26	75	6

ANGLESEY LEAGUE
(Kitchen Medic)

	P	W	D	L	F	A	Pt
Bro Goronwy	16	13	2	1	66	23	41
Trearddur Bay	16	11	2	3	72	21	35
Holyhead Town	16	8	6	2	43	33	30
Llanfairpwll Res.	16	7	4	5	43	36	25
Cemaes Bay	16	6	4	6	35	41	22
Llanerchymedd	16	5	5	6	26	30	20
Menai Bdge Tigers	16	5	1	10	45	40	16
Llangoed & Dist.	16	4	1	11	30	63	13
Llandegfan	16	0	1	15	13	86	1

CAERNARFON & DISTRICT LEAGUE
(Safeflue)

Division One	P	W	D	L	F	A	Pt
Bangor City Res.	18	16	1	1	82	24	49
Mynydd Llandegai	18	12	2	4	69	28	38
Caernarfon Bor. *-3*	18	10	4	4	57	29	31
Y Felinhei	18	8	3	7	46	38	27
Llanrug Utd Res.	18	8	1	9	28	48	25
Waunfawr	18	7	3	8	44	57	24
Talysarn Celts	18	6	3	9	43	59	21
Mountain Rangers	18	6	2	10	52	62	20
Blaenau FA Res.	18	3	2	13	25	67	11
Nefyn United Res.	18	2	3	13	31	65	9

Division Two	P	W	D	L	F	A	Pt
Barmouth Res.	14	9	4	1	46	21	31
Deganwy	14	9	2	3	44	23	29
Penrhyndeudraeth	14	6	5	3	31	22	23
Bangor Univ. Res.	14	7	2	5	27	30	23
Pwllheli Res.	14	4	5	5	22	25	17
Bethesda Res. *-3*	14	5	4	5	41	36	16
Machno United	14	3	0	11	21	46	9
Llanystumdwy Res.	14	1	2	11	20	49	5

CARDIFF COMBINATION

Premier Division	P	W	D	L	F	A	Pt
STM Sports	18	16	0	2	85	21	48
RAFA Boys	18	16	0	2	85	23	48
Llanedyrn Builders	18	10	3	5	53	46	33
Cardiff Hibernian	18	9	3	6	56	40	30
Avenue Hotspur	18	9	2	7	69	46	29
AC Central	18	9	0	9	37	46	27
Thornhill	18	6	1	11	29	44	19
Heath Park United	18	4	2	12	33	64	14
Jug & Bottle	18	2	2	14	23	68	8
Cathays United	18	1	3	14	23	95	6

Division One	P	W	D	L	F	A	Pt
Tiger Bay	18	13	2	3	53	27	41
DUI Dragons	18	12	2	4	54	30	38
AFC Highcroft	18	11	3	4	41	22	36
Roath Park Ryls	18	10	3	5	46	32	33
Pontprenn Pumas	18	8	5	5	39	32	29
Cathays Cons	18	7	3	8	32	35	24
Tremorfa	18	6	1	11	33	50	19
Cathays Pk Revol.	18	4	2	12	33	45	14
Celtic Rangers	18	3	4	11	29	55	13
BTD Stars	18	2	3	13	27	59	9

Division Two	P	W	D	L	F	A	Pt
Cardiff Hibs Res.	16	12	3	1	64	30	39
Jug & Bottle Res.	16	8	5	3	69	42	29
RAFA Boys Res.	16	8	5	3	46	36	29
AFC Butetown Res.	16	7	1	8	53	49	22
AFC W'church Res.	16	6	4	6	33	30	22
Llanedyrn B. Res.	16	6	2	8	31	39	20
Avenue Hot. Res.	16	6	1	9	37	42	19
Cardiff Drac. Res.	16	5	2	9	48	67	17
AC Central Res.	16	2	1	13	27	73	7

CARDIGANSHIRE LEAGUE
(Costcutter)

Division One	P	W	D	L	F	A	Pt
Cardigan Town	22	17	3	2	69	24	54
New Quay	22	15	3	4	73	24	48
Lampeter Town	22	14	2	6	54	27	44
Aberaeron	22	12	4	6	56	29	40
St Dogmaels	22	12	3	7	61	43	39
Maesglas	22	11	3	8	52	35	36
Crannog	22	9	6	7	53	44	33
Dewi Stars	22	9	3	10	41	48	30
Llanboidy	22	6	2	14	26	51	20
Aberporth	22	4	3	15	31	59	15
Ffostrasol	22	3	1	18	18	66	10
Llandysul *-6*	22	3	1	18	20	104	4

Division Two	P	W	D	L	F	A	Pt
Pencader United	22	17	4	1	94	32	55
Felinfach	22	13	2	7	57	43	41
Bargod Rangers	22	12	4	6	48	24	40
Llanybydder	22	12	3	7	70	47	39
Aberaeron Res.	22	13	0	9	68	61	39
Saron	22	12	2	8	68	68	38
N. Emlyn Res. *-3*	22	9	6	7	56	48	30
St Dogmaels Res.	22	7	2	13	59	77	23
Cardigan Res. *-3*	22	7	3	12	45	49	21
New Quay Res.	22	6	2	14	51	73	20
Maesglas Res. *-3*	22	4	3	15	34	75	12
SDUC	22	3	3	16	33	86	12

MERTHYR TYDFIL LEAGUE
(Working Links)

Premier Division	P	W	D	L	F	A	Pt
Bluebirds	18	13	4	1	85	28	43
Pantyscallog VJ	18	14	1	3	69	21	43
Aberfan SDC	18	12	2	4	56	30	38
Georgetown BGC	18	10	1	7	41	41	31
Court House *-3*	18	7	4	7	37	45	22
Gelideg F'dation	18	7	0	11	40	58	21
Abercanaid	18	4	8	6	40	41	20
Gorden Lennox *-3*	18	5	2	11	33	56	14
Pentrebach Labour	18	3	4	11	34	54	13
Caeharris Guest	18	1	2	15	21	82	5

Division One	P	W	D	L	F	A	Pt
Park View	24	21	3	0	146	35	66
White Horse	24	18	0	6	93	54	54
Drovers	24	17	1	6	119	45	52
Trelewis W. Res.	24	15	1	8	77	46	46
Penydarren Res.	24	12	4	8	87	73	40
Merthyr Sts Res.	24	12	0	12	77	87	36
Baili Glas *-3*	24	11	2	11	73	75	32
FC Brunswick	24	9	2	13	49	85	29
Quar Park Rgrs	24	8	2	14	68	74	26
Treharris Ath.W. A	24	8	2	14	62	94	26
Bedlinog	24	8	1	15	62	75	25
Llew Goch *-6*	24	4	3	17	43	142	9
Gurnos SC	24	1	3	20	55	126	6

MID-WALES LEAGUE
(SOUTH)

	P	W	D	L	F	A	Pt
Builth Wells	36	30	5	1	149	16	95
Llandrindod Wells	36	30	3	3	155	22	93
Rhosgoch Rgrs	36	27	5	4	135	29	86
Talgarth Town	36	25	5	6	141	44	80
Presteigne Res.	36	25	4	7	101	33	79
Hay St Marys Res.	36	21	4	11	102	81	67
Newcastle-on-Clun	36	18	9	9	88	59	63
Knighton Town	36	20	2	14	100	71	62
Talgarth Rovers	36	17	7	12	79	75	58
Rhayader T. Res.	36	17	6	13	92	54	57
Penybont United	36	15	2	19	72	86	47
Sennybridge	36	12	4	20	55	96	40
Builth Wednesday	36	9	4	23	56	119	31
CP Llanandras	36	6	8	22	49	102	26
Radnor Valley	36	7	5	24	58	128	26
Newbridge Res.	36	7	4	25	54	140	25
Llan. Wells Colts	36	4	6	26	37	128	18
Penybont Athletic	36	3	6	27	31	129	15
St Harmon	36	3	3	30	35	177	12

NEATH LEAGUE
(Eagle Heating & Plumbing)

Premier Division	P	W	D	L	F	A	Pt
Giants Grave	20	16	3	1	72	27	51
Bryn Rovers	20	16	1	3	60	28	49
Sunnybank WMC	20	12	5	3	35	19	41
Ystradgynlais	20	10	3	7	49	35	33
FC Clydach	20	7	7	6	40	32	28
Cwm Wanderers	20	8	4	8	30	29	28
AFC Caerwern	20	7	4	9	32	46	25
AFC Pontardawe	20	5	3	12	45	60	18
Park Travellers	20	5	2	13	37	46	17
Ynysgerwen	20	4	1	15	22	59	13
Ynysmeudwy	20	2	3	15	30	71	9

Onllwyn - record expunged

Division One	P	W	D	L	F	A	Pt
Lonlas Youth	18	16	0	2	80	28	48
Coelbran Athletic	18	10	2	6	47	31	32
St Ives	18	10	2	6	51	41	32
CMB	18	8	5	5	39	33	29
Glynneath Town	18	9	1	8	55	42	28
Cilfrew Rovers	18	7	4	7	45	53	25
Rhos	18	7	3	8	49	35	24
Clydach Sports	18	4	4	10	18	51	16
FC Nedd	18	4	1	13	29	84	13
Godregraig Ath.	18	2	4	12	35	50	10

Division Two	P	W	D	L	F	A	Pt
Tonna	18	16	1	1	86	22	49
Resolven	18	12	2	4	62	28	38
Seven Sisters Res.	18	9	6	3	58	35	33
Harp Rovers	18	8	5	5	60	43	29
INCO Vale	18	7	4	7	58	56	25
The Miners	18	8	1	9	54	71	25
Cimla FSC	18	7	4	7	56	51	22
Cwmamman Res.	18	5	3	10	54	63	18
Borough	18	3	0	15	29	90	9
Longford FC	18	2	0	16	35	93	6

Reserve Div One	P	W	D	L	F	A	Pt
Giants Grave Res.	18	14	1	3	76	17	43
AFC P'dawe Res.	18	12	1	5	82	31	37
Lonlas Yth Res.	18	9	4	5	57	39	31
Sunnybank Res.	18	9	2	7	44	50	29
Bryn Rovers Res.	18	8	3	7	54	42	27
Ynysygerwen Res.	18	7	3	8	37	66	24
Rhos Res.	18	6	4	8	38	56	22
Resolven Res.	18	5	2	11	36	67	17
Cwm Wders Res.	18	4	2	12	42	67	14
Park Trav. Res.	18	4	2	12	34	65	14

Reserve Div Two	P	W	D	L	F	A	Pt
Glynneath Res.	18	14	2	2	78	29	44
CMB Res.	18	12	2	4	56	34	38
Ynysymeudwy Res.	18	11	2	5	46	26	35
Cilfrew R. Res.	18	8	3	7	43	40	27
INCO Vale Res.	18	8	1	9	36	43	25
Clydach S. Res.	18	8	1	9	27	43	25
AFC Caewern Res.	18	7	3	8	40	34	24
FC Clydach Res.	18	5	3	10	29	42	18
Bryn Rovers A	18	4	2	12	28	61	14
AFC P'dawe A	18	2	3	13	34	65	9

Reserve Div Three	P	W	D	L	F	A	Pt
Tonna Res.	18	14	3	1	60	17	45
Harp Rovers Res.	18	10	3	5	69	31	33
Godregraig Res.	18	10	2	6	70	43	32
Sunnybank A	18	9	2	7	53	43	29
Longford FC Res.	18	8	2	8	47	56	26
Ystradgynlais Res.	18	7	3	8	45	57	24
Glynneath Town A	18	7	2	9	51	58	23
Rhos A	18	5	6	7	36	43	21
Borough Res.	18	4	4	10	47	80	16
INCO Vale A	18	2	1	15	27	77	7

NEWPORT & DISTRICT LEAGUE
(Monmouth Building Society)

Premier Division X	P	W	D	L	F	A	Pt
Marshfield	22	17	4	1	91	26	55
K-2	22	17	3	2	97	32	54
St Julians	22	14	6	2	89	27	48
Pontnewydd Utd	22	15	1	6	68	32	46
Malpas	22	13	2	7	72	45	41
Graig-Y-Rhacca	22	11	2	9	81	45	35
Tredegar Arms	22	8	2	12	66	72	26
Shaftesbury Youth	22	7	4	11	52	69	25
Cwmcarn Athletic	22	7	3	12	45	60	24
Pill Hibernians	22	7	1	14	38	79	22
Caerleon Town	22	1	1	20	21	116	4
Henllys Rangers	22	0	1	21	22	139	1

Machen - record expunged

Premier Division Y	P	W	D	L	F	A	Pt
Cwmbran Celtic A	24	16	5	3	96	36	53
AC P'mister Res.	24	16	5	3	93	33	53
Albion Rov. Res.	24	15	6	3	102	37	51
Lliswerry Res.	24	15	3	6	67	54	48
Pill Res.	24	13	6	5	71	40	45
Coed Eva Res.	24	11	5	8	76	57	38
Lucas Cwm. Res.	24	11	2	11	66	67	35
Spencer Y&B Res.	24	7	4	13	57	69	25
Cromwell Yth Res.	24	7	4	13	55	79	25
Villa D. C.'ch Res.	24	5	5	14	41	80	20
Trethomas Res.	24	6	1	17	38	102	19
Newport Cor. Res.	24	4	5	15	42	78	17
Rogerstone Res.	24	4	1	19	29	101	13

Malpas Gladiators Res. - record expunged

Division One	P	W	D	L	F	A	Pt
Lliswerry A	26	21	3	2	102	48	66
Pontnewydd Res.	26	19	2	5	104	47	59
Albion Rovers A	26	17	4	5	111	51	55
CCYP	26	12	4	10	88	69	40
Ponthir	26	12	3	11	80	59	39
AC Pontymister A	26	12	3	11	61	43	39
Ty-Sign	26	9	8	9	74	69	35
K-2 Res.	26	10	5	11	80	87	35
Malpas Res.	26	10	3	13	69	80	33
Six in Hand	26	9	4	13	69	72	31
Bettws Soc. Club	26	8	7	11	73	77	31
Marshfield Res.	26	7	7	12	56	78	28
Sp. Baneswell Soc.	26	9	0	17	64	107	27
Caerleon T. Res.	26	0	1	25	13	157	1

Division Two	P	W	D	L	F	A	Pt
Oakfield Inn	24	17	4	3	127	53	55
Graig-Y-Rh. Res.	24	17	3	4	80	27	54
Waterfront United	24	17	3	4	105	55	54
Cwmcarn A. Res.	24	14	1	9	70	62	43
Bettws SC Res.	24	12	4	8	68	53	40
Marshfield A	24	10	7	7	72	71	37
Racing C. Newp't	24	8	6	10	69	69	30
Lliswerry B	24	7	7	10	54	56	28
County Athletic	24	7	4	13	62	77	25
Cwmbran Celtic B	24	7	4	13	60	77	25
Cromwell Youth A	24	7	4	13	55	74	25
Rogerstone W. A	24	5	3	16	44	99	18
Newport Eagles	24	2	2	20	52	145	8

Newport Corinthians A - record expunged

Division Three	P	W	D	L	F	A	Pt
St Julians Res.	22	20	2	0	86	23	62
Pill Hibs Res.	22	14	1	7	78	44	43
Pill A	22	12	5	5	72	50	41
FC Llanyravon	22	11	4	7	83	55	37
Lucas Cwmbran A	22	10	3	9	51	54	33
Gaer Park Rgrs	22	9	4	9	74	76	31
Ferns	22	7	4	11	53	68	25
RC Newport Res.	22	6	6	10	45	56	24
Albion Rovers B	22	5	8	9	63	78	23
Ty-Sign Res.	22	5	5	12	42	70	20
Nwp't Eagles Res.	22	5	3	14	54	98	18
Coed Eva Ath. A	22	4	3	15	39	68	15

Royal Mail AFC - record expunged

PEMBROKESHIRE LEAGUE
(Manderwood)

Division One	P	W	D	L	F	A	Pt
Merlins Bridge	26	20	4	2	89	36	64
Haverf'dwest Res.	26	15	7	4	67	33	52
Tenby	26	15	4	7	65	49	49
Goodwick United	26	14	6	6	57	40	48
Hakin United	26	13	6	7	79	40	45
Pennar Robins	26	13	6	7	74	50	45
Narberth *-1*	26	11	7	8	63	45	39
Neyland	26	11	4	11	57	54	37
Kilgetty *+1*	26	7	4	15	53	86	26
Solva	26	6	7	13	54	59	25
Harbrandston	26	6	6	14	46	66	24
Clarbeston Road	26	6	6	14	61	102	24
Prendergast Villa	26	4	4	18	37	84	16
Monkton Swifts	26	5	1	20	42	100	16

Division Two	P	W	D	L	F	A	Pt
Hundleton	26	17	6	3	81	30	57
Johnston	26	16	8	2	57	20	56
St Ishmaels	26	15	2	9	85	42	47
Saundersfoot Sp.	26	13	8	5	68	37	47
Milford United	26	14	2	10	73	43	44
St Clears	26	13	5	8	59	51	44
Milford Athletic	26	12	5	9	58	38	41
Angle	26	11	1	14	53	71	34
Camrose	26	9	5	12	46	54	32
Letterston	26	9	3	14	41	55	30
Carew	26	7	8	11	39	49	29
Pendine	26	6	6	14	36	75	24
Haverfordwest CC	26	6	5	15	48	74	23
Pembroke Boro.	26	1	2	23	19	124	5

PORT TALBOT & DISTRICT LEAGUE

Premier Division	P	W	D	L	F	A	Pt
Cornelly United	20	13	4	3	63	37	43
Real Bay View	20	13	3	4	70	24	42
Gwynfi United	20	12	2	6	40	35	38
Cwmafan *-3*	20	11	4	5	54	28	34
Margam Yth Club	20	9	5	6	40	35	32
Baglan D. Res. *-3*	20	10	1	9	46	52	28
Porthcawl Ath. *-3*	20	9	1	10	51	52	25
Trefelin BGC Res.	20	7	1	12	27	38	22
Cwmafan Welfare	20	7	0	13	37	62	21
Pt Talbot T. Exiles	20	3	3	14	25	53	12
Glyncorrwg	20	2	4	14	32	69	10

Division One	P	W	D	L	F	A	Pt
Cornelly Utd Res.	32	26	4	2	120	41	82
Real Bay View Res.	32	23	4	5	126	56	73
Craddock Galacticos	32	22	5	5	100	44	71
Pt Talbot T. Res. *-6*	32	21	6	5	103	59	63
Ryl Mail Grove Pk	32	17	6	9	72	68	57
Porthcawl Albion *-6*	32	16	6	10	60	56	48
Kenfig Hill Res.	32	12	7	13	64	82	43
Margam YC Res.	32	12	6	14	56	76	42
Newton Wanderers	32	10	8	14	60	61	38
Croeserw United	32	9	10	13	67	65	37
Port Talbot Tigers	32	11	4	17	81	88	37
Gwynfif United Res.	32	11	4	17	67	82	37
Cornelly United A	32	10	4	18	76	88	34
Bell Inn *-6*	32	8	5	19	82	103	23
Cwmafan Res.	32	6	5	21	59	111	23
Afan Lido A	32	5	7	20	44	84	22
Cefn Cribbwr *-3*	32	5	5	22	49	122	17

RHONDDA & DISTRICT LEAGUE

	P	W	D	L	F	A	Pt
Llwynypia BGC	21	17	3	1	91	23	54
Treorchy BGC	21	16	4	1	92	14	52
Max United *-3*	21	13	3	5	79	46	39
Tonyrefail W. Res.	21	7	3	11	42	48	24
The Baglan	21	5	7	9	39	51	22
Penygraig BGC	21	5	1	15	30	87	16
T'refail BGC Res.	21	2	6	13	40	92	12
Ferndale Res. *-3*	21	3	5	13	38	90	11

VALE OF GLAMORGAN LEAGUE

Premier Division	P	W	D	L	F	A	Pt
SW Dockers	20	16	4	0	73	18	52
SP Construction	20	12	6	2	59	29	42
Cardiff Airport	20	12	3	5	64	49	39
Master Mariner	20	11	2	7	45	34	35
AFC Tadross	20	10	2	8	67	51	32
Castle FC	20	6	4	10	38	50	22
Llantwit Mjr Res.	20	6	4	10	42	61	22
Cad. Barry Res.	20	6	3	11	36	50	21
Glenbrook	20	5	5	10	38	48	20
Barry Villa	20	5	5	10	42	61	20
Cadoxton Imps	20	1	2	17	22	75	5

Division One	P	W	D	L	F	A	Pt
Holton Road	24	17	3	4	79	29	54
Sully Sports Res.	24	16	3	5	73	45	51
FC Pumas	24	16	2	6	86	58	50
Park Villa	24	12	6	6	73	50	42
Cogan Cor. Res.	24	12	2	10	80	66	38
SW Dockers Res.	24	10	5	9	59	58	35
St Athan Res.	24	10	4	10	64	61	34
Tynewydd	24	8	8	8	55	61	32
Knap	24	9	4	11	76	82	31
Millwood	24	9	3	12	56	69	30
Wenvoe Exiles	24	9	2	13	77	84	29
C'ton Imps Res. *-1*	24	3	3	18	59	113	11
Cadoxton Athletic	24	0	5	19	39	100	5

Division Two	P	W	D	L	F	A	Pt
Cadoxton Barry A	24	19	2	3	79	42	59
Cowbridge Town	24	14	3	7	81	47	45
Waterfront Wdrs	24	13	5	6	66	33	44
ABC Leasing	24	13	3	8	61	45	42
Cadoxton Imps A	24	11	3	10	60	63	36
Inter Penarth	24	10	2	12	59	61	32
Barry Town Social	24	10	2	12	62	65	32
FC Plumes	24	9	5	10	58	64	32
Tadross Res. *-1*	24	7	6	11	60	67	26
Park Vets *-1*	24	8	1	15	61	75	24
Penarth T. Res.	24	7	3	14	62	91	24
Glenbrook Res.	24	6	4	14	50	94	22
Island Marine *-5*	24	7	5	12	67	79	21

WELSH NATIONAL LEAGUE (WREXHAM AREA)
(Nizam-Druid)

Premier Division	P	W	D	L	F	A	Pt
Rhos Aelwyd	26	18	6	2	90	38	60
Chirk AAA	26	18	4	4	74	38	58
Venture Comm.	26	14	4	8	53	33	46
Corwen Amateurs	26	11	8	7	50	37	41
Castell Alun Colts	26	10	6	10	66	54	36
Coedpoeth United	26	10	6	10	57	69	36
Brymbo	26	9	6	11	44	66	33
Overton Rec.	26	9	5	12	44	49	32
Llay Welfare	26	8	6	12	37	55	30
Hawarden Rgrs	26	8	5	13	41	58	29
FC Cefn	26	6	9	11	61	71	27
Brickfield Rangers	26	7	5	14	49	63	26
Penycae	26	7	5	14	50	66	26
Borras Park Alb.	26	6	7	13	60	79	25

Division One	P	W	D	L	F	A	Pt
Garden Village FC	24	19	2	3	72	30	59
Johnstown Youth	24	19	1	4	91	39	58
Communities First	24	15	4	5	87	50	49
New Brighton Villa	24	14	4	6	64	29	46
Acrefair Youth	24	14	3	7	69	43	45
Penyffordd	24	11	6	7	69	51	39
Penley	24	11	4	9	54	44	37
Llanuwchllyn	24	7	6	11	55	57	27
Buckley United	24	6	3	15	36	62	21
Mold Juniors	24	6	2	16	36	67	20
Glyn Ceiriog	24	2	2	20	28	93	8
Holt Nomads *-3*	24	3	1	20	27	104	7
Hawkesbury *-27*	24	8	4	12	41	60	1

Reserve Division	P	W	D	L	F	A	Pt
Airbus UK Res.	28	22	3	3	118	20	69
Bala Town Res.	28	21	2	5	91	30	65
Ruthin Town Res.	28	15	7	6	84	35	52
Gresford A. Res.	28	16	3	9	63	57	51
Hawarden R. Res.	28	16	2	10	74	63	50
Rhos Aelwyd Res.	28	13	9	6	69	47	48
Chirk AAA Res.	28	11	9	8	53	51	42
Cefn Druids Res.	28	12	5	11	57	54	41
Lex XI Res.	28	11	5	12	62	55	38
Llangollen T. Res.	28	9	6	13	57	61	33
Castell AC Res.	28	9	6	13	64	93	33
Llay Welfare Res.	28	7	5	16	50	95	26
Borras Park Res.	28	7	2	19	46	98	23
Coedpoeth Res.	28	6	3	19	40	82	21
Penycae Res.	28	1	1	26	25	112	4

Res./Colts Div	P	W	D	L	F	A	Pt
Ruthin Town Colts	28	22	4	2	104	29	70
Corwen Ams Res.	28	22	3	3	91	27	69
FC Cefn Res.	28	20	2	6	82	37	62
Brymbo Res.	28	16	3	9	72	56	51
New Brighton Res.	28	15	3	10	90	67	48
Penyffordd Res.	28	14	2	12	76	64	44
Llangollen Colts	28	12	4	12	78	62	40
Garden V. Res.	28	10	6	12	47	53	36
Acrefair Yth Res.	28	10	5	13	73	92	35
Johnstown Y. Res.	28	10	4	14	52	67	34
Penley Res.	28	9	5	14	49	88	32
Overton Rec Res.	28	8	5	15	51	63	29
Brickfield R. Res.	28	6	4	18	51	81	22
Borras Pk Colts	28	6	3	19	51	105	21
Glyn Ceiriog Res.	28	3	1	24	29	105	10

MISCELLANEOUS WELSH CUPS 2009-10

ALFRED SPAREY CUP

(May 16th at Presteigne St Andrews)
Presteigne St Andrews Res. 2 Hay St Mary's Res. 1

BARRITT CUP

(Sponsor: Pentraeth Hona)

FIRST ROUND

Beaumaris Town 3 Nantlle Vale 1
Caernarfon Wanderers 2 **Mochdre Sports** 4
Glan Conwy 6 Brynford United 1
Holywell Town 5 Bethel 5 *aet* (4-1p)
Llandyrnog United 2 Flint Town United 1 *aet*
Sychdyn 2 Llanfairfechan Town 1

SECOND ROUND

Beaumaris Town 0 **Glan Conwy** 3
Blaenau Ffestiniog Amateurs 1 **Mochdre Sports** 2 *aet*
Bodedern Athletic 1 Denbigh Town 0
Bontnewydd 2 Porthmadog Res. 0 *(at Porthmadog)*
Conwy United 2 Llansannan 2 *aet* (4-1p)
Gap Connah's Quay Res. 1 Llanllyfni 0
Gwalchmai 4 Llanrwst United 0
Holywell Town 2 Gaerwen 1
Llandudno Junction 5 Halkyn United 0
Llanrug United 4 Abergele Rovers 1
Llanystumdwy 0 **Aston Park Rangers** 2
Nefyn United 4 Llandyrnog United 1
Prestatyn Town Res. 5 Amlwch Town 1
Pwllheli 3 Llanberis 1
Rhydymwyn 5 Penmaenmawr Phoenix 0
Sychdyn 1 **Barmouth & Dyffryn United** 5

THIRD ROUND

Barmouth & Dyffryn United 1 Rhydymwyn 0
Bontnewydd 1 **Conwy United** 4 *(at Conwy United)*
Gap Connah's Quay Res. 3 Aston Park Rangers 1
Glan Conwy 8 Prestatyn Town Res. 1
Gwalchmai 1 Llanrug United 0
Holywell Town 2 **Pwllheli** 6 *(at Pwllheli)*
Llandudno Junction 4 Mochdre Sports 3
Nefyn United 5 Bodedern Athletic 5 *aet* (4-3p)

QUARTER-FINALS

Conwy United 3 **Glan Conwy** 3 *aet* (2-4p)
Gap Connah's Quay Res. 0 **Llandudno Junction** 3
Nefyn United 1 **Gwalchmai** 5
Pwllheli 2 Barmouth & Dyffryn United 0

SEMI-FINALS

Glan Conwy 2 **Pwllheli** 3
Gwalchmai 1 Llandudno Junction 0

FINAL

(May 9th at Bangor City)
Pwllheli 2 Gwalchmai 0

BAY CUP

(May 22nd at Ffostrasol)
Cardigan Town 3 Pencader United 2 *aet*

CENTRAL WALES CUP

(May 27th at Montgomery Town)
Waterloo Rovers 2
Llanrhaeadr 1

CEREDIGION CUP

(May 3rd at Newcastle Emlyn)
Tregaron Turfs 2 Cardigan Town 1

GWENT SENIOR CUP

PRELIMINARY ROUND

Aberbargoed Buds 2 Tredegar Town 2 *aet* (7-6p)
(at Tredegar Town)
Abertillery Bluebirds 4 Goytre 1
Caerleon 1 Croesyceiliog 0
Monmouth Town 3 Cwmbran Town 1
Newport Civil Service 2 Newport YMCA 2 aet (4-3p)
Risca United 1 **Cwmbran Celtic** 3

QUARTER-FINALS

Aberbargoed Buds 1 **Abertillery Bluebirds** 2
Caerleon v Caldicot Town
Newport Civil Service v Cwmbran Celtic
Newport County 0 **Monmouth Town** 2

SEMI-FINALS

Monmouth Town v Caerleon/Caldicot Town
Newport CS/Cwmbran Celtic v Abertillery Bluebirds
Competition abandoned due to inclement weather

GWENT AMATEUR CUP

(May 8th at Abergavenny Thursdays)
Coed Eva Athletic 2 Undy Athletic 0

J EMRYS MORGAN CUP

(April 24th at Newtown)
Llandrindod Wells 1 Montgomery Town 0 *aet*

LLANSANTFFRAID VILLAGES CUP

(May 14th at Llansantffraid Village)
Abermule 4 Trefonen 1

NORTH EAST WALES CUP

FIRST ROUND

Brickfield Rangers 4 Hawarden Rangers 1
Buckley United 0 **Bala Town Res.** 6 *(at Bala Town)*
Corwen Amateurs 5 Hawkesbury Villa 0
Elements Cefn Druids Res. 3 **Castell Alun Colts** 5
Llay Welfare 5 Acrefair Colts 0
Rhos Aelwyd 8 Johnstown 1
The New Saints Res. 1 **Penyffordd** 2

SECOND ROUND

Brymbo 3 **Overton Recreation** 4
Castell Alun Colts 4 Llanuwchllyn 2
Chirk AAA 5 Borras Park Albion 1
Coedpoeth United 4 **Venture Community** 6
Corwen Amateurs 2 Brickfield Rangers 1
FC Cefn 4 Llay Welfare 3
Holt Nomads 1 **Airbus UK Broughton Res.** 4
Penyffordd 3 **Bala Town Res.** 7 *(at Bala Town)*
Rhos Aelwyd (w/o) v Gwersyllt Athletic

THIRD ROUND

Airbus UK Broughton Res. 2 Venture Community 1
Bala Town Res. 2 Overton Recreation 1
Chirk AAA 5 Mold Alexandra 0
Gresford Athletic 0 **Buckley Town** 3
Lex XI 1 Llangollen Town 1 *aet* (9-8p)
Penycae 0 **Corwen Amateurs** 2
Rhos Aelwyd 3 Castell Alun Colts 0
Ruthin Town 2 **FC Cefn** 3

QUARTER-FINALS

Bala Town Res. 0 **Airbus UK Broughton Res.** 3
Buckley Town 6 Corwen Amateurs 1
Chirk AAA 3 Rhos Aelwyd 0
FC Cefn 1 **Lex XI** 4

SEMI-FINALS

Buckley Town 2 Chirk AAA 1 *(at Brymbo)*
Lex XI 1 **Airbus UK Broughton Res.** 2 *(at Ruthin Town)*

FINAL

(May 4th at Wrexham)
Airbus UK Broughton Res. 0 **Buckley Town** 3

NORTH WALES COAST CUP

(Sponsor: Unite)

PRELIMINARY ROUND

Colwyn Bay 2 Prestatyn Town 0
Flint Town United 1 **Llangefni Town** 2

FIRST ROUND

Bangor City 1 **Porthmadog** 5 *(at Porthmadog)*
Barmouth & Dyffryn United 2 Gap Connah's Quay 1 *aet*
(at Porthmadog)
Caernarfon Town 5 Holywell Town 0

Colwyn Bay 0 **Rhyl** 1
Denbigh Town 3 Llangefni Town 1
Glan Conwy (w/o) v Bethesda Athletic
Holyhead Hotspur 1 **Llandudno Town** 1 *aet* (4-5p)
Llandyrnog United 5 Halkyn United 0
QUARTER-FINALS
Caernarfon Town v **Barmouth & Dyffryn United** (w/o)
Llandudno Town 4 Glan Conwy 3
Llandyrnog United 3 Denbigh Town 2
Rhyl 0 **Porthmadog** 1
SEMI-FINALS
Barmouth & Dyffryn United 2 **Llandudno Town** 3
(at Porthmadog)
Porthmadog 3 Llandyrnog United 1
FINAL
(May 19th at Prestatyn Town)
Porthmadog 1 Llandudno Town 0

NORTH WALES COAST INTERMEDIATE CUP

FINAL
(April 30th at Bangor City)
Prestatyn Town Res. 2 Gwalchmai 1 *aet*

NORTH WALES COAST JUNIOR CUP

FINAL
(May 8th at Porthmadog)
Mynydd Llandegai 2 Bangor City Res. 2 *aet* (6-5p)

PRESTEIGNE-OTWAY CUP

FIRST ROUND
Newbridge-on-Wye (w/o) v Leominster Town
Presteigne St Andrews 2 Hay St Marys 0
FINAL
(May 9th at Presteigne St Andrews)
Presteigne St Andrews 0 Newbridge-on-Wye 0 *aet* (4-3p)

RADNORSHIRE CUP

(Sponsor: Aspidistra)
FIRST ROUND
Builth Wells 4 Newbridge-on-Wye 1
Hay St Marys 0 **Presteigne St Andrews** 3
Penybont United 3 **Llandrindod Wells** 5
Radnor Valley v **Talgarth Town** (w/o)
Rhosgoch Rangers 7 Llanandras 1
QUARTER-FINALS
Builth Wells 2 Llandrindod Wells 0
Knighton Town 4 Llandrindod Wells Colts 1
Rhayader Town 0 **Presteigne St Andrews** 4
Talgarth Town 4 Rhosgoch Rangers 2
SEMI-FINALS
Builth Wells 1 **Talgarth Town** 2
Knighton Town 1 **Presteigne St Andrews** 3
FINAL
(April 5th at Hay St Marys)
Presteigne St Andrews 1 Talgarth Town 0

SOUTH WALES SENIOR CUP

FIRST ROUND
AFC Whitchurch 4 Penrhiwfer 2
Blaenrhondda 2 Llanrumney United 1
Bridgend Street 2 Graig 0
Grange Albion 2 **AFC Caerphilly** 3
Hopkinstown 1 **Llangynwyd Rangers** 9
Trelewis Welfare 0 **Ynyshir & Wattstown BC** 3
SECOND ROUND
Aber Valley YMCA 4 Tonypandy Albion 1
AFC Caerphilly 1 **Lewistown** 2 *(at Lewistown)*
AFC Whitchurch 3 **St Athan** 4
Blaenrhondda 1 **Ynyshir & Wattstown BC** 2
Bridgend Street 2 Merthyr Saints 1
Brynna 4 AFC Bargoed Redz 1
Cadoxton Barry 4 **Penrhiwceiber Cons** 4 *aet* (4-5p)
Cardiff Draconians 1 **Rhydyfelin** 4
Cascade 2 **Nelson Cavaliers** 2 *aet* (5-6p)
Lisvane/Llanishen 3 **Cwm Welfare** 5
Llangynwyd Rangers 4 Stanleytown 0
Rhoose 1 Hirwaun Welfare 0
Splott Albion (w/o) v Ferndale Boys Club
Sully Sports 2 Carnetown BGC 0
Tongwynlais 1 **Penydarren Boys Club** 5
Ynyshir Albion 4 AFC Talbot Green 2
THIRD ROUND
Aber Valley YMCA 1 **Ynyshir & Wattstown BC** 2
Bridgend Street 2 Splott Albion 0
Lewistown 2 **Cwm Welfare** 2 *aet* (5-6p)
Penydarren Boys Club 3 Nelson Cavaliers 2
Rhoose 4 Llangynwyd Rangers 1
Rhydyfelin 3 Brynna 0
Sully Sports 7 Penrhiwceiber Cons 1
St Athan 4 Ynyshir Albion 2 *aet*
QUARTER-FINALS
Cwm Welfare 1 **Sully Sports** 2
Rhoose 3 Penydarren Boys Club 1
Rhydyfelin 2 Bridgend Street 1
Ynyshir & Wattstown BC 5 **St Athan** 5 *aet* (3-4p)
SEMI-FINALS
Rhydyfelin 2 St Athan 1, Sully Sports 1 **Rhoose** 2
FINAL *(May 14th at Aberaman Athletic)*
Rhoose 3 Rhydyfelin 1

SOUTH WALES INTERMEDIATE CUP

FINAL *(May 12th at Taffs Well)*
Clwb Cymric 1 Bryncae 0

TANNERS TOWN CUP

FINAL *(May 22nd at Montgomery Town)*
Montgomery Town 0 **Llanidloes Town** 1 *aet*

WEST WALES INTERMEDIATE CUP

FINAL *(May 12th at Swansea City)*
Coelbren Athletic 3 Blaenymaes 3 *aet* (4-1p)

SCOTLAND

With thanks to Stewart Davidson

SOUTH OF SCOTLAND LEAGUE

	P	W	D	L	F	A	Pts
Threave Rovers	24	19	4	1	94	25	61
Dalbeattie Star A	24	18	3	3	83	25	57
St.Cuthbert Wand.	24	16	4	4	62	24	52
Wigtown & Bladnoch	24	12	4	8	54	42	40
Crichton Royal	24	12	3	9	61	45	39
Stranraer Res	24	10	6	8	69	54	36
Abbeyvale	24	10	2	12	55	66	32
Newton Stewart	24	8	5	11	48	64	29
Mid Annandale	24	8	4	12	35	53	28
Heston Rovers	24	8	3	13	53	65	27
Creetown	24	5	2	17	40	77	17
Fleet Star	24	3	4	17	32	89	13
Nithsdale Wanderers	24	2	6	16	39	96	12

SOUTH OF SCOTLAND CHALLENGE CUP

Semi final

Creetown 1-4 Wigtown & B @Wig'n St

Cuthbert W 3-1 Threave Rovers

Final- Saturday 8 May at St Cuthbert Wanderers

St Cuthbert W 3-1 Wigtown & B

(Redpath, Rudd(pen), Kiltie) (Forrester)

SOUTH OF SCOTLAND LEAGUE CUP

Semi final

Stranraer Res 5-1 N Stewart

Threave Rov disq-WO St Cuthbert W

Final- Saturday 6 February at Stranraer

Stranraer Reserves 3-0 St Cuthbert Wand

(Bradley, Cochrane 2)

TWEEDIE CUP

Semi final

Crichton 5-3* Dalbeattie Star

Threave Rov 4-3 St Cuthbert Wand

Final - Saturday 3 April at Crichton

Crichton 3-3* Threave Rovers

(4-3p)

(Kennedy, Parker, Johnstone) (Donley 2, Warren(pen))

HAIG GORDON MEMORIAL TROPHY

Semi final

St Cuthbert W 4-0 Mid Ann'dale

Threave Rov 1-2 Dalbeattie Star

Final - Monday 10 May at St Cuthbert Wanderers

St Cuthbert Wand 2-1 Dalbeattie Star

(Rudd, Johnstone) (Robinson)

CREE LODGE CUP

Semi final

St Cuthbert W 2-0 Dalbeattie S

Threave Rov 1-3 Stranraer Res

Final - Wednesday 5 May at Stranraer

Stranraer Reserves 1-1* St Cuthbert Wanderers

(8-7p)

(Bradley) (Redpath)

POTTS CUP

Semi final

Crichton 1-3* Stranraer Res

St Cuthbert W wo-disq Threave Rovers

Final - Saturday 13 March at St Cuthbert Wanderers

St Cuthbert Wand 0-2 Stranraer Reserves

(Doyle, Wilson(pen))

EAST OF SCOTLAND LEAGUE

Premier	Pld	W	D	L	G	A	Pts
Spartans	20	17	1	2	63	18	52
Whitehill Welfare	20	12	1	7	30	22	37
Lothian Thistle	20	11	3	6	46	25	36
Tynecastle	20	9	6	5	40	32	33
Civil Service Strollers	20	9	6	5	27	26	33
Heriot Watt Univ	20	10	0	10	42	45	30
Edinburgh City	20	9	1	10	37	39	28
Edinburgh University	20	6	5	9	21	25	23
Preston Athletic	20	5	2	13	27	39	17
Selkirk	20	4	3	13	28	56	15
Coldstream	20	3	2	15	28	62	11

Division One	Pld	W	D	L	G	A	Pts
Stirling University	22	19	2	1	75	16	59
Vale of Leithen	22	19	2	1	63	18	59
Craigroyston	22	14	3	5	57	23	45
Gretna 2008	22	13	4	5	53	20	43
Leith Athletic	22	11	5	6	68	33	38
Easthouses Lily	22	7	6	9	41	38	27
Gala Fairydean	22	8	2	12	42	44	26
Kelso United	22	6	5	11	32	44	23
Ormiston	22	7	0	15	28	54	21
Eyemouth Utd	22	4	7	11	37	51	19
Peebles Rovers	22	3	1	18	23	107	10
Hawick Royal Albert	22	1	3	18	20	91	6

KING CUP

Semi final

Spartans 3-0 Heriot Watt Univ

Stirling Univ 1-0 Preston Ath

Final - Sunday 16 May at Whitehill Welfare

Spartans 2-0 Stirling University

(McLeod-pen, Kader)

IMAGE PRINTERS CUP

Semi final

Gretna 2008 2-1 Edinburgh City

Spartans 1-2 Vale of Leithen

Final - Sunday 28 March at Hawick

Gretna 2008 2-0 Vale of Leithen

(Jeffrey, Jardine)

ALEX JACK CUP

Semi final

Eyemouth U 2-0 Easthouses L

Lothian Th 1-3 Leith Athletic

Final - Sunday 29 November at Preston Ath

Eyemouth Utd 0-2 Leith Athletic

(Campbell, Wallace)

EAST OF SCOTLAND LEAGUE CUP

Ran as a knockout competition this season. As an extraordinary measure (without precedent for future years) five clubs were allowed to opt out at their request due to fixture congestion – Gretna 2008, Peebles Rovers, Stirling University, Vale of Leithen and Whitehill Welfare.

Semi final

Lothian Th	3-2	Tynecastle
Spartans	2-0	Edinburgh University

Final- Wednesday 19 May at Craigroyston

Lothian Th	1-2	Spartans
(Black)		(O'Donnell, King)

HIGHLAND LEAGUE

	Pld	W	D	L	G	A	Pts
Buckie Thistle	34	26	5	3	83	26	83
Cove Rangers	34	23	6	5	97	42	75
Deveronvale	34	21	5	8	91	47	68
Fraserburgh	34	21	5	8	75	48	68
Forres Mechanics	34	20	5	9	72	42	65
Formartine United	34	18	6	10	75	47	60
Huntly	34	19	3	12	66	49	60
Keith	34	17	6	11	77	54	57
Wick Academy	34	16	6	12	79	64	54
Inverurie Loco Works	34	15	6	13	60	47	51
Nairn County	34	15	5	14	61	59	50
Clachnacuddin	34	12	7	15	73	73	43
Turriff United	34	9	4	21	60	86	31
Lossiemouth	34	7	6	21	52	74	27
Brora Rangers	34	6	6	22	32	81	24
Rothes	34	7	3	24	39	102	24
Fort William	34	6	2	26	37	98	20
Strathspey Thistle	34	3	4	27	30	120	13

NUTEL COMMUNICATIONS NORTH OF SCOTLAND CUP

Semi final

North Section

Clachnacuddin	0-2	Inverness CT
Wick Academy	3-0	Brora Rangers

East Section

Fort William	3-4	Rothes
Lossiemouth	0-2	Nairn County

Final

North Section - Wed. 26 August

Wick Academy	1-3	Inverness CT

East Section - Tuesday 25 August

Nairn County	2-1	Rothes

Final - Sunday 13 Sept at Forres

Inverness Caledonian Th	3-2	Nairn County
(Morrison, Sutherland, Rooney)		(Main, Barron)

HIGHLAND LEAGUE CUP

Semi final

Forres Mech	1-0	Lossiemouth
Rothes	3-2	Keith

Final - Saturday 8 May at Buckie Thistle

Forres Mechanics	2-0	Rothes
(Moore, Fraser)		

ABERDEENSHIRE CUP

Semi final

Huntly	0-1	Cove Rangers
Keith	0-3	Buckie Thistle

Final - Saturday 12 September at Turriff United

Buckie Thistle	2-0	Cove Rangers
(Bruce 2)		

ABERDEENSHIRE SHIELD

(sponsored by Morrison Motors)

Semi Final

Cove Rangers	1-5	Peterhead
Fraserburgh	0-2	Inverurie Loco Works

Final - Wednesday 11 November at Peterhead

Inverurie LW	0-3	Peterhead
att - 589		(Cameron, Morrison-og. Ross)

NORTH CALEDONIAN LEAGUE

	Pld	W	D	L	G	A	Pts
Thurso	18	15	3	0	77	13	48
Muir of Ord Rovers	18	15	0	3	63	15	45
Dingwall Thistle	18	12	2	4	54	20	38
Halkirk United	18	12	2	4	54	27	38
Golspie Sutherland	18	11	1	6	54	30	34
Balintore	18	6	1	11	26	57	19
Bonar Bridge	18	5	0	13	21	59	15
Tain	18	5	0	13	20	63	15
Invergordon	18	3	1	14	20	63	10
Fort William	18	1	0	17	22	64	3

LINDSAY'S OF GOLSPIE CUP

Semi final

Halkirk U	3-0	Thurso
M of Ord Rov	1-0	Dingwall Th

Final - Saturday 24 October at Bonar Bridge

Muir of Ord Rovers	2-1	Halkirk United
(Dance 2)		(Sutherland)

SWL CUP

Semi final

Dingwall Th	1-2	Halkirk United
Golspie S	1-2	Muir of Ord Rovers

Final - Saturday 24 April at Thurso

Muir of Ord Rovers	2-0	Halkirk United
(Morrison 2)		

JOCK MACKAY CUP 2009/10

Semi final

Golspie S	3-0	Muir of Ord Rov
Thurso	6-0	Bonar Bridge

Final - Saturday 1 May at Invergordon

Thurso	1-4	Golspie Sutherland
(Nichol)		(Smith, Campbell, Mikula, Bone)

FOOTBALL TIMES CUP 2009/10

(sponsored by Ferries Kitchens)

Semi final

Dingwall Th	3-1	Golspie S.
M of Ord Rov	2-5	Halkirk Utd

Final - Saturday 1 May at Dingwall

Dingwall Th	3-2	Halkirk Utd
(MacLeod, Houston, Taylor-pen)		(Sawyer, Budge)

CHALLENGE CUP – SOUTH

Semi final

Gretna 2008	5-2	Whitehill Welfare
Spartans	2-1	Stirling University

Final - Thursday 13 May at Hearts FC

Gretna 2008	1-3	Spartans
(Rayson)		(Mitchell-og, McLeod, Kader)
	att - c.400	

ACTIVE NATION SCOTTISH CUP

All first and second round matches listed, Thereafter, only matches involving non-league clubs.

First round

Auchinleck T	7-0	Fort William
Brora R	0-2	Irvine Meadow
Buckie Thistle	0-0* (4-1p)	Forres Mechanics
CS Strollers	1-0	Gala Fairydean
Clach'din	2-2 (1-2)	Wick Academy
Coldstream	1-5	Edinburgh City
Dalbeattie S	2-4	Keith
Edinburgh Uni	0-3	Vale Of Leithen
Fraserburgh	1-1 (2-1)	Bonnyrigg Rose
Glasgow Univ	1-4	Girvan
Hawick RA	0-7	Huntly
Inverurie LW	5-0	St Cuthbert Wndrs
Lossiemouth	4-1	Newton Stewart
Nairn County	5-2	Golspie Sutherland
Rothes	1-5	Banks o' Dee
Selkirk	3-0	Preston Ath
Whitehill Welf.	1-1 (3-0)	Wigtown & Bladnoch

Second round

Banks o' Dee	0-3	Montrose
CS Strollers	1-2	Berwick Rangers
Cove Rangers	2-1	Annan Athletic
Deveronvale	2-2 (2-1)	Buckie Thistle
Edinburgh C	5-1	Burntisland Shipyard
Forfar Athletic	4-2	East Stirlingshire
Fraserburgh	1-4	Spartans
Girvan	1-4	Wick Academy
Huntly	1-1 (3-4)	Auchinleck Talbot
Inverurie LW	2-1	Stranraer
Lossiemouth	0-2	Albion Rovers
Nairn County	2-4	Elgin City
Queen's Park	1-3	Livingston
Selkirk	0-3	Irvine Meadow
V Of Leithen	1-3	Keith
Whitehill Welf	1-1 (0-1)	Threave Rovers

Third round

Deveronvale	0-1	Ayr United
Edinburgh C	3-1	Keith
Irvine Meadow	1-0	Arbroath
Spartans	0-1	Forfar Athletic
Stenh's'muir	5-0	Cove Rangers
Stirling Albion	2-1	Auchinleck Talbot
Threave Rov	1-2	Inverurie Loco Works
Wick Acad	4-4	Brechin City (2-4)

Fourth round

Hibernian	3-0	Irvine Meadow
Edinburgh C	1-3	Montrose
Ross County	4-0	Inverurie Loco Works

SFA YOUTH CUP

Matches only involving non-league clubs listed

First round

Dalbeattie S	0-1	N Stewart
Elgin City	3-2	Deveronvale
St Johnstone	10-0	Edinburgh City
Wigtown & B	1-5	St Cuthbert Wand

Second round

Brora R	2-1	Huntly
Clach	1-0	Keith
Cove Rangers	1-5	Aberdeen
Elgin City	2-1	Fraserburgh
Gala F'dean	4-5	St Cuthbert Wand
Nairn Co	1-2	Peterhead
QOS	5-0	N Stewart
Spartans	0-4	Alloa Athletic
Threave Rov	3-1	Annan Athletic

Third round

Brora R'gers	3-0	Civil Service Strollers
Hibernian	8-0	Clach
St Cuthbert W	0-18	Hearts
Threave Rov	0-4	Celtic

JUNIOR FOOTBALL

WEST REGION

West Premier	Pld	W	D	L	G	A	Pts
Beith	22	17	4	1	55	20	55
Arthurlie	22	13	6	3	55	32	45
Auchinleck Talbot	22	13	5	4	60	25	44
Irvine Meadow	22	10	5	7	41	31	35
Pollok	22	9	4	9	40	34	31
Kilbirnie Ladeside	22	9	4	9	43	42	31
Largs Thistle	22	9	3	10	31	43	30
Kirkintilloch Rob Roy	22	8	3	11	27	31	27
Petershill	22	7	3	12	33	47	24
Lanark United	22	6	4	12	34	49	22
Bellshill Athletic	22	5	5	12	32	49	20
Vale of Clyde	22	1	4	17	21	69	7

West Division One	Pld	W	D	L	G	A	Pts
Rutherglen Glencairn	26	18	3	5	60	34	57
Cumnock	26	17	2	7	50	35	53
Clydebank	26	13	6	7	43	35	45
Renfrew	26	11	6	9	47	47	39
Girvan	26	10	8	8	48	41	38
East Kilbride Thistle	26	10	7	9	40	37	37
Glenafton Athletic	26	10	6	10	44	39	36
Ashfield	26	11	3	12	49	47	36
Annbank United	26	11	3	12	45	54	36
Whitletts Victoria	26	10	4	12	31	36	34
Dalry Thistle	26	10	3	13	40	44	33
Maybole	26	8	4	14	35	47	28
Kilsyth Rangers	26	7	4	15	34	47	25
Neilston	26	4	5	17	34	57	17

WEST OF SCOTLAND LEAGUE PLAY OFF
Lanark United won 3-2 on aggregate.

AYRSHIRE LEAGUE

	Pld	W	D	L	G	A	Pts
Hurlford United	22	15	4	3	55	28	49
Kilwinning Rangers	22	15	3	4	59	25	48
Lugar Boswell Thistle	22	15	3	4	50	18	48
Ardrossan Win. Rov.	22	15	0	7	64	34	45
Kello Rovers	22	13	2	7	56	33	41
Craigmark Burnt.	22	10	3	9	31	26	33
Troon	22	10	3	9	31	27	33
Irvine Victoria	22	8	3	11	42	31	27
Darvel	22	7	2	13	32	45	23
Saltcoats Victoria	22	4	4	14	25	54	16
Muirkirk	22	2	3	17	23	83	9
Ardeer Thistle	22	2	2	18	17	81	8

CENTRAL DIVISION 1	Pld	W	D	L	G	A	Pts
Cumbernauld United	24	18	4	2	54	26	58
Shotts Bon Accord	24	15	6	3	56	24	51
St.Anthonys	24	14	4	6	45	33	46
Cambuslang Rangers	24	10	7	7	51	41	37
Vale of Leven	24	11	4	9	42	33	37
Thorniewood United	24	9	3	12	42	51	30
Blantyre Victoria	24	7	8	9	44	40	29
Dunipace	24	7	8	9	43	51	29
Port Glasgow	24	8	5	11	40	48	29
Glasgow Perthshire	24	7	5	12	25	49	26
Lesmahagow	24	6	6	12	35	41	24
Larkhall Thistle	24	4	8	12	39	58	20
Maryhill	24	3	6	15	20	41	15

CENTRAL DIVISION 2	Pld	W	D	L	G	A	Pts
Johnstone Burgh	20	12	6	2	49	27	42
Shettleston	20	13	3	4	41	24	42
Greenock	20	12	4	4	46	22	40
Benburb	20	11	5	4	43	27	38
Yoker Athletic	20	11	2	7	43	31	35
Carluke Rovers	20	6	6	8	33	36	24
St.Rochs	20	7	1	12	30	34	22
Wishaw	20	6	2	12	39	61	20
Forth Wanderers	20	5	2	13	26	56	17
Royal Albert	20	4	4	12	30	47	16
Newmains United	20	4	3	13	20	35	15

NEW COIN AUTOMATICS WEST OF SCOTLAND CUP

Semi final

Irvine M 3-3 Arthurlie
(5-3pens)

K Rob Roy 1-1 Largs Thistle
(4-5p)

Final - Saturday 29 May at Pollok

Irvine Meadow 1-0 Kirkintilloch Rob Roy
(Barr)

ARDAGH GLASS AYRSHIRE SECTIONAL LEAGUE CUP

Semi-Finals

Craigmark B 2-2 Cumnock
(3-4 pens)

Irvine Meadow 0-1 Kiibirnie Ladeside

Final - Sunday 27 September at Irvine Meadow

Kilbirnie Ladeside 3-0 Cumnock
(Longworth 3)

AYRSHIRE WEEKLY PRESS CUP

Semi final

Ardrossan WR 1-6 Girvan

Glenafton Ath 1-1 Cumnock
(3-5pens)

Final - Tuesday 25 May at Auchinleck

Girvan 3-4 Cumnock
(Moffat 2, Shankland) (Cashmore, Tyler, Wilson, Stewart)

CENTRAL SECTIONAL LEAGUE CUP

Semi-Finals

Ashfield 0-0 Arthurlie
(5-6 pens)

Shotts BA 6-1 Vale of Leven

Final - Tuesday 22 September at Maryhill

Arthurlie 1-0 Shotts Bon Accord
(McKeown)

CENTRAL LEAGUE CUP

Semi final

Clydebank 3-2 Petershill

Pollok 3-5 Ashfield

Final - Tuesday 1 June at Pollok

Ashfield 0-2 Clydebank

att - 829 (Lynn, Kilpatrick)

EVENING TIMES CUP WINNERS CUP

Semi final

Cumnock 1-2 Kilbirnle Ladeside

Irvine M 2-0 Hurlford Utd

Final - Saturday 12 June at Pollok

Irvine Meadow 4-0 Kilbrinie Ladeside
(Robertson, McGinty-pen, Hamilton, McGowan)

CLYDESDALE CUP

Semi final

Forth Wand 1-2 Lesmahagow

Lanark Utd 1-0 Carluke Rovers

Final - Monday 27 July at Lanark

Lanark Utd 4-1 Lesmahagow
(Haddow 2, Franch, Jaffrey) (Logan)

EAST REGION

SUPERLEAGUE	Pld	W	D	L	G	A	Pts
Bo'ness United	22	14	6	2	48	18	48
Linlithgow Rose	22	13	6	3	50	25	45
Bathgate Thistle	22	11	4	7	31	32	37
Newtongrange Star	22	9	6	7	41	36	33
Lochee United	22	9	5	8	35	44	32
Camelon	22	9	3	10	36	36	30
Musselburgh Athletic	22	9	2	11	30	34	29
Hill of Beath Hawthorn	22	7	7	8	30	32	28
Kelty Hearts	22	7	6	9	32	38	27
Bonnyrigg Rose	22	8	2	12	37	41	26
Whitburn	22	5	7	10	31	38	22
Glenrothes	22	2	4	16	30	57	10

PREMIER	Pld	W	D	L	G	A	Pts
Tayport	22	15	3	4	39	14	48
Forfar West End	22	14	5	3	53	23	47
Kinnoull	22	13	6	3	45	28	45
Arniston Rangers	22	9	5	8	31	29	32
Carnoustie Panmure	22	9	4	9	35	41	31
Ballingry Rovers	22	8	5	9	30	35	29
Penicuik Athletic	22	8	4	10	23	36	28
St.Andrews United	22	7	6	9	35	39	27
Armadale Thistle	22	6	4	12	41	42	22
Fauldhouse United	22	5	6	11	33	44	21
Blairgowrie	22	5	5	12	33	53	20
Montrose Roselea	22	3	7	12	31	45	16

NORTH DIVISION	Pld	W	D	L	G	A	Pts
Broughty Athletic	22	19	2	1	77	13	59
Violet	22	18	3	1	57	12	57
Arbroath Victoria	22	12	3	7	63	51	39
Kirrie Thistle	22	10	5	7	49	38	35
Downfield	22	10	4	8	38	38	34
Lochee Harp	22	8	4	10	38	40	28
East Craigie	22	7	5	10	36	42	26
North End	22	6	6	10	34	41	24
Brechin Victoria	22	7	3	12	22	36	24
Arbroath SC	22	6	3	13	30	48	21
Forfar Albion	22	5	4	13	24	55	19
Coupar Angus	22	3	0	19	30	84	9

CENTRAL DIVISION	Pld	W	D	L	G	A	Pts
Thornton Hibs	26	19	4	3	69	35	61
Oakley United	26	18	4	4	76	30	58
Kirkcaldy YM	26	17	4	5	72	33	55
Jeanfield Swifts	26	17	2	7	69	39	53
Dundonald Bluebell	26	15	5	6	70	35	50
Lochore Welfare	26	12	3	11	58	51	39
Bankfoot Athletic	26	9	7	10	41	52	34
Rosyth	26	10	3	13	57	46	33
Steelend Victoria	26	10	3	13	60	68	33
Crossgates Primrose	26	9	6	11	38	49	33
Lochgelly Albert	26	6	5	15	44	65	23
Newburgh	26	6	2	18	40	71	20
Scone Thistle	26	6	1	19	44	84	19
Luncarty	26	3	1	22	33	113	10

SOUTH DIVISION	Pld	W	D	L	G	A	Pts
Broxburn Athletic	26	17	6	3	56	27	57
Spartans	26	17	4	5	62	29	55
Tranent	26	17	4	5	55	28	55
Sauchie	26	15	5	6	61	34	50
Blackburn United	26	12	4	10	42	42	40
West Calder United	26	10	4	12	48	59	34
Edinburgh United	26	10	3	13	45	48	33
Dunbar United	26	10	2	14	40	51	32
Dalkeith Thistle	26	8	6	12	45	49	30
Haddington Athletic	26	7	8	11	32	38	29
Stoneyburn	26	8	3	15	35	54	27
Harthill Royal	26	7	4	15	35	53	25
Livingston United	26	6	7	13	35	53	25
Pumpherston	26	5	6	15	34	60	21

FIFE & LOTHIANS CUP
(sponsored by John Walker Painters & Decorators)
Semi final
Bathgate Th 3-2 Tranent
H of B Hawth. 0-3 Musselburgh Ath
Final - Saturday 12 June at Newtongrange
Bathgate Thistle 1-0 Musselburgh Athletic
(Lurinsky)

EAST OF SCOTLAND CUP
Semi final
H of B Hawth. 1-1 Linlithgow R
(4-5p)
Musselburgh 4-1 Oakley United
Final - Saturday 12 June at Bathgate
Linlithgow R 2-1 Musselburgh Ath
(Coyne 2 – 1 a pen) (Devlin)

DECHMONT SOUTH LEAGUE CUP
Semi final
Musselburgh 2-2 Linlithgow R
(3-4p)
Whitburn 1-1 Camelon
(2-4p)
Final - Wednesday 28 April at Linlithgow Rose
Linlithgow Rose 1-2 Camelon
(Tyrell) att- c.600 (Graham, Savage)

ACA SPORTS CENTRAL LEAGUE CUP
Semi final
Kelty Hearts 0-1 H of B Hawthorn
Jeanfield SW. 1-4 Glenrothes
Final - Tuesday 27 April at Dundonald Bluebell
Glenrothes 1-1 Hill of Beath Hawthorn
(Martin) (5-4p) (Smith)

DJ LAING CUP
Semi final
Lochee Utd 3-1 Broughty Ath
Montrose R 2-0 Forfar W End
Final- Sunday 4 October at Carnoustie
Lochee Utd 0-0 Montrose Roselea
(3-4pens)

REDWOOD LEISURE/505050 TAXIS CUP
Semi final
Broughty Ath 1-1 Blairgowrie
(4-5p)
Forfar W End 3-0 St Andrews Utd
Final - Wednesday 16 June at Broughty
Blairgowrie 1-0 Forfar West End
(Neave)

GA ENGINEERING NORTH'TAYIDE INTER REGIONAL CUP
Semi final
Hermes 0-3 Broughty Ath
Sunnybank 2-0 Arbroath Vics
Final - Saturday 29 May at Dundee North End
Broughty Ath 0-4 Sunnybank
(Greig 2, Gordon 2)

NORTH REGION

NORTH LEAGUE

Premier Division	Pld	W	D	L	G	A	Pts
Sunnybank	26	20	2	4	64	20	62
Culter	26	17	1	8	65	29	52
Banchory St.Ternan	26	14	5	7	50	37	47
Dyce	26	14	5	7	48	37	47
Banks O'Dee	26	14	1	11	55	43	43
Hermes	26	12	5	9	53	38	41
Maud	26	10	6	10	48	49	36
Lewis United	26	11	3	12	44	47	36
Longside	26	8	6	12	34	48	30
Ellon United	26	7	7	12	32	39	28
Hall Russell United	26	7	4	15	35	47	25
FC Stoneywood	26	6	7	13	35	63	25
Buchanhaven Hearts*	26	6	5	15	39	78	23
East End	26	4	7	15	29	56	19

*Play-Off Thurs 3 June at Sunnybank
Stonehaven 3-2 Buchanhaven Hearts

Division One	Pld	W	D	L	G	A	Pts
Fraserburgh United	26	19	3	4	65	33	60
Inverness City	26	18	4	4	77	35	58
Stonehaven*	26	14	4	8	73	31	46
Glentanar	26	13	6	7	50	28	45
Deveronside	26	11	8	7	56	49	41
Lossiemouth Utd	26	12	4	10	67	61	40
Buckie Rovers	26	10	7	9	45	44	37
New Elgin	26	10	7	9	38	47	37
Bishopmill United	26	10	3	13	43	58	33
Hillhead	26	9	5	12	40	33	32
Forres Thistle	26	8	7	11	40	54	31
Islavale	26	7	7	12	38	47	28
Dufftown	26	1	8	17	30	68	11
Parkvale	26	2	3	21	29	103	9

Division Two	Pld	W	D	L	G	A	Pts
Burghead Thistle (-6 pts)	20	16	3	1	59	19	45
Nairn St.Ninian	20	11	5	4	47	32	38
Fochabers	20	10	4	6	53	40	34
RAF Lossiemouth	20	6	3	11	37	46	21
Cruden Bay	20	6	3	11	28	37	21
Whitehills	20	1	2	17	22	72	5

GRILL LEAGUE CUP

Semi final

Culter	2-5	Sunnybank
Longside	4-0	Banchory St Ternan

Final - Sunday 22 November at East End FC

Sunnybank	3-1	Longside
(Gordon 3)		(Danton)

NORTH REGIONAL CUP

Semi final

Ellon Utd	2-3	Hermes
Sunnybank	0-0 (3-4p)	FC Ston'wood

Final - Friday 28 May at Sunnybank

Hermes	3-5	FC Stoneywood
(Hamilton, Sinclair 2)		(Stevenson, Skinner, Brooks 2, Campbell-og)

MCLEMAN CUP (for Premier Division clubs)

Semi final

Culter	4-1	Hall Russell U
Hermes	2-0	FC Stoneywood

Final - Friday 4 June at Hillhead

Culter	2-1	Hermes
(McKimmie, Cooper)		(Smith)

MORRISON CUP (for Division One clubs)

Semi final

Inverness City	8-1	Parkvale
Stonehaven	1-1 (6-5p)	Forres Thistle

Final - Sunday 23 May at Islavale

Inverness City	2-2	Stonehaven (4-5p)
(McLeod, Mason)		(Low, Stewart)

ELGINSHIRE CUP (for Division Two clubs)

Semi final

Burghead Th	1-0	Whitehills
Fochabers	scr-WO	Cruden Bay

Final - Sunday 16 May at Buckie Rovers

Burghead Th	1-0	Cruden Bay
(Milne)		

GUERNSEY F.A.

Tel: 01481 200 443 Fax: 01481 200 451 Email: michael.kinder@guernseyfa.com
GFA Headquarters, Corbet Field, Grand Fort Road, St Sampson's, Guernsey GY2 4FG.
Secretary: Mike Kinder. **Chairman:** Mark Le Tissier.

SENIOR COUNTY LEAGUE

DIVISION 1	P	W	D	L	F	A	GD	Pts
Belgrave Wanderers	21	17	1	3	79	30	49	52
St. Martin's	21	16	2	3	75	28	47	50
Northerners	21	10	3	8	51	42	9	33
Vale Recreation	21	9	3	9	34	37	-3	30
Rangers	21	9	2	10	42	45	-3	29
Athletics	21	8	2	11	31	46	-15	26
Sylvans	21	4	2	15	23	59	-36	14
Rovers	21	3	1	17	13	61	-48	10
DIVISION 2								
St. Martin's Res.	24	21	2	1	107	33	74	65
Vale Recreation R.	24	14	3	7	88	44	44	45
Belgrave W. Res.	24	15	0	9	90	61	29	45
Centrals	24	12	1	11	78	85	-7	37
Rangers Reserves	24	11	2	11	68	63	5	35
Bavaria Nomads	24	10	3	11	50	47	3	33
Northerners Res.	24	10	2	12	45	66	-21	32
Sylvans Reserves	24	5	4	15	42	79	-37	19
Rovers Reserves	24	0	3	21	17	107	-90	3
DEVELOPMENT U21 LEAGUE								
Belgrave Wanderers	18	14	1	3	81	27	54	43
Vale Recreation	18	12	2	4	60	32	28	38
Northerners	18	12	2	4	55	30	25	38
St. Martin's	18	7	0	11	40	53	-13	21
Sylvans	18	6	0	11	35	57	-22	19
Rovers	18	5	0	13	30	77	-47	15
Rangers	18	3	2	13	31	56	-25	11

J W LOVERIDGE CUP UNDER 18S	P	W	D	L	F	A	GD	Pts
Vale Recreation	6	5	1	0	24	2	22	16
Northerners	6	5	1	0	25	5	20	16
Sylvans	6	3	1	2	11	11	0	10
Belgrave Wanderers	6	3	0	3	17	16	1	9
Rangers	6	2	0	4	11	24	-13	6
Rovers	6	1	1	4	8	20	-12	4
St. Martin's	6	0	0	6	9	27	-18	0
U16 DEVELOPMENT								
Northerners	18	16	0	2	126	11	115	48
St. Martin's	18	14	1	3	92	21	71	43
Vale Recreation	18	11	1	6	58	33	25	34
Belgrave Wanderers	18	11	0	7	79	48	31	33
Rovers	18	6	1	11	46	55	-9	19
Sylvans	18	3	1	14	32	88	-56	10
Rangers	18	0	0	18	8	185	-177	0
U14 DEVELOPMENT LEAGUE								
Northerers	18	16	1	1	106	19	87	49
Vale Recreation	18	14	1	3	114	28	86	43
Sylvans	18	12	3	3	124	28	96	39
Belgrave Wanderers	18	6	0	12	48	114	-66	18
St Martin's	18	5	2	11	56	86	-30	17
Rovers	18	3	1	14	37	93	-56	10
Rangers	18	2	2	14	26	143	-117	8
WOMEN'S LEAGUE								
Sylvans	12	11	1	0	70	14	56	34
St. Martin's	12	7	1	4	30	17	13	22
Rovers	12	3	2	7	20	45	-25	11
Rangers	12	3	1	8	21	38	-17	10
Vale Recreation	12	3	1	8	18	45	-27	10

JERSEY F.A.

Tel: 01534 730 433 Fax: 01534 730 434 Email: paul.creeden@jerseyfa.com
Springfield Stadium, Jarvin Road, St Helier, Jersey JE2 4LF.
Chief Executive Officer: Paul Creeden.

PREMIERSHIP	P	W	D	L	F	A	GD	Pts
St. Paul's	16	13	3	0	58	7	51	42
Grouville	16	10	4	2	39	14	25	34
Trinity	16	7	3	6	30	23	7	24
Portuguese Club	16	6	5	5	30	22	8	23
St. Ouen	16	5	6	5	24	24	0	21
St. Peter	16	5	6	5	17	32	-15	21
Jersey Scottish	16	3	6	7	31	27	4	15
Rozel Rovers	16	3	3	10	16	55	-39	12
First Tower United	16	1	2	13	12	53	-41	5
CHAMPIONSHIP								
Jersey Wanderers	***18***	***18***	***0***	***0***	***71***	***13***	***58***	***54***
St. Clement	***18***	***12***	***2***	***4***	***50***	***26***	***24***	***38***
Sporting Academics	18	10	1	7	44	36	8	31
St. Lawrence	18	9	2	7	39	22	17	29
St. John	18	7	4	7	26	27	-1	25
St. Brelade	18	6	6	6	34	40	-6	24
Magpies	18	6	2	10	30	44	-14	20
Beeches Old Boys	18	5	2	11	33	54	-21	17
St. Martin/S.C.F.	18	4	0	14	23	49	-26	12
Jersey Nomads	18	2	3	13	22	61	-39	9
Division One Reserves								
Grouville	16	14	1	1	51	17	34	43
St. Ouen	16	11	3	2	39	19	20	36
St. Paul's	16	8	3	5	49	28	21	27
First Tower United	16	7	4	5	37	29	8	25
Rozel Rovers	16	6	2	7	23	31	-8	20
Jersey Wanderers	16	4	5	7	38	37	1	17
Jersey Scottish	16	4	3	9	21	39	-18	15
Sporting Academics	16	3	2	11	23	62	-39	11
St. Peter	16	1	5	10	25	44	-19	8

Division Two Reserves	P	W	D	L	F	A	GD	Pts
Trinity	***16***	***12***	***2***	***2***	***65***	***16***	***49***	***38***
Portuguese Club	***16***	***11***	***2***	***3***	***49***	***20***	***29***	***35***
St. Clement	16	8	1	7	42	45	-3	25
St. Martin/S.C.F.	16	8	1	7	30	59	-29	25
St. John (-3)	16	8	1	7	48	35	13	22
Magpies	16	7	1	8	40	34	6	22
St. Lawrence (-1)	16	7	2	7	36	32	4	22
St. Brelade	16	4	0	12	20	51	-31	12
Beeches O.B. (-3)	16	1	2	13	17	54	-37	2
Division Three (C teams)								
Grouville	16	13	0	3	82	16	76	39
Rozel Rovers	16	11	1	4	53	24	29	34
Jersey Wanderers	16	9	4	3	25	21	4	31
St. John	16	9	2	5	40	42	-2	29
Magpies	16	7	1	8	35	35	0	22
St. Ouen	16	4	6	6	27	33	-6	18
St. Peter	16	5	1	10	16	27	-11	16
St. Clement	16	3	1	12	24	67	-43	10
Sporting Academics (-1)	16	2	2	12	21	58	-37	7
Women's								
St. Paul's	12	12	0	0	59	9	50	36
First Tower United	12	8	0	4	51	20	31	24
St. John	12	5	2	5	34	27	7	17
Jersey Wanderers	12	2	1	9	25	53	-28	7
St. Brelade	12	1	1	10	12	72	-60	4

CHANNEL ISLAND CUP FINALS

Muratti Semi Final	Alderney	0	-	3	Jersey
Muratti Final	Jersey	0	-	1	Guernsey
Upton Park C.I. Club Championship	Belgrave Wanderers (Guernsey)	1	-	3	St. Paul's (Jersey)
Women's Centenary Bowl	Sylvans (Guernsey)	0	-	1	St. Paul's (Jersey)
J.F.A. Wheway Cup Final	St. Paul's	2	-	1	Portuguese Club
J.F.A. Charity Cup	St. Paul's	3	-	1	Trinity
G.F.A. Jeremie Cup Final	St. Martin's (Guernsey)	1	-	2	St. Paul's (Jersey)
Le Riche Cup Final	Portuguese Club	0	-	4	St. Paul's
Under 21 Muratti	Guernsey	3	-	3*	(Won 4-5 on pens) Jersey
Under 18 Muratti	Guernsey	1	-	6	Jersey
Under 16 Muratti	Jersey	2	-	0	Guernsey
Ladies Muratti	Jersey	8	-	0	Guernsey
Under 18 Portsmouth Trophy	Jersey Wanderers	4	-	0	Vale Recreation (Guernsey)
John Leatt Trophy U16	Northerns (Guernsey)	3	-	1	First Tower United (Jersey)

*AET

ISLE OF MAN F.A.

Tel: 01624 615 576 Fax: 01624 615 578 Email: frank.stennett@isleofmanfa.com
PO Box 53, The Bowl, Douglas, Isle of Man IM99 1GY.
Chief Exective: Frank Stennett.

CANADA LIFE PREMIER

	P	W	D	L	F	A	Gd	Pts
Rushen	24	20	3	1	64	17	47	63
St Marys	24	19	1	4	85	28	57	58
Laxey	24	17	5	2	69	21	48	56
Peel (-3)	24	16	3	5	72	31	41	48
St Georges (-3)	24	13	4	7	61	30	31	40
DHSOB	24	12	3	9	53	45	8	39
Castletown	24	9	2	13	39	48	-9	29
Gymnasium	24	9	2	13	53	66	-13	29
Corinthians	24	8	2	14	36	57	-21	26
Ramsey	24	6	6	12	30	52	-22	24
Michael	24	4	4	16	33	80	-47	16
St Johns	24	4	1	19	24	71	-47	13
Union Mills	24	1	0	23	22	95	-73	3

JCK DIVISION TWO

	P	W	D	L	F	A	Gd	Pts
Douglas Royal	24	19	1	4	103	48	55	58
Ayre United	24	18	2	4	100	30	70	56
Colby	24	13	4	7	70	41	29	43
Pulrose	24	14	1	9	60	45	15	43
Braddan	24	13	3	8	61	48	13	42
Marown (-3)	24	13	3	8	76	47	29	39
Foxdale	24	11	6	7	54	50	4	39
RYCOB	24	9	5	10	58	59	-1	32
Onchan	24	6	6	12	35	54	-19	24
Ronaldsway	24	6	4	14	42	89	-47	22
Malew	24	6	3	15	35	77	-42	21
Douglas & District	24	5	2	17	38	90	-52	17
Police	24	2	2	20	29	83	-54	8

CANADA LIFE COMBINATION ONE

	P	W	D	L	F	A	Gd	Pts
DHSOB Combi	24	21	2	1	110	20	90	65
Peel Combi	24	17	3	4	80	28	52	54
St Georges Combi (-12)	24	17	5	2	77	28	49	44
Laxey Combi	24	13	3	8	67	58	9	42
St Marys Combi	24	12	3	9	89	56	33	39
Rushen Combi	24	11	6	7	73	57	16	39
Corinthians Combi	24	9	5	10	54	52	2	32
Ramsey Combi	24	9	4	11	49	75	-26	31
Castletown Combi	24	8	5	11	66	60	6	29
Union Mills Combi	24	5	5	14	38	77	-39	20
St Johns Combi	24	5	2	17	41	81	-40	17
Gymnasium Combi	24	5	1	18	52	92	-40	16
Michael Combi	24	1	2	21	22	134	-112	5

JCK COMBINATION TWO

	P	W	D	L	F	A	Gd	Pts
Onchan Combi	24	17	2	5	85	36	49	53
Ayre Combi	24	17	2	5	80	42	38	53
Douglas Royal Combi	24	16	2	6	91	34	57	50
Marown Combi (-9)	24	18	2	4	116	34	82	47
Colby Combi	24	14	2	8	70	52	18	44
Braddan Combi	24	13	4	7	63	52	11	43
RYCOB Combi	24	11	2	11	65	71	-6	35
Foxdale Combi	24	10	2	12	61	63	-2	32
Pulrose Combi	24	8	0	16	46	78	-32	24
Ronaldsway Combi	24	6	2	16	42	84	-42	20
Police Combi	24	6	2	16	38	82	-44	20
Malew Combi	24	5	1	18	43	107	-64	16
Douglas & D. Combi	24	2	3	19	27	92	-65	9

WOMEN'S DIVISION ONE

	P	W	D	L	F	A	Gd	Pts
Corinthians	8	7	0	1	35	9	26	21
Douglas Royal	8	6	1	1	39	13	26	19
Gymnasium	8	3	1	4	23	27	-4	10
Castletown	8	2	2	4	16	24	-8	8
Peel	8	0	0	8	9	49	-40	0

the
FOOTBALL ASSOCIATION COMPETITIONS

ENGLAND C

RESULTS 2009-10

No.	Date	Comp	H/A	Opponents	Att:	Result	Goalscorers
1	Sept 15	F	A	Hungary	-	D 1-1	Briscoe 41
2	Nov 17	F	A	Poland	-	**W** 2-1	Holroyd, Barnes-Homer 74
3	May 26	ICT GrB	A	Republic of Ireland	-	**W** 2-1	Fleming 27, Porter 63

ICT - International Challenge Trophy. F - Friendly

'ENGLAND C ' ENJOY ANOTHER SUCCESSFUL SEASON.

At a time when the football fraternity of England are recovering from a summer of disappointment, it might be a good time to promote England's most successful team. England C, looked after by Paul Fairclough, Steve Burr an excellent supporting team, plus caring and hard working administrative colleagues, have persistently taken on and beaten more experienced European international opposition.

The International Challenge Trophy has provided England C with the chance of producing some excellent achievements and they have been worthy winners in 2005-2006 and runners up in 2008-2009. Two superb results, away to Hungary's national Under 20 squad and Poland's professional Under 23 team, prepared Paul Fairclough's squad for the first of their two qualifying ICT ties and a fine 2-1 victory was gained in Ireland.

The England C squad is continually changing, as bright young professionals who have been released by League clubs are thrilled to receive international recognition with non-league clubs, and respond brilliantly to the dedicated care shown by the England management. This international squad must surely be the most successful in the country for their results and the way the young players develop and move back to senior football. Look out for them when they play Estonia in October.

THE PLAYERS - 2009-10

NAME		CLUB	2009-10 CAPS	09-10 GOALS	TOTAL CAPS	TOTAL GOALS
Barnes-Homer	Matthew	Luton Town	2	1	2	1
Briscoe	Louis	Mansfield Town	1	1	1	1
Brodie	Richard	York City	1	0	2	0
Cadmore	Tom	Hayes & Yeading United	3	0	3	0
Charles	Darius	Ebbsfleet United	1	0	2	0
Deering	Sam	Oxford United	1	0	1	0
Densmore	Shaun	Altrincham	2	0	4	0
Fleming	Andrew	Wrexham	1	1	2	1
Garner	Scott	Mansfield Town	1	0	1	0
Green	Matt	Oxford United	1	0	1	0
Gregory	Steven	AFC Wimbledon	1	0	1	0
Hall	Ryan	Bromley	1	0	1	0
Hedge	John	FC Halifax Town	1	0	1	0
Holroyd	Chris	Cambridge United	2	1	2	1
Howells	Jake	Luton Town	1	0	1	0
Jarvis	Rossi	Luton Town	3	0	3	0
Knight-Percival	Nat	Histon	1	0	1	0
McFadzean	Kyle	Alfreton Town	2	0	2	0
Morgan-Smith	Amari	Ilkeston Town	1	0	1	0
Newton	Sean	AFC Telford Utd	2	0	4	0
Nix	Kyle	Mansfield Town	1	0	1	0
Obeng	Curtis	Wrexham	1	0	1	0
Porter	Max	Rushden & Diamonds	2	1	2	1
Reason	Jai	Cambridge United	1	0	1	0
Rents	Sam	Crawley Town	1	0	1	0
Reynolds	Callum	Luton Town	1	0	1	0
Roberts	Dale	Rushden & Diamonds	3	0	4	0
Rodman	Alex	Oxford United	1	0	1	0
Shaw	Tom	Tamworth	1	0	2	0
Simpson	Josh	Histon	1	0	1	0
Vaughan	Lee	AFC Telford United	1	0	1	0
Welch	Joe	Histon	1	0	1	0
Wright	Nick	Tamworth	2	0	2	0

INTERNATIONAL CHALLENGE TROPHY

GROUP A	P	W	D	L	F	A	Pts	GD
BELGIUM	2	2	0	0	2	0	6	2
ITALY	2	1	1	0	3	1	4	2
ROMANIA	2	0	1	1	0	1	1	-1
MALTA	2	0	0	2	1	4	0	-3
GROUP B	**P**	**W**	**D**	**L**	**F**	**A**	**Pts**	**GD**
ENGLAND	1	1	0	0	2	1	3	1
ESTONIA	0	0	0	0	0	0	0	0
REPUBLIC OF IRELAND	1	0	0	1	1	2	0	-1
GROUP C	**P**	**W**	**D**	**L**	**F**	**A**	**Pts**	**GD**
PORTUGAL	2	1	1	0	7	2	4	5
NORTHERN IRELAND	1	0	1	0	2	2	1	0
POLAND	1	0	1	0	0	0	1	0
WALES	1	0	1	1	4	9	1	-5

ROBERTS	DENSMORE	NEWTON	CADMORE	CHARLES	HOWELLS	PORTER	JARVIS	WRIGHT	HOLROYD	BRODIE	HEDGE	REASON	SHAW	BARNES-HOMER	GREGORY	MCFADZEAN	MORGAN-SMITH	FLEMING	DEERING	PORTER	OBENG	RODMAN	HALL	GARNER	MIMMS	SAAH	BRISCOE	REYNOLDS	RENTS	GARNER	NIX	KNIGHT-PERCIVAL	VAUGHAN	WELCH	SIMPSON	GREEN
X			X				X	X	X							S											X	X	X	X	X	X	S	S	S	S
X	X	X	X	X	X	X	X	X	X	X	S	S	S	S																						
X	X	X	X				S							X	X	X	X	X	X	X	S	S	S	U	U	U										
Total Appearances																																				
2	2	2	2	1	1	1	1	1	1	1	0	0	0	1	1	1	1	1	1	1	0	0	0	0	0	0	1	1	1	1	1	1	0	0	0	0
0	0	0	0	0	0	0	1	0	0	0	1	1	1	1	0	0	0	0	0	0	1	1	1	0	0	0	0	0	0	0	0	0	1	1	1	1
0	0	0	0	0	0	0	0	0	0	0	0	0	0	0	1	1	1	0	0	0	0	0	0	1	1	1	0	0	0	0	0	0	0	0	0	0

ENGLAND'S RESULTS 1979 - 2010

BARBADOS
02.06.08 Bridgetown 2 - 0

BELGIUM
11.02.03 KV Ostend 1 - 3
04.11.03 Darlington 2 - 2
15.11.05 FC Racing Jets 2 - 0
19.05.09 Oxford United 0 - 1

BOSNIA & HERZEGOVINA
16.09.08 Grbavia Stadium 2 - 6

FINLAND UNDER-21
14.04.93 Woking 1 - 3
30.05.94 Aanekoski 0 - 2
01.06.07 FC Hakka 1 - 0
15.11.07 Helsinki 2 - 0

GIBRALTAR
27.04.82 Gibraltar 3 - 2
31.05.95 Gibraltar 3 - 2
21.05.08 Colwyn Bay 1 - 0

GRENADA
31.05.08 St. George's 1 - 1

HOLLAND
03.06.79 Stafford 1 - 0
07.06.80 Zeist 2 - 1
09.06.81 Lucca 2 - 0
03.06.82 Aberdeen 1 - 0
02.06.83 Scarborough 6 - 0
05.06.84 Palma 3 - 3
13.06.85 Vleuten 3 - 0
20.05.87 Kirkaldy 4 - 0
11.04.95 Aalsmeer 0 - 0
02.04.96 Irthlingborough 3 - 1
18.04.97 Appingedam 0 - 0
03.03.98 Crawley 2 - 1
30.03.99 Genemuiden 1 - 1
21.03.00 Northwich 1 - 0
22.03.01 Wihemina FC 3 - 0
24.04.02 Yeovil Town 1 - 0
25.03.03 BV Sparta 25 0 - 0
16.02.05 Woking 3 - 0
29.11.06 Burton Albion 4 - 1

HUNGARY
15.09.09 Szekesfehervar 1 - 1

IRAQ
27.05.04 Macclesfield 1 - 5

IRISH PREMIER LEAGUE XI
13.02.07 Glenavon FC 1 - 3

ITALY
03.06.80 Zeist 2 - 0
13.06.81 Montecatini 1 - 1
01.06.82 Aberdeen 0 - 0
31.05.83 Scarborough 2 - 0
09.06.84 Reggio Emilia 0 - 1
11.06.85 Houten 2 - 2
18.05.87 Dunfermline 1 - 2
29.01.89 La Spezia 1 - 1
25.02.90 Solerno 0 - 2
05.03.91 Kettering 0 - 0
01.03.99 Hayes 4 - 1
01.03.00 Padova 1 - 1
20.11.02 AC Cremonese 3 - 2
11.02.04 Shrewsbury 1 - 4
10.11.04 US Ivrea FC 1 - 0
15.02.06 Cambridge United 3 - 1
12.11.08 Benevento 2 - 2

MALTA UNDER-21
17.02.09 Malta 4 - 0

NORWAY UNDER-21
01.06.94 Slemmestad 1 - 2

POLAND
17.11.09 Gradiszk Wielpolski 2 - 1

REPUBLIC OF IRELAND
24.05.86 Kidderminster 2 - 1
26.05.86 Nuneaton 2 - 1
25.05.90 Dublin 2 - 1
27.05.90 Cork 3 - 0
27.02.96 Kidderminster 4 - 0
25.02.97 Dublin 0 - 2
16.05.02 Boston 1 - 2
20.05.03 Merthyr Tydfil 4 - 0
18.05.004 Deverondale 2 - 3
24.05.05 Cork 1 - 0
23.05.06 Eastbourne Boro' 2 - 0
22.05.07 Clachnacuddin 5 - 0
26.05.10 Waterford United 2 - 1

SCOTLAND
31.05.79 Stafford 5 - 1
05.06.80 Zeist 2 - 4
11.06.81 Empoli 0 - 0
05.06.82 Aberdeen 1 - 1
04.06.83 Scarborough 2 - 1
07.06.84 Modena 2 - 0
15.06.85 Harderwijk 1 - 3
23.05.87 Dunfermline 2 - 1
18.05.02 Kettering 2 - 0
24.05.03 Carmarthen Town 0 - 0
23.05.04 Deverondale 3 - 1
28.05.05 Cork 3 - 2
27.05.06 Eastbourne Boro' 2 - 0
25.05.07 Ross County 3 - 0
22.05.08 Colwyn Bay 1 - 0

USA
20.03.02 Stevenage Boro. 2 - 1
09.06.04 Charleston USA 0 - 0

WALES
27.03.84 Newtown 1 - 2
26.03.85 Telford 1 - 0
18.03.86 Merthyr Tydfil 1 - 3
17.03.87 Gloucester 2 - 2
15.03.88 Rhyl 2 - 0
21.03.89 Kidderminster 2 - 0
06.03.90 Merthyr Tydfil 0 - 0
17.05.91 Stafford 1 - 2
03.03.92 Aberystwyth 1 - 0
02.03.93 Cheltenham 2 - 1
22.02.94 Bangor 2 - 1
28.02.95 Yeovil Town 1 - 0
23.05.99 St Albans 2 - 1
16.05.00 Llanelli 1 - 1
13.02.01 Rushden & Dia. 0 - 0
14.05.02 Boston 1 - 1
22.05.03 Merthyr Tydfil 2 - 0
20.05.04 Keith FC 0 - 2
26.05.05 Cork 1 - 0
25.05.06 Eastbourne Boro' 1 - 1
27.05.07 Clachnacuddin 3 - 0
21.02.08 Exeter City 2 - 1
24.05.08 Rhyl 3 - 0

RESULTS SUMMARY 1979 - 2010	P	W	D	L	F	A
Barbados	1	1	0	0	2	0
Belgium	4	1	1	2	5	6
Bosnia & Herzegovina	1	0	0	1	2	6
Finland Under-21	4	2	0	2	4	5
Grenada	1	0	1	0	1	1
Gibraltar	3	3	0	0	7	4
Holland	19	14	5	0	40	8
Hungary	1	0	1	0	1	1
Iraq	1	0	0	1	1	5
Irish Premier League XI	1	0	0	1	1	3
Italy	17	5	7	4	23	21
Malta	1	1	0	0	4	0
Norway Under-21	1	0	0	1	1	2
Poland	1	1	0	0	2	1
Republic of Ireland	13	10	0	3	30	11
Scotland	15	10	3	2	30	15
USA	2	1	1	0	2	1
Wales	23	13	6	4	32	18
TOTALS	**109**	**62**	**25**	**21**	**188**	**108**

GOALSCORERS 1979 - 2010

13 GOALS...
Carter, Mark

7 GOALS...
Cole, Mitchell

6 GOALS...
Ashford, Noel

5 GOALS...
Davison, Jon
Williams, Colin

4 GOALS...
Culpin, Paul
D'Sane, Roscoe
Johnson, Jeff
Mackhail-Smith, Craig

3 GOALS...
Adamson, David
Guinan, Steve
Grayson,Neil
Hatch, Liam
Kirk, Jackson
Morison, Steve
Morrison, Michael
Opponents
Watkins, Dale

2 GOALS...
Alford, Carl
Barrett, Keith
Bishop, Andrew
Burgess, Andrew
Casey, Kim
Cordice, Neil
Elding, Anthony
Hayles, Barry
Hill, Kenny
Howell, David
Mutrie, Les
Patmore, Warren

2 goals continued....
Richards, Justin
Seddon, Gareth
Southam, Glen
Watson, John
Weatherstone, Simon
Whitbread, Barry

1 GOAL...
Agana, Tony
Anderson, Dale
Ashton, John
Barnes-Homer, Matthew
Benson, Paul
Blackburn, Chris
Boardman, Jon
Bolton, Jimmy
Boyd, George
Bradshaw, Mark
Briscoe, Louis
Brown, Paul
Browne, Corey
Carey-Bertram, Daniel
Carr, Michael
Cavell, Paul
Charles, Lee
Charley, Ken
Charnock, Kieran
Constable, James
Crittenden, Nick
Davies, Paul
Day, Matt
Densmore, Shaun
Drummond, Stewart
Fleming, Andrew
Furlong, Paul
Grant, John
Harrad, Shaun
Hine, Mark
Holroyd, Chris
Humphreys, Delwyn
Kennedy, John
Kerr, Scott
Kimmins,Ged
King, Simon
Leworthy, David
McDougald, Junior
Mayes, Bobby
Moore, Neil
Moore, Luke
Newton, Sean
O'Keefe, Eamon
Oli, Dennis
Penn, Russell
Pitcher, Geoff
Porter, Max
Ricketts, Sam
Robbins, Terry
Robinson, Mark
Roddis,Nick
Rodgers, Luke
Rogers, Paul
Ryan, Tim
Sellars, Neil
Shaw, John
Sheldon, Gareth
Simpson, Josh
Sinclair, Dean
Smith, Ian
Smith, Ossie
Stansfield, Adam
Stephens,Mickey
Stott, Steve
Taylor, Steve
Thurgood, Stuart
Tubbs, Matthew
Venables, David
Way, Darren
Webb, Paul
Wilcox, Russ

ENGLAND SEMI-PROFESSIONALS, NATIONAL GAME XI AND ENGLAND 'C' CAPS 1979 - 2010

KEY TO COUNTRY CODES:

Ba - Barbados B - Belgium BH - Bosnia & Herzegovina
E - Eire F - Finland G - Gibraltar Gr - Granada H - Holland Hu - Hungary
I - Italy IP - Irish Premier Lge IQ - Iraq M - Malta N - Norway P - Poland
S - Scotland W - Wales US - U.S.A.

2009-10 DEBUTANTS	
Matthew Barnes-Homer (Luton Town) **10** v P, E	2
Louis Briscoe (Mansfield Town) **10** v Hu	1
Tom Cadmore (Hayes & Yeading United) **10** v H, E	2
Sam Deering (Oxford United) **10** v E	1
Scott Garner **10** v Hu	1
Matt Green **10** v Hu	1
Steven Gregory (AFC Wimbledon) **10** v E	1
Ryan Hall (Bromley) **10** v E	1
John Hedge (FC Halifax Town) **10** v P	1
Chris Holroyd (Cambridge United) **10** v H, P	2
Jake Howells (Luton Town) **10** v P	1
Rossi Jarvis (Luton Town) **10** v H, P, E	3
Natt Knight-Percival **10** v Hu	1
Kyle McFadzean (Alfreton Town) **10** v H, E	2
Amari Morgan-Smith (Ilkeston Town) **10** v E	1
Kyle Nix **10** v Hu	1
Curtis Obeng (Wrexham) **10** v E	1
Max Porter (Rushden & Diamonds) **10** v P, E	2
Jai Reason (Cambridge United) **10** v P	1
Sam Rents **10** v Hu	1
Callum Reynolds (Luton Town) **10** v Hu	1
Alex Rodman (Oxford United) **10** v E	1
Josh Simpson **10** v Hu	1
Lee Vaughan **10** v Hu	1
Joe Welch **10** v Hu	1
Nick Wright (Tamworth) **10** v H, P	2
Gary Abbott (Welling) **87** v I(s), S(s), 92 W(s)	3
David Adamson (Boston Utd) **79 v** S, H **80** v I,S, H	5
Les Afful (Forest Green Rovers) **07** v H, IP	2
Tony Agana (Weymouth) **86** v E	1
Junior Agogo (Barnet) **03** v H, i (s), S	3
Danny Alcock (Stafford Rangers) **07** v IP	1
Carl Alford (Kettering T. & Rushden & Ds) **96** v E,H	2
Dale Anderson (Burton Albion) **02** v H **03** v I	2
Mark Angel (Boston United) **02** v W(s), E, S	3
Ian Arnold (Kettering Town) **95** v W(s), H	2
Jim Arnold (Stafford Rangers) **79** v S, H	2
Nathan Arnold (Mansfield Town) **09** v BH	1
Steve Arnold (Grays Athletic) **09** v M	1
Nick Ashby (Kettering & Rushden & Diamonds) **94** v F, N, **95** v G **96** v E, H	5
Noel Ashford (Enfield & Redbridge Forest.) **82 v** G,H,S. **83 v** I,H,S, **84** W,H,S,I, **85** W,I(s), **86** E,E, **87** W(s), I,H,S. **90** v W,E **91** I(s)	21
John Ashton (Rushden & Diamonds) **07** v E, S, W, F	4
John Askey (Macclesfield) **90** v W	1
Ryan Austin (Burton Albion) **06** v I. **07** v H.	2
Danny Bacon (Hucknall Town) **04** v IQ	1
Carl Baker (Southport) **06** v I. **07** v F.	2
Matt Baker (Hereford United) **03** v I, S, **04** E,S,IQ,US	6
Nicky Bailey (Barnet) **05** v H, E, S, W.	4
Stephen Bailey (Grays Athletic) **09** v BH	1
Paul Bancroft (Kidderminster H.) **89** v I,W **90** I,W.E, **91** v W	6
Chris Banks (Cheltenham T.) **98** v H, 99 W	2
Keith Barrett (Enfield) **81** v H,S,I **82 v** G,I,H,S **83** v I,H,S **84** v W(s), H, S **85** I,H,S	16
Adam Bartlett (Blyth Spartans) **07** v F. **08** v G,W,Ba. **09** v I,B	6
Laurence Batty (Woking) **93** v F(s), **95** v W,H,G	4
Mark Beeney (Maidstone) **89** v I(s)	1
Paul Beesley (Chester C.) **01** v H(s)	1
Dean Bennett (Kidderminster H) **00** v W(s)	1
Paul Benson (Dagenham & Redbridge) **07** v IP.	1
Graham Benstead (Kettering) **94** v W,F,N(s)	3
Kevin Betsy (Woking) **98** v H(s)	1
Marcus Bignot (Kidderminster H) **97** v H	1
Andy Bishop (York City) **05** v I,H. **06** v B,I.	4
Neil Bishop (York City) **07** v E, W.	2
James Bittner (Exeter City) **04** v B,I	2
Chris Blackburn (Chester C. & Morecambe) **03** v I. **05** v I,H. **06** v I.	4
Shane Blackett (Dagenham & Red). **06** v E,S.	2
Greg Blundell (Northwich Victoria) **03** v H	1
Jon Boardman (Woking) **03** v I, S. **04** I,W,US	5
Jimmy Bolton (Kingstonian) **95** v G	1
Steve Book (Cheltenham Town) **99 v** I,H,W	3
Michael Bostwick (Stevenage Borough) **09** v I	1
George Boyd (Stevenage Boro') **06** v B,I,E,W,S. **07** v H.	6
Adam Boyes (York City) **09** v M	1
Lee Boylan (Canvey Island) **04** v US	1
Gary Brabin (Runcorn) **94 v** W,F,N	3
Mark Bradshaw (Halifax T.) **98** v H	1
Leon Braithwaite (Margate) **02** v US	1
John Brayford (Burton Albion) **08** v F,W,G,S,W,Gr,Ba.	7
Paul Brayson (Northwich Victoria) **07** v S.	1
Colin Brazier (Kidderminster) **87** v W	1
David Bridges (Cambridge Utd) **06** v I	1
Stewart Brighton (Bromsgrove) **94** v W	1
Richard Brodie (York City) **09** v BH. **10** v P	2
Steve Brooks (Cheltenham) **88** v W(s) **90** v W,E	3
Derek Brown (Woking) **94 v** F(s),N	2
Kevan Brown (Woking) **95** v W,H,G **96** v H **97** v E	5
Paul Brown (Barrow) **09** v M	1
Wayne Brown (Chester C.) **01** v W, H(s), **02** v US, H(s),W,S. **03** v H	7
Corey Browne (Dover) **94** v F(s),N(s), **95** v H(s)	3
Liam Brownhill (Witton Albion) **08** v F,W.	2

David Buchanan (Blyth) **86** v E(s),E	2
Nicki Bull (Aldershot Town) **03** v B. **04** v I, H, E.	4
Andrew Burgess (Oxford United/Rushden & Dia.) **07** v E,S,W. **08** v G,S,W,Gr,Ba.	8
Brian Butler (Northwich) **93** v F	1
Steve Butler (Maidstone) **88** v W, **89** **v** I,W	3
Gary Butterworth (Rushden & Diamonds) **97** v E,H **98** **v** H **99** v I,H,W **00** v I	7
Chris Byrne (Macclesfield T.) **97** v H	1
Joel Byrom (Northwich Victoria) **09** v B	1
Michael Byron (Droylsden) **09** v M	1
DJ Campbell (Yeading) **05** v E, S.	2
Paul Carden (Burton Albion) **07** v E,W.	2
Daniel Carey-Bertram (Hereford Utd) **06** v B	1
Danny Carlton (Morecambe) **04** v IQ	1
Michael Carr (Northwich) **06** v B,I,E,W,S. **07** v H.IP.	7
Mark Carter (Runcorn & Barnet) v **87** **v** W,I,H,S **88** v W, **89** **v** I,W, **90** v I,E, **91** v I,W(s)	11
Kim Casey (Kidderminster) **86** v W,E,E(s), **87** **v** W,I	5
Paul Cavell (Redbridge) **92** v W **93** v F	2
Peter Cavanagh (Accrington) **04** v B,I,E	3
Jon Challinor (Aldershot Town) **04** v B,I	2
Lewis Chalmers (Altrincham/Aldershot) **07** v H,E,S,F. **08** v F,W,G,W,Gr,Ba.	10
Darius Charles (Ebbsfleet United) **09** v B. **10** v P	2
Lee Charles (Hayes) **99** v I(s), H(s), W(s)	3
Anthony Charles (Aldershot/Farnborough) **04** v B,I	2
Kevin Charlton (Telford) **85** v W,I	2
Ken Charlery (Boston U) **01** v H(s)	1
Kieran Charnock (Northwich) **05** v E,W. **06** v B,I,E,W,S. **07** v H,IP,E,W.	11
Andrew Clarke (Barnet) **90** v E,E	2
David Clarke (Blyth Spartans) **80** v I,S(s),H, **81** v H,S,I **82** v I,H,S **83** v H,S **84** v H,S,I	14
Gary Clayton (Burton) **86** v E	1
Paul Clayton (Alfreton Town) **09** v M,B	2
Robert Codner (Barnet) **88** v W	1
Mitchell Cole (Stevenage Borough) **07** v E,S,W,F. **08** v W,G,S,W,Gr,Ba. **09** v BH,I.	12
John Coleman (Morecambe) **93** v F(s)	1
Darren Collins (Enfield) **93** v F(s), **94** v W,F,N	4
Matt Collins (Nuneaton Borough) **04** v I	1
Andy Comyn (Hednesford T.) **98** **v** H(s), **99** **v** I(s),H(s),W(s)	4
Steve Conner (Dartford, Redbridge & Dagenham & R) **90** v I **91** v I,W **92** v W **93** v F.	5
James Constable (Kidderminster & Oxford Utd) **08** v F. **09** I,B	3
David Constantine (Altrincham) **85** v I,H,S **86** **v** W	4
Robbie Cooke (Kettering) **89** v W(s), **90** v I	2
Scott Cooksey (Hednesford T.) **97** v E, **98** vH(s) **01** v W(s),H	4
Alan Cordice(Wealdstone)**83** v I,H,S **84** vW,S(s), I(s),**85** I,H,S	9
Rob Cousins (Yeovil Town) **00** **I** v I(s),H,W	3
Gavin Cowan (Canvey Island) **04** v B,IQ	2
Ken Cramman (Gateshead & Rushden & Diamonds) **96** v E **97** v E,H	3
Ian Craney (Altrincham & Accrington) **03** v B. **04** US. **05** I. **06** v B,I,E,W.	7
Nick Crittendon (Yeovil Town) **02** v US (s)	1
Lance Cronin (Ebbsfleet United) **07** v H,E,W,F. **08** v F,W. **09** vBH	7
Paul Cuddy (Altrincham) **87** v I,H,S	3
Paul Culpin (Nuneaton B) **84** v W, **85** v W(s) ,I,H,S	5
Jonathan D'Laryea (Mansfield Town) **09** v Bh,I.	2
Michael Danzey (Woking) **99** v I,H	2
Paul Davies (Kidderminster H.) **86** v W, **87** **v** W,I,S, **88** **v** W **89** v W	6
John Davison (Altrincham) **79** v S,H **80** v I,S, **81** **v** H,S ,I. **82** **v** G,I,H,S **83** I,H,S. **84** W,H,I,S **85** **v** I,H,S 86 **v** W,E,E.	24
Matt Day (Oxford United) **09** v BH	1
John Denham (Northwich Victoria) **80** v H	1
Peter Densmore (Runcorn) **88** v W **89** v I	2
Shaun Densmore (Altrincham) **09** v M,B. **10** v P,E.	4
Phil Derbyshire (Mossley) **83** v H(s) S(s)	2
Scott Doe (Weymouth) **09** v M.	1
Mick Doherty (Weymouth) **86** v W(s)	1
Neil Doherty (Kidderminster H.) **97** v E	1
Clayton Donaldson (York City) **07** v H,IP.	2
Stuart Drummond (Morecambe) **00** v I(s),H ,W **01** **v** W ,H **02** v US, W,E(s), S **03** v H, I, W, S (s)	13
Roscoe D'Sane (Aldershot Town) **03** v B(s),H(s),E,W,S. **04** B,I	7
Chris Duffy (Canvey Island) **03** v B	1
Neil Durkin (Leigh RMI) **02** v H(s)	1
Lee Elam (Morecambe) **03** v H,E,W,S)s)	4
Anthony Elding (Stevenage Borough) **04** v B. **05** v I,H,E,W,S.	6
Paul Ellender (Scarborough) **01** v W(s)	1
Lee Endersby (Harrow Bor.) **96** **v** H	1
Mick Farrelly (Altrincham) **87** **v** I,H,S	3
Steve Farrelly (Macclesfield & Kingstonian) **95** v H(s),G(s), **00** v I,H,W(s)	5
Trevor Finnegan (Weymouth) **81** v H,S	2
Murray Fishlock (Yeovil Town) **99** v H(s)	1
Andrew Fleming (Wrexham) **09** v B. **10** v E.	2
Richard Forsyth (Kidderminster) **95** v W,H,G	3
Danny Foster (Dagenham & Redbridge) **07** v E,S,F.	3
Ian Foster (Kidderminster H) **00** v W(s)	1
Luke Foster (Oxford United) **09** v BH.	1
Amos Foyewa (Woking) **04** v E,W,S	3
Barry Fuller (Stevenage Borough) **07** v IP.	1
Paul Furlong (Enfield) **90** **v** I,E,E **91** v I,W	5
Mark Gardiner (Macclesfield T.) **97** v E	1
Exodus Geohaghon (Kettering Town) **09** v I,B.	2
Jerry Gill (Yeovil T.) **97** v E	1

MANAGERS 1979 - 2010

		P	W	D	L	F	A
1979	Howard Wilkinson	2	2	0	0	6	1
1980 - 1984	Keith Wright	17	9	5	3	30	16
1985 - 1988	Kevin Verity	12	7	2	3	23	15
1989 - 1996	Tony Jennings	19	10	4	5	27	18
1997	Ron Reid	2	0	1	1	0	2
1998 - 2002	John Owens	14	8	5	1	22	10
2002 -	Paul Fairclough	43	26	8	9	80	46

Matt Glennon (Carlisle Utd) **05** v W,S. 2
Dan Gleeson (Cambridge Utd) **08** v F,W,G,S,Gr,Ba. **09** v I. 7
John Glover (Maidstone Utd) **85** v W,I,H,S 4
Mark Golley (Sutton Utd.) **87** v H(s),S, **88** v W, **89** v I,W, **92** v W 6
Jason Goodliffe (Hayes) **00** v I, H,W, **01** W **02** US, W,E,S. 8
Paul Gothard (Dagenham & Redb.) **97** v E(s), **99** v I(s),W(s) 3
Jeff Goulding (Fisher Athletic) **08** v W. 1
Mark Gower (Barnet) **02** v H, W, E, S(s) 4
Simon Grand (Carlisle) **05** v H. 1
John Grant (Aldershot Town) **07** v E,S,W,F. 4
Neil Grayson (Cheltenham T.) **98** v H **99** v I,H,W 4
Phil Gridelet (Hendon & Barnet) **89** v I,W, **90** v W,E,E 5
Scott Griffiths (Dagenham & Redbridge) **07** v H,IP. 2
Steve Guinan (Hereford) **04** v E,W,S,US 4
Steve Guppy (Wycombe W.) **93** v W 1
Scott Guyett (Southport) **01** v H, **03** v H,I,W,S. 5
Tim Hambley (Havant & Waterlooville) **02** v H 1
Steve Hanlon (Macclesfield) **90** v W 1
Ben Harding (Aldershot) **08** v W,G,W. 3
David Harlow (Farnborough T.) **97** v E(s),H 2
Shaun Harrad (Burton Albion) **07** v F. **08** v F,W,G,S,W,Gr,Ba. **09** v BH,I. 8
Stephen Haslam (Halifax) **05** v E,W,S. 3
Liam Hatch (Barnet) **04** v E,W,S,IQ,US. **05** H. 6
Wayne Hatswell (Chester City/Cambridge Utd) **03** v E(s),W(s). **08** v S,W,Gr,Ba. 6
Karl Hawley (Carlisle Utd) **05** v I,H. 2
Barry Hayles (Stevenage Bor.) **96** v E,H 2
Greg Heald (Barnet) **02** v H 1
Brian Healy (Morecambe) **98** v H 1
Liam Hearn (Alfreton Town) **09** v B. 1
Ronnie Henry (Stevenage Boro) **06** v S. **07** v IP. **08** v F,W. 4
Tony Hemmings (Northwich) **93** v F 1
Andy Hessenthaler (Dartford) **90** v I 1
Kenny Hill (Maidstone Utd) **80** v I,S,H 3
Mark Hine (Gateshead) **95** v W(s),H 2
Simeon Hodson (Kidderminster) **94** v W,F,N 3
Lewis Hogg (Barnet) **04** v B 1
Colin Hogarth (Guiseley) **95 v** W,H 2
Steven Holden (Kettering) **94** v W,F,N(s) **95** v H,G 5
Ricky Holmes (Chelmsford City) **08** v W. 1
Mark Hone (Welling United) **90** v I **93** v F, **94** vW(s),F(s),N 5
Gary Hooley (Frickley) **85** v W 1
Dean Hooper (Kingstonian) **98** v H 1
Keith Houghton (Blyth Spartans) **79** v S 1
Barry Howard (Altrincham) **81** v H,S,I **82** v G,I,H,S 7
Neil Howarth (Macclesfield) **95** v H(s) **97** v E 2
David Howell (Enfield) **85** v H(s),S(s) **86** v W,E **87** v W,I,H,S **88** v W, **89** v I,W **90** v I,E,E 14
Lee Howells (Cheltenham T.) **98** v H **99 v** W 2
Lee Hughes (Kidderminster Harriers) **96** v E,H **97** v E,H 4
Delwyn Humphreys (Kidderminster H.) **91** v W(s) **92** v W **94** v W,F,N **95** v W,H 7
Steve Humphries (Barnet) **87** v H(s) 1
Nicky Ironton (Enfield) **83** H(s) **84** v W 2
Jimmy Jackson (Gravesend & Northfleet) 03 v H(s) 1
Simon Jackson (Woking) **05** v I. 1
Justin Jackson (Morecambe & Rushden & Diamonds) **00** v W **01** v W 2
Kirk Jackson (Stevenage Borough) **02** v US, E,S,(Yeovil Town) **03** v E,W,S(s) 6

Shwan Jalal (Woking) **05** v H. **06** v I,E,W,S. 5
Mark Janney (Dagenham & Redbridge) **03** v H 1
Tony Jennings (Enfield) **79** v S,H **80** v I,S,H **81 v** H,S,I **82** v G,I,H,S 12
Jeff Johnson (Altrincham) **81** v S,I **82** v G,I,H,S **83** v I,H,S **84 v** H,S,I **84 v** I,H,S **86** v W(s),E,E 18
Lee Johnson (Yeovil Town) **03** v I, H(s), E, W, S 5
Paul Jones (Exeter City) **06** v I 1
Steve Jones (Leigh RMI) **01** v H 1
Tom Jones (Weymouth) **87** v W 1
Tom Jordan (Tamworth) **04** v B 1
Antone Joseph(Telford U. & Kidderm'terH.)**84** v S(s), **85** v W,I, H,S **86** v W(s), **87** W,I(s),H, **88** v W **89** v I,W **90 v** I,E,E 15
John Keeling (Purfleet) **03** v B(s) 1
Marcus Kelly (Rushden & Diamonds) **07** v IP. 1
Darran Kempson (Morecambe) **06** v E,W. 2
John Kennedy (Canvey Island) **03** v I, B, H, E, W, S. **04** IQ,US 8
Jon Kennedy (Accrington) **04** v I,IQ,US 3
Andy Kerr (Wycombe) **93** v W 1
Scott Kerr (Scarborough) **04** v E,W,S,IQ. **05** v I,H,E,W,S 9
Lance Key (Kingstonian) 03 v B 1
Ged Kimmins (Hyde Utd.) **96** v E(s),H(s) **97 v** E(s) 3
Simon King (Barnet) **05** v I,H,S. 3
Scott Laird (Stevenage Borough) **09** v B. 1
Mike Lake (Macclesfield) **89** v I 1
Martin Lancaster (Chester City) **03** vI (s)
Andy Lee (Telford U. & Witton A.) **89** I(s), **91** v I,W 3
Arran Lee-Barrett (Weymouth) **07** v H. 1
Stuart Lewis (Stevenage Borough) **08** v F. 1
David Leworthy (Farnborough & Rushden & Diamonds) **93 v** W, **94** v W **97** v E,H 4
Adam Lockwood (Yeovil Town) **02** v E **03** v I 2
Stacey Long (Gravesend & Northfleet) **07** v IP. 1
Kenny Lowe (Barnet) **91 v** I,W 2
Craig McAllister (Basingstoke Town) **03** v B 1
Martin McDonald (Macclesfield) **95** v G(s) 1
Danny McDonnell (Worcester City) **04** v W 1
Junior MacDougald (Dagenham & Redbridge) **01** v H(s) **02** W, E(s), S(s) 4
Mark McGregor (Forest Green Rovers & Nuneaton Borough) **00** v I(s),H(s) **01** v W(s) 3
Kevin McIntyre (Doncaster Rovers) **00 v** H(s)W, **01 v** W(s)H 4
John McKenna (Boston Utd) **88 v** W(s), **90** v I,E,E. **91 v** I,W, **92** vW 7
Aaron McLean (Aldershot & Grays) **04** v B,I. **06** v E,W,S. 5
Lewis McMahon (Gainsborough Trinity) **09** v M. 1
David McNiven (Leigh RMI) **04** v W,S,IQ,US 4
Chris McPhee (Ebbsfleet Utd) **08** v G,S,W. 3
Craig Mackhail-Smith (Dag. & Red.) **05** v W,S. **06** v I,E,W,S. **07** v H. 7
Tamika Mkandawire (Hereford Utd) **06** v B,I. 2
Fiston Manuella (Aylesbury United) **03** v B 1
John Margerrison (Barnet) **87 v** W 1
Simon Marples (Doncaster Rovers) **00 v** I,H 2
John Martin (Stevenage Borough) **08** v G,S,W. 3
Leroy May (Stafford R.) **95 v** G(s) 1
Bobby Mayes (Redbridge) **92 v** W
Paul Mayman (Northwich Vic) **80 v** I,S 2
Stewart Mell (Burton) **85v** W 1
Neil Merrick (Weymouth) **80** v I(s),S 2
Adam Miller (Aldershot Town) **04** v I 1
Russell Milton (Dover) 94 v F,N 2

MOST CAPPED PLAYER

	Club	Caps	Seasons
John Davison	Altrincham	24	1979 - 1986

Player	Caps
Mark Molesley (Aldershot Town) **07** v E,S,W,F.	4
Luke Moore (Ebbsfleet United) **09** v BH.	1
Neil Moore (Telford United) **02** v US (s),H, W, E,S	5
Steve Morison (Stevenage Borough) **07** v H,IP,F. **08** v G,S,W,Gr,Ba.	8
Trevor Morley (Nuneaton) **84 v** W,H,S,I **85 v** W,S(s)	6
Michael Morrison (Cambridge Utd) **07** v H. **08** v F,W,G,S,W,Gr,Ba.	8
Dean Moxey (Exeter City) **05** v H. **08** v W,S.	3
Chris Murphy (Telford United) **04** v B	1
Karl Murrphy (Woking) **04** v B,I	2
Tarkan Mustafa (Rushden & Diamonds) **01** v W,H	2
Les Mutrie (Blyth Spartans) **79 v** S,H, **80** v I,S,H	5
Mark Newson (Maidstone U) **84 v** W,H,S,I, **85 v** W	5
Doug Newton (Burton) **85** v W,H,S	3
Shaun Newton (Droylsden) **09** v M,B. **10** v P,E.	4
Paul Nicol (Kettering T) **91 v** I,W, **92** v W	3
Kevin Nicholson (Forest Green Rovers/Torquay Utd) **07** v E.S.W. **08** v G,S,W,Gr,Ba.	8
Richard Norris (Northwich Victoria) **03** v H, S,	2
Steve Norris (Telford) **88** v W(s)	1
John Nutter (Grays) **06** v E,W,S.	3
Joe O'Connor (Hednesford T.) **97 v** E,H(s)	2
Eamon O'Keefe (Mossley) **79 v** S,H	2
Erkan Okay (Histon) **08** v F.	1
Dennis Oli (Grays) **06** v B,E,W,S. **07** v H.	5
Luke Oliver (Woking) **05** v H.	1
Frank Ovard (Maidstone) **81** v H(s),S(s),I(s)	3
Andy Pape (Harrow Bor. & Enfield) **85** v W(s,)H,S. **86** v W(s),E, **87** v W,I,H,S **88** v W, **89** IW, **90** I,W,E	15
Brian Parker (Yeovil Town) **80 v** S	1
Warren Patmore (Yeovil Town) **99** v I,H,W, **00 v** I,H, **01** W,H	7
Gary Patterson (Kingstonian) **99** v I,H, **00** v H,W, **01 v** W,H	7
Steve Payne (Macclesfield T.) **97 v** H	1
Trevor Peake (Nuneaton Bor) **79 v** S,H	2
David Pearce (Harrow Bor) **84 v** I(s)	1
Russell Penn (Kidderminster) **08** v F,W,G,W,Gr,Ba. **09** v I,B.	8
David Perkins (Morecambe) **04** v B,I,E,S,IQ,US. **05** v I. **06** v B,I.	9
Warren Peyton (Nuneaton Borough) **02** v H(s) **03** v I	2
Brendan Phillips (Nuneaton Bor. & Kettering T.), **79 v** S,H, **80 v** S(s),H.	4
Gary Philips (Barnet) **82 v** G	1
Owen Pickard (Yeovil T.) **98** v H(s)	1
Geoff Pitcher (Kingstonian) **99 v** W, **00 v** I,H,W, **01** v W,H	6
Jon-Paul Pitman (Crawley Town) **09** v I.	1
Phil Power (Macclesfield T.) **96** v E(s),H(s)	2
Ryan Price (Stafford R. & Macclesfield) **92** v W(s) **93** v W,F. **96** v E,H **97** v H.	6
Steve Prindiville **98 v** H(s)	1
Andy Proctor (Accrington Stanley) **04** v IQ	1
Marc Pullan (Crawley Town) **03** v B	1
Robert Purdie (Hereford United) **04** v I. **05** v I.	2
Wayne Purser (Barnet) **03** v I	1
Mark Quayle (Telford United) **02** v H	1
Adam Quinn (Halifax Town) **07** v H,IP,E,S,W,F.	6
Simon Read (Farnborough) **92** v W(s)	1
Matt Redmile (Barnet) **04** v E,W,S	3
Andy Reid (Altrincham) **95 v** W	1
Martin Rice (Exeter City) **07** v IP.	1
Carl Richards (Enfield) **86 v** E	1
Justin Richards (Woking) **06** v E,W,S.	3
Derek Richardson (Maidstone U) **83 v** I, **84 v** W, **86** v E	4
Ian Richardson (Dagenham & Red) **95 v** G	1
Kevin Richardson (Bromsgrove) **94** v W,F,N	3
Paul Richardson (Redbridge) **92** v W, **93 v** W, F	3
Scott Rickards (Tamworth) **03** v B. **04** B	2
Sam Ricketts (Telford) **04** v B,E,W,S	4
Adriano Rigoglioso (Morecambe) **03** v H(s)	1
Martin Riley (Kidderminster Harriers) **09** v M.	1
Anthony Rivierre (Welling United) **03** v B	1
Terry Robbins (Welling) **92 v** W, **93** v W,F, **94** v W,F,N	6
Dale Roberts (Rushden & Diamonds) **09** v M. **10** v H,P,E.	4
Gary Roberts (Accrington) **06** v I,E,W,S.	4
Anton Robinson (Weymouth) **09** v BH,I.	2
Mark Robinson (Hereford) **05** v E,W,S.	3
Peter Robinson (Blyth S) **83 v** I,H,S **84** W,I 85 v W	6
Ryan Robinson (Morecambe) **06** v B.	1
Nick Roddis (Woking) **01 v** H **02** US,H,W,E(s),S	6
Luke Rodgers (Shrewsbury) **04** v B,I.	2
John Rogers (Altrincham) **81 v** H,S,I **82 v** I(s),S	5
Paul Rogers (Sutton) **89** v W, **90** v I, E(2), **91** I,W	6
Colin Rose (Witton Alb.) **96 v** E(s), H	2
Kevin Rose (Kidderminster) **94 v** F(s),N	2
Michael Rose (Hereford United) **03** v I, H, E, S	4
Brian Ross (Marine) **93 v** W(s),F(s), **94** v W(s) **95 v** W,H	5
Carl Ruffer (Chester City) **01** v H(s)	1
Tim Ryan (Southport & Doncaster Rovers) **98 v** H. **99 v** I,H,W, **00 v** I,H,W **01** v W,H **02** v US,H,W,I,S	14
Gareth Seddon (Hyde United) **07** v E.W.	2
Jake Sedgemore (Shrewsbury) **04** v E,W,S,IQ,US.	5
Neil Sellars (Scarboro) **81** v H,S,I **82** v G,H(s),S, **83 v** I,H,S	9
Mark Shail (Yeovil T.) **93** v W	1
John Shaw (Halifax Town) **08** v G,S,W,Gr,Ba.	5
Jon Shaw (Burton Albion) **06** v I.	1
Simon Shaw (Doncaster Rovers) **99** v I,H	2
Tom Shaw (Tamworth) **09** v M. **10** v P.	2
Peter Shearer (Cheltenham) **89 v** I(s)	1
Gareth Sheldon (Exeter) **04** v I,E,W,S,IQ,US.	6
Paul Shirtliff (Frickley A. & Boston U.) **86** vE,E **87** v W,I,H. **88** v W **89 v** I, W, **90 v** I,W,E,E, **92 v** W **93** v W,F	15
Paul Showler (Altrincham) **91** v I(s),W	2
Tim Sills (Kingstonian) **03** v B	1
Gordon Simmonite (Boston United) **79** v S(s,)H(s), **80** v I,S,H	5
Gary Simpson(Stafford R.) **86** v E,E, **87** v I,H,S,**90** v I,W,E,E	9
Josh Simpson (Histon) **09** v I.	1
Wayne Simpson (Stafford) **94** v F,N(s)	2
Dean Sinclair (Barnet) **05** v I,H,E,W,S.	5
Terry Skiverton (Yeovil Town) **01 v** W **02 v** US **03** v 1,W,	4
Glenn Skivington (Barrow) **90** v I,W,E **91** v I,W	5
Jamie Slabber (Grays) **06** v B.	1

Player	Caps
Adrian Smith (Kidderminster H) **00** v I(s),H(s),W	3
Alan Smith (Alvechurch) **82** v G,I,S	3
Ian Smith (Mossley) **80** v I,S,H(s)	3
James Smith (Ebbsfleet Utd) **08** v Gr,Ba. **09** v BH,I.	4
Mark Smith (Stevenage Bor.) **96** v E,H **98** v H **99** v I,H,W. **00** v I,H,W(s).	9
Ossie Smith (Runcorn) **84** v W	1
Phil Smith (Margate) **04** v B	1
Tim Smithers (Nuneaton) **85** v W(s),I **86** v W	3
Guiseppe Sole (Woking) **07** v H,IP,F.	3
Adam Sollitt (Kettering Town) **00** v I(s),H(s),W	3
Leon Solomon (Welling United) **07** v F.	1
Glen Southam (Bishop's Stort' & Dag & R.) **04** v E,W,S,IQ,US. **05** v W,S. **06** v S. **07** v E,S,W,F.	12
Craig Stanley (Hereford & Morecambe) **05** v E,W. **07** v H,IP.	4
Adam Stansfield (Yeovil Town & Hereford) **02** v W (s), I, S **05** v E,S.	5
Simon Stapleton (Wycombe) **93** v W	1
Mickey Stephens (Sutton), **82** v G,S(s) **86 v** W,E,E(s)	5
Jamie Stevens (Crawley Town) **09** v BH.	1
Billy Stewart (Southport) **98** v H	1
Mark Stimson (Canvey Islland) **02** v US	1
Bob Stockley (Nuneaton Borough) **80** v H	1
David Stockdale (York) **05** v I.	1
Darren Stride (Burton Albion) **02** v H	1
Steve Stott (Kettering T., Rushden & Ds & Yeovil T.) **95** v W,H(s),G **96** v E,H **99** v H,W(s)	7
Ryan Sugden (Chester City) 03 v I	1
Ben Surey (Gravesend & Nflt.) **05** v I.	1
Andy Taylor (Exeter City) **05** v E,W,S.	3
James Taylor (Havant & Waterlooville) **02** v H,W, E(s),S(s)	4
Peter Taylor (Maidstone) **84** v HSI	3
Steve Taylor (Bromsgrove R.) **95** v G	1
Shaun Teale (Weymouth) **88** v W	1
Paul Terry (Dagenham & Redbridge) **03** vE (s), W(s), S	3
Stuart Terry (Altrincham) **95** v W	1
Brian Thompson(Yeovil & Maidstone) **79** v S,H **81** v H,S,I. **82** v I,H,S **83** v I,H,S **84** v W,H,S,I	15
Neil Thompson (Scarborough) **87** v W,I,H,S	4
Garry Thompson (Morecambe) **03** v I. **04** v E,W,IQ,US	5
Steve Thompson (Wycombe) **93** v W	1
Stuart Thurgood (Grays Ath.) **05** v I,H. **06** v E,W,S.	5
Kevin Todd (Berwick Rangers) **91** v W	1
Lee Tomlin (Rushden & Diamonds) **09** v M,B.	2
Mike Tomlinson (Runcorn F.C.Halton) **03** v B (s)	1
Anthony Tonkin (Yeovil Town) **02** v US	1
Simon Travis (Forest Green R & Hereford) **02 v** US, H. **05** v E. **06** v E,W,S.	6
Carl Tremarco (Wrexham) **09** v I.	1
Andy Tretton (Hereford) **04** v E,W,S,US	4
Matthew Tubbs (Salisbury City) **07** v E. **08** v F.	2
Mark Tucker (Woking) **96** v E	1
Tony Turner (Telford) **85 v** W	1
Scott Tynan (Rushden & Diamonds) **07** v S,W. **08** v S,Gr.	4
Paul Underwood (Rushden & D) **99** v I,H **00 v** I01 v W	4
David Venables(Stevenage B)**94 v** W(s)**95 v** H,G**96 v** E,H(s)	5
Jamie Victory (Cheltenham T.) **98** vH(s)	1
Ashley Vickers (Dagenham & Redbridge) **04** v IQ	1
David Waite (Enfield) **82** v G	1
Steve Wales (Yeading) **06** v B.	1
Jason Walker (Barrow) **09** v M.	1
Paul Walker (Blyth) **86 v** W,E,E(s), **87 v** S(s)	4
Steve Walters (Northwich Victoria) **97** v H	1
Mark Ward (Northwich Victoria) **83** v S(s)	1
Steve Ward (Canvey Island) **03** v B	1
Dale Watkins (Cheltenham T.) **98** v H **99** v I(s), **00** v I,H,W	5
John Watson (Wealdstone, Scarborough & Maidstone) **79** v S(s),H **80** v I,S,H **81** v H,S,I **82** v I,H,S **83** v I,H,S **84** v W(s),H,S,I	18
Steve Watson (Farnborough Town) **02** v US(s), W(s), S	3
Liam Watson (Marine) **95** v W,H(s)	2
Paul Watts (Redbridge Forest) **89** v W **90** v I,E,E **91** v I **92** v W **93** v W,F	8
Darren Way (Yeovil Town) **03** vI (s), E, W	3
Chris Weale (Yeovil Town) **03** v I (s), H (s), E, W.	4
Simon Weatherstone (Boston United) **02** v W(s),E,S(s)	3
Paul Webb (Bromsgrove R & Kidderminster H) **93** v F **94** v W,F,N(s) **95** v W,H,G **96** v E,H **97** v E,H	11
Aaron Webster (Burton Albion) **02 v** H(s),W,S(s) **03** v I	3
Ishmael Welsh (Grays Athletic) **09** v M,B.	2
Mark West (Wycombe W) **91** v W	1
Steve West (Woking) **01** v W(s)	1
Barry Whitbread (Runcorn & Altrincham) **79 v** S,H **80** v I,S,H, **81 v** I	6
Tristram Whitman (Doncaster Rovers) **03** v W(s), S	2
Russ Wilcox (Frickley) **86** v W,E	2
Adam Wilde (Worcester City) **03** v B	1
Barry Williams (Nuneaton Borough) **99** v H(s),W	2
Colin Williams (Scarborough & Telford Utd.) **81** v H,S. **82** v I,H,S. **84** v H,S,I. **85** v I,H,S.	12
Roger Willis (Barnet) **91** v I(s)	1
Paul Wilson (Frickley Athletic) **86** v W	1
Martyn Woolford (York City) **08** v Gr,Ba.	2
Andy Woods (Scarborough) **02** v US,H(s),W,S.	4
Simon Wormull (Dover Athletic) **99** v I(s),W **02 v** W,E,S.	5
Mark Wright (Thurrock) **09** v BH.	1
Jake Wright (Tamworth) **09** v I.	1
Nicky Wroe (Torquay United) **09** v M,B.	2
Adam Yates (Morecambe) **07** v H,S,W.	3
Mark Yates (Cheltenham Town) **99** v I, W	2
Ismail Yakubu (Barnet) **04** v I,US. **05** v I,E,W,S.	6

FULL INTERNATIONAL HONOURS

To date three players have played for England at both Full International and Semi-Professional/England C levels.

Peter Taylor	Full: 1976	SPro: 1984	whilst at Maidstone United
Alan Smith	Full: 1988	SPro: 1982	whilst at Alvechurch
Steve Guppy	Full: 1999	SPro: 1993	whilst at Wycombe Wanderers

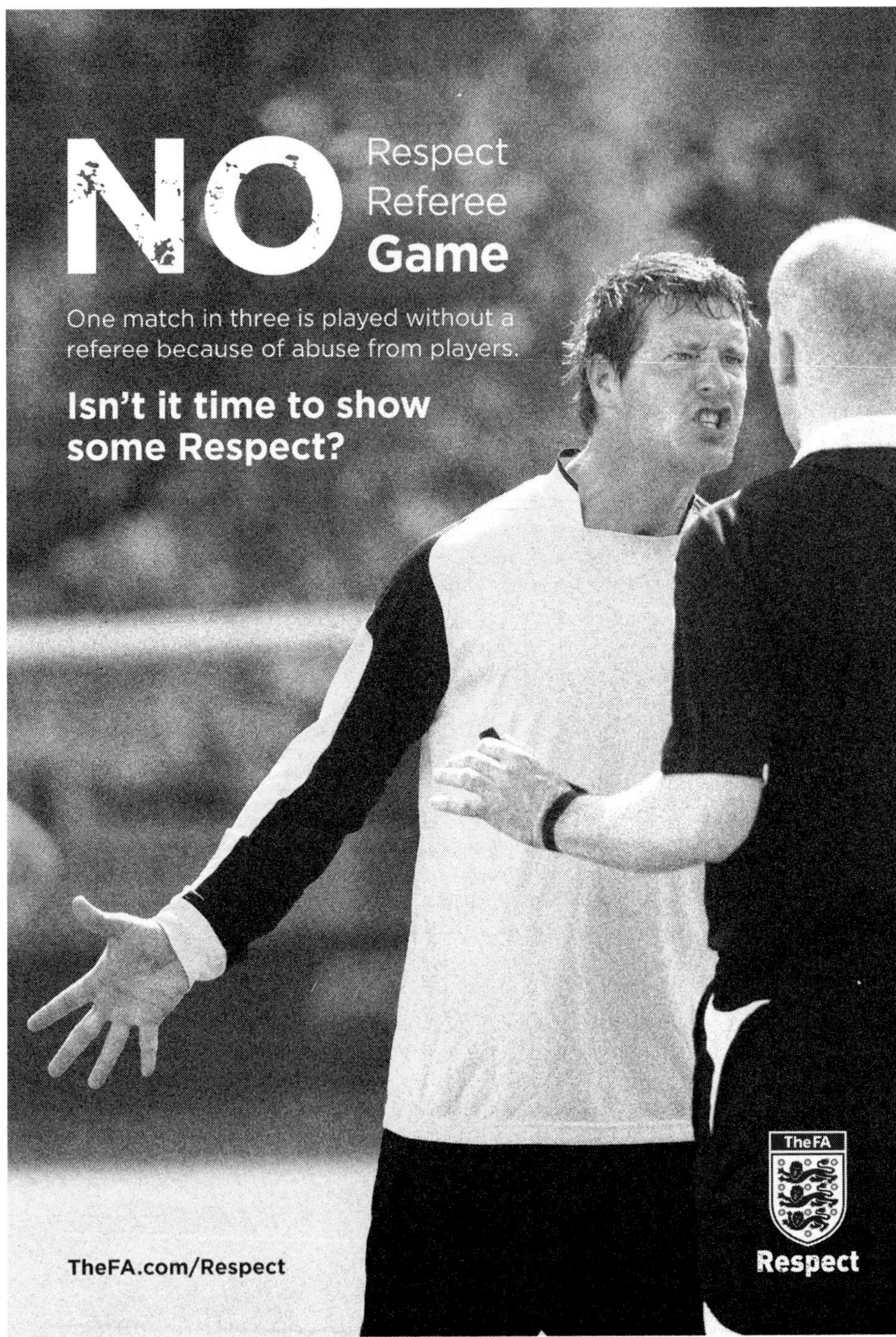
NO
Respect
Referee
Game
One match in three is played without a referee because of abuse from players.
Isn't it time to show some Respect?
TheFA.com/Respect
TheFA
Respect

2009-10

Once again a record 762 clubs entered the F.A. Challenge Cup but before they were due to compete in the First Qualifying Round, Newcastle Blue Star pulled out. Non-league clubs playing in leagues below Step Four featured in the Extra Preliminary Round and Division One clubs from the Northern Premier, Isthmian and Southern Division entered the competition in the Preliminary Round with the Premier Division clubs in these three leagues joining in the First Qualifying Round.

The Conference clubs in the North and South Divisions enter in the Second Qualifying Round but the Premier Conference clubs are spared until the Fourth Qualifying Round, with the Football League clubs joining the competition as usual in the First Round Proper.

Non-League clubs very rarely last further than the Third Round but the prize money available in the early rounds can be an inspiration to a small club at the beginning of a season.

Extra Preliminary Round
(203 Winners @ Prize Money £750)

When 203 clubs were eliminated from the F.A.Cup on the 15th August in the second week of the season and with the Final not being played until mid May, the knock out competition can surely be described as the biggest and probably the best of its type in world football.

The winners were rewarded with a £750 win bonus and little known clubs such as A.F.C. Wulfrunians (West Midlands Premier), Badshot Lea (Combined Counties) and East Preston (Sussex County Division Two) who were to make a name for themselves in this year's competition, enjoyed their first victories.

Best victories of the round

At home:

8 Alresford Town (Wessex Premier)
0 Shaftesbury (Wessex Div. One)

7 Hebburn (Northern Div Two)
0 Eccleshill United (Northern Co.East Div 1)

7 Stone Dynamoes (North West Div 1)
0 Cadbury Athletic (Midland Comb Div 1)

Away:

1 Abbey Hey (North West Co Premier)
6 Hallam (Northern Co. East Premier)

1 Langford (Spartan S.Mids Premier)
6 Aylesbury F.C. (Spartan S.Mids Prem)

2 Hall Road Rangers (Northern Co.East Prem)
6 Bishop Auckland (Northern Div 1)

Highest attendances

608 Scarbrough Athletic (N.Co East Premier) v Guisborough Town (Northern Division 2)
348 Whitley Bay (Northern Division 1) v Dunston UTS (Northern Division 1)

Action from the Desborough Town v Newmarket Town Extra Preliminary Round match, which Desborough won 4-1. Photo: Peter Barnes.

Lingfield's J Greaves fires a powerful shot past two Hailsham Town defenders during this Extra Preliminary tie which saw his side comfortably through to the next round courtesy of a 7-1 victory. Photo: Roger Turner.

EXTRA PRELIMINARY ROUND

1	Bridlington Town	v Esh Winning	0-0	170
	Esh Winning	v Bridlington Town	2-2*	80
	(Bridlington Town won 4-2 on penalties)			
2	Spennymoor Town	v Ashington	5-1	171
3	Seaham Red Star	v Morpeth Town	1-4	43
4	Sunderland RCA	v Ryton	1-3	75
5	Bedlington Terriers	v Thackley	2-0	102
6	Hebburn Town	v Eccleshill United	7-0	44
7	Jarrow Roofing Boldon CA	v Armthorpe Welfare	2-1	26
8	Whickham	v Chester-Le-Street Town	2-0	98
	(tie awarded to Chester-Le-Street Town – Whickham removed for playing ineligible player) (at Dunston UTS FC)			
9	Scarborough Athletic	v Guisborough Town	1-2	608
10	Selby Town	v Leeds Carnegie	0-0	98
	Leeds Carnegie	v Selby Town	1-3	70
11	Consett	v Billingham Town	5-0	148
12	Team Northumbria	v Marske United	4-0	32
13	Hall Road Rangers	v Bishop Auckland	2-6	74
14	Norton & Stockton Ancients	v Pickering Town	3-0	100
15	Shildon	v Northallerton Town	0-0	91
	Northallerton Town	v Shildon	1-2	164
16	South Shields	v Newcastle Benfield	1-4	105
17	Pontefract Collieries	v Penrith	1-4	70
18	Stokesley	v Crook Town	3-1	78
19	West Auckland Town	v Brandon United	2-2	30
	Brandon United	v West Auckland Town	2-1	108
20	Whitley Bay	v Dunston UTS	2-2	348
	Dunston UTS	v Whitley Bay	0-2	251
21	Billingham Synthonia	v Birtley Town	1-1	87
	Birtley Town	v Billingham Synthonia	1-3	69
22	Horden CW	v Tow Law Town	0-0	58
	Tow Law Town	v Horden CW	1-2	94
23	West Allotment Celtic	v Liversedge	3-2	79
24	Silsden	v Colne	3-1	56
25	Congleton Town	v Dinnington Town	3-2	142
26	Abbey Hey	v Hallam	1-6	45
27	Chadderton	v Atherton Collieries	2-2	35
	Atherton Collieries	v Chadderton	3-1	72
28	Maltby Main	v Rossington Main	1-3	42
29	Parkgate	v St Helens Town	1-3	66
30	Holker Old Boys	v Padiham	0-2	40
31	Bacup Borough	v Atherton LR	1-1	100
	Atherton LR	v Bacup Borough	1-0*	53
32	Maine Road	v Alsager Town	3-1	65
33	Squires Gate	v Staveley MW	2-2	55
	Staveley MW	v Squires Gate	2-2*	70
	(Staveley MW won 5-3 on penalties)			
34	Ashton Athletic	v Bootle	1-2	48
35	Runcorn Linnets	v AFC Emley	4-1	198
36	Nostell MW	v Oldham Town	2-1	72
37	Ramsbottom United	v Cheadle Town	5-1	103
38	Flixton	v Winsford United	3-3	50
	Winsford United	v Flixton	4-6	60
39	Formby	v Glossop North End	1-1	95
	Glossop North End	v Formby	3-1	220
40	Meir KA	v Tipton Town	0-4	46
41	Bewdley Town	v Alvechurch	0-2	146
42	Cradley Town	v Biddulph Victoria	3-3	36
	Biddulph Victoria	v Cradley Town	0-1	37
43	Eccleshall	v Tividale	1-3	57
44	Westfields	v Bolehall Swifts	5-0	71
45	Stone Dominoes	v Cadbury Athletic	7-0	35
46	Causeway United	v Wellington	3-1	43
	(at Boldmere St Michaels FC)			
47	Studley	v Pershore Town	1-0	87
48	Dudley Sports	v Southam United	2-1	43
49	Coleshill Town	v Bridgnorth Town	2-0	56
50	Pegasus Juniors	v Ellesmere Rangers	5-1	40
51	Norton United	v Newcastle Town	2-5	80
52	Dudley Town	v Walsall Wood	3-2	48
53	Coventry Sphinx	v Bromyard Town	3-2	116
54	Heath Hayes	v Lye Town	2-1	46
55	Brocton	v Shifnal Town	5-1	33
56	Castle Vale	v Goodrich	4-2	79
57	Stratford Town	v Pilkington XXX	5-0	174
58	AFC Wulfrunians	v Boldmere St Michaels	2-0	85
59	Rocester	v Wednesfield	2-1	69
60	Nuneaton Griff	v Shawbury United	3-1	60
61	Highgate United	v Malvern Town	3-3	71
	Malvern Town	v Highgate United	2-1	52
62	Holwell Sports	v Ellistown	2-2	130
	Ellistown	v Holwell Sports	2-1	132
63	Hinckley Downes	v Boston Town	1-4	133
64	Borrowash Victoria	v Greenwood Meadows	3-0	45
65	Barwell	v Long Eaton United	1-2	101
66	Holbrook Miners Welfare	v Heanor Town	5-0	118
67	Radford	v Rainworth MW	0-3	102
68	Oadby Town	v Kirby Muxloe	2-3	136
69	Bardon Hill Sports	v Arnold Town	3-2	117
70	Coalville Town	v Barrow Town	3-2	155
71	Bottesford Town	v New Mills	1-5	74
72	Dunkirk	v Winterton Rangers	1-3	65
73	Lincoln Moorlands Railway	v St Andrews	2-3	72
74	Shirebrook Town	v Holbeach United	2-2	95
	Holbeach United	v Shirebrook Town	1-2	137
75	Sleaford Town	v Loughborough University	2-0	126
76	Gresley	v Heather St Johns	2-2	202
	Heather St Johns	v Gresley	1-0	179
77	Teversal	v Bourne Town	1-1	79
	Bourne Town	v Teversal	3-0	81
78	Deeping Rangers	v Friar Lane & Epworth	1-1	95
	Friar Lane & Epworth	v Deeping Rangers	3-0	65
79	Gedling MW	v Blackstones	1-1	46
	Blackstones	v Gedling MW	2-1	58
80	Gedling Town	v Barton Town Old Boys	2-2	37
	Barton Town Old Boys	v Gedling Town	2-1	86
81	Long Buckby	v Hadleigh United	3-2	83
82	Cornard United	v Gorleston	0-4	22
83	Yaxley	v Rothwell Corinthians	1-2	83
84	Great Yarmouth Town	v Raunds Town	1-1	147
	Raunds Town	v Great Yarmouth Town	1-3	104
85	Ely City	v Wisbech Town	0-1	122
86	Whitton United	v Daventry Town	0-5	62
87	Walsham Le Willows	v Kirkley & Pakefield	1-1	99
	Kirkley & Pakefield	v Walsham Le Willows	1-0	214
88	St Ives Town	v Daventry United	6-1	152
89	Needham Market	v Felixstowe & Walton United	1-0	130
90	Wellingborough Town	v Wroxham	0-2	129
91	Woodbridge Town	v St Neots Town	1-4	126
92	Desborough Town	v Newmarket Town	4-1	77
93	Diss Town	v Cogenhoe United	2-3	130
94	Dereham Town	v Leiston	3-1	213
95	Godmanchester Rovers	v Haverhill Rovers	0-0	45
	Haverhill Rovers	v Godmanchester Rovers	0-1	67
96	Stewarts & Lloyds	v Norwich United	1-2	36
97	Northampton Spencer	v March Town United	1-0	86
98	Stowmarket Town	v Mildenhall Town	0-3	105
99	Clapton	v Kingsbury London Tigers	2-5	48
100	St Margaretsbury	v Hullbridge Sports	0-0	65
	Hullbridge Sports	v St Margaretsbury	0-1	43
101	Thame United	v Bedford	1-0	84
102	Wembley	v Basildon United	2-3	69

Ben Yiadom lobs the ball over Ampthill Town 'keeper, Leigh Woodcroft, to open the scoring for Erith Town in the Extra Preliminary Round. Photo: Alan Coomes.

Lee Barnett of Chatham, gets above Eastbourne United's Lee Jules to score the first goal of this Preliminary Round tie. Photo: Alan Coomes.

Stamford's Phil Stebbing lifts the ball over the Sleaford 'keeper and, unfortunately, over the cross bar too during his side's 1-3 defeat in the Preliminary Round. Photo: Gordon Whittington.

EXTRA PRELIMINARY ROUND

No.	Home	Away	Score	Att
103	Erith Town	v Ampthill Town	2-0	48
104	Leverstock Green	v Burnham Ramblers	2-1	59
105	Oxhey Jets	v Brimsdown Rovers	0-1	68
106	Eton Manor	v Stanway Rovers	1-2	55
107	Wootton Blue Cross	v Sporting Bengal United	1-0	40
108	Hertford Town	v Newport Pagnell Town	1-2	211
109	Flackwell Heath	v Welwyn Garden City	4-0	92
110	Bicester Town	v Dunstable Town	1-4	54
111	FC Clacton	v London APSA	2-1	99
112	Tiptree United	v Colney Heath	3-2	72
113	Buckingham Town	v Hanwell Town	1-3	71
114	Broxbourne Borough V&E	v Enfield 1893	1-4	187
115	Biggleswade United	v Stotfold	2-0	76
116	Hillingdon Borough	v Kentish Town	2-3	63
117	Hatfield Town	v Southend Manor	2-2	84
	Southend Manor	v Hatfield Town	0-3	46
118	London Colney	v Harwich & Parkeston	4-1	59
119	Halstead Town	v Wivenhoe Town	1-1	102
	Wivenhoe Town	v Halstead Town	1-4	110
120	Potton United	v Hoddesdon Town	2-2	142
	Hoddesdon Town	v Potton United	2-0	71
	(at Hertford Town FC)			
121	North Greenford United	v Cockfosters	0-2	48
122	Stansted	v Royston Town	2-5	159
	(at Bishop's Stortford FC)			
123	Chalfont St Peter	v Toknygton Manor	3-2	28
124	Witham Town	v Saffron Walden Town	2-1	117
125	Barkingside	v Bowers & Pitsea	1-4	83
126	Crawley Green	v Cranfield United	3-1	102
127	Langford	v Aylesbury	0-6	80
128	Barking	v Tring Athletic	2-3	56
129	Harefield United	v Haringey Borough	1-1	115
	Haringey Borough	v Harefield United	1-3	78
130	Tunbridge Wells	v Sevenoaks Town	2-2	117
	Sevenoaks Town	v Tunbridge Wells	2-1	156
131	Raynes Park Vale	v Farnham Town	2-2	42
	Farnham Town	v Raynes Park Vale	0-3	37
132	Hailsham Town	v Lingfield	1-7	62
133	Worthing United	v Badshot Lea	0-2	73
134	Hartley Wintney	v Holmesdale	1-2	98
135	Wick	v Frimley Green	4-0	102
136	Deal Town	v Arundel	3-2	130
137	Littlehampton Town	v Cobham	1-1	153
	Cobham	v Littlehampton Town	2-1	72
138	Southwick	v Herne Bay	2-1	63
139	Chessington & Hook United	v Chertsey Town	0-2	149
140	Egham Town	v Ringmer	2-2	58
	Ringmer	v Egham Town	2-0	86
141	Whitehawk	v Hythe Town	1-2	100
142	Banstead Athletic	v Pagham	1-1	41
	Pagham	v Banstead Athletic	1-1*	75
	(Pagham won 3-2 on penalties)			
143	Camberley Town	v East Preston	1-2	91
144	Oakwood	v Lordswood	2-4	46
145	Croydon	v Shoreham	2-5	68
146	East Grinstead Town	v Feltham	4-1	56
147	Eastbourne United	v Redhill	3-1	53
148	Erith & Belvedere	v Sandhurst Town	1-1	78
	Sandhurst Town	v Erith & Belvedere	2-4	63
149	Wealden	v Epsom & Ewell	1-3	45
150	Cove	v Bookham	4-0	40
151	Crowborough Athletic	v Bedfont	1-1	84
	Bedfont	v Crowborough Athletic	3-2	86
152	Slade Green	v Faversham Town		
	(walkover for Faversham Town – Slade Green withdrawn)			
153	Binfield	v Colliers Wood United	3-5	155
154	Peacehaven & Telscombe	v Mile Oak	1-3	107
155	Lancing	v Selsey	0-2	93
156	Dorking	v Horley Town	0-0	56
	Horley Town	v Dorking	3-0	101
157	Crawley Down	v Westfield	4-1	44
158	Molesey	v Sidley United	2-1	56
159	Guildford City	v St Francis Rangers	4-1	65
160	Three Bridges	v Chichester City	1-3	54
161	Hassocks	v Ash United	1-4	74
162	Wootton Bassett Town	v Westbury United	2-2	38
	Westbury United	v Wootton Bassett Town	2-3	91
163	New Milton Town	v Cowes Sports	4-1	48
164	Petersfield Town	v Brockenhurst	0-2	149
165	Ringwood Town	v Christchurch	2-1	99
166	Downton	v Calne Town	1-1	51
	Calne Town	v Downton	1-0	60
167	Milton United	v Corsham Town	3-0	70
168	Bournemouth	v Highworth Town	1-2	64
169	Fareham Town	v Moneyfields	1-2	152
170	Hamble ASSC	v Wantage Town	2-2	62
	Wantage Town	v Hamble ASSC	4-1	52
171	Romsey Town	v Hayling United	3-0	120
172	Lydney Town	v Totton & Eling	0-5	220
173	Alresford Town	v Shaftesbury	8-0	73
174	Warminster Town	v Amesbury Town	5-1	116
175	Bitton	v Newport (IW)	1-1	93
	Newport (IW)	v Bitton	2-1	153
176	Laverstock & Ford	v Alton Town	1-3	51
177	Devizes Town	v Shrivenham	0-5	75
178	Almondsbury Town	v Longwell Green Sports	2-0	115
179	Marlow United	v Hallen	1-2	26
180	Ardley United	v Witney United	2-2	96
	Witney United	v Ardley United	2-1	113
181	Kidlington	v Abingdon Town	1-0	154
182	Winchester City	v Bemerton Heath Harlequins	1-4	107
183	Brading Town	v Fairford Town	1-0	181
184	Carterton	v Bristol Manor Farm	2-2	25
	Bristol Manor Farm	v Carterton	1-1*	48
	(Bristol Manor Farm won 3-2 on penalties)			
185	Shortwood United	v Blackfield & Langley	1-0	93
186	Reading Town	v Melksham Town	2-0	52
187	Lymington Town	v Harrow Hill	6-0	75
	(at Bashley FC)			
188	Wellington Town	v Bideford	1-3	118
	(at Elmore FC)			
189	Launceston	v Clevedon United	2-0	63
190	Bridport	v Keynsham Town	3-1	111
191	Gillingham Town	v Cullompton Rangers	5-1	209
192	Larkhall Athletic	v Shepton Mallet	4-1	70
193	Radstock Town	v Wimborne Town	0-1	85
194	Dawlish Town	v Elmore	3-0	88
195	Barnstaple Town	v Tavistock	3-1	124
196	Bishop Sutton	v Bodmin Town	1-2	81
197	Willand Rovers	v Street	2-2	80
	Street	v Willand Rovers	0-1	97
198	Buckland Athletic	v Hamworthy United	1-1	229
	Hamworthy United	v Buckland Athletic	3-2	129
199	Saltash United	v Chard Town	6-2	118
200	Portishead Town	v Brislington	1-1	115
	Brislington	v Portishead Town	1-2	70
201	Ilfracombe Town	v Falmouth Town	0-1	130
202	Sherborne Town	v St Blazey	4-1	138
203	Poole Town	v Welton Rovers	3-2	212

Preliminary Round
(167 Winners @ Prize Money - £1,500)

A second massive round was completed before the end of August with 167 clubs leaving the competition. A.F.C. Wulfrunians claimed an impressive scalp by beating Chasetown (N.P.L. Div 1 South) after a replay and two comparatively new names F.C.Halifax Town (N.P.L. Div 1 North) won 6-0 at Brandon (Northern Div 2) and A.F.C. Fylde (N.P.L.Div 1 North) achieved another resounding away victory with a 4-2 scoreline at Padiham (N.W.Co. East Prem.).

At this early stage of the season, as many clubs had dramatically changed their playing staff in the close season, comparative strengths were difficult to judge. However, Hamworthy United (Western Premier) must have been pleased to beat Zamaretto new boys Frome Town 3-2 and Gillingham Town (Western Div 1) followed their 5-1defeat of Cullompton Rangers (S.W.Peninsula) with a splendid 6-0 victory over Portishead (Western Div 1).

Best victories of the round

At Home:	Away:
7 Enfield 1893 (Essex Premier)	0 Brandon Town (Northern Div.2)
1 St.Andrews (East Midland Co- East)	6 F.C.HalifaxTown (N.P.L. Div.1 North)
7 Poole Town (Wessex Premier)	0 Cobham (Combined Co Div 1)
2 Barnstaple Town (Western Premier)	6 V.T.F.C. (Zamaretto Div 1 SW)

Highest attendances:

639 Lowestoft Town (Ryman Division 1 North)	v Gt.Yarmouth Town (Eastern Co Div 1)
476 Worthing (Ryman Division One South)	v Raynes Park Vale (Combined Co. Premier)
427 AFC Wulfrunians (West Midlands Premier)	v Chasetown (Northern Premier League Div 1 South)

Maidstone's James Pinnock is blocked by Liam Hind of Bedfont during this 1st Qualifying Round match.
Photo: Alan Coomes.

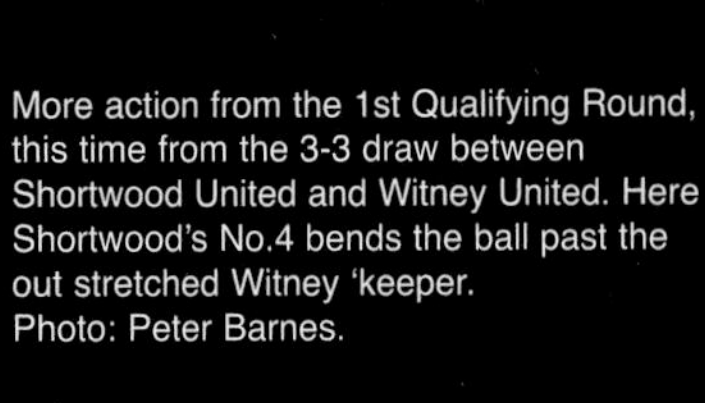

More action from the 1st Qualifying Round, this time from the 3-3 draw between Shortwood United and Witney United. Here Shortwood's No.4 bends the ball past the out stretched Witney 'keeper.
Photo: Peter Barnes.

PRELIMINARY ROUND

No	Home	Away	Score	Att
1	Bedlington Terriers	v Garforth Town	2-3	150
2	Chester-Le-Street Town	v Norton & Stockton Ancients	0-5	69
3	Morpeth Town	v Billingham Synthonia	4-3	53
4	Selby Town	v Ryton	1-2	101
5	Bridlington Town	v Shildon	1-0	203
6	Wakefield	v Guisborough Town	0-0	105
	Guisborough Town	v Wakefield	1-0	149
7	Team Northumbria	v Ossett Albion	1-2	36
8	Stokesley	v Spennymoor Town	1-3	135
9	Jarrow Roofing Boldon CA	v Penrith	2-0	46
10	Hebburn Town	v Bishop Auckland	3-4	90
11	Horden CW	v West Allotment Celtic	2-2	51
	West Allotment Celtic	v Horden CW	2-3*	98
12	Newcastle Benfield	v Whitley Bay	1-2	357
13	Brandon United	v FC Halifax Town	0-6	217
14	Consett	v Harrogate Railway	0-0	130
	Harrogate Railway	v Consett	1-1*	165
	(Harrogate Railway won 4-3 on penalties)			
15	Warrington Town	v Leigh Genesis	1-0	167
16	Clitheroe	v Staveley MW	1-1	157
	Staveley MW	v Clitheroe	1-3	106
17	Padiham	v AFC Fylde	2-4	156
18	Bootle	v Woodley Sports	1-4	136
19	Silsden	v Hallam	1-4	67
20	Sheffield	v Flixton	4-0	174
21	Trafford	v Rossendale United	2-2	127
	Rossendale United	v Trafford	3-1	137
22	Rossington Main	v Glossop North End	1-2	110
23	Curzon Ashton	v Lancaster City	2-2	164
	Lancaster City	v Curzon Ashton	3-2	182
24	Chorley	v Nostell MW	2-1	191
25	Colwyn Bay	v St Helens Town	2-4	262
26	Cammell Laird	v Mossley	2-1	71
27	Maine Road	v Ramsbottom United	2-1	93
28	Atherton LR	v Prescot Cables	1-0	66
29	Atherton Collieries	v Radcliffe Borough	0-1	96
30	Bamber Bridge	v Runcorn Linnets	6-0	247
31	Witton Albion	v Congleton Town	0-1	194
32	Salford City	v Skelmersdale United	3-2	96
33	Castle Vale	v Studley	5-1	90
34	Kidsgrove Athletic	v Alvechurch	1-0	109
35	Dudley Town	v Bromsgrove Rovers	3-3	159
	Bromsgrove Rovers	v Dudley Town	3-0	148
36	Nuneaton Griff	v Stratford Town	1-4	138
37	Coventry Sphinx	v Stourport Swifts	4-4	108
	Stourport Swifts	v Coventry Sphinx	0-2	110
38	Heath Hayes	v Tividale	0-1	64
39	Pegasus Juniors	v Willenhall Town	2-2	59
	Willenhall Town	v Pegasus Juniors	0-2	95
40	Malvern Town	v Cradley Town	1-1	36
	Cradley Town	v Malvern Town	2-1	52
41	Atherstone Town	v Romulus	1-2	147
42	Stone Dominoes	v Market Drayton Town	0-1	75
43	Coleshill Town	v Causeway United	0-2	65
44	Dudley Sports	v Rocester	2-0	68
45	Chasetown	v AFC Wulfrunians	1-1	307
	AFC Wulfrunians	v Chasetown	2-2*	427
	(AFC Wulfrunians won 5-4 on penalties)			
46	Sutton Coldfield Town	v Tipton Town	2-1	102
47	Leek Town	v Bedworth United	2-3	214
48	Newcastle Town	v Westfields	1-2	64
49	Brocton	v Rushall Olympic	0-2	96
50	Carlton Town	v New Mills	4-2	100
51	Borrowash Victoria	v Quorn	0-0	58
	Quorn	v Barrowash Victoria	4-1	165
52	Blackstones	v Shepshed Dynamo	3-2	93
53	Barton Town Old Boys	v Kirby Muxloe	6-3	86
54	Brigg Town	v Spalding United	4-0	95
55	Lincoln United	v Friar Lane & Epworth	5-2	75
56	Winterton Rangers	v St Andrews	6-1	58
57	Coalville Town	v Bardon Hill Sports	0-1	245
58	Glapwell	v Ellistown	3-1	83
59	Sleaford Town	v Stamford	3-1	263

No	Home	Away	Score	Att
60	Rainworth MW	v Heather St Johns	3-1	84
61	Long Eaton United	v Loughborough Dynamo	0-2	91
62	Grantham Town	v Mickelover Sports	2-2	194
	Mickleover Sports	v Grantham Town	3-1	160
63	Shirebrook Town	v Boston Town	0-2	80
64	Belper Town	v Holbrook Miners Welfare	1-1	228
	Holbrook Miners Welfare	v Belper Town	1-0	251
65	Bourne Town	v Goole	3-1	109
66	Desborough Town	v Daventry Town	1-1	88
	Daventry Town	v Desborough Town	2-1	123
67	Norwich United	v Long Buckby	0-1	56
68	Woodford United	v AFC Sudbury	1-2	76
69	Rothwell Town	v Bury Town	0-1	108
70	Needham Market	v Wisbech Town	4-0	147
71	Lowestoft Town	v Great Yarmouth Town	3-0	639
72	Kirkley & Pakefield	v Cogenhoe United	4-0	151
73	Gorleston	v Northampton Spencer	1-1	134
	Northampton Spencer	v Gorleston	3-2	79
74	Rothwell Corinthians	v Godmanchester Rovers	0-0	82
	Godmanchester Rovers	v Rothwell Corinthians	3-0	63
75	Dereham Town	v Wroxham	3-0	259
76	Soham Town Rangers	v St Ives Town	0-0	156
	St Ives Town	v Soham Town Rangers	2-1*	202
77	Mildenhall Town	v St Neots Town	3-0	207
78	Great Wakering Rovers	v Waltham Forest	0-0	80
	Waltham Forest	v Great Wakering Rovers	1-0	76
79	Windsor & Eton	v Bowers & Pitsea	3-1	105
80	Northwood	v St Margaretsbury	3-1	118
81	Potters Bar Town	v Cockfosters	1-1	83
	Cockfosters	v Potters Bar Town	1-4	120
82	Harlow Town	v Kingsbury London Tigers	1-1	
	Kingsbury London Tigers	v Harlow Town	2-1	70
83	Chesham United	v Chalfont St Peter	2-0	247
84	Marlow	v Ilford	3-0	93
85	Witham Town	v London Colney	3-6	107
86	Newport Pagnell Town	v Heybridge Swifts	0-2	179
87	Aylesbury United	v Tiptree United	2-1	136
88	Hanwell Town	v Concord Rangers	1-3	46
89	Enfield Town	v Leverstock Green	2-0	157
90	Enfield 1893	v Crawley Green	7-0	76
91	Harefield United	v Biggleswade Town	2-1	98
92	FC Clacton	v Hitchin Town	0-1	159
93	Barton Rovers	v Ware	2-3	100
94	Thame United	v Wootton Blue Cross	2-0	74
95	Thamesmead Town	v Tilbury	4-2	48
96	Leighton Town	v Aylesbury	0-0	156
	Aylesbury	v Leighton Town	1-0	121
97	Burnham	v Kentish Town	2-1	77
98	Biggleswade United	v Halstead Town	1-2	76
99	Stanway Rovers	v Beaconsfield SYCOB	2-0	86
100	Cheshunt	v Maldon Town	2-3	106
101	Tring Athletic	v Slough Town	0-4	232
102	Dunstable Town	v Wingate & Finchley	0-2	62
103	Arlesey Town	v Hatfield Town	2-0	147
104	Hoddesdon Town	v Royston Town	0-1	137
	(at Hertford Town FC)			
105	Erith Town	v Basildon United	3-0	55
106	Brimsdown Rovers	v Flackwell Heath	2-4	136
107	East Thurrock United	v Brentwood Town	2-0	105
108	Redbridge	v Romford	0-1	128
109	Croydon Athletic	v Godalming Town	2-0	102
110	Sittingbourne	v Horley Town	0-0	119
	Horley Town	v Sittingbourne	0-2	138
111	Worthing	v Raynes Park Vale	4-0	476
112	Merstham	v Faversham Town	2-2	114
	Faversham Town	v Merstham	4-4*	150
	(Faversham Town won 5-4 on penalties)			
113	Dulwich Hamlet	v Sevenoaks Town	1-1	161
	Sevenoaks Town	v Dulwich Hamlet	0-2	170
114	Ashford Town	v Mile Oak	6-1	147
115	Folkestone Invicta	v AFC Hayes	1-0	218
116	Selsey	v Epsom & Ewell	1-0	162
117	Chertsey Town	v Metropolitan Police	0-1	197

First Qualifying Round
(116 ties with £3,000 for the winners)

With the entry of the Step Three clubs, the surviving 'minnows' had the chance of some comparative 'giant-killing' and the prize money was certainly worth winning.

Surprise results

2 Bury Town (Zamaretto Div 1 Mids.)
0 King's Lynn (N.P.L. Premier)

1 Hednesford Town (Zamaretto Premier)
4 Pegasus Juniors (Hellenic Premier)

0 Leamington (Zamaretto Premier)
2 Market Drayton (N.P.L. Div 1 South)

1 Warrington Town (N.P.L. Div 1 North)
0 Nantwich Town (N.P.L. Premier)

2 Whitstable Town (Ryman Div 1 South)
1 Carshalton Athletic (Ryman Premier)

Best attendances

1208 Sheffield v FC United
941 Boston United v Loughbrough Dynamo
779 Lowestoft Town v Dereham Town
716 Farnborough v Hastings United
604 Bury Town v King's Lynn
520 Leamington v Market Drayton

Leading individual goalscorers

Ryan O'Toole (Uxbridge) 4 (2pens) v Ash United
Tony Battersby (Bedford Town) 3 (2pens) v Kingsbury LT.
Josh Thompson (Cammell Laird) 3 v St Helens Tn
Carl Osman (Kendal Town) 3 v Guisborough Town
Alex Taylor (Kendal Town) 3 v Guisborough Town
Andy Baird (Oxford City) 3 v Kidlington
Matt Jackson (Sutton Coldfield) 3 (1pen) v Westfields

Best victories of the round

At home

9 Kendal Town (N.P.L. Premier)
1 Guisborough Town (Northern Div 2)

6 Rugby Town (Zamaretto Premier)
0 Dudley Sports (West Mids Premier)

6 Spennymoor Town (Northern Div 1)
0 Ryton (Northern Div 1)

6 Concord Rangers (Ryman Div 1 N)
0 Romford (Ryman Div 1 North)

Away from Home

1 Chipstead (Ryman Div 1 South)
6 Dartford (Ryman Premier)

0 Westfields (Combined Counties Div 1)
6 Sutton Coldfield (Zamaretto Div 1 Midlands)

0 Brigg Town (N.P.L. Div 1 South)
5 Nuneaton Town (Zamaretto Premier)

0 Bridport (Western Div 1)
7 Truro City (Zamaretto Premier)

This North Leigh player directs his superb diving header towards the Cirencester goal during his side's 2-1 defeat in the 1st Qualifying Round.
Photo: Peter Barnes.

PRELIMINARY ROUND

118	Gosport Borough	v East Preston	0-1	143
119	Lordswood	v Whitstable Town	1-1	83
	Whitstable Town	v Lordswood	2-1*	127
120	Horsham YMCA	v Wick	5-3	134
121	Shoreham	v Crawley Down	1-2	134
122	Chichester City	v AFC Totton	1-3	160
123	Pagham	v Walton Casuals	1-2	74
124	Fleet Town	v Walton & Hersham	1-1	167
	Walton & Hersham	v Fleet Town	2-2*	140
	(Walton & Hersham won 5-4 on penalties)			
125	Lingfield	v Southwick	0-0	107
	(at East Grinstead Town FC)			
	Southwick	v Lingfield	0-3	53
126	Burgess Hill Town	v Chipstead	2-3	183
127	Andover	v Molesey	2-3	111
128	Chatham Town	v Eastbourne United	1-1	167
	Eastbourne United	v Chatham Town	1-2*	102
129	East Grinstead Town	v Cove	4-2	72
130	Cobham	v VT	0-6	58
131	Leatherhead	v Bedfont Green	3-0	118
132	Guildford City	v Ramsgate	3-1	110
133	Hythe Town	v Eastbourne Town	4-0	152
134	Ash United	v Erith & Belvedere	4-0	86
135	Bedfont	v Colliers Wood United	4-2	65
136	Holmesdale	v Badshot Lea	1-3	86
137	Deal Town	v Ringmer	4-1	130
138	Corinthian Casuals	v VCD Athletic	1-3	88
139	Whyteleafe	v Uxbridge	0-1	95
140	Hallen	v Lymington Town	0-0	74
	Lymington Town	v Hallen	0-4	56
141	Shortwood United	v Romsey Town	5-1	75
142	Highworth Town	v Bemerton Heath Harlequins	1-0	175
143	Totton & Eling	v Kidlington	1-4	118
	(at AFC Totton)			
144	Wootton Bassett Town	v Brockenhurst	0-1	70
145	Yate Town	v Alton Town	3-1	141
146	Mangotsfield United	v Bracknell Town	2-0	134
147	Calne Town	v Shrivenham	0-1	45
148	Bishop's Cleeve	v Reading Town	3-1	95
149	Bristol Manor Farm	v Warminster Town	4-4	62
	Warminster Town	v Bristol Manor Farm	2-4	230
150	North Leigh	v Milton United	2-1	89
151	Almondsbury Town	v Cinderford Town	2-1	75
152	Wantage Town	v Newport (IW)	5-0	102
153	Moneyfields	v Hungerford Town	3-4	100
154	Ringwood Town	v Abingdon United	1-3	59
155	Brading Town	v Alresford Town	3-2	130
156	Witney United	v New Milton Town	3-1	124
157	Cirencester Town	v Thatcham Town	2-1	106
158	Wimborne Town	v Sherborne Town	2-1	197
159	Paulton Rovers	v Bideford	3-1	123
160	Falmouth Town	v Willand Rovers	1-1	130
	Willand Rovers	v Falmouth Town	2-1	86
161	Taunton Town	v Bodmin Town	2-1	210
162	Poole Town	v Barnstaple Town	7-2	232
163	Launceston	v Bridgwater Town	2-3	141
164	Bridport	v Dawlish Town	3-3	137
	Dawlish Town	v Bridport	1-2	92
165	Gillingham Town	v Portishead Town	6-0	209
166	Larkhall Athletic	v Saltash United	0-2	96
167	Hamworthy United	v Frome Town	3-2	117

FIRST QUALIFYING ROUND

1	Horden CW	v Durham City	2-2	101
	Durham City	v Horden CW	1-3	115
2	North Ferriby United	v Harrogate Railway	2-0	121
3	Newcastle Blue Star	v Ossett Albion		
	(walkover for Ossett Albion – Newcastle Blue Star withdrawn)			
4	Kendal Town	v Guisborough Town	9-1	161
5	Spennymoor Town	v Ryton	6-0	202
6	Morpeth Town	v Ossett Town	0-1	38
7	Norton & Stockton Ancients	v FC Halifax Town	0-4	390
8	Bridlington Town	v Whitby Town	0-1	374
9	Bradford (Park Avenue)	v Bishop Auckland	4-1	246
10	Jarrow Roofing Boldon CA	v Garforth Town	1-0	56
11	Guiseley	v Whitley Bay	2-0	301
12	Hallam	v Burscough	0-4	135
13	Cammell Laird	v St Helens Town	3-1	75
14	Maine Road	v Bamber Bridge	1-4	86
15	Clitheroe	v Stocksbridge Park Steels	0-2	201
16	Atherton LR	v Congleton Town	1-1	89
	Congleton Town	v Atherton LR	5-0	197
17	Warrington Town	v Nantwich Town	1-0	204
18	Worksop Town	v Frickley Athletic	1-1	178
	Frickley Athletic	v Worksop Town	2-1	228
19	Lancaster City	v Ashton United	0-3	191
20	Glossop North End	v Chorley	2-3	295
21	AFC Fylde	v Rossendale United	4-1	253
22	Salford City	v Marine	2-1	159
23	Woodley Sports	v Radcliffe Borough	0-1	141
	(at Cheadle Town FC)			
24	Sheffield	v FC United of Manchester	1-3	1208
25	Causeway United	v Bedworth United	0-0	138
	Bedworth United	v Causeway United	3-0	163
26	Westfields	v Sutton Coldfield Town	0-6	102
27	Hednesford Town	v Pegasus Juniors	1-4	274
28	Evesham United	v Tividale	0-0	131
	Tividale	v Evesham United	1-2*	140
29	Cradley Town	v Stratford Town	0-1	76
30	Bromsgrove Rovers	v Stourbridge	1-1	465
	Stourbridge	v Bromsgrove Rovers	3-1	255
31	Kidsgrove Athletic	v AFC Wulfrunians	2-3	212
32	Coventry Sphinx	v Rushall Olympic	1-0	196
33	Leamington	v Market Drayton Town	0-2	530
34	Romulus	v Castle Vale	2-1	95
35	Rugby Town	v Dudley Sports	6-0	212
36	Rainworth MW	v Holbrook Miners Welfare	2-1	151
37	Bourne Town	v Boston Town	3-1	125
38	Buxton	v Winterton Rangers	2-1	256
39	Retford United	v Lincoln United	1-1	258
	Lincoln United	v Retford United	2-1	182
40	Bardon Hill Sports	v Barton Town Old Boys	5-0	120
41	Blackstones	v Hucknall Town	2-4	121
42	Quorn	v Mickleover Sports	0-2	150
43	Brigg Town	v Nuneaton Town	0-5	239
44	Matlock Town	v Sleaford Town	1-1	155
	(at Belper Town FC)			
	Sleaford Town	v Matlock Town	1-2	425
45	Glapwell	v Carlton Town	0-1	63
46	Boston United	v Loughborough Dynamo	4-2	941
47	Lowestoft Town	v Dereham Town	3-1	779
48	Godmanchester Rovers	v Northampton Spencer	1-2	120
49	St Ives Town	v Kirkley & Pakefield	1-2	272
50	Bury Town	v Kings Lynn	2-0	604
51	AFC Sudbury	v Needham Market	0-2	362
52	Long Buckby	v Mildenhall Town	1-1	89
	Mildenhall Town	v Long Buckby	4-3*	178
53	Cambridge City	v Daventry Town	2-0	264
54	Harefield United	v Maldon Town	3-1	112
55	Canvey Island	v Hitchin Town	3-3	323
	Hitchin Town	v Canvey Island	0-1	251
56	Enfield 1893	v Halstead Town	3-3	98
	Halstead Town	v Enfield 1893	1-1*	171
	(Enfield 1893 won 2-0 on penalties)			
57	Flackwell Heath	v Royston Town	2-1	85
58	Chesham United	v Harrow Borough	1-1	286
	Harrow Borough	v Chesham United	0-2	158

Second Qualifying Round
(80 winners @ £4,500)

Eighty ties presented a marvellous chance for clubs to boost funds to the tune of £4,500 for each winner. But in this round many of the senior clubs really flexed their muscles and put some of the junior challengers firmly in their place.

Ashford Town (Middx) (Ryman Premier)	10-0	Badshot Lea (Combined Counties)
Dover Athletic (Ryman Premier)	8-0	East Preston (Sussex Division 2)
Northwich Victoria (Blue Square North)	8-0	Bardon Hill Sports (East Midlands Counties-East)
Blyth Spartans (Blue Square North)	7-1	Ossett Albion (Northern Premier League Div 1 North)
Alfreton Town (Blue Square North)	6-0	A.F.C.Wulfrunians (West Midlands Premier)
Stocksbridge Park Steels (Unibond Premier)	2-7	Stalybridge Celtic (Blue Square North)
Witney Town (Hellenic Premier)	1-6	Eastleigh (Blue Square South)

Surprise results

Bishops Cleeve (Zamaretto Division 1 S. W.	3-0	Weymouth (Blue Square South)
Lowestoft (Zamaretto Division 1 Midlands)	1-0	Boston United (Blue Square North)
Chorley (Northern Premier Division 1 North)	2-0	Ashton United (Unibond Premier)
Droylsden (Blue Square North)	0-2	F.C.Halifax Town (Unibond Div 1North)
Maidenhead United (Blue Square South)	2-5	Truro City (Zamaretto Premier)
Stafford Rangers (Blue Square North)	2-2	Coventry Sphinx (Midland Allaince)
Coventry Sphinx (Midland Alliance)	3-2	Stafford Rangers (Blue Square North)

Highest attendances

AFC Telford United v Pegasus Juniors	1136
Lowestoft Town v Boston United	1134
Nuneaton Town v Carlton Town	903
Droylsden v F.C.Halifax Town	902
North Ferriby United v F.C. United	838

Note that four of the five top attendances featured clubs who had recently re-formed.

The F.A.Cup traditionally lifts some clubs more than others, so it was interesting to see some Second Round ties and league games contested by the same two clubs with just one week between the meetings. Corby Town won at Eastwood Town in the cup the week before being held to a 1-1 draw at home by the same team in the league, and Evesham United although achieving a league point, failed to score in two consecutive games with Stourbridge. However, the biggest contrast was at Chippenham Town, who lost 1-5 at home to Merthyr Tydfil in the Zamaretto Premier on 19th September but sent the Welshman packing the following week with a 4-1 F.A.Cup victory!

The Gillingham Town supporters saw their heroes knocked out of the cup at Mangotsfield United in a replay but what fun they enjoyed on the way. The Western League Division One club had scored 21 goals in their five previous ties - in a lively start to the season!

Bury Town of the Zamaretto Division One Midlands enjoyed a fabulous F.A.Cup run in the previous campaign when they reached the First Round Proper and must have set their hearts on a return to the national headlines. At this stage they had already beaten Rothwell Town (A) 1-0, King's Lynn (H) 2-0, Matlock Town (A) 2-2 and (H) 2-0 but there were two more qualifying rounds to survive and the big clubs from the Blue Square Premier were joining the competition at the Fourth Round determined to qualify for the most exciting draw of the competition.

The chase is on! Bedford Town and Romulus players compete to get to the ball first - 3rd Qualifying Rnd. Photo: Peter Barnes.

Darren Acton is beaten but this Gainsborough Trinity header hits the Nuneaton post - 3rd Qualifying Rnd. Photo: Bill Wheatcroft.

FIRST QUALIFYING ROUND

59	Erith Town	v Aylesbury	3-3	72
	Aylesbury	v Erith Town	2-1	84
60	Heybridge Swifts	v Stanway Rovers	1-1	168
	Stanway Rovers	v Heybridge Swifts	0-0*	186
	(Heybridge Swifts won 4-3 on penalties)			
61	Waltham Abbey	v Enfield Town	0-1	260
62	Thamesmead Town	v Windsor & Eton	1-2	59
63	Arlesey Town	v Wealdstone	1-2	236
64	Thame United	v Burnham	0-2	113
65	East Thurrock United	v Ware	4-1	115
66	Northwood	v Wingate & Finchley	2-2	142
	Wingate & Finchley	v Northwood	3-1	85
67	Hemel Hempstead Town	v Slough Town	1-1	395
	Slough Town	v Hemel Hempstead Town	2-1	249
68	Marlow	v Hendon	0-2	150
69	AFC Hornchurch	v Billericay Town	0-3	453
70	Aylesbury United	v Potters Bar Town	0-0	135
	Potters Bar Town	v Aylesbury United	2-0	72
71	London Colney	v Aveley	1-1	102
	Aveley	v London Colney	4-2	146
72	Boreham Wood	v Waltham Forest	1-0	81
73	Bedford Town	v Kingsbury London Tigers	5-1	295
74	Romford	v Concord Rangers	1-1	102
	Concord Rangers	v Romford	6-0	122
75	Guildford City	v East Preston	4-4	73
	East Preston	v Guildford City	2-2*	104
	(East Preston won 4-3 on penalties))			
76	Molesey	v Bashley	2-3	92
77	Walton & Hersham	v Cray Wanderers	2-1	108
78	Chatham Town	v Walton Casuals	0-0	160
	Walton Casuals	v Chatham Town	2-1*	114
79	Farnborough	v Hastings United	2-1	716
80	Whitstable Town	v Carshalton Athletic	2-1	179
81	Crawley Down	v Ashford Town (Middx)	2-3	101
82	Leatherhead	v Ashford Town	2-0	163
83	Uxbridge	v Ash United	4-3	116
84	Bognor Regis Town	v Kingstonian	1-4	402
85	Folkestone Invicta	v Sittingbourne	0-1	360
86	Maidstone United	v Bedfont	2-1	294
87	Hythe Town	v Faversham Town	2-1	215
88	AFC Totton	v VCD Athletic	5-0	185
89	Lingfield	v Badshot Lea	4-4	144
	Badshot Lea	v Lingfield	2-1	148
90	Chipstead	v Dartford	1-6	321
91	Tooting & Mitcham United	v Horsham	4-2	346
92	Deal Town	v Selsey	1-1	120
	Selsey	v Deal Town	3-0	145
93	VT	v Dulwich Hamlet	1-0	173
94	Tonbridge Angels	v Metropolitan Police	1-0	352
95	Croydon Athletic	v Worthing	0-1	161
96	Horsham YMCA	v East Grinstead Town	1-0	116
97	Margate	v Sutton United	2-2	402
	Sutton United	v Margate	3-2*	301
98	Almondsbury Town	v Yate Town	1-1	202
	Yate Town	v Almondsbury Town	1-2	205
99	Brading Town	v Hallen	1-1	124
	Hallen	v Brading Town	3-0	89
100	Banbury United	v Chippenham Town	0-0	361
	Chippenham Town	v Banbury United	3-2	306
101	Brackley Town	v Swindon Supermarine	1-0	180
102	Bishop's Cleeve	v Brockenhurst	5-2	67
103	Oxford City	v Kidlington	4-2	320
104	Mangotsfield United	v Wantage Town	3-0	146
105	Shortwood United	v Witney United	3-3	108
	Witney United	v Shortwood United	2-1	151
106	Highworth Town	v Abingdon United	0-3	134
107	Hungerford Town	v Bristol Manor Farm	4-0	137
108	Didcot Town	v Shrivenham	5-0	226
109	Cirencester Town	v North Leigh	2-1	144
110	Bridgwater Town	v Hamworthy United	3-1	249
111	Saltash United	v Gillingham Town	1-1	203
	Gillingham Town	v Saltash United	6-5*	381
112	Truro City	v Bridport	1-1	473
	Bridport	v Truro City	0-7	335
113	Taunton Town	v Merthyr Tydfil	0-3	340
114	Willand Rovers	v Poole Town	1-0	163
115	Paulton Rovers	v Tiverton Town	1-0	243
116	Clevedon Town	v Wimborne Town	4-2	132

SECOND QUALIFYING ROUND

1	Whitby Town	v Vauxhall Motors	0-5	286
2	Warrington Town	v Radcliffe Borough	1-1	234
	Radcliffe Borough	v Warrington Town	3-1	169
3	Congleton Town	v Frickley Athletic	0-1	294
4	Lincoln United	v Jarrow Roofing Boldon CA	2-1	151
5	Kendal Town	v Ossett Town	2-0	183
6	Droylsden	v FC Halifax Town	0-2	902
7	Horden CW	v Burscough	1-4	82
8	Blyth Spartans	v Ossett Albion	7-1	507
9	North Ferriby United	v FC United of Manchester	0-1	838
10	Hyde United	v Salford City	2-2	276
	Salford City	v Hyde United	1-0	391
11	Chorley	v Ashton United	2-1	294
12	Southport	v Spennymoor Town	3-1	554
13	Bradford (Park Avenue)	v Harrogate Town	4-0	375
14	Northwich Victoria	v Bardon Hill Sports	8-0	502
15	Fleetwood Town	v Farsley Celtic	3-1	730
16	Workington	v Cammell Laird	4-1	302
17	Stocksbridge Park Steels	v Stalybridge Celtic	2-7	352
18	Guiseley	v Bamber Bridge	2-0	298
19	Buxton	v AFC Fylde	5-0	292
20	Coventry Sphinx	v Stafford Rangers	2-2	312
	Stafford Rangers	v Coventry Sphinx	2-3	465
21	Matlock Town	v Bury Town	2-2	341
	Bury Town	v Matlock Town	2-0*	518
22	Nuneaton Town	v Carlton Town	1-1	905
	Carlton Town	v Nuneaton Town	0-3	254
23	Bedford Town	v Romulus	2-1	283
24	Evesham United	v Stourbridge	0-1	262
25	Alfreton Town	v AFC Wulfrunians	6-0	353
26	Bedworth United	v Rainworth MW	2-1	210
27	AFC Telford United	v Pegasus Juniors	4-1	1136
28	Sutton Coldfield Town	v Needham Market	3-1	161
29	Hinckley United	v Kirkley & Pakefield	2-1	322
30	Lowestoft Town	v Boston United	1-0	1134
31	Redditch United	v Stratford Town	1-1	361
	Stratford Town	v Redditch United	0-2	481
32	Market Drayton Town	v Gainsborough Trinity	1-2	205
33	Ilkeston Town	v Mildenhall Town	4-1	321
34	Eastwood Town	v Corby Town	2-1	484
35	Worcester City	v Bourne Town	3-0	555
36	Mickleover Sports	v Solihull Moors	3-4	240
37	Rugby Town	v Hucknall Town	1-3	224
38	Cambridge City	v Northampton Spencer	4-1	243
39	Enfield 1893	v Chelmsford City	0-5	306
40	Walton Casuals	v Selsey	1-0	127
41	Canvey Island	v Tooting & Mitcham United	0-2	376
42	Heybridge Swifts	v St Albans City	1-0	201
43	Burnham	v Aveley	1-1	109
	Aveley	v Burnham	3-1	116
44	Chesham United	v Billericay Town	4-2	422
45	Sutton United	v Uxbridge	3-0	365
46	Lewes	v Leatherhead	1-1	480
	Leatherhead	v Lewes	0-1*	308
47	Bishop's Stortford	v Thurrock	2-3	425
48	Hythe Town	v Woking	2-2	557
	Woking	v Hythe Town	5-1	761
49	Tonbridge Angels	v Horsham YMCA	4-0	366

Third Qualifying Round
(40 winners @ £7,5000)

Life becomes a little more serious and although the Blue Square Premier clubs would soon be joining the competition only two more games need to be won before a place in the the First Round draw with the 'elite' of Divisions One and Two could be achieved.

Only five senior clubs had been unbeaten all season before this round of the cup, but Cambridge City and Dartford really collapsed in front of their own supporters in the two biggest defeats of the round. Hinckley United winning at Milton Road 5-0 and Chelmsford City recording an excellent 4-1 victory at Princes Park Stadium. Newport County also lost their unbeaten record but only went down 0-1 at Paulton Rovers.

Bury Town are still on course to equal last season's excellent F.A.Cup run, but they did it the hard way by drawing 1-1 at home with Bedford Town before winning a thrilling replay 4-3. Lowestoft Town have hit the headlines in recent seasons with two good F.A.Vase runs and promotion into the Isthmian League, but they also needed an away replay victory to dispose of Sutton Coldfield Town.

Best attendances:

F.C.United v Stalybridge Celtic	2819	Stalybridge Celtic v F.C.United	1923
Dartford v Chelmsford City	1830	AFC Telford Utd v Worcester C	1459
F.C.Halifax v Burscough	1459	Woking v Maidstone United	1434
Lowestoft v Sutton Coldfield T	1210	Ilkeston Town v Eastwood Town	1128
Dover Athletic v Welling United	1042	Bury Town v Bedford Town	1003

The Heroes

Aylesbury F.C.from the Spartan South Midlands Premier Division

Extra Preliminary Rd.	v	Langford	(A)	W 6-0 Price, Henney 3 Brennan & Schmid
Preliminary Rd.	v	Leighton	(A)	D 0-0
Replay	v	Leighton	(H)	W 1-0 Price
1st Qualifying Rd.	v	Erith Town	(A)	D 3-3 Henney 3
Replay	v	Erith Town	(H)	W 2-1 Hayward and Henney
2nd Qualifying Rd	v	Wingate&F	(A)	D 2-2 Brennan and Price
Replay	v	Wingate&F	(H)	W 2-1 Henney and Graham
3rd Qualifying Rd	v	Chesham U	(H)	W 4-3 Henney 3 & Gudgeon

With eight ties already completed Aylesbury had won £17,250 and Craig Henney was top F.A.Cup goalscorer in the competition with eleven.

The Fourth Qualifying Round
(32 winners @ £12,500)

One of the best days of the football season highlights the desperate battles in the Fourth Qualifying Round to see who will take on the Football League clubs. This year, joining the twenty four Blue Square Premier teams (11 home and 13 away) were Blue Square North 10 (with 6 home ties and 4 away), Blue Square South 9 (5+4), Unibond 5 (2+3), Ryman 6 (3+3) and Zamaretto 9 (4+5) with Aylesbury F.C. from the Spartan South Midland League drawn at home.

Not surprisingly, apart from the Blue Square Premier clubs, The Blue Square North and South clubs provided most of the other qualifiers for the First Round Proper with five Southern clubs, Bath City, Bromley, Eastleigh, Staines Town and Woking all through at the first attempt. Outstanding results were earned by Eastleigh, with a 5-3 victory at Dover and Staines Town who won 1-0 at Hayes & Yeading.

Their Northern colleagues claimed the scalps of Premier clubs Histon, who were beaten 2-1 at Hinckley United and Tamworth, who lost 0-2 at Ilkeston Town. Northwich Victoria enjoyed entertaining F.C.United in front of 2,615 and won 3-0 with Mark Danks claiming his fourteenth goal of the season.

Excellent replay victories were achieved by Fleetwood Town who beat Kidderminster Harriers 3-1 in front of an impressive 1,698 and AFC Telford United won 4-0 against Blyth Spartans who were playing their fifth F.A.Cup tie in four weeks.

Of the 32 non-league representatives joining the 48 Football League clubs in the draw, 14 Blue Square Premier clubs were favoured with nine home ties, one of which featured unbeaten Oxford United who were given a wonderful home tie with Yeovil Town. The Somerset Division One club were the scourge of the Football League teams in the competition when they were a non-league club themselves, but since they gained senior status they had hardly won a tie.

The Blue Square North and South produced five clubs each but the Steps Three and Four leagues were not so well balanced.The Ryman League were represented by Sutton United, Tooting & Mitcham United and Wealdstone, all with great F.A.Cup memories and capable of surprise results.

One other Ryman club representing Division One North was Lowestoft Town who really had caught the imagination of the local football public with their progress from the Preliminary Round and their impressive attendances:

Preliminary Round	639	v Great Yarmouth Town
1st Qualifying Round	779	v Dereham Town
2nd Qualifying Round	1134	v Boston United
3rd Qualifying Round	1210	v Sutton Coldfield Town
4th Q. Round Replay	2247	v Gloucester City

The Zamaretto League senior representatives were Oxford City, Stourbridge and Nuneaton Town but it was their 'little brother' Paulton Rovers from Division One South West who received all the publicity with a home draw and a live televised match with Norwich City.

The Unibond League, representing the Step Three and Four clubs in the North of England experienced a disappointing and extremely unusual situation with no representative in the First Round.

SECOND QUALIFYING ROUND

50	Dover Athletic	v East Preston	8-0	757
51	Boreham Wood	v Wealdstone	2-4	249
52	Windsor & Eton	v Farnborough	0-1	478
53	Hendon	v Kingstonian	2-1	226
54	Potters Bar Town	v Whitstable Town	3-0	118
55	Bromley	v Flackwell Heath	2-0	442
56	Braintree Town	v Hampton & Richmond B.	0-0	327
	Hampton & Richmond B.	v Braintree Town	4-1	261
57	Harefield United	v Maidstone United	0-2	323
58	Wingate & Finchley	v Aylesbury	2-2	119
	Aylesbury	v Wingate & Finchley	2-1	87
59	Sittingbourne	v Staines Town	2-3	196
60	Worthing	v Dartford	1-2	611
61	Welling United	v East Thurrock United	2-0	404
62	Walton & Hersham	v Enfield Town	3-2	228
63	Ashford Town (Middx)	v Badshot Lea	10-0	102
64	Slough Town	v Concord Rangers	2-0	279
65	Bishop's Cleeve	v Weymouth	3-0	249
66	Dorchester Town	v Hungerford Town	4-0	307
67	Bashley	v Gloucester City	1-2	287
68	Gillingham Town	v Mangotsfield United	3-3	505
	Mangotsfield United	v Gillingham Town	3-0	263
69	Abingdon United	v Cirencester Town	0-0	134
	Cirencester Town	v Abingdon United	3-1	106
70	Willand Rovers	v Bath City	0-5	422
71	Almondsbury Town	v AFC Totton	1-4	100
72	Weston Super Mare	v Havant & Waterlooville	0-1	298
73	Brackley Town	v Basingstoke Town	0-1	326
74	Clevedon Town	v Newport County	1-3	623
75	Chippenham Town	v Merthyr Tydfil	4-1	533
76	Witney United	v Eastleigh	1-6	245
77	VT	v Oxford City	0-1	234
78	Bridgwater Town	v Hallen	1-0	380
79	Maidenhead United	v Truro City	2-5	313
80	Didcot Town	v Paulton Rovers	0-2	225

THIRD QUALIFYING ROUND

1	Salford City	v Blyth Spartans	2-2	271
	Blyth Spartans	v Salford City	2-1	534
2	Fleetwood Town	v Vauxhall Motors	3-2	951
3	Northwich Victoria	v Chorley	4-1	617
4	Buxton	v Bradford (Park Avenue)	2-2	533
	Bradford (Park Avenue)	v Buxton	0-1	375
5	Guiseley	v Kendal Town	1-1	405
	Kendal Town	v Guiseley	1-0	333
6	Workington	v Radcliffe Borough	3-0	318
7	Alfreton Town	v Southport	2-2	613
	Southport	v Alfreton Town	2-1	553
8	FC Halifax Town	v Burscough	1-0	1459
9	FC United of Manchester	v Stalybridge Celtic	3-3	2819
	Stalybridge Celtic	v FC United of Manchester	0-1	1923
10	Lincoln United	v Frickley Athletic	1-1	273
	Frickley Athletic	v Lincoln United	1-1*	274
	(Lincoln United won 3-1 on penalties)			
11	Cambridge City	v Hinckley United	0-5	466
12	Solihull Moors	v Redditch United	0-2	492
13	Stourbridge	v Hucknall Town	0-0	384
	Hucknall Town	v Stourbridge	1-6	324
14	Ilkeston Town	v Eastwood Town	1-1	1128
	Eastwood Town	v Ilkeston Town	1-3	1205
15	Bury Town	v Bedford Town	1-1	1003
	Bedford Town	v Bury Town	3-4	481
16	Coventry Sphinx	v Bedworth United	0-1	871
17	Lowestoft Town	v Sutton Coldfield Town	0-0	1210
	Sutton Coldfield Town	v Lowestoft Town	1-2	201
18	AFC Telford United	v Worcester City	0-0	1459
	Worcester City	v AFC Telford United	0-1	1062
19	Nuneaton Town	v Gainsborough Trinity	1-0	930
20	Hampton & Richmond B.	v Aveley	1-1	485
	Aveley	v Hampton & Richmond B.	1-2	205
21	Dartford	v Chelmsford City	1-4	1830
22	Wealdstone	v Lewes	3-0	530
23	Thurrock	v Potters Bar Town	4-2	155
24	Hendon	v Ashford Town (Middx)	0-0	236
	Ashford Town (Middx)	v Hendon	2-2*	226
	(Hendon won 9-8 on penalties)			
25	Tonbridge Angels	v Bromley	0-2	944
26	Dover Athletic	v Welling United	2-0	1042
27	Tooting & Mitcham United	v Slough Town	3-2	551
28	Sutton United	v Walton & Hersham	1-0	536
29	Aylesbury	v Chesham United	4-3	448
30	Walton Casuals	v Staines Town	0-3	238
31	Woking	v Maidstone United	2-0	1434
32	Heybridge Swifts	v Farnborough	0-0	295
	Farnborough	v Heybridge Swifts	3-0*	567
33	Paulton Rovers	v Newport County	1-0	703
34	Dorchester Town	v Gloucester City	1-2	498
35	Oxford City	v Cirencester Town	2-0	311
36	Eastleigh	v Basingstoke Town	2-0	681
37	Bishop's Cleeve	v Bath City	1-4	398
38	Truro City	v Mangotsfield United	1-1	574
	Mangotsfield United	v Truro City	1-1*	529
	(Mangotsfield United won 4-3 on penalties)			
39	AFC Totton	v Bridgwater Town	3-2	419
40	Havant & Waterlooville	v Chippenham Town	1-2	620

FOURTH QUALIFYING ROUND

1	Hinckley United	v Histon	2-1	778
2	Nuneaton Town	v Kendal Town	1-0	1103
3	FC Halifax Town	v Wrexham	0-1	2843
4	Gateshead	v Southport	3-0	402
5	Workington	v Rushden & Diamonds	0-3	724
6	Mansfield Town	v Altrincham	3-0	2410
7	Buxton	v Stourbridge	0-4	793
8	Blyth Spartans	v AFC Telford United	0-0	642
	AFC Telford United	v Blyth Spartans	4-0	1398
9	Ilkeston Town	v Tamworth	2-0	699
10	Lincoln United	v Cambridge United	1-3	837
11	Kettering Town	v Redditch United	1-1	1403
	Redditch United	v Kettering Town	0-1*	1101
12	Northwich Victoria	v FC United of Manchester	3-0	2615
13	Barrow	v Chester City	1-1	1579
	Chester City	v Barrow	0-4	1287
14	Kidderminster Harriers	v Fleetwood Town	0-0	1257
	Fleetwood Town	v Kidderminster Harriers	3-1	1698
15	York City	v Bedworth United	2-0	1869
16	Hendon	v Woking	0-5	528
17	Gloucester City	v Lowestoft Town	1-1	539
	Lowestoft Town	v Gloucester City	4-2	2247
18	Farnborough	v Salisbury City	0-0	1247
	Salisbury City	v Farnborough	4-2	1200
19	Mangotsfield United	v Forest Green Rovers	1-2	946
20	Crawley Town	v AFC Wimbledon	1-1	2204
	AFC Wimbledon	v Crawley Town	3-1	2467
21	Oxford City	v Bury Town	2-1	580
22	Bromley	v Ebbsfleet United	3-0	1133
23	Chelmsford City	v Stevenage Borough	1-2	1702
24	Aylesbury	v Wealdstone	2-4	682
25	Dover Athletic	v Eastleigh	3-5	1161
26	Hayes & Yeading United	v Staines Town	0-1	602
27	Luton Town	v Grays Athletic	3-0	2721
28	Oxford United	v Thurrock	2-0	3296
29	Bath City	v AFC Totton	3-2	740
30	Paulton Rovers	v Chippenham Town	3-0	931
31	Tooting & Mitcham United	v Eastbourne Borough	3-3	687
	Eastbourne Borough	v Tooting & Mitcham United	3-4*	906
32	Hampton & Richmond B.	v Sutton United	1-3	669

The First Round Proper
(40 winners @ £18,000)

There is an extra incentive for non-league clubs lucky enough to have their cup ties televised from the First Round onwards. The fees offered are:-

First Round Proper	£67,500 for A Live Broadcast	£33,750 A live replay broadcast	£6,750 for highlights
Second Round	£72,000	£36,000	£6,750
Third Round	£144,000	£72,000	£6,750

Despite many Premier League clubs appearing to lose their respect for the F.A.Challenge Cup, you won't find a non-league player who would turn down a chance to face a Football League club in the famous knock out competition. The wonderful win bonus now adds to the glamour, so you can imagine how Bath City players felt on returning with a 2-0 victory at Grimsby and the celebrations as little Staines Town won at Shrewsbury Town and Kettering Town returned with the Hartlepool scalp.

Winners of all non league clashes, were Barrow, 2-1 victors over Eastleigh, Rushden & Diamonds 3-1 winners against Hinckley United, Wrexham 1-0 winners over a brave Lowestoft Town, Cambridge United who convincingly beat Ilkeston Town 4-0, plus Forest Green Rovers who won after a replay at Mansfield Town.

York City beat Crewe Alexandra 3-2, Luton Town won after a replay at Rochdale and Oxford United eliminated the once famous cup fighters Yeovil Town. However, Paulton Rovers representing a little Somerset village enjoyed the glamour and finances of a live televised match even though they took a bit of a beating from a very good Norwich City side.

Our highlight of the round was probably an outstanding televised performance by Northwich Victoria who beat Division One leaders Charlton Athletic 1-0 but this was a performance they couldn't repeat.

The Second Round
(20 winners @ £27,000)

Sadly, the two West Country clubs, Bath City and Forest Green Rovers, were drawn against each other, but at least one would be representing non-league football in the prestigious Third Round and it turned out to be Forest Green Rovers who won 2-1 at Twerton Park

Another all non-league tie was won by Barrow after a replay at Holker Street against Oxford United and two more replays brought differing rewards, with Staines Town losing away to Millwall but Luton Town achieving an excellent 3-0 home result against Rotherham United.

There was a special memory for Kettering Town who drew at home to high flying Leeds United but sadly they were well beaten 5-1 when it appeared that fitness told after extra time at Elland Road.

The Third Round
(32 winners @ £67,500)

The previous season's record of eight non-league clubs in the F.A.Cup Third Round was not challenged and the three representing our level of the game didn't have the best of luck with the draw.

Barrow appreciated 25,190 attending their exciting visit to Premier League Sunderland and Luton Town were also well respected at Southampton, where 18,766 were rewarded with a single goal which was enough for the Saints to win the tie. Sadly, Forest Green Rovers completed a hat trick of defeats in this round but had to wait until 15th January before they could play their tie at Notts County.

Another F.A.Challenge Cup campaign was over for the non-league clubs and although it didn't produce many spectacular results, try telling anyone at Aylesbury F.C. or Paulton Rovers that the competition was losing its magic!

Eastleigh's Richard Gillespie scores in the Spitfires' 2-0 victory over local rivals Basingstoke Town in the 3rd Qualifying Round. Photo: Graham Brown.

FIRST ROUND PROPER

1	Gillingham	v Southend United	3-0	4605
2	Grimsby Town	v Bath City	0-2	2103
3	Gateshead	v Brentford	2-2	1150
	Brentford	v Gateshead	5-2	1960
4	Chesterfield	v AFC Bournemouth	1-3	3277
5	AFC Telford United	v Lincoln City	1-3	2809
6	Stockport County	v Tooting & Mitcham United	5-0	3076
7	Burton Albion	v Oxford City	3-2	2207
8	Barrow	v Eastleigh	2-1	1655
9	Oldham Athletic	v Leeds United	0-2	5552
10	Cambridge United	v Ilkeston Town	4-0	2395
11	York City	v Crewe Alexandra	3-2	3070
12	Wycombe Wanderers	v Brighton & Hove Albion	4-4	2749
	Brighton & Hove Albion	v Wycombe Wanderers	2-0	3383
13	Hereford United	v Sutton United	2-0	1713
14	Nuneaton Town	v Exeter City	0-4	2510
15	Bristol Rovers	v Southampton	2-3	6446
16	Carlisle United	v Morecambe	2-2	4181
	Morecambe	v Carlisle United	0-1	3307
17	Forest Green Rovers	v Mansfield Town	1-1	1149
	Mansfield Town	v Forest Green Rovers	1-2	2496
18	Oxford United	v Yeovil Town	1-0	6144
19	Paulton Rovers	v Norwich City	0-7	2070
20	Swindon Town	v Woking	1-0	4805
21	Port Vale	v Stevenage Borough	1-1	3999
	Stevenage Borough	v Port Vale	0-1	2894
22	Luton Town	v Rochdale	3-3	3167
	Rochdale	v Luton Town	0-2	1982
23	Bromley	v Colchester United	0-4	4242
24	Accrington Stanley	v Salisbury City	2-1	1379
25	Millwall	v AFC Wimbledon	4-1	9453
26	Stourbridge	v Walsall	0-1	2014
27	Shrewsbury Town	v Staines Town	0-1	3539
28	Wealdstone	v Rotherham United	2-3	1638
29	Torquay United	v Cheltenham Town	3-1	2370
30	Barnet	v Darlington	3-1	1654
31	Notts County	v Bradford City	2-1	4213
32	Huddersfield Town	v Dagenham&Redbridge	6-1	5858
33	Milton Keynes Dons	v Macclesfield Town	1-0	4868
34	Rushden & Diamonds	v Hinckley United	3-1	1540
35	Northwich Victoria	v Charlton Athletic	1-0	2153
36	Aldershot Town	v Bury	2-0	2590
37	Wrexham	v Lowestoft Town	1-0	2402
38	Hartlepool United	v Kettering Town	0-1	2645
39	Tranmere Rovers	v Leyton Orient	1-1	3180
	Leyton Orient	v Tranmere Rovers	0-1	1518
40	Northampton Town	v Fleetwood Town	2-1	3077

SECOND ROUND PROPER

1	Northwich Victoria	v Lincoln City	1-3	3544
2	Northampton Town	v Southampton	2-3	4858
3	Hereford United	v Colchester United	0-1	2225
4	Tranmere Rovers	v Aldershot Town	0-0	3742
	Aldershot Town	v Tranmere Rovers	1-2	4016
5	Kettering Town	v Leeds United	1-1	4837
	Leeds United	v Kettering Town	5-1*	10670
6	Gillingham	v Burton Albion	1-0	4996
7	Wrexham	v Swindon Town	0-1	3011
8	Brighton & Hove Albion	v Rushden & Diamonds	3-2	3638
9	Rotherham United	v Luton Town	2-2	3210
	Luton Town	v Rotherham United	3-0	2518
10	Milton Keynes Dons	v Exeter City	4-3	4867
11	Brentford	v Walsall	1-0	2611
12	Carlisle United	v Norwich City	3-1	3936
13	Accrington Stanley	v Barnet	2-2	1301
	Barnet	v Accrington Stanley	0-1	1288
14	Oxford United	v Barrow	1-1	6082
	Barrow	v Oxford United	3-1	2754
15	AFC Bournemouth	v Notts County	1-2	6082
16	Stockport County	v Torquay United	0-4	1690
	(at Macclesfield Town FC)			
17	Cambridge United	v York City	1-2	3505
18	Bath City	v Forest Green Rovers	1-2	3325
19	Port Vale	v Huddersfield Town	0-1	5311
20	Staines Town	v Millwall	1-1	2753
	Millwall	v Staines Town	4-0	3452

THIRD ROUND PROPER

1	Tottenham Hotspur	v Peterborough United	4-0	35862
2	Brentford	v Doncaster Rovers	0-1	2883
3	Middlesbrough	v Manchester City	0-1	12474
4	Stoke City	v York City	3-1	15586
5	Notts County	v Forest Green Rovers	2-1	4389
6	Huddersfield Town	v West Bromwich Albion	0-2	13472
7	Sheffield United	v Queens Park Rangers	1-1	11461
	Queens Park Rangers	v Sheffield United	2-3	5780
8	Milton Keynes Dons	v Burnley	1-2	11816
9	Chelsea	v Watford	5-0	40912
10	Nottingham Forest	v Birmingham City	0-0	20975
	Birmingham City	v Nottingham Forest	1-0	9399
11	Preston North End	v Colchester United	7-0	7621
12	West Ham United	v Arsenal	1-2	25549
13	Aston Villa	v Blackburn Rovers	3-1	25543
14	Portsmouth	v Coventry City	1-1	11214
	Coventry City	v Portsmouth	1-2*	7097
15	Sunderland	v Barrow	3-0	25190
16	Wigan Athletic	v Hull City	4-1	5335
17	Everton	v Carlisle United	3-1	31196
18	Sheffield Wednesday	v Crystal Palace	1-2	8690
19	Tranmere Rovers	v Wolverhampton W.	0-1	7476
20	Blackpool	v Ipswich Town	1-2	7332
21	Fulham	v Swindon Town	1-0	19623
22	Torquay United	v Brighton & Hove Albion	0-1	4028
23	Scunthorpe United	v Barnsley	1-0	5457
24	Southampton	v Luton Town	1-0	18786
25	Bristol City	v Cardiff City	1-1	7289
	Cardiff City	v Bristol City	1-0	6731
26	Reading	v Liverpool	1-1	23656
	Liverpool	v Reading	1-2*	31063
27	Millwall	v Derby County	1-1	10531
	Derby County	v Millwall	1-1*	7183
	(Derby County won 5-3)			
28	Plymouth Argyle	v Newcastle United	0-0	16451
	Newcastle United	v Plymouth Argyle	3-0	15805
29	Leicester City	v Swansea City	2-1	12307
30	Bolton Wanderers	v Lincoln City	4-0	11193
31	Accrington Stanley	v Gillingham	1-0	1323
32	Manchester United	v Leeds United	0-1	74526

Marc Pullen, Eastbourne Borough, out jumps Tooting and Mitcham's Paul Vines to head the ball during this 4th Qualifying Round match.
Photo: Roger Turner.

Action below from the 2nd Round tie between Bath City and Forest Green Rovers, which Rovers went on to win 2-1.
Photo: Peter Barnes.

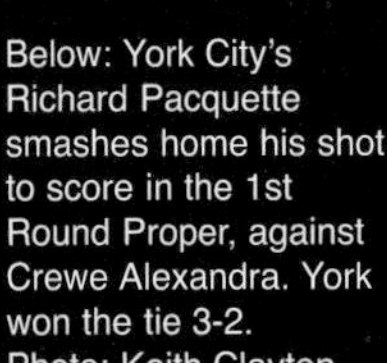

Below: York City's Richard Pacquette smashes home his shot to score in the 1st Round Proper, against Crewe Alexandra. York won the tie 3-2.
Photo: Keith Clayton.

Bluefin

FOURTH ROUND PROPER

1	Southampton	v Ipswich Town	2-1	20446
2	Reading	v Burnley	1-0	12910
3	Derby County	v Doncaster Rovers	1-0	11316
4	Cardiff City	v Leicester City	4-2	10961
5	Stoke City	v Arsenal	3-1	19735
6	Notts County	v Wigan Athletic	2-2	9073
	Wigan Athletic	v Notts County	0-2	5519
7	Scunthorpe United	v Manchester City	2-4	8861
8	West Bromwich Albion	v Newcastle United	4-2	16102
9	Everton	v Birmingham City	1-2	30875
10	Accrington Stanley	v Fulham	1-3	3712
11	Bolton Wanderers	v Sheffield United	2-0	14572
12	Portsmouth	v Sunderland	2-1	10315
13	Preston North End	v Chelsea	0-2	23119
14	Aston Villa	v Brighton & Hove Albion	3-2	39725
15	Wolverhampton W.s	v Crystal Palace	2-2	14449
	Crystal Palace	v Wolverhampton W.	3-1	10282
16	Tottenham Hotspur	v Leeds United	2-2	35750
	Leeds United	v Tottenham Hotspur	1-3	37704

FIFTH ROUND PROPER

1	Crystal Palace	v Aston Villa	2-2	20486
	Aston Villa	v Crystal Palace	3-1	31874
2	Manchester City	v Stoke City	1-1	28019
	Stoke City	v Manchester City	3-1*	21813
3	Derby County	v Birmingham City	1-2	21043
4	Bolton Wanderers	v Tottenham Hotspur	1-1	13596
	Tottenham Hotspur	v Bolton Wanderers	4-0	31436
5	Chelsea	v Cardiff City	4-1	40827
6	Fulham	v Notts County	4-0	16132
7	Reading	v West Bromwich Albion	2-2	18008
	West Bromwich Albion	v Reading	2-3*	13985
8	Southampton	v Portsmouth	1-4	31375

SIXTH ROUND PROPER

1	Chelsea	v Stoke City	2-0	41322
2	Fulham	v Tottenham Hotspur	0-0	24533
	Tottenham Hotspur	v Fulham	3-1	35432
3	Reading	v Aston Villa	2-4	23174
4	Portsmouth	v Birmingham City	2-0	20456

SEMI FINAL

Portsmouth	v Tottenham Hotspur	2-0	84,602
Chelsea	v Astpn Villa	3-0	85,472

THE FINAL

CHELSEA	1	0	PORTSMOUTH	88,335

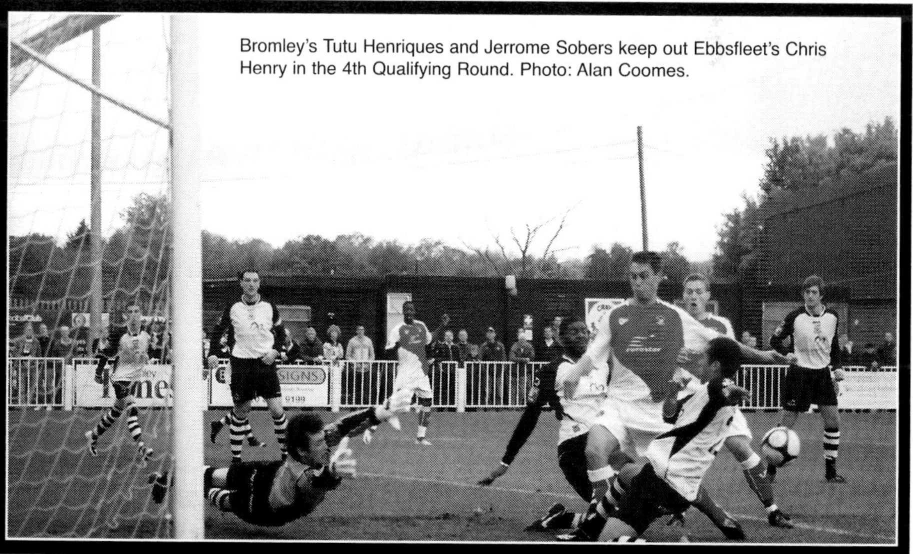

Bromley's Tutu Henriques and Jerrome Sobers keep out Ebbsfleet's Chris Henry in the 4th Qualifying Round. Photo: Alan Coomes.

Northwich Victoria's Wayne Riley....
breaks through the Charlton Athletic defence....
gets his toe to the ball....
and slips it past Randolph to win this First Round tie.
Photos: Keith Clayton.

Kettering Town's Elding sends in a shot whilst playing Leeds United in the 2nd Round.
Photo: Keith Clayton.

2009-10

Preliminary Round - 3rd October
52 winners@ £2,000

For clubs promoted into the Southern, Isthmian and Northern Premier Leagues for the first time, the difference from being senior fancied clubs in the F.A.Vase to become the minnows playing in the very first qualifying round in the F.A.Trophy, is massive. One very early defeat can leave a club out of contention very quickly as far as national knock out cups are concerned, and the first F.A.Trophy tie has to be faced at the beginning of October.

New Isthmians Lowestoft Town, who were losing finalists in the F.A.Vase Final at Wembley just five months previously, entertained Redbridge and attracted an impressive 642 fans to watch their 4-1 victory. Hellenic Champions Hungerford Town, who had stepped up to the Southern Division One South West, had competed in every F.A.Vase competition since its inaugural season in 1974-1975. They had known the agony of losing three Vase semi-finals but now they were travelling to Stourport Swifts for a Trophy Preliminary Round tie and managed a very tight 1-0 victory.

Clubs with Trophy pedigree in this round included Witton Albion (1992 Finalists) 2-0 winners at Colwyn Bay, Leek Town (1990 finalists) who beat Kidsgrove Athletic 1-0 away and Leatherhead (1978 finalists), who shared six goals at home with Thamesmead Town.

Nathan Jack of Totton battles with Johno Richardson of Andover (in the stripes) during the Stags' 2-0 win in the Preliminary Round.
Photo: Graham Brown.

PRELIMINARY ROUND

1	Colwyn Bay	v Witton Albion	0-2	326
2	Woodley Sports	v Harrogate Railway	2-2	81
	Harrogate Railway	v Woodley Sports	2-1	82
3	Clitheroe	v Belper Town	1-1	164
	Belper Town	v Clitheroe	1-4	152
4	Mossley	v Bedworth United	5-2	113
5	Curzon Ashton	v Brigg Town	1-2	85
6	Warrington Town	v Sheffield	5-2	142
7	Rossendale United	v Chorley	1-2	139
8	Glapwell	v Grantham Town	2-2	125
	Grantham Town	v Glapwell	2-3	149
9	Radcliffe Borough	v Mickleover Sports	6-3	111
10	Kidsgrove Athletic	v Leek Town	0-1	285
11	Ossett Albion	v Shepshed Dynamo	2-3	118
12	Cammell Laird	v Stamford	3-1	91
13	Lincoln United	v Chasetown	1-2	83
14	Market Drayton Town	v Bamber Bridge	1-1	124
	Bamber Bridge	v Market Drayton Town	4-0	153
15	Prescot Cables	v Lancaster City	1-2	198
16	Trafford	v FC Halifax Town	3-4	298
17	Wakefield	v Carlton Town	1-1	72
	Carlton Town	v Wakefield	2-2*	81
	(Carlton Town won 3-1 on penalties)			
18	Potters Bar Town	v Arlesey Town	0-0	95
	Arlesey Town	v Potters Bar Town	3-2	106
19	Heybridge Swifts	v VCD Athletic	0-3	149
20	Barton Rovers	v Ilford	1-1	80
	Ilford	v Barton Rovers	2-3*	71
21	Leatherhead	v Thamesmead Town	3-3	146
	Thamesmead Town	v Leatherhead	1-2	81
22	Chatham Town	v Concord Rangers	1-4	159
23	Croydon Athletic	v Bury Town	2-1	71
24	Burgess Hill Town	v Dulwich Hamlet	2-0	173
25	Enfield Town	v Eastbourne Town	4-0	224
26	Corinthian Casuals	v Worthing	2-2	121
	Worthing	v Corinthian Casuals	0-1	164
27	Folkestone Invicta	v Hitchin Town	0-1	255
28	Brentwood Town	v Great Wakering Rovers	3-0	96
29	Whitstable Town	v Walton & Hersham	2-2	154
	Walton & Hersham	v Whitstable Town	3-3*	122
	(Walton & Hersham won 3-1 on penalties)			
30	Tilbury	v Biggleswade Town	1-2	61
31	Waltham Forest	v East Thurrock United	2-0	55
32	Walton Casuals	v Whyteleafe	0-0	75
	Whyteleafe	v Walton Casuals	2-1	100
33	Romford	v AFC Sudbury	0-7	142
34	Soham Town Rangers	v Cheshunt	3-1	103
35	Sittingbourne	v Wingate & Finchley	1-1	104
	Wingate & Finchley	v Sittingbourne	1-2*	71
36	Ramsgate	v Leyton	3-2	133
37	Chipstead	v Horsham YMCA	3-1	75
38	Metropolitan Police	v Maldon Town	1-0	65
39	Lowestoft Town	v Redbridge	4-1	642
40	Leighton Town	v Harlow Town	3-0	108
41	Bedfont Green	v Chesham United	1-2	144
42	North Leigh	v Burnham	2-3	64
43	AFC Totton	v Andover	2-0	195
44	Beaconsfield SYCOB	v Aylesbury United	2-1	109
45	Bishop's Cleeve	v Yate Town	1-2	77
46	Stourport Swifts	v Hungerford Town	0-1	92
47	Slough Town	v Mangotsfield United	1-1	241
	Mangotsfield United	v Slough Town	0-1	149
48	AFC Hayes	v Bridgwater Town	1-4	73
49	Godalming Town	v VT	3-1	111
50	Fleet Town	v Bromsgrove Rovers	2-0	124
51	Rothwell Town	v Gosport Borough	0-1	100
52	Windsor & Eton	v Paulton Rovers	2-1	139

Wingate & Finchley 'keeper, Gavin King, and defender, Craig Ellis, keep out Sittingbourne's Jon Neal (stripes) during their Preliminary Round match.
Photo: Alan Coomes.

First Qualifying Round- 17th October
72 winners @ £2.300

This is the biggest round in the competition but it comes very quickly after the Preliminary Round, so before the end of October half the entries of the competition have been eliminated. The best attendances were attracted by clubs playing under new names as F.C. United attracted 729 down the road to see their 3-1 victory at Ashton United and F.C. Halifax welcomed 936 for the 2-0 victory over Romulus F.C.

The top goalscorers were Thatcham who scored eight at luckless Bracknell Town and Merstham who won 6-1 at Hastings United. Away sides certainly had little trouble finding the net, as Bashley scored four with the help of a Justin Keeler hat trick to beat Beaconsfield SYCOB and Carshalton Athletic smacked five in at Aveley. Brackley Town, Fleet Town and Truro City all hit four away to win at Clevedon Town, Swindon Supermarine and Tiverton Town respectively.

High scoring thrillers were enjoyed at Horsham, who drew 4-4 with Barton Rovers and at Hungerford, who beat Taunton Town by the odd goal in seven. Two Midland clubs on their way back from troubled times, attracted good attendances. Leamington were watched by 615, but lost 1-2 to Midland rivals Stourbridge and Nuneaton Town's 1-1draw with Hucknall Town attracted a creditable 660.

V.C.D. Athletic's Jason Barton, gets in a powerful header against Concord Rangers in the 1st Qualifying Round.
Photo: Alan Coomes.

Seen here in the 2nd Qualifying Round is Dartford's Jay May who sees this effort go over the Chipstead bar.
Photo: Alan Coomes.

FIRST QUALIFYING ROUND

1	Radcliffe Borough	v Quorn	2-2	123
	Quorn	v Radcliffe Borough	6-3	
2	Spalding United	v Mossley	1-3	92
3	Shepshed Dynamo	v Harrogate Railway	2-1	156
4	North Ferriby United	v Worksop Town	1-1	202
	Worksop Town	v North Ferriby United	4-4*	127
	(North Ferriby United won 5-4 on penalties)			
5	Boston United	v Chorley	3-2	889
6	Cammell Laird	v Guiseley	0-3	101
7	Retford United	v Nantwich Town	0-1	222
8	Atherstone Town	v Leigh Genesis	1-3	195
9	Whitby Town	v Warrington Town	5-2	274
10	Brigg Town	v Burscough	3-2	105
11	Leek Town	v Kendal Town	2-1	316
12	Rushall Olympic	v Carlton Town	0-1	90
13	Lancaster City	v Chasetown	1-1	195
	Chasetown	v Lancaster City	1-4	254
14	Skelmersdale United	v Goole	5-0	203
15	Bradford (Park Avenue)	v Clitheroe	0-1	310
16	Salford City	v Durham City	3-0	103
17	Witton Albion	v Sutton Coldfield Town	1-1	200
	Sutton Coldfield Town	v Witton Albion	2-3*	103
18	Garforth Town	v AFC Fylde	0-3	135
19	Marine	v Kings Lynn	0-1	240
20	Nuneaton Town	v Hucknall Town	1-1	660
	Hucknall Town	v Nuneaton Town	0-3	215
21	FC Halifax Town	v Romulus	2-0	936
22	Stocksbridge Park Steels	v Glapwell	1-2	120
23	Matlock Town	v Loughborough Dynamo	2-1	236
24	Ossett Town	v Willenhall Town	1-2	91
25	Buxton	v Hednesford Town	1-0	352
26	Frickley Athletic	v Bamber Bridge	2-1	171
27	Ashton United	v FC United of Manchester	1-3	729
28	Croydon Athletic	v Ashford Town (Middx)	2-1	89
29	AFC Hornchurch	v Brentwood Town	2-1	235
30	Wealdstone	v Margate	3-1	265
31	Aveley	v Carshalton Athletic	2-5	117
32	Ramsgate	v Leatherhead	3-0	198
33	Soham Town Rangers	v Harrow Borough	2-2	125
	Harrow Borough	v Soham Town Rangers	5-1	91
34	Cray Wanderers	v Burgess Hill Town	1-2	149
35	Corinthian Casuals	v Arlesey Town	0-3	80
36	Waltham Abbey	v Boreham Wood	0-2	67
37	Metropolitan Police	v Kingstonian	0-1	296
38	Biggleswade Town	v Chipstead	2-2	117
	Chipstead	v Biggleswade Town	2-2*	77
	(Chipstead won 4-2 on penalties)			
39	AFC Sudbury	v Billericay Town	3-3	312
	Billericay Town	v AFC Sudbury	2-2*	252
	(Billericay Town won 3-1 on penalties)			
40	VCD Athletic	v Concord Rangers	0-1	128
41	Horsham	v Barton Rovers	4-4	234
	Barton Rovers	v Horsham	4-3	88
42	Canvey Island	v Hitchin Town	1-2	285
43	Tooting & Mitcham United	v Walton & Hersham	3-0	233
44	Ware	v Enfield Town	1-3	239
45	Bognor Regis Town	v Ashford Town	3-1	248
46	Sittingbourne	v Dartford	0-1	473
47	Waltham Forest	v Maidstone United	1-1	126
	Maidstone United	v Waltham Forest	1-0	152
48	Leighton Town	v Whyteleafe	0-3	116
49	Hastings United	v Merstham	1-6	358
50	Sutton United	v Tonbridge Angels	0-2	319
51	Hendon	v Lowestoft Town	2-0	174
52	Cirencester Town	v Godalming Town	1-3	136
53	Hemel Hempstead Town	v Farnborough	0-1	316
54	Burnham	v Cinderford Town	3-2	79
55	Beaconsfield SYCOB	v Bashley	1-4	78
56	Swindon Supermarine	v Fleet Town	2-4	107
57	Bracknell Town	v Thatcham Town	1-8	95
58	Banbury United	v Bridgwater Town	2-2	247
	Bridgwater Town	v Banbury United	0-1	196
59	AFC Totton	v Woodford United	2-2	263
	Woodford United	v AFC Totton	1-4	68
60	Didcot Town	v Cambridge City	0-1	195
61	Northwood	v Abingdon United	1-0	93
62	Yate Town	v Bedford Town	2-1	138
63	Tiverton Town	v Truro City	0-4	487
64	Leamington	v Stourbridge	1-2	615
65	Merthyr Tydfil	v Marlow	0-0	250
	Marlow	v Merthyr Tydfil	4-2	115
66	Hungerford Town	v Taunton Town	4-3	122
67	Chippenham Town	v Frome Town	3-1	431
68	Evesham United	v Windsor & Eton	1-1	85
	Windsor & Eton	v Evesham United	0-2	104
69	Rugby Town	v Gosport Borough	0-1	184
70	Clevedon Town	v Brackley Town	2-4	108
71	Uxbridge	v Slough Town	1-1	217
	Slough Town	v Uxbridge	2-0	200
72	Chesham United	v Oxford City	2-2	306
	Oxford City	v Chesham United	2-0	213

SECOND QUALIFYING ROUND

1	Salford City	v Clitheroe	5-3	143
2	Frickley Athletic	v Guiseley	0-3	254
3	Boston United	v Quorn	0-0	917
	Quorn	v Boston United	3-2	251
4	Willenhall Town	v Nuneaton Town	0-6	335
5	AFC Fylde	v Glapwell	2-1	217
6	Whitby Town	v Kings Lynn	0-2	251
7	Carlton Town	v North Ferriby United	0-3	92
8	Witton Albion	v Brigg Town	4-1	220
9	Nantwich Town	v Leek Town	4-1	579
10	Cambridge City	v Matlock Town	0-1	276
11	Shepshed Dynamo	v FC Halifax Town	0-5	481
12	Lancaster City	v FC United of Manchester	3-3	743
	FC United of Manchester	v Lancaster City	1-0*	792
13	Leigh Genesis	v Skelmersdale United	4-1	220
14	Brackley Town	v Mossley	1-1	176
	Mossley	v Brackley Town	3-1*	132
15	Buxton	v Stourbridge	0-1	262
16	Boreham Wood	v Slough Town	3-2	167
17	Hitchin Town	v Gosport Borough	3-1	268
18	Concord Rangers	v Enfield Town	2-0	198
19	Barton Rovers	v Billericay Town	2-2	140
	Billericay Town	v Barton Rovers	3-0	207
20	Dartford	v Chipstead	3-0	1002
21	Croydon Athletic	v Burnham	1-1	130
	Burnham	v Croydon Athletic	2-1	83
22	Carshalton Athletic	v AFC Totton	3-1	249
23	Fleet Town	v Ramsgate	0-2	118
24	Bashley	v Marlow	2-1	211
25	Godalming Town	v Banbury United	1-1	188
	Banbury United	v Godalming Town	1-3	205

2nd Qualifying Round - 31st October
36 winners @ £3,000

Two more famous clubs trying desperately to re-establish themselves and still well supported, were Boston United who attracted 917 to see a 0-0 draw with Quorn before losing away in the replay and Dartford, who were watched by 1002 when they beat Chipstead 3-0. Nuneaton Town with a 6-1 win at Willenhall and F.C.Halifax 5-0 at Shepshed Dynamo, once again showed their determination to show they were on the way back.

Other high scoring clubs in the round were Farnborough with five against Burgess Hill and Salford City 5-3 winners against Clitheroe, while Chippenham Town (4-1 v Tooting & Mitcham), Kingstonian (4-2 v Hendon), Leigh Genesis (4-1 v Skelmersdale United), Witton Albion (4-1 v Brigg Town), Nantwich Town (4-1 v Leek Town) and Truro City who scored four for the second consecutive round, with a 4-1 victory over Thatcham Town, all thrilled their fans at home.

One more Qualifying Round would see the introduction of Conference North and South teams but those within the lower levels of the non-league game are always keen to test themselves against the senior clubs which is often the only chance they get to attempt a little giant killing.

Third Qualifying Round - 21st November
40 winners @ £4,000

One more victory and you're in the draw with the Blue Square Premier clubs and the Competition Proper, but the five clubs, who had reached this Round having started out in the Preliminary Round two months ago, fell at the last hurdle. Home defeats for Godalming Town against Arlesey Town 0-3, Ramsgate against Bishop's Stortford by the same score and Mossley AFC 0-2 in a replay against Ilkeston Town, plus away losses for Hungerford Town at Boreham Wood 0-1 and F.C.Halifax at Guiseley 1-3, ended five mini cup runs after three successful rounds.

A surprising win was Farsley Celtic's 5-2 defeat of Droylsden and the highest scoring club was Woking who celebrated a 6-0 victory over St Albans City. Two high scoring battles that led to replays were the Essex local 'derby' between Chelmsford City and AFC Hornchurch which finished at 4-4, and a 3-3 deadlock between Hyde United and Nuneaton Town.

An excellent crowd enjoyed the clash between two clubs keen to continue their great start to the season, as 1,012 watched Dover Athletic beat Dartford 3-2 in a thriller, while F.C.United lost in front of 1,166, the best attendance of the round as Harrogate Town won 3-2.

With Farsley Celtic struggling to survive despite a good Trophy result, it was equally disappointing to note that King's Lynn, another club to fade during the season, also attracted a very solid 889 to see their 1-0 victory over Salford City, and Weymouth, who were constantly struggling during the campaign, won 3-0 against local rivals Dorchester Town in front of 1,032.

First Round Proper - 12th December
32 winners @ £5,000

Since two clubs were offered promotion into The Football League from The Conference at the end of every season, one can understand that a run in the F.A.Trophy has lost a little of its attraction to the ambitious clubs in the top half of the table. Having said that however, a Final at Wembley Stadium will never lose its appeal to supporters and players alike, so perhaps the Stevenage method is the one that all clubs should adopt!

As F.A.Trophy holders, Graham Westley's superb squad's consistent form ensured the championship was clinched in style, leaving enough time for the players to be made available and motivated to take the F.A.Trophy competition seriously.

One sensed that clubs recently relegated sometimes found F.A.Trophy motivation difficult. Cambridge United eased out Luton Town 3-1, Chester City lost at home by the only goal to Fleetwood Town and Wrexham lost after a replay at Altrincham. As the annual competition develops however, fans can appreciate a 'cup run' and the loyal support attracted by AFC Wimbledon were appreciative of their 2-1 victory over Boreham Wood and I suspect would really enjoy roaring their side on to a Wembley appearance before they return to The Football League!

A special tie was the meeting of two 'Cities', Chelmsford and the little Truro club, that had worked through from relative obscurity in deepest South West to challenge in non-league football's senior knock out competition. Following a 2-2 draw in Essex, Chelmsford won by the only goal of the game in a long distance mid week replay.

SECOND QUALIFYING ROUND

26	Kingstonian	v Hendon	4-2	276
27	Farnborough	v Burgess Hill Town	5-2	584
28	Tonbridge Angels	v Merstham	6-1	386
29	Arlesey Town	v Oxford City	2-1	170
30	Northwood	v Evesham United	0-0	104
	Evesham United	v Northwood	1-2	98
31	Harrow Borough	v Wealdstone	2-2	513
	Wealdstone	v Harrow Borough	2-1	315
32	Yate Town	v Hungerford Town	1-1	135
	Hungerford Town	v Yate Town (3/11)	3-0	127
33	Truro City	v Thatcham Town	4-1	371
34	Bognor Regis Town	v Maidstone United	0-2	252
35	Chippenham Town	v Tooting & Mitcham United	4-1	429
36	Whyteleafe	v AFC Hornchurch	1-1	143
	AFC Hornchurch	v Whyteleafe	4-0	154

THIRD QUALIFYING ROUND

1	King's Lynn	v Salford City	1-0	889
2	Ilkeston Town	v Mossley	1-1	271
	Mossley	v Ilkeston Town	0-2	183
3	Fleetwood Town	v Northwich Victoria	2-0	847
4	FC United of Manchester	v Harrogate Town	2-3	1166
5	Farsley Celtic	v Droylsden	5-2	220
6	Hyde United	v Nuneaton Town	3-3	328
	Nuneaton Town	v Hyde United	1-0	464
7	North Ferriby United	v Gainsborough Trinity	2-2	176
	Gainsborough Trinity	v North Ferriby United	3-3*	226
	(Gainsborough Trinity won 3-2 on penalties)			
8	Workington	v Solihull Moors	1-1	188
	Solihull Moors	v Workington	2-4	117
9	Blyth Spartans	v Stafford Rangers	2-0	442
10	Eastwood Town	v Nantwich Town	0-3	312
11	Quorn	v Vauxhall Motors	2-3	175
12	Leigh Genesis	v Redditch United	0-1	283
13	Stalybridge Celtic	v AFC Telford United	1-1	422
	AFC Telford United	v Stalybridge Celtic	1-2	938
14	Stourbridge	v Southport	0-0	319
	Southport	v Stourbridge	4-2	268
15	Witton Albion	v Matlock Town	1-1	254
	Matlock Town	v Witton Albion	4-3*	256
16	Guiseley	v FC Halifax Town	3-1	992
17	Corby Town	v Alfreton Town	1-1	306
	Alfreton Town	v Corby Town	1-2*	268
18	AFC Fylde	v Hinckley United	1-1	224
	Hinckley United	v AFC Fylde	7-3	194
19	Weston Super Mare	v Carshalton Athletic	1-1	199
	Carshalton Athletic	v Weston Super Mare	3-1	214
20	Bromley	v Maidstone United	0-1	655
21	Billericay Town	v Hitchin Town	0-0	327
	Hitchin Town	v Billericay Town	0-1	219
22	Eastleigh	v Lewes	1-1	261
	Lewes	v Eastleigh	1-0	211
23	Truro City	v Gloucester City	1-0	217
24	Welling United	v Tonbridge Angels	3-2	510
25	Bashley	v Staines Town	2-1	268
26	Woking	v St Albans City	6-0	823
27	Boreham Wood	v Hungerford Town	1-0	89
28	Thurrock	v Havant & Waterlooville	1-4	142
29	Maidenhead United	v Bath City	1-0	272
30	Dover Athletic	v Dartford	3-2	1084
31	Godalming Town	v Arlesey Town	0-3	154
32	Farnborough	v Wealdstone	3-0	1012
33	Chelmsford City	v AFC Hornchurch	4-4	635
	AFC Hornchurch	v Chelmsford City	1-2	370
34	Hampton & Richmond B.	v Concord Rangers	3-2	264
35	Worcester City	v Burnham	2-1	377
36	Weymouth	v Dorchester Town	3-0	1032
37	Ramsgate	v Bishop's Stortford	0-3	298
38	Newport County	v Braintree Town	2-1	684
39	Kingstonian	v Chippenham Town	0-2	388
40	Northwood	v Basingstoke Town	2-1	178

FIRST ROUND PROPER

1	Vauxhall Motors	v King's Lynn		
	(tie awarded to Vauxhall Motors – King's Lynn withdrew)			
2	Mansfield Town	v Tamworth	0-2	1467
3	Gateshead	v Harrogate Town	1-1	302
	Harrogate Town	v Gateshead	0-2	160
4	Corby Town	v Farsley Celtic	2-0	242
5	Workington	v Nuneaton Town	2-1	319
6	Guiseley	v Redditch United	1-0	245
7	Hinckley United	v York City	0-0	506
	York City	v Hinckley United	3-1	853
8	Wrexham	v Altrincham	0-0	1065
	Altrincham	v Wrexham	1-0	407
9	Kettering Town	v Barrow	0-1	763
10	Chester City	v Fleetwood Town	0-1	518
11	Matlock Town	v Kidderminster Harriers	0-2	460
12	Nantwich Town	v Stalybridge Celtic	0-3	581
13	Southport	v Gainsborough Trinity	2-2	478
	Gainsborough Trinity	v Southport	1-0	218
14	Blyth Spartans	v Ilkeston Town	2-0	419
15	Welling United	v Eastbourne Borough	0-1	437
16	Bishop's Stortford	v Maidenhead United	1-2	245
17	Chelmsford City	v Truro City	2-2	701
	Truro City	v Chelmsford City	0-1	322
18	Stevenage Borough	v Ebbsfleet United	2-0	809
19	AFC Wimbledon	v Boreham Wood	2-1	1306
20	Hampton & Richmond B.	v Lewes	0-0	256
	Lewes	v Hampton&Richmond B.	3-1	217
21	Rushden & Diamonds	v Billericay Town	1-0	696
22	Havant & Waterlooville	v Dover Athletic	2-3	483
23	Bashley	v Crawley Town	2-3	335
24	Arlesey Town	v Chippenham Town	1-1	221
	Chippenham Town	v Arlesey Town	2-0	235
25	Oxford United	v Hayes & Yeading United	1-0	1803
26	Woking	v Forest Green Rovers	1-0	956
27	Weymouth	v Salisbury City	0-1	642
28	Farnborough	v Newport County	1-3	805
29	Carshalton Athletic	v Northwood	1-1	231
	Northwood	v Carshalton Athletic	0-5	142
30	Cambridge United	v Luton Town	3-1	1665
31	Worcester City	v Grays Athletic	3-1	545
32	Maidstone United	v Histon	0-3	238
	(at Ashford Town FC) (tie awarded to Maidstone United – Histon expelled)			

Second Round - 9th January
16 winners @ £6,000

Frozen pitches completely ruined this round, so the games were staged over three weeks wherever grounds were considered safe. With no geographical boundaries, Workington entertained Rushden & Diamonds and won 2-1, Dover Athletic travelled all the way to Fleetwood and were rewarded by a 1-0 victory and little Chippenham Town covered new ground by playing at Gateshead, but lost by the only goal of the game.

Holders Stevenage Borough received a second home tie and celebrated by beating Vauxhall Motors 6-0, and also playing in front of their home supporters for the second time were AFC Wimbledon, who beat Altrincham 3-1 and Oxford United, who produced another 1-0 victory, this time over Woking.

Chelmsford City enjoyed a tough 2-1 success against Crawley Town and Kiddderminster Harriers, perhaps surprisingly, found difficulty in beating Lewes 3-2 at home. Supporters of Barrow and York City always seem to enjoy their away games, maybe feeling they have to cover more miles than most. Consequently they find away victories more enjoyable and satisfying, so Barrow's success at Maidenhead United and York City's draw at the high flying Newport County were fully appreciated.

Third Round - 30th January
8 winners @ £7,000

Frozen pitches once again affected the competition and just half the ties were contested on the allotted date. Workington, travelled all the way to South London, where AFC Wimbledon appreciating their third home draw attracted a fine attendance of 2.301, but lost a five goal thriller four minutes from time.

The holders were also given a third home tie and Stevenage Borough celebrated with more goals, scoring four against Dover Athletic. The senior clubs certainly 'pulled rank' in this round, as Oxford United beat Chelmsford City 4 -1 away with two goals from Jack Midson and York City won at home against Corby Town thanks to a 40th minute Andy Ferrell penalty in front of 2,205 at The Kit Kat Stadium.

A very Northern clash between East and West produced a replay at Gateshead after a 1-1 draw at Barrow but disappointing support at The International Stadium may have encouraged the visitors to clinch a place in the last eight with a 3-2 victory.

Fourth Round - 20th February
4 winners @ £8,000

Only Conference North club Workington had prevented the Blue Square Premier dominance of the last eight but they were the latest club providing holders Stevenage Borough with home opposition in this season's F.A.Trophy Competition, and so far the holders goal difference was an impressive 12-1! Not surprisingly Borough reached the Semi-Finals but only after a tough battle.

With the Barrow v York City tie postponed, the score in all three completed games was 2-1, bringing Salisbury City victory at home to Tamworth, and Kidderminster Harriers a surprising victory at Oxford United in front of 3,358. United's league form had wavered and the club appeared to be desperate to regain their early season form - perhaps it would be easier without the complication of the F.A.Trophy? On the other hand, a successful cup run lifts morale -it was a difficult problem, but defeat meant United would definitely be concentrating on promotion!

The fourth Semi-Final place was claimed by Barrow with a 2-1 victory over the 2009 Finalists and a semi-final place brought back memories for their older supporters of 1990, when they faced Colne Dynamoes in the Semi-Finals and qualified to beat Leek Town 3-0 at Wembley.

Semi-Finals - 13th March & 20th March
2 winners @ £16,000

When playing your first leg of an important Semi-Final away from home, the main aim will be to stay in the tie with, at worst, an odd goal deficit. So Barrow bringing back a one goal lead from Salisbury was more than could be expected, but Stevenage Borough's quite staggering 5-1 victory at Kidderminster Harriers must have been mind blowing for all concerned .

Those involved with 'Kiddy' could surely see no point in turning up at Lamex Stadium the following week and Stevenage Borough could seriously concentrate on promotion. What an anti climax as far as the F.A.Trophy was concerned but what an uplifting bonus for all the Borough players battling for their Football League place but also given every chance of a bonus day out at Wembley.

Not surprisingly, the second leg produced a 0-0 draw in front of just 1,622 at Stevenage and much to the Barrow fans' delight, two Jason Walker goals clinched a 3-1 aggregate win for 'The Bluebirds' in front of a 3,070 crowd at Holker Street, providing a just reward for a season of loyal travelling following their club all over the country.

By the time the F.A.Trophy Final would be played, Stevenage Borough would know if they had clinched a Football League place but to Barrow this was the chance of a special day in their history, and anyway, they always won at Wembley and the prize money was £50,000 for the winners and £25,000 for the runners-up. What a thought!

SECOND ROUND PROPER

1	AFC Wimbledon	v Altrincham	3-1	1450
2	Worcester City	v Carshalton Athletic	1-1	468
	Carshalton Athletic	v Worcester City	0-4	259
3	Stevenage Borough	v Vauxhall Motors	6-0	678
4	Blyth Spartans	v Guiseley	1-2	350
5	Cambridge United	v Eastbourne Borough	2-2	913
	Eastbourne Borough	v Cambridge United	0-2	525
6	Gateshead	v Chippenham Town	1-0	216
7	Oxford United	v Woking	1-0	1581
8	Stalybridge Celtic	v Corby Town	1-2	253
9	Kidderminster Harriers	v Lewes	3-2	654
10	Newport County	v York City	0-0	1040
	York City	v Newport County	1-0	1469
11	Workington	v Rushden & Diamonds	2-1	252
12	Chelmsford City	v Crawley Town	2-1	715
13	Fleetwood Town	v Dover Athletic	0-1	871
14	Gainsborough Trinity	v Tamworth	0-0	291
	Tamworth	v Gainsborough Trinity	2-1	392
15	Maidenhead United	v Barrow	0-1	301
16	Salisbury City	v Maidstone United	2-0	746

THIRD ROUND PROPER

1	York City	v Corby Town	1-0	2205
2	Guiseley	v Tamworth	0-1	281
3	Worcester City	v Kidderminster Harriers	0-1	1693
4	AFC Wimbledon	v Workington	2-3	2301
5	Cambridge United	v Salisbury City	0-0	1237
	Salisbury City	v Cambridge United	2-1	592
6	Stevenage Borough	v Dover Athletic	4-1	1203
7	Barrow	v Gateshead	1-1	1200
	Gateshead	v Barrow	2-3	312
8	Chelmsford City	v Oxford United	1-3	1347

FOURTH ROUND PROPER

1	Stevenage Borough	v Workington	2-1	1510
2	Salisbury City	v Tamworth	2-1	1012
3	Barrow	v York City	2-1	1525
4	Oxford United	v Kidderminster Harriers	1-2	3358

SEMI-FINALS

1ST LEG

1	Salisbury City	v Barrow	0-1	1782
2	Kidderminster Harriers	v Stevenage Borough	1-5	2433

2ND LEG

1	Barrow	v Salisbury City	2-1	3070
2	Stevenage Borough	v Kidderminster Harriers	0-0	1622

Left: A closely fought battle between Matt Tubbs and Michael Briscoe during the quarter-final that saw Salisbury City take on Tamworth. Photo: Graham Brown.

Below: This early chance goes begging for the visitors, Chippenham Town, in this drawn 1st Round tie against Arlesey Town. Photo: Gordon Whittington.

It was noticeable that the ground staff forking the pitch were 11 in number before the game began. The same 11 pitch poking prodders were in evidence at half time and at the close, yet Barrow and Stevenage began with 11 in number but neither side finished with that complement. Therein lies the main contributor to the eventual result, Barrow finishing with 10 men, Stevenage with 9.

The opening minutes of this 41st Trophy final belonged to the underdogs from the north. They gained an early corner which was fired in low, enabling Jason Walker, the only Barrow native in the squad, to shoot strongly, a defender stoically falling to block the effort. Two further Barrow corners led to Phil Bolland's shot suffering a similar fate and a spate of head tennis before the third was cleared. Yet, in the tenth minute, having survived that early pressure, Stevenage took the lead. Out of nothing a left foot lob cum shot by Andy Drury, from the penalty area edge, sailed accurately and presumably deliberately past a stunned and stationary Stuart Tomlinson's right into the top of his net. Just as most had anticipated Stevenage were set to be easy victors.

Matters changed however when David Bridge's 28th minute lunge, directly in front of the technical areas, brought his studs in contact with the top of Andy Bond's thigh. A red card was unhesitatingly held high by referee Lee Probert and the Hertfordshire Trophy holders were left stunned, a man short. Yet, with the lively Yemi Odubade successfully making mazy runs down the wing, Stevenage still looked the more dangerous. Odubade's shot narrowly missed Tomlinson's post before forcing the keeper to tip over his threatening cross.

Combining well for once, Walker and Greg Blundell threatened an equaliser at the start of the second period but Stevenage were still in the ascendancy. Despite their numerical handicap a fine pass from Jon Ashton set Odubade clear, his effort fizzing into the side netting. Next it took a finely timed tackle from Simon Spender to stop Chris Beardsley getting on the end of a threatening pass.

Substitute Carlos Logan's pace and dribbling brought some hope for Barrow. Andy Bond shot narrowly wide and Walker just failed to make contact with Logan's cross. 11 minutes were left when substitute Lee McEvilly, an easily recognisable figure, cantering with the unforgettably short strides of a dressage horse, was in the right place at the far post to head Logan's centre accurately back across the helpless Day. The two substitutes had combined to bring Barrow back to level terms.

Stevenage had just been forced into a third and final substitution, the injured Day being replaced in goal by Ashley Bayes who immediately had to save from Logan when there came the decisive moment. The minutes of added time had just started to tick away when Robin Hulbert was judged by referee Probert to have deliberately elbowed Charlie Griffin. For the second time in the match the red card was instantly flourished. Both sides were even in score and personnel but only for seconds as a stretcher was needed for Griffin who looked in a bad way and was immediately taken off to hospital. Stevenage were 9 against 10 with their sub allocation already used. The incident led to some later friction between the two managements with Stevenage mutterings of "assault" and "GBH" being refuted by Barrow as "sour grapes".

So extra time began. With only 9, Stevenage set up in 3/4/1 formation. The respective number 11s, Logan and Odubade, still looked dangerously swift but tiredness was taking its toll and increased for Stevenage when Walker, from the edge of the area, shot home in the same spot Drury had hit 107 minutes previously.

the wrong side the post of an open goal, almost as if he sympathised with the fatigued opposition

Ahead for the first time, Barrow were understandably the stronger although Tomlinson still had to make a full stretch save from one of his defenders to prevent an equaliser as Stevenage understandably shed any semblance of defence. Left unmarked, McEvilly carefully placed the ball the wrong side the post of an open goal, almost as if he sympathised with the fatigued opposition, before referee Probert brought proceedings to an end.

Rather sadly, particularly in view of their Conference triumph and elevation to Football League status, streams of disappointed Stevenage supporters surged for the exits rather than wait a few minutes to applaud their deserving nine men who had so courageously fought to the final whistle. On second thoughts, perhaps it was a wise move to avoid the wild, ranting exhortations of the stadium announcer, whose attempts to excite the crowd are so false and out of place in a Wembley final setting. If that was their reason, I am on their side. Give me a rendering of "Abide with me" any day, rather than throbbing, thudding, deafening, presumably 'heavy metal', whatever that is, rumblings. This is an English football, not American soccer or baseball, occasion. Ship out him and/or his style. Perhaps next time you change the pitch? Please.

ARTHUR EVANS.

BARROW 2

McEvilly 79, Walker 117

STEVENAGE BOROUGH 1

Drury 10

Wembley Stadium - Attendance: 21,223

Left: Jason Walker scores the winning goal. Photo: Keith Clayton.

Above: Scott Laird leaps high for Stevenage in an attempt to holt Barrow's Paul Rutherford. Photo: Alan Coomes.

Above: Barrow's Edwards evades the in coming tackle from Stevenage's Ashton. Photo: Keith Clayton.

2009-10 F.A. Trophy winners Barrow celebrate after the match. Photo: Roger Turner.

Barrow: Stuart Tomlinson, Simon Spender, Paul Jones, Phil Bolland, Paul Edwards, Simon Wiles (sub Carlos Logan 63rd min), Robin Hulbert, Andy Bond, Paul Rutherford (sub Mark Boyd 109th min), Jason Walker, Gregg Blundell (sub Lee McEvilly 73rd min). Subs not used – Tim Deasy and Mike Pearson.

Stevenage Borough: Chris Day (sub Ashley Bayes 90th min), Ronnie Henry, Jon Ashton, Mark Roberts, Scott Laird, Joel Byrom (sub Lawrie Wilson 58th min), David Bridges, Michael Bostwick, Andy Drury, Chris Beardsley (sub Charlie Griffin 64th min), Yemi Odubade. Subs not used – Stacey Long and Peter Vincenti.

Man of the match – Paul Rutherford.

Referee Lee Probert, assisted by Stephen Child and David Coote. Fourth official – James Linington.

2nd Qualifying Round: Dean Gilbert's well placed shot beats Gosport's 'keeper to put Hitchin in front. Photo: Gordon Whittington.

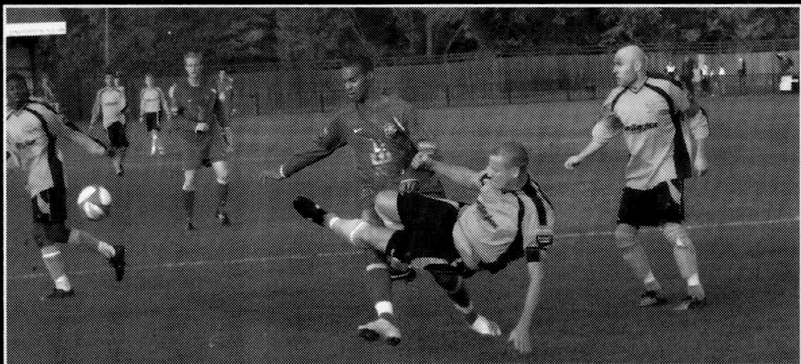

2nd Qualifying Round: Craig Vernon, Merstham, makes a flying tackle to beat Tonbridge Angels' Cumberbatch to the ball. Photo: Roger Turner.

3rd Qualifying Round: Lee Allinson's penalty proved to be the only goal of the game seeing Boreham Wood progress at the expense of Hungerford Town. Photo: Gordon Whittington.

PAST FINALS

1970 MACCLESFIELD TOWN 2 (Lyons, B Fidler) TELFORD UNITED 0 **Att: 28,000**
Northern Premier League *Southern League*
Macclesfield: Cooke, Sievwright, Bennett, Beaumont, Collins, Roberts, Lyons, B Fidler,Young, Corfield, D Fidler.
Telford: Irvine, Harris, Croft, Flowers, Coton, Ray,Fudge, Hart, Bentley, Murray, Jagger. Ref: K Walker

1971 TELFORD UTD 3 (Owen, Bentley, Fudge) HILLINGDON BORO. 2 (Reeve, Bishop) **Att: 29,500**
Southern League *Southern League*
Telford: Irvine, Harris, Croft, Ray, Coton, Carr, Fudge, Owen, Bentley, Jagger ,Murray.
Hillingdon B.: Lowe, Batt, Langley, Higginson, Newcombe, Moore, Fairchild,Bishop, Reeve, Carter, Knox. Ref: D Smith

1972 STAFFORD RANGERS 3 (Williams 2, Cullerton) BARNET 0 **Att: 24,000**
Northern Premier League *Southern League*
Stafford R.: Aleksic, Chadwick, Clayton, Sargeant, Aston, Machin, Cullerton, Chapman,Williams, Bayley, Jones.
Barnet: McClelland, Lye, Jenkins, Ward, Embrey, King, Powell, Ferry, Flatt, Easton, Plume . Ref: P Partridge

1973 SCARBOROUGH 2 (Leask, Thompson) WIGAN ATHLETIC 1 (Rogers) aet **Att:23,000**
Northern Premier League *Northern Premier League*
Scarborough: Garrow, Appleton, Shoulder, Dunn, Siddle, Fagan, Donoghue, Franks,Leask (Barmby), Thompson, Hewitt.
Wigan: Reeves, Morris, Sutherland, Taylor,Jackson, Gillibrand, Clements, Oats (McCunnell), Rogers, King, Worswick. Ref: H Hackney

1974 MORECAMBE 2 (Richmond, Sutton) DARTFORD 1 (Cunningham) **Att: 19,000**
Northern Premier League *Southern League*
Morecambe: Coates, Pearson, Bennett, Sutton, Street, Baldwin, Done, Webber,Roberts (Galley), Kershaw, Richmond.
Dartford: Morton, Read, Payne, Carr, Burns,Binks, Light, Glozier, Robinson (Hearne), Cunningham, Halleday. Ref: B Homewood

1975 (1) MATLOCK TOWN 4 (Oxley, Dawson, T Fenoughty, N Fenoughty) SCARBOROUGH 0 **Att: 21,000**
Northern Premier League *Northern Premier League*
Matlock: Fell, McKay, Smith, Stuart, Dawson, Swan, Oxley, N Fenoughy, Scott, T Fenoughty, M Fenoughty.
Scarborough: Williams, Hewitt, Rettitt, Dunn, Marshall, Todd, Houghton, Woodall, Davidson, Barnby, Aveyard. Ref: K Styles

1976 SCARBOROUGH 3 (Woodall, Abbey, Marshall(p)) STAFFORD R. 2 (Jones 2) aet **Att: 21,000**
Northern Premier League *Northern Premier League*
Scarborough: Barnard, Jackson, Marshall, H Dunn, Ayre (Donoghue), HA Dunn, Dale,Barmby, Woodall, Abbey, Hilley.
Stafford: Arnold, Ritchie, Richards, Sargeant,Seddon, Morris, Chapman, Lowe, Jones, Hutchinson, Chadwick. Ref: R Challis

1977 SCARBOROUGH 2 (Dunn(p), Abbey) DAGENHAM 1 (Harris) **Att: 21,500**
Northern Premier League *Isthmian League*
Scarborough: Chapman, Smith, Marshall (Barmby), Dunn, Ayre, Deere, Aveyard,Donoghue, Woodall, Abbey, Dunn.
Dagenham: Hutley, Wellman, P Currie, Dunwell,Moore, W Currie, Harkins, Saul, Fox, Harris, Holder. Ref: G Courtney

1978 ALTRINCHAM 3 (King, Johnson, Rogers) LEATHERHEAD 1 (Cook) **Att: 20,000**
Northern Premier League *Isthmian League*
Altrincham: Eales, Allan, Crossley, Bailey, Owens, King, Morris, Heathcote,Johnson, Rogers, Davidson (Flaherty).
Leatherhead: Swannell, Cooper, Eaton, Davies,Reid, Malley, Cook, Salkeld, Baker, Boyle (Bailey). Ref: A Grey

1979 STAFFORD RANGERS 2 (A Wood 2) KETTERING TOWN 0 **Att: 32,000**
Northern Premier League *Southern League*
Stafford: Arnold, F Wood, Willis, Sargeant, Seddon, Ritchie, Secker, Chapman, A Wood, Cullerton, Chadwick (Jones).
Kettering: Lane, Ashby, Lee, Eastell, Dixey,Suddards, Flannagan, Kellock, Phipps, Clayton, Evans (Hughes). Ref: D Richardson

1980 (2) DAGENHAM 2 (Duck, Maycock) MOSSLEY 1 (Smith) **Att: 26,000**
Isthmian League *Northern Premier League*
Dagenham: Huttley, Wellman, Scales, Dunwell, Moore, Durrell, Maycock, Horan,Duck, Kidd, Jones (Holder).
Mossley: Fitton, Brown, Vaughan, Gorman, Salter, Polliot, Smith, Moore, Skeete, O'Connor, Keelan (Wilson). Ref: K Baker

1981 (3) BISHOP'S STORTFORD 1 (Sullivan) SUTTON UNITED 0 **Att: 22,578**
Isthmian League *Isthmian League*
Bishop's Stortford: Moore, Blackman, Brame, Smith (Worrell), Bradford, Abery, Sullivan,Knapman, Radford, Simmonds, Mitchell.
Sutton Utd.: Collyer, Rogers, Green, J Rains,T Rains, Stephens (Sunnucks), Waldon, Pritchard, Cornwell, Parsons, Dennis. Ref: J Worrall

1982 ENFIELD 1 (Taylor) ALTRINCHAM 0 **Att: 18,678**
Alliance Premier League *Alliance Premier League*
Enfield: Jacobs, Barrett, Tone, Jennings, Waite, Ironton, Ashford, Taylor,Holmes, Oliver (Flint), King. Ref: B Stevens
Altrincham: Connaughton, Crossley, Davison, Bailey, Cuddy, King (Whitbread), Allan, Heathcote, Johnson, Rogers, Howard.

Notes:
1 The only occasion three members of the same family played in the same FA Trophy Final team.
2 The first of the Amateurs from the Isthmian League to win the FA Trophy.
3 Goalkeeper Terry Moore had also won an Amateur Cup Winners Medal with Bishop's Stortford in 1974.
All games played at Wembley (old & new) unless stated.

1983 **TELFORD UTD 2 (Mather 2) NORTHWICH VICTORIA 1 (Bennett)** **Att: 22,071**
Alliance Premier League *Alliance Premier League*
Telford: Charlton, Lewis, Turner, Mayman (Joseph), Walker, Easton, Barnett,Williams, Mather, Hogan, Alcock.
Northwich: Ryan, Fretwell, Murphy, Jones, Forshaw, Ward, Anderson, Abel (Bennett), Reid, Chesters, Wilson. Ref: B Hill

1984 **NORTHWICH VICTORIA 1 (Chester) BANGOR CITY 1 (Whelan)** **Att: 14,200**
Replay **NORTHWICH VICTORIA 2 (Chesters(p), Anderson) BANGOR CITY 1 (Lunn)** **Att: 5,805 (at Stoke)**
Alliance Premier League *Alliance Premier League*
Northwich: Ryan, Fretwell, Dean, Jones, Forshaw (Power 65), Bennett, Anderson,Abel, Reid, Chesters, Wilson. Ref: J Martin
Bangor: Letheren, Cavanagh, Gray, Whelan, Banks,Lunn, Urqhart, Morris, Carter, Howat, Sutcliffe (Westwood 105) . Same in replay.

1985 **WEALDSTONE 2 (Graham, Holmes) BOSTON UNITED 1 (Cook)** **Att: 20,775**
Alliance Premier League *Alliance Premier League*
Wealdstone: Iles, Perkins, Bowgett, Byatt, Davies, Greenaway, Holmes, Wainwright,Donnellan, Graham (N Cordice 89), A Cordice.
Boston: Blackwell, Casey, Ladd,Creane, O'Brien, Thommson, Laverick (Mallender 78), Simpsom, Gilbert, Lee, Cook. Ref: J Bray

1986 **ALTRINCHAM 1 (Farrelly)** **RUNCORN 0** **Att: 15,700**
Gola League *Gola League*
Altrincham: Wealands, Gardner, Densmore, Johnson, Farrelly, Conning, Cuddy,Davison, Reid, Ellis, Anderson. Sub: Newton.
Runcorn: McBride, Lee, Roberts,Jones, Fraser, Smith, S Crompton (A Crompton), Imrie, Carter, Mather, Carrodus. Ref: A Ward

1987 **KIDDERMINSTER HARRIERS 0** **BURTON ALBION 0** **Att: 23,617**
Replay **KIDDERMINSTER HARRIERS 2 (Davies 2) BURTON ALBION 1 (Groves)** **Att: 15,685 (at West Brom)**
Conference *Southern League*
Kidderminster: Arnold, Barton, Boxall, Brazier (sub Hazlewood in rep), Collins (sub Pearson 90 at Wembley), Woodall, McKenzie, O'Dowd, Tuohy, Casey, Davies. sub:Jones.
Burton: New, Essex, Kamara, Vaughan, Simms, Groves, Bancroft, Land, Dorsett, Redfern, (sub Wood in replay), Gauden. Sub: Patterson. Ref: D Shaw

1988 **ENFIELD 0** **TELFORD UNITED 0** **Att: 20,161**
Replay **ENFIELD 3 (Furlong 2, Howell)TELFORD 2 (Biggins, Norris(p))** **Att: 6,912 (at W Brom)**
Conference *Conference*
Enfield: Pape, Cottington, Howell, Keen (sub Edmonds in rep), Sparrow (sub Hayzleden at Wembley), Lewis (sub Edmonds at Wembley), Harding, Cooper, King,Furlong, Francis.
Telford: Charlton, McGinty, Storton, Nelson, Wiggins, Mayman (sub Cunningham in rep (sub Hancock)), Sankey, Joseph, Stringer (sub Griffiths at Wembley, Griffiths in replay), Biggins, Norris. Ref: L Dilkes

1989 **TELFORD UNITED 1 (Crawley)** **MACCLESFIELD TOWN 0** **Att: 18,102**
Conference *Conference*
Telford: Charlton, Lee, Brindley, Hancock, Wiggins, Mayman, Grainger, Joseph, Nelson, Lloyd, Stringer. Subs: Crawley, Griffiths.
Macclesfield: Zelem, Roberts, Tobin, Edwards, Hardman, Askey, Lake, Hanton, Imrie, Burr, Timmons. Subs: Devonshire, Kendall.

1990 **BARROW 3 (Gordon 2, Cowperthwaite)** **LEEK TOWN 0** **Att: 19,011**
Conference *Northern Premier League*
Barrow: McDonnell, Higgins, Chilton, Skivington, Gordon, Proctor, Doherty (Burgess), Farrell (Gilmore), Cowperthwaite, Lowe, Ferris.
Leek: Simpson, Elsby (Smith), Pearce, McMullen, Clowes, Coleman (Russell),Mellor, Somerville, Sutton, Millington, Norris Ref: T Simpson

1991 **WYCOMBE W. 2 (Scott, West)KIDDERMINSTER HARRIERS 1 (Hadley)** **Att: 34,842**
Conference *Conference*
Wycombe: Granville, Crossley, Cash, Kerr, Creaser, Carroll, Ryan, Stapleton,West, Scott, Guppy (Hutchinson). Ref: J Watson
Kidderminster: Jones, Kurila, McGrath, Weir, Barnett, Forsyth, Joseph (Wilcox), Howell (Whitehouse), Hadley, Lilwall, Humphries

1992 **COLCHESTER UTD* 3 (Masters, Smith, McGavin)WITTON ALBION 1 (Lutkevitch)** **Att: 27,806**
Conference *Conference*
Colchester: Barrett, Donald, Roberts, Knsella, English, Martin, Cook, Masters,McDonough (Bennett 65), McGavin, Smith. Ref: K P Barratt
Witton: Mason, Halliday, Coathup, McNeilis, Jim Connor, Anderson, Thomas, Rose, Alford, Grimshaw (Joe Connor), Lutkevitch (McCluskie)

1993 **WYCOMBE W*. 4 (Cousins, Kerr, Thompson, Carroll)RUNCORN 1 (Shaughnessy)** **Att: 32,968**
Conference *Conference*
Wycombe: Hyde, Cousins, Cooper, Kerr, Crossley, Thompson (Hayrettin 65),Carroll, Ryan, Hutchinson, Scott, Guppy. Sub: Casey.
Runcorn: Williams, Bates, Robertson, Hill, Harold (Connor 62), Anderson, Brady (Parker 72), Brown, Shaughnessy, McKenna, Brabin

1994 **WOKING 2 (D Brown, Hay)** **RUNCORN 1 (Shaw (pen))** **Att: 15,818**
Conference *Conference*
Woking: Batty, Tucker, L Wye, Berry, Brown, Clement, Brown (Rattray 32), Fielder, Steele, Hay (Puckett 46), Walker. Ref: Paul Durkin
Runcorn: Williams, Bates, Robertson, Shaw, Lee, Anderson, Thomas, Connor, McInerney (Hill 71), McKenna, Brabin. Sub: Parker

1995 **WOKING 2 (Steele, Fielder)KIDDERMINSTER HARRIERS 1 aet (Davies)** **Att: 17,815**
Conference *Conference*
Woking: Batty, Tucker, L Wye, Fielder, Brown, Crumplin (Rattray 42), S Wye, Ellis, Steele, Hay (Newberry 112), Walker. (Sub: Read(gk)
Kidderminster: Rose, Hodson, Bancroft, Webb, Brindley (Cartwright 94), Forsyth, Deakin, Yates, Humphreys (Hughes 105), Davies, Purdie. Sub: Dearlove (gk) Ref: D J Gallagher

1996 **MACCLESFIELD TOWN 3 (Payne, OG, Hemmings)** **NORTHWICH VICTORIA 1 (Williams)** **Att: 8,672**
Conference *Conference*
Macclesfield: Price, Edey, Gardiner, Payne, Howarth(C), Sorvel, Lyons, Wood (Hulme 83), Coates, Power, Hemmings (Cavell 88).
Northwich: Greygoose, Ward, Duffy, Burgess (Simpson 87), Abel (Steele), Walters, Williams, Butler (C), Cooke, Humphries, Vicary.
Ref: M Reed

1997 **WOKING 1 (Hay 112)** **DAGENHAM & REDBRIDGE 0** **Att: 24,376**
Conference *Isthmian League*
Woking: Batty, Brown, Howard, Foster, Taylor, S Wye, Thompson (sub Jones 115), Ellis, Steele (L Wye 108), Walker, Jackson (Hay 77).
Dagenham: Gothard, Culverhouse, Connor, Creaser, Jacques (sub Double 75), Davidson, Pratt (Naylor 81), Parratt, Broom, Rogers, Stimson (John 65).
Ref: J Winter

1998 **CHELTENHAM TOWN 1 (Eaton 74)** **SOUTHPORT 0** **Att: 26,387**
Conference *Conference*
Cheltenham: Book, Duff, Freeman, Banks, Victory, Knight (Smith 78), Howells, Bloomer, Walker (sub Milton 78), Eaton, Watkins. Sub: Wright.
Southport: Stewart, Horner, Futcher, Ryan, Farley, Kielty, Butler, Gamble, Formby (sub Whittaker 80), Thompson (sub Bollard 88), Ross. Sub: Mitten.
Ref: G S Willard

1999 **KINGSTONIAN 1 (Mustafa 49)** **FOREST GREEN ROVERS 0** **Att: 20,037**
Conference *Conference*
Kingstonian: Farrelly, Mustafa, Luckett, Crossley, Stewart, Harris, Patterson, Pitcher, Rattray, Leworthy (Francis 87), Akuamoah. Subs (not used): John, Corbett, Brown, Tranter
Forest Green Rovers: Shuttlewood, Hedges, Forbes, Bailey (Smart 76), Kilgour, Wigg (Cook 58), Honor (Winter 58), Drysdale, McGregor, Mehew, Sykes. Subs (not used): Perrin, Coupe
Ref: A B Wilkie

2000 **KINGSTONIAN 3 (Akuamoah 40, 69, Simba 75)** **KETTERING TOWN 2 (Vowden 55, Norman 64p)** **Att: 20,034**
Conference *Conference*
Kingstonian: Farelly, Mustafa, Luckett, Crossley, Stewart (Saunders 77), Harris, Kadi (Leworthy 83), Pitcher, Green (Basford 86), Smiba, Akuamoah. Subs (not used): Hurst, Allan
Kettering Town: Sollit, McNamara, Adams, Perkins, Vowden, Norman (Duik 76), Fisher, Brown, Shutt, Watkins (Hudson 46), Setchell (Hopkins 81). Subs (not used): Ridgway, Wilson
Ref: S W Dunn

2001 **CANVEY ISLAND 1 (Chenery)** **FOREST GREEN ROVERS 0** **Att: 10,007**
Isthmian League *Conference* **at Villa Park**
Forest Green Rovers: Perrin, Cousins, Lockwood, Foster, Clark, Burns, Daley, Drysdale (Bennett 46), Foster (Hunt 75), Meecham, Slater. Subs (not used): Hedges, Prince, Ghent
Canvey Island: Harrison, Duffy, Chenery, Bodley, Ward, Tilson, Stimson (Tanner 83), Gregory, Vaughan (Jones 76), Parmenter. Subs (not used): Bennett, Miller, Thompson.
Ref: A G Wiley

2002 **YEOVIL TOWN 2 (Alford, Stansfield)** **STEVENAGE BOROUGH 0** **Att: 18,809**
Conference *Conference* **at Villa Park**
Yeovil Town: Weale, Lockwood, Tonkin, Skiverton, Pluck (White 51), Way, Stansfield, Johnson, Alford (Giles 86), Crittenden (Lindegaard 83), McIndoe. Subs (not used): O'Brien, Sheffield
Stevenage Borough: Wilkerson, Hamsher, Goodliffe, Trott, Fraser, Fisher, Wormull (Stirling 71), Evers (Williams 56), Jackson, Sigere (Campbell 74), Clarke. Subs (not used): Campbell, Greygoose
Ref: N S Barry

2003 **BURSCOUGH 2 (Martindale 25, 55)** **TAMWORTH 1 (Cooper 78)** **Att: 14,265**
Northern Premier *Southern Premier* **at Villa Park**
Burscough: Taylor, Teale, Taylor, Macauley (White 77), Lawless, Bowen, Wright, Norman, Martindale (McHale 80), Byrne (Bluck 84), Burns. Subs (not used): McGuire (g/k) Molyneux.
Tamworth: Acton, Warner, Follett, Robinson, Walsh, Cooper, Colley, Evans (Turner 64), Rickards (Hatton 88), McGorry, Sale (Hallam 54). Subs (not used): Grocutt, Barnes (g/k).
Ref: U D Rennie

2004 **HEDNESFORD TOWN 3 (Maguire 28, Hines 53, Brindley 87)** **CANVEY ISLAND 2 (Boylan 46, Brindley 48 og)** **Att: 6,635**
Southern Premier *Isthmian Premier Champions* **at Villa Park**
Hednesford Town: Young, Simkin, Hines, King, Brindley, Ryder (Barrow 59), Palmer, Anthrobus, Danks (Piearce 78), Maguire, Charie (Evans 55). Subs (not used): Evans (g/k) McGhee.
Canvey Island: Potter, Kennedy, Duffy, Chenery, Cowan, Gooden (Dobinson 89), Minton, Gregory (McDougald 80), Boylan, Midgley (Berquez 73), Ward. Subs (not used): Theobald, Harrison (g/k).
Ref: M L Dean

2005 **GRAYS ATHLETIC 1 (Martin 65) Pens: 6** **HUCKNALL TOWN 1 (Ricketts 75) Pens: 5** **Att: 8,116**
Conference South *Conference North* **at Villa Park**
Grays Athletic: Bayes, Brennan, Nutter, Stuart, Matthews, Thurgood, Oli (Powell 80), Hopper (Carthy 120), Battersby (sub West 61), Martin, Cole. Subs (not used): Emberson, Bruce..
Hucknall Town: Smith, Asher, Barrick (Plummer 30), Hunter, Timons, Cooke, Smith (Ward 120), Palmer (Heathcote 94), Ricketts, Bacon, Todd. Subs (not used): Winder, Lindley.
Ref: P Dowd

2006 **GRAYS ATHLETIC 2 (Oli, Poole)** **WOKING 0** **Att: 13,997**
Conference *Conference* **at Upton Park**
Grays Athletic: Bayes, Sambrook, Nutter, Stuart, Hanson, Kightly (Williamson 90), Thurgood, Martin, Poole, Oli, McLean.
Subs (not used): Eyre (g/k), Hooper, Olayinka, Mawer.
Woking: Jalal, Jackson, MacDonald, Nethercott (Watson 60), Hutchinson, Murray, Smith (Cockerill 60), Evans (Blackman 85), Ferguson, McAllister, Justin Richards. Subs (not used): Davis (g/k), El-Salahi.
Ref: Howard Webb (Sheffield)

2007 **KIDDERMINSTER HARRIERS 2 (Constable 2)** **STEVENAGE BOROUGH 3 (Cole, Dobson, Morrison)** **Att: 53,262**
Conference *Conference* **(New Trophy record)**
Kidderminster Harriers: Bevan, Kenna, Hurren, Creighton, Whitehead, Blackwood, Russell, Penn, Smikle (Reynolds 90), Christie (White 75) , Constable.
Subs not used: Taylor, Sedgemore, McGrath.
Stevenage Borough: Julian, Fuller, Nutter, Oliver, Gaia, Miller, Cole, Morrison, Guppy (Dobson 63), Henry, Beard.
Subs not used: Potter, Slabber, Nurse, McMahon.
Ref: Chris Foy (Merseyside)

2008 **EBBSFLEET UNITED 1 (McPhee)** **TORQUAY UNITED 0** **Att: 40,186**

Blue Square Premier *Blue Square Premier*

Ebbsfleet United: Cronin, Hawkins, McCarthy, Smith, Opinel, McPhee, Barrett, Bostwick, Long (MacDonald 84), Moore, Akinde.
Subs not used: Eribenne, Purcell, Ricketts, Mott.
Torquay United: Rice, Mansell, Todd, Woods, Nicholson, D'Sane (Benyon 66), Hargreaves, Adams, Zebroski, Sills (Hill 88), Phillips (Stevens 46). Subs not used: Hockley and Robertson. Ref: Martin Atkinson (West Riding)

2009 **STEVENAGE BOROUGH 2 (Morison, Boylan)YORK CITY 0** **Att: 27,102**

Blue Square Premier *Blue Square Premier*

Stevenage Borough: Day, Henry, Bostwick, Roberts, Wilson, Mills, Murphy, Drury, Vincenti (Anaclet 86), Boylan, Morison.
Subs not used: Bayes, Albrighton, Maamria and Willock.
York City:Ingham, Purkiss, McGurk, Parslow, Pejic, Mackin, Greaves(McWilliams 74), Rusk (Russell 80), Brodie, McBreen (Sodje 60), Boyes. Subs not used – Mimms and Robinson. Referee: Michael Jones.

Barrow's Simon Spender gets in the tackle on Stevenage Borough's Chris Beardsley during the F.A. Trophy final at Wembley Stadium. Photo: Keith Clayton.

2009-10

First Qualifying Round- 5th September
116 winners @ £800

The Football Association were pleased to accept 515 entries for this, the 36th F.A Vase competition but as usual, a national cup tie in the very first week of the season is a great risk for many little clubs with ambitions for a morale lifting cup run. Important squad players may be on holiday and it is most unlikely that close season signings have settled down with their new colleagues.

Some clubs with Wembley memories still reasonably fresh in their supporters' minds featured in The First Qualifying Round which was played on 5th September. In the North, Bedlington Terriers (1999 Finalists) achieved a lively 4-2 victory at Esh Winning but St Helens Town (1987 Winners) lost a thriller by 4-3 at Padiham. In the South, Hoddesdon Town, the first Vase winners in 1975, won at Clapton, who used to be a proud member of the original Isthmian League, and Deal Town (2000 Winners) lost by two goals at Ringmer.

Goals seemed to be flowing freely in the Eastern Counties and among the clubs who gave notice that they were taking the competition seriously were Ely City who beat Cornard United 7-0, with Halstead Town scoring six without reply at Harwich & Parkeston, while Alvechurch achieved the same scoreline at Pershore Town.

Lordswood's Ben Hilden (3) heads just wide of the Crawley Down goal in the 1st Qualifying Round. Photo: Alan Coomes.

Teversal 'keeper, Danny Herring, misses the ball but luckily for him the ball is cleared before any Sleaford Town players can get to it during this 1st Qualifying Round tie.
Photo: Bill Wheatcroft.

More 1st Qualifying Round action this time from the 3-1 away win by Daventry Town over Raunds Town.
Photo: Peter Barnes.

FIRST QUALIFYING ROUND

1	Washington	v Morpeth Town	1-4	72
2	Stokesley	v Thackley	5-1	66
3	West Auckland Town	v Yorkshire Amateur	1-0	49
4	Sunderland RCA	v Armthorpe Welfare	0-2	62
5	Bishop Auckland	v Billingham Town	1-0	64
6	Esh Winning	v Bedlington Terriers	2-4	106
7	Billingham Synthonia	v Brandon United	3-2	88
8	Eccleshill United	v Norton & Stockton Ancients	0-7	25
9	Glasshoughton Welfare	v Tadcaster Albion	1-2	77
10	Formby	v Chadderton	1-2	33
11	Padiham	v St Helens Town	4-3	109
12	Ashton Athletic	v Alsager Town	0-2	26
13	Atherton LR	v Colne	1-2	43
14	Ramsbottom United	v Wigan Robin Park (8/9)	4-1*	123
15	AFC Blackpool	v Maine Road	1-0	58
16	Runcorn Linnets	v Staveley MW	4-3*	171
17	Birstall United	v Cradley Town	0-2	58
18	Anstey Nomads	v Coleshill Town	1-2	111
19	Dosthill Colts	v Barrow Town	1-0	105
20	Tipton Town	v Rocester	3-0	57
21	Coventry Copsewood	v Pilkington XXX	1-3	34
	(tie awarded to Coventry Copsewood – Pilkington XXX expelled)			
22	Nuneaton Griff	v Holwell Sports	1-2	72
23	Leek CSOB	v Biddulph Victoria	1-2	122
24	Heath Hayes	v Bartley Green	0-2	76
25	Castle Vale JKS	v Castle Vale	5-2	80
26	Wolverhampton Casuals	v Pelsall Villa	3-2	45
27	Sporting Kalsa	v Goodrich	2-4*	
28	Pershore Town	v Alvechurch	0-6	63
29	Wellington	v Eccleshall	2-2*	66
	Eccleshall	v Wellington (8/9)	2-4	53
30	Shifnal Town	v Wednesfield	0-4	61
31	St Andrews	v Cadbury Athletic	2-0	26
32	Causeway United	v Ellesmere Rangers	2-0	75
33	Gornal Athletic	v Knowle	2-0	
34	Bewdley Town	v Warstone Wanderers	6-0	66
35	Westfields	v Bridgnorth Town	5-4	41
36	Bolehall Swifts	v Lye Town	1-0	47
37	Ashby Ivanhoe	v Coventry Sphinx	0-2	57
38	AFC Wulfrunians	v Dudley Sports	4-1	78
39	Gedling MW	v Grimsby Borough	1-2*	44
40	Holbeach United	v Newark Town	1-0	89
41	Teversal	v Sleaford Town	0-1	86
42	Ollerton Town	v Barton Town Old Boys	1-0	50
43	Cambridge Regional College	v Huntingdon Town	5-1	192
44	Ely City	v Cornard United	7-1	64
45	Haverhill Rovers	v Swaffham Town	4-1*	70
46	Woodbridge Town	v Great Yarmouth Town	2-1	93
47	Raunds Town	v Daventry Town	1-3	84
48	Godmanchester Rovers	v Rothwell Corinthians	1-1*	
	Rothwell Corinthians	v Godmanchester Rovers	3-3*	52
	(Rothwell Corinthians won 4-2 on penalties)			
49	Sileby Rangers	v March Town United	2-3*	42
50	Team Bury	v Mildenhall Town	3-2*	212
51	Mauritius Sports Association UK	v Eton Manor	2-0*	19
	(tie awarded to Eton Manor – Mauritius Sports Association UK expelled)			
52	Oxhey Jets	v Aylesbury	4-3	69
53	Wootton Blue Cross	v Wembley	1-3	53
54	Buckingham Town	v Barking	2-5	81
55	Ampthill Town	v Bethnal Green United	1-2	51
56	Colney Heath	v Sporting Bengal United	2-1	46
57	Tokyngton Manor	v Cockfosters	2-1	
	(tie awarded to Cockfosters – Tokyngton Manor expelled)			
58	Leverstock Green	v Bowers & Pitsea	3-2	36
59	Clapton	v Hoddesdon Town	0-1	20
60	Brimsdown Rovers	v Buckingham Athletic	6-0	69
61	AFC Kempston Rovers	v Welwyn Garden City	1-0	42
62	Kentish Town	v Cranfield United	3-1	41
63	Erith Town	v Canning Town	7-0	59
64	Saffron Walden Town	v Hanwell Town	1-3	88
65	Hatfield Town	v Kingsbury London Tigers	3-4*	
66	Hullbridge Sports	v Hertford Town	1-3	40
67	Baldock Town Letchworth	v Wivenhoe Town	1-1*	195
	(Wivenhoe Town won 6-5 on penalties)			
68	Harpenden Town	v Haringey Borough	0-0*	48
	Haringey Borough	v Harpenden Town (8/9)	1-2	60
69	St Margaretsbury	v Crawley Green	3-1	
70	Winslow United	v Takeley		
	(walkover for Takeley – Winslow United withdrew)			
71	Harwich & Parkeston	v Halstead Town	0-6	127
72	Bedfont	v Mile Oak	2-0	64
73	Norton Sports	v Lingfield	1-2*	63
74	Three Bridges	v Oakwood	4-1*	90
75	East Preston	v Ash United	1-3	39
76	Peacehaven & Telscombe	v Hailsham Town	2-1	102
77	Southwick	v Selsey	1-3*	30
78	Feltham	v Holmesdale	1-5	68
79	Slade Green	v Frimley Green		
	(walkover for Frimley Green – Slade Green withdrew)			
80	Whitehawk	v Littlehampton Town	2-1	78
81	Camberley Town	v Cobham	4-2	82
82	Beckenham Town	v Wealden	6-1	48
83	Chichester City	v Colliers Wood United	4-1	65
84	Lordswood	v Crawley Down	2-5	32
85	Ringmer	v Deal Town	2-0	63
86	Raynes Park Vale	v Horley Town	1-2	40
87	Chessington & Hook Utd	v East Grinstead Town	0-1	56
88	St Francis Rangers	v Egham Town	1-3	56
89	Hassocks	v Sevenoaks Town	3-1*	
90	Badshot Lea	v Rye United	2-1	46
91	Erith & Belvedere	v Sidley United	2-1	112
92	Worthing United	v Haywards Heath Town	0-0*	45
	(Worthing United won 5-4 on penalties)			
93	Newhaven	v Cove	0-6	88
94	Guildford City	v Westfield	3-0	40
95	Flackwell Heath	v Romsey Town	6-0	34
96	Blackfield & Langley	v Harrow Hill		
	(walkover for Blackfield & Langley – Harrow Hill withdrawn)			
97	Melksham Town	v Marlow United	3-1	61
98	Holyport	v Brading Town	4-1	68
99	Amesbury Town	v Milton United	1-2	81
100	Clanfield	v Carterton	1-1*	48
	Carterton	v Clanfield (8/9)	1-0	55
101	Henley Town	v Abingdon Town	3-4	41
102	Westbury United	v AFC Wallingford	4-3*	47
103	Bournemouth	v Petersfield Town	1-0	47
104	Laverstock & Ford	v Lydney Town	4-0	52
105	Malmesbury Victoria	v Hook Norton	2-1	21
106	Calne Town	v Ardley United	2-4*	35
107	Wootton Bassett Town	v Hamble ASSC	2-3	68
108	Warminster Town	v Hayling United	0-5	112
109	Binfield	v New Milton Town	1-2*	49
110	Sandhurst Town	v Highworth Town	0-2	53
111	Cowes Sports	v Almondsbury UWE	2-1	66
112	Radstock Town	v Street	1-2	75
113	Ilfracombe Town	v Tavistock	0-2	83
114	Hamworthy United	v Saltash United	0-2	75
115	Bodmin Town	v Portishead Town	2-1*	85
116	Wadebridge Town	v Penzance	3-4	104

Second Qualifying Round -19th September
168 winners @ £900

This a truly massive round and clubs with serious ambitions in the competition may need luck on their side as early season form can vary as teams just haven't settled down. Home advantage is important at this stage but most ties in this Round are against reasonably local opposition who are well known.

One of the games of the round must have been Guisborough Town's 6-5 victory at Silsden but two clubs managed nine goals of their own, with Blackstones beating Radford at home and Haverhill Rovers away to Fakenham Town also gained their huge victory without conceding.

Another goal festival was enjoyed at Kingsbury who beat Takeley 5-4, while Biggleswade United scored seven at home to Codicote and St Blazey also scored seven at Chard Town.

Very hard earned victories were ground out by Wells City, 3-2 at home Minehead, Tow Law Town 3-2 at Billingham Synthonia, Winterton Rangers by the same score at Shirebrook Town and Burnham Ramblers 4-3 at AFC Kempston. This is a very special round to survive, as the competition proper starts in October and the draw will gradually give clubs further to travel. Wroxham featured for the first time in this round but needed a replay to eliminate Gorleston.

So, in the first week of September with holiday traffic ensuring that Saturday journeys needed serious planning, 279 clubs had already lost their interest in their main national knock out competition, although those who had already won through two rounds could perhaps consider themselves already on a cup run!

The Ampthill defender ensures his hands are well away from the ball as he clears the danger during his side's defeat by Bethnal Green in the 1st Qualifying Round.
Photo: Gordon Whittington.

Action from the 2nd Qualifying round tie between Rushden & Higham United and March Town.
Photo: Peter Barnes.

Bluefin

SECOND QUALIFYING ROUND

No.	Home	Away	Score	Att
1	Willington	v West Auckland Town	1-2	54
2	Easington Colliery	v Shildon	0-1	90
3	Ashington	v Armthorpe Welfare	0-1	156
4	Northallerton Town	v Team Northumbria	2-1	96
5	South Shields	v Pontefract Collieries	5-0	103
6	Brighouse Town	v Tadcaster Albion	2-3	
7	Pickering Town	v Horden CW	2-1	110
8	Hebburn Town	v North Shields	1-3	68
9	Bedlington Terriers	v Jarrow Roofing Boldon CA	3-0	
10	Silsden	v Guisborough Town	5-6	50
	(at Guisborough Town FC)			
11	Ryton	v Crook Town	0-1	80
12	Norton & Stockton Ancients	v West Allotment Celtic	3-0	94
13	Morpeth Town	v Thornaby	4-2*	26
14	Seaham Red Star	v Stokesley	1-4	52
15	Billingham Synthonia	v Tow Law Town	3-3*	79
	Tow Law Town	v Billingham Synthonia	2-2*	80
	(Tow Law Town won 5-4 on penalties)			
16	Liversedge	v Chester-Le-Street Town	4-1	80
17	Whickham	v Darlington Railway Athletic	2-0	65
18	Hall Road Rangers	v Bishop Auckland	3-0	67
19	Birtley Town	v Leeds Carnegie	0-3	33
20	Ramsbottom United	v Nostell MW	1-0	114
21	Ashton Town	v Worsbrough Bridge Athletic	1-3	
22	Penrith	v Squires Gate	2-0	140
23	Daisy Hill	v Runcorn Linnets	2-1	92
24	Flixton	v Hallam	1-3	
25	Rossington Main	v Atherton Collieries	1-0	55
26	Winsford United	v Parkgate	1-0	81
27	Whitehaven	v Cheadle Town	0-2	40
28	AFC Blackpool	v Oldham Town	2-4	45
29	Chadderton	v Padiham	2-2*	47
	Padiham	v Chadderton	3-0	118
30	AFC Liverpool	v Dinnington Town	1-2	
31	Bacup Borough	v Holker Old Boys	2-1	
32	Nelson	v Abbey Hey	5-1	58
33	Irlam	v Colne	1-2	88
34	Maltby Main	v Hemsworth MW	2-3	64
35	AFC Emley	v Alsager Town	2-3	91
36	Hinckley Downes	v Bewdley Town (20/9)	0-3	90
37	Pegasus Juniors	v Walsall Wood	2-3	41
38	Biddulph Victoria	v Bardon Hill Sports	5-0	55
39	Shawbury United	v Tividale	1-3	43
40	Ledbury Town	v Friar Lane & Epworth	1-3	42
41	St Andrews	v Studley	3-6*	49
42	Brocton	v Norton United	0-1	40
43	Ellistown	v Kirby Muxloe	1-2*	43
44	Castle Vale JKS	v Wolverhampton Casuals	2-5*	35
45	Causeway United	v Coventry Sphinx	4-0	108
46	Alvechurch	v Tipton Town	1-5	81
47	Dudley Town	v Loughborough University	1-1*	27
	Loughborough University	v Dudley Town	2-0	50
48	Gornal Athletic	v Wellington	0-1	50
49	Blaby & Whetstone Athletic	v Meir KA	2-1	74
50	Goodrich	v Coleshill Town	1-3	46
51	Wednesfield	v Holwell Sports	2-1	56
52	AFC Wulfrunians	v Heather St Johns	4-0	114
53	Bartley Green	v Bolehall Swifts	2-0	54
54	Dosthill Colts	v Coventry Copsewood	3-3*	51
	Coventry Copsewood	v Dosthill Colts	2-3	45
55	Westfields	v Bromyard Town	3-0	48
56	Oadby Town	v Cradley Town	3-2	97
57	Southam United	v Highgate United	0-0*	
	Highgate United	v Southam United	0-3	
58	Blackstones	v Radford	9-0	61
59	Calverton MW	v Ollerton Town	0-2	52
60	Blackwell MW	v Louth Town	2-6	64
61	Boston Town	v Bottesford Town	0-1	55
62	Shirebrook Town	v Winterton Rangers	2-3	65
63	Bourne Town	v Graham St Prims	2-0	50
64	Gedling Town	v Appleby Frodingham	1-1*	
	Appleby Frodingham	v Gedling Town	2-3*	44
65	Arnold Town	v Kimberley Town	2-1	104
66	Borrowash Victoria	v Greenwood Meadows	2-1	59
67	Grimsby Borough	v Holbrook Miners Welfare	3-1	55
68	Sleaford Town	v Sutton Town	5-0	107
69	Lincoln Moorlands Railway	v Holbeach United	2-1	71
70	Rainworth MW	v Radcliffe Olympic	2-0	83
71	Heanor Town	v Dunkirk	4-4*	
	Dunkirk	v Heanor Town	2-1	78
72	Walsham Le Willows	v Kirkley & Pakefield	0-5	65
73	Bugbrooke St Michaels	v Team Bury	4-2	80
74	Long Melford	v Whitton United	2-2*	58
	Whitton United	v Long Melford	3-1	81
75	Fakenham Town	v Haverhill Rovers	0-9	40
76	Thrapston Town	v Wellingborough Town	0-1*	196
77	Diss Town	v Ely City	2-2*	117
	Ely City	v Diss Town	5-4*	98
78	Gorleston	v Wroxham	0-0*	117
	Wroxham	v Gorleston	3-0	147
79	Daventry Town	v Stowmarket Town	5-0	109
80	Wisbech Town	v Northampton Spencer	0-1	126
81	Brantham Athletic	v Cambridge Regional College	0-1	
82	Woodbridge Town	v Desborough Town	4-0	89
83	Newmarket Town	v St Neots Town	2-1	135
84	Felixstowe & Walton Utd	v Yaxley	2-1	81
85	Daventry United	v Thetford Town	6-1	
86	Rushden & Higham Utd	v March Town United	1-2	69
87	Eynesbury Rovers	v Ipswich Wanderers	3-0	95
88	Rothwell Corinthians	v Hadleigh United	3-2*	58
89	Norwich United	v Long Buckby	1-3	65
	(at Wroxham FC)			
90	Old Woodstock Town	v Bethnal Green United	1-3	44
91	Brimsdown Rovers	v Colney Heath	4-2	48
92	Tiptree United	v Barkingside	3-1	68
93	Bicester Town	v Leverstock Green	1-3	44
94	Barking	v Basildon United	2-2*	61
	Basildon United	v Barking	1-0	83
95	Hadley	v Harpenden Town	2-0	83
96	AFC Kempston Rovers	v Burnham Ramblers	3-4	39
97	Tring Athletic	v Stansted	3-4	89
98	Kentish Town	v London Colney	2-3	38
99	Eton Manor	v Erith Town	0-2	55
100	Wembley	v St Margaretsbury	1-0	48
101	Wivenhoe Town	v Potton United	2-1	70
102	Hoddesdon Town	v Oxhey Jets	4-3	57
103	London APSA	v Royston Town	0-3	20
104	Halstead Town	v Thame United	1-1*	
	Thame United	v Halstead Town	0-1*	
105	Bedford	v Hanwell Town	2-1	38
106	Langford	v Hertford Town	1-0	95
107	Biggleswade United	v Codicote	7-0	48
108	Kingsbury London Tigers	v Takeley	5-4*	28
109	Cockfosters	v Bucks Student Union (BSU)	3-1	60
110	Saltdean United	v Peacehaven & Telscombe	0-2	172
111	Camberley Town	v Selsey	3-2*	68
112	Farnham Town	v Herne Bay	0-4	61
113	Pagham	v Frimley Green	1-0	83
114	Ash United	v Tunbridge Wells	3-1	93
115	Molesey	v Hassocks	2-0	90
116	Beckenham Town	v Banstead Athletic	2-0	68
117	Lancing	v Dorking	2-4*	94

First Round Proper - 3rd October
103 Winners@ £1000

Another hundred clubs leave the competition including respected Vase names such as North Shields and Tow Law Town from the North East and Arnold Town who lost at home to Long Eaton United in the East Midlands. However, Friar Lane & Epworth revived memories of early Vase runs with a fine 5-1 victory away to AFC Wulfrunians.

As it was still very early in the season, few clubs had achieved reliable form, but the West Country produced some impressive games with a few clues as to possible future challengers in the later rounds. Shortwood United (Hellenic Premier) won 3-1 at home to Wessex League Winchester City (winners 2004), Willand Rovers (Western League) thrilled their supporters with a 5-2 victory over Newquay (S.W. Peninsula League) and Plymouth Parkway enjoyed a splendid 4-2 victory over the much fancied St Blazey, who both provided another example of the quality in the Peninsula's deep South West.

However, another local club with a fine Vase reputation did come a cropper, as Porthleven, quarter finalists in 1998, lost by eight goals at Brislington, although Wimborne, winners of one the best finals ever in 1992, beat Gillingham Town 6-1 at home and looked a very good side.

Danny Firkins, Greenwich Borough goalkeeper, taps a header over the bar from Eastbourne United's No.10 Lucas Mann in the 1st Round Proper. Photo: Roger Turner.

Above: More 1st Round action - Steven Willis scores Bethnal Green's only goal during their 2-1 defeat by London Colney in Photo: Gordon Whittington.

Whilst left: Wulfrunians Tony Collins battles with Friar Lane & Epworth's Chris Goodman. Photo: Bill Wheatcroft.

SECOND QUALIFYING ROUND

118	Chichester City	v South Park	4-4*	80
	South Park	v Chichester City (22/9)	0-4	136
119	Bedfont	v Crawley Down	1-0	78
120	Three Bridges	v Badshot Lea	1-6	70
121	Egham Town	v Farnborough North End	1-2	46
122	Whitehawk	v Lingfield	3-1	75
123	Bookham	v Redhill	1-2*	75
124	Worthing United	v Shoreham	1-2	86
125	Cove	v Ringmer	2-3	
126	Hartley Wintney	v East Grinstead Town	1-2*	58
127	Guildford City	v Mole Valley SCR	1-2	31
128	Horley Town	v Erith & Belvedere	1-2	60
129	Holmesdale	v Greenwich Borough	1-2*	58
130	Bemerton Heath Harlequins	v Blackfield & Langley	1-0	72
131	Cheltenham Saracens	v Bradford Town	1-4	45
132	Malmesbury Victoria	v Flackwell Heath	2-4	40
133	Alton Town	v Longwell Green Sports	0-2	66
134	Totton & Eling	v Ardley United	2-3	58
135	Kidlington	v New Milton Town	2-1	72
136	Melksham Town	v Fairford Town	5-2	50
137	Holyport	v Fareham Town	2-3	81
138	Lymington Town	v United Services Portsmouth	0-4	
139	Ringwood Town	v Shrivenham	0-1	47
140	Hamble ASSC	v Milton United	3-0	58
141	Westbury United	v Devizes Town	3-2	72
142	Bournemouth	v Brockenhurst	1-2	59
143	Cowes Sports	v Almondsbury Town	2-3	81
144	Carterton	v Newport (IW)	3-2	45
145	Corsham	v Hallen	2-1	61
146	Wantage Town	v Abingdon Town	3-1	94
147	Downton	v Reading Town	3-2	61
148	Bristol Manor Farm	v Pewsey Vale	3-0	40
149	Alresford Town	v Hayling United	2-0	42
150	Highworth Town	v Laverstock & Ford	1-2	90
151	Wells City	v Minehead	3-2	65
152	Elmore	v Liskeard Athletic	2-4	52
153	Odd Down	v Welton Rovers	0-3	70
154	Buckland Athletic	v Saltash United	2-4*	75
155	Sherborne Town	v Bishop Sutton	0-5	63
156	Torpoint Athletic	v Tavistock	1-2	138
157	Budleigh Salterton	v Barnstaple Town	0-5	63
158	Penzance	v Wellington Town	1-2	185
159	Newquay	v Bridport	4-2	88
160	Brislington	v Street	5-2*	65
161	Bodmin Town	v Shaftesbury	0-1	77
	(tie awarded to Bodmin Town – Shaftesbury removed)			
162	Shepton Mallet	v Porthleven	0-2	74
163	Chard Town	v St Blazey	0-7	85
164	Swanage Town & Herston	v Plymouth Parkway	1-1*	
	Plymouth Parkway	v Swanage Town & Herston	4-0	198
165	Gillingham Town	v Launceston	1-0	150
166	Penryn Athletic	v Keynsham Town	0-1	54
167	Falmouth Town	v Clevedon United	0-3	121
168	Cullompton Rangers	v Verwood Town	1-2*	92

FIRST ROUND PROPER

1	Bridlington Town	v South Shields	2-0	179
2	Leeds Carnegie	v Shildon	2-3	
3	Consett	v Bedlington Terriers	0-2	135
4	North Shields	v Pickering Town	2-3	126
5	West Auckland Town	v Hall Road Rangers	5-1	45
6	Armthorpe Welfare	v Liversedge	3-1	61
7	Whickham	v Tadcaster Albion	1-0*	66
8	Guisborough Town	v Norton & Stockton Ancients	1-2	100
9	Crook Town	v Northallerton Town	2-0	101
10	Stokesley	v Morpeth Town	0-2	50
11	Newcastle Benfield	v Tow Law Town	1-0	57
12	Rossington Main	v Alsager Town	0-3	56
13	Colne	v Hallam	0-4	40
14	Padiham	v Hemsworth MW	4-2	103
15	Ramsbottom United	v Bacup Borough	2-4*	158
16	Penrith	v Dinnington Town	5-0	80
17	Daisy Hill	v Worsbrough Bridge Ath.	6-2	37
18	Oldham Town	v Winsford United	0-1	51
19	Cheadle Town	v Congleton Town	2-2*	68
	Congleton Town	v Cheadle Town	5-2	133
20	Nelson	v Selby Town	2-0	59
21	Loughborough University	v Causeway United	1-1*	
	Causeway United	v Loughborough University	2-1	67
22	Bewdley Town	v Coleshill Town	2-1	72
23	AFC Wulfrunians	v Friar Lane & Epworth	1-5	82
24	Southam United	v Oadby Town	1-2*	59
25	Blaby & Whetstone Ath.	v Malvern Town	3-1	95
26	Wellington	v Dosthill Colts	4-1	55
27	Walsall Wood	v Westfields	0-2	41
28	Studley	v Boldmere St Michaels	0-1	63
29	Tipton Town	v Kirby Muxloe	3-1	57
30	Tividale	v Wolverhampton Casuals	3-2*	49
31	Wednesfield	v Barwell	0-3	48
32	Biddulph Victoria	v Norton United	2-1	62
33	Bartley Green	v Newcastle Town	1-2*	61
34	Bourne Town	v New Mills (14/11)	2-2*	81
	(New Mills won 5-4 on penalties)			
	(3/10, tie ordered to be replayed as a result of an FA investigation, 0-1)			
35	Dunkirk	v Winterton Rangers	2-0*	58
36	Grimsby Borough	v Gresley	1-3	65
37	Blackstones	v Lincoln Moorlands Railway	1-2	55
38	Louth Town	v Sleaford Town	3-4*	215
39	Bottesford Town	v Ollerton Town	0-1	49
40	Borrowash Victoria	v Gedling Town	0-4	57
41	Arnold Town	v Long Eaton United	0-1	102
42	Rainworth MW	v Deeping Rangers	2-1	118
43	Ely City	v Eynesbury Rovers	3-2	104
44	Daventry United	v Wellingborough Town	2-3*	45
45	Cambridge Regional College	v March Town United	7-1	193
46	Kirkley & Pakefield	v Newmarket Town	3-1	136
47	Whitton United	v Woodbridge Town	1-3	99
48	Haverhill Rovers	v Bugbrooke St Michaels	2-3	79
49	Northampton Spencer	v Wroxham	0-3	79
50	Daventry Town	v Rothwell Corinthians	2-0	82
51	Felixstowe & Walton Utd	v Long Buckby	1-1*	103
	Long Buckby	v Felixstowe & Walton Utd	5-1	74
52	Halstead Town	v Dunstable Town	3-0	
53	Burnham Ramblers	v Bedford	1-2	58
54	Witham Town	v Hoddesdon Town	1-2	
55	Broxbourne Borough V&E	v Stotfold	1-2	48
56	Royston Town	v Basildon United	5-3	134
57	Hillingdon Borough	v Brimsdown Rovers	1-2	38
58	Langford	v Wembley	1-2	84
59	Tiptree United	v Harefield United	1-0*	70
60	Newport Pagnell Town	v Erith Town	5-1	75
61	London Colney	v Bethnal Green United	2-1	47
62	Leverstock Green	v Hadley	0-1	55
63	Enfield 1893	v Southend Manor	1-0	64
64	Wivenhoe Town	v Stansted	1-3	63
65	Cockfosters	v North Greenford United	1-2	68

Second Round - 14th November
64 winners @ £1,200

The senior clubs with exemption until this stage of the competition are welcomed, and holders Whitley Bay took advantage of a home tie against Alsager Town with a 2-0 victory. Also in the North East, the new Spennymoor club produced a superb performance to win 5-1 at Bedlington Terriers and Bridlington Town also showed good form to win 5-2 at Scarborough Athletic.

Poor weather in the southern half of the country ruined the Vase fixture list but encouraging victories were gained by Shortwood United who beat Bemerton Heath Harlequins at home 3-0 and Epsom & Ewell, the original losing finalists in 1975, who won 3-2 away at Moneyfields. A fine 3-2 victory was also earned by S.W.Peninsula club Plymouth Parkway who beat powerful Western League club Bitton 3-2.

Highest scorers were Witney United who won their home match with Erith & Belvedere 5-1 and Peacehaven & Telscombe who gained a spectacular away victory by the same score at Chafont St Peter. In the postponed fixtures, another Hellenic club, Almondsbury Town, won 5-2 at Christchurch and five goals were scored by Penrith and Needham Market at home against Hallam and Bedford respectively.

The weather certainly affected this round but some powerful clubs were making their ambitions known and with just thirty two left, a Wembley appearance wasn't nesssarily an impossibility for any ambitious club in the Third Round draw.

Action from Shortwood United 3-0 victory over Bemerton Heath Harlequins in the 2nd Round.
Photo: Peter Barnes.

Greenwich Borough 'keeper, Danny Firkins, can only watch as Holmesdale's Tony Atkins' effort goes wide in the 2nd Round.
Photo: Alan Coomes.

Ben Hiscox, Bristol Manor Farm (right) and Craig Hall of Peacehaven & Telscombe, race for the ball during their 3rd Round tie.
Photo: Roger Turner.

FIRST ROUND PROPER

66	Biggleswade United	v Kingsbury London Tigers	2-1	58
67	Ringmer	v Crowborough Athletic	2-3	77
68	Erith & Belvedere	v Pagham	2-1	92
69	Ash United	v Badshot Lea	3-4*	164
70	East Grinstead Town	v Whitehawk	0-5	101
71	Bedfont	v Shoreham	1-1*	71
	Shoreham	v Bedfont	2-0*	83
72	Mole Valley SCR	v Beckenham Town	0-1	
73	Epsom & Ewell	v Farnborough North End	3-2*	64
74	Eastbourne United	v Greenwich Borough	4-3*	60
75	Molesey	v Arundel	1-2	85
76	Peacehaven & Telscombe	v Chichester City	3-1	
77	Herne Bay	v Hythe Town	1-0	170
78	Redhill	v Camberley Town	3-1*	85
79	Wick	v Faversham Town	1-2	105
80	Dorking	v Chertsey Town	0-2	74
81	Longwell Green Sports	v Wantage Town	2-1	73
82	Westbury United	v Carterton	0-1	64
83	Laverstock & Ford	v Brockenhurst	1-2	63
84	Kidlington	v Bradford Town	1-2	95
85	Bemerton Heath Harlequins	v Alresford Town	1-1*	
	Alresford Town	v Bemerton Heath Harlequins	1-5	
86	Ardley United	v Moneyfields	0-1	47
87	Shrivenham	v Flackwell Heath	0-2	56
88	Almondsbury Town	v Melksham Town	3-1	40
89	Bristol Manor Farm	v Corsham	2-1	50
90	US Portsmouth	v Hamble ASSC	0-1	29
91	Downton	v Fareham Town	2-4*	85
92	Shortwood United	v Winchester City	3-1	115
93	Poole Town	v Bishop Sutton	4-1	219
94	Dawlish Town	v Liskeard Athletic	3-0	74
95	Willand Rovers	v Newquay	5-2	89
96	Wellington Town	v Barnstaple Town	3-1	67
97	Wells City	v Verwood Town	3-0	131
98	Welton Rovers	v Keynsham Town	6-0	69
99	Clevedon United	v Tavistock	3-5	52
100	Brislington	v Porthleven	8-0	85
101	Bodmin Town	v Saltash United (7/10)	1-2	
102	Plymouth Parkway	v St Blazey	4-2*	205
103	Wimborne Town	v Gillingham Town	6-1	296

SECOND ROUND PROPER

1	Padiham	v Norton & Stockton Ancients	2-4	76
2	Winsford United	v Pickering Town	1-2	101
3	Crook Town	v Bacup Borough	2-0	157
4	Nelson	v Morpeth Town	3-1	75
5	West Auckland Town	v Whickham	4-0	69
6	Bedlington Terriers	v Spennymoor Town	1-5	301
7	Penrith	v Hallam	5-2	70
8	Daisy Hill	v Armthorpe Welfare	2-3*	48
9	Newcastle Benfield	v Marske United	1-2	79
10	Glossop North End	v Dunston UTS	1-0	378
11	Whitley Bay	v Alsager Town	2-0	606
12	Bootle	v Stone Dominoes	2-1	69
13	Congleton Town	v Shildon	0-2	237
14	Scarborough Athletic	v Bridlington Town	2-5	1002
15	Wellington	v Stratford Town	3-0	99
16	Coalville Town	v Oadby Town	4-2*	115
17	Blaby & Whetstone Ath.	v Boldmere St Michaels	0-1	122
18	Dunkirk	v Lincoln Moorlands Railway	3-1	67
19	New Mills	v Tividale	6-1	150
20	Barwell	v Long Eaton United	2-0	108
21	Biddulph Victoria	v Gedling Town	1-0*	59
22	Gresley	v Ollerton Town	3-1	181
23	Causeway United	v Newcastle Town	3-2	135
24	Friar Lane & Epworth	v Tipton Town	1-2	27
25	Westfields	v Rainworth MW	1-2	101
26	Sleaford Town	v Bewdley Town	2-1	114
27	Long Buckby	v Stansted	2-1	49
28	Cambridge Regional College	v Enfield 1893	4-1	176
29	Newport Pagnell Town	v Dereham Town	3-1	184
30	North Greenford United	v Daventry Town	0-1	120
31	Kirkley & Pakefield	v Biggleswade United	2-0	155
32	Ely City	v Woodbridge Town	1-1*	79
	(tie awarded to Ely City – Woodbridge Town expelled)			
33	Bugbrooke St Michaels	v Leiston	0-4	120
34	Needham Market	v Bedford	5-0	256
35	Wellingborough Town	v Royston Town	0-4	111
36	Stanway Rovers	v Hadley	1-0	82
37	Wroxham	v Halstead Town	0-0*	85
	Halstead Town	v Wroxham	1-3	137
38	FC Clacton	v St Ives Town	0-2	162
39	Brimsdown Rovers	v London Colney	3-2	145
40	Wembley	v Hoddesdon Town	1-2	59
41	Stewarts & Lloyds	v Stotfold	2-4*	35
42	Tiptree United	v Cogenhoe United	4-3*	51
	(at Maldon Town FC)			
43	Chertsey Town	v Croydon	2-0	107
44	Eastbourne United	v Hamble ASSC	4-2	63
45	Whitehawk	v Fareham Town	3-2*	120
46	Herne Bay	v Flackwell Heath	0-1	160
47	Arundel	v Crowborough Athletic	4-0	43
48	Badshot Lea	v Faversham Town	2-1	101
49	Beckenham Town	v Carterton	2-1	85
50	Witney United	v Erith & Belvedere	5-1	121
51	Chalfont St Peter	v Peacehaven & Telscombe	1-5	105
52	Moneyfields	v Epsom & Ewell	2-3	50
53	Redhill	v Shoreham	1-2	73
54	Plymouth Parkway	v Bitton	3-2	135
55	Wellington Town	v Bradford Town	3-2	50
56	Shortwood United	v Bemerton Heath Harlequins	3-0	103
57	Tavistock	v Brockenhurst	1-3	139
58	Wells City	v Larkhall Athletic	2-3*	103
59	Bristol Manor Farm	v Saltash United	2-1	64
60	Dawlish Town	v Wimborne Town	3-1	100
61	Christchurch	v Almondsbury Town	2-5	87
62	Bideford	v Welton Rovers	0-2	174
63	Longwell Green Sports	v Willand Rovers	2-3*	108
64	Brislington	v Poole Town	0-4	100

Third Round - 5th December
32 winners @ £1,300

Contenders for Wembley were making their challenge from all over the country in this round and unbeaten Midland Alliance leaders Barwell beat Glossop North End 2-0. In the North East two famous names clashed as Shildon won 4-2 at Crook Town.

Top scorers were a little Devon village club Willand Rovers, who had been overshadowed in recent years by the Vase triumphs of local rivals Tiverton Town and Taunton Town. They beat Welton Rovers 6-1 while powerful Hellenic club Shortwood United won 2-0 at home to Shoreham.

High scoring home victories were celebrated by Long Buckby who beat Wellington 5-2, New Mills 5-1 victors over West Auckland Town while away triumphs were enjoyed by Bootle 4-1 at Penrith and Kirkley & Pakefield 4-0 at Hoddesdon Town.

Wroxham won their sixth F.A.Vase tie of the campaign with a 3-1 triumph at Flackwell Heath and Whitley Bay quietly moved on by a similar score at home to Boldmere St Michaels. There were now only thirty two clubs left and surely everyone had a chance.

Fourth Round - 16th January
16winners @ £1,500

Waterlogged pitches were responsible for eleven postponements but some brilliant matches did beat the conditions. Gresley Rovers scored in the 90th minute to take the tie into extra time at 4-4 but there were no more goals. Needham Market beat Kirkley & Pakefield 5-3 in an Eastern 'derby' and St Ives scored seven without reply at Tiptree United while Whitley Bay enjoyed home advantage against Poole Town and another 3-1 victory. To complete a total of 32 goals in just five Vase ties, Long Buckby beat Epsom & Ewell 3-2 at home.

The Fourth Round was completed the following Saturday with Gresley and Dawlish drawing again after 120 minutes but the past finalists from the East Midlands eventually won 7-6 on penalties. Chertsey's John Pomroy scored four in a surprisingly easy victory over Plymouth Parkway, who had built a good reputation during their best ever Vase run.

Barwell showed their potential with a fine 3-0 victory at Shortwood United and Willand Rovers also made club history by reaching the Fifth Round with a 2-0 home victory over Causeway United. The last sixteen clubs were nicely balanced geographically across the country and they all looked forward to a little luck in the important draw for the last eight ties.

Once again Wroxham needed a replay and even then the tie wasn't decided against Armthorpe Welfare until penalties gave the Eastern Counties club a 3-0 winning margin a week later than all the other ties. As this was their eighth Vase match, perhaps it really was going to be their year!

Fifth Round - 6th February
8 winners @ £2,000

Although being drawn at home in the later rounds of the competition is considered an advantage, there is something to be said for an exciting away trip to face unknown opposition, possibly a bonding overnight stop and of course, no administrative duties for any club officials. Looking at the results in this round it can be noted that there is only one home victory from the original seven Saturday fixtures.

With attendances increasing and the thought of their local lads walking out at Wembley, the regional favourites from all areas of the country flexed their muscles and we saw Whitley Bay drawing at the well fancied Chertsey Town, before going through 2-1 in a well fought replay and joining North Eastern rivals Shildon, who had won 3-1 with all the goals in extra-time at St Ives in Cambridgeshire. Over 6000 had watched both these ties.

Barwell, who were still unbeaten in their league, were many peoples favourites and they played out a 2-2 thriller at Willand before winning the replay in extra time. Most of the matches were hard fought and Gresley again won a high scoring battle with a 4-3 triumph at Long Buckby, but Wroxham caught up a week late with another away match, and this time they produced a tremendous 5-0 victory against Royston Town.

Sixth Round - 27th February
4 winners @ £5,000

Holders Whitley Bay drew another away tie at their local Northern League rivals Shildon, while Wroxham were paired with Needham Market another Eastern Counties League club. The two local clashes attracted 1,345 and 601 respectively and both games resulted in away wins, 5-1 at Shildon and 2-1 at Needham Market.

A third away club completed a hat trick of victories for clubs beginning beginning with W as Whitehawk from Sussex travelled to bring Gresley's high scoring Vase campaign to an end with a 3-1 scoreline. This left Barwell, the Midland Alliance favourites, to take on a third Northern League club, Norton & Stockton Ancients, and reach the Semi-Finals late due to another waterlogged pitch.

Semi-Finals - 27th March & 3rd April
2 winners @ £7,000

Barwell, still unbeaten, and holders Whitley Bay, were undoubtedly the favourites, but the luck of the draw paired them together in the Semi-Final and the two produced a couple of outstanding ties. The holders took the lead in the first match at Barwell and then slipped to 1-3 down before Paul Chow scored two late goals to take a 3-3 scoreline back to the North East. In the second leg the lead changed hands twice before a last minute diving header from Whitley Bay's Paul Robinson clinched a thriller and ensured the holders would be back at Wembley.

Wroxham, on the other hand, won both legs of their semi-final with Whitehawk, 2-0 in Sussex and 2-1 at home. As they had played twelve F.A.Vase ties during their long campaign which had started out in September, no one could possibly begrudge them their first ever Wembley appearance and a day which would be treasured by everyone involved with the club.

THIRD ROUND PROPER

1	Marske United	v Nelson	5-0	256
2	Whitley Bay	v Boldmere St Michaels	3-1	567
3	Armthorpe Welfare	v Bridlington Town	2-1	140
4	Rainworth MW	v Norton & Stockton Ancients	1-2	134
5	Pickering Town	v Dunkirk	1-1*	156
	Dunkirk	v Pickering Town	2-2*	129
	(Pickering Town won 5-4 on penalties)			
6	Crook Town	v Shildon	2-4	267
7	Biddulph Victoria	v Causeway United	1-3	73
8	New Mills	v West Auckland Town	5-1	164
9	Penrith	v Bootle	1-4	100
10	Coalville Town	v Tipton Town	0-2	72
11	Barwell	v Glossop North End	2-0	306
12	Gresley	v Spennymoor Town	1-0	372
13	Tiptree United	v Beckenham Town	3-2	67
14	Chertsey Town	v Sleaford Town	3-2*	192
15	Brimsdown Rovers	v Newport Pagnell Town	3-2*	135
16	Cambridge Regional College	v Needham Market	1-2	236
17	Royston Town	v Stanway Rovers	2-1	229
18	Long Buckby	v Wellington	5-2	86
19	Stotfold	v Badshot Lea	3-1	84
20	Hoddesdon Town	v Kirkley & Pakefield	0-4	169
21	Flackwell Heath	v Wroxham	1-3	53
22	St Ives Town	v Ely City	3-0	338
23	Leiston	v Daventry Town	3-4*	223
24	Eastbourne United	v Poole Town	3-5*	123
25	Plymouth Parkway	v Arundel	4-2*	206
26	Willand Rovers	v Welton Rovers	6-1	93
27	Larkhall Athletic	v Whitehawk	0-2	128
28	Shortwood United	v Shoreham	2-0	104
29	Witney United	v Almondsbury Town	4-0	142
30	Peacehaven & Telscombe	v Bristol Manor Farm	0-3	198
31	Wellington Town	v Epsom & Ewell	2-3*	76
32	Dawlish Town	v Brockenhurst	3-1*	67

FOURTH ROUND PROPER

1	New Mills	v Witney United	2-1	260
2	Tiptree United	v St Ives Town	0-7	168
3	Needham Market	v Kirkley & Pakefield	5-3	329
4	Whitley Bay	v Poole Town	3-1	906
5	Shortwood United	v Barwell	0-3	197
6	Brimsdown Rovers	v Daventry Town	1-4	150
7	Bristol Manor Farm	v Whitehawk	1-3	132
8	Norton & Stockton Ancients	v Bootle	4-2	144
9	Pickering Town	v Marske United	1-2	236
10	Armthorpe Welfare	v Wroxham	1-1*	130
	Wroxham	v Armthorpe Welfare	1-1*	175
	(Wroxham won 3-0 on penalties)			
11	Willand Rovers	v Causeway United	2-0	130
12	Long Buckby	v Epsom & Ewell	3-2	164
13	Dawlish Town	v Gresley	4-4*	222
	Gresley	v Dawlish Town	1-1*	469
	(Gresley won 7-6 on penalties)			
	(16/1, tie abandoned after 119 mins due to waterlogged pitch, 4-4)			
14	Royston Town	v Tipton Town	2-1*	365
15	Chertsey Town	v Plymouth Parkway	6-0	312
16	Stotfold	v Shildon	0-2	252

FIFTH ROUND PROPER

1	St Ives Town	v Shildon	1-3*	669
2	New Mills	v Norton & Stockton Ancients	0-2	403
3	Whitehawk	v Marske United	1-1*	370
	Marske United	v Whitehawk	2-3	425
4	Long Buckby	v Gresley	3-4	380
5	Willand Rovers	v Barwell	2-2*	368
	Barwell	v Willand Rovers	2-1*	384
6	Royston Town	v Wroxham	0-5	650
7	Needham Market	v Daventry Town	2-0	411
8	Chertsey Town	v Whitley Bay	1-1*	617
	Whitley Bay	v Chertsey Town	2-1	1103

FIFTH ROUND PROPER

1	Shildon	v Whitley Bay	1-5	1345
2	Needham Market	v Wroxham	1-2	601
3	Barwell	v Norton & Stockton Ancients	3-0	606
4	Gresley	v Whitehawk	1-3	861

SEMI-FINALS

1ST LEG

1	Barwell	v Whitley Bay	3-3	1279
2	Whitehawk	v Wroxham	0-2	1331

2ND LEG

1	Whitley Bay	v Barwell	3-2	2720
2	Wroxham	v Whitehawk	2-1	1262

With so few spectators gathered in the vastness of the stadium empty spaces dominated, despite the evident enthusiasm of those present. Such sparseness does question the wisdom of holding this event at the national stadium although the 515 entrants for the year would be bound to differ. Perhaps Vase and Trophy could be held the same day with a subsequent reduction in costs. Many Bay supporters, having been to Wembley previously, had apparently decided to forego a further trip, the novelty value having diminished whereas Wroxham do not have a substantial following or catchment area from which to attract in the first place.

How pleasing it was to see the East Anglian team numbered traditionally 1 to 11. With the exception of 16 for 5 the Seahorses had nearly managed the same. Generally the Vase final is a more open, competitive, and thus entertaining contest than its senior brother, the Trophy. This 2010 final was an exception in not following that pattern.

Barely had the starting whistle sounded than we had the first score. What can only be described as a 'lumped up ball' was jettisoned into the Yachtsmen's penalty area. Skipper Graham Challen looked at his keeper, Scott Howie, Howie looked back at him. The ball hardly bounced but Paul Chow, quick to take advantage, made contact with a plunging header as Challen and Howie's hesitation deferred immediate intervention, the ball trickling into the unguarded net. Bay supporters leapt to their feet; East Anglian heads bowed unbelievingly. Statisticians ecstatically debated the timing of the goal, eventually agreeing that, at 21 seconds, it had been the fastest goal ever scored at the NEW Wembley. This was no consolation to Wroxham.

it had been the fastest goal ever scored at the NEW Wembley. This was no consolation to Wroxham.

With only Paul Cook on his own up front an East Anglian response looked distinctly unlikely as every time the ball went anywhere near him it was soon back in Bay's control. But wait. A free kick from Shaun Howes, knocked on by Cook, was blocked by Terry Burke's feet and, as the keeper fell backwards, Cook reacted quickly to equalise in the 12th minute.

Four minutes later Bay were again in the lead. As a free kick came across Andy Easthaugh's attempted clearance was sufficient to deflect the ball just inside his own post despite a team mate's attempt at blocking. Adam Johnston, profiting from Chow's distracting the defence, would have scored an immediate third but for Challen's last ditch intervention. Howie tipped over Johnston's header and Cook almost profited from Burke's flappy punch at the other end as the half drew to a close with Bay 2-1 up.

Perhaps Vase and Trophy could be held the same day with a subsequent reduction in costs.

Whitley Bay opened the second half just as they had the first, by scoring. This was a stunner from the impressively untiring Lee Kerr with a perfectly placed shot. The fourth Bay score came after good saves by Howie from efforts by Leon Ryan and Kerr left Johnston to knock home. Contest over.

Naturally Wroxham had to try and push forward, risking the deficit becoming even greater. Cook headed over a cross from the intermittently threatening winger Steve Spriggs and a succession of shots ended securely in Burke's grasp. Bay missed a good chance with some over elaborate passing before Crouch lookalike, sub Phil Bell, raced clear, only to slide a chance past the post as he ignored better placed team mates. Number five arrived though when Paul Robinson broke clear of a bedraggled and tiring Wroxham defence to beat Howie with a low shot. More embarrassment followed when Josh Gillies was put through to slide the sixth past the stranded Howie just before Mr Taylor's whistle halted further scoring. Yet again the Northern League had vanquished more southerly opposition, this time with the highest score in a Vase final and Bay matching Billericay's three triumphs. What is to stop them achieving a third consecutive victory in 2011 to make it four?

ARTHUR EVANS.

Bluefin

WHITLEY BAY 6

Chow 21(sec), Easthaugh 16 (og), Kerr, Johnston, Robinson, Gillies

WROXHAM 1

Cook 12

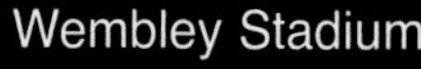

Wembley Stadium

TODAY'S ATTENDANCE
8,920

Damon Robson (left), Whitley Bay, is closed down by Wroxham's Danny White. Photo: Roger Turner.

Wroxham's Scott Howie makes a fine save. Photo: Peter Barnes.

Photo: Alan Coomes.

Whitley Bay: Terry Burke, Craig McFarlane, Callum Anderson, Richard Hodgson, (sub Lee Picton 69th min), Darren Timmons, Leon Ryan, Adam Johnston (sub Joshua Gillies 77th min), Damon Robson, Lee Kerr, Paul Chow (sub Phillip Bell 61st min), Paul Robinson. Subs not used – Tom Kindley and Chris Reid.

Wroxham: Scott Howie, Gavin Pauling (sub Ross Durrant 57th min), Shaun Howes, Graham Challen, Martin McNeil (sub Josh Carus 46th min), Andy Easthaugh (sub Owen Paynter 69th min), Steve Spriggs, Gavin Lemmon, Paul Cook, Danny White, Gary Gilmore. Subs not used – Danny Self and Gareth Simpson.

Referee – Anthony Taylor, assistants Paul Marsden and Dean Mohareb. Fourth official, Neil Swarbrick.

Chertsey Town 'keeper, Liam Stone, watches as a Whitley Bay corner is cleared during an anxious second half of their 5th Round tie.
Photo: Graham Brown.

Paul Cook (No.9) scores Wroxham's first goal at Whitehawk in the 1st leg of their Semi-Final.
Photo: Roger Turner.

Danny Brunskill, Marske United, beats Whitehawk's Justin Harris to the ball during their 5th Round match.
Photo: Roger Turner.

PAST FINALS

1975 **HODDESDON TOWN 2 *(South Midlands)*** **EPSOM & EWELL 1 *(Surrey Senior)*** **Att: 9,500**
Sedgwick 2 **Wales** **Ref: Mr R Toseland**
Hoddesdon: Galvin, Green, Hickey, Maybury, Stevenson, Wilson, Bishop, Picking, Sedgwick, Nathan, Schofield
Epsom & Ewell: Page, Bennett, Webb, Wales, Worby, Jones, O'Connell, Walker, Tuite, Eales, Lee

1976 **BILLERICAY TOWN 1 *(Essex Senior)*** **STAMFORD 0 (aet) *(United Counties)*** **Att: 11,848**
Aslett **Ref: Mr A Robinson**
Billericay: Griffiths, Payne, Foreman, Pullin, Bone, Coughlan, Geddes, Aslett, Clayden, Scott, Smith
Stamford: Johnson, Kwiatowski, Marchant, Crawford, Downs, Hird, Barnes, Walpole, Smith, Russell, Broadbent

1977 **BILLERICAY TOWN 1 *(Essex Senior)*** **SHEFFIELD 1 (aet) *(Yorkshire)*** **Att: 14,000**
Clayden **Coughlan og** **Ref: Mr J Worrall**
Billericay: Griffiths, Payne, Bone, Coughlan, Pullin, Scott, Wakefield, Aslett, Clayden,Woodhouse, McQueen. Sub: Whettell
Sheffield: Wing, Gilbody, Lodge, Hardisty, Watts, Skelton, Kay, Travis, Pugh, Thornhill,Haynes. Sub: Strutt
Replay **BILLERICAY TOWN 2** **SHEFFIELD 1** **Att: 3,482**
Aslett, Woodhouse **Thornhill** **at Nottingham Forest**
Billericay: Griffiths, Payne, Pullin, Whettell, Bone, McQueen, Woodhouse, Aslett, Clayden, Scott, Wakefield
Sheffield: Wing, Gilbody, Lodge, Strutt, Watts, Skelton, Kay, Travis, Pugh, Thornhill, Haynes

1978 **NEWCASTLE BLUE STAR 2 *(Wearside)*** **BARTON ROVERS 1 *(South Midlands)*** **Att: 16,858**
Dunn, Crumplin **Smith** **Ref: Mr T Morris**
Newcastle: Halbert, Feenan, Thompson, Davidson, S Dixon, Beynon, Storey, P Dixon, Crumplin, Callaghan, Dunn. Sub: Diamond
Barton Rovers: Blackwell, Stephens, Crossley, Evans, Harris, Dollimore, Dunn, Harnaman, Fossey, Turner, Smith. Sub: Cox

1979 **BILLERICAY TOWN 4 *(Athenian)*** **ALMONDSBURY GREENWAY 1 *(Glos. Co)*** **Att: 17,500**
Young 3, Clayden **Price** **Ref: Mr C Steel**
Billericay: Norris, Blackaller, Bingham, Whettell, Bone, Reeves, Pullin, Scott, Clayden,Young, Groom. Sub: Carrigan
Almondsbury: Hamilton, Bowers, Scarrett, Sulllivan, Tudor, Wookey, Bowers, Shehean, Kerr, Butt, Price. Sub: Kilbaine

1980 **STAMFORD 2 *(United Counties)*** **GUISBOROUGH TOWN 0 *(Northern Alliance)*** **Att: 11,500**
Alexander, McGowan **Ref: Neil Midgeley**
Stamford: Johnson, Kwiatkowski, Ladd, McGowan, Bliszczak I, Mackin, Broadhurst, Hall,Czarnecki, Potter, Alexander. Sub: Bliszczak S
Guisborough: Cutter, Scott, Thornton, Angus, Maltby, Percy, Skelton, Coleman, McElvaney,Sills, Dilworth. Sub: Harrison

1981 **WHICKHAM 3 *(Wearside)*** **WILLENHALL 2 (aet) *(West Midlands)*** **Att: 12,000**
Scott, Williamson, Peck og **Smith, Stringer** **Ref: Mr R Lewis**
Whickham: Thompson, Scott, Knox, Williamson, Cook, Ward, Carroll, Diamond, Cawthra,Robertson, Turnbull. Sub: Alton
Willenhall: Newton, White, Darris, Woodall, Heath, Fox, Peck, Price, Matthews, Smith,Stringer. Sub: Trevor

1982 **FOREST GREEN ROVERS 3 *(Hellenic)*** **RAINWORTH M.W 0 *(Notts Alliance)*** **Att: 12,500**
Leitch 2, Norman **Ref: Mr K Walmsey**
Forest Green: Moss, Norman, Day, Turner, Higgins, Jenkins, Guest, Burns, Millard, Leitch, Doughty. Sub: Dangerfield
Rainworth M.W: Watson, Hallam, Hodgson, Slater, Sterland, Oliver, Knowles, Raine, Radzi, Reah, Comerford. Sub: Robinson

1983 **V.S. RUGBY 1 *(West Midlands)*** **HALESOWEN TOWN 0 *(West Midlands)*** **Att: 13,700**
Crawley **Ref: Mr B Daniels**
VS Rugby: Burton, McGinty, Harrison, Preston, Knox, Evans, ingram, Setchell, Owen,Beecham, Crawley. Sub: Haskins
Halesowen Town: Coldicott, Penn, Edmonds, Lacey, Randall, Shilvock, Hazelwood, Moss, Woodhouse,P Joinson, L Joinson. Sub: Smith

1984 **STANSTED 3 *(Essex Senior)*** **STAMFORD 2 *(United Counties)*** **Att: 8,125**
Holt, Gillard, Reading **Waddicore, Allen** **Ref: Mr T Bune**
Stanstead: Coe, Williams, Hilton, Simpson, Cooper, Reading, Callanan, Holt, Reevs,Doyle, Gillard. Sub: Williams
Stamford: Parslow, Smitheringate, Blades, McIlwain, Lyon, Mackin, Genovese, Waddicore,Allen, Robson, Beech. Sub: Chapman

1985 **HALESOWEN TOWN 3 *(West Midlands)*** **FLEETWOOD TOWN 1 *(N W Counties)*** **Att: 16,715**
L Joinson 2, Moss **Moran** **Ref: Mr C Downey**
Halesowen: Coldicott, Penn, Sherwood, Warner, Randle, Heath, Hazlewood, Moss (Smith),Woodhouse, P Joinson, L Joinson
Fleetwood Town: Dobson, Moran, Hadgraft, Strachan, Robinson, Milligan, Hall, Trainor, Taylor(Whitehouse), Cain, Kennerley

1986 **HALESOWEN TOWN 3 *(West Midlands)*** **SOUTHALL 0 *(Isthmian 2 South)*** **Att: 18,340**
Moss 2, L Joinson **Ref: Mr D Scott**
Halesowen: Pemberton, Moore, Lacey, Randle (Rhodes), Sherwood, Heath, Penn, Woodhouse, PJoinson, L Joinson, Moss
Southall: Mackenzie, James, McGovern, Croad, Holland, Powell (Richmond), Pierre,Richardson, Sweales, Ferdinand, Rowe

1987 **ST. HELENS 3 *(N W Counties)*** **WARRINGTON TOWN 2 *(N W Counties)*** **Att: 4,254**
Layhe 2, Rigby **Reid, Cook** **Ref: Mr T Mills**
St Helens: Johnson, Benson, Lowe, Bendon, Wilson, McComb, Collins (Gledhill), O'Neill,Cummins, Lay, Rigby. Sub: Deakin
Warrington: O'Brien. Copeland, Hunter, Gratton, Whalley, Reid, Brownville (Woodyer), Cook,Kinsey, Looker (Hill), Hughes

1988 **COLNE DYNAMOES 1 *(N W Counties)*** **EMLEY 0 *(Northern Counties East)*** **Att: 15,000**
Anderson **Ref: Mr A Seville**
Colne Dynamoes: Mason, McFafyen, Westwell, Bentley, Dunn, Roscoe, Rodaway, Whitehead (Burke),Diamond, Anderson, Wood (Coates)
Emley: Dennis, Fielding, Mellor, Codd, Hirst (Burrows), Gartland (Cook), Carmody,Green, Bramald, Devine, Francis

1989 **TAMWORTH 1 *(West Midlands)*** **SUDBURY TOWN 1 (aet) *(Eastern)*** **Att: 26,487**
Devaney **Hubbick** **Ref: Mr C Downey**
Tamworth: Bedford, Lockett, Atkins, Cartwright, McCormack, Myers, Finn, Devaney, Moores,Gordon, Stanton. Subs: Rathbone, Heaton
Sudbury Town: Garnham, Henry, G Barker, Boyland, Thorpe, Klug, D Barker, Barton, Oldfield,Smith, Hubbick. Subs: Money, Hunt
REPLAY **TAMWORTH 3** **SUDBURY TOWN 0** **Att: 11,201**
Stanton 2, Moores **at Peterborough**
Tamworth: Bedford, Lockett, Atkins, Cartwright, Finn, Myers, George, Devaney, Moores,Gordon, Stanton. Sub: Heaton
Sudbury Town: Garnham, Henry, G Barker, Boyland, Thorpe, Klug, D Barker, Barton, Oldfield,Smith, Hubbick. Subs: Money, Hunt

1990 **YEADING 0 *(Isthmian 2 South)*** **BRIDLINGTON TOWN 0 (aet) *(N Co East)*** **Att: 7,932**
Ref: Mr R Groves
Yeading: Mackenzie, Wickens, Turner, Whiskey (McCarthy), Croad, Denton, Matthews, James(Charles), Sweates, Impey, Cordery
Bridlington: Taylor, Pugh, Freeman, McNeill, Warburton, Brentano, Wilkes (Hall), Noteman,Gauden, Whiteman, Brattan (Brown)

Replay **YEADING 1** **BRIDLINGTON TOWN 0** **Att: 5,000**
Sweales **at Leeds Utd FC**
Yeading: Mackenzie, Wickens, Turner, Whiskey, Croad (McCarthy), Schwartz, Matthews,James, Sweates, Impey (Welsh), Cordery
Bridlington: Taylor, Pugh, Freeman, McNeill, Warburton, Brentano, Wilkes (Brown), Noteman,Gauden (Downing), Whiteman, Brattan

1991 **GRESLEY ROVERS 4 *(West Midlands)*** **GUISELEY 4 (aet) *(Northern Co East)*** **Att: 11,314**
Rathbone, Smith 2, Stokes **Tennison 2, Walling, A Roberts** **Ref: Mr C Trussell**
Gresley: Aston, Barry, Elliott (Adcock), Denby, Land, Astley, Stokes, K Smith, Acklam,Rathbone, Lovell (Weston)
Guiseley: Maxted, Bottomley, Hogarth, Tetley, Morgan, McKenzie, Atkinson (Annan),Tennison, Walling, A Roberts, B Roberts

Replay **GUISELEY 3** **GRESLEY ROVERS 1** **Att: 7,585**
Tennison, Walling, Atkinson **Astley** **at Bramall Lane**
Guiseley: Maxted, Annan, Hogarth, Tetley, Morgan, McKenzie (Bottomley), Atkinson,Tennison (Noteman), Walling, A Roberts, B Roberts
Gresley: Aston, Barry, Elliott, Denby, Land, Astley, Stokes (Weston), K Smith, Acklam, Rathbone, Lovell (Adcock)

1992 **WIMBORNE TOWN 5 *(Wessex)*** **GUISELEY 3 *(Northern Premier Div 1)*** **Att: 10,772**
Richardson, Sturgess 2, Killick 2 **Noteman 2, Colville** **Ref: Mr M J Bodenham**
Wimborne: Leonard, Langdown, Wilkins, Beacham, Allan, Taplin, Ames, Richardson, Bridle,Killick, Sturgess (Lovell), Lynn
Guiseley: Maxted, Atkinson, Hogarth, Tetley (Wilson), Morgan, Brockie, A Roberts,Tennison, Noteman (Colville), Annan, W Roberts

1993 **BRIDLINGTON TOWN 1 *(NPL Div 1)*** **TIVERTON TOWN 0 *(Western)*** **Att: 9,061**
Radford **Ref: Mr R A Hart**
Bridlington: Taylor, Brentano, McKenzie, Harvey, Bottomley, Woodcock, Grocock, A Roberts, Jones, Radford (Tyrell), Parkinson. Sub: Swailes
Tiverton Town: Nott, J Smith, N Saunders, M Saunders, Short (Scott), Steele, Annunziata, KSmith, Everett, Daly, Hynds (Rogers)

1994 **DISS TOWN 2 *(Eastern)*** **TAUNTON TOWN 1 *(Western)*** **Att: 13,450**
Gibbs (p), Mendham **Fowler** **Ref: Mr K. Morton**
Diss Town: Woodcock, Carter, Wolsey (Musgrave), Casey (Bugg), Hartle, Smith, Barth, Mendham, Miles, Warne, Gibbs
Taunton Town: Maloy, Morris, Walsh, Ewens, Graddon, Palfrey, West (Hendry), Fowler, Durham, Perrett (Ward), Jarvis

1995 **ARLESEY TOWN 2 *(South Midlands)*** **OXFORD CITY 1 *(Ryman 2)*** **Att: 13,670**
Palma, Gyalog **S Fontaine** **Ref: Mr G S Willard**
Arlesey: Young, Cardines, Bambrick, Palma (Ward), Hull, Gonsalves, Gyalog, Cox, Kane,O'Keefe, Marshall (Nicholls). Sub: Dodwell
Oxford: Fleet, Brown (Fisher), Hume, Shepherd, Muttock, Hamilton (Kemp), Thomas, Spittle, Sherwood, S Fontaine, C Fontaine. Sub: Torres

1996 **BRIGG TOWN 3 *(N Co East)*** **CLITHEROE 0 *(N W Counties)*** **Att: 7,340**
Stead 2, Roach **Ref: Mr S J Lodge**
Brigg: Gawthorpe, Thompson, Rogers, Greaves (Clay), Buckley (Mail), Elston, C Stead, McLean, N Stead (McNally), Flounders, Roach
Clitheroe: Nash, Lampkin, Rowbotham (Otley), Baron, Westwell, Rovine, Butcher, Taylor (Smith), Grimshaw, Darbyshire, Hill (Dunn)

1997 **WHITBY TOWN 3 *(Northern)*** **NORTH FERRIBY UTD. 0 *(N Co East)*** **Att: 11,098**
Williams, Logan, Toman **Ref: Graham Poll**
North Ferriby: Sharp, Deacey, Smith, Brentano, Walmsley, M Smith, Harrison (Horne), Phillips (Milner), France (Newman), Flounders, Tennison
Whitby Town: Campbell, Williams, Logan, Goodchild, Pearson, Cook, Goodrick (Borthwick), Hodgson, Robinson, Toman (Pyle), Pitman (Hall)

1998 **TIVERTON TOWN 1** ***(Western)*** **TOW LAW TOWN 0** ***(Northern)*** **Att: 13,139**
Varley **Ref: M A Riley**
Tiverton: Edwards, Felton, Saunders, Tatterton, Smith J, Conning, Nancekivell (Rogers), Smith K (Varley), Everett, Daly, Leonard (Waters)
Tow Law: Dawson, Pickering, Darwent, Bailey, Hague, Moan, Johnson, Nelson, Suddick, Laidler (Bennett), Robinson.

1999 **TIVERTON TOWN 1** ***(Western)*** **BEDLINGTON TERRIERS 0** ***(Northern)*** **Att: 13, 878**
Rogers 88 **Ref: W. C. Burns**
Bedlington Terriers: O'Connor, Bowes, Pike, Boon (Renforth), Melrose, Teasdale, Cross, Middleton (Ludlow), Gibb, Milner, Bond. Subs: Pearson, Cameron, Gowans
Tiverton Town: Edwards, Fallon, Saunders, Tatterton, Tallon, Conning (Rogers), Nancekivell (Pears), Varley, Everett, Daly, Leonard. Subs: Tucker, Hynds, Grimshaw

2000 **DEAL TOWN 1** ***(Kent)*** **CHIPPENHAM TOWN 0** ***(Western)*** **Att: 20,000**
Graham 87 **Ref: E. K. Wolstenholme**
Deal Town: Tucker, Kempster, Best, Ash, Martin, Seager, Monteith, Graham, Lovell, Marshall, Ribbens. Subs: Roberts, Warden, Turner
Chippenham Town: Jones, James, Andrews, Murphy, Burns, Woods, Brown, Charity, Tweddle, Collier, Godley. Subs: Tiley, Cutler

2001 **TAUNTON TOWN 2** ***(Western)*** **BERKHAMPSTED TOWN 1** ***(Isthmian 2)*** **(at Villa Park) Att: 8,439**
Fields 41, Laight 45 **Lowe 71** **Ref: E. K. Wolstenholme**
Taunton Town: Draper, Down, Chapman, West, Hawkings, Kelly, Fields (Groves), Laight, Cann (Tallon), Bastow, Lynch (Hapgood). Subs: Ayres, Parker
Berkhampsted Town: O'Connor, Mullins, Lowe, Aldridge, Coleman, Brockett, Yates, Adebowale, Richardson, Smith, Nightingale. Subs: Ringsell, Hall, Knight, Franklin, Osborne

2002 **WHITLEY BAY 1** ***(Northern)*** **TIPTREE UNITED 0** ***(Eastern)*** **(at Villa Park) Att: 4742**
Chandler 97 **Ref: A Kaye**
Whitley Bay: Caffrey, Sunderland, Walmsley, Dixon (Neil), Anderson, Locker, Middleton, Bowes (Carr), Chandler, Walton, Fenwick (Cuggy). Subs: Cook, Livermore
Tiptree United: Haygreen, Battell, Wall, Houghton, Fish, Streetley (Gillespie), Wareham (Snow), Daly, Barefield, Aransibia (Parnell), Brady. Subs: Powell, Ford.

2003 **A.F.C SUDBURY 1** ***(Eastern Counties)*** **BRIGG TOWN 2** ***(Northern Co.East)*****(at Upton Park) Att: 6,634**
Raynor 30 **Housham 2, Carter 68** **Ref: M Fletcher**
AFC Sudbury:- Greygoose, Head (Norfolk 63), Spearing, Tracey, Bishop, Anderson (Owen 73), Rayner, Gardiner (Banya 79), Bennett, Claydon, Betson. Subs (not used) Taylor, Hyde.
Brigg Town:- Steer, Raspin, Rowland, Thompson, Blanchard, Stones, Stead (Thompson 41), Housham, Borman (Drayton 87), Roach, Carter. Subs (not used) Nevis, Gawthorpe.

2004 **A.F.C SUDBURY 0** ***(Eastern Counties)*** **WINCHESTER CITY 2** ***(Wessex)*** **(at St Andrews) Att: 5,080**
Forbes 19, Smith 73 (pen) **Ref: P Crossley**
AFC Sudbury:- Greygoose, Head, Wardley, Girling, Tracey, Norfolk, Owen (Banya 62), Hyde (Calver 57), Bennett, Claydon, Betson (Francis 73n). Subs (not used) - Rayner, Nower.
Winchester City:- Arthur, Dyke (Tate 83), Bicknell, Redwood, Goss, Blake, Webber, Green, Mancey, Forbes (Rogers 70), Smith (Green 90). Subs (not used) - Lang and Rastall.

2005 **A.F.C SUDBURY 2** ***(Eastern Counties)*** **DIDCOT TOWN 3** ***(Hellenic)*** **(at White Hart Lane) Att: 8,662**
Wardley, Calver (pen) **Beavon (2), Wardley (og)** **Ref: R Beeeby**
AFC Sudbury:- Greygoose, Girling, Wardley, Bennett, Hyde (Hayes 78), Owen (Norfolk 65), Claydon (Banya 59), Head, Calver, Betson, Terry Rayner. Subs (not used) – Howlett, Nower.
Didcot Town:- Webb, Goodall, Heapy, Campbell, Green, Parrott, Hannigan, Ward, Concannon (Jones 88), Beavon (Bianchini 90), Powell. Subs (not used) – Cooper, Allen, Spurrett.

2006 **HILLINGDON BOROUGH 1** ***(Spartan S.Mids P.)*** **NANTWICH TOWN 3** ***(NWC 1)*** **(at St Andrews) Att: 3,286**
Nelson **Kinsey (2), Scheuber**
Hillingdon Borough:- Brown, Rundell (Fenton 80),Kidson, Phillips, Croft, Lawrence, Duncan (Nelson 46), Tilbury, Hibbs, Wharton (Lyons 38). Subs (not used): O'Grady, White.
Nantwich Town:- Hackney, A.Taylor, T.Taylor, Smith, Davis, Donnelly, Beasley, Scheuber (Parkinson 69), Kinsey (Marrow 69), Blake (Scarlett 86) and Griggs. Subs (not used): O'Connor and Read.

2007 **AFC TOTTON 1** ***(Wessex Division 1)*** **TRURO 3** ***(Western Division 1)*** **Att: 27,754 (New Vase record)**
Potter **Wills (2), Broad** **Ref: P Joslin**
AFC Totton: Brunnschweiler, Reacord, Troon (Stevens 60), Potter (Gregory 82), Bottomley, Austen, Roden, Gosney, Hamodu (Goss 89), Osman, Byres. Subs not used: Zammit, McCormack.
Truro City: Stevenson, Ash, Power, Smith, Martin (Pope 84), Broad, Wills, Gosling, Yetton, Watkins, Walker (Ludlam 90). Subs not used: Butcher, Routledge, Reski.

2008	**KIRKHAM & WESHAM 2** ***(North West Co. Div.2)*** **Walwyn (2)**	**LOWESTOFT TOWN 1** ***(Eastern Co. Premier)*** **Thompson (og)**	**Att: 19,537 Ref: A D'Urso**

Kirkham and Wesham: Summerfield, Jackson (Walwyn 79), Keefe (Allen 55), Thompson, Shaw, Eastwood, Clark, Blackwell, Wane, Paterson (Sheppard 90), Smith. Subs not used: Moffat and Abbott

Lowestoft Town: Reynolds, Poppy, Potter, Woodrow, Saunders, Plaskett (McGee 79), Godbold, Darren Cockrill (Dale Cockrill 46), Stock, Hough, King (Hunn 55). Subs not used: McKenna and Rix.

2009	**GLOSSOP NORTH END 0** ***(North West Co. Prem)***	**WHITLEY BAY 2** ***(Northern Division One)*** **Kerr, Chow**	**Att: 12,212 Ref: K Friend**

Glossop North End: Cooper, Young, Kay, Lugsden, Yates, Gorton, Bailey (Hind 57), Morris, Allen (Balfe 65), Hamilton (Bailey 72), Hodges. Subs not used: Whelan and Parker.

Whitley Bay: Burke, Taylor, Picton, McFarlane (Fawcett 60), Coulson, Ryan, Moore, Robson, Kerr, Chow (Robinson 73), Johnston (Bell 60). Subs not used: McLean and Reay.

All Finals at Wembley unless otherwise stated.

Wroxham's Paul Cook (stripes), tries to go around Whitley Bay's Leon Ryan at Wembley. Photo: Alan Coomes.

The same player, this time complete with head bandage, looks to control the ball under pressure from a Whitley Bay defender. Photo: Roger Turner.

WELSH CUP 2009-10

PRELIMINARY ROUND

AFC Llwydcoed 3 AFC Porth 1 *aet (Aug 15)*
Barmouth & Dyffryn United 2 Dyffryn Banw 0 *(Aug 15)*
Blaenau Ffestiniog Amateurs 0 **Glan Conwy** 3 *(Aug 15)*
Borras Park Albion 4 Rhos Aelwyd 1 *(Aug 15)*
Bow Street 0 **Aberbargoed Buds** 1 *(Aug 15)*
Brickfield Rangers 0 **Hawarden Rangers** 4 *(Aug 15)*
Cardiff Bay Harlequins 2 UWIC 0 *(Aug 15)*
Coedpoeth United (w/o) v Llanllyfni *(Aug 15)*
Corwen Amateurs 1 **Chirk AAA** 2 *(Aug 15)*
Cwmamman Utd 4 **Presteigne St And.** 5 *aet (Aug 15)*
Dolgellau AA 7 Llanfyllin Town 2 *(Aug 15)*
Garw SGBC 0 **Cwmbran Celtic** 4 *(Aug 15)*
Halkyn United 1 **Tywyn & Bryncrug** 2 *(Aug 15)*
Hay St Marys 1 Monmouth Town 1 *aet* (5-3p) *(Aug 14)*
Holywell Town 0 **Llanrug United** 5 *(Aug 15)*
Llandudno Junction 3 Castell Alun Colts 2 *(Aug 15)*
Llanwern 0 **South Gower** 5 *(Aug 15)*
Maesteg Pk 2 **Llantwit Fardre** 4 *aet (at Llantwit Fardre) (Aug 15)*
Newport YMCA 3 **Croesyceiliog** 5 *(Aug 15)*
Pwllheli 6 Nantlle Vale 0 *(Aug 15)*
Rhayader Town 0 **Newport Civil Service** 2 *(Aug 15)*
Seven Sisters 2 Briton Ferry Llansawel 0 *(Aug 15)*
Tredegar Town 3 **Pontyclun** 0 *(Aug 15) (Tredegar Town expelled)*
Troedyrhiw 3 Cwmbran Town 1 *(Aug 15)*

FIRST ROUND

Amlwch Town 2 **Penrhyncoch** 3 *(Sep 12)*
Barmouth & Dyffryn United 3 Buckley Town 2 *(Sep 12)*
Barry Town 1 **Ely Rangers** 5 *(Sep 12)*
Berriew 3 Mold Alexandra 1 *(Sep 12)*
Brymbo 1 **Llangefni Town** 6 *(Sep 12)*
Bryntirion Athletic 4 Cardiff Corinthians 2 *(Sep 12)*
Caerau Ely 2 Bettws 0 *(Sep 12)*
Cambrian/Clydach Vale BGC 4 Ammanford 0 *(Sep 12)*
Carno 2 **Conwy United** 3 *(Sep 12)*
Chirk AAA 1 **Gresford Athletic** 3 *(Sep 12)*
Coedpoeth United 2 Penparcau 0 *(Sep 12)*
Corus Steel 0 **Garden Village** 1 *(Sep 12)*
Croesyceiliog 1 Risca United 0 *(Sep 12)*
Cwmaman Institute 1 **Cwmbran Celtic** 7 *(Sep 12)*
Glan Conwy 2 Denbigh Town 1 *(Sep 12)*
Goytre United 3 Pentwyn Dynamos 1 *(Sep 12)*
Guilsfield 1 **Llangollen Town** 3 *(Sep 12)*
Hawarden Rangers 0 **Ruthin Town** 2 *(Sep 12)*
Hay St Marys 2 Dinas Powys 1 *aet (Sep 12)*
Lex XI 5 Dolgellau AA 3 *(Sep 12)*
Llanberis 1 **Flint Town United** 2 *(Sep 12)*
Llandudno Junction 3 Llanrhaedr 1 *(Sep 12)*
Llandudno Town 1 Bethesda Athletic 0 *(Sep 12)*
Llanfairpwll 2 Penycae 1 *(Sep 12)*
Llanrug United 4 Nefyn United 3 *(Sep 12)*
Llanrwst United 0 **Llangeinor** 2 *(Sep 12)*
Llansantffraid Village 3 Llay Welfare 1 *(Sep 12)*
Llantwit Fardre 0 **Aberbargoed Buds** 1 *(Sep 12)*
Newcastle Emlyn 1 **AFC Llwydcoed** 2 *(Sep 12)*
Overton Recreation 1 **Holyhead Hotspur** 2 *aet (Sep 12)*
Penrhiwceiber Rangers 3 Caerleon 1 *(Sep 12)*
Pontardawe Town 4 Presteigne St Andrews 1 *(Sep 12)*
Pontyclun 7 Goytre 2 *(Sep 12)*
Pontypridd Town 3 Newport Civil Service 0 *(Sep 12)*
Porthcawl Town 2 **Ton Pentre** 4 *(Sep 12)*
Pwllheli 2 Tywyn & Bryncrug 0 *aet (Sep 12)*
Rhydymwyn 2 Llandyrnog United 0 *(Sep 12)*
Seven Sisters 0 **Afan Lido** 7 *(Sep 12)*
South Gower 0 **Caldicot Town** 5 *(Sep 12)*
Treharris Athletic 3 **Cardiff Bay Harlequins** 4 *(Sep 12)*
Troedyrhiw 2 Abertillery Bluebirds 1 *(Sep 12)*
Venture Community 3 **Borras Pk Albion** 4 *aet (Sep 12)*
West End 6 **Taffs Well** 6 *aet* (2-4p) *(Sep 12)*

SECOND ROUND

Aberaman Athletic 3 Penrhiwceiber Rangers 2 *(Oct 3)*
Afan Lido 5 Croesyceiliog 1 *(Oct 3)*
Bangor City 4 Elements Cefn Druids 1 *(Oct 3)*
Borras Park Albion 1 **Bala Town** 8 *(at Bala) (Oct 3)*
Bridgend Town 2 Ton Pentre 0 *(Oct 3)*
Bryntirion Athletic 0 **Aberystwyth Town** 3 *(Oct 3)*
Caerau Ely 5 Hay St Marys 1 *(Oct 3)*
Cambrian & Clydach Vale BGC 3 Troedyrhiw 1 *(Oct 3)*
Cardiff Bay Harlequins 3 Aberbargoed Buds 2 *(Oct 3)*
Carmarthen Town 4 Pontypridd Town 1 *(Oct 3)*
Conwy United 0 **The New Saints** 2 *(Oct 3)*
Ely Rangers 3 AFC Lwydcoed 2 *(Oct 3)*
Flint Town United 7 Barmouth & Dyffryn Utd 1 *(Oct 3)*
Gap Connah's Quay 2 Pwllheli 0 *(Oct 3)*
Garden Village 2 **Caldicot Town** 6 *aet (Oct 3)*
Goytre United 0 **Pontardawe Town** 3 *(Oct 3)*
Gresford Athletic 2 **Llanrug United** 3 *(Oct 3)*
Holyhead Hotspur 1 Newtown 1 *aet* (4-3p) *(Oct 3)*
Lex XI 1 **Airbus UK Broughton** 3 *(Oct 3)*
Llandudno Town 3 Berriew 0 *aet (Oct 3)*
Llanfairpwll 1 **Rhyl** 3 *(Oct 3)*
Llangefni Town 1 **Llandudno Junction** 2 *(Oct 3)*
Llangeinor 2 Pontyclun 1 *aet (Oct 3)*
Llangollen Town 1 Glan Conwy 0 *(Oct 3)*
Llansantffraid Village 1 **Coedpoeth United** 3 *(Oct 3)*
Neath 2 **Llanelli** 2 *aet* (2-3p) *(Oct 3)*
Penrhyncoch 0 **Porthmadog** 1 *(Oct 3)*
Port Talbot Town 5 Cwmbran Celtic 0 *(Oct 3)*
Rhydymwyn 1 Caernarfon Town 0 *(Oct 3)*
Ruthin Town 1 **Caersws** 2 *(Oct 3)*
Taffs Well 0 **Haverfordwest County** 2 *(Oct 3)*
Welshpool Town 2 **Prestatyn Town** 3 *(Oct 3)*

THIRD ROUND

Aberaman Athletic 2 Ely Rangers 0 *(Oct 31)*
Bala Town 1 Llanrug United 0 *(Oct 31)*
Caerau Ely 1 **Afan Lido** 2 *(Oct 31)*
Caersws 4 Coedpoeth United 1 *(Oct 31)*
Caldicot Town 0 **Port Talbot Town** 3 *(Oct 31)*
Cambrian/Clydach VBGC 0 **The New Saints** 2 *(Oct 31)*
Flint Town United 0 **Bangor City** 1 *(Oct 31)*

Gap Connah's Quay 3 Airbus Broughton 2 *aet (Oct 31)*
Haverfordwest County 1 **Aberystwyth Town** 2 *(Oct 31)*
Llanelli 3 Carmarthen Town 1 *(Oct 31)*
Llangeinor 1 **Holyhead Hotspur** 6 *(Oct 31)*
Llangollen Town 1 **Llandudno Junction** 3 *(Oct 31)*
Pontardawe Town 2 Llandudno Town 0 *(Oct 31)*
Porthmadog 3 Rhydymwyn 1 *(Oct 31)*
Prestatyn Town 3 Cardiff Bay Harlequins 0 *(Oct 31)*
Rhyl 4 Bridgend Town 2 *(Oct 31)*

FOURTH ROUND

Aberystwyth Town 0 **Port Talbot Town** 2 *(Jan 30)*
Afan Lido 2 Gap Connah's Quay 1 *(Jan 30)*
Bala Town 2 Caersws 0 *(Jan 30)*
Bangor City 3 Aberaman Athletic 1 *(Jan 30)*
Llandudno Junction 0 **The New Saints** 6 *(Jan 30)*
Llanelli 4 Holyhead Hotspur 0 *(Jan 30)*
Prestatyn Town 1 Porthmadog 0 *(Jan 30)*
Rhyl 7 Pontardawe Town 0 *(Jan 30)*

QUARTER-FINALS

Bala Town 2 Afan Lido 0 *(Feb 27)*
Bangor City 2 Llanelli 0 *(Feb 27)*
Prestatyn Town 4 Rhyl 4 *aet* (5-3p) *(Feb 27)*
The New Saints 2 **Pt Talbot Town** 2 *aet* (3-4p) *(Feb 27)*

SEMI-FINALS

Bangor City 2 Prestatyn Town 0 *(at Newtown) (Apr 11)*
Port Talbot Town 1 Bala T. 0 *(at Aberystwyth) (Apr 10)*

FINAL

(May 1st at Llanelli Scarlets RFC)

Bangor City 3 Port Talbot Town 2

F.A.W TROPHY 2009-10

FIRST ROUND

AFC Whitchurch 0 **Rhydyfelin** 4 *(Aug 28)*
Bow Street (w/o) v Rogerstone Welfare *(Aug 28)*
FC Brunswick 1 **Hay St Marys** 8 *(Aug 28)*
Llandyrnog United 4 Llanuwchllyn 0 *(Aug 28)*
Overton Recreation 4 Tywyn & Bryncrug 0 *(Aug 28)*
Panteg 5 Graig 1 *(Aug 28)*
Trelewis Welfare 4 Newbridge-on-Wye 1 *(Aug 28)*
Waterloo Rovers 14 Glyn Ceiriog 2 *(Aug 28)*
Winch Wen 3 Splott Albion 0 *(Aug 28)*

SECOND ROUND

Baglan Dragons 1 **Cadoxton Barry** 2 *(Sep 19)*
Blaenavon Blues 4 Llandrindod Wells 1 *(Sep 19)*
Bodedern Athletic (w/o) v Llanfyllin Town *(Sep 19)*
Borras Park Albion 1 **Venture Community** 3 *(Sep 19)*
Carno 0 **Overton Recreation** 1 *(Sep 19)*
Clydach Wasps 2 Carnetown BGC 0 *(Sep 19)*
Cogan Coronation 3 Kenfig Hill 0 *(Sep 19)*
Glan Conwy 6 Brickfield Rangers 3 *(Sep 19)*
Hay St Marys 3 Nelson Cavaliers 0 *(Sep 19)*
Johnstown Youth 0 **Rhydymwyn** 2 *(Sep 19)*
Llanberis 3 Brymbo 2 *aet (Sep 19)*
Llandudno Junction 3 Llansantffraid Village 1 *(Sep 19)*
Llandyrnog United 1 **Corwen Amateurs** 2 *(Sep 19)*
Llanidloes Town 1 **Llanystumdwy** 1 *aet* (5-6p) *(Sep 19)*
Llanrhaedr 2 Coedpoeth United 1 *(Sep 19)*
Llanrug United 1 **Pwllheli** 2 *(Sep 19)*
Llanrwst United 3 Greenfield 1 *(Sep 19)*
Llay Welfare 0 **Rhos Aelwyd** 3 *(Sep 19)*
Mardy 2 **Llanharry** 4 *(Sep 19)*
Nefyn United 4 **Waterloo Rovers** 5 *(Sep 19)*
Panteg 0 **Sully Sports** 2 *(Sep 19)*
Penmaenmawr Phoenix 6 Penycae 3 *(Sep 19)*
Presteigne St Andrews 2 Bonymaen Colts 1 *(Sep 19)*
Rhayader Town 2 **Bow Street** 2 *aet* (0-3p) *(Sep 19)*
South Gower 4 Trefelin BGC 2 *(Sep 19)*
STM Sports 9 AFC Bargoed Redz 1 *(Sep 19)*
Temple Bar 1 **Ragged School** 3 *(Sep 19)*
Ton & Gelli Boys Club 5 Pentwynmawr Ath. 2 *(Sep 19)*
Trelewis Welfare 3 **Maltsters Sports** 4 *(Sep 19)*
Turberville Arms 0 **Rhydyfelin** 3 *(Sep 19)*
Winch Wen 5 Abercarn United 4 *(Sep 19)*
Y Felinheli 2 **Chirk AAA** 4 *(Sep 19)*

THIRD ROUND

Blaenavon Blues 3 Cadoxton Barry 2 *(Oct 17)*
Bodedern Athletic 1 **Llandudno Junction** 5 *(Oct 17)*
Clydach Wasps 5 Maltsters Sports 0 *(Oct 17)*
Cogan Coronation 2 **Ragged School** 3 *aet (Oct 17)*
Glan Conwy 2 Corwen Amateurs 1 *aet (Oct 17)*
Llanharry 6 Bow Street 2 *(Oct 17)*
Llanrhaedr 2 **Rhos Aelwyd** 3 *(Oct 17)*
Llanystumdwy 1 **Llanberis** 2 *(Oct 17)*
Overton Recreation 3 Chirk AAA 1 *(Oct 17)*
Penmaenmawr Phoenix 2 Pwllheli 1 *(Oct 17)*
Presteigne St Andrews 2 **Hay St Marys** 3 *aet (Oct 17)*
Rhydyfelin 0 **South Gower** 1 *(Oct 17)*
Rhydymwyn 1 Llanrwst United 1 *aet* (4-2p) *(Oct 17)*
Sully Sports 3 STM Sports 1 *(Oct 17)*
Venture Community 6 Waterloo Rovers 2 *(Oct 17)*
Winch Wen 2 **Ton & Gelli Boys Club** 4 *(Oct 17)*

FOURTH ROUND

Blaenavon Blues 1 **Ton & Gelli Boys Club** 2 *aet (Dec 5)*
Clydach Wasps 4 Hay St Marys 2 *(Nov 28)*
Llanberis 2 Rhydymwyn 2 *aet* (3-1p) *(Nov 28)*
Llandudno Junction 1 **Glan Conwy** 3 *(Nov 28)*
Llanharry 2 South Gower 2 *aet* (8-7p) *(Nov 21)*
Overton Recreation 1 **Venture Community** 3 *(Nov 21)*
Ragged School 0 **Sully Sports** 3 *(Nov 28)*
Rhos Aelwyd 5 Penmaenmawr Phoenix 3 *(Nov 21)*

QUARTER-FINALS

Llanharry 1 **Clydach Wasps** 2 *aet (Feb 13)*
Rhos Aelwyd 0 **Glan Conwy** 0 *aet* (2-4p) *(Feb 13)*
Ton & Gelli Boys Club 0 **Llanberis** 2 *(Feb 13)*
Venture Community 1 Sully Sports 0 *(Feb 13)*

SEMI-FINALS

Llanberis 0 **Glan Conwy** 2 *(at Bangor City) (Mar 13)*
Venture 1 **Clydach Wasps** 4 *(at Rhayader) (Mar 13)*

FINAL

(April 17th at Aberystwyth Town)

Glan Conwy 5 Clydach Wasps 1

PRELIMINARY ROUND

1	Seaham Red Star	v Whitley Bay	8-0	22
2	Lancaster City	v Salford City	4-0	69
3	Nantwich Town	v Chester City	0-1	159
4	Curzon Ashton	v Woodley Sports	0-1	80
5	Fleetwood Town	v Wrexham	1-2	221
6	Southport	v Colne	6-1	86
7	Cammell Laird	v Northwich Victoria	2-0	83
8	Formby	v Prescot Cables	2-1	
9	Altrincham	v Daisy Hill	7-1	120
10	Nostell MW	v Hemsworth MW	3-2	62
11	Pontefract Collieries	v Hallam	1-3	47
12	Yorkshire Amateur	v Glasshoughton Welfare	3-4	44
13	Ossett Albion	v Goole	0-6	
14	North Ferriby United	v Garforth Town	3-0	61
15	Farsley Celtic	v Eccleshill United	6-0	70
16	Barwell	v Boston United	1-3	74
17	St Andrews	v Matlock Town	0-6	27
18	Blaby & Whetstone Ath.	v Grantham Town	4-2	44
19	Hinckley United	v Deeping Rangers	1-0	48
20	Mansfield Town	v Ilkeston Town		
	(walkover for Mansfield Town – Ilkeston Town withdrawn)			
21	Stamford	v Lincoln United	1-4	39
22	Bedworth United	v Chasetown	5-3	64
23	Boldmere St Michaels	v Willenhall Town	3-0	20
24	Kidderminster Harriers	v Coventry Sphinx	4-2	96
25	Atherstone Town	v Sutton Coldfield Town	2-1	90
26	Rugby Town	v Stratford Town	2-1	
27	Redditch United	v Stone Dominoes	0-1	30
28	Stourbridge	v Newcastle Town	5-0	72
29	Lye Town	v Pegasus Juniors	1-0	
30	Rocester	v Bromyard Town	4-0	35
31	Ellesmere Rangers	v Eccleshall	7-1	34
32	Nuneaton Griff	v Stafford Rangers	4-3*	35
33	Solihull Moors	v Worcester City		
	(walkover for Solihull Moors – Worcester City withdrew)			
34	Nuneaton Town	v Malvern Town	3-4*	35
35	Dosthill Colts	v AFC Telford United	1-2	34
	(tie awarded to Dosthill Colts – AFC Telford United expelled)			
36	Tipton Town	v Dudley Town	2-2*	
	(Tipton Town won 5-4 on penalties)			
37	Gornal Athletic	v Pershore Town	2-1	43
38	Histon	v Long Melford	8-2	53
39	Stowmarket Town	v Ely City (17/9)	3-0	37
	(10/9, tie abandoned after 25 mins due to serious injury to player, 0-0)			
40	Newmarket Town	v Kirkley & Pakefield	0-3	45
41	Thetford Town	v Dereham Town	0-3	60
42	Leiston	v Wroxham	5-2	30
43	Cambridge United	v Diss Town	12-0	99
44	Hadleigh United	v Great Yarmouth Town	2-5	107
45	Fakenham Town	v Cornard United	1-2	35
46	March Town United	v Kings Lynn	1-6	80
47	Ipswich Wanderers	v Lowestoft Town	1-5	53
48	Huntingdon Town	v Stotfold	2-1	70
49	Rushden & Diamonds	v Stewarts & Lloyds	9-0	78
50	Luton Town	v Northampton Spencer	6-0	412
51	Cranfield United	v Yaxley	5-1*	25
52	Cogenhoe United	v AFC Kempston Rovers	2-3	40
53	St Ives Town	v Rothwell Town	0-3	65
54	Corby Town	v Raunds Town	0-2	120
55	Sileby Rangers	v Rothwell Corinthians	4-1	43
56	Bugbrooke St Michaels	v Wellingborough Town	1-4	138
57	Halstead Town	v Witham Town	2-1	
58	FC Clacton	v Braintree Town	1-2*	70
59	Chelmsford City	v Romford	5-0	
60	Bishop's Stortford	v Hoddesdon Town	4-1	76
61	St Margaretsbury	v Bowers & Pitsea	3-0	39
62	Brightlingsea Regent	v Thurrock		
	(walkover for Thurrock – Brightlingsea Regent withdrew)			
63	Boreham Wood	v Billericay Town	3-1	54
64	Brentwood Town	v London Colney	1-2	54
65	Grays Athletic	v Hemel Hempstead Town	4-2	113
66	AFC Hornchurch	v Stevenage Borough	3-0	78
67	Southend Manor	v St Albans City	1-1*	
	(St Albans City won 6-5 on penalties)			
68	Ilford	v Harpenden Town	2-0	72
69	Corinthian Casuals	v Hillingdon Borough	2-1	90
70	Tokygnton Manor	v Clapton	1-1*	30
	(Clapton won 5-4 on penalties)			
	(at Viking Sports Ground,Perivale, Greenford)			
71	Staines Town	v Harefield United	2-1	81
72	Thamesmead Town	v Haringey Borough	2-0	34
73	Hayes & Yeading United	v Welling United	4-0	71
74	AFC Wimbledon	v Kentish Town	2-1	87
75	Hampton & Richmond B.	v Leyton		
	(walkover for Hampton & Richmond Borough – Leyton withdrew)			
76	Kingsbury London Tigers	v Ashford Town (Middx)	0-11	10
77	Croydon Athletic	v Redbridge	2-0	
78	Hanwell Town	v North Greenford United	2-3	41
79	Haywards Heath Town	v Croydon	0-4	
	(at Croydon FC)			
80	Oakwood	v Whyteleafe	1-2	52
81	St Francis Rangers	v Eastbourne Borough	1-6	77
	(at Eastbourne Borough FC)			
82	Lewes	v Folkestone Invicta	4-0	41
83	Margate	v Merstham	1-0	48
84	Eastbourne Town	v Redhill	5-3	34
85	Three Bridges	v Dartford	2-6	19
86	Maidstone United	v Crawley Down	5-1	50
87	Chatham Town	v South Park	6-0	106
88	Hastings United	v Deal Town	4-1	59
89	Ramsgate	v VCD Athletic	4-3	62
90	Tonbridge Angels	v Chipstead	1-2	72
91	Carshalton Athletic	v Burgess Hill Town	8-0	
92	Walton & Hersham	v Lancing	5-2	49
93	Horsham	v Tooting & Mitcham Utd	1-4	95
94	Sutton United	v Epsom & Ewell	5-0	82
95	Colliers Wood United	v Chichester City	6-0	60
96	Wick	v Worthing United	1-2	103
97	Worthing	v Woking	1-4	
98	Thatcham Town	v Fleet Town	4-1	71
99	Slough Town	v Thame United	3-3*	84
	(Slough Town won 4-2 on penalties)			
100	Wokingham Town & Em.	v Didcot Town		
	(walkover for Didcot Town – Wokingham Town & Emmbrook expelled)			
101	Binfield	v Basingstoke Town	0-3	40
102	Alton Town	v Oxford United	0-6	111
103	Farnborough	v Aylesbury United		
	(walkover for Farnborough – Aylesbury United withdrew)			
104	Maidenhead United	v Newport Pagnell Town	4-0	16
105	Windsor & Eton	v Abingdon United	4-5	45
106	Chesham United	v Chalfont St Peter	4-3	40
107	Cove	v Flackwell Heath	1-3*	
108	Buckingham Town	v Banbury United	3-0	64
109	Winchester City	v Salisbury City	0-5	
	(at Salisbury City FC)			
110	Moneyfields	v Bournemouth	4-2	
111	Dorchester Town	v Eastleigh	1-3	81
112	Christchurch	v AFC Totton	3-2	42
113	Gosport Borough	v VT	1-2	58
114	Bishop's Cleeve	v Almondsbury UWE	2-1	62
115	Weston Super Mare	v Tiverton Town	4-1	101
116	Wootton Bassett Town	v Chard Town	1-2	58
117	Portishead Town	v Clevedon Town	1-2	50
118	Elmore	v Bridgwater Town		
	(walkover for Elmore – Bridgwater Town withdrawn)			
119	Yate Town	v Mangotsfield United	2-1	

FIRST QUALIFYING ROUND

1	Chester-Le-Street Town	v Birtley Town		
	(walkover for Chester-Le-Street Town – Birtley Town withdrew)			
2	Scarborough Town	v Bedlington Terriers	3-1	

No.	Home		Away	Score	Att.
3	Ryton	v	Prudhoe Town	2-3	56
4	Dunston UTS	v	Seaham Red Star	2-1	89
5	Sunderland RCA	v	Gateshead	2-1	87
6	Guisborough Town	v	York City	1-5	103
7	Ashton Town	v	Vauxhall Motors	1-4	41
8	Marine	v	Chester City	0-1	
9	Wrexham	v	Leigh Genesis	12-0	106
10	Woodley Sports	v	Southport	2-3	138
11	Altrincham	v	Cammell Laird	4-2	106
12	Workington	v	Bootle	1-1*	69
	(Workington won 6-5 on penalties)				
13	Stalybridge Celtic	v	Ashville	7-2	30
14	Warrington Town	v	Lancaster City		
	(walkover for Lancaster City – Warrington Town withdrew)				
15	Burscough	v	Congleton Town	0-2*	60
16	Ashton Athletic	v	Formby	0-5	56
17	Glasshoughton Welfare	v	Sheffield	2-2*	
	(Glasshoughton Welfare won 4-3 on penalties)				
18	Liversedge	v	Ossett Town	4-3*	33
19	Staveley MW	v	Wakefield	3-1	40
20	Nostell MW	v	Stocksbridge Park Steels	1-5	57
21	Hallam	v	FC Halifax Town	2-1	30
22	Worksop Town	v	Goole	0-2	85
	(at Goole FC)				
23	North Ferriby United	v	Farsley Celtic	2-3	67
24	Bradford (Park Avenue)	v	Thackley	3-4	
25	Carlton Town	v	Holwell Sports	5-2*	83
26	Teversal	v	Matlock Town	1-5	
27	Hinckley United	v	Arnold Town	1-2*	61
28	Blaby & Whetstone Ath.	v	Mansfield Town	0-4	73
29	Gresley	v	Lincoln United	3-1	33
30	Oadby Town	v	Rainworth MW	2-0	46
31	New Mills	v	Long Eaton United	1-2	48
32	Loughborough Dynamo	v	Boston United	3-1	58
33	Retford United	v	Mickleover Sports	0-3	31
34	Holbeach United	v	Glossop North End		
	(walkover for Glossop North End – Holbeach United withdrew)				
35	Stone Dominoes	v	Dosthill Colts	0-2*	51
36	Gornal Athletic	v	Malvern Town	2-4	
37	Hednesford Town	v	Bromsgrove Rovers	2-4	72
38	Nuneaton Griff	v	Bewdley Town	3-0	54
39	Tipton Town	v	Stourbridge	1-5	61
40	Pelsall Villa	v	Highgate United	0-3	43
41	Lye Town	v	Solihull Moors	1-2	75
42	Kidderminster Harriers	v	Wednesfield	2-3	79
43	Boldmere St Michaels	v	Atherstone Town	2-5	47
44	Rocester	v	Bedworth United	5-3	20
45	Stourport Swifts	v	Ellesmere Rangers	1-2	
46	Wellington	v	Rugby Town	1-0	39
47	Kirkley & Pakefield	v	Great Yarmouth Town	2-2*	
	(Kirkley & Pakefield won 5-4 on penalties)				
48	Felixstowe & Walton Utd	v	Needham Market	1-2*	50
49	Cornard United	v	Woodbridge Town	2-2*	35
	(Cornard United won 4-2 on penalties)				
50	Histon	v	Kings Lynn	3-2	68
51	Stowmarket Town	v	Bury Town	2-3	90
52	Lowestoft Town	v	Dereham Town	1-2	81
53	Leiston	v	Cambridge United	0-6	50
54	Soham Town Rangers	v	Walsham Le Willows	4-3*	95
55	Luton Town	v	Raunds Town	7-1	164
56	Daventry Town	v	FCV Reds	3-0	41
57	Sileby Rangers	v	Thrapston Town	3-0	28
58	Huntingdon Town	v	Wellingborough Town	2-1	62
59	Rushden & Diamonds	v	Leighton Town	5-0	93
60	Arlesey Town	v	Cranfield United	2-2*	
	(Arlesey Town won 5-4 on penalties)				
61	AFC Kempston Rovers	v	Rothwell Town	1-2	61
62	Dunstable Town	v	Kettering Town	4-1	65
63	Thurrock	v	Burnham Ramblers	9-1	
64	Harlow Town	v	Aveley	0-10	54
65	Hullbridge Sports	v	Leverstock Green	1-6	32
66	St Albans City	v	Hitchin Town	3-1	81
67	East Thurrock United	v	Boreham Wood	2-3	112
68	Colney Heath	v	Tilbury	2-5	40
69	London Colney	v	Ilford	1-0*	
70	Chelmsford City	v	Waltham Abbey	1-1*	108
71	Braintree Town	v	Bishop's Stortford	1-4	62
72	Grays Athletic	v	Halstead Town	2-2*	
73	Royston Town	v	AFC Hornchurch	1-5	111
74	Cheshunt	v	St Margaretsbury	0-6	127
75	Staines Town	v	Hampton & Richmond B.	5-0	90
76	Enfield Town	v	Northwood	2-1	67
77	Ashford Town (Middx)	v	Wealdstone	1-1*	74
78	Corinthian Casuals	v	Croydon Athletic	0-2	61
79	Clapton	v	Wingate & Finchley	2-0	36
80	North Greenford United	v	Thamesmead Town	1-2	47
81	Hayes & Yeading United	v	AFC Wimbledon	0-3	113
82	Dulwich Hamlet	v	Uxbridge	3-0	68
83	Eastbourne Town	v	Bromley	0-2	36
84	Ebbsfleet United	v	Ashford Town	4-0	104
85	Faversham Town	v	Peacehaven & Telscombe	4-3	78
86	Ramsgate	v	East Grinstead Town	0-4	61
87	Dover Athletic	v	Dartford	3-5*	143
88	Crawley Town	v	Whitstable Town	2-3*	114
89	Maidstone United	v	Chipstead	3-0	80
90	Eastbourne Borough	v	Horley Town	4-1	84
91	Whyteleafe	v	Lewes	0-4	44
92	Chatham Town	v	Croydon	1-0	77
93	Saltdean United	v	Hastings United	1-4	56
94	Lingfield	v	Margate	0-1	57
	(at Margate FC)				
95	Tooting & Mitcham United	v	Woking	0-5	74
96	Westfield	v	Mile Oak	3-0	56
97	Camberley Town	v	Shoreham	2-3	
98	Carshalton Athletic	v	Chertsey Town	3-2*	
99	Walton & Hersham	v	Molesey	2-3	79
100	Cobham	v	Sutton United	1-2	21
101	Colliers Wood United	v	Worthing United	3-2	53
102	Kingstonian	v	Pagham	2-0	50
103	Farnborough	v	Bracknell Town	3-0	78
104	Marlow	v	Beaconsfield SYCOB	4-3	68
105	Reading Town	v	Oxford City	0-1	41
106	Buckingham Town	v	Kidlington	4-4*	52
	(Buckingham Town won 4-3 on penalties)				
107	Burnham	v	Maidenhead United	0-2	135
108	Henley Town	v	Sandhurst Town		
109	Abingdon United	v	AFC Wallingford	0-7	35
110	Didcot Town	v	Andover	2-1	47
111	Slough Town	v	Basingstoke Town	0-2	86
112	Chesham United	v	Thatcham Town	2-4	51
113	Witney United	v	Flackwell Heath	3-2	30
114	Carterton	v	Oxford United		
	(walkover for Oxford United – Carterton withdrawn)				
115	Eastleigh	v	Moneyfields	4-1	91
116	Weymouth	v	Havant & Waterlooville	0-1	75
117	Poole Town	v	Petersfield Town	1-0	27
118	Christchurch	v	Salisbury City	3-3*	84
	(Christchurch won 5-4 on penalties)				
119	Shaftesbury	v	VT		
120	Sherborne Town	v	Bashley		
	(walkover for Sherborne Town – Bashley withdrew)				
121	Chard Town	v	Bitton	2-3	75
122	Paulton Rovers	v	Radstock Town	3-5	120
	(tie awarded to Paulton Rovers – Radstock Town expelled)				
123	Cheltenham Saracens	v	Newport County	0-5	21
124	Bishop's Cleeve	v	Cirencester Town	0-3	71
125	Weston Super Mare	v	Bath City	1-0	104
126	Forest Green Rovers	v	Clevedon Town	6-0	102
127	Elmore	v	Yate Town	1-5	
128	Gloucester City	v	Merthyr Tydfil	5-1	55

SECOND QUALIFYING ROUND

1	Chester-Le-Street Town	v York City	1-2	120
2	Dunston UTS	v Sunderland RCA	1-0	95
3	Prudhoe Town	v Scarborough Town	0-4	60
4	Formby	v Southport	0-3	125
5	Vauxhall Motors	v Altrincham	1-2	79
6	Lancaster City	v Chester City	0-1	110
7	Wrexham	v Stalybridge Celtic	4-5aet	103
8	Congleton Town	v Workington	1-0	87
9	Goole	v Farsley Celtic	0-5	115
10	Hallam	v Glasshoughton Welfare	3-0	25
11	Stocksbridge PS	v Staveley MW	2-3	96
12	Liversedge	v Thackley	0-7	30
13	Glossop North End	v Mansfield Town	2-7	100
14	Carlton Town	v Gresley	6-0	54
15	Loughborough Dynamo	v Matlock Town	4-1	63
16	Arnold Town	v Long Eaton United	3-1	120
17	Mickleover Sports	v Oadby Town	3-2	70
18	Bromsgrove Rovers	v Malvern Town	3-5aet	35
19	Atherstone Town	v Ellesmere Rangers	4-2aet	80
20	Highgate United	v Wellington	10-2	34
21	Nuneaton Griff	v Dosthill Colts	0-2	74
22	Solihull Moors	v Stourbridge	2-1	49
23	Wednesfield	v Rocester	2-5	35
24	Dereham Town	v Cambridge United	0-4	103
25	Bury Town	v Kirkley & Pakefield	5-2	51
26	Histon	v Cornard United	4-1	65
	(at Cornard United FC) (6/10, tie abandoned after 45 mins due to floodlight fire, 2-0)			
27	Needham Market	v Soham Town Rangers	5-2	67
28	Arlesey Town	v Rothwell Town	1-7	42
29	Rushden & Diamonds	v Luton Town	2-0	207
30	Huntingdon Town	v Sileby Rangers	2-1aet	54
31	Daventry Town	v Dunstable Town	0-1	43
32	Leverstock Green	v Aveley	3-6aet	60
33	Bishop's Stortford	v AFC Hornchurch	2-0	107
34	Tilbury	v St Margaretsbury	4-1	31
35	St Albans City	v Thurrock	2-1	72
36	London Colney	v Boreham Wood	1-2	
37	Chelmsford City	v Halstead Town	3-1	177
38	Thamesmead Town	v AFC Wimbledon	1-3	115
39	Clapton	v Staines Town	0-0aet	38
	(Clapton won 4-2 on penalties)			
40	Croydon Athletic	v Ashford Town (Middx)	0-1	34
41	Enfield Town	v Dulwich Hamlet	1-4	61
42	Faversham Town	v Ebbsfleet United	2-5	159
43	Lewes	v Hastings United	3-0	76
44	Whitstable Town	v Margate	0-1	65
45	East Grinstead Town	v Bromley	1-3	90
46	Maidstone United	v Dartford	3-2	91
47	Eastbourne Borough	v Chatham Town	3-4	111
48	Sutton United	v Colliers Wood United	3-1aet	74
49	Molesey	v Woking	1-4	72
50	Carshalton Athletic	v Shoreham	3-4	
51	Westfield	v Kingstonian	1-3	46
52	Oxford City	v Marlow	2-3	90
53	Basingstoke Town	v Witney United	1-0	95
54	Henley Town	v Oxford United	0-1	86
55	Buckingham Town	v Farnborough	2-2aet	71
	(Farnborough won 3-1 on penalties)			
56	AFC Wallingford	v Maidenhead United	2-1	47
57	Didcot Town	v Thatcham Town	0-3	81
58	Eastleigh	v Sherborne Town	2-0	73
59	Christchurch	v VT	2-3	90
60	Poole Town	v Havant & Waterlooville	0-1	58
61	Forest Green Rovers	v Yate Town	7-2	75
62	Weston Super Mare	v Bitton	1-5	84
63	Cirencester Town	v Newport County	0-1	68
64	Paulton Rovers	v Gloucester City	1-7	89

THIRD QUALIFYING ROUND

1	Southport	v Hallam	8-0	90
2	Stalybridge Celtic	v Altrincham	3-2	146
3	Thackley	v Chester City	0-4	85
4	Congleton Town	v Dunston UTS	3-2	125
5	Farsley Celtic	v Staveley MW	5-3	75
6	York City	v Scarborough Town	3-1	393
7	Rocester	v Rushden & Diamonds	0-5	111
8	Loughborough Dynamo	v Mansfield Town	1-3	85
9	Mickleover Sports	v Malvern Town	3-4	65
10	Histon	v Needham Market	6-1	80
11	Bury Town	v Huntingdon Town	3-0	62
12	Dosthill Colts	v Atherstone Town	0-2	157
13	Rothwell Town	v Cambridge United	0-1	111
14	Highgate United	v Arnold Town	3-0	63
15	Carlton Town	v Solihull Moors	5-1	49
16	Boreham Wood	v Dunstable Town	1-2	126
17	Bishop's Stortford	v Clapton	2-1	90
18	Aveley	v St Albans City	2-5*	86
19	Dulwich Hamlet	v Chelmsford City	4-1	116
20	Tilbury	v AFC Wimbledon	0-2	55
21	Shoreham	v Marlow	1-4	71
22	Sutton United	v Margate	2-1	85
23	Chatham Town	v Bromley	0-3	146
24	Kingstonian	v Ebbsfleet United	0-3	83
	(at Raynes Park Vale FC)			
25	Ashford Town (Middx)	v Woking	2-2*	70
	(Woking won 5-4 on penalties)			
26	Lewes	v Maidstone United	2-3	75
27	Bitton	v VT	1-3	53
28	Newport County	v Oxford United	3-4	126
29	Forest Green Rovers	v AFC Wallingford	1-0	88
30	Basingstoke Town	v Havant & Waterlooville	2-1	118
31	Gloucester City	v Thatcham Town	4-2*	78
32	Farnborough	v Eastleigh	2-0	115

FIRST ROUND PROPER

1	Macclesfield Town	v Bury	2-0	160
2	Hartlepool United	v Lincoln City	3-1*	95
3	Oldham Athletic	v Stalybridge Celtic	4-1	279
4	Darlington	v Huddersfield Town	1-2*	
5	Bradford City	v Southport	3-1	184
6	Accrington Stanley	v Carlisle United	1-1*	103
	(at Carlisle United FC) (Carlisle United won 9-8 on penalties)			
7	Grimsby Town	v York City	1-2	
8	Congleton Town	v Rochdale	0-3	201
9	Leeds United	v Crewe Alexandra	0-1	241
10	Tranmere Rovers	v Farsley Celtic	3-0	271
11	Chester City	v Morecambe	0-4	87
12	Rotherham United	v Stockport County	3-3*	144
	(Stockport County won 4-3 on penalties)			
13	Bury Town	v Walsall	3-2	141
14	Rushden & Diamonds	v Northampton Town	1-2*	432
15	Carlton Town	v Burton Albion	2-1	108
16	Histon	v Cambridge United	0-4	313
17	Chesterfield	v Mansfield Town	4-1	341
18	Atherstone Town	v Highgate United	2-0	90
19	Shrewsbury Town	v Port Vale	2-1	
20	Malvern Town	v Notts County	0-1*	140
21	Milton Keynes Dons	v Dunstable Town	2-1	609
22	Maidstone United	v Wycombe Wanderers	3-5	246
23	Barnet	v Brighton & Hove Albion	0-4	352
24	Woking	v Dagenham & Redbridge	3-1	187
25	AFC Wimbledon	v Sutton United	2-1*	209
26	Charlton Athletic	v Gillingham	3-0	846
27	Leyton Orient	v Bromley	2-1	196
28	St Albans City	v Colchester United	1-0	133
29	Millwall	v Southend United	3-1	352
30	Bishop's Stortford	v Marlow	7-1	121
31	Ebbsfleet United	v Brentford	2-1*	180

32	Dulwich Hamlet	v Norwich City	1-1*	112
	(Norwich City won 4-2 on penalties)			
33	Aldershot Town	v Southampton	0-4	179
34	Forest Green Rovers	v Farnborough	1-2	96
35	Bristol Rovers	v AFC Bournemouth	1-3	238
36	VT	v Torquay United	2-3*	138
37	Basingstoke Town	v Hereford United	3-4	138
38	Oxford United	v Gloucester City	5-2	135
	(at Oxford City FC)			
39	Exeter City	v Cheltenham Town	0-4	461
40	Swindon Town	v Yeovil Town	6-0	223

SECOND ROUND PROPER

1	Bradford City	v Crewe Alexandra	1-2*	
	(at Crewe Alexandra FC)			
2	Stockport County	v Carlton Town	2-0	116
	(at Carlton Town FC)			
3	Oldham Athletic	v Rochdale	3-5	312
4	Notts County	v Hartlepool United	0-2	341
5	Northampton Town	v Chesterfield	2-1	203
6	Shrewsbury Town	v Morecambe	5-2	
7	York City	v Carlisle United	1-2	264
8	Huddersfield Town	v Atherstone Town	5-0	189
9	Bury Town	v Macclesfield Town	1-1*	258
	(Bury Town won 4-3 on penalties)			
10	Tranmere Rovers	v Cambridge United	3-1	242
11	Millwall	v Oxford United	1-0	
12	Southampton	v Hereford United	6-0	345
13	Cheltenham Town	v Farnborough	3-2	213
14	Swindon Town	v Leyton Orient	1-2*	337
15	Milton Keynes Dons	v Bishop's Stortford	2-1	317
16	Charlton Athletic	v Woking	3-1	553
17	AFC Wimbledon	v AFC Bournemouth	0-5	210
18	Brighton & Hove Albion	v Ebbsfleet United	2-0	94
19	St Albans City	v Wycombe Wanderers	2-2*	217
	(Wycombe Wanderers won 4-2 on penalties)			
20	Torquay United	v Norwich City	1-0	546

THIRD ROUND PROPER

1	Manchester United	v Birmingham City	2-0	635
2	Derby County	v Peterborough United	6-1	303
3	Middlesbrough	v Everton	0-1*	100
4	Wigan Athletic	v Tottenham Hotspur	0-1	721
5	Cheltenham Town	v Reading	1-2*	310
6	Nottingham Forest	v Bury Town	5-2	384
7	Milton Keynes Dons	v Leyton Orient	1-3	240
8	Shrewsbury Town	v Hull City	1-2	245
9	Watford	v Wycombe Wanderers	3-0	686
10	Liverpool	v Wolverhampton W.	2-0	1141
11	Hartlepool United	v Sheffield United	2-1	143
12	Crystal Palace	v Bristol City	3-2*	567
13	Stockport County	v Fulham	0-3	101
	(at Hyde United FC)			
14	Preston North End	v Manchester City	2-1	590
15	Cardiff City	v Barnsley	1-2	475
16	Torquay United	v Millwall	1-3	564
17	Arsenal	v Crewe Alexandra	3-3*	335
	(Arsenal won 5-4 on penalties) (at Barnet FC)			
18	Tranmere Rovers	v Ipswich Town	0-2	247
19	Scunthorpe United	v Burnley	1-4	273
20	Plymouth Argyle	v West Ham United	0-1*	1500
21	Portsmouth	v Huddersfield Town	1-0	350
22	Northampton Town	v Brighton & Hove Albion	1-3	174
23	Sheffield Wednesday	v Sunderland	2-7	190
24	Aston Villa	v Rochdale	4-0	723
25	Carlisle United	v Stoke City	0-1	204
26	Swansea City	v West Bromwich Albion	0-3	139
27	Coventry City	v Leicester City	2-3	356
28	Bolton Wanderers	v AFC Bournemouth	3-1	530
29	Blackburn Rovers	v Blackpool	3-0	452
30	Charlton Athletic	v Chelsea	1-2	1033
31	Doncaster Rovers	v Newcastle United	0-3*	525
32	Queens Park Rangers	v Southampton	3-1	414

FOURTH ROUND PROPER

1	Stoke City	v Hull City	1-2	250
2	West Ham United	v Queens Park Rangers	3-0	972
3	Millwall	v Barnsley	5-4*	314
4	Blackburn Rovers	v Leyton Orient	1-0	561
5	Bolton Wanderers	v Fulham	2-2*	492
	(Fulham won 5-3 on penalties)			
6	Reading	v Newcastle United	1-3	192
7	Brighton & Hove Albion	v Everton	0-2	915
8	Tottenham Hotspur	v Portsmouth	0-1	551
9	Crystal Palace	v Derby County	2-0	637
10	Leicester City	v Liverpool	1-5	1881
11	West Bromwich Albion	v Aston Villa	0-2	515
12	Burnley	v Manchester United	1-5	1036
13	Hartlepool United	v Watford	0-2	242
14	Nottingham Forest	v Chelsea	0-4	786
15	Sunderland	v Preston North End	2-2*	613
	(Preston North End won 3-0 on penalties)			
16	Arsenal	v Ipswich Town	0-2	436
(at Barnet FC)				

FIFTH ROUND PROPER

1	Blackburn Rovers	v Manchester United	3-0	874
2	Preston North End	v Everton	0-3	1531
3	Chelsea	v Portsmouth	1-0	1605
4	Liverpool	v Watford	0-1	2199
5	West Ham United	v Newcastle United	0-3	1157
6	Hull City	v Crystal Palace	1-4	320
	(at North Ferriby United FC)			
7	Ipswich Town	v Fulham	1-3	1495
8	Aston Villa	v Millwall	4-1	717

SIXTH ROUND PROPER

1	Watford	v Chelsea	0-4	2270
2	Newcastle United	v Crystal Palace	4-2	1291
3	Blackburn Rovers	v Everton	2-1	1148
4	Fulham	v Aston Villa	2-2aet	772
	(Aston Villa won 3-1 on penalties)			

SEMI-FINALS - 1ST LEG

1	Aston Villa	v Newcastle United	1-1	2457
2	Blackburn Rovers	v Chelsea	0-1	1332

SEMI-FINALS - 2ND LEG

1	Newcastle United	v Aston Villa	0-1	4959
	(Aston Villa won 2-1 on aggregate)			
2	Chelsea	v Blackburn Rovers	4-0	1750
	(Chelsea won 5-0 on aggregate)			

THE FINAL - 1ST LEG

Aston Villa	v Chelsea	1-1	3359

THE FINAL - 2ND LEG

Chelsea	v Aston Villa	2-1	10464

PREVIOUS TEN FINALS

				Aggregate Score
2009	Arsenal	v	Liverpool	6-2
2008	Manchester City	v	Chelsea	4-2
2007	Liverpool	v	Manchester Utd	2-2*, 4-3p
2006	Liverpool	v	Manchester City	3-2
2005	Ipswich Town	v	Southampton	3-2
2004	Middlesbrough	v	Aston Villa	4-0
2003	Manchester United	v	Middlesbrough	3-1
2002	Aston Villa	v	Everton	4-2
2001	Arsenal	v	Blackburn Rovers	6-3
2000	Arsenal	v	Coventry City	5-1

FIRST ROUND

1	Cumberland	v	North Riding	0-2
2	West Riding	v	Cheshire	0-0*
	(West Riding won 5-4 on penalties)			
	(at West Riding County FA, Woodlesford)			
3	Westmorland	v	Manchester	2-3
4	Leicestershire & Rutland	v	Shropshire	3-1
5	Staffordshire	v	East Riding	0-4
6	Gloucestershire	v	Bedfordshire	1-4
7	Guernsey	v	Berks & Bucks	3-6
8	Norfolk	v	Suffolk	0-3
9	London	v	Northamptonshire	3-1
	(at Dulwich Hamlet FC)			
10	Hertfordshire	v	Cornwall	1-2
11	Essex	v	Hampshire	1-7
12	Herefordshire	v	Amateur Football Alliance	0-1
13	Somerset	v	Devon	2-1
14	Cambridgeshrie	v	Oxfordshire	3-2

Byes

Birmingham, Dorset, Durham, Huntingdonshire, Isle of Man, Jersey, Kent, Lancashire, Lincolnshire, Liverpool, Middlesex, Northumberland, Nottinghamshire, Sheffield & Hallamshire, Surrey, Sussex, Wiltshire, Worcestershire.

SECOND ROUND

1	Northumberland	v	West Riding	0-2
2	Lancashire	v	Manchester	3-1
3	Liverpool	v	North Riding	2-0
4	Birmingham	v	Leicestershire & Rutland	4-0
5	Lincolnshire	v	East Riding	2-2*
6	Sheffield & Hallamshire	v	Isle of Man	2-0
7	Nottinghamshire	v	Durham	1-5
8	Suffolk	v	Cambridgeshire	5-4
9	London	v	Cornwall	1-4*
10	Sussex	v	Dorset	4-1
11	Middlesex	v	Huntingdonshire	5-0
12	Somerset	v	Kent	1-5
13	Surrey	v	Berks & Bucks	3-1
14	Bedfordshire	v	Amateur Football Alliance	3-0
15	Worcestershire	v	Jersey	5-2
16	Wiltshire	v	Hampshire	1-0

THIRD ROUND

1	Middlesex	v	Lancashire	1-2
2	Birmingham	v	Suffolk	3-4
3	Wiltshire	v	Cornwall	2-4*
4	East Riding	v	Durham	1-3
5	Surrey	v	Liverpool	1-3
6	Bedfordshire	v	West Riding	0-2
7	Sheffield & Hallamshire	v	Worcestershire	2-1*
8	Kent	v	Sussex	1-0

FOURTH ROUND

1	Lancashire	v	Suffolk	1-0
2	Liverpool	v	Cornwall	3-0
3	Durham	v	Kent	1-2
4	Sheffield & Hallamshire	v	West Riding	2-0

SEMI-FINALS

1	Sheffield & Hallamshire	v	Lancashire	1-0
2	Liverpool	v	Kent	3-5*

THE FINAL

Kent	v	Sheffield & Hallamshire	1-0
At Gillingham FC			Att: 778

PREVIOUS TEN FINALS

2009	Birmingham FA	v	Kent FA	2-1
2008	Suffolk FA	v	Cambridgeshire FA	2-1
2007	West Riding FA	v	Suffolk FA	1-1*, 4-3p
2006	Bedfordshie FA	v	Durham FA	3-2
2005	Suffolk FA	v	Hampshire FA	2-1
2004	Durham FA	v	North Riding FA	4-0
2003	Northumberland FA	v	Liverpool FA	1-0
2002	Birmingham FA	v	Durham FA	2-1
2001	Northamptonshire FA	v	Birmingham FA	3-0
2000	Birmingham FA	v	Surrey FA	2-1

Bluefin

THE F.A. SUNDAY CUP

PRELIMINARY ROUND

1	Tower	v	Crossflatts	4-1
2	Brow	v	Rawdon Old Boys	4-0
3	Queens Park	v	Alder	3-2
4	Seymour KFCA	v	Towngate	2-3
5	Shankhouse United	v	St Sebastians	3-1
6	Belt Road	v	Station Gates	4-0
7	Hawkins Sports	v	Warstones Wanderers (Sunday)	0-4
8	Baldon Sports	v	London Maccabi Lions	2-3*
9	Broadfields United	v	Crawley Green (Sunday)	3-1
10	Dunstable White Swan	v	AC Sportsman & Ravensborough	3-1
11	Comets Sports Club	v	AC Cadoza	3-2
12	Offley Moat	v	St Margarets	3-2
13	Blackwater Valley	v	Battersea Ironsides	2-3

FIRST ROUND

1	Bolton Woods	v	Paddock	0-2
2	Tower	v	Salisbury Athletic	0-6
3	Cleator Moor	v	West Lee	1-3
4	Mirehouse	v	Thirly	3-2
5	Brow	v	Thornhill Lees	4-2
6	Fforde Grene Brazil	v	Sandstone	1-3
7	Hetton Lyons Cricket Club	v	Allerton	7-0
8	Towngate	v	Queens Park	1-3
9	Kelloe WMC	v	Witton Park Rose & Crown	3-4
10	Silsden (Sunday)	v	Salford Celtic	2-1
11	Britannia	v	BRNESC	5-0
12	St Bees Village	v	Shamrocks	0-4
13	Shankhouse United	v	Hartlepool Lion Hillcarter	2-1*
14	East End Park WMC	v	Canada	1-2
15	AFC Blackburn Leisure	v	Obiter	3-0
16	Huddersfield Irish Centre	v	Chapeltown Brazil	4-1
17	Dengo United	v	Home & Bargain	4-0
18	Beverley United	v	Western Approaches	0-4
19	Lindley WMC	v	JOB	0-3
20	Halton Moor	v	Flat House	
	(tie abandoned after 20 mins due to misconduct – 1-0)			
	(both clubs removed after being found guilty of causing the abandonment)			
21	Ford Motors	v	Poulton Royal	0-4
22	Hessle Rangers	v	Kempston St Gym	
	(walkover for Kempston St Gym – Hessle Rangers withdrawn)			
23	Langley Celtic	v	Dawdon Colliery Welfare	4-2
24	Sunderland RCA Barnes	v	Lobster	0-4
25	Swanfield	v	Nicosia	3-2
26	Mariners	v	Murton Victoria	3-0
27	Loughborough Saints	v	Leicester Polska	7-1
28	Belt Road	v	Sporting Dynamo	3-2
29	Barcabullona	v	Bartley Green Sunday	1-3
30	Birstall Stamford	v	Britannia Revolution	2-0
31	Travellers	v	Brereton Town	2-0
32	Anstey Swifts OB	v	Barwell Sports Bar	
	(walkover for Barwell Sports Bar – Anstey Swifts OB withdrawn)			
33	Thatch	v	Harp FC 2003	4-1
34	Warstones Wanderers (Sunday)	v	Duke or Rutland	2-0
35	Robinson's Garage	v	Magnet Tavern	1-5
36	Bungay Town	v	Sawston Keys	2-0
37	Shelford Falcons	v	Wisbech St Mary	0-1
38	Royal Falcons	v	London Maccabi Lions	3-2
39	Greengate	v	Enfield Rangers	0-2
40	Sungate	v	Luton Old Boys	7-1
41	FC Houghton Centre	v	Hammer	0-3
42	Britannia United	v	North West Neasden	2-4*
43	Club Lewsey	v	Broadfields United	5-4
44	Standens Barn	v	Stanbridge & Tilsworth	0-1
45	Belstone	v	Bury Park Saracens	4-5*
46	Gossoms End	v	Dunstable White Swan	3-2*
47	Unity Nirankari	v	Silsoe Park Rangers	3-1
48	St Josephs (Luton)	v	Bedfont Sunday	2-3
49	61 FC (Sunday)	v	Comets Sports Club	0-4
50	Northampton Trotters	v	Rumours	1-0
51	Westoning	v	CB Hounslow United (Sunday)	5-0
52	Wycombe Town	v	Offley Moat	3-0
53	Richfield Rovers	v	Greyhound	0-3
54	Seven Allstars	v	Downend	1-3
55	Brixton United	v	Ajax LA	6-0
56	Knighton Arms	v	Battersea Ironsides	3-1
57	Totton Town	v	Hazelhurst	
	(walkover for Hazelhurst – Totton Town withdrawn)			
58	Goring Rangers	v	Kerria Sports	1-0
59	Whitenap	v	Airport Motors	1-1*
	(Whitenap won 4-1 on penalties)			60
	Sporting Bristol	v	Lebeq Tavern Courage	0-3
61	Lakeside Athletic	v	Hanham Sunday	3-2
62	Bristol Athletic	v	Windmill	2-3

SECOND ROUND

1	West Lee	v	Silsden (Sunday)	2-4
2	Salisbury Athletic	v	Paddock	4-1
3	Sandstone	v	Mariners	1-0
4	Brow	v	Mirehouse	3-3*
	(Mirehouse won 5-4 on penalties)			5
	Queens Park	v	Lobster	0-3
6	Hetton Lyons Cricket Club	v	Canada	6-0
7	Western Approaches	v	Langley Celtic	1-4
8	Huddersfield Irish Centre	v	Britannia	3-2
9	Oyster Martyrs	v	Witton Park Rose & Crown	4-2
10	Kempston St Gym	v	Shamrocks	1-3*
11	Shankhouse United	v	Halton Moor or Flat House	
	(tie awarded to Shankhouse United – Halton Moor and Flat House expelled)			
12	Dengo United	v	AFC Blackburn Leisure	3-3*
	(Dengo Utd won 6-5 on penalties)			
13	Swanfield	v	Scots Grey	
	(walkover for Swanfield – Scots Grey withdrawn)			
14	Poulton Royal	v	JOB	6-5*
15	Magnet Tavern	v	Loughborough Saints	3-0*
16	Belt Road	v	Wisbech St Mary	2-0
17	Birstall Stamford	v	Bartley Green Sunday	4-0
18	Thatch	v	Warstones Wanderers (Sunday)	3-2
19	Barwell Sports Bar	v	Travellers	0-5
20	Enfield Rangers *(tie reversed)*	v	Stanbridge & Tilsworth	1-6
21	Royal Falcons	v	Bungay Town	1-2
22	Bury Park Saracens	v	Sungate	1-2
23	North West Neasden	v	Hammer	4-1
24	Comets Sports Club *(tie reversed)*	v	Northampton Trotters	7-2
25	Unity Nirankari	v	Club Lewsey	4-1
26	Bedfont Sunday	v	Westoning	4-2*
27	Wycombe Town	v	Gossoms End	3-2
28	Greyhound	v	Lakeside Athletic	2-1
29	Downend	v	Knighton Arms	0-4
30	Whitenap	v	Lebeq Tavern Courage	0-4
31	Windmill	v	Goring Rangers	5-3
32	Hazelhurst *(tie reversed)*	v	Brixton United	2-0*

THIRD ROUND

1	Sandstone	v	Silsden (Sunday)	2-1*
2	Salisbury Athletic	v	Mirehouse	3-2
3	Langley Celtic	v	Lobster	1-0
4	Oyster Martyrs	v	Huddersfield Irish Centre	
5	Shankhouse United	v	Dengo United	2-1
6	Swanfield	v	Shamrocks	3-4*
7	Poulton Royal *(tie reversed)*	v	Hetton Lyons Cricket Club	0-2
8	Birstall Stamford	v	Thatch	5-0
9	Travellers	v	Belt Road	3-1
10	Stanbridge & Tilsworth	v	Magnet Tavern	0-4
11	North West Neasden	v	Bungay Town	3-1
12	Sungate	v	Comets Sports Club	4-1
13	Wycombe Town	v	Unity Nirankari	10-2
	(31/1, tie ordered to be replayed as a result of an FA investigation, 4-1)			
14	Bedfont Sunday	v	Hazelhurst	1-3
15	Lebeq Tavern Courage	v	Greyhound	7-0
16	Knighton Arms *(tie reversed)*	v	Windmill	2-3

FOURTH ROUND

1	Salisbury Athletic	v	Langley Celtic	1-0*
2	Hetton Lyons Cricket Club	v	Huddersfield Irish Centre	1-0
3	Shankhouse Utd *(tie reversed)*	v	Shamrocks	2-2*
	(Shankhouse United won 2-1 on penalties)			
4	Birstall Stamford	v	Sandstone	3-2
5	Magnet Tavern	v	Travellers	3-0
6	Sungate	v	North West Neasden	6-4
7	Wycombe Town	v	Lebeq Tavern Courage	3-5*
8	Hazelhurst	v	Windmill	6-1

FIFTH ROUND

1	Lebeq Tavern Courage	v	Magnet Tavern	1-3
2	Hazelhurst	v	Sungate	4-1
3	Hetton Lyons Cricket Club	v	Salisbury Athletic	2-1
4	Shankhouse United	v	Birstall Stamford	0-1

SEMI-FINALS

1	Birstall Stamford	v	Magnet Tavern	1-2
	At Hinckley United FC			
2	Hazelhurst	v	Hetton Lyons Cricket Club	1-2
	At Sutton United FC			

THE FINAL

	Hetton Lyons Cricket Club	v	Magnet Tavern	4-2
	At Liverpool FC			*Att: 856*

PRELIMINARY ROUND

1	Nottinghamshire Senior Lge	v	Teesside Football Lge	0-1
2	Cumberland County Lge	v	Yorkshire Old Boys Lge	4-5
3	Midland Football Comb. (Div 1)	v	West Yorkshire Football Lge	1-0
4	Isle of Man Lge	v	Manchester Lge	1-0
5	Wearside Lge	v	Cambridgeshire County Lge	1-2
6	Northamptonshire Combination	v	Peterborough & District Lge	2-1
7	Brighton Hove & District Lge	v	Dorset Premier Lge	0-3
8	Guernsey Senior County Lge	v	Kent County Lge	6-0
9	Mid Sussex Lge	v	Bedfordshire Football Lge	0-4
10	Jersey Football Combination	v	Spartan South Mid Lge (Div 2)	2-0
11	Reading Football Lge	v	Middlesex County Lge	4-1
12	Northampton Town Lge	v	Hampshire Premier Lge	2-1

Byes - 19

Anglian Combination	Lancashire & Cheshire Amateur Lge
Amateur Football Combination	Liverpool County Premier Lge
Birmingham & District Amateur Lge	Northern Football Alliance
Cheshire Football Lge	Somerset County Lge
Essex Olympian Lge	Sussex County Lge (Div 3)
Essex & Suffolk Border Lge	West Cheshire Lge
Gloucestershire County Lge	West Riding County Amateur Lge
Hertfordshire Senior County Lge	Wiltshire Football Lge
Humber Premier Lge	Worthing & District Lge
Lancashire Amateur Lge	

Exemptions –
Southern Amateur Lge – Holders to Round 1

FIRST ROUND

1	Humber Premier Lge	v	West Cheshire Lge	2-1
	(tie awarded to West Cheshire Lge – Humber Premier Lge removed)			
2	Lancashire Amateur Lge	v	Anglian Combination	3-2
3	Cheshire Football Lge	v	Yorkshire Old Boys Lge	1-3
4	Lancashire & Cheshire Am. Lge	v	Birmingham & District Am. Lge	4-2
5	Northamptonshire Combination	v	West Riding County Amateur Lge	1-4
	(at Harborough Town FC)			
6	Teesside Football Lge	v	Cambridgeshire County Lge (26/9)	1-3
7	Northern Football Alliance	v	Liverpool County Premier Lge (19/9)	2-3
	(at Whitley Bay FC)			
8	Midland Football Comb. (Div 1)	v	Isle of Man Lge	0-3
9	Dorset Premier Lge	v	Sussex County Lge (Div 3)	5-2aet
10	Bedfordshire Football Lge	v	Amateur Football Combination	0-0aet
	(Bedfordshire Football Lge won 4-3 on penalties, at Biggleswade Town FC)			
11	Worthing & District Lge	v	Essex Olympian Lge	2-9
12	Hertfordshire County Senior Lge	v	Essex & Suffolk Border Lge	1-0
13	Wiltshire Football Lge	v	Jersey Football Combination	0-3
14	Northampton Town Lge	v	Guernsey Senior County Lge	0-2
15	Southern Amateur Lge (Holders)	v	Gloucestershire County Lge	2-0
16	Somerset County Lge	v	Reading Football Lge	3-4

SECOND ROUND

1	Lancashire & Cheshire Am.	v	Cambridgeshire County	0-5
2	West Riding County Amateur	v	Yorkshire Old Boys	0-3
3	Liverpool County Premier	v	Isle of Man	2-1
4	Lancashire Amateur	v	West Cheshire Lge	2-3
5	Essex Olympian	v	Jersey Combination	0-1
6	Bedfordshire	v	Dorset Premier	1-2
7	Guernsey Senior County	v	Southern Amateur	3-2
8	Reading	v	Hertfordshire Senior County	2-3

THIRD ROUND

1	Liverpool County Premier Lge	v	Cambridgeshire County Lge	3-1aet
2	West Cheshire Lge	v	Yorkshire Old Boys Lge	2-3
3	Jersey Football Combination	v	Dorset Premier Lge	0-1
4	Guernsey Senior County Lge	v	Herts Senior County Lge	3-2

SEMI-FINALS

1	Guernsey Senior County Lge	v	Dorset Premier Lge	3-2
	at Corbet Field, St Sampson,			
2	Liverpool County Premier Lge	v	Yorkshire Old Boys Lge	3-2
	at The Liverpool Soccer Centre			

THE FINAL

Guernsey Senior County Lge v Livepool County Premier League 5-2

at The Track, St Sampson, Guernsey.

PRELIMINARY ROUND

1	Forest Hall Women's YPC	v	Stokesley Ladies	
	(walkover for Forest Hall Women's YPC – Stokesley Ladies withdrawn)			
2	Newcastle Medics	v	Gateshead Rutherford Ravens	0-9
3	Prudhoe Youth Club	v	Tynedale Ladies	1-3
4	Gateshead Cleveland Hall	v	North Shields Ladies	0-7
5	Accrington Girls & Ladies	v	Harraby Catholic Club	0-1
6	Dearne & District Ladies	v	Kirklees	2-1
7	Tipton Town Ladies	v	Stourport Swifts	16-0
8	Woodford United	v	Brackley Sports	0-4
9	Saffron Walden Town	v	C&K Basildon	1-5
10	Runwell Hospital	v	Hutton Ladies	2-1
11	Eastleigh Ladies	v	Boscombe Albion	5-0
12	Christchurch	v	New Forest Ladies	3-3*
	(New Forest Ladies won 4-1 on penalties)			

FIRST QUALIFYING ROUND

1	Gateshead Rutherford Ravens	v	Birtley Town Ladies	0-3
2	Forest Hall Women's YPC	v	North Shields Ladies	1-5
3	Whitley Bay Women	v	Teesside Athletic	7-0
4	Tynedale Ladies	v	Brandon United	3-0
5	Blyth Spartans	v	Peterlee Town	
	(walkover for Peterlee Town – Blyth Spartans withdrew)			
6	Abbeytown Women's	v	Warrington Town	1-2*
7	Birkenhead Ladies	v	Middleton Athletic	2-3
8	Whitehaven Ladies	v	Bury Girls & Ladies	3-1
9	Chester City	v	Wigan Athletic Ladies	0-2
10	Harraby Catholic Club	v	Dalton United Ladies	1-0
11	Bolton Wanderers	v	Preston Rangers	10-1
12	Barnsley	v	Hull City	1-2*
13	Dearne & District Ladies	v	Huddersfield Town	3-1
14	Steel City Wanderers	v	Sheffield United Junior Blades Ladies	2-0
15	Guiseley Ladies	v	Sheffield Ladies	1-2
16	Keighley Ladies	v	Sheffield United Community	1-5
17	Rolls Royce Leisure	v	Market Warsop	2-1
18	Mansfield Town	v	Peterborough	2-1
19	Sandiacre Town	v	Retford United	4-0
20	Friar Lane & Epworth	v	Long Eaton United	2-4
21	Peterborough Azure	v	West Bridgford	5-0
22	Hinckley United Ladies	v	Loughborough Students	1-4
23	Huntingdon Town Ladies	v	Oadby & Wigston Girls & Ladies	1-2
24	Linby CW	v	Shepshed Dynamo	1-7
25	Hereford Phoenix Ladies	v	Cottage Farm Rangers	5-0
26	Tipton Town Ladies	v	Southam United	0-4
27	Leamington Lions	v	Cannock Ladies	3-1
28	Hereford Pegasus	v	Allscott	3-2
29	Worcester City	v	Stratford Town	0-1*
30	Crusaders Ladies	v	Coventry Ladies Development	
	(walkover for Coventry Ladies Development – Crusaders Ladies expelled)			
31	Lichfield Diamonds	v	Dudley United	1-6
32	Haverhill Rovers	v	Stalham Town Ladies	1-0
33	Cambridge University	v	West Lynn	1-2
34	Bungay Town	v	Woodbridge Town	0-9
35	AFC Kempston Rovers	v	Raunds Town	3-0
36	Daventry Town	v	Corby S&L	1-3
37	Bedford Ladies	v	Kingsthorpe Ladies & Girls	7-0
38	Leighton Linslade Ladies	v	Whitwell Ladies	3-0
39	Brackley Sports	v	Arlesey Town Ladies	0-3
40	Kettering Town	v	Hitchin Hearts	3-0
41	London Colney	v	Brentwood Town	
	(walkover for Brentwood Town – London Colney withdrew)			
42	C&K Basildon	v	Barking	0-5
43	Royston Town	v	Braintree Town	1-2
44	Hemel Hempstead Town	v	Billericay Town	3-2
45	Tring Athletic	v	Stevenage Borough	2-1
46	Runwell Hospital	v	Chelmsford City	2-5
47	Sawbridgeworth Town	v	Garston	2-1
48	Haringey Borough	v	Wandgas	4-1
49	MSA Ladies	v	Manford Way Ladies	4-1
50	Leyton Ladies	v	Panthers	0-4
51	Tower Hamlets	v	Westfield Ladies	3-0
52	AFC Wimbledon Ladies	v	Horley Town	3-1
53	Old Actonians	v	Denham United	2-1
54	Ashford Girls	v	Crowborough Athletic	5-1
55	Rottingdean Village	v	Canterbury City	0-2
56	Ramsgate	v	Maidstone Town	0-9
57	Bexhill United	v	Haywards Heath Town	0-3
58	Eastbourne Town	v	London Corinthians	5-1
59	Aldershot Town	v	Southampton Saints	1-0
60	Crawley Wasps	v	Chichester City	3-0
61	BTC Southampton Ladies	v	Shanklin	
	(walkover for Shanklin – BTC Southampton Ladies withdrew)			
62	Southampton	v	University of Portsmouth	1-5
63	Eastleigh Ladies	v	Basingstoke Town Ladies	0-5
64	Littlehampton Town Devils & Ladies	v	New Forest Ladies	2-1
65	Bracknell Town	v	Cheltenham Town Ladies	3-0
66	Wycombe Wanderers	v	Forest of Dean	4-1*
67	Chippenham Town Ladies	v	Stoke Lane Athletic	3-6
68	Stony Stratford Town	v	Reading Girls	5-4
69	MK Wanderers	v	Oxford United	0-3
70	Launton	v	Marlow Ladies	4-1
71	Maidenhead United Ladies	v	Banbury United	14-0
72	Slough	v	Newent Town Ladies	9-0
73	Reading	v	Swindon Supermarine Ladies	1-3
74	Poole Town	v	Keynsham Town Development	0-6
75	Launceston	v	Saltash United	0-2
76	Frome Town	v	Weymouth Ladies	2-0

SECOND QUALIFYING ROUND

1	Birtley Town Ladies	v	Whitley Bay Women	2-10
2	Tynedale Ladies	v	Peterlee Town	0-2
3	North Shields Ladies	v	Harraby Catholic Club	1-5
4	Warrington Town	v	Hull City	0-8
5	Bolton Wanderers	v	Dearne & District Ladies	3-1
6	Sheffield Ladies	v	Middleton Athletic	11-0
7	Whitehaven Ladies	v	Wigan Athletic Ladies	0-2
8	Sheffield United Community	v	Steel City Wanderers	3-1
9	Peterborough Azure	v	Rolls Royce Leisure	2-1
10	Shepshed Dynamo	v	Loughborough Students	1-3
11	Sandiacre Town	v	Mansfield Town	3-0
12	Long Eaton United	v	Oadby & Wigston Girls & Ladies	4-1*
13	Stratford Town	v	Hereford Phoenix Ladies	1-3
14	Corby S&L	v	Coventry Ladies Development	4-0
15	Leamington Lions	v	Southam United	3-0
16	Hereford Pegasus	v	Dudley United	2-5
17	Bedford Ladies	v	Haverhill Rovers	3-0
18	Kettering Town	v	Leighton Linslade Ladies	2-1
19	Woodbridge Town	v	West Lynn	3-0
20	AFC Kempston Rovers	v	Arlesey Town Ladies	1-3
21	Brentwood Town	v	Chelmsford City	1-4
22	Tring Athletic	v	Sawbridgeworth Town	2-3*
23	MSA Ladies	v	Barking	2-6
24	Braintree Town	v	Hemel Hempstead Town	4-3
25	Panthers	v	Haringey Borough	3-4
26	Tower Hamlets	v	Maidstone Town	1-3
27	Canterbury City	v	Haywards Heath Town	2-3
28	Aldershot Town	v	AFC Wimbledon Ladies	5-0
29	Old Actonians	v	Ashford Girls	6-0

30	Crawley Wasps	v	Eastbourne Town	1-2
31	Launton	v	Wycombe Wanderers	1-4
32	Shanklin	v	Bracknell Town	5-0
33	University of Portsmouth	v	Basingstoke Town Ladies	3-2
34	Oxford United	v	Stony Stratford Town	7-1
35	Littlehampton Town Devils & Ladies	v	Maidenhead United Ladies	3-2*
36	Slough	v	Stoke Lane Athletic	8-3
37	Keynsham Town Development	v	Swindon Supermarine Ladies	2-4
38	Frome Town	v	Saltash United	0-1

THIRD QUALIFYING ROUND

1	Sheffield Ladies	v	Whitley Bay Women	1-2
2	Wigan Athletic Ladies	v	Peterlee Town	2-6
3	Harraby Catholic Club	v	Hull City	1-12
	(tie reversed - at Hull University Sports Centre)			
4	Bolton Wanderers	v	Sheffield United Community	0-7
5	Long Eaton United	v	Peterborough Azure	2-0
6	Leamington Lions	v	Corby S&L	4-1*
7	Hereford Phoenix Ladies	v	Loughborough Students	3-5
8	Dudley United	v	Sandiacre Town	2-1
9	Woodbridge Town	v	Chelmsford City	3-3*
	(Woodbridge Town won 8-7 on penalties)			
10	Braintree Town	v	Sawbridgeworth Town	0-3
11	Kettering Town	v	Barking	1-5
12	Bedford Ladies	v	Arlesey Town Ladies	2-1
13	Aldershot Town	v	Old Actonians	3-5
14	Haywards Heath Town	v	Maidstone Town	1-2
15	Haringey Borough	v	Eastbourne Town	2-1
16	Wycombe Wanderers	v	Littlehampton Town Devils & Ladies	1-7
17	Slough	v	Swindon Supermarine Ladies	0-5
18	Shanklin	v	Oxford United	1-0
19	Saltash United	v	University of Portsmouth	2-0

FIRST ROUND PROPER

1	Liverpool Feds	v	Peterlee Town	4-0
2	Salford Ladies	v	Darlington RA	
	(walkover for Salford Ladies – Darlington RA withdrew)			
3	Stockport County	v	Bradford City	3-1
4	Whitley Bay Women	v	Blackpool Wren Rovers	7-1
5	Hull City	v	Rochdale AFC Ladies	0-9
6	Tranmere Rovers	v	Rotherham United	1-6
7	Sheffield United Community	v	Middlesbrough	1-2
8	South Durham GSK Royals	v	Wakefield Ladies	1-2
9	Wolverhampton Wanderers	v	Sporting Club Albion	1-3
10	Stoke City	v	Loughborough Students	5-4*
11	Long Eaton United	v	Coventry City	0-2
12	Leafield Athletic	v	Leamington Lions	8-0
13	Copsewood (Coventry)	v	Scunthorpe United	7-1
14	Leicester City Ladies	v	Loughborough Foxes	2-3*
15	Dudley United	v	TNS	2-1
16	Haringey Borough	v	Barking	3-1
17	Enfield Town	v	Maidstone Town	3-1
18	Tottenham Hotspur	v	Northampton Town	0-1
19	Littlehampton Town Devils & Ladies	v	Ebbsfleet United	2-1*
20	Cambridge Womens	v	Sawbridgeworth Town	5-0
21	MK Dons Ladies	v	Old Actonians	3-0
22	Gillingham	v	Oxford City	6-0
23	Lewes	v	Ipswich Town	5-2
24	Dagenham & Redbridge	v	Norwich City Ladies	
	(walkover for Norwich City Ladies – Dagenham & Redbridge withdrew)			
25	Welwyn Garden City	v	Woodbridge Town	
	(walkover for Woodbridge Town – Welwyn Garden City withdrew)			
26	Bedford Ladies	v	Chesham United	0-3
27	Shanklin	v	Havant & Waterlooville	0-2
28	Plymouth Argyle	v	Swindon Supermarine Ladies	5-1
	(tie reversed - at Swindon Supermarine FC)			
29	Saltash United	v	Yeovil Town	0-3
30	Cullompton Rangers	v	Forest Green Rovers	
	(tie awarded to Forest Green Rovers – Cullompton Rangers withdrew)			
31	Swindon Town	v	Winscombe	3-2
32	Reading Town	v	Newquay	1-7

SECOND ROUND PROPER

1	Whitley Bay Women	v	Rochdale AFC Ladies	2-3
	(29/11, tie abandoned after 45mins due to waterlogged pitch, 0-1)			
2	Salford Ladies	v	Middlesbrough	0-2
	(tie reversed – at Billingham Synthonia FC)			
3	Rotherham United	v	Liverpool Feds	2-3
	(tie reversed – at Heswall FC)			
4	Stockport County	v	Wakefield Ladies	1-0
5	Coventry City	v	Leafield Athletic	7-0
6	Sporting Club Albion	v	Loughborough Foxes	4-1
7	Copsewood (Coventry)	v	Stoke City	2-3
8	Cambridge Women's	v	Dudley United	2-1*
9	Norwich City Ladies	v	Chesham United	3-1
	(tie reversed – at Chesham United FC)			
10	Lewes	v	Haringey Borough	5-1
11	Woodbridge Town	v	Littlehampton Tn Devils & Ladies	0-1
12	Enfield Town	v	Gillingham	0-3
13	MK Dons Ladies	v	Northampton Town	2-0
14	Newquay	v	Swindon Town	2-0
15	Plymouth Argyle	v	Havant & Waterlooville	2-5
	(tie reversed – at Fort Blockhouse, Portsmouth)			
16	Yeovil Town	v	Forest Green Rovers	4-1

THIRD ROUND PROPER

1	Liverpool Feds	v	Rochdale AFC Ladies	1-0
2	Liverpool	v	Preston North End	4-1
3	Sheffield Wednesday	v	Stockport County	5-2
4	Middlesbrough	v	Curzon Ashton	1-2
5	Leeds City Vixens	v	Manchester City	1-0
6	Ooh Lincoln Ladies	v	Newcastle United	2-2*
	(Ooh Lincoln Ladies won 3-2 on penalties)			
7	Aston Villa	v	Sporting Club Albion	3-2
8	Stoke City	v	Leicester City	2-6
9	Luton Town Ladies	v	Cambridge Women's	4-1*
	(tie reversed – at Cambridge City FC)			
10	Coventry City	v	Derby County	1-4
11	Reading Women	v	Brighton & Hove Albion	1-0
12	Charlton Athletic	v	West Ham United	0-3
13	Gillingham	v	Barnet Ladies	1-4
14	Lewes	v	Queens Park Rangers	0-5
15	Crystal Palace	v	WFC Fulham	0-0*
	(WFC Fulham won 5-4 on penalties)	16		MK Dons Ladies
v	Norwich City Ladies	3-5		
	(tie reversed – at Norwich United FC)			
17	Colchester United	v	Littlehampton Town Devils & Ladies	4-0
18	Yeovil Town	v	Newquay	3-1
	(tie reversed – at Newquay FC)			
19	Keynsham Town	v	Portsmouth	2-3
20	Havant & Waterlooville	v	Cardiff City	2-1
	(tie reversed – at Cardiff Athletics Stadium)			

FOURTH ROUND PROPER

1	Liverpool Feds	v Curzon Ashton	0-5
2	Bristol Academy	v West Ham United	1-2
3	Ooh Lincoln Ladies	v Sheffield Wednesday	3-1
4	Portsmouth	v Luton Town	2-1
5	WFC Fulham	v Blackburn Rovers	0-6
6	Everton	v Queens Park Rangers	6-2
7	Reading Women	v Aston Villa	1-1*
	(Aston Villa won 5-4 on penalties)	8	Liverpool
v	Chelsea	1-2*	
9	Norwich City Ladies	v Yeovil Town	1-3
10	Nottingham Forest	v Leeds City Vixens	3-2
11	Leeds Carnegie Ladies	v Watford	4-1
12	Leicester City	v Millwall Lionesses	0-3
13	Arsenal	v Sunderland	4-1*
14	Doncaster Rovers Belles	v Havant & Waterlooville	6-1
15	Birmingham City	v Derby County	4-1
16	Colchester United	v Barnet Ladies	2-3*

FIFTH ROUND PROPER

1	Blackburn Rovers	v Ooh Lincoln Ladies	1-0*
2	Curzon Ashton	v Aston Villa	1-2
3	Birmingham City	v Doncaster Rovers Belles	0-1
4	West Ham United	v Barnet Ladies	2-3*
5	Yeovil Town	v Nottingham Forest	0-1
6	Everton	v Portsmouth	7-0
7	Arsenal	v Leeds Carnegie Ladies	3-2
8	Chelsea	v Millwall Lionesses	3-1*

SIXTH ROUND PROPER

1	Aston Villa	v Chelsea	3-4*
2	Barnet Ladies	v Nottingham Forest	3-2
3	Arsenal	v Doncaster Rovers Belles	5-0
4	Everton	v Blackburn Rovers	2-1

SEMI-FINALS

1	Everton	v Barnet Ladies	2-0
	At Southport FC		*Att: 252*
2	Chelsea	v Arsenal	0-4
	At Staines Town FC		*Att: 605*

THE FINAL

Arsenal	v Everton	2-3*
At Nottingham Forest FC		*Att: 17,505*

QUALIFYING LEAGUES

NORTH	P	W	D	L	F	A	GD	Pts
SHEFFIELD	14	11	2	1	108	43	65	35
MANCHESTER	14	10	2	2	81	39	42	32
TRANMERE VICTORIA	14	8	3	3	77	45	32	27
MIDDLESBROUGH	14	6	1	7	72	67	5	19
LEEDS	14	5	2	7	73	78	-5	17
OLDHAM ATHLETIC	14	4	0	10	60	100	-40	12
LIVERPOOL	14	3	1	10	58	96	-38	10
FC GRIMSBY	14	3	1	10	41	102	-61	10

MIDLANDS	P	W	D	L	F	A	GD	Pts
TEAM UTD BIRMINGHAM	12	9	0	3	75	42	33	27
CHIPPENHAM	12	8	0	4	84	70	14	24
BIRMINGHAM TIGERS	12	6	2	4	82	72	10	20
TEAM BATH FUTSAL	12	6	1	5	51	44	7	19
HARTPURY FUTSAL	12	4	3	5	67	67	0	15
LOUGHBOROUGH	12	5	0	7	53	73	-20	15
HEREFORD	12	1	0	11	49	93	-44	3

SOUTH	P	W	D	L	F	A	GD	Pts
SPARTANS FC	14	12	2	0	120	34	86	38
HELVECIA FC	14	11	1	2	123	45	78	34
FC BALTIC	14	7	3	4	77	66	11	24
LONDON UNITED FC	14	6	3	5	73	67	6	21
KICKERS FC	14	5	1	8	66	77	-11	16
GENESIS FC	14	4	2	8	86	91	-5	14
FC ENFIELD	14	3	3	8	78	122	-44	12
BRENTFORD CST FC	14	0	1	13	72	193	-121	1

THE FINALS

GROUP A	P	W	D	L	F	A	Gd	Pts
HELVECIA	2	2	0	0	25	6	19	6
SHEFFIELD	2	1	0	1	14	15	-1	3
CHIPPENHAM	2	0	0	2	6	24	-18	0

Results

Sheffield	v	Chippenham	12-2
Chippenham	v	Helvecia	4-12
Sheffield	v	Helvecia	2-13

GROUP B	P	W	D	L	F	A	Gd	Pts
SPARTANS	2	2	0	0	11	5	6	6
TEAM UTD BIRMINGHAM	2	1	0	1	4	8	-4	3
MANCHESTER	2	0	0	2	6	8	-2	0

Results

Spartans	v	Team Utd Birmingham	6-1
Team Utd Birmingham	v	Manchester	3-2
Spartans	v	Manchester	5-4

THE FINAL

Helvecia	v	Spartans	11-8 (aet)

GOLDEN BOOT

Name (Club)	Match 1	Match 2	Match 3	Total
Adriano Hoelzle (Helvecia)	2	1	5	8
Raoni Medina (Helvecia)	3	3	1	7
Bruno Ferrage (Spartans)	2	2	1	5
William Neubecker (Helvecia)	1	2	2	5
Elizandro Lima (Helvecia)	2	1	1	4
Joel Rocha (Sheffield)	2	1	0	3
Luke Ballinger (Chippenham)	0	3	0	3
Sergio Raul (Spartans)	2	1	0	3
Ricardo Ferreira (Spartans)	0	0	3	3

ENGLAND FUTSAL RESULTS 2009-10

DATE	COMPETITION	HOME/AWAY	OPPONENT	RESULT	SCORE
09/10/2009	Other	H	Isreal	L	1 - 3
10/10/2009	Other	H	Isreal	L	1 - 3
04/12/2009	Friendly	A	Libya	D	1 - 1
05/12/2009	Friendly	A	Libya	**W**	2 - 1
05/02/2010	Friendly	A	Cyprus	L	0 - 3
06/02/2010	Friendly	A	Cyprus	L	1 - 3
02/04/2010	Four Nations	H	Malta	**W**	5 - 0
03/04/2010	Four Nations	H	Turkey	L	3 - 4

COUNTY FOOTBALL ASSOCIATIONS

BEDFORDSHIRE F.A.

Tel: 01582 565 111 Fax: 01582 565 222

Email: peter.brown@bedfordshirefa.com

Century House, Skimpot Road,

Dunstable, Bedfordshire LU5 4JU

Chief Executive: Peter D Brown.

BERKS & BUCKS F.A.

Tel: 01367 242 099 Fax: 01367 242 158

Email: brian.moore@berks-bucksfa.com

15a London Street, Faringdon,

Oxon SN7 7HD

Chief Executive: Brian Moore

BIRMINGHAM COUNTY F.A.

Tel: 0121 357 4278 Fax: 0121 358 1661

Email: info@birminghamfa.com

Ray Hall Lane, Great Barr, Birmingham

B43 6JF

Secretary: David Shelton

CAMBRIDGESHIRE F.A.

Tel: 01223 209 020 Fax: 01223 209 030

Email: info@cambridgeshirefa.com

Bridge Road, Impington, Cambridgeshire

CB24 9PH

Chief Executive: Roger Pawley

CHESHIRE F.A.

Tel: 01606 871 166 Fax: 01606 871 292

Email: info@cheshirefa.com

Hartford House, Hartford Moss Rec. Centre,

Winnington, Northwich CW8 4BG

Chief Executive: Maureen Dunford

CORNWALL F.A.

Tel: 01208 269 010 Fax: 01208 892 665

Email: barry.cudmore@cornwallfa.com

Kernow House, 15 Callywith Gate

Launceston Road, Bodmin

Cornwall PL31 2RQ

Secretary: Barry Cudmore

CUMBERLAND F.A.

Tel: 01900 872 310 Fax: 01900 61647

Email: info@cumberlandfa.com

17 Oxford Street, Workington, Cumbria,

CA14 2AL

Chief Executive: Geoff Turrell.

DERBYSHIRE F.A.

Tel: 01332 361 422 Fax: 01332 360 130

Email: info@derbyshirefa.com

Units 8-9 Stadium Business Court,

Millennium Way, Pride Park, Derby DE24 8HP

Chief Executive: Miss Dawn Heron.

DEVON F.A.

Tel: 01626 332 077 Fax: 01626 336 814

Email: info@devonfa.com

County Headquarters, Coach Road,

Newton Abbot, Devon TQ12 1EJ

Chief Executive: Paul Morrison.

DORSET F.A.

Tel: 01202 682 375 Fax: 01202 666 577

Email: sue.hough@dorsetfa.com

County Ground, Blandford Close,

Hamworthy, Poole BH15 4BF

Chief Executive: Sue Hough.

DURHAM F.A.

Tel: 0191 387 2929 Fax: 0191 387 2919

Email: info@durhamfa.com

'Codeslaw', Riverside South,

Chester le Street, Co.Durham DH3 3SJ

Secretary: John Topping.

EAST RIDING F.A.

Tel: 01482 221 158 Fax: 01482 221 169

Email: info@eastridingfa.com

Roy West Centre, 220 Inglemire Lane,

Hull HU6 7TS

Chief Executive: Adam Lowthorpe.

ESSEX F.A.

Tel: 01245 393 079 Fax: 01245 393 089

Email: info@essexfa.com

The County Office, Springfield Lyons Approach,

Springfield, Chelmsford CM2 5LB

Chief Executive: Phil Sammons.

GLOUCESTERSHIRE F.A.

Tel: 01454 615 888 Fax: 01454 618 088

Email: info@gloucestershirefa.com

Oaklands Park, Almondsbury, Bristol

BS32 4AG

Chief Executive: David Neale.

HAMPSHIRE F.A.

Tel: 01256 853 000 Fax: 01256 357 973

Email: info@hampshirefa.com

Winklebury Football Complex,

Winklebury Way, Basingstoke RG23 8BF

Chief Executive: Neil Cassar.

HEREFORDSHIRE F.A.

Tel: 01432 342 179 Fax: 01432 279 265

Email: info@herefordshirefa.com

County Ground Offices,

Widemarsh Common, Hereford HR4 9NA

Chief Executive: Jim Lambert.

HERTFORDSHIRE F.A.

Tel: 01462 677 622 Fax: 01462 677 624

Email: info@hertfordshirefa.com

County Ground, Baldock Road, Letchworth,

Herts SG6 2EN

Chief Executive: Nick Perchard.

HUNTINGDONSHIRE F.A.

Tel: 01480 414 422 Fax: 01480 447 489

Email: info@huntsfa.com

Cromwell Chambers, 8 St Johns Street,

Huntingdon, Cambs PE29 3DD

Secretary: Mark Frost.

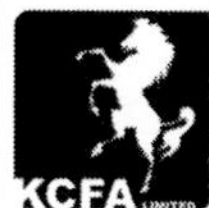

KENT F.A.

Tel: 01622 791 850 Fax: 01622 792 140

Email: info@kentfa.com

Suite A1, Cobdown House,

London Road, Ditton, Aylesford

Kent ME20 6DQ

Chief Executive: Keith Masters.

LANCASHIRE F.A.

Tel: 01772 624 000 Fax: 01772 624 700

Email: secretary@lancashirefa.com

The County Ground, Thurston Road, Leyland

PR25 2LF

Chief Executive: David Burgess.

LEICESTERSHIRE & RUTLAND F.A.

Tel: 0116 286 7828 Fax: 0116 286 4858

Email: info@leicestershirefa.com

Holmes Park, Dog & Gun Lane, Whetstone

LE8 6FA

Chief Executive: Laurence Jones.

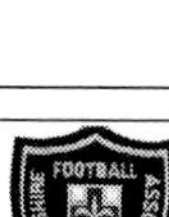

LINCOLNSHIRE F.A.

Tel: 0844 967 0708 Fax: 0844 967 0709

Email: john.griffin@lincolnshirefa.com

Deepdale Enterprise Park, Deepdale Lane,

Nettleham, Lincs LN2 2LL

Secretary: John Griffin.

LIVERPOOL F.A.

Tel: 0151 523 4488 Fax: 0151 523 4477

Email: info@liverpoolfa.com

Liverpool Soccer Centre, Walton Hall Park,

Walton Hall Avenue, Liverpool L4 9XP

Secretary: David Pugh.

LONDON F.A.

Tel: 0207 610 8360 Fax: 0207 610 8370

Email: info@londonfa.com

11 Hurlingham Business Park, Sulivan Road,

Fulham, London SW6 3DU

Chief Executive: David Fowkes.

MANCHESTER F.A.

Tel: 0161 604 7620 Fax: 0161 604 7622

Email: info@manchesterfa.com

Salford Sports Village, Littleton Road,

Lower Kersal, Salford, Manchester M7 3NQ

Chief Executive: Colin Bridgford

MIDDLESEX F.A.

Tel: 020 8515 1919 Fax: 020 8515 1910

Email: info@middlesexfa.com

39 Roxborough Road, Harrow, Middlesex

HA1 1NS

Chief Executive: Peter Clayton.

NORFOLK F.A.

Tel: 01603 704 050 Fax: 01603 704 059

Email: info@norfolkfa.com

11 Meridian Way, Thorpe St Andrew, Norwich

NR7 0TA

Chief Executive: Shaun Turner.

NORTH RIDING F.A.

Tel: 01642 717 770 Fax: 01642 717 776

Email: info@northridingfa.com

Broughton Road, Stokesley, Middlesbrough

TS9 5NY

Chief Executive: Tom Radigan.

NORTHAMPTONSHIRE F.A.

Tel: 01604 670 741 Fax: 01604 670 742

Email: info@northamptonshirefa.com

9 Duncan Close, Red House Square,

Moulton Park, Northampton NN3 6WL

Chief Executive: David Payne.

NORTHUMBERLAND F.A.

Tel: 0191 270 0700

Email: rowland.maughan@northumberlandfa.com

Whitley Park, Whitley Road,

Newcastle upon Tyne NE12 9FA

Chief Executive: Rowland E Maughan.

NOTTINGHAMSHIRE F.A.

Tel: 0115 983 7400 Fax: 0115 946 1977

Email: info@nottnghamshirefa.com

Unit 6b, Chetwynd Business Park,

Chilwell, Nottinghamshire NG9 6RZ

Chief Executive: Elaine Oram.

OXFORDSHIRE F.A.

Tel: 01993 778 586 Fax: 01993 772 191

Email: info@oxfordshirefa.com

PO Box 62, Witney, Oxon

OX28 1HA

Secretary: Ian Mason.

SHEFFIELD & HALLAMSHIRE F.A.

Tel: 0114 241 4999 Fax: 0114 241 4990

Email: info@sheffieldfa.com

Clegg House, 69 Cornish Place, Cornish St.,

Sheffield S6 3AF

Chief Executive: James Hope-Gill.

SHROPSHIRE F.A.

Tel: 01743 362 769 Fax: 01743 270 494

Email: secretary@shropshirefa.com

The New Stadium, Oteley Road,

Shrewsbury, Shropshire SY2 6ST

Chief Executive: David Rowe.

SOMERSET F.A.

Tel: 01761 410 280 Fax: 01761 410 477

Email: info@somersetfa.com

Charles Lewin House,

Unit 5 & 10 Landmark House,

Wirral Bus. Est., Glastonbury, Somerset

BA6 9FR

Chief Executive: Jon Pike.

STAFFORDSHIRE F.A.

Tel: 01785 256 994 Fax: 01785 279 837

Email: brain.adshead@staffordshirefa.com

Unit F, Dyson Court, Staffordshire Tech. Pk,

Beaconside, Stafford ST18 0LQ

Chief Executive: Brian Adshead.

SUFFOLK F.A.

Tel: 01449 616 606 Fax: 01449 616 607

Email: info@suffolkfa.com

The Buntings, Cedars Park, Stowmarket,

Suffolk IP14 5GZ

Chief Executive: Martin Head.

SURREY F.A.

Tel: 01372 373 543 Fax: 01372 361 310

Email: info@surreyfa.com

Connaught House, 36 Bridge Street,

Leatherhead, Surrey KT22 8BZ

Secretary: Ray Ward.

SUSSEX F.A.

Tel: 01903 753 547 Fax: 01903 761 608

Email: info@sussexfa.com

Culver Road, Lancing, West Sussex

BN15 9AX

Chief Executive: Ken Benham.

WEST RIDING F.A.

Tel: 0113 282 1222 Fax: 0113 282 1525

Email: info@wrcfa.com

Fleet Lane, Woodlesford, Leeds

LS26 8NX

Chief Executive: Roy Carter.

WESTMORLAND F.A.

Tel: 01539 730 946 Fax: 01539 740 567

Email: info@westmorlandfa.com

Unit 1, Riverside Business Park, Natland Rd,

Kendal, Cumbria LA9 7SX

Chief Executive: Peter Ducksbury.

WILTSHIRE F.A.

Tel: 01793 486 047 Fax: 01793 692 699

Email: mike.benson@wiltshirefa.com

Units 2/3 Dorcan Business Village, Dorcan,

Swindon, Wiltshire SN3 5HY

Secretary: Mike Benson.

WORCESTERSHIRE F.A.

Tel: 01905 827 137 Fax: 01905 798 963

Email: info@worcestershirefa.com

Craftsman House, De Salis Drive,

Hampton Lovett Ind.Est., Droitwich WR9 0QE

Secretary: Mervyn Leggett.

Crawley Green after their Bedfordshire Senior Trophy success over Potton United.
Photo: Gordon Whittington.

Newport Pagnell Town of the United Counties League and Berks & Bucks Senior Trophy winners.
Photo: Gordon Whittington.

COUNTY CUPS 2009-10

BEDFORDSHIRE PREMIER CUP
(July 29th at Biggleswade Town)
Biggleswade Town 2 Luton Town 2 (4-1p)

BEDFORDSHIRE SENIOR CUP
FIRST ROUND
Biggleswade United 0 **Stotfold** 2
Dunstable 0 **Biggleswade Town** 4 *(at Biggleswade Town)*
QUARTER-FINALS
Arlesey Town 5 Bedford Town 1 *aet*
Barton Town 2 **Stotfold** 3
Biggleswade Town 5 Luton Town 1
Langford 0 **Leighton Town** 5
SEMI-FINALS
Biggleswade Town 1 **Leighton Town** 4
Stotfold 1 **Arlesey Town** 0 *(Stotfold expelled)*
FINAL
(May 21st at Luton Town)
Leighton Town 2 **Arlesey Town** 2 *aet* (1-3p)

BEDFORDSHIRE SENIOR TROPHY
FIRST ROUND
AFC Kempston Rovers 0 Renhold United 0 *aet* (4-2p)
AFC Kempston Town 5 Westoning Recreation Club 1
Ampthill Town 2 **Caddington** 5
Bedford 1 Brache Sparta 0
Biggleswade United Res. (w/o) v Meltis Corinthians
Blunham 1 **Potton United** 3 *aet*
Cranfield United 4 Kent Athletic 0
Crawley Green 3 Totternhoe 1
Ickwell & Old Warden 5 Wilshamstead 1
Riseley Sports 1 **AFC Dunstable** 11
Southill Alexander 3 **The 61 FC (Luton)** 4
Woburn 1 **Campton** 3
Wootton Blue Cross 4 Oakley Sports 0
SECOND ROUND
AFC Dunstable 7 Ickwell & Old Warden 2
AFC Kempston Town 3 Cranfield United 1
Bedford 0 **Crawley Green** 4
Biggleswade United Res. 0 **Caddington** 1
Campton v **AFC Kempston Rovers** (w/o)
Dunton 4 Sharnbrook 2
Potton United 3 Caldecote 0
The 61 FC (Luton) 4 Wootton Blue Cross 2
QUARTER-FINALS
AFC Dunstable 3 Caddington 1
AFC Kempston Rovers 3 Dunton 1
AFC Kempston Town 1 **Potton United** 3 *aet*
Crawley Green 3 The 61 FC (Luton) 1
SEMI-FINALS
Crawley Green 3 AFC Dunstable 1
Potton United 1 AFC Kempston Rovers 0
FINAL
(April 7th at Arlesey Town)
Crawley Green 1 Potton United 1 *aet* (5-4p)

BEDFORDSHIRE INTERMEDIATE CUP
FINAL *(April 14th at Biggleswade United)*
Leighton Town Res. 3 Lewsey Park 0

BEDFORDSHIRE JUNIOR CUP
FINAL *(April 23rd at Potton United)*
Potton Wanderers 4 Renhold Village 2

BERKS & BUCKS SENIOR CUP
FIRST ROUND
Beaconsfield SYCOB 1 **Abingdon United** 3
Burnham 8 Bracknell Town 0
Maidenhead United 3 Chesham United 0
Thatcham Town 2 Hungerford Town 1 *aet*
Wycombe Wanderers 3 Didcot Town 1
QUARTER-FINALS
Abingdon United 1 **Maidenhead United** 2
Slough Town 2 Marlow 1
Thatcham Town 4 Burnham 2
Windsor & Eton 0 **Wycombe Wanderers** 1
SEMI-FINALS
Slough Town 0 **Wycombe Wanderers** 1
Thatcham Town 2 **Maidenhead United** 4 *aet*
FINAL *(May 3rd at Marlow)*
Maidenhead United 3 Wycombe Wanderers 2 *aet*

BERKS & BUCKS SENIOR TROPHY
FIRST ROUND
Ascot United 1 **Binfield** 3 *aet*
Aylesbury 1 **Milton United** 3 *aet (at Milton United)*
Chalfont St Peter 1 **Abingdon Town** 3
Sandhurst Town 1 Flackwell Heath 0
Wantage Town 2 **Shrivenham** 3
QUARTER-FINALS
Marlow United 2 **Newport Pagnell Town** 4 *aet*
Milton United 1 **Abingdon Town** 3
Sandhurst Town 2 Binfield 1
Shrivenham 0 **Reading Town** 2
SEMI-FINALS
Abingdon Town 0 **Reading Town** 2
Newport Pagnell Town 5 Sandhurst Town 3
FINAL
(April 13th at Chesham United)
Reading Town 2 **Newport Pagnell Town** 6

BERKS & BUCKS INTERMEDIATE CUP
FINAL *(May 8th at Buckingham Athletic)*
New Bradwell St Peter 3 Bucks CC 0

BERKS & BUCKS JUNIOR CUP
FINAL *(April 24th at Newport Pagnell Town)*
P & IC United 3 Reading Rapids 0

BIRMINGHAM SENIOR CUP
FIRST ROUND
Alvechurch 1 Bedworth United 0
Atherstone Town 1 **Cradley Town** 3
Banbury United 5 Studley 1
Boldmere St Michaels 2 Walsall 0
Causeway United 2 Highgate United 0
Coleshill Town 1 **Burton Albion** 4
Coventry Sphinx 1 **Nuneaton Town** 3
Halesowen Town 0 **West Bromwich Albion** 2
Hednesford Town 1 **Sutton Coldfield Town** 3
Leamington 5 Bromsgrove Rovers 1
Redditch United 1 **Stourbridge** 2
Romulus 2 Rushall Olympic 1
Rugby Town 6 Stratford Town 2
Solihull Moors 1 **Birmingham City** 3
Tamworth 1 **Wolverhampton Wanderers** 2
Willenhall Town 0 **Tipton Town** 0 *aet* (2-3p)
SECOND ROUND
Alvechurch 2 Rugby Town 1
Boldmere St Michaels 0 **Burton Albion** 3
Causeway United 0 **Romulus** 3
Cradley Town 0 **Stourbridge** 3
Leamington 3 Birmingham City 2
Nuneaton Town 3 Banbury United 2
Sutton Coldfield Town 4 West Bromwich Albion 1
Tipton Town 2 **Wolverhampton Wanderers** 2 *aet* (2-4p)
QUARTER-FINALS
Alvechurch 2 Wolverhampton Wanderers 0
Nuneaton Town 3 Leamington 2
Romulus 2 Burton Albion 1
Stourbridge 4 Sutton Coldfield Town 1
SEMI-FINALS
Romulus 1 **Alvechurch** 3 *aet*
Stourbridge 0 **Nuneaton Town** 4
FINAL
(May 4th at Nuneaton Town)
Nuneaton Town 2 Alvechurch 1

BIRMINGHAM FLOODLIGHT CUP

FIRST ROUND

AFC Wulfrunians 2 Cadbury Athletic 0
Bustleholme 0 **Boldmere St Michaels Res.** 3
Coventry Copsewood 2 **Racing Club Warwick** 4
Dosthill Colts 0 **Oldbury Athletic** 4
Gornal Athletic 4 Dudley Town 3
Knowle 1 **Castle Vale JKS** 2
Lye Town 2 **Bartley Green** 4
Nuneaton Griff 4 **Castle Vale** 5
Tividale 2 Pilkington XXX 1
Wednesfield 3 Continental Star 2

SECOND ROUND

Bartley Green 5 AFC Wulfrunians 3 *aet*
Boldmere St Michaels Res. 2 Racing Club Warwick 1
Bolehall Swifts 1 **Oldbury Athletic** 5
Castle Vale JKS 3 **Wednesfield** 4
Dudley Sports 1 **Massey-Ferguson** 2
Goodrich 0 **Tividale** 1
Gornal Athletic 2 Darlaston Town 1
Southam United 3 Castle Vale 1

QUARTER-FINALS

Bartley Green 2 Southam United 0
Gornal Athletic 4 Wednesfield 2 *aet*
Massey-Ferguson 5 Boldmere St Michs Res. 5 aet (4-2p)
Tividale 2 **Oldbury Athletic** 3

SEMI-FINALS

Massey-Ferguson 0 **Gornal Athletic** 1
Oldbury Athletic 0 **Bartley Green** 1

FINAL

(April 28th at Halesowen Town)
Bartley Green 1 Gornal Athletic 0

BIRMINGHAM VASE

FINAL *(April 14th at Tamworth)*
Alvis 2 Stretton Eagles 2 *aet* (5-4p)

BIRMINGHAM JUNIOR CUP

FINAL *(March 27th at BCFA, Great Barr)*
Silhill 3 Somers A 1

CAMBRIDGESHIRE PROFESSIONAL CUP

(August 3rd at Cambridge United)
Cambridge United 1 **Histon** 2

CAMBRIDGESHIRE INVITATION CUP

(Sponsor: Ridgeons)

FIRST ROUND

Ely City 1 **CRC** 5
Godmanchester Rovers 0 **Fulbourn Institute** 1
Histon Res. 2 Newmarket Town 0
March Town United 1 **Lakenheath** 5
Mildenhall Town (w/o) v Saffron Walden Town
Wisbech Town 3 Cambridge University Press 2

QUARTER-FINALS

Cambridge City 3 Fulbourn Institute 1
Mildenhall Town 3 CRC 1
Soham Town Rangers 3 Histon Res. 0
Wisbech Town 3 Lakenheath 1

SEMI-FINALS

Cambridge City 0 **Mildenhall Town** 3
Wisbech Town 3 Soham Town Rangers 2

FINAL

(April 29th at Cambridge United)
Mildenhall Town 3 Wisbech Town 1

CLIFF BULLEN CAMBRIDGESHIRE CHALLENGE CUP

FIRST ROUND

Castle Camps 3 **Haddenham Rovers** 5
Coates Athletic 3 Swavesey Institute 1
Girton United 7 Wisbech Town Res. 1
Great Chesterford 1 Cherry Hinton 0
Milton 3 March Town United Res. 2 *aet*
Saffron Crocus 1 Outwell Swifts 3 *(Outwell expelled)*
Soham United 1 **Chatteris Town** 5

SECOND ROUND

Coates Athletic 4 Milton 2
Comberton United 0 **Fulbourn Institute** 2
Ely City Res. 4 Girton United 3
Fowlmere 0 **Foxton** 4
Great Shelford 4 Sawston United 1
Hardwick 3 Whittlesey United 2
Leverington Sports 0 Histon A 0 *aet* (4-1p)
Linton Granta 2 **Haddenham Rovers** 3
Over Sports 0 **Chatteris Town** 1
Parson Drove 3 Fordham 0
RHS United 2 **Great Chesterford** 3
Waterbeach 0 **Littleport Town** 3
West Wratting 1 Cambridge University Press 0
Whittlesford United 1 **Cottenham United** 3
Wimblington 2 Saffron Crocus 0
Wisbech St Mary 3 Soham Town Rangers Res. 1

THIRD ROUND

Chatteris Town 0 **Hardwick** 1
Ely City Res. 1 Great Chesterford 0
Foxton 2 Haddenham Rovers 0
Rematch: Haddenham Rovers 1 **Foxton** 6
Fulbourn Institute 8 Wisbech St Mary 3
Great Shelford 2 Cottenham United 2 aet (4-1p)
Littleport Town 3 Leverington Sports 0
Parson Drove 1 **Coates Athletic** 5
West Wratting 6 Wimblington 1

QUARTER-FINALS

Coates Athletic 1 **Hardwick** 2 *aet*
Fulbourn Institute 3 Foxton 1
Great Shelford 3 Ely City Res. 2
West Wratting 0 **Littleport Town** 1

SEMI-FINALS

Fulbourn Institute 1 **Great Shelford** 2
Littleport Town 0 Hardwick 0 *aet* (4-1p)

FINAL *(April 6th at Cambridge City)*
Great Shelford 1 Littleport Town 0

CAMBRIDGESHIRE JUNIOR INVITATION CUP

FINAL *(April 28th at Histon)*
Dullingham 1 **Longstanton** 5

CAMBRIDGESHIRE LOWER JUNIOR CUP

FINAL *(May 11th at Histon)*
Chatteris Town Res. 3 Orwell 0

CHESHIRE PREMIER CUP

FIRST ROUND

Stockport County 2 **Crewe Alexandra** 5
Tranmere Rovers 2 **Macclesfield Town** 4

FINAL

(April 27th at Crewe Alexandra)
Crewe Alexandra 2 Macclesfield Town 1

CHESHIRE SENIOR CUP

FIRST ROUND

Altrincham 1 **Witton Albion** 2
Nantwich Town 3 Hyde United 1
Northwich Victoria 6 Cheadle Town 0
Runcorn Linnets 4 Congleton Town 0
Stalybridge Celtic 1 **Chester City** 2
Vauxhall Motors 4 Warrington Town 3 *(at Warrington)*
Winsford United 2 **Cammell Laird** 3
Woodley Sports 4 Alsager Town 1

QUARTER FINALS

Cammell Laird 4 Nantwich Town 3 *aet*
Chester City 0 **Northwich Victoria** 2 *aet*
Witton Albion 0 **Runcorn Linnets** 1
Woodley Sports 1 Vauxhall Motors 0

SEMI-FINALS

Cammell Laird 2 **Woodley Sports** 4
Northwich Victoria 7 Runcorn Linnets 1

FINAL

(March 24th at Altrincham)
Northwich Victoria 1 Woodley Sports 1 *aet* (5-4p)

CHESHIRE AMATEUR CUP

FIRST ROUND

AFC Bebington Athletic 2 Legion 1 *aet*
Bronze Social 0 **Barnton** 2
Capenhurst Villa (w/o) v Broadheath Central
Chester Nomads 2 Grappenhall Sports 1
Christleton 6 Mersey Royal 0
Club AZ 3 Mallaby 1
Dukinfield Town 11 Bentley 0
Ellesmere Port 2 Blacon Youth Club 1
Govan Athletic 1 **Old Altrinchamians** 3
Hazel Grove 3 FC Pensby 0
Lostock Gralam 0 **Runcorn Town** 4
Lostock Rangers v **Castrol Social** (w/o)
Lymm 0 **Styal** 2
Malpas 2 **Halton** 4
Manor Athletic 2 **Vauxhall Motors Res.** 3
Mellor 0 **Helsby** 2
Moore United 3 Poynton 1
New Brighton 2 Warrington Town Res. 1 *aet*
Newton 2 Heswall 1
Shaftesbury Youth Club v **Crewe** (w/o)
Spurley Hey 2 Upton AA 2 *aet*
Replay: **Upton AA** 4 Spurley Hey 1
St Werburghs 1 **Linotype & Cheadle HN** 10
Stoconians 3 Knutsford 0

SECOND ROUND

AFC Bebington Athletic 5 Hazel Grove 2
Barnton 4 Stoconians 0
Capenhurst Villa 1 **Stockport Georgians** 3
Chester Nomads 2 Stalybridge Celtic Res. 2 *aet*
Replay: Stalybridge Celtic Res. 1 **Chester Nomads** 3
Crewe 1 **Newton** 3
Dukinfield Town 0 **Castrol Social** 1
Ellesmere Port 3 Old Altrinchamians 1
Grange Athletic 3 Christleton 2
Halton 2 **West Kirby** 3
Helsby 3 Club AZ 1 *aet*
Linotype & Cheadle HN 1 Styal 1 *aet*
Replay: **Styal** 3 Linotype & Cheadle HN 2
Moore United 3 **Woodley** 4 *aet*
New Brighton 1 Middlewich Town 1 *aet*
Replay: **Middlewich Town** 3 New Brighton 2
Upton AA 5 **Ashville** 6
Vauxhall Motors Res. 0 **Runcorn Town** 2
Willaston 2 Cammell Laird Res. 1

THIRD ROUND

AFC Bebington Athletic 3 Willaston 3 *aet*
Replay: **Willaston** 3 AFC Bebington Athletic 0
Ashville 1 **Castrol Social** 2
Barnton 0 Chester Nomads 0 *aet*
Replay: **Chester Nomads** 3 Barnton 2
Ellesmere Port 3 Middlewich Town 0
Newton 1 Stockport Georgians 0
Runcorn Town 4 Helsby 3 *(at Helsby)*
West Kirby 4 Styal 0
Woodley 10 Grange Athletic 1

QUARTER-FINALS

Ellesmere Port 0 **Castrol Social** 1
Newton 4 Chester Nomads 3 *aet (at Chester Nomads)*
West Kirby 2 Runcorn Town 0
Woodley 0 **Willaston** 2 *(at Willaston)*

SEMI-FINALS

Castrol Social 2 Newton 1 *(at Vauxhall Motors)*
Willaston 1 **West Kirby** 3 *aet (at Cammell Laird)*

FINAL *(April 16th at Vauxhall Motors)*
Castrol Social 0 **West Kirby** 1

CORNWALL SENIOR CUP

(Sponsor: Westinsure)

PRELIMINARY ROUND

Helston Athletic 5 Biscovey 1
Holmans Sports Club 1 **Troon** 6
Lanreath 1 **Morwenstow** 3
Nanpean Rovers 3 **St Stephens Borough** 5
Perranwell 1 Sticker 1 *aet*
Replay: **Sticker** 2 Perranwell 1
Portreath 0 **St Ives Town** 8
Probus 3 St Dennis 3 *aet*
Replay: **St Dennis** 3 Probus 0
St Agnes 3 St Dominick 1
St Day 3 Mullion 1
St Just 4 Roche 0
St Stephen 1 RNAS Culdrose 3 *(RNAS Culdrose expelled)*

FIRST ROUND

Bude Town 1 **St Day** 2
Helston Athletic 5 Sticker 1
Morwenstow 5 Polperro 1
St Agnes 2 **St Dennis** 4
St Just 7 Ludgvan 2
St Stephen 2 **Edgcumbe** 6
St Stephens Borough 4 St Ives Town 2
Troon 1 **Illogan RBL** 5

SECOND ROUND

Bodmin Town 5 Newquay 0
Camelford 4 Torpoint Athletic 2
Dobwalls 2 **Millbrook** 3
Foxhole Stars 2 **St Dennis** 7
Godolphin Atlantic 5 Edgcumbe 0
Hayle 1 Penzance 0
Helston Athletic 2 **Perranporth** 4
Launceston 3 Falmouth Town 2
Liskeard Athletic 11 Wendron United 1
Morwenstow 2 **St Day** 3
Mousehole 1 **St Austell** 4
Penryn Athletic 2 Truro City 0
Porthleven 5 St Stephens Borough 0
Saltash United 5 Callington Town 3
St Blazey 2 Wadebridge Town 2 *aet*
Replay: Wadebridge Town 3 **St Blazey** 3 *aet* (2-3p)
St Just 1 Illogan RBL 1 *aet*
Replay: **Illogan RBL** 1 St Just 0

THIRD ROUND

Godolphin Atlantic 1 Millbrook 0
Hayle 0 **Camelford** 1
Liskeard Athletic 1 **St Austell** 2
Penryn Athletic 4 St Dennis 1
Perranporth 0 **St Blazey** 1
Porthleven 1 **Launceston** 2
Saltash United 0 **Illogan RBL** 1
St Day 0 **Bodmin Town** 3

QUARTER-FINALS

Bodmin Town 2 Launceston 0
Camelford 3 Godolphin Atlantic 3 *aet*
Replay: Godolphin Atlantic 0 **Camelford** 1
Penryn Athletic 1 St Austell 0
St Blazey 1 **Illogan RBL** 3

SEMI-FINALS

Bodmin Town 4 Penryn Athletic 0 *(at St Blazey)*
Illogan RBL 1 **Camelford** 2 *(at Wadebridge Town)*

FINAL *(April 5th at Truro City)*
Bodmin Town 3 Camelford 1

DURNING LAWRENCE CORNWALL CHARITY CUP

FIRST ROUND

Dobwalls 3 Millbrook 1
Foxhole Stars 1 **Camelford** 6
Hayle 1 **St Austell** 5
Penryn Athletic 4 Callington Town 1
Perranwell 4 Mousehole 0
Porthleven 2 **Godolphin Atlantic** 4 *aet*
Truro City Res. 3 **Perranporth** 5 *aet*
Wendron United 2 **Newquay** 12

QUARTER-FINAL

Newquay 5 Camelford 3
Penryn Athletic 1 **St Austell** 3
Perranporth 1 **Dobwalls** 4
Perranwell 1 Godolphin Atlantic 0

SEMI-FINAL

Dobwalls 1 **Newquay** 2 *(at Liskeard Athletic)*
St Austell 1 Perranwell 0 *(at Penryn Athletic)*

FINAL *(May 12th at St Blazey)*
Newquay 2 St Austell 0

CORNWALL JUNIOR CUP

FINAL

(April 5th at Truro City)

St Buryan 3 Looe Town 0

CUMBERLAND SENIOR CUP

FIRST ROUND

Aspatria 3 Alston Moor Sports Club 1
Cockermouth 13 Whitehaven Miners Social 1
FC32 3 St Bees 2
Frizington White Star 2 **Wetheriggs United** 4 *aet*
Kirkoswald 2 **Longtown** 2 *aet* (2-4p)
Langwathby United 1 **Wigton Athletic** 4
Mirehouse 1 Wigton Harriers 0
Netherhall 6 Keswick 2

SECOND ROUND

Braithwaite 0 **Longtown** 5
Bransty Rangers 1 **Netherhall** 5
Carlisle Amateurs 1 Northbank Carlisle 0
FC32 0 **Aspatria** 3
Greystoke 5 Wigton Athletic 3
Harraby Catholic Club 4 Windscale 0
Hearts of Liddlesdale 2 Cockermouth 1
Mirehouse 3 Penrith Rangers 2 *aet*
Parton United 2 Cleator Moor Celtic 0
Silloth 0 **Wetheriggs United** 2
Workington South 1 **Carlisle City** 3

THIRD ROUND

Gillford Park 2 Carlisle City 1
Harraby Catholic Club 5 Parton United 0
Longtown 0 **Carlisle Amateurs** 1
Mirehouse 2 **Aspatria** 3
Penrith 7 Netherhall 0
Wetheriggs United 2 Carlisle United 1
Whitehaven Amateurs (w/o) v Hearts of Liddlesdale
Workington 3 Greystoke 0

QUARTER-FINALS

Carlisle Amateurs 0 **Workington** 3
Gillford Park 2 Wetheriggs United 1 *aet*
Harraby Catholic Club 1 Whitehaven Amateurs 0
Penrith 3 Aspatria 0

SEMI-FINALS

Gillford Park 1 Workington 0
Harraby Catholic Club 0 **Penrith** 3

FINAL *(May 7th at Carlisle United)*

Penrith 6 Gillford Park 0

DERBYSHIRE SENIOR CUP

FIRST ROUND

Chapel Town 1 Stapenhill 0
Dronfield Town 3 **Pinxton** 6
Gamesley 3 **Shirebrook Town** 5
Gresley 2 Borrowash Victoria 0
Holbrook Miners Welfare 2 Heanor Town 0
Long Eaton United 5 Blackwell Miners Welfare 0
New Mills 7 Parkhouse 4 *aet*
Newhall United 3 **Glossop North End** 8
South Normanton 0 **Graham Street Prims** 1 *aet*

SECOND ROUND

Alfreton Town 7 Holbrook Miners Welfare 2
Buxton 6 Graham St Prims 3
Glossop North End 0 **Glapwell** 2
Gresley 0 **Belper Town** 3
Ilkeston Town 3 Pinxton 1
Long Eaton United 2 Chapel Town 0
Matlock Town 2 Mickleover Sports 1 *aet*
Shirebrook Town 0 **New Mills** 3

QUARTER FINALS

Buxton 1 Ilkeston Town 1
Replay: **Ilkeston Town** 3 Buxton 1 *aet*
Glapwell 1 **Belper Town** 1 *aet* (4-5p)
Long Eaton United 2 **New Mills** 3
Matlock Town 3 Alfreton Town 1

SEMI-FINALS

Ilkeston Town 0 **Belper Town** 1
Matlock Town 2 New Mills 1

FINAL

(April 20th at Derby County)

Belper Town 0 **Matlock Town** 2

DERBYSHIRE DIVISIONAL CUP NORTH

FINAL

(April 13th at Buxton)

Whaley Bridge Athletic 6 Grindleford 0

DERBYSHIRE DIVISIONAL CUP SOUTH

FINAL

(April 6th at Belper Town)

Allenton United 3 Ashbourne 0

DERBYSHIRE JUNIOR CUP NORTH

FINAL

(April 22nd at Glapwell)

Pinxton North End 1 **Three Horse Shoes Brimington** 9

DERBYSHIRE JUNIOR CUP SOUTH

FINAL

(April 14th at Long Eaton United)

Mickleover RBL Res. 3 Acorn Athletic 1

DEVON ST LUKES BOWL

(Sponsor: Westinsure)

FIRST ROUND

Buckland Athletic 6 Elburton Villa 0
Cullompton Rangers 3 Clyst Rovers 0
Dawlish Town 8 Bovey Tracey 1
Holsworthy 3 **Ivybridge Town** 4 *aet*
Ilfracombe Town 4 Witheridge 2 *aet*

SECOND ROUND

Barnstaple Town 4 Cullompton Rangers 3 *aet*
Buckland Athletic 1 **Plymouth Argyle** 3
Dartmouth 0 **Bideford** 6
Dawlish Town 0 **Willand Rovers** 2
Elmore 2 **Tiverton Town** 5
Ilfracombe Town 1 **Exeter City** 4
Ivybridge Town 3 Tavistock 1 *(at Tavistock)*
Plymouth Parkway 0 **Torquay United** 6
(at Torquay United)

QUARTER-FINALS

Barnstaple Town 1 **Plymouth Argyle** 3
Bideford 2 Torquay United 1
Ivybridge Town 1 **Exeter City** 2 *aet*
(at Newton Abbot Spurs)
Willand Rovers 2 **Tiverton Town** 2 *aet* (4-5p)

SEMI-FINALS

Bideford 1 Plymouth Argyle 0
Tiverton Town 1 **Exeter City** 1 *aet* (5-6p)

FINAL

(May 6th at Willand Rovers)

Exeter City 1 **Bideford** 2

DEVON PREMIER CUP

(Sponsor: Graddon Vending)

FINAL

(April 22nd at Tiverton Town)

Royal Marines 3 **Appledore** 5 *aet*

DEVON SENIOR CUP

(Sponsor: Jail Ale)

FINAL

(April 29th at DCFA, Newton Abbot)

Buckland Athletic Res. 4 Elburton Villa Res. 2 *aet*

DEVON INTERMEDIATE CUP

FINAL *(April 8th at DCFA, Newton Abbot)*

Woolsery 4 Windsor Car Sales 2

DORSET SENIOR CUP
FIRST ROUND
Bridport 1 **Chickerell United** 2
Cobham Sports 4 Sturminster Newton Utd 1
Gillingham Town 3 Blandford United 2
Holt United 4 Cranborne 1
Parley Sports 5 Shaftesbury 3 *aet*
Swanage Town & Herston 2 Hamworthy Recreation 1
SECOND ROUND
Chickerell United 0 **Gillingham Town** 1 *aet*
Parley Sports 0 **Swanage Town & Herston** 2
Poole Borough 1 Holt United 0 *aet*
Portland United 0 **Hamworthy United** 1
Sturminster Marshall 4 Cobham Sports 1 *aet*
Verwood Town 2 **Dorchester Town** 7
Weymouth 3 Poole Town 1
Wimborne Town 3 Sherborne Town 2
QUARTER-FINALS
Dorchester Town 1 **Wimborne Town** 4
Gillingham Town 1 Weymouth 0 *(at Weymouth)*
Hamworthy United 2 Swanage Town & Herston 1
Sturminster Marshall 1 **Poole Borough** 4
SEMI-FINALS
Gillingham Town 1 Hamworthy United 0
(at Dorchester Town)
Wimborne Town 2 Poole Borough 1
(at Hamworthy United)
FINAL
(April 13th at Dorchester Town)
Wimborne Town 1 **Gillingham Town** 2 *aet*

DORSET SENIOR TROPHY
FINAL
(April 7th at Weymouth)
Weymouth Sports 2 **Bridport Res.** 3

DORSET INTERMEDIATE CUP
FINAL
(April 15th at Wimborne Town)
Blandford Sports 3 Ferndown Town 1

DORSET JUNIOR CUP
FINAL
(April 20th at Dorchester Town)
Bridport A 0 **FC Windowman** 1

DORSET MINOR CUP
FINAL
(April 1st at Hamworthy United)
Corfe Mullen 1 South Coast Demolition 0

DURHAM CHALLENGE CUP
PRELIMINARY ROUND
Boldon Community Association 5 Hebburn Town 2
Hartlepool United 0 **Washington** 1 *(at Washington)*
Horden Colliery Welfare 4 **Crook Town** 5 *aet*
(at Crook Town)
Houghton Town 0 **Bishop Auckland** 5
Jarrow 1 Annfield Plain 0
Newton Aycliffe 2 Peterlee Town 0
Seaham Red Star 1 **Esh Winning** 4
Silksworth CC 2 **Ryhope Colliery Welfare** 3
Spennymoor Town 8 Willington 0
Whickham 0 **Billingham Town** 2
FIRST ROUND
Billingham Synthonia 3 Ryhope Colliery Welfare 1
Billingham Town 4 Coxhoe Athletic 1
Birtley Town 3 Darlington Railway Athletic 0
Brandon United 1 **Boldon Community Association** 2 *aet*
Darlington 1 **Crook Town** 3
Dunston UTS 4 Easington Colliery 0
Durham City 1 Washington 0
Esh Winning 3 **Consett** 4
Jarrow 3 **West Auckland Town** 3 *aet* (2-4p)
Jarrow Roofing Boldon CA 1 Spennymoor Town 0
Newton Aycliffe 4 Ashbrooke Belford House 1
Norton & Stockton Ancients 2 Bishop Auckland 0
Ryton 3 Sunderland Ryhope CA 0
South Shields 4 Hartlepool 2
Tow Law Town 0 **Chester-le-Street Town** 5
Wolviston 0 **Shildon** 2
SECOND ROUND
Billingham Town 2 **Billingham Synthonia** 3
Boldon Community Association 2 **Crook Town** 5
Chester-le-Street Town 2 Dunston UTS 0
Durham City 1 **Shildon** 3 *aet*
Newton Aycliffe 2 Birtley Town 1
Norton & Stockton Ancients 1 **Consett** 3
South Shields 0 **Jarrow Roofing Boldon CA** 1
West Auckland Town 0 **Ryton** 4
QUARTER-FINALS
Billingham Synthonia 3 Newton Aycliffe 0
Chester-le-Street Town 2 **Ryton** 6
Crook Town 2 Consett 1
Jarrow Roofing Boldon CA 1 **Shildon** 3
SEMI-FINALS
Crook Town 0 **Ryton** 1
Shildon 1 **Billingham Synthonia** 2 *aet*
FINAL
(April 2nd at Eppleton Colliery Welfare)
Billingham Synthonia 2 Ryton 0

DURHAM CHALLENGE TROPHY
FINAL
(March 26th at Eppleton Colliery Welfare)
Hebburn Reyrolle 2 **Whitehills** 4

DURHAM MINOR CUP
FINAL
(April 7th at Peterlee Town)
Hartlepool Millhouse 2 **South Shields United** 3 *aet*

EAST RIDING SENIOR CUP
FIRST ROUND
Beverley Town 3 Pocklington Town 1
Reckitts 4 Easington United 1
Westella & Willerby 5 Hedon Rangers 1
SECOND ROUND
Bridlington Town 1 Westella & Willerby 0
Hall Road Rangers 3 Beverley Town 2
Hessle Rangers 1 **Hull City** 2
Hessle Sporting Club 1 **Malet Lambert Youth Club** 2
Hornsea Town 4 St Andrews 1
(at Leconfield)
North Ferriby United 7 Hutton Cranswick United 0
Reckitts 2 **Chalk Lane** 3
Sculcoates Amateurs 3 Hall Road Rangers 2
QUARTER-FINALS
Chalk Lane 5 Hornsea Town 2
Hall Road Rangers 1 **Sculcoates Amateurs** 4
Malet Lambert Youth Club 0 **Bridlington Town** 1
(at Bridlington Town)
North Ferriby United 3 Hull City 0
SEMI-FINALS
Bridlington Town 2 Sculcoates Amateurs 0
(at ERCFA, Hull)
North Ferriby United 7 Chalk Lane 0
(at ERCFA, Hull)
FINAL
(May 4th at Hull City)
Bridlington Town 2 **North Ferriby United** 3 *aet*

EAST RIDING COUNTRY CUP
FINAL
(May 11th at Bridlington Town)
Riccall 3 Hodgsons 0

EAST RIDING INTERMEDIATE CUP
FINAL
(May 3rd at ERCFA, Hull)
Kingburn Athletic 3 Little Weighton 0

ESSEX SENIOR CUP

FIRST ROUND

London APSA 4 FC Clacton 1
Saffron Walden Town 3 Harwich & Parkeston 0
Wivenhoe Town 1 **Halstead Town** 3

SECOND ROUND

Bowers & Pitsea 3 Stansted 1
Burnham Ramblers 7 Eton Manor 1
Hullbridge Sports 2 Tiptree United 1
London APSA 1 Basildon Utd 3 *(Basildon Utd expelled)*
Saffron Walden Town 4 Takeley 2
Southend Manor 1 Barkingside 1 *aet* (5-4p)
Stanway Rovers 4 Barking 2 *aet*
Witham Town 2 **Halstead Town** 2 *aet* (1-4p)

THIRD ROUND

Aveley 2 Brentwood Town 1
Bowers & Pitsea 1 Southend United 0
Braintree Town 3 Canvey Island 1
Burnham Ramblers 1 **Billericay Town** 2
Dagenham & Redbridge 3 Great Wakering Rovers 3 *aet* (5-4p)
East Thurrock United 4 Thurrock 3
Halstead Town 0 **Harlow Town** 4
Heybridge Swifts 3 **Chelmsford City** 4
Ilford 0 **Colchester United** 1
London APSA 0 **Hullbridge Sports** 2
Maldon Town 3 Tilbury 0
Romford 0 **Grays Athletic** 5
Saffron Walden Town 0 **Concord Rangers** 3
Southend Manor 3 **Redbridge** 4
Stanway Rovers 2 **Waltham Abbey** 3 *aet*
Waltham Forest 0 **AFC Hornchurch** 2

FOURTH ROUND

Aveley 4 Billericay Town 2
Chelmsford City 1 Grays Athletic 0
Concord Rangers 1 **Maldon Town** 2
East Thurrock United 0 **AFC Hornchurch** 4
Harlow Town 2 **Dagenham & Redbridge** 3
Hullbridge Sports 1 Braintree Town 0
Redbridge 1 **Colchester United** 3 *(at Colchester United)*
Waltham Abbey 4 Bowers & Pitsea 1

QUARTER-FINALS

Chelmsford City 5 Aveley 0
Colchester United 7 Maldon Town 1
Dagenham & Redbridge 1 Hullbridge Sports 0
Waltham Abbey 0 **AFC Hornchurch** 1

SEMI-FINALS

AFC Hornchurch 4 Chelmsford City 3
Dagenham & Redbridge 0 **Colchester United** 1

FINAL

(August 3rd at AFC Hornchurch)
AFC Hornchurch 1 **Colchester United** 2

ESSEX PREMIER CUP

FIRST ROUND

Boxted Lodgers 1 **Epping** 7
Faces 0 **Canning Town** 3
Gas Recreation 3 Basildon Town 0
Gosfield United 0 **Bowers & Pitsea Res.** 4
Great Wakering Rovers Res 2 **Foxash Social** 2 *aet* (4-5p)
Hannakins Farm 2 Rayleigh Town 1
Harold Wood Athletic 3 Ryan 1
Herongate Athletic 1 **Witham Town Res.** 3
Heybridge Swifts Res. 4 Wivenhoe Town Res. 1
Lawford Lads 0 **Mountnessing Boca** 2
Leigh Ramblers 10 Burnham Ramblers Res. 1
Newbury Forest 4 Hutton 2
Romford Res. 1 **Old Chelmsfordians** 5
Runwell Hospital 4 Dedham Old Boys 3
Shenfield Association 5 Stanway Rovers Res. 0
Takeley Res. 2 **Benfleet** 3 *aet*
Upminster 1 **White Notley** 4
West Bergholt 1 Stansted Res. 0
Westhamians 3 Rowhedge 1
White Ensign 5 M & B Club 1

SECOND ROUND

Alresford Colne Rangers 1 **Leigh Ramblers** 2 *aet*
Barking Res. 2 **Benfleet** 3 *(at Benfleet)*
Brampton Park 0 **Buckhurst Hill** 4
Brightlingsea Regent 1 Shell Club Corringham 0
Canning Town 2 **Harold Wood Athletic** 3
Catholic United 0 **Manford Way** 3
Clacton United 1 Great Bentley 0
Earls Colne (w/o) v Ramsden
Foxash Social 2 **Galleywood** 3
Gas Recreation 4 Writtle 1
Halstead Town Res. 2 **Grays Athletic Res.** 4
Hannakins Farm 6 Shenfield Association 1
Heybridge Swifts Res. 1 **Frenford Senior** 2
Kelvedon Hatch 3 Holland 2
Lakeside 5 Kirby Athletic 0
Leytonstone United 1 **Springfield** 2 *aet*
Little Oakley 3 **Newbury Forest** 3 *aet* (2-4p)
Maldon St Marys 1 Waltham Abbey Res. 0
Mountnessing Boca 7 Mersea Island 1
Old Chelmsfordians 0 **Epping** 3
Ongar Town 1 **Wadham Lodge** 2
Roydon 2 **White Ensign** 3
Runwell Hospital 2 **Sandon Royals** 3
Southminster St Leonards 1 **Barking Boro.** 1 *aet* (3-4p)
Sungate 3 Bowers & Pitsea Res. 1
Thurrock Res. 4 Debden Sports 2 *aet*
Tiptree Jobserve 0 **Coggeshall Town** 1
Toby 2 Barnston 0
Weeley Athletic 1 **West Essex** 2
West Bergholt 1 Bradfield Rovers 0
Westhamians 5 Hatfield Peverel 0
Witham Town Res. 0 **White Notley** 5

THIRD ROUND

Barking Borough 1 **White Notley** 4
Benfleet 1 **Westhamians** 3
Brightlingsea Regent 1 Leigh Ramblers 0
Buckhurst Hill 1 Epping 0 *(at Epping)*
Clacton United 1 **Toby** 4
Frenford Senior 9 Earls Colne 0
Galleywood 3 Kelvedon Hatch 1
Harold Wood Athletic 3 Coggeshall Town 0
Lakeside 0 **Grays Athletic Res.** 1
Manford Way 1 **Newbury Forest** 2
Mountnessing Boca 2 **Hannakins Farm** 2 *aet* (4-5p)
Springfield 0 **Thurrock Res.** 4
Sungate 4 White Ensign 2
Wadham Lodge 2 Sandon Royals 0
West Bergholt 3 Maldon St Marys 2
West Essex v **Gas Recreation** (w/o)

FOURTH ROUND

Brightlingsea Regent 2 **West Bergholt** 3
Buckhurst Hill 4 Westhamians 3
Frenford Senior 2 Hannakins Farm 0
Galleywood 1 Harold Wood Athletic 0
Gas Recreation 7 Sungate 5 *aet*
Newbury Forest 5 Wadham Lodge 1
Thurrock Res. 2 Grays Athletic Res. 1
Toby 2 **White Notley** 3

QUARTER FINALS

Frenford Senior 1 **Galleywood** 2 *aet*
Thurrock Res. 0 **Buckhurst Hill** 3
West Bergholt 6 Gas Recreation 2 *aet*
White Notley 2 **Newbury Forest** 4 *aet*

SEMI-FINALS

Buckhurst Hill 1 **Galleywood** 1 *aet* (3-4p)
Newbury Forest 1 **West Bergholt** 3

FINAL

(April 14th at Billericay Town)
West Bergholt 2 Galleywood 1

ESSEX JUNIOR CUP

FINAL

(April 21st at Great Wakering Rovers)
Byfleet Rangers 0 **Old Southendians** 1

ESSEX JUNIOR TROPHY
FINAL
(April 28th at Billericay Town)
St Clere's 1 **Beacon Hill Rovers Res.** 2 *aet*

GLOUCESTERSHIRE SENIOR CUP
FIRST ROUND
Cinderford Town 2 Cirencester Town 1
Mangotsfield United 3 Yate Town 1
QUARTER-FINALS
Bishops Cleeve 1 **Bristol Rovers** 3
Cheltenham Town 0 **Gloucester City** 4
Cinderford Town 1 **Bristol City** 4 *aet*
Mangotsfield United 1 Forest Green Rovers 0
SEMI-FINALS
Bristol Rovers 1 **Bristol City** 3
Gloucester City 4 Mangotsfield United 3 *aet*
FINAL
(May 5th at Bristol City)
Bristol City 2 Gloucester City 0

GLOUCESTERSHIRE CHALLENGE TROPHY
FIRST ROUND
Bitton 5 Fairford Town 1
Kings Stanley 3 Thornbury Town 1
Lydney Town 1 **Longwell Green Sports** 3
Rockleaze Avonside 0 **Shirehampton** 1
Slimbridge 6 AXA 2
Tuffley Rovers (w/o) v Hardwicke
Tytherington Rocks 2 Chipping Sodbury 2 *aet* (4-2p)
SECOND-ROUND
Almondsbury Town 2 Berkeley Town 0
Bitton 1 Hallen 0
Cadbury Heath 5 Ellwood 0
Cheltenham Saracens 7 Cirencester Town Res. 1
Hanham Athletic 1 Harrow Hill 0
Henbury 1 **Highridge United** 6
Mangotsfield United Res. v **Longwell Green Sports** (w/o)
Oldland Abbotonians 4 Kings Stanley 1
Patchway Town 4 DRG Stapleton 1
Shirehampton 1 **Almondsbury UWE** 2
Shortwood United 3 Brimscombe & Thrupp 0
Taverners 0 **Bishops Cleeve Res.** 1
Tuffley Rovers 1 **Slimbridge** 2
Tytherington Rocks 1 Roman Glass St George 1 *aet* (3-2p)
Winterbourne United 4 Kingswood 1 *aet*
Yate Town Res. 0 **Bristol Manor Farm** 3
THIRD ROUND
Almondsbury UWE 3 Bishops Cleeve Res. 0
(at Almondsbury Town)
Bitton 2 Cadbury Heath 1 *aet*
Cheltenham Saracens 2 **Almondsbury Town** 4
Highridge United 4 Tytherington Rocks 1
Oldland Abbotonians 3 Bristol Manor Farm 2
Shortwood United 2 Longwell Green Sports 1
Slimbridge 3 **Hanham Athletic** 4 *aet*
Winterbourne United 0 **Patchway Town** 1 *aet*
QUARTER-FINALS
Almondsbury UWE 3 Highridge United 0
Bitton 3 **Almondsbury Town** 3 *aet* (3-5p)
Oldland Abbotonians 0 **Shortwood United** 5
Patchway Town 1 **Hanham Athletic** 2
SEMI-FINALS
Hanham Athletic 3 **Almondsbury Town** 7
Shortwood United 7 Almondsbury UWE 1
FINAL
(April 29th at Almondsbury Town)
Shortwood United 2 **Almondsbury Town** 3

GLOUCESTERSHIRE SENIOR AMATEUR CUP NORTH
FINAL *(April 15th at Slimbridge)*
Cheltenham Saracens Res. 1 **Sharpness** 2

GLOUCESTERSHIRE SENIOR AMATEUR CUP SOUTH
FINAL
(April 27th at Almondsbury Town)
Mendip United 0 **Southmead Athletic** 1

GLOUCESTERSHIRE INTERMEDIATE CUP NORTH
FINAL
(April 22nd at Almondsbury Town)
Gloucester Elmleaze 0 **FC Barometrics Res.** 1

GLOUCESTERSHIRE INTERMEDIATE CUP SOUTH
FINAL
(April 13th at Almondsbury Town)
Eden Grove 3 DRG Stapleton Res. 2

GLOUCESTERSHIRE JUNIOR CUP NORTH
FINAL
(May 6th at Shortwood United)
Marshall Langston 2 Newent Town 0

GLOUCESTERSHIRE JUNIOR CUP SOUTH
FINAL
(April 20th at Almondsbury Town)
Ashley 3 St Aldhelms Res. 1

GLOUCESTERSHIRE MINOR CUP NORTH
FINAL
(April 27th at Cirencester Town)
Cheltenham & Gloucester 6 Tetbury Town A 3

GLOUCESTERSHIRE MINOR CUP SOUTH
FINAL
(March 30th at Almondsbury Town)
St George Rangers 2 Woodlands Rangers 1

GLOUCESTERSHIRE PRIMARY CUP NORTH
FINAL *(April 13th at Tuffley Rovers)*
Bush 1 FC Lakeside 0

GLOUCESTERSHIRE PRIMARY CUP SOUTH
FINAL
(March 13th at Almondsbury Town)
Real Thornbury 5 Hallen A 2

HAMPSHIRE SENIOR CUP
(Sponsor: BSA-Regal Group)
FIRST ROUND
AFC Portchester 4 Alton Town 2
Andover New Street 3 **Hayling United** 7
Belgrave Wanderers 1 **Moneyfields** 4
Blackfield & Langley 4 United Services Portsmouth 2
Bournemouth 2 Guernsey Athletic 1
Christchurch 3 Fawley 1
Cowes Sports 0 **Hamble ASSC** 1
Eversley 1 Petersfield Town 0 *(at Petersfield Town)*
Fareham Town 3 Alresford Town 3 *aet* (5-4p)
Farnborough North End 4 Ringwood Town 1
Hythe & Dibden 4 Lymington Town 3
New Milton Town 1 Stockbridge 0
Romsey Town 2 Brading Town 0
Tadley Calleva 0 **Newport IOW** 6
Totton & Eling 5 Horndean 0
Whitchurch United 3 Hartley Wintney 0

SECOND ROUND
AFC Portchester 0 **Basingstoke Town** 4
Aldershot Town 6 Romsey Town 0
Andover 2 Winchester City 1 *aet*
Bashley 2 **Farnborough** 3
Bournemouth 4 Hayling United 0
Christchurch 2 Eastleigh 1 *aet*
Cove 3 Whitchurch United 1
East Cowes Victoria Athletic 0 **Moneyfields** 2 *aet*
Eversley 1 **Brockenhurst** 4 *(at Brockenhurst)*
Fareham Town 1 **AFC Totton** 2
Fleet Spurs 2 **Farnborough North End** 3 aet
Fleet Town 3 Blackfield & Langley 0
Hamble ASSC 3 **Gosport Borough** 6 *aet*
Hythe & Dibden 1 **Havant & Waterlooville** 6
New Milton Town 1 Newport IOW 0
VTFC 1 Totton & Eling 0
THIRD ROUND
Bournemouth 1 Havant & Waterlooville 0
Brockenhurst 0 **AFC Totton** 5
Cove 0 **Aldershot Town** 1 *aet*
Farnborough 3 Gosport Borough 3 *aet* (5-4p)
Farnborough North End 2 **Christchurch** 6
Fleet Town 5 New Milton Town 0
Moneyfields 2 Andover 1
VTFC 1 Basingstoke Town 0
QUARTER-FINALS
Bournemouth 1 **AFC Totton** 3
Christchurch 4 Moneyfields 0
Farnborough 1 **Aldershot Town** 2
Fleet Town 2 VTFC 1
SEMI-FINALS
AFC Totton 3 Christchurch 0
Fleet Town 1 **Aldershot Town** 1 *aet* (3-4p)
FINAL
(April 22nd at AFC Bournemouth)
Aldershot Town 0 **AFC Totton** 4

HAMPSHIRE RUSSELL COTES CUP
(Sponsor: Harold G Walker)
FIRST ROUND
Farnborough North End 2 **Bemerton Heath Harlequins** 4
Fleet Spurs 2 **Hythe & Dibden** 3 *aet*
Newport IOW 3 AFC Portchester 1
Petersfield Town 3 **Amesbury Town** 3 *aet* (7-8p)
Ringwood Town 2 **Totton & Eling** 3
SECOND ROUND
Andover 3 Amesbury Town 2
Brockenhurst 5 Hythe & Dibden 1
Fareham Town 7 Hamble ASSC 0
Fleet Town 2 **Newport IOW** 3 *aet*
Gosport Borough 1 Hayling United 0
Moneyfields (w/o) v Andover New Street
Romsey Town 4 **Bemerton Heath Harlequins** 5 *aet*
Totton & Eling 3 Christchurch 1 *aet*
QUARTER-FINALS
Fareham Town 1 **Brockenhurst** 4
Gosport Borough 3 Bemerton Heath Harlequins 0
Newport IOW 0 **Moneyfields** 0 *aet* (3-4p)
Totton & Eling 6 Andover 2
SEMI-FINALS
Gosport Borough 2 Brockenhurst 0
Totton & Eling 3 Moneyfields 2
FINAL *(April 20th at Gosport Borough)*
Gosport Borough 1 **Totton & Eling** 3 *aet*

HAMPSHIRE INTERMEDIATE CUP
(Sponsor: Genesis Reflective Products)
FINAL *(April 16th at Andover New Street)*
Liphook United 2 Netley Central Sports 0

HAMPSHIRE JUNIOR A CUP
(Sponsor: JD Fives)
FINAL *(April 10th at Andover New Street)*
FC Censo 3 Headley Athletic 0

HAMPSHIRE JUNIOR B CUP
(Sponsor: JD Fives)
FINAL
(April 10th at Andover New Street)
Richmond Park Con Club 2 Compton Res. 0

HEREFORDSHIRE CHALLENGE CUP
FIRST ROUND
Hinton (w/o) v Woofferton
Holme Lacy 1 **Hereford Lads Club** 4
Kington Town 0 **Ledbury Town** 6
Leominster Town 5 Fownhope 4
Pegasus Juniors 6 Ewyas Harold 1
Wellington 2 **Westfields** 4
QUARTER-FINALS
Hinton 1 Bromyard Town 0
Pegasus Juniors 4 **Ledbury Town** 6
Ross Town v **Leominster Town** (w/o)
Westfields 7 Hereford Lads Club 0
SEMI-FINALS
Ledbury Town 2 Leominster Town 1
Westfields 4 Hinton 0
FINAL
(April 5th at Hereford United)
Westfields 0 **Ledbury Town** 3

HEREFORDSHIRE CHARITY BOWL
FIRST ROUND
Hereford Lads Club 2 Fownhope 1
Holme Lacy 2 **Wellington Res.** 7
Kington Town 4 **Hinton** 6
Leominster Town 15 Bromyard Town Res. 0
Ross Town 0 **Ewyas Harold** 7
Woofferton v **Pegasus Juniors Res.** (w/o)
QUARTER-FINALS
Ewyas Harold 1 **Ledbury Town Res.** 2
Leominster Town 11 Hereford Lads Club 1
Wellington Res. 4 Hinton 2
Westfields Res. 0 **Pegasus Juniors Res.** 2
SEMI-FINALS
Leominster Town 5 Ledbury Town Res. 1
Pegasus Juniors Res. 5 Wellington Res. 3
FINAL
(March 17th at Wellington)
Pegasus Juniors Res. 1 **Leominster Town** 5

HERTFORDSHIRE SENIOR CUP
FIRST ROUND
Broxbourne Borough V & E 2 Colney Heath 1
Hemel Hempstead Town 4 Watford 1
Leverstock Green 2 Hitchin Town 1
Oxhey Jets 4 Hertford Town 2
Royston Town 3 Boreham Wood 1
Ware 3 Tring Athletic 1
SECOND ROUND
Barnet 3 **Hemel Hempstead Town** 5
(at Hemel Hempstead Town)
Bishop's Stortford 6 Hatfield Town 2 *aet*
Leverstock Green 1 **Stevenage Borough** 4
Oxhey Jets 1 Potters Bar Town 0
Sawbridgeworth Town 1 **Cheshunt** 2
St Albans City 0 **Royston Town** 2
St Margaretsbury 1 Ware 0
Welwyn Garden City 2 Broxbourne Borough V & E 1 *aet*
QUARTER-FINALS
Bishop's Stortford 3 St Margaretsbury 1
Hemel Hempstead Town 5 Welwyn Garden City 0
Royston Town 2 **Cheshunt** 3
Stevenage Borough 9 Oxhey Jets 0
SEMI-FINALS
Bishop's Stortford 8 Stevenage Borough 2
Cheshunt 2 Hemel Hempstead Town 2
aet (2-1p)
FINAL
(April 13th at HCFA, Letchworth)
Bishop's Stortford 4 Cheshunt 0

HERTFORDSHIRE CHARITY CUP

FIRST ROUND

Bishop's Stortford 1 **Broxbourne Boro. V & E** 1 *aet* (3-4p)
Hemel Hempstead Town 1 Leverstock Green 0
Hitchin Town 2 Cheshunt 1 *aet*
Potters Bar Town 2 Ware 2 *aet* (5-4p)

SEMI-FINALS

Hitchin Town 1 **Broxbourne Borough V & E** 5
Potters Bar Town 0 **Hemel Hempstead Town** 4

FINAL *(May 6th at HCFA, Letchworth)*

Hemel Hempstead Town 2 Broxbourne Borough V & E 1

HERTFORDSHIRE SENIOR CENTENARY TROPHY

FIRST ROUND

Bovingdon 0 **Wodson Park** 4
Codicote 4 Harpenden Town 2
Evergreen 1 **Metropolitan Police Bushey** 3
Hadley 0 **Tring Corinthians** 2
Hertford Heath 1 **Berkhamsted** 6
Kings Langley 0 Sandridge Rovers 0 *aet* (10-9p)
Lemsford 4 Mill End Sports 0
Sun Postal Sports 1 **Baldock Town Letchworth** 5
Wormley Rovers 2 Cuffley 1 *aet*

SECOND ROUND

Baldock Town Letchworth 2 **Wormley Rovers** 2 *aet* (1-3p)
Codicote 3 Tring Corinthians 2
Hoddesdon Town 3 Metropolitan Police Bushey 1 *aet*
Kings Lanley 5 Croxley Guild 3 *aet*
Lemsford 2 **Chipperfield Corinthians** 5
London Lions 2 Standon & Puckeridge 0
Park Street Village 0 **London Colney** 1
Wodson Park 5 Berkhamsted 2

QUARTER-FINALS

Chipperfield Corinthians 3 **Codicote** 3 *aet* (1-3p)
London Colney 3 Hoddesdon Town 0
Wodson Park 1 **Kings Langley** 4
Wormley Rovers 3 London Lions 0

SEMI-FINALS

London Colney 2 Kings Langley 0 *aet*
Wormley Rovers 3 Codicote 0

FINAL

(March 17th at at HCFA, Letchworth)

London Colney 4 Wormley Rovers 0

HERTFORDSHIRE CHARITY SHIELD

FIRST ROUND

Colney Heath 0 **Hoddesdon Town** 3
Harpenden Town 0 **Metropolitan Police Bushey** 2
Hertford Town 2 Royston Town 0
Kings Langley 1 **London Colney** 3
London Lions 0 **Welwyn Garden City** 1
Oxhey Jets 4 Sun Postal Sports 0
Sawbridgeworth Town 0 **St Margaretsbury** 4
Tring Athletic 3 Hatfield Town 1 *aet*

QUARTER-FINALS

Hertford Town 2 **London Colney** 4
Hoddesdon Town 0 Tring Athletic 0 *aet* (3-2p)
Oxhey Jets 4 Metropolitan Police Bushey 1
St Margaretsbury 3 Welwyn Garden City 1

SEMI-FINALS

Hoddesdon Town 1 **Oxhey Jets** 2
London Colney 0 **St Margaretsbury** 1

FINAL

(May 11th at HCFA, Letchworth)

St Margaretsbury 2 **Oxhey Jets** 4

HERTFORDSHIRE INTERMEDIATE CUP

FINAL

(March 24th at HCFA, Letchworth)

Hemel Hempstead Town Res. 3 Oxhey Jets Res. 0

HERTFORDSHIRE JUNIOR CUP

FINAL *(April 2nd at HCFA, Letchworth)*

Berkhamsted Sports 5 Broxbourne Badgers 3 *aet*

HUNTINGDONSHIRE SENIOR CUP

FIRST ROUND

Alconbury 5 Eaton Socon 3
Needingworth United 1 **AFC Fletton** 6
Ramsey Town 4 Eynesbury Rovers 2 *aet*

QUARTER-FINALS

AFC Fletton 1 **Yaxley** 5
Godmanchester Rovers 1 **St Ives Town** 3
Huntingdon Town 0 **Ramsey Town** 2
St Neots Town 6 Alconbury 0

SEMI-FINALS

Ramsey Town 0 **St Neots Town** 2
Yaxley 1 St Ives Town 0

FINAL *(May 3rd at Huntingdon Town)*

St Neots Town 1 Yaxley 0

HUNTINGDONSHIRE SCOTT GATTY CUP

FINAL *(March 24th at Godmanchester Rovers)*

Somersham Town 1 **St Neots Town Res.** 6

HUNTINGDONSHIRE BENOVOLENT CUP

FINAL *(April 21st at St Ives Town)*

Somersham Town 0 **St Neots Town Res.** 0 *aet* (6-7p)

HUNTINGDONSHIRE JUNIOR CUP

FINAL *(April 14th at Huntingdon Town)*

Eaton Socon Res. 7 Somersham Town Res. 2

HUNTINGDONSHIRE LOWER JUNIOR CUP

FINAL *(March 17th at St Neots Town)*

Fenstanton Res. 1 Gransden Chequers Res. 0

KENT SENIOR CUP

FIRST ROUND

VCD Athletic 4 Thamesmead Town 2

SECOND ROUND

Bromley 1 **Sittingbourne** 4
Cray Wanderers 3 Whitstable Town 0
Dartford 1 **Welling United** 3
Ebbsfleet United 1 **Maidstone United** 3
Folkestone Invicta 2 Dover Athletic 0
Margate 1 Chatham Town 0
Tonbridge Angels 2 Ramsgate 1
VCD Athletic 1 **Ashford Town** 2

QUARTER-FINALS

Cray Wanderers 3 Ashford Town 1
Folkestone Invicta 2 Maidstone United 1
Tonbridge Angels 2 **Sittingbourne** 2 *aet* (0-3p)
Welling United 2 Margate 0

SEMI-FINALS

Cray Wanderers 1 **Sittingbourne** 1 *aet* (3-4p)
Folkestone Invicta 2 Welling United 1

FINAL *(May 4th at Folkestone Invicta)*

Folkestone Invicta 1 **Sittingbourne** 3

KENT SENIOR TROPHY

(Sponsor: Umbro)

FIRST ROUND

Holmesdale 8 West Wickham 0

SECOND ROUND

Beckenham Town 3 **Holmesdale** 3 *aet* (4-5p)
Deal Town 2 Norton Sports 2 *aet* (3-2p)
Erith & Belvedere 3 **Hollands & Blair** 3 *aet* (1-3p)
Erith Town 1 **Lordswood** 1 *aet* (4-5p)
Greenwich Borough 3 Bearsted 1 *aet*
Hythe Town 0 **Faversham Town** 2
Milton & Fulston United 0 **Sevenoaks Town** 3
Tunbridge Wells 1 **Herne Bay** 2

QUARTER-FINALS

Deal Town 1 Sevenoaks Town 0
Faversham Town 2 Hollands & Blair 1
Greenwich Borough 3 Lordswood 0
Herne Bay 3 Holmesdale 1

SEMI-FINAL

Faversham Town 2 Deal Town 1
Greenwich Borough 3 Herne Bay 2 *aet*

FINAL *(April 18th at Welling United)*

Faversham Town 2 Greenwich Borough 1

KENT INTERMEDIATE CHALLENGE SHIELD

FIRST ROUND

Kennington 1 **Crockenhill** 1 *aet* (1-4p)
Oakwood 3 Guru Nanak 2
Phoenix Sports 3 Premier 0
Sutton Athletic 2 Old Bexleians 0
Woodstock Park 1 Staplehurst & Monarchs United 0

SECOND ROUND

Bly Spartans 3 AFC Sheppey 1
Bromley Green 1 Canterbury City 0
Charlton Athletic Community 1 **Gillingham Green** 2
Chipstead 0 **Wickham Park** 2
Coney Hall 0 **APM Mears** 4
Cray Valley Paper Mills 4 Corinthian 1
Lydd Town v **Stansfeld O & B Club** (w/o)
Oakwood 0 **Larkfield & New Hythe Wdrs** 4
Orpington 1 **Crockenhill** 3
Otford United 2 **Fleet Leisure** 4 *aet*
Phoenix Sports 2 Greenways 0
Rusthall 0 **New Romney** 2
Sheerness East 1 Tudor Sports 1 *aet* (4-1p)
Sutton Athletic 0 **Belvedere** 1
Tonbridge Invicta 6 Snodland 2
Woodstock Park 4 Farnborough Old Boys Guild 2

THIRD ROUND

Belvedere 0 **Crockenhill** 1
Bromley Green 0 **Tonbridge Invicta** 4
Cray Valley Paper Mills 3 Gillingham Green 0
Fleet Leisure 3 **Woodstock Park** 3 *aet* (3-4p)
Larkfield & New Hythe Wdrs 4 Wickham Park 1
New Romney 2 APM Mears 0
Phoenix Sports 5 Bly Spartans 4
Sheerness East 1 Stansfeld O & B Club 0

QUARTER-FINALS

Cray Valley Paper Mills 4 Tonbridge Invicta 2
Crockenhill 1 **Sheerness East** 2
Larkfield & New Hythe Wdrs 1 **Phoenix Sports** 4
New Romney 2 Woodstock Park 1

SEMI-FINALS

Cray Valley Paper Mills 4 New Romney 1
Sheerness East 0 **Phoenix Sports** 3

FINAL

(May 8th at Beckenham Town)
Cray Valley Paper Mills 0 **Phoenix Sports** 1

KENT INTERMEDIATE CUP

FINAL *(April 27th at Ebbsfleet United)*
Dartford Res. 2 Tonbridge Angels Res. 0

KENT JUNIOR A CUP

FINAL *(May 1st at Lordswood)*
Swale United 5 BAE Sports & Social 2

KENT JUNIOR B CUP

FINAL *(April 17th at Thamesmead Town)*
Insulators 2 Bexley 0

LANCASHIRE SENIOR CUP

(Sponsor: Canterbury)

FIRST ROUND

Accrington Stanley 2 Bury 2 *aet* (3-0p)
Manchester United 1 **Liverpool** 1 *aet* (3-4p)
Morecambe 0 **Preston North End** 2
Wigan Athletic 2 Blackburn Rovers 0

QUARTER-FINALS

Accrington Stanley 0 **Oldham Athletic** 3
Bolton Wanderers 0 **Liverpool** 2
Preston North End 7 Blackpool 0
Wigan Athletic 1 Rochdale 1 *aet* (3-2p)

SEMI-FINALS

Preston North End 0 **Oldham Athletic** 2
Wigan Athletic 0 **Liverpool** 2

FINAL

(July 24th at LCFA, Leyland)
Liverpool 3 Oldham Athletic 0

LANCASHIRE TROPHY

(Sponsor: United Co-operatives)

FIRST ROUND

AFC Fylde 3 **Clitheroe** 4
Ashton Athletic 3 Bacup Borough 2
Atherton Collieries 1 **Padiham** 4
Atherton LR 4 **Leigh Genesis** 4 *aet* (3-4p)
Burscough 2 Kendal Town 0
Colne 1 Chorley 0
Lancaster City 7 AFC Blackpool 3
Leigh Genesis 4 Atherton LR 4 *aet* (4-3p)
Marine 4 Bamber Bridge 2
Ramsbottom United 3 Nelson 2
Rochdale Town 0 **Daisy Hill** 1
Rossendale United 4 Squires Gates 1
Wigan Robin Park 0 **Holker Old Boys** 3

SECOND ROUND

Barrow 3 Rossendale United 1
Clitheroe 3 Fleetwood Town 0
Colne 4 Padiham 3
Lancaster City 4 Ramsbottom United 1 *aet*
Leigh Genesis 3 Ashton Athletic 0 *(at Ashton Athletic)*
Marine 4 Daisy Hill 0
Radcliffe Borough 2 Burscough 1
Southport 3 Holker Old Boys 1 *aet*

QUARTER-FINALS

Colne 1 **Leigh Genesis** 3
Marine 0 **Clitheroe** 4
Radcliffe Borough 3 **Lancaster City** 4
Southport 4 Barrow 2

SEMI-FINALS

Clitheroe 3 Leigh Genesis 1 *(at LCFA, Leyland)*
Lancaster City 2 **Southport** 5 *(at LCFA, Leyland)*

FINAL

(April 14th at Bolton Wanderers)
Southport 4 Clitheroe 0

LANCASHIRE AMATEUR SHIELD

FINAL

(April 16th at LCFA, Leyland)
Garstang 3 **Blackpool Wren Rovers** 4 *aet*

LANCASHIRE AMATEUR CUP

(Sponsor: Sharrocks)

FINAL

(April 7th at LCFA, Leyland)
Hurst Green 2 Highgrove 0

LEICESTERSHIRE CHALLENGE CUP

(Sponsor: Westerby Homes)

FIRST ROUND

Friar Lane & Epworth 3 Anstey Nomads 1
Hinckley United 6 Barrow Town 1
Loughborough Dynamo 1 Kirby Muxloe SC 0
Loughborough University 1 **Oadby Town** 2

QUARTER-FINALS

Coalville Town 5 Friar Lane & Epworth 0
Hinckley United 0 **Barwell** 1
Quorn 2 **Loughborough Dynamo** 5
Shepshed Dynamo 1 **Oadby Town** 2 *aet*

SEMI-FINALS

Loughborough Dynamo 2 Coalville Town 1
(at LCFA, Holmes Park)
Oadby Town 0 **Barwell** 2
(at LCFA, Holmes Park)

FINAL

(May 18th at Leicester City)
Loughborough Dynamo 2 Barwell 1

LEICESTERSHIRE CUP WINNERS CUP

(Sponsor: Westerby Homes)
(October 13th at Barwell)
Barwell 0 **Leicester City** 1

LEICESTERSHIRE SENIOR CUP
(Sponsor: Jelson Homes)
FIRST ROUND
Anstey Nomads 1 **Harborough Town** 4
Asfordby Amateurs 0 **Ashby Ivanhoe** 6
Bardon Hill Sports 1 **Ratby Sports** 2
Barrow Town 4 Cottesmore Amateurs 0
Birstall United 1 **Hinckley Downes** 2
Ellistown 1 **Ibstock United** 2
Highfield Rangers 1 **Uppingham Town** 3
Lutterworth Athletic 0 **Rothley Imperial** 1
Rutland Rangers 1 **Thurmaston Town** 3
Saffron Dynamo 1 Blaby & Whetstone Athletic 0
St Andrews SC 5 Aylestone Park 0
SECOND ROUND
Ashby Ivanhoe 3 Harborough Town 2
Barrow Town 2 Sileby Town 1
Heather St John 7 Uppingham Town 0
Hinckley Downes 3 Holwell Sports 1
Rothley Imperial 1 **Ibstock United** 3
St Andrews SC 4 Ratby Sports 0
Thurmaston Town 2 Leics Constabulary 1
Thurnby Nirvana 4 Saffron Dynamo 1
QUARTER-FINALS
Ashby Ivanhoe 3 Ibstock United 1
Barrow Town 2 **Heather St John** 5
Hinckley Downes 1 **Thurmaston Town** 2
Thurnby Nirvana 2 St Andrews SC 1
SEMI-FINALS
Thurmaston Town 3 Ashby Ivanhoe 1
(at LCFA, Holmes Park)
Thurnby Nirvana 2 **Heather St John** 5
(at LCFA, Holmes Park)
FINAL
(May 4th LCFA, Holmes Park)
Thurmaston Town 0 **Heather St John** 1

LEICESTERSHIRE SHIELD
FINAL *(April 20th at LCFA, Holmes Park)*
Birstall United Res. 2 Thurmaston Town Res. 1

LEICESTERSHIRE PLATE
FINAL *(March 23rd at LCFA, Holmes Park)*
Quorn Res. 1 Kirby Muxloe SC Res. 0

LEICESTERSHIRE TROPHY
FINAL *(April 13th at LCFA, Holmes Park)*
Greenhill Youth Club 1 Witherley 0

LEICESTERSHIRE INTERMEDIATE CUP
FINAL *(April 5th at LCFA, Holmes Park)*
FC Dynamo 7 Mountsorrel Amateurs 2

LEICESTERSHIRE VASE
FINAL
(March 11th at LCFA, Holmes Park)
Revive 2 North Kilworth Sports 1

LINCOLNSHIRE SENIOR CUP
SEMI-FINAL
Grimsby Town 0 **Scunthorpe United** 3
FINAL
(July 30th at Lincoln City)
Lincoln City 1 **Scunthorpe United** 1 (2-4p)

LINCOLNSHIRE SHIELD
FIRST ROUND
Brigg Town 0 **Boston United** 1
Spalding United 0 **Grantham Town** 1
Stamford 0 **Gainsborough Trinity** 4
SEMI-FINAL
Grantham Town 2 Gainsborough Trinity 1
Lincoln United 1 **Boston United** 4
FINAL
(March 16th at Grantham Town)
Grantham Town 0 **Boston United** 1

LINCOLNSHIRE TROPHY
FIRST ROUND
Bottesford Town 4 Boston Town 2
Grimsby Borough v **Nettleham** (w/o)
Holbeach United 4 Barton Town Old Boys 0
Lincoln Moorlands Railway 3 Blackstones 2
Louth Town 5 Appleby Frodingham 1
Sleaford Town 3 Grantham Rangers 1
Winterton Rangers 3 Bourne Town 1 *aet*
QUARTER-FINALS
Bottesford Town 2 Nettleham 1 *aet*
Lincoln Moorlands Railway 2 Deeping Rangers 1
Sleaford Town 0 **Louth Town** 2
Winterton Rangers 3 Holbeach United 2
SEMI-FINALS
Louth Town 1 Bottesford Town 1 *aet* (4-2p)
Winterton Rangers 2 Lincoln Moorlands Railway 1
FINAL
(May 4th at Scunthorpe United)
Winterton Rangers 1 Louth Town 0

LINCOLNSHIRE SHIELD
FINAL
(April 17th at Brigg Town)
AFC Brumby 2 Waltham Tea Gardens 1

LIVERPOOL SENIOR CUP
FIRST ROUND
AFC Liverpool 2 Formby 0 *(at Formby)*
Bootle 5 Burscough 2 *aet*
St Helens Town 1 **Warrington Town** 2 *aet*
SECOND ROUND
Ashton Town 2 Prescot Cables 1
Marine 0 **Cammell Laird** 2
Skelmersdale United 5 AFC Liverpool 2
Warrington Town 0 **Bootle** 1
QUARTER-FINALS
Ashton Town 0 **Liverpool** 4
Bootle 2 **Everton** 4
Cammell Laird 0 **Tranmere Rovers** 2
Skelmersdale United 7 Southport 0
SEMI-FINALS
Skelmersdale United 2 Everton 0
Liverpool 3 Tranmere Rovers 0 *(at Liverpool Academy)*
FINAL
(July 31st at Skelmersdale United)
Skelmersdale United 2 **Liverpool** 3

LIVERPOOL CHALLENGE CUP
FIRST ROUND
Albany Athletic 2 **Bootle Res.** 3
Angus Village 3 Pilkington 1
BRNESC 1 **Roma** 1 *aet* (2-4p)
Cronton Villa 1 **Copperas Hill** 1 *aet* (4-5p)
Eagle Sports 1 Southport Trinity 0
East Villa 2 **Sacre Coeur Former Pupils** 4
Ford Motors 1 **South Sefton Borough** 2
Greenalls Padgate St Oswalds 2 Old Xaverians 1
Halewood Town 2 NELTC 1
Lucas Sports 3 **Red Rum** 3 *aet* (2-4p)
Mackets 4 **Warrington Town Res.** 4 *aet* (3-4p)
Page Celtic 3 Edge Hill BCOB 2
South Liverpool 7 Garswood United 2
St Aloysius 2 Old Holts 1
Warbreck 2 **Birchfield** 3 *aet*
SECOND ROUND
Aigburth People's Hall 3 Kingsley United 0
Angus Village 1 **South Sefton Borough** 2
Birchfield 4 Copperas Hill 2
Cheshire Lines 2 **St Aloysius** 3
Collegiate Old Boys v **Crosfields-Rylands** (w/o)
Fleetwood Hesketh 0 **Bootle Res.** 2
Formby Res. 0 **Red Rum** 4
Greenalls Padgate St Oswalds 2 **Page Celtic** 3 *aet*
Halewood Town 1 **Maghull** 1 *aet* (3-4p)
Marine Res. 3 Halebank 1

Mossley Hill Athletic 1 **Leyfield** 3
REMYCA United 1 AFC Liverpool Res. 0
Sacre Coeur Former Pupils 1 **Eagle Sports** 2
South Liverpool 1 **Stoneycroft** 2
Warrington Town Res. 1 **Essemmay Old Boys** 2
Waterloo Dock 8 Roma 0

THIRD ROUND

Crosfields-Rylands 3 Red Rum 1
Eagle Sports 4 REMYCA United 2
Essemmay Old Boys 1 **Waterloo Dock** 3
Leyfield 1 **Birchfield** 1 *aet* (1-4p)
Maghull 3 Stoneycroft 3 *aet* (4-2p)
Marine Res. 0 **Aigburth People's Hall** 3 *aet*
Page Celtic 3 **St Aloysius** 4
South Sefton Borough 3 Bootle Res. 2

QUARTER-FINALS

Aigburth People's Hall 3 Eagle Sports 1 *aet*
Crosfields-Rylands 1 **St Aloysius** 2
Maghull 1 **Waterloo Dock** 3
South Sefton Borough 2 Birchfield 0

SEMI-FINALS

St Aloysius 2 South Sefton Borough 1 *aet*
Waterloo Dock 2 **Aigburth People's Hall** 4

FINAL

(May 11th LCFA, Wavertree)
Aigburth People's Hall 3 St Aloysius 1

LIVERPOOL INTERMEDIATE CUP

FINAL

(April 20th at LCFA, Wavertree)
Hale 1 Old Cathinians 0

LIVERPOOL JUNIOR CUP

FINAL

(May 4th at LCFA, Wavertree)
Marshalls 4 Pinewoods 1

LONDON SENIOR CUP

FIRST ROUND

Barking 2 **Brimsdown Rovers** 3 *aet*
Civil Service v **Erith Town** (w/o)
Cockfosters 4 **Hanwell Town** 4 *aet* (3-4p)
Croydon 2 Lewisham Borough (Community) 0
Fisher 2 Kingsbury London Tigers 1
Haringey Borough 3 Erith & Belvedere 1
Hoddesdon Town 1 **Beckenham Town** 4
South Kilburn 3 Clapton 0

SECOND ROUND

Beckenham Town 2 Mauritius Sports Association 1
Brimsdown Rovers 4 Redbridge 1
Corinthian Casuals 1 **Wingate & Finchley** 3
Dulwich Hamlet 1 **South Kilburn** 2 *aet*
Erith Town 2 Leyton 1
Hanwell Town 6 Croydon 5 *aet*
Haringey Borough 1 **Fisher** 2
Thamesmead Town 2 **Metropolitan Police** 3

THIRD ROUND

Brimsdown Rovers 4 Hanwell Town 1
Bromley 1 Erith Town 0
Fisher 2 Cray Wanderers 2 *aet* (4-3p)
Harrow Borough 3 Beckenham Town 0
Metropolitan Police 0 Wingate & Finchley 0 *aet* (4-3p)
South Kilburn 2 **Hendon** 3
Tooting & Mitcham United 2 **AFC Wimbledon** 2 *aet* (3-4p)
Welling United 1 **Croydon Athletic** 2

QUARTER FINALS

Brimsdown Rovers 1 Hendon 0 *aet*
Bromley 1 **Metropolitan Police** 1 *aet* (3-5p)
Fisher 1 **Croydon Athletic** 1 *aet* (4-5p)
Harrow Borough 2 **AFC Wimbledon** 3

SEMI-FINALS

AFC Wimbledon 3 Croydon Athletic 0
Metropolitan Police 7 Brimsdown Rovers 1

FINAL

(April 28th at Harrow Borough)
Metropolitan Police 4 AFC Wimbledon 4 *aet* (4-3p)

LONDON INTERMEDIATE CUP

FIRST ROUND

Bridon Ropes 1 **Cockfosters Res.** 5
Corinthian Casuals Res. 1 **Old Roan** 3
Cray Valley Paper Mills 2 Barking Res. 0
Eltham Town v **Newham United** (w/o)

QUARTER-FINALS

Cray Wanderers Res. 0 **Cray Valley Paper Mills** 3
Erith Town Res. 0 Tooting & Mitcham United Res. 0 *ae* (4-2p)
Metrogas 2 **Cockfosters Res.** 3
Old Roan 7 Newham United 4

SEMI-FINALS

Cockfosters Res. 0 **Cray Valley Paper Mills** 1
Old Roan 1 **Erith Town Res.** 1 *aet* (3-4p)

FINAL

(March 27th at Metropolitan Police)
Cray Valley Paper Mills 2
Erith Town Res. 1

LONDON JUNIOR CUP

FINAL

(April 17th at Croydon Athletic)
Flanders 3 FC Team 0

MANCHESTER PREMIER CUP

FIRST ROUND

Abbey Hey 2 **Glossop North End** 2 *aet* (4-5p)
Ashton United 2 **Curzon Ashton** 3
Irlam 1 **Hyde United** 4
Mossley 4 Maine Road 0
Salford City 2 **Radcliffe Borough** 6
Trafford 4 Oldham Boro 1

QUARTER-FINALS

Curzon Ashton 0 **Droylsden** 2
Glossop North End 2 Mossley 1
Radcliffe Borough 1 Chadderton 0
Trafford 3 Hyde United 0

SEMI-FINALS

Droylsden 2 Glossop North End 0
Trafford 2 Radcliffe Borough 1

FINAL

(April 20th at Hyde United)
Droylsden 2 Trafford 0

MANCHESTER CHALLENGE TROPHY

FIRST ROUND

Curzon Ashton Res. 1 **East Manchester** 4
Dukinfield Town v **Beechfield United** (w/o)
Fives Athletic 0 **Maine Road Res.** 1
Hollinwood 7 Chorltonians 0
Irlam 4 Moorside Rangers 0
Manchester Juniors v **Newton** (w/o)
Trafford Res. 1 AVRO 1 *aet* (3-1p)

QUARTER-FINALS

East Manchester 5 Newton 0
Irlam 0 **Hollinwood** 2
Trafford Res. 3 **Maine Road Res.** 3 *aet* (2-3p)
Wythenshawe Town 2 **Beechfield United** 3

SEMI-FINALS

(played over two legs)
Beechfield United 3 Maine Road Res. 2,
Maine Road Res. 1 **Beechfield United** 2
Hollinwood 2 East Manchester 1,
East Manchester 1 **Hollinwood** 3

FINAL

(March 18th at Salford City)
Hollinwood 5 Beechfield United 0

MANCHESTER AMATEUR CUP

FINAL

(April 15th at Irlam)
Dukinfield Town Res. 5
Heaton Mersey 0

MIDDLESEX SENIOR CUP

FIRST ROUND

Hanwell Town 1 **Bedfont Green** 4
Hanworth Villa 4 Wingate & Finchley 3
Hillingdon Borough 1 **Enfield Town** 2
Northwood 2 Bedfont 0
Wembley 3 Enfield 2

SECOND ROUND

Enfield Town 2 Harefield United 0
Hampton & Richmond Borough 0 **Northwood** 1
Hanworth Villa 2 Hendon 2 *aet* (5-4p)
Harrow Borough 0 **Bedfont Green** 3
Hayes & Yeading United 1 **Staines Town** 4
Uxbridge 5 Ashford Town (Middx) 4 *aet*
Wealdstone 2 North Greenford United 1
Wembley 2 **AFC Hayes** 3 *aet*

QUARTER-FINALS

Bedfont Green 0 **Staines Town** 1
Enfield Town 3 AFC Hayes 2
Hanworth Villa 0 **Northwood** 3
Wealdstone 2 **Uxbridge** 3

SEMI-FINALS

Enfield Town 0 **Staines Town** 3
Uxbridge 2 Northwood 0

FINAL

(April 5th Staines Town)
Staines Town 2
Uxbridge 0

MIDDLESEX CHARITY CUP

FIRST ROUND

Uxbridge 1 **AFC Hayes** 3

SECOND ROUND

Harefield United 3 AFC Hayes 1
Hillingdon Borough 2 Enfield 1
Wealdstone v **Hanworth Villa** (w/o)

QUARTER-FINALS

Bedfont 4 Hillingdon Borough 0
Hanwell Town v **Enfield Town** (w/o)
Harefield United (w/o) v Hanworth Villa
Harrow Borough 1 **North Greenford United** 2

SEMI-FINALS

Enfield Town 2 Bedfont 1 *aet*
Harefield United 2 **North Greenford United** 3 *aet*

FINAL

(May 3rd at Hampton & Richmond Borough)
North Greenford United 1
Enfield Town 0

MIDDLESEX PREMIER CUP

FIRST ROUND

Northwood Res. 0 **Bedfont Res.** 3
Tokyngton Manor 8 Hanworth Villa Res. 0

SECOND ROUND

Bedfont Green Res. 0 **Harefield United Res.** 9
Bedfont Res. 2 **Ashford Town (Middx) Res.** 4
Bedfont Sports 2 Staines Lammas 0
CB Hounslow United 1 **Rayners Lane** 3
Feltham 1 Tokyngton Manor 0 *aet*
Hayes & Yeading United Res. 3 Harrow Borough Res. 1
North Greenford United Res. 1 **Uxbridge Res.** 6
Wealdstone Res. 1 **AFC Hayes Res.** 5

QUARTER-FINALS

Ashford Town (Middx) Res. 3 AFC Hayes Res. 2
Feltham 0 **Bedfont Sports** 1
Rayners Lane 1 Harefield United Res. 3 *aet*
(at Harefield United) (Harefield United expelled)
Uxbridge Res. v **Hayes & Yeading United Res.** (w/o)

SEMI-FINALS

Bedfont Sports 3 Ashford Town (Middx) Res. 2
Hayes & Yeading United Res. 2 Rayners Lane 0

FINAL

(May 11th at Hayes & Yeading United)
Bedfont Sports 3 Hayes & Yeading United Res. 1

MIDDLESEX INTERMEDIATE CUP

FINAL

(April 28th at Northwood)
Park View 4 Broadfields United 0

MIDDLESEX JUNIOR CUP

FINAL

(April 14th at North Greenford United)
Chiswick Homefields 3 Hillingdon 1

MIDDLESEX JUNIOR TROPHY

FINAL

(April 21st at Uxbridge)
Uxbridge Town 1 Christchurch Roxeth 0

NORFOLK SENIOR CUP

FIRST ROUND

Long Stratton 2 Holt United 2 *aet*
Replay: Holt United 2 **Long Stratton** 4
Poringland Wanderers 3 Hindringham 3 *aet*
Replay: **Hindringham** 2 Poringland Wanderers 1
Scole United 3 Caister 1
Stalham Town 0 **Horsford United** 4

SECOND ROUND

Horsford United 1 **Reepham Town** 3
Norwich St Johns 5 Long Stratton 1
Wells Town 3 Hindringham 2
Wymondham Town 0 **Scole United** 1

THIRD ROUND

Acle United 0 **Diss Town** 1
Blofield United 3 Reepham Town 1
Cromer Town 0 Sprowston Athletic 0 *aet*
Replay: Sprowston Athletic 1 **Cromer Town** 4
Dersingham Rovers 1 **Great Yarmouth Town** 4
Fakenham Town 1 Hempnall 0
Gorleston 3 Norwich St Johns 2
Loddon United 3 Downham Town 1
Mattishall 6 Watton United 2
North Walsham Town 3 Wells Town 1
Scole United 2 St Andrews 1
Sheringham 4 Swaffham Town 2
Spixworth United 4 Thetford Town 2

FOURTH ROUND

Blofield Town 2 **Cromer Town** 3 *aet*
Diss Town 1 **Mattishall** 2 *aet*
Gorleston 2 Sheringham 1
Great Yarmouth Town 1 Wroxham 1 *aet*
Replay: **Wroxham** 1 Great Yarmouth Town 0
King's Lynn Res. 0 **Spixworth United** 2
(at Spixworth United)
Loddon United 4 Scole United 2
North Walsham Town 1 **Dereham Town** 2
Norwich United 3 Fakenham Town 0

QUARTER-FINALS

Dereham Town 3 Gorleston 1
Loddon United 0 **Mattishall** 1 *aet*
Spixworth United 1 **Cromer Town** 3
Wroxham 1 **Norwich United** 2

SEMI-FINALS

Cromer Town 0 **Norwich United** 3
Dereham Town 0 **Mattishall** 1

FINAL

(April 12th at Norwich City)
Mattishall 1 Norwich United 1
aet (5-4p)

NORFOLK JUNIOR CUP

FINAL

(April 13th at Norwich City)
West Lynn SSC 2 Foulsham 1

NORFOLK PRIMARY CUP

FINAL

(April 9th at Dereham Town)
Old Hunstanton 4
Great Yarmouth Town Hall 2

Hertfordshire Junior Cup winners Berkhamsted Sports, who beat Broxbourne Badgers 5-3, celebrate their win.
Photo: Gordon Whittington.

O.N.Chenecks celebrating making history, after lifting the Northamptonshire Junior Cup for the first time.
Photo: Gordon Whittington.

NORTH RIDING SENIOR CUP

FIRST ROUND

Scarborough Town 7 New Marske Sports Club 2

SECOND ROUND

Fishburn Park 1 **Scarborough Town** 3
Grangetown Boys Club 4 Guisborough Town HC 0
South Bank St Peters 0 **Kirkbymoorside** 2
Teesside Athletic 3 Nunthorpe Athletic 2

THIRD ROUND

Guisborough Town 3 Teesside Athletic 0
Kirkbymoorside 1 **Pickering Town** 4 *(at Pickering Town)*
Marske United 1 **Stokesley** 1 *aet* (3-4p)
Scarborough Town 0 **Northallerton Town** 3
(at Whitby Town)
Thornaby 1 Grangetown Boys Club 1 *aet* (6-5p)
Whitby Town 1 **Scarborough Athletic** 1 *aet* (2-3p)

QUARTER-FINALS

Middlesbrough 3 Pickering Town 3 *aet* (4-3p)
(at Pickering Town)
Northallerton Town 3 Scarborough Athletic 1
Stokesley 4 Thornaby 2
York City 3 Guisborough Town 0

SEMI-FINAL

Northallerton Town 3 **York City** 3 *aet* (2-4p)
Stokesley 2 Middlesbrough 1

FINAL *(April 20th at Stokesley)*
York City 2 Stokesley 0

NORTH RIDING COUNTY CUP

(Sponsor: A66 Trophies)

FINAL *(March 10th at Stokesley)*
Cargo Fleet 3 Old Malton St Marys 2

NORTH RIDING CHALLENGE CUP

(Sponsor: Sportsguard)

FINAL *(April 14th at Stokesley)*
Cargo Fleet Res. 0 **Thirsk Falcons** 3

NORTHAMPTONSHIRE SENIOR CUP

(Sponsor: Hillier)

FIRST ROUND

Cogenhoe United 1 **Corby Town** 3
Daventry Town 2 Stewarts & Lloyds Corby 0
Daventry United 2 **Rushden & Diamonds** 5
Desborough Town 2 Raunds Town 0
Long Buckby 3 Rothwell Town 1
Northampton Spencer 2 **Kettering Town** 4
Wellingborough Town 2 Rothwell Corinthians 1
Woodford United 2 Brackley Town 1

QUARTER-FINALS

Daventry Town 2 Long Buckby 1
Rushden & Diamonds 1 **Kettering Town** 2 *aet*
Wellingborough Town 0 **Desborough Town** 1
Woodford United 2 **Corby Town** 4

SEMI-FINALS

Daventry Town 3 Desborough Town 2
Kettering Town 0 **Corby Town** 2

FINAL *(March 17th at Corby Town)*
Corby Town 3 Daventry Town 2

NORTHAMPTONSHIRE JUNIOR CUP

FINAL *(April 14th at Rushden & Diamonds)*
Northampton ON Chenecks 1 N'pton Sileby Rangers 0

NORTHAMPTONSHIRE LOWER JUNIOR CUP

FINAL *(April 27th at Raunds Town)*
Peterbor. Northern Star Res. 4 Bugbrooke St M. Res. 2

NORTHUMBERLAND SENIOR CUP

FIRST ROUND

North Shields 2 **Bedlington Terriers** 3 *aet*
Team Northumbria 0 **Ashington** 3

QUARTER-FINALS

Bedlington Terriers 0 **Ashington** 3
Blyth Spartans 3 Morpeth Town 1
Newcastle United 4 Newcastle Benfield 2 *aet*
West Allotment Celtic 1 **Whitley Bay** 3

SEMI-FINALS

Ashington 3 Blyth Spartans 2 *aet*
Whitley Bay 3 Newcastle United 1

FINAL *(April 19th at Whitley Bay)*
Whitley Bay 2 Ashington 1

NORTHUMBERLAND BENEVOLENT BOWL

FIRST ROUND

Alnwick Town 3 Walker Central 0
Ashington Colliers 3 Cramlington Town 2 *aet*
Cullercoats 3 Heddon 2
Killingworth Sporting 2 Ponteland United 1
Seaton Delaval Amateurs 1 **Heaton Stannington** 2
Stocksfield 2 Newcastle University 1
Wark 4 Shankhouse 0
Whitley Bay A 4 **Blyth Town** 6 *aet*

QUARTER-FINALS

Blyth Town 2 **Killingworth Sporting** 4
Cullercoats 2 **Alnwick Town** 3 *aet*
Heaton Stannington 5 Stocksfield 1 *(at Prudhoe Town)*
Wark 2 Ashington Colliers 1

SEMI-FINALS

Heaton Stannington 2 Killingworth Sporting 1
Wark 0 **Alnwick Town** 3

FINAL *(May 21st at West Allotment Celtic)*
Alnwick Town 2 Heaton Stannington 1 *aet*

NORTHUMBERLAND MINOR CUP

FINAL

(May 19th at West Allotment Celtic)
Morpeth Sporting Club 1 Percy Main Amateurs 0

NOTTINGHAMSHIRE SENIOR CUP

FIRST ROUND

Basford United 1 Ollerton Town 0
Bilborough Pelican 5 Wollaton 5 *aet* (9-8p)
Blidworth Welfare 2 Clipstone Welfare 0
Boots Athletic 2 Sutton Town 1
Hucknall Rolls Leisure 2 Radcliffe Olympic 1
Keyworth United 1 **Kirkby Town** 4
Kimberley Town 2 Kimberley Miners Welfare 1 *aet*
Magdala Amateurs 2 **Greenwood Meadows** 3
Newark Flowserve 2 Linby Colliery Welfare 1
Newark Town 4 Calverton Miners Welfare 0
Radford 0 **Southwell City** 2
Teversal 2 Cotgrave Welfare 0

SECOND ROUND

Basford United 3 **Southwell City** 4
Bilborough Pelican 2 **Kirkby Town** 4
Boots Athletic 5 Kimberley Town 1
Hucknall Rolls Leisure 1 **Blidworth Welfare** 4
Newark Flowserve v **Teversal** (w/o)
Newark Town 4 Greenwood Meadows 1

THIRD ROUND

Carlton Town 2 **Gedling Miners Welfare** 3
Eastwood Town 3 Arnold Town 1 *aet*
Forest Town 3 Boots Athletic 2
Kirkby Town 1 Blidworth Welfare 0
Newark Town 1 **Dunkirk** 2
Rainworth Miners Welfare 2 Teversal 1
Retford United 3 Hucknall Town 0
Southwell City (w/o) v Gedling Town

QUARTER-FINALS

Gedling Miners Welfare 1 **Forest Town** 2
Kirkby Town 0 **Eastwood Town** 6
Rainworth Miners Welfare 2 **Dunkirk** 4
Retford United 3 Southwell City 1

SEMI-FINALS

Forest Town 0 **Eastwood Town** 1
Retford United 4 Dunkirk 0

FINAL

(May 7th at Notts County)
Retford United 3 **Eastwood Town** 4 *aet*

NOTTINGHAMSHIRE INTERMEDIATE CUP
FINAL
(April 27th at Rainworth Miners Welfare)
Gedling Southbank 0 **Retford Town** 1

NOTTINGHAMSHIRE JUNIOR CUP
FINAL
(May 11th at Dunkirk)
Awsworth Villa Res. 3 Burton Joyce 0

NOTTINGHAMSHIRE MINOR CUP
FINAL *(April 29th at Hucknall Town)*
Carlton Town Colts 5 Coronation 4

OXFORDSHIRE SENIOR CUP
FIRST ROUND
BCS Bardwell 1 **Horspath** 4
Bicester Town 1 **Marston Saints** 2
Bletchingdon 2 **Carterton** 3
Easington Sports 5 Enstone Sports 0
Garsington 2 Chadlington 1
Headington Amateurs 4 Clanfield 2
Kidlington 4 Henley Town 3 *aet*
Launton Sports 1 **Ardley United** 5
Oxford University Press 3 **Adderbury Park** 5 *aet*
Rover Cowley 3 Fritwell 1
Stonesfield Sports 3 Eynsham Association 0
Thame United 2 Old Woodstock Town 1
Warborough & Shillingford 2 **Chinnor** 4 *aet*
Woodcote & Stoke Row 2 **Oxford City Nomads** 4
SECOND ROUND
Carterton 2 Witney United 1
Chinnor 2 **Rover Cowley** 3 *aet*
Easington Sports 5 Headington Amateurs 5 *aet* (4-3p)
Garsington 0 **Kidlington** 1
Hook Norton 2 Adderbury Park 1
Horspath 7 Marston Saints 1
Oxford City Nomads 6 Stonesfield Sports 1
Thame United 1 **Ardley United** 2 *aet*
THIRD ROUND
Carterton 1 **Kidlington** 3
Easington Sports 4 Ardley United 0 *aet*
Horspath 2 Hook Norton 1
Rover Cowley 0 **Oxford City Nomads** 5
QUARTER-FINALS
Easington Sports 0 **Banbury United** 3
(at Banbury United)
Horspath 0 **North Leigh** 7
Kidlington 2 **Oxford United** 3 *aet*
Oxford City 3 Oxford City Nomads 2
SEMI-FINALS
Banbury United 3 North Leigh 0 *(at Oxford City)*
Oxford City 1 **Oxford United** 2
FINAL *(April 7th at Oxford United)*
Oxford United 3 Banbury United 1

OXFORDSHIRE CHARITY CUP
FINAL *(April 24th at Witney United)*
Kidlington Old Boys 1 Stonesfield Sports 0

OXFORDSHIRE INTERMEDIATE CUP
FINAL *(April 20th at Oxford City)*
Henley Town Res. 4 Charlton United 1

OXFORDSHIRE JUNIOR SHIELD
FINAL *(May 1st at Witney United)*
Quarry 2 Hailey 0

SHEFFIELD & HALLAMSHIRE SENIOR CUP
FIRST ROUND
AFC Emley 3 Yorkshire Main 0
Brodsworth Miners Welfare 0 **Mexborough Main Street** 1
Dinnington Town 3 Kinsley Boys 1
Hallam 2 Athersley Recreation 0
Handsworth 4 Harworth Colliery 1
Hemsworth Miners Welfare 6 Parramore Sports 1
Nostell Miners Welfare 9 Bentley Colliery 1
Parkgate 4 **Mexborough Pocket** 4 *aet* (3-4p)
Penistone Church 4 FC Brimington 2
Rossington Main 1 Worsbrough Bridge MW 0
Sheffield 4 Frecheville CA 0
South Kirkby Colliery 1 **Maltby Main** 3
Staveley Miners Welfare 1 Phoenix Sports & Social 0
SECOND ROUND
Hallam 2 Frickley Athletic 1
Handsworth 2 **Dinnington Town** 5
Hemsworth Miners Welfare 1 **Nostell Miners Welfare** 2
Mexborough Pocket 0 **Mexborough Main Street** 8
Penistone Church 1 **Stocksbridge Park Steels** 3
Rossington Main 0 **Sheffield** 7
Staveley Miners Welfare 4 Maltby Main 3
Worksop Town 1 **AFC Emley** 2 *(at AFC Emley)*
QUARTER-FINALS
Hallam 2 AFC Emley 1
Mexborough Main Street 1 **Nostell Miners Welfare** 4
(at Nostell Miners Welfare)
Staveley Miners Welfare 2 Dinnington Town 0
Stocksbridge Park Steels 4 **Sheffield** 5
SEMI-FINALS
Nostell Miners Welfare 1 **Hallam** 4
Staveley Miners Welfare 3 **Sheffield** 4 *aet*
FINAL
(May 4th at Sheffield Wednesday)
Sheffield 4 Hallam 2

SHEFFIELD & HALLAMSHIRE ASSOCIATION CUP
(Sponsor: Rosehill Press)
FINAL
(April 16th at Staveley Miners Welfare)
Sheffield Res. 2 Dearne Colliery MW 1

SHEFFIELD & HALLAMSHIRE JUNIOR CUP
(Sponsor: Owlerton Stadium)
FINAL *(May 1st at Barnsley)*
Skelmanthorpe 3 HSBC Bank A 1

SHROPSHIRE SENIOR CUP
(November 17th at AFC Telford United)
AFC Telford United 1 **Shrewsbury Town** 2

SHROPSHIRE CHALLENGE CUP
FIRST ROUND
Impact United 0 **Ellesmere Rangers** 3
Shifnal Town 8 Clee Hill United 0
Wellington Amateurs 3 Morda United 0
SECOND ROUND
Broseley Juniors 0 **Hanwood United** 1
Ellesmere Rangers 4 Bridgnorth Town 1
Market Drayton Town 10 St Martins 1
Shifnal Town 4 Ludlow Town 1 *aet*
Shifnal United 0 **Haughmond** 1
Wellington Amateurs 6 Newport County Borough 1
Wem Town 1 Shawbury United 1 *aet* (4-2p)
Whitchurch Alport 2 Telford Juniors 0
QUARTER-FINALS
Hanwood United 1 **Shifnal Town** 2
Haughmond 1 **Wellington Amateurs** 2
Market Drayton Town (w/o) v Wem Town
Whitchurch Alport 0 **Ellesmere Rangers** 1
SEMI-FINAL
Ellesmere Rgrs 1 Wellington Ams 0 *(at Shifnal Town)*
Market Drayton Town 2 Shifnal Town 0
(at Sundorne Sports Village)
FINAL
(April 20th at Shrewsbury Town)
Market Drayton Town 1 **Ellesmere Rangers** 3

SHROPSHIRE JUNIOR CUP
(Sponsor: Williams & Picken)
FINAL
(March 30th at Shrewsbury Town)
Newport Town 4 Ellesmere Rangers Res. 2

SOMERSET PREMIER CUP
FIRST ROUND
Bishop Sutton 5 Clevedon Town 1
Bridgwater Town 3 Bath City 0
Brislington 1 Odd Down 0
Clevedon United 3 Portishead Town 2
Radstock Town 1 **Wells City** 1 *aet* (3-4p)
Street 4 Shepton Mallet 1
Wellington Town 3 Minehead Town 1
Welton Rovers 3 Paulton Rovers 1
Yeovil Town (w/o) v Team Bath
SECOND ROUND
Bristol Manor Farm 0 **Bishop Sutton** 1
Chard Town 0 **Welton Rovers** 3
Clevedon United 0 **Bridgwater Town** 4
Frome Town 3 Weston-super-Mare 1
Street 4 Larkhall Athletic 2 *aet*
Wellington Town 3 Keynsham Town 2
Wells City 1 Taunton Town 0
Yeovil Town 2 Brislington 0
QUARTER-FINALS
Frome Town 0 **Bridgwater Town** 2
Street 0 **Wells City** 0 *aet* (7-8p)
Wellington Town 3 **Welton Rovers** 4
Yeovil Town 2 Bishop Sutton 0 *(at Bishop Sutton)*
SEMI-FINALS
Wells City 0 **Bridgwater Town** 2
Welton Rovers 2 Yeovil Town 0
FINAL
(May 4th at Yeovil Town)
Bridgwater Town 0 **Welton Rovers** 0 *aet* (2-4p)

SOMERSET SENIOR CUP
FIRST ROUND
Berrow 4 Portishead Town Res. 1
Bishop Sutton Res. 0 **Stockwood Green Robinsons** 2
Broad Plain House Old Boys 0 **Clevedon United Res.** 3
Burnham United 5 Backwell United 2
Churchill Club 0 **Nailsea United** 2
Clutton 1 **Brislington Res.** 4
Combe St Nicholas (w/o) v Langford Rovers
Creech St Michael 4 Welton Rovers Res. 1
Cutters Friday 2 Congresbury 0
Frome Collegians 3 Bridgwater Town Res. 3 *aet* (5-4p)
Fry Club 12 Shepton Mallet Res. 1
Glastonbury Town 1 **CTK Southside** 3
Hartcliffe 2 **St George Easton-in-Gordano** 2 *aet* (1-3p)
Hengrove Athletic 3 Winscombe 2
Imperial Bristol 1 **Ashton United** 3
Larkhall Athletic Res. 1 **Purnell Sports** 3
Odd Down Res. 2 **Cheddar** 3
Paulton Rovers Res. 2 **Taunton Blackbrook** 6
Peasedown Athletic 0 **Bishops Lydeard** 11
Radstock Town Res. 2 Yatton Athletic 2 *aet* (4-3p)
Street Res. 4 Keynsham Town Res. 2 *aet*
Teyfant Athletic v **Weston St Johns** (w/o)
Timsbury Athletic 5 Dundry Athletic 0
Tunley Athletic 1 **Westland United** 5
Vale Recreation 3 Castle Cary 2
Watchet Town 2 Wellington Town Res. 0
Wells City Res. 0 **Banwell** 3
Westfield 3 Cleeve West Town 2 *aet*
Whitchurch 0 **Wrington-Redhill** 3
Wincanton Town 0 **Ilminster Town** 2
Worle 2 **Westland Sports** 5
SECOND ROUND
Ashton United 3 Berrow 1
Brislington Res. 2 St George Easton-in-Gordano 1
Burnham United 2 Radstock Town Res. 1
Combe St Nicholas v **Banwell** (w/o)
Creech St Michael 2 Timsbury Athletic 0
Cutters Friday 1 Fry Club 1 *aet* (3-1p)
Saltford 2 Hengrove Athletic 1
Street Res. 0 **Purnell Sports** 3
Taunton Blackbrook 3 CTK Southside 1
Vale Recreation 4 Frome Collegians 1
Watchet Town 3 Bishops Lydeard 1
Westfield 4 Stockwood Green Robinsons 3
Westland Sports 1 Ilminster Town 1 *aet* (4-3p)
Westland United 3 **Cheddar** 4 *aet*
Weston St Johns 2 Clevedon United Res. 2 *aet* (3-1p)
Wrington-Redhill 0 **Nailsea United** 7
THIRD ROUND
Ashton United 4 **Burnham United** 4 *aet* (5-6p)
Brislington Res. (w/o) v Taunton Blackbrook
Cutters Friday 1 Vale Recreation 0
Nailsea United 0 **Westland Sports** 1
Saltford 4 Banwell 1
Watchet Town 2 Purnell Sports 0
Westfield 5 Creech St Michael 0
Weston St Johns 3 **Cheddar** 6
QUARTER-FINALS
Cheddar 4 Burnham United 0
Watchet Town 0 **Saltford** 1
Westfield 2 **Brislington Res.** 3
Westland Sports 2 Cutters Friday 0
SEMI-FINALS
Brislington Res. 1 **Westland Sports** 3
Saltford 0 **Cheddar** 3 *aet*
FINAL *(May 7th at Street)*
Cheddar 1 **Westland Sports** 2

SOMERSET JUNIOR CUP
FINAL *(April 21st at Shepton Mallet)*
Chew Valley 0 **South Petherton** 2

SOMERSET INTERMEDIATE CUP
FINAL *(May 18th at Street)*
Barwick & Stoford 1 Tor 0

STAFFORDSHIRE SENIOR CUP
FIRST ROUND
Hednesford Town 3 Biddulph Victoria 1
Leek Town 0 **Newcastle Town** 4
Rushall Olympic 1 **Chasetown** 4
QUARTER-FINALS
Hednesford Town 2 **Port Vale** 5
Kidsgrove Athletic 3 Stoke City 0
Newcastle Town 6 Rocester 0
Stafford Rangers 0 **Chasetown** 4
SEMI-FINALS
Kidsgrove Athletic 2 **Port Vale** 3 *aet*
Newcastle Town 3 Chasetown 1
FINAL
(April 26th at Port Vale)
Newcastle Town 6 Port Vale 1

STAFFORDSHIRE VASE
FIRST ROUND
Pelsall Villa 0 **Wolverhampton Casuals** 1
Riverway 1 **Bloxwich United** 4
SECOND ROUND
Barlaston Town 1 **Foley** 4
Bilston Town 1 **Leek CSOB** 4
Bloxwich United 1 Stafford Town 0
Brereton Social 1 **Ball Haye Green** 3
Brocton 4 Wolverhampton Casuals 1
Burntwood Town 1 **Warstones Wanderers** 2
Eccleshall 3 Heath Town Rangers 2
Eccleshall AFC 1 **Abbey Hulton United** 4
Florence 1 Holt JCB 0
Heath Hayes 2 Redgate Clayton 0
Manor Inne 1 **Wolstanton United** 3
Norton 3 Meir KA 2
Norton United 4 Hanley Town 0
Sporting Khalsa 0 **Bilbrook** 3

Stone Dominoes 5 Goldenhill Wanderers 1
Walsall Wood 2 Shenstone Pathfinder 0
THIRD ROUND
Abbey Hulton United 0 **Wolstanton United** 2
Bilbrook 3 Florence 1
Bloxwich United 5 Walsall Wood 4
Brocton 1 **Stone Dominoes** 3
Heath Hayes 4 Ball Haye Green 0
Leek CSOB 0 **Foley** 4
Norton United 0 **Eccleshall** 2
Warstones Wanderers 0 **Norton** 4 *(at Norton United)*
QUARTER-FINALS
Bilbrook 1 **Heath Hayes** 4
Bloxwich United 3 Eccleshall 1
Stone Dominoes 1 Foley 0
Wolstanton United 6 Norton 2
SEMI-FINALS
Bloxwich United 1 **Heath Hayes** 2
Wolstanton United 1 **Stone Dominoes** 2
FINAL
(April 12th at Stafford Rangers)
Heath Hayes 0 **Stone Dominoes** 3

STAFFORDSHIRE CHALLENGE CUP
FIRST ROUND
Bentley 4 **Wolstanton United Res.** 6
Chasetown Res. 4 Stone Dominoes Res. 0
Chesterton 3 Talbot Athletic 1
Hanley Town Res. 1 **Brocton Res.** 2
Penkridge Town 4 Northwood Town 2
Redgate Clayton Res. 3 **Longton Harriers** 6
Wyrley Juniors 3 Cheadle Town Old Boys 2
SECOND ROUND
Brocton Res. 0 **Kidsgrove Athletic Youth** 8
Chesterton 2 **Penkridge Town** 5
Lichfield City 2 Heath Town Rangers Res. 2 *aet* (7-6p)
Newcastle Town Res. 3 Keele University 2
Stone Old Alleynians 5 Hawkins Sports 1
Walsall Wood Res. 1 **Alsager Town Res.** 3
Wolstanton United Res. 4 Chasetown Res. 1
Wyrley Juniors 4 Longton Harriers 2
QUARTER-FINALS
Newcastle Town Res. 1 **Lichfield City** 1 *aet* (2-4p)
Penkridge Town 7 Alsager Town Res. 1
Stone Old Alleynians 6 Wyrley Juniors 0
Wolstanton United Res. 0 **Kidsgrove Athletic Youth** 6
SEMI-FINALS
Kidsgrove Athletic Youth 2 Penkridge Town 1 *aet*
Lichfield City 3 **Stone Old Alleynians** 3 *aet* (4-5p)
FINAL *(March 22nd at Eccleshall)*
Stone Old Alleynians 1 **Kidsgrove Athletic Youth** 5

STAFFORDSHIRE PRESIDENT'S CUP
FINAL *(March 15th at Wolverhampton Casuals)*
Pendeford Santos 3 Sikh Hunters 2

SUFFOLK PREMIER CUP
(Sponsor: LB Group)
FIRST ROUND
Debenham Leisure Centre 1 **Bury Town** 2
Hadleigh United 2 **Felixstowe & Walton United** 3
Haverhill Rovers 2 Newmarket Town 2 *aet* (4-2p)
Ipswich Town 2 Leiston 1 *(at Leiston)*
Kirkley & Pakefield 2 Lowestoft Town 0
Needham Market 4 Mildenhall Town 1
Woodbridge Town 1 **AFC Sudbury** 4
QUARTER-FINALS
AFC Sudbury 2 **Bury Town** 3
Felixstowe & Walton United 2 **Needham Market** 7
Ipswich Town 4 Haverhill Rovers 0
Walsham-le-Willows 1 **Kirkley & Pakefield** 4 *aet*
SEMI-FINALS
Bury Town 0 **Ipswich Town** 3
Kirkley & Pakefield 0 **Needham Market** 2
FINAL *(April 19th at Ipswich Town)*
Ipswich Town 4 Needham Market 1

SUFFOLK SENIOR CUP
FIRST ROUND
Beccles Town 2 **Corton** 3
Brantham Athletic 5 Conard United 0
Bungay Town 2 **Leiston St Margarets** 3
Coplestonians 3 Framlingham Town 2
East Bergholt United 0 **Grundisburgh** 4
Hundon 2 **Lakenheath** 3
Ipswich Athletic 3 Whitton United 1
Ipswich Wanderers 3 Crane Sports 1
Long Melford 1 **Ransomes Sports** 3
Melton St Audrys 0 **Stowmarket Town** 3
Old Newton United 0 **Capel Plough** 3
Stowupland Falcons 1 **Team Bury** 3
Westerfield United 2 Sole Bay United 1
Woodbridge Athletic 6 Brandon Town 1
SECOND ROUND
Coplestonians 6 Stowmarket Town 1
Felixstowe United 0 **Capel Plough** 1
Ipswich Wanderers 1 **Brantham Athletic** 3
Lakenheath 7 Achilles 1
Leiston St Margarets 2 **Grundisburgh** 5
Team Bury 3 Ipswich Athletic 1
Westerfield United 3 **Ransomes Sports** 3 *aet* (2-4p)
Woodbridge Athletic 2 Corton 0
QUARTER-FINALS
Capel Plough 3 Brantham Athletic 1
Coplestonians 1 **Team Bury** 2
Ransomes Sports 7 Lakenheath 1
Woodbridge Athletic 0 **Grundisburgh** 1
SEMI-FINALS
Ransomes Sports 0 **Capel Plough** 1
Team Bury 2 Grundisburgh 1
FINAL
(April 12th at Ipswich Town)
Team Bury 2 Capel Plough 0

SUFFOLK RESERVES CUP
FINAL
(May 8th at Needham Market)
Lowestoft Town Res. 3 Haverhill Rovers Res. 2

SUFFOLK JUNIOR CUP
FINAL
(April 7th at Ipswich Town)
Bacton 2 Sudbury Athletic 1

SUFFOLK PRIMARY CUP
FINAL
(April 20th at Hadleigh United)
Somersham 3 Glemsford & Cavendish United 2

SURREY SENIOR CUP
FIRST ROUND
Chipstead 3 Walton Casuals 1
Kingstonian 4 Beckenham Town 0
Leatherhead 1 **Corinthian Casuals** 3 *aet*
Lingfield 2 Horley Town 0
Whyteleafe 3 Metropolitan Police 2 *aet*
SECOND ROUND
Ash United 1 **AFC Wimbledon** 7
Banstead Athletic 1 **Croydon Athletic** 6
Carshalton Athletic 0 **Badshot Lea** 1
Chessington & Hook United 3 Bookham 0
Chipstead 3 Lingfield 1 *aet*
Colliers Wood United 0 **Egham Town** 3
Corinthian Casuals 1 **Raynes Park Vale** 4
Croydon 1 **Camberley Town** 2
Dorking 0 **Woking** 5
Epsom & Ewell 3 Chertsey Town 0
Guildford City 0 Redhill 0 *aet* (5-3p)
Kingstonian 2 **Crystal Palace** 3
Merstham 4 Ashford Town (Middx) 3
Molesey 0 **Godalming Town** 3
Tooting & Mitcham United 0 **Sutton United** 1
Walton & Hersham 3 Whyteleafe 2

THIRD ROUND
AFC Wimbledon 1 Camberley Town 1 *aet* (6-5p)
Badshot Lea 4 Raynes Park Vale 3
Chipstead 4 Egham Town 0
Croydon Athletic 6 Crystal Palace 2 *aet*
Epsom & Ewell 4 **Walton & Hersham** 5
Godalming Town 3 Chessington & Hook United 2
Guildford City 0 **Sutton United** 2
Woking 1 Merstham 1 *aet* (3-0p)
QUARTER-FINALS
Badshot Lea 3 Woking 3 *aet* (5-3p)
Chipstead 3 **AFC Wimbledon** 4
Croydon Athletic 0 **Sutton United** 6
Walton & Hersham 1 **Godalming Town** 2
SEMI-FINALS
Godalming Town 2 AFC Wimbledon 0
Sutton United 2 Badshot Lea 1
FINAL
(May 4th at Metropolitan Police)
Godalming Town 2
Sutton United 1

SURREY PREMIER CUP

FIRST ROUND
Coulsdon United 3 Colliers Wood United Res. 2
(at Chipstead)
Farleigh Rovers 2 Whyteleafe Res. 0
(at Whyteleafe)
Frimley Green 2 Bookham Res. 0
Godalming Town Res. 0 **AFC Wimbledon Res.** 1
Horley Town Res. 3 Shene Old Grammarians 2
Leatherhead Res. 7 Farnham Town 2
Metropolitan Police Res. 5 Molesey Res. 1
Sutton United Res. 2 Staines Lammas 0
Westfield 1 Chobham 0
SECOND ROUND
AFC Wimbledon Res. 3 Crescent Rovers 0
Ash United Res. 1 **Mole Valley SCR** 3
Camberley Town Res. 1 **Corinthian Casuals Res.** 2
Chessington & Hook United Res. 0 **Merton** 1
Chipstead Res. 2 **Knaphill** 2 *aet* (3-4p)
Coulsdon United 1 **Redhill Res.** 2 *aet (at Redhill)*
Croydon Municipal 1 **Westfield** 3
Epsom & Ewell Res. 2 Sheerwater 0
Farleigh Rovers 1 **Tooting & Mitcham United Res.** 2
(at Tooting & Mitcham United)
Frimley Green 0 **Leatherhead Res.** 2
Horley Town Res. 1 **Metropolitan Police Res.** 3
Lingfield Res. 2 **Cobham** 3 *aet*
Old Suttonians 2 Badshot Lea Res. 0
South Park 1 **Worcester Park** 4
Sutton United Res. 5 Ashford Town (Middx) Res. 0
Woking Res. v **Warlingham** (w/o)
THIRD ROUND
Cobham 4 Merton 1
Corinthian Casuals Res. 3 Epsom & Ewell Res. 1
Leatherhead Res. 1 **Mole Valley SCR** 4 *(at Cobham)*
Redhill Res. 2 Old Suttonians 0
Tooting & Mitcham United Res. 2 **Knaphill** 5
Warlingham 1 **Sutton United Res.** 3
Westfield 1 **Metropolitan Police Res.** 2
Worcester Park 2 AFC Wimbledon Res. 0
(at Walton Casuals)
QUARTER-FINALS
Cobham 4 Worcester Park 1
Metropolitan Police Res. 6 Knaphill 2
Mole Valley SCR 2 Corinthian Casuals Res. 0
Sutton United Res. 3 Redhill Res. 1
SEMI-FINAL
Mole Valley SCR 2 Cobham 1
Sutton United Res. 5 Metropolitan Police Res. 0
FINAL
(May 7th at Carshalton Athletic)
Mole Valley SCR 1 **Sutton United Res.** 1
aet (4-5p)

SURREY INTERMEDIATE CUP

FINAL
(May 5th at Walton Casuals)
Virginia Water 1 Epsom Eagles 0

SURREY JUNIOR CUP

FINAL
(May 12th at Merstham)
Clayton & Ditton 0 Chessington KC 0 *aet* (4-3p)

SURREY LOWER JUNIOR CUP

FINAL
(May 13th at Banstead Athletic)
Abbey Rangers 2 AFC Waltham & Hersham 1

SUSSEX SENIOR CUP

FIRST ROUND
Clymping 1 **Chichester City** 3
Hassocks 2 **East Preston** 3
Lancing 1 **Mile Oak** 2
Little Common 2 **East Grinstead Town** 6
Pagham 1 Midhurst & Easebourne Utd 0 *aet*
Peacehaven & Telscombe 4 St Francis Rangers 0
Ringmer 1 **Westfield** 2 *aet*
Rye United 2 Selsey 1
Seaford Town 0 **Hailsham Town** 1
Sidley United 5 Oakwood 1
Southwick 2 Storrington 1
Steyning Town 0 **Loxwood** 1
Wealden 4 Crawley Down 1
Whitehawk 3 Rustington 0
Worthing United 0 **Littlehampton Town** 2
SECOND ROUND
Arundel 1 **Lewes** 2
Bognor Regis Town 3 Horsham 2 *aet*
Brighton & Hove Albion 5 Southwick 1 *(at Lancing)*
Burgess Hill Town 1 **Eastbourne Borough** 4
Crowborough Athletic 0 **Crawley Town** 1
East Grinstead Town 6 Chichester City 5
Eastbourne United Association 3 Hailsham Town 2 *aet*
Horsham YMCA 2 **Worthing** 3 *aet*
Loxwood 0 **Eastbourne Town** 3
Mile Oak 2 **Whitehawk** 3
Pagham 4 Wealden 2
Peacehaven & Telscombe 3 Wick 2
Rye United 0 **Hastings United** 2
(at Hastings United)
Sidley United 2 Littlehampton Town 2 *aet*
Replay: Littlehampton Town 1 **Sidley United** 3
Three Bridges 1 **Shoreham** 2
Westfield 1 **East Preston** 2
THIRD ROUND
Crawley Town 1 **Brighton & Hove Albion** 2
Eastbourne Borough 8 Sidley United 1
Eastbourne United Association 2 East Preston 1
Lewes 1 Hastings United 1 *aet*
Replay: **Hastings United** 1 Lewes 0
Pagham 0 **Peacehaven & Telscombe** 2
Shoreham 1 East Grinstead Town 0
Whitehawk 1 Eastbourne Town 0
Worthing 0 **Bognor Regis Town** 2
QUARTER-FINALS
Brighton & Hove Albion 6 Eastbourne Utd Association 0
(at Lancing)
Hastings United 2 Shoreham 1
Peacehaven & Telscombe 1 **Bognor Regis Town** 2
Whitehawk 0 **Eastbourne Borough** 1
SEMI-FINAL
Bognor Regis Town 1 Eastbourne Borough 0
(at Three Bridges)
Brighton & Hove Albion 5 Hastings United 0
(at Eastbourne Town)
FINAL
(May 3rd at Eastbourne Borough)
Brighton & Hove Albion 4
Bognor Regis Town 0

SUSSEX RUR CHARITY CUP
(Sponsor: Principal)

FIRST ROUND

Arundel 1 **Lingfield** 2
East Preston 0 **Rye United** 2
Pagham 0 **Chichester City** 3
Redhill 3 Rustington 0
Selsey 3 Lancing 0
Sidley United 2 Steyning Town 0

SECOND ROUND

Clymping 1 **Shoreham** 2 *aet*
Crawley Down 4 Sidley United 1
Eastbourne United Association 1 Mile Oak 0
Hassocks 2 **Selsey** 4
Lingfield 3 Three Bridges 1
Littlehampton Town 0 **East Grinstead Town** 2
Midhurst & Easebourne Utd 1 **Southwick** 3
Oakwood 6 Crowborough Athletic 1
Peacehaven & Telscombe 3 Redhill 1
Ringmer 3 Chichester City 1
Rye United 3 Westfield 0
Storrington 2 Little Common 1
Wealden 1 **Seaford Town** 2
Whitehawk 2 Loxwood 2 *aet* (3-2p)
Wick 4 Hailsham Town 1
Worthing United 2 **St Francis Rangers** 3

THIRD ROUND

Crawley Down 2 Rye United 1 *(at Rye United)*
East Grinstead Town 0 **Shoreham** 0 *aet* (3-4p)
Eastbourne United Association 0 **Wick** 1
Lingfield 1 **Seaford Town** 2
Peacehaven & Telscombe 4 Ringmer 2
St Francis Rangers 1 Oakwood 0
Storrington 1 **Southwick** 2
Whitehawk 3 Selsey 1

QUARTER-FINALS

Crawley Down 1 St Francis Rangers 0
Peacehaven & Telscombe 3 Seaford Town 1
Southwick 0 **Whitehawk** 8
Wick 3 Shoreham 2

SEMI-FINALS

Peacehaven & Telscombe 2 Crawley Down 2 *aet* (3-0p)
(at Shoreham)
Whitehawk 0 **Wick** 1 *(at Hassocks)*

FINAL

(April 28th at Lancing)
Wick 1 **Peacehaven & Telscombe** 6

SUSSEX INTERMEDIATE CUP
Competition abandoned due to inclement weather

SUSSEX JUNIOR CUP
FINAL

(April 14th at Lancing)
Wadhurst United 3 Worthing Leisure 0

WEST RIDING COUNTY CUP

FIRST ROUND

Armthorpe Welfare 1 **Ossett Albion** 4
Askern Villa 3 Leeds Carnegie 1
Harrogate Railway Athletic 0 **FC Halifax Town** 1
Harrogate Town 3 Goole 2
Selby Town 4 Pontefract Collieries 0
Silsden 5 Glasshoughton Welfare 2
Tadcaster Albion 2 **Guiseley** 3 *aet*
Thackley 1 **Ossett Town** 2
Wakefield 3 Eccleshill United 2

SECOND ROUND

Askern Villa 3 **Garforth Town** 4
Brighouse Town 1 **Barnoldswick Town** 3
Farsley Celtic 2 FC Halifax Town 1
Ossett Albion 2 **Liversedge** 3
Ossett Town 1 **Guiseley** 4
Selby Town 1 **Yorkshire Amateur** 2 *(at Yorkshire Amats)*
Silsden 5 **Bradford Park Avenue** 6 *aet*
Wakefield 2 Harrogate Town 2 *aet* (4-3p)

QUARTER-FINALS

Barnoldswick Town 3 Yorkshire Amateur 0
Bradford Park Avenue 0 **Guiseley** 3
Garforth Town 1 Farsley Celtic 0
Wakefield 6 Liversedge 3

SEMI-FINALS

Garforth Town 4 Wakefield 3 *aet*
Guiseley 1 **Barnoldswick Town** 1 *aet* (2-4p)

FINAL

(April 14th at WRCFA, Woodlesford)
Garforth Town 5 Barnoldswick Town 4

WEST RIDING CHALLENGE CUP
FINAL

(April 30th at WRCFA, Woodlesford)
Albion Sports 1 **Knaresborough Town** 3

WEST RIDING CHALLENGE TROPHY
FINAL

(April 26th at WRCFA, Woodlesford)
Thornhill 4 Beeston St Anthony's Res. 1

WESTMORLAND SENIOR CUP
FIRST ROUND

Alston Moor Sports Club 2 Endmoor KGR 1
Ambleside United 5 **Shap** 7
Burton Thistle 1 **Appleby** 2
Carvetii United 2 Staveley United 1
Kendal Celtic 0 **Penrith Rangers** 4
Kendal County 6 Lunesdale United 2
Kirkby Lonsdale 4 Greystoke 1
Wetheriggs United 10 Coniston 0
Windermere SC 2 **Milnthorpe Corinthians** 3

SECOND ROUND

Appleby 3 **Ibis** 3 *aet* (2-4p)
Braithwaite 0 **Alston Moor Sports Club** 6
Burneside 2 Kendal County 1
Carvetii United 2 **Penrith Rangers** 4
Kirkoswald 5 Langwathby United 0
Milnthorpe Corinthians 3 Keswick 2 *aet*
Shap 3 Sedbergh Wanderers 2
Wetheriggs United 4 Kirkby Lonsdale 0

QUARTER-FINALS

Alston Moor Sports Club 0 **Kirkoswald** 8
Burneside 3 Penrith Rangers 0
Ibis 1 **Milnthorpe Corinthians** 7
Wetheriggs United 4 Shap 3 *aet*

SEMI-FINALS

Milnthorpe Corinthians 2 Burneside 1
Wetheriggs United 1 **Kirkoswald** 2

FINAL

(April 24th at Kendal Town)
Milnthorpe Corinthians 0 **Kirkoswald** 0 *aet* (3-4p)

WESTMORLAND BENEVOLENT TROPHY
FIRST ROUND

Ambleside United 7 Burneside 2
Braithwaite 2 **Ibis** 6
Carvetii United 6 Endmoor KGR 3
Dent 0 **Coniston** 4
Greystoke (w/o) v Windermere SC
Shap 2 **Keswick** 4

SECOND ROUND

Appleby 1 **Kendal County** 6
Carvetii United 6 Kendal Celtic 1
Coniston 0 **Penrith Rangers** 5
Greystoke 2 **Keswick** 9
Ibis 3 **Ambleside United** 4
Kendal United 2 Alston Moor Sports Club 1
Lunesdale United 3 **Milnthorpe Corinthians** 4
Staveley United 2 Wetheriggs United 1

QUARTER-FINALS

Carvetii United 2 **Keswick** 5
Kendal United 2 Penrith Rangers 1 *aet*
Milnthorpe Corinthians 2 **Ambleside United** 2 *aet* (8-7p)
(Milnthorpe Corinthians expelled)
Staveley United 3 Kendal County 2 *aet*

SEMI-FINALS
Ambleside United 2 Kendal United 0
Staveley United 1 **Keswick** 7
FINAL
(April 14th at Kendal Town)
Ambleside United 0 **Keswick** 1

WESTMORLAND JUNIOR CUP
FINAL
(April 22nd at Kendal Town)
Appleby Res. 0 **Kendal United** 1

WILTSHIRE PREMIER SHIELD
FIRST ROUND
(played over two legs)
Salisbury City 1 Swindon Town 2,
Swindon Town 7 Salisbury City 2
Swindon Supermarine 4 Chippenham Town 2,
Chippenham Town 1 **Swindon Supermaine** 2
FINAL
(April 27th at Swindon Supermarine)
Swindon Supermarine 1 **Swindon Town** 2

WILTSHIRE SENIOR CUP
FIRST ROUND
Calne Town 3 FC Chippenham Youth 2 *aet*
Corsham Town 10 Westside 1
Devizes Town 4 Cricklade Town 3
Downton 2 KC 0
Malmesbury Victoria 3 Wroughton 1
Marlborough Town 2 Westbury United 1
Pewsey Vale 2 **Shrewton United** 7
Purton 3 New College Swindon 0
Trowbridge Town 1 Amesbury Town 0
SECOND ROUND
Bemerton Heath Harlequins 4 Downton 1 *aet*
Calne Town 2 Bradford Town 2 *aet* (4-3p)
Malmesbury Victoria 2 Devizes Town 1
Marlborough Town 0 **Highworth Town** 4
Melksham Town 2 Trowbridge Town 1
Purton 3 **Laverstock & Ford** 4
Shrewton United 4 Wootton Bassett Town 3
Warminster Town 1 **Corsham Town** 2
QUARTER-FINALS
Corsham Town 2 **Bemerton Heath Harlequins** 3 *aet*
Laverstock & Ford 3 Highworth Town 2 *aet*
Malmesbury Victoria 1 **Melksham Town** 3
Shrewton United 0 **Calne Town** 3
SEMI-FINALS
Bemerton Heath Harlequins 1 **Calne Town** 2 *aet*
(at Warminster Town)
Melksham Town 1 **Laverstock & Ford** 5
(at Warminster Town)
FINAL
(May 4th at Salisbury City)
Laverstock & Ford 3 **Calne Town** 4

WILTSHIRE JUNIOR CUP
FINAL
(April 24th at Laverstock & Ford)
Minety 4 Redlynch & Woodfalls United 2

WORCESTERSHIRE SENIOR CUP
FIRST ROUND
Bromsgrove Rovers 1 **Kidderminster Harriers** 3
Halesowen Town 2 Stourport Swifts 2 *aet* (4-2p)
Stourbridge 1 Evesham United 0
Worcester City 4 Redditch United 1
SEMI-FINALS
Halesowen Town 3 Stourbridge 1
Worcester City 2 **Kidderminster Harriers** 3
FINAL
(April 22nd at Kidderminster Harriers)
Kidderminster Harriers 2 Halesowen Town 0

WORCESTERSHIRE SENIOR URN
FIRST ROUND
Bewdley Town 2 Pershore Town 1
QUARTER-FINALS
Alvechurch 2 GSA Sport 1
Bewdley Town 2 Lye Town 2 *aet* (6-5p)
Dudley Sports 1 Bromsgrove Rovers Res. 0
Malvern Town 2 **Studley** 5
SEMI-FINALS
Bewdley Town 0 **Alvechurch** 3
Dudley Sports 1 Studley 0
FINAL
(April 27th at Kidderminster Harriers)
Dudley Sports 0 **Alvechurch** 2

WORCESTERSHIRE JUNIOR CUP
FINAL
(March 31st at Worcester City)
Archdale 3 Inkberrow 1

MISCELLANEOUS CUPS 2009-10

ALDERSHOT SENIOR CUP
FIRST ROUND
Bagshot 2 Fleet Spurs Res. 1
Camberley Town 3 Headley United 0
Cove 7 Frensham RBL 1
Farnborough North End 1 Frimley Green 0
Frimley Select 2 **Overton United** 3 *aet*
Hale Rovers 6 Hindhead Athletic 6 *aet* (4-3p)
Hartley Wintney 7 Frimley 1
Liphook United 0 **Farnham Town** 1
(at Farnham Town)
Petersfield Town 0 **Ash United** 6
Sandhurst Town 1 **Sandhurst Devels** 2
South Farnborough 5 Sandhurst Sports 3
Yateley 1 **Alton Town** 7
(at Alton Town)
SECOND ROUND
Alton Town 2 **Hartley Wintney** 3
Camberley Town 0 **Ash United** 2
Farnborough 7 Bagshot 1
Farnborough North End 2 Sandhurst Devels 1
Farnham Town 2 Badshot Lea 0
Hale Rovers 1 **Fleet Town** 11
Overton United 4 Liss Athletic 0
South Farnborough 0 **Cove** 10 *(at Cove)*
QUARTER-FINALS
Cove 2 Farnborough North End 1
(at Farnborough North End)
Farnborough 2 Ash United 1 *aet*
Farnham Town 3 Overton United 1
Fleet Town 2 Hartley Wintney 1
SEMI-FINALS
Cove 2 Farnborough 0
Farnham Town 1 **Fleet Town** 4
FINAL *(May 8th at Fleet Town)*
Fleet Town 5 Cove 0

AXMINSTER HOSPITAL CUP
FIRST ROUND
Alphington (w/o) v Ottery St Mary
Budleigh Salterton 4 Axminster Town 1
Colaton Raleigh 2 **Elmore** 3 *(at Elmore)*
Ilminster Town (w/o) v Chard Town
Seaton Town 3 Millwey Rise 1
Sidmouth Town 1 Feniton 0
QUARTER-FINALS
Alphington (w/o) v Crewkerne
Exmouth Town 5 Elmore 1
Ilminster Town 1 Sidmouth Town 0
Seaton Town 0 **Budleigh Salterton** 3

SEMI-FINALS
Budleigh Salterton 0 **Alphington** 1
Exmouth Town 5 Ilminster Town 2 *aet*
FINAL
(May 9th at Axminster Town)
Alphington 1 Exmouth Town 1 *aet* (5-4p)

BRIGHTON CHARITY CUP 2008-09
(three ties held over
to pre-season 2009-10)
QUARTER-FINALS
East Preston 1 Southwick 0
SEMI-FINALS
Seaford Town 1 **East Preston** 1 *aet* (4-5p)
FINAL *(September 8th at Worthing)*
East Preston 1 Shoreham 0

BRIGHTON CHARITY CUP
FIRST ROUND
Littlehampton Town 2 **Horsham** 3
Mile Oak 2 **Worthing United** 3
Pagham 2 East Preston 1
Seaford Town 1 **Peacehaven & Telscombe** 2
Shoreham 1 Rustington 0
Southwick 3 **Ringmer** 4
Storrington 1 **Chichester City** 3
Wick 4 Clymping 0
QUARTER-FINALS
Chichester City 3 Horsham 2 *aet*
Ringmer 2 Peacehaven & Telscombe 1 *aet*
Shoreham 2 Pagham 1
Wick 3 Worthing United 1 *aet*
SEMI-FINALS
Ringmer 2 Shoreham 1 *aet*
Wick 2 Chichester City 1
FINAL
(May 13th at Worthing)
Wick 3 Ringmer 0

BUCKINGHAMSHIRE CHARITY CUP
FIRST ROUND
Banbury United 2 Brackley Town 0
Stony Stratford Town 2 Mursley United 1
QUARTER-FINALS
Banbury United 4 Ampthill Town 2
Buckingham Town 1 **Olney Town** 4
New Bradwell St Peter 2 Leighton Town 1
Stony Stratford Town 3 Buckingham Athletic 2 *aet*
SEMI-FINALS
Banbury United 2 New Bradwell St Peter 0
Stony Stratford Town 2 **Olney Town** 4
FINAL
(May 11th at Buckingham Town)
Banbury United 4 Olney Town 0

BUCKINGHAM JUNIOR CHARITY CUP
(all ties played at Buckingham Town)
FIRST ROUND
Great Horwood 1 **Stewkley** 3
Grendon Rangers 3 Steeple Claydon 2
Potterspury 3 Marsh Gibbon 0
Syresham 2 **Kempston Hammers** 3 *aet*
Thornbrough Athletic 2 Deanshanger Athletic 1
Westbury 1 **Wicken Sports** 7
QUARTER-FINALS
Charlton 1 **Brackley Sports** 4
Kempston Hammers 0 **Wicken Sports** 4
Potterspury 2 **Thornborough Athletic** 3
Stewkley 3 **Grendon Rangers** 1 *aet (Stewkley expelled)*
SEMI-FINALS
Brackley Sports 2 Wicken Sports 0
Thornborough Athletic 4 Grendon Rangers 2 *aet*
FINAL
(April 22nd at Buckingham Town)
Thornborough Athletic 3
Brackley Sports 1

CAPITAL COUNTIES FEEDER LEAGUES TROPHY
(Sponsor: Anagram Records)
FIRST ROUND
Berkhamsted 2 Pitstone & Ivinghoe 1
Bovingdon 1 **Sandridge Rovers** 1 *aet* (2-4p)
Brache Sparta v **Westhamians** (w/o)
Croxley Guild 1 **Manford Way** 3
Epping 5 Chipperfield Corinthians 0
Frenford Senior 3 Aston Clinton 2 *aet*
Hanworth Villa 2 **The 61 FC (Luton)** 0
(Hanworth Villa expelled)
Hutton 5 Bletchley Town 3 *aet*
Kent Athletic 3 **Broadfields United** 4 *aet*
Lemsford 1 **Cuffley** 2
London Lions 3 Evergreen 0
Metropolitan Police Bushey 3 Mill End Sports 1
Old Bradwell United 1 **Padbury United** 5
Park Street Village 1 **MK Wanderers** 2
Sheerwater 3 Standon & Puckeridge 2
Wormley Rovers 2 White Ensign 0
SECOND ROUND
Berkhamsted 3 Cuffley 1
Epping 4 Sandridge Rovers 1
Frenford Senior 3 Metropolitan Police Bushey 1
Hutton 0 **Padbury United** 1
MK Wanderers 1 **London Lions** 4
The 61 FC (Luton) 5 Sheerwater 1
Westhamians 3 **Manford Way** 4
Wormley Rovers 1 **Broadfields United** 2
QUARTER-FINALS
Berkhamsted 1 **Padbury United** 3
Epping 2 Broadfields United 1
Frenford Senior 1 **The 61 FC (Luton)** 2
Manford Way 1 London Lions 0
SEMI-FINALS
Epping 1 **Padbury United** 4
The 61 FC (Luton) 2 Manford Way 1
FINAL
(May 23rd at HCFA, Letchworth)
The 61 FC (Luton) 2 **Padbury United** 3

FARINGDON THURSDAY MEMORIAL CUP
FIRST ROUND
Bampton Town 0 **Highworth Town Res.** 1
Childrey United 2 **Faringdon Town** 2 *aet* (2-4p)
Fairford United Res. 4 Clanfield 0
Lambourn Sports 7 Coleshill United 1
Letcombe 4 Hanney United 0
Lower Stratton 1 CHQ United 0 *(at CHQ United)*
Shrivenham Res. 5 Saxton Rovers 0
Wantage Town Res. 7 Stanford-in-Vale 0
QUARTER FINALS
Faringdon Town 1 Wantage Town Res. 1 *aet* (6-5p)
Highworth Town Res. 5 Fairford Town Res. 1
Lambourn Sports 5 Lower Stratton 1
Letcombe 2 **Shrivenham Res.** 3
SEMI-FINALS
Faringdon Town 1 Shrivenham Res. 0
Lambourn Sports 3 Highworth Town Res. 1
FINAL
(May 6th at Faringdon Town)
Faringdon Town 1 Lambourn Sports 1
aet (4-3p)

HASTINGS SENIOR CUP
FIRST ROUND
Sidley United 1 Westfield 0 *aet*
SEMI-FINALS
Rye United 1 **Bexhill United** 2
Sidley United 1 Little Common 0 *aet*
FINAL
(April 13th at Sidley United)
Sidley United 2 Bexhill United 1

HINCHINGBROOKE CUP

PRELIMINARY ROUND

Huntingdon Town 2 **Yaxley** 3 *aet*
Potton United 1 **St Ives Town** 2
Rushden & Higham United 4 Bourne Town 1
St Neots Town 1 **Wootton Blue Cross** 3

FIRST ROUND

Biggleswade Town 3 Cranfield United 1
Biggleswade United 0 **Stotfold** 1
Deeping Rangers 2 AFC Kempston Rovers 1
Godmanchester Rovers 2 St Ives Town 0 *aet*
Peterborough Northern Star 4 Eynesbury Rovers 2
Rothwell Corinthians 4 Wootton Blue Cross 4 *aet* (4-2p)
Rushden & Higham United 1 **Yaxley** 4
Wellingborough Whitworth 0 **Blackstones** 3

QUARTER-FINALS

Biggleswade Town 2 Yaxley 1
Peterborough Northern Star 1 Blackstones 0
Rothwell Corinthians 2 Godmanchester Rovers 1
Stotfold 3 Deeping Rangers 1

SEMI-FINALS

Rothwell Corinthians 3 **Peterborough Northern Star** 5
Stotfold 0 **Biggleswade Town** 1

FINAL *(May 4th at Huntingdon Town)*

Peterborough Northern Star 4 Biggleswade Town 1

J W HUNT CUP

FIRST ROUND

Alvechurch 0 **Penkridge Town** 2
Bilston Town 4 **Penn Croft** 6 *aet*
Bloxwich United 5 Wolverhampton Casuals 2
Brereton Social 1 **Walsall Wood** 3
Chasetown Res. 1 AFC Wombourne United 0
Darlaston Town 4 Warstones Wanderers 2
Dudley Town 2 Black Country Rangers 1 *aet*
Heath Town Rangers 1 **Continental Star** 2
Pelsall Villa 1 **Heath Hayes** 2
Riverway 1 **GSA Sports** 3
Stafford Town 5 Goodrich 1
Tipton Town 1 **Brocton** 3
Warley Development 2 Wolverhampton United 0
Wednesfield 2 **AFC Wulfrunians** 4
Wrens Nest 2 **Newport County Borough** 3
Wyrley Juniors 8 Blackheath Town 1

SECOND ROUND

Chasetown Res. 4 Heath Hayes 3
Continental Star 0 **Bloxwich United** 3
Darlaston Town 3 Newport County Borough 1
Dudley Town 3 Penn Croft 0
GSA Sports 2 **Brocton** 4
Stafford Town 3 AFC Wulfrunians 2
Walsall Wood 4 Wyrley Juniors 1
Warley Development 0 **Penkridge Town** 2

QUARTER-FINALS

Bloxwich United 5 Penkridge Town 0
Chasetown Res. 2 Brocton 1
Stafford Town 4 Dudley Town 0
Walsall Wood 1 **Darlaston Town** 3

SEMI-FINALS

Bloxwich United (w/o) v Darlaston Town *(at Goodrich)*
Chasetown Res. 0 **Stafford Town** 1 *(at Goodrich)*

FINAL *(May 14th at AFC Wulfrunians)*

Bloxwich United 2 Stafford Town 0

MORRISON BELL CUP

FIRST ROUND

Budleigh Salterton 2 Royal Marines 1 *aet*
Feniton 0 **Clyst Valley** 3
Ottery St Mary 1 **East Budleigh** 1 *aet* (3-4p)

SEMI-FINALS

Budleigh Salterton 2 Sidmouth Town 1
aet (at Ottery St Mary)
East Budleigh 0 **Clyst Valley** 2 *(at Ottery St Mary)*

FINAL

(May 29th at Ottery St Mary)
Budleigh Salterton 2 Clyst Valley 0

NORTH BEDFORDSHIRE CHARITY CUP

FIRST ROUND

Arlesey Town v **Stotfold** (w/o)
Biggleswade United 3 **Langford** 4
Cranfield United 0 **Biggleswade Town** 10
Wootton Blue Cross (w/o) v Potton United

SEMI-FINALS

Langford 2 **Biggleswade Town** 5
Wootton Blue Cross 0 **Stotfold** 2 *(at Langford)*

FINAL *(May 7th at Langford)*

Biggleswade Town 0 **Stotfold** 3

NORTH HAMPSHIRE SENIOR CUP

FIRST ROUND

Alresford Town 8 Winchester Castle 1
Fleet Town 8 Overton United 0
Winchester City 4 Stockbridge 0

QUARTER-FINALS

AFC Aldermaston 2 **Whitchurch United** 5
Andover 3 **Alresford Town** 3 *aet* (4-5p)
Andover New Street 2 Tadley Calleva 1
Fleet Town 2 Winchester City 1

SEMI-FINAL

Alresford Town 4 Whitchurch United 2 *aet*
Fleet Town (w/o) v Andover New Street

FINAL *(May 10th at Andover New Street)*

Fleet Town 2 Alresford Town 0

PORTSMOUTH SENIOR CUP

FIRST ROUND

Clanfield 1 **Paulsgrove** 2
Fareham Town 1 **Gosport Borough** 2
Hayling United 3 Waterlooville Social 1
Horndean 2 Paulsgrove Res. 0
Locks Heath 3 Fleetlands 1
Moneyfields 3 Portsmouth Royal Navy 1
Petersfield Town 4 University of Portsmouth 2
Wymering 7 Shearer United 1

QUARTER-FINALS

Hayling United 3 Moneyfields 2
Horndean 2 **Locks Heath** 3
Paulsgrove 5 Wymering 2
Petersfield Town 3 Gosport Borough 3 *aet* (8-7p)

SEMI-FINALS

Hayling United 3 Paulsgrove 2 *aet*
Petersfield Town 4 Locks Heath 2

FINAL *(April 28th at Moneyfields)*

Hayling United 1 Petersfield Town 0

ROLLESTON CHARITY CUP

FIRST ROUND

Anstey Nomads 1 **Birstall United** 4
Ibstock United 0 **Barwell** 2
Oadby Town 2 St Andrews SC 0

SEMI-FINALS

Barwell 0 Birstall United 0 *aet* (5-4p)
Hinckley United 4 Oadby Town 0

FINAL *(May 3rd at LCFA, Holmes Park)*

Hinckley United 0 **Barwell** 3

SOUTH MIDLANDS FLOODLIGHT CUP

FIRST ROUND

Broxbourne Borough V & E 3 Hoddesdon Town 2 *aet*
Potton United 2 Wormley Rovers 1
Hertford Town 5 **Stansted** 1 *(Hertford Town expelled)*
St Margaretsbury 1 **Oxhey Jets** 2

QUARTER-FINALS

Biggleswade Town 1 **Broxbourne Borough V & E** 2
Bedford 2 Potton United 0
Oxhey Jets 2 Cheshunt 0
Stansted 0 **Royston Town** 5

SEMI-FINALS

Broxbourne Borough V & E 3 Bedford 1
Royston Town 3 Oxhey Jets 2

FINAL *(May 16th at Broxbourne Borough V & E)*

Broxbourne Borough V & E 1 **Royston Town** 2

SOUTHERN COMBINATION CUP

FIRST ROUND

Crawley Down v **Ashford Town (Middx)** (w/o)
Feltham 3 **Cobham** 5 *aet*
Frimley Green 1 **Sandhurst Town** 5
Guildford City 2 Knaphill 1
Staines Lammas 1 **Hanworth Villa** 3
(at Hanworth Villa)

SECOND ROUND

Ashford Town (Middx) (w/o) v Westfield
Chertsey Town 3 Cobham 2
Cove 1 **Leatherhead** 2
Guildford City 2 **Molesey** 3
Hanworth Villa 5 Sandhurst Town 0
Hartley Wintney 4 Chessington & Hook United 2
Reading Town 2 Dorking 1
Staines Town 2 **Old Hamptonians** 3 *aet*

QUARTER-FINALS

Ashford Town (Middx) v **Reading Town** (w/o)
Hanworth Villa (w/o) v Chertsey Town
Molesey 1 Leatherhead 0
Old Hamptonians 2 Hartley Wintney 0
(at Hartley Wintney)

SEMI-FINALS

Old Hamptonians 0 **Hanworth Villa** 1
Reading Town 2 Molesey 1

FINAL

(May 13th at Reading Town)
Reading Town 4 Hanworth Villa 1

TOLLESHUNT DARCY MEMORIAL CUP

FIRST ROUND

Braintree Town 1 Beacon Hill Rovers 0
Burnham Ramblers 2 Hatfield Peverel 1
Halstead Town 1 **Earls Colne** 4
Heybridge Swifts 3 Southminster St Leonards 1
Hullbridge Sports 0 **Tiptree Jobserve** 1
Stanway Rovers 2 White Notley 0
Witham Town 2 Maldon St Marys 1
Wivenhoe Town v **Coggeshall Town** (w/o)

QUARTER-FINALS

Coggeshall Town (w/o) v Heybridge Swifts
Earls Colne 0 **Burnham Ramblers** 1 *(at Halstead Town)*
Tiptree Jobserve 3 Stanway Rovers 3 *aet* (4-1p)
Witham Town 2 Braintree Town 0

SEMI-FINAL

Burnham Ramblers 7 Tiptree Jobserve 2
Coggeshall Town 2 **Witham Town** 2 *aet* (0-3p)

FINAL

(May 19th at Witham Town)
Witham Town 2 **Burnham Ramblers** 3

WALSALL SENIOR CUP

FIRST ROUND

Bloxwich United 4 Biddulph Victoria 1
Bolehall Swifts (w/o) v Tividale
Chasetown 6 Walsall Wood 1
Continental Star 3 Wolverhampton Casuals 1
Darlaston Town 1 Bridgnorth Town 1 *aet* (4-2p)
Heath Hayes 7 Oldbury Athletic 0
Romulus 1 Pelsall Villa 0
Rushall Olympic 1 Boldmere St Michaels 0

QUARTER-FINALS

Bloxwich United 2 Chasetown 1
Continental Star 4 Bolehall Swifts 2
Darlaston Town 0 **Rushall Olympic** 3
Heath Hayes 0 **Romulus** 4

SEMI-FINALS

Continental Star 2 **Bloxwich United** 2 *aet* (2-3p)
Rushall Olympic 3 Romulus 1

FINAL

(May 18th at Walsall)
Bloxwich United 1 Rushall Olympic 0

OTHER CUP FINALS 2009-10

ALDERSHOT JUNIOR CUP
(May 3rd at Aldershot Town)
Yateley Green Res. 3 Liphook United Res. 1

ANCASTER CUP
(May19th at Bourne Town)
Sleaford Town Res. 2 **Deeping Rangers Res.** 2 *aet* (3-5p)

ANDOVER OPEN CUP
(April 21st at Andover)
Otterbourne 2 Stockbridge 1

ASHBY BENEFIT CUP
(December 29th at Bottesford Town)
Grimsby Borough 2 Bottesford Town 1 *aet*

AUCKLAND CHARITY CUP
(April 12th at West Auckland Town)
Coundon & Leeholme 0 Shildon Railway 0 *aet* (5-4p)

BARKSTON ASH CUP
(April 5th at Tadcaster Albion)
Sherburn White Rose 3 Aberford Albion 2

BASINGSTOKE SENIOR CUP
(May 12th at Thatcham Town)
Fleet Town 3 Alton Town 1

BASS CHARITY VASE
(July 30th at Burton Albion)
Burton Albion 1 Derby County 0

BEDWORTH NURSING CUP
(April 2nd at Bedworth United)
Collycroft Sports 4 Broughton & Frankton 1

BIGGLESWADE & DISTRICT CUP
(May 12th at Biggleswade United)
Langford 1 Stotfold Res. 1 *aet* (7-6p)

BOLTON HOSPITAL CUP
(May 10th at Bolton Wanderers)
Eagley 2 Stoneclough 1

BRADFORD SENIOR CUP
(May 5th at Thackley)
Campion 2 Field Sports & Social 0

BRAUNTON CUP
(May 9th at Barnstaple Town)
Braunton 2 Barnstaple AAC 1

CPO NATIONAL CHRISTIANS CUP
(May 31st at Bolton Wanderers)
Billingham Crusaders 1 Mill Lane Churches West Derby 0

CHESTER SENIOR CUP
(May 14th at Christleton)
Upton Athletic Assoc. 0 Chester Nomads 0 *aet* (5-4p)

CHESTER CHALLENGE CUP
(April 16th at Christleton)
Christleton Res. 1 **Highfield Athletic** 2

COMMANDER ETHELSTON CUP
(May 3rd at Whitchurch Alport)
Whitchurch Alport 3 Ellesmere Rangers Res. 2

COVENTRY EVENING TELEGRAPH CUP
(May 5th at Coventry City)
Christ The King 1 Alvis 0

COVENTRY CHARITY CUP
(May 4th at Coventry City)
Alveston 2 Coventry Copsewood 1

CRAVEN FA CUP
(May 14th at Barnoldswick Town)
Grassington United 2 **Rimington** 7

CRAVEN FA MORRISON CUP
(May 7th at Settle United)
Barnoldswick Town Res. 2 **Sedbergh Wanderers** 4

CRAVEN FA NORMAN PRATT TROPHY
(April 30th at Settle United)
Rimington Res. 3 Ingleton 3 *aet*
(Replay May 4th at Settle United)
Ingleton 3 Rimington Res. 2

CREWE & DISTRICT CUP
(May 8th at Crewe Alexandra)
Sandbach United 3 MMU Alsager 0

DIDCOT FESTIVAL CUP
(August 29th at Didcot Town)
Crowmarsh Gifford 2 Saxton Rovers 1

EAST HAM MEMORIAL HOSPITAL CUP
(May 19th at Newham United)
Forest United 2 Newham United 0

EASTBOURNE CHALLENGE CUP
(May 4th at Eastbourne Town)
Eastbourne Town Res. 2 Polegate 1

FRY CUP
(Auguest 9th at Fry Club)
Yate Town Res. 2 Henbury 1

GOLESWORTHY CUP
(May 26th at Ottery St Mary)
Beer Albion Res. 4 Clyst Valley Res. 2

GRANDISSON CUP
(May 28th at Ottery St Mary)
Colyton 3 Tipton St John 0

GRANTHAM HOSPITAL CUP
(May 29th at Ancaster Rovers)
Beehive United 4 **Whatton United** 4 *aet* (8-9p)

HADLEIGH CHARITY CUP
(July 18th at Hadleigh United)
Hadleigh United 0 **Ipswich Town** 4

HALIFAX & DISTRICT CUP
(April 26th at FC Halifax Town)
Ovenden West Riding 3 Brighouse Old Boys 1

HANSEN CUP
(May 3rd at Torrington)
Wrey Arms 3 Anchor Braunton 1

HARWICH CHARITY CUP
(April 7th at Brantham Athletic)
Brantham Athletic Res. 3 Great Bentley 1

HASTINGS INTERMEDIATE CUP
(May 8th at Hollington United)
Westfield Res. 4 Punnetts Town 0

HASTINGS JUNIOR CUP
(May 8th at Hollington United)
Catsfield 8 Ticehurst 0

HEAVY WOOLLEN CUP
(May 6th at Ossett Town)
Gildersome Spurs 1 Thornhill 0

HOLMAN CUP
(April 5th at North Molton)
Northam Lions 6 Barnstaple AAC Res. 4

HOYLE CUP
(April 20th at Huddersfield Town)
Bay Athletic 2 Aimbry 1

HUDDERSFIELD & DISTRICT CUP
(April 26th at Huddersfield Town)
Bay Athletic 3 Newsome WMC 1

ISLE OF WIGHT SENIOR (GOLD) CUP
(May 8th at Cowes Sports)
Brading Town 2 Newport IOW 1 *aet*

ISLE OF WIGHT CHALLENGE CUP
(April 29th at East Cowes Victoria Athletic)
Newport IOW Res. 0 **West Wight** 2

ISLE OF WIGHT MEMORIAL CUP
(May 12th at Brading Town)
East Cowes Victoria Athletic Res. 2
West Wight 2 *aet* (5-3p)

ISLE OF WIGHT JUNIOR A CUP
(April 22nd at Brading Town)
Ventnor 3 West Wight Res. 0

JIM NEWMAN CUP
(November 18th at Clanfield)
Witney United 3 Letcombe 2

KEIGHLEY & DISTRICT CUP
(April 12th at Silsden)
Cowling 3 Long Lee Juniors 2 *aet*

KEIGHLEY & DISTRICT SUPPLEMENTARY CUP
(April 8th at Silsden)
Oxenhope Recreation Res. 2
Steeton Res. 1

LAUNCESTON & DISTRICT CUP
(May 9th at Launceston)
Gunnislake 4 Kilkhampton 2 *aet*

LOUGHBOROUGH CHARITY CUP
Competition abandoned due to inclement weather

LUTTERWORTH CHARITY CUP
(December 28th at Lutterworth Town)
Lutterworth Athletic 3 Blaby & Whetstone Athletic 1

MAIDENHEAD NORFOLKIAN CUP
(April 9th at Maidenhead United)
FC Beaconsfield 3 Reading YMCA 2 *aet*

MID-CHESHIRE SENIOR CUP
(April 22th at Northwich Victoria)
Northwich Victoria 4 Winsford United 0

MID-SUSSEX SENIOR CHARITY CUP
(May 5th at Hassocks)
Eastbourne Borough A 1 **Cowfold** 2 *aet*

MID-SUSSEX JUNIOR CHARITY CUP
(March 23rd at Haywards Heath Town)
Newick 2 Lindfield Res. 0

NORTH CAMBRIDGESHIRE JUNIOR CUP
(April 14th at March Town United)
Thorney 1 Manea United 0

NORTH HAMPSHIRE INTERMEDIATE CUP
(March 31st at Whitchurch United)
FC Censo 2 Winchester Castle 1

NORTHAMPTON TOWN FA GORELL BARNES CUP
(May 22nd at Northampton Town)
Delapre Old Boys 1 Fox & Hounds 1
aet (4-2p)

NORTHERN COUNTIES CHAMPIONSHIP
(May 4th at Vauxhall Motors)
Cheshire FA (West Kirby) 0
Lancashire FA (Manchester Gregorians) 1

OLD BOYS SENIOR INVITATION CUP
(March 27th at Old Parkonians)
Old Parmiterians 2 Old Salesians 1

PAULTON HOSPITAL CUP
(April 2nd at Paulton Rovers)
Purnells Sports Res. 3 Meadow Rangers 2

POWELL CHARITY CUP
(May 2nd at Wem Town)
Wem Town 2 Ellesmere Rangers Res. 0

READING SENIOR CUP
(May 12th at Reading)
Westwood United 1 Flackwell Heath 0

READING JUBILEE CUP
(May 1st at Newbury)
Benson Lions 2 Frilsham & Yattendon Res. 0

ROTHERHAM CHARITY CUP
(May 3rd at Parkgate)
Phoenix Sports & Social 1 Grove Social 0

RUNCORN SENIOR CUP
(May 7th at Pavilions, Runcorn)
Runcorn Town 0 **Helsby** 1

RYDE & DISTRICT CHARITY CUP 2008-09
(September 24th at Newport IOWI)
Seaview 5 Kyngs Towne 3

SALISBURY HOSPITAL CUP
(May 5th at Salisbury City)
Downton 3 Chalke Valley 2

SEATON CHALLENGE CUP
(May 20th at Seaton Town)
Seaton Town 1 **Budleigh Salterton** 2 *aet*

SEATON CARLISLE CUP
(May 21st at Seaton Town)
Colaton Raleigh 3 Seaton Town Res. 0

SLOUGH TOWN PREMIER CUP
(April 2nd at Burnham)
Slough Heating 3 Slough Laurencians 0

SLOUGH TOWN JUNIOR CUP
(April 7th at Burnham)
Britwell 4 Alpha Arms 2

SMEDLEY CROOKE MEMORIAL CHARITY CUP
(May 22nd at Bromsgrove Rovers)
Cadbury Athletic 4 Knowle Res. 0

SOUTHAMPTON SENIOR CUP
(April 15th at Southampton)
VTFC Res. 2 Team Solent 0

SOUTHAMPTON JUNIOR A CUP
(April 5th at BTC Southampton)
Warren Social 2 Yacht Sports 1

SOUTH MIDLANDS RESERVES FLOODLIGHT CUP
(May 18th at Royston Town)
Royston Town Res. 3 Stotfold Res. 2

SOUTHEND CHARITY A CUP
(May 7th at Great Wakering Rovers)
Shoebury Town 3 Old Southendians 1

SOUTHEND CHARITY B CUP
(April 29th at White Ensign)
Shenfield Assocaition 3 Stambridge United 1

SOUTHEND CHARITY C CUP
(April 15th at White Ensign)
Ensign 1 Castle Point Gas 1 *aet* (4-1p)

STOCKPORT SENIOR CUP
(May 18th at Woodley Sports)
Cheadle Heath Nomads 6 Cheadle Town Res. 2

STROUD CHARITY A CUP
(May 12th at Shortwood United)
Tetbury Town 3 Stonehouse Town 1

STROUD CHARITY B CUP
(May 10th at Shortwood United)
Frampton United 8 Tetbury Town Res. 0

TORRIDGE CUP
(May 6th at Torrington) **Barnstaple AAC** 1 Braunton 0 *aet*

VERNON WENTWORTH CUP
(May 11th at Worthing)
Rottingdean Village 1 Ferring 0 *aet*

WAKEFIELD & DISTRICT CUP
(April 13th at Wakefield)
Horbury Town 3 Hall Green United 0

WEALD OF KENT CHARITY CUP
(May 31st at Tenterden Town)
Woodstock Park 2 Kennington 0

WEST HERTS ST MARYS CUP
(May 3rd at Hemel Hempstead Town)
Hemel Hempstead Town 2 Oxhey Jets 0

WESTWARD HO! CUP
(May 1st at Barnstaple Town)
Bude Town 3 Boca Seniors 1

WHARFEDALE CUP
(May 3rd at Guiseley)
Otley Town 4 Ventus & Yeadon Celtic 3

WIRRAL SENIOR CUP
(April 30th at Vauxhall Motors) **West Kirby** 2 Heswall 0

WIRRAL AMATEUR CUP
(April 5th at Ashville)
West Kirby Res. 3 New Brighton 0

WORCESTER ROYAL INFIRMARY CUP
(May 16th at Ledbury Town)
Malvern Town 1 Ledbury Town 0

WYCOMBE SENIOR CUP
(May 19th at Wycombe Wanderers)
Chalfont Wasps 1 AC Marlow 0

YMCA CUP
(May 15th at South Molton)
Chittlehampton 3 High Bickington 1

AMATEUR FOOTBALL ALLIANCE

www.amateur-fa.com

AMATEUR COMBINATION

www.amateurfootballcombination.com

	Alb	Bea	Cla	Hon	Aloy	Ham	Mea	Min	Parm	Park
Albanian		0-3	2-0	1-0	6-0	3-1	1-1	1-4	2-0	2-3
Bealonians	1-6	***P***	4-4	2-3	3-1	4-1	1-1	2-2	2-0	1-1
Clapham Old Xaverians	1-5	2-5	***R***	1-2	2-0	2-2	1-1	0-1	0-3	1-3
Honourable Artillery Company	2-2	1-5	6-0	***E***	1-0	1-1	2-1	3-5	3-2	1-1
Old Aloysians	2-3	1-4	4-2	2-4	***M***	2-3	0-2	1-0	2-3	1-4
Old Hamptonians	1-3	3-4	5-1	1-0	4-1		0-2	2-3	1-2	4-3
Old Meadonians	2-2	2-2	2-0	2-1	1-0	2-1	***D***	1-1	0-1	3-2
Old Minchendenians	1-2	2-1	1-0	1-5	5-1	4-2	0-4	***I***	2-2	5-2
Old Parmiterians	1-2	3-4	3-3	6-1	8-0	5-0	3-1	0-1	***V***	1-2
Parkfield	1-5	1-5	2-2	1-0	4-0	0-0	1-1	1-2	1-3	

Premier Division	P	W	D	L	F	A	Pts
Albanian	**18**	**12**	**3**	**3**	**48**	**24**	**39**
O. Minch'nians	**18**	**11**	**3**	**4**	**40**	**30**	**36**
Bealonians	**18**	**10**	**5**	**3**	**53**	**34**	**35**
Old Meadonians	**18**	**8**	**7**	**3**	**29**	**19**	**31**
O. Parmiterians	**18**	**9**	**2**	**7**	**46**	**27**	**29**
Hon. Art. Co.	**18**	**8**	**3**	**7**	**36**	**34**	**27**
Parkfield	**18**	**6**	**5**	**7**	**33**	**37**	**23**
O. Hamptonians	**18**	**5**	**3**	**10**	**32**	**42**	**18**
Clapham Old X.	**18**	**1**	**5**	**12**	**22**	**51**	**8**
O. Aloysians *-5*	**18**	**2**	**0**	**16**	**18**	**59**	**1**

AMATEUR COMBINATION PREMIER DIVISION CONSTITUTION 2010-11

ALBANIAN .... Chase Lodge Playing Fields, Page Street, Barnet NW7 2ED .... None
BEALONIANS .... Redbridge Sports Centre, Forest Road, Ilford IG6 3HD 020 8498 1000
HONOURABLE ARTILLERY CO. London Marathon Spts Ground, Grove Park Rd, Mottingham SE9 4QA .... None
OLD BELGRAVIANS .... South Bank University Sports Ground, Turney Road, London SE21 7JA 020 7737 0677
OLD HAMPTONIANS .... Rectory Farm, Dean Road, Hampton TW12 1AQ 020 8979 2784
OLD MEADONIANS .... Dukes Meadow, Dan Mason Drive, Chiswick W4 2SH 020 8994 8612
OLD MINCHENDENIANS .... Minchenden Association, Bramley Road Sports Ground, Southgate N14 4HP 020 8449 1661
OLD PARMITERIANS .... Douglas Eyre Sports Centre, 148 Coppermill Lane, Walthamstow E17 7HE 07956 251323
OLD SUTTONIANS .... Walch Memorial Playing Fields, Northey Avenue, Cheam SM2 7HJ 020 8642 3423
PARKFIELD .... Merchant Taylor's School, Sandy Lodge Lane, Northwood HA6 2HT 01923 842682

IN: Old Belgravians (P), Old Suttonians (P)
OUT: Clapham Old Xaverians (R), Old Aloysians (R)

Senior Div One	P	W	D	L	F	A	Pt
Old Suttonians	20	14	3	3	43	14	45
Old Belgravians	20	12	3	5	54	33	39
Old Salvatorians	20	12	3	5	42	31	39
UCL Academicals	20	12	2	6	45	27	38
Old Ignatians	20	9	4	7	41	40	31
Hale End Athletic	20	7	4	9	31	29	25
Sinjuns Gramm.	20	8	1	11	39	41	25
Wood Green OB	20	6	4	10	44	62	22
Glyn Old Boys	20	6	2	12	30	50	20
Centymca	20	5	1	14	27	53	16
Old Challoners	20	4	3	13	29	45	15

Senior Div Two	P	W	D	L	F	A	Pt
Old Uffingtonians	20	12	3	5	47	30	39
Southgate County	20	12	0	8	44	26	36
Enfield Old Gram.	20	10	5	5	47	35	35
Old Danes	20	9	4	7	38	43	31
Hon. Art. Co. Res.	20	8	5	7	45	33	29
Economicals	20	7	6	7	48	37	27
Old Hampton. Res.	20	7	6	7	34	39	27
Old Pauline	20	7	5	8	35	37	26
UCL Acad. Res.	20	6	5	9	27	36	23
William Fitt	20	5	6	9	40	51	21
Old Mead. Res.	20	3	3	14	26	64	12

Senior Three North	P	W	D	L	F	A	Pt
Old Edmontonians	20	15	3	2	65	24	48
Bealonians Res.	20	14	0	6	57	26	42
Old Kolsassians	20	12	4	4	57	31	40
Leyton Co. Old B.	20	11	3	6	51	41	36
O Woodhouseians	20	7	5	8	34	43	26
Old Vaughanians	20	8	1	11	44	49	25
Parkfield Res.	20	7	3	10	37	54	24
Latymer Old Boys	20	6	5	9	45	61	23
Old Aloysians Res.	20	5	3	12	38	51	18
Old Manorians	20	4	4	12	38	61	16
O Salvat. Res. *-3*	20	5	1	14	30	55	13

Senior Three South	P	W	D	L	F	A	Pt
Pegasus	20	13	3	4	46	18	42
Shene Old Gram	20	11	5	4	43	29	38
Old Thorntonians	20	11	5	4	43	33	38
Old Josephians	20	8	5	7	50	39	29
Old Bromleians	20	7	6	7	58	56	27
Dorkinians	20	7	6	7	44	42	27
Ful. Compton OB	20	6	8	6	33	34	26
Chert. O Salesians	20	7	3	10	39	40	24
Kings Old Boys	20	6	6	8	41	47	24
H'pstd Heathens	20	5	3	12	30	49	18
Old Guildfordians	20	3	2	15	22	62	11

Intermediate North	P	W	D	L	F	A	Pt
Albanian Res.	20	16	3	1	69	20	51
O. Parm'ians Res.	20	11	5	4	42	22	38
Globe Rangers	20	11	3	6	52	34	36
Old Minchen. Res.	20	9	6	5	44	23	33
O. Magdalenians	20	7	8	5	41	31	29
Enfield Old G. Res.	20	9	1	10	47	56	28
Hale End Ath. Res.	20	7	4	9	43	46	25
UCL Academicals A	20	8	1	11	34	58	25
Old Aloysians A	20	5	5	10	28	41	20
Egbertian	20	3	3	14	30	69	12
Old Kingsburians	20	2	5	13	35	65	11

Intermediate South	P	W	D	L	F	A	Pt
Old Tenisonians	22	20	2	0	87	16	62
Old Tiffinians	21	11	4	6	49	42	37
Clapham OX Res.	22	10	7	5	41	38	37
Old Meadonians A	22	11	3	8	42	29	36
Old Sedcopians	22	10	3	9	59	45	33
Ryl Bank of Scot.	22	9	3	10	38	39	30
O. Suttonians Res.	22	7	6	9	45	52	27
Old Wokingians	22	7	5	10	45	54	26
Wandsworth Boro.	22	7	3	12	37	54	24
Nat West Bank	22	5	4	13	30	53	19
Fitzwilliam OB *-6*	21	6	6	9	32	38	18
Mickleham O. Box.	22	4	2	16	34	79	14

Intermediate West	P	W	D	L	F	A	Pt
Old Isleworthians	20	15	2	3	48	26	47
Birkbeck College	20	14	4	2	60	20	46
Old Salvatorians A	20	10	2	8	58	54	32
O. Hamptonians A	20	9	3	8	46	51	30
Old Meadonians B	20	7	7	6	40	35	28
O Manorians Res.	20	7	6	7	46	41	27
Brent	20	7	6	7	38	46	27
O. Vaughan. Res.	20	8	2	10	47	43	26
O. Uff'tonians Res.	20	6	4	10	48	62	22
London Welsh	20	5	4	11	33	49	19
Parkfield A	20	1	2	17	21	58	5

Phoenix Old Boys - record expunged

Division One North	P	W	D	L	F	A	Pt
William Fitt Res.	20	17	2	1	64	19	53
Old Tollingtonians	20	12	4	4	60	32	40
Lea Valley	20	9	7	4	53	26	34
Bealonians A	20	10	2	8	41	41	32
Old Aloysians B	20	8	5	7	52	41	29
Southgate Co. Res.	20	8	3	9	29	40	27
Old Buckwellians	20	7	5	8	39	35	26
Old Ignatians Res.	20	8	1	11	39	53	25
Old Edmont. Res.	20	4	5	11	34	56	17
Leyton C. OB Res.	20	4	3	13	25	51	15
Mill Hill Co. OB	20	3	3	14	24	66	12

Division One South	P	W	D	L	F	A	Pt
Old St Marys	20	15	3	2	57	25	48
Old Pauline Res.	20	14	3	3	58	19	45
Marsh	20	15	0	5	62	29	45
Witan	20	11	2	7	61	47	35
Economicals Res.	20	10	1	9	37	34	31
Glyn O. Boys Res.	20	7	4	9	34	34	25
Sinjuns Gram. Res.	20	7	2	11	37	38	23
City of London	20	7	1	12	29	38	22
John Fisher Old B.	20	5	4	11	40	56	19
Kings Old B. Res.	20	4	2	14	26	73	14
O Tenisonians Res.	20	3	2	15	25	73	11

Division One West	P	W	D	L	F	A	Pt
Birkbeck Coll. Res.	20	16	1	3	84	25	49
Old Danes Res.	20	15	1	4	64	20	46
Old K'burians Res.	20	14	3	3	76	40	45
Shene Old G. Res.	20	11	1	8	56	53	34
Old Pegasonians	20	8	5	7	35	47	29
Old Manorians A	20	9	1	10	53	58	28
Chertsey OS Res.	20	8	2	10	43	53	26
Old I'wthians Res.	20	7	1	12	35	62	22
O. Challoners Res.	20	5	1	14	39	60	16
Old Salvatorians B	20	3	4	13	32	56	13
O. Vaughanians A	20	4	0	16	38	81	12

Division Two North	P	W	D	L	F	A	Pt
Albanian A	18	17	1	0	57	16	52
Mayfield Athletic	18	11	3	4	66	29	36
Egbertian Res.	18	9	2	7	44	34	29
Queen Mary COB	18	8	3	7	36	37	27
Univ. Hertfordshire	18	7	5	6	43	50	26
Hale End Ath. A	18	7	3	8	42	53	24
Mill Hill Co. Res.	18	6	1	11	40	54	19
Globe Rgrs Res.	18	5	3	10	46	55	18
Wood Green Res	18	5	1	12	36	51	16
Old Aloysians C	18	2	4	12	28	59	10

Division Two South	P	W	D	L	F	A	Pt
Economicals A	20	16	4	0	67	16	52
Nat West Bk Res.	20	14	1	5	61	29	43
Clapham Old X. A	20	10	3	7	49	49	33
O Wokingians Res.	20	9	3	8	41	36	30
Tilburg Regents	20	10	0	10	39	35	30
Old Meadonians C	20	9	0	11	41	64	27
Sinjuns Gramm. A	20	7	3	10	36	39	24
Reigatians	20	6	4	10	41	51	22
Old Suttonians A	20	6	3	11	32	46	21
Old Whitgiftian	20	6	3	11	39	57	21
Old Tenisonians A	20	4	2	14	37	61	14

Division Two West	P	W	D	L	F	A	Pt
Old Salvatorians C	20	14	4	2	60	23	46
O. Hamptonians B	20	13	6	1	63	22	45
O. Isleworthians A	20	12	5	3	60	34	41
Old Manorians B	20	11	4	5	54	31	37
Teddington	20	11	0	9	54	42	33
Phoenix Res. *-3*	20	8	4	8	50	45	25
O. Kingsburians A	20	7	3	10	42	54	24
O. Vaughanians B	20	7	3	10	46	63	24
Parkfield B	20	4	3	13	29	60	15
Hampst'd H. Res.	20	3	3	14	22	56	12
Brent Res.	20	1	3	16	22	72	6

Division Two West title withheld

Div. Three North	P	W	D	L	F	A	Pt
RBL Loughton	18	11	7	0	49	22	40
Old Parmiterians A	18	10	3	5	54	30	33
Latymer OB Res.	18	10	3	5	49	28	33
Oakhill Tigers	18	8	5	5	58	41	29
O. Edmontonians A	18	8	4	6	35	32	28
Old Ignatians A	18	7	5	6	50	50	26
Enfield Old G. A	18	5	4	9	31	41	19
Q. Mary COB Res.	18	6	1	11	32	52	19
Albanian B	18	4	5	9	36	50	17
Old Buckwell. Res.	18	1	3	14	24	72	6

Div. Three West	P	W	D	L	F	A	Pt
Heathrow Seniors	20	15	2	3	66	27	47
Old Manorians C	20	14	1	5	78	30	43
Cardinal Manning	20	14	1	5	62	40	43
O. Magdalen. Res.	20	10	4	6	49	34	34
O. Kolsass. Res.	20	9	3	8	49	41	30
Ealing Association	20	7	4	9	46	43	25
Old Uxonians	20	7	4	9	36	59	25
Parkfield C	20	7	3	10	41	55	24
Old Islew'thians B	20	4	3	13	33	74	15
Phoenix OB A *-3*	20	4	4	12	37	68	13
L'don Welsh Res.	20	3	3	14	29	55	12

Div. Three South	P	W	D	L	F	A	Pt
Nat West Bank A	18	14	0	4	58	17	42
Ryl Bk Scot. Res.	18	12	2	4	55	28	38
Dorkinians Res.	18	9	3	6	53	30	30
Clapham Old X. B	18	9	3	6	38	29	30
Old Crosbeians	18	9	3	6	33	34	30
Royal Sun Alliance	18	8	5	5	41	46	29
Glyn Old Boys A	18	6	2	10	32	45	20
Reigatians Res.	18	6	0	12	27	49	18
Temple Bar	18	5	0	13	23	46	15
The Comets	18	2	2	14	17	53	8

Division Four North	P	W	D	L	F	A	Pt
Old Parmiterians B	16	12	4	0	67	15	40
Bealonians B	16	12	2	2	61	38	38
Egbertian A	16	7	5	4	47	32	26
Wood Green OB A	16	8	1	7	45	39	25
Hale End Ath. B	16	6	3	7	30	40	21
UCL Acad'cals B	16	5	4	7	38	48	19
Old Buckwellians A	16	4	1	11	44	67	13
London Hosp. *-3*	16	3	4	9	22	39	10
Mill Hill Co. OB A	16	2	2	12	26	62	8

Old Camdenians A - record expunged

Division Four South	P	W	D	L	F	A	Pt
Citigroup	20	13	5	2	64	30	44
Standard Chart. Bk	20	12	4	4	52	32	40
O. Bromleians Res.	20	11	4	5	81	34	37
Economicals B	20	9	7	4	44	38	34
Old Sedcop. Res.	20	8	9	3	56	37	33
Witan Res.	20	7	5	8	33	41	26
Wandsw'th B. Res.	20	7	3	10	33	43	24
Old Wokingians A	20	4	8	8	34	51	20
Old Suttonians B	20	3	8	9	27	30	17
Old Meadonians D	20	4	4	12	25	64	16
Clapham Old X. C	20	2	3	15	24	73	9

Division Four West	P	W	D	L	F	A	Pt
Old Uffingtonians A	14	11	2	1	55	24	35
Old Manorians D	14	9	2	3	44	26	29
Phoenix Old B. B	14	7	3	4	42	38	24
Old Salvatorians D	14	7	2	5	22	18	23
Brent A	14	6	0	8	29	36	18
O. Vaughanians C	14	5	0	9	30	42	15
Ealing A. Res. *-1*	14	4	1	9	28	44	12
Old Challoners A	14	1	2	11	12	34	5

Division Five North	P	W	D	L	F	A	Pt
Old Minch'nians A	20	13	5	2	60	26	44
Leyton Co. OB A	20	14	2	4	70	41	44
Bealonians C	20	12	2	6	66	32	38
O. W'hseians Res.	20	10	2	8	56	48	32
Latymer Old B.A	20	9	5	6	56	53	32
Albanian C	20	8	4	8	55	44	28
O Toli'tonians Res.	20	8	2	10	40	57	26
Southgate Co. A	20	7	4	9	39	44	25
Egbertian B	20	7	0	13	48	80	21
Goffs Old Boys	20	6	1	13	46	54	19
Old Aloysians D	20	2	1	17	35	92	7

Division Five South	P	W	D	L	F	A	Pt
Old Thornton. Res.	18	14	1	3	67	30	43
Old St Marys Res.	18	10	3	5	51	27	33
Glyn Old Boys B	18	9	3	6	44	34	30
Old Tiffinians Res.	18	6	5	7	43	55	23
Old Guildf'dns Res.	18	5	7	6	38	37	22
Dorkinians A	18	6	4	8	43	52	22
Old Wokingians B	18	6	3	9	35	53	21
Old Suttonians C	18	5	5	8	36	36	20
City of L'don Res.	18	6	1	11	36	52	19
Old Sedcopians A	18	4	6	8	35	52	18

Old Tenisonians B - record expunged

Division Six North	P	W	D	L	F	A	Pt
Lea Valley Res.	16	12	2	2	61	34	38
Ravenscroft Old B.	16	11	3	2	62	35	36
Old Parmiterians C	16	10	2	4	52	27	32
Latymer Old B. B	16	8	1	7	38	34	25
O Edmontonians B	16	7	2	7	35	42	23
O. Minch. B *-3*	16	7	3	6	53	29	21
Globe Rangers A	16	6	0	10	57	44	18
Mill Hill Co. OB *-3*	16	3	2	11	40	68	8
Wood Green B *-3*	16	0	1	15	24	109	-2

Davenant Wanderers Old Boys, Old Camdenians Res. - records expunged

Division Six South	P	W	D	L	F	A	Pt
Old Meadonians E	20	15	2	3	60	36	47
Old Suttonians D	20	15	1	4	76	36	46
Old Grantonians	20	13	3	4	63	32	42
Ful. Compton Res.	20	12	4	4	59	34	40
Reigatians A	20	12	2	6	58	53	38
O Josephians Res.	20	10	2	8	71	54	32
O. Thorntonians A	20	6	2	12	45	59	20
John Fisher Res.	20	6	1	13	54	70	19
Shene Old G. A	20	4	4	12	32	50	16
Glyn Old Boys C	20	3	2	15	39	68	11
Old Bromleians A	20	2	1	17	40	105	7

Div. Seven North	P	W	D	L	F	A	Pt
UCL Acad'cals C	18	16	1	1	75	26	49
Oakhill Tigers Res.	18	15	1	2	97	33	46
Old Parmiterians D	18	11	4	3	55	30	37
O. W'dhouseians A	18	7	4	7	30	45	25
Leyton Co. OB B	18	6	4	8	48	40	22
Albanian D	18	6	4	8	45	57	22
Old Ignatians B	18	5	5	8	48	58	20
Bealonians D	18	4	2	12	27	68	14
Enfield Old G. B	18	3	3	12	29	60	12
Mill Hill Village	18	2	2	14	35	72	8

Old Camdenians A - record expunged

Div. Seven South	P	W	D	L	F	A	Pt
Economicals C	18	15	1	2	79	20	46
Fulham Compton A	18	10	3	5	38	29	33
Old Pauline A	18	9	3	6	63	45	30
Old Guildfordians A	18	9	2	7	49	36	29
Kings Old Boys A	18	9	1	8	41	35	28
Old Suttonians E	18	8	2	8	33	49	26
O. Bromleians B *-6*	18	9	1	8	52	49	22
Old Sedcopians B	18	6	3	9	33	44	21
City of London A	18	3	2	13	28	59	11
Clapham Old X. D	18	2	2	14	19	69	8

Div. Eight North	P	W	D	L	F	A	Pt
Old Parmiterians E	18	18	0	0	86	14	54
Queen Mary C. A	18	11	1	6	65	36	34
Old Edm'tonians C	18	10	3	5	59	40	33
Ravenscroft Res.	18	10	3	5	53	38	33
Old Ignatians C	18	9	1	8	61	66	28
Leyton Co. OB C	18	7	1	10	39	45	22
Mill Hill V. Res. *-3*	18	7	1	10	43	51	19
Southgate Co. B	18	5	2	11	30	51	17
O. W'dhouseians B	18	4	2	12	28	73	14
Goffs Old B. Res.	18	1	2	15	17	67	5

Old Camdenians B - record expunged

Div. Eight South	P	W	D	L	F	A	Pt
Old Wokingians C	16	12	3	1	59	17	39
John Fisher OB A	16	11	1	4	71	43	34
Fulham Compton B	16	10	2	4	59	24	32
O. Guildfordians B	16	10	2	4	35	22	32
Reigatians B	16	5	3	8	29	48	18
Mick OB Res. *-2*	16	4	2	10	28	63	13
Glyn Old Boys D	16	3	3	10	24	41	12
Old Tiffinians A	16	3	3	10	30	49	12
Dorkinians B	16	2	5	9	22	50	11

Old Tenisonians C - record expunged

Division Nine North	P	W	D	L	F	A	Pt
UCL Acad'cals D	18	14	1	3	78	25	43
Mayfield Ath. Res.	18	12	2	4	53	20	38
Latymer Old B. C	18	11	0	7	65	52	33
Old Parmiterians F	18	10	2	6	58	42	32
Bealonians E	18	7	4	7	36	40	25
Enfield Old G. C	18	5	4	9	60	53	19
Old Kingsburians B	18	5	4	9	26	52	19
O Edmontonians D	18	5	2	11	41	56	17
Old Uff'nians B -3	18	6	1	11	36	76	16
Old Minch'dns C	18	4	2	12	37	74	14

Division Nine South	P	W	D	L	F	A	Pt
John Fisher OB B	18	15	1	2	62	25	46
Ful. Compton C	18	15	0	3	55	23	45
O. Whitgiftian Res.	18	10	1	7	60	35	31
Old St Marys A	18	9	4	5	58	37	31
Old Wokingians D	18	9	1	8	46	45	28
Reigatians C	18	8	3	7	32	31	27
Sinjuns Gram. B	18	7	1	10	31	41	22
Old Pauline B	18	6	1	11	41	58	19
Tilburg Reg. Res.	18	2	2	14	21	64	8
Old Suttonians F	18	2	0	16	20	67	6

Division Ten South	P	W	D	L	F	A	Pt
O. Tenisonians D	18	14	3	1	92	27	45
Old Sedcopians C	18	11	3	4	64	29	36
Wandsworth B. A	18	11	2	5	60	29	35
Old Suttonians G	18	10	1	7	64	42	31
Old Wokingians E	18	10	1	7	64	48	31
Shene Old G. B	18	7	1	10	47	73	22
Reigatians D	18	7	0	11	44	66	21
O. Guildfordians C	18	6	2	10	47	57	20
Old Meadonians F	18	5	2	11	34	79	17
Old St Marys B	18	0	3	15	31	97	3

ARTHURIAN LEAGUE

www.arthurianleague.com

	King	Lanc	Ald	Bren	Cart	Chol	For	Harr	Sale	Wes
Kings Wimbledon		2-2	n/a	3-2	1-5	3-2	4-5	3-2	1-2	2-4
Lancing Old Boys	2-2	***P***	2-1	2-4	0-3	1-3	2-1	1-1	4-3	3-1
Old Aldenhamians	3-2	n/a	***R***	3-0	0-2	n/a	0-1	2-4	n/a	n/a
Old Brentwoods	L-W	1-3	n/a	***E***	1-2	5-1	0-1	0-1	3-0	3-2
Old Carthusians	0-0	5-0	4-1	6-0	***M***	6-1	10-0	1-3	8-2	3-1
Old Cholmeleians	D-D	0-1	n/a	4-2	0-6		2-2	0-3	1-1	3-1
Old Foresters	4-4	0-5	n/a	2-3	0-2	1-2	***D***	2-3	4-3	4-1
Old Harrovians	2-1	2-1	n/a	3-4	3-1	4-1	3-0	***I***	4-2	3-0
Old Salopians	3-3	5-2	0-2	1-0	1-1	2-2	3-2	0-2	***V***	2-1
Old Westminsters	1-8	3-1	0-1	1-4	1-2	0-0	1-1	0-3	3-2	

Premier Division	**P**	**W**	**D**	**L**	**F**	**A**	**Pts**
Old Harrovians	**16**	**13**	**1**	**2**	**42**	**17**	**40**
Old Carthusians	**16**	**12**	**2**	**2**	**61**	**14**	**38**
Kings Wim'don	**16**	**5**	**6**	**5**	**37**	**36**	**21**
Old Brentwoods	**16**	**7**	**0**	**9**	**32**	**32**	**21**
Lancing Old B.	**16**	**6**	**3**	**7**	**30**	**36**	**21**
Old Salopians	**16**	**5**	**4**	**7**	**32**	**41**	**19**
O. Cholmeleians	**16**	**4**	**5**	**7**	**22**	**38**	**17**
Old Foresters	**16**	**4**	**3**	**9**	**29**	**48**	**15**
O. Westminsters	**16**	**3**	**2**	**11**	**21**	**44**	**11**

Old Aldenhamians - record expunged

ARTHURIAN LEAGUE PREMIER DIVISION CONSTITUTION 2010-11

LANCING OLD BOYS . . . . Tolworth Court Sports Ground, Old Kingston Road, Tolworth KT4 7QH 020 8330 2865
OLD BRENTWOODS . . . . . . The Society of Old Brentwoods, Ashwells Road, Bentley, Brentwood CM15 9SE. 01277 374070
OLD CARTHUSIANS . . . . Charterhouse School, Godalming GU7 2DX 01483 29154/291679
OLD CHIGWELLIANS . . . . Old Chigwellians Club, Roding Lane, Chigwell IG7 6BE. 020 8500 2477
OLD CHOLMELEIANS. . . . . Hendon Wood Lane, Mill Hill NW7 4HR 020 8959 6566
OLD ETONIANS. . . . . Dutchmans, Eton College, Eton Road, Windsor SL4 6DW 01753 565325
OLD FORESTERS . . . . The Park, Forest School, College Place, Snaresbrook E17 3PY. 020 8520 1744
OLD HARROVIANS . . . . The Philatelic Ground, Harrow School, Besborough Road, Harrow-on-the-Hill HA1 4AA . . . . None
OLD KINGS WIMBLEDON Raynes Park Spts Grnd, All England LTClub, 216 Grand Drive, Raynes Park SW20 9NB. 020 8542 2391
OLD SALOPIANS . . . . Riverside Lands Playing Fields, Dukes Meadows, Chiswick W4 2SH. 020 8994 8612

IN: Old Chigwellians (P), Old Etonians (P)

OUT: Old Aldenhamians (WS), Old Westminsters (R)

ARTHUR DUNN CUP

FIRST ROUND

Old Bradfieldians 3 Old Cholmeleians 2
Old Brentwoods 9 Old Berkhamstedians 0
Old Carthusians 7 Old Radleians 0
Old Chigwellians 0 **Old Foresters** 1
Old Eastbournians 1 **Old Oundlelians** 11
Old Etonians 2 Old Haileyburians 0
Old Reptonians 3 Old Haberdashers 0
Old Salopians 0 **Old Westminsters** 1
Old Tonbridgians 3 Old Malvernians 0
Old Wellingburians 3 Old Amplefordians 0
Old Wykehamists 1 **Old Harrovians** 4

SECOND ROUND

Kings Wimbledon 6 Old Wellingburians 1
Old Aldenhamians 2 Old Bradfieldians 1
Old Brentwoods (w/o) v Old Wellingtonians
Old Carthusians 8 Old King's Scholars 1
Old Harrovians 4 Lancing Old Boys 3
Old Oundelians 2 **Old Foresters** 3
Old Reptonians 4 **Old Etonians** 5
Old Tonbridgians 4 Old Westminsters 2

QUARTER-FINALS

Old Aldenhamians 2 Old Tonbridgians 2
Replay: **Tonbridgians** (w/o) v Old Alds
Old Brentwoods 3 Old Foresters 2
Old Carthusians 1 **Old Etonians** 2
Old Harrovians 2 **Kings Wimbledon** 3

SEMI-FINALS

Kings Wimbledon 1 Old Tonbridgians 1
Replay: Old Tonbridgians 1 **Kings Wimbledon** 2
Old Brentwoods 1 **Old Etonians** 5

FINAL

(April 17th at Imperial University)
Old Etonians 2 Kings Wimbledon 1

Division One	P	W	D	L	F	A	Pt
Old Chigwellians	16	13	1	2	52	14	40
Old Etonians	16	12	2	2	38	11	38
Old Wykehamists	16	7	2	7	32	29	23
Old Malvernians	16	7	2	7	31	31	23
Old Haileyburians	16	6	4	6	21	27	22
Old Radleians	16	5	3	8	19	32	18
Old King's Scholars	16	3	5	8	22	36	14
Old Tonbridgians	16	4	2	10	16	33	14
Old Reptonians -3	16	4	1	11	27	45	10

Division Two	P	W	D	L	F	A	Pt
Old Carthusians Res.	14	9	2	3	34	16	29
Old Chigwellians Res.	14	8	1	5	30	20	25
Old Carthusians A	14	6	5	3	26	19	23
Old Foresters Res.	14	6	1	7	28	32	19
Old Haberdashers	14	5	2	7	33	35	17
Old Bradfieldians	14	5	2	7	30	33	17
Old Brentwoods Res.	14	3	6	5	22	32	15
Old Harrovians Res.	14	4	1	9	35	51	13

Division Three	P	W	D	L	F	A	Pt
Old Etonians Res.	14	10	2	2	34	16	32
Old Oundelians	14	9	2	3	58	28	29
Old Brentwoods A	14	7	2	5	21	31	23
Old Wellingtonians	14	5	5	4	34	33	20
Old Salopians Res.	14	6	2	6	27	28	20
Lancing OB Res.	14	4	4	6	21	23	16
Old Bradf. Res. -3	14	3	2	9	31	38	8
O W'minst Res. -3	14	1	3	10	22	51	3

Division Four	P	W	D	L	F	A	Pt
Old Amplefordians	14	8	3	3	33	15	27
Old Eastbournians	14	7	4	3	33	22	25
O. Cholmeleians A	14	6	3	5	23	25	21
Old Foresters B	14	6	2	6	26	32	20
Old Cholm. Res.	14	4	6	4	27	30	18
Old Chigwellians A	14	4	5	5	26	25	17
Old Foresters A	14	3	4	7	22	26	13
Old Harrovians A	14	3	3	8	24	39	12

Division Five	P	W	D	L	F	A	Pt
Old Berk'stedians	12	7	4	1	32	9	25
Kings W'don Res.	12	7	1	4	48	22	22
Old Brentwds B -3	12	8	0	4	34	18	21
Old Wyk'ists Res.	12	6	1	5	30	31	19
O Malvernians Res.	12	4	4	4	22	23	16
Old Epsomians	12	3	1	8	24	36	10
Old Cholm. B -6	12	0	3	9	8	59	-3

SOUTHERN AMATEUR LEAGUE

www.southernamateurleague.co.uk

	Broomfield	Civil Service	Nottsborough	Old Actonians Association	Old Owens	Old Salesians	Old Wilsonians	Polytechnic	Weirside Rangers	West Wickham	Winchmore Hill
Broomfield	***S***	2-1	2-1	1-1	0-2	6-0	1-2	3-2	1-3	0-0	3-1
Civil Service	1-2	***E***	0-1	2-2	1-1	2-1	0-0	4-0	2-0	0-2	3-3
Nottsborough	3-1	1-0	***N***	5-0	0-1	0-0	1-0	3-1	0-0	1-2	0-1
Old Actonians Association	0-2	2-0	2-6	***I***	2-1	1-0	2-1	1-1	2-0	2-1	2-3
Old Owens	3-0	6-5	0-1	4-2	***O***	2-4	1-1	4-5	1-1	1-1	3-4
Old Salesians	3-0	1-0	1-0	3-2	1-0	***R***	3-1	2-1	1-0	1-1	2-3
Old Wilsonians	1-0	2-0	4-1	2-3	2-1	1-3		0-6	3-1	0-1	1-3
Polytechnic	1-2	3-1	0-3	1-1	0-1	2-3	1-6		1-2	0-1	0-3
Weirside Rangers	1-0	1-1	0-2	0-2	0-1	0-1	3-0	1-2	***O***	3-1	2-4
West Wickham	1-2	2-2	0-2	0-4	3-0	2-0	0-0	2-3	2-1	***N***	2-0
Winchmore Hill	1-2	1-0	1-2	1-1	1-2	1-0	1-0	0-1	2-0	2-1	***E***

Senior Division One	**P**	**W**	**D**	**L**	**F**	**A**	**Pts**
Nottsborough	**20**	**12**	**2**	**6**	**33**	**16**	**38**
Winchmore Hill	**20**	**12**	**2**	**6**	**36**	**27**	**38**
Old Salesians	**20**	**12**	**2**	**6**	**30**	**25**	**38**
Broomfield	**20**	**10**	**2**	**8**	**30**	**28**	**32**
Old Actonians Assoc.	**20**	**9**	**5**	**6**	**34**	**34**	**32**
West Wickham	**20**	**8**	**5**	**7**	**25**	**24**	**29**
Old Owens	**20**	**8**	**4**	**8**	**35**	**34**	**28**
Old Wilsonians	**20**	**7**	**3**	**10**	**27**	**32**	**24**
Polytechnic	**20**	**6**	**2**	**12**	**31**	**43**	**20**
Weirside Rangers	**20**	**5**	**3**	**12**	**19**	**29**	**18**
Civil Service	**20**	**3**	**6**	**11**	**25**	**33**	**15**

SOUTHERN AMATEUR LEAGUE SENIOR DIVISION ONE CONSTITUTION 2010-11

BROOMFIELD. . . . . Hazlewood Sports Club, Madeira Road, Hedge Lane, London N13 5SR 020 8886 999
CARSHALTON . . . . Beddington Park, Church Road, Wallington SM6 7NN 020 8647 748
EAST BARNET OLD GRAMMARIANS. . . . . Alan Drive, Mays Lane, Barnet EN5 2PU. 020 8449 432
NOTTSBOROUGH. . Kingston University Sports Ground, Tolworth Court, Old Tolworth Rd, Worcester Park KT4 7QH 020 8330 286
OLD ACTONIANS ASSOCIATION. . . Old Actonians Association, Gunnersbury Drive, Ealing W5 4LL 020 8567 455
OLD OWENS . . . . Coopers Lane, Northaw, Potters Bar EN6 4NF 01707 64698
OLD SALESIANS . . . . Salesian College Sports Ground, Old Schools Lane, Ewell KT17 1TW 020 8393 982
OLD WILSONIANS . . . . Old Wilsonians Sports Ground, Hayes Hill, Hayes, Kent BR2 7HN. 020 8462 260
POLYTECHNIC. . . . . . University of Westminster Sports Ground, Main Pavilion, Cavendish Road, London W4 3UH 020 8994 155
WEST WICKHAM. . . . . West Wickham Sports Club, Corkscrew Hill, West Wickham BR4 9BA 020 8777 344
WINCHMORE HILL . . . . Paulin Grond, Fords Grove, Winchmore Hill, London N21 3ER 020 8360 127

IN: Carshalton (P), East Barnet Old Grammarians (P)
OUT: Civil Service (R), Weirside Rangers (R)

Senior Division Two		**P**	**W**	**D**	**L**	**F**	**A**	**Pts**
East Barnet Old Gram.		**20**	**13**	**5**	**2**	**73**	**28**	**44**
Carshalton		**20**	**12**	**6**	**2**	**49**	**21**	**42**
Norsemen		**20**	**13**	**2**	**5**	**55**	**27**	**41**
Alleyn Old Boys		**20**	**8**	**5**	**7**	**47**	**35**	**29**
Crouch End Vampires		**20**	**9**	**2**	**9**	**45**	**35**	**29**
Old Finchleians		**20**	**8**	**5**	**7**	**40**	**45**	**29**
BB Eagles		**20**	**8**	**3**	**9**	**48**	**42**	**27**
Old Esthameians		**20**	**7**	**5**	**8**	**48**	**52**	**26**
HSBC		**20**	**5**	**2**	**13**	**40**	**70**	**17**
Lloyds TSB Bank		**20**	**4**	**3**	**13**	**31**	**63**	**15**
Kew Association	*-3*	**20**	**4**	**0**	**16**	**29**	**87**	**9**

Senior Division Three	**P**	**W**	**D**	**L**	**F**	**A**	**Pts**
Old Parkonians	**20**	**18**	**0**	**2**	**75**	**11**	**54**
Alexandra Park	**20**	**10**	**5**	**5**	**51**	**35**	**35**
Merton	**20**	**10**	**4**	**6**	**46**	**27**	**34**
Southgate Olympic	**20**	**10**	**4**	**6**	**33**	**31**	**34**
South Bank Cuaco	**20**	**9**	**5**	**6**	**48**	**36**	**32**
Ibis	**20**	**10**	**0**	**10**	**39**	**50**	**30**
Old Stationers	**20**	**6**	**7**	**7**	**38**	**44**	**25**
Old Latymerians	**20**	**6**	**4**	**10**	**29**	**39**	**22**
Old Lyonians	**20**	**5**	**2**	**13**	**31**	**60**	**17**
O. Westminster Citzns	**20**	**5**	**0**	**15**	**32**	**58**	**15**
Bank of England	**20**	**4**	**3**	**13**	**22**	**53**	**15**

Intermediate One	P	W	D	L	F	A	Pt
O. Actonians Res.	20	15	4	1	70	26	49
Nottsborough Res.	20	14	4	2	44	18	46
Civil Service Res.	20	10	4	6	35	26	34
W. Wickham Res.	20	10	1	9	45	36	31
Old Owens Res.	20	8	3	9	42	44	27
Winchmore H Res.	20	7	3	10	27	31	24
East Barnet Res.	20	7	1	12	41	51	22
Merton Res.	20	6	4	10	20	45	22
Carshalton Res.	20	5	6	9	34	37	21
Polytechnic Res.	20	5	6	9	32	48	21
O. Salesians Res.	20	3	4	13	24	52	13

Intermediate Two	P	W	D	L	F	A	Pt
Alleyn Old B. Res.	20	13	2	5	47	32	41
Norsemen Res.	20	11	5	4	57	31	38
O. W'minster Res.	20	11	4	5	59	45	37
O. Esth'mns Res.	20	11	3	6	53	39	36
O Parkonians Res.	20	10	1	9	44	39	31
BB Eagles Res.	20	8	4	8	42	42	28
HSBC Res.	20	8	2	10	36	42	26
Weirside R. Res.	20	7	3	10	39	40	24
O Wilsonians Res.	20	7	3	10	37	41	24
Crouch End Res.	20	5	2	13	32	55	17
Southgate O. Res.	20	3	3	14	37	77	12

Intermediate Three	P	W	D	L	F	A	Pt
Alexandra Pk Res.	20	10	5	5	49	29	35
O Finchleians Res.	20	9	8	3	64	49	35
Kew A. Res. *-4*	20	12	2	6	43	38	34
O. Stationers Res.	20	10	2	8	55	39	32
Old Latymer. Res.	20	9	5	6	64	53	32
Ibis Res.	20	8	5	7	38	42	29
Broomfield Res.	20	8	2	10	48	53	26
Bank of Eng.Res.	20	7	3	10	31	53	24
Lloyds TSB Res.	20	7	2	11	40	41	23
S. Bk Cuaco Res.	20	6	3	11	40	46	21
Old Lyonians Res.	20	4	3	13	38	67	15

Junior Div One	P	W	D	L	F	A	Pt
Nottsborough A	20	19	0	1	69	15	57
Winchmore Hill A	20	15	3	2	61	31	48
East Barnet OG A	20	13	1	6	63	28	40
Old Actonians A	20	10	4	6	53	38	34
Alleyn OB A *-3*	20	10	3	7	40	38	30
Old Owens A	20	8	4	8	57	40	28
Weirside Rgrs A	20	8	3	9	42	41	27
O. Westminster A	20	7	1	12	50	78	22
Carshalton A	20	3	4	13	22	61	13
Kew Assoc. A	20	3	0	17	25	66	9
Crouch End V. A	20	2	1	17	29	75	7

Junior Div Two	P	W	D	L	F	A	Pt
O. Esthameians A	20	15	2	3	75	30	47
West Wickham A	20	14	3	3	60	36	45
Norsemen A	20	11	4	5	41	30	37
Civil Service A	20	10	2	8	48	43	32
Old Salesians A	20	9	2	9	43	42	29
Old Parkonians A	20	8	3	9	44	49	27
Old Stationers A	20	7	4	9	34	35	25
Old Wilsonians A	20	7	1	12	35	54	22
Polytechnic A	20	6	3	11	31	44	21
Alexandra Park A	20	5	2	13	35	58	17
HSBC A	20	4	2	14	36	61	14

Junior Div Three	P	W	D	L	F	A	Pt
BB Eagles A	20	18	2	0	72	23	56
Broomfield A	20	12	4	4	70	37	40
Merton A	20	12	3	5	49	35	39
Lloyds TSB Bk A	20	9	3	8	40	43	30
Ibis A	20	8	4	8	46	43	28
Sth Bank Cuaco A	20	8	2	10	38	38	26
Southgate Oly. A	20	8	2	10	39	43	26
Old Finchleians A	20	5	5	10	41	54	20
Bank of England A	20	5	2	13	36	55	17
Old Lyonians A	20	5	2	13	31	71	17
Old Latymerians A	20	4	3	13	36	56	15

Minor Division One	P	W	D	L	F	A	Pt
Nottsborough B	20	15	3	2	57	18	48
Old Actonians B	20	15	2	3	45	21	47
Civil Service B	20	12	3	5	59	36	39
Old Owens B	20	11	3	6	58	45	36
Winchmore Hill B	20	9	3	8	62	40	30
Polytechnic B	20	8	2	10	39	49	26
Old Actonians C	20	6	3	11	25	38	21
Alexandra Park B	20	6	3	11	44	62	21
Old Parkonians B	20	6	2	12	35	54	20
Civil Service C	20	4	4	12	30	50	16
Carshalton B	20	3	2	15	36	77	11

Minor Two North	P	W	D	L	F	A	Pt
Old Owens D	20	15	1	4	77	28	46
Norsemen C	20	15	1	4	76	41	46
Winchmore Hill D	20	14	2	4	79	50	44
Winchmore Hill C	20	10	2	8	51	40	32
East Barnet B *-3*	20	9	1	10	53	58	25
Norsemen B	20	7	3	10	36	43	24
Southgate Oly. B	20	6	4	10	51	69	22
Old Owens C	20	6	2	12	31	50	20
Crouch End V. B	20	6	2	12	28	49	20
Crouch End V. C	20	5	5	10	30	53	20
Alexandra Park C	20	4	3	13	35	66	15

Minor Two North title withheld

Minor Two South	P	W	D	L	F	A	Pt
Polytechnic D	20	15	4	1	66	38	49
Old Actonians D	20	11	3	6	53	33	36
HSBC B	20	11	3	6	47	33	36
Weirside Rgrs B	20	9	4	7	52	43	31
Kew Assoc. B	20	9	3	8	47	43	30
Polytechnic C	20	7	6	7	42	47	27
Carshalton C	20	8	1	11	54	47	25
West Wickham B	20	7	4	9	43	49	25
Civil Service D	20	6	4	10	38	47	22
Old Wilsonians B	20	5	4	11	32	43	19
W. Wickham C *-3*	20	3	2	15	27	78	8

Minor Two South title withheld

Minor Three North	P	W	D	L	F	A	Pt
Old Stationers B	20	16	0	4	76	36	48
Old Finchleians B	20	11	3	6	55	34	36
Broomfield C	20	10	2	8	40	45	32
Winch. Hill E *-3*	20	11	1	8	61	51	31
Old Finchleians C	20	9	3	8	35	40	30
East Barnet OG C	20	9	2	9	59	59	29
Norsemen D	20	9	1	10	44	41	28
O. Esthameians B	20	8	1	11	35	44	25
Broomfield B	20	8	1	11	41	56	25
Old Parkonians C	20	7	3	10	51	48	24
Crouch End V. D	20	3	1	16	32	75	10

Minor Three South	P	W	D	L	F	A	Pt
BB Eagles C	20	16	3	1	61	19	51
BB Eagles B	20	13	4	3	67	24	43
Alleyn Old Boys B	20	12	5	3	50	31	41
Kew Assoc. C	20	8	3	9	34	42	27
Old Wilsonians C	20	8	2	10	34	46	26
Carshalton D *-3*	20	8	4	8	44	50	25
Ibis B	20	8	1	11	50	62	25
O. Westminster B	20	7	3	10	42	46	24
Alleyn Old Boys C	20	6	3	11	28	48	21
HSBC C	20	4	2	14	39	60	14
Merton B	20	3	4	13	33	54	13

Minor Four North	P	W	D	L	F	A	Pt
Old Parkonians E	20	16	2	2	84	38	50
Winchmore Hill G	20	12	2	6	64	46	38
Norsemen F	20	11	5	4	59	48	38
Old Finchleians D	20	12	1	7	60	37	37
Winchmore Hill F	20	7	6	7	57	48	27
Norsemen E	20	8	3	9	39	57	27
East Barnet OG D	20	7	2	11	41	58	23
Old Parkonians D	20	6	4	10	53	48	22
Crouch End V. E	20	7	1	12	59	75	22
Alexandra Park D	20	4	4	12	53	47	16
Crouch End V. F	20	4	2	14	42	109	14

Minor Four North title withheld

Minor Four South	P	W	D	L	F	A	Pt
Old Westminster C	20	12	5	3	87	43	41
Carshalton E	20	10	7	3	57	34	37
HSBC D	20	10	5	5	52	38	35
Old Actonians E	20	10	5	5	41	35	35
SB Cuaco B *-3*	20	10	4	6	65	51	31
Lloyds TSB Bk B	20	7	8	5	42	30	29
Kew Assoc. D	20	7	2	11	50	65	23
Merton C	20	5	5	10	35	52	20
Old Lyonians B	20	5	3	12	44	82	18
Lloyds TSB Bk C	20	5	2	13	35	65	17
W. Wickham D *-3*	20	4	4	12	47	60	13

Minor Five North	P	W	D	L	F	A	Pt
Southgate Oly. D	22	20	0	2	107	19	60
Southgate Oly. C	22	18	1	3	84	46	55
Old Parkonians F	22	16	2	4	82	35	50
Old Stationers C	22	13	1	8	65	51	40
Old Finchleians E	22	11	4	7	65	44	37
Broomfield D	22	11	3	8	55	45	36
Old Parkonians G	22	7	3	12	62	66	24
Winchmore Hill H	22	7	0	15	47	68	21
East Barnet OG E	22	6	1	15	53	84	19
Alexandra Park E	22	4	4	14	46	90	16
Alexandra Park F	22	4	2	16	25	90	14
East Barnet OG F	22	4	1	17	35	88	13

Minor Five South	P	W	D	L	F	A	Pt
Old Actonians F	18	14	1	3	72	29	43
Polytechnic E	18	13	1	4	66	25	40
Polytechnic F	18	12	2	4	73	31	38
Old Salesians B	18	10	2	6	59	35	32
Sth Bank Cuaco C	18	9	2	7	42	48	29
Kew Association E	18	6	2	10	40	47	20
Old Wilsonians D	18	6	1	11	32	61	19
Bank of England B	18	4	4	10	25	62	16
Old Wilsonians E	18	3	6	9	30	48	15
Old West. Czns D	18	1	3	14	19	72	6

Minor Six South	P	W	D	L	F	A	Pt
HSBC F	22	15	1	6	66	40	46
S. Bk Cuaco D *-3*	22	15	3	4	70	36	45
Old Actonians G	22	13	4	5	74	35	43
HSBC E	22	12	1	9	55	42	37
Civil Service E	22	11	3	8	53	49	36
Weirside Rgrs C	22	10	4	8	64	48	34
BB Eagles D	22	10	4	8	46	37	34
Kew Assoc. F *-3*	22	8	5	9	39	48	28
Lloyds TSB Bk D	22	8	4	10	43	59	28
Polytechnic G	22	7	3	12	48	65	24
Lloyds TSB Bk E	22	3	1	18	26	71	10
Civil Service F	22	2	3	17	40	94	9

Minor Seven South	P	W	D	L	F	A	Pt
Lloyds TSB Bk F	22	20	0	2	121	21	60
Old Actonians I	22	19	2	1	85	37	59
Carshalton F	22	15	2	5	70	44	47
S. Bank Cuaco E	22	11	1	10	78	67	34
BB Eagles E	22	10	4	8	61	51	34
Alleyn Old Boys D	22	9	4	9	44	50	31
Merton D	22	6	7	9	47	46	25
Bank of England C	22	7	3	12	62	68	24
Old Wilsonians G	22	6	4	12	28	62	22
Old Actonians H	22	6	2	14	73	62	20
Old Wilsonians F	22	4	5	13	27	86	17
Lloyds TSB Bk G	22	1	2	19	30	132	5

Minor Seven South title withheld

AMATEUR FOOTBALL ALLIANCE SENIOR CUP 2009-10

FIRST ROUND

Albanian 9 HSBC 1
Alexandra Park 5 Parkfield 2 *aet*
Alleyn Old Boys 2 **Old Ignations** 3 *aet*
BB Eagles 2 **Centymca** 3 *aet*
Carshalton 5 Bank of England 0
Clapham Old Xaverians 2 **Old Esthameians** 3
East Barnet Old Grammarians 1 **Old Brentwoods** 3
Enfield Old Grammarians 3 Old Hamptonians 2
Globe Rangers 6 Old Buckwellians 0
Honourable Artillery Company 3 Old Kolsassians 1
Ibis 3 Dorkinians 1
Kings Old Boys 2 Old Stationers 1
Old Belgravians 3 **Latymer Old Boys** 4 *aet*
Old Chigwellians 1 Old Latymerians 0
Old Foresters 4 Lancing Old Boys 2
Old Lyonians 0 **Old Finchleians** 1
Old Manorians 2 FC Romania 1
Old Salesians 2 **Old Parkonians** 4
Old Salopians 0 **Old Edmontonians** 4
Old Salvatorians 0 **Hale End Athletic** 1
Old Uffingtonians 4 Old Aldenhamians 1
Old Vaughanians 5 Old Guildfordians 2
Old Westminster Citizens 2 **Kew Association** 3 *aet*
Old Wilsonians 7 Hampstead Heathens 1
Old Woodhouseians 2 **William Fitt** 5 *aet*
Pegasus 1 Chertsey Old Salesians 0
South Bank Cuaco 0 **Old Carthusians** 4
Southgate County 2 Old Aloysians 0
Southgate Olympic 1 **Glyn Old Boys** 6
St Albans Rangers v **Old Paulines** (w/o)
West Wickham 7 Old Bromleians 1
Wood Green Old Boys 3 **Economicals** 4

SECOND ROUND

Carshalton 0 **Albanian** 4
Centymca 2 **Polytechnic** 4
Crouch End Vampires 2 **Old Carthusians** 5
Fulham Compton Old Boys 2 **Old Danes** 2 *aet* (1-3p)
Honourable Artillery Company 5 Civil Service 1
Ibis 0 **Weirside Rangers** 2
Lloyds TSB Bank 5 Latymer Old Boys 0
Merton 0 **Old Meadonians** 4
National Westminster Bank 4 Old Tiffinians 0
Norsemen (w/o) Bromleians Sports
Nottsborough 12 Kew Association 0
Old Actonians Association 10 Old Vaughanians 0
Old Chigwellians 1 **Broomfield** 5
Old Cholmeleians 2 **Alexandra Park** 2 *aet* (3-4p)
Old Edmontonians 2 **Old Parkonians** 3
Old Esthameians 4 Economicals 3
Old Foresters 4 Sinjuns Grammarians 3 *aet*
Old Ignatians 4 Kings Old Boys 2
Old Josephians 1 **Hale End Athletic** 4
Old Malvernians v **William Fitt** (w/o)
Old Minchendenians 12 Mill Hill Village 0
Old Owens 11 Wandsworth Borough 1
Old Paulines 4 Glyn Old Boys 1
Old Suttonians 2 Bealonians 1 *aet*
Old Thorntonians 2 **Old Brentwoods** 3
Old Uffingtonians 6 Old Finchleians 2
Old Wilsonians 1 **Old Parmiterians** 3
Pegasus 2 Globe Rangers 1
UCL Academicals 2 Leyton County Old Boys 1
Wake Green Amateurs 4 Enfield Old Grammarians 2
West Wickham 9 Old Manorians 2
Winchmore Hill 4 Southgate County 1 *aet*

THIRD ROUND

Hale End Athletic 2 Old Actonians Association 1
Honourable Artillery Company 1 Old Suttonians 0
Norsemen 8 Old Paulines 1
Old Brentwoods 0 **Old Meadonians** 2
Old Carthusians 0 **Broomfield** 1
Old Esthameians 1 **Old Parkonians** 4
Old Foresters 0 **Albanian** 7
Old Ignatians 4 Weirside Rangers 0
Old Minchendenians 7 Lloyds TSB Bank 0
Old Owens 5 National Westminster Bank 1
Old Parmiterians 3 Pegasus 2
Old Uffingtonians 5 **Polytechnic** 5 *aet* (3-4p)
Wake Green Amateurs 8 Old Danes 1
West Wickham 0 **Nottsborough** 2
William Fitt 1 UCL Academicals 0
Winchmore Hill 3 Alexandra Park 0

FOURTH ROUND

Albanian 3 **Honourable Artillery Company** 4
Broomfield 3 Polytechnic 0
Hale End Athletic 1 **Old Ignatians** 4
Nottsborough 1 Old Parmiterians 0
Old Meadonians 2 **Norsemen** 4
Old Owens 6 Old Parkonians 0
Wake Green Amateurs 0 **Winchmore Hill** 1
William Fitt 0 **Old Minchendenians** 5

QUARTER-FINALS

Broomfield 7 Norsemen 2
Old Ignatians 0 **Old Owens** 2
Old Minchendenians 0 **Nottsborough** 2
Winchmore Hill 2 Honourable Artillery Company 1

SEMI-FINALS

Broomfield 4 **Nottsborough** 5 *aet*
Old Owens 0 **Winchmore Hill** 1 *aet*

FINAL *(April 10th at Norsemen)*

Winchmore Hill 3 Nottsborough 0

OTHER AMATEUR FOOTBALL ALLIANCE FINALS 2009-10

GREENLAND CUP *(September 5th at East Barnet Old Grammarians)* **Bealonians** 3 Nottsborough 2
MIDDLESEX / ESSEX SENIOR CP *(March 20th at Old Actonians)* **Albanian** 4 Old Parkonians 3
SURREY / KENT SENIOR CUP *(March 20th at Bank of England)* **Old Salesians** 2 Nottsborough 1
INTERMEDIATE CUP *(March 27th at Old Finchleians)* **Old Actonians Association Res.** 2 Norsemen Res. 1
MIDDLESEX / ESSEX INTERMEDIATE *(March 27th at Old Parmiterians)* **Icarus** 3 Winchmore Hill Res. 3 *aet* (4-2p
SURREY / KENT CUP INTERMEDIATE *(March 27th at Old Dorkinians)* **Nottsborough Res.** 3 West Wickham Res
JUNIOR CUP *(March 13th at HSBC)* Nottsborough A 1 **Old Stationers A** 2
MINOR CUP *(March 27th at East Barnet Old Grammarians)* **Old Meadonians B** 4 Old Hamptonians B 3 *aet*
SENIOR NOVETS CUP *(March 13th at East Barnet Old Grammarians)* **BB Eagles B** 1 Economicals 0
INTERMEDIATE NOVETS CUP *(March 27th at Phoenix Old Boys Slough)* **Polytechnic** D 6 Civil Service D 2
JUNIOR NOVETS CUP *(March 13th at West Wickham)* Polytechnic F 3 **Old Parmiterians E** 5

ARMED FORCES FOOTBALL

INTER SERVICES CUP

MEN'S COMPETITION

	P	W	D	L	F	A	Pts
Royal Air Force	2	1	1	0	4	1	4
Royal Navy	2	0	2	0	3	3	2
Army	2	0	1	1	2	4	1

Inter Service Champions 2008/09: Royal Air Force

Inter Service Champions 2007/08: Royal Air Force

Inter Service Champions 2006/07: Army

Inter Service Champions 2005/06: Army

Inter Service Champions 2004/05: Army

Inter Service Champions 2003/04: Royal Navy

WOMEN'S COMPETITION

	P	W	D	L	F	A	Pts
Royal Air Force	2	2	0	0	2	0	6
Army	2	0	1	1	2	3	1
Royal Navy	2	0	1	1	2	3	1

Inter Service Champions 2008/09: Royal Air Force

Inter Service Champions 2007/08: Army

Inter Service Champions 2006/07: Army

Inter Service Champions 2005/06: Royal Air force

Inter Service Champions 2004/05: Army

Inter Service Champions 2003/04: Army

ARMY

F.A. CUP (from the Quarter Final Stages)

QUARTER FINALS

2 Para	v	24 Cdo Engr Regt	4-2
4 Ls Regt	v	SEAE	2-3
6 Bn REME	v	2 Sig Regt	5-2

SEMI FINALS

2 Para	v	SEAE	3-0
6 Bn REME	v	QRH (BA (G))	3-1

FINAL

2 Para	v	6 Bn REME	3-1

MASSEY TROPHY - DIVISION ONE 2009-10

		P	W	D	L	F	A	GD	Pts
1.	SIGNALS	12	9	3	0	42	22	20	30
2.	REME	12	7	3	2	31	20	11	24
3.	ENGINEERS	12	6	2	4	20	19	1	20
4.	INFANTRY	12	4	4	4	29	23	6	16
5.	RLC	12	3	3	6	19	25	-6	12
6.	PT CORPS	12	2	2	8	10	24	-14	8
7.	ARTILLERY	12	1	3	8	11	29	-18	6

MASSEY TROPHY DIVISION TWO 2009-10

		P	W	D	L	F	A	GD	Pts
1.	AGC	8	6	0	2	16	8	7	18
2.	INT CORPS	8	5	1	2	14	6	8	16
3.	RAC	8	5	0	3	19	15	4	15
4.	AMS	8	2	0	6	5	14	-10	6
5.	AAC	8	1	1	6	11	22	-11	4

ROYAL AIR FORCE - SENIOR MEN'S RESULTS 2008-09

Date	Opponents	Venue	Competition	Result
Mar 3	Army	Elgin City FC	Inter-Services	**W** 2-0
Mar 10	Royal Navy	Portsmouth	Inter-Services	D 1-1

F.A. CUP FINAL RESULT

RAF COSFORD 1 - 0 RAF LEEMING

ROYAL NAVY - SENIOR MEN'S RESULTS 2009-10

Date	Opponents	Venue	Competition	Result
Oct 28	South Down Academy FC	Portsmouth	Friendly	L 2-3
Nov 11	AFA	Portsmouth	SC Cup	**W** 3-0
Nov 25	London FA	London	SC Cup	**W** 6-0
Dec 9	Sussex FA	Lacing	SC Cup	D 1-1
Jan 20	Prison Service	Portsmouth	Friendly	**W** 1-0
Mar 10	Royal Arir Force	Portsmouth	Inter-Services	D 1-1
Mar 17	Army	Aldershot	Inter-Services	D 2-2

F.A. CUP (from the Quarter Final Stages)

QUARTER FINALS

HMS Illustrious	v	HMS Sultan	2-1
HMS Sutherland	v	HMS Heron	1-2
42 Cdo Rm	v	CTCRM	2-4
45 Cdo Rm	v	HMS Neptune	3-1

SEMI FINALS

HMS Heron	v	HMS Illustrious	3-3* 8-7p
45 Cdo Rm	v	CTCRM	4-3*

FINAL

45 Cdo RM	v	HMS Heron	3-2*

BRITISH UNIVERSITIES FOOTBALL

MEN'S CHAMPIONSHIP FINAL

BOURNEMOUTH	1	2	LOUGHBOROUGH

MEN'S NORTHERN CONFERENCE CUP FINAL

LANCASTER	2	1	SHEFFIELD HALLAM 2nds

MEN'S MIDLANDS CONFERENCE CUP FINAL

CAMBRIDGE	1	2	STAFFORDSHIRE

MEN'S WESTERN CONFERENCE CUP FINAL

WINCHESTER	4	2	GLAMORGAN

MEN'S SOUTH EASTERN CONFERENCE CUP FINAL

GREENWICH	2	2	ESSEX (WON 3-2 ON PENS)

PREMIER LEAGUE FINAL STANDINGS

NORTH		SOUTH
LEEDS	1	UWE HARTPURY
LOUGHBOROUGH	2	CARDIFF
BIRMINGHAM	3	BRIGHTON
NORTHUMBRIA	4	BATH
NOTTINGHAM	5	HERTFORDSHIRE
MANCHESTER	6	EXETER

CONFERENCE STANDINGS

NORTHERN		WESTERN
LEEDS MET	1	BOURNEMOUTH
SHEFFIELD HALLAM	2	GLOUCESTERSHIRE
YORK ST. JOHNS	3	UWE
CENTRAL LANCASHIRE	4	SWANSEA
SUNDERLAND	5	BATH 3rds
EDGE HILL	6	BATH 2nds

MIDLANDS		SOUTH EASTERN
NOTTINGHAM TRENT	1	BRUNEL - WEST LONDON
LOUGHBOROUGH 2nds	2	ST. MARY'S
OXFORD	3	BRIGHTON 2nds
LINCOLN	4	BUCKINGHAMSHIRE
NOTTINGHAM 2nds	5	CHICHESTER
LOUGHBOROUGH 3rds	6	KENT

ENGLISH SCHOOLS' FOOTBALL ASSOCIATION

4, Parker Court, Staffordshire Technology Park, Beaconside, Stafford ST18 0WP
Tel : 01785 785 970; website :www..esfa.co.uk
Chief Executive
John Read (john.read@schoolsfa.com)
Competitions Manager
Mike Spinks (mike.spinks@schoolsfa.com)
Non-League Directory Contributor
Mike Simmonds (0115 9313299)
m.simmonds31@btinternet.com
Photos : RWT Photography
website: www.rwt-photography.co.uk

THE INTERNATIONAL SEASON

THE CARNEGIE CENTENARY SCHOOLS' SHIELD (UNDER 18)

FINAL TABLE 2009-10	P	W	D	L	F	A	Pts
REPUPLIC of Ireland	4	3	0	1	7	3	9
England	4	2	1	1	8	3	7
Northern Ireland	4	1	2	1	4	6	5
Scotland	4	1	1	2	7	12	4
Wales	4	0	2	2	3	5	2
Places are calculated on points only.							

RESULTS

Northern Ireland	1-4	England	Crusaders FC
Northern Ireland	1-1	Scotland	Forfar Athletic FC
Wales	0-0	England	Llanelli AFC
Republic of Ireland	0-1	Northern Ireland	Tullamore Town FC
Scotland	3-2	Wales	Airdrie United FC
Wales	0-1	Republic of Ireland	Haverfordwest FC
Republic of Ireland	5-2	Scotland	Finn Harps FC
Northern Ireland	1-1	Wales	Windsor Park
England	4-1	Scotland	Carlisle United FC
England	0-1	Republic of Ireland	Burton Albion FC

ENGLAND U18 SCHOOLS' SQUAD
Back row (L to R): Daren Regis, Connor Gater, Reece Yorke, Andrew Kelly, Tim Rivers, Dale Whitham, Lewis Robinson, Robert Thompson-Brown.
Middle row: Shaun Hemming (Goalkeeper Coach), Andy Williams (Assistant Manager), Cliff Moyo, Kenny Reeves, Adam Molloy, Josh Hart, Liam Williams, Kris Wilkinson, Dave Burns (Physio), Dr Arthur Tabor (Team Doctor).
Front row: Tom Boakye, Matt Whitehead, Phil Nardiello (Manager), Paul Rickard (Chairman), John Read (Chief Executive), Dave Woollaston (Chairman of Selection & Coaching), Nick Hancock, Luke Boyce.

ENGLISH SCHOOLS' F.A NATIONAL COMPETITIONS

The major feature of the last ten years of the English Schools' F.A. has been the great increase in the number of national competitions. 23 national competitions were played last season compared with less than half that number which were featured in the Non-League Directory ten years ago. Apart from the four Primary competitions, the finals of which were played on the excellent facilities of the Watford Training ground and the two Under 12 indoor competitions, the remainder of the National Finals were played with six F.A. Premier Clubs providing their facilities and clubs as far apart geographically as Accrington Stanley and Exeter City playing host to a Cup Final. This, of course, gave nearly 550 students the chance of playing on a League club ground, something which the vast majority will remember for the rest of their lives. In addition, the E.S.F.A. has developed links with the Royal School for the Deaf and has organised a number of competitions in partnership with them while Futsal has been introduced to the programme

Broadening the base of the E.S.F.A. is the major aim in extending the number of competitions which are organised. This has certainly been successful as some figures illustrate. The Under 11 Boys' 7-a-side last season attracted over 3000 entries from Primary and Junior sides while 1687 girls' teams participated in the parallel competition. At Secondary level, the largest entry was at Under 16 Individual Schools' Level with over 1000 entries for the boys' Cup and 556 for the girls' competition. Entries for the other competitions varied between 1100 and 600 and when one considers the myriad events organised by County and Local Associations, it can be seen that schools' football is still flourishing.

Most of last season's finals were well contested although it was disappointing that the Association's oldest competition, the Under 15 Inter-Association Trophy which began in the 1904-05 season was a one-sided affair. Congratulations, nevertheless, go to Liverpool who went further ahead in the list of national winners. Two of the most exciting finals were in the Under 15 Boys' Cup and the Girls' Under 16 County Championship; in the former, Harefield Academy, whose Under 16 team also won the National title, opened the scoring only for Lancaster of Leicester to draw level before half-time. Harefield raced into a 3-1 lead soon after the break but the Leicester school forced extra time before Jordan Bholo netted the winner for Harefield

In the Under 16 Girls' inter-county final, Grace Teah gave Leicestershire and Rutland the lead and Jesse Hickey added a second just after the break. Wiltshire then mounted a great fight-back thanks to goals from Abby Picton and Niamh Rawlins before Jesse Hickey scored the winner in added time. Another game to go to extra time was the Under 13 Girls Final and it need penalties before Thomas Telford just pipped Maiden Erlegh. Full results and goal scorers are displayed below.

PRIMARY (Under 11)

SMALL SCHOOLS SOCCER SEVENS
Saturday 1st May. University College, London (Watford F.C. Training Ground)
Winners: LANCING COLLEGE PREPARATORY SCHOOL (Brighton, Hove and Portslade SFA)
Runners-up : ST. AIDANS RC PRIMARY SCHOOL (Huyton SFA)

UNDER 11 INTER-ASSOCIATION 7-A-SIDE TROPHY
Saturday, May 1st : University College, London (Watford F.C. Training Ground)
Winners : LIVERPOOL SFA
Runners-up : SOUTH BIRMINGHAM PSFA

UNDER 11 BOYS 7-A-SIDE CUP
Saturday, May 1st : University College, London (Watford F.C. Training Ground)
Winners : FOLVILLE JUNIOR SCHOOL (Leicester SFA)
Runners-up : STANFORD LE HOPE PRIMARY SCHOOL (Thurrock SFA)

UNDER 11 GIRLS 7-A-SIDE CUP
Saturday, May 1st : University College, London (Watford F.C. Training Ground)
Joint Winners : NEWBOTTLE PRIMARY SCHOOL (Lambton and Hetton SFA) and
THOMAS JOYFFE PRIMARY SCHOOL (South Warwickshire SFA)

Lancing College Prep School, Winners of the Small Schools 'Soccer Sevens'

Determined action from Balby Carr School and John Madejski School (Horizontal stripes) in the Under 18 Girls Trophy Final.

SECONDARY INDIVIDUAL SCHOOLS (11-18)

GIRLS

UNDER 12 GIRLS INDOOR 5-A-SIDE CUP FINAL
Monday, March 1st : Power League Soccerdome, Derby
PRIORY SCHOOL (Shrewsbury and District SFA) 2
QUEENS SCHOOL (Watford and District SFA) 1

UNDER 13 GIRLS NATIONAL FINAL
Saturday, May 1st : Pirelli Stadium, Burton Albion F.C.
THOMAS TELFORD SCHOOL (Telford and Wrekin SFA) 1 (Courtney Owen)
MAIDEN ERLEIGH SCHOOL (Reading SFA) 1 (Laura Harris-Steers)
Thomas Telford won 4-3 on penalties.

UNDER 15 GIRLS NATIONAL FINAL
Wednesday, May 12th : St. James' Park, Exeter City F.C.
ST, JULIE'S SCHOOL ((Liverpool SFA) 3 (Shannon Beckwith 3)
HABERDASHERS' ASKE KNIGHTS SCHOOL (Blackheath SFA) 1 (Vyan Simpson)

UNDER 16 GIRLS NATIONAL CUP FINAL
Wednesday, May 5th ; The Hawthorns, West Bromwich Albion F.C.)
WILLIAM FARR SCHOOL (Lincoln and Gainsborough SFA) 2 (Martha Harris, Caitlyn Lynch)
THOMAS TELFORD SCHOOL (Telford and Wrekin SFA) 0

UNDER 18 GIRLS (SCHOOLS) TROPHY FINAL
Monday, March 29th : Madejski Stadium, Reading F.C.
BALBY CARR SCHOOL (Doncaster SFA) 6 (Jenny Knibbs 3, Lauren Rodway, Becky Kendall, Beth Smith)
JOHN MADEJSKI SCHOOL (Reading SFA) 2 (Danielle Puddifoot, Francesca Kirby)

UNDER 18 GIRLS (COLLEGES) TROPHY FINAL
Wednesday, March 17th : Fraser Eagle Stadium, Accrington Stranley F.C.
ACCRINGTON AND ROSSENDALE COLLEGE (Hyndburn and Ribble SFA) 1 (Jayde Clegg)
FILTON COLLEGE (Glucestershire SFA) 4 (Connie Short, Gabby Bird, Nadine Grogan, Daisy Allen)

BOYS

UNDER 12 BOYS INDOOR 5-A-SIDE CUP FINAL
Monday, March 1st : Power League Soccerdome, Derby
TRINITY SCHOOL (Carlisle SFA) 3
KIBWORTH SCHOOL (South Leicestershire SFA) 1

UNDER 12 E.S.F.A. BOYS CUP FINAL(SPONSORED BY DANONE NATIONS UK)
Monday, May 17th : Stamford Bridge, Chelsea F.C.)
WHITGIFT SCHOOL (Croydon SFA) 1 (Andre Coker)
ST. CUTHBERT'S SCHOOL (Rochdale SFA) 0

UNDER 13 BOYS CUP FINAL
Tuesday, May 18th : Goodison Park, Everton F.C.
ARCHBISHOP BECK SCHOOL (Liverpool SFA) 1 (Brian Ellison)
GRANGE SCHOOL (Bristol and South Gloucestershire SFA) 0

UNDER 14 BOYS CUP : FINAL (SPONSORED BY THE F.A. PREMIER LEAGUE)
Thursday, May 6th : Craven Cottage, Fulham F.C.
THOMAS TELFORD SCHOOL (Telford and Wrekin SFA) 2 (Chaquille Buchanan,Ben Carter)
QUEEN'S SCHOOL (Watford SFA) 0

UNDER 15 BOYS CUP FINAL
Monday, May 24th : Ashton Gate, Bristol City F.C.
HAREFIELD ACADEMY (Hillingdon SFA) 4
(Bernard Mensah 2, Afolabi Obafemi, Jordan Bholo)
LANCASTER SCHOOL (Leicester SFA) 3
(Jamaal Quailey, Sam Rogers, Elliot Francis)
(after extra time)

UNDER 16 BOYS CUP FINAL
Tuesday, May 11th : Boundary Park, Oldham F.C.
HAREFIELD ACADEMY (Hillingdon SFA) 4
(Michael Kalu, Frankie Sutherland, Trey Horne, Mani O'Sullivan)
MANCHESTER GRAMMAR SCHOOL (Manchester SFA) 1

UNDER 18 BOYS (SCHOOLS) TROPHY FINAL
Tuesday, May 18th : Goodison Park, Everton F.C.
BARKING ABBEY SCHOOL (Barking and Dagenham SFA) 3
(Joe Bricknell, Michael Thalassitis, Glenn O'Hanlon)
ST. MARGARET'S SCHOOL (Liverpool SFA) 0

UNDER 18 BOYS (COLLEGES) TROPHY FINAL
Wednesday, March 17th : Christie Park, Morecambe F.C.
HARTPURY COLLEGE (West Glucestershire SFA) 2 (Callum Preece, Jack Wood)
GATESHEAD COLLEGE (Gateshead SFA) 1 (Lee Dial)

Whitgift School celebrate the victory in the Under 12 DANONE Final at Stamford Bridge

Harefield Academy's Under 15 side, part of a national double with their Under 16 team.

Warrington Schools' at the Reebok Stadium after their victory in the Final.

Leicester and Rutland in jubilant mood.

BOYS INTER-DISTRICT COMPETITIONS
E.S.F.A UNDER 13 INTER-ASSOCIATION TROPHY FINAL
Friday, May 14th : Reebok Stadium, Bolton Wanderers F.C.
WARRINGTON SCHOOLS' F.A. 1 (George Cooper)
BARNET SCHOOLS' F.A. 0

E.S.F.A UNDER 15 INTER-ASSOCIATION TROPHY FINAL
Tuesday, May 11th : Anfield, Liverpool F.C.
LIVERPOOL SCHOOLS' F.A. 8
(Ryan Cox 5, Joel Kerwin, Kellen Daly)
CAMBRIDGE AND DISTRICT SCHOOLS' F.A. 0

INTER-COUNTY COMPETITIONS (BOYS AND GIRLS)
E.S.F.A UNDER 16 BOYS COUNTY CHAMPIONSHIP : FINAL
Wednesday, May 12th : Hillsborough, Sheffield Wednesday F.C.
GREATER MANCHESTER COUNTY SCHOOLS' F.A. 5 (Jay Mehmet 3, Kyle Riley, Godwin Abadaki)
SUFFOLK COUNTY SCHOOLS' F.A. 1 (Charlie King)

E.S.F.A. UNDER 16 GIRLS COUNTY CHAMPIONSHIP : FINAL
Thursday, March 18th : Sincil Bank, Lincoln City F.C.
LEICESTERHIRE AND RUTLAND COUNTY SFA 3 (Grace Teah, Jess Hickey 2)
WILTSHIRE COUNTY SCHOOLS' F.A. 2 (Abby Picton, Niamh Rawlins)

PHOTO IMG 6032 Leicester and Rutland in jubilant mood

E.S.F.A. UNDER 18 BOYS COUNTY CHAMPIONSHIP : FINAL
Wednesday, May 5th : Bramall Lane, Sheffield United F.C.
GWENT COUNTY SCHOOLS' F.A. 2 (Jamie Davies, Josh Brown)
DURHAM COUNTY SCHOOLS' F.A. 0

WOMEN'S FOOTBALL

NATIONAL DIVISION 2009-10

		P	W	D	L	F	A	GD	Pts
1	**Arsenal**	22	20	1	1	79	19	60	61
2	**Everton**	22	16	2	4	67	19	48	50
3	**Chelsea**	22	16	1	5	60	27	33	49
4	**Leeds United**	22	15	2	5	50	16	34	47
5	**Sunderland WFC**	22	12	1	9	36	35	1	37
6	**Doncaster Rovers B.**	22	9	7	6	36	37	-1	34
7	**Blackburn Rovers**	22	7	3	12	27	45	-18	24
8	**Millwall Lionesses**	22	6	3	13	24	43	-19	21
9	**Watford**	22	4	5	13	23	60	-37	17
10	**Birmingham City**	22	4	4	14	21	41	-20	16
11	**Nottingham Forest**	22	3	4	15	16	51	-35	13
12	**Bristol Academy**	22	3	1	18	12	58	-46	10

NORTHERN DIVISION 2009-10

		P	W	D	L	F	A	GD	Pts
1	**Liverpool**	22	19	2	1	59	19	40	59
2	**OOH Lincoln**	22	15	4	3	46	22	24	49
3	Leicester City	22	11	6	5	53	35	18	39
4	Manchester City	22	10	6	6	36	25	11	36
5	Curzon Ashton	22	9	4	9	37	39	-2	31
6	Aston Villa	22	7	8	7	37	35	2	29
7	Leeds City Vixens	22	9	2	11	41	48	-7	29
8	Newcastle United	22	7	6	9	38	48	-10	27
9	Preston North End	22	6	6	10	56	54	2	24
10	Derby County	22	5	5	12	30	51	-21	20
11	Sheffield Wednesday	22	4	6	12	29	50	-21	18
12	Luton Town	22	1	3	18	12	48	-36	6

SOUTHERN DIVISION 2009-10

		P	W	D	L	F	A	GD	Pts
1	**Barnet FC**	22	16	4	2	53	18	35	52
2	**Reading FC**	22	13	5	4	43	28	15	44
3	Keynsham Town	22	12	5	5	55	36	19	41
4	Portsmouth FC	22	11	6	5	42	32	10	39
5	West Ham United	22	9	9	4	38	24	14	36
6	Cardiff City	22	10	5	7	44	32	12	35
7	Charlton Athletic	22	10	4	8	24	20	4	34
8	Brighton & Hove Albion	22	6	8	8	33	33	0	26
9	Colchester United FC	22	6	5	11	19	40	-21	23
10	Queens Park Rangers	22	5	5	12	42	43	-1	20
11	WFC Fulham	22	2	2	18	14	63	-49	8
12	Crystal Palace	22	1	4	17	12	50	-38	7

WOMEN'S SUPER LEAGUE

March 2011 will see the start of a new Super League in Women's Football

NATIONAL DIVISION 2009-10	NORTHERN DIVISION 2009-10	SOUTHERN DIVISION 2009-10
Barnet	Aston Villa	Brighton & Hove Albion
Blackburn Rovers	Coventry City	Cardiff City
Leeds United	Curzon Ashton	Charlton Athletic
Millwall Lionesses	Derby County	Colchester United
Nottingham Forest	Leeds City Vixens	Gillingham
Reading	Leicester City	Keynsham Town
Sunderland	Manchester City	Portsmouth
Watford	Newcastle United	Queens Park Rangers
	Preston North End	West Ham United
	Rochdale	Yeovil Town

LEAGUE CUP

FIRST ROUND

Brighton & H.A.	v	Portsmouth	1-3
Barnet	v	Colchester United	5-0
Derby County	v	Curzon Ashton	1-2
OOH Lincoln	v	Newcastle United	3-1
Bristol Academy	Bye		

SECOND ROUND

Blackburn Rovers	v	Manchester City	4-2
Birmingham City	v	OOH Lincoln	6-2
Aston Villa	v	Derby County	3-0
Leeds United	v	Nottingham Forest	1-0
Cardiff City	v	Bristol Academy	0-4
Portsmouth	v	WFC Fulham	5-2
Chelsea	v	Barnet	6-2
Keynsham Town	v	Crystal Palace	7-1
Charlton Athletic	v	Luton Town	1-0
West Ham United	v	Millwall Lionesses	0-0*, 1-4p
Watford	v	Arsenal (H)	1-4
Leeds City Vixens	v	Doncaster Rovers Belles	0-5
Leicester City	v	Preston North End	3-2
Sheffield Wednesday	v	Everton	0-5
Sunderland	v	Liverpool	5-1

THIRD ROUND

Birmingham City	v	Blackburn Rovers	1-2
Aston Villa	v	Leeds United	2-4
Bristol Academy	v	Reading	HW
Portsmouth	v	Chelsea	0-1
Keynsham Town	v	Charlton Athletic	3-1
Millwall Lionesses	v	Arsenal (H)	0-2
Doncaster Rovers Belles	v	Leicester City	3-1
Everton	v	Sunderland	4-0

QUARTER-FINALS

Everton	v	Doncaster Rovers Belles	3-0
Arsenal (H)	v	Keynsham Town	4-0
Chelsea	v	Bristol Academy	8-0
Leeds United	v	Blackburn Rovers	5-0

SEMI-FINALS

Everton	v	Arsenal (H)	2-1
Chelsea	v	Leeds United	0-2

THE FINAL

Everton	v	Leeds United	1-3

ENGLAND SENIOR TEAM - 2009/10

Results

	Date	Opponents	H/A	Comp	Result		Goalscorers
1	Aug 25	Italy	N	Euro Grp C	L	1-2	Williams 38 (pen)
2	28	Russia	N	Euro Grp C	**W**	3-2	Carney 24, Aluko 32, Kelly Smith 42
3	31	Sweden	N	Euro Grp C	D	1-1	White 28
4	Sept 3	Finland	N	Euro	**W**	3-2	Aluko 14, 67, Williams 49
5	6	Holland	N	Euro SF	**W**	2-1	Kelly Smith 61, Jill Scott 116
6	10	Germany	N	Euro Final	L	2-6	Carney 24, Kelly Smith 55
7	Oct 25	Malta	H	WC Q	**W**	8-0	White 5, Williams 20,37,65, Clarke 35,75 Westwood 77, Unitt 88
8	Nov 26	Turkey	A	WC Q	**W**	3-0	Scott 76, Sanderson 80, Unitt 84
9	Feb 24	South Africa	N	Cyprus Cup	**W**	1-0	
10	27	Canada	N	Cyprus Cup	L	0-1	
11	Mar 1	Switzerland	N	Cyprus Cup	D	2-2	
12	3	Italy	N	Cyprus Cup	**W**	3-2	
13	25	Austria	H	WC Q	**W**	3-0	Sanderson 16, Aluko 68, E. White 90
14	Apr 1	Spain	H	WC Q	**W**	1-0	Chapman 29
15	May 20	Malta	A	WC Q	**W**	6-0	F.White 7, Smith 15, Williams 29,82, Clarke 56, E.White 67
16	Jun 19	Spain	A	WC Q	D	2-2	Unitt 78, F.White 88
17	Jul 29	Turkey	H	WC Q	**W**	3-0	Yankey 22, E.White 58, Clarke 76
18	Aug 21	Austria	A	WC Q	**W**	4-0	Smith 7,30, A.Scott 40, E.White 80

WORLD CUP QUALIFYING - GROUP 5

		P	W	D	L	F	A	Pts
1.	**ENGLAND**	**8**	**7**	**1**	**0**	**30**	**2**	**22**
2.	SPAIN	8	6	1	1	37	4	19
3.	AUSTRIA	7	3	0	4	12	10	9
4.	TURKEY	7	2	0	5	8	21	6
5.	MALTA	8	0	0	8	1	51	0

England now qualify for a two legged play-off to be played 11-12 and 15-16 September.

The Squad selected for Austria match 21st August 2010

	Club	Caps	Goals
Goalkeepers			
Rachel Brown	Everton	70	0
Siobhan Chamberlain	Chelsea	16	0
Defenders			
Laura Bassett	Unattached	17	0
Sophie Bradley	Lincoln Ladies	0	0
Steph Houghton	Unattached	0	0
Lindsay Johnson	Everton	40	1
Claire Rafferty	Chelsea	2	0
Alex Scott	Boston Breakers	67	12
Casey Stoney	Chelsea	80	4
Dunia Susi	Chelsea	8	0
Rachel Unitt	Everton	80	7
Faye White	Arsenal	81	11
Midfielders			
Karen Carney	Chicago Red Stars	29	5
Katie Chapman	Chicago Red Stars	80	8
Jessica Clarke	Lincoln Ladies	0	0
Jill Scott	Everton	38	5
Sue Smith	Lincoln Ladies	87	14
Fara Williams	Everton	85	32
Rachel Yankey	Arsenal	101	13
Forwards			
Kelly Smith	Boston Breakers	95	41
Eniola Aluko	Atlanta Beat	48	10
Ellen White	Arsenal	5	3

NON-LEAGUE PUBLICATIONS

Despite the shattering disappointment of 'our special game's' World Cup competition, where England were desperately bad, and the Final itself produced a winning side who appeared to dive at every tackle and runners up who gave them every excuse to fall over with consistently foul challenges, the game of football survives.

So it is a perfect time for the Non-League competitions to show what excellent entertainment they can supply within a competitive but friendly atmosphere.To highlight this special non-league world we have a wonderful selection of publications which do indeed present the very best aspects of the sport that still attracts millions.

The wonderful quarterly magazine **'Groundtastic'** (80 pages) gives a comprehensive review of all grounds old and new.
(email: editors@groundtastic.co.uk and website: www.groundtastic.co.uk).
Editors: Vince Taylor & Paul Claydon

'Non-League 24' A new exciting monthly magazine, edited by David Watters, has completed a year and covers
the Non-League game with a balance of features, statistics and photographs in its 116 pages.

'Non League Digest' (60 pages) gives a very thorough monthly round-up of features including all aspects of the game that interest groundhoppers.
(email: steveking@nonleaguedigest.com and website: www.nonleaguedigest.com).
Editor: Steve KIng.

'Non League Retrospect' The National Game History magazine (46 pages) is packed with fascinating historical facts and features.
(email: enquiries@3-2books.co.uk and website: www.3-2books.com)
Editors: Fred Hawthorn and Ronald Price.

The Football Traveller is a weekly publication giving you up to date details of fixtures from over a hundred competitions plus news and features on programmes and travel around the country.
(email: berrytft@googlemail.com and website: www.thefootballtraveller.co.uk)
Editor: Bill Berry.

Soccer History Magazine (56 pages) is a quarterly publication covering all aspects of the history of the game.
Website: www.soccer-history.co.uk

INDEX OF CLUBS

For clubs at Steps 1-4, the page number refers to their directory page.
For clubs at Step 5 and below, the page number refers to the club's 2009-10 league table.
Clubs promoted to Step 4 show their directory page in brackets.
New or renamed clubs are asterisked, with the page number indicating their directory entry.

INDEX

Y